Visit classzone.com and get connected

Online resources provide instruction, practice, and learning support correlated to your text.

- **Misconceptions database** provides solutions for common student misconceptions about science and their world.
- **Professional development links,** including SciLinks, offer additional teaching resources.
- **Animations and visualizations** help improve comprehension.
- **Math Tutorial** helps strengthen students' math skills.
- **Flashcards** help students review vocabulary.
- **State test practice** prepares students for assessments.

You have immediate access to *ClassZone's* teacher resources.

MCDTCOWDMSSZ

Use this code to create your own username and password.

Also visit *ClassZone* to learn more about these innovative and updated online resources.

- eEdition Plus Online
- eTest Plus Online
- EasyPlanner Plus Online
- Content Review Online

Now it all clicks!™

McDougal Littell

TEACHER'S EDITION

McDougal Littell

Life SCIENCE

Human Biology

Ecology

Life Over Time

Diversity of Living Things

Cells and Heredity

Unit 1 Credits
5B © Frans Lanting/Minden Pictures; Illustration by George Kelvin; **5C** Illustration by Debbie Maizels; **37B** *left* Illustration by Debbie Maizels; *right* Illustration by Keith Kasnot; **37C** Illustration by Debbie Maizels; **69B** © Will & Deni McIntyre/Photo Researchers, Inc.; **69C** © David B. Fleetham/Visuals Unlimited; **97B** Illustration by Robin Storesund; **131B** © Gladden Willis/Visuals Unlimited; Illustration by Steve Oh/KO Studios; **131C** © Getty Images.

Unit 2 Credits
165B *left* © Mark A. Schneider/Photo Researchers, Inc.; *right* © Sinclair Stammers/Photo Researchers, Inc.; Illustration by Peter Scott/Wildlife Art Ltd.; **165C** Illustration by Laurie O'Keefe; © Mark A. Schneider/Photo Researchers, Inc.; **199B** © Tom Brakefield/Bruce Coleman, Inc.; **199C** © Biophoto Associates/Photo Researchers, Inc.; **237B** © Stephen J. Krasemann/DRK Photo; **237C** NASA.

Unit 3 Credits
277B Illustration by Steve Oh/KO Studios; **277C** *left* Illustration by Steve Oh/KO Studios; *right* Illustration by Peter Bull/Wildlife Art Ltd.; **311B** Illustration by Robin Storesund; **353B** Illustration by Debbie Maizels; **353C** Illustration by Debbie Maizels; © Ed Reschke; **391B** Illustration by Laurie O'Keefe; **391C** Illustration by Ian Jackson/Wildlife Art, Inc.; **425B** Illustration by Laurie O'Keefe **425C** *left* © Fritz Polking/Visuals Unlimited; *right* © Comstock.

Unit 4 Credits
469B © Grant Heilman Photography; Illustration by Martin Macrae/nbillustration.co.uk; **469C** Illustration by Richard Bonson/Wildlife Art Ltd.; **505C** *both* Illustrations by Luigi Galante.

Unit 5 Credits
581B *center* Illustration by Linda Nye; *right* Illustration by Bart Vallecoccia; **581C** Illustration by Debbie Maizels; **609B** *both* Illustrations by Bart Vallecoccia; © Martin Rotker/Phototake; *bottom left* © Michael Newman/PhotoEdit; **609C** Illustration by Bart Vallecoccia; **637B** Illustration by Linda Nye; **637C** Illustration by Debbie Maizels; **673B** Illustration by Steve Oh/KO Studios; **673C** Illustration by Linda Nye; **705B** © Tom Galliher/Corbis; **705C** © Dr. Kari Lounatmaa/Photo Researchers, Inc.

Acknowledgments
Excerpts and adaptations from *National Science Education Standards* by the National Academy of Sciences. Copyright © 1996 by the National Academy of Sciences. Reprinted with permission from the National Academies Press, Washington, D.C. Excerpts and adaptations from *Benchmarks for Science Literacy: Project 2061.* Copyright © 1993 by the American Association for the Advancement of Science. Reprinted with permission.

Printed in the United States of America.

ISBN: 0-618-61519-9 2 3 4 5 6 7 8 VJM 08 07 06

Internet Web Site: http://www.mcdougallittell.com

McDougal Littell Science

Effective Science Instruction Tailored for Middle School Learners

Life Science Teacher's Edition Contents

Consultants and Reviewers

Science Consultants

Chief Science Consultant

James Trefil, Ph.D. is the Clarence J. Robinson Professor of Physics at George Mason University. He is the author or co-author of more than 25 books, including *Science Matters* and *The Nature of Science.* Dr. Trefil is a member of the American Association for the Advancement of Science's Committee on the Public Understanding of Science and Technology. He is also a fellow of the World Economic Forum and a frequent contributor to *Smithsonian* magazine.

Rita Ann Calvo, Ph.D. is Senior Lecturer in Molecular Biology and Genetics at Cornell University, where for 12 years she also directed the Cornell Institute for Biology Teachers. Dr. Calvo is the 1999 recipient of the College and University Teaching Award from the National Association of Biology Teachers.

Kenneth Cutler, M.S. is the Education Coordinator for the Julius L. Chambers Biomedical Biotechnology Research Institute at North Carolina Central University. A former middle school and high school science teacher, he received a 1999 Presidential Award for Excellence in Science Teaching.

Instructional Design Consultants

Douglas Carnine, Ph.D. is Professor of Education and Director of the National Center for Improving the Tools of Educators at the University of Oregon. He is the author of seven books and over 100 other scholarly publications, primarily in the areas of instructional design and effective instructional strategies and tools for diverse learners. Dr. Carnine also serves as a member of the National Institute for Literacy Advisory Board.

Linda Carnine, Ph.D. consults with school districts on curriculum development and effective instruction for students struggling academically. A former teacher and school administrator, Dr. Carnine also co-authored a popular remedial reading program.

Sam Miller, Ph.D. is a middle school science teacher and the Teacher Development Liaison for the Eugene, Oregon, Public Schools. He is the author of curricula for teaching science, mathematics, computer skills, and language arts.

Donald Steely, Ph.D. serves as principal investigator at the Oregon Center for Applied Science (ORCAS) on federal grants for science and language arts programs. His background also includes teaching and authoring of print and multimedia programs in science, mathematics, history, and spelling.

Vicky Vachon, Ph.D. consults with school districts throughout the United States and Canada on improving overall academic achievement with a focus on literacy. She is also co-author of a widely used program for remedial readers.

Content Reviewers

John Beaver, Ph.D.
Ecology
Professor, Director of Science Education Center
College of Education and Human Services
Western Illinois University
Macomb, IL

Donald J. DeCoste, Ph.D.
Matter and Energy, Chemical Interactions
Chemistry Instructor
University of Illinois
Urbana-Champaign, IL

Dorothy Ann Fallows, Ph.D., MSc
Diversity of Living Things, Microbiology
Partners in Health
Boston, MA

Michael Foote, Ph.D.
The Changing Earth, Life Over Time
Associate Professor
Department of the Geophysical Sciences
The University of Chicago
Chicago, IL

Lucy Fortson, Ph.D.
Space Science
Director of Astronomy
Adler Planetarium and Astronomy Museum
Chicago, IL

Elizabeth Godrick, Ph.D.
Human Biology
Professor, CAS Biology
Boston University
Boston, MA

Isabelle Sacramento Grilo, M.S.
The Changing Earth
Lecturer, Department of the Geological Sciences
San Diego State University
San Diego, CA

David Harbster, MSc
Diversity of Living Things
Professor of Biology
Paradise Valley Community College
Phoenix, AZ

Richard D. Norris, Ph.D.
Earth's Waters
Professor of Paleobiology
Scripps Institution of Oceanography
University of California, San Diego
La Jolla, CA

Donald B. Peck, M.S.
Motion and Forces; Waves, Sound, and Light; Electricity and Magnetism
Director of the Center for Science Education (retired)
Fairleigh Dickinson University
Madison, NJ

Javier Penalosa, Ph.D.
Diversity of Living Things, Plants
Associate Professor, Biology Department
Buffalo State College
Buffalo, NY

Raymond T. Pierrehumbert, Ph.D.
Earth's Atmosphere
Professor in Geophysical Sciences (Atmospheric Science)
The University of Chicago
Chicago, IL

Brian J. Skinner, Ph.D.
Earth's Surface
Eugene Higgins Professor of Geology and Geophysics
Yale University
New Haven, CT

Nancy E. Spaulding, M.S.
Earth's Surface, The Changing Earth, Earth's Waters
Earth Science Teacher (retired)
Elmira Free Academy
Elmira, NY

Steven S. Zumdahl, Ph.D.
Matter and Energy, Chemical Interactions
Professor Emeritus of Chemistry
University of Illinois
Urbana-Champaign, IL

Susan L. Zumdahl, M.S.
Matter and Energy, Chemical Interactions
Chemistry Education Specialist
University of Illinois
Urbana-Champaign, IL

Safety Consultant

Juliana Texley, Ph.D.
Former K–12 Science Teacher and School Superintendent
Boca Raton, FL

English Language Advisor

Judy Lewis, M.A.
Director, State and Federal Programs for reading proficiency and high risk populations
Rancho Cordova, CA

Research-Based Solutions for Your Classroom

The distinguished program consultant team and a thorough, research-based planning and development process assure that *McDougal Littell Science* supports all students in learning science concepts, acquiring inquiry skills, and thinking scientifically.

Standards-Based Instruction

Concepts and skills were selected based on careful analysis of national and state standards.

- National Science Education Standards
- Project 2061 Benchmarks for Science Literacy
- Comprehensive database of state science standards

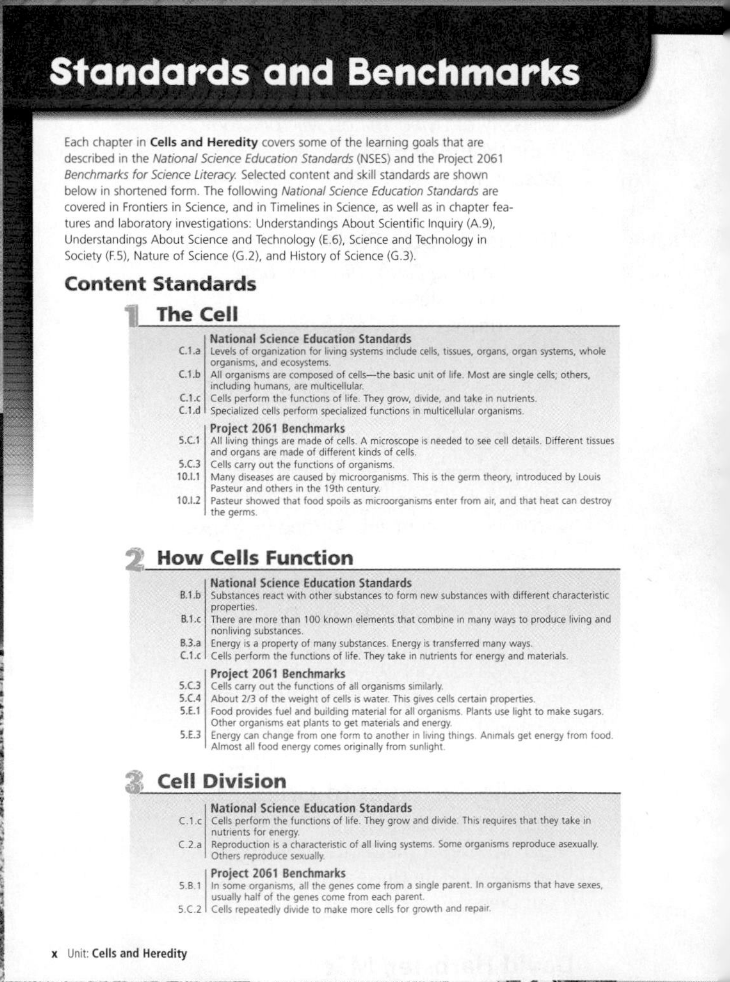

Standards and Benchmarks

Each chapter in **Cells and Heredity** covers some of the learning goals that are described in the *National Science Education Standards* (NSES) and the Project 2061 *Benchmarks for Science Literacy.* Selected content and skill standards are shown below in shortened form. The following *National Science Education Standards* are covered in Frontiers in Science, and in Timelines in Science, as well as in chapter features and laboratory investigations: Understandings About Scientific Inquiry (A.9), Understandings About Science and Technology (E.6), Science and Technology in Society (F.5), Nature of Science (G.2), and History of Science (G.3).

Content Standards

1 The Cell

National Science Education Standards

C.1.a Levels of organization for living systems include cells, tissues, organs, organ systems, whole organisms, and ecosystems.
C.1.b All organisms are composed of cells—the basic unit of life. Most are single cells; others, including humans, are multicellular.
C.1.c Cells perform the functions of life. They grow, divide, and take in nutrients.
C.1.d Specialized cells perform specialized functions in multicellular organisms.

Project 2061 Benchmarks

5.C.1 All living things are made of cells. A microscope is needed to see cell details. Different tissues and organs are made of different kinds of cells.
5.C.3 Cells carry out the functions of organisms.
10.I.1 Many diseases are caused by microorganisms. This is the germ theory, introduced by Louis Pasteur and others in the 19th century.
10.I.2 Pasteur showed that food spoils as microorganisms enter from air, and that heat can destroy the germs.

2 How Cells Function

National Science Education Standards

B.1.b Substances react with other substances to form new substances with different characteristic properties.
B.1.c There are more than 100 known elements that combine in many ways to produce living and nonliving substances.
B.3.a Energy is a property of many substances. Energy is transferred many ways.
C.1.c Cells perform the functions of life. They take in nutrients for energy and materials.

Project 2061 Benchmarks

5.C.3 Cells carry out the functions of all organisms similarly.
5.C.4 About 2/3 of the weight of cells is water. This gives cells certain properties.
5.E.1 Food provides fuel and building material for all organisms. Plants use light to make sugars. Other organisms eat plants to get materials and energy.
5.E.3 Energy can change from one form to another in living things. Animals get energy from food. Almost all food energy comes originally from sunlight.

3 Cell Division

National Science Education Standards

C.1.c Cells perform the functions of life. They grow and divide. This requires that they take in nutrients for energy.
C.2.a Reproduction is a characteristic of all living systems. Some organisms reproduce asexually. Others reproduce sexually.

Project 2061 Benchmarks

5.B.1 In some organisms, all the genes come from a single parent. In organisms that have sexes, usually half of the genes come from each parent.
5.C.2 Cells repeatedly divide to make more cells for growth and repair.

x Unit: Cells and Heredity

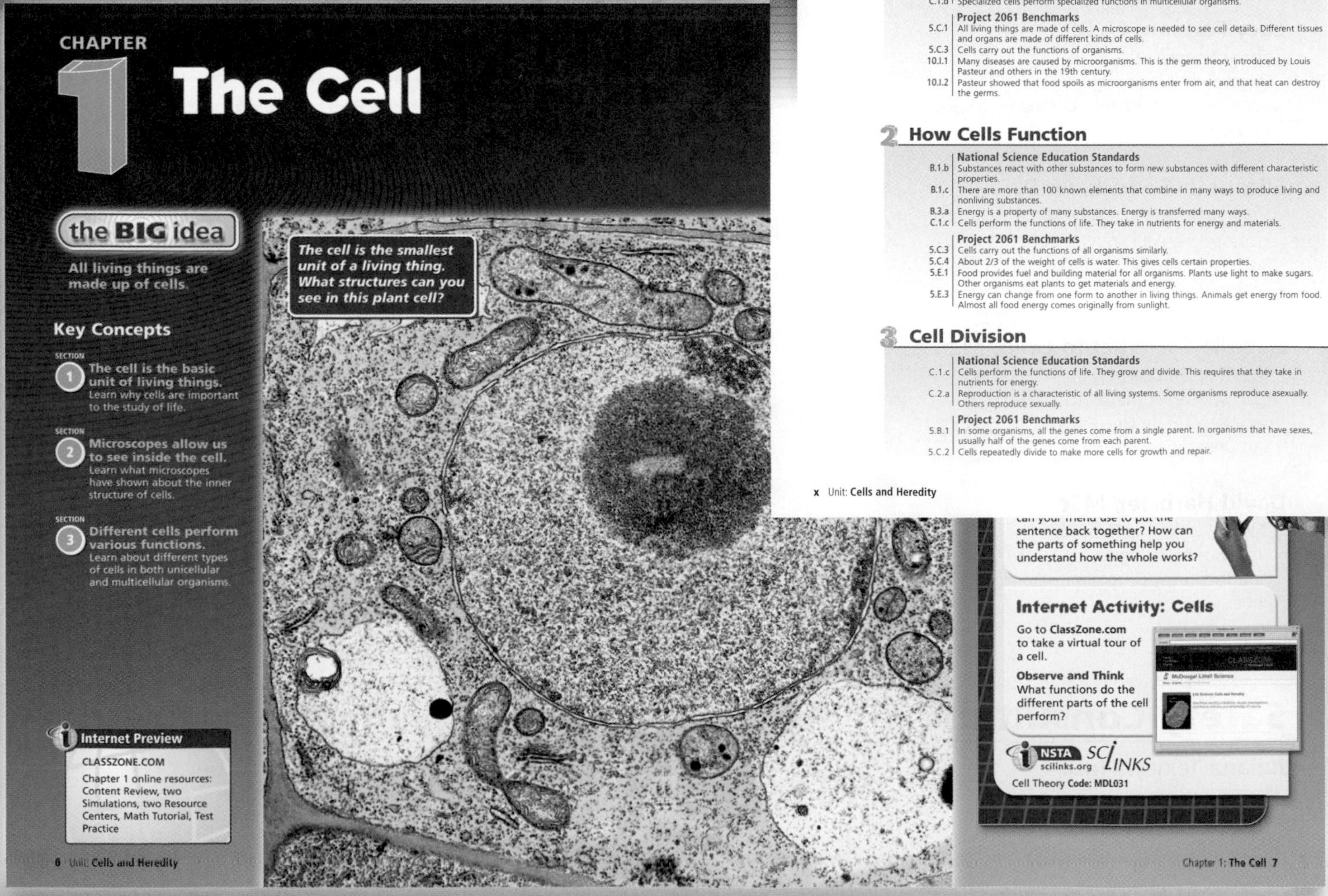

CHAPTER 1

The Cell

the BIG idea

All living things are made up of cells.

Key Concepts

SECTION 1 The cell is the basic unit of living things. Learn why cells are important to the study of life.

SECTION 2 Microscopes allow us to see inside the cell. Learn what microscopes have shown about the inner structure of cells.

SECTION 3 Different cells perform various functions. Learn about different types of cells in both unicellular and multicellular organisms.

The cell is the smallest unit of a living thing. What structures can you see in this plant cell?

Internet Preview

CLASSZONE.COM

Chapter 1 online resources: Content Review, two Simulations, two Resource Centers, Math Tutorial, Test Practice

6 Unit: Cells and Heredity

sentence back together? How can the parts of something help you understand how the whole works?

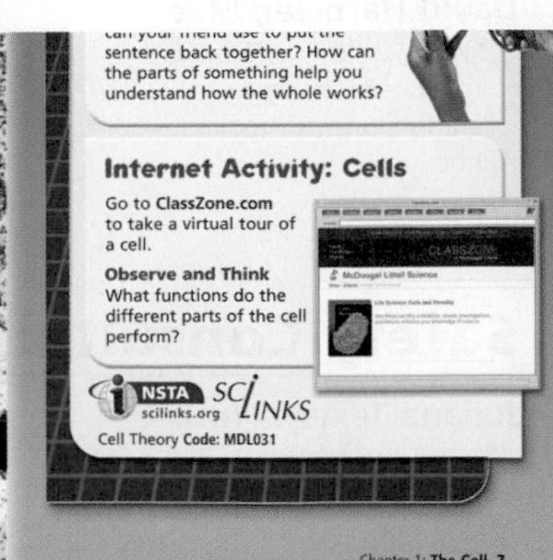

Chapter 1: The Cell 7

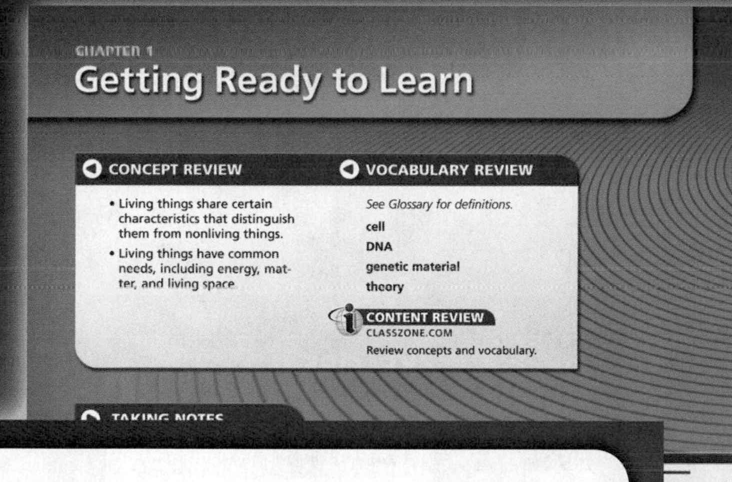

Effective Instructional Strategies

McDougal Littell Science incorporates strategies that research shows are effective in improving student achievement. These strategies include

- Note taking and nonlinguistic representations (Marzano, Pickering, and Pollock)
- A focus on big ideas (Kame'enui and Carnine)
- Background knowledge and active involvement (Project CRISS)

Robert J. Marzano, Debra J. Pickering, and Jane E. Pollock, *Classroom Instruction That Works: Research-Based Strategies for Increasing Student Achievement* (ASCD, 2001)

Edward J. Kame'enui and Douglas Carnine, *Effective Teaching Strategies That Accommodate Diverse Learners* (Pearson, 2002)

Project CRISS (Creating Independence Through Student-Owned Strategies)

Comprehensive Research, Review, and Field Testing

An ongoing program of research and review guided the development of *McDougal Littell Science.*

- Program plans based on extensive data from classroom visits, research surveys, teacher panels, and focus groups
- All pupil edition activities and labs classroom-tested by middle school teachers and students
- All chapters reviewed for clarity and scientific accuracy by the Content Reviewers listed on page T5
- Selected chapters field-tested in the classroom to assess student learning, ease of use, and student interest

Content Organized Around Big Ideas

Each chapter develops a big idea of science, helping students to place key concepts in context.

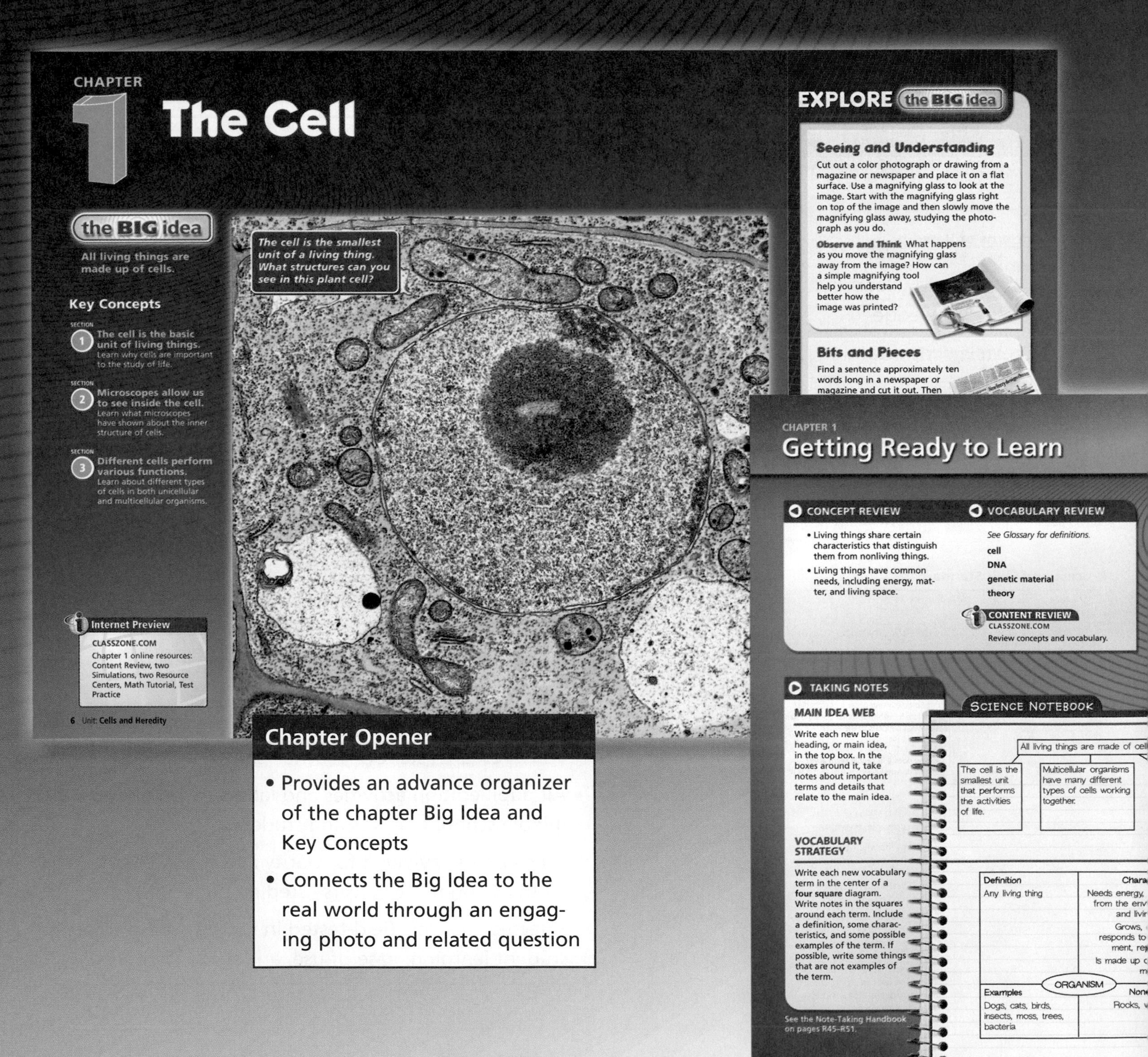

Chapter Opener

- Provides an advance organizer of the chapter Big Idea and Key Concepts
- Connects the Big Idea to the real world through an engaging photo and related question

Visual Summary

- Summarizes Key Concepts using both text and visuals
- Reinforces the connection of Key Concepts to the Big Idea

1 Chapter Review

the BIG idea

All living things are made up of cells.

CONTENT REVIEW
CLASSZONE.COM

KEY CONCEPTS SUMMARY

1 The cell is the basic unit of living things.

All living things are made up of one or more cells. **Organisms** share the following characteristics:

- organization
- ability to grow and develop
- ability to respond
- ability to reproduce

Multicellular organisms include this frog and these water-lily plants.

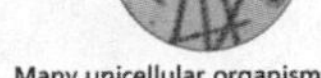

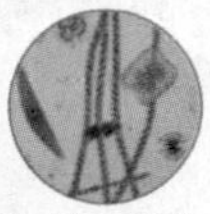

Many unicellular organisms live in pond water.

VOCABULARY
organism p. 9
unicellular p. 11
multicellular p. 11
microscope p. 12
bacteria p. 14

2 Microscopes allow us to see inside the cell.

A **prokaryotic cell** is relatively simple in structure, with no nucleus or other organelles. A **eukaryotic cell** is more complex, with many different organelles inside it.

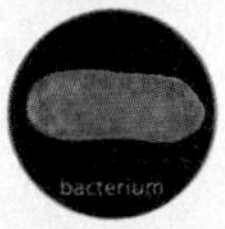

bacterium

A bacterium consists of a single prokaryotic cell.

plant cell   animal cell

Plants and animals are made up of many eukaryotic cells.

VOCABULARY
cell membrane p. 20
cytoplasm p. 20
nucleus p. 20
eukaryotic cell p. 20
prokaryotic cell p. 20
organelle p. 20
cell wall p. 21
chloroplast p. 23
mitochondria p. 23

3 Different cells perform v... functions.

- The single cell of a unicellular or... that is necessary for the organism to s...
- A multicellular organism is a com... **specialized** cells.
- Scientific models make it easier t... cells.

The tarsier ... of organiza...

Reviewing Vocabulary

1–5. Use a vocabulary term to identify each numbered part of this plant cell.

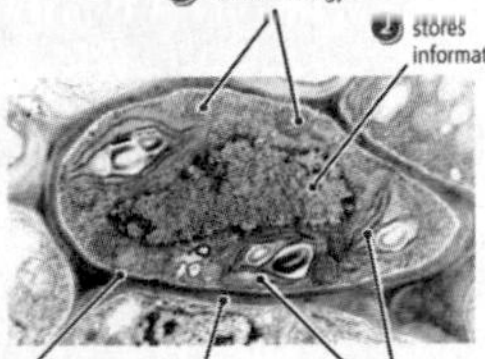

1 releases energy
2 stores information
3 captures energy
4 provides protection and support
5 encloses cytoplasm and organelles

In one or two sentences, describe how the terms in each of the following pairs are related. Underline each term in your answer.

6. unicellular, multicellular
7. cell, organelle
8. prokaryotic cell, eukaryotic cell
9. tissue, organ

Reviewing Key Concepts

... the best ... f the cell ... gs. ... ell mem- ... ght. ... cells.

Section Opener

- Highlights the Key Concept
- Connects new learning to prior knowledge
- Previews important vocabulary

KEY CONCEPT

1.1 The cell is the basic unit of living things.

BEFORE, you learned
- Living things have common characteristics
- Living things have common needs
- A theory is something that explains what is observed in nature

NOW, you will learn
- How living things are different from nonliving things
- How the microscope led to the discovery of cells
- About the cell theory

VOCABULARY
organism p. 9
unicellular p. 11
multicellular p. 11
microscope p. 12
bacteria p. 14

EXPLORE Activity and Life

Does a candle show signs of life?

PROCEDURE
1. Carefully light one candle.
2. Sit quietly and observe the candle. Note its behavior. What does the flame do? What happens to the wax?

WHAT DO YOU THINK?
- How does a lit candle seem alive?
- How do you know for sure that it is not?

MATERIALS
- small candle
- candleholder
- matches

Living things are different from nonliving things.

MAIN IDEA WEB
Make a main idea web about living things, including how they differ from nonliving things.

You know life when you see it. Perhaps your class takes a field trip to a local state park to collect water samples. You are surrounded by trees. There is a stream, with rocks covered with moss and green algae. There are fish and frogs; there are birds and insects. You are surrounded by life. But how would you define it?

One way to answer the question is to think about what makes a living thing different from a nonliving thing. You might ask if a thing uses energy. Or maybe you would observe it to see if it moves. You could investigate whether it consumes food and water. These are characteristics of living things, or organisms. Any individual form of life that uses energy to carry out its activities is an **organism**. Most organisms move. All organisms get water and other materials from the environment.

Chapter 1: **The Cell 9**

Thinking Critically

Questions 18–20 refer to polar bears and their cells as examples of animals and animal cells.

18. **PREDICT** Some polar bears go through long periods of sleep during the cold winter months. In what two ways might their fat cells help the bears survive during these periods?
19. **PROVIDE EXAMPLES** Animals do not get energy directly from the Sun as plants do. Give one or two examples of body systems in a polar bear that help it obtain and process food.
20. **COMPARE AND CONTRAST** Consider the fat cells in a polar bear and compare them with the single body cell of a bacterium. How are the cells alike, and how are they different?
21. **CONNECT** The cell theory applies to all organisms, including you. State the three parts of the cell theory and describe briefly how they relate to you.
22. **ANALYZE** Louis Pasteur designed the swan-necked flask to use in his experiments. In one experiment, he used two flasks of nutrient broth. One flask he heated; the other he left untouched. Bacteria grew in the untouched flask. Nothing grew in the flask that had been heated, or sterilized. How did this experiment help disprove the theory of spontaneous generation?

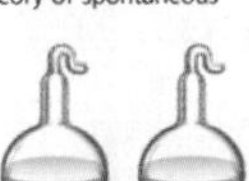

Both ends of flasks are open.

23. **PREDICT** What would happen if the neck of the sterilized swan-necked flask were broken?
24. **IDENTIFY CAUSE** Why does pasteurized milk eventually spoil?
25. **COMPARE AND CONTRAST** A plant cell has a number of structures and organelles that an animal cell does not. Copy the table below and place a check in the appropriate box of each row. The first two are done for you.

	Animal Cell	Plant Cell
Cell wall		✓
Cell membrane	✓	✓
Cytoplasm		
Nucleus		
Central vacuole		
Chloroplast		
Mitochondrion		

the BIG idea

26. **CLASSIFY** Look again at the photograph on pages 6–7. Can you identify any of the structures shown? Can you identify the type of microscope used to make the photograph? How do you know?
27. **CONNECT** What are three ways that an understanding of cells has changed the way people live? **Hint:** Think about Pasteur and his work.

UNIT PROJECTS

If you are doing a unit project, make a folder for your project. Include in your folder a list of the resources you will need, the date on which the project is due, and a schedule to track your progress. Begin gathering data.

36 Unit: **Cells and Heredity**

The Big Idea Questions

- Help students connect their new learning back to the Big Idea
- Prompt students to synthesize and apply the Big Idea and Key Concepts

Many Ways to Learn

Because students learn in so many ways, *McDougal Littell Science* gives them a variety of experiences with important concepts and skills. Text, visuals, activities, and technology all focus on Big Ideas and Key Concepts.

Hands-on Learning

- Activities that reinforce Key Concepts
- Skill Focus for important inquiry and process skills
- Multiple activities in every chapter, from quick Explores to full-period Chapter Investigations

Considerate Text

- Clear structure of meaningful headings
- Information clearly connected to main ideas
- Student-friendly writing style

KEY CONCEPT

4.2 Patterns of heredity can be predicted.

BEFORE, you learned

- Genes are passed from parents to offspring
- Offspring inherit genes in predictable patterns

NOW, you will learn

- How Punnett squares can be used to predict patterns of heredity
- How ratios and probability can be used to predict patterns of heredity

VOCABULARY

Punnett square p. 110
ratio p. 112
probability p. 112
percentage p. 112

EXPLORE Probability

How can probability help predict results?

PROCEDURE

1. Toss both coins 10 times. For each toss, record the combination of heads and/or tails.
2. For each combination (two heads, two tails, or a head and a tail), add up the number of tosses.

MATERIALS

- two coins
- pencil and paper

WHAT DO YOU THINK?

- Which combination happened most often?
- If you tossed both coins one more time, which combination would be the most likely result? Can you know for sure? Why or why not?

Punnett squares show possible outcomes for inheritance.

NOTETAKING STRATEGY
Use a strategy from an earlier chapter or design one of your own to take notes on how Punnett squares show possible patterns of heredity.

Mendel noticed that traits are inherited in patterns. One tool for understanding the patterns of heredity is a graphic called a Punnett square. A **Punnett square** illustrates how the parents' alleles might combine in offspring.

Each parent has two alleles for a particular gene. An offspring receives one allele from each parent. A Punnett square shows how the parents' alleles may be passed on to potential offspring.

The Punnett square on page 111 shows how alleles for pea-plant height would be distributed among offspring in Mendel's first-generation cross. The dominant allele (D) is regular height, and the recessive allele (d) is dwarf height.

The top of the Punnett square shows one parent's alleles for this trait—two dominant regular alleles (DD). The side of the Punnett square shows the other parent's alleles for this trait—two recessive dwarf alleles (dd).

Each box in the Punnett square shows a way the alleles from each parent would combine in potential offspring. You can see that each potential offspring would have the same genotype: one dominant and one recessive allele (Dd). The phenotype of each offspring would show the dominant allele, in this case regular height.

READING TIP
As you read about Punnett squares, connect each sentence with the diagram below.

CHECK YOUR READING What is a Punnett square?

Using Punnett Squares

The Punnett square below shows the possible allele combinations for an offspring of one parent with two dominant (D) regular-height alleles and one parent with two recessive (d) dwarf-height alleles.

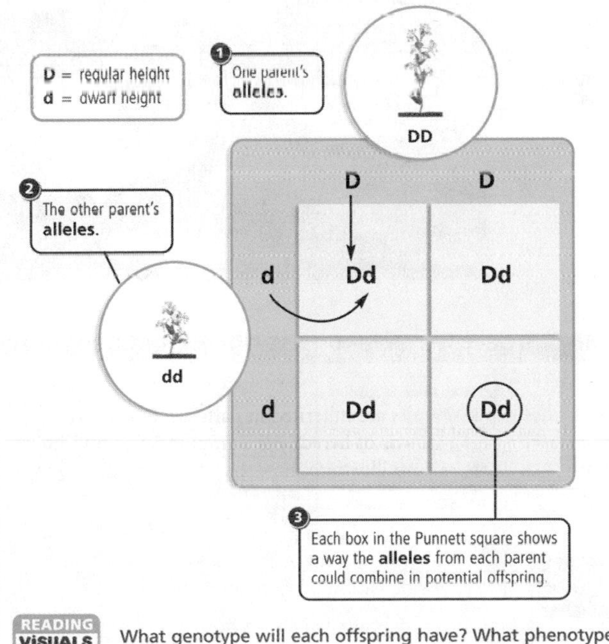

READING VISUALS What genotype will each offspring have? What phenotype?

Predict offspring traits with virtual Punnett squares.

Integrated Technology

- Interaction with Key Concepts through Simulations and Visualizations
- Easy access to relevant Web resources through Resource Centers and SciLinks
- Opportunities for review through Content Review and Math Tutorials

Visuals that Teach

- Information-rich visuals directly connected to the text
- Thoughtful pairing of diagrams and real-world photos
- Reading Visuals questions to support student learning

Differentiated Instruction

A full spectrum of resources for differentiating instruction supports you in reaching the wide range of learners in your classroom.

1.1 INSTRUCT

Develop Critical Thinking

COMPARE AND CONTRAST Have students list characteristics that a flower, a puppy, a house, and a cup of water have in common and ways that they are different. *All four can respond to their environment—if the house has a thermostat. Water can freeze or vaporize. All are organized, including the molecules of water. But only the flower and the puppy can grow, develop, and reproduce.*

Integrate the Sciences

Explorations of the planet Mars have shown it to be cold and sterile. Some scientists believe that Mars once held a vast ocean, however, and if there is or once was water, there is a chance that we'll find life or its traces on Mars. Almost everywhere on Earth that water is found, there is life. So NASA's current exploration strategy for Mars is to follow the water—present or past—in hopes that it will lead to evidence of life.

Ongoing Assessment

CHECK YOUR READING *Answer: organization, ability to develop and grow, ability to respond to the environment, ability to reproduce*

PHOTO CAPTION Answer: Birds and fish both get energy from eating other living things, while grasses get energy from the Sun. They all live near or in the water, and get materials from their surroundings.

Characteristics of Life

Living things have these characteristics:

- organization
- the ability to develop and grow
- the ability to respond to the environment
- the ability to reproduce

An organism's body must be organized in a way that enables it to meet its needs. Some organisms, like bacteria, are very simple. A more complex organism, such as the kingfisher shown in the photograph below, is organized so that different parts of its body perform different jobs, called functions. For example, a kingfisher has wings for flying, a heart for pumping blood, and eyes for seeing.

Another characteristic of organisms is that they grow and, in most cases, develop into adult forms. Some organisms change a great deal in size and appearance throughout their lifetimes, whereas others grow and change very little. Organisms also respond to the world outside them. Think of how the pupils of your eyes get smaller in bright light. Finally, organisms can reproduce, producing new organisms that are similar to themselves.

CHECK YOUR READING What four characteristics are common to all living things?

Needs of Life

Organisms cannot carry out the activities that characterize life without a few necessities: energy, materials, and living space. What does it mean to need energy? You know that if you want to run a race, you need energy. But did you know that your body also needs energy to sleep or to breathe or even to think? All organisms require a steady supply of energy to stay alive. Where does this energy come from, and how does an organism get it? A

APPLY Identify three living things in this photograph. How do they meet their needs?

The energy used by almost all forms of life on Earth comes from the Sun. Some organisms, like plants and some bacteria, are able to capture this energy directly. Your body, like the bodies of other animals, uses food as a source of energy. The food animals eat comes from plants or from organisms that eat plants. Food also provides the materials necessary for growth and reproduction. These materials include substances such as carbon dioxide, nitrogen, oxygen, and water. Finally, all organisms need space to live and grow. If any one of these requirements is missing, an organism will die. B

All living things are made of cells.

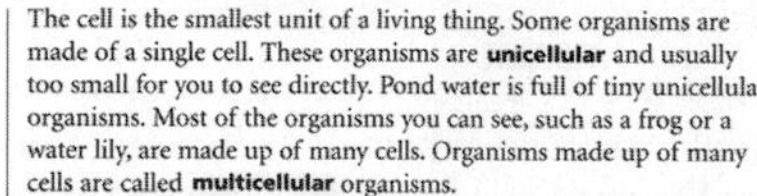

C The cell is the smallest unit of a living thing. Some organisms are made of a single cell. These organisms are **unicellular** and usually too small for you to see directly. Pond water is full of tiny unicellular organisms. Most of the organisms you can see, such as a frog or a water lily, are made up of many cells. Organisms made up of many cells are called **multicellular** organisms.

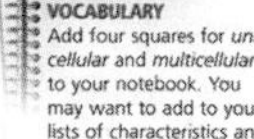

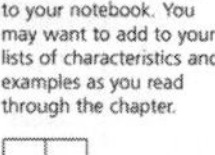

VOCABULARY Add four squares for *unicellular* and *multicellular* to your notebook. You may want to add to your lists of characteristics and examples as you read through the chapter.

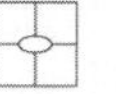

D The needs and characteristics of a single cell in a unicellular organism are the same as those for any organism. Each of the tiny single-celled organisms found in a drop of pond water performs all the activities that characterize life. Multicellular organisms, like a frog or a water lily, have bodies that are more complex. Different parts of the body of a multicellular organism perform different functions. A water lily's roots hold it in the soil and its leaves capture energy from the Sun. A frog moves with its arms and legs and eats with its mouth.

Multicellular organisms have different types of cells that make up their body parts and help the organisms meet their needs. Roots are made of root cells, which are different from leaf cells. Muscle cells have special parts that allow them to move. In a multicellular organism, many cells work together to carry out the basic activities of life.

Multicellular and Unicellular Organisms

READING VISUALS What are some differences between the multicellular and unicellular organisms in this photograph? some similarities?

DIFFERENTIATE INSTRUCTION

More Reading Support

A What does life need a steady supply of? *energy*

B Where does almost all the energy used by life on Earth come from? *the Sun*

English Learners Have students write the definitions for *organism, cell, unicellular, multicellular,* and *microscope* in their Science Word Dictionaries. English learners may not have prior knowledge of how English words can change with a prefix or suffix. For example, compare the meanings of *produce* and *reproduce.* Other words to compare are *characteristic* and *characterize, cell, unicellular,* and *multicellular.*

DIFFERENTIATE INSTRUCTION

More Reading Support

C What is the smallest structure that can perform life activities? *the cell*

D Is a frog a multicellular organism or a unicellular organism? *multicellular*

Advanced Stage a debate among two teams of students about whether or not living things may exist—or ever have existed—in parts of the Solar System other than Earth. Have each team take an opposite position. Their arguments should be persuasive, skeptical, and well-researched.

Have students who are interested in conditions necessary for life read the following article:

R Challenge Reading, pp. 43–44

Teacher's Edition

- More Reading Support for below-level readers
- Strategies for below-level and advanced learners, English learners, and inclusion students

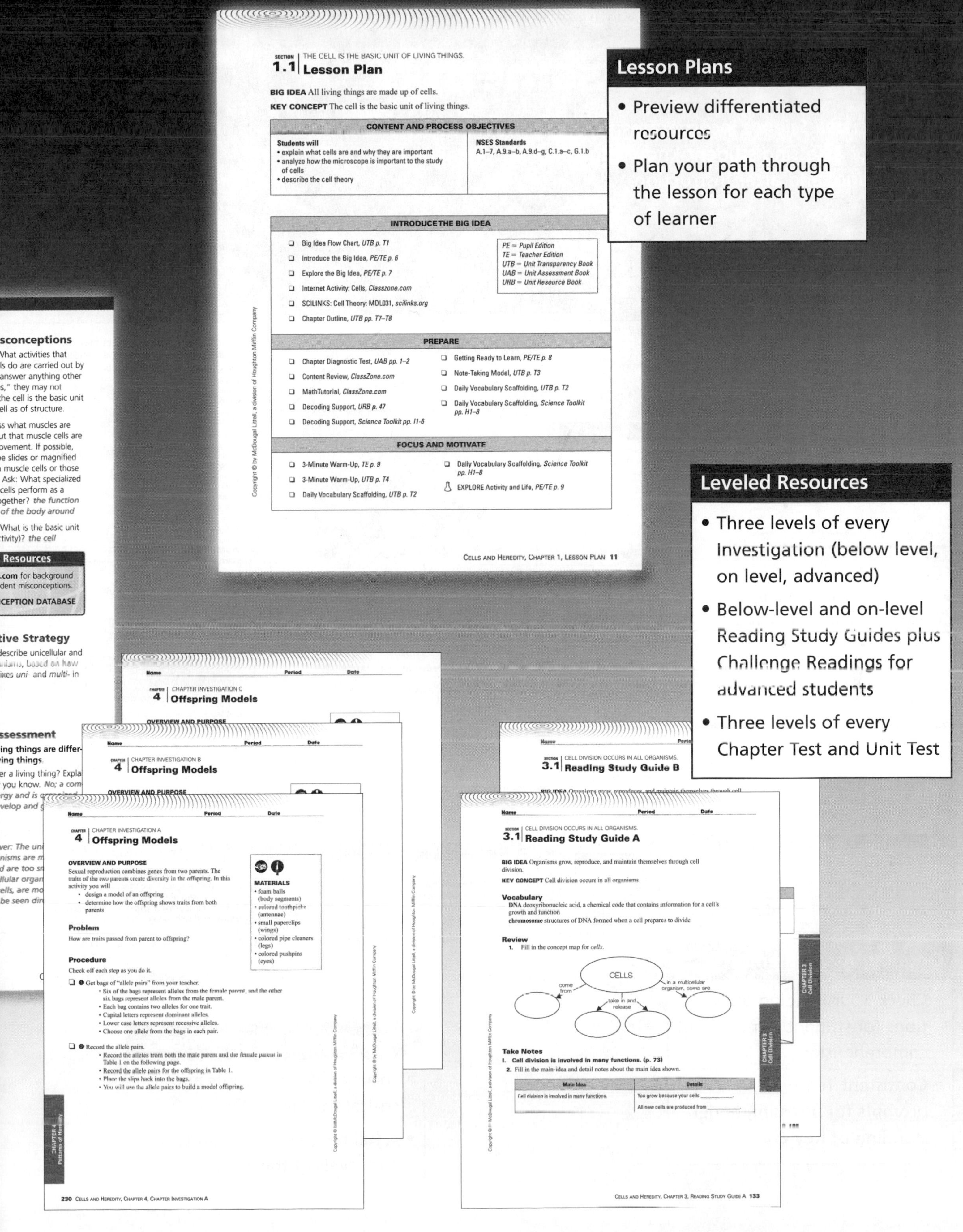

Lesson Plans
• Preview differentiated resources
• Plan your path through the lesson for each type of learner
Leveled Resources
• Three levels of every Investigation (below level, on level, advanced)
• Below-level and on-level Reading Study Guides plus Challenge Readings for advanced students
• Three levels of every Chapter Test and Unit Test
SECTION 1.1 THE CELL IS THE BASIC UNIT OF LIVING THINGS.
Lesson Plan
BIG IDEA All living things are made up of cells.
KEY CONCEPT The cell is the basic unit of living things.
CONTENT AND PROCESS OBJECTIVES
Students will
• explain what cells are and why they are important
• analyze how the microscope is important to the study of cells
• describe the cell theory
NSES Standards
A.1–7, A.9.a–b, A.9.d–g, C.1.a–c, G.1.b
INTRODUCE THE BIG IDEA
Big Idea Flow Chart, UTB p. T1
Introduce the Big Idea, PE/TE p. 6
Explore the Big Idea, PE/TE p. 7
Internet Activity: Cells, Classzone.com
SCILINKS: Cell Theory: MDL031, scilinks.org
Chapter Outline, UTB pp. T7–T8
PE = Pupil Edition
TE = Teacher Edition
UTB = Unit Transparency Book
UAB = Unit Assessment Book
URB = Unit Resource Book
PREPARE
Chapter Diagnostic Test, UAB pp. 1–2
Content Review, ClassZone.com
MathTutorial, ClassZone.com
Decoding Support, URB p. 47
Decoding Support, Science Toolkit pp. I1-6
Getting Ready to Learn, PE/TE p. 8
Note-Taking Model, UTB p. T3
Daily Vocabulary Scaffolding, UTB p. T2
Daily Vocabulary Scaffolding, Science Toolkit pp. H1–8
FOCUS AND MOTIVATE
3-Minute Warm-Up, TE p. 9
3-Minute Warm-Up, UTB p. T4
Daily Vocabulary Scaffolding, UTB p. T2
Daily Vocabulary Scaffolding, Science Toolkit pp. H1–8
EXPLORE Activity and Life, PE/TE p. 9
Copyright © by McDougal Littell, a division of Houghton Mifflin Company
CELLS AND HEREDITY, CHAPTER 1, LESSON PLAN 11
CHAPTER 4 CHAPTER INVESTIGATION C Offspring Models
CHAPTER 4 CHAPTER INVESTIGATION B Offspring Models
CHAPTER 4 CHAPTER INVESTIGATION A Offspring Models
SECTION 3.1 CELL DIVISION OCCURS IN ALL ORGANISMS. Reading Study Guide B
SECTION 3.1 CELL DIVISION OCCURS IN ALL ORGANISMS. Reading Study Guide A

Effective Assessment

McDougal Littell Science incorporates a comprehensive set of resources for assessing student knowledge and performance before, during, and after instruction.

Diagnostic Tests

- Assessment of students' prior knowledge
- Readiness check for concepts and skills in the upcoming chapter

Pasteur's Experiments

Pasteur's experiments showed that bacteria are present in the air. They do not grow spontaneously.

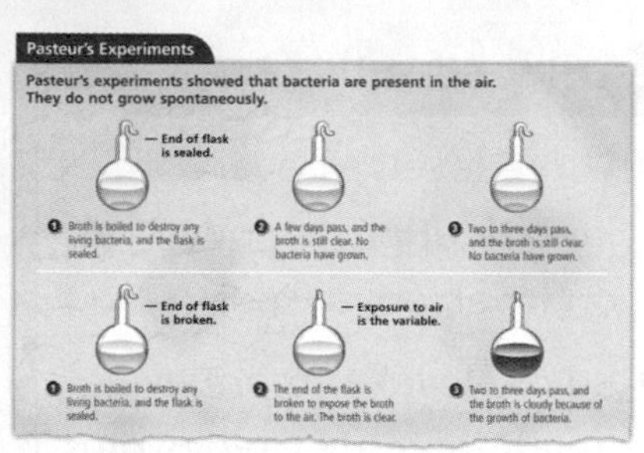

a now-famous series of experiments that disproved spontaneous generation and confirmed the cell theory. He showed that cells come only from other cells. Two of those experiments are shown above. Both began with a sealed flask containing boiled broth. In the first experiment, the flask remained sealed, while in the second experiment, the top of the flask was broken to expose the contents to air. Bacteria grew only in the second flask.

1.1 Review

KEY CONCEPTS

1. Name four characteristics of living things.
2. How did the microscope change human understanding of life?
3. Explain the three concepts that make up the cell theory.

CRITICAL THINKING

4. **Analyze** Relate the characteristics of a scientific theory to the cell theory.
5. **Compare and Contrast** Draw a Venn diagram to compare and contrast multicellular and unicellular organisms.

CHALLENGE

6. **Synthesize** Explain how Pasteur's experiment supported the cell theory and disproved the theory of spontaneous generation.

Chapter 1: **The Cell** 15

ANSWERS

1. organization, growth and development, response to environment, reproduction

2. It allowed people to see cells. Before the microscope humans did not realize that life could be so small.

3. Every living thing is made of one or more cells; cells carry out the functions needed to support life; cells come only from other living cells.

4. The cell theory is widely accepted and explains observations of nature, and is supported by evidence such as Pasteur's experiments.

5. multicellular: many cells, complex, easier to see; unicellular: one cell, cannot be seen directly; both: need energy, materials, and living space

6. In Pasteur's experiment, bacteria did not grow spontaneously. They came from the environment, which indicates that cells come from other cells.

Teach from Visuals

To help students interpret the diagram of Pasteur's experiments, ask:

- What is the difference between the two flasks? *The end of one is broken off so it is open to the air.*
- How would the observer know if a flask was contaminated? *Its contents would be cloudy instead of clear.*

Reinforce (the BIG idea)

Have students relate the section to the Big Idea.

R Reinforcing Key Concepts, p. 20

1.1 ASSESS & RETEACH

Assess

A Section 1.1 Quiz, p. 3

Reteach

Use a triangle diagram to show the three main concepts of cell theory:

Cells — carry out all necessary functions; come only from other cells; are in all living things, even the smallest

- Ask volunteers to give an example for each corner of the triangle.
- Ask volunteers to state their own reasons for why each concept is important.

Technology Resources

Have students visit **ClassZone.com** for reteaching of Key Concepts.

CONTENT REVIEW

CONTENT REVIEW CD-ROM

Chapter 1 **15**

Ongoing Assessment

- Check Your Reading questions for student self-check of comprehension
- Consistent Teacher's Edition prompts for assessing understanding of Key Concepts

Reviewing Vocabulary

1–5. *Use a vocabulary term to identify each numbered part of this plant cell.*

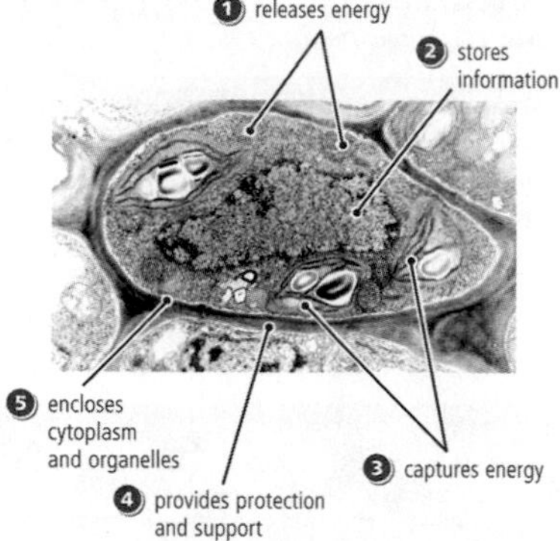

In one or two sentences, describe how the terms in each of the following pairs are related. Underline each term in your answer.

6. unicellular, multicellular
7. cell, organelle
8. prokaryotic cell, eukaryotic cell
9. tissue, organ

Reviewing Key Concepts

Multiple Choice *Choose the letter of the best answer.*

10. Which statement about cells is part of the cell theory?
    a. Cells are found in most living things.
    b. Cells with cell walls do not have cell membranes.
    c. All cells capture energy from sunlight.
    d. Cells come only from other living cells.

11. What structure does a plant cell have that is not found in an animal cell and that allows a plant cell to capture energy from the Sun?
    a. cell wall
    b. chloroplast
    c. mitochondrion
    d. central vacuole

12. Which technology was important to the development of the cell theory?
    a. computer
    b. scientific model
    c. microscope
    d. refrigeration

13. Organisms can be divided into domains on the basis of the characteristics of their cells. What are these domains?
    a. Archaea, Bacteria, and Eukarya
    b. prokaryotes and eukaryotes
    c. plants, animals, and bacteria
    d. unicellular and multicellular

14. Cells in a complex multicellular organism have different levels of organization. What is the order of these levels?
    a. cell membrane, cytoplasm, nucleus
    b. tissues, organs, organ systems
    c. tissues, organs, specialized cells
    d. cell membrane, organelles, nucleus

15. What is the function of the genetic material in a cell?
    a. provides transport of materials from the nucleus to the cell membrane
    b. breaks down materials brought into the cell
    c. provides information a cell needs to function and grow
    d. controls what comes into a cell and what goes out

Short Answer *Write a short answer to each question.*

16. What are four characteristics common to all living things?
17. What are three needs common to all living things?

Chapter 1: **The Cell** 35

Section and Chapter Reviews

- Focus on Key Concepts and critical thinking skills
- A full range of question types and levels of thinking

Leveled Chapter and Unit Tests

- Three levels of test for every chapter and unit
- Same Big Ideas, Key Concepts, and essential skills assessed on all levels

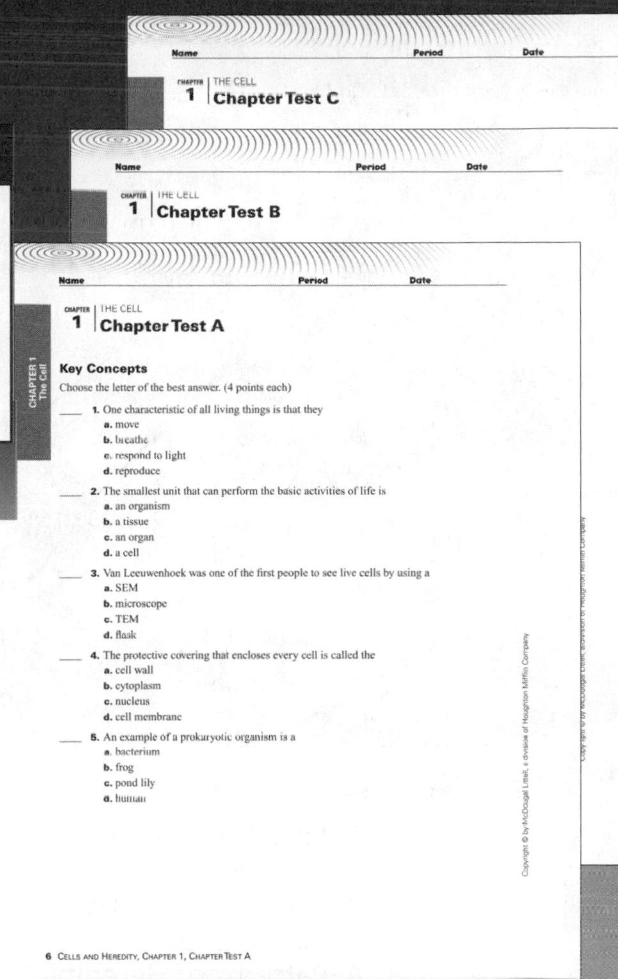

Name Period Date

CHAPTER 1 | THE CELL
Chapter Test C

Name Period Date

CHAPTER 1 | THE CELL
Chapter Test B

Name Period Date

CHAPTER 1 | THE CELL
Chapter Test A

Key Concepts

Choose the letter of the best answer. (4 points each)

____ 1. One characteristic of all living things is that they
a. move
b. breathe
c. respond to light
d. reproduce

____ 2. The smallest unit that can perform the basic activities of life is
a. an organism
b. a tissue
c. an organ
d. a cell

____ 3. Van Leeuwenhoek was one of the first people to see live cells by using a
a. SEM
b. microscope
c. TEM
d. flask

____ 4. The protective covering that encloses every cell is called the
a. cell wall
b. cytoplasm
c. nucleus
d. cell membrane

____ 5. An example of a prokaryotic organism is a
a. bacterium
b. frog
c. pond lily
d. human

Copyright © by McDougal Littell, a division of Houghton Mifflin Company

6 CELLS AND HEREDITY, CHAPTER 1, CHAPTER TEST A

Thinking Critically

Questions 18–20 refer to polar bears and their cells as examples of animals and animal cells.

18. PREDICT Some polar bears go through long periods of sleep during the cold winter months. In what two ways might their fat cells help the bears survive during these periods?

19. PROVIDE EXAMPLES Animals do not get energy directly from the Sun as plants do. Give one or two examples of body systems in a polar bear that help it obtain and process food.

20. COMPARE AND CONTRAST Consider the fat cells in a polar bear and compare them with the single body cell of a bacterium. How are the cells alike, and how are they different?

21. CONNECT The cell theory applies to all organisms, including you. State the three parts of the cell theory and describe briefly how they relate to you.

22. ANALYZE Louis Pasteur designed the swan-necked flask to use in his experiments. In one experiment, he used two flasks of nutrient broth. One flask he heated; the other he left untouched. Bacteria grew in the untouched flask. Nothing grew in the flask that had been heated, or sterilized. How did this experiment help disprove the theory of spontaneous generation?

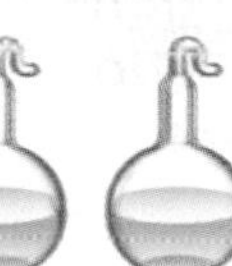

Both ends of flasks are open.

23. PREDICT What would happen if the neck of the sterilized swan-necked flask were broken?

24. IDENTIFY CAUSE Why does pasteurized milk eventually spoil?

25. COMPARE AND CONTRAST A plant cell has a number of structures and organelles that an animal cell does not. Copy the table below and place a check in the appropriate box of each row. The first two are done for you.

	Animal Cell	Plant Cell
Cell wall		✓
Cell membrane	✓	✓
Cytoplasm		
Nucleus		
Central vacuole		
Chloroplast		
Mitochondrion		

the BIG idea

26. CLASSIFY Look again at the photograph on pages 6–7. Can you identify any of the structures shown? Can you identify the type of microscope used to make the photograph? How do you know?

27. CONNECT What are three ways that an understanding of cells has changed the way people live? **Hint:** Think about Pasteur and his work.

UNIT PROJECTS

If you are doing a unit project, make a folder for your project. Include in your folder a list of the resources you will need, the date on which the

36 Unit: Cells and Heredity

Rubrics

- Rubrics in Teacher's Edition for all extended-response questions
- Rubrics for all Unit Projects
- Alternative Assessment with rubric for each chapter
- A wide range of additional rubrics in the Science Toolkit

McDougal Littell Science: Life, Earth, Physical Series

Each book in this three-book series provides comprehensive coverage of life, earth, or physical science.

- Carefully sequenced units and chapters that consistently connect new learning to prior knowledge
- Focused integration of selected concepts from other sciences and technology
- Complete Student Resource Handbooks in every book

Life Science Units

1 ▶ Cells and Heredity
1. The Cell
2. How Cells Function
3. Cell Division
4. Patterns of Heredity
5. DNA and Modern Genetics

2 ▶ Life Over Time
6. The History of Life on Earth
7. Classification of Living Things
8. Population Dynamics

3 ▶ Diversity of Living Things
9. Single-Celled Organisms and Viruses
10. Introduction to Multicellular Organisms
11. Plants
12. Invertebrate Animals
13. Vertebrate Animals

4 ▶ Ecology
14. Ecosystems and Biomes
15. Interactions Within Ecosystems
16. Human Impact on Ecosystems

5 ▶ Human Biology
17. Systems, Support, and Movement
18. Absorption, Digestion, and Exchange
19. Transport and Protection
20. Control and Reproduction
21. Growth, Development, and Health

Earth Science Units

1 ▶ Earth's Surface
1. Views of Earth Today
2. Minerals
3. Rocks
4. Weathering and Soil Formation
5. Erosion and Deposition

2 ▶ The Changing Earth
6. Plate Tectonics
7. Earthquakes
8. Mountains and Volcanoes
9. Views of Earth's Past
10. Natural Resources

3 ▶ Earth's Waters
11. The Water Planet
12. Freshwater Resources
13. Ocean Systems
14. Ocean Environments

4 ▶ Earth's Atmosphere
15. Earth's Changing Atmosphere
16. Weather Patterns
17. Weather Fronts and Storms
18. Climate and Climate Change

5 ▶ Space Science
19. Exploring Space
20. Earth, Moon, and Sun
21. Our Solar System
22. Stars, Galaxies, and the Universe

Physical Science Units

TEACHER'S EDITION
McDougal Littell
Physical SCIENCE
Chemical Interactions
Waves, Sound, and Light
Matter and Energy
Motion and Forces
Electricity and Magnetism

1 ▶ Matter and Energy
1. Introduction to Matter
2. Properties of Matter
3. Energy
4. Temperature and Heat

2 ▶ Chemical Interactions
5. Atomic Structure and the Periodic Table
6. Chemical Bonds and Compounds
7. Chemical Reactions
8. Solutions
9. Carbon in Life and Materials

3 ▶ Motion and Forces
10. Motion
11. Forces
12. Gravity, Friction, and Pressure
13. Work and Energy
14. Machines

4 ▶ Waves, Sound, and Light
15. Waves
16. Sound
17. Electromagnetic Waves
18. Light and Optics

5 ▶ Electricity and Magnetism
19. Electricity
20. Circuits and Electronics
21. Magnetism

Teaching Resources

A wealth of print and technology resources help you adapt the program to your teaching style and to the specific needs of your students.

Book-Specific Print Resources

Unit Resource Book provides all of the teaching resources for the unit organized by chapter and section.

- Family Letters
- *Scientific American Frontiers* Video Guide
- Unit Projects
- Lesson Plans
- Reading Study Guides (Levels A and B)
- Spanish Reading Study Guides
- Challenge Readings
- Challenge and Extension Activities
- Reinforcing Key Concepts
- Vocabulary Practice
- Math Support and Practice
- Investigation Datasheets
- Chapter Investigations (Levels A, B, and C)
- Additional Investigations (Levels A, B, and C)
- Summarizing the Chapter

Unit Assessment Book contains complete resources for assessing student knowledge and performance.

- Chapter Diagnostic Tests
- Section Quizzes
- Chapter Tests (Levels A, B, and C)
- Alternative Assessments
- Unit Tests (Levels A, B, and C)

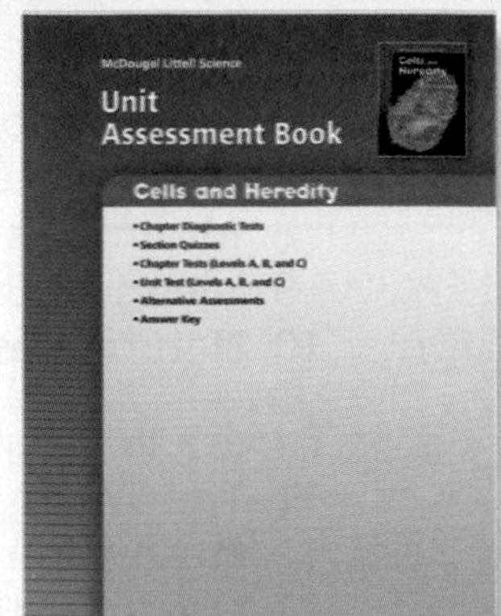

Unit Transparency Book includes instructional visuals for each chapter.

- Three-Minute Warm-Ups
- Note-Taking Models
- Daily Vocabulary Scaffolding
- Chapter Outlines
- Big Idea Flow Charts
- Chapter Teaching Visuals

Lab Manual

Note-Taking/ Reading Study Guide

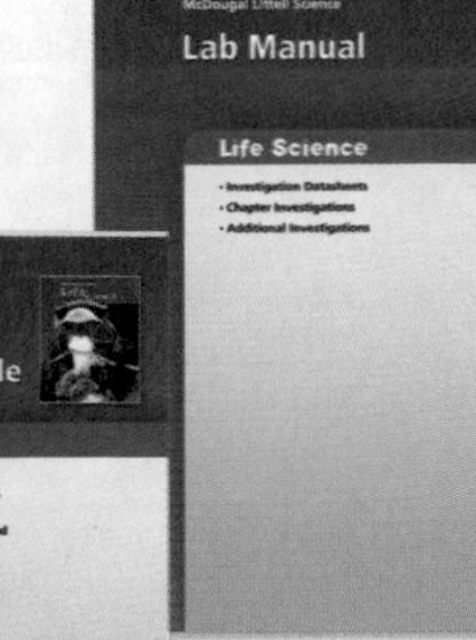

Program-Wide Print Resources

Process and Lab Skills

Problem Solving and Critical Thinking

Standardized Test Practice

Science Toolkit

City Science

Visual Glossary

Multi-Language Glossary

English Learners Package

***Scientific American Frontiers* Video Guide**

How Stuff Works Express
This quarterly magazine offers opportunities to explore current science topics.

Technology Resources

***Scientific American Frontiers* Video Program**
Each specially tailored segment from this award-winning PBS series correlates to a unit; available on VHS and DVD

Audio CDs Complete chapter texts read in both English and Spanish

Lab Generator CD-ROM
A searchable database of all activities from the program plus additional labs for each unit; edit and print your own version of labs

Test Generator CD-ROM

eEdition CD-ROM

EasyPlanner CD-ROM

Content Review CD-ROM

Power Presentations CD-ROM

Online Resources

- ClassZone.com
- Content Review Online
- eEdition Plus Online
- EasyPlanner Plus Online
- eTest Plus Online

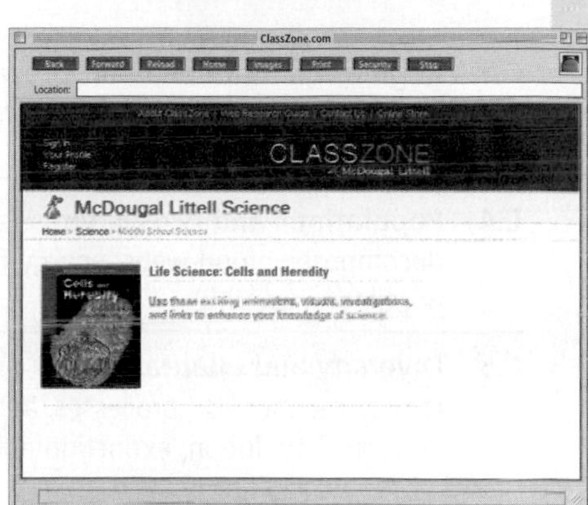

Correlation to National Science Education Standards

This chart provides an overview of how the five units of *McDougal Littell Life Science* address the National Science Education Standards. The complete wording of the standards can be found at the end of this Teacher's Edition.

	A. Science as Inquiry	Chapter and Section
A.1–A.8	**Abilities necessary to do scientific inquiry** Identify questions for investigation; design and conduct investigations; use evidence; think critically and logically; analyze alternative explanations; communicate; use mathematics.	pp. R2–R44, all Chapter Investigations, all Think Science features
A.9	**Understandings about scientific inquiry** Different kinds of investigations for different questions; investigations guided by current scientific knowledge; importance of mathematics and technology for data gathering and analysis; importance of evidence, logical argument, principles, models, and theories; role of legitimate skepticism; scientific investigations lead to new investigations.	pp. xxxviii–xli, 4.3, 6.3, 12.3, 15.2, 17.1

	B. Physical Science	Chapter and Section
B.1	**Properties and changes of properties in matter** Physical properties; substances, elements, and compounds; chemical reactions.	2.1, 3.1 (Connecting Sciences)
B.2	**Motions and forces** Position, speed, direction of motion; balanced and unbalanced forces.	13.2 (Connecting Sciences)
B.3	**Transfer of energy** Energy transfer; forms of energy; heat and light; electrical circuits; sun as source of Earth's energy.	2.2, 14.3, 20.2 (Connecting Sciences)

	C. Life Science	Chapter and Section
C.1	**Structure and function in living systems** Systems; structure and function; levels of organization; cells and cell activities; specialization; human body systems; disease.	1.1, 1.2, 1.3, 2.1, 2.2, 2.3, 3.1, 6, 9.1, 10, 12, 15.1, 17.1, 17.2, 17.3, 18.1, 18.2, 18.3, 19.1, 19.2, 19.3, 20.1, 20.2, 20.3, 21.1, 21.2, 21.3
C.2	**Reproduction and heredity** Sexual and asexual reproduction; heredity and genes; traits determined by heredity and environment.	3.2, 3.3, 4.1, 4.2, 4.3, 5.1, 5.2, 7.1, 9.1, 9.2, 10.4, 11.3, 11.4, 12.2, 12.3, 12.4, 13.2, 13.3, 13.4, 20.3
C.3	**Regulation and behavior** Growth, reproduction, and maintenance of stable internal environment; regulation; behavior; evolution of behavior through adaptation to environment.	9.1, 10.1, 12.1, 13.1, 13.2, 13.3, 13.4, 17.1, 20.1, 20.2, 21.1, 21.2
C.4	**Populations and ecosystems** Populations; ecosystems; producers, consumers, and decomposers; food webs; energy flow; population size and resource availability; population growth.	8.1, 8.2, 8.3, 11.1,14.1, 14.2, 14.3, 15.1, 15.2, 15.3, 16.1, 16.2, 16.3
C.5	**Diversity and adaptations of organisms** Unity and diversity; similarities in internal structures, chemical processes, and evidence of common ancestry; adaptation and biological evolution; extinction and fossil evidence.	6.1, 6.2, 6.3, 7.1, 7.2, 7.3, 12.1, 12.2, 12.3, 12.4, 13.1, 13.2, 13.3, 13.4

D. Earth and Space Science		Chapter and Section
D.1	**Structure of the earth system** Lithosphere, mantle, and core; plate movement and earthquakes, volcanoes, and mountain building; constructive and destructive forces on landforms; soil, weathering, and erosion; water and water cycle; atmosphere, weather, and climate; living organisms in earth system.	8.3, 14.1
D.2	**Earth's history** Continuity of earth processes; impact of occasional catastrophes; fossil evidence.	6.1, pp. R58–R63
D.3	**Earth in the solar system** Sun, planets, asteroids, comets; regular and predictable motion and day, year, phases of the moon, and eclipses; gravity and orbits; sun as source of energy for earth; cause of seasons.	14.3

E. Science and Technology		Chapter and Section
E.1– E.5	**Abilities of technological design** Identify problems; design a solution or product; implement a proposed design; evaluate completed designs or products; communicate the process of technological design.	pp.xlii–xliii, Unit 2 (p. 5)
E.6	**Understandings about science and technology** Similarities and differences between scientific inquiry and technological design; contributions of people in different cultures; reciprocal nature of science and technology; nonexistence of perfectly designed solutions; constraints, benefits, and unintended consequences of technological designs.	pp. xlii–xliii, Frontiers in Science and Timelines in Science features, 5.3, 16.1, 16.2

F. Science in Personal and Social Perspectives		Chapter and Section
F.1	**Personal health** Exercise; fitness; hazards and safety; tobacco, alcohol, and other drugs; nutrition; STDs; environmental health.	10.4, 16.2, 18.2, 21.2, 21.3
F.2	**Populations, resources, and environments** Overpopulation and resource depletion; environmental degradation.	8.2, 8.3, 16.1, 16.2, 16.3
F.3	**Natural hazards** Earthquakes, landslides, wildfires, volcanic eruptions, floods, storms; hazards from human activity; personal and societal challenges.	16.2
F.4	**Risks and benefits** Risk analysis; natural, chemical, biological, social, and personal hazards; decisions based on risks and benefits.	5.3, 16.3, 21.2
F.5	**Science and technology in society** Science's influence on knowledge and world view; societal challenges and scientific research; technological influences on society; contributions from people of different cultures and times; work of scientists and engineers; ethical codes; limitations of science and technology.	5.3, all Timelines in Science features

G. History and Nature of Science		Chapter and Section
G.1	**Science as a human endeavor** Diversity of people working in science, technology, and related fields; abilities required by science.	pp. xxxviii–xli, all Frontiers in Science features
G.2	**Nature of science** Observations, experiments, models; tentative nature of scientific ideas; differences in interpretation of evidence; evaluation of results of investigations, experiments, observations, theoretical models, and explanations; importance of questioning, response to criticism, and communication.	6.2, 6.3, 7.3
G.3	**History of science** Historical examples of inquiry and relationships between science and society; scientists and engineers as valued contributors to culture; challenges of breaking through accepted ideas.	6.2, 21.3 All Frontiers in Science and Timelines in Science features

Correlation to Benchmarks

This chart provides an overview of how the five units of *McDougal Littell Life Science* address the Project 2061 Benchmarks for Science Literacy. The complete wording of the benchmarks can be found at the end of this Teacher's Edition.

1. The Nature of Science	Chapter and Section
	The Nature of Science (pp. xxxiii–xli); 18.3; Think Science Features: 3.1, 7.2, 10.1, 12.2, 16.2, 19.1; Scientific Thinking Handbook (pp R2–R9); Lab Handbook (pp. R10–R35)
3. The Nature of Technology	**Chapter and Section**
	The Nature of Technology (pp. xlii–xliii); 5.3, 8.3, 16.3; Timelines in Science Features
4. The Physical Setting	**Chapter and Section**
4.B THE EARTH	8.3, 14.1, 14.2, 15
4.C PROCESSES THAT SHAPE THE EARTH	8.3, 11.4, 16.1, 16.2
4.D STRUCTURE OF MATTER	2.1, 14.2
4.E ENERGY TRANSFORMATIONS	6.3, 10.2
5. The Living Environment	**Chapter and Section**
5.A DIVERSITY OF LIFE	
5.A.1 Differences among plants, animals, and other organisms	9.1, 10.2, 10.3, 10.4, 14.3
5.A.2 Body plans and internal structures for food and reproduction.	7, 10.2, 10.3, 11, 12, 13
5.A.3 Similarities among organisms in internal and external structures used to determine relatedness	7.1, 7.2, 7.3, 12.1, 12.2, 12.3, 12.4
5.A.4 For sexually reproducing organisms, a species comprises all organisms that can mate with one another to produce fertile offspring.	15.1
5.A.5 Interconnected global food webs and cycles	11.4, 14.3
5.B HEREDITY	
5.B.1 In some species, all the genes come from a single parent; whereas in organisms that have sexes, typically half of the genes come from each parent.	3.3, 4
5.B.2 Sexual reproduction and the transmission of genetic information	4.1, 4.3, 5.1, 10.1, 20.3
5.B.3 New varieties of plants and domestic animals from selective breeding	5.2, 5.3, 6.2
5.C CELLS	
5.C.1 All living things are composed of cells; tissues and organs	1, 9, 10.1
5.C.2 Cells divide to make more cells for growth and repair. Various organs and tissues function to serve the needs of cells for food, air, and waste removal.	3.1, 3.2, 3.3, 10.1
5.C.3 Within cells, many basic functions of organisms are carried out; way in which cells function is similar in all living organisms.	1.2, 2, 9, 10.1
5.C.4 About two thirds of the weight of cells is accounted for by water, which gives cells many of their properties.	2.1

	Chapter and Section
5.D INTERDEPENDENCE OF LIFE	
5.D.1 In all environments, organisms with similar needs may compete for resources; growth and survival of organisms depend on the physical conditions	8.1, 8.2, 14.1, 15.2
5.D.2 Producer/consumer, predator/prey, or parasite/host relationships; scavengers and decomposers; competitive or mutually beneficial relationships.	10.1, 10.2, 10.3, 10.4, 14.3, 15.2
5.E FLOW OF MATTER AND ENERGY	
5.E.1 Food molecules as fuel and building material for all organisms; photosynthesis and producers; consumers.	2.1, 2.2, 10.2, 10.3, 11.1, 14.3
5.E.2 Flow of energy through living systems; amount of matter remains constant, even though its form and location change.	14.2, 14.3
5.E.3 Energy can change from one form to another in living things; almost all food energy comes originally from sunlight.	1.2, 2.2, 10.2, 10.3, 14.3
5.F EVOLUTION OF LIFE	
5.F.1 Small differences between parents and offspring can accumulate in successive generations so that descendants are very different from their ancestors.	5.2, 5.3, 6.2, 6.3
5.F.2 Individual organisms with certain traits are more likely than others to survive and have offspring. Changes in environmental conditions can affect the survival of individual organisms and entire species.	6.1, 6.2, 13
5.F.3 Sedimentary rock layers as evidence for the long history of the earth and of changing life forms whose remains are found in the rocks.	6.1, Unit 2 pp. R52–R57

6. The Human Organism	Chapter and Section
6.A HUMAN IDENTITY	17, 18, 19, 20
6.B HUMAN DEVELOPMENT	10.1, 13.4, 20, 21
6.C BASIC FUNCTIONS	10.1, 13.4, 17, 18, 19, 20
6.E PHYSICAL HEALTH	9.2, 9.3, 9.4, 16.2, 19, 21
8. The Designed World	5.3, 8.3, 14.3, 16.2, 16.3
9. The Mathematical World	All Math in Science Features
10. Historical Perspectives	1.1, 1.2

12. Habits of Mind	Chapter and Section
12.A VALUES AND ATTITUDES	Think Science Features: 1.3, 4.3, 6.3, 12.3, 15.2, 17.1
12.B COMPUTATION AND ESTIMATION	All Math in Science Features, Lab Handbook (pp. R10–R35)
12.C MANIPULATION AND OBSERVATION	All Investigates and Chapter Investigations
12.D COMMUNICATION SKILLS	All Chapter Investigations, Lab Handbook (pp. R10–R35)
12.E CRITICAL-RESPONSE SKILLS	Think Science Features: 1.3, 4.3, 6.3, 12.3, 15.2, 17.1; Scientific Thinking Handbook (pp. R2–R9)

Planning the Unit

The Pacing Guide provides suggested pacing for all chapters in the unit as well as the two unit features shown below.

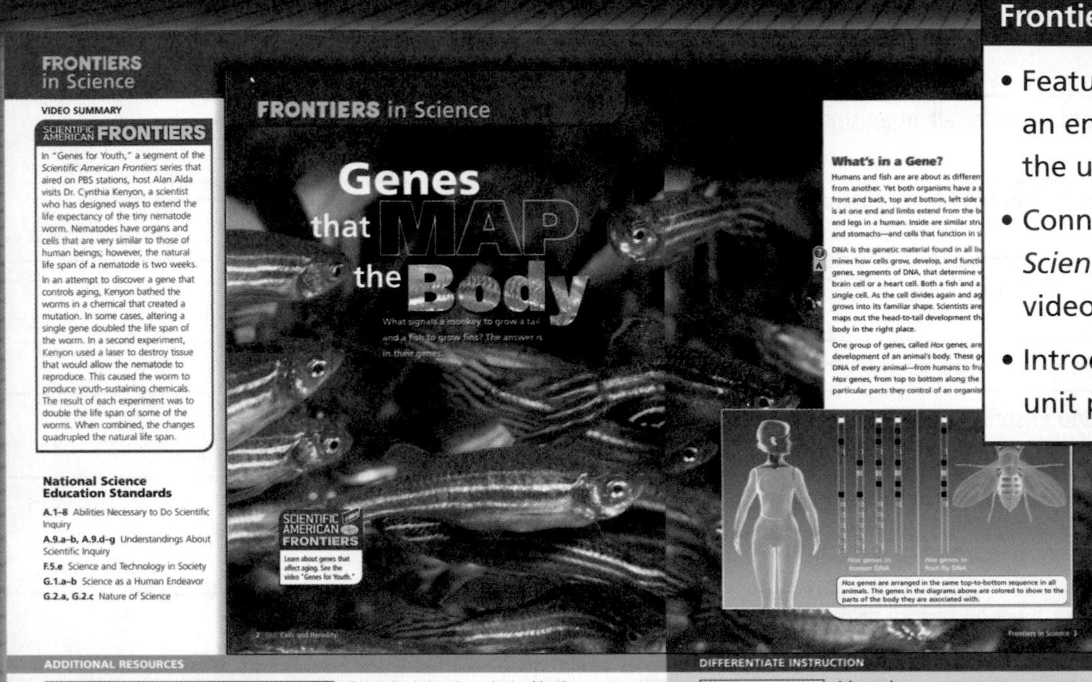

Frontiers in Science

- Features cutting-edge research as an engaging point of entry into the unit
- Connects to an accompanying *Scientific American Frontiers* video and viewing guide
- Introduces three options for unit projects

Timelines in Science

- Traces the history of key scientific discoveries
- Highlights interactions between science and technology

Cells and Heredity Pacing Guide

The following pacing guide shows how the chapters in *Cells and Heredity* can be adapted to fit your specific course needs. If you need to cover 5 units in a year, reduce the number of periods spent on the last section of each chapter by making the Chapter Review the homework.

	TRADITIONAL SCHEDULE (DAYS)	BLOCK SCHEDULE (DAYS)
Frontiers in Science: Genes That Map the Body	1	0.5
Chapter 1 The Cell		
1.1 The cell is the basic unit of living things.	2	1
1.2 Microscopes allow us to see inside the cell.	2	1
1.3 Different cells perform various functions.	3	1.5
Chapter Investigation	1	0.5
Chapter 2 How Cells Function		
2.1 Chemical reactions take place inside cells.	2	1
2.2 Cells capture and release energy.	2	1
2.3 Materials move across the cell's membranes.	3	1.5
Chapter Investigation	1	0.5
Chapter 3 Cell Division		
3.1 Cell division occurs in all organisms.	2	1
3.2 Cell division is part of the cell cycle.	2	1
3.3 Both sexual and asexual reproduction involve cell division.	3	1.5
Chapter Investigation	1	0.5
Chapter 4 Patterns of Heredity		
4.1 Living things inherit traits in patterns.	2	1
4.2 Patterns of heredity can be predicted.	2	1
4.3 Meiosis is a special form of cell division.	3	1.5
Chapter Investigation	1	0.5
Timelines in Science: The Story of Genetics	1	0.5
Chapter 5 DNA and Modern Genetics		
5.1 DNA and RNA are required to make proteins.	2	1
5.2 Changes in DNA can produce variation.	2	1
5.3 Modern genetics uses DNA technology.	3	1.5
Chapter Investigation	1	0.5
Total Days for Unit	**42**	**21**

Life Over Time Pacing Guide

The following pacing guide shows how the chapters in ***Life Over Time*** can be adapted to fit your specific course needs. If you need to cover 5 units in a year, reduce the number of periods spent on the last section of each chapter by making the Chapter Review the homework.

	TRADITIONAL SCHEDULE (DAYS)	BLOCK SCHEDULE (DAYS)
Frontiers in Science: Life by Degrees	1	0.5
Chapter 6 The History of Life on Earth		
6.1 Earth has been home to living things for about 3.8 billion years.	2	1
6.2 Species change over time.	2	1
6.3 Many types of evidence support evolution.	3	1.5
Chapter Investigation	1	0.5
Chapter 7 Classification of Living Things		
7.1 Scientists develop systems for classifying living things.	2	1
7.2 Biologists use seven levels of classification.	2	1
7.3 Classification systems change as scientists learn more.	3	1.5
Chapter Investigation	1	0.5
Timelines in Science: Life Unearthed	1	0.5
Chapter 8 Population Dynamics		
8.1 Populations have many characteristics.	2	1
8.2 Populations respond to pressures.	2	1
8.3 Human populations have unique responses to change.	3	1.5
Chapter Investigation	1	0.5
Total Days for Unit	**26**	**13**

Diversity of Living Things Pacing Guide

The following pacing guide shows how the chapters in ***Diversity of Living Things*** can be adapted to fit your specific course needs. If you need to cover 5 units in a year, reduce the number of periods spent on the last section of each chapter by making the Chapter Review the homework.

	TRADITIONAL SCHEDULE (DAYS)	BLOCK SCHEDULE (DAYS)
Frontiers in Science: Chilling Changes	1	0.5
Chapter 9 Single-Celled Organisms and Viruses		
9.1 Single-celled organisms have all the characteristics of living things.	2	1
9.2 Bacteria are single-celled organisms without nuclei.	2	1
9.3 Viruses are not alive but affect all living things.	2	1
9.4 Protists are a diverse group of organisms.	3	1.5
Chapter Investigation	1	0.5
Chapter 10 Introduction to Multicellular Organisms		
10.1 Multicellular organisms meet their needs in different ways.	2	1
10.2 Plants are producers.	2	1
10.3 Animals are consumers.	2	1
10.4 Most fungi are decomposers.	3	1.5
Chapter Investigation	1	0.5
Chapter 11 Plants		
11.1 Plants are adapted to living on land.	2	1
11.2 Most mosses and ferns live in moist environments.	2	1
11.3 Seeds and pollen are reproductive adaptations.	2	1
11.4 Many plants reproduce with flowers and fruit.	3	1.5
Chapter Investigation	1	0.5
Timelines in Science: Discoveries in Biodiversity	1	0.5
Chapter 12 Invertebrate Animals		
12.1 Most animals are invertebrates.	2	1
12.2 Cnidarians and worms have different body plans.	2	1
12.3 Most mollusks have shells and echinoderms have spiny skeletons.	2	1
12.4 Arthropods have exoskeletons and joints.	3	1.5
Chapter Investigation	1	0.5
Chapter 13 Vertebrate Animals		
13.1 Vertebrates are animals with endoskeletons.	2	1
13.2 Amphibians and reptiles are adapted for life on land.	2	1
13.3 Birds meet their needs on land, in water, and in the air.	2	1
13.4 Mammals live in many environments.	3	1.5
Chapter Investigation	1	0.5
Total Days for Unit	**52**	**26**

Ecology Pacing Guide

The following pacing guide shows how the chapters in ***Ecology*** can be adapted to fit your specific course needs. If you need to cover 5 units in a year, reduce the number of periods spent on the last section of each chapter by making the Chapter Review the homework.

	TRADITIONAL SCHEDULE (DAYS)	BLOCK SCHEDULE (DAYS)
Frontiers in Science: Ecosystems on Fire	1	0.5
Chapter 14 Ecosystems and Biomes		
14.1 Ecosystems support life.	2	1
14.2 Matter cycles through ecosystems.	2	1
14.3 Energy flows through ecosystems.	2	1
14.4 Biomes contain many ecosystems.	3	1.5
Chapter Investigation	1	0.5
Chapter 15 Interactions Within Ecosystems		
15.1 Groups of living things interact within ecosystems.	2	1
15.2 Organisms can interact in different ways.	2	1
15.3 Ecosystems are always changing.	3	1.5
Chapter Investigation	1	0.5
Timelines in Science: Wilderness Conservation	1	0.5
Chapter 16 Human Impact on Ecosystems		
16.1 Human population growth presents challenges.	2	1
16.2 Human activities affect the environment.	2	1
16.3 People are working to protect ecosystems.	3	1.5
Chapter Investigation	1	0.5
Total Days for Unit	**28**	**14**

Human Biology Pacing Guide

The following pacing guide shows how the chapters in ***Human Biology*** can be adapted to fit your specific course needs. If you need to cover 5 units in a year, reduce the number of periods spent on the last section of each chapter by making the Chapter Review the homework.

	TRADITIONAL SCHEDULE (DAYS)	BLOCK SCHEDULE (DAYS)
Frontiers in Science: Surprising Senses	1	0.5
Chapter 17 Systems, Support, and Movement		
17.1 The human body is complex.	2	1
17.2 The skeletal system provides support and protection.	2	1
17.3 The muscular system makes movement possible.	3	1.5
Chapter Investigation	1	0.5
Chapter 18 Absorption, Digestion, and Exchange		
18.1 The respiratory system gets oxygen and removes carbon dioxide.	2	1
18.2 The digestive system breaks down food.	2	1
18.3 The urinary system removes waste materials.	3	1.5
Chapter Investigation	1	0.5
Chapter 19 Transport and Protection		
19.1 The circulatory system transports materials.	2	1
19.2 The immune system defends the body.	2	1
19.3 The integumentary system shields the body.	3	1.5
Chapter Investigation	1	0.5
Timelines in Science: Seeing Inside the Body	1	0.5
Chapter 20 Control and Reproduction		
20.1 The nervous system responds and controls.	2	1
20.2 The endocrine system helps regulate body conditions.	2	1
20.3 The reproductive system allows the production of offspring.	3	1.5
Chapter Investigation	1	0.5
Chapter 21 Growth, Development, and Health		
21.1 The human body changes over time.	2	1
21.2 Systems in the body function to maintain health.	2	1
21.3 Science helps people prevent and treat disease.	3	1.5
Chapter Investigation	1	0.5
Total Days for Unit	**42**	**21**

Planning the Chapter

Complete planning support precedes each chapter.

Previewing Content

- Section-by-section science background notes
- Common Misconceptions notes

CHAPTER 1 **The Cell**

Life Science
UNIFYING PRINCIPLES

PRINCIPLE 1 All living things share common characteristics.

PRINCIPLE 2 All living things share common needs.

PRINCIPLE 3 Living things r... needs through... with the envir...

PRINCIPLE 4

Unit 1: Cells and Heredity
BIG IDEAS

CHAPTER 1 The Cell All living things are made up of cells.

CHAPTER 2 How Cells Function All cells need energy and materials for life processes.

CHAPTER 3 Cell Division Organisms grow, reproduce, and maintain themselves through cell division.

CHAPTER 1
KEY CONCEPTS

SECTION 1

The cell is the basic unit of living things.
1. Living things are different from nonliving things.
2. All living things are made of cells.
3. The microscope led to the discovery of cells.
4. Cells come from other cells.
5. The cell theory is important to the study of biology.

SECTION 2

Microscopes allow us to see inside the cell.
1. The microscope is an important too...
2. Cells are diverse.
3. Plants and animals have eukaryotic cells.

The Big Idea Flow Chart is available on p. T1 in the **UNIT TRANSPARENCY BOOK**

5A Unit: **Cells and Heredity**

Previewing Content

SECTION  **The cell is the basic unit of living things.** pp. 9–17

1. **Living things are different from nonliving things.** **Organisms** are individual forms of life that use energy to carry out activities. To be classified as living, something must
   - be organized;
   - grow and develop;
   - respond to its environment; and

SECTION 2

1. The m... Three... Light m... micros... smaller... The di...

Previewing Content

SECTION 3 **Different cells perform various functions.** pp. 26–33

1. **Organisms can be classified by their cell type.** Most organisms on Earth are **unicellular.** They can be in one of three domains.
   - **Archaea** are prokaryotes that mostly live in extreme environments.
   - **Bacteria** are prokaryotes that share some similarities with archaea, but grow virtually everywhere on Earth.
   - **Eukarya** are eukaryotes, which include multicellular organisms (plants, animals, fungi, and some protists) and unicellular organisms (some protists).

   Note: Domains, kingdoms, and other classifications remain in flux and debated within the scientific community. Some scientists recognize just five kingdoms (rather than six). Some may refer to domains.

2. **Cells in multicellular organisms specialize.** All multicellular organisms begin life as a single fertilized egg cell. As cells divide, they specialize to perform specific jobs. The more **specialization** there is, the more complex the organism is.

3. **A multicellular organism is a community of cells.** Organisms have different degrees of organization. For example, sponges have specialized cells, but are not strictly organized.
   - Similar cells group together to form **tissues.**
   - Tissues act together to form **organs.**
   - Organs and tissues act together in organ systems.

4. **Scientists use models to study cells.** Scientists use models to make complicated structures or processes easier to understand. Some examples of models include mathematical or chemical equations, diagrams, process models, or physical models.

Complex organisms have a hierarchy of organization, pictured below.

Common Misconceptions

PLANT AND ANIMAL SIMILARITIES Students may think that plants and animals are totally different, even at the cellular level. In fact, the two types of organisms have both differences and similarities.

TE This misconception is addressed on p. 23.

MISCONCEPTION DATABASE
CLASSZONE.COM Background on student misconceptions

TWO KINDS OF CELLS Students often think that all cells are either plant or animal. Many, of course, are neither.

TE This misconception is addressed on p. 28.

5C Unit: **Cells and Heredity**

Previewing Chapter Resources

- Section-by-section listing of all print and technology resources
- Suggested pacing
- Correlations to National Science Education Standards

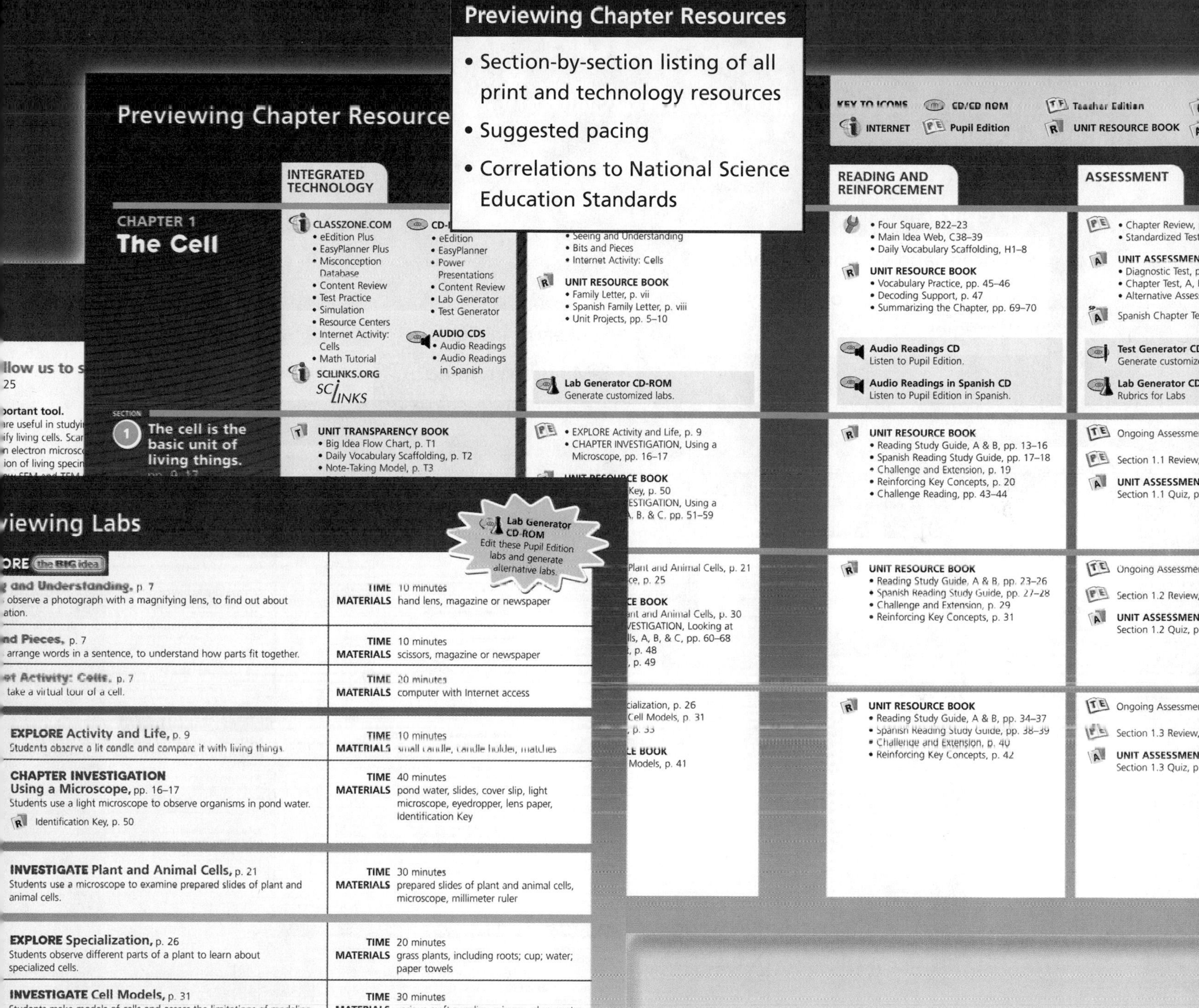

Previewing Labs

- Brief descriptions of all chapter labs and activities
- Time and materials required for each activity

Planning the Lesson

Point-of-use support for each lesson provides a wealth of teaching options.

1. Prepare

- Concept and vocabulary review
- Note-taking and vocabulary strategies

2. Focus

- Set Learning Goals
- 3-Minute Warm-up

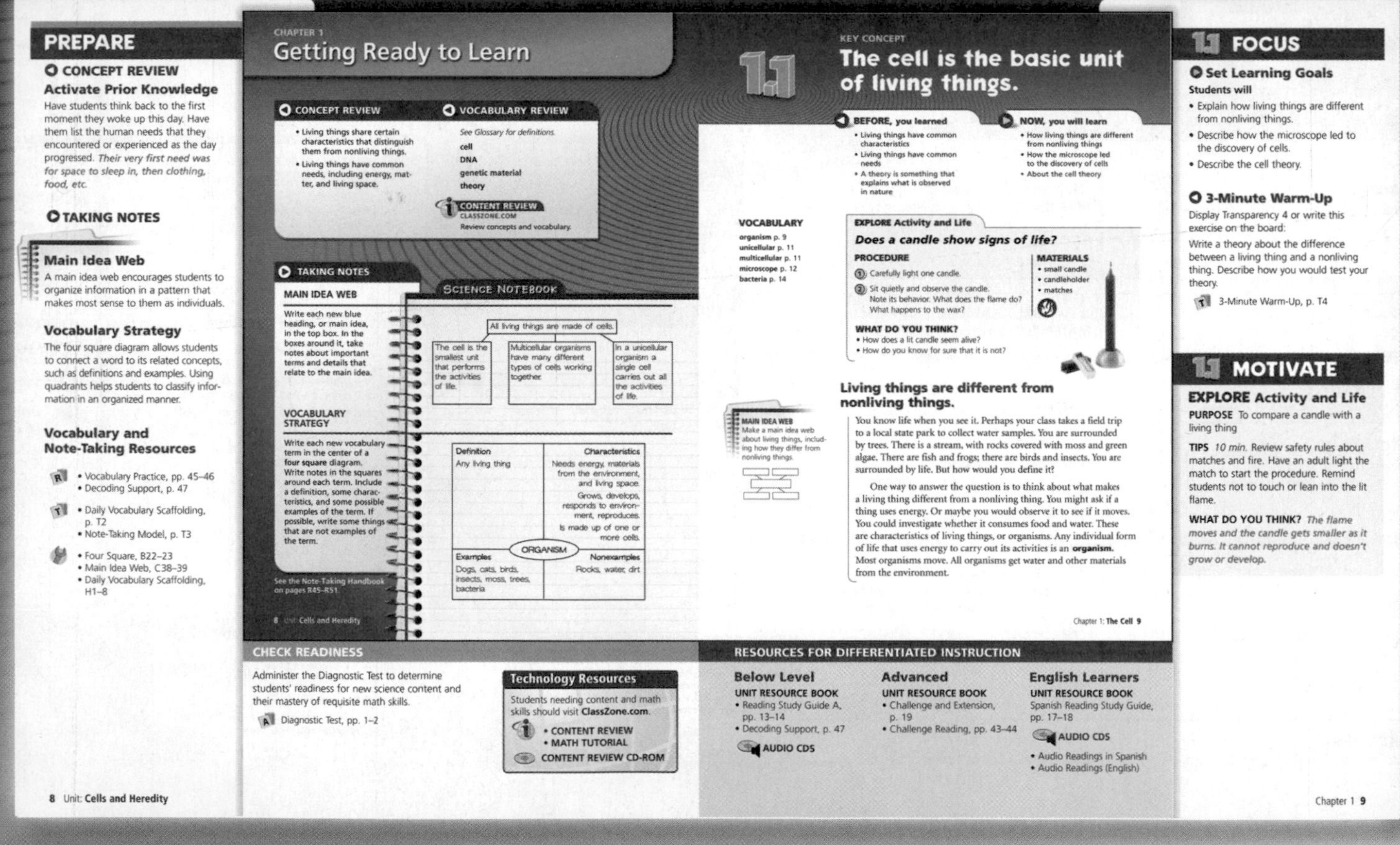

PREPARE

CONCEPT REVIEW

Activate Prior Knowledge

Have students think back to the first moment they woke up this day. Have them list the human needs that they encountered or experienced as the day progressed. *Their very first need was for space to sleep in, then clothing, food, etc.*

TAKING NOTES

Main Idea Web

A main idea web encourages students to organize information in a pattern that makes most sense to them as individuals.

Vocabulary Strategy

The four square diagram allows students to connect a word to its related concepts, such as definitions and examples. Using quadrants helps students to classify information in an organized manner.

Vocabulary and Note-Taking Resources

- Vocabulary Practice, pp. 45–46
- Decoding Support, p. 47
- Daily Vocabulary Scaffolding, p. T2
- Note-Taking Model, p. T3
- Four Square, B22–23
- Main Idea Web, C38–39
- Daily Vocabulary Scaffolding, H1–8

CHAPTER 1

Getting Ready to Learn

CONCEPT REVIEW

- Living things share certain characteristics that distinguish them from nonliving things.
- Living things have common needs, including energy, matter, and living space.

VOCABULARY REVIEW

See Glossary for definitions.

cell
DNA
genetic material
theory

CONTENT REVIEW
CLASSZONE.COM
Review concepts and vocabulary.

TAKING NOTES

MAIN IDEA WEB

Write each new blue heading, or main idea, in the top box. In the boxes around it, take notes about important terms and details that relate to the main idea.

VOCABULARY STRATEGY

Write each new vocabulary term in the center of a **four square** diagram. Write notes in the squares around each term. Include a definition, some characteristics, and some possible examples of the term. If possible, write some things that are not examples of the term.

See the Note-Taking Handbook on pages R45–R51.

SCIENCE NOTEBOOK

All living things are made of cells.
The cell is the smallest unit that performs the activities of life.
Multicellular organisms have many different types of cells working together.
In a unicellular organism a single cell carries out all the activities of life.

Definition: Any living thing
Characteristics: Needs energy, materials from the environment, and living space. Grows, develops, responds to environment, reproduces. Is made up of one or more cells.
ORGANISM
Examples: Dogs, cats, birds, insects, moss, trees, bacteria
Nonexamples: Rocks, water, dirt

8 Unit: Cells and Heredity

KEY CONCEPT

1.1 The cell is the basic unit of living things.

BEFORE, you learned

- Living things have common characteristics
- Living things have common needs
- A theory is something that explains what is observed in nature

NOW, you will learn

- How living things are different from nonliving things
- How the microscope led to the discovery of cells
- About the cell theory

VOCABULARY

organism p. 9
unicellular p. 11
multicellular p. 11
microscope p. 12
bacteria p. 14

EXPLORE Activity and Life

Does a candle show signs of life?

PROCEDURE

1. Carefully light one candle.
2. Sit quietly and observe the candle. Note its behavior. What does the flame do? What happens to the wax?

MATERIALS

- small candle
- candleholder
- matches

WHAT DO YOU THINK?

- How does a lit candle seem alive?
- How do you know for sure that it is not?

Living things are different from nonliving things.

MAIN IDEA WEB
Make a main idea web about living things, including how they differ from nonliving things.

You know life when you see it. Perhaps your class takes a field trip to a local state park to collect water samples. You are surrounded by trees. There is a stream, with rocks covered with moss and green algae. There are fish and frogs; there are birds and insects. You are surrounded by life. But how would you define it?

One way to answer the question is to think about what makes a living thing different from a nonliving thing. You might ask if a thing uses energy. Or maybe you would observe it to see if it moves. You could investigate whether it consumes food and water. These are characteristics of living things, or organisms. Any individual form of life that uses energy to carry out its activities is an **organism.** Most organisms move. All organisms get water and other materials from the environment.

Chapter 1: The Cell 9

1.1 FOCUS

Set Learning Goals

Students will

- Explain how living things are different from nonliving things.
- Describe how the microscope led to the discovery of cells.
- Describe the cell theory.

3-Minute Warm-Up

Display Transparency 4 or write this exercise on the board:

Write a theory about the difference between a living thing and a nonliving thing. Describe how you would test your theory.

3-Minute Warm-Up, p. T4

1.1 MOTIVATE

EXPLORE Activity and Life

PURPOSE To compare a candle with a living thing

TIPS *10 min.* Review safety rules about matches and fire. Have an adult light the match to start the procedure. Remind students not to touch or lean into the lit flame.

WHAT DO YOU THINK? *The flame moves and the candle gets smaller as it burns. It cannot reproduce and doesn't grow or develop.*

CHECK READINESS

Administer the Diagnostic Test to determine students' readiness for new science content and their mastery of requisite math skills.

Diagnostic Test, pp. 1–2

Technology Resources

Students needing content and math skills should visit **ClassZone.com.**

- CONTENT REVIEW
- MATH TUTORIAL

CONTENT REVIEW CD-ROM

RESOURCES FOR DIFFERENTIATED INSTRUCTION

Below Level
UNIT RESOURCE BOOK
- Reading Study Guide A, pp. 13–14
- Decoding Support, p. 47

AUDIO CDS

Advanced
UNIT RESOURCE BOOK
- Challenge and Extension, p. 19
- Challenge Reading, pp. 43–44

English Learners
UNIT RESOURCE BOOK
Spanish Reading Study Guide, pp. 17–18

AUDIO CDS
- Audio Readings in Spanish
- Audio Readings (English)

8 Unit: Cells and Heredity

Chapter 1 9

3. Motivate

- Engaging entry into the section
- Explore activity or Think About question

1.1 INSTRUCT

Develop Critical Thinking

COMPARE AND CONTRAST Have students list characteristics that a flower, a puppy, a house, and a cup of water have in common and ways that they are different. *All four can respond to their environment—if the house has a thermostat. Water can freeze or vaporize. All are organized, including the molecules of water. But only the flower and the puppy can grow, develop, and reproduce.*

Integrate the Sciences

Explorations of the planet Mars have shown it to be cold and sterile. Some scientists believe that Mars once held a vast ocean, however, and if there is or once was water, there is a chance that we'll find life or its traces on Mars. Almost everywhere on Earth that water is found, there is life. So NASA's current exploration strategy for Mars is to follow the water—present or past—in hopes that it will lead to evidence of life.

Ongoing Assessment

CHECK YOUR READING *Answer: organization, ability to develop and grow, ability to respond to the environment, ability to reproduce*

PHOTO CAPTION Answer: Birds and fish both get energy from eating other living things, while grasses get energy from the Sun. They all live near or in the water, and get materials from their surroundings.

Characteristics of Life

Living things have these characteristics:

- organization
- the ability to develop and grow
- the ability to respond to the environment
- the ability to reproduce

An organism's body must be organized in a way that enables it to meet its needs. Some organisms, like bacteria, are very simple. A more complex organism, such as the kingfisher shown in the photograph below, is organized so that different parts of its body perform different jobs, called functions. For example, a kingfisher has wings for flying, a heart for pumping blood, and eyes for seeing.

Another characteristic of organisms is that they grow and, in most cases, develop into adult forms. Some organisms change a great deal in size and appearance throughout their lifetimes, whereas others grow and change very little. Organisms also respond to the world outside them. Think of how the pupils of your eyes get smaller in bright light. Finally, organisms can reproduce, producing new organisms that are similar to themselves.

CHECK YOUR READING What four characteristics are common to all living things?

Needs of Life

Organisms cannot carry out the activities that characterize life without a few necessities: energy, materials, and living space. What does it mean to need energy? You know that if you want to run a race, you need energy. But did you know that your body also needs energy to sleep or to breathe or even to think? All organisms require a steady supply of energy to stay alive. Where does this energy come from, and how does an organism get it? A

The energy used by almost all forms of life on Earth comes from the Sun. Some organisms, like plants and some bacteria, are able to capture this energy directly. Your body, like the bodies of other animals, uses food as a source of energy. The food animals eat comes from plants or from organisms that eat plants. Food also provides the materials necessary for growth and reproduction. These materials include substances such as carbon dioxide, nitrogen, oxygen, and water. Finally, all organisms need space to live and grow. If any one of these requirements is missing, an organism will die. B

APPLY Identify three living things in this photograph. How do they meet their needs?

Food is a source of **energy** and **materials**.

Water provides **materials** and **living space**.

10 Unit: Cells and Heredity

All living things are made of cells.

C The cell is the smallest unit of a living thing. Some organisms are made of a single cell. These organisms are **unicellular** and usually too small for you to see directly. Pond water is full of tiny unicellular organisms. Most of the organisms you can see, such as a frog or a water lily, are made up of many cells. Organisms made up of many cells are called **multicellular** organisms.

D The needs and characteristics of a single cell in a unicellular organism are the same as those for any organism. Each of the tiny single-celled organisms found in a drop of pond water performs all the activities that characterize life. Multicellular organisms, like a frog or a water lily, have bodies that are more complex. Different parts of the body of a multicellular organism perform different functions. A water lily's roots hold it in the soil and its leaves capture energy from the Sun. A frog moves with its arms and legs and eats with its mouth.

Multicellular organisms have different types of cells that make up their body parts and help the organisms meet their needs. Roots are made of root cells, which are different from leaf cells. Muscle cells have special parts that allow them to move. In a multicellular organism, many cells work together to carry out the basic activities of life.

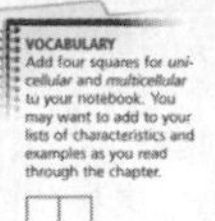

VOCABULARY Add four squares for unicellular and multicellular to your notebook. You may want to add to your lists of characteristics and examples as you read through the chapter.

Multicellular and Unicellular Organisms

Both multicellular and unicellular organisms live in this pond.

There are many **unicellular organisms** in this drop of pond water, magnified 75×.

The frog and water lilies are **multicellular organisms**.

READING VISUALS What are some differences between the multicellular and unicellular organisms in this photograph? some similarities?

Chapter 1: The Cell 11

DIFFERENTIATE INSTRUCTION

More Reading Support

A What does life need a steady supply of? *energy*

English Learners Have students write the definitions for *organism, cell, unicellular, multicellular* and *microscope* in their Science Word Dictionaries. English learners may not have prior knowledge of how English words can change with a prefix or ... compare the meanings of *produce* and ... words to compare are *characteristic* and ... *unicellular,* and *multicellular*.

DIFFERENTIATE INSTRUCTION

More Reading Support

C What is the smallest structure that can perform life activities? *the cell*

D Is a frog a multicellular organism or a unicellular ...

Advanced Stage a debate among two teams of students about whether or not living things may exist—or ever have existed—in parts of the Solar System other than Earth. Have each team take an opposite position. Their arguments should be persuasive, skeptical, and well-researched.

Have students who are interested in conditions necessary for life ...

Address Misconceptions

IDENTIFY Ask: What activities that plants and animals do are carried out by cells? If students answer anything other than "All activities," they may not understand that the cell is the basic unit of function, as well as of structure.

CORRECT Discuss what muscles are made of. Point out that muscle cells are specialized for movement. If possible, display microscope slides or magnified images of human muscle cells or those of other animals. Ask: What specialized functions do the cells perform as a group working together? *the function of moving parts of the body around*

REASSESS Ask: What is the basic unit of function (or activity)? *the cell*

Technology Resources

Visit **ClassZone.com** for background on common student misconceptions.

MISCONCEPTION DATABASE

Metacognitive Strategy

Ask students to describe unicellular and multicellular organisms, based on how they use the prefixes *uni-* and *multi-* in other words.

Ongoing Assessment

Explain how living things are different from nonliving things.

Ask: Is a computer a living thing? Explain scientifically how you know. *No; a computer needs energy and is organized, but it cannot develop and grow; it cannot reproduce.*

READING VISUALS *Answer: The unicellular organisms are made of only one cell and are too small to see directly. Multicellular organisms are made of many cells, are more complex, and can usually be seen directly.*

Chapter 1 11

4. Instruct

- Teaching strategies
- Reading support
- Ongoing assessment
- Addressing misconceptions
- Differentiated instruction activities and tips

Pasteur's Experiments

Pasteur's experiments showed that bacteria are present in the air. They do not grow spontaneously.

End of flask is sealed.

1 Broth is boiled to destroy any living bacteria, and the flask is sealed.

2 A few days pass, and the broth is still clear. No bacteria have grown.

3 Two to three days pass, and the broth is still clear. No bacteria have grown.

End of flask is broken.

Exposure to air is the variable.

1 Broth is boiled to destroy any living bacteria, and the flask is sealed.

2 The end of the flask is broken to expose the broth to the air. The broth is clear.

3 Two to three days pass, and the broth is cloudy because of the growth of bacteria.

a now-famous series of experiments that disproved spontaneous generation and confirmed the cell theory. He showed that cells come only from other cells. Two of those experiments are shown above. Both began with a sealed flask containing boiled broth. In the first experiment, the flask remained sealed, while in the second experiment, the top of the flask was broken to expose the contents to air. Bacteria grew only in the second flask.

1.1 Review

KEY CONCEPTS

1. Name four characteristics of living things.
2. How did the microscope change human understanding of life?
3. Explain the three concepts that make up the cell theory.

CRITICAL THINKING

4. **Analyze** Relate the characteristics of a scientific theory to the cell theory.
5. **Compare and Contrast** Draw a Venn diagram to compare and contrast multicellular and unicellular organisms.

CHALLENGE

6. **Synthesize** Explain how Pasteur's experiment supported the cell theory and disproved the theory of spontaneous generation.

Chapter 1: The Cell 15

ANSWERS

1. organization, growth and development, response to environment, reproduction

2. It allowed people to see cells. Before the microscope humans did not realize that life could be so small.

3. Every living thing is made of one or more cells; cells carry out the functions needed to support life; cells come only from other living cells.

4. The cell theory is widely accepted and explains observations of nature, and is supported by evidence such as Pasteur's experiments.

5. multicellular: many cells, complex, easier to see; unicellular: one cell, cannot be seen directly; both: need energy, materials, and living space

6. In Pasteur's experiment, bacteria did not grow spontaneously. They came from the environment, which indicates that cells come from other cells.

Teach from Visuals

To help students interpret the diagram of Pasteur's experiments, ask:

- What is the difference between the two flasks? *The end of one is broken off so it is open to the air.*
- How would the observer know if a flask was contaminated? *Its contents would be cloudy instead of clear.*

Reinforce (the BIG idea)

Have students relate the section to the Big Idea.

Reinforcing Key Concepts, p. 20

1.1 ASSESS & RETEACH

Assess

Section 1.1 Quiz, p. 3

Reteach

Use a triangle diagram to show the three main concepts of cell theory:

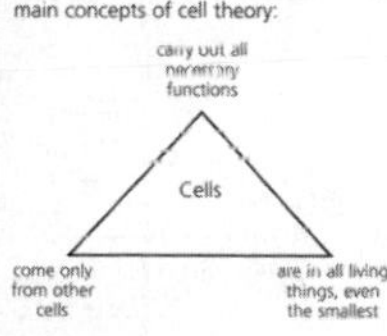

- Ask volunteers to give an example for each corner of the triangle.
- Ask volunteers to state their own reasons for why each concept is important.

Technology Resources

Have students visit **ClassZone.com** for reteaching of Key Concepts.

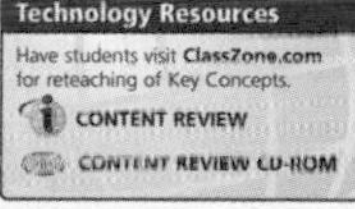

Chapter 1 13

5. Assess & Reteach

- Answers to Section Review
- Reteaching activity
- Resources for review and assessment

Lab Materials List

The following charts list the consumables, nonconsumables, and equipment needed for all activities. Quantities are per group of four students. Lab aprons, goggles, water, books, paper, pens, pencils, and calculators are assumed to be available for all activities.

Materials kits are available. For more information, please call McDougal Littell at 1-800-323-5435.

Consumables

Description	Quantity per Group	Explore *page*	Investigate *page*	Chapter Investigation *page*
albumen solution, 1%	20 mL			632
apple	2 1/4	379, 659	489	
artificial sweetener	3 tsp			344
bacterial amylase	20 mL		623	
bag, zip-top, 1/2 gallon	3		456	
bag, zip-top, sandwich	1	480		
bag, clear plastic	5–7	628, 650		
bag, paper lunch	17	545, 677		108, 516
baking soda	16 oz		297	
ball, Styrofoam, 2"–3"	5–7		31	108
balloon	2		53, 615	
banana	1/8–1/4		489	
bean, dry	30–40		254	
bean, white kidney, dry	1/2–1 cup			516
bleach	2–4 cups			604
bottle, clear plastic, 1/2 liter	1		366	
bottle, clear plastic, 1 liter	1		615	
bottle, clear plastic, 1 liter with cap	1		489	
bottle, plastic, pint	1		53	
candle, small taper	1	9		
cardboard tube, 8"–12"	1–2		31	
cardboard, 10 cm x 10 cm	20		521	
carrot	1/4		418	
celery	1/4	323		
chicken leg, uncooked	1			604
chicken wing, uncooked	1			604
cinnamon	1–3 sticks	677		
clay, modeling	1/2 stick	169		
cloth, white cotton, 12"x 12"	1	650		
clothespin	8			344
cornstarch	1/4 cup			570
cornstarch solution, 1%	100 mL			64
cotton ball	20		661	570
cotton swab, sterile	3			294, 684

Description	Quantity per Group	Explore *page*	Investigate *page*	Chapter Investigation *page*
cover slip	4		285, 303	16
craft stick	156		76	266
crayon, colored	5			228
culture, daphnia	1 mL		285	
culture, hydra	1 mL		285	
cup, clear plastic	9	26, 296, 323, 338, 527		
cup, paper	37		254, 297, 324, 529	376, 684
earthworm	6–11	400		406
egg, hardboiled	3		62, 442	
feathers, assorted	6	445		570
filter paper, fine, 4"	5			406, 478, 632
flour	1 1/2 cup			344
flower	1		383	
foam packing pellet	1–2 cups		84	
food coloring, blue	1 bottle	56, 650	44, 62	684
glitter	4–6 tbs	724		
glucose solution, 1%	20 mL			632
glue, white	1 bottle		31, 84	
gravel	1 cup		489	
hand soap, liquid	20 mL			730
hydrochloric acid, 0.1 M dilute	50 mL		489	
ice	2–4 cups		456	
index card	12		212, 555	
indicator strip, glucose	2			632
indicator strip, protein	2			632
indicator strip, salinity	2			632
iodine	5 mL	323		
iodine solution, 2%	15 mL			64
iodine solution, 5%	15 mL			64
iodine solution, 10%	15 mL			64
Isopropyl alcohol	190 mL		661, 690	142, 570
jug, plastic, gallon	1		119	
kelp granules	2 tbs		366	
knife, plastic	5	379	62, 396, 442, 623	
label, adhesive	10			376
leaf, assorted	20	357	206, 489	228
lens cleaning paper	1			16
liquid dish detergent	1/3 cup	621		570
liquid dishwashing detergent solution, 25%	20 mL			142
marker, colored	3–5		31, 84, 193	344
marker, permanent black	1	486, 509, 527	114, 489, 555, 655	294, 376, 730
marker, permanent blue	1			516

Description	Quantity per Group	Explore page	Investigate page	Chapter Investigation page
marker, permanent red	1			516
match, wood	2	9		
mealworm	10		418	
milk	75 mL		44	
millet seed	2 cups			452
mushroom, fresh	1	338		
newspaper, sheet	1		146	
nutrient agar, sterile	200 mL			294, 730
nutrition label, bag of fresh carrots	1		719	
nutrition label, canned spaghetti in sauce	1		719	
nutrition label, carbonated soft drink	1		719	
nutrition label, fruit juice	1		719	
nutrition label, plain popcorn kernels	1		719	
nutrition label, potato chips	1		719	
nutrition label, unsweetened apple sauce	1		719	
oat bran	2 cups		418	
orange peel	1	677		
owl pellet	1		332	
paper, 3 cm x 3 cm	200		521	
paper, 5" x 5"	3			478
paper, construction, 3" x 3"	7		193	
paper, construction, 8.5" x 11"	1	486		
paper, graph, 8.5" x 11"	8	258, 709	262, 499, 521, 690, 713	648
paper, graph, large-grid, 8.5" x 11"	1	509		
paper, newsprint, 24" x 36"	1		586	
paper, tracing, 8.5" x 11"	11		548	228
paper, white, 8.5" x 11"	2	338		684
paper circle, hole punch	20–30		146	
paper clip	45		316	108, 142
paper towel	1 roll	379	62, 374	376, 570, 604, 684
pasta, dry	2 cups			452
pea pod	1	379		
pear	1/8	323		
pencil, blue	1	258	262, 499, 521	
pencil, red	1	258	262, 499, 521	
petroleum jelly	2 tbs		555	
phenolphthalein	50 mL		297	
pill bug	5	414		
pin	1	650		
pine branch, small	1	677		
pine cone, dry and open	1		374	

Description	Quantity per Group	Explore *page*	Investigate *page*	Chapter Investigation *page*
pipe cleaner	40		31, 84, 119	
pipe cleaner, blue	2	117		
pipe cleaner, orange	6			108
pipe cleaner, red	2	117		
pipe cleaner, yellow	6			108
plant, bean seedling	3		324	
plant, grass with root	1	26		
plant, houseplant cutting	1		91	
plant, live moss	1	364		
plant, small houseplant	1	480		
plastic wrap, 20 cm x 20 cm	1			64
plate, paper	1	296		
poster board, 12" x 12"	1		31	
poster board, 24" x 36"	1		84	
potato, raw	3	323	396, 418, 623	
pushpin, blue	2			108
pushpin, green	2			108
reinforcement ring, binder paper	1			684
rice	1/2 cup	509		
salt solution, 1%	20 mL			632
salt solution, 8%	20 mL			142
salt, table	3/4 cup	296		344
sand	5 lbs			406, 478, 570
sea shell, whole or crushed	1–2		483	
seaweed, stem	2			570
seed, radish	25–50		529	
seed, vegetable, 5–10 varieties	3–5 of each			376
sesame seed	100 mL	296		
shoebox, cardboard	1			228
shoebox, cardboard with lid	1	414		
slide	4		285, 303	16
slide, animal cell	1		21	
slide, egg cell	1	694		
slide, onion root tip cell	1			86
slide, plant cell	1		21	
slide, sperm cell	1	694		
soil, clay	50 mL			478
soil, loam	50 mL			478
soil, local	3 cups	400		
soil, potting	20 lbs	562	91, 254, 324, 489, 529	376, 406
sponge	1			570

Description	Quantity per Group	Explore *page*	Investigate *page*	Chapter Investigation *page*
spoon, plastic	4		62, 396	478, 570
stirring rod	2	527	44	
straw, clear drinking	8			344
string	42"		366, 555	
sugar	4 1/4 tsp	527		344
sugar solution, 10%	300 mL		53	
tape, duct	6"		615	
tape, masking	1 roll	480, 486, 628	114, 396, 489, 521, 655	294, 344, 730
thread	15 cm	486		
toothpick	1			478
toothpick, blue	2			108
toothpick, purple	2			108
toothpick, red	2			108
turmeric	1–2 mL			570
vegetable oil	120 mL	621	44	570
vegetable shortening	1 lb		456	
vinegar, white	1/8–1/4 cup		483	
water, distilled	860 mL	400		142, 406
water, pond	3 mL		303	16
wheat germ, raw	1 gram			142
yarn, blue	30 cm		76	
yarn, colored	600 cm		31, 84, 119	570
yarn, green	30 cm		76	
yarn, red	30 cm		76	
yarn, yellow	30 cm		76	
yeast, dry	2 tsp	527	53	
yeast, quick-rise	1 tsp			344

Nonconsumables

Description	Quantity per Group	Explore *page*	Investigate *page*	Chapter Investigation *page*
aquarium, small	1	429		406
baking sheet	1			344
balance, triple beam	1		324	
bead, colored	10–25		31	
beaker, 100 mL	1			632
beaker, 250 mL	3	56	44, 62, 483	406, 478, 570
beaker, 400 mL	1			570
beaker, 500 mL	1		374	
beaker, 600 mL	3			478
blindfold	2–4	73		
bowl, plastic, extra-large	1		456	

Description	Quantity per Group	Explore *page*	Investigate *page*	Chapter Investigation *page*
bowl, plastic, large	1	650		
box, small cardboard	2		316	
button, white	1		366	
candleholder	1	9		
census data, local	1		262	
coffee can, 1/2 pound	1			266
coin, penny	2		114	
coin, quarter	2	110	114	
computer graphing program	1		713	
container, clear plastic, small with lid	4–6	414	655	406, 452
dice, numbered	2			186
dictionary	1		212	
eyedropper	2	323, 621	297, 303, 623, 661	16, 64, 452, 478
film canister	1		119	
flashlight with batteries	1			406
flower pot, plastic with draining dish	2	562	91	
funnel, small plastic	3			478, 632
graduated cylinder, 50 mL	1			632
graduated cylinder, 100 mL	1			64
hand lens	1	296, 338, 357, 364, 414	206, 303, 383, 555	228, 294, 478, 730
jar, glass, 26 oz	1			452
jar, glass, 26 oz with air holes in lid	1		418	
jar, baby food with lid	1			64
knife, sharp	1	338		
lamp, gooseneck desk	1	486		
light bulb, 60 watt	1	486		
map, local land use or zoning	1		548	
measuring cup, 1/4 cup	1			344
measuring cup, 1 cup	1	562		
measuring cup, 2 cup/500 mL	1	527		
measuring spoon, 1/4 teaspoon	1			344
measuring spoon, 1/2 teaspoon	1	527		
measuring spoon, tablespoon	1		366	
measuring spoon, teaspoon	1	527	53, 297	344
meter stick	1	436		
microscope	1	694	21, 285, 303	16, 86
mollusk shell	1–2		410	
mortar and pestle	1		483	
needle tool	1		332	
pan, metal, 10" x 14"	1			570

Description	Quantity per Group	Explore *page*	Investigate *page*	Chapter Investigation *page*
paper hole punch	1		555	
paper clip, blue plastic-coated	16			186
paper clip, red plastic-coated	16			186
paper clip, yellow plastic-coated	16			186
petri dish, with lid	4	169	418	294, 730
pliers	1–2			452
puzzle piece	5–10		171	
rubber band	50			452
ruler, metric	1	527	21, 62, 366, 529, 548	344
sand dollar	1–2		410	
scissors	1	486	31, 84, 489, 555	604
scoop, small	1			142
sea star	1–2		410	
sieve	1	296		
sock, pair	12–24	73		
spoon, slotted	1–2			452
spray bottle, 250 mL	1	400		406
stopwatch	1–2	73, 250, 473, 562, 628, 641	690	266, 406, 452, 478, 648
tape measure, flexible	1	709		
test tube	4–6	621		142, 452
test tube rack	1	621		452
test tube stopper	1	621		
thermometer	1	473		
thermometer, mercury-free	1		690	
tray, dissection	1	400	332	604
tweezers	1		332, 418	452
vegetable peeler	1	659		

Unit Resource Book Datasheet

Description	Explore *page*	Investigate *page*	Chapter Investigation *page*
Bone Identification Key		332	
Climate Graph		499	

Safety Equipment

Description	Explore *page*	Investigate *page*	Chapter Investigation *page*
gloves	323, 400, 562	332, 396, 418	228, 376, 406, 478, 570, 604

McDougal Littell

Life SCIENCE

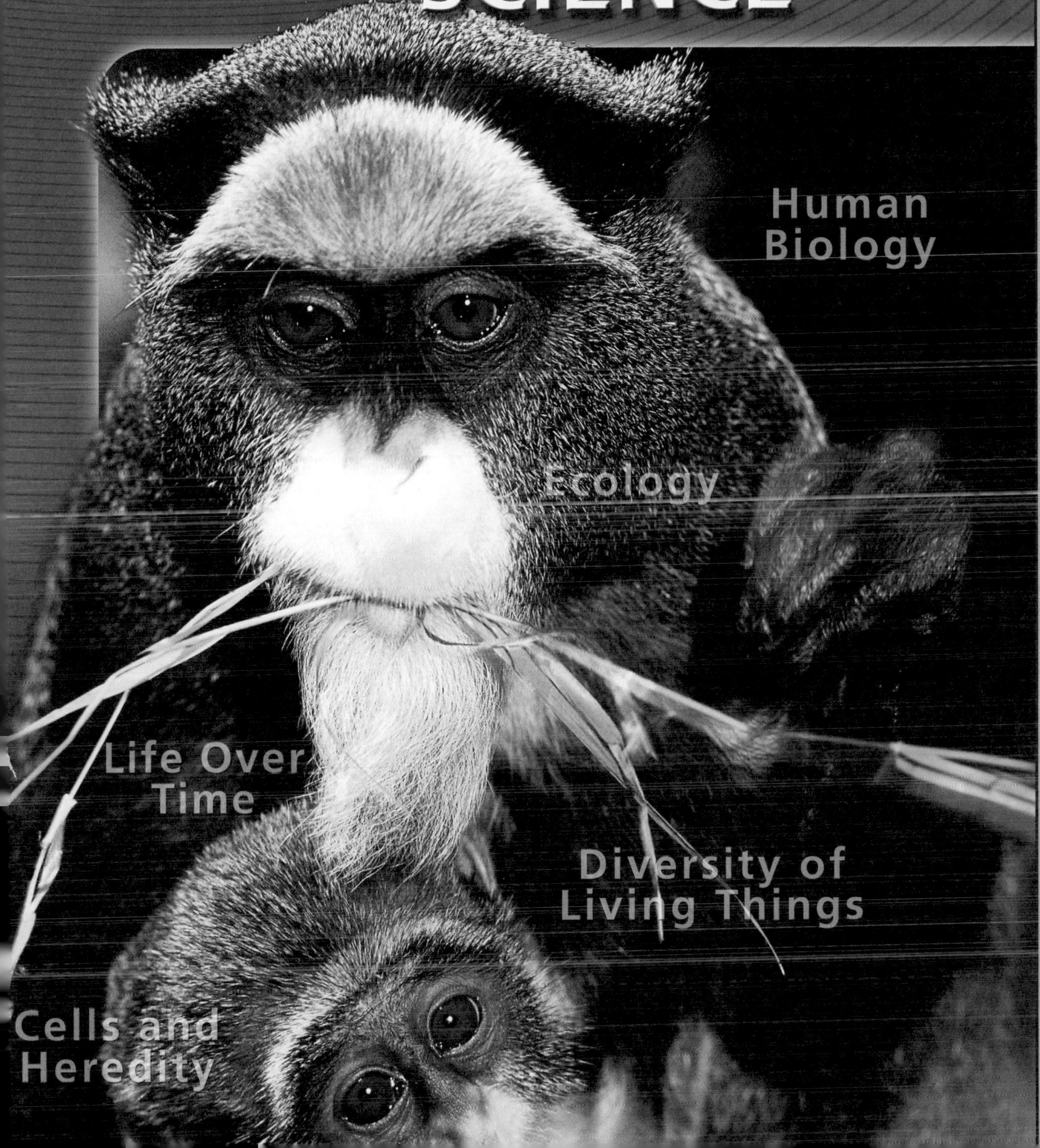

Human Biology

Ecology

Life Over Time

Diversity of Living Things

Cells and Heredity

LIFE SCIENCE

Acknowledgments: Excerpts and adaptations from *National Science Education Standards* by the National Academy of Sciences. Copyright © 1996 by the National Academy of Sciences. Reprinted with permission from the National Academies Press, Washington, D.C.

Excerpts and adaptations from *Benchmarks for Science Literacy: Project 2061.* Copyright © 1993 by the American Association for the Advancement of Science. Reprinted with permission.

Printed in the United States of America

ISBN: 0-618-61518-0 X 2 3 4 5 6 7 8 VJM 09 08 07 06 05

Internet Web Site: http://www.mcdougallittell.com

Science Consultants

Chief Science Consultant

James Trefil, Ph.D. is the Clarence J. Robinson Professor of Physics at George Mason University. He is the author or co-author of more than 25 books, including *Science Matters* and *The Nature of Science.* Dr. Trefil is a member of the American Association for the Advancement of Science's Committee on the Public Understanding of Science and Technology. He is also a fellow of the World Economic Forum and a frequent contributor to *Smithsonian* magazine.

Rita Ann Calvo, Ph.D. is Senior Lecturer in Molecular Biology and Genetics at Cornell University, where for 12 years she also directed the Cornell Institute for Biology Teachers. Dr. Calvo is the 1999 recipient of the College and University Teaching Award from the National Association of Biology Teachers.

Kenneth Cutler, M.S. is the Education Coordinator for the Julius L. Chambers Biomedical Biotechnology Research Institute at North Carolina Central University. A former middle school and high school science teacher, he received a 1999 Presidential Award for Excellence in Science Teaching.

Instructional Design Consultants

Douglas Carnine, Ph.D. is Professor of Education and Director of the National Center for Improving the Tools of Educators at the University of Oregon. He is the author of seven books and over 100 other scholarly publications, primarily in the areas of instructional design and effective instructional strategies and tools for diverse learners. Dr. Carnine also serves as a member of the National Institute for Literacy Advisory Board.

Linda Carnine, Ph.D. consults with school districts on curriculum development and effective instruction for students struggling academically. A former teacher and school administrator, Dr. Carnine also co-authored a popular remedial reading program.

Sam Miller, Ph.D. is a middle school science teacher and the Teacher Development Liaison for the Eugene, Oregon, Public Schools. He is the author of curricula for teaching science, mathematics, computer skills, and language arts.

Donald Steely, Ph.D. serves as principal investigator at the Oregon Center for Applied Science (ORCAS) on federal grants for science and language arts programs. His background also includes teaching and authoring of print and multimedia programs in science, mathematics, history, and spelling.

Vicky Vachon, Ph.D. consults with school districts throughout the United States and Canada on improving overall academic achievement with a focus on literacy. She is also co-author of a widely used program for remedial readers.

iii

Content Reviewers

John Beaver, Ph.D.
Ecology
Professor, Director of Science Education Center
College of Education and Human Services
Western Illinois University
Macomb, IL

Donald J. DeCoste, Ph.D.
Matter and Energy, Chemical Interactions
Chemistry Instructor
University of Illinois
Urbana-Champaign, IL

Dorothy Ann Fallows, Ph.D., MSc
Diversity of Living Things, Microbiology
Partners in Health
Boston, MA

Michael Foote, Ph.D.
The Changing Earth, Life Over Time
Associate Professor
Department of the Geophysical Sciences
The University of Chicago
Chicago, IL

Lucy Fortson, Ph.D.
Space Science
Director of Astronomy
Adler Planetarium and Astronomy Museum
Chicago, IL

Elizabeth Godrick, Ph.D.
Human Biology
Professor, CAS Biology
Boston University
Boston, MA

Isabelle Sacramento Grilo, M.S.
The Changing Earth
Lecturer, Department of the Geological Sciences
San Diego State University
San Diego, CA

David Harbster, MSc
Diversity of Living Things
Professor of Biology
Paradise Valley Community College
Phoenix, AZ

Richard D. Norris, Ph.D.
Earth's Waters
Professor of Paleobiology
Scripps Institution of Oceanography
University of California, San Diego
La Jolla, CA

Donald B. Peck, M.S.
Motion and Forces; Waves, Sound, and Light; Electricity and Magnetism
Director of the Center for Science Education (retired)
Fairleigh Dickinson University
Madison, NJ

Javier Penalosa, Ph.D.
Diversity of Living Things, Plants
Associate Professor, Biology Department
Buffalo State College
Buffalo, NY

Raymond T. Pierrehumbert, Ph.D.
Earth's Atmosphere
Professor in Geophysical Sciences (Atmospheric Science)
The University of Chicago
Chicago, IL

Brian J. Skinner, Ph.D.
Earth's Surface
Eugene Higgins Professor of Geology and Geophysics
Yale University
New Haven, CT

Nancy E. Spaulding, M.S.
Earth's Surface, The Changing Earth, Earth's Waters
Earth Science Teacher (retired)
Elmira Free Academy
Elmira, NY

Steven S. Zumdahl, Ph.D.
Matter and Energy, Chemical Interactions
Professor Emeritus of Chemistry
University of Illinois
Urbana-Champaign, IL

Susan L. Zumdahl, M.S.
Matter and Energy, Chemical Interactions
Chemistry Education Specialist
University of Illinois
Urbana-Champaign, IL

Safety Consultant

Juliana Texley, Ph.D.
Former K–12 Science Teacher and School Superintendent
Boca Raton, FL

English Language Advisor

Judy Lewis, M.A.
Director, State and Federal Programs for reading proficiency and high risk populations
Rancho Cordova, CA

iv

Teacher Panel Members

Carol Arbour
Tallmadge Middle School,
Tallmadge, OH

Patty Belcher
Goodrich Middle School,
Akron, OH

Gwen Broestl
Luis Munoz Marin Middle School,
Cleveland, OH

Al Brofman
Tehipite Middle School,
Fresno, CA

John Cockrell
Clinton Middle School,
Columbus, OH

Jenifer Cox
Sylvan Middle School,
Citrus Heights, CA

Linda Culpepper
Martin Middle School,
Charlotte, NC

Melvin Figueroa
New River Middle School,
Ft. Lauderdale, FL

Doretha Grier
Kannapolis Middle School,
Kannapolis, NC

Robert Hood
Alexander Hamilton Middle School,
Cleveland, OH

Scott Hudson
Covedale Elementary School,
Cincinnati, OH

Loretta Langdon
Princeton Middle School,
Princeton, NC

Carlyn Little
Glades Middle School,
Miami, FL

Ann Marie Lynn
Amelia Earhart Middle School,
Riverside, CA

James Minogue
Lowe's Grove Middle School,
Durham, NC

Kathleen Montagnino-DeMatteo
Jefferson Davis Middle School,
West Palm Beach, FL

Joann Myers
Buchanan Middle School,
Tampa, FL

Barbara Newell
Charles Evans Hughes Middle School,
Long Beach, CA

Anita Parker
Kannapolis Middle School,
Kannapolis, NC

Greg Pirolo
Golden Valley Middle School,
San Bernardino, CA

Laura Pottmyer
Apex Middle School,
Apex, NC

Lynn Prichard
Williams Middle Magnet School,
Tampa, FL

Jacque Quick
Walter Williams High School,
Burlington, NC

Robert Glenn Reynolds
Hillman Middle School,
Youngstown, OH

Stacy Rinehart
Lufkin Road Middle School,
Apex, NC

Theresa Short
Abbott Middle School,
Fayetteville, NC

Rita Slivka
Alexander Hamilton Middle School,
Cleveland, OH

Marie Sofsak
B F Stanton Middle School,
Alliance, OH

Nancy Stubbs
Sweetwater Union Unified School District,
Chula Vista, CA

Sharon Stull
Quail Hollow Middle School,
Charlotte, NC

Donna Taylor
Bak Middle School of the Arts,
West Palm Beach, FL

Sandi Thompson
Harding Middle School,
Lakewood, OH

Lori Walker
Audubon Middle School & Magnet Center,
Los Angeles, CA

Teacher Lab Evaluators

Andrew Boy
W.E.B. DuBois Academy,
Cincinnati, OH

Jill Brimm-Byrne
Albany Park Academy,
Chicago, IL

Gwen Broestl
Luis Munoz Marin Middle School,
Cleveland, OH

Al Brofman
Tehipite Middle School,
Fresno, CA

Michael A. Burstein
The Rashi School,
Newton, MA

Trudi Coutts
Madison Middle School,
Naperville, IL

Jenifer Cox
Sylvan Middle School,
Citrus Heights, CA

Larry Cwik
Madison Middle School,
Naperville, IL

Jennifer Donatelli
Kennedy Junior High School,
Lisle, IL

Melissa Dupree
Lakeside Middle School,
Evans, GA

Carl Fechko
Luis Munoz Marin Middle School,
Cleveland, OH

Paige Fullhart
Highland Middle School,
Libertyville, IL

Sue Hood
Glen Crest Middle School,
Glen Ellyn, IL

William Luzader
Plymouth Community Intermediate School,
Plymouth, MA

Ann Min
Beardsley Middle School,
Crystal Lake, IL

Aileen Mueller
Kennedy Junior High School,
Lisle, IL

Nancy Nega
Churchville Middle School,
Elmhurst, IL

Oscar Newman
Sumner Math and Science Academy,
Chicago, IL

Lynn Prichard
Williams Middle Magnet School,
Tampa, FL

Jacque Quick
Walter Williams High School,
Burlington, NC

Stacy Rinehart
Lufkin Road Middle School,
Apex, NC

Seth Robey
Gwendolyn Brooks Middle School,
Oak Park, IL

Kevin Steele
Grissom Middle School,
Tinley Park, IL

v

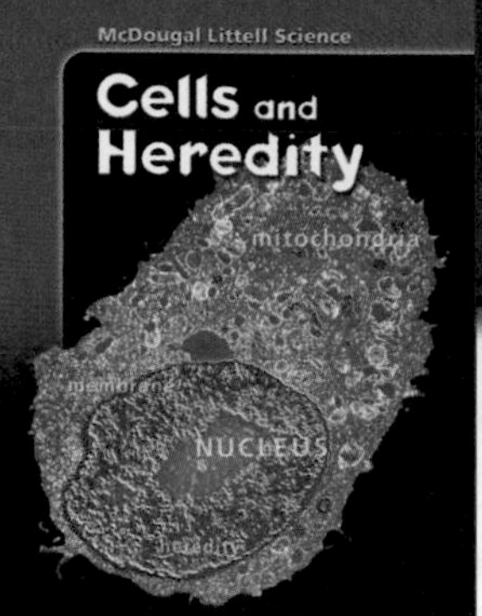

eEdition

UNIT 1
Cells and Heredity

Unit Features

How do plants like these sunflowers change energy from the Sun?
page 38

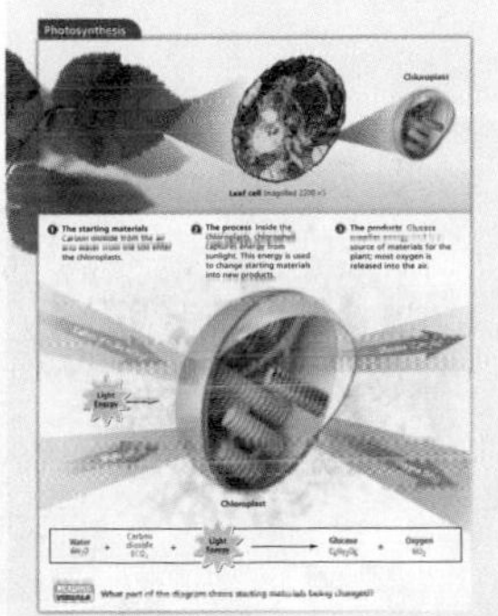

Visual Highlights

UNIT 2

Life Over Time

eEdition

Unit Features

6 The History of Life on Earth 166

the BIG idea

Living things, like Earth itself, change over time.

How do scientists learn about the history of life on Earth? page 166

How many different types of organisms do you see and how would you group them? page 200

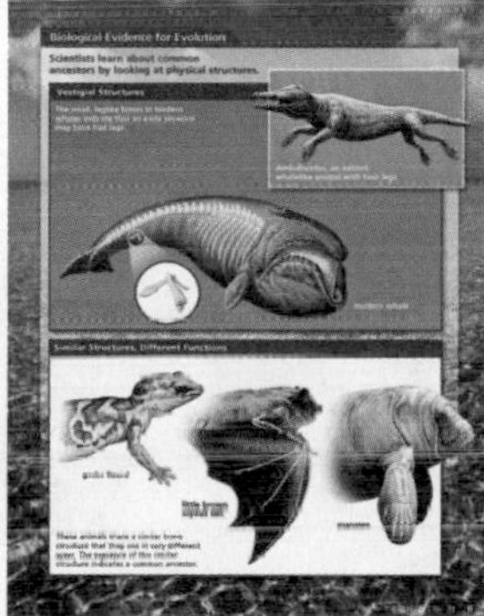

Visual Highlights

ix

eEdition

UNIT 3
Diversity of Living Things

Unit Features

9 Single-Celled Organisms and Viruses 278

the BIG idea

Bacteria and protists have the characteristics of living things, while viruses are not alive.

10 Introduction to Multicellular Organisms 312

the BIG idea

Multicellular organisms live in and get energy from a variety of environments.

How does an organism get energy and materials from its environment? *page 312*

Visual Highlights

eEdition

UNIT 4
Ecology

Unit Features

14 Ecosystems and Biomes 470

the BIG idea

Matter and energy together support life within an environment.

How many living and nonliving things can you identify in this photograph? *page 470*

How do living things interact? page 506

Visual Highlights

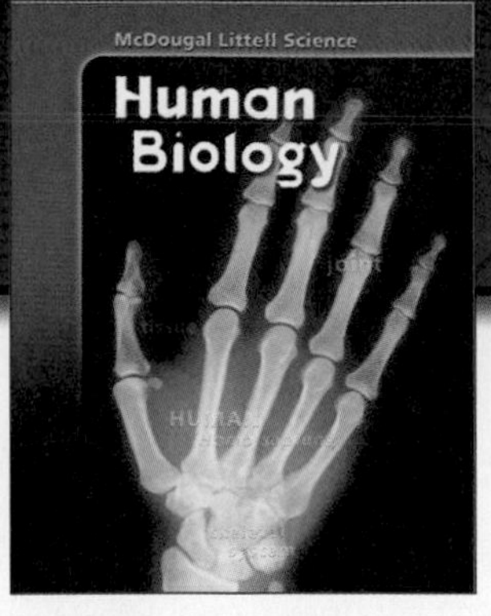

eEdition

UNIT 5
Human Biology

Unit Features

What materials does your body need to function properly? *page 610*

Red blood cells travel through a blood vessel. How do you think blood carries materials around your body? page 638

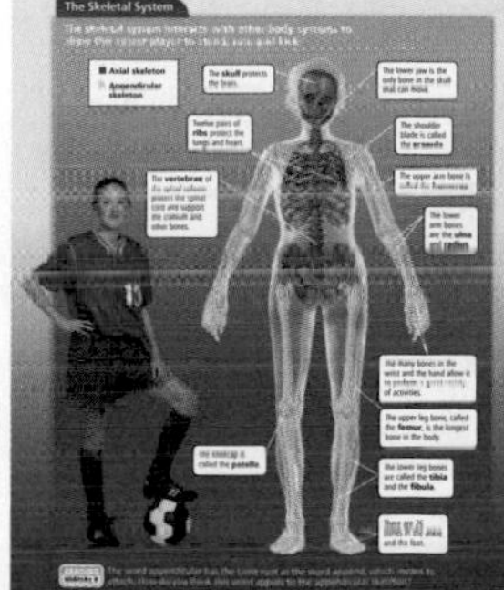

Visual Highlights

Features

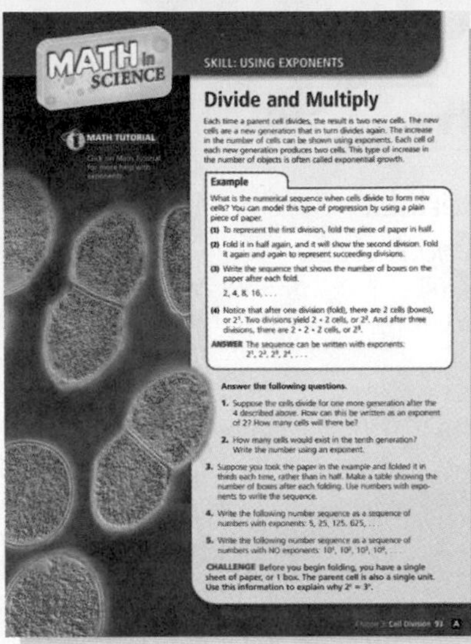
MATH in SCIENCE

SKILL: USING EXPONENTS

Divide and Multiply

Math in Science

Think Science

Connecting Sciences

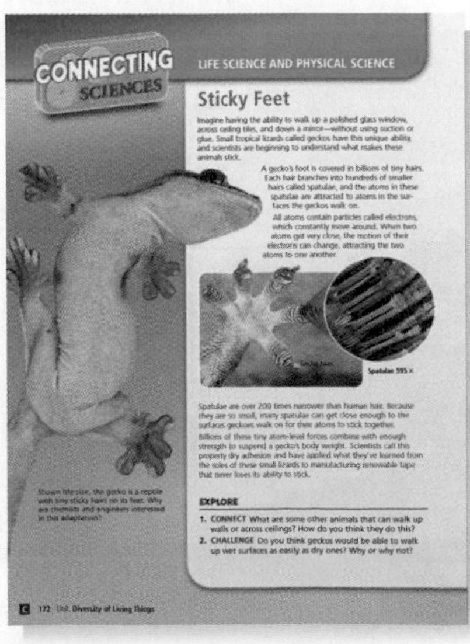
CONNECTING SCIENCES

LIFE SCIENCE AND PHYSICAL SCIENCE

Sticky Feet

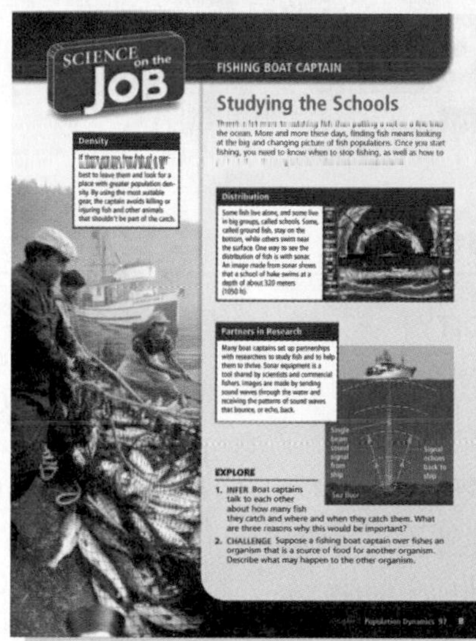

Frontiers in Science

Science on the Job

Extreme Science

Timelines in Science

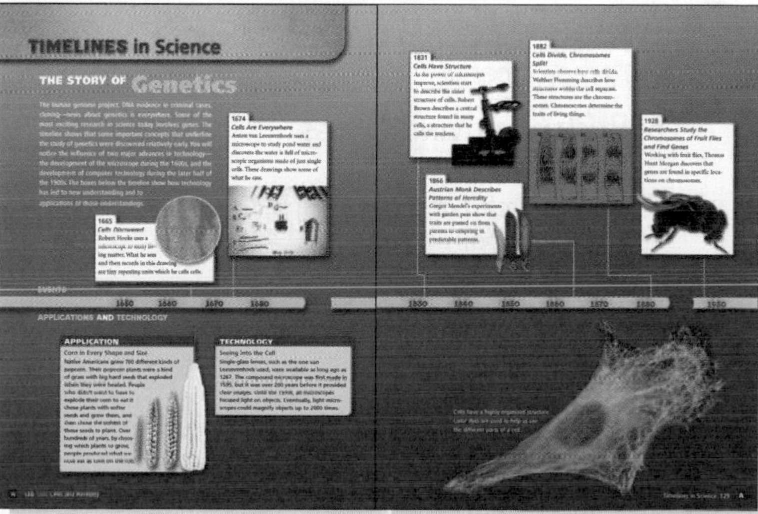

xvii

Internet Resources @ ClassZone.com

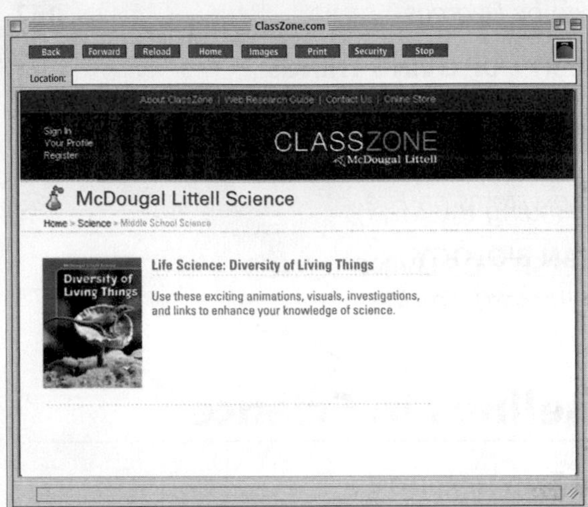

Simulations

Visualizations

Career Centers

Resource Centers

CELLS AND HEREDITY
Resources for the following topics may be found at ClassZone.com: *Cell Structures, Unicellular Organisms, Macromolecules, Diffusion, Nerve Regeneration, Cell Cycle, Asexual Reproduction, Sexual Reproduction, Meiosis, Genetics Research, Human Genome Project, DNA, Mutations, DNA Technology.*

LIFE OVER TIME
Resources for the following topics may be found at ClassZone.com: *Mass Extinctions, Natural Selection, Evidence Supporting Evolution, Linnaeus, Taxonomy, New Insect Species, Modern Classification, Current Fossil and Living Fossil Finds, Population Dynamics, Human Population Growth, Introduced Species in the United States.*

DIVERSITY OF LIVING THINGS
Resources for the following topics may be found at ClassZone.com: *Single-Celled Organisms and the Human Body, Bacteria, Viruses, Bee Dance, Plant Adaptations, Animal Adaptations, Fungi, Biodiversity Discoveries and Research, Plant Systems, Plant Evolution, Seeds, Extreme Seeds, Invertebrate Diversity, Worms, Mollusks, Arthropods, Fish, Amphibians, Reptiles, Mammals.*

ECOLOGY
Resources for the following topics may be found at ClassZone.com: *Prairie Ecosystems, Ecosystems, Cycles in Nature, Land and Aquatic Biomes, Symbiotic Relationships, Succession, Conservation Efforts, The Environment, Urban Expansion, Natural Resources, Ecosystem Recovery.*

HUMAN BIOLOGY
Resources for the following topics may be found at ClassZone.com: *Shackleton Expedition, Skeletal System, Muscles, Respiratory System, Urinary System, Circulatory System, Blood Types, Lymphatic System, Skin, Current Medical Imaging Techniques, Senses, Nervous System, Endocrine System, Human Health, Nutrition, Fighting Disease.*

Math Tutorials

NSTA SciLinks

Codes for use with the NSTA SciLinks site may be found on every chapter opener.

Content Review

There is a content review for every chapter at ClassZone.com

Test Practice

There is a standardized test practice for every chapter at ClassZone.com

Explore the Big Idea

Chapter Opening Inquiry

Each chapter opens with hands-on explorations that introduce the chapter's Big Idea.

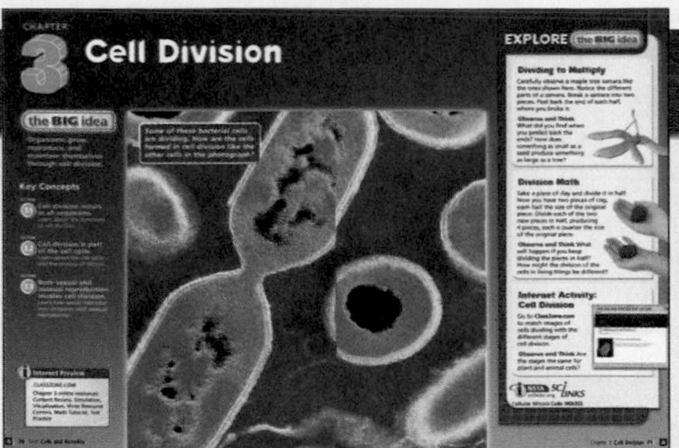

Chapter Investigations

Full-Period Labs

The Chapter Investigations are in-depth labs that let you form and test a hypothesis, build a model, or sometimes design your own investigation.

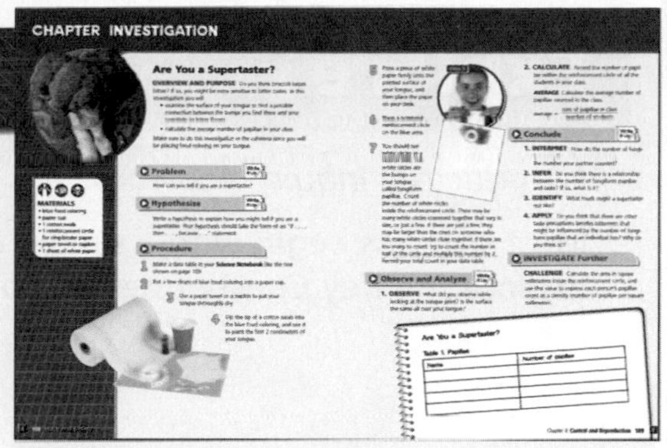

xxi

Explore

Introductory Inquiry Activities

Most sections begin with a simple activity that lets you explore the Key Concept before you read the section.

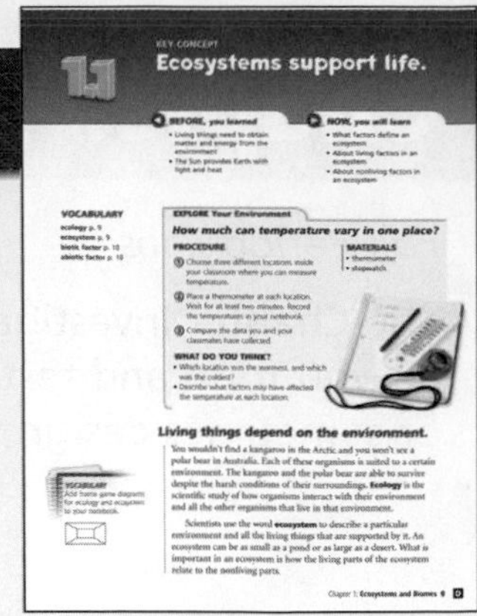

Investigate

Skill Labs

Each Investigate activity gives you a chance to practice a specific science skill related to the content that you're studying.

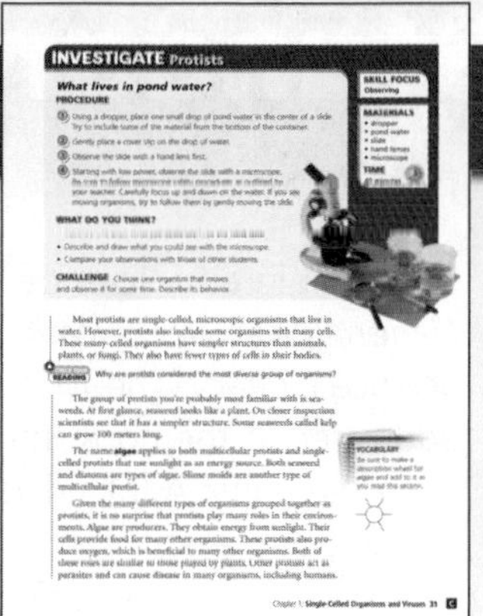

xxiii

Standards and Benchmarks

Each unit in **Life Science** addresses some of the learning goals described in the *National Science Education Standards* (NSES) and the Project 2061 *Benchmarks for Science Literacy.* The following National Science Education Standards are also addressed in the book introduction, unit and chapter features, and lab investigations in all the units: A.9 Understandings About Scientific Inquiry, E.6 Understandings About Science and Technology, F.5 Science and Technology in Society, G.1 Science as a Human Endeavor, G.2 Nature of Science, G.3 History of Science.

National Science Education Standards

Content Standards

UNIT 1 Cells and Heredity

B.1.c	There are more than 100 known elements that combine in many ways to produce living and nonliving substances.
B.3.a	Energy is a property of many substances. Energy is transferred many ways.
C.1.a	Levels of organization for living systems include cells, tissues, organs, organ systems, whole organisms, and ecosystems.
C.1.b	All organisms are composed of cells—the basic unit of life. Most are single cells; others, including humans, are multicellular.
C.1.c	Cells perform the functions of life.
C.1.d	Specialized cells perform specialized functions in multicellular organisms.
C.2.a	Reproduction is a characteristic of all living systems. Some organisms reproduce asexually. Others reproduce sexually.
C.2.b	In many species, females produce eggs and males produce sperm. The egg and sperm come together to produce offspring with genetic material from both parents.
C.2.c	Every organism requires a set of instructions for specifying its traits.
C.2.d	Heredity information is contained in genes in the chromosomes of each cell.
C.2.e	The characteristics of an organism are a combination of traits. Some traits are inherited and others result from interactions with the environment.
F.5.c	Needs, attitudes, and values influence decisions about technology.

UNIT 2 Life Over Time

C.2.e	The characteristics of an organism are a combination of traits. Some traits are inherited and others result from interactions with the environment.
C.4.a	A population consists of all individuals of a species that occur together at a given place and time.
C.4.d	Resources and other factors can limit population growth.
C.5.a	Millions of species of animals, plants, and microorganisms are alive today. Relationships among organisms can be found by looking at internal structures, chemical processes, and the evidence of common ancestry.
C.5.b	Biological evolution has led to greater species diversity over time. Biological adaptations include changes in structures, behaviors, or physiology that enhance survival in a particular environment.
C.5.c	Species may become extinct if they cannot survive changes in the environment.
D.2.b	Fossils provide evidence of how life and the environment have changed.
F.2.a	When an area becomes overpopulated, increased use of resources degrades the environment.
G.2.a	Scientists change their ideas about nature when they find new evidence that does not match their existing explanations.

UNIT 3 Diversity of Living Things

C.1.b	All organisms are composed of cells—the basic unit of life. Most are single cells; others, including humans, are multicellular.
C.1.c	Cells perform the functions of life. They grow and divide. They take in nutrients for energy and materials.
C.1.d	Specialized cells perform specialized functions in multicellular organisms.
C.1.f	Some diseases are the result of breakdown of structures or by infection by other organisms.
C.2.a	Reproduction is a characteristic of all living systems. Some organisms reproduce asexually. Others reproduce sexually.
C.2.b	In many species, females produce eggs and males produce sperm. The egg and sperm come together to produce offspring with genetic material from both parents.
C.3.a	All organisms must be able to obtain and use resources, grow, reproduce, and maintain stable internal conditions.
C.3.b	Regulation of an organism's internal environment keeps conditions within the range required to survive.
C.3.c	Behavior is one kind of response an organism makes.
C.4.c	Most energy in ecosystems enters as sunlight, gets transferred by producers into chemical energy, and passes from organism to organism as food.
C.5.a	Millions of species of animals, plants, and microorganisms are alive today.
F.1.e	Food provides energy and nutrients for growth and development.

UNIT 4 Ecology

C.4.a	A population consists of all individuals of a species that occur together at a given place and time. An ecosystem includes both living and nonliving things.
C.4.b	Different populations have different roles in an ecosystem. Food webs show the relationship between producers and consumers.
C.4.c	Most energy in ecosystems enters as sunlight, gets transferred by producers into chemical energy through photosynthesis, and passes from organism to organism as food.
C.4.d	Factors can limit population growth.
D.1.f	Water circulates through Earth's crust, oceans, and atmosphere.
D.3.d	The Sun is the major source of energy affecting plant growth, winds, ocean currents, the water cycle, and seasonal variations.
E.6.e	All designs have limits, including availability, safety, and environmental impact.
F.2.a	Human overpopulation can cause increased use of resources, decline in resources, and decline in other populations.
F.2.b	Causes of pollution and resource loss vary from place to place.

UNIT 5 Human Biology

C.1.a	Levels of organization for living systems include: cells, tissues, organs, organ systems, whole organisms, and ecosystems.
C.1.e	The human organism has systems that perform specific functions.
C.1.f	Some diseases are the result of infection by other organisms.
C.2.a	Reproduction is a characteristic of all living systems.
C.2.b	In many species, females produce eggs and males produce sperm. The egg and sperm come together to produce offspring with genetic material from both parents.
C.3.a	All organisms must be able to obtain and use resources, grow, reproduce, and maintain stable internal conditions.
C.3.b	Regulation of an organism's internal environment keeps conditions within the range required to survive.
F.1.c	Tobacco use increases the risk of illness.
F.1.d	Alcohol and other drugs can increase the risk of illness.
F.1.e	Food provides energy and nutrients for growth and development.

xxv

Process and Skill Standards

A.1	Identify questions that can be answered through scientific methods.
A.2	Design and conduct a scientific investigation.
A.3	Use appropriate tools and techniques to gather and analyze data.
A.4	Use evidence to describe, predict, explain, and model.
A.5	Think critically to find relationships between results and interpretations.
A.6	Give alternative explanations and predictions.
A.7	Communicate procedures and explanations.
A.8	Use mathematics in scientific inquiry.
A.9.a	Different types of questions suggest different types of scientific investigations.
A.9.b	Current scientific knowledge guides scientific investigations.
E.6.b	Many different people in different cultures have made and continue to make contributions to science and technology.
G.1.b	The work of science relies on qualities, such as reasoning, insight, energy, skill, and creativity.

Project 2061 Benchmarks

Content Benchmarks

UNIT 1 Cells and Heredity

5.B.1	In some organisms, all genes come from a single parent. In organisms that have sexes, typically half of the genes come from each parent.
5.B.2	In sexual reproduction, a specialized cell from a female joins one from a male.
5.C.1	All living things are made of cells.
5.C.2	Cells continually divide to make more cells.
5.C.3	Cells carry out the functions of organisms.
5.C.4	About 2/3 of the weight of cells is water which gives cells certain properties.
5.E.1	Food provides fuel and building material for all organisms.
5.E.3	Energy can change form in living things.
5.F.1	Differences between parents and offspring enlarge over generations.
8.A.2	People control characteristics of plants and animals by selective breeding.
10.I.1	Many diseases are caused by microorganisms. This is the germ theory.
10.I.2	Pasteur showed food spoils as germs enter, and heat can destroy germs.

UNIT 2 Life Over Time

5.A.3	In classifying organisms, biologists consider internal and external structures.
5.B.3	New species have resulted from selective breeding.
5.D.1	In all environments, organisms with similar needs may compete.
5.F.1	Small differences between parents and offspring accumulate in successive generating.
5.F.2	Individual organisms with certain traits are more likely than others to survive.

UNIT 3 Diversity of Living Things

5.A.1	One general distinction among organisms is between plants and animals. Many organisms are neither plants or animals.
5.A.2	Organisms have diverse body plans.
5.A.3	Organisms share similar features.
5.B.2	In sexual reproduction a specialized cell from a female joins one from a male.
5.C.1	All living things are made of cells.
5.E.1	Food provides organisms with fuel and materials.
5.E.3	Energy can change form in living things.
6.B.3	Patterns of human development are similar to those of other vertebrates.
6.C.1	Organs and organ systems are composed of cells and help provide basic needs.
6.E.3	Viruses, bacteria, fungi, and parasites may infect the human body.

UNIT 4 Ecology

3.C.6	Rarely are technology issues simple.
4.B.8	Water is, necessary for life, limited, and becoming depleted and polluted.
4.C.7	Human activities affect the environment.
5.A.5	All organisms are part of two connected food webs.
5.D.1	Species with similar needs may compete.
5.D.2	Populations may interact in diverse ways.
5.E.2	Matter is transferred between living things and the environment.
5.E.3	Energy can change form in living things.
6.E.5	The health of individuals requires keeping soil, air, and water safe.
11.A.2	Studying a system involves studying interactions among its parts.

UNIT 5 Human Biology

6.A.1	Human beings have body systems for diverse body functions
6.C.2	For the body to use food it must be digested and transported to cells.
6.C.3	Cells take in oxygen for combustion of food, and eliminate carbon dioxide.
6.C.4	Specialized cells and molecules identify and/or destroy microbes.
6.B.1	Fertilization occurs when a sperm cell enters an egg cell.
6.B.3	Cells divide and specialize as a fetus develops from the embryo.
6.B.5	Body changes occur as humans age.
6.C.5	Hormones are chemical messengers.
6.C.6	Interactions among senses, nerves, and the brain make learning possible.
6.E.2	Toxic substances, diet, and behavior may harm one's health.
6.E.4	White blood cells engulf invaders or produce antibodies.

Process and Skill Benchmarks

9.A.2	Use a number line and negative numbers.
9.A.3	Write numbers in different forms.
9.A.4	Use addition, subtraction, multiplication, division.
9.B.2	Use mathematics to describe change.
9.B.3	Use graphs to show relationships.
9.C.4	Use a graphic display of numbers to show trends, rates, gaps, or clusters.
9.D.3	The mean, median, and mode tell different things about a data set.
9.D.5	Use a large, well-chosen sample to represent the whole.
11.A.2	Think about things as systems.
11.A.3	See how systems are interconnected.
11.B.1	Use models to think about processes.
11.C.4	Use equations to summarize changes.
11.C.5	Understand how symmetry (or the lack of it) can determine properties.
11.D.2	With complex systems, use summaries, averages, ranges, and examples.
12.A.1	Know why it is important in science to keep honest, clear, and accurate records.
12.A.2	Investigate, using hypotheses.
12.A.3	See multiple ways to interpret results.
12.B.3	Calculate volumes of rectangular solids.
12.B.7	Determine, use, and convert units.
12.C.3	Use and read measurement instruments.
12.D.1	Use tables and graphs to organize information and identify relationships.
12.D.2	Read, interpret, and describe tables and graphs.
12.D.3	Locate information in reference books and other resources.
12.D.4	Understand charts and graphs.
12.E.3	Be skeptical of biased samples.
12.E.4	See more than one way to interpret results.
12.E.5	Criticize faulty reasoning.

Introducing Life Science

Scientists are curious. Since ancient times, they have been asking and answering questions about the world around them. Scientists are also very suspicious of the answers they get. They carefully collect evidence and test their answers many times before accepting an idea as correct.

In this book you will see how scientific knowledge keeps growing and changing as scientists ask new questions and rethink what was known before. The following sections will help get you started.

UNIFYING PRINCIPLES of Life Science

What Is Life Science?

Life science is the study of living things. As you study life science, you will observe and read about a variety of organisms, from huge redwood trees to the tiny bacteria that cause sore throats. Because Earth is home to such a great variety of living things, the study of life science is rich and exciting.

But life science doesn't simply include learning the names of millions of organisms. It includes big ideas that help us to understand how all these living things interact with their environment. Life science is the study of characteristics and needs that all living things have in common. It's also a study of changes—both daily changes as well as changes that take place over millions of years. Probably most important, in studying life science, you will explore the many ways that all living things—including you—depend upon Earth and its resources.

The text and visuals in this book will invite you into the world of living things and provide you with the key concepts you'll need in your study. Activities offer a chance for you to investigate some aspects of life science on your own. The four unifying principles listed below provide a way for you to connect the information and ideas in this program.

- **All living things share common characteristics.**
- **All living things share common needs.**
- **Living things meet their needs through interactions with the environment.**
- **The types and numbers of living things change over time.**

the BIG idea

Each chapter begins with a big idea. Keep in mind that each big idea relates to one or more of the unifying principles.

UNIFYING PRINCIPLE

All living things share common characteristics.

Birds nest among the plants of a reed marsh as sunlight shines and a breeze blows. Which of these is alive? Warblers and plants are living things, but sunlight and breezes are not. All living things share common characteristics that distinguish them from nonliving things.

What It Means

This unifying principle helps you explore one of the biggest questions in science, "What is life?" Let's take a look at four characteristics that distinguish living things from nonliving things: organization, growth, reproduction, and response.

Organization

If you stand a short distance from a reed warbler's nest, you can observe the largest level of organization in a living thing—the **organism** itself. Each bird is an organism. If you look at a leaf under a microscope, you can observe the smallest level of organization capable of performing all the activities of life, a **cell.** All living things are made of cells.

Growth

Most living things grow and develop. Growth often involves not only an increase in size, but also an increase in complexity, such as a tadpole growing into a frog. If all goes well, the small warblers in the picture will grow to the size of their parent.

Reproduction

Most living things produce offspring like themselves. Those offspring are also able to reproduce. That means that reed warblers produce reed warblers, which in turn produce more reed warblers.

Response

You've probably noticed that your body adjusts to changes in your surroundings. If you are exploring outside on a hot day, you may notice that you sweat. On a cold day, you may shiver. Sweating and shivering are examples of response.

Why It's Important

People of all ages experience the urge to explore and understand the living world. Understanding the characteristics of living things is a good way to start this exploration of life. In addition, knowing about the characteristics of living things helps you identify

- similarities and differences among various organisms
- key questions to ask about any organism you study

UNIFYING PRINCIPLE

All living things share common needs.

What do you need to stay alive? What does an animal like a fish or a coral need to stay alive? All living things have common needs.

What It Means

Inside every living thing, chemical reactions constantly change materials into new materials. For these reactions to occur, an organism needs energy, water and other materials, and living space.

Energy

You use energy all the time. Movement, growth, and sleep all require energy, which you get from food. Plants use the energy of sunlight to make sugar for energy. Almost all animals get their energy by eating either plants or other animals that eat plants.

Water and Other Materials

Water is an important material in the cells of all living things. The chemical reactions inside cells take place in water, and water plays a part in moving materials around within organisms.

Other materials are also essential for life. For example, plants must have carbon dioxide from the air to make sugar. Plants and animals both use oxygen to release the energy stored in sugar. You and other animals that live on land get oxygen when you breathe in air. The fish swimming around the coral reef in the picture have gills, which allow them to get oxygen that is dissolved in the water

Living Space

You can think of living space as a home—a space that protects you from external conditions and a place where you can get materials such as water and air. The ocean provides living space for the coral that makes up this coral reef. The coral itself provides living space for many other organisms.

Why It's Important

Understanding the needs of living things helps people make wise decisions about resources. This knowledge can also help you think carefully about

- the different ways in which various organisms meet their needs for energy and materials
- the effects of adding chemicals to the water and air around us
- the reasons why some types of plants or animals may disappear from an area

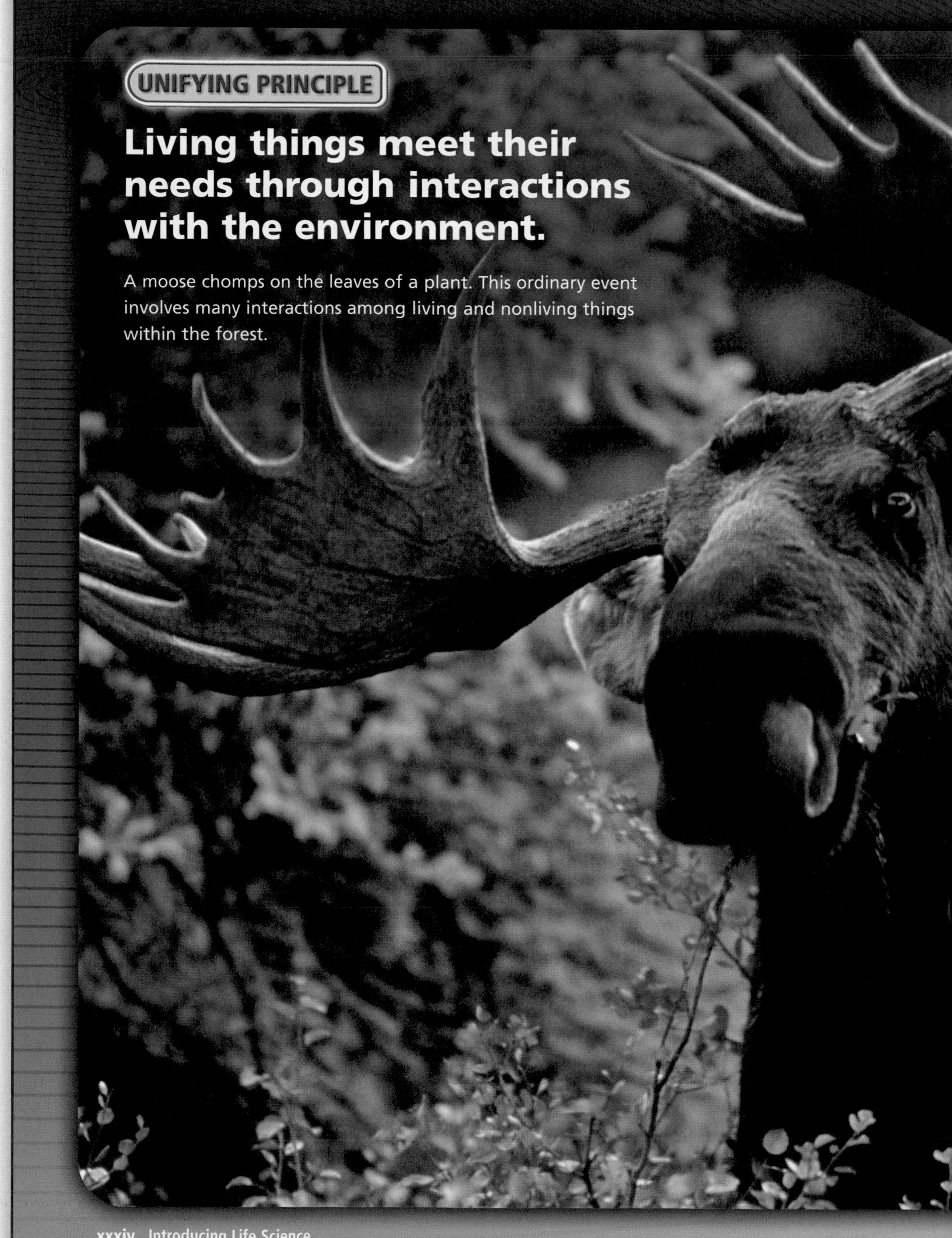

UNIFYING PRINCIPLE

Living things meet their needs through interactions with the environment.

A moose chomps on the leaves of a plant. This ordinary event involves many interactions among living and nonliving things within the forest.

What It Means

To understand this unifying principle, take a closer look at the words *environment* and *interactions.*

Environment

The **environment** is everything that surrounds a living thing. An environment is made up of both living and nonliving factors. For example, the environment in this forest includes rainfall, rocks, and soil as well as the moose, the evergreen trees, and the birch trees. In fact, the soil in these forests is called "moose and spruce" soil because it contains materials provided by the animals and evergreens in the area.

Interaction

All living things in an environment meet their needs through interactions. An **interaction** occurs when two or more things act in ways that affect one another. For example, trees and other forest plants can meet their need for energy and materials through interactions with materials in soil and with air and light from the Sun. New plants get living space as birds, wind, and other factors carry seeds from one location to another.

Animals like this moose meet their need for food through interactions with other living things. The moose gets food by eating leaves off trees and other plants. In turn, the moose becomes food for wolves.

Why It's Important

Learning about living things and their environment helps scientists and decision makers address issues such as

- predicting how a change in the moose population would affect the soil in the forest
- determining the ways in which animals harm or benefit the trees in a forest
- developing land for human use without damaging the environment

UNIFYING PRINCIPLE

The types and numbers of living things change over time.

The story of life on Earth is a story of changes. Some changes take place over millions of years. At one time, animals similar to modern fish swam in the area where this lizard now runs.

xxxvi Introducing Life Science

What It Means

To understand how living things change over time, let's look closely at the terms *diversity* and *adaptation.*

Diversity

You are surrounded by an astonishing variety of living things. This variety is called **biodiversity.** Today, scientists have described and named 1.4 million species. There are even more species that haven't been named. Scientists use the term *species* to describe a group of closely related living things. Members of a **species** are so similar that they can produce offspring that are able to reproduce. Lizards, such as the one you see in the photograph, are so diverse that they make up many different species.

Over the millions of years that life has existed on Earth, new species have originated and others have disappeared. The disappearance of a species is called **extinction.** Fossils, like the one in the photograph, provide evidence of some of the organisms that lived millions of years ago.

Adaptation

Scientists use the term **adaptation** to mean a characteristic of a species that allows members of that species to survive in a particular environment. Adaptations are related to needs. A lizard's legs are an adaptation that allows it to move on land.

Over time, species either develop adaptations to changing environments or they become extinct. The history of living things on Earth is related to the history of the changing Earth. The presence of a fishlike fossil indicates that the area shown in this photograph was once covered by water.

Why It's Important

By learning how living things change over time, you will gain a better understanding of the life that surrounds you and how it survives. Discovering more about the history of life helps scientists to

- identify patterns of relationships among various species
- predict how changes in the environment may affect species in the future

The Nature of Science

You may think of science as a body of knowledge or a collection of facts. More important, however, science is an active process that involves certain ways of looking at the world.

Scientific Habits of Mind

Scientists are curious. They are always asking questions. A scientist who observes that the number of plants in a forest preserve has decreased might ask questions such as, "Are more animals eating the plants?" or "Has the way the land is used affected the numbers of plants?" Scientists around the world investigate these and other important questions.

Scientists are observant. They are always looking closely at the world around them. A scientist who studies plants often sees details such as the height of a plant, its flowers, and how many plants live in a particular area.

Scientists are creative. They draw on what they know to form a possible explanation for a pattern, an event, or a behavior that they have observed. Then scientists create a plan for testing their ideas.

Scientists are skeptical. Scientists don't accept an explanation or answer unless it is based on evidence and logical reasoning. They continually question their own conclusions as well as conclusions suggested by other scientists. Scientists trust only evidence that is confirmed by other people or methods.

A white-tailed deer feeds on many plants, including the trillium shown here.

By measuring the growth of this tree, a scientist can study interactions in the ecosystem.

Science Processes at Work

You can think of science as a continuous cycle of asking and seeking answers to questions about the world. Although there are many processes that scientists use, scientists typically do each of the following:

- Observe and ask a question
- Determine what is known
- Investigate
- Interpret results
- Share results

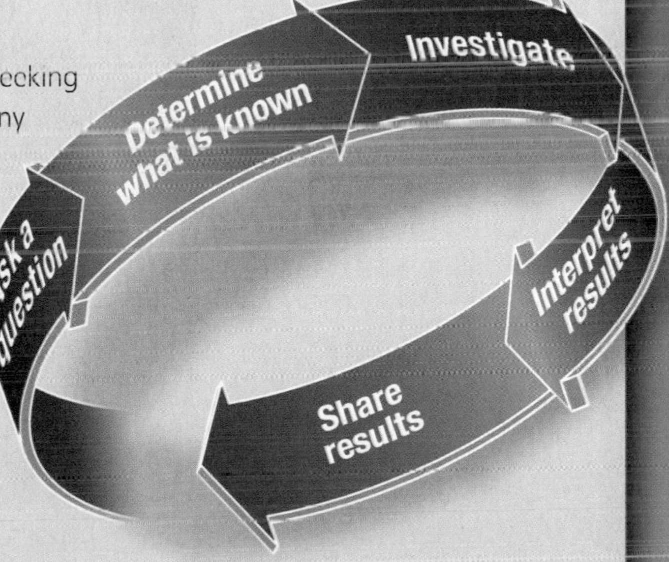

Observe and Ask a Question

It may surprise you that asking questions is an important skill. A scientific investigation may start when a scientist asks a question. Perhaps scientists observe an event or a process that they don't understand, or perhaps answering one question leads to another.

Determine What Is Known

When beginning an inquiry, scientists find out what is already known about a question. They study results from other scientific investigations, read journals, and talk with other scientists. A biologist who is trying to understand how the change in the number of deer in an area affects plants will study reports of censuses taken for both plants and animals.

Investigate

Investigating is the process of collecting evidence. Two important ways of collecting evidence are observing and experimenting.

Observing is the act of noting and recording an event, a characteristic, a behavior, or anything else detected with an instrument or with the senses. For example, a scientist notices that plants in one part of the forest are not thriving. She sees broken plants and compares the height of the plants in one area with the height of those in another.

An **experiment** is an organized procedure during which all factors but the one being studied are controlled. For example, the scientist thinks the reason some plants in the forest are not thriving may be that deer are eating the flowers off the plants. An experiment she might try is to mark two similar parts of an area where the plants grow and then build a fence around one part so the deer can't get to the plants there. The fence must be constructed so the same amounts of light, air, and water reach the plants. The only factor that changes is contact between plants and the deer.

Close observation of the Colorado potato beetle led scientists to a biological pesticide that can help farmers control this insect pest.

Ask a question

Forming hypotheses and making predictions are two other skills involved in scientific investigations. A **hypothesis** is a tentative explanation for an observation or a scientific problem that can be tested by further investigation. For example, since at least 1900, Colorado potato beetles were known to be resistant to chemical insecticides. Yet the numbers of beetles were not as large as expected. It was hypothesized that bacteria living in the beetles' environment were killing many beetles. A **prediction** is an expectation of what will be observed or what will happen and can be used to test a hypothesis. It was predicted that certain bacteria would kill Colorado potato beetles. This prediction was confirmed when a bacterium called *Bt* was discovered to kill Colorado potato beetles and other insect pests.

xl

Interpret Results

As scientists investigate, they analyze their evidence, or data, and begin to draw conclusions. **Analyzing data** involves looking at the evidence gathered through observations or experiments and trying to identify any patterns that might exist in the data. Often scientists need to make additional observations or perform more experiments before they are sure of their conclusions. Many times scientists make new predictions or revise their hypotheses.

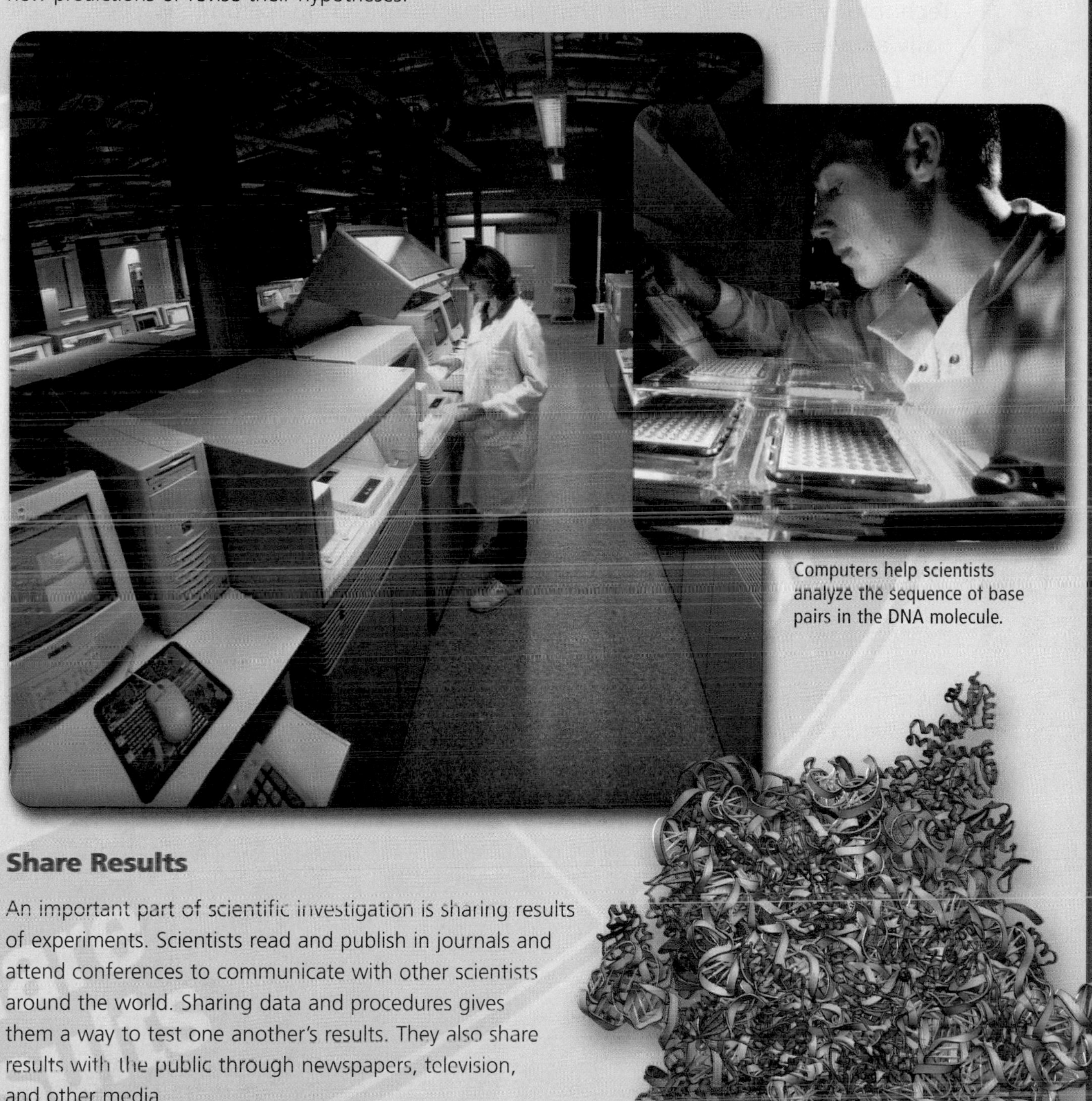

Computers help scientists analyze the sequence of base pairs in the DNA molecule.

Share Results

An important part of scientific investigation is sharing results of experiments. Scientists read and publish in journals and attend conferences to communicate with other scientists around the world. Sharing data and procedures gives them a way to test one another's results. They also share results with the public through newspapers, television, and other media.

Living things contain complex molecules such as RNA and DNA. To study them, scientists often use models like the one shown here.

The Nature of Technology

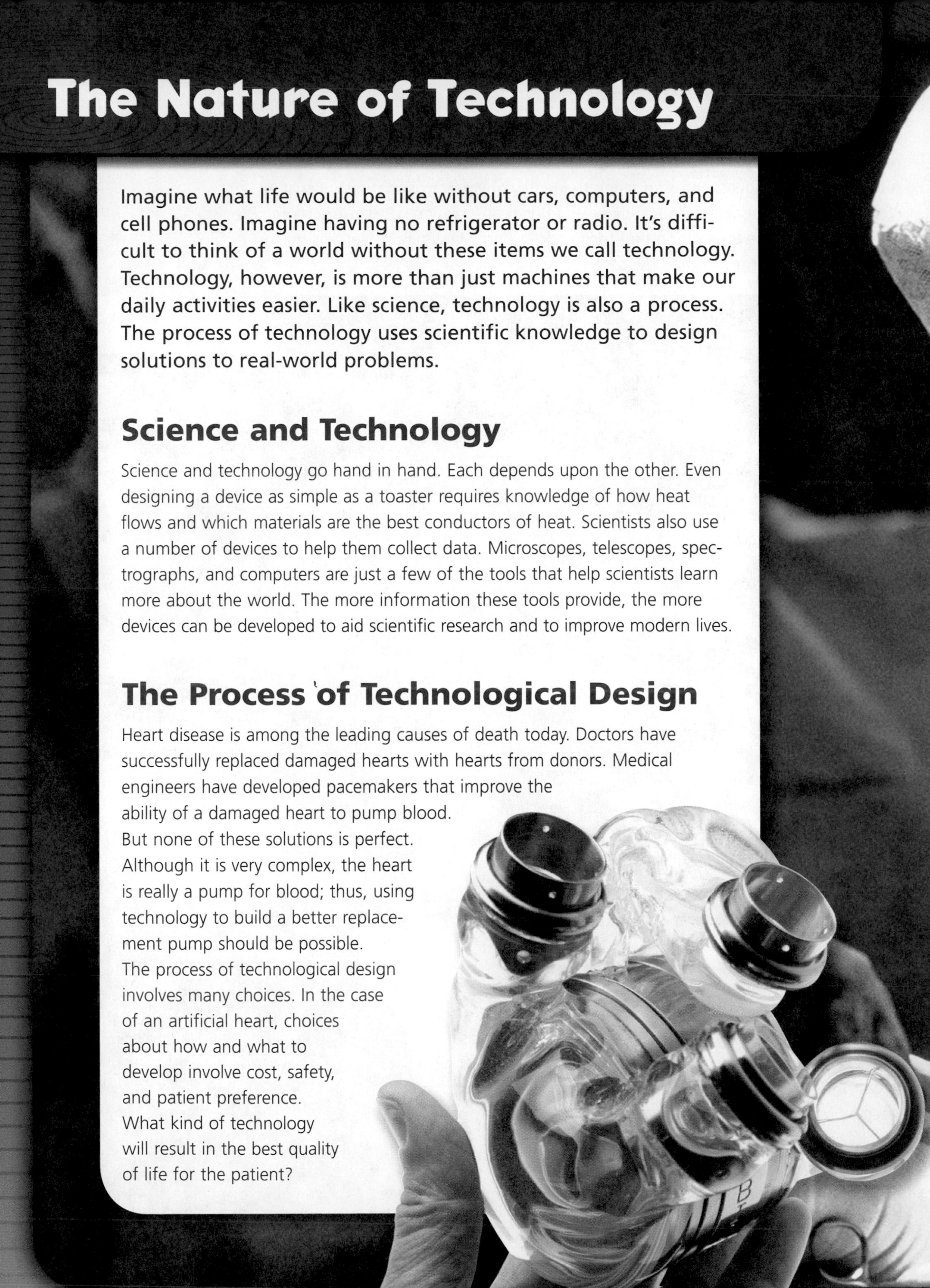

Imagine what life would be like without cars, computers, and cell phones. Imagine having no refrigerator or radio. It's difficult to think of a world without these items we call technology. Technology, however, is more than just machines that make our daily activities easier. Like science, technology is also a process. The process of technology uses scientific knowledge to design solutions to real-world problems.

Science and Technology

Science and technology go hand in hand. Each depends upon the other. Even designing a device as simple as a toaster requires knowledge of how heat flows and which materials are the best conductors of heat. Scientists also use a number of devices to help them collect data. Microscopes, telescopes, spectrographs, and computers are just a few of the tools that help scientists learn more about the world. The more information these tools provide, the more devices can be developed to aid scientific research and to improve modern lives.

The Process of Technological Design

Heart disease is among the leading causes of death today. Doctors have successfully replaced damaged hearts with hearts from donors. Medical engineers have developed pacemakers that improve the ability of a damaged heart to pump blood. But none of these solutions is perfect. Although it is very complex, the heart is really a pump for blood; thus, using technology to build a better replacement pump should be possible. The process of technological design involves many choices. In the case of an artificial heart, choices about how and what to develop involve cost, safety, and patient preference. What kind of technology will result in the best quality of life for the patient?

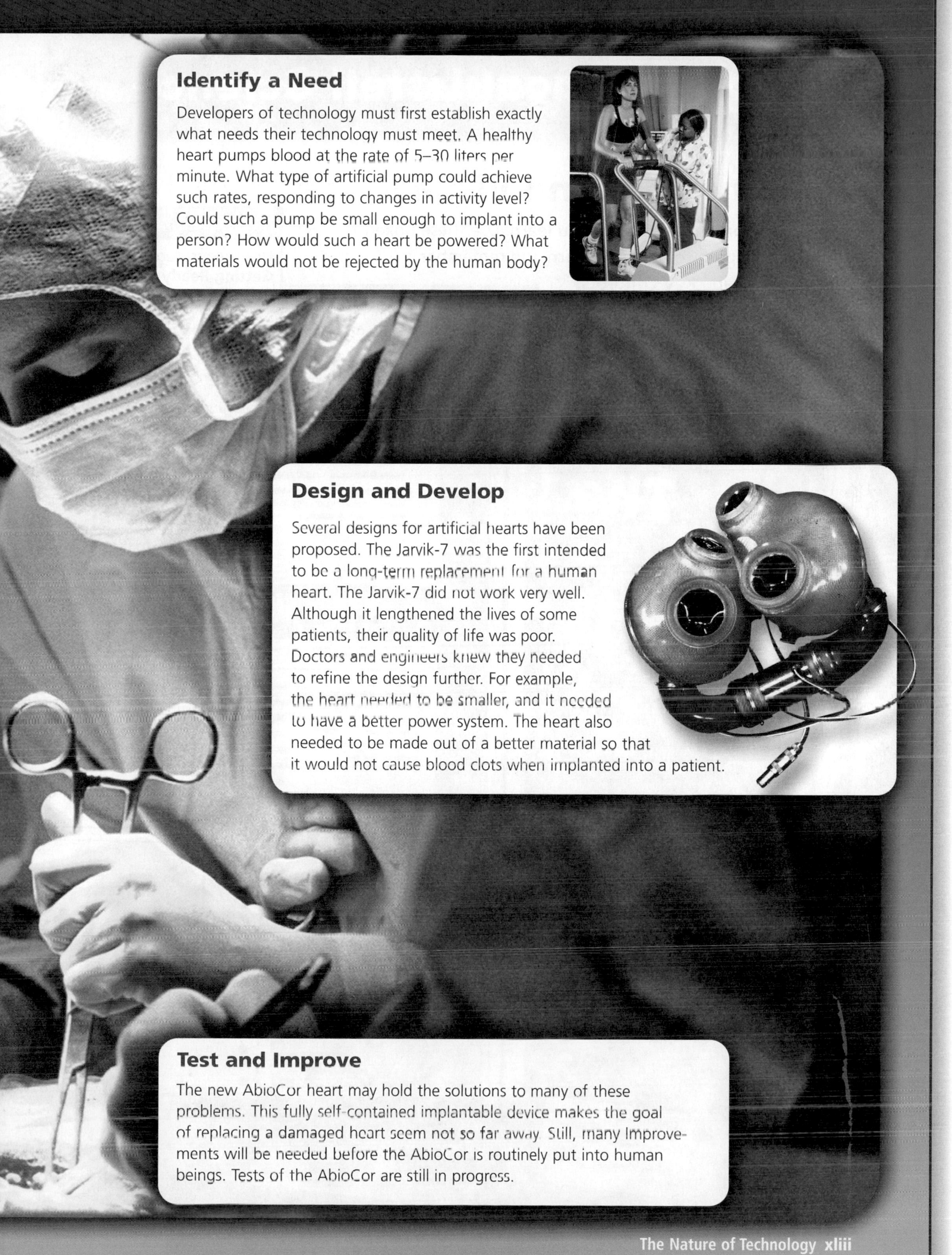

Identify a Need

Developers of technology must first establish exactly what needs their technology must meet. A healthy heart pumps blood at the rate of 5–30 liters per minute. What type of artificial pump could achieve such rates, responding to changes in activity level? Could such a pump be small enough to implant into a person? How would such a heart be powered? What materials would not be rejected by the human body?

Design and Develop

Several designs for artificial hearts have been proposed. The Jarvik-7 was the first intended to be a long-term replacement for a human heart. The Jarvik-7 did not work very well. Although it lengthened the lives of some patients, their quality of life was poor. Doctors and engineers knew they needed to refine the design further. For example, the heart needed to be smaller, and it needed to have a better power system. The heart also needed to be made out of a better material so that it would not cause blood clots when implanted into a patient.

Test and Improve

The new AbioCor heart may hold the solutions to many of these problems. This fully self-contained implantable device makes the goal of replacing a damaged heart seem not so far away. Still, many improvements will be needed before the AbioCor is routinely put into human beings. Tests of the AbioCor are still in progress.

Using McDougal Littell Science

Reading Text and Visuals

This book is organized to help you learn. Use these boxed pointers as a path to help you learn and remember the **Big Ideas** and **Key Concepts.**

Take notes.

Use the strategies on the **Getting Ready to Learn** page.

Read the Big Idea.

As you read **Key Concepts** for the chapter, relate them to **the Big Idea.**

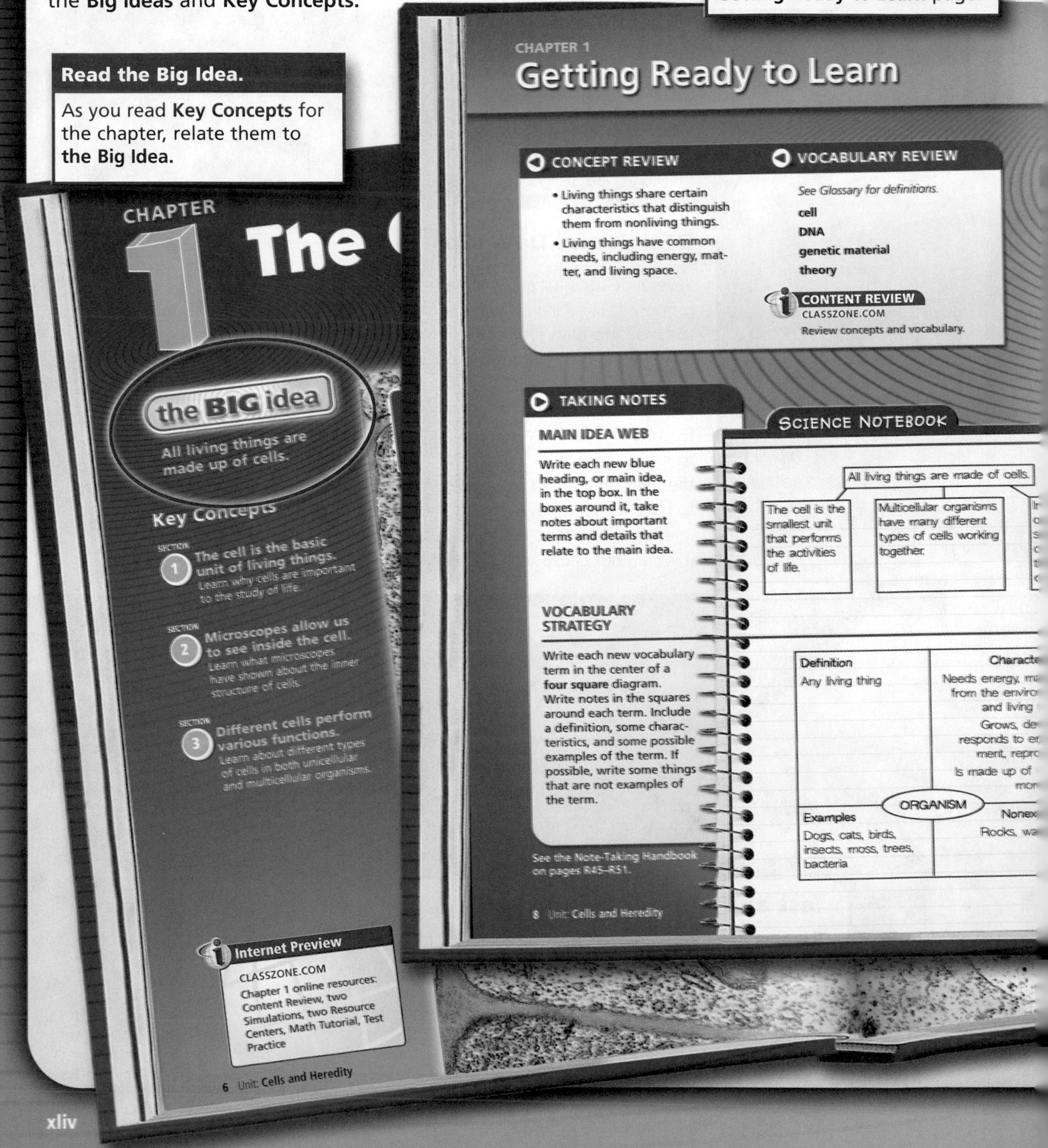

CHAPTER 1 The

the BIG idea

All living things are made up of cells.

Key Concepts

SECTION 1 The cell is the basic unit of living things. Learn why cells are important to the study of life.

SECTION 2 Microscopes allow us to see inside the cell. Learn what microscopes have shown about the inner structure of cells.

SECTION 3 Different cells perform various functions. Learn about different types of cells in both unicellular and multicellular organisms.

Internet Preview
CLASSZONE.COM
Chapter 1 online resources: Content Review, two Simulations, two Resource Centers, Math Tutorial, Test Practice

6 Unit: Cells and Heredity

CHAPTER 1
Getting Ready to Learn

CONCEPT REVIEW
- Living things share certain characteristics that distinguish them from nonliving things.
- Living things have common needs, including energy, matter, and living space.

VOCABULARY REVIEW
See Glossary for definitions.
cell
DNA
genetic material
theory

CONTENT REVIEW
CLASSZONE.COM
Review concepts and vocabulary.

TAKING NOTES

MAIN IDEA WEB
Write each new blue heading, or main idea, in the top box. In the boxes around it, take notes about important terms and details that relate to the main idea.

VOCABULARY STRATEGY
Write each new vocabulary term in the center of a **four square** diagram. Write notes in the squares around each term. Include a definition, some characteristics, and some possible examples of the term. If possible, write some things that are not examples of the term.

See the Note-Taking Handbook on pages R45–R51.

SCIENCE NOTEBOOK

All living things are made of cells.

The cell is the smallest unit that performs the activities of life.

Multicellular organisms have many different types of cells working together.

Definition: Any living thing

Characte[ristics]: Needs energy, ma[tter] from the enviro[nment] and living [space]. Grows, de[velops], responds to en[viron]ment, repro[duces]. Is made up of [one or] mor[e cells]

ORGANISM

Examples: Dogs, cats, birds, insects, moss, trees, bacteria

Nonex[amples]: Rocks, wa[ter]

8 Unit: Cells and Heredity

Read each heading.

See how it fits in the outline of the chapter.

KEY CONCEPT

1.1 The cell is the basic unit of living things.

BEFORE, you learned
- Living things have common characteristics
- Living things have common needs
- A theory is something that explains what is observed in nature

NOW, you will learn
- How living things are different from nonliving things
- How the microscope led to the discovery of cells
- About the cell theory

Remember what you know.

Think about concepts you learned earlier and preview what you'll learn now.

VOCABULARY
- organism p. 9
- unicellular p. 11
- multicellular p. 11
- microscope p. 12
- bacteria p. 14

EXPLORE Activity and Life

Does a candle show signs of life?

PROCEDURE
1. Carefully light one candle.
2. Sit quietly and observe the candle. Note its behavior. What does the flame do? What happens to the wax?

MATERIALS
- small candle
- candleholder
- matches

WHAT DO YOU THINK?
- How does a lit candle seem alive?
- How do you know for sure that it is not?

Try the activities.

They will introduce you to science concepts.

Living things are different from nonliving things.

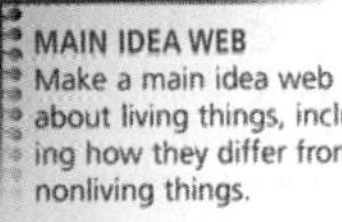

MAIN IDEA WEB
Make a main idea web about living things, including how they differ from nonliving things.

You know life when you see it. Perhaps your class takes a field trip to a local state park to collect water samples. You are surrounded by trees. There is a stream, with rocks covered with moss and green algae. There are fish and frogs; there are birds and insects. You are surrounded by life. But how would you define it?

One way to answer the question is to think about what makes a living thing different from a nonliving thing. You might ask if a thing uses energy. Or maybe you would observe it to see if it moves. You could investigate whether it consumes food and water. These are characteristics of living things, or organisms. Any individual form of life that uses energy to carry out its activities is an **organism.** Most organisms move. All organisms get water and other materials from the environment.

Learn the vocabulary.

Take notes on each term.

Chapter 1: **The Cell** 9

Reading Text and Visuals

Cells come from other cells.

The studies of Hooke and Leeuwenhoek made people ask if all living things have cells. People continued to observe samples taken from all sorts of living matter. They continued to find cells, although often these cells looked very different from one another. Still, it was clear that all living matter was made of cells.

There was another important question scientists were trying to answer: Where do cells come from? The answer to this question was settled by the 1850s. People studying all types of living cells observed the same thing—that cells divide. One living cell divides into two living cells. Here, under the microscope, was evidence of where cells come from. Life comes from life—that is, one cell comes from another cell.

CHECK YOUR READING What do scientists mean when they say that life comes from life? Your answer should include the word *cells*.

The observations and evidence gathered over a long time by many scientists are summarized in the three concepts of the cell theory:

1. Every living thing is made of one or more cells.
2. Cells carry out the functions needed to support life.
3. Cells come only from other living cells.

The Cell Theory

The importance of the cell to life is summarized in the cell theory.

1. **Every living thing is made up of one or more cells.** A polar bear is a multicellular organism.
2. **Cells carry out the functions needed to support life.** Fat cells are animal cells that provide energy as well as insulation.
3. **Cells come only from other living cells.** Each polar bear cub began as a single cell.

400 ×

Chapter 1: **The Cell** 13

Read one paragraph at a time.

Look for a topic sentence that explains the main idea of the paragraph. Figure out how the details relate to that idea. One paragraph might have several important ideas; you may have to reread to understand.

Answer the questions.

Check Your Reading questions will help you remember what you read.

Study the visuals.

- Read the title.
- Read all labels and captions.
- Figure out what the picture is showing. Notice the information in the captions.

Doing Labs

To understand science, you have to see it in action. Doing labs helps you understand how things really work.

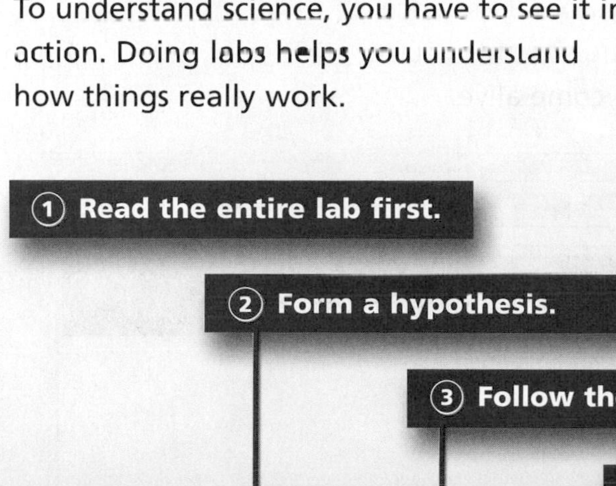

① **Read the entire lab first.**

② **Form a hypothesis.**

③ **Follow the procedure.**

④ **Record the data.**

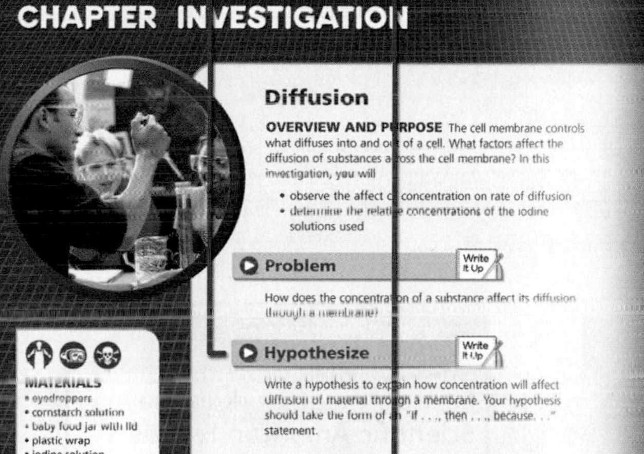

⑤ **Analyze your results.**

⑥ **Write your lab report.**

Using Technology

The Internet is a great source of information about up-to-date science. The ClassZone Web site and NSTA SciLinks have exciting sites for you to explore. Video clips and simulations can make science come alive.

Look for red banners.

Go to **ClassZone.com** to see simulations, visualizations, resource centers, and content review.

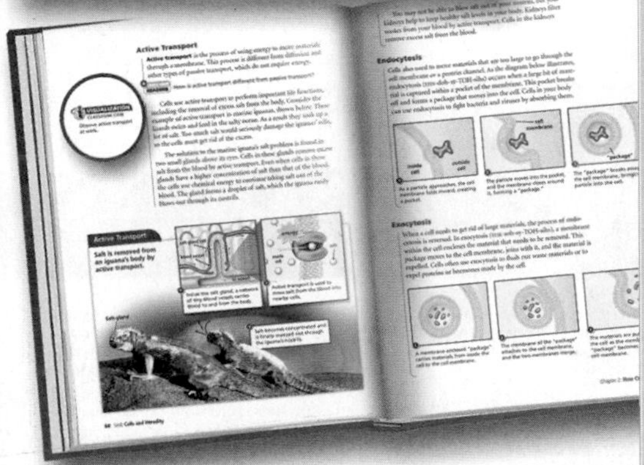

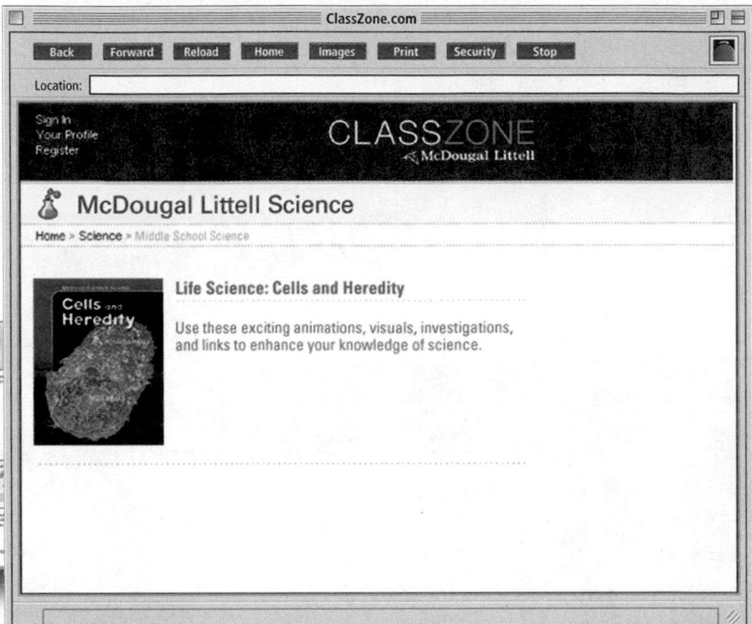

Watch the video.

See science at work in the **Scientific American Frontiers** video.

Look up SciLinks.

Go to **scilinks.org** to explore the topic.

Heredity **Code: MDL034**

xlviii

McDougal Littell Science

Cells and Heredity

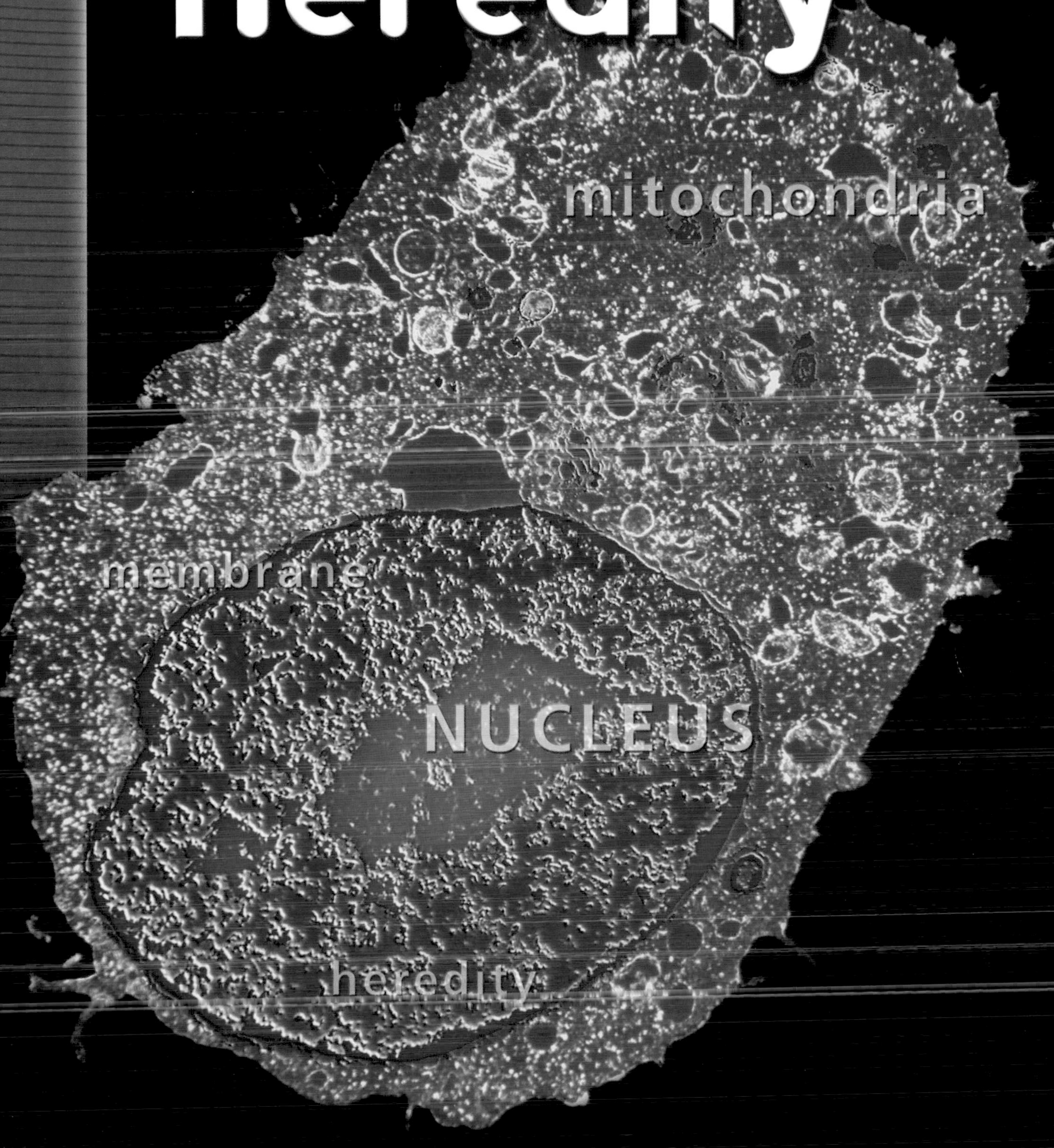

mitochondria

membrane

NUCLEUS

heredity

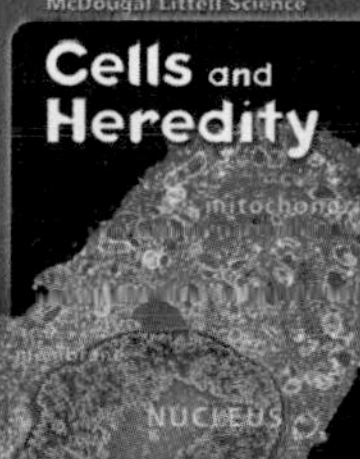

Cells and Heredity
Contents Overview

Unit Features

FRONTIERS in Science

VIDEO SUMMARY

SCIENTIFIC AMERICAN FRONTIERS

In "Genes for Youth," a segment of the *Scientific American Frontiers* series that aired on PBS stations, host Alan Alda visits Dr. Cynthia Kenyon, a scientist who has designed ways to extend the life expectancy of the tiny nematode worm. Nematodes have organs and cells that are very similar to those of human beings; however, the natural life span of a nematode is two weeks.

In an attempt to discover a gene that controls aging, Kenyon bathed the worms in a chemical that created a mutation. In some cases, altering a single gene doubled the life span of the worm. In a second experiment, Kenyon used a laser to destroy tissue that would allow the nematode to reproduce. This caused the worm to produce youth-sustaining chemicals. The result of each experiment was to double the life span of some of the worms. When combined, the changes quadrupled the natural life span.

National Science Education Standards

A.1–8 Abilities Necessary to Do Scientific Inquiry

A.9.a–b, A.9.d–g Understandings About Scientific Inquiry

F.5.e Science and Technology in Society

G.1.a–b Science as a Human Endeavor

G.2.a, G.2.c Nature of Science

FRONTIERS in Science

Genes that MAP the Body

What signals a monkey to grow a tail and a fish to grow fins? The answer is in their genes.

SCIENTIFIC AMERICAN FRONTIERS

Learn about genes that affect aging. See the video "Genes for Youth."

2 Unit 1: **Cells and Heredity**

ADDITIONAL RESOURCES

Technology Resources

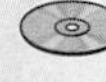
Scientific American Frontiers Video: *Genes for Youth:* 8-minute video segment that introduces the unit.

ClassZone.com
CAREER LINK, Molecular Biologist

Guide student viewing and comprehension of the video:

Video Teaching Guide, pp. 1–2; Video Viewing Guide, p. 3; Video Wrap-Up, p. 4

Scientific American Frontiers Video Guide, pp. 1–2

Unit projects procedures and rubrics:

Unit Projects, pp. 5–10

What's in a Gene?

Humans and fish are about as different as one animal can be from another. Yet both organisms have a similar body pattern: front and back, top and bottom, left side and right side. The head is at one end and limbs extend from the body—fins in a fish, arms and legs in a human. Inside are similar structures—brains, hearts, and stomachs—and cells that function in similar ways.

A DNA is the genetic material found in all living things. DNA determines how cells grow, develop, and function. Within the DNA are genes, segments of DNA, that determine whether a cell becomes a brain cell or a heart cell. Both a fish and a human start out life as a single cell. As the cell divides again and again, each organism grows into its familiar shape. Scientists are studying what it is that maps out the head-to-tail development that gets every part of a body in the right place.

One group of genes, called *Hox* genes, are critical in the early development of an animal's body. These genes are found in the DNA of every animal—from humans to fruit flies. The position of *Hox* genes, from top to bottom along the DNA, matches up to the particular parts they control of an organism's body. B

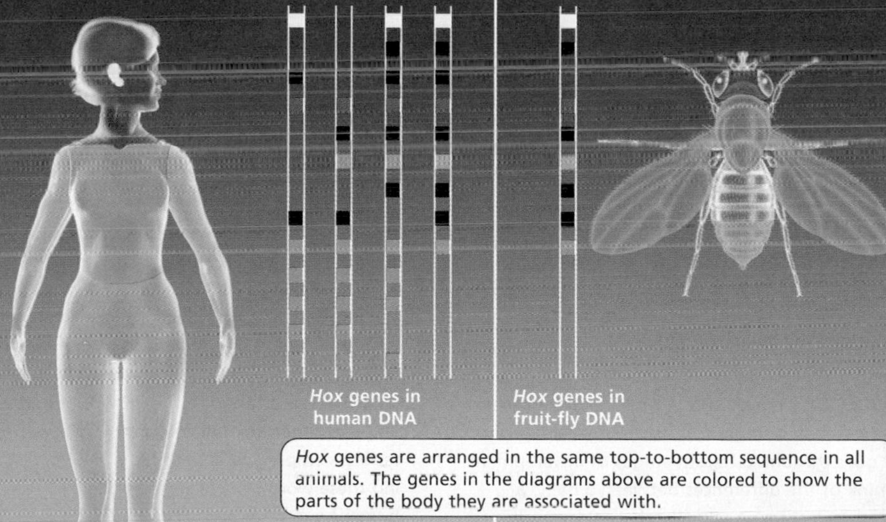

Hox genes are arranged in the same top-to-bottom sequence in all animals. The genes in the diagrams above are colored to show the parts of the body they are associated with.

FOCUS

Set Learning Goals

Students will

- Examine the purpose and function of Hox genes.
- Analyze how the development process can differ between animals.
- Complete a unit project relating to DNA forensics, cell processes, or the DNA molecule.

Remind students that a frontier is an area where new advances in science can be made, and that the "Genes for Youth" video shows scientists applying technology to investigate and manipulate genes. Have students look at the photos on pp. 2–3 and predict the similarities that scientists might find among fish, flies, and humans.

INSTRUCT

Determining What Is Known

Point out that the study of genes begins with the knowledge that all living things share certain common characteristics, among these is the ability to grow, develop, and reproduce. Ask: What common characteristic did people discover with early microscopes? *Organisms have cells.*

Teach from Visuals

Draw students' attention to the diagrams of genes on chromosomes. Ask: What is one obvious difference between the human and fruit-fly genes? *Humans have more* Hox *genes.* How are the genes similar? *They appear in the same sequence in both organisms.*

DIFFERENTIATE INSTRUCTION

More Reading Support

A What do genes in DNA do? *control how cells grow, develop, and function*

B What do *Hox* genes do? *control development of body parts*

Advanced Have students investigate the research that has been done using fruit flies. Ask them to report on why fruit flies are good subjects for this type of study.

Teach from Visuals

Have students compare and contrast the photos of the zebrafish embryo. Ask: What is one clue that different types of structures are developing? *The third photo shows structures of different sizes and shapes.*

Scientific Process

Ask students to identify the skills that scientists use most to study *Hox* genes. *experimentation and observation*

Sharing Results

Ask students why it is important that scientists share what they find out about *Hox* genes. *Sample answer: Scientists who share information enable other scientists to build on this information. Experiments are then altered and may be performed without redundancy. And, new experiments can be done. In this way, researchers get more and better information that may lead to ways to treat certain genetic conditions.*

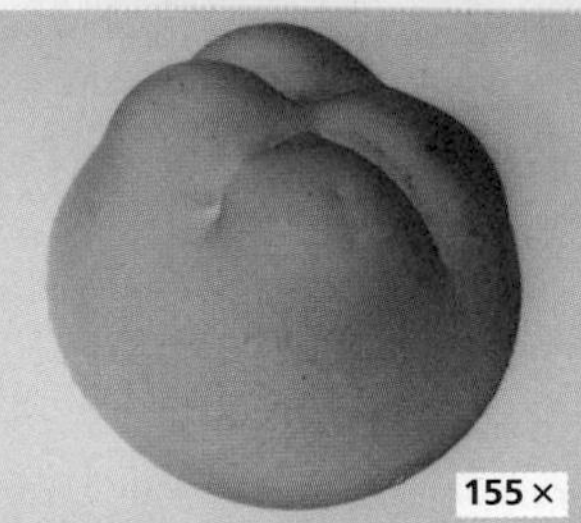

The egg of a zebrafish starts to divide after fertilization.

SOURCE for three images, Dr. Richard Kessel and Dr. Gene Shih/Visuals Unlimited

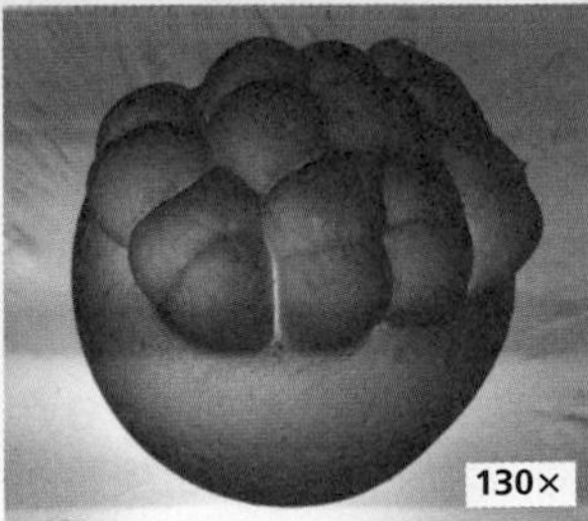

The egg now has 16 cells, all of which are similar in size and shape.

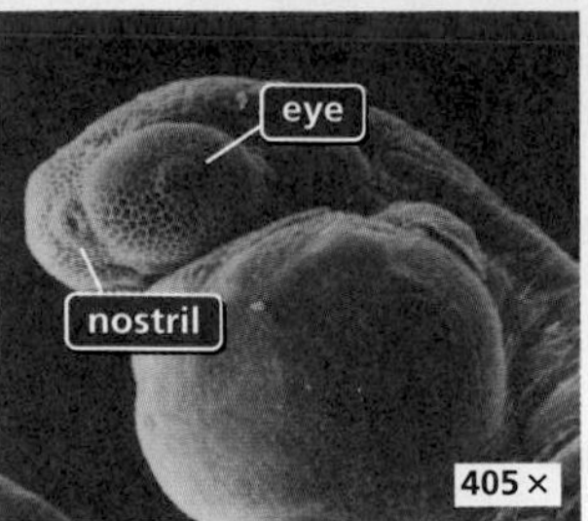

Many hours later, the cells have started to develop into different parts of the body.

How *Hox* Genes Work

Hox genes act like switches. A particular *Hox* gene turns on the development of a particular structure in an animal's body. One type of *Hox* gene switches on the development of structures in the head—for example, eyes and ears. Another switches on the development of limbs—the arms, legs, fins, or wings of an animal. The position of the genes within an animal's DNA matches to the part of the body it controls. *Hox* genes at the top control development of parts of the head. Those toward the middle control development of the main part of the body and the limbs.

How a Limb Develops

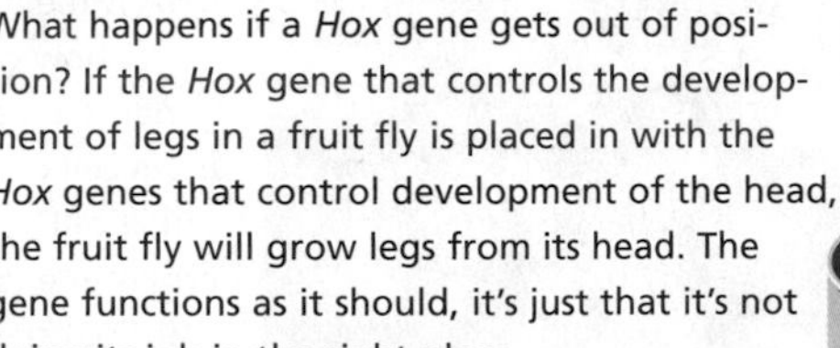

What happens if a *Hox* gene gets out of position? If the *Hox* gene that controls the development of legs in a fruit fly is placed in with the *Hox* genes that control development of the head, the fruit fly will grow legs from its head. The gene functions as it should, it's just that it's not doing its job in the right place.

Another interesting thing about *Hox* genes is that they are active only for a certain period of time. They "switch off" when the part of the body they control has developed. Studies of the zebrafish have provided clues as to how this happens.

View the "Genes for Youth" segment of your Scientific American Frontiers video to learn about the role of genes in aging.

IN THIS SCENE FROM THE VIDEO ▶ **biologist Cynthia Kenyon observes the activity level of some unusual worms that remain active much longer than other worms.**

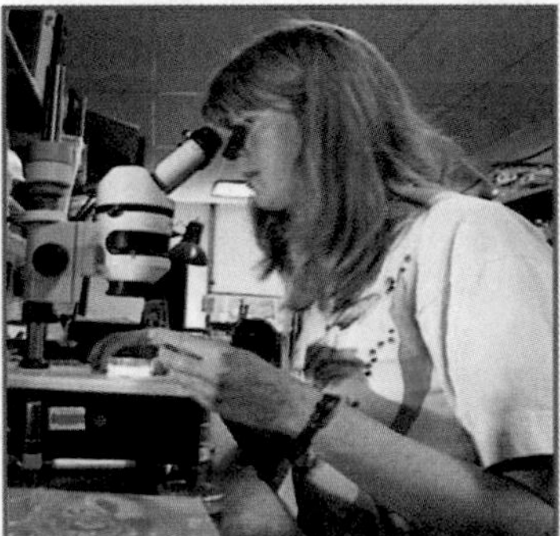

UNDERSTANDING AGING A multicellular organism starts life as a single cell. As an organism grows, it goes through different stages of development. Think of the differences between a baby, a teenager, a young adult, and an older person.

Kenyon is interested in what controls aging in worms. She studies how the genes in long-living worms affect the activity of their cells. She looks for differences between the cells of unusual worms and those of normal worms. Because cells of animals function in similar ways, she is interested in how what she learns about aging in worms might apply to other animals. Even though a worm is far less complex an animal than a human, studying these worms may provide clues into how humans age.

DIFFERENTIATE INSTRUCTION

More Reading Support

C What do *Hox* genes act like? *switches*

D What happens if a *Hox* gene is missing or damaged? *Abnormalities can occur.*

Below Level Have students draw two sequences of events, one beginning with a switch labeled "on" and the other with a switch labeled "off," to show how *Hox* genes work. *On: cells develop, buds form, limbs form; off: growth stops.*

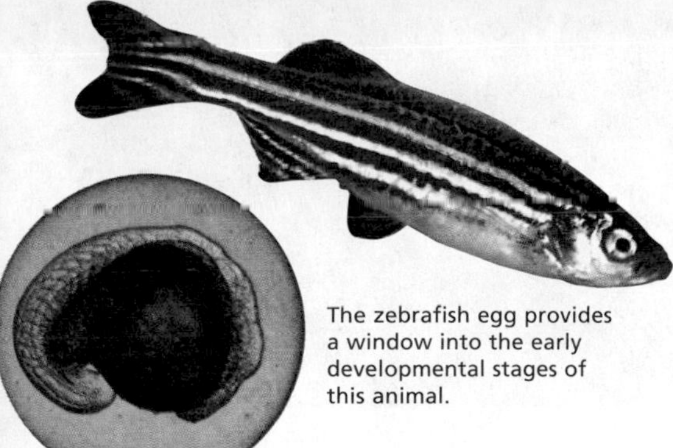

The zebrafish egg provides a window into the early developmental stages of this animal.

A Window on Development

Zebrafish are tiny fish that hatch in about three days. Scientists can actually see through the fish egg to watch its body develop. Working with the *Hox* genes of zebrafish, one researcher studied the amount of time that the *Hox* gene that controls fin development was active. The gene "turned on" for a short period of time, the fin developed, then the gene "turned off."

This research led scientists to think about the length of time the same *Hox* gene is active in other animals. It's possible that limbs are longer in larger animals because their *Hox* genes are active for a longer period of time. Researchers are excited because what they learn about the *Hox* genes of a simple animal can provide clues into the development of larger, more complex animals.

UNANSWERED Questions

There are many unanswered questions about the role *Hox* genes play in the development of body plans:

- Which *Hox* genes control which stages of development and how long are the genes active?
- What is it that signals the genes to "turn on and off"?
- How can research on *Hox* genes be used by medical researchers to help them treat genetic diseases or disorders that affect how a body develops?

UNIT PROJECTS

As you study this unit, work alone or with a group on one of the projects below.

Design an Experiment

Use fast plants to observe differences among plants.

- Follow directions for growing fast plants.
- Observe the plants as they grow and identify different characteristics.
- Use your observations to form a question about genes and plant characteristics.
- Design an experiment to answer your question.

Living Cell

Work cooperatively to present a "living cell" demonstration. Model cell processes, such as photosynthesis and cellular respiration.

- Design a model that shows parts of the cell at work.
- Include structures such as membranes, the nucleus, chloroplasts, and mitochondria. Represent energy and materials that move into and out of a cell.
- Have one student narrate each process.

DNA Detective Work

Prepare an oral presentation about how DNA technology is used to solve crimes.

Explain the science behind police and detective work.

CAREER CENTER
CLASSZONE.COM

Learn more about careers in molecular biology.

UNANSWERED Questions

Have students read the questions and think of some of their own. Remind them that scientists always end up with more questions—that inquiry is the driving force of science.

- With the class, generate on the board a list of new questions.
- Students can add to the list after they watch the *Scientific American Frontiers* Video.
- Students can use the list as a springboard for choosing their Unit Projects.

UNIT PROJECTS

Encourage students to pick the project that most appeals to them. Point out that each is long-term and will take several weeks to complete. You might group or pair students to work on projects and in some cases guide student choice. Some of the projects have student choice built into them. Each project has two worksheet pages, including a rubric. Use the pages to guide students through criteria, process, and schedule.

 Unit Projects, pp. 5–10

REVISIT concepts introduced in this article:

Chapter 1
- Cells come from other cells, p. 13
- Cells in multicellular organisms specialize, p. 28

Chapter 2
- Chemical reactions take place inside cells, pp. 41–46

Chapter 3
- Cell division is involved in growth, development, and repair, pp. 76–78

Chapter 4
- Living things inherit traits in patterns, pp. 101–107

Chapter 5
- DNA is the information molecule, pp. 135–138
- Changes in DNA can produce variation, pp. 144–148
- Modern genetics uses DNA technology, pp. 150–154

DIFFERENTIATE INSTRUCTION

More Reading Support

E Why do some scientists think that animals develop longer limbs? *because their Hox genes signal for a longer time*

Differentiate Unit Projects Projects are appropriate for varying abilities. Allow students to choose the ones that interest them most and let them vary their product. Encourage below level students to give visual or oral presentations or to record audio presentations about their topic.

Below Level Encourage students to try "Living Cell."

Advanced Challenge students to complete "DNA Detective Work."

CHAPTER 1 The Cell

Life Science UNIFYING PRINCIPLES

PRINCIPLE 1
All living things share common characteristics.

PRINCIPLE 2
All living things share common needs.

PRINCIPLE 3
Living things meet their needs through interactions with the environment.

PRINCIPLE 4
The types and numbers of living things change over time.

Unit 1: Cells and Heredity BIG IDEAS

CHAPTER 1
The Cell
All living things are made up of cells.

CHAPTER 2
How Cells Function
All cells need energy and materials for life processes.

CHAPTER 3
Cell Division
Organisms grow, reproduce, and maintain themselves through cell division.

CHAPTER 4
Patterns of Heredity
In sexual reproduction, traits are passed from parents to offspring in predictable patterns.

CHAPTER 5
DNA and Modern Genetics
DNA is a set of instructions for making cell parts.

CHAPTER 1 KEY CONCEPTS

SECTION 1

The cell is the basic unit of living things.

1. Living things are different from nonliving things.
2. All living things are made of cells.
3. The microscope led to the discovery of cells.
4. Cells come from other cells.
5. The cell theory is important to the study of biology.

SECTION 2

Microscopes allow us to see inside the cell.

1. The microscope is an important tool.
2. Cells are diverse.
3. Plants and animals have eukaryotic cells.

SECTION 3

Different cells perform various functions.

1. Organisms can be classified by their cell type.
2. Cells in multicellular organisms specialize.
3. A multicellular organism is a community of cells.
4. Scientists use models to study cells.

The Big Idea Flow Chart is available on p. T1 in the **UNIT TRANSPARENCY BOOK.**

Previewing Content

SECTION

The cell is the basic unit of living things. pp. 9–17

1. Living things are different from nonliving things.
Organisms are individual forms of life that use energy to carry out activities. To be classified as living, something must
- be organized;
- grow and develop;
- respond to its environment; and
- be able to reproduce.

All organisms need energy, materials, and living space. All energy used by life on Earth comes from the Sun.

2. All living things are made of cells.
The **cell** is the smallest unit that can perform the basic activities of life. **Multicellular** organisms have specialized cells that, together, meet the basic needs.

3. The microscope led to the discovery of cells.
Robert Hooke and Anton van Leeuwenhoek first described cells in the 1660s and 1670s. **Microscopes** were the new technology that led to their discoveries.

4. Cells come from other cells.
In the 1850s people knew for sure that cells come from other cells. This fact is part of the cell theory:
- All living things are made of one or more cells.
- Cells carry out the functions needed to support life.
- Cells come only from other living cells.

5. The cell theory is important to the study of biology.
A theory is an explanation of what is observed, and must be supported by evidence. Louis Pasteur used the cell theory as a foundation for his studies. He found that
- Bacteria causes food spoilage, sour milk, and many diseases.
- Living things do not arise by spontaneous generation.

SECTION

Microscopes allow us to see inside the cell. pp. 18–25

1. The microscope is an important tool.
Three types of microscopes are useful in studying cells. Light microscopes can magnify living cells. Scanning electron microscopes and transmission electron microscopes can magnify smaller objects, but preparation of living specimens kills them. The diagrams below show how SEM and TEM work.

Scanning Electron Microscope

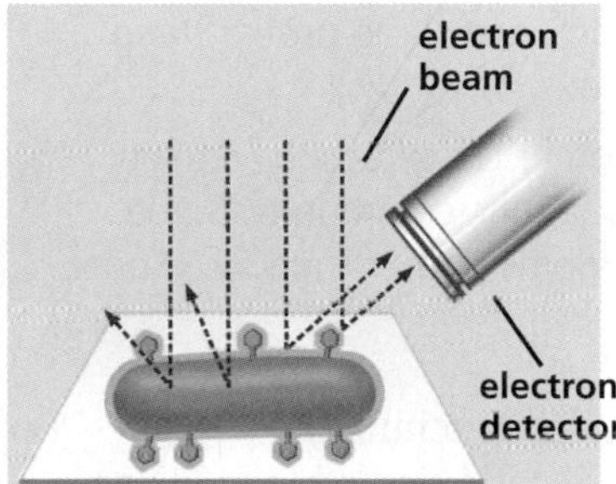

Transmission Electron Microscope

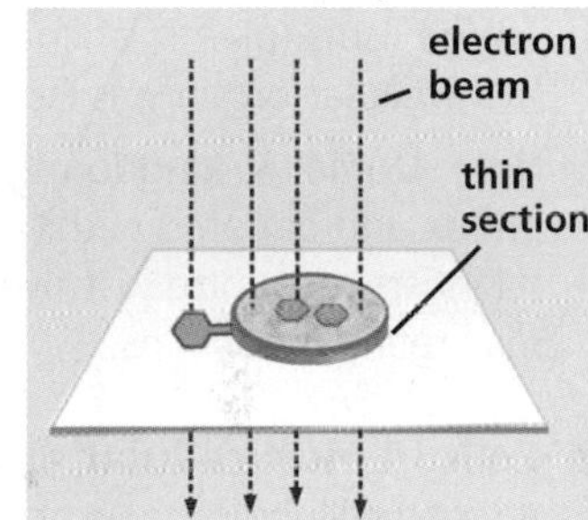

2. Cells are diverse.
All cells have **cell membranes** as a protective covering. They all contain **cytoplasm,** a thick fluid where most of the work of the cell is done. Most cells also have genetic material, DNA.
- In prokaryotic cells, DNA is in the cytoplasm.
- In eukaryotic cells, DNA is separated from the rest of the cytoplasm in a **nucleus.**

3. Plants and animals have eukaryotic cells.
Eukaryotic cells are much larger than prokaryotic cells. They have many complex structures, including **organelles.** Organelles called **chloroplasts** use energy from sunlight to make sugar. Cells have **mitochondria** to make energy available to the organism. The endoplasmic reticulum, ribosomes, and Golgi apparatus process and transport materials. Other organelles such as vacuoles and lysosomes store and recycle water and waste.

Common Misconceptions

MISCONCEPTION DATABASE
CLASSZONE.COM Background on student misconceptions

BASIC UNIT OF STRUCTURE AND FUNCTION Students easily understand the cell as a unit of structure but may not grasp that it is a unit of function. Functionality can be inferred from experiments with cells.

 This misconception is addressed on p. 11.

INSIDE OF A CELL Students may think of cells as mostly empty with isolated structures inside. In fact, cells are full of cytoplasm, a thick fluid, which in turn contains nutrients, wastes, and cell structures and is full of activity as well.

TE This misconception is addressed in More Reading Support on p. 20.

Previewing Content

SECTION

Different cells perform various functions. pp. 26–33

1. **Organisms can be classified by their cell type.**
   Most organisms on Earth are **unicellular.** They can be in one of three domains.
   - **Archaea** are prokaryotes that mostly live in extreme environments.
   - **Bacteria** are prokaryotes that share some similarities with archaea, but grow virtually everywhere on Earth.
   - **Eukarya** are eukaryotes, which include multicellular organisms (plants, animals, fungi, and some protists) and unicellular organisms (some protists).

   Note: Domains, kingdoms, and other classifications remain in flux and debated within the scientific community. Some scientists recognize just five kingdoms (rather than six). Some may refer to domains.

2. **Cells in multicellular organisms specialize.**
   All multicellular organisms begin life as a single fertilized egg cell. As cells divide, they specialize to perform specific jobs. The more **specialization** there is, the more complex the organism is.

3. **A multicellular organism is a community of cells.**
   Organisms have different degrees of organization. For example, sponges have specialized cells, but are not strictly organized.
   - Similar cells group together to form **tissues.**
   - Tissues act together to form **organs.**
   - Organs and tissues act together in organ systems.

4. **Scientists use models to study cells.**
   Scientists use models to make complicated structures or processes easier to understand. Some examples of models include mathematical or chemical equations, diagrams, process models, or physical models.

Complex organisms have a hierarchy of organization, pictured below.

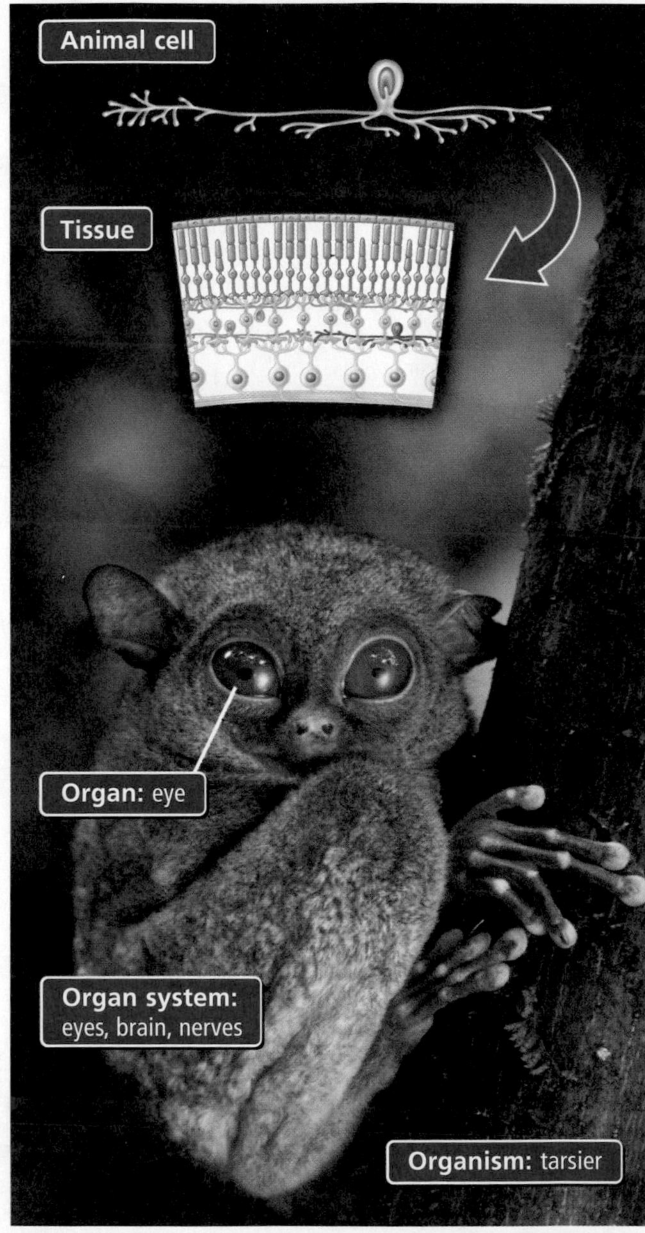

Common Misconceptions

PLANT AND ANIMAL SIMILARITIES Students may think that plants and animals are totally different, even at the cellular level. In fact, the two types of organisms have both differences and similarities.

 This misconception is addressed on p. 23.

MISCONCEPTION DATABASE
CLASSZONE.COM Background on student misconceptions

TWO KINDS OF CELLS Students often think that all cells are either plant or animal. Many, of course, are neither.

 This misconception is addressed on p. 28.

Previewing Labs

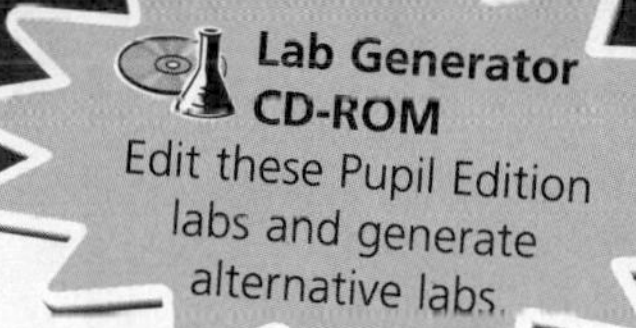

EXPLORE the BIG idea

Seeing and Understanding, p. 7 Students observe a photograph with a magnifying lens to find out about magnification.	**TIME** 10 minutes **MATERIALS** hand lens, magazine or newspaper
Bits and Pieces, p. 7 Students arrange words in a sentence to understand how parts fit together.	**TIME** 10 minutes **MATERIALS** scissors, magazine or newspaper
Internet Activity: Cells, p. 7 Students take a virtual tour of a cell.	**TIME** 20 minutes **MATERIALS** computer with Internet access

SECTION 1

EXPLORE Activity and Life, p. 9 Students observe a lit candle and compare it with living things.	**TIME** 10 minutes **MATERIALS** small candle, candle holder, matches
CHAPTER INVESTIGATION **Using a Microscope,** pp. 16–17 Students use a light microscope to observe organisms in pond water. R Identification Key, p. 50	**TIME** 40 minutes **MATERIALS** pond water, slides, cover slip, light microscope, eyedropper, lens paper, Identification Key

SECTION 2

INVESTIGATE Plant and Animal Cells, p. 21 Students use a microscope to examine prepared slides of plant and animal cells.	**TIME** 30 minutes **MATERIALS** prepared slides of plant and animal cells, microscope, millimeter ruler

SECTION 3

EXPLORE Specialization, p. 26 Students observe different parts of a plant to learn about specialized cells.	**TIME** 20 minutes **MATERIALS** grass plants, including roots; cup; water; paper towels
INVESTIGATE Cell Models, p. 31 Students make models of cells and assess the limitations of modeling.	**TIME** 30 minutes **MATERIALS** various craft supplies, scissors, glue, poster board, markers

R **Additional INVESTIGATION,** Looking at Your Own Cells, A, B, & C, pp. 60–68; Teacher Instructions, pp. 308–309

Previewing Chapter Resources

CHAPTER 1
The Cell

INTEGRATED TECHNOLOGY

CLASSZONE.COM
- eEdition Plus
- EasyPlanner Plus
- Misconception Database
- Content Review
- Test Practice
- Simulation
- Resource Centers
- Internet Activity: Cells
- Math Tutorial

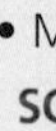

SCILINKS.ORG

SCILINKS

CD-ROMS
- eEdition
- EasyPlanner
- Power Presentations
- Content Review
- Lab Generator
- Test Generator

AUDIO CDS
- Audio Readings
- Audio Readings in Spanish

LABS AND ACTIVITIES

EXPLORE the Big Idea, p. 7
- Seeing and Understanding
- Bits and Pieces
- Internet Activity: Cells

UNIT RESOURCE BOOK
- Family Letter, p. vii
- Spanish Family Letter, p. viii
- Unit Projects, pp. 5–10

Lab Generator CD-ROM
Generate customized labs.

SECTION

1 The cell is the basic unit of living things.
pp. 9–17

Time: 3 periods (1.5 blocks)

 Lesson Plan, pp. 11–12

UNIT TRANSPARENCY BOOK
- Big Idea Flow Chart, p. T1
- Daily Vocabulary Scaffolding, p. T2
- Note-Taking Model, p. T3
- 3-Minute Warm-Up, p. T4

- EXPLORE Activity and Life, p. 9
- CHAPTER INVESTIGATION, Using a Microscope, pp. 16–17

UNIT RESOURCE BOOK
- Identification Key, p. 50
- CHAPTER INVESTIGATION, Using a Microscope, A, B, & C, pp. 51–59

SECTION

2 Microscopes allow us to see inside the cell.
pp. 18–25

Time: 2 periods (1 block)

 Lesson Plan, pp. 21–22

- **RESOURCE CENTER,** Cell Structures
- **SIMULATION,** Microscopes
- **MATH TUTORIAL**

UNIT TRANSPARENCY BOOK
- Daily Vocabulary Scaffolding, p. T2
- 3-Minute Warm-Up, p. T4
- "Parts of a Eukaryotic Cell" Visual, p. T6

- INVESTIGATE Plant and Animal Cells, p. 21
- Math in Science, p. 25

UNIT RESOURCE BOOK
- Datasheet, Plant and Animal Cells, p. 30
- Additional INVESTIGATION, Looking at Your Own Cells, A, B, & C, pp. 60–68
- Math Support, p. 48
- Math Practice, p. 49

SECTION

3 Different cells perform various functions.
pp. 26–33

Time: 3 periods (1.5 blocks)

 Lesson Plan, pp. 32–33

RESOURCE CENTER, Unicellular Organisms

UNIT TRANSPARENCY BOOK
- Big Idea Flow Chart, p. T1
- Daily Vocabulary Scaffolding, p. T2
- 3-Minute Warm-Up, p. T5
- Chapter Outline, pp. T7–T8

- EXPLORE Specialization, p. 26
- INVESTIGATE Cell Models, p. 31
- Think Science, p. 33

UNIT RESOURCE BOOK
Datasheet, Cell Models, p. 41

KEY TO ICONS

 CD/CD-ROM

 Teacher Edition

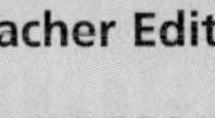 UNIT TRANSPARENCY BOOK

 SPANISH ASSESSMENT BOOK

INTERNET

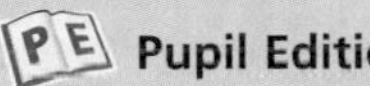 Pupil Edition

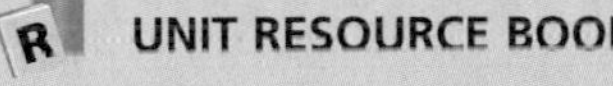 UNIT RESOURCE BOOK

 UNIT ASSESSMENT BOOK

SCIENCE TOOLKIT

READING AND REINFORCEMENT	ASSESSMENT	STANDARDS
 • Four Square, B22–23 • Main Idea Web, C38–39 • Daily Vocabulary Scaffolding, H1–8  **UNIT RESOURCE BOOK** • Vocabulary Practice, pp. 45–46 • Decoding Support, p. 47 • Summarizing the Chapter, pp. 69–70 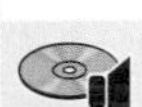 **Audio Readings CD** Listen to Pupil Edition.  **Audio Readings in Spanish CD** Listen to Pupil Edition in Spanish.	• Chapter Review, pp. 34–36 • Standardized Test Practice, p. 37  **UNIT ASSESSMENT BOOK** • Diagnostic Test, pp. 1–2 • Chapter Test, A, B, & C, pp. 6–17 • Alternative Assessment, pp. 18–19  Spanish Chapter Test, pp. 1–4  **Test Generator CD-ROM** Generate customized tests.  **Lab Generator CD-ROM** Rubrics for Labs	National Standards A.1–8, A.9.a–g, C.1.a–d, G.1.b See p. 6 for the standards.
 **UNIT RESOURCE BOOK** • Reading Study Guide, A & B, pp. 13–16 • Spanish Reading Study Guide, pp. 17–18 • Challenge and Extension, p. 19 • Reinforcing Key Concepts, p. 20 • Challenge Reading, pp. 43–44	 Ongoing Assessment, pp. 10–14  Section 1.1 Review, p. 15  **UNIT ASSESSMENT BOOK** Section 1.1 Quiz, p. 3	National Standards A.1–7, A.9.a–b, A.9.d–g, C.1.a–c, G.1.b
 **UNIT RESOURCE BOOK** • Reading Study Guide, A & B, pp. 23–26 • Spanish Reading Study Guide, pp. 27–28 • Challenge and Extension, p. 29 • Reinforcing Key Concepts, p. 31	 Ongoing Assessment, pp. 19–20, 23–24  Section 1.2 Review, p. 24  **UNIT ASSESSMENT BOOK** Section 1.2 Quiz, p. 4	National Standards A.2–8, A.9.a–c, A.9.e–f, C.1.a–c, G.1.b
 **UNIT RESOURCE BOOK** • Reading Study Guide, A & B, pp. 34–37 • Spanish Reading Study Guide, pp. 38–39 • Challenge and Extension, p. 40 • Reinforcing Key Concepts, p. 42	 Ongoing Assessment, pp. 27–31  Section 1.3 Review, p. 32  **UNIT ASSESSMENT BOOK** Section 1.3 Quiz, p. 5	National Standards A.2–7, A.9.a–b, A.9.e–f, C.1.a–d, G.1.a–b

Previewing Resources for Differentiated Instruction

CHAPTER INVESTIGATION

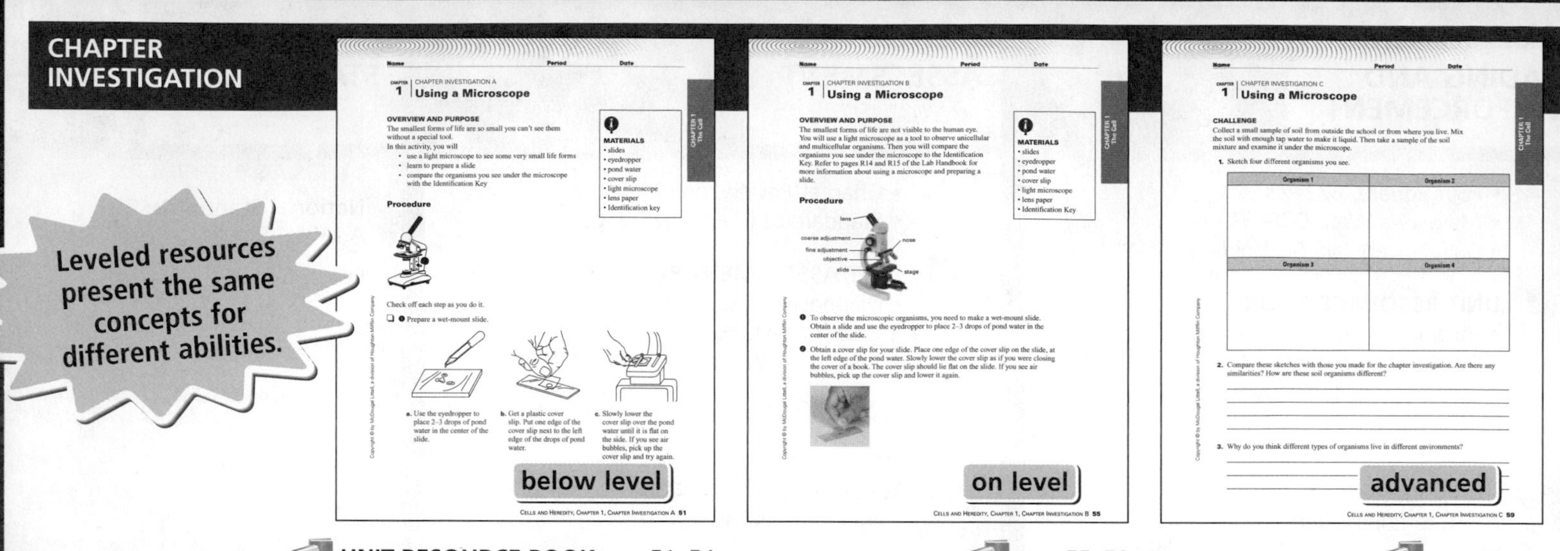

UNIT RESOURCE BOOK, pp. 51–54

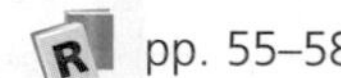
pp. 55–58

pp. 55–59

READING STUDY GUIDE

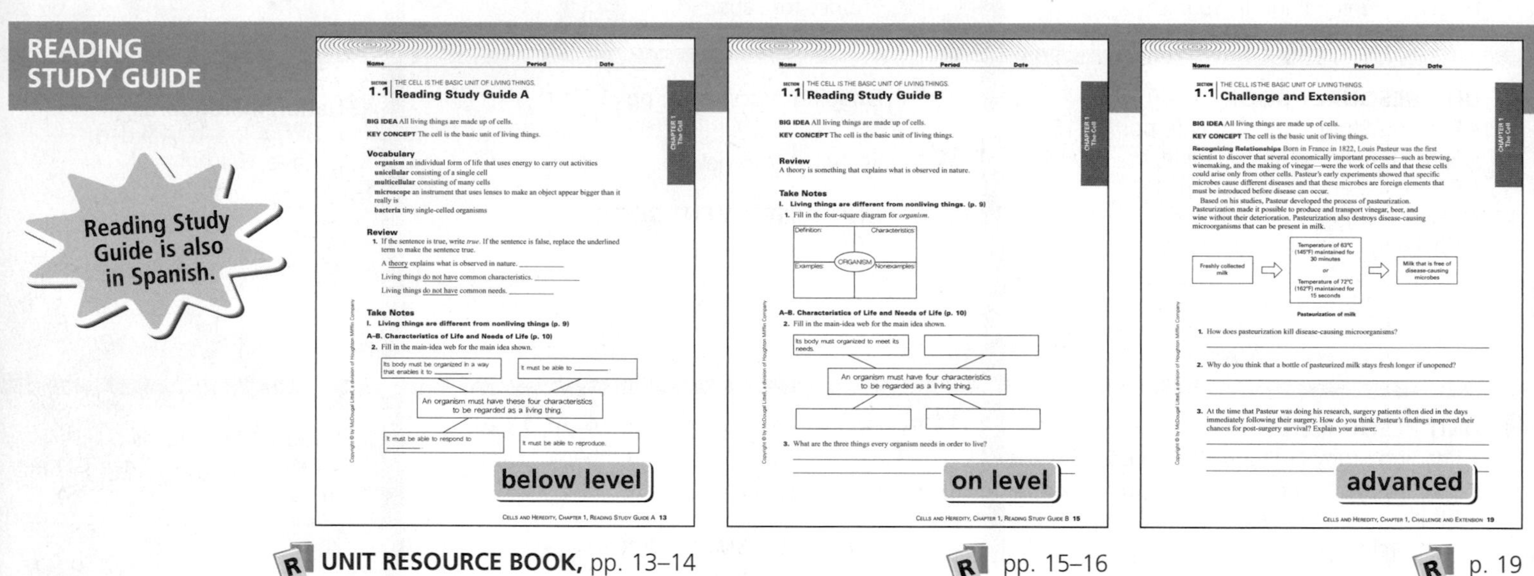

UNIT RESOURCE BOOK, pp. 13–14

pp. 15–16

p. 19

CHAPTER TEST

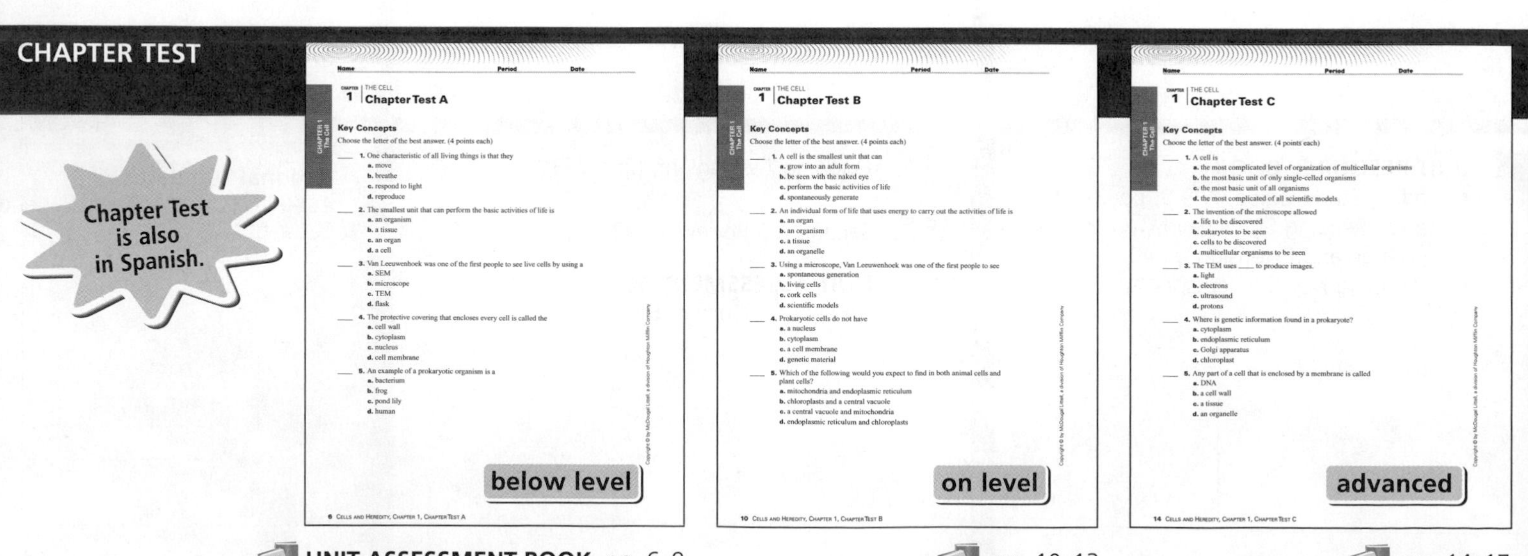

UNIT ASSESSMENT BOOK, pp. 6–9

pp. 10–13

pp. 14–17

TECHNOLOGY

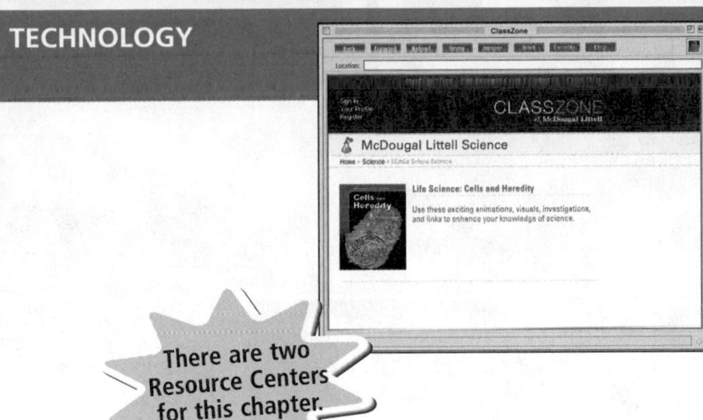

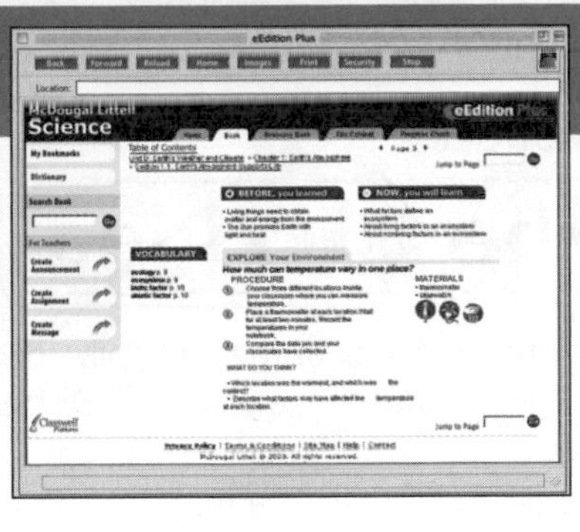

CLASSZONE.COM

CD/CD-ROMS

CLASSZONE.COM

VISUAL CONTENT

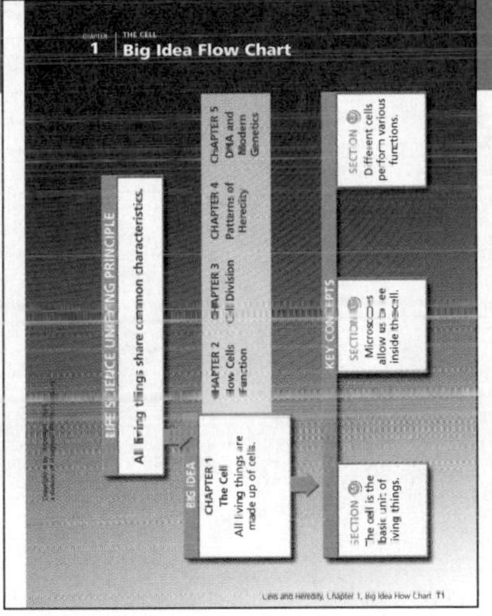

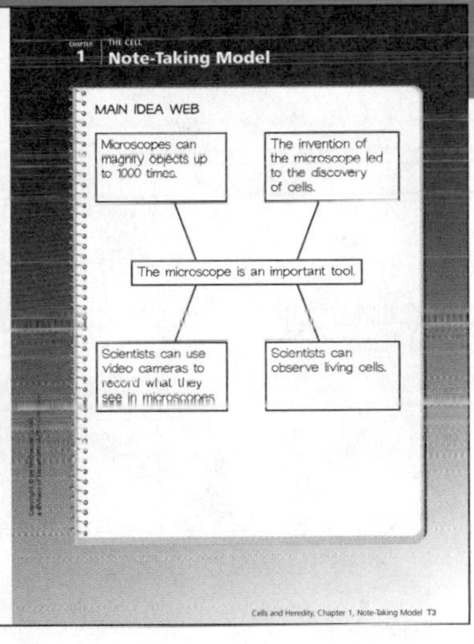

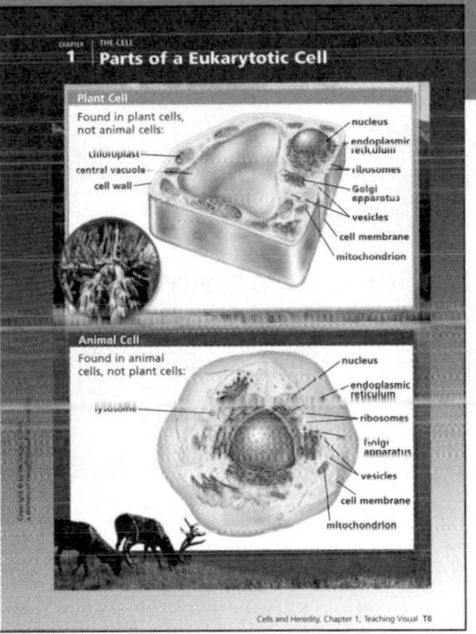

UNIT TRANSPARENCY BOOK, p. T1

p. T3

p. T6

MORE SUPPORT

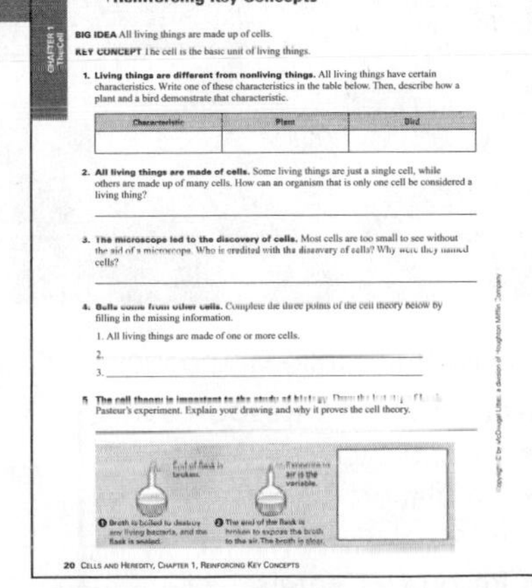

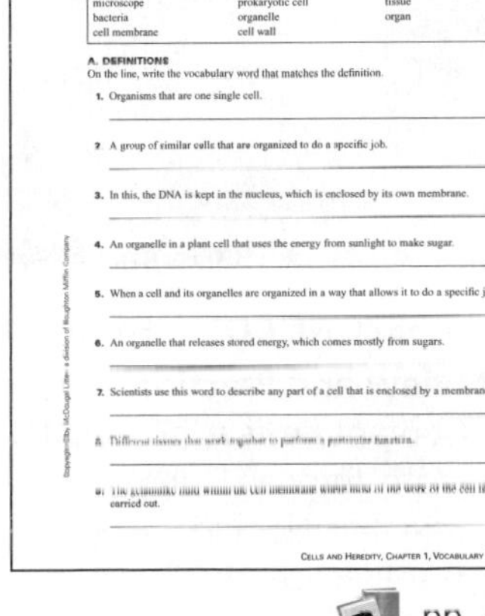

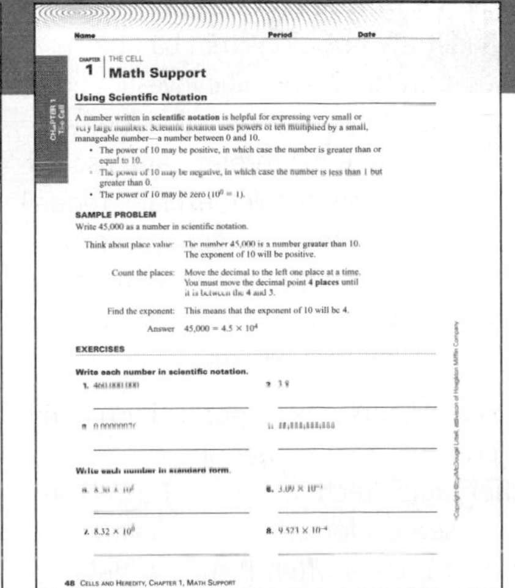

UNIT RESOURCE BOOK, p. 20

pp. 45–46

p. 48

INTRODUCE

the BIG idea

Have students look at the artificially colored micrograph of the plant cell. Discuss the question in the box:

- Ask students to find three structures, or organelles, in the cell.
- Point out that there are plant cells in paper (no longer alive).

National Science Education Standards

Content

C.1.a Levels of organization for living systems include cells, tissues, organs, organ systems, organisms, and ecosystems.

C.1.b All organisms are composed of cells—the basic unit of life. Most are single cells; others, including humans, are multicellular.

C.1.c Cells perform the functions of life. They grow, divide, and take in nutrients.

C.1.d Regulation of an organism's internal environment involves sensing the internal environment and changing to keep conditions within range.

Process

A.1–8 Identify questions that can be answered through scientific investigations; design and conduct an investigation; use tools to gather and interpret data; use evidence to describe, predict, explain, model; think critically to relate evidence to explanation; recognize different explanations and predictions; communicate procedures and results; use mathematics.

A.9.a–g Understand scientific inquiry by using different investigations, methods, mathematics, technology, and explanations based on logic, evidence, and skepticism. Data often results in new investigations.

CHAPTER

The Cell

the BIG idea

All living things are made up of cells.

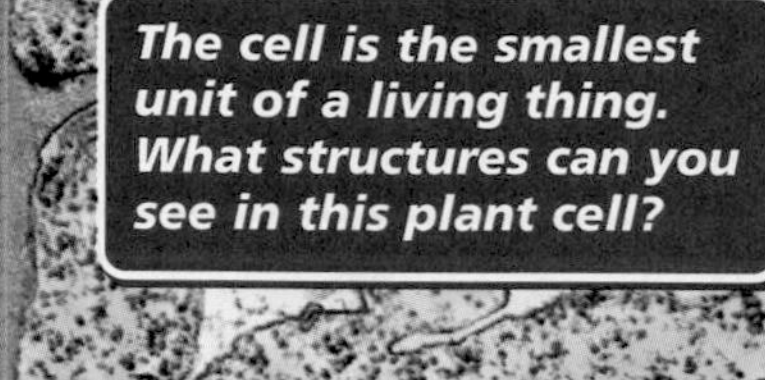

The cell is the smallest unit of a living thing. What structures can you see in this plant cell?

Key Concepts

SECTION

1 **The cell is the basic unit of living things.** Learn why cells are important to the study of life.

SECTION

2 **Microscopes allow us to see inside the cell.** Learn what microscopes have shown about the inner structure of cells.

SECTION

3 **Different cells perform various functions.** Learn about different types of cells in both unicellular and multicellular organisms.

Internet Preview

CLASSZONE.COM

Chapter 1 online resources: Content Review, two Simulations, two Resource Centers, Math Tutorial, Test Practice

6 Unit 1: **Cells and Heredity**

INTERNET PREVIEW

CLASSZONE.COM For student use with the following pages:

Review and Practice

- Content Review, pp. 8, 34
- Math Tutorial: Using Scientific Notation, p. 25
- Test Practice, p. 37

Activities and Resources

- Internet Activity: Cells, p. 7
- Simulation: Microscopes, p. 19
- Resource Centers: Cell Structures, p. 21; Unicellular Organisms, p. 27

Cell Theory **Code: MDL031**

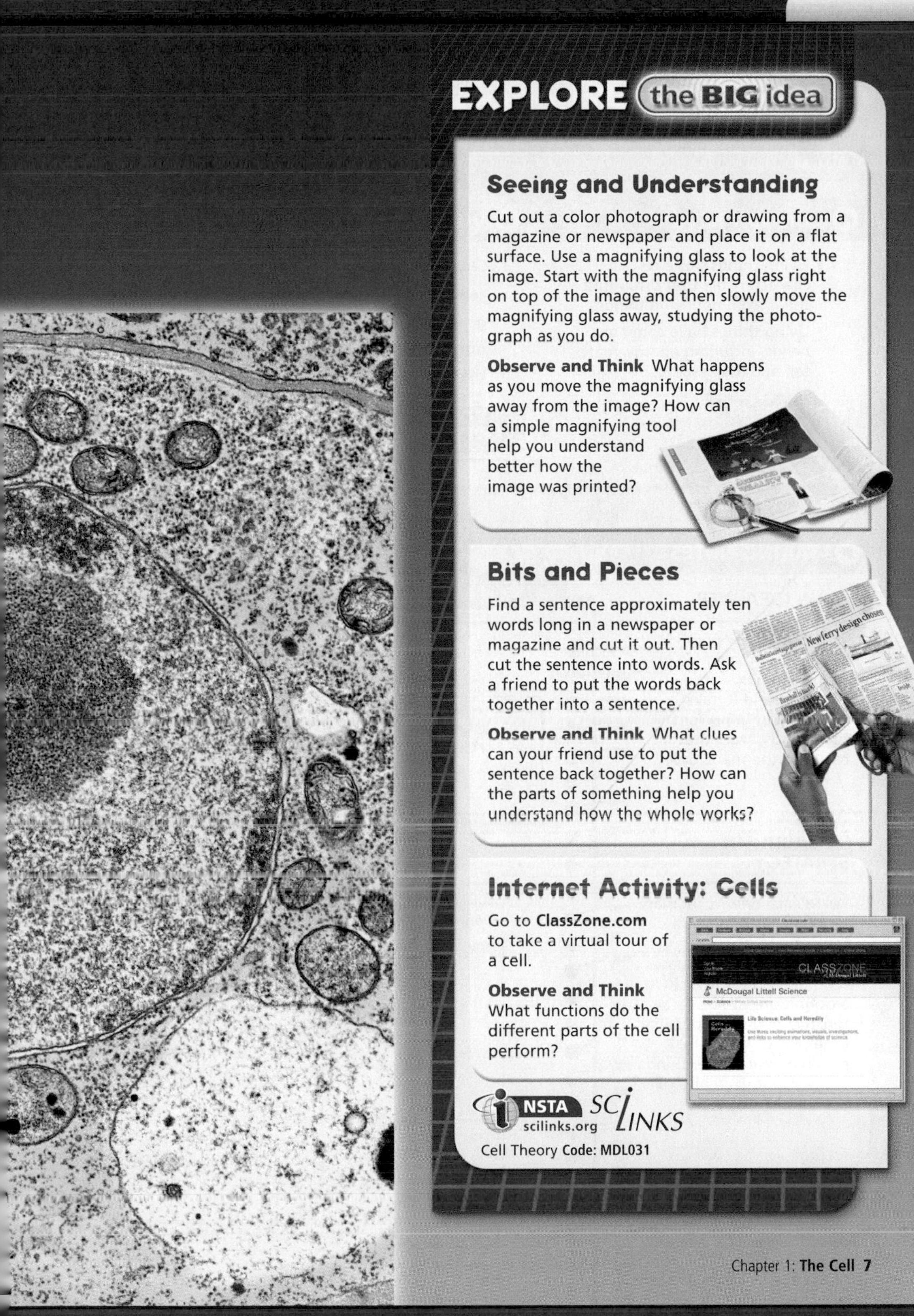

EXPLORE the BIG idea

Seeing and Understanding

Cut out a color photograph or drawing from a magazine or newspaper and place it on a flat surface. Use a magnifying glass to look at the image. Start with the magnifying glass right on top of the image and then slowly move the magnifying glass away, studying the photograph as you do.

Observe and Think What happens as you move the magnifying glass away from the image? How can a simple magnifying tool help you understand better how the image was printed?

Bits and Pieces

Find a sentence approximately ten words long in a newspaper or magazine and cut it out. Then cut the sentence into words. Ask a friend to put the words back together into a sentence.

Observe and Think What clues can your friend use to put the sentence back together? How can the parts of something help you understand how the whole works?

Internet Activity: Cells

Go to **ClassZone.com** to take a virtual tour of a cell.

Observe and Think What functions do the different parts of the cell perform?

NSTA SCILINKS scilinks.org

Cell Theory **Code: MDL031**

TEACHING WITH TECHNOLOGY

PC Microscope If available, use a PC microscope to view the microorganisms during the Chapter Investigation, pp. 16–17 and for "Investigate Plant and Animal Cells," p. 21. Display the magnified images of the organisms on a computer monitor, or project them as part of the activity or during a parent open house.

Digital Camera Create a photo album of the cell models constructed on p. 31. Display the album in the classroom. Use the video function and macro setting to create up-close tours inside the cells.

EXPLORE the BIG idea

These inquiry-based activities are appropriate for use at home or as a supplement to classroom instruction.

Seeing and Understanding

PURPOSE To explore the concept of magnification by viewing a magazine photo under a hand lens.

TIP *10 min.* Printing processes for magazines are based on four colors (cyan, magenta, yellow, and black) known as "CMYK." Students should see dots of these colors.

Sample answer: The image gets larger. The magnifying glass shows that the image is printed in dots, which blend together when seen by the naked eye.

REVISIT after p. 12.

Bits and Pieces

PURPOSE To rearrange words in a sentence to explore the importance of structure and organization.

TIP *10 min.* Remind students to look for the capital letter to start the sentence, then the subject and verb.

Sample answer: placement of capital letters, parts of speech; understanding the function of the parts helps you understand the whole

REVISIT after p. 31.

Internet Activity: Cells

PURPOSE To use details of cells to distinguish them.

TIP *20 min.* Have students work in small groups if computer access is limited. One student may give a "narrated tour" to others.

Sample answers: nucleus: stores genetic material; chloroplast: makes food; mitochondria: releases energy; vacuole: stores materials; ribosome, endoplasmic reticulum, Golgi apparatus: process and transport materials; cell membrane: protects; cell wall: supports and protects

REVISIT after p. 22

PREPARE

CONCEPT REVIEW

Activate Prior Knowledge

Have students think back to the first moment they woke up this day. Have them list the human needs that they encountered or experienced as the day progressed. *Their very first need was for space to sleep in, then clothing, food, etc.*

TAKING NOTES

Main Idea Web

A main idea web encourages students to organize information in a pattern that makes most sense to them as individuals.

Vocabulary Strategy

The four square diagram allows students to connect a word to its related concepts, such as definitions and examples. Using quadrants helps students to classify information in an organized manner.

Vocabulary and Note-Taking Resources

- Vocabulary Practice, pp. 45–46
- Decoding Support, p. 47

- Daily Vocabulary Scaffolding, p. T2
- Note-Taking Model, p. T3

- Four Square, B22–23
- Main Idea Web, C38–39
- Daily Vocabulary Scaffolding, H1–8

CHAPTER 1

Getting Ready to Learn

CONCEPT REVIEW

- Living things share certain characteristics that distinguish them from nonliving things.
- Living things have common needs, including energy, matter, and living space.

VOCABULARY REVIEW

See Glossary for definitions.

cell
genetic material
organism
theory

CLASSZONE.COM

Review concepts and vocabulary.

TAKING NOTES

MAIN IDEA WEB

Write each new blue heading, or main idea, in the top box. In the boxes around it, take notes about important terms and details that relate to the main idea.

VOCABULARY STRATEGY

Write each new vocabulary term in the center of a **four square** diagram. Write notes in the squares around each term. Include a definition, some characteristics, and some possible examples of the term. If possible, write some things that are not examples of the term.

See the Note-Taking Handbook on pages R45–R51.

SCIENCE NOTEBOOK

All living things are made of cells.

- The cell is the smallest unit that performs the activities of life.
- Multicellular organisms have different types of cells working together.
- In a unicellular organism a single cell carries out all the activities of life.

Definition	Characteristics
Any living thing	Needs energy, materials from the environment, and living space. Grows, develops, responds to environment, reproduces. Is made up of one or more cells.
ORGANISM	
Examples	**Nonexamples**
Dogs, cats, birds, insects, moss, trees, bacteria	Rocks, water, dirt

8 Unit 1: Cells and Heredity

CHECK READINESS

Administer the Diagnostic Test to determine students' readiness for new science content and their mastery of requisite math skills.

 Diagnostic Test, pp. 1–2

Technology Resources

Students needing content and math skills should visit **ClassZone.com**.

- **CONTENT REVIEW**
- **MATH TUTORIAL**

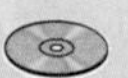 **CONTENT REVIEW CD-ROM**

KEY CONCEPT

The cell is the basic unit of living things.

BEFORE, you learned
- Living things have common characteristics
- Living things have common needs
- A theory is something that explains what is observed in nature

NOW, you will learn
- How living things are different from nonliving things
- How the microscope led to the discovery of cells
- About the cell theory

VOCABULARY

unicellular p. 11
multicellular p. 11
microscope p. 12
bacteria p. 14

EXPLORE Activity and Life

Does a candle show signs of life?

PROCEDURE

1. Carefully light one candle.
2. Sit quietly and observe the candle. Note its behavior. What does the flame do? What happens to the wax?

MATERIALS
- small candle
- candleholder
- matches

WHAT DO YOU THINK?
- How does a lit candle seem alive?
- How do you know for sure that it is not?

Living things are different from nonliving things.

MAIN IDEA WEB
Make a main idea web about living things, including how they differ from nonliving things.

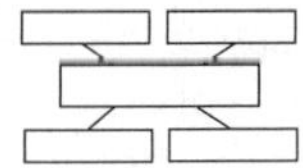

You know life when you see it. Perhaps your class takes a field trip to a local state park to collect water samples. You are surrounded by trees. There is a stream, with rocks covered with moss and green algae. There are fish and frogs; there are birds and insects. You are surrounded by life. But how would you define it?

One way to answer the question is to think about what makes a living thing different from a nonliving thing. You might ask if a thing uses energy. Or maybe you would observe it to see if it moves. You could investigate whether it consumes food and water. These are characteristics of living things, or organisms. Any individual form of life that is capable of growing and reproducing is an organism. All organisms get water and other materials from the environment.

1.1 FOCUS

Set Learning Goals

Students will
- Explain how living things are different from nonliving things.
- Describe how the microscope led to the discovery of cells.
- Describe the cell theory.

3-Minute Warm-Up

Display Transparency 4 or write this exercise on the board:

Write a theory about the difference between a living thing and a nonliving thing. Describe how you would test your theory.

3-Minute Warm-Up, p. T4

1.1 MOTIVATE

EXPLORE Activity and Life

PURPOSE To compare a candle with a living thing

TIPS *10 min.* Review safety rules about matches and fire. Have an adult light the match to start the procedure. Remind students not to touch or lean into the lit flame.

WHAT DO YOU THINK? *The flame moves and the candle gets smaller as it burns. It cannot reproduce and doesn't grow or develop.*

RESOURCES FOR DIFFERENTIATED INSTRUCTION

Below Level

UNIT RESOURCE BOOK
- Reading Study Guide A, pp. 13–14
- Decoding Support, p. 47

AUDIO CDS

Advanced

UNIT RESOURCE BOOK
- Challenge and Extension, p. 19
- Challenge Reading, pp. 43–44

English Learners

UNIT RESOURCE BOOK
Spanish Reading Study Guide, pp. 17–18

AUDIO CDS
- Audio Readings in Spanish
- Audio Readings (English)

1.1 INSTRUCT

Develop Critical Thinking

COMPARE AND CONTRAST Have students list characteristics that a flower, a puppy, a house, and a cup of water have in common and ways that they are different. *All four can respond to their environment—if the house has a thermostat. Water can freeze or vaporize. All are organized, including the molecules of water. But only the flower and the puppy can grow, develop, and reproduce.*

Integrate the Sciences

Explorations of the planet Mars have shown it to be cold and sterile. Some scientists believe that Mars once held a vast ocean, however, and if there is or once was water, there is a chance that we'll find life or its traces on Mars. Almost everywhere on Earth that water is found, there is life. So NASA's current exploration strategy for Mars is to follow the water—present or past—in hopes that it will lead to evidence of life.

Ongoing Assessment

CHECK YOUR READING *Answer: organization, ability to develop and grow, ability to respond to the environment, ability to reproduce*

PHOTO CAPTION Answer: Birds and fish both get energy from eating other living things, while grasses get energy from the Sun. They all live near or in the water, and get materials from their surroundings.

Characteristics of Life

Living things have these characteristics:

- organization
- the ability to develop and grow
- the ability to respond to the environment
- the ability to reproduce

An organism's body must be organized in a way that enables it to meet its needs. Some organisms, like bacteria, are very simple. A more complex organism, such as the kingfisher shown in the photograph below, is organized so that different parts of its body perform different jobs, called functions. For example, a kingfisher has wings for flying, a heart for pumping blood, and eyes for seeing.

Another characteristic of organisms is that they grow and, in most cases, develop into adult forms. Some organisms change a great deal in size and appearance throughout their lifetimes, whereas others grow and change very little. Organisms also respond to the world outside them. Think of how the pupils of your eyes get smaller in bright light. Finally, organisms can reproduce, producing new organisms that are similar to themselves.

CHECK YOUR READING What four characteristics are common to all living things?

Needs of Life

Organisms cannot carry out the activities that characterize life without a few necessities: energy, materials, and living space. What does it mean to need energy? You know that if you want to run a race, you need energy. But did you know that your body also needs energy to sleep or to breathe or even to think? All organisms require a steady supply of energy to stay alive. Where does this energy come from, and how does an organism get it?

APPLY Identify three living things in this photograph. How do they meet their needs?

The energy used by almost all forms of life on Earth comes from the Sun. Some organisms, like plants and some bacteria, are able to capture this energy directly. Your body, like the bodies of other animals, uses food as a source of energy. The food animals eat comes from plants or from organisms that eat plants. Food also provides the materials necessary for growth and reproduction. These materials include substances such as carbon dioxide, nitrogen, oxygen, and water. Finally, all organisms need space to live and grow. If any one of these requirements is missing, an organism will die.

DIFFERENTIATE INSTRUCTION

More Reading Support

A What does life need a steady supply of? *energy*

B Where does almost all the energy used by life on Earth come from? *the Sun*

English Learners Have students write the definitions for *organism, cell, unicellular, multicellular,* and *microscope* in their Science Word Dictionaries. English learners may not have prior knowledge of how English words can change with a prefix or suffix. For example, compare the meanings of *produce* and *reproduce.* Other words to compare are *characteristic* and *characterize, cell, unicellular,* and *multicellular.*

All living things are made of cells.

The cell is the smallest unit of a living thing. Some organisms are made of a single cell. These organisms are **unicellular** and usually too small for you to see directly. Pond water is full of tiny unicellular organisms. Most of the organisms you can see, such as a frog or a water lily, are made up of many cells. Organisms made up of many cells are called **multicellular** organisms.

The needs and characteristics of a single cell in a unicellular organism are the same as those for any organism. Each of the tiny single-celled organisms found in a drop of pond water performs all the activities that characterize life. Multicellular organisms, like a frog or a water lily, have bodies that are more complex. Different parts of the body of a multicellular organism perform different functions. A water lily's roots hold it in the soil and its leaves capture energy from the Sun. A frog moves with its arms and legs and eats with its mouth.

Multicellular organisms have different types of cells that make up their body parts and help the organisms meet their needs. Roots are made of root cells, which are different from leaf cells. Muscle cells have special parts that allow them to move. In a multicellular organism, many cells work together to carry out the basic activities of life.

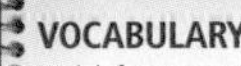

VOCABULARY
Add four squares for *unicellular* and *multicellular* to your notebook. You may want to add to your lists of characteristics and examples as you read through the chapter.

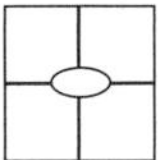

Multicellular and Unicellular Organisms

Both multicellular and unicellular organisms live in this pond.

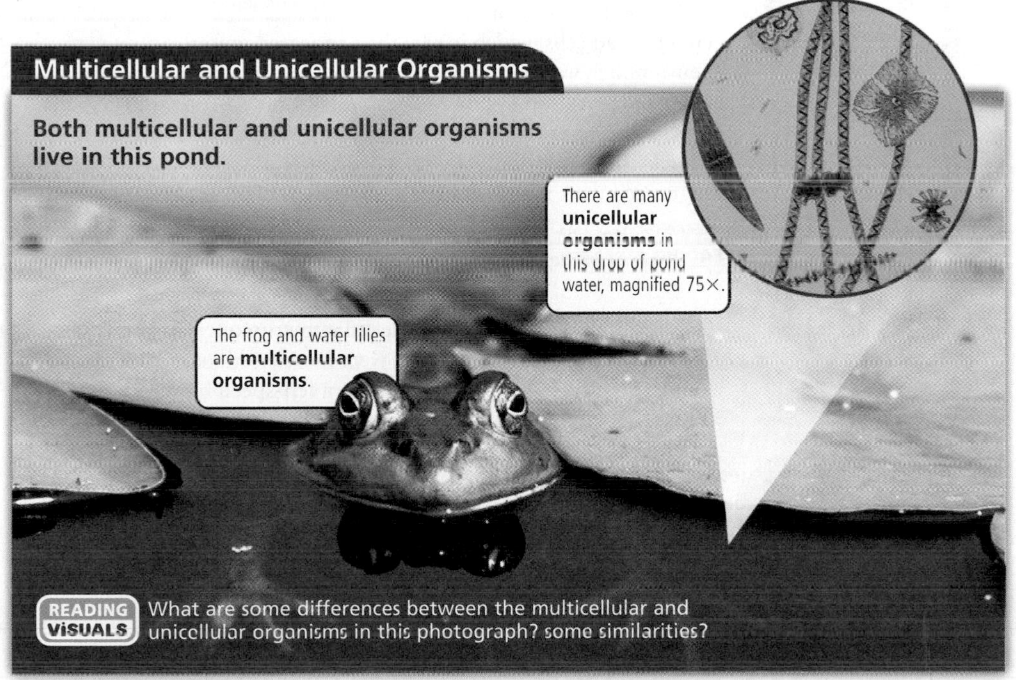

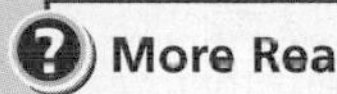

READING VISUALS What are some differences between the multicellular and unicellular organisms in this photograph? some similarities?

Address Misconceptions

IDENTIFY Ask: What activities that plants and animals do are carried out by cells? If students answer anything other than "All activities," they may not understand that the cell is the basic unit of function, as well as of structure.

CORRECT Discuss what muscles are made of. Point out that muscle cells are specialized for movement. If possible, display microscope slides or magnified images of human muscle cells or those of other animals. Ask: What specialized functions do the cells perform as a group working together? *the function of moving parts of the body around*

REASSESS Ask: What is the basic unit of function (or activity)? *the cell*

Technology Resources

Visit **ClassZone.com** for background on common student misconceptions.

MISCONCEPTION DATABASE

Metacognitive Strategy

Ask students to describe unicellular and multicellular organisms, based on how they use the prefixes *uni-* and *multi-* in other words.

Ongoing Assessment

Explain how living things are different from nonliving things.

Ask: Is a computer a living thing? Explain scientifically how you know. *No; a computer needs energy and is organized, but it cannot develop and grow; it cannot reproduce.*

READING VISUALS *Answer: The unicellular organisms are made of only one cell and are too small to see directly. Multicellular organisms are made of many cells, are more complex, and can usually be seen directly.*

DIFFERENTIATE INSTRUCTION

More Reading Support

C What is the smallest structure that can perform life activities? *the cell*

D Is a frog a multicellular organism or a unicellular organism? *multicellular*

Advanced Stage a debate among two teams of students about whether or not living things may exist—or ever have existed—in parts of the Solar System other than Earth. Have each team take an opposite position. Their arguments should be persuasive, skeptical, and well-researched.

Have students who are interested in conditions necessary for life read the following article:

 Challenge Reading, pp. 43–44

History of Science

People have used lenses since ancient times. Greek and Roman writings from around 100 A.D. mention "burning glasses" used to focus sunlight to ignite fires. True lenses for magnifying images were probably first manufactured in Europe during the 13th century. Glass lenses are still made much as they were then, though new polishing materials have been developed. Nowadays, plastic is often used to make lenses. Instead of being ground, plastic lenses are molded. They are less expensive, lighter, and stronger than glass lenses.

EXPLORE the BIG idea

Revisit "Seeing and Understanding" on p. 7. Ask students how they could use the technology to discover something about life.

Ongoing Assessment

Describe how the microscope led to the discovery of cells.

Ask: Why were cells not discovered before the microscope was invented? *Cells are too small to be seen without a microscope. When Hooke and van Leeuwenhoek began to look at materials under a microscope, they saw cells and tiny organisms for the first time.*

CHECK YOUR READING *Answer: It allowed people to see cells for the first time.*

The microscope led to the discovery of cells.

READING TIP The word *microscopic* is an adjective made from the noun *microscope*. Things that are microscopic are too small to see without the use of a microscope.

Most cells are microscopic, too small to see without the aid of a microscope. A **microscope** is an instrument which makes an object appear bigger than it is. It took the invention of this relatively simple tool to lead to the discovery of cells. In the 1660s, Robert Hooke began using microscopes to look at all sorts of materials. Anton van Leeuwenhoek took up similar work in the 1670s. They were among the first people to describe cells. E

Hooke's Drawing of Cells

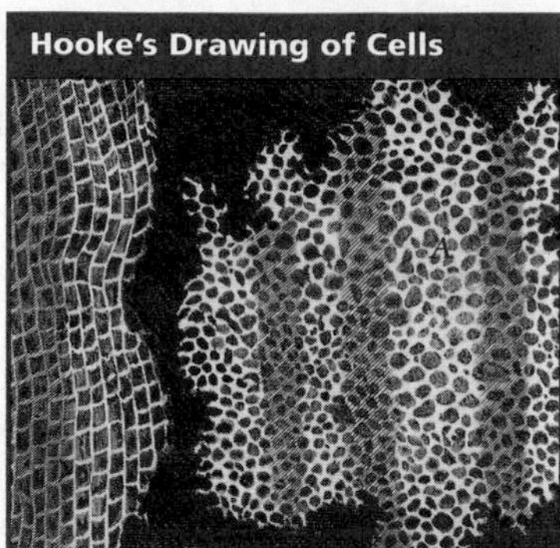

Robert Hooke published this drawing of dead cork cells in 1665. The microscope he used, shown at left, has two lenses.

Robert Hooke gave the cell its name. While looking at a sample of cork, a layer of bark taken from an oak tree, he saw a group of similarly shaped compartments that looked to him like tiny empty rooms, or cells. You can see from his drawing, shown at right, how well these cells fit Hooke's description. Hooke used a microscope that magnified objects 30 times (30 ×). In other words, objects appeared thirty times larger than their actual size.

The bark cells Hooke saw were actually dead cells, which is why they appeared empty. Anton van Leeuwenhoek was one of the first people to describe living cells. He looked at a drop of pond water under a microscope. Imagine his surprise when he saw that a drop of water was full of living things! Using lenses that could magnify an object almost 300 ×, he observed tiny unicellular organisms like those shown on page 11.

CHECK YOUR READING How did the invention of the microscope change the study of biology?

You can understand how powerful a microscope is if you think of how big a penny would be if it were increased in size 30 ×. It would be a little bigger than the tire of a ten-speed bicycle. Enlarged 300 ×, that penny would be so big that you would need a tractor-trailer to move it. Magnify your best friend 30 × (supposing a height of 1.5 meters, or almost 5 ft), and your friend would appear to be 45 meters (147 ft) tall. That's almost the height of Niagara Falls. Change the magnification to 300 ×, and your friend would appear to be 450 meters (1470 ft) tall—taller than the Empire State Building. F

DIFFERENTIATE INSTRUCTION

More Reading Support

E What invention led to the discovery of cells? *the microscope*

F Which looks larger, a cell magnified 5 × or magnified 100 ×? *100 ×*

Advanced Have students research how the use of plastics has changed lens use and manufacturing, and present their findings in an oral report to the class.

R Challenge and Extension, p. 19

Cells come from other cells.

The studies of Hooke and Leeuwenhoek made people ask if all living things have cells. People continued to observe samples taken from all sorts of living matter. They continued to find cells, although often these cells looked very different from one another. Still, it was clear that all living matter was made of cells.

G

There was another important question scientists were trying to answer: Where do cells come from? The answer to this question was settled by the 1850s. People studying all types of living cells observed the same thing—that cells divide. One living cell divides into two living cells. Here, under the microscope, was evidence of where cells come from. Life comes from life—that is, one cell comes from another cell.

H

CHECK YOUR READING What do scientists mean when they say that life comes from life? Your answer should include the word *cells*.

The observations and evidence gathered over a long time by many scientists are summarized in the three concepts of the cell theory:

1. Every living thing is made of one or more cells.
2. Cells carry out the functions needed to support life.
3. Cells come only from other living cells.

The Cell Theory

The importance of the cell to life is summarized in the cell theory.

Integrate the Sciences

The word *cell,* which meant "empty room" to Robert Hooke, can refer to other structures besides the basic unit of life. The cell in a table is the spot at the intersection of a row and a column. Cellular phones cover a geographic area called a cell, a space within which certain broadcast frequencies are used. Batteries are made of electrical cells, compartments that hold chemicals and convert their energy to electrical energy.

Teach from Visuals

To help students interpret the photograph of the polar bears, ask:

- What is a polar bear made of? *cells*
- What is a fat cell? *a specialized cell that provides energy and insulation*
- How did the polar bear cubs begin life? *as a single fertilized egg cell*

Ongoing Assessment

CHECK YOUR READING *Answer: Cells come from other cells.*

DIFFERENTIATE INSTRUCTION

More Reading Support

G What is the basic unit that all living things have? *the cell*

H Where do cells come from? *other cells*

Below Level Help students construct a concept map to organize the information on cell theory. Use "living things" as the central idea from which you can lay out stems to explain cells and what they do.

History of Science

Louis Pasteur (1822–1895) is known as the founder of microbiology for his work with microorganisms. In his work with alcoholic beverages, he demonstrated that yeast caused the desirable fermentation process, while bacteria caused souring. Bacteria could be removed by heating the original solution. Pasteur also inoculated sheep with weakened anthrax to demonstrate that it would provide immunity to anthrax. His development of vaccines made him a hero.

Teach Difficult Concepts

Students sometimes find the concept of spontaneous generation difficult to understand. Have them look up *spontaneous* in the dictionary. Explain that *generation* in this context means creation. Use the Teacher Demo below to show why people believed in spontaneous generation until microscopes produced evidence against it.

Teacher Demo

Bring in a ripe peach or other soft fruit and allow it to sit in a bowl until fruit flies develop. This demonstration is especially effective if you have a net dome to put over the fruit.

Ongoing Assessment

Describe the cell theory.

Ask: What are the three parts of the cell theory? *All living things are made of one or more cells. Cells carry out the functions needed to support life. Cells come only from other living cells.*

CHECK YOUR READING *Answer: It is a widely accepted explanation for what is observed in nature, and it must be supported by evidence.*

The cell theory is important to the study of biology.

The three ideas on page 13 are so important that they are grouped together using the word *theory.* A scientific theory is a widely accepted explanation of things observed in nature. A theory must be supported by evidence, including experimental evidence and observations. A theory proves its value when it explains new discoveries and observations.

CHECK YOUR READING What are two characteristics of a scientific theory?

Theories are important for a number of reasons. Certainly they satisfy scientists' desire to understand the natural world, and they serve as foundations for further research and study. Theories can also lead to research that has some practical benefit for society.

Louis Pasteur

The work of the French scientist Louis Pasteur shows how an understanding of cell theory can have practical uses. Pasteur lived in the 1800s, when there was no mechanical refrigeration in homes. People were used to having foods spoil, like milk going sour. During this time, many people died from diseases such as typhoid fever, tuberculosis, and diphtheria. Pasteur's work showed that microscopic organisms were involved both in the spoilage of food and in disease.

The milk that you get from the school cafeteria has been pasteurized so that it will stay fresh longer.

Pasteur observed that milk that turned sour contained large numbers of tiny single-celled organisms called **bacteria** (bak-TEER-ee-uh). He developed a process, now known as pasteurization, in which heat is used to kill the bacteria. Killing the bacteria keeps milk fresh longer. The fact that bacteria cause milk to sour or "sicken" made Pasteur wonder whether microscopic organisms could also be the cause of sickness in humans and animals.

Bacteria and Spontaneous Generation

Using a microscope to study air, water, and soil, Pasteur found microorganisms everywhere. He found bacteria in the blood of animals, including people who were sick. Pasteur referred to the microorganisms he observed as "germs." He realized that an understanding of germs might help prevent disease. Pasteur's work led to the first animal vaccinations for cholera and anthrax and to a treatment for rabies in humans.

At the time that Pasteur was doing his research, there were scientists who thought that bacteria grew from nonliving materials, an idea called spontaneous generation. Pasteur conducted a now-

DIFFERENTIATE INSTRUCTION

I How is evidence related to a theory? *Evidence supports or disproves a theory.*

J What causes food spoilage? *bacteria*

Advanced Have students choose a disease and research how vaccination works against it in the body. They can make a public interest brochure to display their findings.

Pasteur's Experiments

Pasteur's experiments showed that bacteria are present in the air. They do not appear spontaneously.

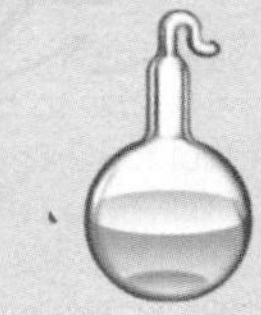

1. Broth is boiled to destroy any living bacteria, and the flask is sealed.
2. A few days pass, and the broth is still clear. No bacteria have grown.
3. More days pass, and the broth is still clear. No bacteria have grown.

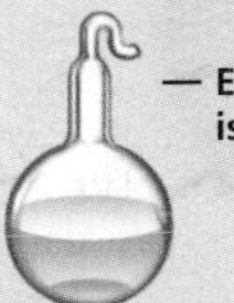

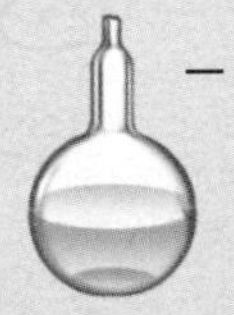

1. Broth is boiled to destroy any living bacteria, and the flask is sealed.
2. A few days pass, and the broth is clear. The end of the flask is then broken to expose the broth to the air.
3. Two to three days pass, and the broth is cloudy because of the growth of bacteria.

famous series of experiments that did not support the idea of spontaneous generation and confirmed the cell theory. He showed that cells come only from other cells. Two of Pasteur's experiments are shown above. Both began with a sealed flask containing boiled broth. In the first experiment, the flask remained sealed, while in the second experiment, the top of the flask was broken to expose the contents to air. Bacteria grew only in the second flask.

1.1 Review

KEY CONCEPTS

1. Name four characteristics of living things.
2. How did the microscope change human understanding of life?
3. Explain the three concepts that make up the cell theory.

CRITICAL THINKING

4. **Analyze** Relate the characteristics of a scientific theory to the cell theory.
5. **Compare and Contrast** Draw a Venn diagram to compare and contrast multicellular and unicellular organisms.

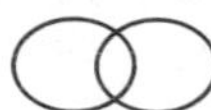

CHALLENGE

6. **Synthesize** Explain how Pasteur's experiment supported the cell theory and failed to support the theory of spontaneous generation.

ANSWERS

1. organization, growth and development, response to environment, reproduction

2. It allowed people to see cells. Before the microscope humans did not realize that life could be so small.

3. Every living thing is made of one or more cells; cells carry out the functions needed to support life; cells come only from other living cells.

4. The cell theory is widely accepted and explains observations of nature, and is supported by evidence such as Pasteur's experiments.

5. multicellular: many cells, complex, easier to see; unicellular: one cell, cannot be seen directly; both: need energy, materials, and living space

6. In Pasteur's experiment, bacteria did not grow spontaneously. They came from the environment, which indicates that cells come from other cells.

Teach from Visuals

To help students interpret the diagram of Pasteur's experiments, ask:

- What is the difference between the two flasks? *The end of one is broken off so it is open to the air.*
- How would the observer know if a flask was contaminated? *Its contents would be cloudy instead of clear.*

Reinforce the BIG idea

Have students relate the section to the Big Idea.

 Reinforcing Key Concepts, p. 20

1.1 ASSESS & RETEACH

Assess

 Section 1.1 Quiz, p. 3

Reteach

Use a triangle diagram to show the three main concepts of cell theory:

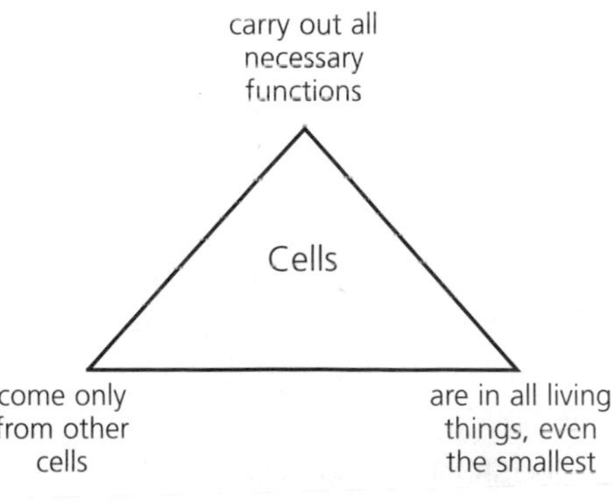

- Ask volunteers to give an example for each corner of the triangle.
- Ask volunteers to state their own reasons for why each concept is important.

Technology Resources

Have students visit **ClassZone.com** for reteaching of Key Concepts.

 **CONTENT REVIEW**

 **CONTENT REVIEW CD-ROM**

CHAPTER INVESTIGATION

Focus

PURPOSE To use a light microscope to observe microorganisms

OVERVIEW Students will make wet-mount slides of pond water. They will use both low and high magnification to observe organisms in the water. They will draw what they see and compare their sketches with a key to identify the organisms they find. Students will find the following:

- A microscope allows them to see living organisms that are otherwise invisible.
- A drop of pond water has many organisms in it.

Lab Preparation

- Be sure to demonstrate use of the light microscope. You may want to do your own trial run before class to be sure it is working properly.
- Prior to the investigation, have students read through it and prepare their data tables. Or you may wish to copy and distribute datasheets and rubrics.

UNIT RESOURCE BOOK, pp. 50–59

SCIENCE TOOLKIT, F15

Lab Management

Focusing the microscope is generally a skill that takes practice, encourage students to be patient and make multiple attempts.

INCLUSION Students with good fine motor skills can team up with those who have disabilities to place the cover slip on the samples.

INCLUSION Students with vision impairments will have difficulty focusing the microscope and looking through it. A PC or projection microscope can help, or have another student describe the play-by-play.

Teaching with Technology

If a PC microscope is available, make movies of the pond organisms on the slides. Play them during wait times at parent conferences.

CHAPTER INVESTIGATION

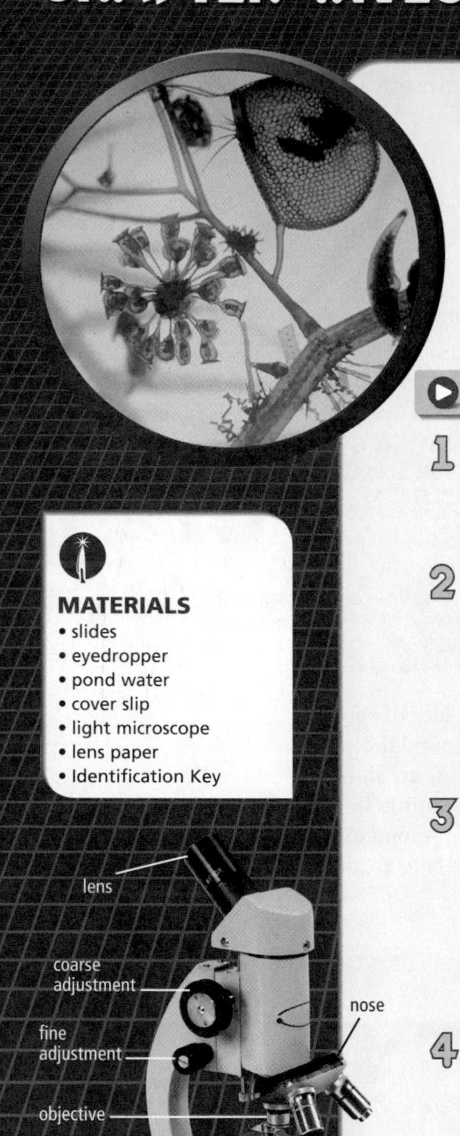

MATERIALS
- slides
- eyedropper
- pond water
- cover slip
- light microscope
- lens paper
- Identification Key

Using a Microscope

OVERVIEW AND PURPOSE The smallest forms of life are not visible to the human eye. You will use a light microscope as a tool to observe very small unicellular and multicellular organisms. Then you will compare the organisms you see under the microscope to the Identification Key. Refer to pages R14 and R15 of the Lab Handbook for more information about using a microscope and preparing a slide.

Procedure

1. Make a data table like the one shown on page 17. To observe the microscopic organisms, you need to make a wet-mount slide. Obtain a slide and use the eyedropper to place 2–3 drops of pond water in the center of the slide.

2. Obtain a cover slip for your slide. Place one edge of the cover slip on the slide, at the left edge of the pond water. Slowly lower the cover slip as if you were closing the cover of a book. The cover slip should lie flat on the slide. If you see air bubbles, pick up the cover slip and lower it again.

step 2

3. Clean the lenses of the microscope with lens paper. Choose the lowest magnification, then place the slide on the stage. Start with the objective at its lowest point and raise the objective to focus. First focus with the coarse adjustment, which is usually the larger knob. Begin your search for living organisms. Use the fine adjustment to make the image clearer. Be patient when looking for life on your slide. It may take some time.

4. When you find something interesting, carefully switch to a higher magnification. Turn the nose of the microscope until another objective snaps into place. Use only the fine adjustment when viewing at high power, to avoid scratching the microscope or the slide. Move the slide gently from side to side as you look through the microscope. Search different parts of the sample for different organisms.

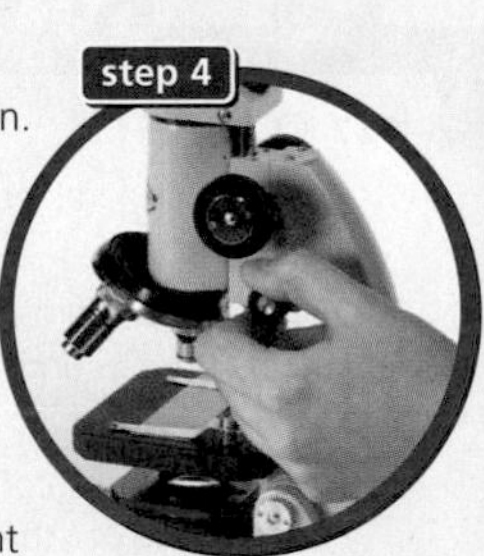

16 Unit 1: Cells and Heredity

INVESTIGATION RESOURCES

CHAPTER INVESTIGATION, Using a Microscope
- Identification Key, p. 50
- Level A, pp. 51–54
- Level B, pp. 55–58
- Level C, p. 59

Advanced students should complete Levels B & C.

Writing a Lab Report, D12–13

Technology Resources

Customize this student lab as needed or look for an alternative. Print rubrics to assess student lab reports.

Lab Generator CD-ROM

Observe and Analyze

1. Answers will vary depending on students' observations.

Conclude

1. Answers will depend on students' observations.
2. Most cells are too small to see without a microscope. Some organisms are made of only one cell and so you need a microscope to see them.
3. The lowest magnification objective can be used for looking at the whole of a thing, while the objective with the highest magnification is useful for looking at details.
4. A microscope would let a doctor look for those microscopic organisms and thereby determine if a patient has a disease caused by them, and know which disease based on which organisms are there.
5. Sample answer: A biologist might use a microscope to study the organisms rather than just look for and identify the organisms.

INVESTIGATE Further

CHALLENGE It is likely that at least some of the organisms, if not all, will be different from those in the pond water sample. Different organisms have different ways of meeting their needs in their environments.

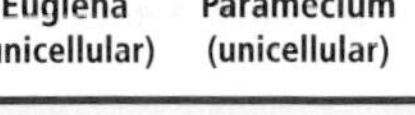

Identification Key

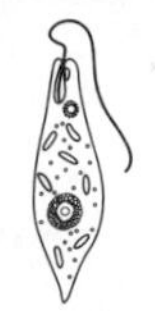
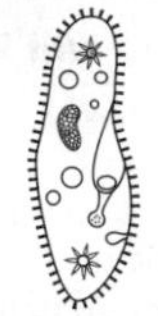
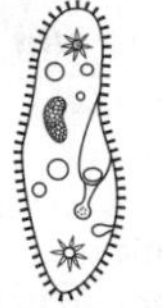

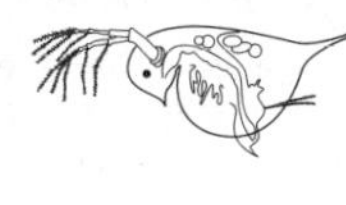

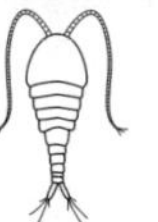
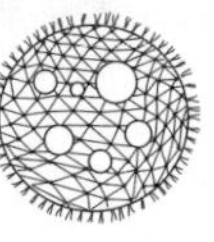

Euglena (unicellular)	Paramecium (unicellular)	Stentor (unicellular)	Desmid (unicellular)	Water flea (multicellular)	Hydra (multicellular)	Copepod (multicellular)	Volvox (multicellular)

5 Make a sketch of each of the different organisms that you see. Record any movement or behavior you observe. Include the magnification of the objective lens that you used.

Observe and Analyze

1. **CLASSIFY** Use the Identification Key above to identify the organism. If you cannot make an identification, write *unknown*.

Conclude

1. **COLLECT DATA** Compare your sketches with those of your classmates. How many different organisms in total did your class find? How many were identified as unicellular? How many were identified as multicellular?
2. **COMMUNICATE** Why is the microscope an important tool for studying cells and entire organisms?
3. **INTERPRET** Using what you learned in this chapter and in this investigation, explain the ways in which you would use the different objectives on a microscope.
4. **APPLY** Many diseases, such as strep throat, are caused by microscopic organisms. Why might a microscope be an important tool for a doctor?
5. **APPLY** How might the way a biologist uses a microscope be different from the way a doctor uses a microscope?

INVESTIGATE Further

Collect a small sample of soil from outside the school or your home. Mix the soil with enough tap water to make it liquid. Then take a sample of the soil mixture and examine it under the microscope. Sketch some of the organisms you see. Are they similar to those in the pond-water sample? Why do you think different types of organisms live in different environments?

Using a Microscope

Table 1. Identifying Microorganisms

Organism 1
Magnification used:
Movement/behavior:
Sketch:

Name:

Organism 2
Magnification used:
Movement/behavior:
Sketch:

Name:

Post-Lab Discussion

- Ask for a show of hands to make a census of the organisms that students found. List them on the board.
- Ask: Would you have wanted to live before the invention of the microscope? Why or why not?
- Ask students what new questions for research they can formulate based on watching the organisms' movements. How might they design an investigation to help answer one of the questions?

1.2 FOCUS

Set Learning Goals

Students will

- Describe different types of microscopes.
- Describe prokaryotic and eukaryotic cells.
- Compare plant and animal cells.
- Use a microscope to observe plant and animal cells.

3-Minute Warm-Up

Display Transparency 4 or copy this exercise on the board:

Decide if these statements are true. If not true, correct them.

1. All organisms are multicellular. *Some organisms are multicellular.*
2. The telescope is necessary to study cells. *The microscope is necessary to study cells.*
3. The cell theory says the cell is the basic unit of life. *true*

 3-Minute Warm-Up, p. T4

1.2 MOTIVATE

THINK ABOUT

PURPOSE To foster a sense of the scale of microorganisms

DISCUSS Have students look at the photographs of the dime and the bacteria cells while reading the text. Ask:

- How many bacteria cells will it take to make a line across the dime? *17,000*
- Which is larger, a bacteria cell or an animal cell? *an animal cell*
- Do you think a real dime has bacteria on it? Why or why not? *yes; because bacteria live almost everywhere on Earth*

KEY CONCEPT

1.2 Microscopes allow us to see inside the cell.

BEFORE, you learned

- Some organisms are unicellular and some are multicellular
- A microscope is necessary to study most cells
- The cell theory describes the cell as the fundamental unit of life

NOW, you will learn

- About different types of microscopes
- About prokaryotic and eukaryotic cells
- How plant and animal cells are similar and different

VOCABULARY

cell membrane p. 20
cytoplasm p. 20
nucleus p. 20
eukaryotic cell p. 20
prokaryotic cell p. 20
organelle p. 20
cell wall p. 21
chloroplast p. 23
mitochondria p. 23

THINK ABOUT

How small are cells?

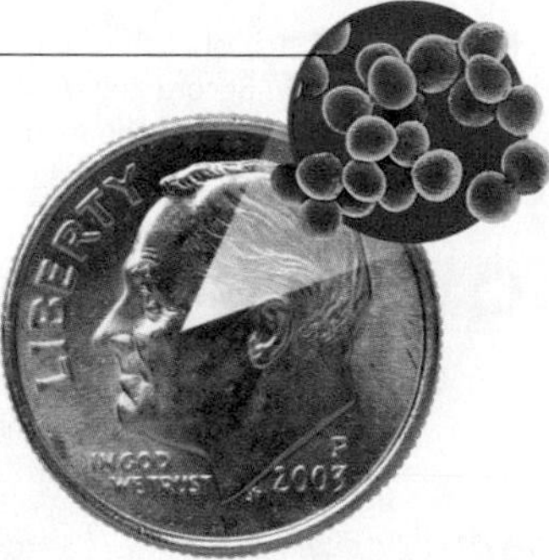

Because cells are so small, describing them requires a very small unit of measure: the micrometer (μm). A micrometer is one millionth of a meter. Most cells range in size from about 1 micrometer (some bacteria) to 1000 micrometers (some plant and animal cells). To get a sense of the sizes of cells, consider that it would take about 17,000 tiny bacterial cells lined up to reach across a dime. How many of these cells might fit on your fingertip?

MAIN IDEA WEB
Make a main idea web that explains the importance of the microscope.

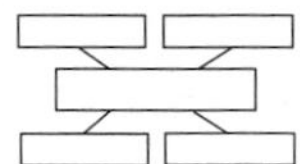

The microscope is an important tool.

The invention of the light microscope led to the discovery of cells and to the development of cell theory. In light microscopes, lenses are used to bend light and make objects appear bigger than they are. Modern light microscopes can magnify objects up to 1000 times.

The light microscope is still used today to study cells. Over many years scientists have found ways to make light microscopes more useful. Cell samples are treated with dyes to make structures in the cells easier to see. Scientists use video cameras and computer processing to observe the movement of cell parts and materials within cells. One important advantage of light microscopes is that scientists can observe living cells with them.

RESOURCES FOR DIFFERENTIATED INSTRUCTION

Below Level

UNIT RESOURCE BOOK

- Reading Study Guide A, pp. 23–24
- Decoding Support, p. 47

AUDIO CDS

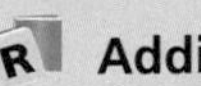 **Additional INVESTIGATION,** Looking at Your Own Cells, A, B, & C, pp. 60–68; Teacher Instructions, pp. 308–309

Advanced

UNIT RESOURCE BOOK

Challenge and Extension, p. 29

English Learners

UNIT RESOURCE BOOK

Spanish Reading Study Guide, pp. 27–28

 **AUDIO CDS**

- Audio Readings in Spanish
- Audio Readings (English)

Two other types of microscopes are important in the study of cells. The scanning electron microscope (SEM) and the transmission electron microscope (TEM) can produce images of objects as small as 0.002 micrometers. The light microscope can be used only for objects that are larger than 0.2 micrometers. Therefore, although a light microscope can be used to see many of the parts of a cell, only the SEM and TEM can be used for looking at the details of those parts.

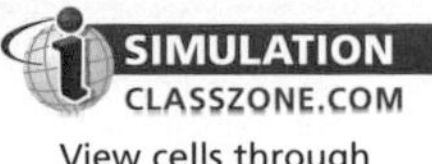

View cells through different types of microscopes.

In both the SEM and the TEM, tiny particles called electrons, not light, are used to produce images. The advantage of these microscopes is that they can magnify objects up to a million times. The disadvantage is that they cannot be used to study live specimens.

Compare light microscopes with electron microscopes. What are the advantages and disadvantages of each?

To be viewed with an SEM, a cell sample is coated in a heavy metal, such as gold. Then a beam of electrons is run back and forth over the surface of the cell. The electrons bounce off the coating and are read by a detector that produces a three-dimensional image of the surface.

A cell viewed with a TEM is sliced extremely thin. Electrons pass through a section. Images produced by a TEM appear two-dimensional.

Electron Microscopes

SEM

bacterial cell
viruses
heavy metal coating
electron beam
electron detector

1 An infected bacterial cell is coated with a heavy metal.

2 Beams of electrons bounce off the surface of the coated cell.

3 Images produced by an SEM appear three-dimensional.

TEM

bacterial cell
virus
thin section
electron beam
thin section

1 An infected bacterial cell is sliced into very thin sections.

2 Beams of electrons pass through the thin section.

3 Images produced by a TEM appear two-dimensional.

1.2 INSTRUCT

Teacher Demo

To illustrate how a lens collects and bends light, put some lint from the clothes dryer in a shallow metal pan. Focus sunlight through a magnifying glass onto the lint. Soon it will begin to smoke. You could also melt an ice cube in this way, using a second ice cube as a control to show how the lens intensifies the heat.

Teach from Visuals

To help students interpret the diagrams of electron microscopes, ask:

- Which microscope looks at a thin slice of the bacteria cell? *the TEM*
- Which microscope produces three-dimensional images? *the SEM*
- What kind of beams do both microscopes use? *electron beams*

Real World Example

About the size of a small car, the cryo-electron microscope can magnify specimens one million times. In other words, they can make a dime look about 12 miles wide. Resolution is about three times what is possible with standard electron microscopes; the cryo-electron microscope can focus on cell components that are smaller than one nanometer.

Ongoing Assessment

Describe different types of microscopes.

Ask: What is the difference between light microscopes and electron microscopes? *A light microscope uses lenses to bend light into your eye. An electron microscope runs a beam of electrons that bounces into a detector. Electron microscopes magnify more.*

CHECK YOUR READING *Answer: Light microscopes use lenses to bend light and make an object appear bigger. Electron microscopes use tiny particles called electrons to produce images. Electron microscopes can magnify objects that light microscopes miss, but cannot be used to study live specimens.*

DIFFERENTIATE INSTRUCTION

More Reading Support

A Why do we use electron microscopes? *to look at the details of the parts of a cell*

B What produces images in the SEM and TEM? *electrons*

English Learners Descriptions and processes can often be difficult for English learners. Have students who have a good understanding of how SEM and TEM microscopes work explain the processes to a partner who is new to English. As they explain, they should use two methods: first, explaining aloud, and second, diagramming or sketching. Then, have English learners write down or repeat aloud what they learned, and ask questions. Remind students to pronounce *SEM* as "S.E.M." not "sem."

Integrate the Sciences

Optics is the science of light—how to create it, how to change it, what changes it produces, and other related phenomena. Physical optics deals with the nature and characteristics of light itself. Geometrical optics deals with the devices that use light, such as lenses and mirrors. Fiber optics is the transmission of data, sound, and images by passing light through thin, usually glass, wires.

Teach from Visuals

To help students interpret the diagram of eukaryotic and prokaryotic cells, ask:

- Which cells have a nucleus? *eukaryotic*
- Which cells are smaller? *prokaryotic*
- Which cells have a cell membrane and cytoplasm? *both types*

Ongoing Assessment

Describe prokaryotic and eukaryotic cells.

Ask: How are prokaryotic and eukaryotic cells alike and different? *Both have cell membranes and cytoplasm. Eukaryotic cells have their DNA in a nucleus, while prokaryotic cells have it in the cytoplasm.*

Cells are diverse.

Very early on, the people studying cells knew that cells have a great diversity of sizes and shapes. As microscopes were improved, scientists could see more and more details of cells. What they saw was that the inside of one cell can be very different from that of another cell.

VOCABULARY
Add a four square for *cell membrane* to your notebook. Try to include the word *cytoplasm* in your diagram.

Every cell has a boundary that separates the inside from the outside. That boundary is the **cell membrane,** a protective covering that encloses the entire cell. (C) Any material coming into or out of the cell must pass through the cell membrane. Contained inside the cell membrane is a gelatin-like material called **cytoplasm** (SY-tuh-PLAZ-uhm). Most of the work of the cell is carried out in the cytoplasm. (D)

Scientists separate cells into two broad categories based on one key difference: the location of the genetic material cells need to reproduce and function. In a **eukaryotic cell** (yoo-KAR-ee-AHT-ihk) the genetic material is in a structure called the **nucleus** (NOO-klee-uhs), a structure enclosed by its own membrane. Scientists use the word **organelle** (AWR-guh-NEHL) to describe any part of a cell that is enclosed by membrane.

In a **prokaryotic cell** (proh-KAR-ee-AWT-ihk) there is no separate compartment for the genetic material. Instead, it is in the cytoplasm. There are no organelles. Most unicellular organisms are prokaryotic cells. Almost all multicellular organisms are eukaryotic.

Eukaryotic and Prokaryotic Cells

Eukaryotic cells have a nucleus while prokaryotic cells do not. On average, eukaryotic cells are about 100 times larger than prokaryotic cells.

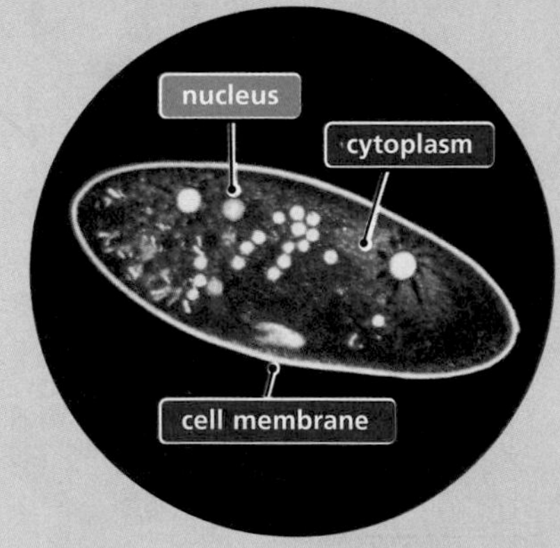

A **eukaryotic cell** has a nucleus. The paramecium shown here is magnified 133×.

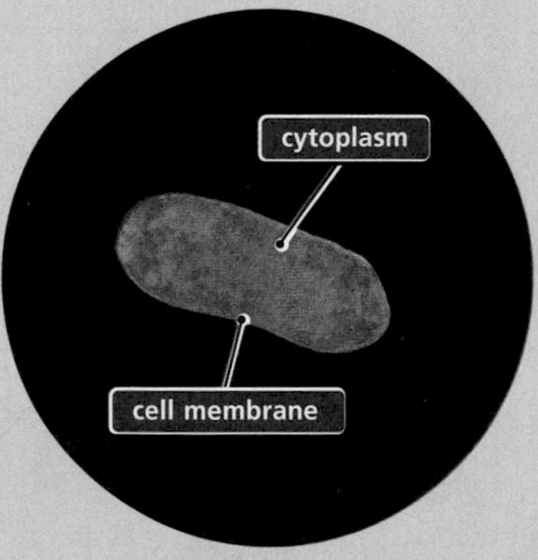

A **prokaryotic cell** does not have a nucleus. The bacterium shown here is magnified 12,000×.

DIFFERENTIATE INSTRUCTION

More Reading Support

C What do you call a protective covering that encloses the cell? *cell membrane*

D Where is most of the work of a cell carried out? *in the cytoplasm*

English Learners There are an unusual number of vocabulary terms highlighted on p. 20, and they are nearly all illustrated in the micrographs of "Eukaryotic and Prokaryotic Cells," p. 20. The term that is shown but not labeled is *organelle,* which students can see clear examples of in the *eukaryotic cell.* Encourage students to trace or sketch the micrographs and add labels. Pronounce each term aloud.

INVESTIGATE Plant and Animal Cells

How do plant and animal cells compare?

PROCEDURE

1. Choose the objective lens with the lowest magnification. Place the plant-cell slide on the stage and turn on the light source. Handle the slide carefully.
2. Observe the cells at low magnification. Make a drawing of one of the cells.
3. Observe the cells at high magnification. Fill in details. Return to the low-magnification lens before removing the slide.
4. Repeat steps 1–3 with the animal-cell slide.

WHAT DO YOU THINK?

- Compare the drawings you made. How are the plant and animal cells alike, and how are they different?
- Compare the thickness of plant cell's cell membrane and cell wall with the thickness of the animal cell's cell membrane.

CHALLENGE Placing a ruler on top of the slides, view each slide at low power. Estimate and compare the sizes of the two cells.

SKILL FOCUS
Observing

MATERIALS
- prepared slides
- microscope
- *for Challenge:* millimeter ruler

TIME
30 minutes

Plants and animals have eukaryotic cells.

 E

Plant and animal cells, like all eukaryotic cells, are divided into two main compartments. The nucleus, usually the largest organelle, is the compartment that stores the instructions a cell needs to function. You will learn more about how cells use this information in Chapter 5.

Surrounding the nucleus is the cytoplasm. The cell membrane is the boundary between the cytoplasm and the outside of the cell. Plant cells also have cell walls. A **cell wall** is a tough outer covering that lies just outside the cell membrane. The cell wall supports and protects the cell. Having a cell wall is one important way in which plant cells differ from animal cells.

F

RESOURCE CENTER
CLASSZONE.COM

Find out more about cell structures.

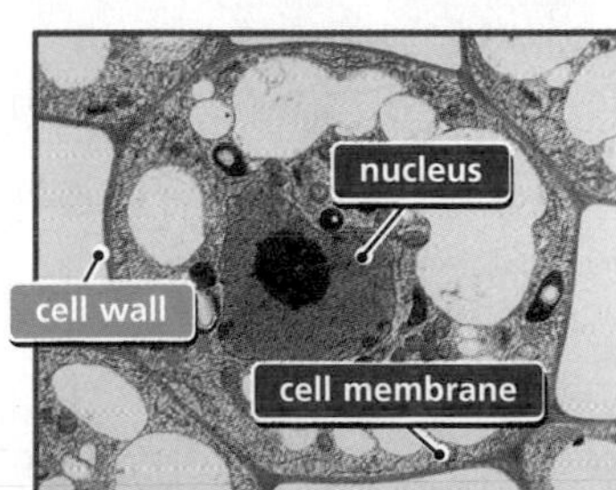

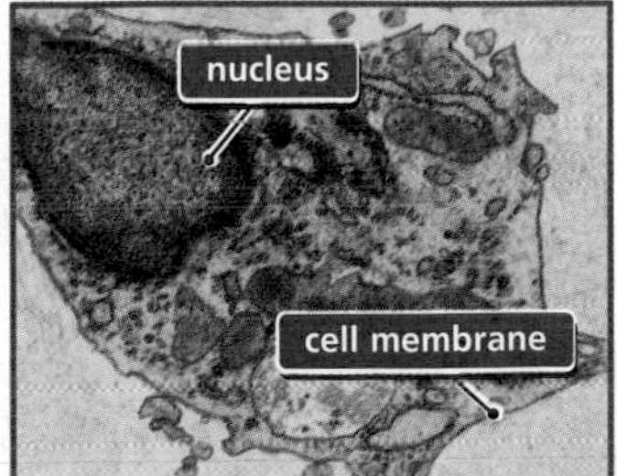

Both a plant cell (shown at left magnified 1750 ×) and an animal cell (shown at right magnified 12,000 ×) have a nucleus and a cell membrane. Plant cells also have a cell wall.

DIFFERENTIATE INSTRUCTION

More Reading Support

E What do you call any part of a cell enclosed by a membrane? *an organelle*

F What is one way plant cells differ from animal cells? *cell wall (plants)*

Advanced Have students research how advanced electron micrography is aiding the study of the human genome. Have them make a list of the technologies that are essential for mapping the genome.

 Challenge and Extension, p. 29

INVESTIGATE Plant and Animal Cells

PURPOSE To observe parts of a cell

TIPS *30 min.* Focusing the microscope is generally a skill that takes practice. Caution students that microscope slides may be sharp-edged, and if dropped will break. They should not touch broken glass.

WHAT DO YOU THINK? *Students may observe that both cells have a nucleus and a cell membrane. Students may say that plant cells have cell walls, look greener, have fewer structures within the cytoplasm. The cell wall of the plant cell is thicker than the cell membrane of the animal cell.*

CHALLENGE *Accept all reasonable responses. Check that answers are based on observations.*

 Datasheet, Plant and Animal Cells, p. 30

Technology Resources

Customize this student lab as needed or look for an alternative. Print rubrics to assess student lab reports.

 **Lab Generator CD-ROM**

Teaching with Technology

Use a PC microscope to take pictures of the cells that students observe. Have them available for students to view at their leisure.

History of Science

The first electron microscope was built in 1933 by a German electrical engineer, Ernst Ruska. He knew that a light microscope is limited by the wavelength of light. He also knew that electrons have the properties of waves that are thousands of times shorter than those of light. Putting these pieces of information together, Ruska developed an electron lens that could focus electrons on an object, just as light could be focused. He built the first electron microscope by putting several of these lenses together in a series.

Teach from Visuals

To help students interpret the diagrams of plant and animal cells, ask:

- Which structures are found in plant cells but not animal cells? *chloroplasts, central vacuole, cell wall*
- Which structures are found in animal cells but not plant cells? *lysosomes*
- Which structures are found in both plant and animal cells? *nucleus, endoplasmic reticulum, ribosomes, Golgi apparatuses, vesicles, mitochondria, cell membrane*

The visual "Parts of a Eukaryotic Cell" is available as T6 in the Unit Transparency Book.

Metacognitive Strategy

Have students brainstorm ways to organize information about the similarities and differences of plant and animal cells.

EXPLORE the BIG idea

Revisit "Internet Activity: Cells" on p. 7. Have students compare the cells in the activity to the ones in the illustrations on p. 22. What is familiar or similar?

Arts Connection

The abstract and geometric forms of cells and organelles have inspired contemporary painters and sculptors. Have students create designs for a stained glass window that incorporate motifs from cell structures. Students can cut colored acetate to execute their designs. They can piece their "windows" together using clear tape and a cardboard frame. Display these works on a class window.

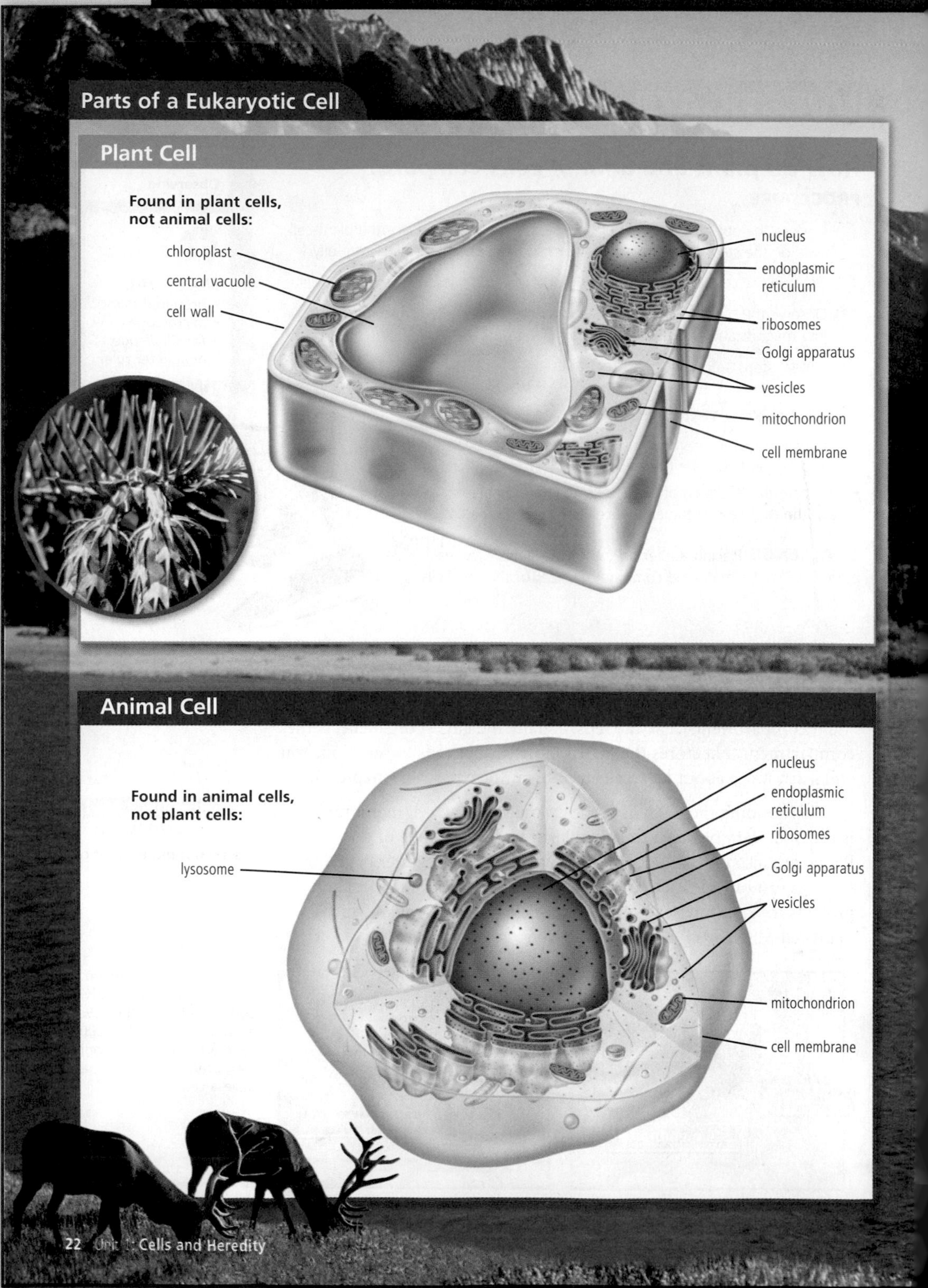

Parts of a Eukaryotic Cell

Plant Cell

Found in plant cells, not animal cells:

chloroplast
central vacuole
cell wall

nucleus
endoplasmic reticulum
ribosomes
Golgi apparatus
vesicles
mitochondrion
cell membrane

Animal Cell

Found in animal cells, not plant cells:

lysosome

nucleus
endoplasmic reticulum
ribosomes
Golgi apparatus
vesicles
mitochondrion
cell membrane

22 Unit 1: Cells and Heredity

DIFFERENTIATE INSTRUCTION

Alternative Assessment Have students create unlabeled diagrams of plant and animal cells. Copy their diagrams and have them label the organelles on the master copy. Pair students for peer review, using the unlabeled diagrams to test knowledge and the master copy to check it.

Structures That Process Information

The nucleus is often the largest organelle in a cell. It contains information a cell needs to function. Some of the information is translated by ribosomes, tiny structures located in the cytoplasm and the endoplasmic reticulum. Ribosomes use the information to build important molecules called proteins.

Organelles That Provide Energy

G No cell can stay alive without energy. Cells need energy to perform all the activities of life. Plants get their energy directly from the Sun. Within plant cells are **chloroplasts** (KLAWR-uh-PLASTS), organelles in which the energy from sunlight is used to make sugar. Plants use some of the sugar immediately, to keep their cells functioning. The rest of the sugar is stored in the cells.

H Animal cells do not contain chloroplasts. As a result, animals are not able to use the energy of the Sun directly. Instead, animals get their energy from food. Much of the food an animal uses for energy comes from the sugar that plant cells have stored. Animals can get this energy by eating plants or by eating animals that have eaten plants.

mitochondria

chloroplast

This plant cell is magnified 6000×.

CHECK YOUR READING How can a chloroplast, a structure found in plant cells but not in animal cells, provide energy for both plants and animals?

Both plant cells and animal cells must be able to use energy to do work. The energy is made available by organelles found in all eukaryotic cells. **Mitochondria** (MY-tuh-KAHN-dree-uh) are the organelles that use oxygen to get energy from processing food.

READING TIP *Mitochondria* is plural. The singular form is *mitochondrion*.

Organelles That Process and Transport

You know that plant and animal cells get their energy from the sugars that the organisms make or consume. Sugars are also an important part of the starting materials that cells use to maintain themselves and grow. The job of making cell parts from the starting materials that enter a cell is divided among a number of structures in the cytoplasm.

In the illustrations on page 22, you can see that the endoplasmic reticulum is a system of twisting and winding membranes. Some of the endoplasmic reticulum contains ribosomes, which manufacture proteins. The endoplasmic reticulum manufactures parts of the cell membrane.

Address Misconceptions

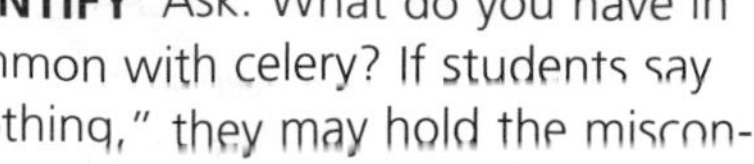

IDENTIFY Ask: What do you have in common with celery? If students say "nothing," they may hold the misconception that plants are totally different from animals.

CORRECT Discuss the criteria for life. Ask whether celery meets the criteria, and how that makes it like humans.

REASSESS Ask: What are the similarities between plants and animals? *Both are made of cells; they have some similar needs; and both engage in life processes.*

Technology Resources

Visit **ClassZone.com** for background on common student misconceptions.

MISCONCEPTION DATABASE

Ongoing Assessment

CHECK YOUR READING *Answer: Plants use their chloroplasts to create sugars, which animals eat to get energy.*

DIFFERENTIATE INSTRUCTION

More Reading Support

G Where do plants get their energy? *from the Sun*

H Where do animals get their energy? *from eating plants or other animals that have eaten plants*

Additional Investigation To reinforce Section 1.2 learning goals, use the following full-period investigation:

Additional INVESTIGATION, Looking at Your Own Cells, A, B, & C, pp. 60–68, 308–309
(Advanced students should complete Levels B and C.)

Below Level If students are confused by the chain of energy flowing from the Sun through plants to animals, remind them that they may have encountered the concept before, called a food chain or food web. Draw a chain (for example: grass > grasshopper > toad > snake > hawk > bacteria).

Ongoing Assessment

Compare plant and animal cells.

Ask: How are plant and animal cells alike and different? *Both have organelles that process and transport. Only plants have chloroplasts to capture energy from sunlight. Only plant cells have cell walls and central vacuoles. Only animal cells take in food.*

CHECK YOUR READING *Answer: Lysosomes in animal cells contain wastes and store and break down nutrients. The central vacuole in plant cells stores and holds water. Both are vacuoles.*

Develop Critical Thinking

CONNECT Ask: How is a cell like a factory? *Raw materials come in, different jobs are done, waste and other products emerge.*

Reinforce the BIG idea

Have students relate the section to the Big Idea.

 Reinforcing Key Concepts, p. 29

The endoplasmic reticulum is also part of the cellular transport system. Portions of endoplasmic reticulum break off to form small packages called vesicles. The vesicles transport processed materials to an organelle called the Golgi apparatus. The folded membranes of the Golgi apparatus make it look something like a stack of pancakes. The Golgi apparatus takes the materials manufactured by the endoplasmic reticulum and finishes processing them.

Organelles for Storage, Recycling, and Waste

Cells store water, sugar, and other materials, which they use to function. Cells must also store waste materials until they can be removed. Inside plant and fungus cells are sacs called vacuoles. Vacuoles are enclosed by a membrane and can hold water, waste, and other materials. Vacuoles function with the cell membrane to move materials either into or out of the cell. A plant cell has a large central vacuole in which water and other materials can be stored. Water in the vacuole provides support for smaller plants.

Animal cells do not have central vacuoles. What animal cells do have are similar structures called lysosomes. Lysosomes are vesicles that contain chemicals that break down materials taken into the cell, as well as old cell parts. Remember that animals, unlike plants, take in food. Nutrients brought into the cell need to be broken down, as well as wastes contained.

CHECK YOUR READING Compare and contrast lysosomes and central vacuoles.

1.2 Review

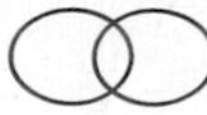

KEY CONCEPTS

1. What advantages and disadvantages does a light microscope have in comparison with an electron microscope?
2. What is the difference between a eukaryotic cell and a prokaryotic cell?
3. List three structures found in plant cells that are not in animal cells.

CRITICAL THINKING

4. **Synthesize** What organelles can be said to act like an assembly line within a cell? Explain.
5. **Compare and Contrast** Make a Venn diagram comparing and contrasting plant and animal cells.

CHALLENGE

6. **Synthesize** Identify the type of microscope used to capture the image at the right, and indicate whether the cell is a plant cell or an animal cell. How do you know?

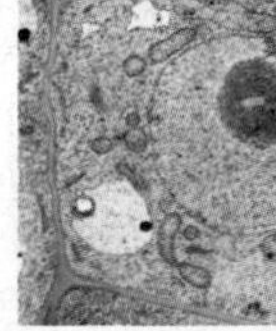

(magnified 27,9

1.2 ASSESS & RETEACH

Assess

 Section 1.2 Quiz, p. 4

Reteach

Have students use the "Parts of a Eukaryotic Cell" diagram on p. 22 to create drawings of plant and animal cells, using a color system to draw attention to similarities and differences.

Technology Resources

Have students visit **ClassZone.com** for reteaching of Key Concepts.

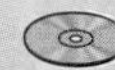 CONTENT REVIEW

CONTENT REVIEW CD-ROM

ANSWERS

1. With a light microscope you can view live specimens, but you can magnify only 1000 times.

2. A eukaryotic cell has DNA in a nucleus, and a prokaryotic cell has DNA throughout the cytoplasm.

3. chloroplast, central vacuole, cell wall

4. The endoplasmic reticulum uses materials from ribosomes to make proteins and cell membrane parts. Vesicles take those materials to the Golgi apparatus, which finishes processing them.

5. plant cells: chloroplast, central vacuole, cell wall; animal cells: lysosome; both: eukaryotic, all the other organelles

6. light microscope; plant cell, because it has chloroplasts, a cell wall, and a central vacuole

MATH TUTORIAL

CLASSZONE.COM

Click on Math Tutorial for more help with scientific notation.

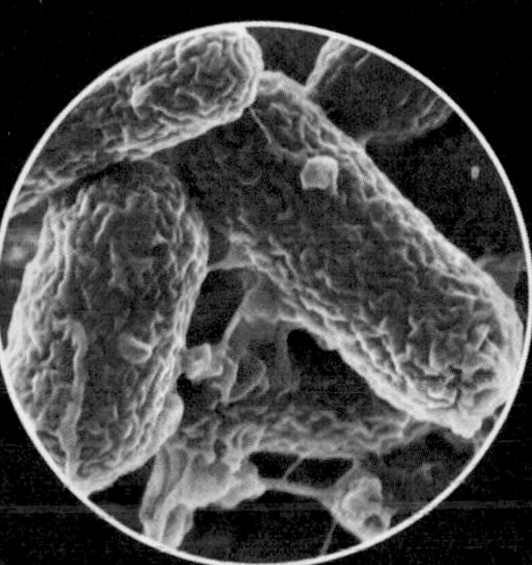

How many bacteria can fit on the head of a pin? The bacteria are magnified 50,000 × in this photograph. The head of the pin below is magnified 7 ×.

SKILL: USING SCIENTIFIC NOTATION

Comparing Sizes

Measuring the sizes of very small things like atoms or very large things like planets requires numbers with many places. For example, the diameter of the nucleus of a cell is around 1/100,000 of a meter, while the diameter of Earth is 12,756,000 meters. How can you compare these sizes?

Example

(1) Express a large number as a number between 1 and 10 multiplied by a power of 10.

$12{,}756{,}000 = 1.2756 \times 10^7$

The exponent is the number of places following the first place.

(2) Express any number smaller than 1 as a negative power of 10.

$\frac{1}{100{,}000} = 0.00001 = 1 \times 10^{-5}$

The exponent is the number of places following the decimal point.

(3) Compare −5 and 7 to see that 7 is 12 more than −5.

ANSWER Earth's diameter is roughly 10^{12} times bigger than the diameter of a cell's nucleus.

Answer the following questions.

1. An oxygen atom measures 14/100,000,000,000 of a meter across. Write the width of the oxygen atom as a decimal number.
2. Write the width of the oxygen atom in scientific notation.
3. A chloroplast measures 5 millionths of a meter across. Write its width in standard form and in scientific notation.
4. A redwood tree stands 100 meters tall. There are 1000 millimeters in a meter. Express the height of the redwood tree in millimeters. Write the number in scientific notation.
5. A typical plant cell measures 1 millionth of a meter in width. Express the width in standard form and in scientific notation.

CHALLENGE **The yolk of an ostrich egg is about 8 centimeters in diameter. The ostrich itself is about 2.4 meters tall. Write each of these lengths in the same unit, and express them in scientific notation. Then tell how many times taller the ostrich is than the yolk.**

MATH IN SCIENCE

Math Skills Practice for Science

Set Learning Goal

To use scientific notation to express very large and very small numbers

Present the Science

You don't have to leave Earth to find huge differences in numbers that you might want to compare. Some organisms have only one cell, while the largest, the blue whale, has around 1×10^{15}. A small rotifer weighs about 6×10^{-9} gram, while a large whale weighs more than 1.7×10^8 grams.

Develop Number Sense

- Remind students that exponents indicate how many times a base number is multiplied by itself.
- When you are using 10 as the base number, the number of zeros in the final answer equals the exponent.

DIFFERENTIATION TIP For some students, manipulatives such as bead chains or an abacus may be helpful.

Close

Ask: Why would we need scientific notation when talking about the cells in our bodies? *The cells are microscopic, and there are so many of them in a body.*

- Math Support, p. 48
- Math Practice, p. 49

Technology Resources

Students can visit **ClassZone.com** to practice scientific notation.

MATH TUTORIAL

ANSWERS

1. 0.000000000014 m

2. 1.4×10^{-11} m

3. 0.000005 m; 5×10^{-6} m

4. 100,000 mm; 1×10^5 mm

5. 0.000001 m; 1×10^{-6} m

CHALLENGE *8 cm, 240 cm (8×10^{-2} m, 2.4×10^{-2} m); 30 times*

1.3 FOCUS

Set Learning Goals

Students will

- Describe how organisms are classified by cell type.
- Explain specialization of cells.
- Explain how cells, tissues, and organs are organized into systems.
- Make models of cells and assess the limitations of modeling.

3-Minute Warm-Up

Display Transparency 5 or copy this exercise on the board:

Match the definition to the correct term.

Definitions

1. a cell with no nucleus *b*
2. a cell with a cell wall and a nucleus *e*
3. a device for viewing microorganisms *c*

Terms

a. eukaryotic
b. prokaryotic
c. microscope
d. telescope
e. plant cell

3-Minute Warm-Up, p. T5

1.3 MOTIVATE

EXPLORE Specialization

PURPOSE To infer where chloroplasts are found and to discover that plants have specialized parts

TIPS *20 min.* Clean all dirt off roots so the shape of the roots is apparent. Students may draw blades and roots before describing them in words.

WHAT DO YOU THINK? *The grass blades are green, and the roots are white and brown. Because the grass blades are green, they probably have chloroplasts and can produce sugar.*

KEY CONCEPT

1.3 Different cells perform various functions.

BEFORE, you learned

- Modern microscopes reveal details of cell structures
- Some cells are prokaryotic and some are eukaryotic
- Plant and animal cells have similarities and differences

NOW, you will learn

- How organisms are classified into three domains
- About specialization in multicellular organisms
- How cells, tissues, and organs are organized

VOCABULARY

specialization p. 28
tissue p. 29
organ p. 30

EXPLORE Specialization

How do roots differ from leaves?

PROCEDURE

1. Soak the grass plant in a cup of water to clean away any dirt.
2. Compare the color of the roots with the color of the blades or leaves. Record your observations.
3. Wash your hands when you have finished.

MATERIALS

- grass plants
- cup
- water

WHAT DO YOU THINK?

- How does the color of the grass roots compare with that of the grass blades?
- Chloroplasts contain a chemical that gives leaves their green color. What does this suggest to you about the functions of the grass blades and roots?

Organisms can be classified by their cell type.

MAIN IDEA WEB
Make a web of the important terms and details about the main idea: *Organisms can be classified by their cell type.*

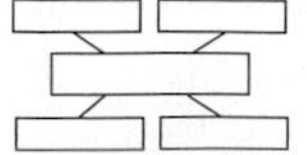

Look around you at this moment. The living organisms you see may number 10, 20, 100, or 1000, depending on where you are. What you are not seeing, but what is also there, is a huge number of unicellular organisms. For example, there are at least 2–3 million bacteria living on each square centimeter of your skin.

Most of the organisms alive on Earth today are made of a single cell. One of the most interesting scientific discoveries made recently had to do with a group of unicellular organisms. These organisms were found living where no one expected to find any life at all.

RESOURCES FOR DIFFERENTIATED INSTRUCTION

Below Level

UNIT RESOURCE BOOK

- Reading Study Guide A, pp. 34–35
- Decoding Support, p. 47

AUDIO CDS

Advanced

UNIT RESOURCE BOOK
Challenge and Extension, p. 40

English Learners

UNIT RESOURCE BOOK
Spanish Reading Study Guide, pp. 38–39

AUDIO CDS

- Audio Readings in Spanish
- Audio Readings (English)

Archaea and Bacteria

In the early 1980s, scientists discovered unicellular organisms living in rather extreme environments. Some were living deep in the ocean, at thermal vents where there is extreme heat and little oxygen. Others were found in the salty waters of the Great Salt Lake and in the hot sulfur springs of Yellowstone Park.

REMINDER

The genetic material in a prokaryotic cell is not enclosed in a nucleus. In eukaryotic cells genetic material is stored in a nucleus.

At first, these organisms were referred to as archaebacteria. The organisms were similar in appearance to bacteria. The prefix *archae* comes from a Greek word that means "ancient." Many of these organisms live in environments that scientists think are like the environments of ancient Earth.

Archaea are prokaryotic organisms that can live in extreme environments like these thermal vents. In a thermal vent, temperatures can reach 600 degrees Celsius.

A It took a while for scientists to realize that these organisms that looked like bacteria were genetically very different from bacteria. Scientists decided to establish a separate category for them, a domain called Archaea (AHR kee-uh). A domain is a broad category of living things that is based on characteristics of their cells. Scientists have identified three domains. Bacteria are classified in the domain Bacteria. A third domain includes organisms with eukaryotic cells.

Organisms that belong to the domains Bacteria and Archaea are similar in some important ways. They are prokaryotes, which are unicellular organisms with prokaryotic cells. Their cytoplasm contains ribosomes but no organelles, so the structure of a prokaryote is simple. Another feature of a prokaryote is a tough cell wall that protects the organism.

RESOURCE CENTER
CLASSZONE.COM

Learn more about unicellular organisms.

CHECK YOUR READING Why did scientists decide to establish separate domains for archaea and bacteria?

1.3 INSTRUCT

Real World Example

Biologists once believed that all living things could be classified as either plant or animal. That began changing in the 17th century with the invention of the microscope. By the 1950s, most scientists realized that this did not account for fungi, protists, or bacteria, so a system of five kingdoms was developed, including prokaryotic bacteria and four eukaryotic kingdoms. Most scientists today add Archaea as a separate kingdom, for a six-kingdom system. Carl Woese proposed in 1977 that three domains exist, based on DNA sequences: Archaea, Bacteria, and Eukarya. Domains are used as an organizational level above kingdoms.

History of Science

Carl Woese, an American microbiologist born in 1928, pioneered classification of organisms by their ribosomal RNA. The technique led to Woese's most famous work, the discovery that the Archaea constituted an entirely separate domain of life from bacteria and eukaryotes. The discovery of Archaea transformed most scientists' view of biology.

Ongoing Assessment

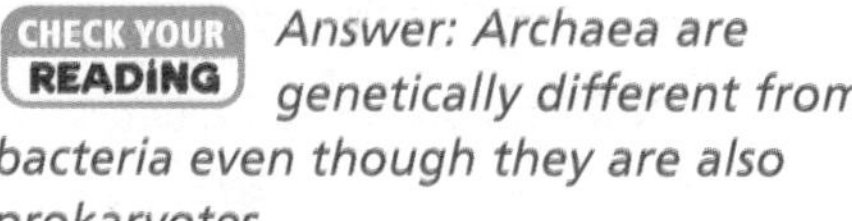

CHECK YOUR READING *Answer: Archaea are genetically different from bacteria even though they are also prokaryotes.*

DIFFERENTIATE INSTRUCTION

More Reading Support

A What is a domain in biology? ***a broad category of living things based on characteristics of the cell***

English Learners Place the terms *Archaea, Bacteria,* and *Eukarya* on the Science Word Wall with brief definitions of each. Place a micrograph, photograph, or illustration next to each word as well. Reinforce for students that each word is a title for one of the three domains of living things. Also model correct pronunciation.

Address Misconceptions

IDENTIFY Ask: What are the basic types of cells? If students answer "plant and animal cells," they may hold the misconception that all life can be divided into plants and animals.

CORRECT Point out that differences between some organisms can only be seen using sophisticated equipment. Explain that prokaryotic and eukaryotic cells are very different, and are the basic types of cells. Refer to p. 20, and ask students to describe differences between the two types.

REASSESS Ask: Is a bacterium a plant or an animal? What type of cell is it? *neither; prokaryotic*

Technology Resources

Visit **ClassZone.com** for background on common student misconceptions.

MISCONCEPTION DATABASE

Real World Example

Once specialized cells have matured, they usually cannot reproduce. Instead, the body gets new specialized cells from stem cells. Stem cells have the property of self-replication—they can reproduce themselves over and over again, each time producing one new specialized cell and one new stem cell. Stem cells do not always produce the same specialized cell—they receive signals telling them which to produce.

Ongoing Assessment

Describe how organisms are classified by cell type.

Ask: How are the three domains of cells categorized? *according to genetic differences*

CHECK YOUR READING *Answer: Eukaryotes have cells with a nucleus and other organelles. Some eukaryotes are single-celled organisms, but they are larger than prokaryotes.*

CHECK YOUR READING *Answer: The cell and its organelles are organized to allow it to do a specific job.*

Eukarya

B

The third domain is the domain Eukarya. Organisms in this domain have cells with a nucleus. This domain includes almost all the multicellular organisms on Earth: plants, animals, and fungi. It also includes many unicellular organisms called protists. The cells of unicellular eukaryotes are more complex in structure and larger than the cells of prokaryotes.

CHECK YOUR READING How are eukaryotes different from prokaryotes?

The paramecium is one of the most complex of all unicellular eukaryotes. Its body is lined with hairlike strands, called cilia (SIHL-ee-uh), that allow it to move. It has dartlike structures that carry a substance used in healing and, perhaps, defense. Along the outside of the cell is a long oral groove lined with cilia that leads to a mouth pore. In addition to a nucleus, the cell of a paramecium has organelles that enable it to digest food and remove water and wastes. The paramecium has all it needs to live as a single cell. By comparison, in most multicellular eukaryotes, no individual cell can survive on its own.

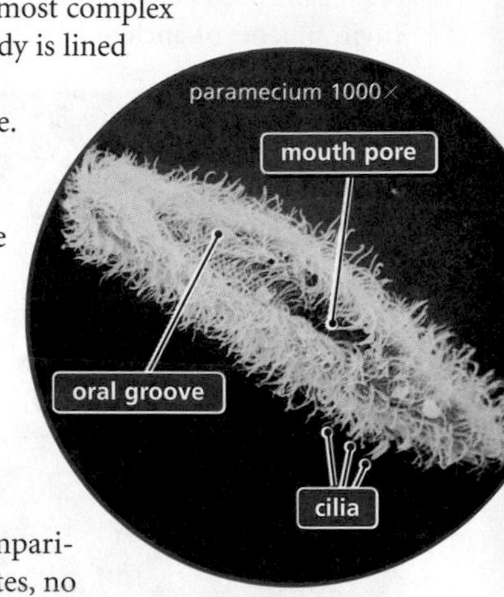

Cells in multicellular organisms specialize.

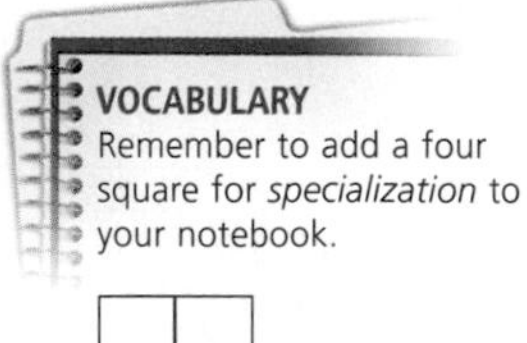
VOCABULARY
Remember to add a four square for *specialization* to your notebook.

Most multicellular organisms consist of many different types of cells that do different jobs. For example, most animals have blood cells, nerve cells, and muscle cells. The cells are specialized. **Specialization** of cells means that specific cells perform specific functions. This specialization is why a single cell from a multicellular organism cannot survive on its own. A blood cell can help you fight infection or deliver oxygen to your muscles, but it cannot cause your body to move as a muscle cell can. Plants have cells that function in photosynthesis, and other cells that draw water from the soil, and still others that function mainly to support the plant's weight.

? C

CHECK YOUR READING What does it mean for a cell to be specialized?

28 Unit 1: Cells and Heredity

DIFFERENTIATE INSTRUCTION

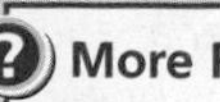
More Reading Support

B What domain includes almost all the multicellular organisms? *Eukarya*

C What is a specialized cell? *a cell that does a specific job*

Below Level Have students make and use flash cards of the three domains, with one characteristic—for instance, "lives in extreme environments"—on the back of each card.

Specialization

A fully grown salamander has many specialized cells.

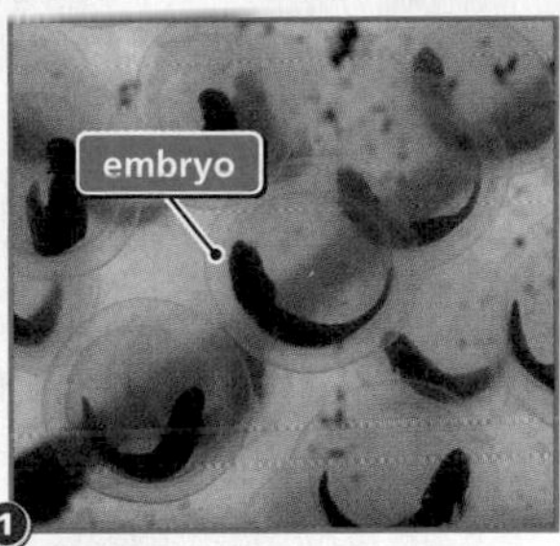

1 A salamander, like all multicellular organisms, begins life as an egg. After fertilization, the egg develops into an embryo.

2 As the cells divide, they begin to specialize. The amount of specialization depends on the complexity of the organism.

3 A salamander's body has many specialized cells. These include skin cells, blood cells, bone cells, muscle cells, and nerve cells.

D

A multicellular organism is a community of cells.

Cells in a multicellular organism are specialized. The ways in which the cells work together and interact depend on the organism. You can think of the cells of an organism as members of a community. The size and complexity of the community differ from organism to organism.

A sponge is an animal that is fairly simple in its organization. It spends its life attached to the ocean floor, filtering food and other nutrients from the water. Like all animals, the sponge is organized at a cellular level. Different types of cells in its body perform different functions. For example, certain cells take in food, and other cells digest it. However, cells in a sponge are not very highly specialized. A piece broken from a living sponge will actually regenerate itself as new cells replace the lost ones.

E

In more complex organisms, such as plants and animals, cells are not only specialized but grouped together in tissues. A **tissue** is a group of similar cells that are organized to do a specific job. If you look at your hand, you will see the top layer of tissue in your skin. Humans have two layers of skin tissue, layered one on top of the other. Together these skin tissues provide protection and support.

CHECK YOUR READING In what way is a tissue an organization of cells?

Teacher Demo

Use a plant leaf to show students the sequence of cell to tissue to organ. Bring in a leaf of lettuce, preferably a variety such as romaine, with large stems. Locate a rib in the leaf and bend it back against the curve until it snaps. You should be able to see the edges of a thin layer of tissue. Use tweezers or forceps to gently peel the tissue off the lettuce for students to see. This tissue is one cell thick.

Develop Critical Thinking

COMPARE Ask: How is an organism like a city? *Cells do different jobs to keep the organism going, just as people keep the city going. Organisms have tissues; cities have roads, fences, and greenbelts.*

Ongoing Assessment

Explain specialization of cells.

Ask: Why is a blood cell called a specialized cell? *A blood cell is specialized because it performs specific jobs, such as carrying oxygen or fighting infection, that help a multicellular organism survive.*

CHECK YOUR READING *Answer: A tissue is a group of similar cells organized to do a specific job.*

DIFFERENTIATE INSTRUCTION

More Reading Support

D How do all multicellular organisms begin life? *as a single fertilized egg cell*

E What do you call a group of similar cells that do a specific job? *a tissue*

Advanced Have students research biologists' search for the universal ancestor—the first organism from which all other life evolved. They might focus on particular scientists or on the genetic mapping process.

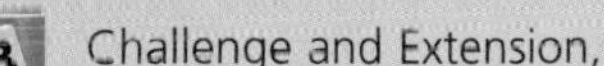

R Challenge and Extension, p. 40

Teach from Visuals

To help students interpret the diagram of levels of organization, ask:

- What structures make up a tissue? *cells*
- What are some examples of organs? *leaf, eye*
- What are components of an animal organ system? *sensory organs, brain, spinal cord, nerves*

Integrate the Sciences

Extracellular matrix (ECM) is the nonliving scaffold within which tissues take shape. In bone, for instance, it is composed of collagen, calcium, and phosphorus. The cells not only grow within the ECM, they create it, remodel it, and are regulated by it. An ECM made of collagen has been fairly successful at engineering skin tissue, and currently a scaffold made of sea coral is being tried for engineering bone.

Ongoing Assessment

CHECK YOUR READING *Answer: Tissues make up organs.*

Different tissues working together to perform a particular function represent another level of organization, the **organ.** The eye is an organ that functions with the tarsier's brain to allow sight. A leaf is an organ that provides a plant with energy and materials. It has tissue that brings in water and nutrients, tissue that uses the Sun's energy to make sugar, and tissue that moves sugar to other parts of the plant.

What is the relationship between tissues and organs?

DIFFERENTIATE INSTRUCTION

Alternative Assessment Have students demonstrate their mastery of the levels of organization by making a drawing of an organism of their choice and chaining backwards to the cell level.

Below Level Have students create collages of the levels of organization, using pictures cut from magazines.

Different organs and tissues working together form an organ system. An organism may have only a few organ systems. The organ systems of plants include roots, stems, and leaves. Other organisms have many organ systems. Humans have 11 major organ systems, made up of about 40 organs and over 200 types of tissue. The human nervous system, for example, includes the brain, the spinal cord, nerves, and sensory organs, such as the ears and eyes.

? F An organism itself represents the highest level of organization. It is at this level that we see all the characteristics we associate with life. If an organism is a complex organism—a human, for example—it will consist of trillions of cells grouped into tissues, organs, and organ systems. However, a simple organism, like a sponge, meets its needs with a body made up of only a few types of specialized cells.

CHECK YOUR READING What level of organization is an organism? What do we see at this level of organization?

INVESTIGATE Cell Models

What are some of the limitations of using a model to represent a cell?

SKILL FOCUS
Making models

PROCEDURE

1. Work with a partner to choose a type of cell to model and to determine the types of organelles to include.
2. Using the poster board as a base, construct the model from available supplies. Make the model as accurate as you can.
3. Use a marker to label each organelle, and include a description of its function.
4. Compare your cell model with those made by your classmates.

MATERIALS
- craft supplies
- scissors
- glue
- poster board
- markers

TIME
30 minutes

WHAT DO YOU THINK?

- What are some of the limitations of using a model to represent a cell?
- What are some of the benefits of making a three dimensional model of a cell?

CHALLENGE Think of something to which you might compare the activities of a cell—perhaps the activities of a factory or a school. Add labels to your model to show how the comparison applies to each of the cell's structures.

INVESTIGATE Cell Models

PURPOSE To make models of cells and assess limitations of modeling

TIP *30 min.* Remind students that a model represents a real item but is not the same thing as the real item.

WHAT DO YOU THINK? *Sample answer: Actual cells are fully three-dimensional, full of activity, smaller, and perform functions. It is more like an actual cell than an entirely two-dimensional model such as an illustration.*

CHALLENGE *Answers will vary depending on models.*

R Datasheet, Cell Models, p. 41

Technology Resources

Customize this student lab as needed or look for an alternative. Print rubrics to assess student lab reports.

Lab Generator CD-ROM

Teaching with Technology

Use a digital camera to take virtual tours of student models. Use the video capability and macro setting. Display them in an album in the classroom.

EXPLORE the BIG idea

Revisit "Bits and Pieces" on p. 7. Have students explain their results.

Ongoing Assessment

Explain how cells, tissues, and organs are organized into organ systems.

Ask: What are the components of an organ system? *Specialized cells make up a tissue; tissues act together to form an organ; different organs serve a common function like digestion in an organ system.*

CHECK YOUR READING *Answer: the highest level; all characteristics associated with life*

DIFFERENTIATE INSTRUCTION

? More Reading Support

F What is the highest level of organization in a living thing? *the organism*

Inclusion Students who are literal thinkers, especially those with learning disabilities such as Asperger's syndrome or autism, may draw too many parallels between the cell models and real cells. Emphasize clear differences such as size, activity, function, detail, and shape.

History of Science

Rosalind Franklin (1920–1958)'s groundbreaking x-ray crystallography work provided information crucial to the model of DNA produced by James Watson and Francis Crick in 1953. Unfortunately, her contributions were not given their due weight by her peers at the time, and her early death at the age of 37 meant that when James Watson and Francis Crick won the Nobel Prize in 1962, they shared the prize with Franklin's colleague Maurice Wilkins instead of with Franklin herself, as the Nobel Prize can only be awarded to living people.

Reinforce the BIG idea

Have students relate the section to the Big Idea.

 Reinforcing Key Concepts, p. 42

1.3 ASSESS & RETEACH

Assess

 Section 1.3 Quiz, p. 5

Reteach

Put two graphic organizers on the board to summarize the section. Have students help you fill in a classification tree for Archaea, Eukarya, and Bacteria. Use a pyramid graphic to summarize the levels of organization.

Technology Resources

Have students visit **ClassZone.com** for reteaching of Key Concepts.

 CONTENT REVIEW

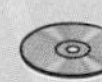 CONTENT REVIEW CD-ROM

Scientists use models to study cells.

Any drawing or photograph on a flat page is two-dimensional. In addition, diagrams of cells are often simplified to make them easier to understand. If you look at plant or animal cells under a microscope, you will notice some differences between real cells and the diagrams on page 22. In order to study cell structures and their functions, scientists use many types of models, including three-dimensional models. One of the most important discoveries in science involved the use of models.

Scientific Models

Scientists use several different types of models.

Watson and Crick used a model made from wire and tin.

DNA is the genetic material common to all cells. (You will read more about the structure and function of DNA later in this unit.) In the early 1950s, scientists had a good idea what DNA was made up of. The problem was that they could not figure out how all the pieces of the molecule fit together.

A scientist named Rosalind Franklin used x-rays to produce images of DNA. The x-ray provided an important clue as to the shape of the molecule. Two other scientists, James Watson and Francis Crick, were then able to put together a three-dimensional model of DNA and present it to the world in 1953.

Today's scientists have many different tools for making models. The images at the left show a computer model of DNA along with Watson and Crick's famous model.

1.3 Review

KEY CONCEPTS

1. What are the three domains, and what type of cells do the organisms in each domain have?
2. Define specialization in your own words.
3. Describe the levels of organization in a tree.

CRITICAL THINKING

4. **Synthesize** In what way does a specialized cell in a multicellular organism differ from the cell of a unicellular organism?
5. **Compare and Contrast** How is a model similar to the real object it represents? How is it different?

CHALLENGE

6. **Evaluate** The organism below is called *Chlamydomonas*. What domain does it belong to, and what do the internal structures tell you about it?

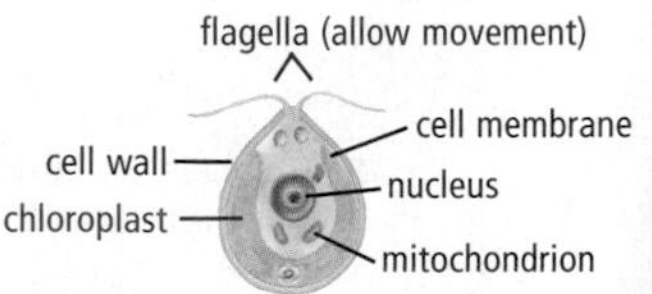

ANSWERS

1. Archaea and Bacteria have prokaryotic cells. Eukarya have eukaryotic cells.

2. Sample answer: when different cells perform different functions

3. A tree is an organism made of plant cells that form tissue. Different tissues work together to form an organ, the leaf. The organ system includes leaves, stems, and roots.

4. In a unicellular organism, one cell must do all the tasks required to keep the organism alive. A specialized cell does just one task.

5. A model represents a real object, but it is not the real object.

6. Eukarya; it can make its own food because it has a chloroplast.

SKILL: MAKING COMPARISONS

Cells and Spacesuits

What do a space suit and a unicellular organism have in common? Both have to support life. And both can support life in difficult environments. What are some of the similarities—and differences—between the cell body of a unicellular organism and a space suit that supports an astronaut in outer space?

Some Features of Spacesuits

FEATURE	FUNCTION
Strong outer material...	...protects the astronaut from space particles.
A special jet-propelled backpack...	...helps the astronaut move in the weightlessness of space.
Tanks of compressed air...	...provide oxygen for the astronaut to breathe.

Some Features of Cells

FEATURE	FUNCTION
Tail-like flagella on the outside of some cells...	...help cells move.
An outer membrane...	...keeps harmful particles out
Tiny openings in a cell's membrane...	...let oxygen move into the cell.

Make Comparisons

On Your Own Match each cell feature with a similar spacesuit feature. What characteristics do the cell and spacesuit have in common? What is one key difference?

As a Group Use your comparisons to make a Venn diagram.

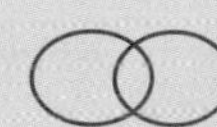

CHALLENGE An analogy uses a familiar thing to help explain or describe something new. Come up with your own analogies to describe the cell or some of its organelles.

flagella

This cell has flagella, which help it move.

THINK SCIENCE
Scientific Methods of Thinking

Set Learning Goal

To compare items that seem unlike by finding similarities as well as differences

Present the Science

Other functions that a spacesuit must perform include keeping the astronaut's environment at the right temperature and pressure. At the low atmospheric pressures in space, the astronaut's body fluids would boil. Since space has no atmosphere to filter sunlight, temperatures are also extreme: when an astronaut is outside the spacecraft, the side of the suit facing the Sun could be as hot as 120°C, while the side in darkness might be −155°C.

Guide the Activity

- Students might begin by matching functions, where the similarities are easiest to see.
- If students are unfamiliar with Venn diagrams, show them a sample one for reference with circles labeled as "Only Spacesuits," "Only Cells," and the overlapping area labeled "Both."

Close

Ask: What other functions does a cell perform that a spacesuit also must perform? *It gets rid of waste and allows materials (nutrients) to enter.*

ANSWERS

ON YOUR OWN *Strong outer material = an outer membrane; a special jet-propelled backpack = tail-like flagella on the outside of some cells; tanks of compressed air = tiny openings in cell membrane. The cell and spacesuits have similar needs—oxygen, protection, and movement. But the spacesuit comes with oxygen, while the cell gets its oxygen from its environment.*

AS A GROUP *cell: openings in cell membrane to allow oxygen in; spacesuit: tank of oxygen; both: structures for movement, outer covering for protection*

CHALLENGE *Sample answer: a factory, a city, a community, a ship, a planet*

BACK TO

the BIG idea

Ask: In what ways do cells exhibit the characteristics of living things? *consume energy to carry out complex activities, highly organized, move, grow, respond to their environment, and reproduce*

KEY CONCEPTS SUMMARY

SECTION 1.1

Ask: How is a car similar to and different from a living organism? *A car is made up of a number of parts that are organized into a system to perform complex activities. It consumes energy and moves around. Unlike a living thing, a car cannot respond to the environment, grow, or reproduce.*

SECTION 1.2

Ask: What details of a cell can be seen with an electron microscope that cannot be seen with a light microscope? *An electron microscope can show details of a cell's organelles.*

Ask: Name the three categories of organelles and list the organelles that belong to each. *information-processing organelles: nucleus, ribosomes; energy-providing organelles: chloroplasts, mitochondria; processing and transporting organelles: endoplasmic reticulum, vesicles, Golgi apparatus; storage, recycling, and waste-elimination organelles: vacuoles, lysosomes*

SECTION 1.3

Ask: How do organisms in Archaea domain differ from those in Bacteria domain? *They live in extreme environments in which bacteria could not survive, such as boiling hot thermal vents deep in the ocean, the extremely salty water of the Great Salt Lake.*

Ask: List the five levels of organization in multicellular organisms, in order from simplest to most complex. *cell, tissue, organ, organ system, organism*

Review Concepts

- Big Idea Flow Chart, p. T1
- Chapter Outline, pp. T7–T8

1 Chapter Review

the BIG idea

All living things are made up of cells.

KEY CONCEPTS SUMMARY

The cell is the basic unit of living things.

All living things are made up of one or more cells. **Organisms** share the following characteristics:

Multicellular organisms include this frog and these water-lily plants.

- organization
- ability to grow and develop
- ability to respond
- ability to reproduce

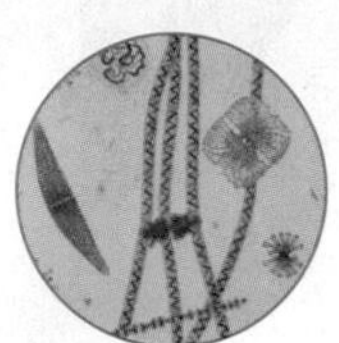

Many unicellular organisms live in pond water.

VOCABULARY
unicellular p. 11
multicellular p. 11
microscope p. 12
bacteria p. 14

Microscopes allow us to see inside the cell.

A **prokaryotic cell** is relatively simple in structure, with no nucleus or other organelles. A **eukaryotic cell** is more complex, with many different organelles inside it.

bacterium

A bacterium consists of a single prokaryotic cell.

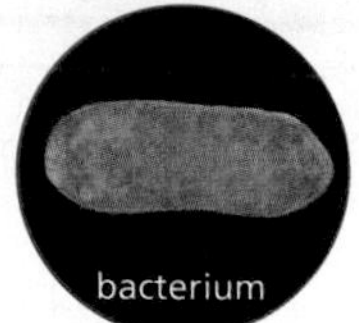

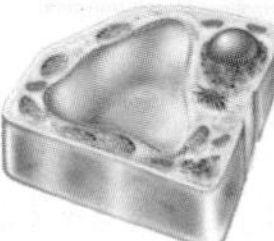

plant cell animal cell

Plants and animals are made up of many eukaryotic cells.

VOCABULARY
cell membrane p. 20
cytoplasm p. 20
nucleus p. 20
eukaryotic cell p. 20
prokaryotic cell p. 20
organelle p. 20
cell wall p. 21
chloroplast p. 23
mitochondria p. 23

Different cells perform various functions.

- The single cell of a unicellular organism does all that is necessary for the organism to survive.
- A multicellular organism is a community of **specialized** cells.
- Scientific models make it easier to understand cells.

tarsier

The tarsier has many levels of organization in its body.

VOCABULARY
specialization p. 28
tissue p. 29
organ p. 30

34 Unit 1: **Cells and Heredity**

Technology Resources

Have students visit **ClassZone.com** or use the CD-ROM for a cumulative review of concepts.

CONTENT REVIEW

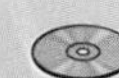

CONTENT REVIEW CD-ROM

Engage students in a whole-class interactive review of Key Concepts. Edit content as you wish.

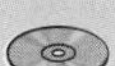

POWER PRESENTATIONS

Reviewing Vocabulary

1–5. *Use a vocabulary term to identify each numbered part of this plant cell.*

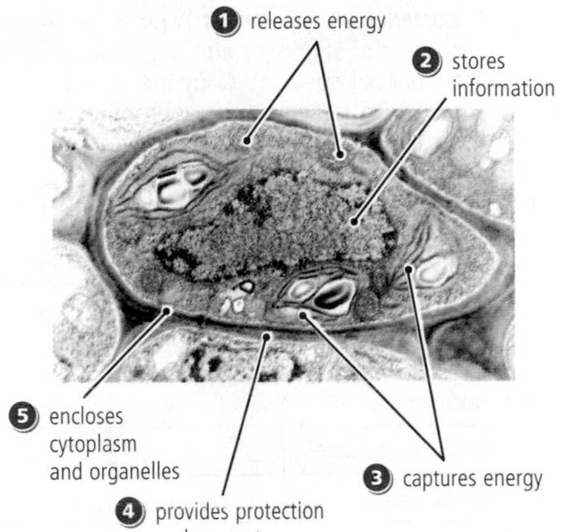

In one or two sentences, describe how the terms in each of the following pairs are related. Underline each term in your answer.

6. unicellular, multicellular

7. cell, organelle

8. prokaryotic cell, eukaryotic cell

9. tissue, organ

Reviewing Key Concepts

Multiple Choice *Choose the letter of the best answer.*

10. Which statement about cells is part of the cell theory?
- **a.** Cells are found in most living things.
- **b.** Cells with cell walls do not have cell membranes.
- **c.** All cells capture energy from sunlight.
- **d.** Cells come only from other living cells.

11. What structure does a plant cell have that is not found in an animal cell and that allows a plant cell to capture energy from the Sun?
- **a.** cell wall
- **b.** chloroplast
- **c.** mitochondrion
- **d.** central vacuole

12. Which technology was important to the development of the cell theory?
- **a.** computer
- **b.** scientific model
- **c.** microscope
- **d.** refrigeration

13. Organisms can be divided into domains on the basis of the characteristics of their cells. What are these domains?
- **a.** Archaea, Bacteria, and Eukarya
- **b.** prokaryotes and eukaryotes
- **c.** plants, animals, and bacteria
- **d.** unicellular and multicellular

14. A complex multicellular organism has different levels of organization. What is the order of these levels?
- **a.** cell membrane, cytoplasm, nucleus
- **b.** tissues, organs, organ systems
- **c.** tissues, organs, specialized cells
- **d.** cell membrane, organelles, nucleus

15. What is the function of the genetic material in a cell?
- **a.** provides transport of materials from the nucleus to the cell membrane
- **b.** breaks down materials brought into the cell
- **c.** provides information a cell needs to function and grow
- **d.** controls what comes into a cell and what goes out

Short Answer *Write a short answer to each question.*

16. What are four characteristics common to all living things?

17. What are three needs common to all living things?

ASSESSMENT RESOURCES

UNIT ASSESSMENT BOOK
- Chapter Test A, pp. 6–9
- Chapter Test B, pp. 10–13
- Chapter Test C, pp. 14–17
- Alternative Assessment, pp. 18–19

SPANISH ASSESSMENT BOOK
Spanish Chapter Test, pp. 1–4

Technology Resources

Edit test items and answer choices.

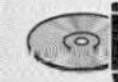

Test Generator CD-ROM

Visit **ClassZone.com** to extend test practice.

Test Practice

Reviewing Vocabulary

1. mitochondrion
2. nucleus
3. chloroplast
4. cell wall
5. cell membrane
6. Both describe how many cells an organism has. Unicellular organism: consists of a single cell; multicellular organism: made up of many cells
7. Cell is basic unit of life. Many cells have smaller structures called organelles.
8. Both refer to types of organisms. A prokaryote is an organism whose cells do not have a nucleus, whereas a eukaryote is an organism whose cells do have a nucleus.
9. A tissue is a group of similar cells that are specialized to do a particular function. An organ contains different types of tissues that work together to do a particular function.
10. d
11. b
12. c
13. a
14. b
15. c
16. All living things are made up of cells, they develop and grow, they respond to their environment, and they can reproduce.
17. All living things need energy, materials, and living space.

(Answers to items that appear on p. 36)

Thinking Critically

18. Fat cells provide insulation to keep the bears from freezing as they sleep and store energy-rich material.
19. Polar bears have muscles that enable them to move, a nervous system that allows them to respond to the environment to get food, a digestive system to break food down, a circulatory system that delivers food to the body, and a system to remove wastes.

(Answers to items 18 and 19 appear on p. 35.)

Thinking Critically

20. *The cells in both organisms need to support life. Bacterium: a single cell carries out all the functions needed for survival. Polar bear: fat cell is specialized. It works together with other cells to support life. Both have a cell membrane, but the bacterial cell is prokaryotic and the fat cell is eukaryotic.*
21. *All living things are made up of one or more cells. Cells carry out the functions needed to support life. Cells come only from other living cells. You are made up of many cells that carry out the functions you need to live, grow, and develop. The cells in your body came from a single living cell that divided many times. As you grew, cells specialized.*
22. *If bacteria can appear spontaneously, then they should appear in the broth of both flasks, whether or not the broth has been heated. If no bacteria appear in sterilized broth, that suggests heat has killed the living cells.*
23. *Bacteria will start to grow in the flask. These bacteria come from the air, into the broth.*
24. *Bacteria in the air will get into milk and cause it to spoil.*
25. *cytoplasm: animal, plant; nucleus: animal, plant; central vacuole: plant; chloroplast: plant; mitochondria: animal, plant*

the BIG idea

26. *Students should identify the nucleus or a mitochondrion or chloroplast. Light microscope; shows the whole cell*
27. *Sample answer: We wash our hands and face to remove germs. We generally keep everything cleaner. We pasteurize milk.*

UNIT PROJECTS

Give students the appropriate Unit Project worksheets. Both directions and rubrics can be used as a guide.

 Unit Projects, pp. 5–10

Thinking Critically

Questions 18–20 refer to polar bears and their cells as examples of animals and animal cells.

18. **PREDICT** Some polar bears go through long periods of sleep during the cold winter months. In what two ways might their fat cells help the bears survive during these periods?
19. **PROVIDE EXAMPLES** Animals do not get energy directly from the Sun as plants do. Give one or two examples of body systems in a polar bear that help it obtain and process food.
20. **COMPARE AND CONTRAST** Consider the fat cells in a polar bear and compare them with the single body cell of a bacterium. How are the cells alike, and how are they different?
21. **CONNECT** The cell theory applies to all organisms, including you. State the three parts of the cell theory and describe briefly how they relate to you.
22. **ANALYZE** Louis Pasteur designed the swan-necked flask to use in his experiments. In one experiment, he used two sealed flasks of nutrient broth. One flask he heated; the other he left untouched. Bacteria grew in the untouched flask. Nothing grew in the flask that had been heated, or sterilized. How did this experiment provide evidence against the theory of spontaneous generation?

23. **PREDICT** What would happen if the neck of the sterilized swan-necked flask were broken?
24. **IDENTIFY CAUSE** Why does pasteurized milk eventually spoil?
25. **COMPARE AND CONTRAST** A plant cell has a number of structures and organelles that an animal cell does not. Copy the table below and place a check in the appropriate box of each row. The first two are done for you.

	Animal Cell	Plant Cell
Cell wall		✓
Cell membrane	✓	✓
Cytoplasm		
Nucleus		
Central vacuole		
Chloroplast		
Mitochondrion		

the BIG idea

26. **CLASSIFY** Look again at the photograph on pages 6–7. Can you identify any of the structures shown? Can you identify the type of microscope used to make the photograph? How do you know?
27. **CONNECT** What are three ways that an understanding of cells has changed the way people live? **Hint:** Think about Pasteur and his work.

UNIT PROJECTS

If you are doing a unit project, make a folder for your project. Include in your folder a list of the resources you will need, the date on which the project is due, and a schedule to track your progress. Begin gathering data.

MONITOR AND RETEACH

If students are having difficulty answering questions 22–24, suggest that they review spontaneous generation on pp. 14–15 and the diagram of Pasteur's experiments on p. 15. Then have them create a two-column chart comparing conditions in the flask exposed to air with those in the sealed flask.

Students may benefit from summarizing one or more sections of the chapter.

 Summarizing the Chapter, pp. 69–70

Standardized Test Practice

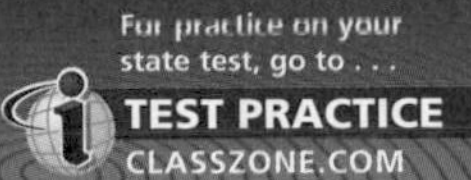

The Euglena Puzzle

Read the following description of euglenas and how scientists classify them. Then answer the questions below.

Plants and animals are typically multicellular organisms. For a long time, scientists tried to classify any unicellular organism that had a nucleus as either a single-celled plant or a single-celled animal. One group of unicellular organisms, *Euglenas,* was particularly difficult to classify. These tiny organisms can be found living in most ponds. What is puzzling about *Euglenas* is that they have characteristics of both plants and animals.

Some scientists argued that *Euglenas* are more like plants because many of them have chloroplasts. Chloroplasts are cellular structures that enable both plants and *Euglenas* to capture energy from the Sun. Other scientists argued that *Euglenas* are more like animals because they can take in food particles from the water. *Euglenas* also have flagella, tail-like structures that enable them to swim. The *Euglena* even has an eyespot for sensing light.

1. What cellular structures enable plants and *Euglenas* to capture energy from the Sun?
   a. flagella **c.** nuclei
   b. chloroplasts **d.** eyespots

2. What cellular structures are common to plants, animals, and *Euglenas*?
   a. flagella **c.** nuclei
   b. chloroplasts **d.** eyespots

3. In what way are *Euglenas* different from both plants and animals?
   a. They have no nuclei. **c.** They live in ponds.
   b. They are unicellular. **d.** They get energy from food.

4. What does an eyespot do?
   a. senses light **c.** provides energy
   b. captures food **d.** senses movement

5. Having flagella makes *Euglenas* similar to animals because it allows *Euglenas* to do what?
   a. eat food **c.** sense light
   b. get energy **d.** move about

Extended Response

Answer the following questions in detail. Include some of the terms in the word box. In your answers, underline each term you use.

sunlight	energy	food
eyespot	flagellum	move

6. A jar of water containing *Euglenas* is placed in a sunny window. After a while, a noticeable cloud forms in the water, near where the light shines into the water. Over the course of the day, the position of the Sun changes. As it does, the cloud keeps moving toward the light. On the basis of your reading, what do you think is happening and why?

7. Suppose there is a small pond near your school. The pond is surrounded by many tall trees that tend to block sunlight around the edges of the pond. In this situation, explain why it is an advantage for *Euglenas* to have the characteristics they do. Which of these characteristics do you associate with plants? with animals?

METACOGNITIVE ACTIVITY

Have students answer the following questions in their **Science Notebook:**

1. What study strategies can you use to help you review the chapter?
2. What concepts about cells were tricky or confused you?
3. What progress have you made on your Unit Project?

Analyzing Data

1. b 2. c 3. b 4. a 5. d

Extended Response

6. RUBRIC

4 points for a response that correctly answers the question and cites at least four details that describe the situation.

Sample answer: The cloud is a group of Euglenas *that are attracted to the light. They use the light to capture energy. A* Euglena *is able to sense the position of the Sun with its eyespot, and it can move using its flagellum.*

3 points for a response that correctly answers the question and cites three details that describe the situation
2 points for a response that correctly answers the question and cites two details that describe the situation
1 point for a response that correctly answers the question and cites one detail that describes the situation

7. RUBRIC

4 points for a response that demonstrates an understanding of how the characteristics of *Euglenas* contribute to their overall adaptation to this environment and cites three of *Euglenas'* animal-like and plantlike characteristics.

Sample answer: The trees block sunlight and keep the water dark. The fact that Euglenas *can get food from the water is an advantage if no sunlight is available. Because they have an eyespot that senses light and have a flagellum that allows them to swim, they can also move into an open area of the pond, where there is plenty of light. Then they get their energy directly from the light.*

3 points for a response that demonstrates an understanding of *Euglenas'* need to be able to move toward light and cites two of *Euglenas'* animal-like and plantlike characteristics
2 points for a response that demonstrates an understanding of *Euglenas'* need to be able to move toward light and cites one of *Euglenas'* animal-like and plantlike characteristics
1 point for a response that demonstrates an understanding of *Euglenas'* need to be able to move toward light but shows little understanding of *Euglenas'* animal-like and plantlike characteristics

CHAPTER

How Cells Function

Life Science UNIFYING PRINCIPLES

PRINCIPLE 1
All living things share common characteristics.

PRINCIPLE 2
All living things share common needs.

PRINCIPLE 3
Living things meet their needs through interactions with the environment.

PRINCIPLE 4
The types and numbers of living things change over time.

Unit 1: Cells and Heredity BIG IDEAS

CHAPTER 1
The Cell
All living things are made up of cells.

CHAPTER 2
How Cells Function
All cells need energy and materials for life processes.

CHAPTER 3
Cell Division
Organisms grow, reproduce, and maintain themselves through cell division.

CHAPTER 4
Patterns of Heredity
In sexual reproduction, genes are passed from parents to offspring in predictable patterns.

CHAPTER 5
DNA and Modern Genetics
DNA is a set of instructions for making cell parts.

CHAPTER 2 KEY CONCEPTS

SECTION 1

Chemical reactions take place inside cells.

1. All cells are made of the same elements.
2. Large molecules support cell function.
3. About two thirds of every cell is water.

SECTION 2

Cells capture and release energy.

1. All cells need energy.
2. Some cells capture light energy.
3. All cells release energy.

SECTION 3

Materials move across the cell's membranes.

1. Some materials move by diffusion.
2. Some transport requires energy.
3. Cell size affects transport.

T The Big Idea Flow Chart is available on p. T9 in the **UNIT TRANSPARENCY BOOK.**

Previewing Content

SECTION

Chemical reactions take place inside cells. pp. 41–46

1. All cells are made of the same elements.
There are about 100 elements; 25 of them are necessary for life. The smallest unit of an element is the atom. Atoms bond together in **chemical reactions** to form molecules.

2. Large molecules support cell function.
All large molecules in living things contain carbon. Carbon atoms can form long chains, leading to a huge number of possible compounds. There are four types of large molecules:

- **Carbohydrates** are sugar, starch, and cellulose. They provide cells with energy and structural support.
- **Lipids** are fats, oils, and waxes that cannot mix with water. Lipids often provide cells with energy.
- **Proteins** are made of smaller molecules—amino acids. Proteins control chemical reactions, support growth and repair of tissue, allow movement, fight infections, and deliver oxygen.
- **Nucleic acids** hold the instructions for maintenance, growth, and reproduction of the cell. The two types are DNA and RNA.

3. About two thirds of every cell is water.
A water molecule, which consists of two hydrogen atoms and one oxygen atom, is a polar molecule. Because its two sides have slightly different charges, water is an excellent solvent.

Cell membranes are composed of special lipids that have one end that repels water. Cell membranes have double layers of lipids. Both sides of a membrane have water-repellent ends facing out.

The cell membrane is made of a double layer of lipids.

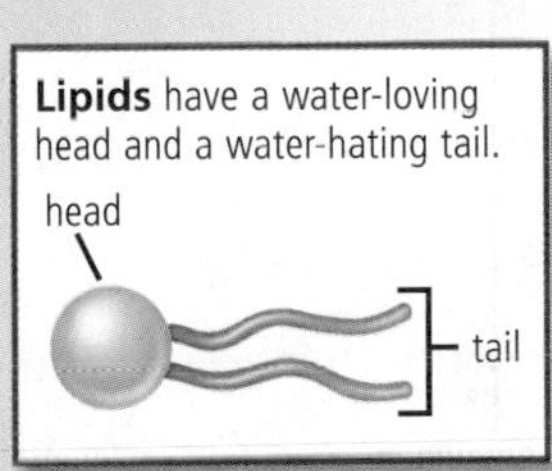

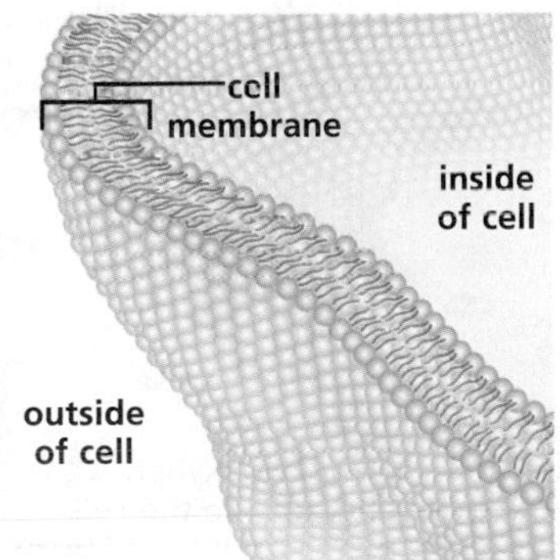
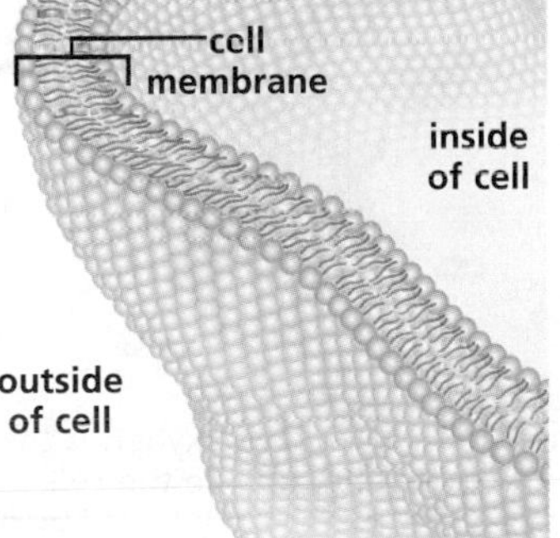

SECTION

Cells capture and release energy. pp. 47–55

1. All cells need energy.
Molecules store **chemical energy** in the bonds between their atoms. **Glucose** is the energy source for most cells.

2. Some cells capture light energy.
Plants capture light energy from the sun through **photosynthesis.** This process takes place in plant cells that have chloroplasts.
Plants take water from the soil and carbon dioxide from the air. In chloroplasts a pigment called **chlorophyll** absorbs light. The cell uses the energy to break water into hydrogen and oxygen. The freed hydrogen and the carbon dioxide from the air are combined to make glucose. Most of the oxygen from water is released into the air.

3. All cells release energy.
All cells, plant and animal, break down glucose for energy. In **cellular respiration,** the mitochondria in cells convert small glucose molecules into energy, carbon dioxide, and water. This process is the other half of the energy cycle.
Photosynthesis and cellular respiration are the two processes in the energy cycle, shown below.

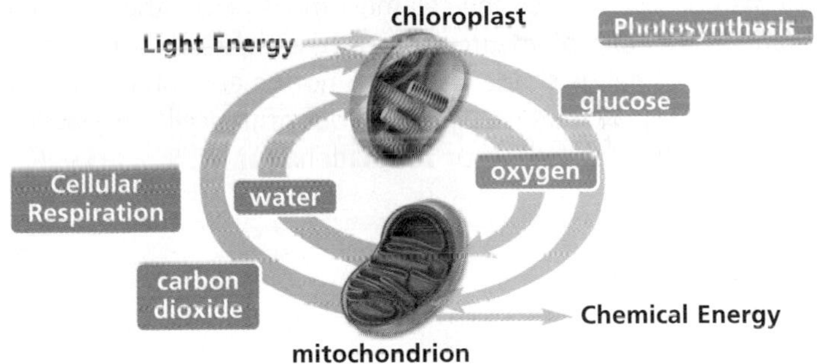

Fermentation allows cells to release energy without oxygen. It releases small amounts of energy and can produce either carbon dioxide and alcohol or lactic acid. When you run out of oxygen while exercising, your muscles use fermentation to break down sugar. This results in lactic-acid buildup, which makes muscles sore.

Common Misconceptions

MISCONCEPTION DATABASE
CLASSZONE.COM Background on student misconceptions

HIERARCHY OF ATOMS, MOLECULES, AND CELLS Students confuse cells and molecules and atoms. They are not sure, at this point, what comprises what, and often do not see a hierarchy. Cells are made of molecules, which are made of atoms.

 This misconception is addressed on p. 42.

CELLS IN NONLIVING THINGS Students may think that cells are the components of nonliving things, including carbohydrates and proteins, as well as living things.

TE This misconception is addressed on p. 44.

CELLULAR RESPIRATION Students commonly think that cellular respiration takes place in animal cells but not in plant cells. In fact, both plant and animal cells use cellular respiration to release stored energy.

 This misconception is addressed on p. 50.

Previewing Content

SECTION

Materials move across the cell's membranes. pp. 56–65

1. Some materials move by diffusion.
Diffusion occurs when molecules spread out until they are evenly mixed.
- Molecules move from a higher concentration to a lower one.
- Small molecules diffuse through membranes during **passive transport.**
- The diffusion of water through a membrane is called **osmosis.**

2. Some transport requires energy.
Cells use chemical energy for **active transport.** This type of transport is necessary for two purposes.
- Cells need to move materials from lesser concentrations to greater. Our kidneys use active transport to remove excess salt from our bodies.
- Cells need to move large molecules. Molecules move into the cell through endocytosis and out of it through exocytosis. In both cases, the cell membrane encloses the molecule in a pocket, pinches off the pocket, and moves it.

3. Cell size affects transport.
All materials needed by the cell must move across the cell membrane. If the ratio of volume to surface area is too large and the cell doesn't change shape, there will not be enough membrane area to transport materials into and out of the cell. Cells avoid this problem by one of three adaptations:
- staying small
- dividing
- changing shape

Materials move across a cell membrane continuously.

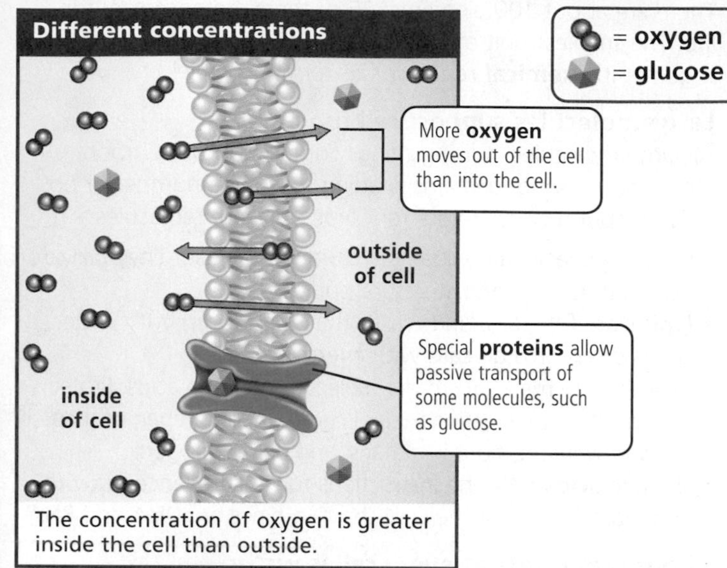

The concentration of oxygen is greater inside the cell than outside.

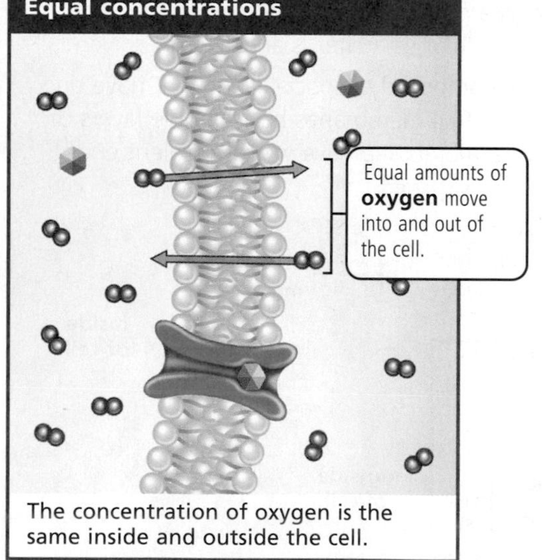

The concentration of oxygen is the same inside and outside the cell.

Common Misconceptions

THE PRIMACY OF DIFFUSION Students may think that a cell gets all it needs through diffusion. However, a cell also needs other transport mechanisms.

 This misconception is addressed on p. 61.

MISCONCEPTION DATABASE
CLASSZONE.COM Background on student misconceptions

Previewing Labs

Lab Generator CD-ROM
Edit these Pupil Edition labs and generate alternative labs.

EXPLORE the BIG idea

Leaves Underwater, p. 39 Students observe leaves in jars of water placed in sunlight to find that plants absorb water.	**TIME** 10 minutes, split by 2 hours for results to develop **MATERIALS** shallow dish, 2 leaves, 2 baby food jars, sinkful of water
Just a Spoonful of Sugar, p. 39 Students observe osmosis rates for raisins submerged in both sugar water and plain water.	**TIME** 10 minutes, split by 4 hours for results to develop **MATERIALS** 2 cups, 8 spoonfuls of sugar, several raisins, warm water
Internet Activity: Photosynthesis, p. 39 Students view plant cells to see how plants use sunlight and air to make sugar.	**TIME** 20 minutes **MATERIALS** computer with Internet access

SECTION 

EXPLORE Food Molecules, p. 41 Students research molecules in our food supply to find sources of protein, carbohydrates, and lipids.	**TIME** 10 minutes **MATERIALS** notebook, reference materials
INVESTIGATE Oil and Water, p. 44 Students mix water with oil and milk to observe that fat is not water-soluble.	**TIME** 10 minutes **MATERIALS** 5 drops vegetable oil, water, 5 drops milk, 3 beakers, 10 drops food coloring, stirring stick

SECTION 

INVESTIGATE Fermentation, p. 53 Students create a yeast-and-sugar solution to observe that fermentation produces gas.	**TIME** 30 minutes **MATERIALS** 1/2 teaspoon dry yeast, spoon, small water bottle, warm sugar solution (1 T sugar to 1 cup warm water), balloon

SECTION 

EXPLORE Diffusion, p. 56 Students observe food coloring diffusing in water.	**TIME** 10 minutes **MATERIALS** beaker, water, 3 drops food coloring
INVESTIGATE Cells, p. 62 Students model how surface area is related to a cell's ability to get resources.	**TIME** 30 minutes **MATERIALS** 2 hard-boiled peeled eggs, plastic knife, ruler, 100 mL water, glass beaker, 10 drops dark food coloring, eyedropper, spoon, paper towel
CHAPTER INVESTIGATION Diffusion, pp. 64–65 Students observe diffusion through plastic wrap to determine the effect of concentration on diffusion.	**TIME** 40 minutes **MATERIALS** eyedroppers, cornstarch solution (1 Tbsp cornstarch to 1 cup water), baby food jar with lid, plastic wrap, iodine solution [1 teaspoon of bottled iodine (available in drug stores) added to 1 cup of water], graduated cylinder

 **Additional INVESTIGATION,** Cells and Osmosis, A, B, & C, pp. 120–128; Teacher Instructions, pp. 308–309

Previewing Chapter Resources

CHAPTER 2
How Cells Function

INTEGRATED TECHNOLOGY

CLASSZONE.COM
- eEdition Plus
- EasyPlanner Plus
- Misconception Database
- Content Review
- Test Practice
- Visualizations
- Resource Centers
- Internet Activity: Photosynthesis
- Math Tutorial

SCILINKS.ORG

SCILINKS

CD-ROMS
- eEdition
- EasyPlanner
- Power Presentations
- Content Review
- Lab Generator
- Test Generator

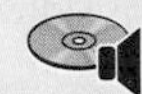

AUDIO CDS
- Audio Readings
- Audio Readings in Spanish

LABS AND ACTIVITIES

EXPLORE the Big Idea, p. 39
- Leaves Underwater
- Just a Spoonful of Sugar
- Internet Activity: Photosynthesis

UNIT RESOURCE BOOK
Unit Projects, pp. 5–10

Lab Generator CD-ROM
Generate customized labs.

SECTION

1 Chemical reactions take place inside cells.
pp. 41–46

Time: 2 periods (1 block)

 Lesson Plan, pp. 71–72

Integrated Technology

RESOURCE CENTER, Molecules

UNIT TRANSPARENCY BOOK
- Big Idea Flow Chart, p. T9
- Daily Vocabulary Scaffolding, p. T10
- Note-Taking Model, p. T11
- 3-Minute Warm-Up, p. T12

Labs and Activities

- EXPLORE Food Molecules, p. 41
- INVESTIGATE Oil and Water, p. 44
- Science on the Job, p. 46

UNIT RESOURCE BOOK
Datasheet, Oil and Water, p. 80

SECTION

2 Cells capture and release energy.
pp. 47–55

Time: 2 periods (1 block)

 Lesson Plan, pp. 82–83

Integrated Technology

MATH TUTORIAL

UNIT TRANSPARENCY BOOK
- Daily Vocabulary Scaffolding, p. T10
- 3-Minute Warm-Up, p. T12
- "Photosynthesis and Respiration Cycle" Visual, p. T14

Labs and Activities

- INVESTIGATE Fermentation, p. 53
- Math in Science, p. 55

UNIT RESOURCE BOOK
- Datasheet, Fermentation, p. 91
- Math Support, p. 109
- Math Practice, p. 110

SECTION

3 Materials move across the cell's membranes.
pp. 56–65

Time: 4 periods (2 blocks)

R Lesson Plan, pp. 93–94

Integrated Technology

- **RESOURCE CENTER,** Diffusion
- **VISUALIZATION,** Transport at Work

UNIT TRANSPARENCY BOOK
- Big Idea Flow Chart, p. T9
- Daily Vocabulary Scaffolding, p. T10
- 3-Minute Warm-Up, p. T13
- Chapter Outline, pp. T15–T16

Labs and Activities

- EXPLORE Diffusion, p. 56
- INVESTIGATE Cells, p. 62
- CHAPTER INVESTIGATION, Diffusion, pp. 64–65

UNIT RESOURCE BOOK
- Datasheet, Cells, p. 102
- Additional INVESTIGATION, Cells and Osmosis, A, B, & C, pp. 120–128
- CHAPTER INVESTIGATION, Diffusion, A, B, & C, pp. 111–119

KEY TO ICONS

 CD/CD-ROM

 Pupil Edition

INTERNET

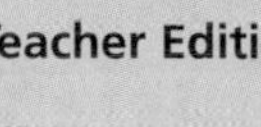 Teacher Edition

UNIT RESOURCE BOOK

UNIT TRANSPARENCY BOOK

UNIT ASSESSMENT BOOK

 SPANISH ASSESSMENT BOOK

SCIENCE TOOLKIT

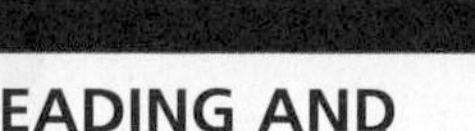

READING AND REINFORCEMENT

ASSESSMENT

STANDARDS

- Word Triangle, B18–19
- Outline, C43
- Daily Vocabulary Scaffolding, H1–8

UNIT RESOURCE BOOK
- Vocabulary Practice, pp. 106–107
- Decoding Support, p. 108
- Summarizing the Chapter, pp. 129–130

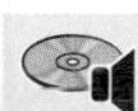

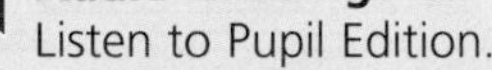

Audio Readings CD
Listen to Pupil Edition.

Audio Readings in Spanish CD
Listen to Pupil Edition in Spanish.

- Chapter Review, pp. 66–68
- Standardized Test Practice, p. 69

UNIT ASSESSMENT BOOK
- Diagnostic Test, pp. 20–21
- Chapter Test, A, B, & C, pp. 25–36
- Alternative Assessment, pp. 37–38

Spanish Chapter Test, pp. 5–8

Test Generator CD-ROM
Generate customized tests.

Lab Generator CD-ROM
Rubrics for Labs

National Standards
A.1–8, A.9.a–c, A.9.e–g, B.1.b–c, B.3.a, C.1.c, G.1.b

See p. 38 for the standards.

UNIT RESOURCE BOOK
- Reading Study Guide, A & B, pp. 73–76
- Spanish Reading Study Guide, pp. 77–78
- Challenge and Extension, p. 79
- Reinforcing Key Concepts, p. 81
- Challenge Reading, pp. 104–105

Ongoing Assessment, pp. 43–45

Section 2.1 Review, p. 45

UNIT ASSESSMENT BOOK
Section 2.1 Quiz, p. 22

National Standards
A.2–7, A.9.a–b, A.9.e–f, B.1.b–c, C.1.c, G.1.b

UNIT RESOURCE BOOK
- Reading Study Guide, A & B, pp. 84–87
- Spanish Reading Study Guide, pp. 88–89
- Challenge and Extension, p. 90
- Reinforcing Key Concepts, p. 92

Ongoing Assessment, pp. 48–53

Section 2.2 Review, p. 54

UNIT ASSESSMENT BOOK
Section 2.2 Quiz, p. 23

National Standards
A.2–8, A.9.a–c, A.9.e–f, B.3.a, C.1.c, G.1.b

UNIT RESOURCE BOOK
- Reading Study Guide, A & B, pp. 95–98
- Spanish Reading Study Guide, pp. 99–100
- Challenge and Extension, p. 101
- Reinforcing Key Concepts, p. 103

Ongoing Assessment, pp. 57–58, 60–61

Section 2.3 Review, p. 63

UNIT ASSESSMENT BOOK
Section 2.3 Quiz, p. 24

National Standards
A.1–7, A.9.a–b, A.9.e–g, C.1.c, G.1.b

Previewing Resources for Differentiated Instruction

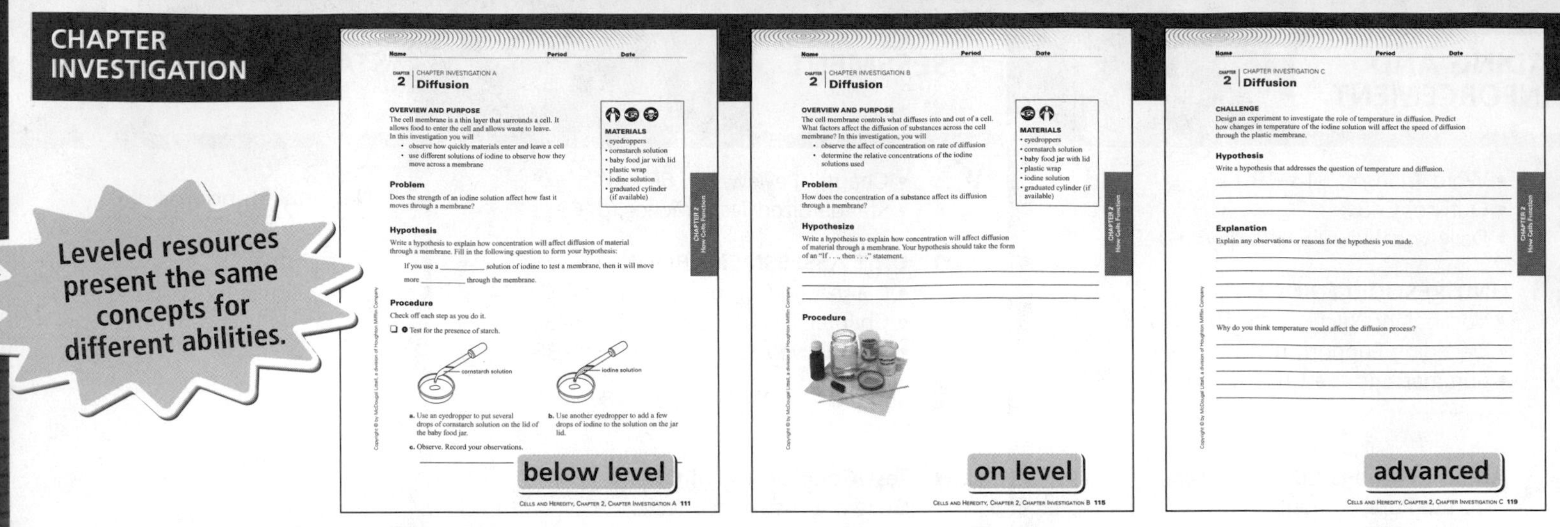

UNIT RESOURCE BOOK, pp. 111–114 | pp. 115–118 | pp. 115–119

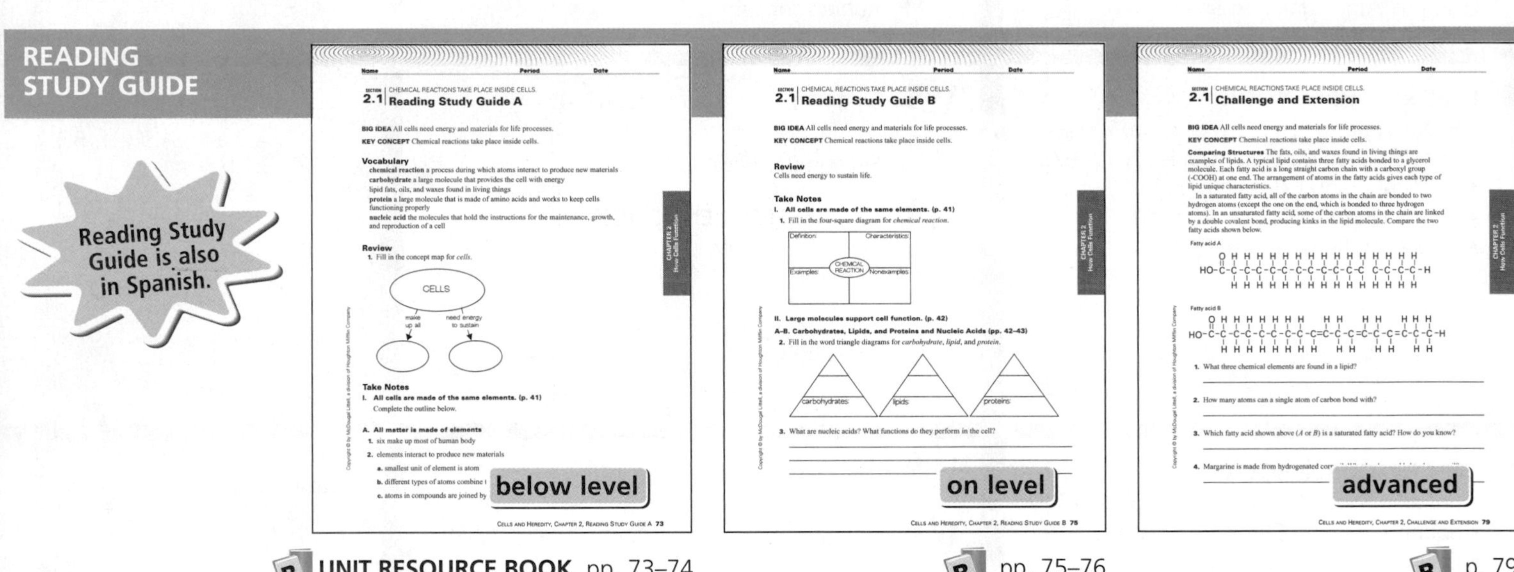

UNIT RESOURCE BOOK, pp. 73–74 | pp. 75–76 | p. 79

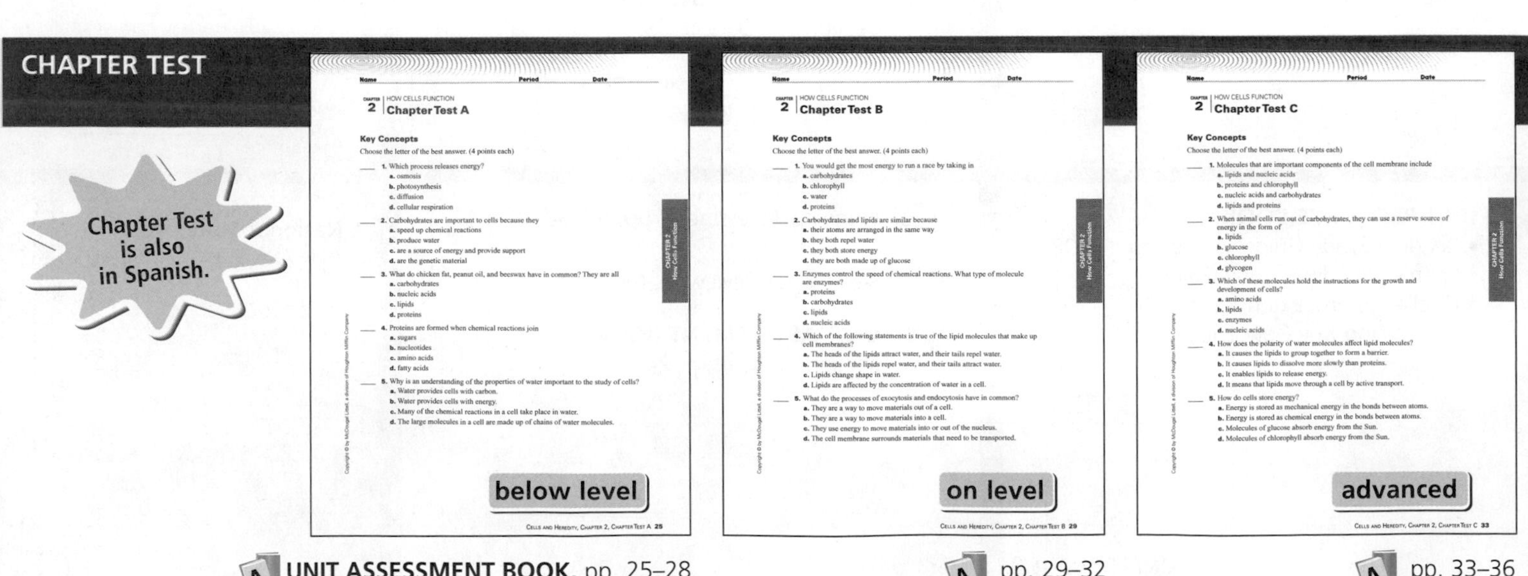

UNIT ASSESSMENT BOOK, pp. 25–28 | pp. 29–32 | pp. 33–36

TECHNOLOGY

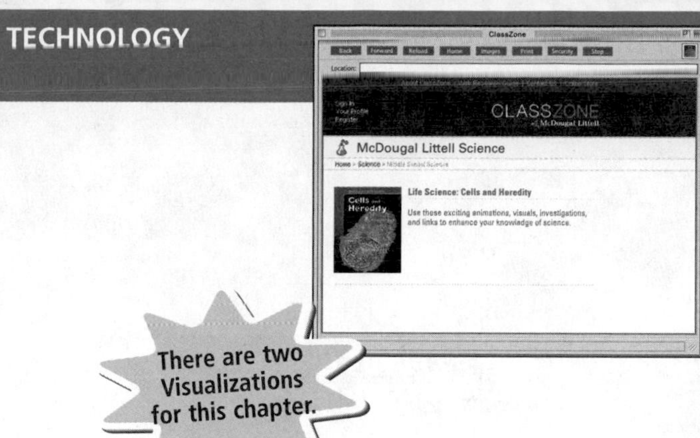

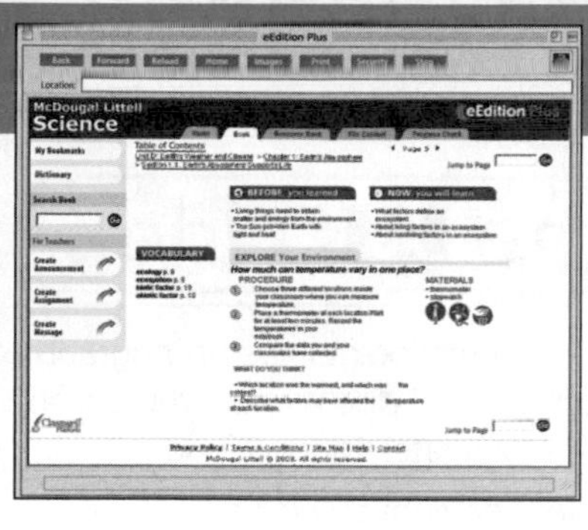

CLASSZONE.COM

CD/CD-ROMS

CLASSZONE.COM

VISUAL CONTENT

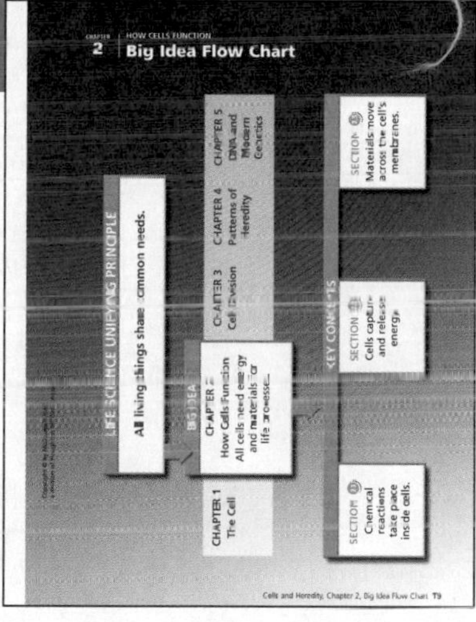

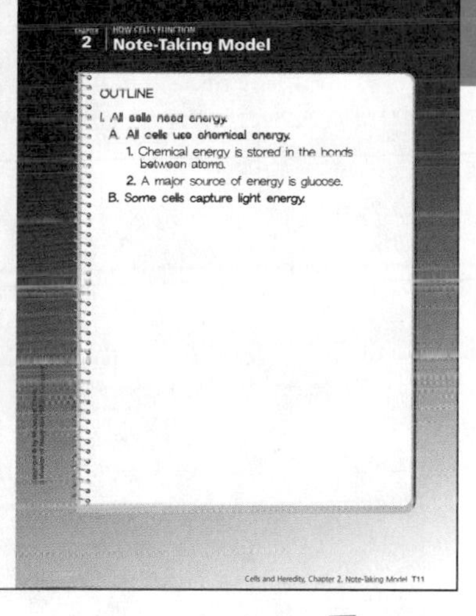

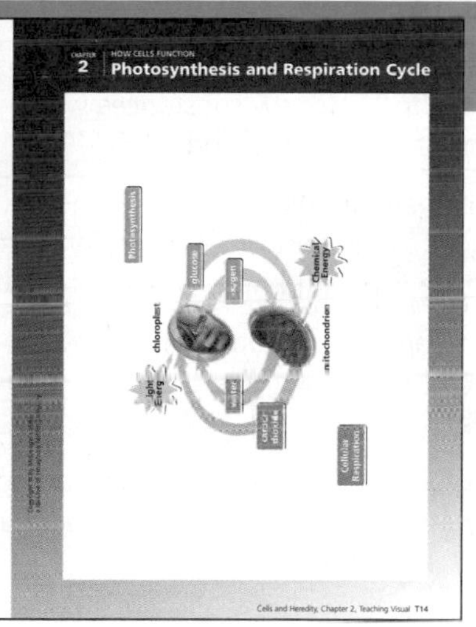

UNIT TRANSPARENCY BOOK, p. T9

p. T11

p. T14

MORE SUPPORT

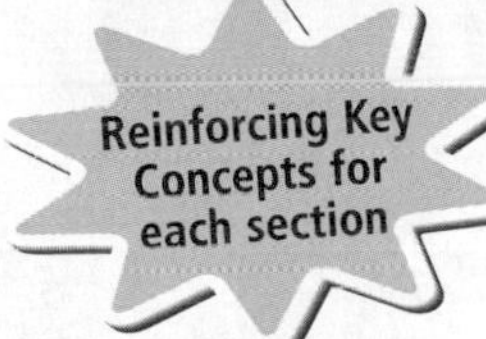

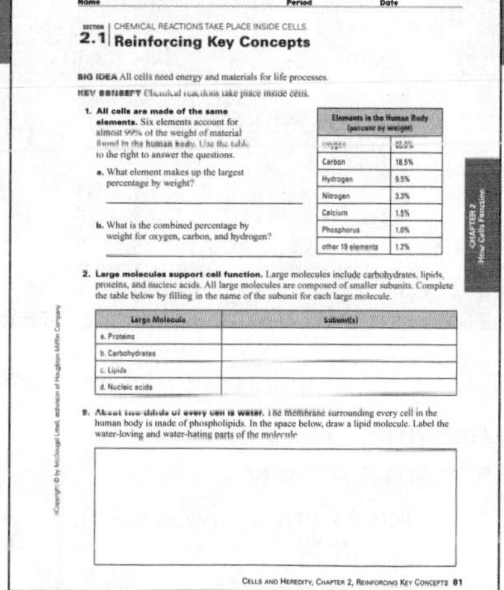

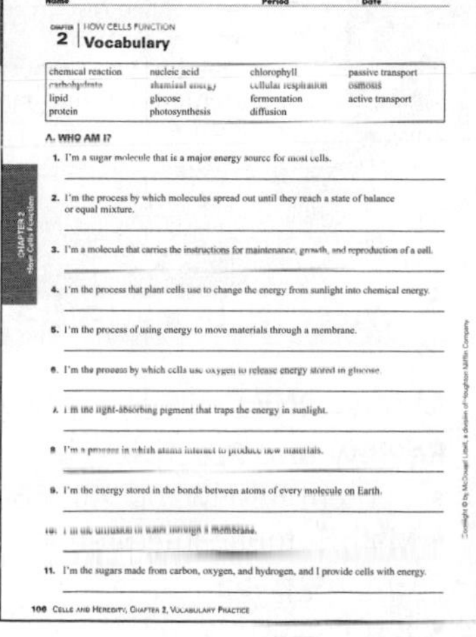

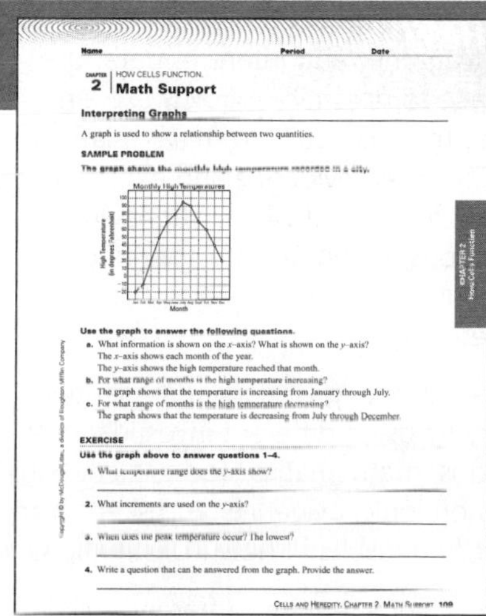

UNIT RESOURCE BOOK, p. 81

pp. 106–107

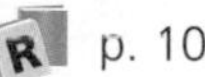
p. 109

CHAPTER 2 How Cells Function

INTRODUCE

the BIG idea

Have students look at the photograph of sunflowers and discuss how the question in the box relates to the Big Idea. Ask:

- How do sunflowers use energy?
- How do sunflowers get the materials to grow from seeds to tall stalks?

National Science Education Standards

Content

B.1.b Substances react with other substances to form new substances with different characteristic properties.

B.1.c There are more than 100 known elements that combine in many ways to produce living and nonliving substances.

B.3.a Energy is a property of many substances. Energy is transferred in many ways.

C.1.c Cells perform the functions of life. They grow and divide. This requires that they take in nutrients.

Process

A.1–8 Identify questions that can be answered by scientific investigation. Design and conduct an investigation; use tools to gather and interpret data; use evidence to describe, predict, explain, model; think critically to make relationships between evidence and explanation; recognize different explanations and predictions; communicate scientific procedures and explanations; use mathematics.

A.9.a–c, A.9.e–g Understand scientific inquiry by using different investigations, methods, mathematics, and explanations based on logic, evidence, and skepticism. Data often results in new investigations.

G.1.b Science requires different abilities.

CHAPTER 2 How Cells Function

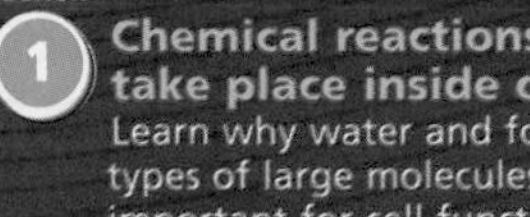

All cells need energy and materials for life processes.

How do plants like these sunflowers change energy from the Sun?

Key Concepts

SECTION

Chemical reactions take place inside cells. Learn why water and four types of large molecules are important for cell functions.

SECTION

Cells capture and release energy. Learn about the process of photosynthesis and the two ways cells release energy.

SECTION

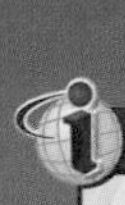

Materials move across the cell's membranes. Learn about the different ways materials move through cells.

Internet Preview

CLASSZONE.COM

Chapter 2 online resources: Content Review, two Visualizations, two Resource Centers, Math Tutorial, and Test Practice.

INTERNET PREVIEW

CLASSZONE.COM For student use with the following pages:

Review and Practice
- Content Review, pp. 40, 66
- Math Tutorial: Interpreting Graphs, p. 55
- Test Practice, p. 69

Activities and Resources
- Internet Activity, p. 39
- Resource Centers: Molecules, p. 42; Diffusion, p. 57
- Visualization: Transport at Work, p. 60

Photosynthesis
Code: MDL032

Leaves Underwater

Put a dish, two plant leaves, and two baby food jars in a sink full of water. Fill one jar with water and both leaves, then turn the jar upside down on the dish. Fill the other jar with just water and do the same. Remove your set-up from the sink and place it in sunlight for two hours.

Observe and Think What happened in the jars? Why do you think these things happened?

Just a Spoonful of Sugar

Pour a little warm water into each of two cups. Stir eight spoonfuls of sugar into one of the cups. Drop several raisins into each cup and wait for six hours. After six hours, compare the raisins in each cup.

Observe and Think How are the raisins different? How would you explain your observation?

Internet Activity: Photosynthesis

Go to **ClassZone.com** to examine how plants use sunlight to make sugar molecules.

Observe and Think What are the starting materials of photosynthesis? What are the products?

NSTA scilinks.org SCILINKS
Photosynthesis **Code: MDL032**

TEACHING WITH TECHNOLOGY

Digital Camera If you have access to a digital camera, you might photograph the changes that occur during the investigations on p. 53 and p. 62. Have students post the lab on a school Web site or class site, using the photographs to illustrate it.

PC Microscope If you have access to a PC microscope, have students use it to look at cells as they complete the investigation on p. 62. Separate onion layers with tweezers and put them on slides or use prepared slides.

EXPLORE the BIG idea

These inquiry-based activities are appropriate for use at home or as a supplement to classroom instruction.

Leaves Underwater

PURPOSE To observe that leaves absorb water. Students observe leaves in jars of water in the sunlight.

TIPS *10 min.* Setup and analysis time are about 5 minutes each, with a period of 2 hours for results to develop. Hold the plate over the filled jar, and then flip the jar and plate together. You may want to use two dishes, one for each jar.

Answer: The water level is lower in the jar with leaves. The leaves have bubbles on them, because they are producing gas.

REVISIT after p. 63.

Just a Spoonful of Sugar

PURPOSE To model osmosis. Students observe raisins submerged in both sugar water and plain water.

TIP *10 min.* Setup and analysis time are about 10 minutes, with a period of 6 hours for results to develop.

Answer: The raisins in the plain water are plumper. More plain water moved into the raisins because plain water and raisins contain very different concentrations of sugar.

REVISIT after p. 57.

Internet Activity: Photosynthesis

PURPOSE To observe how plants use sunlight to make sugar molecules for energy.

TIP *20 min.* If students are using a classroom computer, have them work in pairs.

Answer: carbon dioxide and water; glucose and oxygen

REVISIT after p. 49.

PREPARE

CONCEPT REVIEW

Activate Prior Knowledge

Display a potted plant and have students examine the leaves and stems with a hand lens. Ask:

How are plant and animal cells similar and different? *They have similar structures, but only plant cells have cell walls and chloroplasts.*

Point out that all living things—and only living things—are made up of cells, and that each cell is itself a living thing.

TAKING NOTES

Outline

Remind students to use the blue headings and red subheadings as they take notes in their outlines.

- For summarizing text in their own words, it may help students to work in pairs. If they summarize concepts orally before they write them down, they will learn to find their own wording.
- Encourage students to add examples or contexts from their own experience or knowledge to the details of the outline. Check that their additions are accurate.

Vocabulary Strategy

A word triangle requires students to stack information in a pattern that will enhance their memory. Drawing a picture at the top of the stack expresses the information in a way that uses their visual memory.

Vocabulary and Note-Taking Resources

- Vocabulary Practice, pp. 106–107
- Decoding Support, p. 108

- Daily Vocabulary Scaffolding, p. T10
- Note-Taking Model, p. T11

- Word Triangle, B18–19
- Outline, C43
- Daily Vocabulary Scaffolding, H1–8

CHAPTER 2

Getting Ready to Learn

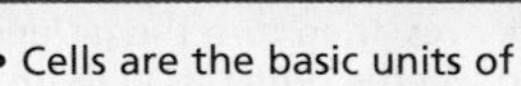

CONCEPT REVIEW

- Cells are the basic units of living things.
- Some cells have organelles that perform special functions for the cell.
- Animal cells and plant cells have similar structures, but plant cells have cell walls and chloroplasts.

VOCABULARY REVIEW

cell membrane, p. 20
organelle, p. 20
chloroplast, p. 23
mitochondria, p. 23

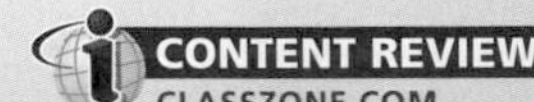

CONTENT REVIEW
CLASSZONE.COM
Review concepts and vocabulary.

TAKING NOTES

OUTLINE

As you read, copy the headings on your paper in the form of an outline. Then add notes in your own words that summarize what you read.

VOCABULARY STRATEGY

Draw a **word triangle** diagram for each new vocabulary term. On the bottom line, write and define the term. Above that, write a sentence that uses the term correctly. At the top, draw a small picture to show what the term looks like.

See the Note-Taking Handbook on pages R45–R51.

SCIENCE NOTEBOOK

OUTLINE

I. ALL CELLS ARE MADE OF THE SAME ELEMENTS.
  A. ALL MATTER IS MADE OF ELEMENTS.
    1. 6 make up most of human body
    2. elements interact to produce new materials
      a. smallest unit of element is atom

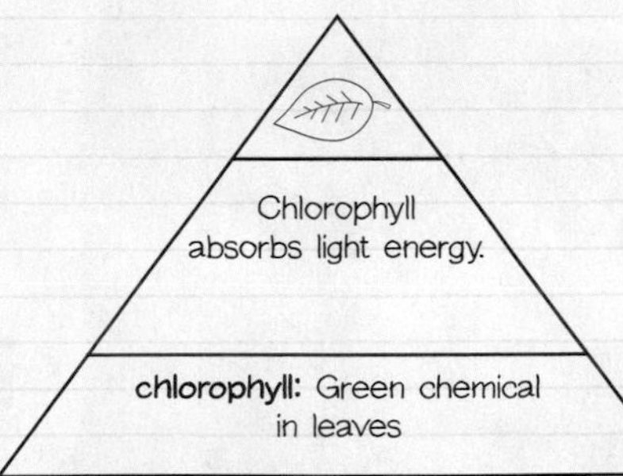

CHECK READINESS

Administer the Diagnostic Test to determine students' readiness for new science content and their mastery of requisite math skills.

 Diagnostic Test, pp. 20–21

Technology Resources

Students needing content and math skills should visit **ClassZone.com**.

- CONTENT REVIEW
- MATH TUTORIAL

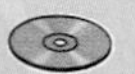 CONTENT REVIEW CD-ROM

KEY CONCEPT

Chemical reactions take place inside cells.

BEFORE, you learned

- All living things are made of cells
- Cells need energy to sustain life
- Plant and animal cells have similarities and differences

NOW, you will learn

- About the types of elements found in all cells
- About the functions of large molecules in the cell
- Why water is important to the activities of the cell

VOCABULARY

chemical reaction p. 42
carbohydrate p. 42
lipid p. 43
protein p. 43
nucleic acid p. 43

EXPLORE Food Molecules

How are different types of molecules important in your everyday life?

PROCEDURE

1. Examine the foods shown in the photograph. Protein, carbohydrates, and lipids (fats) are important substances in the food you eat. Locate at least one source of protein, carbohydrates, and lipids in the food.
2. Use your textbook and additional resource materials to find out a little more about these molecules in our food supply.

MATERIALS

- notebook
- reference materials

WHAT DO YOU THINK?

What foods do you eat that supply protein, carbohydrates, and lipids?

OUTLINE

Continue the outline begun on page 40.

I. Main idea
  A. Supporting idea
    1. Detail
    2. Detail
  B. Supporting idea

All cells are made of the same elements.

The microscope allowed people to observe the tiny cells that make up all living things. Even smaller, too small for a light microscope to show, is the matter that makes up the cell itself.

All matter in the universe—living and nonliving—can be broken down into basic substances called elements. About a hundred different elements are found on Earth. Each element has its own set of properties and characteristics. For example, the characteristics of oxygen include that it is colorless, odorless, and on Earth, it exists in the form of a gas.

2.1 FOCUS

Set Learning Goals

Students will

- Describe the functions of large molecules in the cell.
- Describe the types of molecules found in all cells.
- Explain why water is important to the activities of the cell.
- Observe solubility of fats in an experiment.

3-Minute Warm-Up

Display Transparency 12 or copy this exercise on the board:

Write whether each statement is true for animal cells, plant cells, or both.

1. They need energy to sustain life. *both*
2. They have organelles. *both*
3. They have cell walls. *plant cells*

 3-Minute Warm-Up, p. T12

2.1 MOTIVATE

EXPLORE Food Molecules

PURPOSE To research the foods that provide the proteins, carbohydrates, and lipid molecules that nourish cells

TIP *10 min.* Many nutrition or diet books and Web sites give the number of grams of protein, fat, and carbohydrates in common foods.

WHAT DO YOU THINK? *Meat, fish, eggs, cheese, some beans provide protein; bread, pasta, potatoes, crackers provide carbohydrates; oils provide lipids.*

History of Science

Robert Hooke coined the word *cell* in 1665 for the walled spaces he saw in cork under a microscope. He described similar structures in the tissues of trees and plants.

RESOURCES FOR DIFFERENTIATED INSTRUCTION

Below Level

UNIT RESOURCE BOOK

- Reading Study Guide A, pp. 73–74
- Decoding Support, p. 108

 **AUDIO CDS**

Advanced

UNIT RESOURCE BOOK

- Challenge and Extension, p. 79
- Challenge Reading, pp. 104–105

English Learners

UNIT RESOURCE BOOK

Spanish Reading Study Guide, pp. 77–78

 **AUDIO CDS**

- Audio Readings in Spanish
- Audio Readings (English)

2.1 INSTRUCT

Address Misconceptions

IDENTIFY Ask: Rank the following from simplest to most complex: *cell, atom, molecule.* If students order them incorrectly, they may be confused about what makes up cells and molecules.

CORRECT Have students use a dictionary or encyclopedia to find definitions of the three concepts. Ask them to draw what the three might look like. Students should use arrows to show progression from simplest to most complex. Ask: What is water? *a molecule* What atoms make up water? *hydrogen and oxygen* Describe how water is related to cells. *All cells contain water.*

REASSESS Have students devise their own graphic organizer that shows the relationships among cells, atoms, and molecules. Students might use concentric circles, a "pyramid," an umbrella, tree, or flow chart, or might show sketches as models. Their organizers should indicate a hierarchy with *cells* overarching *molecules* overarching *atoms*.

Technology Resources

Visit **ClassZone.com** for background on common student misconceptions.

MISCONCEPTION DATABASE

Integrate the Sciences

Carbon is widely distributed in nature and is well known in its elemental form as diamond, coal, graphite, and charcoal. Carbon compounds are vital to living things, and there is almost an infinite number of them due to carbon's ability to form chains and rings.

Social Studies Connection

The U.S. government subsidizes corn crops, so high fructose corn syrup is cheap. Estimates are that Americans consume about 9 percent of their daily calories in the form of fructose. Corn syrup has few nutrients. Studies indicate that it increases cholesterol in the blood.

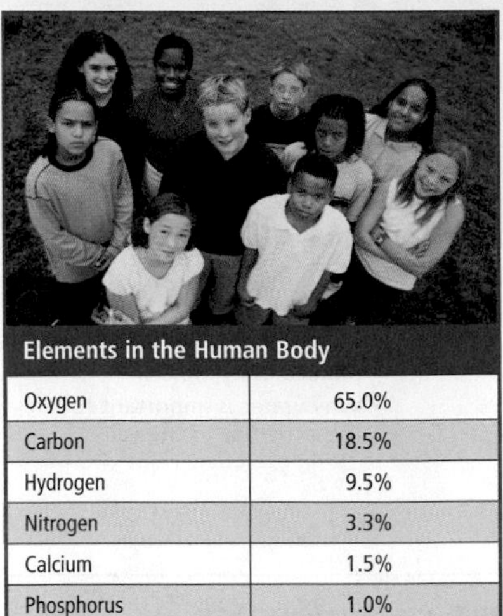

Elements in the Human Body

Oxygen	65.0%
Carbon	18.5%
Hydrogen	9.5%
Nitrogen	3.3%
Calcium	1.5%
Phosphorus	1.0%
other 19 elements	1.2%

Source: CRC Handbook of Chemistry and Physics

Of all the elements found on Earth, about 25 are essential for life. As you can see from the table, just 6 elements account for about 99 percent of the mass of the human body. But very little of this matter exists as pure elements. Instead, most is in the form of compounds, which are substances made up of two or more different elements. For example, water is a compound made of hydrogen and oxygen.

The smallest unit of any element is called an atom. In a compound, atoms of two or more elements are joined together by chemical bonds. Most compounds in cells are made up of atoms bonded together in molecules. For example, a molecule of water is made of one atom of oxygen bonded to two atoms of hydrogen. ? A

Most activities that take place within cells involve atoms and molecules interacting. In this process, called a **chemical reaction,** bonds between atoms are broken and new bonds form to make different molecules. Energy is needed to break bonds between atoms, and energy is released when new bonds form. Cells use chemical energy for life activities.

Large molecules support cell function.

RESOURCE CENTER
CLASSZONE.COM
Explore molecules in living things.

In living things, there are four main types of large molecules: (1) carbohydrates, (2) lipids, (3) proteins, and (4) nucleic acids. Thousands of these molecules work together in a cell. The four types of molecules in all living things share one important characteristic. They all contain carbon atoms. These large molecules are made up of smaller parts called subunits.

Carbohydrates

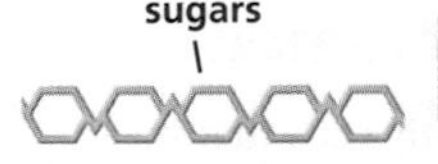

Carbohydrates are used for structure and energy storage. Carbohydrates, such as cellulose, are made of **sugars.**

Carbohydrates (KAHR-boh-HY-DRAYTS) provide the cell with energy. Simple carbohydrates are sugars made from atoms of carbon, oxygen, and hydrogen. Inside cells, sugar molecules are broken down. This process provides usable energy for the cell.

Simple sugar molecules can also be linked into long chains to form more complex carbohydrates, such as starch, cellulose, and glycogen. Starch and cellulose are complex carbohydrates made by plant cells. When a plant cell makes more sugar than it can use, extra sugar molecules are stored in long chains called starch. Plants also make cellulose, which is the material that makes up the cell wall. Animals get their energy by eating plants or other animals that eat plants.

DIFFERENTIATE INSTRUCTION

More Reading Support

A What is the smallest unit of any element? *an atom*

B What provides the cell with energy? *carbohydrates*

English Learners Have English learners write the definitions for *element, atom, molecule, chemical reaction, carbohydrate, lipid, protein,* and *nucleic acid* in their Science Word Dictionaries.

This section has a variety of introductory clauses and phrases. For example, "Of all the elements found on Earth, about 25 are essential for life" (p. 42). Have students find the comma that separates the introductory clause or phrase from the rest of the sentence. Then, help them locate the subject of the sentence.

Lipids

Lipids are the fats, oils, and waxes found in living things. Like carbohydrates, simple lipids are made of atoms of carbon, oxygen, and hydrogen and can be used by cells for energy and for making structures. However, the atoms in all lipids are arranged differently from the atoms in carbohydrates. Many common lipids consist of a molecule called glycerol bonded to long chains of carbon and hydrogen atoms called fatty acids. This structure gives lipids unique properties. One extremely important property of lipids is that they cannot mix with water.

glycerol

fatty acids

Lipids make up the membranes surrounding the cell and organelles. Lipids are made of **fatty acids** and **glycerol.**

 How do cells use carbohydrates and lipids?

Proteins

Proteins are made of smaller molecules called amino acids. Amino acids contain the elements carbon, oxygen, hydrogen, nitrogen, and sometimes sulfur. In proteins, amino acids are linked together into long chains that fold into three-dimensional shapes. The structure and function of a protein is determined by the type, number, and order of the amino acids in it.

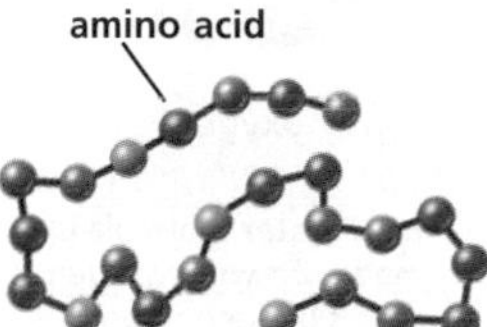

Proteins are made up of **amino acids.** Proteins carry out most of the chemical activity in cells.

Your body gets amino acids from protein in food, such as meat, eggs, cheese, and some beans. After taking in amino acids, your cells use them to build proteins needed for proper cell functioning. Some amino acids can be made by the body, but others must be taken in from an outside food source.

There are many types of proteins. Enzymes are proteins that control chemical reactions in the cells. Other proteins support the growth and repair of living matter. The action of proteins in your muscles allows you to move. Some of the proteins in your blood fight infections. Another protein in your blood delivers oxygen to all the cells in your body. Proteins are also important parts of cell membranes. Some proteins in the cell membrane transport materials into and out of the cell.

Nucleic Acids

Nucleic acids (noo-KLEE-ihk) are the molecules that hold the instructions for the maintenance, growth, and reproduction of a cell. There are two types of nucleic acids: DNA and RNA. Both DNA and RNA are made from carbon, oxygen, hydrogen, nitrogen, and phosphorus. The subunits of nucleic acids are called nucleotides.

DNA provides the information used by the cell for making proteins a cell needs. This information takes the form of a code contained in the specific order of different nucleotides in the DNA.

nucleotide

Nucleic acids store and translate the genetic information a cell needs to function. Nucleic acids, such as DNA, are made up of **nucleotides.**

DIFFERENTIATE INSTRUCTION

 **More Reading Support**

C What are the large molecules that make up fats and oils? *lipids*

D What molecules are made up of amino acids? *proteins*

Below Level Using pipe cleaners and table-tennis balls, plastic building blocks, or other materials, have students build models of the four large molecules shown on pp. 42–43.

Teach from Visuals

To help students interpret the illustrations of large molecules, ask:

- Why are parts of the illustration shaped and colored differently? *They represent molecules that are joined to make up a larger molecule.*
- How accurate do you think these illustrations are? *They are not accurate representations but rough approximations that differentiate the types of molecules visually.*
- How is a visual model of something that may be too small to see accurately—even with technology—helpful? *The visual model helps people understand how molecules react to each other and how they function in the cell.*

Metacognitive Strategy

Have students brainstorm strategies for testing their knowledge of large molecules.

Teach Difficult Concepts

Students may incorrectly think that the visual model of the molecule denotes the actual shape of the molecule. Explain to them that the picture is only to show how molecules bond; the bonds they make can actually give rise to different shapes for the same molecule.

Ongoing Assessment

Describe the functions of large molecules in the cell.

Ask: What large molecules provide energy? *carbohydrates and lipids*

 *Answer: for energy and structural support*

Real World Example

DNA fingerprinting is a method of isolating and making images of DNA. Since DNA fingerprinting was introduced in 1984, it has been used for researching genetic diseases, solving crimes, and determining paternity.

INVESTIGATE Oil and Water

PURPOSE To observe that fat is not water soluble

TIPS *10 min.* Tell students not to ingest the oil. Use extra droppers to control drops added to water.

WHAT DO YOU THINK? *When combined, oil and water separate into distinct layers. Milk and water mix. Oil and water do not mix because oil is made from lipids. Milk, mostly water, mixes.*

CHALLENGE *Lipids act as a barrier.*

 Datasheet, Oil and Water, p. 80

Technology Resources

Customize this student lab as needed or look for an alternative. Print rubrics to assess student lab reports.

 **Lab Generator CD-ROM**

Address Misconceptions

IDENTIFY Ask: What are the building blocks of proteins? If students answer "cells," they may think that cells can be components of nonliving compounds.

CORRECT Remind them that cells grow and reproduce. Proteins are built of molecules. Cells are alive; atoms and molecules are not.

REASSESS Ask: What is the smallest possible living thing? *a cell*

Technology Resources

Visit **ClassZone.com** for background on common student misconceptions.

 **MISCONCEPTION DATABASE**

Ongoing Assessment

Describe the types of molecules found in all cells.

Ask: What molecules do all cells have? *water and large molecules*

 *Answer: hold instructions for maintenance, growth, and reproduction of cells*

The pattern of nucleotides in DNA is then coded into RNA, which delivers the information into the cytoplasm. Other RNA molecules in the cytoplasm produce the proteins.

 What is the function of DNA and RNA?

About two thirds of every cell is water.

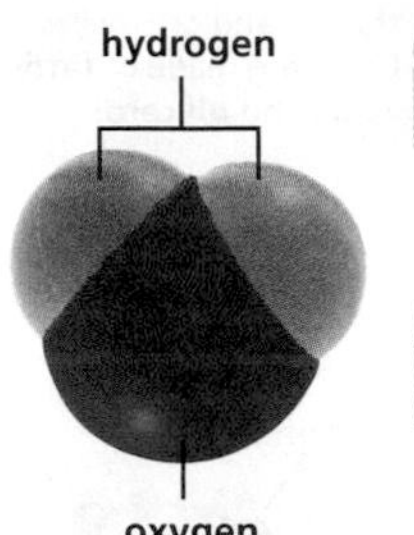

Each **water** molecule is made of two **hydrogen** atoms bonded to one **oxygen** atom.

E All of the chemical reactions inside the cell take place in water. Water is also in the environment outside the cell. For example, water inside cells makes up about 46 percent of your body's mass, and water outside the cells in body fluids accounts for another 23 percent.

F A water molecule consists of two atoms of hydrogen bonded to one atom of oxygen. Because of its structure, a water molecule has a slight positive charge near the hydrogen atoms and a slight negative charge near the oxygen atom. Molecules that have slightly charged ends are said to be polar. Like a magnet, the ends of a polar molecule attract opposite charges and repel charges that are the same. Because water is a polar molecule, many substances dissolve in water. However, not all materials dissolve in water. If you have ever shaken a bottle of salad dressing, you've probably observed that oil and water don't mix.

INVESTIGATE Oil and Water

What happens when you combine oil and water?

PROCEDURE

1. Put a small amount of oil into one beaker and an equal amount of milk into another.
2. Put water into a third beaker and add enough food coloring to make the water darkly colored.
3. Add equal amounts of the colored water to the beaker of oil and the beaker of milk. Stir the liquids to mix them. Record your observations.

WHAT DO YOU THINK?

- Compare and contrast the behavior of the mixture of oil and water with that of the mixture of milk and water.
- Why does a mixture of oil and water behave differently from a mixture of milk and water?

CHALLENGE The outside of a cell is surrounded by water. Explain how the water-hating nature of lipids can keep a cell's inside separated from its outside.

SKILL FOCUS
Observing

MATERIALS
- vegetable oil
- milk
- water
- 3 beakers
- food coloring
- stirring stick

TIME
10 minutes

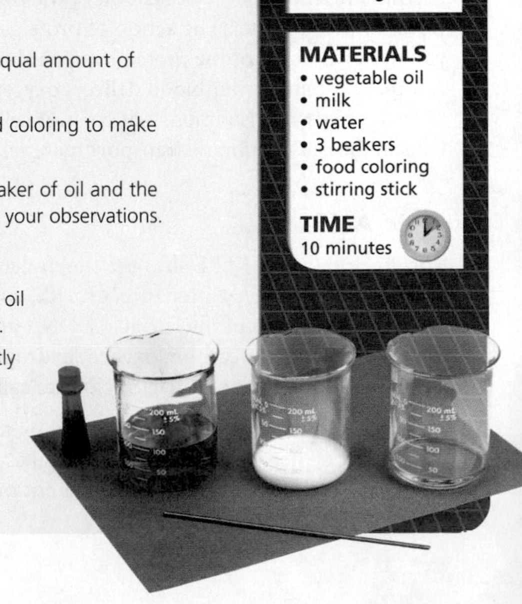

DIFFERENTIATE INSTRUCTION

More Reading Support

E Where do the chemical reactions of a cell take place? *in water*

F What two elements are in water? *hydrogen and oxygen*

Advanced Have students research the science behind low-carbohydrate diets and explain why these diets might lower blood cholesterol more than a low-fat diet would.

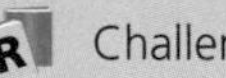 Challenge and Extension, p. 79

Have interested students read more about low-fat fat substitutes.

 Challenge Reading, pp. 104–105

Cell Membrane

The cell membrane is made of a double layer of lipids.

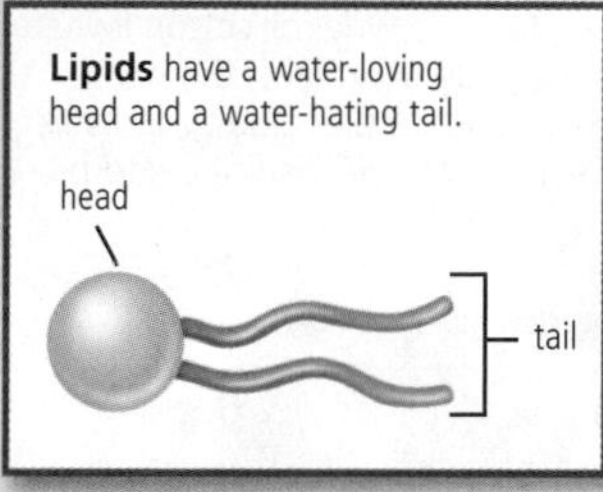

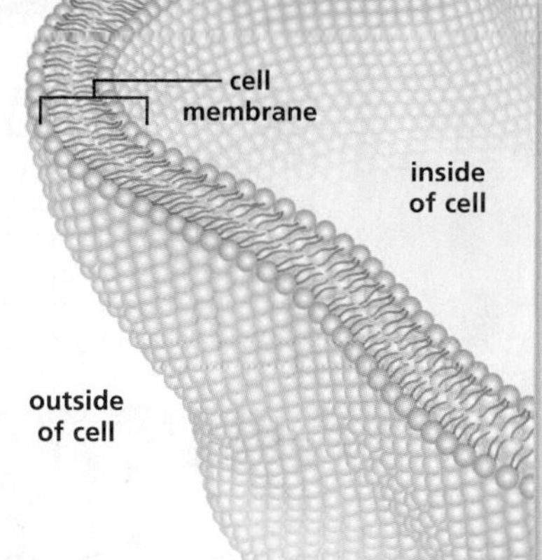

Most lipids do not dissolve in water. A special type of lipid is the major molecule that makes up cell membranes. These special lipid molecules have two parts: a water-loving head and two water-hating tails. In other words, the head of the lipid molecule is polar, while the tails are nonpolar.

Why is it important that cell membranes contain lipids? Remember that cell membranes function as boundaries. That is, they separate the inside of a cell from the outside. Most of the material inside and outside the cell is water. As you can see in the diagram above, the water-hating tails in the lipids repel the water while the head clings to water.

READING TIP

As you read about the properties of cell, notice the arrangements of lipids in the diagram of the cell.

2.1 Review

KEY CONCEPTS

1. Explain how just a few elements can make up all living things.
2. What functions do proteins, carbohydrates, lipids, and nucleic acids perform?
3. What does it mean to describe water molecules as being polar?

CRITICAL THINKING

4. **Compare and Contrast** How are carbohydrates and lipids similar? How are they different?
5. **Draw Conclusions** What do the major types of molecules that make up living things have in common?

CHALLENGE

6. **Model** Some people have compared the nucleic acids DNA and RNA to a blueprint for life. How are DNA and RNA like blueprints? How are they different?

ANSWERS

1. A few types of atoms can combine in various ways to form many different compounds.

2. Proteins control chemical reactions and support cell growth and repair. Lipids and carbohydrates provide energy and structure. Nucleic acids contain instructions for cell reproduction.

3. They have slightly charged ends, one positive and one negative.

4. Both contain carbon, oxygen, and hydrogen and provide energy/structure. Lipids do not dissolve in water, carbohydrates do.

5. They all contain carbon atoms.

6. Blueprints are plans for constructing something, such as a building. RNA and DNA are like a plan for living things. People create and use blueprints. Cells produce and use RNA and DNA.

Teach from Visuals

To help students interpret the diagram of the cell membrane, ask:

- What is a cell membrane made of? *lipids*
- What effect does the double layer of lipids have in cell membranes? *They separate the inside of the cell from the outside of the cell.*

Ongoing Assessment

Explain why water is important to the activities of the cell.

Ask: What fluid makes up most of a cell? *water*

Reinforce the BIG idea

Have students relate the section to the Big Idea.

 Reinforcing Key Concepts, p. 81

2.1 ASSESS & RETEACH

Assess

 Section 2.1 Quiz, p. 22

Reteach

Have students list the foods that are available in the cafeteria. Compile a class list on the board. Be sure to include liquids such as milk, juice, and water. Ask students which foods have the most large molecules of protein, fat, or carbohydrates. Also discuss water content. Discuss how these large molecules and water molecules support the cell.

Technology Resources

Have students visit **ClassZone.com** for reteaching of Key Concepts.

 CONTENT REVIEW

 CONTENT REVIEW CD-ROM

SCIENCE ON THE JOB
Relevance of Science to Non-science Jobs

Purpose
To recognize that textile designers use organic and chemical compounds

Present the Science
Direct dyes can be used on plant, or cellulose, fibers such as cotton, flax, ramie, and rayon. If you applied a direct dye to a protein, or animal, fiber such as silk or wool, you would not get a fast color—the dye would fade or run when washed. You must first treat animal fibers with a mordant, then dye them.

Discussion Questions
- Describe the difference between plant and animal fibers and give examples. *Plant fibers are mostly cellulose and have thick cell walls; examples are cotton, linen, and rayon. Animal fibers are mainly made of protein and have thinner cell walls; examples are silk and wool.*
- How do dyes bond with fibers? *molecule to molecule*
- What is a mordant? *a color fixer*

Close
Ask: What kind of information about fibers and dyes do textile designers need to know? *A fiber's origins are key to the properties it has and how it reacts to different dyes and processes.*

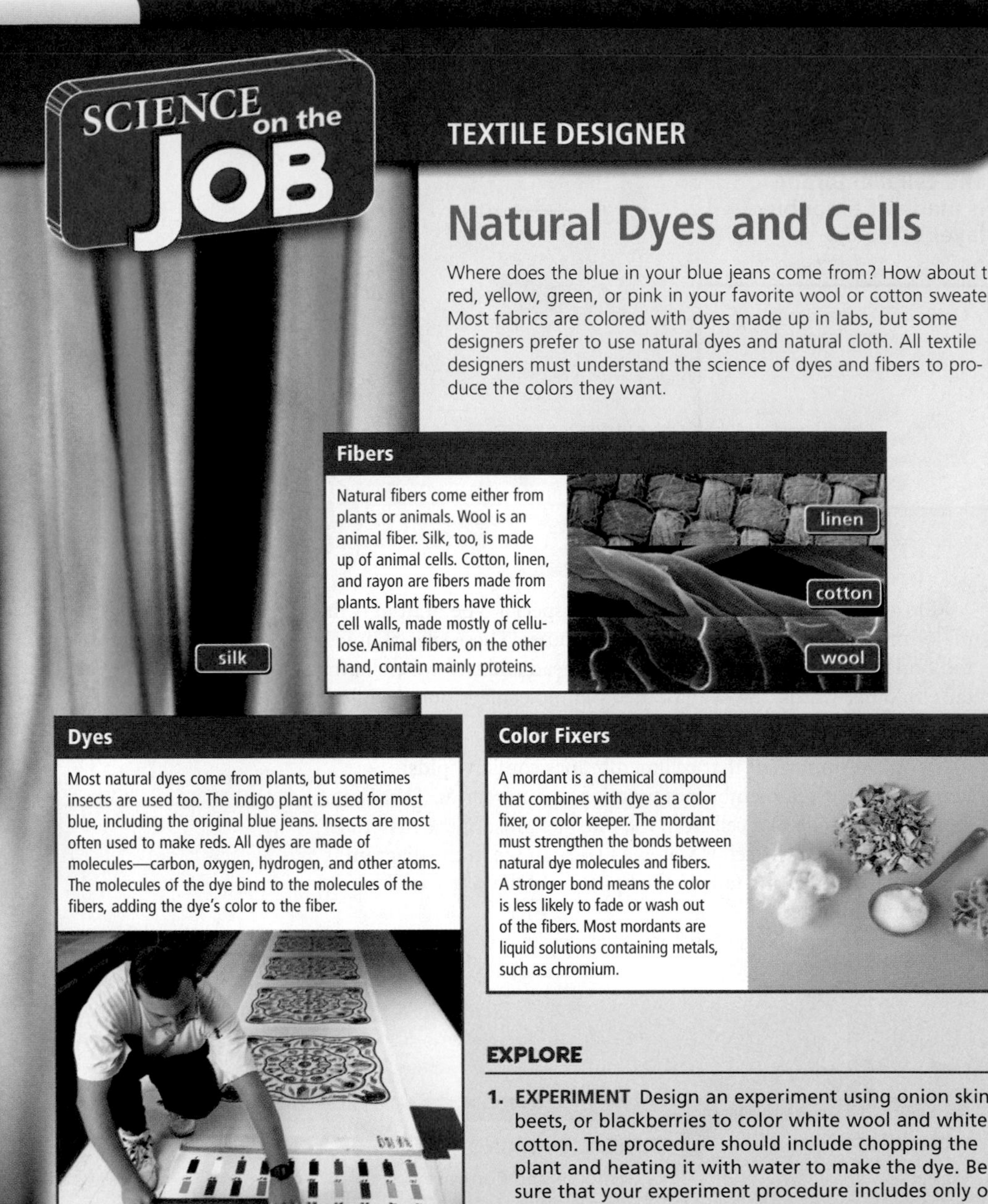

TEXTILE DESIGNER

Natural Dyes and Cells

Where does the blue in your blue jeans come from? How about the red, yellow, green, or pink in your favorite wool or cotton sweater? Most fabrics are colored with dyes made up in labs, but some designers prefer to use natural dyes and natural cloth. All textile designers must understand the science of dyes and fibers to produce the colors they want.

Fibers
Natural fibers come either from plants or animals. Wool is an animal fiber. Silk, too, is made up of animal cells. Cotton, linen, and rayon are fibers made from plants. Plant fibers have thick cell walls, made mostly of cellulose. Animal fibers, on the other hand, contain mainly proteins.

Dyes
Most natural dyes come from plants, but sometimes insects are used too. The indigo plant is used for most blue, including the original blue jeans. Insects are most often used to make reds. All dyes are made of molecules—carbon, oxygen, hydrogen, and other atoms. The molecules of the dye bind to the molecules of the fibers, adding the dye's color to the fiber.

Color Fixers
A mordant is a chemical compound that combines with dye as a color fixer, or color keeper. The mordant must strengthen the bonds between natural dye molecules and fibers. A stronger bond means the color is less likely to fade or wash out of the fibers. Most mordants are liquid solutions containing metals, such as chromium.

EXPLORE
1. **EXPERIMENT** Design an experiment using onion skins, beets, or blackberries to color white wool and white cotton. The procedure should include chopping the plant and heating it with water to make the dye. Be sure that your experiment procedure includes only one variable. Your experiment should start with a question, such as How do the dyes differ? Or Which dye works best?
2. **CHALLENGE** Using different mordants with the same dye can give different colors. For example, dandelion leaf dye gives yellow-green, gray-green, tan, or gold with different mordants. Explain why this happens.

46 Unit 1: Cells and Heredity

EXPLORE
1. ***EXPERIMENT*** *Students should include a question and appropriate hypothesis. The procedure should be clear and controlled. Check that the procedure tests the hypothesis. Check that the procedure follows proper safety guidelines such as using rubber gloves and safety goggles.*
2. ***CHALLENGE*** *Different mordants make different chemical bonds with the dye, producing different colors.*

KEY CONCEPT

Cells capture and release energy.

BEFORE, you learned

- The cell is the basic unit of all living things
- Plant cells and animal cells have similarities and differences
- Plants and animals need energy and materials

NOW, you will learn

- Why cells need energy
- How energy is captured and stored
- How plants and animals get energy

VOCABULARY

chemical energy p. 47
glucose p. 47
photosynthesis p. 48
chlorophyll p. 48
cellular respiration p. 50
fermentation p. 52

THINK ABOUT

What do these cells have in common?

Both muscle cells and plant cells need energy to live. Your muscle cells need energy to help you move and perform other functions. Even though plant cells don't move in the same way that muscles move, they still need energy. How do human muscle cells and plant cells get energy?

OUTLINE
Remember to include this heading in your outline of this section.

I. Main idea
A. Supporting idea
1. Detail
2. Detail
B. Supporting idea

All cells need energy.

To stay alive, cells need a constant supply of energy. Animal cells get energy from food, while plant cells get energy from sunlight. All cells use chemical energy. **Chemical energy** is the energy stored in the bonds between atoms of every molecule. To stay alive, cells must be able to release the chemical energy in the bonds.

A major energy source for most cells is stored in a sugar molecule called **glucose.** When you need energy, cells release chemical energy from glucose. You need food energy to run, walk, and even during sleep. Your cells use energy from food to carry out all of their activities.

Think about muscle cells. When you run, muscle cells release chemical energy from glucose to move your legs. The more you run, the more glucose your muscle cells need. You eat food to restore the glucose supply in muscles. But how do plant cells get more glucose? Plants transform the energy in sunlight into the chemical energy in glucose.

2.2 FOCUS

Set Learning Goals

Students will

- Explain why cells need energy.
- Summarize how energy is captured and stored.
- Describe how plants and animals get energy.
- Observe in an experiment that fermentation produces gas.

3-Minute Warm-Up

Display Transparency 12 or copy this exercise on the board:

Begin a web diagram with the word *cell* in the middle bubble. Branch off with *plant cell* and *animal cell.* Add what you know to each bubble. *Plant cell: has a cell wall, has a nucleus, specialized, photosynthesizes; Animal cell: has a cell membrane, has a nucleus, specialized, does not photosynthesize, processes large molecules.*

 3-Minute Warm-Up, p. T12

2.2 MOTIVATE

THINK ABOUT

PURPOSE To understand what all cells have in common

DISCUSS Have students look at the cell pictures. Ask: These cells look very different. What is similar about them? *They need energy to function.*

RESOURCES FOR DIFFERENTIATED INSTRUCTION

Below Level

UNIT RESOURCE BOOK
- Reading Study Guide A, pp. 84–85
- Decoding Support, p. 108

AUDIO CDS

Advanced

UNIT RESOURCE BOOK
Challenge and Extension, p. 90

English Learners

UNIT RESOURCE BOOK
Spanish Reading Study Guide, pp. 88–89

AUDIO CDS

- Audio Readings in Spanish
- Audio Readings (English)

2.2 INSTRUCT

Real World Example

In addition to capturing energy, photosynthesis helps control the composition of Earth's atmosphere. It removes carbon dioxide and produces oxygen. Rainforests, in particular, serve as carbon sinks, helping to clean up atmospheric pollution, much of which is carbon dioxide. Scientists have considered planting more trees to serve as carbon sinks, especially species that grow faster in high levels of carbon dioxide.

Ongoing Assessment

Explain why cells need energy.

Ask: Why do cells need energy? *to stay alive and to do work*

Summarize how energy is captured and stored.

Ask: How do plant cells capture and store energy? *They capture the energy in sunlight with chlorophyll. With this energy they can turn carbon dioxide and water into glucose, which contains chemical energy that cells can use. Plants store glucose in large carbohydrates called starch.*

CHECK YOUR READING *Sample answer: In photosynthesis plants use energy from sunlight to change carbon dioxide and water into glucose and oxygen.*

Some cells capture light energy.

The source of energy for almost all organisms ultimately comes from sunlight. Plants change the energy in sunlight into a form of energy their cells can use—the chemical energy in glucose. All animals benefit from the ability of plants to convert sunlight to food energy. Animals either eat plants, or they eat other animals that have eaten plants.

A **Photosynthesis** (FOH-toh-SIHN-thih-sihs) is the process that plant cells use to change the energy from sunlight into chemical energy. Photosynthesis takes place in plant cells that have chloroplasts. Chloroplasts contain **chlorophyll** (KLAWR-uh-fihl), a light-absorbing pigment, or colored substance, that traps the energy in sunlight.

The process of photosynthesis involves a series of chemical steps, or reactions. The illustration on the next page shows an overview of how photosynthesis changes starting materials into new products.

READING TIP
As you read each numbered item here, find the number on the diagram on page 49.

1. **The starting materials** of photosynthesis are carbon dioxide and water. The plant takes in carbon dioxide from the air and water from the soil.
2. **The process** takes place when carbon dioxide and water enter the plant's chloroplasts. Chlorophyll captures energy from sunlight, which is used to change carbon dioxide and water into new products.
3. B **The products** of photosynthesis are oxygen and sugars such as glucose. The plant releases most of the oxygen to the air as a waste product and keeps the glucose for its energy needs.

CHECK YOUR READING Summarize photosynthesis. Remember that a summary includes only the most important information.

Plants do not immediately use all of the glucose they make. Some of the glucose molecules are linked together to build large carbohydrates called starch. Plants can store starch and later break it back down into glucose or other sugars when they need energy. Sugars and starches supply food for animals that eat plants.

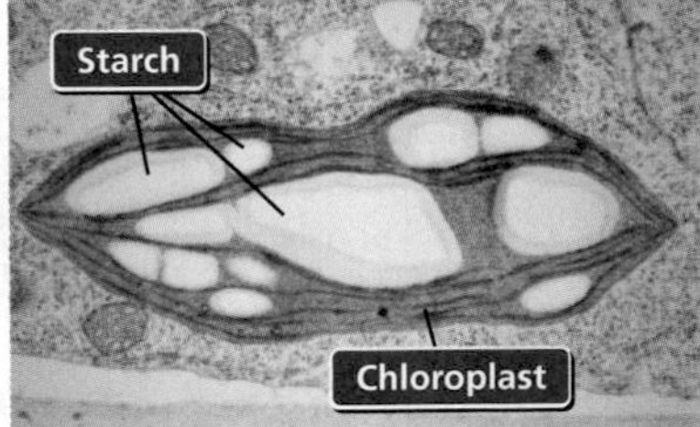

The starch in this plant cell stores energy.

DIFFERENTIATE INSTRUCTION

More Reading Support

A What is photosynthesis? *the process by which plant cells change sunlight to chemical energy*

B What substance is the power source for cells? *glucose*

English Learners Help English learners understand the multiple meanings of words used in this section, such as *material(s), process, product(s), energy,* and *bonds.* Students can draw a sketch to illustrate both meanings, once they have been explained. Knowing the second (everyday) meaning will reinforce understanding of the science meaning.

Photosynthesis

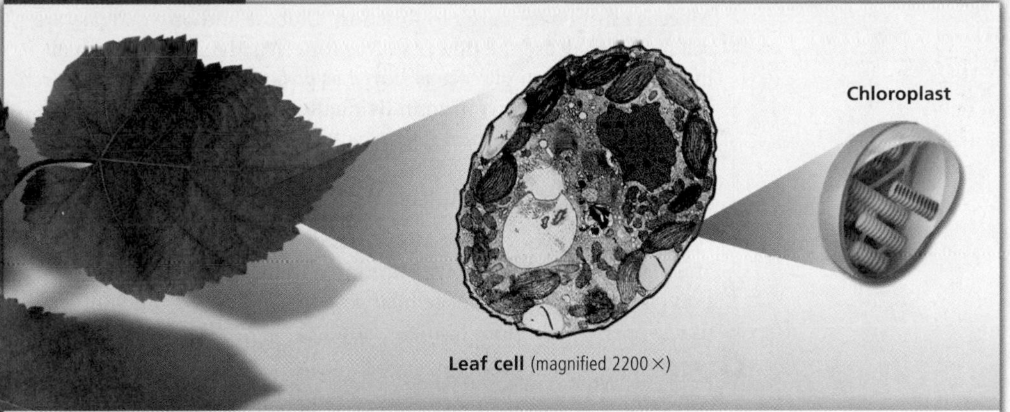

Chloroplast

Leaf cell (magnified 2200×)

1 The starting materials Carbon dioxide from the air and water from the soil enter the chloroplasts.

2 The process Inside the chloroplasts, chlorophyll captures energy from sunlight. This energy is used to change starting materials into new products.

3 The products Glucose supplies energy and is a source of materials for the plant; most oxygen is released into the air.

Carbon dioxide ($6CO_2$)

Light Energy

Water ($6H_2O$)

Glucose ($C_6H_{12}O_6$)

Oxygen ($6O_2$)

Chloroplast

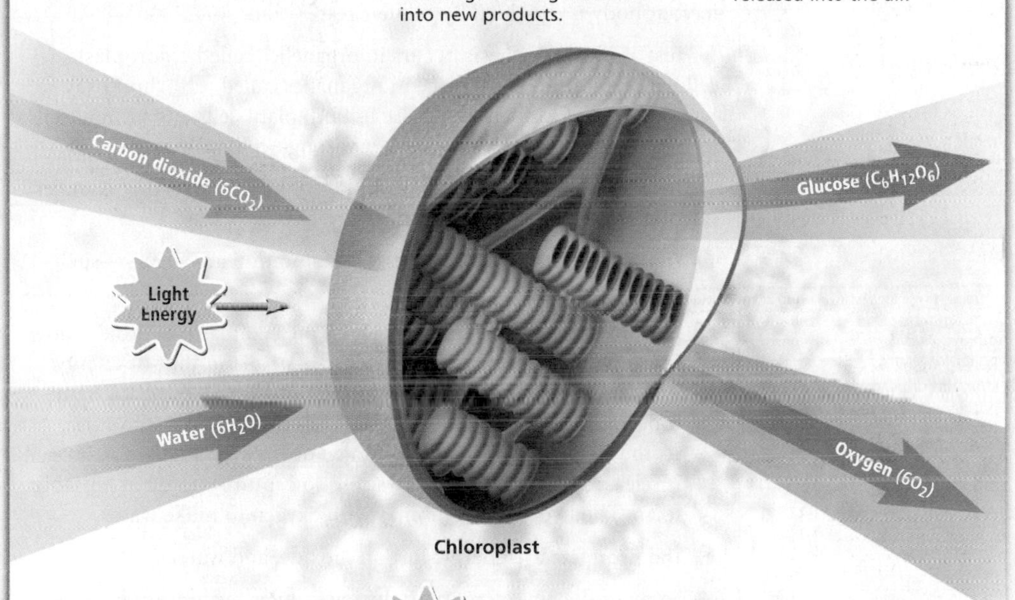

Water $6H_2O$	+	Carbon dioxide $6CO_2$	+	Light Energy	→	Glucose $C_6H_{12}O_6$	+	Oxygen $6O_2$

READING VISUALS What part of the diagram shows starting materials being changed?

Teach from Visuals

To help students interpret the photosynthesis diagram, ask:

- Where do the raw materials for photosynthesis come from? *air and soil*
- What captures the energy from sunlight? *chlorophyll in chloroplasts*
- Where do the products of photosynthesis go? *Glucose stays in the plant and provides energy and materials for it; most oxygen is released into the air.*

Integrate the Sciences

Carbon dioxide is one of a group of gases called greenhouse gases. In the stratosphere, these gases behave somewhat like the glass panes of a greenhouse—when Earth radiates heat, the gases trap some of it in the atmosphere, which raises the temperature on Earth. Since the Industrial Revolution, concentrations of carbon dioxide in the atmosphere have increased by about 25 percent, and over the last century temperatures on Earth's surface have risen 0.5°C to 0.9°C.

EXPLORE the BIG idea

Revisit "Internet Activity: Photosynthesis" on p. 39. Ask students to describe how plants they observed used sunlight. What structures and what materials were involved?

Ongoing Assessment

Answer: inside the chloroplast

DIFFERENTIATE INSTRUCTION

Below Level Have students make a poster of photosynthesis. They can illustrate the materials and products with pictures cut from magazines that represent a graphic, vivid symbol of the concept. At the center of the poster they should draw the plant cell and the chloroplasts. They can add the formulas shown in their textbook, p. 49, as captions.

Integrate the Sciences

Oxygen is a colorless, odorless, and tasteless gas, and is the most abundant element on Earth. By weight oxygen composes more than 21 percent of the atmosphere, more than 85 percent of the oceans, and almost 47 percent of the solid crust. It is found in all living tissues. Oxygen is in many organic and inorganic compounds, and is required for all combustion.

Address Misconceptions

IDENTIFY Ask: How do plant cells release stored energy? If students say "photosynthesis," they may hold the misconception that only animals use cellular respiration and that plants use only photosynthesis.

CORRECT Have students chart the starting materials and products of both processes. Ask: Where do plants get their energy at night? *They use stored energy from glucose, which they convert through cellular respiration.*

REASSESS Ask: When do plant and animal cells use oxygen to get energy to function? *during cellular respiration*

Technology Resources

Visit **ClassZone.com** for background on common student misconceptions.

MISCONCEPTION DATABASE

Ongoing Assessment

Answer: energy

Answer: energy, carbon dioxide, and water

All cells release energy.

All cells must have energy to function. Glucose and other sugars are cell food—they are the power source for cell activities in almost all living things. When glucose is stored as glycogen or taken in as starch, it must be broken down into individual sugar molecules before cells are able to use it. Chemical energy is stored in the bonds of sugars. When a sugar molecule is broken down, a usable form of energy is released for the cell's life functions.

Cells can release energy in two basic processes: cellular respiration and fermentation. Cellular respiration requires oxygen, but fermentation does not. In addition, cellular respiration releases much more usable energy than does fermentation.

What is released when a sugar molecule is broken down?

Cellular Respiration

C

In **cellular respiration,** cells use oxygen to release energy stored in sugars such as glucose. In fact, most of the energy used by the cells in your body is provided by cellular respiration.

Just as photosynthesis occurs in organelles called chloroplasts, cellular respiration takes place in organelles called mitochondria. Remember that mitochondria are in both plant cells and animal cells, so both kinds of cells release energy through cellular respiration.

Like photosynthesis, cellular respiration is a process that changes starting materials into new products.

D

READING TIP
Reread step 2 to make sure you understand what happens to oxygen and glucose.

1. **The starting materials** of cellular respiration are sugars—such as glucose—and oxygen.
2. **The process** begins when glucose in the cytoplasm is broken down into smaller molecules. This releases a small amount of energy. These molecules then move into the mitochondria. At the same time, oxygen enters the cell and travels into the mitochondria. As the smaller molecules are broken down even further, hydrogen is released in a way that allows cells to capture energy in a usable form. The hydrogen combines with oxygen to make water.
3. **The products** are energy, carbon dioxide, and water.

Some of the energy released during cellular respiration is transferred to other molecules, which then carry the energy where it is needed for the activities of the cell. The rest of the energy is released as heat. Carbon dioxide formed during cellular respiration is released by the cell.

What are the three products of cellular respiration?

DIFFERENTIATE INSTRUCTION

More Reading Support

C How do cells release stored energy? *through cellular respiration*

D What are the starting materials of cellular respiration? *sugars, such as glucose, and oxygen*

Below Level Have students create a poster of cellular respiration. They should draw or trace the mitochondrion and cut pictures from magazines to represent the starting materials and products. Have students use their posters of both photosynthesis and cellular respiration to give an oral explanation of how the two processes relate.

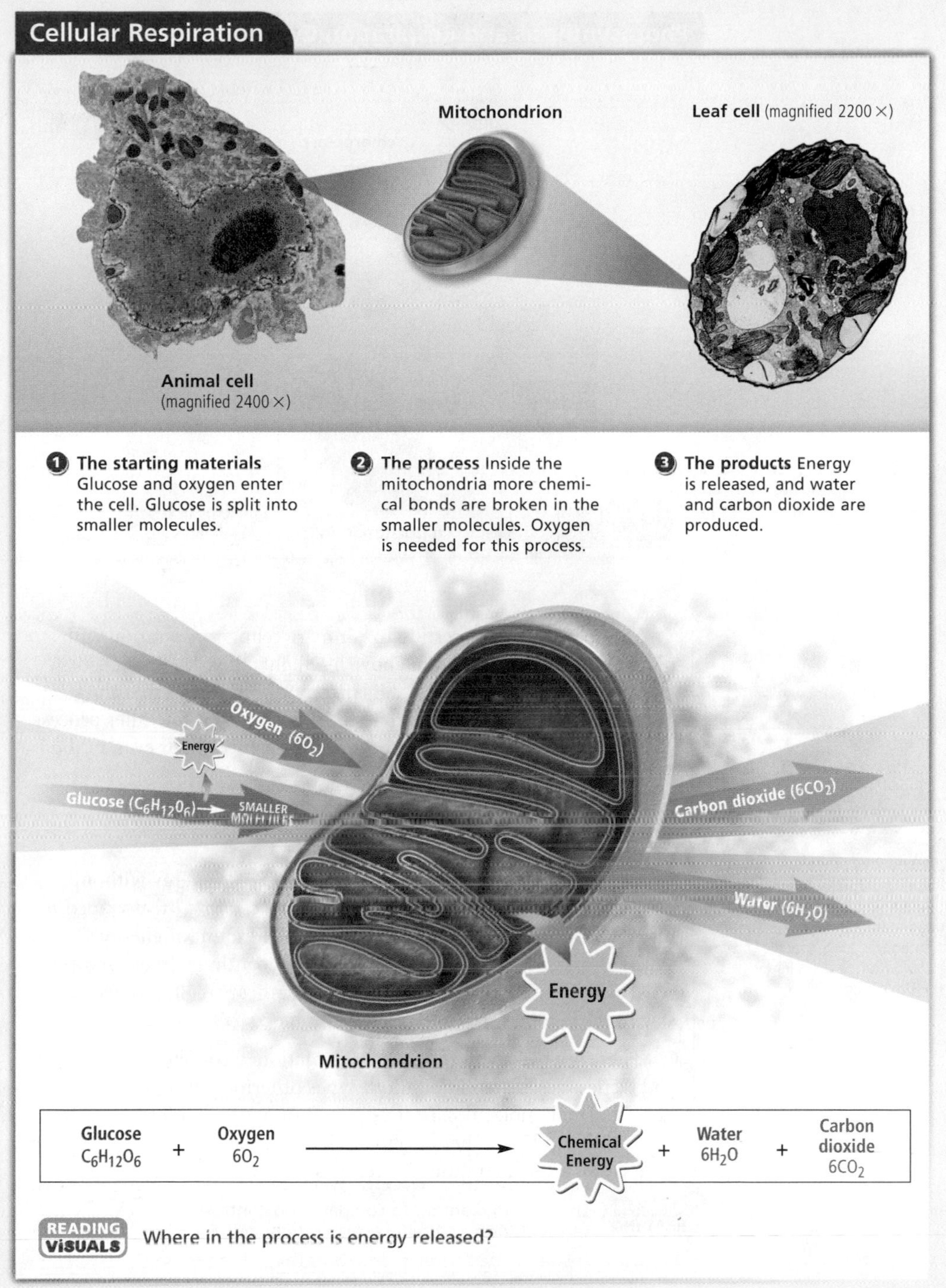

Teach from Visuals

To help students interpret the diagram of cellular respiration, ask:

- What are the starting materials of cellular respiration? *glucose and oxygen*
- What happens to glucose after it enters the cell? *It splits into smaller molecules.*
- What structures in the cell use oxygen to break down glucose's chemical bonds? *mitochondria*

History of Science

Theodor Schwann understood that fermentation of sugar and starch is the result of life processes. A German physiologist, Schwann founded modern histology, the study of tissues. He first defined the cell as the basic unit of animal structure by applying the cell theory of botanist Matthias Schleiden to animals. In 1839, he published his major work on the structure and growth of plants and animals. Schwann also studied muscles and Schwann cells, which are specialized cells that insulate and separate human nerve cells.

Language Arts Connection

Middle school students may find that an author study of novelist Madeleine L'Engle makes science come alive. L'Engle's novel *A Wind in the Door* includes a scene inside a mitchondrion.

Ongoing Assessment

READING VISUALS *Answer: during glucose breakdown in the mitochondrion*

DIFFERENTIATE INSTRUCTION

Advanced Have students research mitochondria and the chemical processes that take place inside them. They can make a mitochondrion model and create an "Owner's Manual" describing how it works.

Challenge and Extension, p. 90

Teach Difficult Concepts

To reinforce students' understanding of the energy cycle, have them start with the Sun and pass the energy through to a student. They could make a graphic organizer of the process: Sun's energy ⟶ captured by (an edible) plant ⟶ photosynthesis ⟶ glucose ⟶ plant eaten by student ⟶ cellular respiration ⟶ student moves.

Teach from Visuals

To help students understand the relationships within the photosynthesis and respiration cycle, ask:

- Chloroplast depends on what products from mitochondrion? *carbon dioxide and water*
- Mitochondrion depends on what products from chloroplast? *glucose and oxygen*
- What does this cycle illustrate about the relationship between photosynthesis and respiration? *Each process depends upon the other process to continue. The products from one process become the starting materials for the other process.*

 The visual "Photosynthesis and Respiration Cycle" is available as T14 in the Unit Transparency Book.

Ongoing Assessment

CHECK YOUR READING *Answer: Fermentation: no oxygen needed to release energy; occurs in cytoplasm; produces alcohol and carbon dioxide, or lactic acid. Cellular respiration: oxygen needed to release energy; occurs in mitochondria; produces water and carbon dioxide. Both: releases energy.*

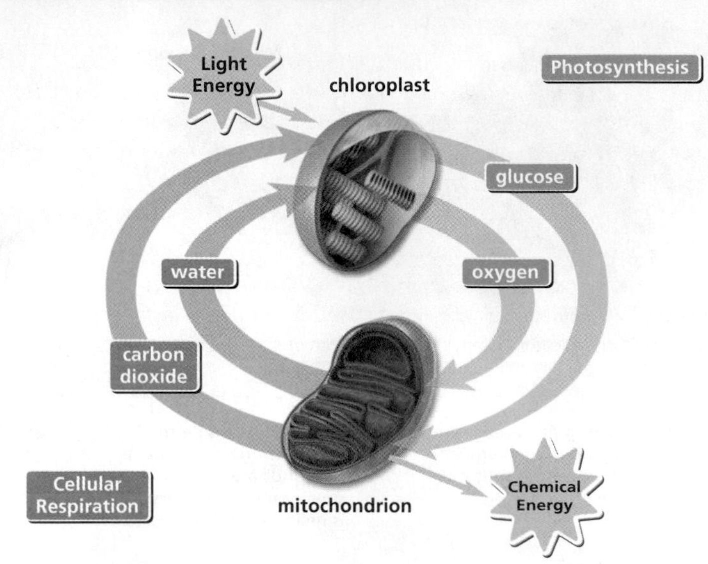

You may find it interesting to compare cellular respiration with photosynthesis. The diagram above highlights the cycle that occurs between photosynthesis and cellular respiration. Notice that the starting materials of one process are also the products of the other process. This cycle does not necessarily occur in the same cell, or even in the same organism.

Fermentation

VOCABULARY
Add a word triangle for *fermentation* to your notebook. Your triangle could include a sketch of a loaf of bread.

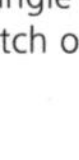

Fermentation is the process by which cells release energy without oxygen. Recall that in cellular respiration the cell first breaks glucose into smaller molecules. This releases a small amount of energy. Without oxygen, cellular respiration cannot continue. In eukaryotic cells, instead of entering the mitochondria, these smaller molecules stay in the cytoplasm, where fermentation occurs.

There are two main types of fermentation: alcoholic fermentation and lactic acid fermentation. Both types of fermentation break sugars down to small molecules. In the absence of oxygen, different reactions occur that produce either alcohol and carbon dioxide or lactic acid. In both cases, a small amount of energy is released.

 Use a Venn diagram to compare and contrast fermentation and cellular respiration. 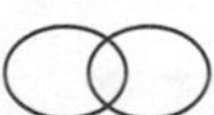

DIFFERENTIATE INSTRUCTION

 **More Reading Support**

E How do cells release energy without oxygen? *by fermentation*

English Learners The diagram on p. 52 will be particularly helpful to English learners. To simplify the concepts in the section, have them review this diagram with a fluent or advanced student. The students can take turns being a "tour guide" for energy's movement through the cycle.

The production of many foods that people eat every day involve either alcoholic fermentation or lactic acid fermentation. Three important foods are bread, yogurt, and cheese.

Bread is often made by mixing flour, milk, and sugar with a microorganism you know as yeast. Yeast runs out of oxygen and uses fermentation to convert the sugar into alcohol and carbon dioxide. Bubbles of carbon dioxide gas forming inside the dough cause it to rise. When the dough is baked, the small amount of alcohol evaporates, the yeast is killed, and the carbon dioxide bubbles give the bread a light, spongy structure.

Some bacteria release energy through lactic acid fermentation. These bacteria convert the sugar found in milk into lactic acid and are used to make yogurt, cheese, and sourdough bread. Lactic acid changes the acidity of a bread mixture to give it a slightly sour flavor. In yogurt and cheese, the buildup of lactic acid causes the milk to partially solidify, producing the creamy texture of yogurt. If fermentation continues for a long time, the milk eventually turns into cheese.

INVESTIGATE Fermentation

How can you tell if fermentation releases material?

PROCEDURE

1. Add 1/2 teaspoon of yeast to the empty water bottle.
2. Fill the bottle about three-quarters full with the sugar solution.
3. Place the balloon tightly around the mouth of the bottle.
4. Gently swirl the bottle to mix the yeast and sugar solution.
5. After 20 minutes, observe the balloon and record your observations.

WHAT DO YOU THINK?

- What changes did you observe? What do you think is the source of energy that caused these changes?
- What accounts for the change in the amount of gas inside the balloon?

CHALLENGE Design an experiment to answer the following question. How might the temperature of the sugar solution affect the process?

SKILL FOCUS
Observing

MATERIALS
- dry yeast
- spoon
- small water bottle
- warm sugar solution
- balloon

TIME
30 minutes

Real World Example

Wine is the fermented juice from grapes. Professional winemakers carefully control the process of fermentation. Grape skins are normally covered with bacteria, molds, and wild yeasts, whose growth must be suppressed, so that only the chosen strain of yeast can work. Temperature is controlled to keep the yeast alive and to extract particular colors and flavors from the grape skins. Contact with the air is restricted to prevent oxidation. Fermentation stops when the amount of fermentable sugar drops to about 0.1 percent.

INVESTIGATE Fermentation

PURPOSE To observe the process of fermentation

TIPS *30 min.* Be sure to use fresh yeast. Allow more time for results if yeast is cold or stale. Students should start by stretching the balloon out as though it were to be inflated. To create a tight seal with the bottle, a piece of duct tape can be added. Tell students not to squeeze the bottle.

WHAT DO YOU THINK? *The balloon filled up. Sugar is the energy source. The yeast and sugar release gas that fills up the balloon.*

CHALLENGE *Students' experiments will vary; temperature of the sugar solution might affect how much gas is produced per minute.*

 Datasheet, Fermentation, p. 91

Technology Resources

Customize this student lab as needed or look for an alternative. Print rubrics to assess student lab reports.

 **Lab Generator CD-ROM**

DIFFERENTIATE INSTRUCTION

More Reading Support

F What are some common foods that have fermentation as part of their production? *bread, yogurt, and cheese*

Advanced Have students design a fermentation experiment and create a product such as cheese or yogurt. The Internet and health food stores are sources for the microorganisms used in these products.

Ongoing Assessment

Describe how plants and animals get energy.

Ask. Do plants and animals get their energy from the same direct source? Explain. *No; plants get their energy from sunlight through photosynthesis. Animals get their energy from eating plants or other organisms.*

Reinforce the BIG idea

Have students relate the section to the Big Idea.

 Reinforcing Key Concepts, p. 92

2.2 ASSESS & RETEACH

Assess

 Section 2.2 Quiz, p. 23

Reteach

Use a chart to help students master the processes of photosynthesis and cellular respiration.

	Photosynthesis	Cellular Respiration
Ingredients	sunlight, CO_2, and water	glucose and O_2
Used By	plants only	plants and animals
Product	glucose and O_2	energy, CO_2, and water

Technology Resources

Have students visit **ClassZone.com** for reteaching of Key Concepts.

 CONTENT REVIEW

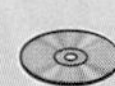 CONTENT REVIEW CD-ROM

Energy and Exercise

Your muscle cells, like some organisms, are able to release energy by both cellular respiration and fermentation. While you are at rest, your muscle cells use specialized molecules to store both energy and oxygen.

During hard or prolonged exercise, your muscle cells may use up all their stores of energy and oxygen. Then your muscle cells rely on fermentation to break down sugars. There is much less energy available to cells that use fermentation, which is why you cannot continue to run rapidly for long distances. When your cells use fermentation to release energy, one of the waste products is lactic acid, which can cause a burning sensation in your muscles.

APPLY Why might these students feel a burning sensation in their arm muscles while doing pull-ups?

When you stop after this type of exercise, your muscles continue to hurt and you continue to breathe hard for many minutes. During this time, your muscles are playing catch-up. They use the oxygen brought into your blood by your heavy breathing to finish breaking down the byproducts of fermentation. As the lactic acid is converted into carbon dioxide and water, the burning sensation in your muscles goes away. Your muscles build back up their stores of energy and oxygen until the next time they are needed.

2.2 Review

KEY CONCEPTS

1. Which form of energy is especially important for living things? Why?
2. How is photosynthesis important to life on Earth?
3. What starting materials do cells need for cellular respiration?

CRITICAL THINKING

4. **Compare and Contrast** How are photosynthesis and cellular respiration similar? How are they different?
5. **Predict** Suppose that in a lab you could remove all the oxygen from a terrarium. What would happen to the plants? Why?

CHALLENGE

6. **Synthesize** In everyday language, the word *respiration* refers to breathing. How is breathing related to *cellular respiration*? **Hint: The air we breathe out contains more carbon dioxide than the air we breathe in.**

ANSWERS

1. Glucose; most cells store their energy in glucose.

2. It produces food for most organisms.

3. glucose and oxygen

4. Cellular respiration and photosynthesis both produce energy, but the starting materials and the products are reversed in the two processes. Photosynthesis uses carbon dioxide and water to convert energy to glucose. Cellular respiration uses glucose and oxygen and produces carbon dioxide and water.

5. They would die. They need oxygen for cellular respiration.

6. Cellular respiration is like breathing because when you exhale, carbon dioxide and water leave your body. When you inhale, oxygen enters your body.

SKILL: INTERPRETING GRAPHS

Carbon Dioxide Levels in Biosphere 2

Biosphere 2 is a research and education center in Arizona that can house people, plants, and animals. It was built to find out whether people could get the food and breathable air needed to survive in a small sealed environment over a two-year period.

Example

Data on carbon dioxide levels in the air of Biosphere 2 were collected at 15-minute intervals for several weeks. The graph below shows the amounts of carbon dioxide (CO_2) in the air on January 20, 1996.

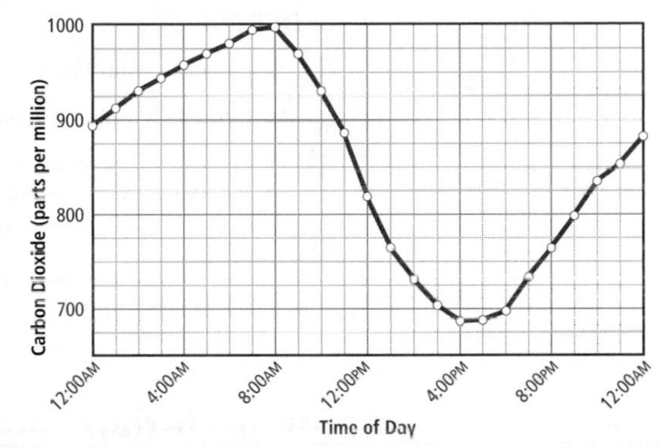

Answer the following questions.

1. What intervals are shown on the *x*-axis? What is shown on the *y*-axis?
2. At what time of day does the carbon dioxide concentration reach its highest point? About how many parts per million of CO_2 are in the air at that time?
3. Between what hours is the CO_2 level decreasing?

CHALLENGE The data in the graph were collected on a sunny day. How might the graph look different if the day had been overcast?

ANSWERS

1. hours; carbon dioxide in parts per million

2. 8 A.M.; about 990 parts per million

3. 8:00 A.M. to 4:00 P.M.

CHALLENGE Plants would not be able to use as much carbon dioxide through photosynthesis as they would on a sunny day, so the graph would show less of a decrease.

MATH IN SCIENCE

Math Skills Practice for Science

Purpose

To interpret a graph of carbon dioxide levels from Biosphere 2

Present the Science

Biosphere 2 was an attempt to model Earth under glass on three acres in Arizona. Eight people aimed to live in the airtight greenhouse for two years, trying to better understand the workings of Earth. Although seven biomes were recreated inside the structure, oxygen limits dipped dangerously low and the attempt failed. The experiment showed how difficult it is to copy Earth's biosphere using human technology.

Develop Graphing Skills

- Review reading from an axis to the curve.
- Point out that the units on the two axes are different.

Close

Discuss how the amount of vegetation affects the amount of carbon dioxide in the air. Ask: How might developing land that is currently forested affect the air? *With fewer trees available to convert carbon dioxide into oxygen through the process of photosynthesis, the percentage of oxygen in the air might drop.*

- Math Support, p. 109
- Math Practice, p. 110

Technology Resources

Students can visit **ClassZone.com** for practice in interpreting graphs.

 MATH TUTORIAL

2.3 FOCUS

Set Learning Goals

Students will

- Describe how materials move into and out of the cell through the cell membrane.
- Explain how energy is involved in transporting some materials.
- Examine how surface area affects diffusion in cells.

3-Minute Warm-Up

Display Transparency 13 or copy this exercise on the board:

Match the definitions to the terms.

Definitions

1. proteins, lipids, and carbohydrates *c*
2. lipid layers that repel water *a*
3. source of chemical energy *b*

Terms

a. cell membrane
b. glucose
c. large molecules
d. small molecules
e. water

 3-Minute Warm-Up, p. T13

2.3 MOTIVATE

EXPLORE Diffusion

PURPOSE To observe how particles move by diffusion

TIP *10 min.* Remind students to use only three drops of food coloring; too much obscures the diffusion.

WHAT DO YOU THINK? *The food coloring gradually colors all the water in the beaker. The food coloring diffused through the water.*

KEY CONCEPT

2.3 Materials move across the cell's membranes.

BEFORE, you learned

- All cells have an outer covering called the cell membrane
- Cells need starting materials for life-sustaining processes
- Cells need to get rid of waste products

NOW, you will learn

- How materials move into and out of the cell through the cell membrane
- How energy is involved in transporting some materials into and out of cells
- How surface area affects transport in cells

VOCABULARY

diffusion p. 56
passive transport p. 58
osmosis p. 59
active transport p. 60

EXPLORE Diffusion

How do particles move?

PROCEDURE

1. Fill the beaker with tap water.
2. Add 3 drops of food coloring to the water.
3. For 10 minutes, observe what happens. Write down your observations.

MATERIALS

- beaker
- water
- food coloring

WHAT DO YOU THINK?

- What changes did you observe?
- What might have caused the changes?

Some materials move by diffusion.

VOCABULARY Add a word triangle for *diffusion* to your notebook. Your triangle could include a sketch of the sun.

When you walk toward the shampoo section in a store, you can probably smell a fragrance even before you get close. The process by which the scent spreads through the air is an example of diffusion. **Diffusion** (dih-FYOO-zhuhn) is the process by which molecules spread out, or move from areas where there are many of them to areas where there are fewer of them.

Diffusion occurs because the molecules in gases, liquids, and even solids are in constant motion in all directions. This random movement of molecules tends to spread molecules out until they are evenly distributed. But diffusion does more than just spread a scent around a room. Cells use diffusion to carry out important life functions. Diffusion helps cells maintain conditions necessary for life. For example, the oxygen needed for respiration enters cells by diffusion. Similarly, the carbon dioxide produced by respiration leaves cells by diffusion.

RESOURCES FOR DIFFERENTIATED INSTRUCTION

Below Level

UNIT RESOURCE BOOK

- Reading Study Guide A, pp. 95–96
- Decoding Support, p. 108

 **AUDIO CDS**

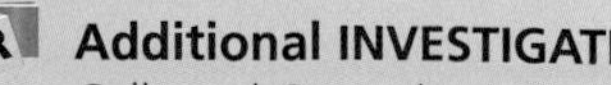 **Additional INVESTIGATION,** Cells and Osmosis, A, B, & C, pp. 120–128; Teacher Instructions, pp. 308–309

Advanced

UNIT RESOURCE BOOK

Challenge and Extension, p. 101

English Learners

UNIT RESOURCE BOOK

Spanish Reading Study Guide, pp. 99–100

 **AUDIO CDS**

- Audio Readings in Spanish
- Audio Readings (English)

Concentration

Diffusion occurs naturally as particles move from an area of higher concentration to an area of lower concentration. The concentration of a substance is the number of particles of that substance in a specific volume. For example, if you dissolved 9 grams of sugar in 1 liter of water, the concentration of the sugar solution would be 9 g/L. When there is a difference in the concentration of a substance between two areas, diffusion occurs.

Generally, the greater the difference in concentration between two areas, the more rapidly diffusion occurs. As the difference in concentration decreases, diffusion slows down. The number of particles moving to one area is balanced by the number moving in the other direction. Particles are still moving in all directions, but these movements do not change the concentrations.

CHECK YOUR READING Summarize what happens during diffusion. (Remember, a summary includes only the most important information.)

Concentration and Diffusion

A sugar cube dissolving in water provides an example of diffusion.

1 Shortly after a sugar cube is placed in a beaker of water, the concentration of sugar is high near the sugar cube and very low elsewhere in the beaker.

2 Over time, diffusion causes the concentration of sugar to become the same throughout the beaker. Particles are still moving.

Diffusion in Cells

Diffusion is one way by which materials move in and out of cells. Small molecules such as oxygen can pass through tiny gaps in the cell membrane by diffusion. For example, consider the conditions that result from photosynthesis in a leaf cell.

- Photosynthesis produces oxygen inside the cell.
- The concentration of oxygen molecules becomes higher inside the cell than outside.
- Oxygen molecules move out of the cell by diffusion.

RESOURCE CENTER CLASSZONE.COM

Learn more about diffusion.

2.3 INSTRUCT

Teacher Demo

To reinforce students' understanding of concentration and diffusion, demonstrate the sugar cube in water as shown on p. 57. Have a volunteer taste the water when the cube is first placed in it and when the cube is dissolved, and report to the class on the difference. (Remind students not to taste unknown substances, unless a teacher tells them it is safe to do so.)

Real World Example

Explain that diffusion happens at levels much easier to see than cells and molecules. Ask students to brainstorm daily examples of diffusion. *Sample answers: cream in coffee, students entering a bus or classroom, cold and hot air, water running over a tub, bowl, or basin, and so on.*

Ongoing Assessment

CHECK YOUR READING *Answer: During diffusion, molecules, which are in constant motion in all directions, spread out in an equal mixture.*

DIFFERENTIATE INSTRUCTION

More Reading Support

A What does concentration mean? *number of particles of that substance in a specific volume*

English Learners Place the words *concentration, diffusion, passive transport, osmosis,* and *active transport* on a classroom Science Word Wall with brief definitions of each. Encourage students to give everyday example of the words *passive, active, transport,* and *concentration.* The everyday context will help to reinforce the science (or cellular) context.

Develop Critical Thinking

CONNECT Ask students to think of examples that expand the concept of diffusion to human interaction. For instance, new ideas, fashions, and gossip diffuse through the population.

Teach from Visuals

To help students interpret the diagrams of diffusion through a membrane, ask:

- Does the oxygen move toward or away from the greater concentration? *away*
- What are protein channels and what is their function? *They are openings that allow molecules through the cell membrane.*
- When is equilibrium reached? *when the concentrations inside and outside the cell are equal*

Teaching with Technology

Use a PC microscope to show students slides of cells. Pull the thin layer between layers of an onion and put it in water on a slide, or use prepared slides. They should be able to view the cell membrane.

Ongoing Assessment

CHECK YOUR READING *Answer: Passive transport allows materials to move without using the cell's energy.*

VOCABULARY
Add a word diagram for *passive transport* to your notebook. You may want to use words instead of a sketch in part of your triangle.

? B

In a plant cell, some of the oxygen produced by photosynthesis is used in cellular respiration. The remaining oxygen diffuses out of the cell. Much of it escapes to the air. Some of it diffuses to other cells where there is a lower concentration of oxygen. This process of diffusion continues from one cell to the next.

? C

Diffusion is a form of passive transport. In **passive transport,** materials move without using the cell's energy. Cells benefit from passive transport because some materials can move through various cell membranes without any input of energy. Whether or not a substance can diffuse across a cell membrane depends on how well the substance dissolves in the lipids that make up the cell membrane. A special form of passive transport allows polar substances, such as glucose, salts, and amino acids, to pass through cell membranes.

All cells need the food energy supplied by glucose. Yet glucose is produced in just some plant cells. Polar substances move into the cell through protein channels—or openings—in their membranes that are specific for each substance. This type of diffusion is still passive transport because it uses no energy.

CHECK YOUR READING What is passive transport? Your answer should mention energy.

Passive Transport

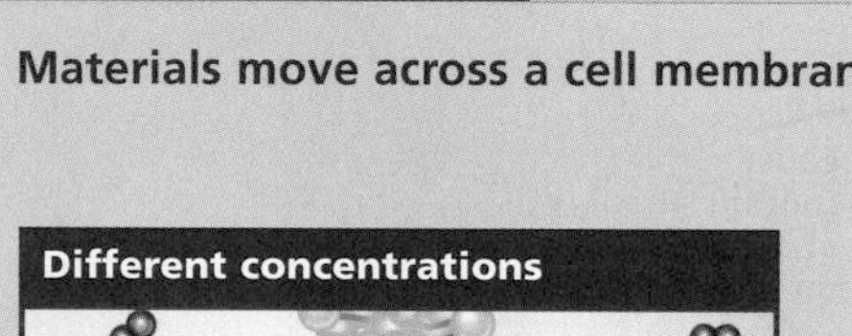

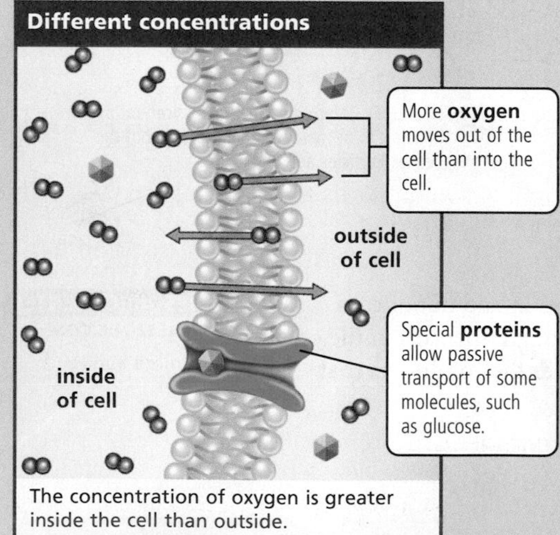

The concentration of oxygen is greater inside the cell than outside.

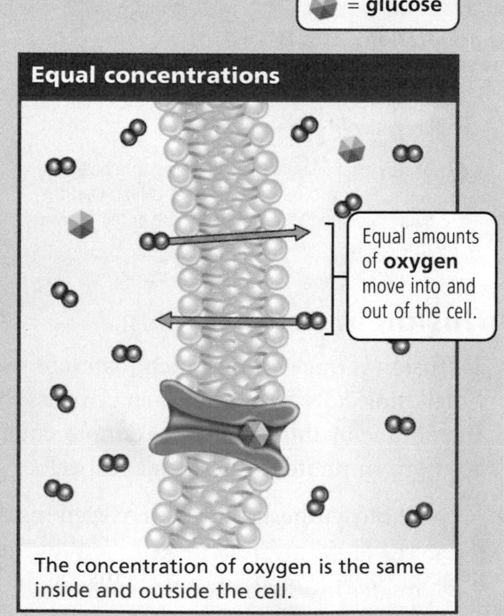

The concentration of oxygen is the same inside and outside the cell.

58 Unit 1: **Cells and Heredity**

DIFFERENTIATE INSTRUCTION

More Reading Support

B How does oxygen get into and out of a cell? *by diffusion*

C How do materials move without using the cell's energy? *by passive transport*

English Learners Have a group of 6 to 8 students model the following science words by acting as molecules and cellular structures: *osmosis, concentration, diffusion, active transport, passive transport.*

Osmosis

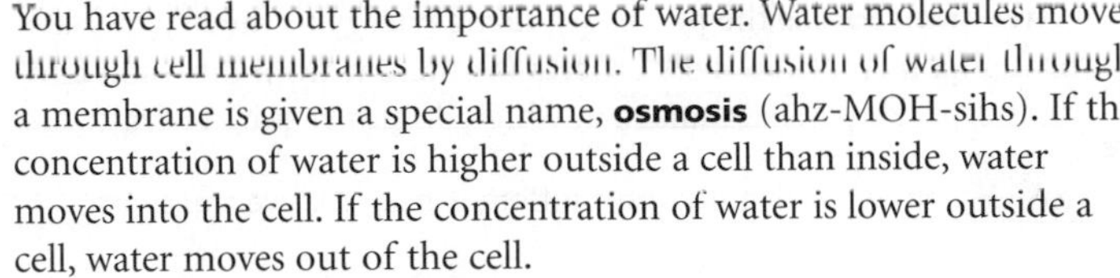

You have read about the importance of water. Water molecules move through cell membranes by diffusion. The diffusion of water through a membrane is given a special name, **osmosis** (ahz-MOH-sihs). If the concentration of water is higher outside a cell than inside, water moves into the cell. If the concentration of water is lower outside a cell, water moves out of the cell.

You can easily observe the effect of osmosis on plants. If you forget to water a plant, it wilts. Why? The soil dries out, and the plant's roots have no water to absorb. As a result, water leaves the plant cells by osmosis and they shrink. If you water the plant, water becomes available to enter the shrunken cells by osmosis. The leaves will return to normal as water moves into the cells.

Without water, a plant droops. The cells have little water in their vacuoles, shown in blue. (magnified 1200×)

Water moves into leaf cells by osmosis and fills the vacuoles, shown in blue. (magnified 1200×)

Some transport requires energy.

Not all materials that move in and out of a cell can do so by diffusion. For cells to carry out life functions, materials must often move from areas of low concentration into areas of high concentration. This process of moving materials against a concentration requires energy.

OUTLINE
Remember to include the heading *Some transport requires energy* and notes on the red headings in your outline.

Teacher Demo

Bring a plant into the classroom and let it go without water for a few days, until it begins to visibly wilt. Have students observe the difference when you resume watering.

Real World Example

If fresh water and salty water are on opposite sides of a membrane, osmosis usually occurs, and the fresh water travels through the membrane into the salty side to dilute it. This process can be reversed, however, by adding pressure to the salty side. Municipal desalinization of water is often accomplished by this process, called reverse osmosis. Pressure pushes the water across the cell membrane, away from the salt, leaving a higher concentration of salt behind.

EXPLORE the BIG idea

Revisit "Just a Spoonful of Sugar" on p. 39. Ask students what made the raisins swell.

DIFFERENTIATE INSTRUCTION

More Reading Support

D What do you call diffusion of water through a membrane? *osmosis*

E If the concentration of water is higher outside a cell, which way will water move? *into the cell*

Advanced Have students put a drop or two of food extract or perfume into a deflated balloon. Blow up the balloon, tie it off, and place it inside a shoe box with the lid taped on. Later, students can remove the lid and smell the contents. Have students write an explanation of why the box smells like the scent when the scent was inside the balloon.

R Challenge and Extension, p. 101

Teach from Visuals

To help students interpret the active transport drawings, ask:

- What structures inside the salt gland carry blood to and from the body? *a network of blood vessels*
- How do cells get rid of salt? *by active transport*
- Where does the concentrated salt go? *to the nostrils*

Integrate the Sciences

Diffusion occurs in many ways in the natural world. Thermal energy diffuses from a high temperature to a low one. A nuclear reactor requires neutrons to diffuse through a special medium that scatters them without absorbing them. The rate of diffusion is proportional to the concentration gradient.

Ongoing Assessment

Describe how materials move into and out of the cell through the cell membrane.

Ask: What two ways can materials move through cell membranes? *Materials can move passively, from high concentration to low, by diffusion. They can move by active transport, where chemical energy moves a material from low concentration to high.*

CHECK YOUR READING *Answer: Active transport requires energy, while passive transport uses no energy.*

Active Transport

Active transport is the process of using energy to move materials through a membrane. This process is different from diffusion and other types of passive transport, which do not require energy.

CHECK YOUR READING How is active transport different from passive transport?

VISUALIZATION CLASSZONE.COM

Observe active transport at work.

Cells use active transport to perform important life functions, including the removal of excess salt from the body. Consider the example of active transport in marine iguanas, shown below. These lizards swim and feed in the salty ocean. As a result they soak up a lot of salt. Too much salt would seriously damage the iguanas' cells, so the cells must get rid of the excess.

The solution to the marine iguana's salt problem is found in two small glands above its eyes. Cells in these glands remove excess salt from the blood by active transport. Even when cells in these glands have a higher concentration of salt than that of the blood, the cells use chemical energy to continue taking salt out of the blood. The gland forms a droplet of salt, which the iguana easily blows out through its nostrils.

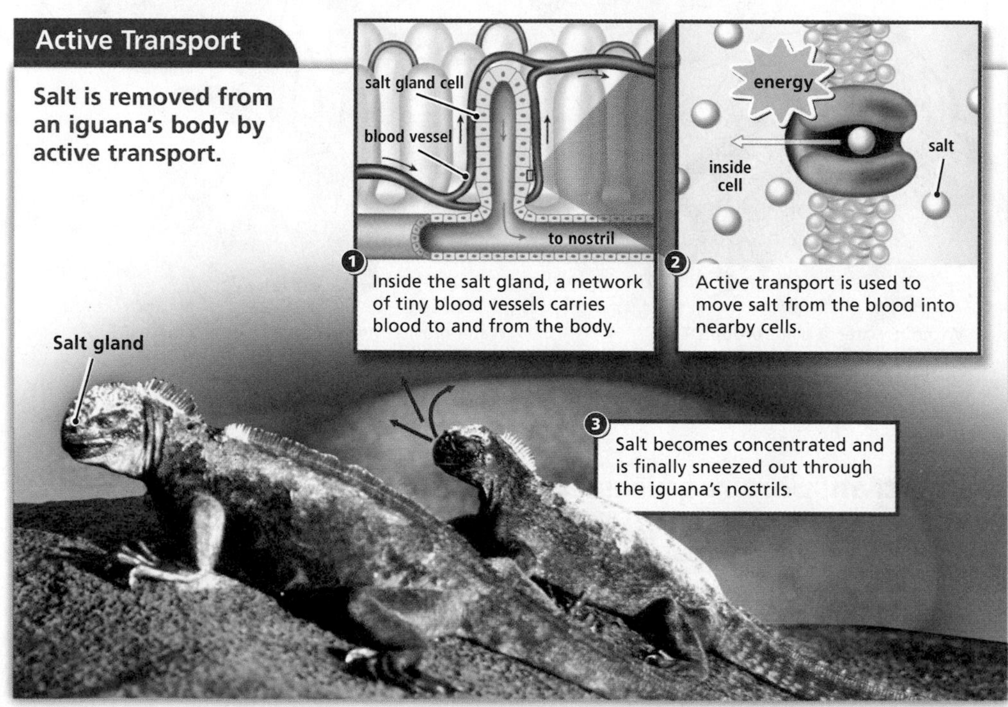

DIFFERENTIATE INSTRUCTION

More Reading Support

F What process involves cells using energy to move materials? *active transport*

G What is one way that cells use active transport? *to remove excess salt*

Additional Investigation

To reinforce Section 2.3 learning goals, use the following full-period investigation:

Additional INVESTIGATION, Cells and Osmosis, A, B, & C, pp. 120–128, 308–309 (Advanced students should complete Levels B and C.)

H You may not be able to blow salt out of your nostrils, but your kidneys help to keep healthy salt levels in your body. Kidneys filter wastes from your blood by active transport. Cells in the kidneys remove excess salt from the blood.

Endocytosis

Cells also need to move materials that are too large to go through the cell membrane or a protein channel. As the diagram below illustrates, endocytosis (EHN-doh-sy-TOH-sihs) occurs when a large bit of material is captured within a pocket of the membrane. This pocket breaks off and forms a package that moves into the cell. Cells in your body can use endocytosis to fight bacteria and viruses by absorbing them.

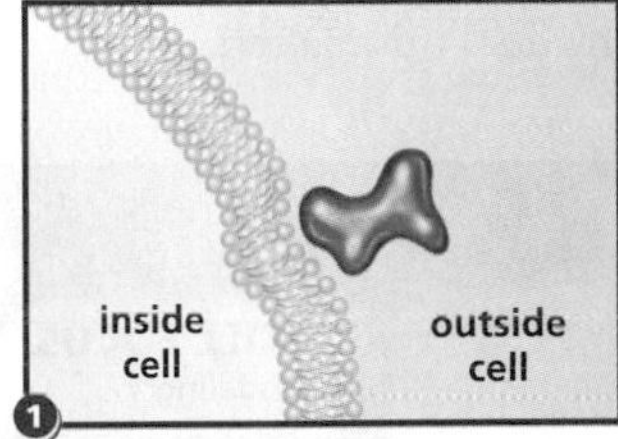

1 As a particle approaches, the cell membrane folds inward, creating a pocket.

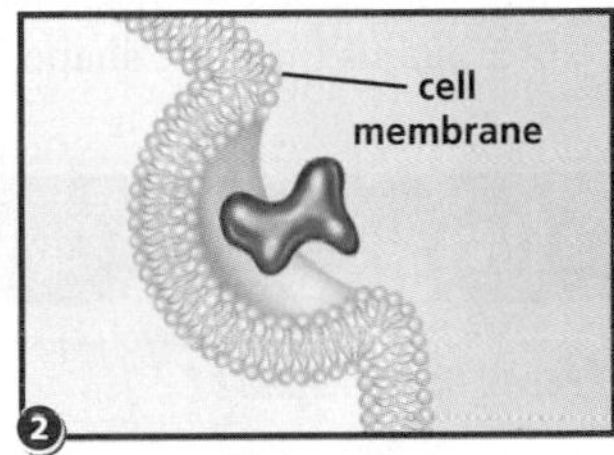

2 The particle moves into the pocket, and the membrane closes around it, forming a "package."

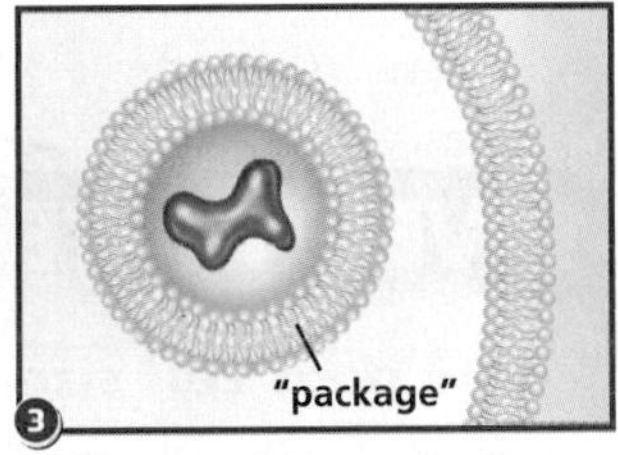

3 The "package" breaks away from the cell membrane, bringing the particle into the cell.

Exocytosis

When a cell needs to get rid of large materials, the process of endocytosis is reversed. In exocytosis (EHK-soh-sy-TOH-sihs), a membrane within the cell encloses the material that needs to be removed. This package moves to the cell membrane, joins with it, and the material is expelled. Cells often use exocytosis to flush out waste materials or to expel proteins or hormones made by the cell.

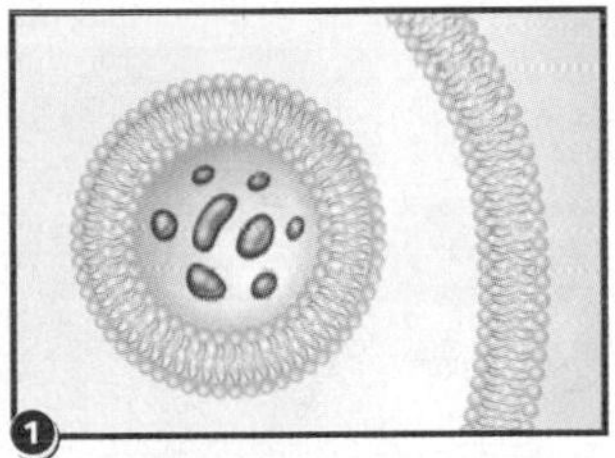

1 A membrane-enclosed "package" carries materials from inside the cell to the cell membrane.

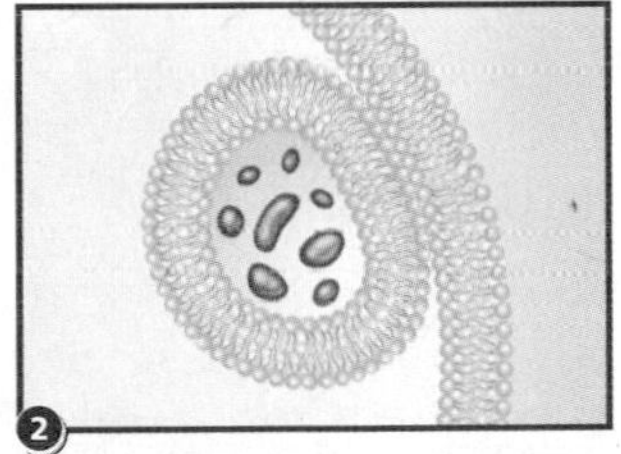

2 The membrane of the "package" attaches to the cell membrane, and the two membranes merge.

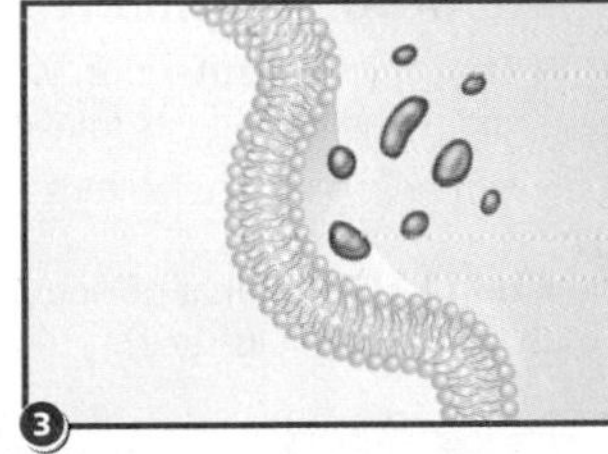

3 The materials are pushed out of the cell as the membrane of the "package" becomes part of the cell membrane.

Develop Critical Thinking

COMPARE Have students explain the similarities between endocytosis and exocytosis. *In both cases, the cell membrane folds to either absorb or release a package of membrane material. In both cases some other material is moved across the cell membrane.*

Metacognitive Strategy

Have students suggest strategies for remembering the difference between *endocytosis* and *exocytosis.*

Address Misconceptions

IDENTIFY Ask: How do cells get the materials they need? If students answer "diffusion," they may hold the misconception that diffusion is the only way that materials move in and out of cells.

CORRECT Remind students of the marine iguana. Point out that the salt concentration in the iguana's body is too high, and salt must be removed. Have students discuss active transport and endocytosis and exocytosis.

REASSESS Ask: Besides diffusion, how do materials move in and out of cells? *by active transport, endocytosis, and exocytosis*

Technology Resources

Visit **ClassZone.com** for background on common student misconceptions.

MISCONCEPTION DATABASE

Ongoing Assessment

Explain how energy is involved in transporting some materials.

Ask: How does active transport remove excess salt from your blood? *It moves salt against concentration gradient from blood into kidneys.*

DIFFERENTIATE INSTRUCTION

More Reading Support

H What organs in the human body use active transport to remove excess salt? *the kidneys*

Below Level Have students make flip books illustrating endocytosis and exocytosis. They can trace the diagrams from the textbook. They should use 4" × 6" notepaper taped at the top, at least 12 sheets. They should draw "in-betweens" to make the action smooth from step to step.

INVESTIGATE Cells

PURPOSE To model how surface area affects diffusion

TIP *30 min. (15 min. setup, 24 hours wait time, 15 min. observation time)* Caution students not to slice toward their hands.

WHAT DO YOU THINK? *The small piece of egg was penetrated more; the small piece had more surface area for the dye to enter.*

CHALLENGE *Very little, if any, dye would get to the white.*

 Datasheet, Cells, p. 102

Technology Resources

Customize this student lab as needed or look for an alternative. Print rubrics to assess student lab reports.

 **Lab Generator CD-ROM**

Teaching with Technology

Use a PC microscope or projection microscope to have students view cells taken from the thinnest layer of a newer onion skin. Or use prepared slides or digital slides. Point out the relationships between a cell's shape, surface area, and volume.

Cell size affects transport.

Most cells are very small. In fact, most cells are too small to be seen without a microscope. The average cell in your body is about 50 micrometers (0.05 mm) in diameter. Most of the cells on this planet are bacteria, which are only 3 to 5 micrometers in diameter. How can something as important as a cell be so tiny? Actually, if cells were not so small, they could never do their jobs.

Everything the cell needs or has to get rid of has to go through the cell membrane. The amount of cell membrane limits the ability of cells to either get substances from the outside or transport waste and other materials to the outside. This ability is related to surface area. The relationship between surface area and volume controls cell size. As a cell gets larger, its volume increases faster than its surface area if the cell maintains the same shape. Why does this matter?

INVESTIGATE Cells

How does cell size affect transport?

Demonstrate how small size helps make it possible for cells to get resources.

PROCEDURE

1. Cut a large piece of egg white from the egg.
2. Use a knife to trim the egg white into one small cube, about 1 cm square, and one large cube, about 2 cm square.
3. Pour 100 mL of water into the beaker. Add 10 drops of blue food coloring and stir. Place both cubes into the solution. Let both stand in the colored water overnight.
4. Remove each gently from the water with a spoon. Place both on a paper towel. With the knife, cut each in half. Use the ruler to measure how far the blue water penetrated into the surface of each one.

WHAT DO YOU THINK?

- Record your observations. Which piece of egg was penetrated more, compared to its total diameter, by the blue water?
- Why was there a difference in water penetration?

CHALLENGE What do you predict would happen to an egg left in its shell?

SKILL FOCUS
Modeling

MATERIALS
- 2 hard-boiled, peeled eggs
- knife
- ruler
- 100 mL water
- glass beaker
- dark blue food coloring
- spoon
- paper towel

TIME
30 minutes

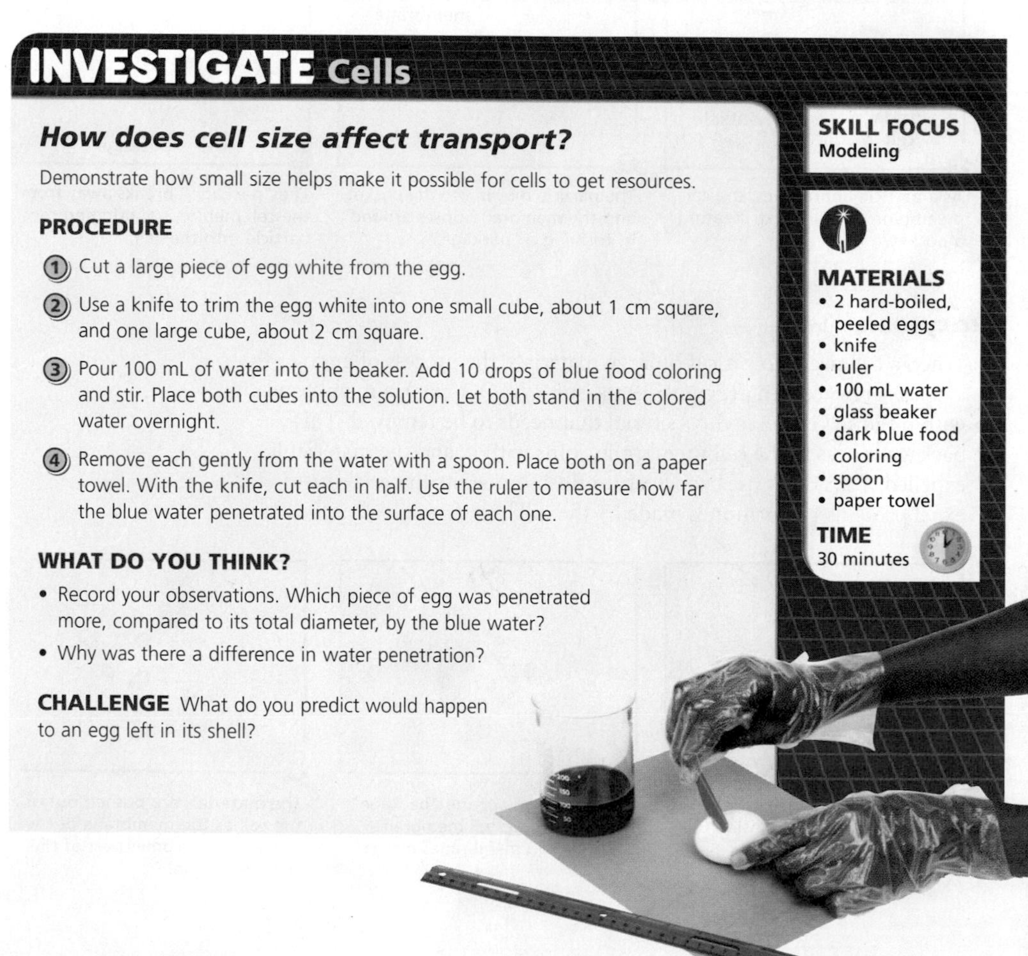

DIFFERENTIATE INSTRUCTION

More Reading Support

I What do you need to see most cells?
a microscope

Below Level Have students work with wooden blocks to model how the ratio of surface area to volume decreases as the cell gets larger. This is an opportunity to reinforce the concept that cells are the "building blocks" or basic units of living things, and that molecules build cells and atoms build molecules. (See Address Misconceptions, p. 42.)

Surface Area and Volumes of Cubes

	Number of Cubes	Side Length	Surface Area	Volume
4 cm	1	4 cm	96 cm^2	64 cm^3
2 cm	8	2 cm	192 cm^2	64 cm^3
1 cm	64	1 cm	384 cm^2	64 cm^3

As the cell gets bigger, there comes a time when its surface area is not large enough to allow resources to travel to all parts of the cell. So the cell stops growing. Bird eggs and frog eggs are much larger than typical cells, but they have a storehouse of food and also rapidly divide to give rise to multicellular embryos. In fact, this multicellular embryo is a good illustration of another way cells get around the surface-area-to-volume problem: they divide. The ratio of surface area to volume in newly divided cells is much higher, giving more surface area for exchanging materials with the outside of cells.

READING TIP

Look at the chart above. Notice that the volumes are all the same, but the surface area changes.

A cell's shape also affects its surface area. For example, some single-celled organisms are thin and flat, providing increased surface area. Other cells, such as nerve cells and muscle cells, are long and skinny, which also gives them a higher ratio of surface area to volume.

2.3 Review

KEY CONCEPTS

1. How are the processes of diffusion and osmosis alike?
2. What is the difference between active and passive transport? Use the term *energy* in your answer.
3. How does the surface area of a cell limit the growth of the cell?

CRITICAL THINKING

4. **Apply** If you put a bouquet of carnations in water, through what process does the water enter the stems?
5. **Predict** If a marine iguana were to spend a few days in a freshwater tank, would it continue to blow salt droplets from its nostrils? Why or why not?

CHALLENGE

6. **Predict** Freshwater protozoa, which are unicellular organisms, have a greater concentration of salt inside them than does the surrounding water. Does water diffuse into or out of the protozoa?

ANSWERS

1. Osmosis is a special term for water diffusion.

2. Active transport uses the cell's energy to move materials, while passive transport does not need energy.

3. The amount of a cell's surface area limits the amount of material that can move into or out of the cell, which in turn limits the size of the cell.

4. osmosis

5. No; it would not be getting extra salt from the environment.

6. into the protozoa

Ongoing Assessment

Examine how surface area affects diffusion in cells.

Ask: After a cell has divided, the two new cells have great ability to exchange materials with the outside of cells. Why? *Newly divided cells have a higher ratio of surface area to volume than the old cell.*

EXPLORE the BIG idea

Revisit "Leaves Underwater" on p. 39. Students should be able to explain why plants thrive on land although they need water to survive.

Reinforce the BIG idea

Have students relate the section to the Big Idea.

 Reinforcing Key Concepts, p. 103

2.3 ASSESS & RETEACH

Assess

 Section 2.3 Quiz, p. 24

Reteach

Split the board in two with a line, which represents a cell membrane. Label one side "inside the cell" and the other "outside the cell." Write different substances on the board and ask how they get to the other side of the cell membrane. Include examples of diffusion, osmosis, endocytosis, exocytosis, passive transport, and active transport, and at least one example of concentration difference on the two sides of the membrane.

Technology Resources

Have students visit **ClassZone.com** for reteaching of Key Concepts.

 **CONTENT REVIEW**

 **CONTENT REVIEW CD-ROM**

CHAPTER INVESTIGATION

Focus

PURPOSE Students will observe diffusion through plastic wrap to determine what factors affect its rate

OVERVIEW Students will place plastic wrap between cornstarch and iodine solutions to observe how diffusion occurs. They will find:

- Cornstarch diffuses through the plastic into the iodine.
- It lessens in concentration.
- Diffusion proceeds more quickly at steeper concentration gradients.

Lab Preparation

- Prepare the cornstarch solution for each group: 1 Tbsp cornstarch dissolved in 1 cup water.
- Prepare the iodine solutions: A—2 tsp bottled iodine solution (available in drugstores) dissolved in 1 cup water; B—1 tsp iodine dissolved in 1 cup water. C—1/2 tsp iodine dissolved in 1 cup water. Give A, B, or C to each group.
- Protect desks with newspaper.
- **SAFETY** Use safety goggles and gloves. Warn students that iodine can cause stains.
- Prior to the investigation, have students read through the investigation and prepare their data tables. Or you may wish to copy and distribute datasheets and rubrics.

 UNIT RESOURCE BOOK, pp. 111–119

 SCIENCE TOOLKIT, F14

Lab Management

- Students should check plastic wrap for holes or rips.
- Tell students to make sure that the plastic wrap extends below the surface of the cornstarch solution before they pour in the iodine solution.

CHAPTER INVESTIGATION

Diffusion

OVERVIEW AND PURPOSE The cell membrane controls what diffuses into and out of a cell. What factors affect the diffusion of substances across the cell membrane? In this investigation, you will

- observe the effect of concentration on rate of diffusion
- determine the relative concentrations of the iodine solutions used

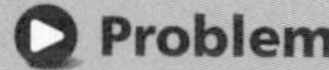

Problem

How does the concentration of a substance affect its diffusion through a membrane?

Hypothesize

Write a hypothesis to explain how concentration will affect diffusion of material through a membrane. Your hypothesis should take the form of an "If . . ., then . . ., because. . ." statement.

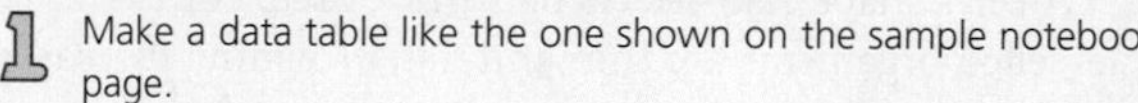

Procedure

1. Make a data table like the one shown on the sample notebook page.

2. To test for the presence of starch, use one eyedropper to put several drops of cornstarch solution on the lid of the baby food jar. With another eyedropper, add a few drops of iodine to the solution on the jar lid. Observe and record what happens.

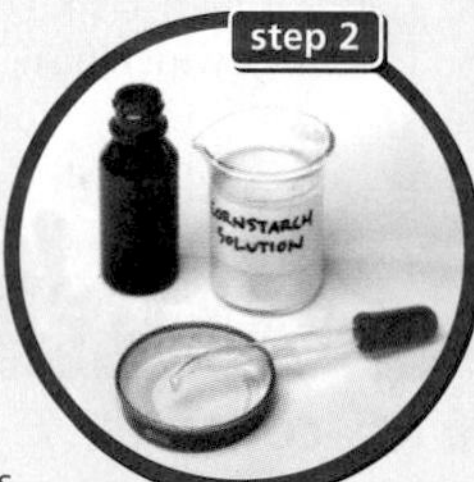

3. Fill the baby food jar about three-fourths full with the cornstarch solution.

   Place the plastic wrap inside the jar so that the plastic extends a little below the surface of the cornstarch solution.

4. Pour 10 mL of the iodine solution that you are given (A, B, or C) on the plastic wrap membrane, enough to cover the top of the plastic wrap. Record your observations.

MATERIALS
- eyedroppers
- cornstarch solution
- baby food jar with lid
- plastic wrap
- iodine solution
- graduated cylinder (if available)

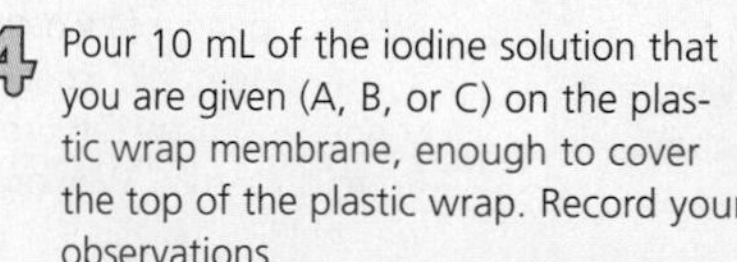

64 Unit 1: Cells and Heredity

INVESTIGATION RESOURCES

 CHAPTER INVESTIGATION, Diffusion
- Level A, pp. 111–114
- Level B, pp. 115–118
- Level C, p. 119

Advanced students should complete Levels B & C.

 Writing a Lab Report, D12–13

Technology Resources

Customize this student lab as needed or look for an alternative. Print rubrics to assess student lab reports.

 **Lab Generator CD-ROM**

5 Examine the solutions above and below the membrane after 20 minutes. Record any color changes, as well as the intensity of any changes, that you observe.

Observe and Analyze

1. **IDENTIFY VARIABLES** Identify the constants. What will stay the same in the experiment for all groups?

   Identify the independent variable. What is being changed?

   Identify the dependent variable. What is being observed and measured?

2. **RECORD OBSERVATIONS** Draw before and after pictures of your setup and label each drawing. Be sure to show the colors of the solutions on both sides of the membrane in each drawing.

   Make a drawing to show the direction in which molecules diffused through the membrane in your experiment.

   Compare the observations you made from your iodine solution with the observations made by your classmates. Be sure to record which iodine solution (A, B, or C) produced which changes.

3. **INFER** From what you've observed, which solution contains larger molecules, cornstarch or iodine? Why weren't the larger molecules able to diffuse through the membrane?

4. **INTERPRET** Which iodine solution (A, B, or C) produced the largest color change?

5. **INTERPRET** Which solution had the highest concentration of iodine, and how do you know?

6. **IDENTIFY LIMITS** Describe any errors that you made in your procedure, or places where errors might have occurred.

7. **APPLY** Identify two real-life situations in which diffusion occurs.

Conclude

1. **INTERPRET** Did starch diffuse through the membrane into the iodine solution? How do you know? Did iodine diffuse through the membrane into the cornstarch solution? How do you know?

2. **INTERPRET** What factors affect the diffusion of different substances through a membrane?

INVESTIGATE Further

CHALLENGE Investigate the role of temperature in diffusion. Predict how changes in the temperature of the iodine solution will affect the speed of diffusion through the plastic membrane. Why do you think temperature would affect the diffusion process?

Diffusion

Table 1. Color Changes

Solution	Color at 0 min		Color at 20 min	
	cornstarch solution	iodine solution	cornstarch solution	iodine solution
A				
B				
C				

Observe and Analyze

1. *constants: the cornstarch solution, the procedure, independent variable: the iodine solution; dependent variable: amount of diffusion*
2. *Answers will vary. However, drawings should generally show cornstarch diffusing through the membrane into the iodine.*

Conclude

1. *Yes, because the color of the iodine solution changed. No, because the color of the cornstarch solution did not change.*
2. *size of molecules in relation to the size of gaps in the membrane, the relative concentrations of the substances on either side of the membrane*
3. *the iodine solution; because they would not fit through the gaps in the membrane*
4. *Solution A*
5. *Solution A, because it produced the largest color change—that is, the most diffusion happened in this case, which means the difference in concentration between the iodine and the cornstarch was greatest.*
6. *Answers will vary. Sample answers: failing to check the plastic wrap for large holes and not making sure the plastic wrap is below the surface of the cornstarch.*
7. *Answers will vary.*

INVESTIGATE Further

CHALLENGE Answers will vary. One good example: An increase in temperature of the iodine solution will increase the speed of diffusion through the plastic membrane. Higher temperatures mean that the molecules are moving faster, which changes the effective concentration.

Post-Lab Discussion

- Discuss the role that the membrane plays in determining which solution moves. Ask: What does this lab tell you about possible problems when using plastic wrap for storage? *Some substances can diffuse through it.*
- Discuss any questions that were raised by the observations or analysis. What sorts of tests might answer those questions? What might be another way to test diffusion? *Answers will vary.*

BACK TO

the BIG idea

Have students choose either a plant cell or an animal cell and discuss what the cell's needs are. Have them summarize the processes that the cell might use to get what it needs. *All cells need energy. Processes include various types of transport, cellular respiration, and photosynthesis.*

KEY CONCEPTS SUMMARY

SECTION 2.1

Ask: What does each type of large molecule contribute to a cell? *Carbohydrates give energy; lipids give energy and form membranes; proteins control chemical reaction, allow movement, deliver oxygen, and more; and nucleic acids contain the instructions for the maintenance, growth, and reproduction of the cell.*

Ask: What property of water makes it so important? *Water is an excellent solvent.*

SECTION 2.2

Ask: How do plants capture light energy from the Sun? *Chlorophyll in the chloroplasts absorbs light.*

Ask: How do cells access the energy stored in glucose? *Cells use glucose in cellular respiration and fermentation.*

SECTION 2.3

Ask: How do materials move into and out of a cell? *by passive transport, active transport, exocytosis, and endocytosis*

Review Concepts

- Big Idea Flow Chart, p. T9
- Chapter Outline, pp. T15–T16

2 Chapter Review

the BIG idea

All cells need energy and materials for life processes.

KEY CONCEPTS SUMMARY

1 Chemical reactions take place inside cells.

All cells are made of the same elements. Cells contain four types of large molecules—**carbohydrates, lipids, proteins,** and **nucleic acids**—that support cell function.

About two thirds of every cell is water. The properties of water are important to cell function.

carbohydrates

lipids

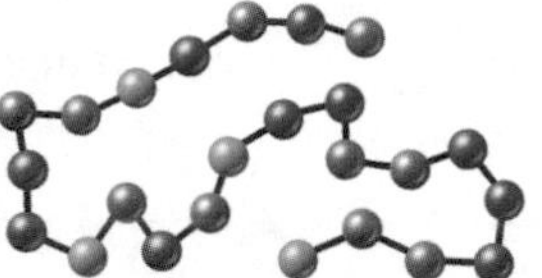
proteins

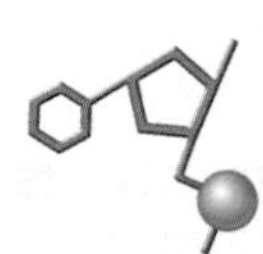
nucleic acids

VOCABULARY
chemical reaction p. 42
carbohydrate p. 42
lipid p. 43
protein p. 43
nucleic acid p. 43

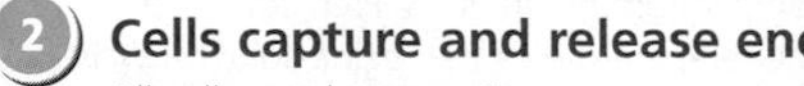

2 Cells capture and release energy.

All cells need energy. Some cells capture light energy through **photosynthesis.** All cells release chemical energy from glucose.

Cellular respiration and **fermentation** are two ways that cells release energy from glucose.

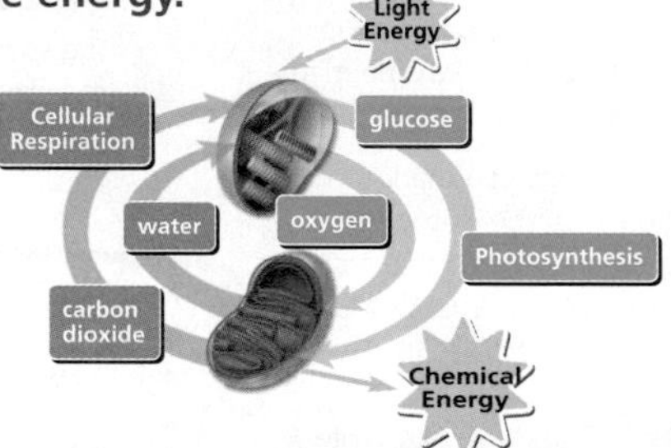

VOCABULARY
chemical energy p. 47
glucose p. 47
photosynthesis p. 48
chlorophyll p. 48
cellular respiration p. 50
fermentation p. 52

3 Materials move across the cell's membranes.

Passive transport is the movement of materials from an area of higher concentration to an area of lower concentration. **Diffusion** and **osmosis** are examples of passive transport.

Active transport is the movement of materials from an area of lower concentration to an area of higher concentration. Cells need energy to perform active transport.

passive transport

active transport

VOCABULARY
diffusion p. 56
passive transport p. 58
osmosis p. 59
active transport p. 60

Technology Resources

Have students visit **ClassZone.com** or use the CD-ROM for a cumulative review of concepts.

CONTENT REVIEW

CONTENT REVIEW CD-ROM

Engage students in a whole-class interactive review of Key Concepts. Edit content as you wish.

POWER PRESENTATIONS

Reviewing Vocabulary

Use words from the vocabulary lists on page 66 to answer these questions.

1. Which molecule stores information?
2. Which word describes the process when two or more atoms bond together?
3. What kind of energy do cells use?
4. Which term describes the process in which cells release energy without using oxygen?
5. Which process occurs in chloroplasts?
6. From what sugar molecule do many living things release energy?
7. Which chemical that aids in photosynthesis do you find in a chloroplast?
8. Which word means "diffusion of water across cell membranes"?
9. Choose two pairs of opposite processes.
10. Use a Venn diagram to compare and contrast passive transport and active transport.

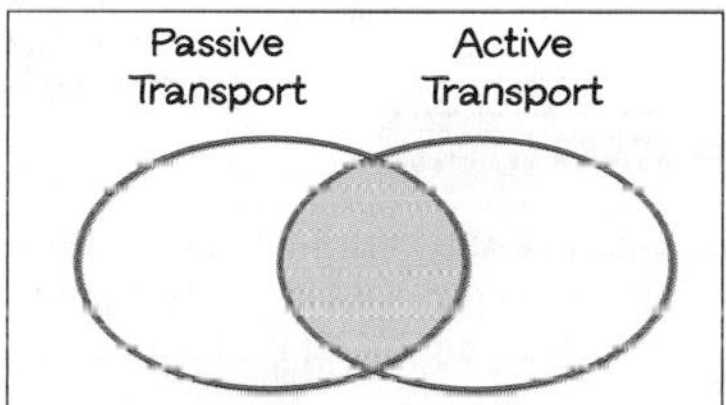

Reviewing Key Concepts

Multiple Choice *Choose the letter of the best answer.*

11. The fats, oils, and waxes found in living things are known as
    a. lipids
    b. proteins
    c. carbohydrates
    d. glucose
12. What do cells use as a source of energy and for energy storage?
    a. proteins
    b. water
    c. cytoplasm
    d. carbohydrates
13. Leaf cells use chlorophyll to absorb
    a. oxygen
    b. light energy
    c. carbon dioxide
    d. glucose
14. The cells of a redwood tree require oxygen for the process of
    a. photosynthesis
    b. cellular respiration
    c. fermentation
    d. endocytosis
15. In fermentation, cells release energy without
    a. alcohol
    b. water
    c. glucose
    d. oxygen
16. Both a whale and a seaweed use which of the following to change glucose into energy?
    a. water
    b. photosynthesis
    c. cellular respiration
    d. bonding
17. The movement of materials across a cell membrane, requiring energy, is called
    a. diffusion
    b. osmosis
    c. passive transport
    d. active transport

Short Answer *Write a short answer to each question.*

18. Why is water needed by cells?
19. Describe the main function of nucleic acids.
20. What is the role of chlorophyll in a plant's leaves?
21. Explain why a carrot feels spongy after being soaked in salt water.
22. Explain how the ways in which plants and animals get their energy differ.

ASSESSMENT RESOURCES

UNIT ASSESSMENT BOOK
- Chapter Test A, pp. 25–28
- Chapter Test B, pp. 29–32
- Chapter Test C, pp. 33–36
- Alternative Assessment, pp. 37–38

SPANISH ASSESSMENT BOOK
Spanish Chapter Test, pp. 5–8

Technology Resources

Edit test items and answer choices.

Test Generator CD-ROM

Visit **ClassZone.com** to extend test practice.

Test Practice

Reviewing Vocabulary

1. *nucleic acid*
2. *chemical reaction*
3. *chemical energy*
4. *fermentation*
5. *photosynthesis*
6. *glucose*
7. *chlorophyll*
8. *osmosis*
9. *active and passive transport; cellular respiration and photosynthesis are complementary.*
10. *Passive Transport: uses no energy; Active Transport: requires energy; Both: moves materials through a membrane*

Reviewing Key Concepts

11. *a*
12. *d*
13. *b*
14. *b*
15. *d*
16. *c*
17. *d*
18. *All the chemical reactions in a cell take place in water.*
19. *They map how to make new cells.*
20. *It captures energy from the Sun. This energy is used to change raw materials into glucose.*
21. *It loses water to the salt water, which has a lower concentration of water than the carrot does.*
22. *Plants get their energy from the Sun by the process of photosynthesis. Animals get their energy from the food they eat.*

23. *Most of a cell's activities require chemical reactions.*
24. *Cell membranes, made of lipids, repel water. It does not illustrate transport across a membrane.*
25. *carbon dioxide and water; oxygen and sugar*
26. *oxygen and sugar; carbon dioxide and water*
27. *Photosynthesis and cellular respiration can cycle into each other.*
28. *Osmosis: no, yes; Active transport: yes, no; Passive transport: no, yes*
29. *Because there was no oxygen, fermentation occurred when the yeast used the sugar in the grape juice.*
30. *It would put too much salt in the body, which would dehydrate the cells.*
31. *It will decrease.*

the BIG idea

32. *Plants need energy from the Sun.*
33. *Yes; ultimately all the energy we get comes from the Sun. Plants convert sunlight to energy. Some they use and some they store. We get energy from eating plants or from eating other animals that ate plants.*
34. *Plants use carbon dioxide to produce energy and they release oxygen, so in a way, they clean the air we breathe. If developers clear a forest for the shopping center, there would be an increase in carbon dioxide from the increased traffic and fewer trees to use the carbon dioxide.*

UNIT PROJECTS

Collect schedules, materials lists, and questions. Be sure dates and materials are obtainable, and questions are focused.

Unit Projects, pp. 5–10

Thinking Critically

23. **RECOGNIZE CAUSE AND EFFECT** Explain why chemical reactions are essential to living creatures.
24. **MODEL** How does a glass filled with oil and water illustrate the properties of a cell membrane? What properties does it not illustrate?

The illustration below summarizes the relationship between photosynthesis and cellular respiration. Use it to answer the next three questions.

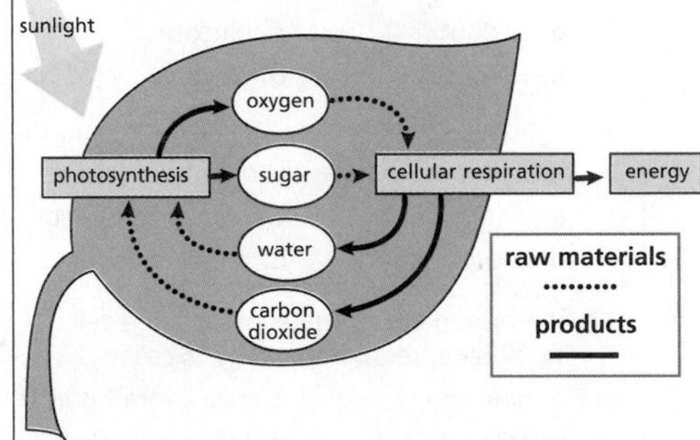

25. **OBSERVE** What are the starting materials of photosynthesis? What are the starting materials of cellular respiration?
26. **OBSERVE** What are the products of photosynthesis? What are the products of cellular respiration?
27. **DRAW CONCLUSIONS** What does the diagram above reveal about the connections between photosynthesis and cellular respiration?

Process	Requires Energy?	Moves from Higher to Lower Concentration?
Diffusion	no	yes
Osmosis		
Active transport		
Passive transport		

28. **CHART INFORMATION** Copy and complete this chart. The first line is done for you.
29. **INFER** The French scientist Louis Pasteur mixed yeast and grape juice in a sealed container. When he opened the container, the grape juice contained alcohol. Explain what happened.
30. **DRAW CONCLUSIONS** Why would it be harmful to your health to drink seawater?
31. **PREDICT** Look at the diagram at the right. The bag has pores that are bigger than the sugar molecules. What will be true of the concentration of the sugar water after a few hours?

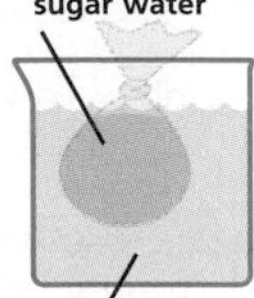

the BIG idea

32. **COMPARE AND CONTRAST** Look again at the picture on pages 38–39. Why do you think the sunflowers are facing the Sun?
33. **INFER** Does your body get all its energy from the Sun? Explain.
34. **WRITE** Imagine that your community has a high level of carbon dioxide emission from cars and factories. A developer wants to build a shopping center on the remaining forest land. Would this action increase or decrease carbon dioxide levels? Why? Write a paragraph explaining your answer.

UNIT PROJECTS

Check your schedule for your unit project. How are you doing? Be sure that you have placed data or notes from your research in your project folder.

MONITOR AND RETEACH

If students have difficulty with items 25–27, refer them to the energy cycle diagram on p. 52. Have them summarize the cycle. Then have students explain why and how diffusion is important to the cycle.

Students may benefit from summarizing one or more sections of the chapter.

Summarizing the Chapter, pp. 129–130

Standardized Test Practice

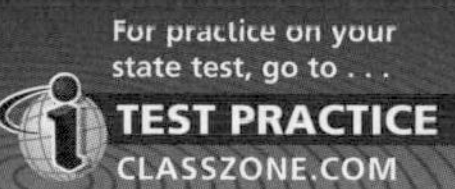

Analyzing Data

Elodea plants in beakers of water were placed at different distances from a light source. The number of bubbles that formed on the plants was counted and recorded. The data table shows the results.

Beaker	Distance from light	Bubbles per minute
1	200 cm	2
2	100 cm	10
3	50 cm	45
4	20 cm	83

Study the data and answer the questions below.

1. What gas do the bubbles consist of?
   a. carbon dioxide c. water vapor
   b. hydrogen d. oxygen
2. What is the relationship between the distance from the light source and the rate of bubble formation?
   a. The rate increases as the distance increases.
   b. The rate decreases as the distance increases.
   c. The rate stays the same as the distance increases.
   d. The rate changes in a way unrelated to distance.
3. If another beaker with *elodea* were placed 150 cm from the light, about how many bubbles would form each minute?
   a. 1 c. 11
   b. 7 d. 24

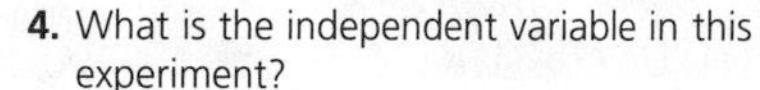

4. What is the independent variable in this experiment?
   a. type of plant c. distance from light
   b. number of bubbles d. amount of time
5. Which graph best represents the data shown in the table?

a.

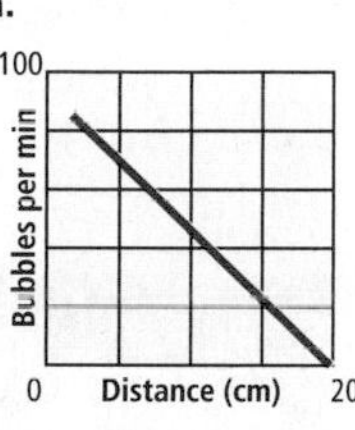

c.

100
Bubbles per min
0 Distance (cm) 200

b.

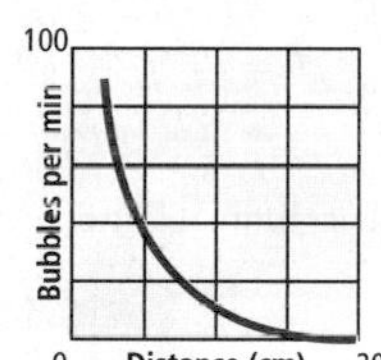

d.

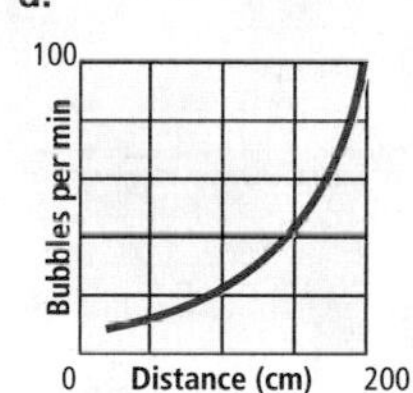

Extended Response

Answer each question. Include some of the terms shown in the word box. In your answers underline each term you use.

chemical energy	cellular respiration
osmosis	chloroplasts
fermentation	glucose
photosynthesis	diffusion

6. A person rides his bicycle several miles. What process is used by the cells in his legs to release energy at the beginning of the ride? At the end of the ride? Explain.
7. A student places a plant in a sealed container and puts the container on a window sill. She leaves the plant there for a week. Will the plant have the starting materials it needs to carry out photosynthesis during the entire week? Explain.

METACOGNITIVE ACTIVITY

Have students answer the following questions in their **Science Notebook:**

1. What helped you understand photosynthesis and cellular respiration?
2. How can you spot an error in your description of photosynthesis and cellular respiration?
3. What's the point of learning about carbohydrates, lipids, proteins, and amino acids? Why is it helpful in your daily life?

Analyzing Data

1. d *3. b* *5. b*
2. b *4. c*

Extended Response

6. RUBRIC

4 points for a response that correctly answers the questions and includes the terms:

- chemical energy
- fermentation
- cellular respiration
- glucose

Sample answer: At the beginning of the ride, muscle cells release chemical energy through cellular respiration. The more a person rides, the more glucose is needed for energy. Near the end of the ride, the muscle cells may have used up their energy and oxygen. Muscle cells then rely on fermentation to break down sugars. The waste product of fermentation is lactic acid, which may cause the person's legs to have a burning sensation.

3 points correctly answers the questions and includes three of the terms shown
2 points correctly answers the questions and includes two of the terms shown
1 point correctly answers the questions and includes at least one term

7. RUBRIC

4 points for a response that correctly answers the question and includes the terms:

- osmosis
- photosynthesis
- chloroplasts
- diffusion

Sample answer: No, the plant cannot carry out photosynthesis for the entire week. For photosynthesis to occur, the plant's chloroplasts need carbon dioxide (from air) and water. The sealed container prevents the plant from obtaining either of these. Some materials may move through cell membranes through diffusion without using the cell's energy. However, osmosis will not occur because the plant will not receive water.

3 points correctly answers the question and includes three of the terms shown
2 points correctly answers the questions and includes two of the terms shown
1 point correctly answers the questions and includes at least one term

CHAPTER

Cell Division

Life Science
UNIFYING PRINCIPLES

PRINCIPLE 1
All living things share common characteristics.

PRINCIPLE 2
All living things share common needs.

PRINCIPLE 3
Living things meet their needs through interactions with the environment.

PRINCIPLE 4
The types and numbers of living things change over time.

Unit 1: Cells and Heredity
BIG IDEAS

CHAPTER 1
The Cell
All living things are made up of cells.

CHAPTER 2
How Cells Function
All cells need energy and materials for life processes.

CHAPTER 3
Cell Division
Organisms grow, reproduce, and maintain themselves through cell division.

CHAPTER 4
Patterns of Heredity
In sexual reproduction, genes are passed from parents to offspring in predictable patterns.

CHAPTER 5
DNA and Modern Genetics
DNA is a set of instructions for making cell parts.

CHAPTER 3
KEY CONCEPTS

SECTION 1

Cell division occurs in all organisms.

1. Cell division is involved in many functions.
2. The genetic material of eukaryotic cells is organized in chromosomes.
3. Cell division is involved in growth, development, and repair.

SECTION 2

Cell division is part of the cell cycle.

1. The cell cycle includes interphase and cell division.
2. Cell division produces two genetically identical cells.

SECTION 3

Both sexual and asexual reproduction involve cell division.

1. Asexual reproduction involves one parent.
2. Sexual reproduction involves two parent organisms.

T The Big Idea Flow Chart is available on p. T17 in the **UNIT TRANSPARENCY BOOK.**

Previewing Content

SECTION

Cell division occurs in all organisms. pp. 73–79

1. Cell division is involved in many functions.
Bodies grow because more cells are formed, not because cells get bigger.

2. The genetic material of eukaryotic cells is organized in chromosomes.
Deoxyribonucleic acid (DNA) is a chemical that directs a cell's growth and functions. DNA is made of two strands of molecules joined in a structure that resembles a twisted ladder, or double helix.

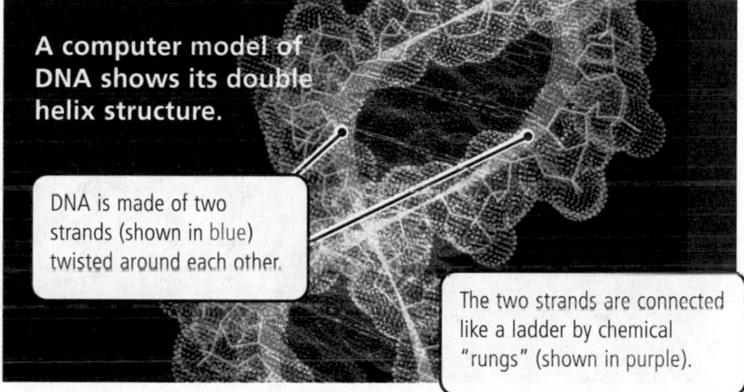

DNA is in the nucleus of a cell, usually as a mass of loose strands. When a cell prepares to divide, the DNA condenses into structures called **chromosomes,** which duplicate themselves.

3. Cell division is involved in growth, development, and repair.
Most multicellular organisms start out as a single cell. A cell must have a certain amount of membrane surface to exchange materials, so cell size is limited by the ratio of surface area to volume.

- Cell division is responsible for the organism's growth.
- Development results when new cells specialize and act with other similar cells to form tissues.

SECTION

Cell division is part of the cell cycle. pp. 80–87

1. The cell cycle includes interphase and cell division.
The cell cycle consists of two main phases.

- **Interphase** is the period when the cell is not dividing. The cell grows and conducts normal functions such as nutrient intake, waste excretion, and cellular respiration. It also duplicates its DNA in preparation for the next phase.

Cell Cycle

The events that happen during the life of a cell are called the cell cycle.

1 **Interphase** The **cell cycle** begins with interphase, which is the longest part of the cell cycle.

2 **Cell Division Phase** After **mitosis** and **cytokinesis** there are two cells. The cell cycle then begins again for each cell.

INTERPHASE
cell grows and carries out normal functions; organelles duplicate
DNA replicates and chromosomes duplicate
cell grows and prepares for mitosis
CYTOKINESIS
MITOSIS
Telophase
Anaphase
Metaphase
Prophase

- **Mitosis** is the part of the cell cycle when the nucleus divides. At the end of mitosis the cell's cytoplasm divides, producing two daughter cells.

2. Cell division produces two genetically identical cells.
Mitosis has four phases.

- During **prophase** the DNA condenses into chromosomes.
- During **metaphase** the chromosomes line up in the middle of the cell.
- During **anaphase** the chromatids split up, forming two chromosomes. These are pulled to opposite sides of the cell.
- During **telophase** a new membrane forms around each group of chromosomes, and the chromosomes revert to threadlike form.

After mitosis, **cytokinesis** divides the parent's cytoplasm. Because two daughter cells are genetically identical, they function the way their parent cell did.

Common Misconceptions

MISCONCEPTION DATABASE
CLASSZONE.COM Background on student misconceptions

CELL DIVISION, ENLARGEMENT, AND DIFFERENTIATION Students sometimes think that living things grow because cells get larger, and they do not understand the role of differentiation. In fact, cells divide and specialize for the multicellular organism's growth.

 This misconception is addressed on p. 77.

THE LOCATION OF CHROMOSOMES Students sometimes think that only brain and/or sex cells have chromosomes. Virtually all cells have chromosomes, however.

 This misconception is addressed on p. 82.

SECTION

3 Both sexual and asexual reproduction involve cell division. pp. 88–93

1. Asexual reproduction involves one parent.
Most single-celled organisms reproduce asexually.
- In binary fission, cell division produces two daughter cells that are two new organisms.
- Some single-celled organisms reproduce by budding. The parent organism produces a protuberance that drops off and becomes a new organism.
- Some multicellular organisms can regenerate from parts. Plants can often grow from cuttings, and starfish can regenerate from fragments that include part of their center disk.
- Rapid generation rate in asexually reproducing organisms makes it more likely that some offspring will have a random genetic change that may be beneficial.

2. Sexual reproduction involves two parent organisms.
In sexual reproduction, genetic material combines equally from the two parents. The chance for genetic variation in offspring is high.

Comparing Asexual and Sexual Reproduction

Asexual Reproduction	Sexual Reproduction
Cell Division	Cell division and other processes
One parent organism	Two parent organisms
Rate of reproduction is rapid	Rate of reproduction is slower than rate for asexual reproduction
Offspring identical to parents	Offspring have genetic information from two parents

Regeneration This starfish is regenerating its legs that were lost.

Common Misconceptions

MISCONCEPTION DATABASE
CLASSZONE.COM Background on student misconceptions

CELL DIVISION AND ASEXUAL REPRODUCTION Students often do not understand or acknowledge asexual reproduction. In asexual reproduction, cell division results not just in a new cell but in a whole new organism. The main difference between the two types of reproduction is the number of parents involved.

This misconception is addressed on p. 89.

Previewing Labs

Lab Generator CD-ROM
Edit these Pupil Edition labs and generate alternative labs.

EXPLORE the BIG idea

Lab	Time and Materials
Dividing to Multiply, p. 71 Students observe maple seeds to understand how splitting them affects reproduction.	**TIME** 10 minutes **MATERIALS** several maple samara (seed pod pairs from any species of maple)
Division Math, p. 71 Students divide clay to model cell division.	**TIME** 10 minutes **MATERIALS** clay
Internet Activity: Cell Division, p. 71 Students take a virtual tour of mitosis to view cell division.	**TIME** 20 minutes **MATERIALS** computer with Internet access

SECTION 

Lab	Time and Materials
EXPLORE Cell Division, p. 73 Students pair socks while blindfolded to explore the benefits of organization in cell division.	**TIME** 10 minutes **MATERIALS** 2 blindfolds; assorted socks, paired and not; stopwatch
INVESTIGATE Chromosomes, p. 76 Students use yarn to model the compaction of DNA.	**TIME** 20 minutes **MATERIALS** 4 long pieces of different-colored yarn, 4 craft sticks

SECTION 

Lab	Time and Materials
INVESTIGATE Cell Division, p. 84 Students model the stages of mitosis, using craft supplies.	**TIME** 30 minutes **MATERIALS** poster board, markers, pipe cleaners, packing peanuts, glue, scissors, yarn
CHAPTER INVESTIGATION **Stages of the Cell Cycle,** pp. 86–87 Students use a microscope to observe mitosis in the root tips of an onion.	**TIME** 40 minutes **MATERIALS** prepared slides of onion root tips, compound light microscope, Cell Division Diagram (PE p. 83, also available as T22 in the Unit Transparency Book)

SECTION 

Lab	Time and Materials
INVESTIGATE Asexual Reproduction, p. 91 Students plant different pieces of a houseplant to conclude which parts are able to regenerate.	**TIME** 15 minutes **MATERIALS** pieces of a houseplant, flowerpot, soil, water

 **Additional INVESTIGATION,** Temperature and Yeast Reproduction, A, B, & C, pp. 180–188; Teacher Instructions, pp. 308–309

Previewing Chapter Resources

CHAPTER 3 Cell Division

	INTEGRATED TECHNOLOGY	LABS AND ACTIVITIES
CHAPTER 3 Cell Division	 **CLASSZONE.COM** • eEdition Plus • EasyPlanner Plus • Misconception Database • Content Review • Test Practice • Visualization • Resource Centers • Internet Activity: Cell Division • Math Tutorial  **SCILINKS.ORG** 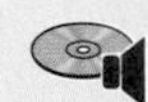 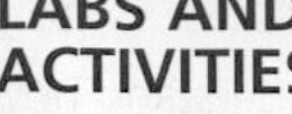 **CD-ROMS** • eEdition • EasyPlanner • Power Presentations • Content Review • Lab Generator • Test Generator 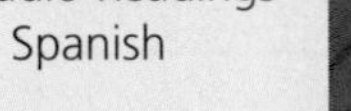 **AUDIO CDS** • Audio Readings • Audio Readings in Spanish	 EXPLORE the Big Idea, p. 71 • Dividing to Multiply • Division Math • Internet Activity: Cell Division  **UNIT RESOURCE BOOK** Unit Projects, pp. 5–10 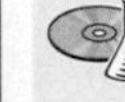 **Lab Generator CD-ROM** Generate customized labs.
 SECTION 1 **Cell division occurs in all organisms.** pp. 73–79 Time: 2 periods (1 block)  Lesson Plan, pp. 131–132	 **RESOURCE CENTER,** Nerve Cell Growth **UNIT TRANSPARENCY BOOK** • Big Idea Flow Chart, p. T17 • Daily Vocabulary Scaffolding, p. T18 • Note-Taking Model, p. T19 • 3-Minute Warm-Up, p. T20	 • EXPLORE Cell Division, p. 73 • INVESTIGATE Chromosomes, p. 76 • Connecting Sciences, p. 79  **UNIT RESOURCE BOOK** Datasheet, Chromosomes, p. 140
 SECTION 2 **Cell division is part of the cell cycle.** pp. 80–87 Time: 3 periods (1.5 block)  Lesson Plan, pp. 142–143	 • **RESOURCE CENTER,** Cell Cycle • **VISUALIZATION,** Mitosis **UNIT TRANSPARENCY BOOK** • Daily Vocabulary Scaffolding, p. T18 • 3-Minute Warm-Up, p. T20 • "Cell Division" Visual, p. T22	 • INVESTIGATE Cell Division, p. 84 • CHAPTER INVESTIGATION, Stages of the Cell Cycle, pp. 86–87  **UNIT RESOURCE BOOK** • Datasheet, Cell Division, p. 151 • CHAPTER INVESTIGATION, Stages of the Cell Cycle, A, B, & C, pp. 171–179
 SECTION 3 **Both sexual and asexual reproduction involve cell division.** pp. 88–93 Time: 3 periods (1.5 blocks)  Lesson Plan, pp. 153–154	 • **MATH TUTORIAL** • **RESOURCE CENTER,** Asexual Reproduction  **UNIT TRANSPARENCY BOOK** • Big Idea Flow Chart, p. T17 • Daily Vocabulary Scaffolding, p. T18 • 3-Minute Warm-Up, p. T21 • Chapter Outline, pp. T23–T24	 • INVESTIGATE Asexual Reproduction, p. 91 • Math in Science, p. 93  **UNIT RESOURCE BOOK** • Datasheet, Asexual Reproduction, p. 162 • Math Support, p. 169 • Math Practice, p. 170 • Additional INVESTIGATION, Temperature and Yeast Reproduction, A, B, & C, pp. 180–188

KEY TO ICONS

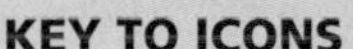

 CD/CD-ROM
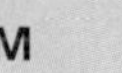
 INTERNET
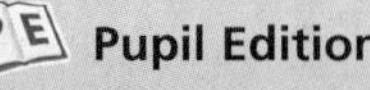 Pupil Edition
 Teacher Edition
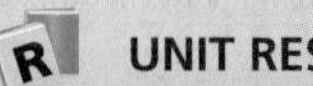 UNIT RESOURCE BOOK
 UNIT TRANSPARENCY BOOK
 UNIT ASSESSMENT BOOK
SPANISH ASSESSMENT BOOK
 SCIENCE TOOLKIT

READING AND REINFORCEMENT

- Frame Game, B26–27
- Combination Notes, C36
- Daily Vocabulary Scaffolding, H1–8

 **UNIT RESOURCE BOOK**
- Vocabulary Practice, pp. 166–167
- Decoding Support, p. 168
- Summarizing the Chapter, pp. 189–190

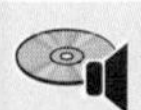 **Audio Readings CD**
Listen to Pupil Edition.

 **Audio Readings in Spanish CD**
Listen to Pupil Edition in Spanish.

ASSESSMENT

- Chapter Review, pp. 94–96
- Standardized Test Practice, p. 97

 **UNIT ASSESSMENT BOOK**
- Diagnostic Test, pp. 39–40
- Chapter Test, A, B, & C, pp. 44–55
- Alternative Assessment, pp. 56–57

 **SPANISH ASSESSMENT BOOK**
Spanish Chapter Test, pp. 9–12

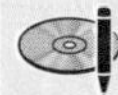 **Test Generator CD-ROM**
Generate customized tests.

 **Lab Generator CD-ROM**
Rubrics for Labs

STANDARDS

National Standards
A.2–8, A.9.a–f, C.1.c, C.2.a, G.1.b

See p. 70 for the standards.

 **UNIT RESOURCE BOOK**
- Reading Study Guide, A & B, pp. 133–136
- Spanish Reading Study Guide, pp. 137–138
- Challenge and Extension, p. 139
- Reinforcing Key Concepts, p. 141

 Ongoing Assessment, pp. 74–75, 77–78

 Section 3.1 Review, p. 78

 **UNIT ASSESSMENT BOOK**
Section 3.1 Quiz, p. 41

National Standards
A.2–7, A.9.a–b, A.9.e–f, C.1.c, G.1.b

 **UNIT RESOURCE BOOK**
- Reading Study Guide, A & B, pp. 144–147
- Spanish Reading Study Guide, pp. 148–149
- Challenge and Extension, p. 150
- Reinforcing Key Concepts, p. 152
- Challenge Reading, pp. 164–165

 Ongoing Assessment, pp. 81–82, 84–85

 Section 3.2 Review, p. 85

 **UNIT ASSESSMENT BOOK**
Section 3.2 Quiz, p. 42

National Standards
A.2–7, A.9.a–b, A.9.d–f, C.1.c, G.1.b

 **UNIT RESOURCE BOOK**
- Reading Study Guide, A & B, pp. 155–158
- Spanish Reading Study Guide, pp. 159–160
- Challenge and Extension, p. 161
- Reinforcing Key Concepts, p. 163

 Ongoing Assessment, pp. 89–92

 Section 3.3 Review, p. 92

 **UNIT ASSESSMENT BOOK**
Section 3.3 Quiz, p. 43

National Standards
A.2–8, A.9.a–c, A.9.e–f, C.2.a, G.1.b

Previewing Resources for Differentiated Instruction

CHAPTER INVESTIGATION

Leveled resources present the same concepts for different abilities.

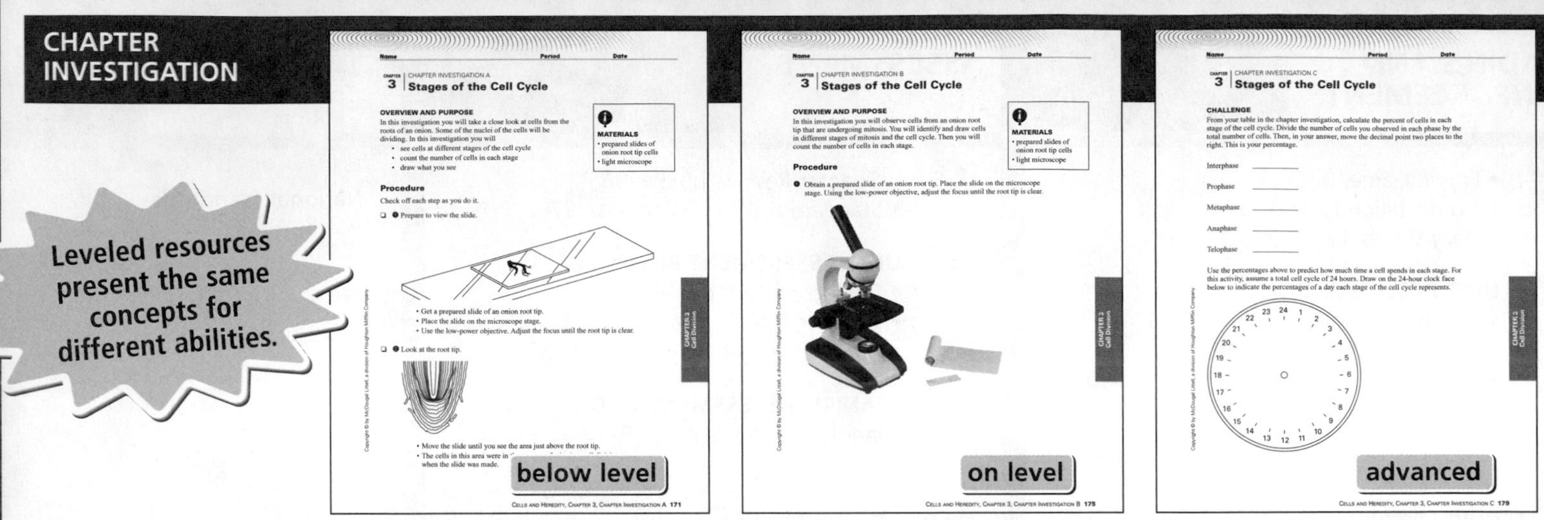

UNIT RESOURCE BOOK, pp. 171–174 | pp. 175–178 | pp. 175–179

READING STUDY GUIDE

Reading Study Guide is also in Spanish.

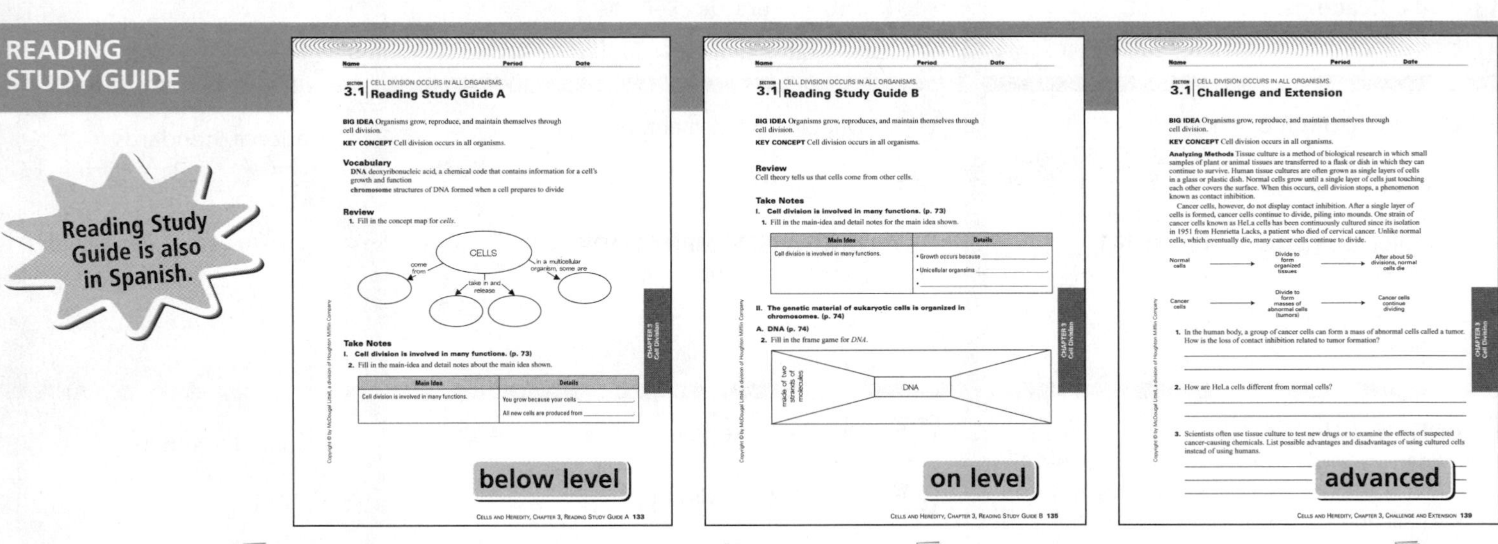

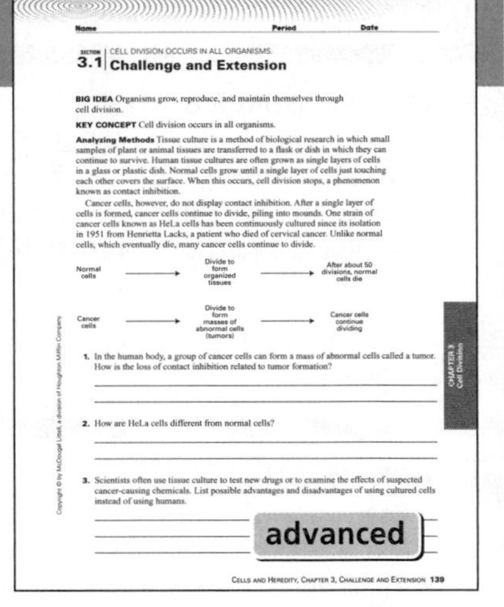

UNIT RESOURCE BOOK, pp. 133–134 | pp. 135–136 | p. 139

CHAPTER TEST

Chapter Test is also in Spanish.

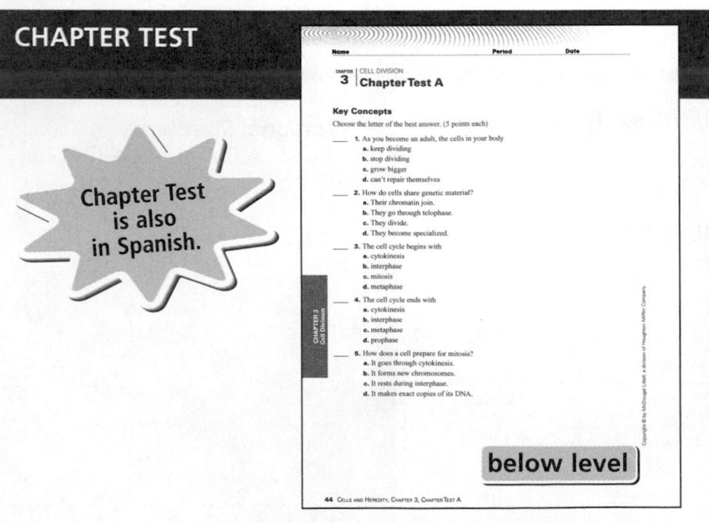

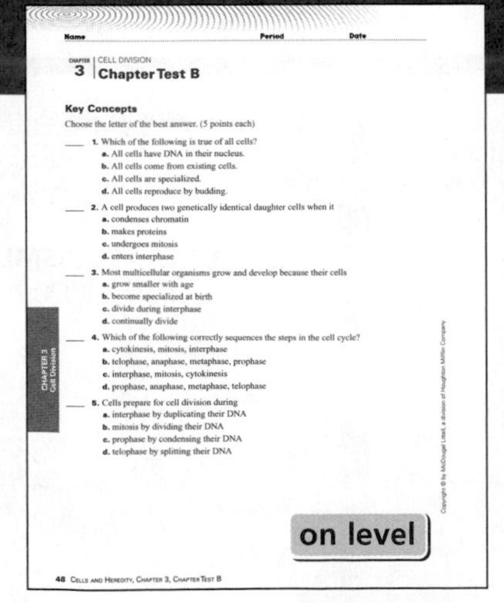

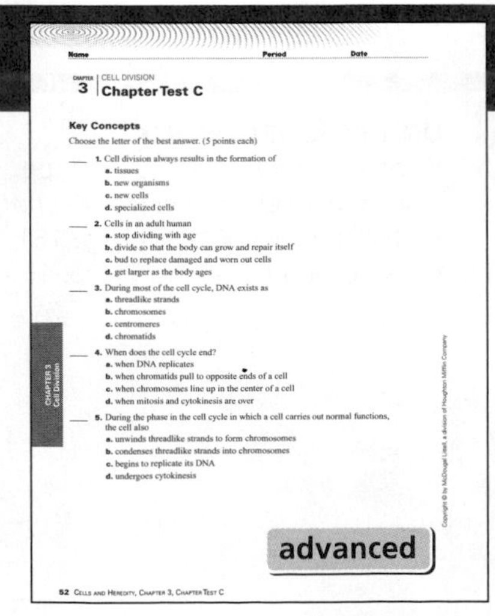

UNIT ASSESSMENT BOOK, pp. 44–47 | pp. 48–51 | pp. 52–55

TECHNOLOGY

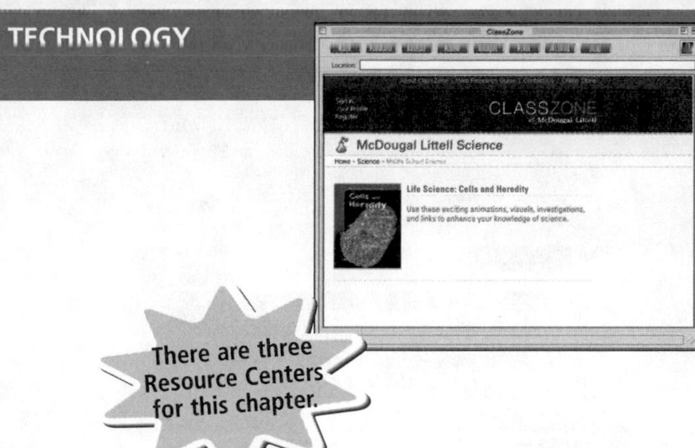

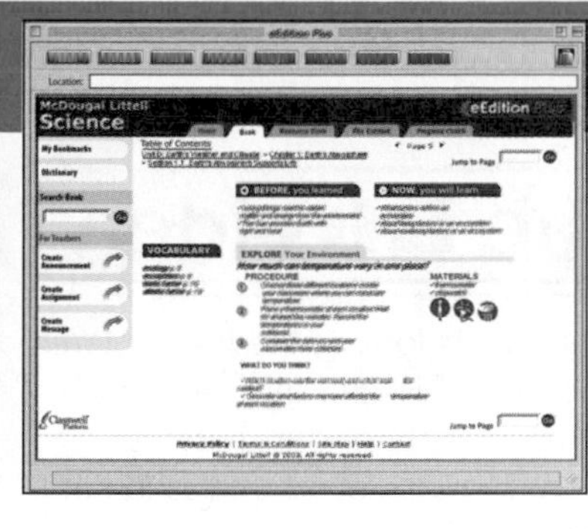

CLASSZONE.COM

CD/CD-ROMS

CLASSZONE.COM

VISUAL CONTENT

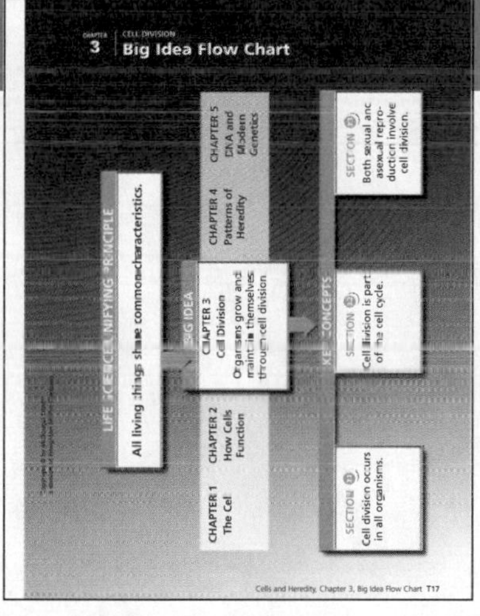

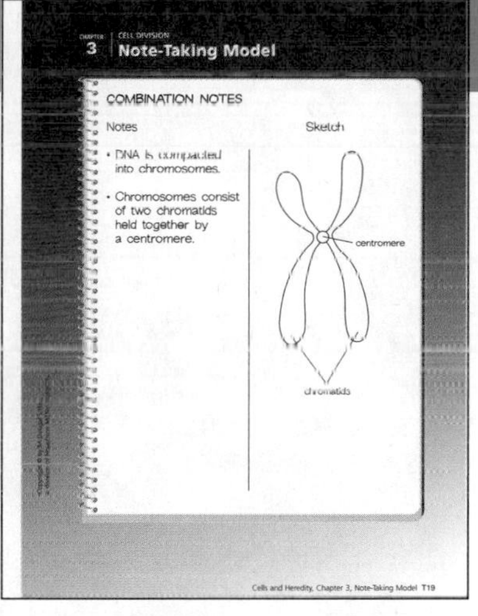

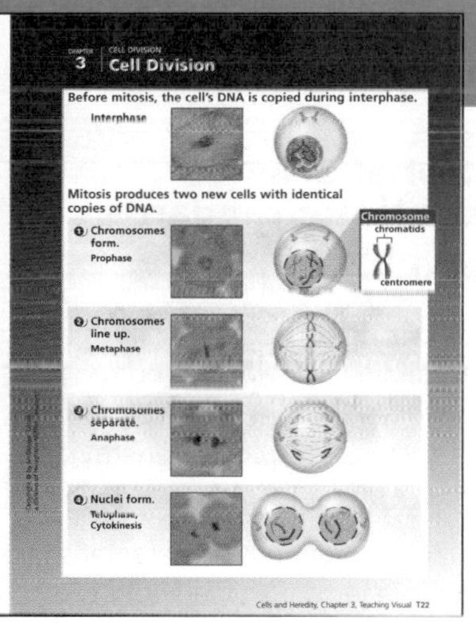

UNIT TRANSPARENCY BOOK, p. T17

p. T19

p. T22

MORE SUPPORT

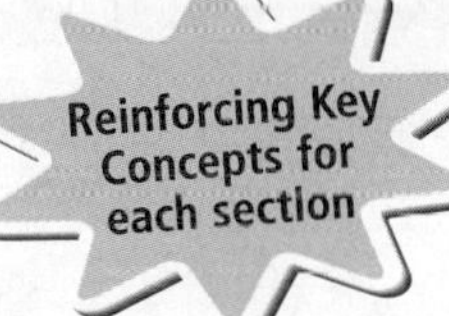

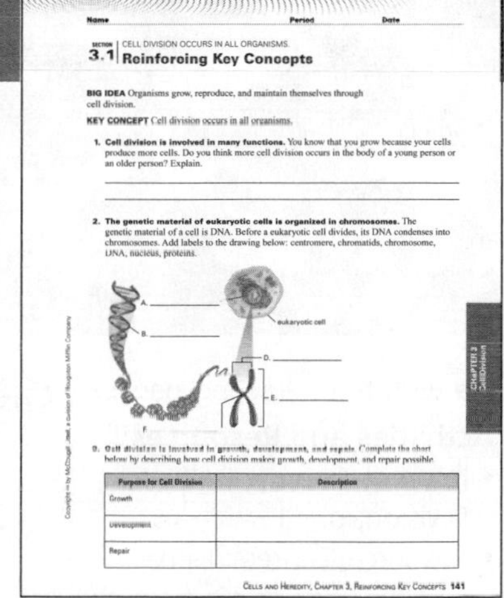

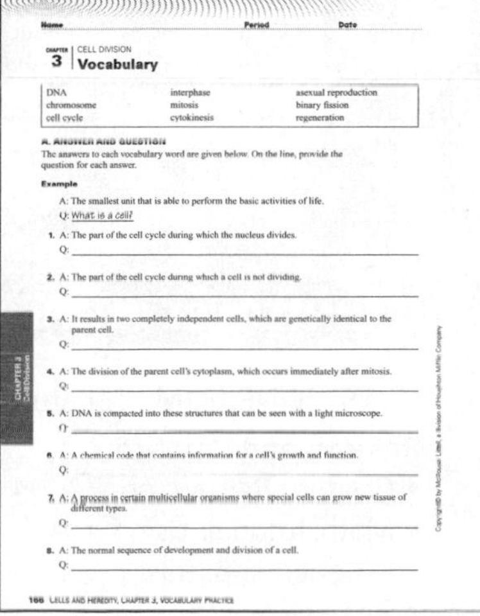

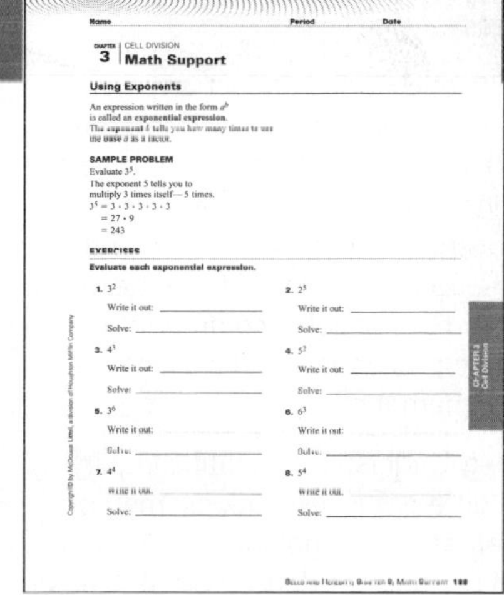

UNIT RESOURCE BOOK, p. 141

pp. 166–167

p. 169

CHAPTER 3 Cell Division

INTRODUCE

the BIG idea

Have students look at the false-colored micrograph of listeria cells (a type of bacteria). The cell in the center is dividing. Discuss how the question in the box links to the Big Idea: Ask:

- How do plants, animals, and other living things grow?
- Point out that the photograph shows growth at a microscopic level. Cells in the picture are dividing and growing, just as cells in the human body—and in every organism—do.
- Ask: Other than for growth, how might new cells help a body?

National Science Education Standards

Content

C.1.c Cells perform the functions needed to sustain life. They grow and divide. This requires that they take in nutrients, which they use to provide energy and materials.

C.2.a Reproduction is a characteristic of all living systems. Reproduction is essential to the continuation of a species. Some organisms reproduce asexually, others sexually.

Process

A.2–8 Design and conduct an investigation; use tools to gather and interpret data; use evidence to describe, predict, explain, model; think critically to make relationships between evidence and explanation; recognize different explanations and predictions; communicate scientific procedures and explanations; use mathematics.

A.9.a–g Understand scientific inquiry by using different investigations, methods, mathematics, technology, explanations based on logic, evidence, and skepticism.

G.1.b Science requires different abilities.

CHAPTER 3 Cell Division

the BIG idea

Organisms grow, reproduce, and maintain themselves through cell division.

Key Concepts

SECTION

Cell division occurs in all organisms.
Learn about the functions of cell division.

SECTION

Cell division is part of the cell cycle.
Learn about the cell cycle and the process of mitosis.

SECTION

Both sexual and asexual reproduction involve cell division.
Learn how sexual reproduction compares with asexual reproduction.

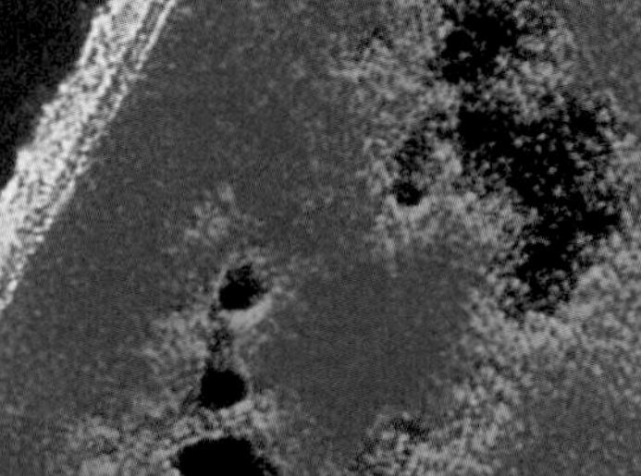

Some of these bacterial cells are dividing. How are the cells formed in cell division like the other cells in the photograph?

Internet Preview

CLASSZONE.COM

Chapter 3 online resources: Content Review, Simulation, Visualization, three Resource Centers, Math Tutorial, Test Practice

INTERNET PREVIEW

CLASSZONE.COM For student use with the following pages:

Review and Practice
- Content Review, pp. 72, 94
- Math Tutorial: Using Exponents, p. 93
- Test Practice, p. 97

Activities and Resources
- Internet Activity: Cell Division, p. 71
- Resource Centers: Nerve Cell Growth, p. 79; Cell Cycle, p. 80; Asexual Reproduction, p. 90
- Visualization: Mitosis, p. 83

Cellular Mitosis
Code: MDL033

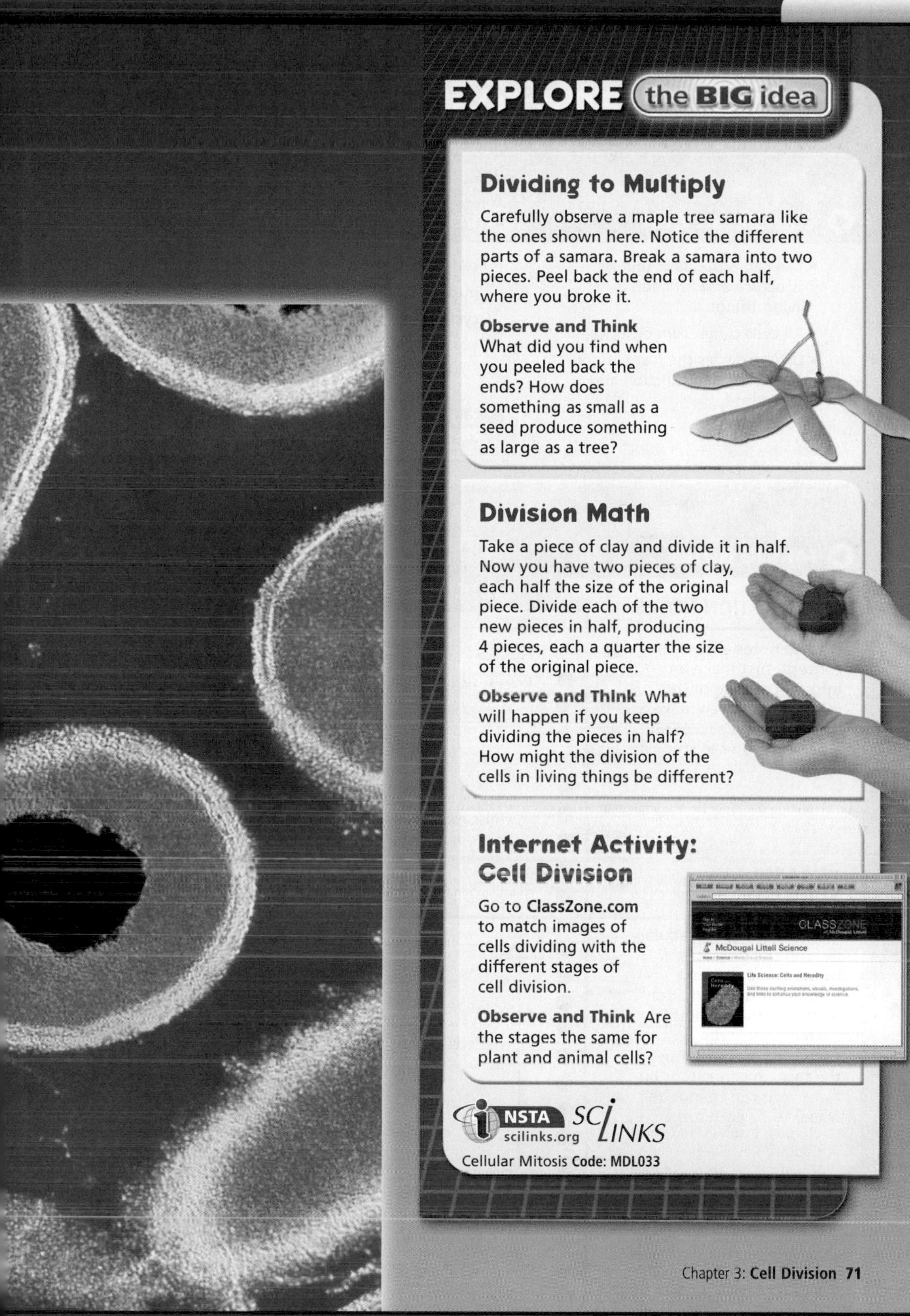

EXPLORE the BIG idea

Dividing to Multiply

Carefully observe a maple tree samara like the ones shown here. Notice the different parts of a samara. Break a samara into two pieces. Peel back the end of each half, where you broke it.

Observe and Think What did you find when you peeled back the ends? How does something as small as a seed produce something as large as a tree?

Division Math

Take a piece of clay and divide it in half. Now you have two pieces of clay, each half the size of the original piece. Divide each of the two new pieces in half, producing 4 pieces, each a quarter the size of the original piece.

Observe and Think What will happen if you keep dividing the pieces in half? How might the division of the cells in living things be different?

Internet Activity: Cell Division

Go to **ClassZone.com** to match images of cells dividing with the different stages of cell division.

Observe and Think Are the stages the same for plant and animal cells?

NSTA scilinks.org SCILINKS
Cellular Mitosis **Code: MDL033**

TEACHING WITH TECHNOLOGY

Modeling Software If 3D modeling software is available, students may wish to render their models of cell division stages (p. 84) electronically. The models can then be compiled into one folder, where they can be viewed and manipulated.

PC Microscope If you have equipment and software to use a microscope with a personal computer, students can view the onion root-tip cells (pp. 86–87) on a classroom monitor. You might also use the monitor as a display for parents while they view student work during an open house.

EXPLORE the BIG idea

These inquiry-based activities are appropriate for use at home or as a supplement to classroom instruction.

Dividing to Multiply

PURPOSE To understand the importance of cells and equal division.

TIPS *10 min.* Provide several samples, and try to use fresh, soft specimens. You can use other species of plants that have a two-part seed pod if maples are not local.

Answer: It has a line where it splits. Cells in the seed will reproduce and grow.

REVISIT after p. 83.

Division Math

PURPOSE To model how cells divide into cells that are smaller than the parent cell.

TIPS *10 min.* You can use this activity to sharpen math skills in both calculating and estimating halved weights. You might wish to have students use a scale or balance to measure weights.

Answer: The pieces get smaller. Cells in living things would have to grow.

REVISIT after p. 83.

Internet Activity: Cell Division

PURPOSE To view images of various stages of cell division and categorize the stages.

TIP *20 min.* Students might generate their own questions from this activity. Encourage them to write a list of three questions about cell division, and to look for answers as they read the chapter.

Answer: yes, except for cytokineisis

REVISIT after p. 92.

PREPARE

CONCEPT REVIEW

Activate Prior Knowledge

- Ask: What are you and every other living thing made of? *cells*
- Ask: Where do cells come from? *other cells*
- Ask: How does a cell know how to function and reproduce? *It has DNA instructions.*

TAKING NOTES

Combination Notes

Many of the important concepts in this chapter are illustrated in diagrams, or may be modeled by students in various activities. As students take notes, they can use these diagrams and models as a reference point for sketches that reinforce the learning of new or difficult concepts or terminology.

Vocabulary Strategy

The frame game provides a structure that sets off the vocabulary word. It provides the flexibility for students to attach any information they deem relevant. For more advanced students, you might challenge them to fill the frame with certain types of words, such as parts, examples, roots, or context clues.

Vocabulary and Note-Taking Resources

- Vocabulary Practice, pp. 166–167
- Decoding Support, p. 168

- Daily Vocabulary Scaffolding, p. T18
- Note-Taking Model, p. T19

- Frame Game, B26–27
- Combination Notes, C36
- Daily Vocabulary Scaffolding, H1–8

CHAPTER 3

Getting Ready to Learn

CONCEPT REVIEW

- The cell is the basic unit of structure and function in living things.
- All cells come from other cells.
- DNA provides the instructions a cell needs to function and reproduce.

VOCABULARY REVIEW

cell membrane p. 20
nucleus p. 20
cycle *See Glossary.*

Review concepts and vocabulary.

TAKING NOTES

COMBINATION NOTES

To take notes about a new concept, first make an informal outline of the information. Then make a sketch of the concept and label it so you can study it later.

VOCABULARY STRATEGY

Write each new vocabulary term in the center of a **frame game** diagram. Decide what information to frame it with. Use examples, description, parts, sentences that use the term in context, or pictures. You can change the frame to fit each term.

See the Note-Taking Handbook on pages R45–R51.

SCIENCE NOTEBOOK

NOTES

Mitosis has four phases
- prophase: chromosomes become visible

- metaphase: chromosomes line up in middle

forms chromosomes when cell is ready to divide

found in nucleus of eukaryotic cells

DNA

is copied during interphase

loose threadlike strands of DNA

CHECK READINESS

Administer the Diagnostic Test to determine students' readiness for new science content and their mastery of requisite math skills.

 Diagnostic Test, pp. 39–40

Technology Resources

Students needing content and math skills should visit **ClassZone.com**.

- **CONTENT REVIEW**
- **MATH TUTORIAL**

 **CONTENT REVIEW CD-ROM**

KEY CONCEPT

Cell division occurs in all organisms.

BEFORE, you learned
- Cells come from other cells
- Cells take in and release energy and materials
- In a multicellular organism, some cells specialize

NOW, you will learn
- How genetic material is organized in cells
- About the functions of cell division in multicellular organisms

VOCABULARY

DNA p. 74
chromosome p. 75

EXPLORE Cell Division

How is organization helpful?

PROCEDURE

1. Work with two other students. Obtain paired and unpaired groups of socks.
2. Two of the students put on blindfolds. One takes the paired group of socks and the other takes the unpaired group.
3. Each blindfolded student tries to separate his or her group of socks into two piles of single socks, one from each pair. The third student keeps track of time and stops the activity after 2 min.

MATERIALS
- 2 blindfolds
- socks
- stopwatch

WHAT DO YOU THINK?
Which group of socks was more accurately separated into two identical sets? Why?

Cell division is involved in many functions.

REMINDER
Most multicellular organisms are made up of eukaryotic cells. Most genetic material in eukaryotic cells is contained in the nucleus.

Cell division occurs in all organisms, but performs different functions. Unicellular organisms reproduce through cell division. In multicellular organisms, cell division is involved in growth, development, and repair, as well as in reproduction.

You are probably bigger this year than you were last year. One characteristic of all living things is that they grow. Your body is made up of cells. Although cells themselves grow, most growth in multicellular organisms occurs when cells dividing produce new cells. In this chapter you will read about cell division in eukaryotic cells.

3.1 FOCUS

Set Learning Goals

Students will
- Explain how genetic material is organized in cells.
- Explain how cells share genetic material.
- Describe the functions of cell division in multicellular organisms.
- Model chromosomes using coiled yarn to show compaction.

3-Minute Warm-Up

Display Transparency 20 or copy this exercise on the board:

Decide if these statements are true. If not true, correct them.

1. Cell theory tells us that cells arise from chemical reactions. *Cell theory tells us that cells arise from other cells.*
2. Cells passively receive energy and nutrients. *Cells actively take in and release energy and nutrients.*
3. In a multicellular organism, some cells specialize. *true*

 3-Minute Warm-Up, p. T20

3.1 MOTIVATE

EXPLORE Cell Division

PURPOSE To understand the benefits of organization in cell division

TIP *10 min.* Have student volunteers provide clean pairs of socks to contribute to the activity. Gather socks the day before class.

WHAT DO YOU THINK? *The folded ones; they were already matched, so it was easy to separate them into two identical piles.*

RESOURCES FOR DIFFERENTIATED INSTRUCTION

Below Level

UNIT RESOURCE BOOK
- Reading Study Guide A, pp. 133–134
- Decoding Support, p. 168

Advanced

UNIT RESOURCE BOOK
Challenge and Extension, p. 139

English Learners

UNIT RESOURCE BOOK
Spanish Reading Study Guide, pp. 137–138

- Audio Readings in Spanish
- Audio Readings (English)

3.1 INSTRUCT

History of Science

In 1962 the Nobel Prize for Physiology or Medicine was given to James Watson, Francis Crick, and Maurice Wilkins for discovering the molecular structure of DNA. Wilkins developed techniques for studying DNA using X-ray diffraction. Using Wilkins's studies as well as those of Rosalind Franklin, Watson and Crick constructed a molecular model consistent with the physical and chemical properties of DNA. Their model was a double helix of sugar and phosphate, bridged horizontally by organic bases. Their work also showed how the molecule could duplicate itself.

Teach Difficult Concepts

Students often have trouble visualizing a double helix. Explain to them that the shape is that of a twisted ladder. You might also try the demonstration below.

Teacher Demo

Make a model of DNA by gluing popsicle sticks to two pieces of string in a ladder pattern. Mark the sticks with colored markers to indicate the base pairs. When you hold the ladder up for the class to see, twist it to make a spiral.

Ongoing Assessment

Answer: the genetic material in cells

The genetic material of eukaryotic cells is organized in chromosomes.

The genetic material of a cell contains information needed for the cell's growth and other activities. When a cell divides into two new cells, each new cell receives a full set of genetic material. The genetic material in cells is contained in DNA molecules.

DNA

VOCABULARY
Make a frame game diagram for the term *DNA*. You can change the frame if you need to.

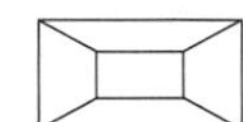

The genetic material in cells is DNA—deoxyribonucleic acid (dee-AHK-see-RY-boh-noo-KLEE-ihk). **DNA** is a chemical that contains information for an organism's growth and functions. You read in chapter 1 that James Watson and Francis Crick worked with other scientists to build a model of DNA in 1953. They showed that DNA is made of two strands of molecules joined in a structure that resembles a twisted ladder or a double helix. You will learn more about DNA later in the unit.

What is DNA?

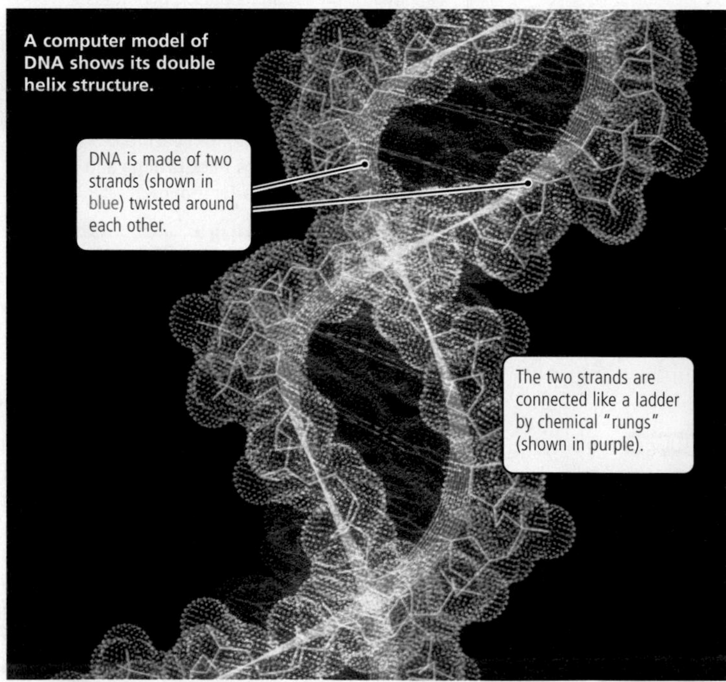

A computer model of DNA shows its double helix structure.

DIFFERENTIATE INSTRUCTION

More Reading Support

A What does a cell's genetic material contain? *instructions for growth and function*

B What is the shape of DNA? *double helix*

English Learners On the Science Word Wall, place the term *deoxyribonucleic acid* with its phonetic spelling in parenthesis next to it. Slowly speak the word parts for the class. Explain how the abbreviation DNA is derived, and add it to the wall as well. Help English learners learn to pronounce complex science words such as this one by reviewing all pronunciations aloud.

Chromosomes

In a eukaryotic cell, most of the cell's DNA is in the nucleus. During most of a cell's life cycle, DNA exists as a mass of loose strands. While the DNA is spread throughout the nucleus, the cell performs the functions needed for survival. During this time, the DNA is duplicated, or copied.

DNA is wrapped around proteins like thread around a spool and compacted into structures called **chromosomes** (KROH-muh-SOHMZ). Before division, the chromosomes compact more and become visible under a light microscope. During division, a duplicated chromosome can be seen as two identical structures called chromatids that are held together by a centromere.

READING TIP Compare the diagram of DNA with the computer model on page 74.

Within each species of organism, the number of chromosomes is constant. For example, humans have 46 chromosomes. Fruit flies, however, have 8 chromosomes, and corn plants have 20.

CHECK YOUR READING Describe the relationship between DNA and chromosomes.

Organization of Genetic Material

The DNA in chromosomes is wrapped around a protein core until it is very condensed.

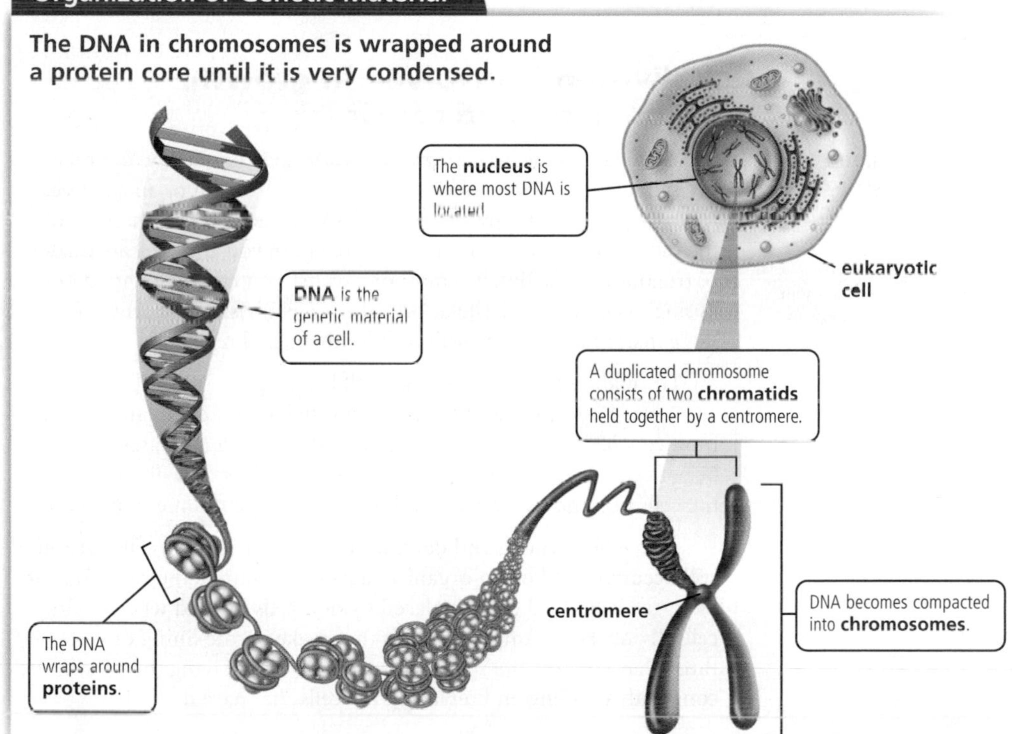

Real World Example

Living cells need to stop or start their various functions at critical times—whether to rest, to reproduce, to specialize, or to die for example. A small number of genes are involved in these stops and starts. Cancer is a group of more than 100 diseases that can occur when these genes somehow get damaged beyond the cell's ability to repair them. In such a case, a cell reproduces unchecked, passing its mutation to its daughter cells, which also reproduce unchecked. None of a normal cell's "stop" signals work. A normal cell will kill itself when it senses that its DNA is damaged beyond repair, but in cancer this mechanism to switch off self-replication does not function.

Teach from Visuals

To help students interpret the diagram of DNA and chromosomes, ask:

- Where are duplicated chromosomes located? *in the nucleus*
- What two identical bodies make up a duplicated chromosome? *chromatids*
- What joins the chromatids? *a centromere*

Ongoing Assessment

Explain how genetic material is organized in cells.

Ask: Describe how genetic material in eukaryotic cells is organized. *The DNA is in the nucleus. The DNA wraps around proteins into chromosomes.*

Answer: Chromosomes consist of compacted DNA.

DIFFERENTIATE INSTRUCTION

More Reading Support

C How is DNA condensed? *It is wrapped around proteins like a spool.*

Below Level Pair students who have difficulty reading with students who read fluently. Have pairs work together to create a comic strip called "Adventures of a DNA Molecule." They should show change in each frame of the strip as they describe the condensing of DNA as it forms into chromosomes. They should show each change in both words and a picture.

INVESTIGATE Chromosomes

PURPOSE To model the various shapes of DNA

TIP *20 min.* As students work, encourage them to discuss the similarities and differences between their models and the process of DNA compaction in real living cells.

WHAT DO YOU THINK? *It is messy, and the ball takes up a lot of room. The loose ball represents the loose mass of threadlike DNA, and the spooled yarn represents DNA as it prepares to divide. Each strand of yarn is right next to the next strand.*

CHALLENGE *The colors are already organized and separated.*

 Datasheet, Chromosomes, p. 140

Technology Resources

Customize this student lab as needed or look for an alternative. Print rubrics to assess student lab reports.

 **Lab Generator CD-ROM**

Teach Difficult Concepts

Students sometimes confuse DNA, the mass of loose threadlike strands, and chromatids. Explain that all refer to DNA, but in different forms. Most of the time, DNA is in loose strands spread out in the nucleus of the cell. A chromatid is also DNA; it is compacted. A chromatid becomes a chromosome when that chromosome is part of a pair of exact duplicates.

INVESTIGATE Chromosomes

How does DNA fit inside the nucleus?

SKILL FOCUS Modeling

MATERIALS
- yarn
- craft sticks

TIME 20 minutes

PROCEDURE

1. Select four pieces of yarn of different colors and four craft sticks. Push the yarn together into a loose ball. Observe how much space it takes up and how the individual pieces are organized.
2. Wrap each piece of yarn around a craft stick. Wrap the yarn so that the coils are tightly packed but do not overlap.

WHAT DO YOU THINK?

- What did you observe about the loosely balled yarn?
- What does the loosely balled yarn represent?
- What does the yarn on the craft sticks represent?
- Why does the yarn on the craft sticks take up less space than the ball of yarn?

CHALLENGE How does the yarn's being wrapped on the craft sticks make it easier to separate the different colors?

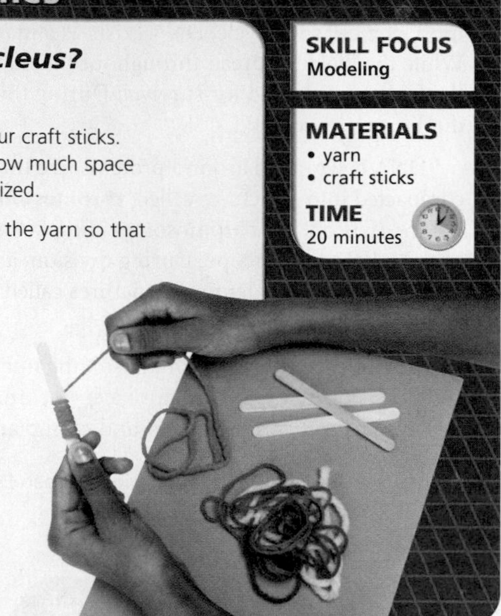

Cell division is involved in growth, development, and repair.

COMBINATION NOTES Remember to take notes and draw sketches to help you understand the main idea: *Cell division is involved in growth, development, and repair.* Be sure to include the red heads in your notes.

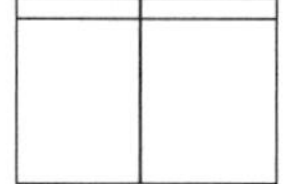

Multicellular organisms vary greatly in size and complexity. You may not think that you have much in common with an ant or an oak tree. Actually, you share many characteristics with these organisms. One of the most important characteristics is that both you and they are made of trillions of cells. But, like most organisms, you and they started out as single cells. In multicellular organisms, cell division is essential for three major functions: growth, development, and repair. 

Through cell division, a single cell becomes two cells. Those two cells divide into four, and the four cells divide into eight, and so on. A multicellular organism grows because cell division increases the number of cells in it. As the organism develops and its cells divide, many of the cells become specialized, and most of them continue to divide.

Even when growth and development appear to stop, cell division is still occurring. When an organism ages or is injured, the worn-out or damaged cells need to be replaced by new cells formed when healthy cells divide. For example, the cells that make up the lining of your throat have a short life span—two to three days. Living throat cells are constantly dividing and replacing the cells that have died.

DIFFERENTIATE INSTRUCTION

More Reading Support

D Why is cell division important? *It is essential for growth, development, and repair.*

Below Level Help students organize the information on the process of cell division by filling in a sequence graphic organizer. For example:

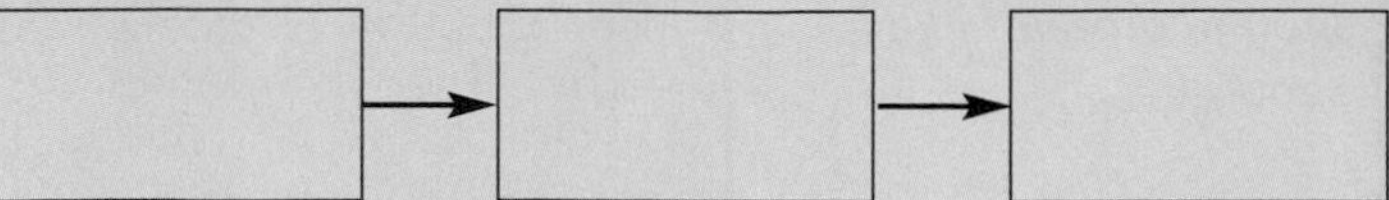

Growth

In general, a large organism does not have larger cells than a small organism; it simply has many more cells than the small organism. When you were small, your body contained fewer cells than it has now. By the time you reach adulthood, your body will be made up of about 100 trillion cells.

Individual cells grow in size, but there are limits to the size that cells can reach. As you learned in Chapter 2, cells need a high ratio of surface area to volume in order to function. As a cell grows, that ratio decreases. When the cell divides into two smaller cells, the ratio of surface area to volume for each cell increases.

Scientists are still searching for answers about how cell size is related to the control of cell division. Some scientists think that there is no single factor that controls cell division. Instead, they think that many cell processes added together control when a cell divides.

CHECK YOUR READING Describe how the number of cells in a multicellular organism changes as the organism grows.

Growth and Development

Organisms, like this sea turtle, grow and develop through cell division.

1

The embryo growing inside this egg started as a single cell.

2

When it hatches, the baby turtle has trillions of cells.

3 The adult turtle has more than a hundred times the cells of the baby turtle.

Development

E
F

Although multicellular organisms begin as single cells, they grow into larger organisms through cell division. However, cell division alone does not allow organisms to develop. If cell division were the only process occurring in cells, all multicellular organisms would end up as spheres of identical cells. But during development, cells become specialized to perform particular functions.

These cells may take on shapes or structures that help them to perform their functions. Some cells might become layered skin cells, while others might become long, thin nerve cells. These cells still have the same set of genetic material as all the other cells in an organism's body, but as the organism develops they specialize.

CHECK YOUR READING Give two examples of specialized cells from the paragraph above.

READING TIP

Connect what you have read about growth and development with the series of sea turtle photographs above.

DIFFERENTIATE INSTRUCTION

More Reading Support

E What makes one organism larger than another? *The larger organism has more cells.*

F What happens during an organism's development? *Cells become specialized.*

Advanced Have students research cells that become specialized and the stages in an organism's life when specialization occurs. They can choose one organism and draw a poster with examples of specialized cells to display in class.

R Challenge and Extension, p. 139

Address Misconceptions

IDENTIFY Ask: What are the purposes of cell division and cell growth? Students may not understand that there are different purposes, perhaps thinking that living things grow because their cells get larger.

CORRECT Ask students to think of the tiny babies they were when first born, and compare the amount of skin they had then with now. Have them think of a recent time when dead skin peeled, or when they clipped a cuticle. Have them imagine what those two processes would be like if the increase in their skin came from cell growth as opposed to cell division.

REASSESS Ask: How do multicellular organisms grow? *by increasing the number of cells through cell division*

Technology Resources

Visit **ClassZone.com** for background on common student misconceptions.

MISCONCEPTION DATABASE

Develop Mathematics Skills

If students find the limitations on cell size difficult to conceptualize, bring in mathematics manipulatives that include small cubes. Put the cubes together into larger and larger cubes. Start with 8, then 27, then 64. Have students count how many sides of small cubes are on one face versus the number of blocks in the whole larger cube. The ratio between these two numbers decreases as the cube grows.

Ongoing Assessment

Describe the functions of cell division in multicellular organisms.

Ask: How does a multicellular organism grow, develop, and repair itself? *Cell division allows the organism to grow by increasing the number of cells it has. Cells can specialize as they divide, so the organism develops. Cell division makes new cells to repair an injury or replace dead cells*

Answer: The number of cells increases.

Answer: layered skin cells and long, thin nerve cells

Ongoing Assessment

CHECK YOUR READING *Answer: Cell division makes new cells to replace damaged or aging cells.*

Develop Critical Thinking

COMPARE AND CONTRAST Have students discuss the similarities and differences between growth and reproduction of a cell and of an organism.

Reinforce the BIG idea

Have students relate the section to the Big Idea.

 Reinforcing Key Concepts, p. 141

3.1 ASSESS & RETEACH

Assess

 Section 3.1 Quiz, p. 41

Reteach

Have students look at the photograph on pp. 70–71. Ask them to pretend that this photograph is shown behind a news broadcaster describing breaking news about a growing bacteria colony. Help students describe in detail what is happening to the colony.

- *First, the DNA in a cell's nucleus compacts from loose strands into coils.*
- *Next, the coils compact further as chromatids form into duplicated chromosomes, each bundled or joined by a centromere.*
- *Finally the cell begins to divide.*
- *The result is twice as many new cells as old, each time a division takes place. The bacteria colony grows. Dead cells are replaced by new ones.*

Technology Resources

Have students visit **ClassZone.com** for reteaching of Key Concepts.

 CONTENT REVIEW

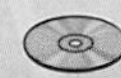 CONTENT REVIEW CD-ROM

Repair

You may have cut yourself at one time or another. Perhaps you have even broken a bone in your arm or leg. The body repairs injuries like these by means of cell division. For example, when your skin is cut, skin cells on either side of the cut make new cells to heal the wound. You can see the process of healing in the diagram below.

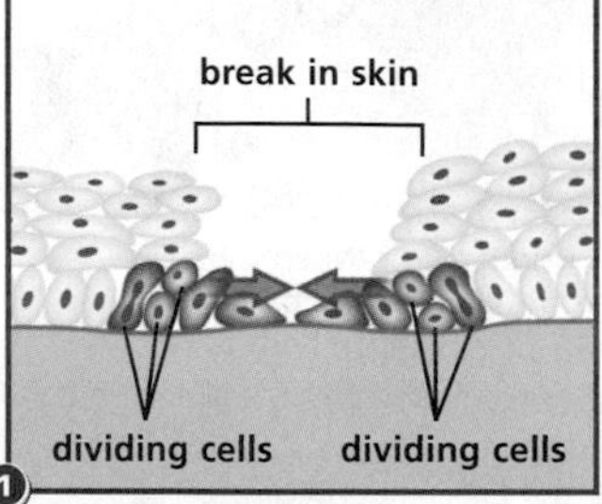

1. Cells in the lower layer begin to divide quickly and move into the break.

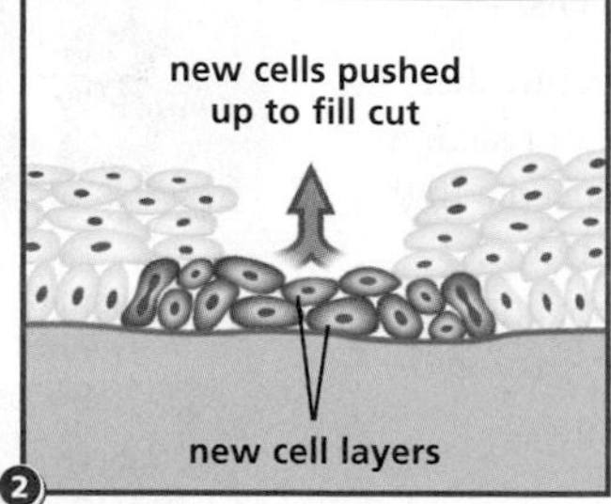

2. New cells begin to fill the area as cells continue to divide.

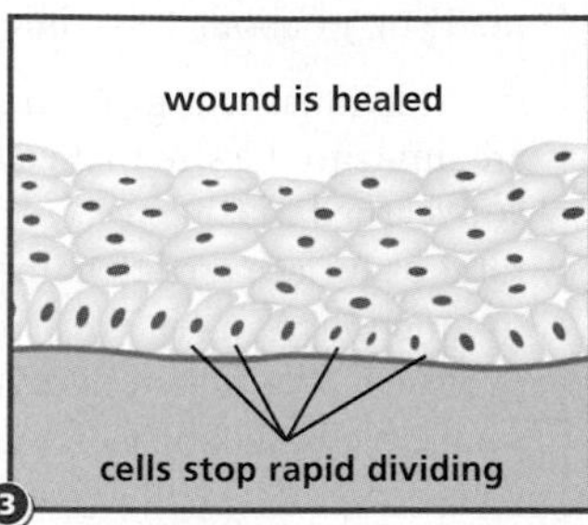

3. Cells stop their rapid dividing once the break is filled.

As cells age and die, they need to be replaced. In the human body—which is made up of about 200 different types of cells—cells are replaced at different rates. Your skin cells wear out quickly, so they need to be replaced often. Every minute or so, your skin loses about 40,000 cells, which are replaced with new ones. In contrast, most of the cells in your brain live a long time and do not divide very often.

 What role does cell division play in healing the body?

3.1 Review

KEY CONCEPTS

1. Why is cell division important?
2. How is genetic material organized in eukaryotic cells?
3. Explain how cell division is involved in the growth, development, and repair of an organism.

CRITICAL THINKING

4. **Summarize** Explain how DNA compacts before a eukaryotic cell divides.
5. **Infer** Why do you think that injuries to the skin generally heal faster than injuries to the brain?

CHALLENGE

6. **Apply** Describe the stages of development in a multicellular organism that is familiar to you.

ANSWERS

1. It leads to growth, development, and repair.

2. It condenses and forms chromosomes.

3. Cells divide to make more cells, which allow multicellular organisms to grow. As cells divide, they can specialize. Damaged cells are also replaced by cell division.

4. It wraps in coils around proteins, and then compacts further as it arranges into chromosomes.

5. Skin cells wear out quickly, so they duplicate frequently. Brain cells usually last a long time and do not replace themselves often. Skin heals faster because its cells are better equipped to replace themselves.

6. Answers will depend on choice of organism.

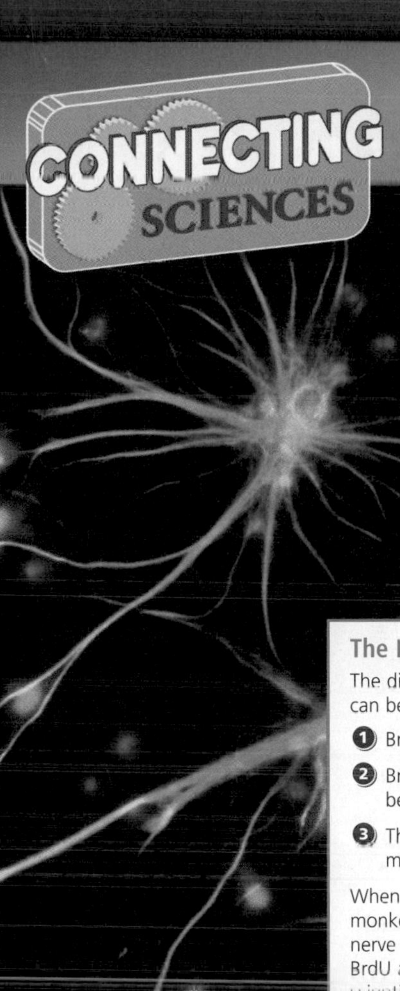

LIFE SCIENCE AND PHYSICAL SCIENCE

Chemical Dyes Show Nerve Growth

For years, the medical community has agreed that nerve tissue, once damaged, does not repair itself. In fact, the opinion was that new nerve cells didn't grow in adults at all. However, a surprising discovery has shown that new nerve cells do grow in the mature brains of both monkeys and people!

Elizabeth Gould noticed that new nerve cells can grow in adult brains

The Discovery

The discovery involves a chemical known as bromodeoxyuridine (BrdU), which can be used to detect new cancer cells.

1. BrdU highlights the DNA of cells that are reproducing, such as cancer cells.
2. BrdU also makes it possible to count the new cells that are being created, because they stand out as well.
3. The cells that have been highlighted with BrdU can be seen under a microscope when they are illuminated with a special light.

When scientists used this technique to examine certain areas in the brains of monkeys and of adult humans who had died of cancer, they found that new nerve cells had grown in the brains of each. Thus, the chemical properties of BrdU allowed scientists to discover new nerve cells growing in places where scientists had previously never expected to see them.

Hope for the Future

If new nerve cells grow in these tissues, it may be possible to stimulate growth in damaged nerve tissue such as that in the spinal cord. If researchers discover how new growth in nerve cells is stimulated, there may be new hope for people who have nervous systems damaged by accidents or by diseases such as Parkinson's disease.

EXPLORE

1. **SYNTHESIZE** How could you use chemicals, such as small dots with a pen, in an experiment to show how your fingernails grow?
2. **CHALLENGE** What are some possible effects of being able to grow new nerve cells?

RESOURCE CENTER
CLASSZONE.COM
Find out more about new nerve cell growth.

EXPLORE

1. *SYNTHESIZE Students might suggest placing a dot in the center of each nail and recording its movement for a week or two.*
2. *CHALLENGE Sample answer: People with damaged spines might regain use of their limbs. People with brain damage might regain brain activity or functions.*

CONNECTING SCIENCES

Integration of Sciences

Set Learning Goal

To synthesize knowledge about cell growth with information about chemical interactions

Present the Science

Researchers use chemical interactions to study cellular activity. They "trick" cells into taking in chemical dyes that are bonded to another molecule that the cell normally takes in. In the past it has been found that if the brain stops receiving signals from an area of the body, it reorganizes itself and becomes unresponsive to those signals. This is partly why areas with nerve damage become paralyzed. Physical therapy and electrical stimulation can help people recover from some paralysis.

Discussion Questions

Ask: Why might experiments be conducted on monkeys as well as humans? *because similarities exist between primates*

Ask: Why are dyes used in biology? *to improve visibility of a specimen*

DIFFERENTIATION TIP If you have students with spinal cord injuries or nerve cell damage in class, you might ascertain privately if they are willing to share their experiences. If they are sensitive about discussing the topic, you might focus discussion on a celebrity example, such as Christopher Reeve.

Close

Discuss the implications that growing new nerve cells might have for people with Alzheimer's, Parkinson's, or other neurological conditions.

Technology Resources

Have students visit **ClassZone.com** to find more about new nerve cell growth.

 **RESOURCE CENTER**

3.2 FOCUS

Set Learning Goals

Students will

- Explain a cell cycle, including interphase and mitosis.
- Describe how cells prepare for mitosis.
- Analyze what happens during mitosis.
- Use a microscope to observe mitosis.

3-Minute Warm-Up

Display Transparency 20 or copy this exercise on the board:

Consider the muscle tissue in your body. What ingredients and processes formed it? How did it become a muscle? *The tissue formed from cells, which came from other cells through cell division. It became a muscle because genetic material from its parent told it to specialize.*

 3-Minute Warm-Up, p. T20

3.2 MOTIVATE

THINK ABOUT

PURPOSE To explore the concept of cycle

DISCUSS Have students look at the photo of trees changing with the seasons. Ask:

- What is causing the trees to change? *the weather cycle*
- Which phases do you think are most active? *flowering and growing seasons*

KEY CONCEPT

Cell division is part of the cell cycle.

BEFORE, you learned

- Cells come from other cells through cell division
- A cell must have a full set of genetic material to function
- Cell division enables multicellular organisms to develop, grow, and repair themselves

NOW, you will learn

- About two main stages in the cell cycle
- About the changes that occur in cells before mitosis
- About the events that take place during mitosis

VOCABULARY

cell cycle p. 80
interphase p. 81
mitosis p. 81
cytokinesis p. 81

THINK ABOUT

What is a cycle?

Many things in your everyday life are cycles. A cycle is any activity or set of events that regularly repeats. Cycles can be short, like the sequence of events that make your heart beat, or they can be very long, like the turning of our galaxy. One example of a cycle is shown at the right. The photographs show a tree during four seasons in a northern climate. How are these seasons a cycle?

The cell cycle includes interphase and cell division.

All living things live, grow, reproduce, and die in a process called a life cycle. The life cycle of a tree, for example, begins with a seed. Under the right conditions, the seed begins to grow. It produces a very small plant, which may grow over many years into a towering tree. When it is mature, the tree makes its own seeds, and the cycle begins again.

RESOURCE CENTER CLASSZONE.COM

Learn about the cell cycle.

Cells have a life cycle too, called the cell cycle. The **cell cycle** is the normal sequence of development and division of a cell. The cell cycle consists of two main phases: one in which the cell carries out its functions, called interphase, and one in which the cell divides, which can include mitosis and cytokinesis. All cells divide, but only eukaryotes undergo mitosis. Each phase in the cell cycle requires a certain period of time—from hours to days or years, depending on the type of cell.

RESOURCES FOR DIFFERENTIATED INSTRUCTION

Below Level

UNIT RESOURCE BOOK

- Reading Study Guide A, pp. 144–145
- Decoding Support, p. 168

 **AUDIO CDS**

Advanced

UNIT RESOURCE BOOK

- Challenge and Extension, p. 150
- Challenge Reading, pp. 164–165

English Learners

UNIT RESOURCE BOOK

Spanish Reading Study Guide, pp. 148–149

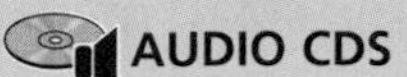 **AUDIO CDS**

- Audio Readings in Spanish
- Audio Readings (English)

Interphase

Interphase is the part of the cell cycle during which a cell is not dividing. Much activity takes place in this phase of the cell's life. During interphase, the cell grows to about twice the size it was when it was first produced. The cell also engages in normal life activities, such as transporting materials in and transporting wastes out. Also, cellular respiration occurs, which provides the energy the cell needs.

Changes that occur during interphase prepare a cell for division. Before a cell can divide, it duplicates its DNA exactly. Correct copying of the DNA is very important. It ensures that, after cell division, each new cell gets a complete set of DNA.

What cell processes occur during interphase?

VOCABULARY
Make a frame game diagram for *interphase*.

Cell Division Phase

Mitosis is the part of the cell cycle during which the nucleus divides. Prokaryotes do not undergo mitosis because they have no nucleus. In most cells, mitosis is the shortest period in the life cycle. The function of mitosis is to move the DNA and other material in the parent cell into position for cell division. When the cell divides, each new cell gets a full set of DNA and other cell structures. **Cytokinesis** (SY-toh-kuh-NEE-sihs) is the division of the parent cell's cytoplasm. Cytokinesis occurs immediately after mitosis.

Cell Cycle

The events that happen during the life of a cell are called the cell cycle.

1 **Interphase**
The **cell cycle** begins with interphase, which is the longest part of the cell cycle.

2 **Cell Division Phase**
After **mitosis** and **cytokinesis** there are two cells. The cell cycle then begins again for each cell.

cell grows and carries out normal functions; organelles duplicate
INTERPHASE
CYTOKINESIS
Telophase
Anaphase
Metaphase
Prophase
MITOSIS
DNA replicates
cell grows and prepares for mitosis

READING TIP
The arrows in the Cell Cycle diagram represent the passage of time. Interphase is in red, mitosis is in purple, and cytokinesis is in yellow.

3.2 INSTRUCT

History of Science

German anatomist Walther Flemming (1843–1905) was one of the founders of the science of cytogenetics, which studies the cell's chromosomes. Flemming was a specialist in using dyes to color specimens. He used this technique to stain cells, which made threadlike bodies in the cells visible. Although he did not understand the function of these bodies, in 1882, he became the first scientist to describe their changes during mitosis. In 1888, Wilhelm von Waldeyer, another German anatomist, named these bodies *chromosomes* ("colored bodies") because they became visible only after they had absorbed dyes.

Develop Mathematics Skills

Some students may have difficulty understanding pie charts, such as the one on this page, showing relationships of parts in relation to one whole. Explain how a pie chart displays information. Use a simple example, such as comparing the number of hours in a school day. Then explain that, in the chart above, each "slice" of the pie represents the length of each phase in the cell cycle in relation to the length of the whole cycle.

Ongoing Assessment

Explain a cell cycle, including interphase and mitosis.

Ask: What occurs in a cell's life besides division? *The cell is in interphase when it is not dividing. During interphase, the cell grows, conducts cellular respiration and other normal life activities, and duplicates its DNA in preparation for division, or mitosis.*

Answer: growth, food intake, transporting waste, and cellular respiration

DIFFERENTIATE INSTRUCTION

More Reading Support

A What is the part of a cell's life when it is not dividing? *interphase*

B What is the part of the cell cycle when the nucleus divides? *mitosis*

English Learners Have a small group of students prepare a "Cell Cycle" wall poster for the class that combines the cell cycle information from the pie chart on p. 81 with the details of each phase in the cycle, illustrated on p. 83. Include English learners and advanced students in the group, and be sure the terms *mitosis, prophase, metaphase, anaphase, telophase,* and *chromosome* are all included on the poster.

Address Misconceptions

IDENTIFY Ask: What type of cells contain DNA? If students answer "brain cells" or "sex cells," they hold the misconception that only these cells have genetic material.

CORRECT Ask students to think about their skin. They know that pressure on the soles of their feet, for example, creates thicker skin, so you can discuss that the body produces more skin cells. Point out that a skin cell has a plan that makes it a skin cell, not, say, a blood cell. The plan is its genetic material.

REASSESS Ask: Which cells in the human body have chromosomes? *all of them*

Technology Resources

Visit **ClassZone.com** for background on common student misconceptions.

MISCONCEPTION DATABASE

Real World Example

Many disorders are genetic in origin. Cystic fibrosis, muscular dystrophy, and juvenile diabetes are all inherited. Other diseases such as AIDS and cancer occur when a gene is miscoded and its instructions change. Some hope for controlling these disorders lies in gene therapy. Gene therapy inserts a gene or genes into a cell to provide it with a new set of instructions, which are then copied as the cell divides. Gene therapy was first used in 1990 to help a four-year-old girl with adenine deaminase deficiency, an inherited disorder that is usually fatal. Eventually gene therapy may be used to treat or prevent many diseases.

Ongoing Assessment

Describe how cells prepare for mitosis.

Ask: How does the cell get ready for mitosis? *During interphase, the cell grows to almost double its original size and duplicates its DNA.*

CHECK YOUR READING *Answer: They are genetically identical.*

As a result of mitosis and cytokinesis, the original—or parent—cell splits into two genetically identical daughter cells. In this case, the term *daughter cell* does not imply gender. It is a term scientists use to refer to these new cells. Each daughter cell receives a complete set of DNA from the parent cell.

Cell division produces two genetically identical cells.

COMBINATION NOTES As you read, begin to take combination notes on the main idea: *Cell division produces two genetically identical cells.*

Recall that many cells in your body are continually dividing into new cells. The new cells help your body grow, develop, repair itself, and replace worn-out parts. Though your body cells divide at different rates, the same process—mitosis—divides their genetic material.

Cell division produces daughter cells that are genetically identical to each other, as well as to their parent cell, which no longer exists. Being genetically identical to their parent cell helps the new cells function properly. A skin cell, for example, divides and produces skin cells genetically identical to it.

CHECK YOUR READING How are daughter cells like the parent cell?

Steps of Mitosis

VISUALIZATION CLASSZONE.COM Watch the process of mitosis in action.

The process of mitosis is essential in evenly dividing the genetic material between the daughter cells. Although mitosis is a continuous process, scientists divide the events of mitosis into four phases.

? C

1. **Chromosomes form.** During prophase, the DNA in the nucleus of a cell condenses and becomes visible under a light microscope. Each chromosome consists of two identical chromatids held together by a centromere. The membrane around the nucleus disappears.
2. **Chromosomes line up.** The chromosomes line up in the middle of the cell. This stage is called metaphase.
3. **Chromosomes separate.** During the stage called anaphase, the chromatids split, resulting in two separate identical chromosomes. These chromosomes are pulled to opposite sides of the cell.
4. **Nuclei form.** A new nuclear membrane forms around each group of chromosomes during telophase. The chromosomes return to their threadlike form.

Mitosis is finished, and the cell's genetic material has been divided. Following telophase the parent cell's cytoplasm is divided to complete the parent cell's division into two entirely separate daughter cells.

DIFFERENTIATE INSTRUCTION

? More Reading Support

C What are the four phases of mitosis? *prophase, metaphase, anaphase, telophase*

Advanced Have students research cell division and specialization, finding out which cells divide the fastest and which the slowest. Ask them to write a paragraph about the implications of the rate of cell division on the ability of a tissue to heal.

R Challenge and Extension, p. 150

Have students who are interested in new understandings about cell division read the following article:

R Challenge Reading, pp. 164–165

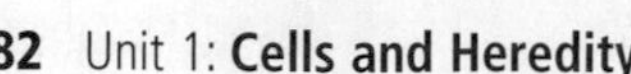

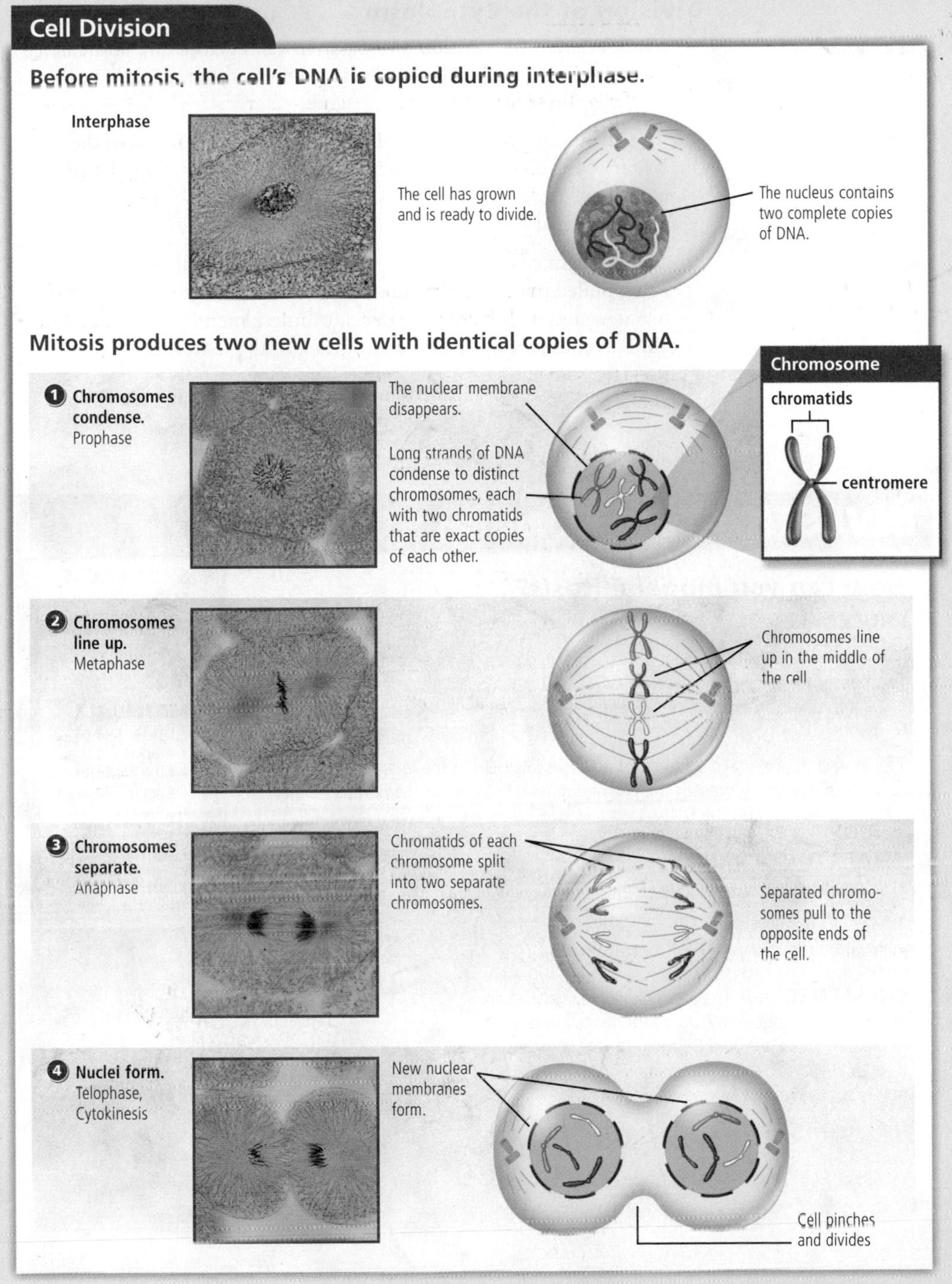

Cell Division

Before mitosis, the cell's DNA is copied during interphase.

Interphase

The cell has grown and is ready to divide.

The nucleus contains two complete copies of DNA.

Mitosis produces two new cells with identical copies of DNA.

Chromosome

chromatids

centromere

1 Chromosomes condense.
Prophase

The nuclear membrane disappears.

Long strands of DNA condense to distinct chromosomes, each with two chromatids that are exact copies of each other.

2 Chromosomes line up.
Metaphase

Chromosomes line up in the middle of the cell.

3 Chromosomes separate.
Anaphase

Chromatids of each chromosome split into two separate chromosomes.

Separated chromosomes pull to the opposite ends of the cell.

4 Nuclei form.
Telophase, Cytokinesis

New nuclear membranes form.

Cell pinches and divides

Teach from Visuals

To help students interpret the illustration of cell division, ask:

- In what phase does the cell's nuclear membrane disappear? *prophase*
- How is a chromosome made? *Long strands of DNA condense.*
- What happens to the chromosomes during anaphase? *They split into two identical chromatids, which pull to opposite ends of the cell.*

The visual "Cell Division" is available as T22 in the Unit Transparency Book.

Develop Critical Thinking

INFER Point out that sometimes a cell inaccurately duplicates its DNA, and its daughter cells are not identical. Ask: What are the results of that inaccuracy likely to be? *Sample answer: The daughter cells may not function the way their parent cell did; they may die.*

EXPLORE the BIG idea

Revisit "Dividing to Multiply" on p. 71. Have students discuss the organization of the maple samara and compare it to a cell's organization during mitosis.

EXPLORE the BIG idea

Revisit "Division Math" on p. 71. Have students explain how the clay compares to cells when they divide.

DIFFERENTIATE INSTRUCTION

Below Level Have students create two sets of sequencing cards for the phases of mitosis, with the names of the phases on one side of both. On one set, have them draw the phases on the other side of the cards. On the other set, explain the phase in words.

INVESTIGATE Cell Division

PURPOSE To model the stages of mitosis

TIP *30 min.* Before the investigation, review mitosis on the board with students.

WHAT DO YOU THINK? *The nuclear membrane is present in interphase and telophase. Telophase has chromatin. Interphase, prophase, metaphase, and anaphase have chromosomes. Arrows show the order of the stages of mitosis.*

CHALLENGE *Prokaryotic cells have no nucleus, so cell division is less complex. (Drawings will vary, but should* not *show the nuclear membrane dissolving.)*

 Datasheet, Cell Division, p. 151

Technology Resources

Customize this student lab as needed or look for an alternative. Print rubrics to assess student lab reports.

 **Lab Generator CD-ROM**

Teaching with Technology

If 3D modeling software is available on a school computer, students can use it to model the stages of mitosis in "Investigate Cell Division." The models can be viewed and manipulated by other students or parents.

Ongoing Assessment

Analyze what happens during mitosis.

Ask: Explain the phases of mitosis. *In prophase the DNA condenses into chromosomes, which are two identical chromatids joined by a centromere. The nuclear membrane dissolves. In metaphase the chromosomes line up in the middle of the cell. During anaphase the chromatids separate and go to opposite ends of the cell. During telophase a new membrane forms around the chromosomes. They become chromatin again.*

 *Answer: In plant cells, a cell plate grows and develops into a new cell wall and cell membrane. In animal cells, the cell membrane pulls inward, and the cell is pinched into two daughter cells.*

READING TIP As you read about cytokinesis refer to the images of plant and animal cells on page 85.

Division of the Cytoplasm

 D

Cytokinesis, or the division of the parent cell's cytoplasm, immediately follows mitosis in eukaryotic cells. Cytokinesis differs slightly in animal cells and plant cells.

During cytokinesis in an animal cell, a fiber ring forms in the center of the dividing cell. The fiber ring contracts, pulling the cell membrane inward. Eventually, the cell is pinched into two daughter cells.

 E

In a plant cell, the cell wall prevents the cell membrane from being pulled inward. A structure called a cell plate grows between the two new nuclei. The cell plate develops into a membrane and eventually becomes part of the cell wall of each of the new cells.

 How does cytokinesis differ in plant cells and animal cells?

INVESTIGATE Cell Division

How can you model mitosis?

PROCEDURE

1. Divide the poster board into six spaces, and draw arrows from one space to the next to indicate a cycle. Label the spaces, in order, "Interphase," "Prophase," "Metaphase," "Anaphase," "Telophase," and "Cytokinesis."
2. In each space, make a model of a cell and its DNA in the indicated phase. Make sure you represent the cell membrane, the nuclear membrane—when it is present—and the DNA.

WHAT DO YOU THINK?

- In which phases is the nuclear membrane present?
- In which phases are the chromosomes condensed?
- What do the arrows in your model show?

CHALLENGE How do you think cell division would differ in prokaryotic cells? Do you think cell division in prokaryotic cells would be more or less complex than in eukaryotic cells? Make drawings to show how you think a prokaryotic cell might divide.

SKILL FOCUS Making models

MATERIALS
- poster board
- markers
- pipe cleaners
- packing peanuts
- glue
- scissors
- yarn

TIME 30 minutes

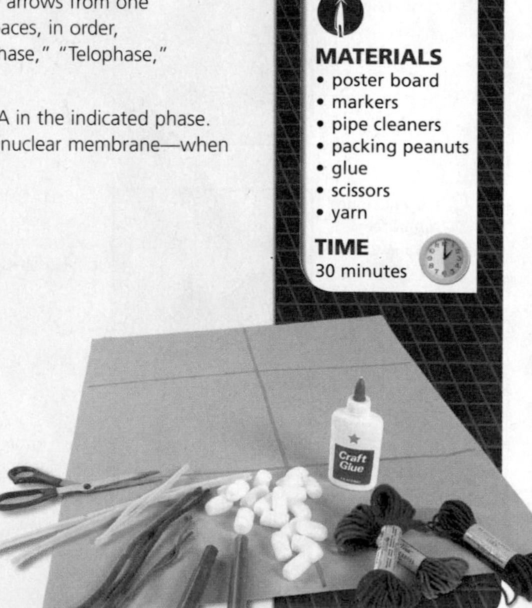

DIFFERENTIATE INSTRUCTION

More Reading Support

D What do you call the division of the parent cell's cytoplasm? *cytokinesis*

E What structure in a plant cell grows between the two new nuclei after mitosis? *the cell plate*

Alternative Assessment Have students temporarily cover any captions or text on the models they made in "Investigate Cell Division." Pair students and have them give verbal summations of each other's models, reviewing both the models and their knowledge of mitosis.

Cytokinesis

Cytokinesis happens in both plant and animal cells.

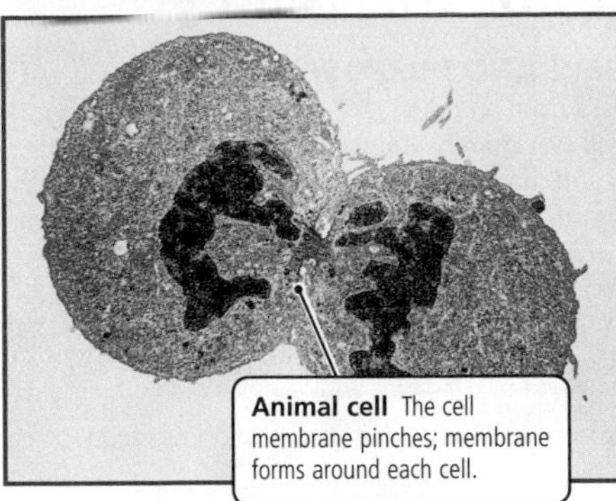

Animal cell The cell membrane pinches; membrane forms around each cell.

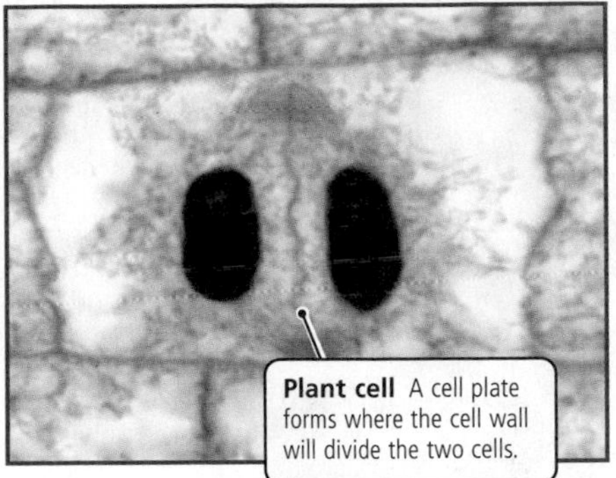

Plant cell A cell plate forms where the cell wall will divide the two cells.

READING VISUALS **COMPARE AND CONTRAST** How does the process of cytokinesis in the animal cell on the left differ from that of the plant cell on the right?

The two daughter cells are now completely separated. Each is surrounded by a cell membrane. Each daughter cell has some of its parent cell's cytoplasm. Though daughter cells are genetically identical to their parent cell, they are smaller. After division, cells may enter a period of growth, during which they take in the resources they need to increase the amount of their cytoplasm and to grow to full size. When cells are fully grown, they are about the same size as the parent cell was before division.

CHECK YOUR READING What happens to cells after cytokinesis?

3.2 Review

KEY CONCEPTS

1. What are the two main parts of the cell cycle?
2. Describe the state of a cell about to start mitosis.
3. How is the genetic material in two daughter cells similar to the genetic material in a parent cell?

CRITICAL THINKING

4. **Sequence** Describe in order the steps that occur during mitosis.
5. **Compare and Contrast** How is cytokinesis in plant cells similar to cytokinesis in animal cells? How is it different?

CHALLENGE

6. **Infer** You know that mitosis does not happen in prokaryotes. Do you think cytokinesis happens in prokaryotes? Explain your answer.

ANSWERS

1. interphase and cell division

2. two complete sets of DNA, twice the size of when it was first formed

3. They are identical.

4. Chromosomes form (prophase), chromosomes line up (metaphase), chromosomes separate (anaphase), nuclei form (telophase).

5. In both plant and animal cells, cytokinesis is the division of the cytoplasm. In plant cells, a cell plate forms and becomes a new cell wall and cell membrane. In animal cells, the cell membrane pulls inward and pinches into two new cells.

6. Yes, because cytokinesis is the division of the cytoplasm, and prokaryotes have cytoplasm to divide.

Ongoing Assessment

READING VISUALS *Answer: In animal cells, cell membranes pinch apart. A plant cell forms a cell plate where the cell will divide.*

CHECK YOUR READING *Answer: They enter a period of growth.*

Reinforce the BIG idea

Have students relate the section to the Big Idea.

Reinforcing Key Concepts, p. 152

3.2 ASSESS & RETEACH

Assess

Section 3.2 Quiz, p. 42

Reteach

Draw a pie-shaped graphic organizer on the board and label it "The Cell Cycle." Have students help you fill in events.

- *The largest part is interphase, when the cell grows, functions, and duplicates DNA.*
- *In prophase DNA condenses to chromosomes, and the nuclear membrane dissolves.*
- *In metaphase the chromosomes line up.*
- *In anaphase the chromatids split apart and move to opposite ends of the cell.*
- *In telophase a new nuclear membrane forms, and DNA returns to chromatin form.*
- *In cytokinesis an animal cell pinches apart, and a plant cell grows a cell plate.*

Technology Resources

Have students visit **ClassZone.com** for reteaching of Key Concepts.

CONTENT REVIEW

CONTENT REVIEW CD-ROM

CHAPTER INVESTIGATION

Focus

PURPOSE To observe mitosis

OVERVIEW Students will view prepared slides of an onion root tip through a microscope. They will locate and sketch cells in each phase of mitosis. Out of a randomly selected 25 cells, they will count and record how many were in each phase of mitosis. Students will find the following:

- Different parts of the cell cycle last different amounts of time.
- Most growth occurs in root tips.

Lab Preparation

- Be sure to obtain enough prepared slides for each microscope station. You can prepare your own slides from layers of onion skin, but root cells will show more variety.
- For homework the night before class, have students set up their observation charts in their Science Notebooks. They should also prepare by reading pp. 86–87 for homework. You may wish to copy and distribute the datasheet and rubric.

 UNIT RESOURCE BOOK, pp. 171–179

 SCIENCE TOOLKIT, F15

Lab Management

SAFETY Demonstrate proper handling of microscope slides. Review precautions for broken glass before students begin.

INCLUSION For students who are unable to manipulate a microscope, you may wish to obtain a projection microscope or PC-based microscope. Alternately have another student describe vividly his or her observations.

Teaching with Technology

Use a PC microscope, if available, to project the onion root-tip cells on a computer monitor. You might also use the monitor as a classroom learning center, or as a display for parents to view alongside students' labwork.

CHAPTER INVESTIGATION

Stages of the Cell Cycle

OVERVIEW AND PURPOSE In this activity you will observe cells from an onion root tip that are undergoing mitosis. You will identify and draw cells in different stages of mitosis and the cell cycle. Then you will count the number of cells in each stage. Remember to record this information in your **Science Notebook.**

MATERIALS
- prepared slides of onion root tip cells
- light microscope

Procedure

1. Make a data table like the one shown on the sample notebook page.
2. Obtain a prepared slide of an onion root tip. Place the slide on the microscope stage. Using the low-power objective, adjust the focus until the root tip is clear. 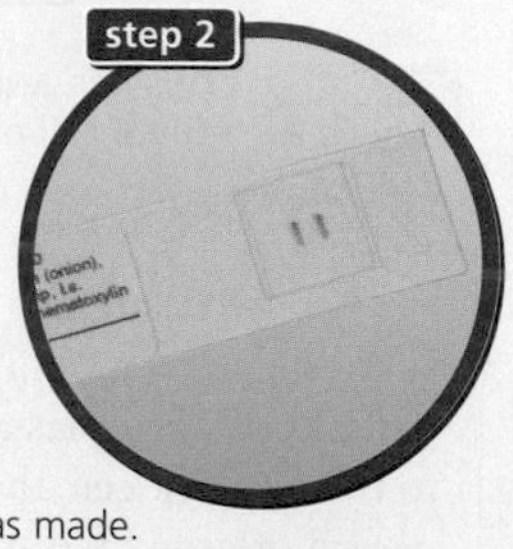
3. Move the slide until you are looking at the region just above the root tip. The cells in this area were in the process of mitosis when the slide was made.
4. Look at the boxlike cells arranged in rows. The DNA in these cells has been stained to make it more visible. Select a cell in interphase. Switch to high power and sketch this cell in your notebook.

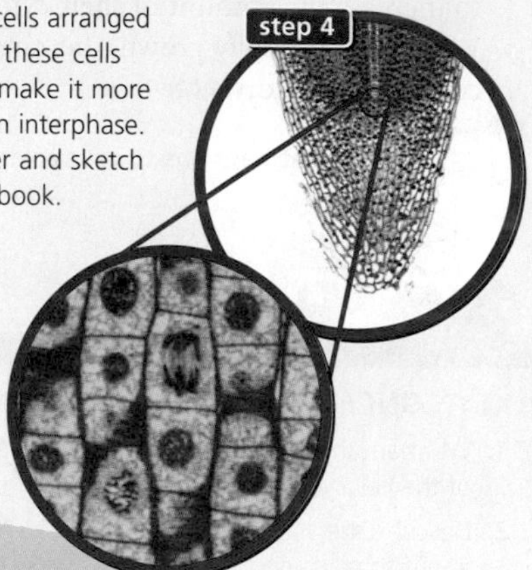

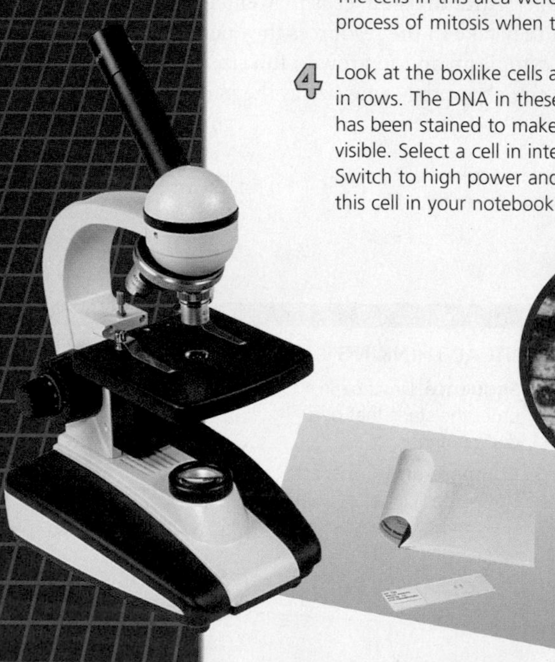

step 2

step 4

86 Unit 1: **Cells and Heredity**

INVESTIGATION RESOURCES

 CHAPTER INVESTIGATION, Stages of the Cell Cycle
- Level A, pp. 171–174
- Level B, pp. 175–178
- Level C, p. 179

Advanced students should complete Levels B & C.

 Writing a Lab Report, D12–13

Technology Resources

Customize this student lab as needed or look for an alternative. Print rubrics to assess student lab reports.

 **Lab Generator CD-ROM**

5 Repeat step 3 for cells in the various stages of mitosis: prophase, metaphase, anaphase, and telophase. Refer to the diagram on page 83 to identify cells in each stage.

6 Arrange your sketches to represent the order of the process of mitosis.

7 Under low-power magnification, choose 25 cells at random. Decide which stage of the cell cycle each cell is in. Record the number of cells in each stage in your data table.

Observe and Analyze

Write It Up

1. **OBSERVE** Look at your sketches of the stages of mitosis. Describe the events in each stage.
2. **ANALYZING DATA** Was there any one stage of the cell cycle that was occurring in the majority of cells you observed? If so, which was it?

Conclude

1. **INFER** What might the differences in the number of cells in each stage of the cell cycle mean?
2. **IDENTIFY LIMITS** Were there any cells that were difficult to classify as being in one particular phase of the cell cycle? What do these cells suggest to you about the process of mitosis?
3. **APPLY** Where does new root growth take place? Explain your answer.

INVESTIGATE Further

CHALLENGE From your data table, calculate the percent of cells in each stage of the cell cycle. Use those numbers to predict how much time a cell spends in each stage. You can base your calculation on a total cell cycle of 24 hours.

Stages of the Cell Cycle

Table 1. Number of Cells in Each Stage of the Cell Cycle

Stage	Number of Cells Observed
Interphase	
Prophase	
Metaphase	
Anaphase	
Telophase	

Observe and Analyze

1. *Sketches and stages will vary. Chromosomes form (prophase), chromosomes line up (metaphase), chromosomes separate (anaphase), nuclei form (telophase).*
2. *Answers may vary, but interphase is most likely.*

Conclude

1. *It may correspond to the amount of time a cell spends in each phase.*
2. *Sample answer: Yes, the process of mitosis is continuous.*
3. *near the tips, which is where most of the mitosis is happening*

INVESTIGATE Further

CHALLENGE: Sample answer: Within a 24-hour day, about 20 hours would be interphase. About 25 minutes each would be spent in prophase, metaphase, anaphase, and telophase, and cytokinesis.

Post-Lab Discussion

- Ask: How much activity is occurring in living things that we cannot see without a microscope? *At the cellular level, activity is always occurring.*
- Ask: Are cells synchronized with each other in regard to mitosis? Explain. *No; different cells are in different phases at one time.*
- Ask: How do plants grow? *Cells divide using mitosis. Gradually the total number of cells increases and the plant gets bigger.*

3.3 FOCUS

Set Learning Goals

Students will

- Explain how some organisms use cell division to reproduce asexually.
- Compare asexual and sexual reproduction.
- Draw experimental conclusions about plant regeneration.

3-Minute Warm-Up

Display Transparency 21 or copy this exercise on the board:

Draw a clock. Instead of numbers, fill in roughly the phases of the cell cycle: interphase and mitosis. Describe what happens during each. *interphase: cell grows and carries out normal functions, organelles duplicate, DNA replicates, and chromosomes duplicate; mitosis: DNA and other material move into position, chromosomes separate and move to opposite sides of cell, new nuclei form, cell pinches, cytoplasm divides, and two new daughter cells enter interphase*

3-Minute Warm-Up, p. T21

3.3 MOTIVATE

THINK ABOUT

PURPOSE To consider the effect of cell division in single-celled organisms

DISCUSS Ask students to imagine what would happen if each person became two people when their cells divided.

Metacognitive Strategy

Have students write down what they already know about reproduction and cell division. Then ask them what they still need to know, or still have questions about.

KEY CONCEPT

Both sexual and asexual reproduction involve cell division.

BEFORE, you learned

- Cells go through a cycle of growth and division
- Mitosis produces two genetically identical cells

NOW, you will learn

- About cell division and asexual reproduction
- How sexual reproduction and asexual reproduction compare

VOCABULARY

asexual reproduction p. 88
binary fission p. 89
regeneration p. 90

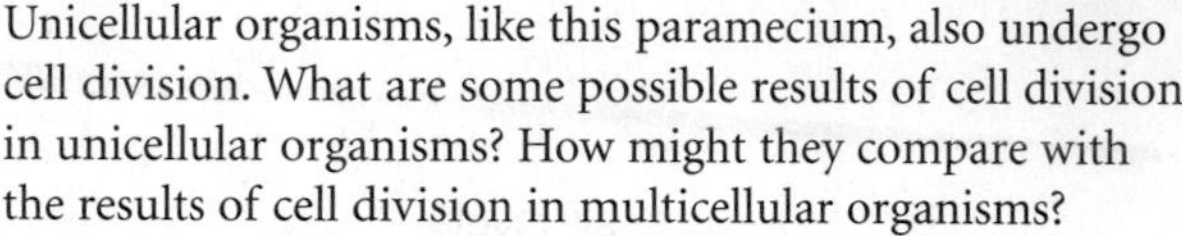

THINK ABOUT

How does cell division affect single-celled organisms?

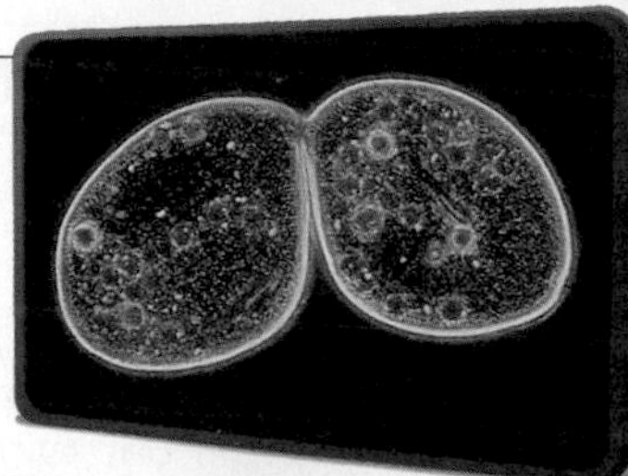

In multicellular organisms, cell division functions in growth, repair, and development. But in unicellular organisms, each cell is itself an organism. Unicellular organisms, like this paramecium, also undergo cell division. What are some possible results of cell division in unicellular organisms? How might they compare with the results of cell division in multicellular organisms?

COMBINATION NOTES Begin taking notes on the main idea: *Asexual reproduction involves one parent.* Be sure to include sketches of each method of reproducing.

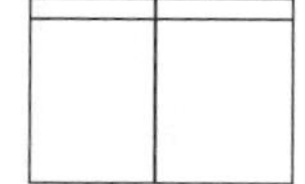

Asexual reproduction involves one parent.

Mitosis and cytokinesis are the processes by which eukaryotic cells divide. In multicellular organisms, the daughter cells that result are separate cells but do not live independent lives. For example, new skin cells are part of skin tissue and cannot live independently. In multicellular organisms, mitosis and cytokinesis are not considered methods by which an organism reproduces.

Most unicellular organisms, and a few multicellular organisms, use cell division to reproduce, in a process called asexual reproduction. In **asexual reproduction,** one organism produces one or more new organisms that are identical to itself and that live independently of it. The organism that produces the new organism or organisms is the parent. Each new organism is an offspring. The offspring produced by asexual reproduction are genetically identical to the parent.

RESOURCES FOR DIFFERENTIATED INSTRUCTION

Below Level

UNIT RESOURCE BOOK

- Reading Study Guide A, pp. 155–156
- Decoding Support, p. 168

Advanced

UNIT RESOURCE BOOK

Challenge and Extension, p. 161

English Learners

UNIT RESOURCE BOOK

Spanish Reading Study Guide, pp. 159–160

- Audio Readings in Spanish
- Audio Readings (English)

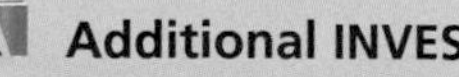

Temperature and Yeast Reproduction, A, B, & C, pp. 180–188; Teacher Instructions, pp. 308–309

Cell Division in Unicellular Organisms

Cell division and reproduction are the same thing in all single-celled organisms. However, the process of cell division in prokaryotes and in single-celled eukaryotes differs.

A **Binary fission** is the form of asexual reproduction occurring in prokaryotes. Binary fission occurs when the parent organism splits in two, producing two completely independent daughter cells. Genetically, the daughter cells are exactly like the parent cell. Since all prokaryotic organisms are single-celled, cell division and reproduction by binary fission are the same process for them.

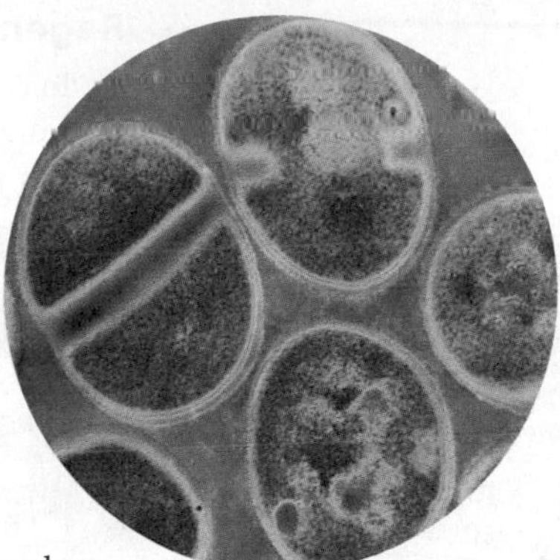

Binary fission results in two nearly equal, independent cells, as shown in these bacteria.

In single-celled eukaryotic organisms, however, reproduction by cell division involves mitosis and cytokinesis. The unicellular organism undergoes mitosis, duplicating and separating its chromosomes. Then its cytoplasm is divided through cytokinesis. The result is two separate, independent, and genetically identical offspring. Examples of single-celled eukaryotic organisms that reproduce by cell division include algae, some yeasts, and protozoans, such as paramecium.

Budding

Both unicellular and multicellular organisms can reproduce by budding. Budding is a process in which an organism develops tiny buds on its body. Each bud forms from the parent's cells, so the bud's genetic material is the same as the parent's. The bud grows until it forms a complete or nearly complete new organism that is genetically identical to the parent.

Budding Hydras reproduce by pinching off small buds.

In some budding organisms, buds can form from any part of the body. In other organisms, buds can be produced only by specialized cells in particular parts of the body. A new organism produced by budding may remain attached to its parent. Most often, when a bud reaches a certain size, it breaks free of the parent and becomes a separate, independent organism.

B Some yeast and single-celled organisms reproduce asexually by budding. But budding is most notable in multicellular organisms. Hydras are freshwater animals that are famous for reproducing by budding. Among plants, the kalanchoe (KAL-uhn-KOH-ee) produces tiny buds from the tips of its leaves. Each kalanchoe bud that lands on a suitable growing surface will develop into a mature kalanchoe plant that is genetically identical to the parent plant.

How is budding different in unicellular and multicellular organisms?

DIFFERENTIATE INSTRUCTION

More Reading Support

A What kind of asexual reproduction do most single-celled organisms use? *binary fission*

B How do some multi-celled organisms reproduce asexually? *by budding*

English Learners Have students write the definitions for the terms *asexual reproduction, parent,* and *offspring* in their Science Word Dictionaries. The term *offspring,* as well as its definition, may be confusing to English learners. Use the analogy that a mother is to a baby as a parent is to an offspring to help students understand.

3.3 INSTRUCT

Address Misconceptions

IDENTIFY Ask: How do you know if a cell is reproducing asexually when it divides? If students cannot answer, they are confused about the difference between sexual and asexual reproduction.

CORRECT Explain that cell division is a part of both asexual and sexual reproduction. In sexual reproduction, however, two organisms of different genders must in some way combine genetic material to produce a new individual organism. In asexual reproduction, one organism alone can produce another entire organism using cell division. Compare the bacteria in the photograph on pp. 70–71 with the seed depicted beside it on p. 71. Ask students to describe how reproduction differs in these two organisms.

REASSESS Ask: What are the two main differences between sexual and asexual reproduction? *1) two parents (sexual) vs. one parent (asexual); 2) offspring are new genetic individual (sexual) vs. identical to parent (asexual)*

Technology Resources

Visit **ClassZone.com** for background on common student misconceptions.

MISCONCEPTION DATABASE

Teacher Demo

Budding is easy to see in a potato that is kept in a bag at room temperature. The "eye" will grow, and if a piece of the potato containing the eye is planted, it will grow into a potato plant.

Ongoing Assessment

Explain how some organisms use cell division to reproduce asexually.

Ask: How can mitosis accomplish reproduction? *If mitosis results in two new organisms, there has been asexual reproduction.*

CHECK YOUR READING *Answer: In unicellular organisms, the bud is a single cell. In multicellular organisms, the bud grows by cell division, becoming multicellular.*

Integrate the Sciences

Hydroponics grows plants without soil. Plants are raised in a chemical solution containing the elements that plants need: nitrogen, phosphorus, potassium, magnesium, sulfur, calcium, iron, manganese, boron, zinc, copper, and sometimes others. To keep the plants upright in the solution, growers put them in gravel or frames. Hydroponics is used to grow plants out of season or where the soil and climate will not support them. Many arid regions obtain vegetables this way. Throughout winter months, tomatoes are one example of a readily available hydroponic crop.

Real World Example

Kerin Lilleeng-Rosenberger, who works for the National Tropical Botanical Garden in Hawaii, develops special techniques to propagate native plants, and has built the largest living collection of endangered plant species in the world. Collectors bring her plants, sometimes traveling by helicopter or rappelling down cliffs to find what may be the last living specimen of a plant. Self-taught, Lilleeng-Rosenberger has had remarkable success inventing protocols to propagate these plants often including asexual reproduction.

Ongoing Assessment

CHECK YOUR READING *Answer: If a starfish is cut in half, each half can regenerate its missing body parts by growing new tissue from cell division.*

Regeneration

In certain multicellular organisms, specialized cells at the site of a wound or lost limb are able to become different types of tissues. The process of new tissue growth at these sites is called **regeneration.** Although one function of regeneration is the regrowth of damaged or missing body parts, in some organisms asexual reproduction is another function of regeneration.

Regeneration This starfish is regenerating its legs that were lost.

Regeneration can be observed in many animals called starfish. If a starfish is cut in half, each half can regenerate its missing body parts from its own cells. The result is two complete, independent, and genetically identical starfish. Sometimes a starfish will drop off one of its limbs. The animal will eventually form a new limb. In these cases, regeneration is considered a form of asexual reproduction.

The growth of plants from cuttings is also a kind of asexual reproduction through regeneration. Cells near a cut made in a plant's stem begin to produce the missing part of the plant. Once the missing part is grown, the cutting can be planted in soil. The cutting will grow into a new, independent plant that is genetically identical to the plant from which the cutting was taken.

CHECK YOUR READING Describe the process of regeneration in starfish.

RESOURCE CENTER CLASSZONE.COM

Learn more about asexual reproduction.

Asexual Reproduction and Health

You have probably had the following experience. In the morning you feel fine. By afternoon, you have a strange feeling that something is not quite right, but you are well enough to function normally. You may even continue to feel well at dinner, and you eat heartily. Then, later that evening, it hits you. You're sick. That tickle in your throat has become a sore throat requiring a visit to the doctor and antibiotics. How did you get so sick so fast?

You could have picked up bacteria in school that morning. Perhaps another student coughed, spreading the bacteria that cause strep throat. A population of bacteria, like populations of other organisms that reproduce asexually through binary fission, increases in number geometrically. Two cells become 4, which become 8, which become 16, and so on.

DIFFERENTIATE INSTRUCTION

More Reading Support

C What process do starfish use to replace broken body parts? *regeneration*

D How do plants use regeneration? *by growing from cuttings*

Below Level Help students organize the information on asexual reproduction. Use a cluster diagram with "asexual reproduction" in the center, and branches for budding, regeneration, and binary fission.

The reason you get sick so fast is that for many bacteria the generation time is very short. Generation time is the time it takes for one generation to produce offspring—the next generation. In fact, some types of bacteria can produce a new generation of cells in less than 30 minutes. In about an hour the number of bacteria can increase to four times the starting number.

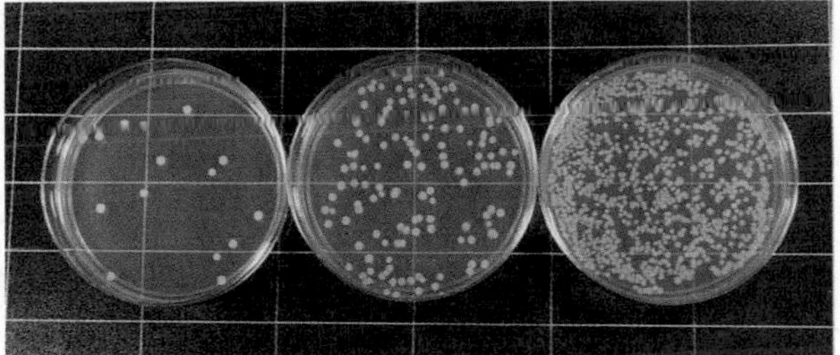

Asexual reproduction These bacteria are quickly multiplying through asexual reproduction.

Although all offspring are genetically identical, the rare genetic random change does occasionally occur during cell division. The rapid reproduction rate makes it more likely that some offspring will have a random genetic change, which may be beneficial.

INVESTIGATE Asexual Reproduction

Which parts of plants can reproduce?

Some organisms can regenerate offspring from any part of their body. Others can regenerate offspring from only one specialized body part. In this activity, you will discover if a houseplant regenerates from various parts.

SKILL FOCUS
Drawing conclusions

MATERIALS
- houseplant
- flowerpot
- soil
- water

TIME
15 minutes

PROCEDURE

1. Obtain a plant part (leaf, stem, stem with leaf, or root) from your teacher. Also get one flowerpot filled with potting soil.
2. Dip the plant part in water and set it into the soil, about 1 in. deep, but make sure that most of the plant part is above the level of the soil. Water the soil lightly.
3. Place all the class's pots on the same window sill. Observe your plant part every day for two to three weeks. Record your observations.

WHAT DO YOU THINK?
- Which plant parts, if any, were able to regenerate a new plant?
- What can you conclude about the ability of different plant parts to grow into new plants?

CHALLENGE How does the plant in the experiment compare with the kalanchoe plant you read about in the text? What accounts for plants' different abilities to produce viable offspring?

INVESTIGATE Asexual Reproduction

PURPOSE To draw experimental conclusions about which plant parts can regenerate

TIPS *15 min.* Students should label the pots with date, type of plant, and part of plant, and give them consistent (even) amounts of water, soil, and Sun.

Some common plants and plant parts:
- Ivy: areas of stem between leaf joints as well as nodes
- Geranium: stem cuttings
- Dahlia: tubers
- Leaf cuttings: begonia rex, African violets, peperomia, crassula
- Shoots: pinks, marguerites
- Roots: papaver, verbascum, campanula, phlox

WHAT DO YOU THINK? *Answers will depend on the type of plant. Not all parts of all plants can regenerate.*

CHALLENGE *Sample answer: Kalanchoe buds grow roots even though they are not planted in soil. Our plant needed to be planted in soil to grow roots and regenerate. The regenerating part has to be able to survive on its own.*

 Datasheet, Regeneration, p. 162

Technology Resources

Customize this student lab as needed or look for an alternative. Print rubrics to assess student lab reports.

 **Lab Generator CD-ROM**

DIFFERENTIATE INSTRUCTION

More Reading Support

E Is the generation time of bacteria long or short? *short*

Additional Investigation

To reinforce Section 3.3 learning goals, use the following full-period investigation:

 **Additional INVESTIGATION,** Temperature and Yeast Reproduction, A, B, & C, pp. 180–188, 308–309 (Advanced students should complete Levels B and C.)

Advanced

R Challenge and Extension, p. 161

Ongoing Assessment

Compare asexual and sexual reproduction.

Ask: Why have some organisms evolved to reproduce asexually? *so they can produce large populations quickly; so that only one individual is needed to continue a species*

Ongoing Assessment

Sample answer: short generation time for asexual reproduction and only one parent organism needed; also, sexual reproduction involves cell division as well as other processes and the offspring have genetic material from two parents.

EXPLORE the BIG idea

Revisit "Internet Activity: Cell Division" on p. 71. Have students share their questions and answers during a class discussion.

Reinforce the BIG idea

Have students relate the section to the Big Idea.

Reinforcing Key Concepts, p. 163

ASSESS & RETEACH

Assess

Section 3.3 Quiz, p. 43

Reteach

Draw a Venn diagram on the board. Label one circle "Asexual Reproduction" and the other circle "Sexual Reproduction." Lead a discussion to fill in the diagram. *Sample answer: Asexual: one parent, identical offspring; Sexual: two parents, new genetic offspring; Common: cell division*

Technology Resources

Have students visit **ClassZone.com** for reteaching of Key Concepts.

CONTENT REVIEW

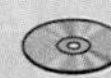
CONTENT REVIEW CD-ROM

Sexual reproduction involves two parent organisms.

Reproduction of multicellular organisms often involves sexual reproduction as well as asexual cell division. The table shows some differences between asexual and sexual reproduction.

Comparing Asexual and Sexual Reproduction

Asexual Reproduction	Sexual Reproduction
Cell Division	Cell division and other processes
One parent organism	Two parent organisms
Rate of reproduction is rapid	Rate of reproduction is slower than rate for asexual reproduction
Offspring identical to parent	Offspring have genetic information from two parents

If you grow a plant from a cutting, the new plant will be identical to the parent. However, plants that grow from seeds contain genetic material from two parents. Plants growing from seeds and animals growing from eggs are examples of organisms that reproduce through sexual reproduction.

Cell division is part of both sexual and asexual reproduction. The process of mitosis produces cells identical to the parent cells. The diversity of life on Earth is in part possible because of the combining of genetic materials from two parents in sexual reproduction. In the next chapter, you will read about cell processes involved in sexual reproduction.

List two major differences between asexual and sexual reproduction.

3.3 Review

KEY CONCEPTS

1. How does binary fission relate to cell division?
2. What is a bud, and where does it form on an organism that reproduces asexually?
3. Compare sexual and asexual reproduction.

CRITICAL THINKING

4. **Predict** Do you think prokaryotes undergo regeneration? Why or why not?
5. **Compare and Contrast** How is binary fission in prokaryotic organisms similar to and different from mitosis and cytokinesis in single-celled eukaryotic organisms?

CHALLENGE

6. **Synthesize** Some bacteria can exchange pieces of genetic material with one another through a process called conjugation. What effect might this exchange have on the offspring of the bacteria that underwent conjugation?

ANSWERS

1. They are the same in prokaryotes.

2. A bud is a bump on the body of a parent that grows until it forms a new organism genetically identical to the parent. In some organisms buds can form anywhere, but in other organisms, buds form at specific places with specialized cells.

3. Asexual reproduction involves only one parent, has a rapid rate, and produces identical offspring. Sexual reproduction involves two parents and produces offspring that have genetic material from both parents.

4. No, because regeneration only happens in multicellular organisms, and prokaryotes are unicellular.

5. Eukaryotic organisms do not undergo binary fission.

6. The offspring would have more genetic variation.

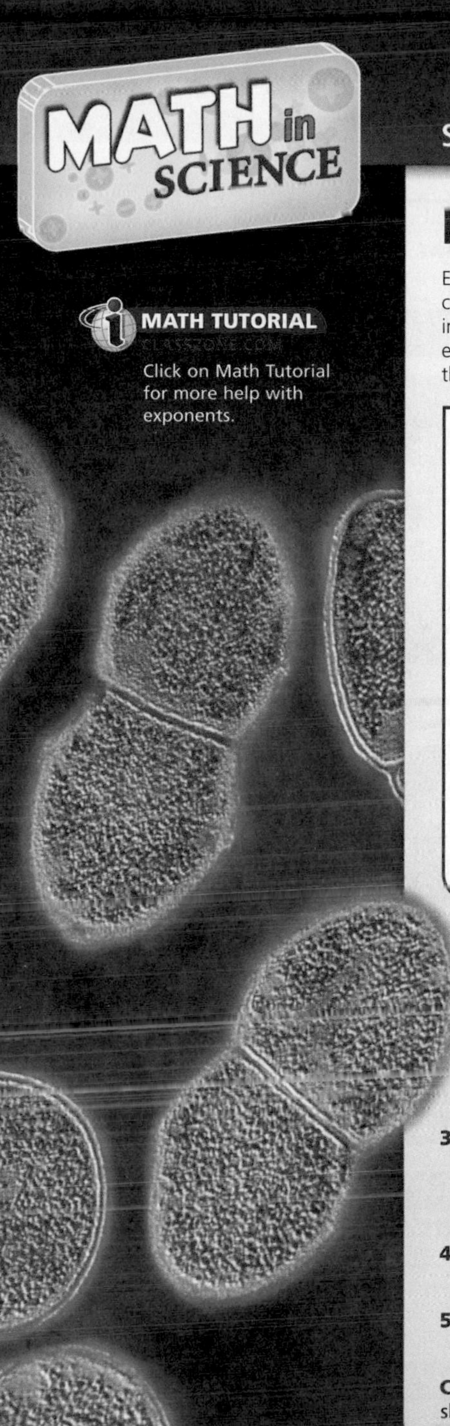

SKILL: USING EXPONENTS

Divide and Multiply

Each time a parent cell divides, the result is two new cells. The new cells are a new generation that in turn divides again. The increase in the number of cells can be shown using exponents. Each cell of each new generation produces two cells. This type of increase in the number of objects is often called exponential growth.

Example

What is the numerical sequence when cells divide to form new cells? You can model this type of progression by using a plain piece of paper.

(1) To represent the first division, fold the piece of paper in half.

(2) Fold it in half again, and it will show the second division. Fold it again and again to represent succeeding divisions.

(3) Write the sequence that shows the number of boxes on the paper after each fold.

2, 4, 8, 16, . . .

(4) Notice that after one division (fold), there are 2 cells (boxes), or 2^1. Two divisions yield $2 \cdot 2$ cells, or 2^2. And after three divisions, there are $2 \cdot 2 \cdot 2$ cells, or 2^3.

ANSWER The sequence can be written with exponents: $2^1, 2^2, 2^3, 2^4, \ldots$

Answer the following questions.

1. Suppose the cells divide for one more generation after the 4 described above. How can this be written as an exponent of 2? How many cells will there be?

2. How many cells would exist in the tenth generation? Write the number using an exponent.

3. Suppose you took the paper in the example and folded it in thirds each time, rather than in half. Make a table showing the number of boxes after each folding. Use numbers with exponents to write the sequence.

4. Write the following number sequence as a sequence of numbers with exponents: 5, 25, 125, 625, . . .

5. Write the following number sequence as a sequence of numbers with NO exponents: $10^1, 10^2, 10^3, 10^4, \ldots$

CHALLENGE Before you begin folding, you have a single sheet of paper, or 1 box. The parent cell is also a single unit. Use this information to explain why $2^0 = 3^0$.

ANSWERS

1. 2^5; 32

2. 2^{10}

3. $3^1, 3^2, 3^3, 3^4, \ldots$

4. $5^1, 5^2, 5^3, 5^4, \ldots$

5. 10, 100, 1000, 10,000

CHALLENGE *No matter how many folds you make, before any folds are made (the* 0th *exponent) the starting state is always 1.* ($10^0 = 1$)

MATH IN SCIENCE

Math Skills Practice for Science

Set Learning Goal

To use exponents to improve understanding of growth rate

Present the Science

Genetic engineering has used exponential growth in single-cell organisms to produce large quantities of medically necessary substances. Insulin, for instance, which used to be available in limited quantities from hogs, is now cloned in large quantities. The human insulin gene is "spliced" into Escherichia coli bacteria, which reproduce quickly. The insulin is then extracted from the bacteria. The technique is also used to obtain large quantities of some vaccines, as well as substances used to treat various medical conditions.

Develop Number Sense

- Remind students that 2 is the first power of 2, or $2^1 = 2$.
- Explain that students are not trying to find out how many offspring come from any one cell, but how many result once one cell (or set of cells) has divided.
- You do not count the very first cell, which constitutes the very first generation or the zero power ($2^0 = 1$).
- Make sure that students count the number of integers in the sequence to get the exponent, not the number of multiplication symbols.

Technology Resources

Students can visit **ClassZone.com** for practice in using exponents.

 **MATH TUTORIAL**

Close

Ask: Where else in life might you encounter exponential growth? *Sample answer: the population of a city, the number of flies in the house*

- Math Support, p. 169
- Math Practice, p. 170

BACK TO

the BIG idea

Ask: How does cell division relate to the growth of plants and animals? *Both plants and animals grow bigger by developing more cells. These additional cells come from the division of existing cells.*

KEY CONCEPTS SUMMARY

SECTION 3.1

Ask: What is DNA? *the genetic instructions for how the cell is to develop, function, and reproduce*

Ask: Where does a new cell get its DNA? *from the parent cell*

SECTION 3.2

Ask: In what phase does a cell spend most of its life? *interphase*

Ask: Summarize what happens during mitosis. *Chromosome duplicates line up and pull to opposite ends of the parent cell, and the cell divides into two daughter cells.*

SECTION 3.3

Ask: What is the difference between cell division and asexual reproduction? *In cell division a new cell forms, while in asexual reproduction, a whole new organism forms.*

Ask: What is advantageous about asexual reproduction? *It produces large populations fast, and one organism can perpetuate the species.*

Review Concepts

- Big Idea Flow Chart, p. T17
- Chapter Outline, pp. T23–T24

3 Chapter Review

the BIG idea

Organisms grow, reproduce, and maintain themselves through cell division.

KEY CONCEPTS SUMMARY

1 Cell division occurs in all organisms.

- In unicellular organisms functions of cell division include reproduction
- In multicellular organisms functions of cell division include growth, development, and repair.

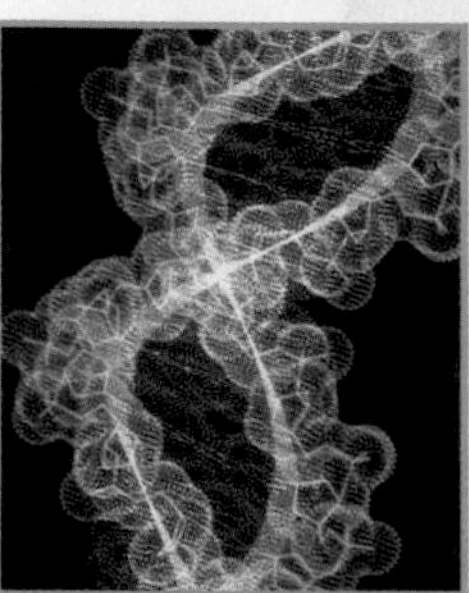

VOCABULARY
DNA p. 74
chromosome p. 75

2 Cell division is part of a cell cycle.

The **cell cycle** has two main phases, **interphase** and **mitosis.** Most of the life cycle of a cell is spent in interphase. During mitosis, cells divide.

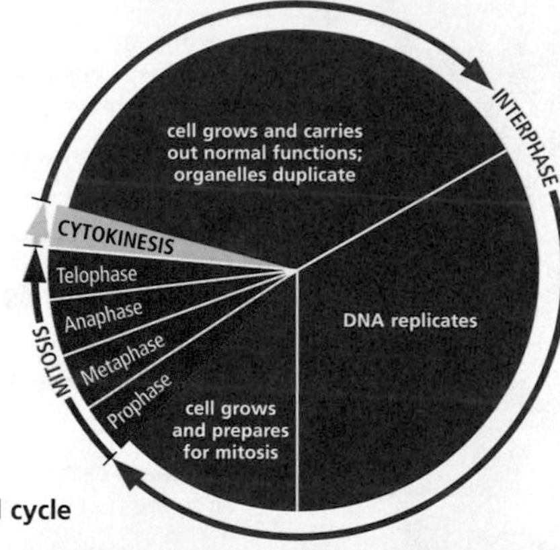

Cell cycle

VOCABULARY
cell cycle p. 80
interphase p. 81
mitosis p. 81
cytokinesis p. 81

3 Both sexual and asexual reproduction involve cell division.

Some organisms reproduce asexually. Both asexual and sexual reproduction involve cell division.

Comparing Asexual and Sexual Reproduction

Asexual Reproduction	Sexual Reproduction
Cell Division	Cell division and other processes
One parent organism	Two parent organisms
Rate of reproduction is rapid	Rate of reproduction is slower than rate for asexual reproduction
Offspring identical to parents	Offspring have genetic information from two parents

VOCABULARY
asexual reproduction p. 88
binary fission p. 89
regeneration p. 90

94 Unit 1: Cells and Heredity

Technology Resources

Have students visit **ClassZone.com** or use the CD-ROM for a cumulative review of concepts.

CONTENT REVIEW

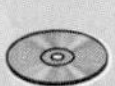
CONTENT REVIEW CD-ROM

Engage students in a whole-class interactive review of Key Concepts. Edit content as you wish.

POWER PRESENTATIONS

Reviewing Vocabulary

On a separate sheet of paper, write a sentence describing the relationship between the two vocabulary words in each pair.

1. cell cycle, interphase
2. mitosis, cytokinesis
3. chromosome, DNA
4. parent, offspring

Reviewing Key Concepts

Multiple Choice *Choose the letter of the best answer.*

5. Most of the growth in your body occurs because your cells
   a. grow larger
   b. take in oxygen
   c. make proteins
   d. divide
6. The stage in a cell's life when it is not in the process of dividing is called
   a. interphase
   b. the cell cycle
   c. mitosis
   d. cell division
7. What material in the cell makes up chromosomes?
   a. carbohydrates
   b. chromatids
   c. the nucleus
   d. nucleic acids
8. What ratio increases when a cell divides into two smaller cells?
   a. volume to length
   b. length to width
   c. surface area to volume
   d. width to surface area
9. The process of cytokinesis results in
   a. two daughter cells that are different from one another
   b. two genetically identical daughter cells
   c. identical pairs of chromosomes
   d. identical pairs of chromatids
10. What is the step that follows mitosis, in which the cytoplasm divides?
    a. prophase
    b. synthesis
    c. anaphase
    d. cytokinesis
11. A cell's chromosomes must be duplicated before mitosis occurs so that
    a. they can form chromatids
    b. they can attach to the spindle
    c. each daughter cell gets a full number of chromosomes
    d. each daughter cell does not have to duplicate its own chromosomes
12. Binary fission differs from mitosis because the new cells
    a. cannot function without the parent
    b. grow from missing limbs
    c. have half the normal number of chromosomes
    d. live independently of the parent cell
13. If a starfish is cut in half, it can regrow its missing body through
    a. binary fission
    b. budding
    c. healing
    d. regeneration
14. Which is an example of reproduction?
    a. binary fission in unicellular organisms
    b. cell division in a multicellular organism
    c. cell division around a broken bone
    d. division of cytoplasm
15. Which sequence is correct for mitosis?
    a. chromosomes form, chromosomes separate, chromosomes line up, nuclei form
    b. chromosomes form, chromosomes line up, chromosomes separate, nuclei form
    c. chromosomes line up, nuclei form, chromosomes separate, chromosomes form
    d. chromosomes separate, chromosomes form, nuclei form, chromosomes line up

Short Answer *Write a short answer to each question.*

16. What is the difference between cytokinesis in plant and animal cells?
17. Describe what happens in a cell during interphase. Your answer should mention DNA.
18. Describe the functions of cell division in both unicellular and multicellular organisms.

ASSESSMENT RESOURCES

UNIT ASSESSMENT BOOK
- Chapter Test A, pp. 44–47
- Chapter Test B, pp. 48–51
- Chapter Test C, pp. 52–55
- Alternative Assessment, pp. 56–57

SPANISH ASSESSMENT BOOK
Spanish Chapter Test, pp. 9–12

Technology Resources

Edit test items and answer choices.

 **Test Generator CD-ROM**

Visit **ClassZone.com** to extend test practice.

 **Test Practice**

Reviewing Vocabulary

1. *Interphase is the longest phase of the cell cycle.*
2. *Cytokinesis, which is the division of cytoplasm, occurs immediately after mitosis.*
3. *Chromosomes consist of compacted DNA.*
4. *Offspring come from parents.*

Reviewing Key Concepts

5. *d*
6. *a*
7. *d*
8. *c*
9. *b*
10. *d*
11. *c*
12. *d*
13. *d*
14. *a*
15. *b*
16. *During animal mitosis, a fiber ring contracts in the center of the dividing cells. In plants, a rigid cell wall is built between the two daughter cells.*
17. *During interphase, the cell grows, performs normal life activities, and duplicates its DNA.*
18. *In multicellular organisms, cell division is involved with growth, development, repair, two types of asexual reproduction (budding, regeneration), and sexual reproduction (along with other processes). In unicellular organisms, cell division results in asexual reproduction.*

Thinking Critically

19. *Cells divide when it is necessary for an organism to grow larger. Cells also divide to repair cells that have been damaged or cells that die.*
20. *leaf*
21. *the nuclei of the cells in the cutting*
22. *They are genetically identical.*
23. *cell division*
24. *The cells in the plants grow and duplicate their DNA during interphase. Then, the DNA condenses and separates into two new nuclei via mitosis, followed by cytokinesis during which two daughter cells are formed. This process keeps happening, resulting in plant growth.*
25. *Both the cutting and the plant that would grow from a seed are organisms separate from the parent organism. However, the cutting is genetically identical to the parent plant, whereas the plant that would grow from a seed may also have genetic material from a second parent plant.*
26. $2^{20} = 1,048,576$
27. *d, a, b, c*
28. *The first drawing would show a cell in interphase, so the DNA should be in a threadlike mass instead of in chromosomes. The second drawing should show two separate daughter cells.*
29. *The model should include the four phases of mitosis.*

the BIG idea

30. *Answers should include the idea that the cells that are dividing are genetically identical to the other cells in the photograph.*
31. *The cell theory states that cells come from other cells. Cell division is the process by which cells come from other cells.*

UNIT PROJECTS

Check to make sure students are working on their projects. Check schedules and work in progress.

Unit Projects, pp. 5–10

Thinking Critically

19. **IDENTIFY CAUSE** Describe some of the reasons that cells divide.

This illustration shows a plant and the cutting that was taken from it, which is growing in a container of water. Use the illustration to answer the next six questions.

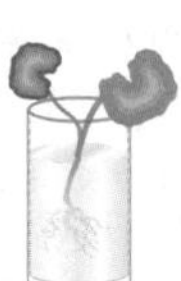

20. **OBSERVE** From which part of the plant was the cutting taken?
21. **INFER** Where did the cutting get the genetic information that controls its development?
22. **INFER** What is the genetic relationship between the original plant and the cutting?
23. **SYNTHESIZE** What process causes both the cutting and the original plant to grow?
24. **SUMMARIZE** Write a brief summary of the process that causes growth in both plants.
25. **PREDICT** These plants can also reproduce from fertilized seeds. How is the cutting the same as the plant that would grow from a seed? How is the cutting different?

26. **CALCULATE** A single bacterium enters your body at 10:00 A.M. These bacteria reproduce at a rate of one generation every 30 minutes. How many bacteria of this type will be in your body by 8:00 P.M. that evening?

The diagrams below show 4 parts of a process. Use them to answer the following three questions.

a.

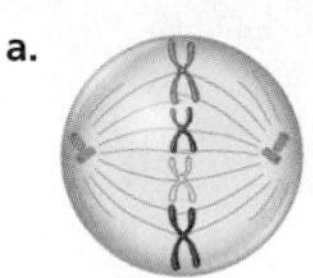

c.

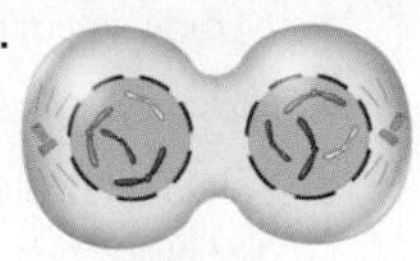

b.

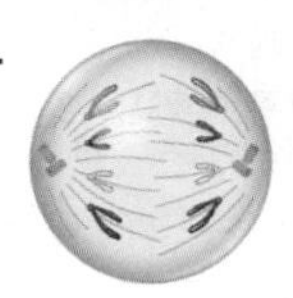

d.

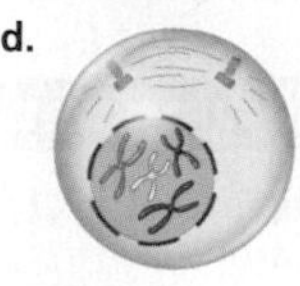

27. **SEQUENCE** What is the correct order of the four diagrams above?
28. **SYNTHESIZE** Draw two diagrams, one showing what you would see before the process shown above begins, and one showing what you would see after the conclusion of the process.
29. **MODEL** On a separate sheet of paper, draw your own simple model of the process of mitosis.

the BIG idea

30. **SUMMARIZE** Look again at the question on the photograph on pages 70–71. Now that you have studied this chapter, how would you change your answer to the question?
31. **SYNTHESIZE** How do the concepts in this chapter relate to the concepts in the cell theory?

UNIT PROJECTS

If you need to do an experiment for your unit project, gather the materials. Be sure to allow enough time to observe results before the project is due.

MONITOR AND RETEACH

If students have difficulty with items 21, 23, and 24, have them imagine they are a starfish who has just lost a leg. What is most likely to happen? How does cell division play a part? *Cells in the wound start mitosis. Daughter cells, genetically identical to the parent cells, multiply. Gradually the starfish replaces missing cells until it regenerates a leg.*

Students may benefit from summarizing one or more sections of the chapter.

Summarizing the Chapter, pp. 189–190

Standardized Test Practice

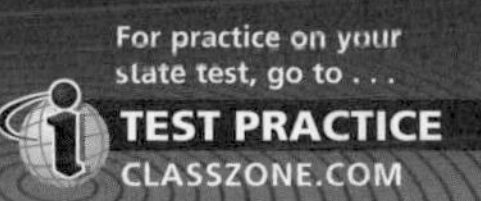

Analyzing Data

This diagram shows the length of the cell cycle for a typical skin cell in the human body.

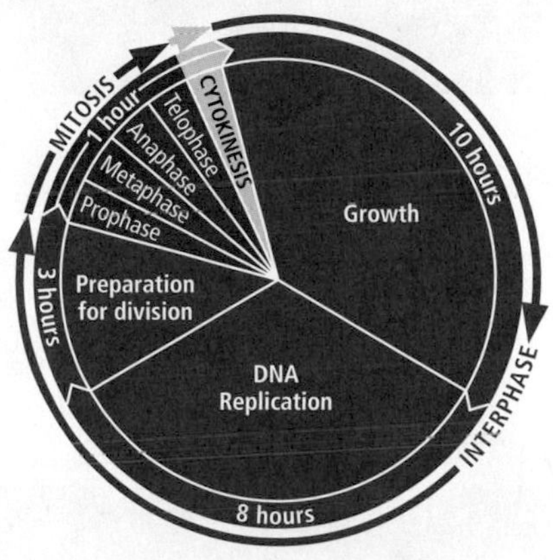

Use the diagram to answer the questions below.

1. How long does the growth phase of the cell cycle take?
   a. 1 hour **c.** 8 hours
   b. 3 hours **d.** 10 hours
2. How much time does the cell cycle spend in interphase?
   a. 1 hour **c.** 21 hours
   b. 10 hours **d.** 22 hours
3. What is the total length of time it takes for the skin cell to complete one full cell cycle?
   a. 10 hours **c.** 21 hours
   b. 18 hours **d.** 22 hours
4. What phase of the cell cycle takes about 8 hours?
   a. DNA replication
   b. mitosis
   c. growth
   d. preparation for cell division
5. Suppose another type of skin cell takes 44 hours to complete one cell cycle. If all of the phases are proportional to the length of time shown in the diagram, how long will the preparation for cell division phase last?
   a. 3 hours **c.** 10 hours
   b. 6 hours **d.** 20 hours
6. According to the diagram, what is the second stage in mitosis?
   a. prophase **c.** telophase
   b. metaphase **d.** cytokinesis

Extended Response

Answer the two questions. Include some of the terms shown in the word box. Underline each term you use in your answers.

cell cycle	metaphase	mitosis
anaphase	prophase	telophase

7. A scientist is studying the stages of cell division in the cells of an onion root. The scientist counts 100 cells and identifies which stage of cell division each cell is in at a given moment. He counts a total of 85 cells in interphase, 8 cells in prophase, 3 cells in metaphase, and 2 cells each in anaphase and telophase. A typical onion cell takes about 12 hours to complete the cell cycle. Using the information in the diagram and the data given here, how can you account for these numbers?
8. Your science class is investigating the effect of temperature on the rate of mitosis in onion plants. You hypothesize that the higher the temperature, the faster cells undergo mitosis. How could you set up an experiment to support your hypothesis? Describe the materials you would use and the steps you would take in your procedure.

METACOGNITIVE ACTIVITY

Have students answer the following questions in their **Science Notebook:**

1. Why do you think it is important for you to learn about cell reproduction?
2. Which topics in this chapter would you like to learn more about?
3. How do the concepts in this chapter relate to your unit project?

Analyzing Data

1. d *3. d* *5. b*
2. c *4. a* *6. b*

Extended Response

7. RUBRIC

4 points for a response that correctly identifies the four phases of mitosis and indicates that interphase accounts for the largest portion of a cell's life.

Sample answer: The stages of prophase, metaphase, anaphase, and telophase are all stages of mitosis. Mitosis is the shortest phase of the cell cycle. Interphase is the longest phase. Most cells in the onion root would be in interphase.

3 points correctly identifies the phases of mitosis but not why more cells are in interphase

2 points does not correctly identify the phases of mitosis but says why more cells are in interphase

1 point demonstrates minimal understanding of mitosis and the cell cycle but cannot answer the question

8. RUBRIC

4 points for a plan for an experiment that will test the hypothesis, including:
- Apply measurable heat differences to onion root tips.
- Assemble slides from the root tips.
- Record results.

Sample answer: Cut off three onion root tips. Put one root tip in the refrigerator for 24 hours, keep one at room temperature for 24 hours, and put one in hot water until the color changes. Examine the tips under a microscope. Count the cells in mitosis and compare the results.

3 points if the plan accounts for only one temperature difference but includes comparing and recording

2 points if the plan does not account for temperature differences but notes that counting and comparing are important

1 point if the plan demonstrates minimal understanding of the task of experimentation

CHAPTER

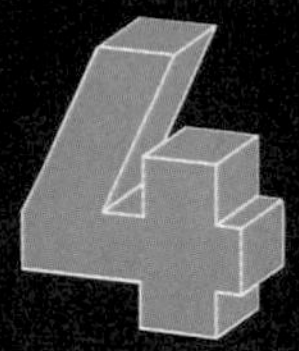

Patterns of Heredity

Life Science

UNIFYING PRINCIPLES

PRINCIPLE 1
All living things share common characteristics.

PRINCIPLE 2
All living things share common needs.

PRINCIPLE 3
Living things meet their needs through interactions with the environment.

PRINCIPLE 4
The types and numbers of living things change over time.

Unit 1: Cells and Heredity

BIG IDEAS

CHAPTER 1
The Cell
All living things are made up of cells.

CHAPTER 2
How Cells Function
All cells need energy and materials for life processes.

CHAPTER 3
Cell Division
Organisms grow, reproduce, and maintain themselves through cell division.

CHAPTER 4
Patterns of Heredity
In sexual reproduction, genes are passed from parents to offspring in predictable patterns.

CHAPTER 5
DNA and Modern Genetics
DNA is a set of instructions for making cell parts.

CHAPTER 4

KEY CONCEPTS

SECTION 1

Living things inherit traits in patterns.

1. Parents and offspring are similar.
2. Genes are on chromosome pairs.
3. Gregor Mendel made some important discoveries about heredity.
4. Alleles interact to produce traits.

SECTION 2

Patterns of heredity can be predicted.

1. Punnett squares show possible outcomes for inheritance.
2. Ratios and percentages can express the probability of outcomes.

SECTION 3

Meiosis is a special form of cell division.

1. Meiosis is necessary for sexual reproduction.
2. Cells divide twice during meiosis.
3. Meiosis and mitosis differ in some important ways.

The Big Idea Flow Chart is available on p. T25 in the **UNIT TRANSPARENCY BOOK.**

Previewing Content

SECTION

Living things inherit traits in patterns. pp. 101–109

1. Parents and offspring are similar.
Some traits are inherited from parents, and some are acquired by learning or affected by environmental influence. Some traits combine both influences.

2. Genes are on chromosome pairs.
A **gene** is a unit of heredity, a segment of DNA that carries a code for a particular function or trait and occupies a specific place on a chromosome. Most functions and traits are coded for by more than one gene.
Humans have 23 pairs of chromosomes, consisting of a homolog from each parent. Homologs may have the same or different **alleles,** different variants of a gene. Human females have cells with two X-chromosomes and human males have cells with one X- and one Y-chromosome. Unlike other homologs (shown below), X- and Y-chromosomes in males have some alleles that are unpaired.

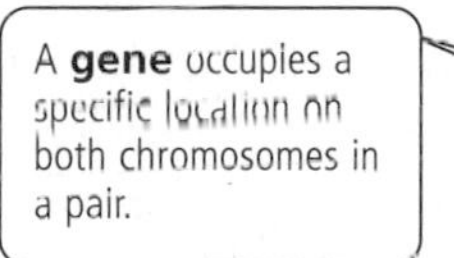

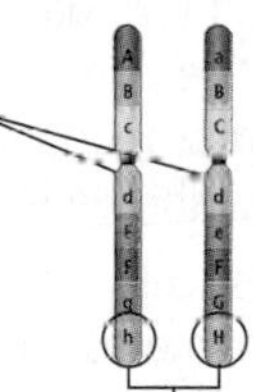

3. Gregor Mendel made some important discoveries about heredity.
Mendel's experiments with pea plants demonstrated that each parent contributes factors of heredity, now known as genes, that affect the traits of their offspring.

4. Alleles interact to produce traits.
An organism's **phenotype** is its observable characteristics. Its **genotype** is the set of genes that it has. Alleles of a gene can be dominant or recessive.

- Only one allele is necessary for a trait to be expressed if the allele is **dominant.**
- If alleles are **recessive,** two recessive alleles must be present for the trait to be expressed.

SECTION

Patterns of heredity can be predicted. pp. 110–116

1. Punnett squares show possible outcomes for inheritance.
A Punnett square shows all possible combinations of the parents' alleles that can combine in their offspring, and what proportion of the offspring is likely to express a particular trait. The Punnett square below shows the possible genotypes for a cross between a parent with two dominant alleles and one with two recessive alleles.

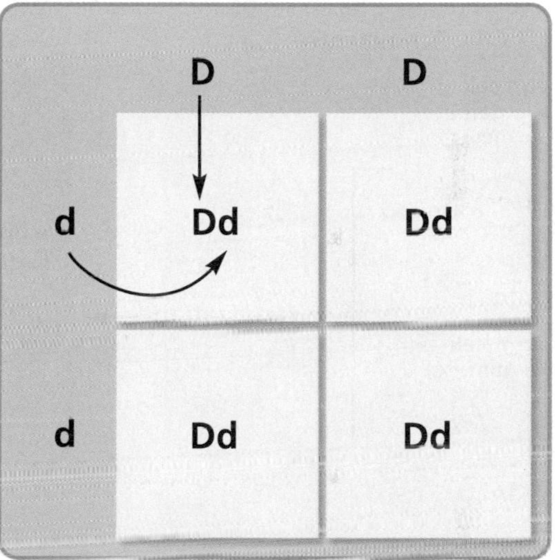

2. Ratios and percentages can express the probability of outcomes.
A **ratio** compares two quantities. **Probability** is the likelihood of an outcome. The ratios in a Punnett square show the probability of an offspring inheriting certain genes. A **percentage** is another way to express probability. In the Punnett square above, the probability that an offspring will have the dominant trait is 4:4, a 100 percent chance.

Common Misconceptions

MISCONCEPTION DATABASE
CLASSZONE.COM Background on student misconceptions

ACQUIRED TRAITS NOT INHERITED
Students sometimes think that all traits are inherited. However some traits are learned, or acquired. Each generation has to relearn or acquire these traits, such as the ability to read or write.

This misconception is addressed on p. 102.

TRAITS ON THE X- AND Y-CHROMOSOMES Students may think that the sex chromosomes only determine the sex of offspring. The X- and Y-chromosomes, sometimes called sex chromosomes, also code for other important traits as well.

This misconception is addressed on p. 103.

PARENTS CONTRIBUTE EQUALLY
Students may think that if an offspring shows the same trait as one particular parent, then the gene for that trait must have come only from that parent. Offspring get genes from both parents, but not all genes are expressed.

This misconception is addressed on p. 104.

Previewing Content

SECTION

Meiosis is a special form of cell division. pp. 117–123

1. Meiosis is necessary for sexual reproduction.
Organisms that reproduce sexually produce **gametes,** sex cells that contain half as many chromosomes as body cells do.

- Female gametes are **eggs.**
- Male gametes are **sperm.**
- Gametes are also called 1*n*, or haploid, cells and are produced by the process of **meiosis.**

In fertilization, two gametes join, as shown below. The resulting cell is 2*n*, or diploid. It has pairs of chromosomes, with a homolog from each parent.

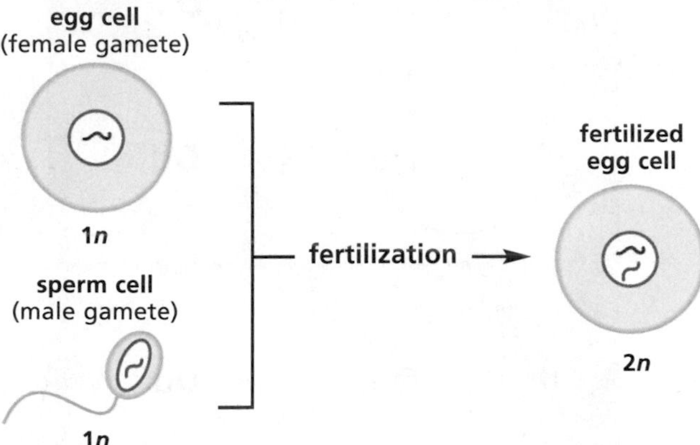

2. Cells divide twice during meiosis.
Before meiosis, the DNA in each homolog is copied. (Recall from the previous chapter that the copies are referred to as chromatids and are held together by a centromere.) Meiosis goes through stages similar to mitosis, with an important difference:

- The genetic material is divided not once, but twice.
- Four 1*n* (haploid) daughter cells are formed.

In meiosis I, the first two daughter cells are formed. They receive one of the homologs.

In meiosis II, these two daughter cells divide again, splitting the homolog so that each cell gets one of the copies.

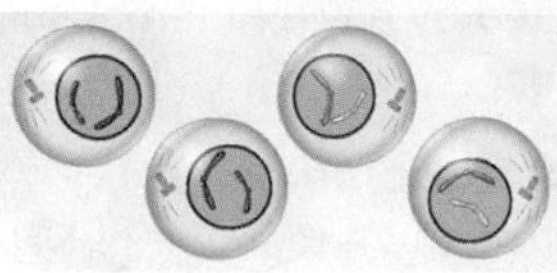

Each of the four resulting daughter cells has half the number of chromosomes needed for offspring.

3. Meiosis and mitosis differ in important ways.
Cells that are to become gametes go through meiosis; all other cells divide by mitosis. In meiosis, DNA is copied, then the cells divide twice. Each cell has only one homolog from one parent. In mitosis, DNA is copied and the cells divide just once. Each cell has two homologs, one from each parent.

- Meiosis produces haploid (1*n*) daughter cells that have half the genetic material of the parents.
- Mitosis produces diploid (2*n*) daughter cells that have the same genetic material as the parents.

Meiosis produces gametes, cells specialized for reproduction. During fertilization, two gametes combine and two haploid cells form into one diploid cell. The cell then divides by mitosis, developing into a multicellular organism.

Common Misconceptions

MISCONCEPTION DATABASE
CLASSZONE.COM Background on student misconceptions

TRAITS CAN BE PREDICTED Students may think Punnett squares predict the offspring's traits. A prediction is not the same thing as a probability. Punnett squares indicate only the probability of a trait being expressed in one of the offspring.

 This misconception is addressed on p. 113.

Previewing Labs

Lab Generator CD-ROM
Edit these Pupil Edition labs and generate alternative labs.

EXPLORE the BIG idea

How Are Traits Distributed? p. 99 Students collect data on human traits to learn how they are distributed in the population.	**TIME** 10 minutes **MATERIALS** paper and pencil
Combinations, p. 99 Students consider ways to combine two sets of materials.	**TIME** 10 minutes **MATERIALS** 4 blue slips of paper, 4 red slips of paper, plastic bags
Internet Activity: Mendel's Experiment, p. 99 Students explore Mendel's work with pea plants.	**TIME** 20 minutes **MATERIALS** computer with Internet access

SECTION 1

CHAPTER INVESTIGATION **Offspring Models,** pp. 108–109 Students design a model of an offspring to determine its genotype and phenotype.	**TIME** 40 minutes **MATERIALS** foam balls, colored toothpicks, small paperclips, colored pipe cleaners, colored pushpins

SECTION 2

EXPLORE Probability, p. 110 Students toss coins to explore probability.	**TIME** 10 minutes **MATERIALS** two coins, pencil and paper
INVESTIGATE Multiple Probabilities, p. 114 Students toss four coins to explore whether probabilities affect each other.	**TIME** 30 minutes **MATERIALS** 2 large coins, 2 small coins, masking tape, marker, datasheet

SECTION 3

EXPLORE Meiosis, p. 117 Students use pipe cleaners to create a model of sexual reproduction showing the necessity of meiosis.	**TIME** 20 minutes **MATERIALS** 2 blue pipe cleaners, 2 red pipe cleaners
INVESTIGATE Fertilization, p. 119 Students use pipe cleaners to design a model to show what happens in a cell during fertilization.	**TIME** 25 minutes **MATERIALS** pipe cleaners, gallon milk jug, film canister, yarn

R **Additional INVESTIGATION,** How Is the Sex of Offspring Determined?, A, B, & C, pp. 239–247; Teacher Instructions, pp. 308–309

Previewing Chapter Resources

CHAPTER 4

Patterns of Heredity

INTEGRATED TECHNOLOGY

CLASSZONE.COM
- eEdition Plus
- EasyPlanner Plus
- Misconception Database
- Content Review
- Test Practice
- Simulation
- Resource Centers
- Internet Activity: Mendel's Experiment
- Math Tutorial

SCILINKS.ORG
SCILINKS

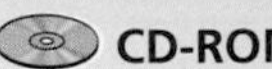
CD-ROMS
- eEdition
- EasyPlanner
- Power Presentations
- Content Review
- Lab Generator
- Test Generator

AUDIO CDS
- Audio Readings
- Audio Readings in Spanish

LABS AND ACTIVITIES

EXPLORE the Big Idea, p. 99
- How Are Traits Distributed?
- Combinations
- Internet Activity: Mendel's Experiment

UNIT RESOURCE BOOK
Unit Projects, pp. 5–10

Lab Generator CD-ROM
Generate customized labs.

SECTION

Living things inherit traits in patterns.
pp. 101–109

Time: 3 periods (1.5 blocks)

 Lesson Plan, pp. 191–192

Integrated Technology

RESOURCE CENTER, Sexual Reproduction

UNIT TRANSPARENCY BOOK
- Big Idea Flow Chart, p. T25
- Daily Vocabulary Scaffolding, p. T26
- Note-Taking Model, p. T27
- 3-Minute Warm-Up, p. T28

Labs and Activities

CHAPTER INVESTIGATION, Offspring Models, pp. 108–109

UNIT RESOURCE BOOK
CHAPTER INVESTIGATION, Offspring Models, A, B, & C, pp. 230–238

SECTION

Patterns of heredity can be predicted.
pp. 110–116

Time: 2 periods (1 block)

 Lesson Plan, pp. 201–202

Integrated Technology

- **SIMULATION,** Punnett Squares
- **MATH TUTORIAL**

UNIT TRANSPARENCY BOOK
- Daily Vocabulary Scaffolding, p. T26
- 3-Minute Warm-Up, p. T28
- "Punnett Square and Probability" Visual, p. T30

Labs and Activities

- EXPLORE Probability, p. 110
- INVESTIGATE Multiple Probabilities, p. 114
- Math in Science, p. 116

UNIT RESOURCE BOOK
- Datasheet, Multiple Probabilities, p. 210
- Math Support, p. 228
- Math Practice, p. 229

SECTION

Meiosis is a special form of cell division.
pp. 117–123

Time: 3 periods (1.5 blocks)

 Lesson Plan, pp. 212–213

Integrated Technology

RESOURCE CENTER, Meiosis

UNIT TRANSPARENCY BOOK
- Big Idea Flow Chart, p. T25
- Daily Vocabulary Scaffolding, p. T26
- 3-Minute Warm-Up, p. T29
- Chapter Outline, pp. T31–T32

Labs and Activities

- EXPLORE Meiosis, p. 117
- INVESTIGATE Fertilization, p. 119
- Think Science, p. 123

UNIT RESOURCE BOOK
- Datasheet, Fertilization, p. 221
- Additional INVESTIGATION, How Is the Sex of Offspring Determined?, A, B, & C, pp. 239–247

KEY TO ICONS  CD/CD-ROM  Teacher Edition  UNIT TRANSPARENCY BOOK SPANISH ASSESSMENT BOOK

 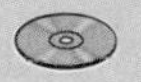 INTERNET 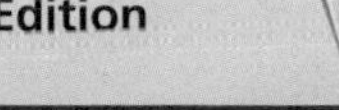 Pupil Edition UNIT RESOURCE BOOK UNIT ASSESSMENT BOOK SCIENCE TOOLKIT

READING AND REINFORCEMENT	ASSESSMENT	STANDARDS
 • Magnet Word, B24–25 • Choose Your Own Strategy, C35–44 • Daily Vocabulary Scaffolding, H1–8  **UNIT RESOURCE BOOK** • Vocabulary Practice, pp. 225–226 • Decoding Support, p. 227 • Summarizing the Chapter, pp. 248–249 **Audio Readings CD** Listen to Pupil Edition. **Audio Readings in Spanish CD** Listen to Pupil Edition in Spanish.	• Chapter Review, pp. 125–126 • Standardized Test Practice, p. 127  **UNIT ASSESSMENT BOOK** • Diagnostic Test, pp. 58–59 • Chapter Test, A, B, & C, pp. 63–74 • Alternative Assessment, pp. 75–76     Spanish Chapter Test, pp. 13–16  **Test Generator CD-ROM** Generate customized tests. **Lab Generator CD-ROM** Rubrics for Labs	National Standards A.1–8, A.9.a–c, A.9.e–g, C.2.a–d, G.1.a–b See p. 98 for the standards.
UNIT RESOURCE BOOK • Reading Study Guide, A & B, pp. 193–196 • Spanish Reading Study Guide, pp. 197–198 • Challenge and Extension, p. 199 • Reinforcing Key Concepts, p. 200	 Ongoing Assessment, pp. 102–107  Section 4.1 Review, p. 107  **UNIT ASSESSMENT BOOK** Section 4.1 Quiz, p. 60	National Standards A.1–7, A.9.a–b, A.9.e–g, C.2.a–d, G.1.a–b
 **UNIT RESOURCE BOOK** • Reading Study Guide, A & B, pp. 203–206 • Spanish Reading Study Guide, pp. 207–208 • Challenge and Extension, p. 209 • Reinforcing Key Concepts, p. 211 • Challenge Reading, pp. 223–224	 Ongoing Assessment, pp. 111–112, 114–115  Section 4.2 Review, p. 115  **UNIT ASSESSMENT BOOK** Section 4.2 Quiz, p. 61	National Standards A.2–8, A.9.a–c, A.9.e–f, C.2.c–d, G.1.a–b
 **UNIT RESOURCE BOOK** • Reading Study Guide, A & B, pp. 214–217 • Spanish Reading Study Guide, pp. 218–219 • Challenge and Extension, p. 220 • Reinforcing Key Concepts, p. 222	 Ongoing Assessment, pp. 117–118, 121–122  Section 4.3 Review, p. 122  **UNIT ASSESSMENT BOOK** Section 4.3 Quiz, p. 62	National Standards A.2–8, A.9.a–b, A.9.e–f, C.2.a, G.1.a–b

Previewing Resources for Differentiated Instruction

CHAPTER INVESTIGATION

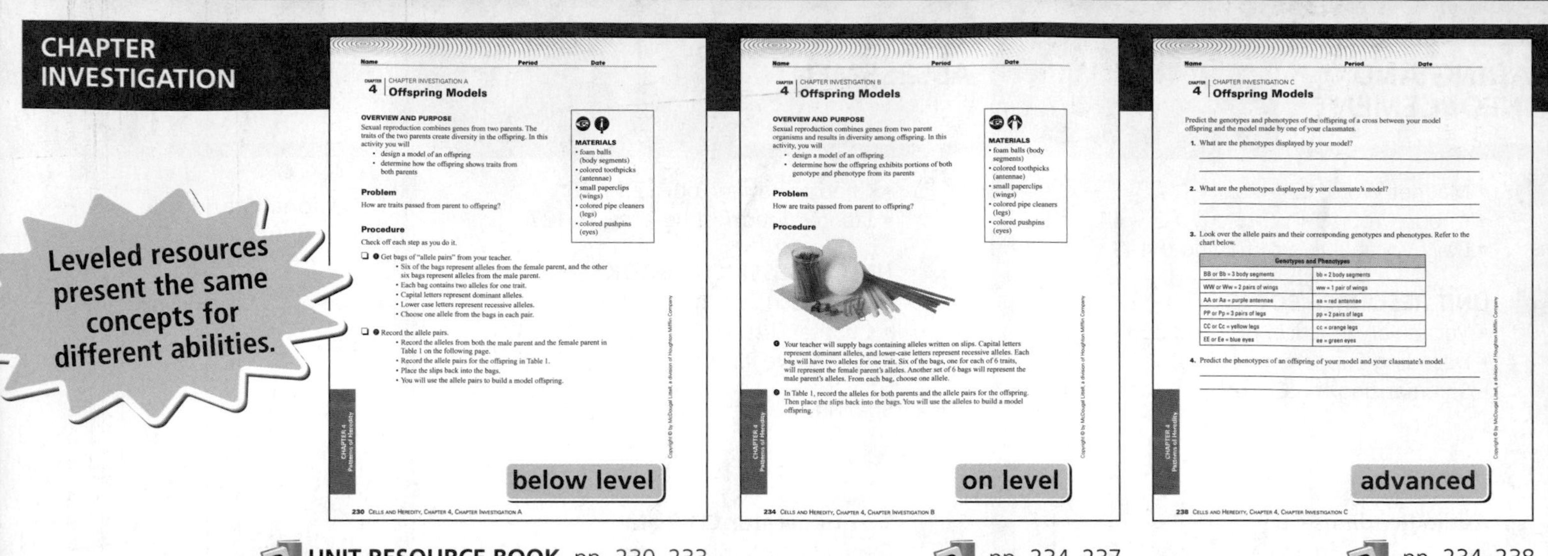

UNIT RESOURCE BOOK, pp. 230–233 | pp. 234–237 | pp. 234–238

READING STUDY GUIDE

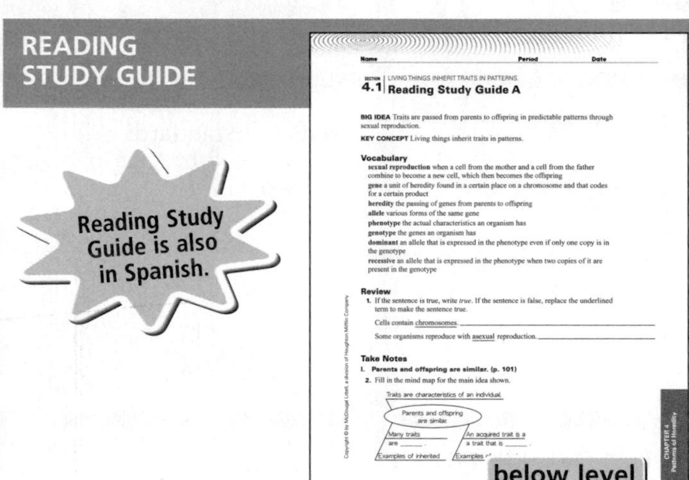

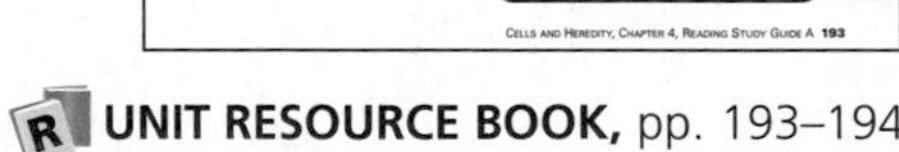

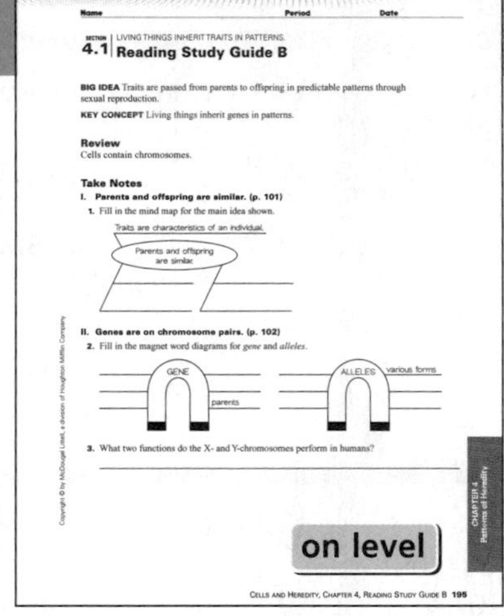

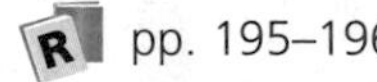

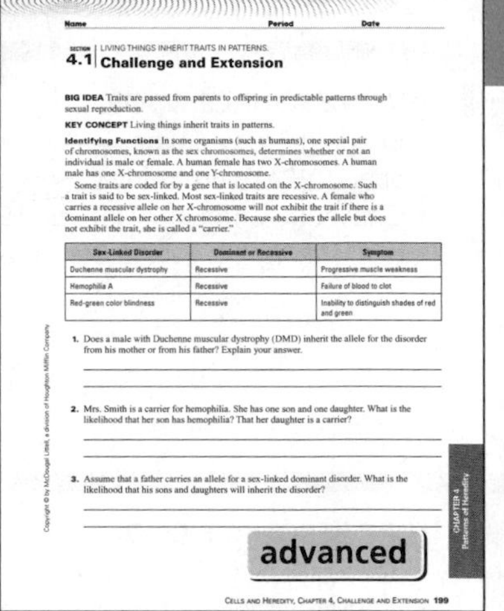

p. 199

CHAPTER TEST

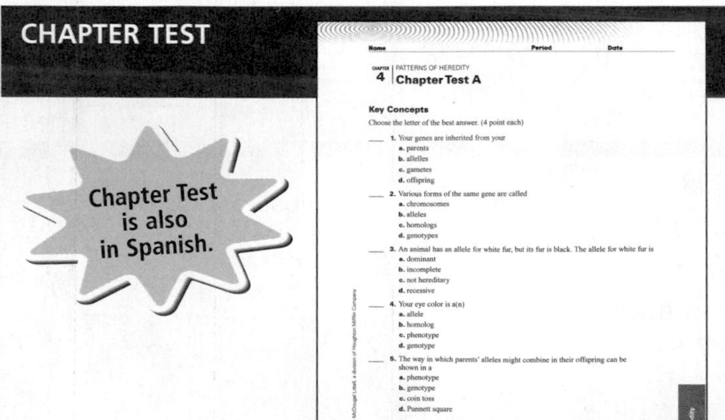

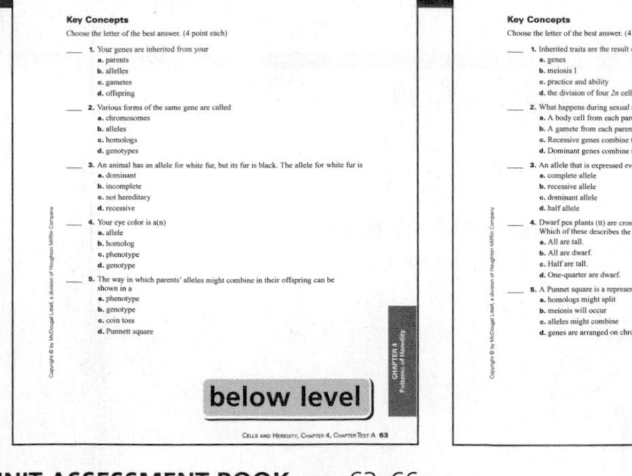

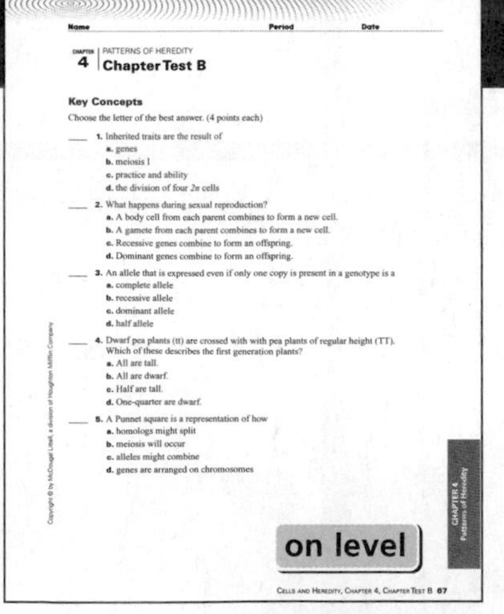

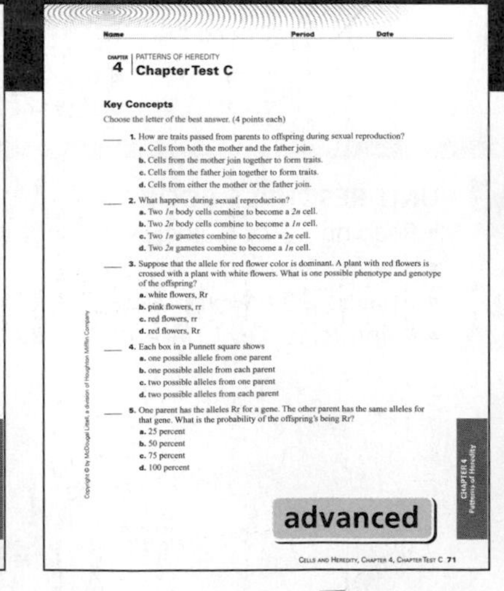

UNIT ASSESSMENT BOOK, pp. 63–66 | pp. 67–70

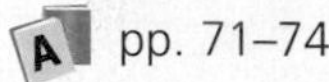

TECHNOLOGY

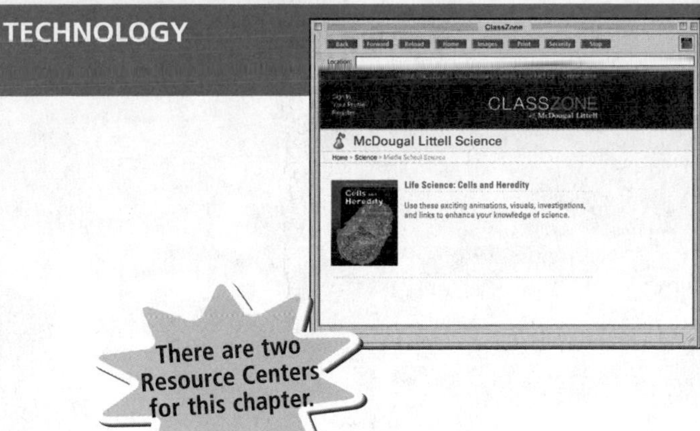

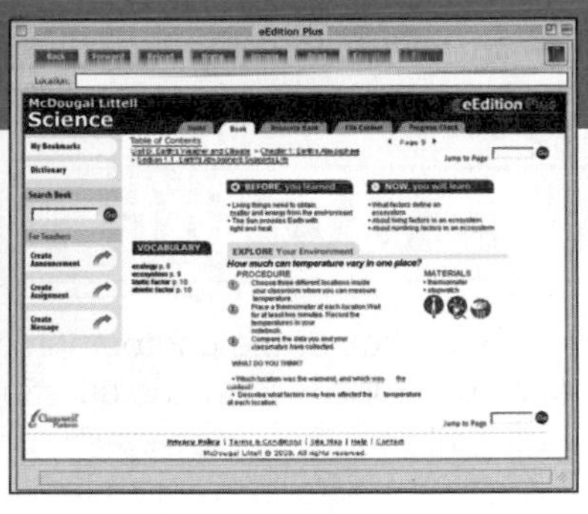

CLASSZONE.COM

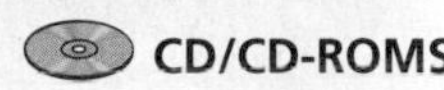
CD/CD-ROMS

CLASSZONE.COM

VISUAL CONTENT

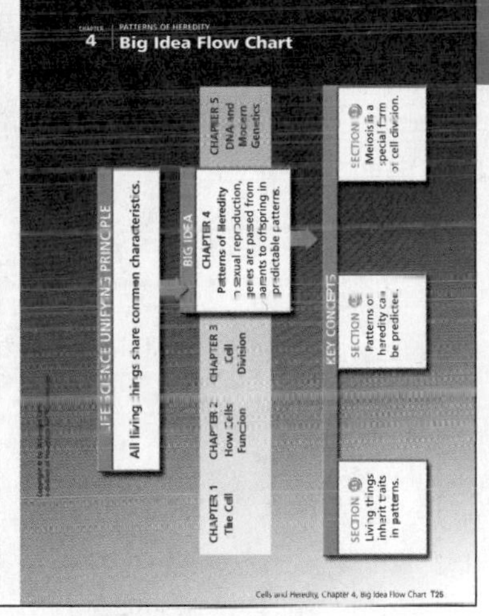

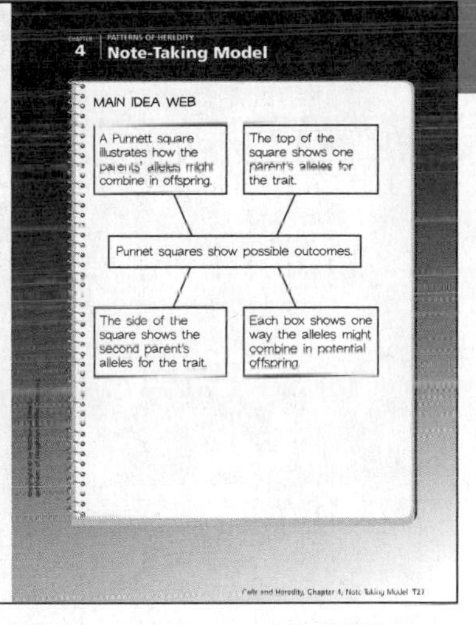

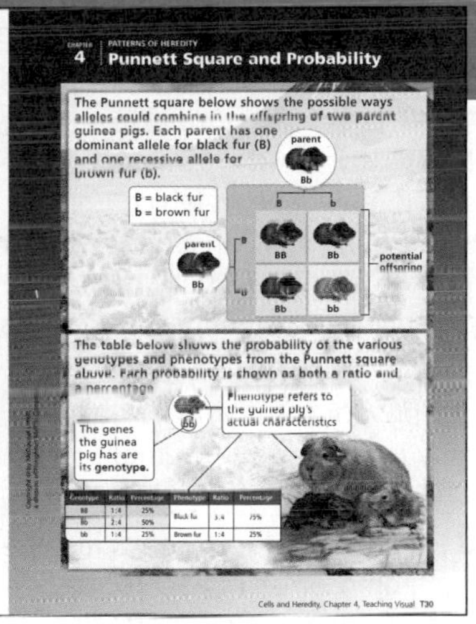

UNIT TRANSPARENCY BOOK, p. T25

p. T27

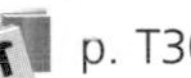
p. T30

MORE SUPPORT

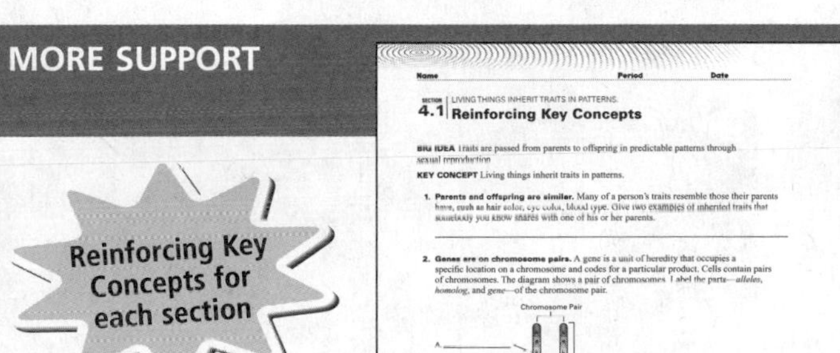

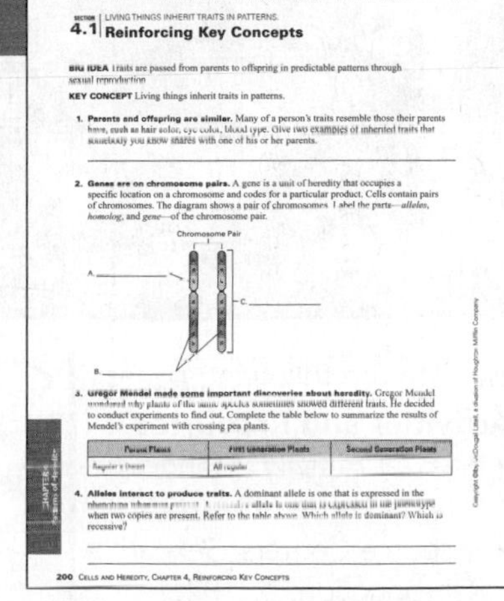

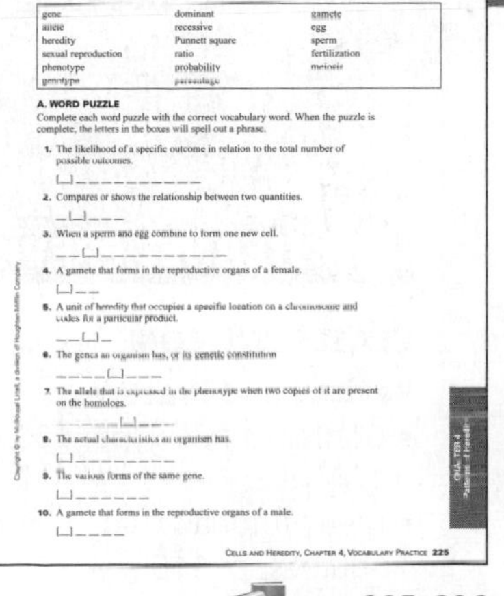

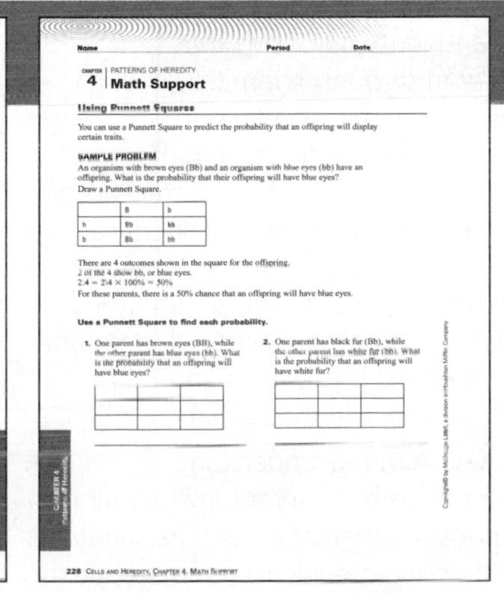

UNIT RESOURCE BOOK, p. 200

pp. 225–226

p. 228

CHAPTER

Patterns of Heredity

INTRODUCE

the BIG idea

Have students look at the photograph of wolf and cubs. Discuss how the question in the box links to the Big Idea. Ask:

- How are the mother's and cubs' body shapes similar and different?
- How about the face shapes and the coat colors?

National Science Education Standards

Content

C.2.a Reproduction is a characteristic of all living systems. Some organisms reproduce asexually, others sexually.

C.2.b In many species, females produce eggs, and males sperm which unite in a new individual. That offspring gets genes from both parents. Sexually produced offspring never are identical to parents.

C.2.c Every organism requires a set of instructions for specifying its traits. Heredity is the passage of these instructions from one generation to another.

C.2.d Hereditary information is in genes in the chromosomes of each cell. Each gene carries one unit of information. A trait is determined by one or more genes.

Process

A.1–8 Identify questions that can be answered through scientific investigations; design and conduct an investigation; use tools to gather and interpret data; use evidence to describe, predict, explain, model; think critically to make relationships between evidence and explanation; recognize different explanations and predictions; communicate scientific procedures and explanations; use mathematics.

A.9.a–c, A.9.e–g Understand scientific inquiry by using different investigations, methods, mathematics, and explanations based on logic, evidence, and skepticism. Data often result in new investigations.

G.1.b Science requires different abilities.

CHAPTER

Patterns of Heredity

the BIG idea

In sexual reproduction, genes are passed from parents to offspring in predictable patterns.

Key Concepts

SECTION

Living things inherit traits in patterns.
Learn about traits and how living things inherit traits from their parents.

SECTION

Patterns of heredity can be predicted.
Learn how math can be used to predict patterns of heredity.

SECTION

Meiosis is a special form of cell division.
Learn about the process of meiosis.

Internet Preview

CLASSZONE.COM

Chapter 4 online resources: Content Review, two Simulations, two Resource Centers, Math Tutorial, Test Practice

98 Unit 1: Cells and Heredity

INTERNET PREVIEW

CLASSZONE.COM For student use with the following pages:

Review and Practice

- Content Review, pp. 100, 124
- Math Tutorial: Using Punnett Squares, p. 116
- Test Practice, p. 127

Activities and Resources

- Internet Activity: Mendel's Experiment, p. 99
- Resource Centers: Sexual Reproduction, p. 102; Meiosis, p. 120
- Simulation: Punnett Squares, p. 111

Heredity **Code: MDL034**

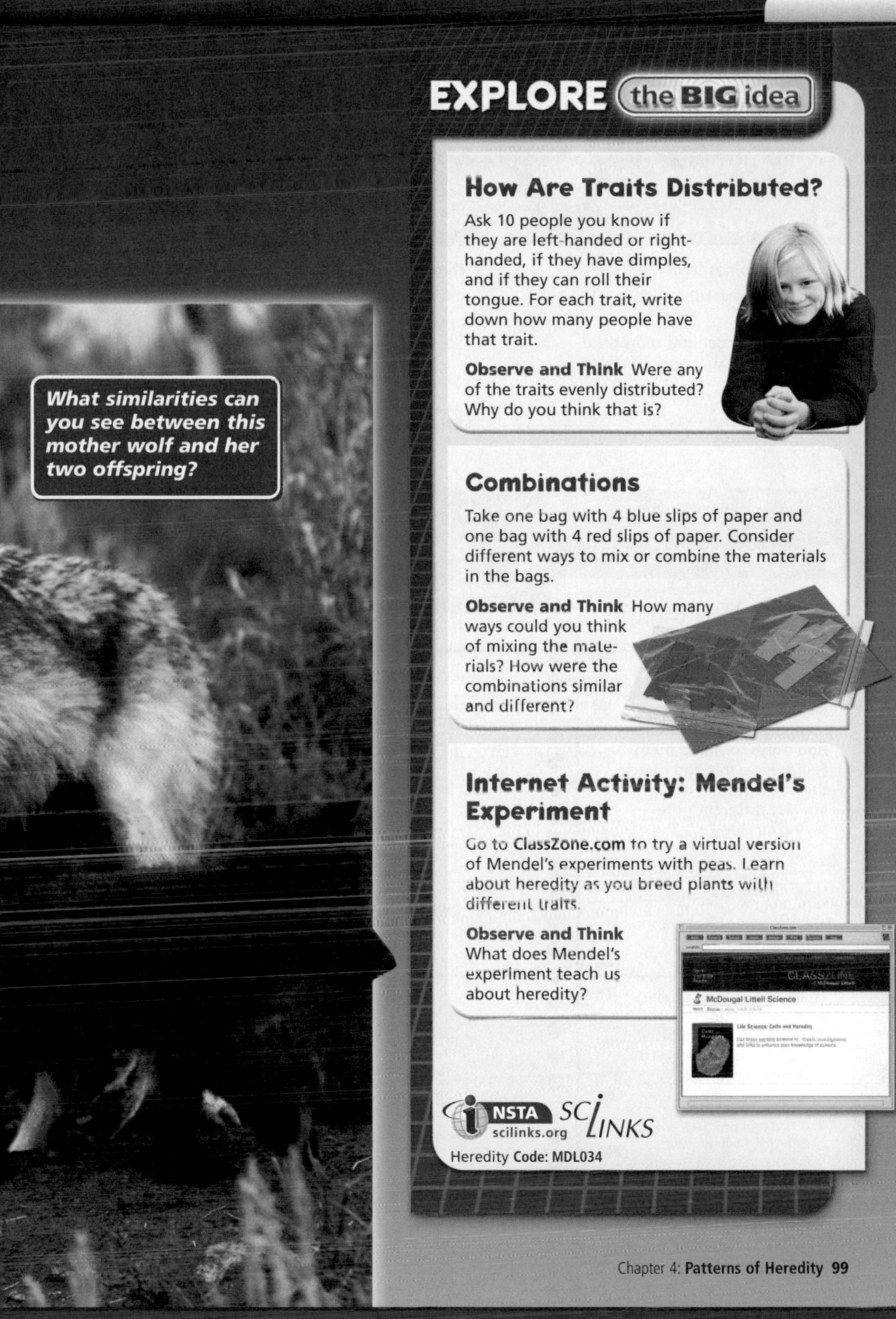

EXPLORE the BIG idea

How Are Traits Distributed?

Ask 10 people you know if they are left-handed or right-handed, if they have dimples, and if they can roll their tongue. For each trait, write down how many people have that trait.

Observe and Think Were any of the traits evenly distributed? Why do you think that is?

Combinations

Take one bag with 4 blue slips of paper and one bag with 4 red slips of paper. Consider different ways to mix or combine the materials in the bags.

Observe and Think How many ways could you think of mixing the materials? How were the combinations similar and different?

Internet Activity: Mendel's Experiment

Go to **ClassZone.com** to try a virtual version of Mendel's experiments with peas. Learn about heredity as you breed plants with different traits.

Observe and Think What does Mendel's experiment teach us about heredity?

NSTA scilinks.org SCILINKS

Heredity **Code: MDL034**

What similarities can you see between this mother wolf and her two offspring?

EXPLORE the BIG idea

These inquiry-based activities are appropriate for use at home or as a supplement to classroom instruction.

How Are Traits Distributed?

PURPOSE To see that traits are distributed differently in a population. Students collect data on traits of their friends.

TIP *20 min.* You might want to limit the data to certain traits and might assign who should collect data from whom.

Answers will vary but should involve that some traits are more common than others in a population.

REVISIT after p. 107.

Combinations

PURPOSE To have students consider the various ways of mixing two sets of materials.

TIP *10 min.* Some possible combinations will involve moving one or more slips from one bag to another. Some involve taking slips from both bags and making an entirely new set.

Answers will vary but students should have found at least three ways, and will likely find more.

REVISIT after p. 104.

Internet Activity: Mendel's Experiment

PURPOSE To introduce students to Mendel's pea experiments.

TIP *20 min.* You might set up an awards or checklist system with the goal of breeding peas for certain traits.

Answer: Plants have two factors for a trait, one from each parent. Some factors can be masked.

REVISIT after p. 105.

TEACHING WITH TECHNOLOGY

Digital Camera If a digital camera is available, take pictures of the creatures created in the Chapter Investigation, pp. 108–109. Combine the photographs with the data tables in a scrapbook to display in class.

PC Microscope If prepared slides are available, let students observe meiosis through the microscope, after studying pp. 120–121.

PREPARE

CONCEPT REVIEW

Activate Prior Knowledge

- Ask students to recap what they know about where life comes from. *Life comes from life.*
- Discuss how a cell produces another cell. Ask: What is the end product of mitosis? *two identical daughter cells*

TAKING NOTES

Choose Your Own Strategy

Encourage students to think about their own learning styles and to choose the strategy that best suits them. They may want to choose a different strategy for each section if they have not tried some of the strategies or want to test out which works best.

Vocabulary Strategy

The magnet word diagram helps students organize information pertaining to words when the information may not fall into a clearly delineated category, such as an example. The magnet shape reinforces that the information is still connected to the word.

Vocabulary and Note-Taking Resources

- Vocabulary Practice, pp. 225–226
- Decoding Support, p. 227

- Daily Vocabulary Scaffolding, p. T26
- Note-Taking Model, p. T27

- Magnet Word, B24–25
- Choose Your Own Strategy, C35–44
- Daily Vocabulary Scaffolding, H1–8

CHAPTER 4

Getting Ready to Learn

CONCEPT REVIEW

- Life comes from life.
- Mitosis produces identical cells.
- Some organisms reproduce with asexual reproduction.

VOCABULARY REVIEW

chromosome p. 75
mitosis p. 81
asexual reproduction p. 88

CONTENT REVIEW
CLASSZONE.COM
Review concepts and vocabulary.

TAKING NOTES

CHOOSE YOUR OWN STRATEGY

Take notes using one or more of the strategies from earlier chapters—**main idea webs, combination notes,** or **mind maps.** Feel free to mix and match the strategies, or use an entirely different note-taking strategy.

VOCABULARY STRATEGY

Think about a vocabulary term as a **magnet word** diagram. Write the other terms or ideas related to that term around it.

See the Note-Taking Handbook on pages R45–R51.

SCIENCE NOTEBOOK

CHECK READINESS

Administer the Diagnostic Test to determine students' readiness for new science content and their mastery of requisite math skills.

 Diagnostic Test, pp. 58–59

Technology Resources

Students needing content and math skills should visit **ClassZone.com**.

- **CONTENT REVIEW**
- **MATH TUTORIAL**

 **CONTENT REVIEW CD-ROM**

KEY CONCEPT

Living things inherit traits in patterns.

BEFORE, you learned
- Life comes from life
- Cells contain chromosomes
- Some organisms reproduce with asexual reproduction

NOW, you will learn
- How genes for traits are passed from parent to offspring
- About discoveries made by Gregor Mendel
- About dominant and recessive alleles

VOCABULARY

sexual reproduction p. 102
gene p. 102
heredity p. 102
allele p. 103
phenotype p. 106
genotype p. 106
dominant p. 107
recessive p. 107

THINK ABOUT

What characteristics might be inherited?

Make a list of characteristics you can observe about the girl in the photograph to the right. Perhaps your list includes the fact that she has pale skin, or that she can read. Some of these characteristics are qualities or abilities learned or acquired from the environment around her. However, some of the characteristics were probably inherited from her parents. Of the characteristics on your list, which do you think were inherited and which do you think were acquired?

Parents and offspring are similar.

NOTETAKING STRATEGY Take notes on the idea that parents and offspring are similar by using a strategy from an earlier chapter or one of your own.

You are an individual who has a unique combination of characteristics. These characteristics are also known as traits. Many of your traits may resemble those your parents have, including your hair color, eye color, and blood type. These characteristics are called inherited traits.

Some traits are acquired, not inherited. An acquired trait is developed during your life. Learned behaviors are one type of acquired trait. For example, your ability to read and write is an acquired trait—a skill you learned. You were not born knowing how to ride a bike, and if you have children, they will not be born knowing how to do it either. They will have to learn the skill just as you did.

RESOURCES FOR DIFFERENTIATED INSTRUCTION

Below Level

UNIT RESOURCE BOOK
- Reading Study Guide A, pp. 193–194
- Decoding Support, p. 227

AUDIO CDS

Advanced

UNIT RESOURCE BOOK
Challenge and Extension, p. 199

English Learners

UNIT RESOURCE BOOK
Spanish Reading Study Guide, pp. 197–198

- Audio Readings in Spanish
- Audio Readings (English)

4.1 FOCUS

Set Learning Goals

Students will
- Explain how traits are passed from parent to offspring.
- Describe how genes are distributed in sexual reproduction.
- Understand that some traits are dominant and others are recessive.
- Design a model to determine genotype and phenotype.

3-Minute Warm-Up

Display Transparency 28 or copy this exercise on the board:

Choose the best term for each definition.

Definitions
1. the results of mitosis *d*
2. genetic material during mitosis *a*
3. process that involves two parent cells *c*

Terms
a. chromosomes
b. asexual reproduction
c. sexual reproduction
d. daughter cells
e. parent cells

 3-Minute Warm-Up, p. T28

4.1 MOTIVATE

THINK ABOUT

PURPOSE To make a distinction between acquired and inherited traits

DISCUSS Ask students for other examples of acquired and inherited traits. Ask: Can you think of traits that might combine inheritance and learning? *Sample answer: musical ability*

4.1 INSTRUCT

Address Misconceptions

IDENTIFY Ask: If a mother works out as a body builder for many years, what are the chances her offspring will inherit strong muscles? If students say there is a good chance of this, then they may hold the misconception that acquired traits can be transmitted genetically.

CORRECT Have students try to imagine how the mother's DNA would find out about her workout habits. Point out that it can't. A muscle grows *if* it is worked, but the child will have to do the same workouts to get big muscles.

REASSESS Ask: If a father speaks several languages fluently, will his children be able to understand what he is saying in different languages? *not unless each child learns the language first*

Technology Resources

Visit **ClassZone.com** for background on common student misconceptions.

MISCONCEPTION DATABASE

Teach from Visuals

To help students interpret the diagrams of chromosomes and genes, ask:

- What do you call the two members of a chromosome pair? *homologs*
- Where does each member of the chromosome pair come from? *one homolog in a pair from each parent*
- What do you call the different forms of a particular gene? *alleles*
- What do the genes of a particular pair of chromosomes have in common? *same type of genes, in the same location*

Ongoing Assessment

CHECK YOUR READING *Answer: Inherited traits are not learned behaviors but are passed from parent to offspring. Eye color is inherited. Acquired traits are learned, such as skill at a sport, or affected by the environment, such as skin tone.*

Some acquired traits are not learned but result from interaction with the environment. Skin color, for example, has both an inherited component and an environmental one. The skin color of many light-skinned people darkens when they are exposed to the Sun.

CHECK YOUR READING How are inherited traits and acquired traits different? Give one example of each.

RESOURCE CENTER CLASSZONE.COM

Find out more about sexual reproduction.

In this chapter, you will learn about inheritance that happens through sexual reproduction. During **sexual reproduction** a cell containing genetic information from the mother and a cell containing genetic information from the father combine into a completely new cell, which becomes the offspring. You will learn more about the mechanics of sexual reproduction in Section 4.3.

Genes are on chromosome pairs.

Inherited traits are controlled by the structures, materials, and processes you learned about in Chapters 1 and 2. In turn, these structures, materials, and processes are coded for by genes. A **gene** is a unit of heredity that occupies a specific location on a chromosome and codes for a particular product. **Heredity** is the passing of genes from parents to offspring.

Individuals inherit their genes from their parents. The genes code for the expression of traits. It is important to understand that an organism does not inherit the traits themselves from its parents. It inherits the genes that code for the traits it has. Most traits are not coded for by just one gene. Some characteristics are affected by many genes in complicated ways. We have much to learn about which genes might affect which characteristics.

Chromosomes and Genes

The letters on the pair of chromosomes below represent alleles.

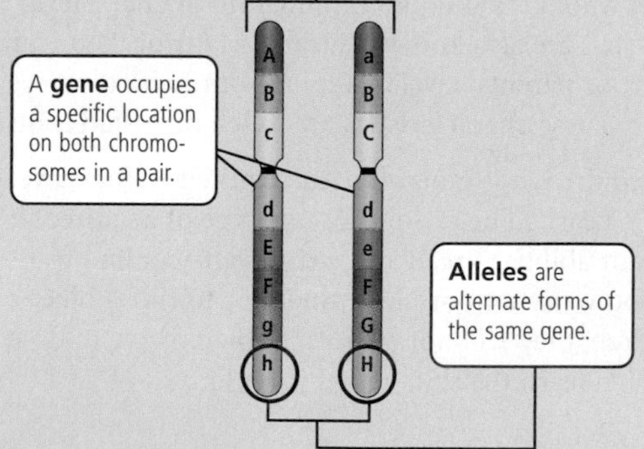

In most eukaryotes, cells contain pairs of chromosomes, with one chromosome of each pair coming from each of two parents. The chromosomes in a pair are called homologs. They resemble each other, having the same size and shape, and carrying genetic information for particular traits.

On each homolog are sites where specific genes are located. Let us say, for example, that the gene that determines

DIFFERENTIATE INSTRUCTION

More Reading Support

A What do genes do? *They code for a particular product.*

B Where do individuals get their genes? *from their parents*

English Learners Have students write the definitions for *gene, allele, heredity, sexual reproduction, phenotype, genotype, dominant,* and *recessive* in their Science Word Dictionaries. When discussing heredity, make sure students understand the concept of cause and effect. Other words that signal cause and effect are *because, due to, since, then, therefore, affect, effect.*

whether or not a plant is tall is located at place A on a pair of homologs. Though both homologs have the gene for height at site A, the genes may not be identical. They may be variations instead. The various forms of the same gene are called **alleles** (uh-LEELZ).

Thus, the homolog from one parent might have an allele for regular height at site A, while the gene from the other parent might have an allele for short height at site A. The alleles on a pair of homologs may or may not be different. Though any one plant can have only two alleles of a gene, there can be many alleles for a particular gene within a population.

READING TIP

The word *homolog* comes from the Greek words *homos*, which means "same," and *logos*, which means "proportion."

What are alleles?

Each species has a characteristic number of chromosomes. Chimpanzees have 24 pairs of chromosomes, for a total of 48 chromosomes. Fruit flies have 4 pairs of chromosomes, or 8 in all. Humans have 23 pairs, for a total of 46 chromosomes. Scientists refer to chromosomes by their number. Human chromosomes are numbered 1 through 22; the 23rd pair are the sex chromosomes.

In humans, the sex chromosomes are called the X-chromosome and the Y-chromosome. A human female has two X-chromosomes, while a human male has one X-chromosome and one Y-chromosome. In addition to determining the sex of an offspring, the X- and Y-chromosomes contain important genes, just as the other, numbered chromosomes do.

Human Chromosomes

Humans have 23 pairs of chromosomes, for a total of 46. One of these pairs, shown below, determines the sex of the offspring.

X-chromosome

Y-chromosome

An offspring with XY, as shown, is male. Female offspring have two X-chromosomes.

Address Misconceptions

IDENTIFY Ask: What traits do the X- and Y-chromosomes carry? If students respond that X and Y code only for sex, they think that sex chromosomes do not carry genes for other traits.

CORRECT Ask students if they have ever seen an orange female cat. There are very few of them. Orange color in cats is a sex-linked trait and appears mostly in males. Explain that X- and Y-chromosomes carry many genes besides those that code for sex.

REASSESS Have students research other traits that are sex-linked.

Technology Resources

Visit **ClassZone.com** for background on common student misconceptions.

MISCONCEPTION DATABASE

Teach from Visuals

To help students interpret the pairs of chromosomes, ask:

- How many pairs of chromosomes do humans have? *23*
- What gender of offspring is produced by two X-chromosomes? *female*

Teach Difficult Concepts

To distinguish among the terms *allele, homolog, gene,* and *chromosome,* try pairing the concepts. Homologs go with chromosomes, alleles go with genes.

Teacher Demo

Link building blocks to construct models of chromosome pairs. Use different shapes to indicate genes for a certain trait, and different colors with the same shape to indicate alleles.

Ongoing Assessment

Explain how traits are passed from parent to offspring.

Ask: How does a child inherit traits from its parents? *Both parents contribute one set of chromosomes. Pairs of chromosomes contain genes that give cells information to produce traits.*

Answer: different forms of the same gene

DIFFERENTIATE INSTRUCTION

More Reading Support

C What do you call various forms of the same gene? *alleles*

D What are the sex chromosomes for humans called? *X- and Y-chromosomes*

Below Level Have students draw a chart with as many traits they can think of, with all the different alleles that might be variants of the gene for that trait. Be sure to emphasize that most traits are not connected to just one allele—this is a simplified model of heredity.

Address Misconceptions

IDENTIFY Ask: If you look most like your mother, do you get most of your traits from her? If students say yes, they may hold the misconception that one parent contributes more traits than the other. Typically they believe that the mother or the same-sex parent contributes more.

CORRECT Remind students that each parent contributes half the chromosomes for each offspring. Even if a child resembles one parent more than the other, the child has the same amount of genetic material from each.

REASSESS Ask: Who gave you most of your genes? *No one—my parents each gave me half.*

Technology Resources

Visit **ClassZone.com** for background on common student misconceptions.

MISCONCEPTION DATABASE

EXPLORE (the BIG idea)

Revisit "Combinations" on p. 99. There are many ways to combine the color slips. Mendel realized units of heredity always followed the same pattern of combination: one from each parent.

Ongoing Assessment

Describe how genes are distributed in sexual reproduction.

Ask: How do offspring of asexual reproduction differ from those of sexual reproduction? *asexual: all genetic material from one parent; sexual: genetic material from two parents*

CHECK YOUR READING *Answer: First generation plants: all are of regular height. Second generation plants: three-fourths are regular height; one-fourth are dwarf height.*

Gregor Mendel made some important discoveries about heredity.

The first major experiments investigating heredity were performed by a monk named Gregor Mendel, who lived in Austria during the mid-1800s. Before Mendel became a monk, he attended university and received training in science and mathematics. This training served him well when he began investigating the inheritance of traits among the pea plants in the monastery's garden.

READING TIP The root of the word *trait* means to "draw out." It was originally used in the sense of drawing out a line. This same idea works in heredity if you think of drawing a connection between parents and offspring.

Mendel took very detailed notes, carefully recording all the data from his many experiments. He worked with seven different traits: plant height, flower and pod position, seed shape, seed color, pod shape, pod color, and flower color. He studied each trait separately, always starting with plants that were true-breeding for that one particular trait. A true-breeding plant is one that will always produce offspring with a particular trait when allowed to self-pollinate.

One Example

In his experiments with plant height, Mendel took two sets of plants, one true-breeding for plants of regular height and the other true-breeding for plants of short or dwarf height.

1. Instead of letting the plants self-pollinate as they do naturally, he deliberately paired as parents one plant from each set. Mendel called the plants that resulted from this cross the first generation. All of the plants from this first generation were of regular height. The dwarf-height trait seemed to have disappeared entirely.
2. Mendel then let the first-generation plants self-pollinate. He called the offspring that resulted from this self-pollination the second generation. About three fourths of the second-generation plants were of regular height, but about one fourth were of dwarf height. So the trait that seemed to disappear in the first generation reappeared in the second generation.

Mendel's experiments with other traits showed similar patterns.

CHECK YOUR READING Summarize the pattern shown in Mendel's experiments with plant height.

Mendel's Conclusions

Mendel drew upon his knowledge of mathematics while analyzing his data in order to suggest a hypothesis that would explain the patterns he observed. Mendel realized that each plant must have two "factors" for each possible trait, one factor from each parent. Some traits, such as dwarf height, could be masked—dwarf height could be seen in the

DIFFERENTIATE INSTRUCTION

More Reading Support

E What organism did Gregor Mendel experiment with? *pea plants*

F What are some examples of pea plants' hereditary traits? *seed and flower color, plant height*

English Learners English learners may be confused by words used in capacities other than their literal meaning. In this section, the verb *draw* is used twice with different meanings. "Mendel *drew* upon his knowledge of mathematics . . . " "Later experiments allowed Mendel to *draw* a number of other conclusions . . . " The first sentence uses *drew upon* to mean "used." The second sentence uses *draw* to mean "make." Encourage students to look up the word *draw* in the dictionary and note how many different definitions it has.

Mendel's Pea Plants

Mendel observed variation in the height of pea plants (regular or dwarf height). By crossing plants with specific traits, he deduced that offspring get factors for each trait from both parents.

1 First generation Crossing a true-breeding regular pea plant with a true-breeding dwarf pea plant produces all regular pea plants in the first generation.

2 Second generation Allowing the first generation pea plants to self-pollinate resulted in about three-fourths regular pea plants and one- fourth dwarf pea plants.

plant only if both of the plant's factors were for dwarf height. All of the plants in the first generation had one dwarf factor and one regular factor. A plant with one dwarf-height factor and one regular-height factor would be of regular height, because the regular-height factor masks the dwarf height factor.

Later experiments allowed Mendel to draw a number of other conclusions about how these factors are distributed. Since the mid-1800s, Mendel's experiments and conclusions have been the basis for most of the scientific thought about heredity. Those things he called "factors" are what we now call genes and alleles.

CHECK YOUR READING How many factors or genes does each plant have for each possible trait?

DIFFERENTIATE INSTRUCTION

More Reading Support

G Today what do we call Mendel's "factors"? *genes and alleles*

Advanced Have students research sickle-cell disease. Ask them to find out why hydroxyurea is used to treat the disease. *It is thought to turn on a gene that codes for production of fetal hemoglobin.*

R Challenge and Extension, p. 199

Teach from Visuals

To help students interpret the diagram of Mendel's experiment, ask:

- What types of plants were the parents? *one of regular height and one dwarf, true breeding*
- What does "true-breeding" mean, in terms of factors of heredity? *The factors (alleles) are the same in each plant: either two factors for regular height or two factors for dwarf height.*
- What does the cross between the two plants and the bracket below indicate? *that the genetic material from the two plants combines to form the next generation (the pollen from one plant is used to pollinate the other plant)*
- What plants were produced in the first generation? *They were all of regular height.*
- How many dwarf plants were in the second generation? *one out of four*

EXPLORE the BIG idea

Revisit "Internet Activity: Mendel's Experiment" on p. 99. Have students describe Mendel's results in their own words.

History of Science

One of Gregor Mendel's other major conclusions came out of his study of multiple traits. He studied a total of 7 traits, and found when looking at the traits together that the inheritance of one did not affect the inheritance of any of the others. That is to say, each trait was determined separately and without any relation to the other traits. We would say today that each trait is determined by a different gene.

Ongoing Assessment

CHECK YOUR READING *Answer: two*

Integrate the Sciences

If unfiltered, ultraviolet rays can damage DNA by causing chemical changes in it. Ozone, a highly active form of oxygen (O_3 instead of O_2), is present in the atmosphere both from natural reactions and from pollution. Low levels high in the atmosphere are a problem. In the stratosphere, ozone shields Earth from ultraviolet radiation from the Sun.

Metacognitive Strategy

Have students brainstorm strategies for remembering the difference between phenotype and genotype.

Develop Critical Thinking

APPLY Have students choose a plant or animal with which they are familiar. Ask them to write a detailed phenotype from their observations, and to construct a genotype that could produce such a phenotype.

Ongoing Assessment

CHECK YOUR READING *Answer: Eye color is a phenotype because it is observable.*

Alleles interact to produce traits.

H

The pea-plant traits Gregor Mendel chose to study were all controlled by single genes, and each of the genes was on a different chromosome. As you learned earlier, most traits are not controlled by only one gene. However, simple examples such as Mendel's peas do help us better understand heredity.

Phenotype and Genotype

The word *phenotype* and *phenomenon* have a similar root word meaning "to appear."

What color eyes do you have? The eye color you see when you look in the mirror is your phenotype. An organism's **phenotype** describes the actual characteristics that can be observed. Your height, the size of your feet, the presence or absence of a fold in your eyelids—all are observable traits and are part of your phenotype.

VOCABULARY
Make word magnet diagrams for the terms *phenotype* and *genotype*.

? I

By contrast, the genes that control the development of eyefolds are part of your genotype. **Genotype** is the name for the genes an organism has. Your genotype is not always obvious from your phenotype. If you have eyefolds, your genotype definitely contains at least one eyefold-producing allele. But it may also have one allele for no eyefolds. Sometimes your genes contain information that is not expressed in your phenotype.

CHECK YOUR READING Which term describes characteristics that can be observed?

COMPARE The photograph above shows **phenotypes** of the eyefold gene. A person with eyefolds is shown to the left, a person without eyefolds to the right.

DIFFERENTIATE INSTRUCTION

More Reading Support

H Are traits controlled by single genes or multiple genes? *mostly by multiple genes*

I Which contains alleles, your phenotype or your genotype? *genotype*

Alternative Assessment Have students draw a chosen phenotype and list possible genotypes to go with it.

Dominant and Recessive Alleles

The eyefold gene, which controls the development of folds in the eyelids, has two alleles: eyefolds and no-eyefolds. If you have even one copy of the allele for eyefolds, you will have eyefolds. This happens because the allele that codes for eyefolds is dominant. A **dominant** allele is one that is expressed in the phenotype even if only one copy is present in the genotype—that is, even if the other allele is an alternative form.

Suppose your genotype contains a no-eyefolds allele. The no-eyefolds allele is recessive. A **recessive** allele is one that is expressed in the phenotype only when two copies of it are present on the homologs. If one chromosome in the pair contains a dominant allele and the other contains a recessive allele, the dominant allele will be expressed in your phenotype. If you do not have eyefolds, it is because you got two no-eyefolds genes—one from each parent.

CHECK YOUR READING Under what conditions is a recessive allele expressed in an offspring's phenotype?

The interaction of dominant and recessive alleles means that it is possible for two brown-haired parents to have a blond child.

Hair color is determined by multiple genes, can be affected by the environment, and sometimes changes over time. However, in some cases it has a dominant-recessive pattern similar to that of the eyefold gene. As in the family shown at right, parents who both have brown hair can have a blond child. The allele for brown hair is dominant, so if both parents have alleles for both brown hair and blond hair, the brown-hair allele is more likely to be expressed. Their child, however, could have two blond-hair alleles (one from each parent) and therefore have blond hair instead of brown.

4.1 Review

KEY CONCEPTS

1. Explain the difference between acquired and inherited traits.
2. Describe the conclusions that Mendel drew from his experiments with pea plants.
3. What type of alleles are expressed only if two identical copies exist on the homologs of the offspring?

CRITICAL THINKING

4. **Compare and Contrast** What is the difference between a genotype and a phenotype?
5. **Analyze** Explain why a person with an allele for a particular trait may not have a phenotype that shows the trait.

CHALLENGE

6. **Apply** In guinea pigs, the allele for black fur is dominant over the allele for brown fur. If you had two parent guinea pigs, each with brown fur, what color fur might the offspring have, and why?

ANSWERS

1. Acquired traits are not determined by genes; inherited traits are.

2. Inherited traits are controlled by two factors, and one factor can mask another.

3. recessive

4. Genotype describes the genes that code for traits; phenotype describes the traits that are expressed.

5. If a person has one recessive and one dominant allele, the dominant allele will be expressed. So a person can have a recessive allele and it will not show in the phenotype.

6. Brown, the parents must both carry two recessive genes for brown fur, otherwise a single dominant black allele makes them black.

EXPLORE the BIG idea

Revisit "How Are Traits Distributed?" on p. 99. Have students speculate on dominance and recessiveness of differently distributed traits.

Ongoing Assessment

Understand that some traits are dominant and others are recessive.

Ask: Why are some parents' traits expressed in their offspring while others are not? *Dominant traits are expressed even if only one copy of the allele codes for them. If a trait is recessive, it is expressed only if both alleles code for it.*

CHECK YOUR READING *Answer: when both alleles are recessive*

Reinforce the BIG idea

Have students relate the section to the Big Idea.

 Reinforcing Key Concepts, p. 200

4.1 ASSESS & RETEACH

Assess

 Section 4.1 Quiz, p. 60

Reteach

Sketch a tall plant and a short plant on the board. Have students help you draw what the next two generations would look like if the two true-breeding plants were crossed. *First generation: all offspring are tall; second generation: one in four offspring is short.*

Technology Resources

Have students visit **ClassZone.com** for reteaching of Key Concepts.

 CONTENT REVIEW

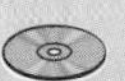 CONTENT REVIEW CD-ROM

CHAPTER INVESTIGATION

Focus

PURPOSE To determine how genotypes of parents affect genotypes and phenotypes of offspring

OVERVIEW Students will select slips of paper from bags to assemble a genotype for their offspring.

- They will record the genotype of offspring using alleles from parents.
- They will use craft supplies to build the offspring according to the phenotype.

Students will find the following:

- Genotypes may have alleles that are not expressed in the phenotype.
- Offspring from the same parents can have different traits.

Lab Preparation

- Purchase foam balls in a craft store, or substitute marshmallows.
- Cut 12 index cards in half. Make a set of allele cards for each parent as follows: B, b, W, w, A, a, P, p, C, c, E, e. Put one pair of alleles in each of 12 bags.
- Prior to the investigation, have students read through the investigation and prepare their data tables. Or you may wish to copy and distribute datasheets and rubrics.

 UNIT RESOURCE BOOK, pp. 230–238

 SCIENCE TOOLKIT, F14

Lab Management

Providing each student or group with an individually packaged set of craft supplies will help minimize mess or confusion.

SAFETY Caution students to carefully keep track of the numerous small objects in the activity.

Teaching with Technology

Take pictures with a digital camera of the offspring that students construct. Combine the photographs with the data tables in a scrapbook to display in class.

CHAPTER INVESTIGATION

Offspring Models

OVERVIEW AND PURPOSE Sexual reproduction combines genes from two parent organisms and results in diversity among offspring. In this activity, you will

- design a model of an offspring
- determine how the offspring exhibits portions of both genotype and phenotype from its parents

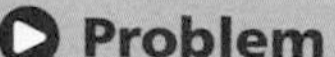

Problem

How are traits passed from parent to offspring?

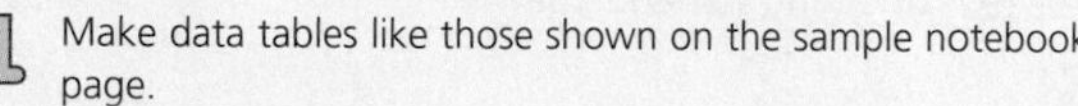

Procedure

1. Make data tables like those shown on the sample notebook page.
2. Your teacher will supply bags containing alleles written on slips. Capital letters represent dominant alleles, and lower-case letters represent recessive alleles. Each bag will have two alleles for one trait. Six of the bags, one for each of 6 traits, will represent the female parent's alleles. Another set of 6 bags will represent the male parent's alleles. From each bag, choose one allele.
3. In Table 1, record the alleles for both parents, and the allele pairs for the offspring. Then place the slips back into the bags. You will use the alleles to build a model offspring.
4. Use the information in the table below to determine the phenotype of the offspring. Write the phenotype in the fourth column in Table 1.

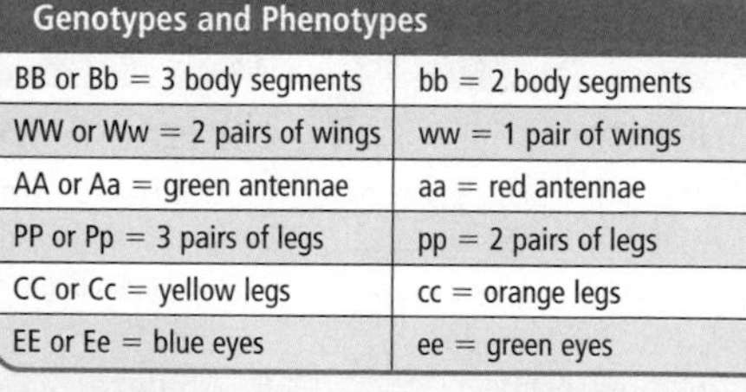

Genotypes and Phenotypes

BB or Bb = 3 body segments	bb = 2 body segments
WW or Ww = 2 pairs of wings	ww = 1 pair of wings
AA or Aa = green antennae	aa = red antennae
PP or Pp = 3 pairs of legs	pp = 2 pairs of legs
CC or Cc = yellow legs	cc = orange legs
EE or Ee = blue eyes	ee = green eyes

MATERIALS
- foam balls (body segments)
- colored toothpicks (antennae)
- small paperclips (wings)
- colored pipe cleaners (legs)
- colored pushpins (eyes)

108 Unit 1: Cells and Heredity

INVESTIGATION RESOURCES

 CHAPTER INVESTIGATION, Offspring Models
- Level A, pp. 230–233
- Level B, pp. 234–237
- Level C, p. 238

Advanced students should complete Levels B & C.

 Writing a Lab Report, D12–13

Technology Resources

Customize this student lab as needed or look for an alternative. Print rubrics to assess student lab reports.

 **Lab Generator CD-ROM**

5 Choose the materials you need to assemble the offspring. You can use toothpicks to attach the body segments. Push the pipe cleaners, toothpicks, and wings into the foam balls. **CAUTION: Take care when handling the pushpins.**

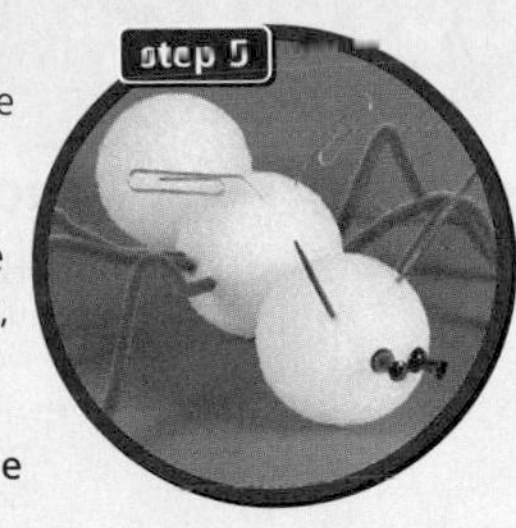

Observe and Analyze

Write It Up

1. **OBSERVE** Does your offspring look the way you would expect either parent to look? Explain.
2. **ANALYZE** How many different genotypes are possible for each trait? Explain.

Conclude

Write It Up

1. **INFER** What are the possible genotypes of the parents? Fill in Table 2.
2. **INTERPRET** Can you tell how the genotypes of the parents differ from that of the offspring? Explain.
3. **INTERPRET** How does your offspring model illustrate what you have learned about heredity?
4. **IDENTIFY LIMITS** What sources of error might you have experienced?
5. **APPLY** In humans, blue eyes are the phenotype for two recessive alleles. Can parents with blue eyes have a brown-eyed offspring? Explain.

INVESTIGATE Further

CHALLENGE Repeat the procedure, but this time use alleles taken from your model offspring and those of a model offspring made by one of your classmates. Record the genotype and determine the phenotype of this second-generation offspring.

Offspring Models

Table 1. Parent and Offspring Family Traits

	Female Allele	Male Allele	Offspring Genotype	Offspring Phenotype
Body segments				
Pairs of wings				
Antennae color				
Pairs of legs				
Color of legs				
Color of eyes				

Table 2. Possible Parent Genotypes

Trait	Female Parent	Male Parent
Body segments		
Pairs of wings		
Antennae color		
Pairs of legs		
Color of legs		
Color of eyes		

Observe and Analyze

1. *Offspring often have traits different from their parents. Unless both parents had all dominant alleles or all recessive alleles, then you would expect parents and offspring to look different.*
2. *three: both dominant, both recessive, or one of each*

Conclude

1. *Student tables should show two possibilities. If parent is known to have one dominant allele, then it will have either both dominant or one dominant and one recessive. If parent is known to have one recessive allele, then it will have either both recessive or one dominant and one recessive.*
2. *If the genotype for one trait of the offspring is a combination of dominant and recessive alleles, it is possible that the parent with the recessive allele could have two recessive alleles and show a recessive trait. If the parent has a dominant allele for a trait, then the parent has the dominant trait, just like the offspring.*
3. *Answers should involve the idea of dominant and recessive alleles and the fact that sometimes offspring can show traits not seen in the parents.*
4. *Students may say they could incorrectly identify the phenotype for a trait.*
5. *No; the offspring would inherit two recessive alleles, which would result in blue eyes.*

INVESTIGATE Further

CHALLENGE Answers should adhere to the genotype and phenotype rules on p. 108.

Post-Lab Discussion

- Ask: What does a recessive trait in the offspring indicate about the genotype of the parents if both parents show all dominant traits? *You know that each parent must have a dominant and recessive allele for that trait because each parent contributes a recessive allele but still shows the dominant trait.*
- Ask students to discuss any question, problems, or puzzling results that arose. Have them identify one question for further investigation.

4.2 FOCUS

Set Learning Goals

Students will

- Use Punnett squares to understand patterns of heredity.
- Use ratios and probability to describe patterns of heredity.
- Analyze experimental data to find probabilities.

3-Minute Warm-Up

Display Transparency 28 or copy this exercise on the board:

Suppose you had a pair of goats, one black and one white. Most of the kids they had were white, although black ones were not rare. Describe the genotype that might be possible for each parent for coat color. *Both parents have white and black alleles; white is dominant, so more offspring are white. But it is possible for both alleles to be black (recessive) some of the time.*

3-Minute Warm-Up, p. T28

4.2 MOTIVATE

EXPLORE Probability

PURPOSE To explore multiple probabilities

TIP *10 min.* Instead of coins, you can use any plastic or cardboard disk with a marker dot on one side, or use a number cube and toss for even vs. odd numbers.

WHAT DO YOU THINK? *Sample answer: A head and a tail. Students should think of the probability of the next double toss as HT, TH, TT, HH. That means there is a greater chance, a 2:4 chance, that a toss will produce a head and a tail. However, it is impossible to predict the outcome because any of the four outcomes is possible.*

KEY CONCEPT

Patterns of heredity can be predicted.

BEFORE, you learned

- Genes are passed from parents to offspring
- Offspring inherit genes in predictable patterns

NOW, you will learn

- How Punnett squares can be used to predict patterns of heredity
- How ratios and probability can be used to predict patterns of heredity

VOCABULARY

Punnett square p. 110
ratio p. 112
probability p. 112
percentage p. 112

EXPLORE Probability

How can probability help predict results?

PROCEDURE

1. Toss both coins 10 times. For each toss, record the combination of heads and/or tails.
2. For each combination (two heads, two tails, or a head and a tail), add up the number of tosses.

MATERIALS

- two coins
- pencil and paper

WHAT DO YOU THINK?

- Which combination happened most often?
- If you tossed both coins one more time, which combination would be the most likely result? Can you know for sure? Why or why not?

Punnett squares show possible outcomes for inheritance.

NOTETAKING STRATEGY
Use a strategy from an earlier chapter or design one of your own to take notes on how Punnett squares show possible patterns of heredity.

Mendel noticed that traits are inherited in patterns. One tool for understanding the patterns of heredity is a graphic called a Punnett square. A **Punnett square** illustrates how the parents' alleles might combine in offspring.

Each parent has two alleles for a particular gene. An offspring receives one allele from each parent. A Punnett square shows how the parents' alleles may be passed on to potential offspring.

The Punnett square on page 111 shows how alleles for pea-plant height would be distributed among offspring in Mendel's first-generation cross. The dominant allele (D) is regular height, and the recessive allele (d) is dwarf height.

RESOURCES FOR DIFFERENTIATED INSTRUCTION

Below Level

UNIT RESOURCE BOOK

- Reading Study Guide A, pp. 203–204
- Decoding Support, p. 227

AUDIO CDS

Advanced

UNIT RESOURCE BOOK

- Challenge and Extension, p. 209
- Challenge Reading, pp. 223–224

English Learners

UNIT RESOURCE BOOK

Spanish Reading Study Guide, pp. 207–208

- Audio Readings in Spanish
- Audio Readings (English)

The top of the Punnett square shows one parent's alleles for this trait—two dominant regular alleles (DD). The side of the Punnett square shows the other parent's alleles for this trait—two recessive dwarf alleles (dd).

Each box in the Punnett square shows a way the alleles from each parent would combine in potential offspring. You can see that each potential offspring would have the same genotype: one dominant and one recessive allele (Dd). The phenotype of each offspring would show the dominant allele, in this case regular height.

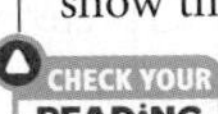

CHECK YOUR READING What is a Punnett square?

READING TIP As you read about Punnett squares, connect each sentence with the diagram below.

Using Punnett Squares

The Punnett square below shows the possible allele combinations for an offspring of one parent with two dominant (D) regular-height alleles and one parent with two recessive (d) dwarf-height alleles.

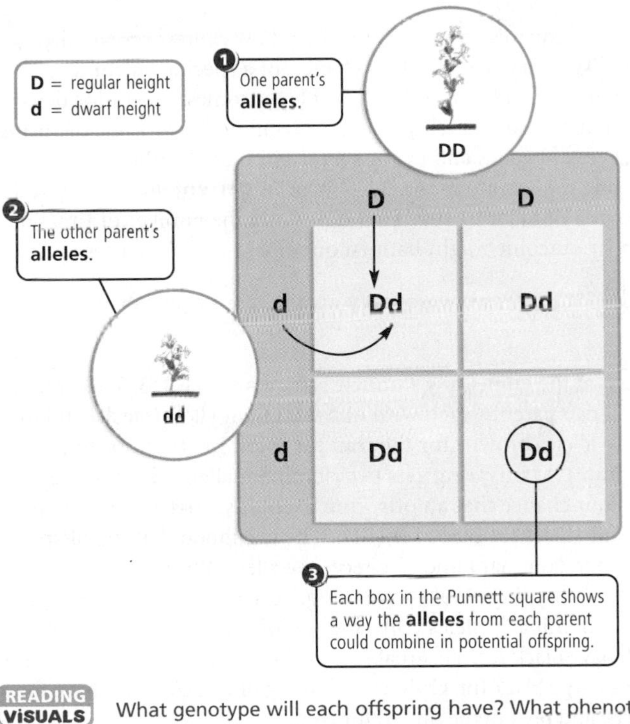

READING VISUALS What genotype will each offspring have? What phenotype?

SIMULATION CLASSZONE.COM

Predict offspring traits with virtual Punnett squares.

4.2 INSTRUCT

Teach from Visuals

To help students interpret the diagram of the Punnett square, ask:

- How is the symbol for each allele the same? *symbolized by the same letter*
- How can you tell which allele is dominant and which is recessive? *A capital letter is used for dominant, and a lowercase letter is used for recessive.* In this Punnett square, which trait is dominant? *regular height, D*
- Which trait is recessive? *dwarf height, d*
- What does each box show? *the alleles of one possible offspring*

History of Science

Thomas Hunt Morgan, an American, was one of the first scientists to provide evidence that genes have a specific location on specific chromosomes—the chromosome theory of heredity. Morgan did his research on fruit flies. He noticed that a rare recessive trait, white eyes, was much more likely to occur in males than females. He reasoned that the eye-color gene must be on the X-chromosome. This would explain why there is a greater chance for white eyes in males, because there would be no second gene to mask the trait. That is because a male has no second X-chromosome.

Ongoing Assessment

Use Punnett squares to understand patterns of heredity.

Ask: What can a Punnett square show us about heredity? *the possible inheritance outcomes for parents with various pairs of alleles*

CHECK YOUR READING *Answer: a tool that illustrates possible allele combinations for offspring*

READING VISUALS *Answer: genotype: Dd; phenotype: regular height*

DIFFERENTIATE INSTRUCTION

More Reading Support

A What do the side and top of Punnett squares show? *the two parents' alleles*

B What does each box of a Punnett square contain? *a possible combination*

English Learners Have English learners practice explaining Punnett squares to an advanced student. They can use words, visuals, or numbers or a combination of all three. The pairs of students should exchange questions about the explanations.

Develop Critical Thinking

APPLY Present this situation: A blue-eyed male and a green-eyed female have four offspring, three with blue eyes and one with green. Ask:

- Which allele is likely to be dominant and which recessive? *blue dominant, green recessive*
- Is it likely that both parents have a pair of like alleles, or mixed alleles? *mixed*

Real World Example

Tay-Sachs is a genetic disease resulting from the lack of an enzyme that prevents buildup of damaging substances in nerve cells in the brain. In people who have the disease, the genes that code for the enzyme are inactive. The inactive alleles are recessive. People who have one active allele are healthy, but they can pass the recessive allele on. If both parents carry the recessive allele, their children who inherit two recessive alleles will have Tay-Sachs disease and die very young. The recessive allele occurs much more frequently in certain populations, in particular among eastern European Jews and the Cajuns in Louisiana.

Teach Difficult Concepts

Some students may find it difficult to distinguish between a ratio and a percentage. Explain that a percentage is a special ratio: one of the quantities being compared is always 100. Demonstrate the relationship between ratios and percentages by using different-colored beans or marbles as manipulatives.

Ongoing Assessment

Answer: as a ratio or as a percentage

Ratios and percentages can express the probability of outcomes.

VOCABULARY Remember to create a word magnet diagram for the term *ratio*.

C D

The Punnett square on page 111 for the first generation of pea plants shows that all potential offspring will be of regular height, because they all have one dominant allele. You can say that 100 percent of the offspring will be of regular height. Or you could say that the ratio of regular-height offspring to total offspring is four to four. A **ratio** compares, or shows the relationship between, two quantities. A ratio is usually written 4:4 and read as "four to four." This can be interpreted as "four out of four." The Punnett square shows that four out of four offspring will express the dominant gene for regular height.

4:4
ratio of blue squares to total squares

1:4 red
3:4 blue

Punnett squares and the ratios they show express probability. **Probability** is the likelihood, or chance, of a specific outcome in relation to the total number of possible outcomes. The ratios derived from a Punnett square tell you the probability that any one offspring will get certain genes and express a certain trait. Another way of expressing probability is as a percentage. A **percentage** is a ratio that compares a number to 100. That is, it states the number of times a particular outcome might happen out of a hundred chances.

What are two ways that you can express a probability?

Look at the guinea-pig Punnett square on page 113. This cross is between two parents, each with one dominant allele (black) and one recessive allele (brown) for the trait fur color. In this cross, only one in four (ratio 1:4) offspring gets two dominant alleles. That is, there is a one in four chance that an offspring from this cross will have two dominant alleles for black fur (BB). The likelihood that the offspring will get one dominant and one recessive allele (Bb) is 2:4—two out of every four offspring would have this genotype. Like the one offspring with two dominant alleles (BB), the two offspring with the genotype Bb will have black fur. This makes a total of three offspring (3:4) with the phenotype black fur. Only 1:4 offspring of this cross will have the genotype and phenotype brown fur (bb).

DIFFERENTIATE INSTRUCTION

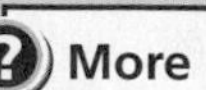

More Reading Support

C What does a ratio show? *the relationship between two quantities*

D How would you write the ratio of one to five? *1:5*

Below Level Have students trace out a two-by-two frame for their Punnett squares, using a white piece of paper. Then have students use red and blue squares of paper to make various combinations in their Punnett squares, like the ones on p. 112. The frame will reinforce the idea that each ratio is made with the total number of squares (four) as the basis for comparison. They can express the relationship between the colored squares and frame using ratios.

Punnett Square and Probability

The Punnett square below shows the possible ways alleles could combine in the offspring of two parent guinea pigs. Each parent has one dominant allele for black fur (B) and one recessive allele for brown fur (b).

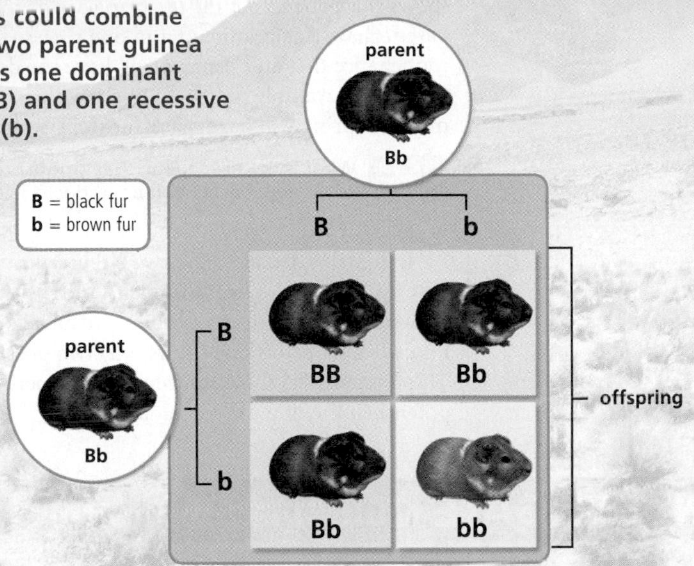

B = black fur
b = brown fur

parent
Bb

parent
Bb

	B	b
B	BB	Bb
b	Bb	bb

offspring

The table below shows the probability of the various genotypes and phenotypes from the Punnett square above. Each probability is shown as both a ratio and a percentage.

(bb)

The genes the guinea pig has are its **genotype.**

Phenotype refers to the guinea pig's actual characteristics.

Genotype	Ratio	Percentage	Phenotype	Ratio	Percentage
BB	1:4	25%	Black fur	3:4	75%
Bb	2:4	50%			
bb	1:4	25%	Brown fur	1:4	25%

READING VISUALS Connect the four shaded sections of the Punnett square to the matching genotypes in the chart.

Chapter 4: Patterns of Heredity 113

Teach from Visuals

To help students interpret the Punnett square and probability charts, ask:

- What kinds of alleles do both parents have? *pairs of one dominant and one recessive*
- What two genotypes produce a phenotype of black fur? *BB and Bb*
- What ratio translates to 25%? *1:4*

The visual "Punnett Square and Probability" is available as T30 in the Unit Transparency Book.

Address Misconceptions

IDENTIFY Point out that human parents have a 1:2 probability of having a boy or a girl with each pregnancy. Ask: If the first child is a girl, what is the probability of their next child being a boy? If students think there is now a higher probability that the child will be a boy, they are confusing potential ratios with actual outcomes.

CORRECT Refer students to the Explore activity on p. 110 to help them understand that one outcome does not influence the next. Remind them that a Punnett square shows possibilities only—the square may show three offspring with one trait and one with another, but in fact all four might be born with the recessive trait.

REASSESS Refer to the Punnett square on p. 113. Ask: If these parents have three offspring, all with black fur, what is the chance their next offspring will be brown? *1:4*

Technology Resources

Visit **ClassZone.com** for background on common student misconceptions.

MISCONCEPTION DATABASE

DIFFERENTIATE INSTRUCTION

Below Level Have students draw a Punnett square for dragons or another fictional organism.

Advanced Have students create Punnett squares for several generations of guinea pigs.

Have students who are interested in traits determined by genes read the following article:

R Challenge Reading, pp. 223–224

INVESTIGATE Multiple Probabilities

PURPOSE To explore multiple probabilities

TIP *30 min.* Instead of coins, you can use any plastic or cardboard discs, or use metal washers.

WHAT DO YOU THINK? *Yy and Rr; The coin tosses do not affect each other; each time they have the same chance of landing up or down. The same is true for alleles turning up in a genotype.*

CHALLENGE *One large coin with "Y" on both sides, one larger coin with "Y" on both sides, one small coin with "R" on both sides; the outcome would always be YyRr.*

 Datasheet, Multiple Probabilities, p. 210

Technology Resources

Customize this student lab as needed or look for an alternative. Print rubrics to assess student lab reports.

 **Lab Generator CD-ROM**

Ongoing Assessment

Use ratios and probabilities to describe patterns of heredity.

Ask: What do ratios and probabilities have to do with heredity? *Ratios and probabilities express the likelihood of how alleles (and the traits they influence) will be inherited by offspring.*

 *Answer: 0 percent*

When one parent has two dominant alleles and the other has two recessive alleles, there is a 100 percent chance that an offspring will have the dominant phenotype. The pea-plant example on page 111 shows this pattern. All the offspring are of regular height. When both parents have one dominant and one recessive allele, there is a 75 percent chance that an offspring will have the dominant phenotype. The guinea-pig example on page 113 shows this pattern. Chances are that more offspring will have black fur than brown fur.

 What is the probability that an offspring from the pea plant cross on page 111 will be of dwarf height?

In humans, females have two X-chromosomes (XX), and males have an X- and a Y-chromosome (XY). The Punnett square on page 115 shows the possible sexes of human offspring. Unlike the guinea-pig Punnett square, this one shows only two possible outcomes, XX and XY. The diagram also shows how to find the percentage chance that a potential offspring will be female.

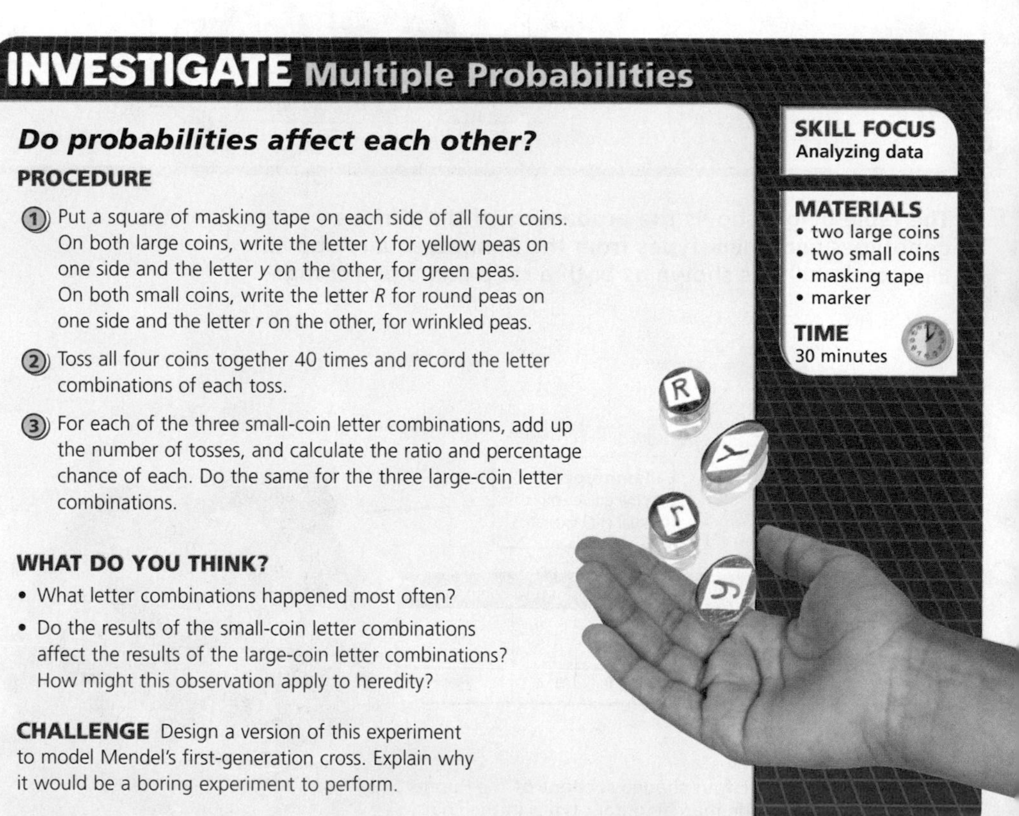

INVESTIGATE Multiple Probabilities

Do probabilities affect each other?

SKILL FOCUS Analyzing data

MATERIALS
- two large coins
- two small coins
- masking tape
- marker

TIME 30 minutes

PROCEDURE

1. Put a square of masking tape on each side of all four coins. On both large coins, write the letter *Y* for yellow peas on one side and the letter *y* on the other, for green peas. On both small coins, write the letter *R* for round peas on one side and the letter *r* on the other, for wrinkled peas.
2. Toss all four coins together 40 times and record the letter combinations of each toss.
3. For each of the three small-coin letter combinations, add up the number of tosses, and calculate the ratio and percentage chance of each. Do the same for the three large-coin letter combinations.

WHAT DO YOU THINK?
- What letter combinations happened most often?
- Do the results of the small-coin letter combinations affect the results of the large-coin letter combinations? How might this observation apply to heredity?

CHALLENGE Design a version of this experiment to model Mendel's first-generation cross. Explain why it would be a boring experiment to perform.

DIFFERENTIATE INSTRUCTION

 **More Reading Support**

 What sex chromosomes do human females and males carry? *XX for females, XY for males*

Advanced Ask students to consider the issue of insurance companies' using genetic differences among people to discriminate as to who gets insurance. Have them lay out their thoughts in a letter to a lawmaker.

Challenge and Extension, p. 209

Calculating Probability

Two humans, a female (XX) and a male (XY), have an offspring. The Punnett square below can be used to calculate the probability that an offspring will be female or male.

1. To find the percentage chance of a female offspring, first find the ratio by counting the number of XX offspring out of the four possible outcomes.

2. 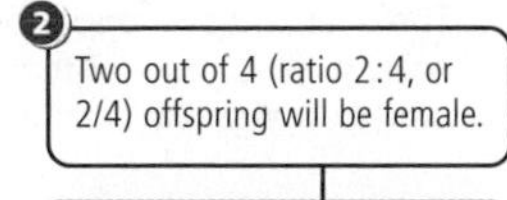

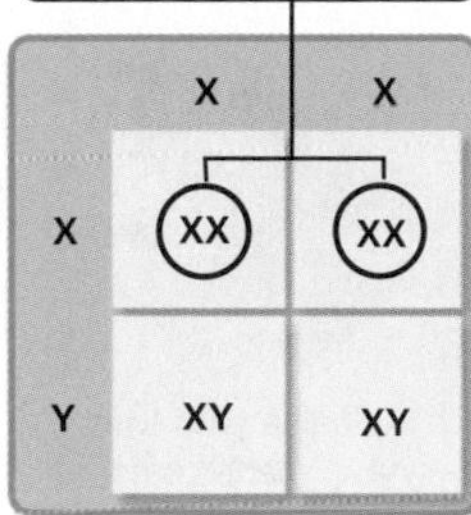

3. Multiply this ratio by 100 to find the probability as a percentage.

4. Two fourths equal 1/2, and 1/2 of 100 is 50. So there is a 50 percent chance that an offspring will be female.

READING VISUALS Compare this Punnett square with the pea-plant Punnett square on page 111 and the guinea-pig Punnett square on page 113. How is it similar? How is it different?

It is important to realize that Punnett squares and probability do not guarantee the outcome of a genetic cross. They indicate the probability of different outcomes. While there is a 75 percent chance that an offspring will have black fur according to the Punnett square on page 113, you cannot know with any certainty what color fur a particular offspring will actually have. Actual experimental results may not match predicted outcomes.

CHECK YOUR READING Can a Punnett square tell you the specific outcome of a genetic cross? Why or why not?

4.2 Review

KEY CONCEPTS

1. Explain how Punnett squares predict the outcomes of a genetic cross.
2. How are ratios and percentages related?
3. How can you find a percentage chance from a Punnett square?

CRITICAL THINKING

4. **Predict** Mendel studied the colors of flowers in his experiments with pea plants. Let P stand for purple and p stand for white. Purple is dominant. Make a Punnett square for a cross between two Pp plants. Find the percentage chance for each outcome.

CHALLENGE

5. **Apply** In pea plants, the allele for smooth peas is dominant over the allele for wrinkled peas. Create a Punnett square and calculate the probability that two smooth-pea plants will have an offspring with wrinkled peas if each parent has one smooth and one wrinkled allele.

ANSWERS

1. They show how the parents' alleles may be passed on to offspring.

2. Ratios compare one number to another number. A percentage is a ratio that compares a number to 100.

3. Determine each possible outcome. Represent it as a ratio in fraction form. Multiply by 100 to find the percentage.

4. Two blocks have one recessive and one dominant allele. One block has two dominant alleles, and one block has two recessive alleles. The chance for each possible outcome is 75 percent green, 25 percent yellow.

5. The probability is 25 percent. Two blocks will show one recessive and one dominant allele. One block will show two dominant alleles. One block will show two recessive alleles.

Ongoing Assessment

READING VISUALS *Answer: All three Punnett squares predict possible allele combinations for offspring. Page 111: one parent, two dominant alleles; other parent, two recessive alleles; 100 percent regular height probability; p. 113: both parents, one dominant and one recessive allele; 75 percent black fur and 25 percent brown fur probability; p. 115: one parent, XX chromosomes; other parent, XY chromosomes; 50 percent female offspring probability*

CHECK YOUR READING *Answer: No; they indicate the probability of different outcomes, but not the specific outcome.*

Reinforce the BIG idea

Have students relate the section to the Big Idea.

 Reinforcing Key Concepts, p. 211

4.2 ASSESS & RETEACH

Assess

 Section 4.2 Quiz, p. 61

Reteach

Set up a Punnett square with one parent having both dominant alleles and the other having both recessive, and another with each parent having a dominant and a recessive. Have students fill in the squares and predict the ratios and percentages.

Technology Resources

Have students visit **ClassZone.com** for reteaching of Key Concepts.

 CONTENT REVIEW

 CONTENT REVIEW CD-ROM

MATH IN SCIENCE
Math Skills Practice for Science

Set Learning Goal
To use a Punnett square to determine the probability of traits

Present the Science
Dogs have lived and worked with humans since the cave dwellers. Through selective breeding the species has become diverse in color and size. The American Kennel Club officially recognizes 138 breeds of dogs, ranging in size from 1.5 to 200 pounds.

Develop Number Sense
- Remind students that m is used for "no merling," rather than N or NM, to indicate that it is merely another form of the same gene, not a different gene.
- Point out that the only way for a recessive trait to be expressed is if there are no dominant alleles (capital letters) in the square.

Close
Tell students that certain traits, such as weight in cattle, speed in horses, and color in dogs, can make them more valuable in the marketplace. Ask: How could a Punnett square help you if you were a professional animal breeder? *You could work out how likely two parents were to have offspring with a particular trait.*

- Math Support, p. 228
- Math Practice, p. 229

Technology Resources

Students can visit **ClassZone.com** for practice in using Punnett squares.

 **MATH TUTORIAL**

SKILL: USING PUNNETT SQUARES

Coat Coloring

The Shetland sheepdog, or Sheltie, has patches of color on its silky coat. A gene controls marbling of the colors, or merling. The merle gene comes in two forms: M for merle, or m for no merle.

A Sheltie with Mm has a merle coat.

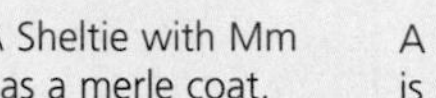

A Sheltie with MM is mostly white.

A Sheltie with mm has solid patches, no merling

Example
One Sheltie parent has a merle coat (Mm), and one has no merling (mm). With these two parents, what is the probability of a puppy with a merle coat?

(1) Make a Punnett square. Put the alleles from one parent on top. Put those of the other on the side.

(2) Fill in the blocks by combining the alleles.

(3) The total number of blocks is the second part of a ratio.
___ : 4

(4) To find the probability of an outcome, count the blocks of that outcome.

	M	m
m	Mm	mm
m	Mm	mm

ANSWER: There is a 2 : 4, or 2 out of 4 probability.

Now, make your own Punnett square for Shelties.

1. Make a Punnett square to show two Sheltie parents, both with merle coats (Mm).
2. What is the probability of a merle puppy?
3. What are the chances of a puppy with no merling?

CHALLENGE Write each of the probabilities in questions 2 and 3 and the example as a percentage.

ANSWERS

1. Punnett square should show both parents as Mm with offspring MM, Mm, Mm, and mm.

2. 2:4

3. 1:4

CHALLENGE *50 percent, 25 percent, 50 percent*

KEY CONCEPT

Meiosis is a special form of cell division.

BEFORE, you learned
- Mitosis produces two genetically identical cells
- In sexual reproduction, offspring inherit traits from both parents
- Genetic traits are inherited in predictable patterns

NOW, you will learn
- Why meiosis is necessary for sexual reproduction
- How cells and chromosomes divide during meiosis
- How meiosis differs from mitosis

VOCABULARY

gamete p. 118
egg p. 118
sperm p. 118
fertilization p. 118
meiosis p. 119

EXPLORE Meiosis

Why does sexual reproduction need a special form of cell division?

PROCEDURE

1. Suppose the cells that combine during sexual reproduction are produced by mitosis, with the same pairs of chromosomes as most cells. Model this combination with the pipe cleaners; both red pipe cleaners and both blue pipe cleaners end up in the new cell.
2. Now model a way for the new cell to end up with the same number of chromosomes as most other cells.

MATERIALS
- 2 blue pipe cleaners
- 2 red pipe cleaners

WHAT DO YOU THINK?
- What was wrong with the new cell produced at the end of step 1?
- Describe your model of the way a new cell could end up with the correct number of chromosomes.

Meiosis is necessary for sexual reproduction.

In Section 4.1 you learned that two cells combine during the process of sexual reproduction. One of the cells contains genetic information from the mother. The other contains genetic information from the father. The two cells combine into a completely new cell, which becomes the offspring.

How does the genetic material of offspring produced by sexual reproduction compare with the genetic material of the parents?

RESOURCES FOR DIFFERENTIATED INSTRUCTION

Below Level

UNIT RESOURCE BOOK
- Reading Study Guide A, pp. 214–215
- Decoding Support, p. 227

Advanced

UNIT RESOURCE BOOK
Challenge and Extension, p. 220

English Learners

UNIT RESOURCE BOOK
Spanish Reading Study Guide, pp. 218–219

- Audio Readings in Spanish
- Audio Readings (English)

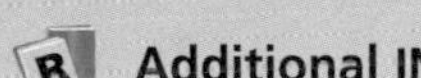

Additional INVESTIGATION, How Is the Sex of Offspring Determined?, A, B, & C, pp. 239–247; Teacher Instructions, pp. 308–309

4.3 FOCUS

Set Learning Goals

Students will
- Explain why meiosis is necessary for sexual reproduction.
- Describe how cells and chromosomes divide during meiosis.
- Analyze how meiosis differs from mitosis.
- Model what takes place inside of cells during fertilization.

3-Minute Warm-Up

Display Transparency 29 or copy this exercise on the board:

Decide if these statements are true. If not true, correct them.

1. Mitosis produces four genetically identical daughter cells. *Mitosis produces two genetically identical daughter cells.*
2. In sexual reproduction, offspring inherit traits from both parents. *true*
3. Genetic traits are inherited in random patterns. *Genetic traits are inherited in predictable patterns.*

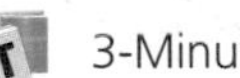

3-Minute Warm-Up, p. T29

4.3 MOTIVATE

EXPLORE Meiosis

PURPOSE To model what would happen if meiosis did not occur before two cells combine during sexual reproduction

TIP *20 min.* You might remind students that two cells join together in sexual reproduction, while one cell splits in two during asexual reproduction.

WHAT DO YOU THINK? *It had the wrong number of chromosomes. Students might describe taking one pipe cleaner of each color instead of two.*

Ongoing Assessment

Answer: The offspring has some genetic material from each parent.

4.3 INSTRUCT

Teach from Visuals

To help students interpret the fertilization diagram, ask:

- Which cells are 1*n*? *the gametes*
- Which cell is 2*n*? *the fertilized egg cell*
- If these were human gametes, how many chromosomes would be pictured in each 1*n* gamete? *23*
- If the fertilized egg shown were a human egg, how many chromosome pairs would be shown in the egg? *23*

Ongoing Assessment

Explain why meiosis is necessary for sexual reproduction.

Ask: Why does sexual reproduction require meiosis? *If meiosis did not occur, a fertilized cell would have twice as many chromosomes as it needs.*

CHECK YOUR READING *Answer: a cell with half the usual number of chromosomes—one from each pair*

A

Most human cells, which can be referred to as body cells, contain 46 chromosomes—the full number of chromosomes that is normal for a human being. Any cell that contains the full number of chromosomes (two sets) for a species is a 2*n* cell, also called a diploid cell. The 2*n* cells for a fruit fly, for example, contain 8 chromosomes.

Think about what would happen if two body cells were to combine. The resulting cell would have twice the normal number of chromosomes. Reproductive cells, called gametes, differ from body cells.

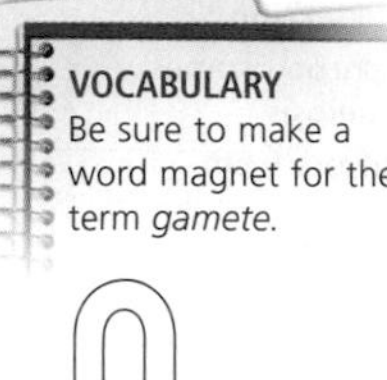

Gametes are cells that contain half the usual number of chromosomes—one chromosome from each pair. Gametes are 1*n* cells, also called haploid cells. Human gametes contain 23 unpaired chromosomes. The gametes of a fruit fly contain 4 unpaired chromosomes. Gametes are found only in the reproductive organs of plants and animals. An **egg** is a gamete that forms in the reproductive organs of a female. A gamete that forms in the reproductive organs of a male is a **sperm**.

CHECK YOUR READING What is a gamete?

B

During sexual reproduction two gametes combine to become a 2*n* cell that can grow into a new offspring. **Fertilization** is the process that takes place when a sperm and an egg combine to form one new cell. The diagram below shows what happens to the chromosomes in gametes during fertilization. In humans, an egg cell with 23 chromosomes joins a sperm cell with 23 chromosomes to form a new 2*n* cell with 46 chromosomes.

Fertilization

During fertilization, a 1*n* egg cell from a female combines with a 1*n* sperm cell from a male, producing a 2*n* fertilized egg cell, which develops into an offspring.

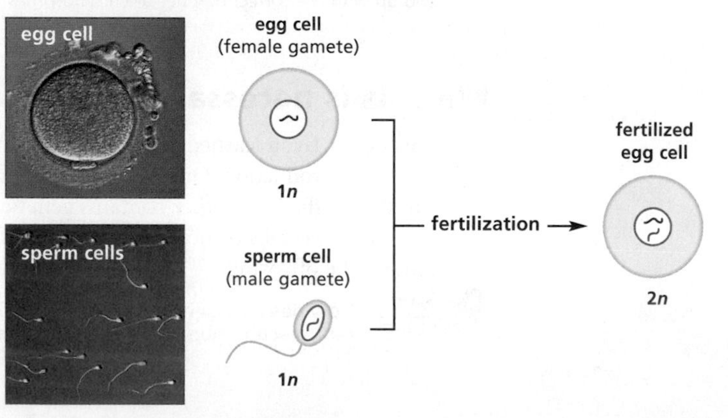

DIFFERENTIATE INSTRUCTION

More Reading Support

A How many chromosomes do human cells contain? *46*

B What is fertilization? *sperm and egg combine to form one new cell*

English Learners Place the terms *gamete, egg, sperm, fertilization,* and *meiosis* on the classroom's Science Word Wall with brief definitions of each. Use the Chapter Summary page to help students with key concepts and vocabulary.

INVESTIGATE Fertilization

How can you model fertilization?

DESIGN — YOUR OWN — EXPERIMENT

In fertilization, a sperm and an egg combine to form a new cell. Design a model of fertilization.

SKILL FOCUS
Designing Experiments

MATERIALS
- pipe cleaners
- gallon milk jug
- film canister
- yarn

TIME
25 minutes

PROCEDURE

1. Use the materials provided to make simple models of an egg and a sperm.
2. Use the sperm and egg models to show the fertilization process.

WHAT DO YOU THINK?

- Describe your model of the cell that exists at the end of the fertilization process.
- How is it different from the sperm cell and egg cell?

CHALLENGE Design a model for fertilization in fruit flies.

You know that body cells divide by the process called mitosis. Mitosis produces two daughter cells, each containing exact copies of the chromosomes in the parent cell. Each daughter cell formed by mitosis is a standard diploid ($2n$) cell.

But to produce gametes, which are haploid, a different kind of cell division is necessary. **Meiosis** is a special kind of cell division that produces haploid ($1n$) cells. During meiosis, a single cell goes through two cell divisions—meiosis I and meiosis II. Meiosis takes place only in the reproductive tissues of an organism.

Cells divide twice during meiosis.

NOTETAKING STRATEGY
Use an earlier strategy or one that you think works well to take notes on the division of cells during meiosis.

Before meiosis begins, the chromosomes of the parent cell are copied. A cell that is ready to divide contains two copies of each chromosome pair—twice as many chromosomes as usual. So to end up with cells that have half the usual number of chromosomes, there must be two divisions.

? C Remember that the two chromosomes in a pair are called homologs. At the beginning of meiosis I, the cell has two copies of each homolog, attached together. During meiosis I the homologs separate. The starting cell divides into two cells. One cell contains the two copies of one homolog of each pair, while the other cell contains the two copies of the other homolog of each pair. Then, during meiosis II, each of the two cells is divided, producing four haploid cells. Each haploid cell has one unpaired set of chromosomes.

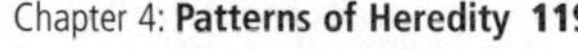

INVESTIGATE Fertilization

PURPOSE To design a model of a cell to show the changes during fertilization

TIP *25 min.* You may wish to have students read the investigation and think over their designs while reading the rest of Section 4.3. Then have them return to the task of completing their models.

WHAT DO YOU THINK? *The model should have pairs of pipe cleaners (half from the sperm, half from the egg). It has twice as many chromosomes.*

CHALLENGE *Fruit flies have 8 chromosomes, so the end model should have 8 pipe cleaners, while the egg and sperm should each have 4 pipe cleaners.*

 Datasheet, Fertilization, p. 221

Technology Resources

Customize this student lab as needed or look for an alternative. Print rubrics to assess student lab reports.

 **Lab Generator CD-ROM**

DIFFERENTIATE INSTRUCTION

 **More Reading Support**

C What happens to homologs during meiosis I? *The homologs split up, one from each parent going into a separate cell.*

Below Level Students might find it helpful to collect the many vocabulary words connected with reproduction, such as *meiosis* and *fertilization,* and make flash cards for learning them.

Advanced

R Challenge and Extension, p. 220

Teach Difficult Concepts

Have students make sequence cards for the process of meiosis, with drawings on one side and verbal explanations on the other. Have them practice rearranging sequence cards that are placed out of order.

Teacher Demo

In order to help students better understand the concept of meiosis, have them act as chromosomes by holding colored ribbons or sheets of construction paper. Have other students hold a long piece of string to represent the cell membrane. Walk students through the stages of meiosis I and II.

CHECK YOUR READING *Answer: The parent cell divides into two daughter cells.*

Meiosis I

D

As you can see in the diagram on page 121, there are four steps in meiosis I: prophase I, metaphase I, anaphase I, and telophase I. Included in telophase I is a cytokinesis, the division of the cytoplasm. The diagram shows what would happen during meiosis I in a species that has four chromosomes in its $2n$ body cells.

READING TIP As you read about meiosis I and meiosis II, match the numbers in the text to the numbers in the diagram on page 121.

1. **Prophase I** The duplicated chromosomes pair up with their partners. There are two sets of each of the chromosome pairs in the parent cell. The chromatids are attached together. There are pairs of doubled homologs.
2. **Metaphase I** The chromosome pairs line up along the center of the cell.
3. **Anaphase I** The two copies of one homolog are pulled apart from the two copies of the other homolog. This separating of the homologs is the most significant step of meiosis I.
4. **Telophase I and Cytokinesis** A new cell membrane forms at the center of the cell, dividing the parent cell into two daughter cells.

CHECK YOUR READING What happens to the parent cell during telophase I?

Meiosis II

RESOURCE CENTER CLASSZONE.COM
Learn more about meiosis.

E

During meiosis I, two daughter cells are formed. The chromosomes of these two cells are not copied before meiosis II begins. Both of these cells divide during meiosis II, to produce a total of four daughter cells. The four steps in meiosis II, shown on page 121, are prophase II, metaphase II, anaphase II, and telophase II (with cytokinesis).

5. **Prophase II** In each daughter cell, there are two copies of each of n chromosomes. The copies are attached together.
6. **Metaphase II** Each duplicated chromosome lines up separately along each cell's center.
7. **Anaphase II** The two attached copies of each chromosome separate and are pulled to opposite poles in each cell.
8. **Telophase II and Cytokinesis** A new cell membrane forms in the center of each cell, as each cell divides into two $1n$ daughter cells, producing a total of four $1n$ cells.

During meiosis, one cell in an organism's reproductive system divides twice to form four $1n$ cells. In male organisms, these gametes become sperm. In female organisms, at least one of these cells becomes an egg. In some species, including humans, only one of the four daughter cells produced by a female during meiosis becomes an egg. The rest dissolve back into the organism or, in some cases, are never produced.

DIFFERENTIATE INSTRUCTION

More Reading Support

D What are the results of meiosis I? *two daughter cells*

E What stage of meiosis II produces 4 daughter cells? *telophase II*

Below Level It may be helpful to students to trace the diagrams on p. 121 using colored pencils. Have them describe to a partner the events that are depicted in each phase.

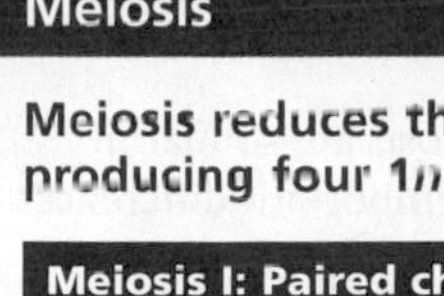

Meiosis reduces the number of chromosomes by half, producing four 1*n* cells.

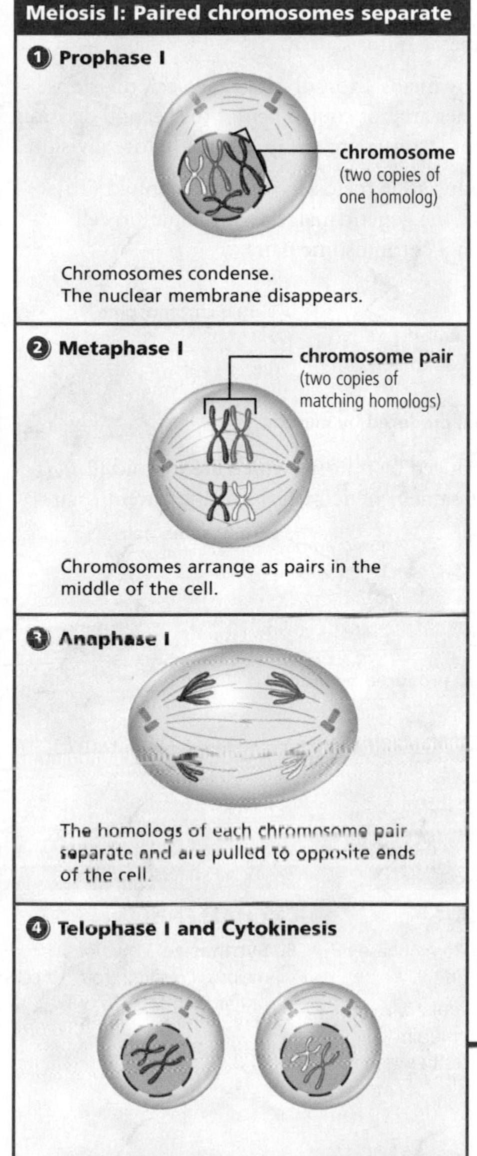

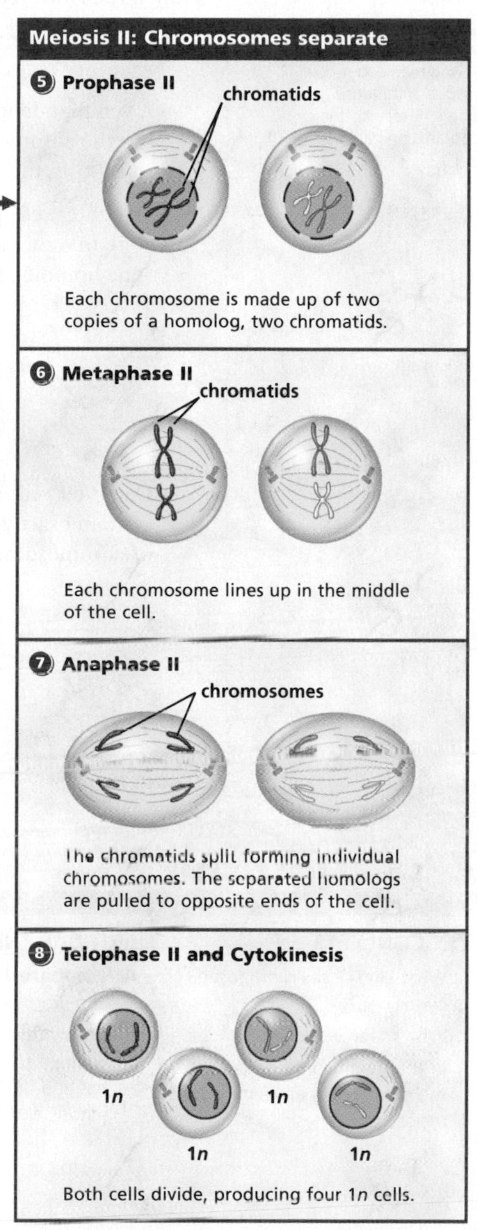

Teach from Visuals

To help students interpret the diagrams of meiosis, ask:

- How many chromosome pairs are there in the cell shown in prophase I? *2 pairs: one green/purple pair, one yellow/red pair*
- What happens to each homolog in the chromosome pairs during anaphase I? *The pairs split, so one homolog (for example, green) goes into one cell and the other homolog (for example, purple) goes into the other.*
- What does each homolog look like in telophase 1? *It still has two copies of DNA.*
- When do the copies of DNA in a single homolog split? *during anaphase II*

Teaching with Technology

If you have a PC microscope, have students look at prepared slides of the different stages of meiosis.

Ongoing Assessment

Describe how cells and chromosomes divide during meiosis.

Ask: What happens to cells and chromosomes during meiosis? *The DNA in the chromosomes is copied, but the cell goes through two divisions. So the DNA is divided twice resulting in half as much DNA as the original cell. In meiosis I, the pair of homologs split up. In meiosis II, each homolog, consisting of two copies of DNA, splits so that the original DNA and the copy go into different cells. This results in four cells with a single set of homologs.*

DIFFERENTIATE INSTRUCTION

Below Level Discuss meiosis in terms of numbers. Start with a number representing the chromosomes in a cell, for example, 4. DNA is doubled, so double the number ($4 \times 2 = 8$). Divide this not once, but twice ($8 \div 2 = 4$; $4 \div 2 = 2$). Ask: What has happened to the number? *It is half what it was.*

Additional Investigation To reinforce Section 4.3 learning goals, use the following full-period investigation:

 **Additional INVESTIGATION,** How Is the Sex of Offspring Determined?, A, B, & C, pp. 239–247, 308–309
(Advanced students should complete Levels B and C.)

Ongoing Assessment

Analyze how meiosis differs from mitosis.

Ask: What are the ending daughter cells like after mitosis and meiosis? *Mitosis forms two genetically identical cells with 2 pairs of chromosomes. Meiosis forms four cells with a set of single chromosomes.*

CHECK YOUR READING *Answer: Meiosis happens only to cells that become gametes; meiosis involves two cell divisions after DNA is copied, mitosis involves one cell division; meiosis produces four haploid (1*n*) daughter cells; mitosis produces two diploid (2*n*) cells.*

Reinforce the BIG idea

Have students relate the section to the Big Idea.

 Reinforcing Key Concepts, p. 222

4.3 ASSESS & RETEACH

Assess

 Section 4.3 Quiz, p. 62

Reteach

Allow students to refer to the diagram on p. 121. Ask students to do a round-robin "guided tour" taking turns narrating as they direct you through drawing the steps in meiosis I and II. You may wish to have them sketch the steps on the board.

Technology Resources

Have students visit **ClassZone.com** for reteaching of Key Concepts.

 CONTENT REVIEW

 CONTENT REVIEW CD-ROM

Meiosis and mitosis differ in some important ways.

READING TIP
As you read about how meiosis and mitosis are different, refer to the diagrams on pages 83 and 121.

You can see that the processes of meiosis and mitosis are similar in many ways. However, they also have several very important differences.

- Only cells that are to become gametes go through meiosis. All other cells divide by mitosis.
- A cell that divides by meiosis goes through two cell divisions, but the chromosomes are not copied before the second division. In mitosis, the chromosomes are always copied before division.
- Daughter cells produced by meiosis, which are haploid (1*n*), contain only half of the genetic material of the parent cell (one homolog from a chromosome pair).

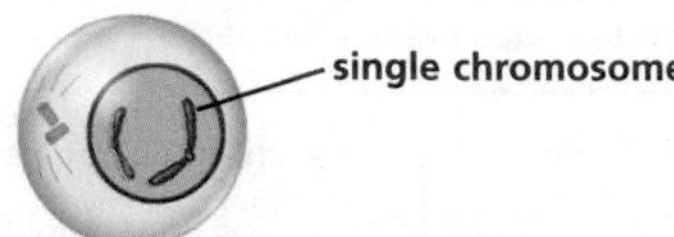

Cell produced by meiosis

- Daughter cells produced by mitosis, which are diploid (2*n*), contain exactly the same genetic material as the parent (pairs of chromosomes).

chromosome pair

Cell produced by mitosis

 What are four ways in which meiosis differs from mitosis?

4.3 Review

KEY CONCEPTS

1. What kind of cell is produced by meiosis?
2. What is fertilization?
3. In your own words, describe the differences between meiosis and mitosis.

CRITICAL THINKING

4. **Compare** How do prophase I and prophase II differ?
5. **Communicate** Make a Venn diagram to show the similarities and differences between mitosis and meiosis.

CHALLENGE

6. **Synthesize** Why does meiosis II result in four 1*n* cells rather than four 2*n* cells?

ANSWERS

1. a gamete (haploid)

2. A sperm and an egg combine to form a new cell.

3. Meiosis produces 4 1n (haploid) gametes instead of 2 2n (diploid) cells. It involves 2 divisions after DNA is copied, rather than 1 division after DNA is copied.

4. Prophase I: one cell contains twice usual number of chromosomes for species; prophase II: two cells each with two copies of one homolog of each chromosome pair.

5. Meiosis: produces 4 1n (haploid) cells, 2 divisions; mitosis: produces 2 2n (diploid) cells, one division; both: DNA copied, chromosomes divide, new cells form

6. One cell divides twice, so one cell produces four. The cells are 1n because DNA was copied only once.

Think SCIENCE

SKILL: DETERMINING RELEVANCE

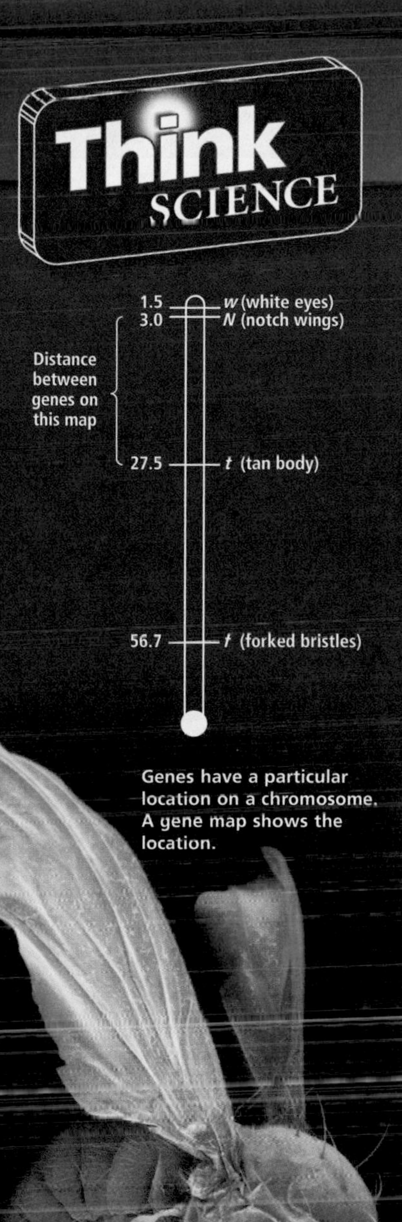

Genes have a particular location on a chromosome. A gene map shows the location.

Are Traits Linked?

Fruit flies are easy to breed in a laboratory and have an assortment of easily recognized genetic traits—different eye colors, body patterns, limb characteristics, and wing shapes. For these reasons, early geneticists studied fruit flies to learn how certain traits were inherited. Sometimes the experiments produced puzzling results. Here is an example from the laboratory of Thomas Hunt Morgan.

Observations

- In a batch of fruit flies, most red-eyed individuals were born with short wings.
- In the same batch, at least one fruit fly was born with red eyes and normal-sized wings.

Hypotheses

Morgan and his coworkers made these hypotheses about the inherited traits:

- The gene for red eyes and the gene for short wings are linked together on a fruit fly's chromosomes. These linked genes are usually inherited together.
- Sometimes during meiosis, one of the linked genes will "cross over" from one chromosome to a homologous one. When this happens, a fruit fly will be born with one but not both of the linked genes—red eyes without short wings.
- Genes that are farthest from each other on a chromosome are most likely to become separated and cross over during meiosis. Genes that are closest (linked) to each other are least likely to.

Further Discoveries

By studying the results of many breeding experiments, Morgan and his student, Alfred Sturtevant, could determine which genes were closest and farthest from each other on the same chromosome. From this information, they drew a simple map showing the location of each of the fruit fly's linked genes.

Determine Relevance

On Your Own Look at the map of a chromosome on this page. Which of the traits are most likely to be inherited together? Which might be most easily separated and cross over during meiosis?

As a Group Is it reasonable to think that information about a fruit fly's genes could apply to the genes of a human being? Discuss this topic in a small group and see if the group can agree.

ANSWERS

On Your Own *W and N (traits that are close together); w and f (the traits that are the farthest apart).*

As a Group *Discussion should include the idea that cells of different species behave in similar ways. Many of the same chemical activities that occur in a fly cell also occur in a human cell, so it's likely that the genes controlling those activities will be similar.*

THINK SCIENCE
Scientific Methods of Thinking

Set Learning Goal

To learn how to make inferences from relevant data

Present the Science

During meiosis I, homologous chromosomes can swap genetic material, a process called crossing over or recombination. It occurs during prophase I, when the homologs are next to each other. The homologs temporarily break and reconnect in a way that causes genes from one homolog to get attached to the other homolog. Remember that alleles are located in the same place on homologs. One allele swaps positions with the other. Scientists noticed that certain genes seem to be linked, that is, if one gene gets swapped, then so will the other gene. They realized that the two must be close together on the chromosome.

Guide the Activity

- Ask: What advantages are there to using fruit flies in genetic studies? *many generations in a short time, easy to breed, clear differences in genetics*
- Discuss why scientists cannot do similar experiments with people.

Close

Discuss reasons to map human genes. These could include social and anthropological reasons as well as scientific or medical ones.

BACK TO

the BIG idea

Ask students to think about how heredity affects them. Ask: Why do you have the hair color, eye color, face shape, foot size, and height that you do? *My parents or other ancestors had the traits, and they were passed on to me through sexual reproduction. Sometimes, interaction with the environment will affect how the traits are expressed.*

KEY CONCEPTS SUMMARY

SECTION 4.1

Ask: What is an allele? *various forms of a gene, which offspring inherit from their parents*

Ask: What are your genotype and phenotype? *The phenotype is a set of observable characteristics; the genotype is the set of alleles that produce them.*

SECTION 4.2

Ask: How can the probability of particular outcomes be expressed? *in ratios and percentages*

Ask: What's the probability that offspring in the Punnett square will have black fur? *3:4, or 75%*

SECTION 4.3

Ask: What is the end product of meiosis I? *two daughter cells, each with two copies of one homolog from each pair of chromosomes*

Ask: What is the end product of meiosis II? *four daughter cells, each with half the chromosomes necessary to become offspring—one homolog from each pair*

Review Concepts

- Big Idea Flow Chart, p. T25
- Chapter Outline, pp. T31–T32

4 Chapter Review

the BIG idea

In sexual reproduction, genes are passed from parents to offspring in predictable patterns.

KEY CONCEPTS SUMMARY

Living things inherit traits in patterns.

Offspring inherit **alleles**, which are forms of **genes**, from their parents. Alleles can be **dominant** or **recessive**. The alleles you have are your **genotype;** the observable characteristics that come from your genotype are your **phenotype**.

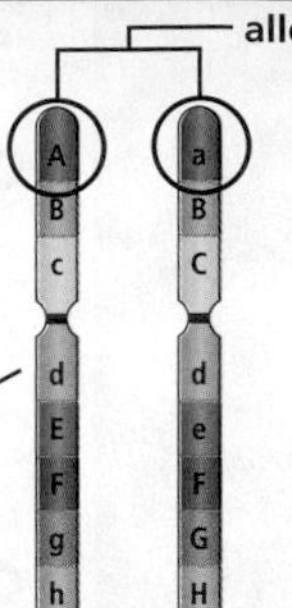

VOCABULARY
sexual reproduction p. 102
gene p. 102
heredity p. 102
allele p. 103
phenotype p. 106
genotype p. 106
dominant p. 107
recessive p. 107

Patterns of heredity can be predicted.

Punnett squares show possible outcomes of heredity. **Ratios** and **percentages** can be used with Punnett squares to express the **probability** of particular outcomes.

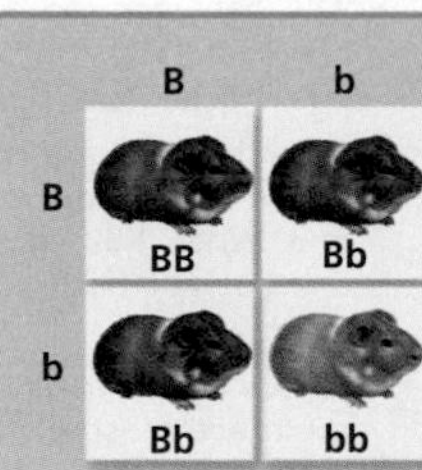

B = black fur
b = brown fur

VOCABULARY
Punnett square p. 110
ratio p. 112
probability p. 112
percentage p. 112

Meiosis is a special form of cell division.

- At the beginning of meiosis I, the parent cell has two copies of each chromosome pair.
- During meiosis I, the homologs of the chromosome pair separate; there are two cells, each with two copies of one homolog from each pair.
- During meiosis II, the two copies of each homolog separate; each daughter cell has one homolog.

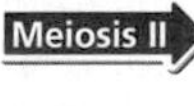

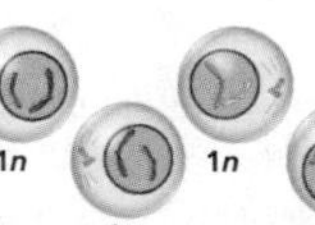

VOCABULARY
gamete p. 118
egg p. 118
sperm p. 118
fertilization p. 118
meiosis p. 119

124 Unit 1: **Cells and Heredity**

Technology Resources

Have students visit **ClassZone.com** or use the CD-ROM for a cumulative review of concepts.

CONTENT REVIEW

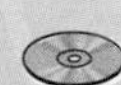
CONTENT REVIEW CD-ROM

Engage students in a whole-class interactive review of Key Concepts. Edit content as you wish.

POWER PRESENTATIONS

Reviewing Vocabulary

Make a frame for each of the vocabulary terms listed below. Write the term in the center. Think about how each term is related to the Big Idea of the chapter. Decide what information to frame it with. Use definitions, examples, descriptions, parts, or pictures.

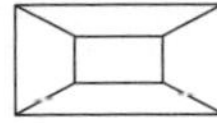

1. allele
2. heredity
3. ratio
4. probability

Describe how the vocabulary terms in the following pairs of words are related to each other. Explain the relationship in a one- or two-sentence answer. Underline each vocabulary word or term in your answers.

5. phenotype, genotype
6. dominant, recessive

Reviewing Key Concepts

Multiple Choice *Choose the letter of the best answer.*

7. Which is an example of an acquired trait?
   a. eye color
   b. hair color
   c. blood type
   d. ability to read
8. The unit of heredity that determines a particular trait is known as
   a. a chromosome
   b. a gamete
   c. a gene
   d. a phenotype
9. A human female would have which set of sex chromosomes?
   a. XX
   b. YY
   c. XY
   d. XxYy
10. If one copy of a dominant allele is present in a genotype, then the trait the allele codes for is
    a. expressed in the phenotype
    b. not expressed in the phenotype
    c. partially expressed in the phenotype
    d. not expressed in an offspring's phenotype
11. In guinea pigs, the allele for black fur (B) is dominant, and the allele for brown fur (b) is recessive. If a BB male mates with a Bb female, what percentage of offspring are likely to have black fur?
    a. 100 percent
    b. 75 percent
    c. 50 percent
    d. 25 percent
12. If one parent has two dominant alleles and another parent has two recessive alleles, the offspring will have
    a. the recessive phenotype
    b. the dominant phenotype
    c. two dominant alleles
    d. two recessive alleles
13. Cells that contain half the usual number of chromosomes are
    a. fertilized egg cells
    b. gametes
    c. alleles
    d. diploid cells
14. The process that produces haploid ($1n$) cells is known as
    a. mitosis
    b. reproduction
    c. meiosis
    d. fertilization
15. What happens when fertilization occurs?
    a. Two $2n$ cells combine in a new cell.
    b. Two $1n$ cells combine into a new cell.
    c. Two $2n$ daughter cells are produced.
    d. Two $1n$ daughter cells are produced.
16. Which does not occur during meiosis?
    a. Four haploid daughter cells are produced.
    b. Two diploid daughter cells are produced.
    c. Only cells that are gametes are produced.
    d. Daughter cells are produced that contain half the chromosomes of the parent cell.

Short Answer *Write a short answer to each question.*

17. In what case would a recessive allele be expressed in the phenotype of an offspring?
18. Describe the purpose of a Punnett square.
19. How does the number of chromosomes in a person's sex cells compare with the number of chromosomes in the body cells?

ASSESSMENT RESOURCES

UNIT ASSESSMENT BOOK
- Chapter Test A, pp. 63–66
- Chapter Test B, pp. 67–70
- Chapter Test C, pp. 71–74
- Alternative Assessment, pp. 75–76

SPANISH ASSESSMENT BOOK
Spanish Chapter Test, pp. 13–16

Technology Resources

Edit test items and answer choices.

Test Generator CD-ROM

Visit **ClassZone.com** to extend test practice.

Test Practice

Reviewing Vocabulary

Sample answers:

1. Alleles are alternative forms of the same gene; they can be either dominant or recessive; alleles are found on chromosomes.

2. Heredity is the passing of traits genetically from parents to offspring: it is controlled by genes; alleles are different forms of a gene.

3. A ratio compares two quantities; Punnett squares show a ratio of possible phenotypes and genotypes.

4. Probability is the likelihood of a specific outcome; taken from ratio based on 100; can be used to express chance of certain phenotypes and genotypes.

5. A phenotype is the expression of a genotype.

6. Dominant traits are expressed in a phenotype if one or more dominant alleles are present, whereas two recessive alleles must be present for a recessive trait to be expressed in the phenotype.

Reviewing Key Concepts

7. d	*12. b*
8. c	*13. b*
9. a	*14. c*
10. a	*15. b*
11. a	*16. b*

17. if both homologs in offspring had the recessive allele

18. It shows the possible genotypes in the offspring of two parents.

19. The sex cells have exactly half of the number of chromosomes as the body cells, a single set of homologs.

(Answer to item that appears on p. 126.)

20. The first generation of a cross between true-breeding dwarf- and regular-height plants produced all plants of regular height. In a cross of second-generation plants, the dwarf trait reappeared. That suggested that the dwarf-height factor was there all along but masked in the first generation. So there had to be two factors for the trait.

Thinking Critically

(Answer for item 20 appears on p. 125.)

21. A gene is the unit of heredity that occupies a specific location on a chromosome. A gene codes for a particular product or trait and is passed from parent to offspring during sexual reproduction.

22. No; if it had a dominant allele, it would be of regular height.

23. The top and sides of the Punnett square show the alleles of the parents' genotypes. The boxes show the possible genotypes and the phenotypes of the offspring.

24. The appearance of the recessive trait (white fur) in the offspring indicates both parents must have one dominant and one recessive allele.

25. 2:4 for both phenotypes

26. 50 percent

27. The egg and sperm cells are haploid. They join to produce a diploid fertilized egg.

28. Meiosis I: DNA in parent cell is copied; the cell divides, forming two cells, each with one homolog. Meiosis II: Cells divide again, and homologs split, resulting in four 1n cells.

the BIG idea

29. Answers should refer to genes as means for passing on traits; may mention dark fur as a possible recessive trait.

30. Answers should mention Mendel's experiments with heredity in pea plants. He determined that offspring have at least two "factors," or genes, for a trait in their genotype. Different alleles, dominant and recessive, affect its phenotype.

UNIT PROJECTS

Students should have begun designing. Remind them to continue researching and to try different solutions to the problems they encounter.

Unit Projects, pp. 5–10

Thinking Critically

20. INFER How was Mendel able to infer that each offspring of two parent pea plants had a pair of "factors" for a particular trait?

21. COMMUNICATE Briefly describe how heredity works. Use the terms *gene* and *chromosome* in your explanation.

22. APPLY Can a dwarf pea plant ever have a dominant allele? Explain.

23. ANALYZE How is a Punnett Square used to show both the genotype and phenotype of both parents and offspring?

24. APPLY In rabbits, the allele for black fur is dominant over the allele for white fur. Two black rabbits have a litter of eight offspring. Six of the offspring have black hair and two have white hair. What are the genotypes of the parents? Explain.

Use the Punnett square below to answer the next two questions.

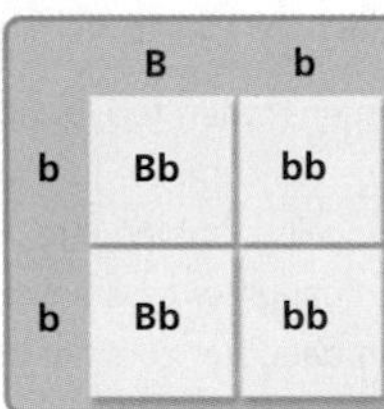

	B	b
b	Bb	bb
b	Bb	bb

25. CALCULATE A parent has one dominant allele for black fur (B) and one recessive allele for white fur (b). The other parent has two recessive alleles for white fur. In this cross what is the chance that an offspring will be born with black fur? With white fur?

26. CALCULATE What is the percentage chance that an offspring will have the recessive phenotype?

27. ANALYZE This diagram shows the process of fertilization. Which of the cells shown are haploid? Explain.

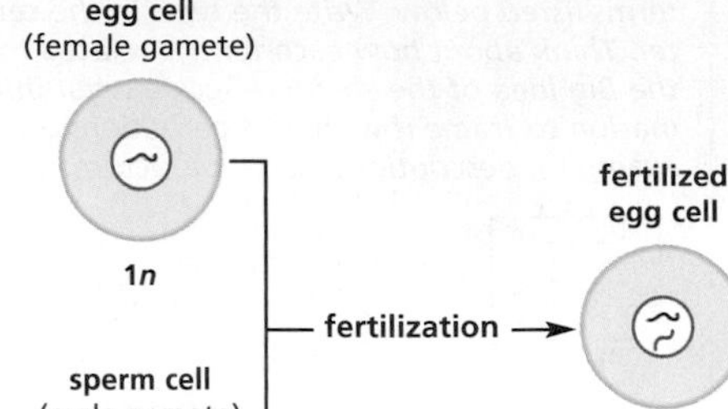

28. SUMMARIZE Briefly describe what happens during meiosis I and meiosis II. What is the function of meiosis?

the BIG idea

29. INFER Look again at the picture on pages 98–99. Now that you have finished the chapter, how would you change or add details to your answer to the question on the photograph?

30. SYNTHESIZE Write one or more paragraphs explaining how Mendel's observations of pea plants contributed to the study of modern genetics. Use these terms in your explanation.

gene	phenotype
allele	dominant
trait	recessive
genotype	

UNIT PROJECTS

If you need to create graphs or other visuals for your project, be sure you have grid paper, poster board, markers, or other supplies.

MONITOR AND RETEACH

If students have difficulty with items 23–26, they may need more practice working with Punnett squares. Students can make a mock Punnett square (a probability square) for a variety of outcomes that are not related to genes and heredity, such as tossing two coins heads or tails, or any paired binary choices. Encourage students to devise their own, and to write problems for each other to solve.

Students may benefit from summarizing one or more sections of the chapter.

Summarizing the Chapter, pp. 248–249

Standardized Test Practice

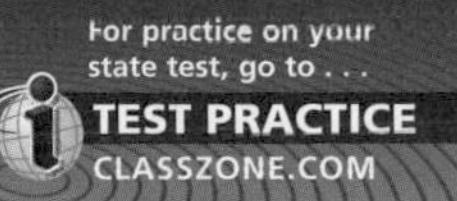

Analyzing data

The chart below shows the phenotypes of pea-plant offspring.

Phenotypes of Pea Plants	
Phenotype	Number of Offspring
Regular (D)	12
Dwarf (d)	4

Use the chart to answer the questions below.

1. What percentage of pea plants showed the dominant phenotype?
- **a.** 100 percent
- **b.** 75 percent
- **c.** 50 percent
- **d.** 25 percent

2. What percentage of pea plants showed the recessive phenotype?
- **a.** 100 percent
- **b.** 75 percent
- **c.** 50 percent
- **d.** 25 percent

3. What is the genotype of the dwarf pea plants?
- **a.** DD
- **b.** Dd
- **c.** dd
- **d.** cannot tell

4. What are the possible genotypes of the regular pea plants?
- **a.** DD and dd
- **b.** DD and Dd
- **c.** Dd and dd
- **d.** cannot tell

5. What are the genotypes of the parents?
- **a.** Dd and dd
- **b.** DD and Dd
- **c.** Dd and Dd
- **d.** dd and dd

6. Which statement is true, based on the data in the chart?
- **a.** If both parents were Dd, then none of the offspring would be dwarf.
- **b.** If both parents were DD, then none of the offspring would be dwarf.
- **c.** If one parent were Dd and the other were dd, then none of the offspring would be regular.
- **d.** If one parent were DD and the other parent were dd, then none of the offspring would be regular.

Extended Response

7. Traits for a widow's peak hairline (W) and curly hair (C) are controlled by dominant alleles. A family of eight has three children with widow's peaks. All six children have curly hair. Use your knowledge of heredity to write one or two paragraphs explaining the possible genotypes of the parents.

8. A student proposes a hypothesis that traits that are dominant are more common in the general population than traits with recessive alleles. Describe a procedure you might use to test this hypothesis.

METACOGNITIVE ACTIVITY

Have students answer the following questions in their **Science Notebook:**

1. Why do you think it is important for you to learn about patterns of heredity?
2. Which topics in this chapter would you like to learn more about?
3. How do you think Punnett squares could be useful to life decisions?

Analyzing Data

1. b *3. c* *5. c*
2. d *4. b* *6. b*

Extended Response

7. RUBRIC

4 points for an answer that indicates correct understanding of these concepts:

- how alleles are denoted
- how a Punnett square would apply to this problem
- the meaning of the ratios of children with widow's peaks and curly hair
- a correct understanding of genotype and phenotype

Sample answer: Since the ratio of children with widow's peaks is 3 out of 6, it is likely that one parent has a genotype of ww and the other parent has a genotype of Ww. A Punnett square would show a 50 percent probability that the offspring would have a widow's peak. Since all six children have curly hair, one parent probably has the genotype CC.

3 points shows understanding of three concepts
2 points shows understanding of two concepts
1 point shows understanding of one concept

8. RUBRIC

4 points for a response that shows understanding of these concepts:

- dominant and recessive alleles
- how alleles combine to form a genotype
- ratios and probabilities
- use of a Punnett square

Sample answer: The experiment should investigate an easily recognizable trait that has dominant and recessive alleles, such as the presence of eye folds. Take a census of a large population and see if the data provides a ratio like that provided by Punnett squares for different combinations.

3 points shows understanding of three concepts
2 points shows understanding of two concepts
1 point shows understanding of one concept

FOCUS

Set Learning Goals

Students will

- Determine how the development of the microscope enabled research into cells and genes.
- Explore experiments with plants that advanced our understanding of heredity.
- Analyze how the development of the computer enabled research into cells and genes.
- Use a lens to examine a water sample.

National Science Education Standards

A.9.a–g Understandings About Scientific Inquiry

E.6.a–c Understandings About Science and Technology

F.5.a–e, F.5.g Science and Technology in Society

G.1.a–b Science as a Human Endeavor

G.2.a Nature of Science

G.3.a–c History of Science

INSTRUCT

The top half of the timeline shows major events in the study of genetics, starting in 1665. The bottom half of the timeline illustrates advances in technology and their application to genetics. The gaps represent blocks of time that have been omitted.

TIMELINES in Science

THE STORY OF Genetics

The human genome project, DNA evidence in criminal cases, cloning—news about genetics is everywhere. Some of the most exciting research in science today involves genes. The timeline shows that some important concepts that underline the study of genetics were discovered relatively early. You will notice the influence of two major advances in technology—the development of the microscope during the 1600s, and the development of computer technology during the later half of the 1900s. The boxes below the timeline show how technology has led to new understanding and to applications of those understandings.

1674

Cells Are Everywhere

Anton van Leeuwenhoek uses a microscope to study pond water and discovers the water is full of microscopic organisms, some made of single cells. These drawings show some of what he saw.

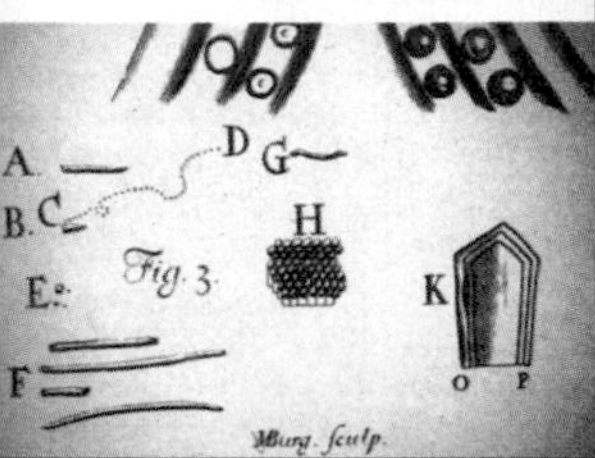

1665

Cells Discovered

Robert Hooke uses a microscope to study living matter. What he sees and then records in this drawing are tiny repeating units, which he calls cells.

EVENTS

1650 | 1660 | 1670 | 1680

APPLICATIONS AND TECHNOLOGY

APPLICATION

Corn in Every Shape and Size

Native Americans grew 700 different kinds of popcorn. Their popcorn plants were a kind of grass with big, hard seeds that exploded when they were heated. People who didn't want to have to explode their corn to eat it chose plants with softer seeds and grew them, and then chose the softest of those seeds to plant. Over hundreds of years, by choosing which plants to grow, people produced what we now eat as corn on the cob.

TECHNOLOGY

Seeing into the Cell

Single-glass lenses, such as the one van Leeuwenhoek used, were available as long ago as 1267. The compound microscope was first made in 1595, but it was over 200 years before it provided clear images. Until the 1930s, all microscopes focused light on objects. Eventually, light microscopes could magnify objects up to 2000 times.

DIFFERENTIATE INSTRUCTION

Below Level Point out how new technology can lead to new discoveries. Discuss which events on the timeline are connected to the use of new technology, for example, microscope and dyes.

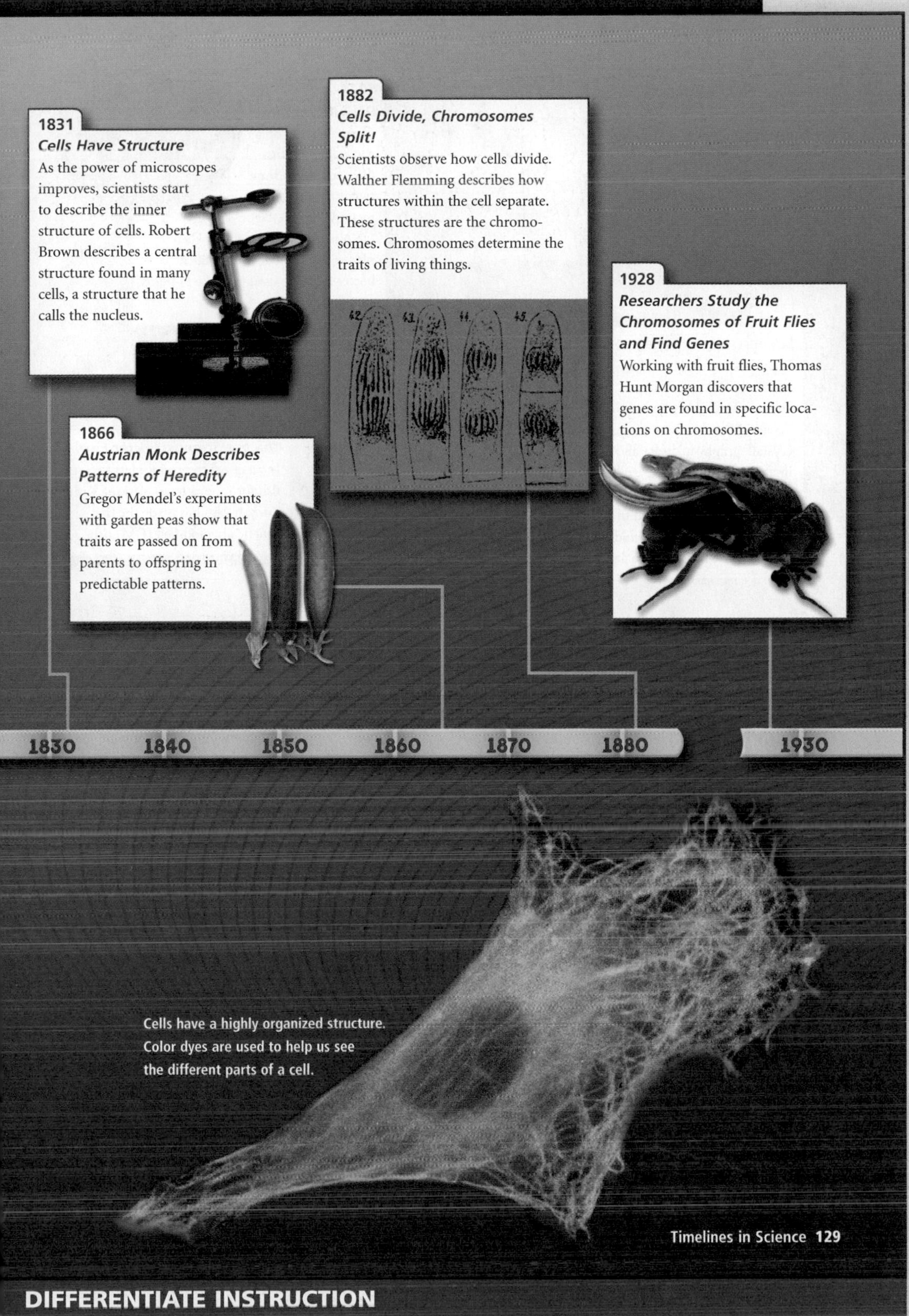

Cells have a highly organized structure. Color dyes are used to help us see the different parts of a cell.

Scientific Process

Scientists must write up and publish their studies for other scientists to review. Thomas Hunt Morgan published two books, *Mechanism of Mendelian Heredity* (1915) and *The Theory of the Gene* (1926). For his work he was awarded the Nobel Prize in physiology or medicine in 1933.

Technology

1866 Although Mendel showed that traits are passed along in predictable patterns, he could not describe what was happening inside the cells. Discuss what might have helped Mendel find out about genes. *use of microscope that would enable him to see chromosomes double and split in dividing cells*

DIFFERENTIATE INSTRUCTION

Advanced Population genetics was given a mathematical basis in 1908 with the formulation of the Hardy-Weinberg law, which describes mathematically the stability of gene and genotype frequencies through a population over successive generations. Have students research this law and prepare a poster on it. They should include the law's assumptions or describe when it does not apply.

Application

1984 China is forging ahead with genetically engineered plants and animals because of the resources needed to feed its large population. China's population is growing, while it has little good farmland. Discuss some methods for increasing crop yield, such as fertilization, pesticides, and use of hybrids. Have students list pros and cons for these methods.

Scientific Process

Building a model is a way to study a hypothesis. Watson and Crick built a model of DNA that accounted for and fit all the known information. The American biochemist Arthur Kornberg later provided experimental proof for their model.

Technology

SEEING MOLECULES Development of the electron microscope began with basic research in physics in the early 20th century, and has continued ever since. Ask: How did this invention open the door to genetic engineering? *It enabled scientists to see the genetic material inside cells and how it behaves.*

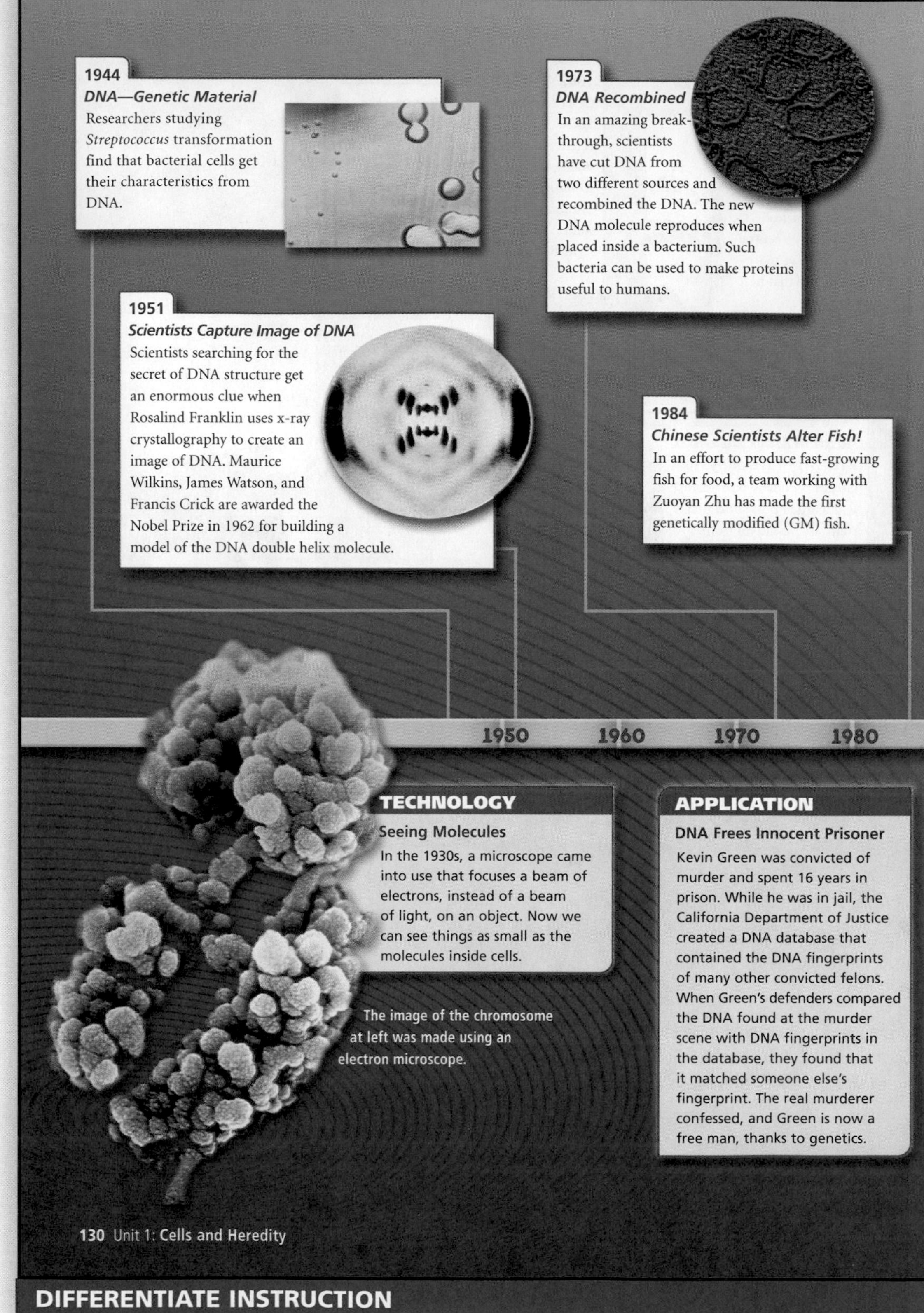

1944
DNA—Genetic Material
Researchers studying *Streptococcus* transformation find that bacterial cells get their characteristics from DNA.

1951
Scientists Capture Image of DNA
Scientists searching for the secret of DNA structure get an enormous clue when Rosalind Franklin uses x-ray crystallography to create an image of DNA. Maurice Wilkins, James Watson, and Francis Crick are awarded the Nobel Prize in 1962 for building a model of the DNA double helix molecule.

1973
DNA Recombined
In an amazing breakthrough, scientists have cut DNA from two different sources and recombined the DNA. The new DNA molecule reproduces when placed inside a bacterium. Such bacteria can be used to make proteins useful to humans.

1984
Chinese Scientists Alter Fish!
In an effort to produce fast-growing fish for food, a team working with Zuoyan Zhu has made the first genetically modified (GM) fish.

1950 1960 1970 1980

TECHNOLOGY
Seeing Molecules
In the 1930s, a microscope came into use that focuses a beam of electrons, instead of a beam of light, on an object. Now we can see things as small as the molecules inside cells.

The image of the chromosome at left was made using an electron microscope.

APPLICATION
DNA Frees Innocent Prisoner
Kevin Green was convicted of murder and spent 16 years in prison. While he was in jail, the California Department of Justice created a DNA database that contained the DNA fingerprints of many other convicted felons. When Green's defenders compared the DNA found at the murder scene with DNA fingerprints in the database, they found that it matched someone else's fingerprint. The real murderer confessed, and Green is now a free man, thanks to genetics.

130 Unit 1: Cells and Heredity

DIFFERENTIATE INSTRUCTION

Below Level Have students draw a cause-and-effect graphic organizer with the discovery of the light microscope as the cause and some of the research that resulted as effects.

1984
Living Things Have Genetic Fingerprints
Human fingers have their own unique fingerprints. In a similar way, the DNA of different people has its own unique patterns. These DNA fingerprints are compared here.

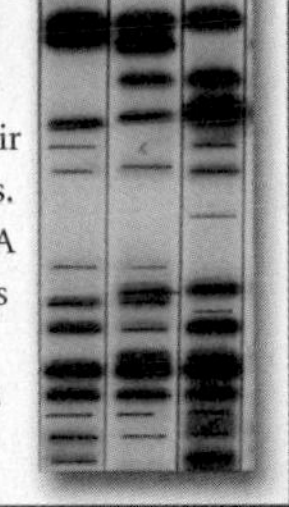

2000
Scientists Sequence Human Genome
Two groups of researchers, Celera and the Human Genome Project, succeed in publishing the first draft of the sequence of DNA for all the chromosomes in the human body.

RESOURCE CENTER
CLASSZONE.COM
Find recent genetics updates.

1990 2000 Today

APPLICATION

Saved by a Gene Donor

In 1986 a baby girl named Ashanti DeSilva was born. One single mistake in her DNA meant that Ashanti's body could not make an important disease-fighting protein.

In 1981, researchers had figured out how to move a working gene from one mammal to another. Ashanti became the first person ever to receive a gene from someone else. Ashanti's doctors injected some of her white blood cells with healthy copies of the sick gene. Now her white blood cells worked. Researchers and doctors are trying to apply the same techniques to other genetic disorders. There is still much work to be done.

INTO THE FUTURE

Genetics is a young science. The timeline spans 350 years, but the real study of genetics began in 1900 with the rediscovery of the work of Gregor Mendel. Since then, scientists have determined the structure and function of DNA—and ways to use this knowledge.

In medicine, genetics is used to identify genes that play a role in inherited diseases. Questions remain about how this knowledge can be used to treat or even prevent disease.

In agriculture, genetics is used to modify the genes of plant and animal stocks to give them desirable traits, such as resistance to disease. Questions remain about what effect modified genes might have once they enter a population of plants or animals.

In biology, genetics is used to determine how different types of organisms have changed over time and how one species relates to another. Questions remain about whether similar genes found in different organisms behave in the same way.

In society, genetic profiles are used to help solve crimes or make identifications. Questions remain about how to protect individuals and their personal information.

ACTIVITIES

Reliving History

Use a hand lens or microscope to study water from a pond or puddle. See if your sample contains structures similar to those drawn by van Leeuwenhoek in 1674.

Writing About Science: Biography

Sharing information is important to scientific discovery. Learn more about individuals or groups involved in the discovery of DNA structure or sequencing the human genome. How important was cooperation in their work?

DIFFERENTIATE INSTRUCTION

Advanced Have students research Rosalind Franklin and X-ray crystallography. Based on their findings, students could debate whether Franklin should have shared in the Nobel Prize, had she been alive when it was awarded.

Sharing Results

Many people believe that Rosalind Franklin should have shared in the Nobel Prize won by Watson and Crick, because Wilkins, her superior at the lab where she worked, shared some of her data with them without Franklin's permission or knowledge. Because she died before the prize was awarded, the question became moot because the prize is never awarded posthumously.

INTO THE FUTURE

Point out that the field of genetics presents humans with some difficult choices and that, as the technology expands, the choices will become more numerous. Have students brainstorm what some of these choices will be.

ACTIVITIES

Reliving History

Students can collect samples of water from many places, including puddles from different locations, fountains, and ponds in a park or at home. Have students chart their results and look for differences. If the same body of water is available for more than a day, they could take samples on different days to see how the organisms in the water change with time.

Writing About Science: Biography

Students will discover that there were many people involved in trying to discover the structure of DNA. In fact, there was almost a race to the finish. Even so, many researchers willingly contributed to the effort. Because of this, Watson and Crick knew what all the pieces of the DNA puzzle were. They just needed to put the puzzle together in the right way.

Technology Resources

Students can visit **ClassZone.com** for current news about genetics.

CHAPTER

DNA and Modern Genetics

Life Science UNIFYING PRINCIPLES

PRINCIPLE 1
All living things share common characteristics.

PRINCIPLE 2
All living things share common needs.

PRINCIPLE 3
Living things meet their needs through interactions with the environment.

PRINCIPLE 4
The types and numbers of living things change over time.

Unit 1: Cells and Heredity BIG IDEAS

CHAPTER 1
The Cell
All living things are made up of cells.

CHAPTER 2
How Cells Function
All cells need energy and materials for life processes.

CHAPTER 3
Cell Division
Organisms grow, reproduce, and maintain themselves through cell division.

CHAPTER 4
Patterns of Heredity
In sexual reproduction, genes are passed from parents to offspring in predictable patterns.

CHAPTER 5
DNA and Modern Genetics
DNA is a set of instructions for making cell parts.

CHAPTER 5 KEY CONCEPTS

SECTION 1

DNA and RNA are required to make proteins.

1. DNA is the information molecule.
2. RNA is needed to make proteins.

SECTION 2

Changes in DNA can produce variation.

1. DNA sequences can change.
2. Mutations can cause genetic disorders.
3. Cancer is a genetic disorder that affects the cell cycle.

SECTION 3

Modern genetics uses DNA technology.

1. Changes in DNA can change an organism.
2. There are risks and benefits associated with genetic engineering.
3. DNA technology has many applications.

T The Big Idea Flow Chart is available on p. T33 in the **UNIT TRANSPARENCY BOOK.**

Previewing Content

SECTION

DNA and RNA are required to make proteins. pp. 135–143

1. DNA is the information molecule.

- DNA stores the information necessary for a cell to put together the correct sequence of amino acids needed to produce specific proteins.
- DNA is a spiral molecule made up of nucleotide bases: adenine, thymine, cytosine, and guanine. It is the sequence of these bases that forms the code for making proteins.
- When a cell divides, DNA **replicates,** or makes a copy of itself. The DNA molecule separates and free nucleotides match up to each open strand. DNA replication is shown in the diagram.

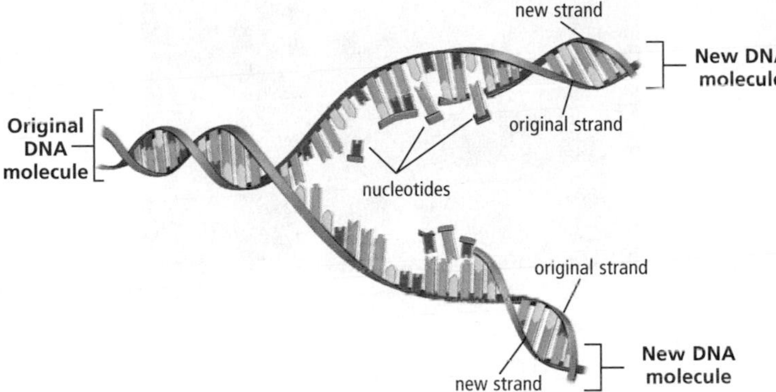

2. RNA is needed to make proteins.

- Three kinds of **RNA** are used to make proteins: messenger RNA, transfer RNA, and ribosomal RNA. Transferring information from DNA to RNA is known as transcription. During this process, a strand of DNA molecule is used to make a single strand of mRNA.
- The assembly of amino acids in their proper sequence to form a protein molecule is known as translation. Proteins are made on ribosomes, structures in the cytoplasm that are made up of ribosomal RNA and proteins.

SECTION

Changes in DNA can produce variation. pp. 144–149

1. DNA sequences can change.

Variations in DNA are what give organisms different characteristics. Any change in DNA is a **mutation.** Mutations can cause no effect, have a minor effect, or a great effect. Some mutations are harmful, such as those that result in genetic disorders. Other mutations can be beneficial if they improve an organism's ability to survive or resist disease.

2. Mutations can cause genetic disorders.

- Mutations that affect the normal functioning of a cell can result in genetic diseases that are passed from parent to offspring. Genetic disorders include Tay-Sachs disease, cystic fibrosis, albinism, and sickle cell disease.
- **Pedigrees** are diagrams of family relationships that include two or more generations. Genetic diseases, such as sickle cell disease, can be traced through a pedigree.

3. Cancer is a genetic disorder that affects the cell cycle.

Cancer is characterized by uncontrolled cell division. Most cancers are caused by mutations to DNA that occur during a person's lifetime. Environmental pollutants called carcinogens cause other cancers. Ultraviolet radiation and x-rays also cause cancer.

Cancer cells such as those shown in the photograph often result from mutations to DNA.

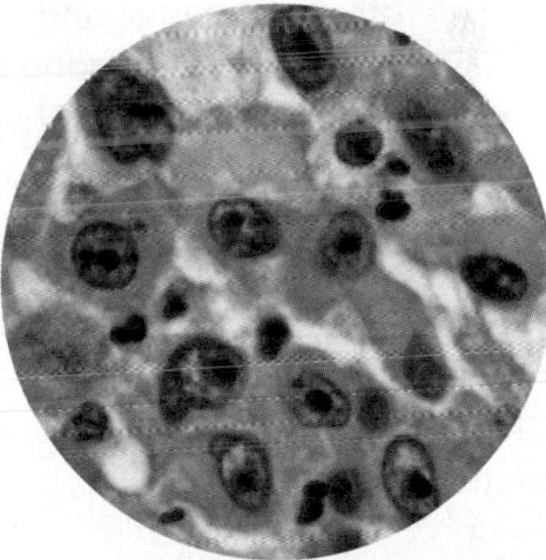

Common Misconceptions

MISCONCEPTION DATABASE
CLASSZONE.COM Background on student misconceptions

DNA, GENES, AND CHROMOSOMES Some students do not understand the relationship among DNA, genes, and chromosomes. Middle-school students will often use the three terms interchangeably. In fact the three exist in a hierarchy. Chromosomes are the form DNA takes when cells divide. DNA is the name of the molecule that makes up each chromosome. Each DNA molecule in turn contains genes, the smaller units of heredity. It may be helpful for students to think of the three in terms of bundles, strands, and beads, or to use some other visual model.

 This misconception is addressed on p. 137.

MODELS OF THE NATURAL WORLD Most middle-school students have some confusion about the accuracy of the various models that scientists use to represent the natural world—from models of molecules and cells, to models of weather patterns and populations. There is never a one-to-one correspondence with the model and that which is represented. There are always attributes that differ between the two.

 This misconception is addressed in the Teacher Demo on p. 138.

Previewing Content

SECTION

Modern genetics uses DNA technology. pp. 150–155

1. Changes in DNA can change an organism.
Selective breeding is controlled by crossing two organisms with desirable traits to produce offspring with those traits. Selective breeding does not produce changes in DNA. **Genetic engineering** is a process that allows humans to change the DNA of an organism by isolating it, changing, and returning it to the organism or another organism. The genetically modified, or transgenic, organisms have traits that are desirable.

2. There are risks and benefits associated with genetic engineering.
Genetic engineering allows scientists to produce organisms such as plants that produce more food, or are resistant to certain diseases or insects, or animals that are modified to grow faster. Scientists, however, are uncertain how the genetically modified organisms might affect natural populations if they are interbred.

3. DNA technology has many applications.
- DNA technology can be used to make foods more nutritious, produce better drugs for treating diseases, or screen for genetic disorders.
- DNA profiles, or fingerprints, are now being used to solve crimes. These profiles are unique and are based on about ten regions of DNA known to vary among individuals.
- Scientists studying **genomes,** all of the genetic material in an organism, have been working toward sequencing all the nucleotide pairs in human DNA and identify about 30,000 genes within the human genome.
- **Cloning** is a technology that makes copies of DNA. It has been used to produce drugs to fight disease, as well as to affect the birth of animals that are genetically identical to one another.

The first cloned mammal, a sheep named Dolly.

Previewing Labs

Lab Generator CD-ROM
Edit these Pupil Edition labs and generate alternative labs.

EXPLORE the BIG idea

What Is the Pattern? p. 133 Students use cards to model the patterns for DNA sequences.	**TIME** 10 minutes **MATERIALS** index cards, marker or pencil
What Vegetable Is That? p. 133 Students observe a broccoflower to describe its properties.	**TIME** 10 minutes **MATERIALS** broccoflower
Internet Activity: Human Genome, p. 133 Students find out how scientists put together a sequence of the DNA in the human genome.	**TIME** 20 minutes **MATERIALS** computer with Internet access

SECTION 1

EXPLORE Templates, p. 135 Students explore relationships among characters to see how a template works.	**TIME** 15 minutes **MATERIALS** paper, pencil
CHAPTER INVESTIGATION **Extract and Observe DNA,** pp. 142–143 Students use simple chemicals that break down the membranes of a cell to extract DNA from raw wheat germ.	**TIME** 40 minutes **MATERIALS** raw wheat germ, scoop, test tube, warm distilled water, detergent solution, salt solution, cold ethyl or isopropyl alcohol, bent paper clip

SECTION 2

EXPLORE Codes, p. 144 Students create codes based on the alphabet to explore the concept of coding.	**TIME** 15 minutes **MATERIALS** pencil, paper
INVESTIGATE Neutral Mutations, p. 146 Students use newspaper to model genetic mutations.	**TIME** 15 minutes **MATERIALS** newspaper, pen, handful of paper-punch circles

Additional INVESTIGATION, DNA Fingerprinting Simulation, A, B, & C, pp. 297–305; Teacher Instructions, pp. 308–309

Previewing Chapter Resources

INTEGRATED TECHNOLOGY | **LABS AND ACTIVITIES**

CHAPTER 5
DNA and Modern Genetics

Integrated Technology

 **CLASSZONE.COM**
- eEdition Plus
- EasyPlanner Plus
- Misconception Database
- Content Review
- Test Practice
- Resource Centers
- Visualization
- Internet Activity: Human Genome
- Math Tutorial

 **SCILINKS.ORG**

SCI LINKS

 **CD-ROMS**
- eEdition
- EasyPlanner
- Power Presentations
- Content Review
- Lab Generator
- Test Generator

 **AUDIO CDS**
- Audio Readings
- Audio Readings in Spanish

Labs and Activities

 EXPLORE the Big Idea, p. 133
- What Is the Pattern?
- What Vegetable Is That?
- Internet Activity: Human Genome

 **UNIT RESOURCE BOOK**
Unit Projects, pp. 5–10

 **Lab Generator CD-ROM**
Generate customized labs.

SECTION

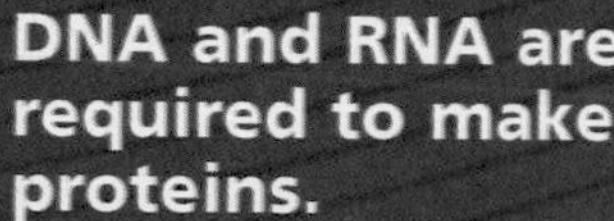

1 DNA and RNA are required to make proteins.
pp. 135–143

Time: 3 periods (1.5 blocks)

 Lesson Plan, pp. 250–251

- **RESOURCE CENTER,** DNA
- **VISUALIZATION,** Protein Synthesis

 **UNIT TRANSPARENCY BOOK**
- Big Idea Flow Chart, p. T33
- Daily Vocabulary Scaffolding, p. T34
- Note-Taking Model, p. T35
- 3-Minute Warm-Up, p. T36
- "Translation" Visual, p. T38

- EXPLORE Templates, p. 135
- CHAPTER INVESTIGATION, Extract and Observe DNA, pp. 142–143

UNIT RESOURCE BOOK
CHAPTER INVESTIGATION, Extract and Observe DNA, pp. 288–296

SECTION

2 Changes in DNA can produce variation.
pp. 144–149

Time: 2 periods (1 block)

 Lesson Plan, pp. 260–261

- **RESOURCE CENTER,** Mutations
- **MATH TUTORIAL**

 **UNIT TRANSPARENCY BOOK**
- Daily Vocabulary Scaffolding, p. T34
- 3-Minute Warm-Up, p. T36

- EXPLORE Codes, p. 144
- INVESTIGATE Neutral Mutations, p. 146
- Math in Science, p. 149

UNIT RESOURCE BOOK
- Datasheet, Neutral Mutations, p. 269
- Math Support, p. 286
- Math Practice, p. 287

SECTION

3 Modern genetics uses DNA technology.
pp. 150–155

Time: 3 periods (1.5 blocks)

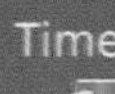 Lesson Plan, pp. 271–272

 **RESOURCE CENTER,** DNA Technology

UNIT TRANSPARENCY BOOK
- Big Idea Flow Chart, p. T33
- Daily Vocabulary Scaffolding, p. T34
- 3-Minute Warm-Up, p. T37
- Chapter Outline, pp. T39–T40

 Extreme Science, p. 155

 **UNIT RESOURCE BOOK**
Additional INVESTIGATION, DNA Fingerprinting Simulation, A, B, & C, pp. 297–305

KEY TO ICONS

 CD/CD-ROM
 Teacher Edition
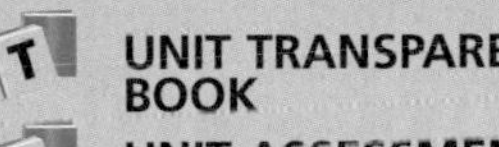 UNIT TRANSPARENCY BOOK
 SPANISH ASSESSMENT BOOK
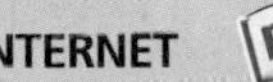 INTERNET
 Pupil Edition
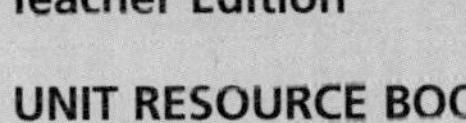 UNIT RESOURCE BOOK
UNIT ASSESSMENT BOOK
SCIENCE TOOLKIT

READING AND REINFORCEMENT	ASSESSMENT	STANDARDS
 • Choose Your Own Strategy, B18–27 • Supporting Main Ideas, C42 • Daily Vocabulary Scaffolding, H1–8  **UNIT RESOURCE BOOK** • Vocabulary Practice, pp. 283–284 • Decoding Support, p. 285 • Summarizing the Chapter, pp. 306–307  **Audio Readings CD** Listen to Pupil Edition.  **Audio Readings in Spanish CD** Listen to Pupil Edition in Spanish.	 • Chapter Review, pp.156–158 • Standardized Test Practice, p. 159  **UNIT ASSESSMENT BOOK** • Diagnostic Test, pp. 77–78 • Chapter Test, A, B, & C, pp. 82–93 • Alternative Assessment, pp. 94–95 • Unit Test, A, B, & C, pp. 96–107  • Spanish Chapter Test, pp. 17–20 • Spanish Unit Test, pp. 21–24 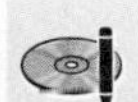 **Test Generator CD-ROM** Generate customized tests.  **Lab Generator CD-ROM** Rubrics for Labs	National Standards A.1–8, A.9.a–c, A.9.e–g, C.2.d–e, F.5.c, G.1.b See p. 132 for the standards.
 **UNIT RESOURCE BOOK** • Reading Study Guide, A & B, pp. 252–255 • Spanish Reading Study Guide, pp. 256–257 • Challenge and Extension, p. 258 • Reinforcing Key Concepts, p. 259	 Ongoing Assessment, pp. 136–138, 141  Section 5.1 Review, p. 141  **UNIT ASSESSMENT BOOK** Section 5.1 Quiz, p. 79	National Standards A.1–7, A.9.a–b, A.9.e–g, C.2.d–e, G.1.b
UNIT RESOURCE BOOK • Reading Study Guide, A & B, pp. 262–265 • Spanish Reading Study Guide, pp. 266–267 • Challenge and Extension, p. 268 • Reinforcing Key Concepts, p. 270	 Ongoing Assessment, pp. 145–148  Section 5.2 Review, p. 148  **UNIT ASSESSMENT BOOK** Section 5.2 Quiz, p. 80	National Standards A.2–8, A.9.a–c, A.9.e–f, C.2.d–e, G.1.b
 **UNIT RESOURCE BOOK** • Reading Study Guide, A & B, pp. 273–276 • Spanish Reading Study Guide, pp. 277–278 • Challenge and Extension, p. 279 • Reinforcing Key Concepts, p. 280 • Challenge Reading, pp. 281–282	Ongoing Assessment, pp. 150–154  Section 5.3 Review, p. 154  **UNIT ASSESSMENT BOOK** Section 5.3 Quiz, p. 81	National Standards A.3–7, C.2.d–e, F.5.c, G.1.b

Previewing Resources for Differentiated Instruction

CHAPTER INVESTIGATION

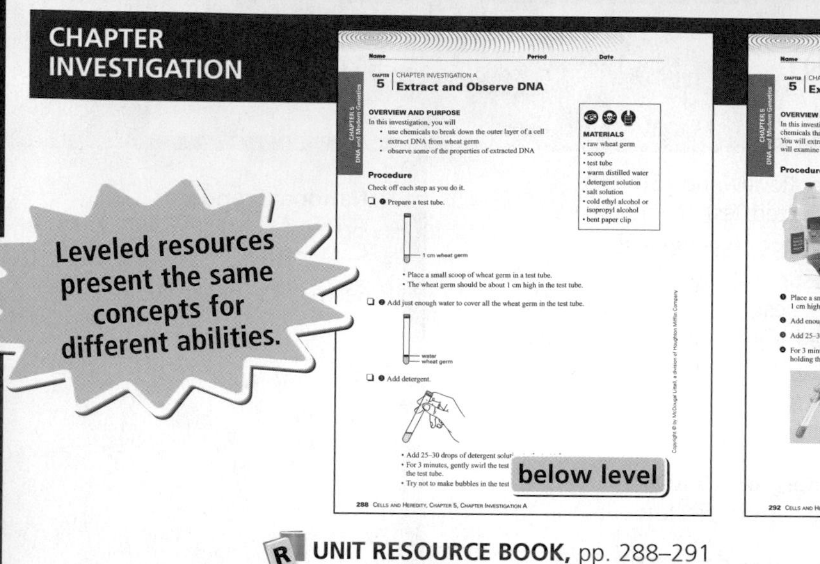

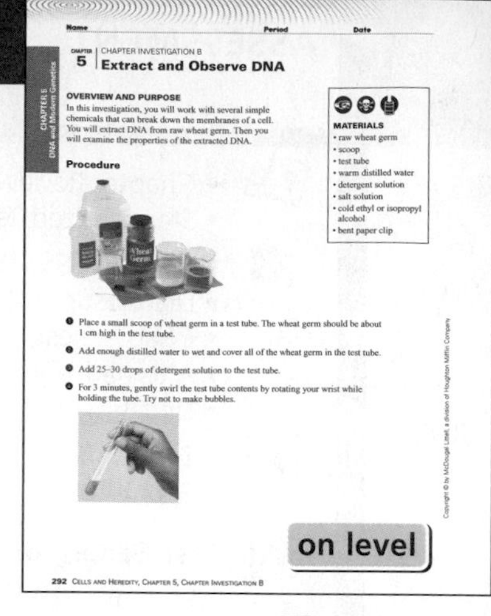

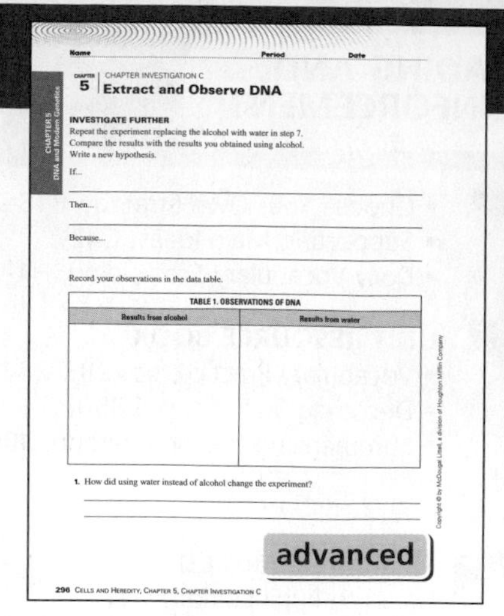

R **UNIT RESOURCE BOOK,** pp. 288–291

R pp. 292–295

R pp. 292–296

READING STUDY GUIDE

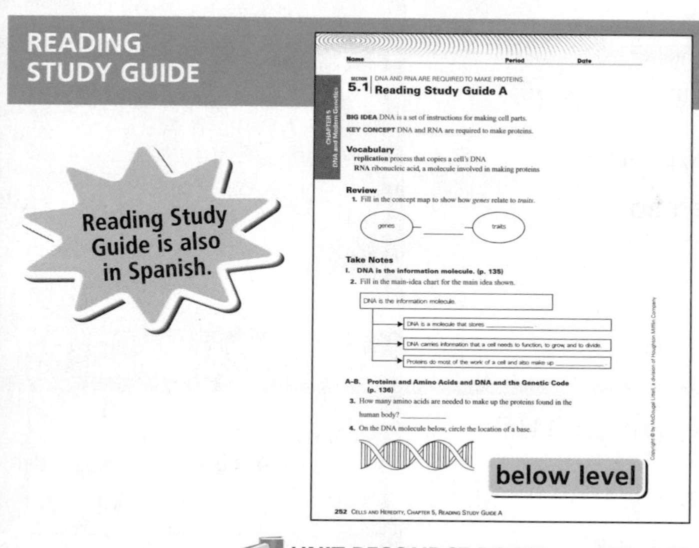

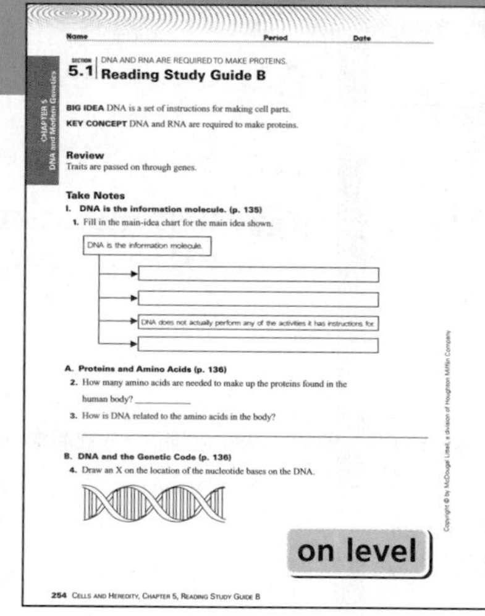

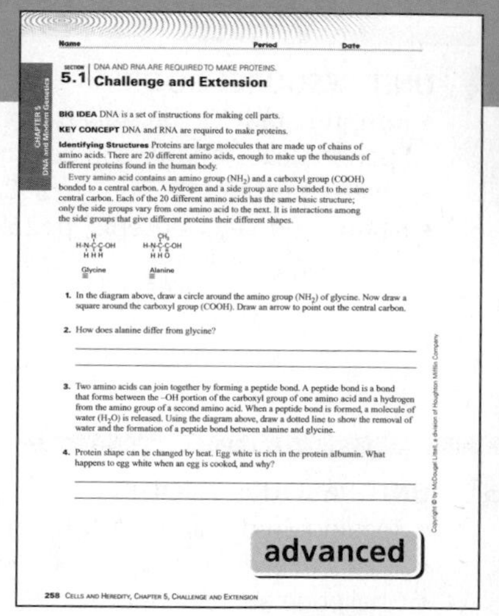

R **UNIT RESOURCE BOOK,** pp. 252–253

R pp. 254–255

R p. 258

CHAPTER TEST

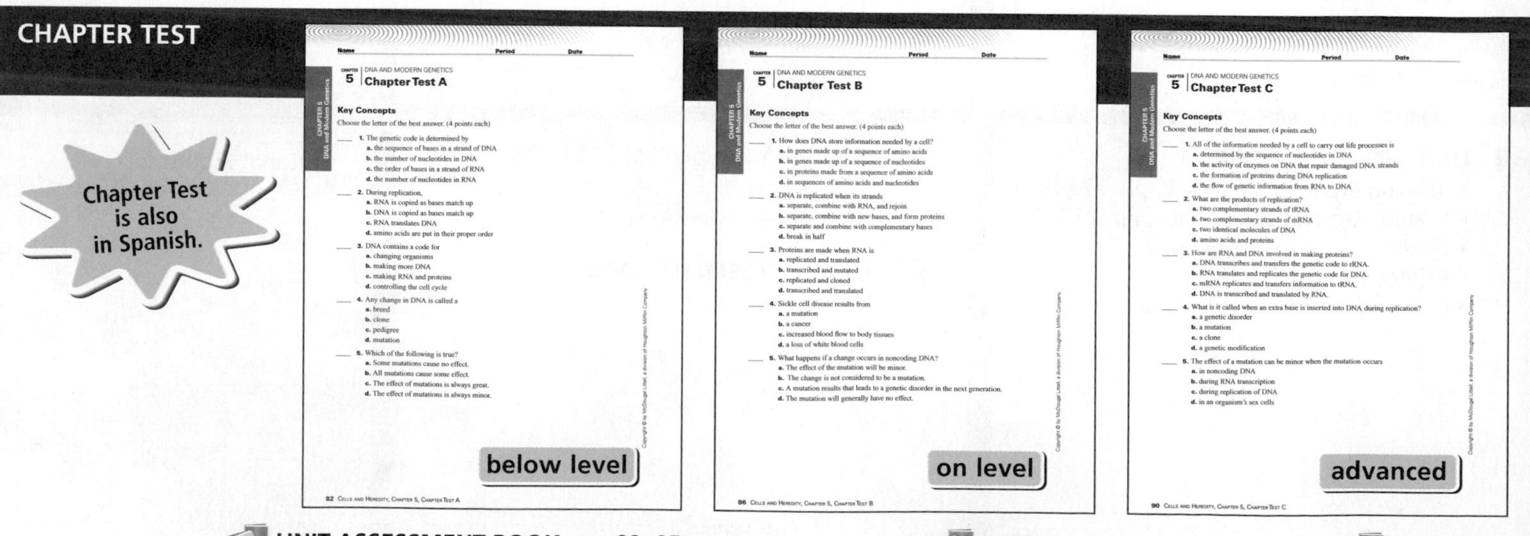

A **UNIT ASSESSMENT BOOK,** pp. 82–85

A pp. 86–89

A pp. 90–93

TECHNOLOGY

VISUAL CONTENT

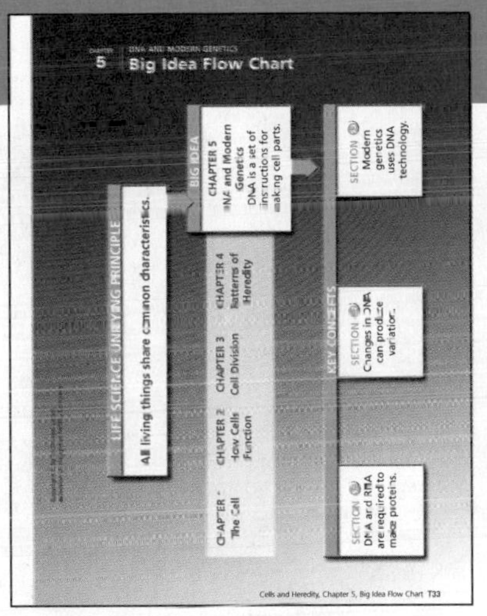

UNIT TRANSPARENCY BOOK, p. T33

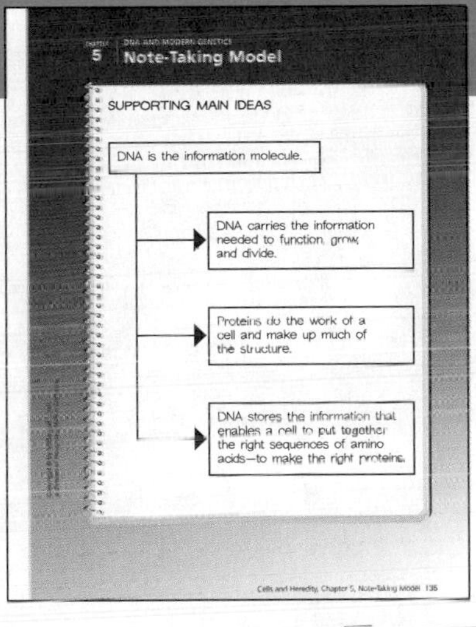

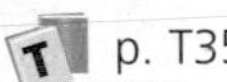

p. T35

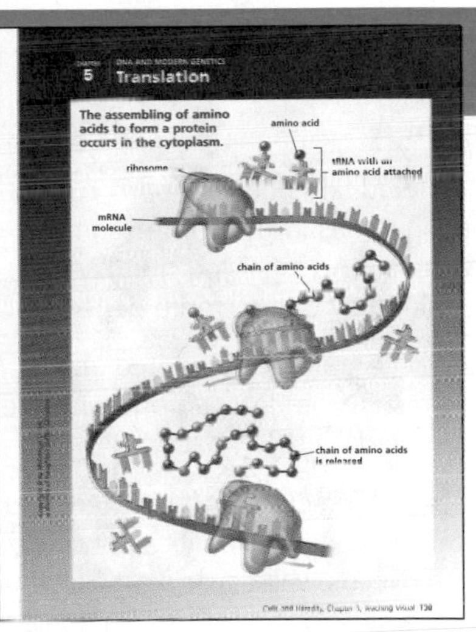

p. T38

MORE SUPPORT

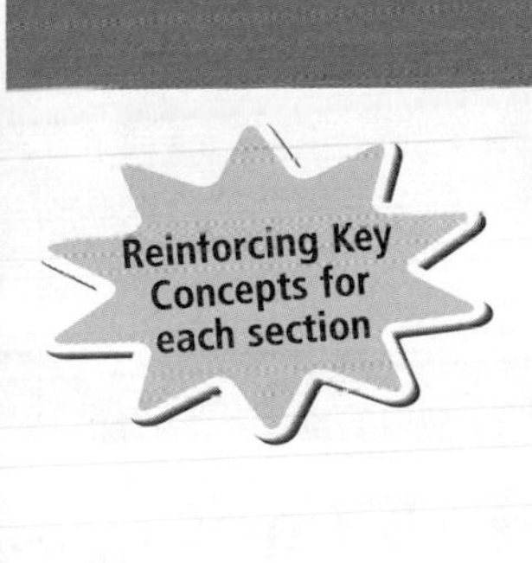

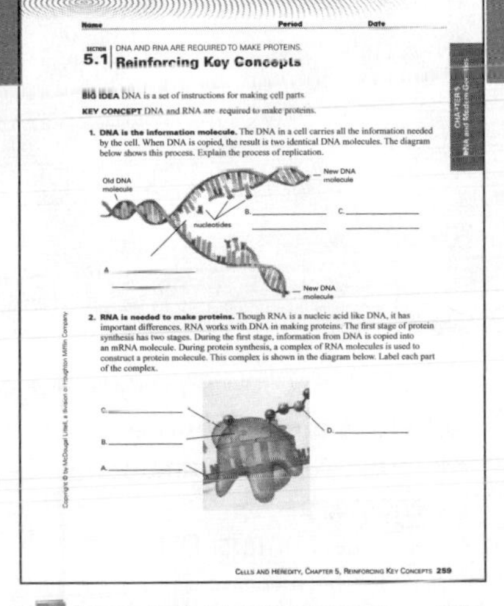

UNIT RESOURCE BOOK, p. 259

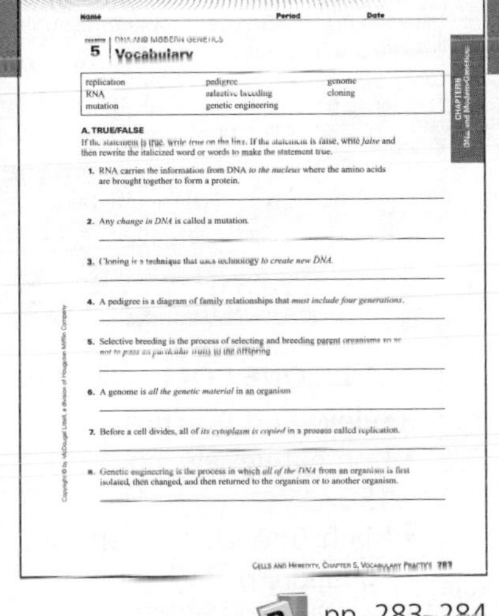

pp. 283–284

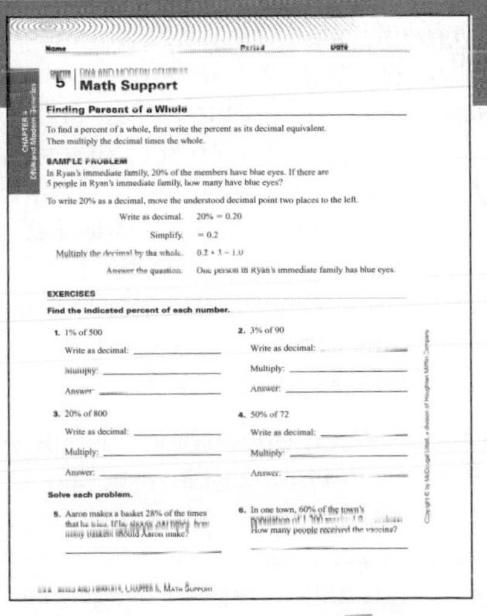

p. 286

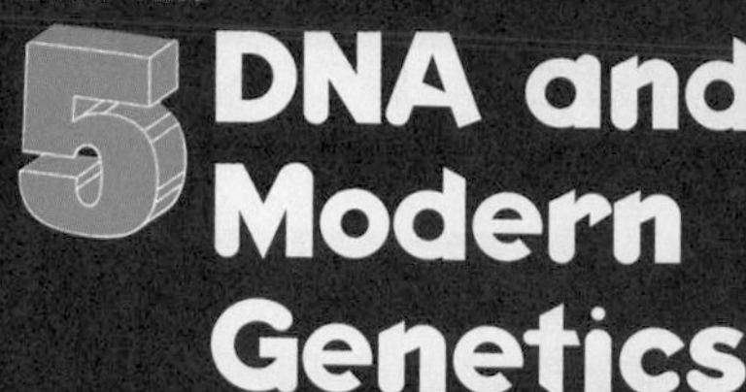

CHAPTER

DNA and Modern Genetics

INTRODUCE

the BIG idea

Have students look at the photograph of a DNA model and discuss how the question in the box links to the Big Idea. Ask:

- What does the model in the photograph represent?
- How large do you think the object modeled in this picture is?

National Science Education Standards

Content

C.2.d Hereditary information is contained in genes in the chromosomes of each cell. An inherited trait can be determined by one or more genes.

C.2.e Some traits are inherited and others result from interactions with the environment.

F.5.c Technology influences society and can cause economic, political, and social change. Needs, values, and attitudes influence decisions about technology.

Process

A.1–8 Identify questions that can be answered through scientific investigations; design and conduct an investigation; use tools to gather and interpret data; use evidence to describe, predict, explain, model; think critically to make relationships between evidence and explanation; recognize different explanations and predictions; communicate scientific procedures and explanations; use mathematics.

A.9.a–c, A.9.e–g Understand scientific inquiry by using different investigations, methods, mathematics, and explanations based on logic, evidence, and skepticism. Data often results in new investigations.

G.1.b Science requires different abilities.

CHAPTER

DNA and Modern Genetics

the BIG idea

DNA is a set of instructions for making cell parts.

Key Concepts

SECTION 1

DNA and RNA are required to make proteins.
Learn about DNA, RNA, and protein synthesis.

SECTION 2

Changes in DNA can produce variation.
Learn about the effects of changes in DNA and how some changes can cause genetic disorders.

SECTION 3

Modern genetics uses DNA technology.
Learn about some applications of DNA technology and the Human Genome Project.

Internet Preview

CLASSZONE.COM

Chapter 5 online resources: Content Review, Visualization, four Resource Centers, Math Tutorial, Test Practice

What can a model of DNA show you about its structure?

INTERNET PREVIEW

CLASSZONE.COM For student use with the following pages:

Review and Practice

- Content Review, pp. 134, 156
- Math Tutorial: The Percent Equation, p. 149
- Test Practice, p. 159

Activities and Resources

- Internet Activity: Human Genome, p. 133
- Resource Centers: DNA, p. 136; Mutations, p. 145; DNA Technology, p. 153
- Visualization: Protein Synthesis, p. 141

Genetics **Code: MDL035**

EXPLORE the BIG idea

What Is the Pattern?

Sometimes by looking at the parts of a whole you can guess how the pieces fit together. Some evidence for the structure of DNA came when people noticed that certain types of chemical subunits came in pairs. Try this activity with a friend. Take 9 index cards and write 2 letters, A T or C G, on each card. Now cut the pairs in half and give your friend the individual pieces. See if he or she can find the pattern.

Observe and Think How long did it take your friend to see the pattern? Were there any other clues that he or she used?

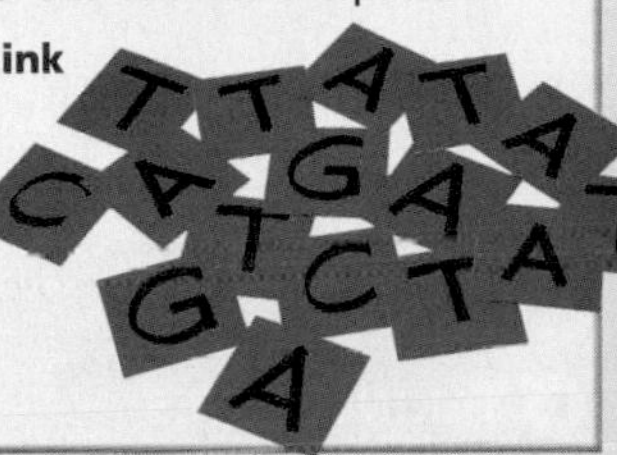

What Vegetable Is That?

Buy a broccoflower from your local supermarket. Describe what it looks like, what it tastes like, and how it smells.

Observe and Think What properties of each vegetable does the broccoflower have? What gives an organism its traits?

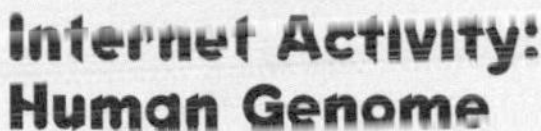

Internet Activity: Human Genome

Go to **ClassZone.com** to find out how scientists put together a sequence of the DNA in the human genome.

Observe and Think What are the benefits of having a map of the human genome?

NSTA scilinks.org SCILINKS

Genetics Code: MDL035

TEACHING WITH TECHNOLOGY

Slide Show Software Have students use slide show software to create a multimedia presentation about DNA, how it is replicated, and how RNA is used to make proteins. Students can create diagrams and drawings based on the illustrations on pp. 136–140.

Video Cameras Students could use video cameras to record the steps of the Chapter Investigation on pp. 142–143. Students can act as science news reporters, narrating the events of the procedure, then giving an analysis of what happened.

EXPLORE the BIG idea

These inquiry-based activities are appropriate for use at home or as a supplement to classroom instruction.

What Is the Pattern?

PURPOSE To model the patterns for DNA sequences.

TIPS *10 min.* Students should write the letters on opposite ends of the cards. To make it easier, they can use a jigsaw puzzle style of edge when cutting the cards.

Answers will vary. Students should recognize that A is always paired with T and that C is always paired with G.

REVISIT after p. 136.

What Vegetable Is That?

PURPOSE To observe the properties of a broccoflower.

TIPS *10 min.* If possible, bring to class broccoli and cauliflower so that students can see each. Have students share their observations. An alternate exploration could be done with a tangelo, which combines traits of an orange and a tangerine.

Answer: The vegetable was formed from a combination of broccoli and cauliflower. It has the color of cauliflower and the texture of broccoli. Genes give an organism its traits.

REVISIT after p. 151.

Internet Activity: Human Genome

PURPOSE To find out how scientists put together a sequence of the DNA in the human genome.

TIP *20 min.* Have students compare their observations.

Answer: Scientists will be better able to identify and locate different genes.

REVISIT after p. 153.

PREPARE

CONCEPT REVIEW

Activate Prior Knowledge

- Ask students to name some traits that all people generally share. *Sample answer: All have a heart, a brain, a skeleton, skin, and so on.*
- Have students predict how people get their traits. Write down their predictions to review at the end of the chapter.

TAKING NOTES

Supporting Main Ideas

Students can rely on the blue and red headings to form the basic headings for the main ideas. Supporting main ideas to put under the headings can be found in the text, photos, and captions. Encourage students to use their supporting main ideas as a study guide.

Vocabulary Strategy

Ask students to share vocabulary strategies for each new vocabulary term. Students can add to their four squares, word triangles, frame games, or magnet words as they read through the chapter.

Vocabulary and Note-Taking Resources

- Vocabulary Practice, pp. 283–284
- Decoding Support, p. 285

- Daily Vocabulary Scaffolding, p. T34
- Note-Taking Model, p. T35

- Choose Your Own Strategy, B18–27
- Supporting Main Ideas, C42
- Daily Vocabulary Scaffolding, H1–8

CHAPTER 5

Getting Ready to Learn

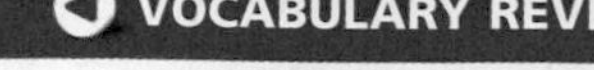

CONCEPT REVIEW

- Traits are controlled by genes on chromosomes.
- Genes can be dominant or recessive.
- Cells have DNA, RNA, and proteins.

VOCABULARY REVIEW

organelle p. 20
protein p. 43
gene p. 102
technology *See Glossary.*

CONTENT REVIEW
CLASSZONE.COM
Review concepts and vocabulary.

TAKING NOTES

SUPPORTING MAIN IDEAS

Make a chart to show main ideas and the information that supports them. Copy each blue heading; then add supporting information, such as reasons, explanations, and examples.

CHOOSE YOUR OWN STRATEGY

Take notes about new vocabulary terms using one or more of the strategies from earlier chapters—**four square, word triangle, frame game,** or **magnet word.** Feel free to mix and match the strategies, or use an entirely different vocabulary strategy.

See the Note-Taking Handbook on pages R45–R51.

SCIENCE NOTEBOOK

DNA sequences can change.
- Variations in DNA make one organism different from another.
- Human DNA has 6 billion base pairs; yeast DNA has 12 million base pairs.

134 Unit 1: Cells and Heredity

CHECK READINESS

Administer the Diagnostic Test to determine students' readiness for new science content and their mastery of requisite math skills.

 Diagnostic Test, pp. 77–78

Technology Resources

Students needing content and math skills should visit **ClassZone.com**.

- **CONTENT REVIEW**
- **MATH TUTORIAL**

 **CONTENT REVIEW CD-ROM**

KEY CONCEPT

DNA and RNA are required to make proteins.

BEFORE, you learned

- Traits pass from parents to offspring in predictable patterns
- Traits are passed on through genes
- In sexual reproduction, offspring get half their genes from each parent

NOW, you will learn

- How the structure of DNA stores information the cell needs
- How DNA is copied
- How RNA uses the information from DNA to make proteins

VOCABULARY

replication p. 137
RNA p. 138

EXPLORE Templates

How does a template work?

PROCEDURE

1. Write a set of rules to describe how the characters in line A relate to the characters in line B.

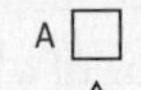   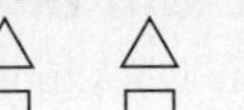

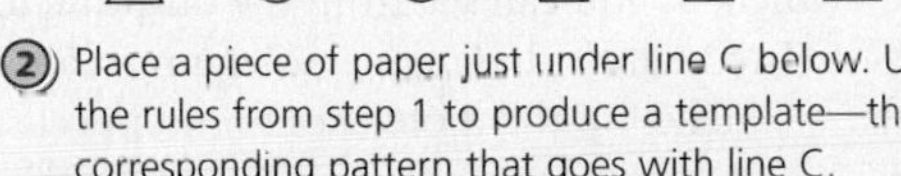

2. Place a piece of paper just under line C below. Use the rules from step 1 to produce a template—the corresponding pattern that goes with line C.

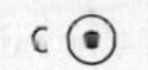  

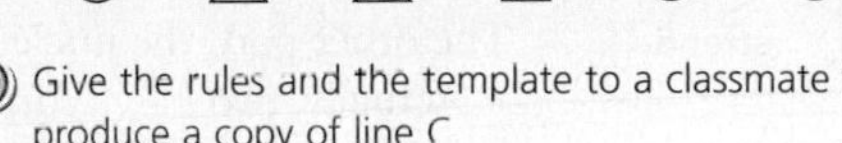

3. Give the rules and the template to a classmate to produce a copy of line C.

MATERIALS

- paper
- pencil

WHAT DO YOU THINK?

What is a template and how does it differ from a copy?

DNA is the information molecule.

SUPPORTING MAIN IDEAS
Make a chart of information supporting the main idea: *DNA is the information molecule.*

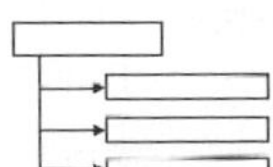

DNA is a molecule that stores information—that's all it does. You could compare the information in DNA to the books in your local library. You might find a book describing how to bake a cake, make a model sailboat, or beat your favorite computer game. The books, however, don't actually do any of those things—you do. The "books" in the DNA "library" carry all the information that a cell needs to function, to grow, and to divide. However, DNA doesn't do any of those things. Proteins do most of the work of a cell and also make up much of the structure of a cell.

5.1 FOCUS

Set Learning Goals

Students will

- Describe how the structure of DNA stores information the cell needs.
- Explain how DNA is copied.
- Explain how RNA uses the information from DNA to make proteins.

3-Minute Warm-Up

Display Transparency 36 or copy this exercise on the board:

Decide if these statements are true. If not true, correct them.

1. Genes are units of heredity that determine traits. *true*
2. A genotype refers to the observable characteristics of an organism. *A phenotype refers to the observable characteristics of an organism.*
3. A dominant trait is expressed only if two alleles are present on a chromosome. *A dominant trait is expressed if one or two alleles are present on a chromosome.*

 3-Minute Warm-Up, p. T36

5.1 MOTIVATE

EXPLORE Templates

PURPOSE To explore how a template works

TIPS *15 min.* Have students compare their rules. Students should note that squares always match up with triangles and that blank circles always match up with circles with dots.

WHAT DO YOU THINK? *A copy is a duplicate of what already exists. A template forms a pattern that enables one to make a copy. It is not the same thing as a copy.*

RESOURCES FOR DIFFERENTIATED INSTRUCTION

Below Level

UNIT RESOURCE BOOK

- Reading Study Guide A, pp. 252–253
- Decoding Support, p. 285

AUDIO CDS

Advanced

UNIT RESOURCE BOOK

Challenge and Extension, p. 258

English Learners

UNIT RESOURCE BOOK

Spanish Reading Study Guide, pp. 256–257

- Audio Readings in Spanish
- Audio Readings (English)

5.1 INSTRUCT

Teach from Visuals

To help students interpret the illustration of a DNA molecule, review the names of the nucleotide subunits with students. Then ask:

- What makes up the rungs of the DNA "ladder?" *the nucleotide bases*
- Why do certain nucleotides always pair with certain others? *They have a specific shape and size that allows them to match up with each other.*

Metacognitive Strategy

Have students devise a strategy for remembering which two nucleotides pair together.

EXPLORE the BIG idea

Revisit "What Is the Pattern?" on p. 133. Ask students how this activity models the DNA molecule. *The index cards formed a pattern of AT and CG, like the paired nucleotide subunits of the DNA molecule.*

Ongoing Assessment

CHECK YOUR READING *Answer: Proteins are made up of chains of amino acids.*

RESOURCE CENTER CLASSZONE.COM
Learn more about DNA.

Proteins and Amino Acids

Proteins are large molecules that are made up of chains of amino acids. Twenty different amino acids come together in enough combinations to make up the thousands of different proteins found in the human body. Some proteins are small. For example, lysozyme is a digestive protein that is made up of a sequence of 129 amino acids. Some proteins are large. For example, dystrophin is a huge structural protein that is made up of 3685 amino acids.

What is the relationship between proteins and amino acids?

DNA stores the information that enables a cell to put together the right sequences of amino acids needed to produce specific proteins. Scientists describe DNA as containing a code. A code is a set of rules and symbols used to carry information. For example, your computer uses a code of ones and zeroes to store data and then translates the code into the numbers, letters, and graphics you see on a computer screen. To understand how DNA functions as a code, you first need to learn about the structure of the DNA molecule.

DNA and the Genetic Code

The DNA molecule takes the shape of a double-stranded spiral, which, as you can see from the diagram, looks something like a twisted ladder. In Chapter 2, you read about different subunits that make up the molecules found in cells. Nucleotide subunits make up each of the two strands of the DNA molecule. One part of the nucleotide forms the side rail of the DNA "ladder." The other part, the nucleotide base, forms the rung. Actually, two bases come together to form the rung, as one nucleotide base attaches to another from the opposite strand. You can see how the parts fit together in the diagram to the left. **A**

There are four different nucleotides in DNA, identified by their bases: adenine (A), thymine (T), cytosine (C), and guanine (G). Because of differences in size and shape, adenine always pairs with thymine (A-T) and cytosine always pairs with guanine (C-G). The bases fit together like two pieces of a jigsaw puzzle. These bases are often referred to simply by their initials—A, T, C, and G. The phrase "all tigers can growl" may help you remember them. **B**

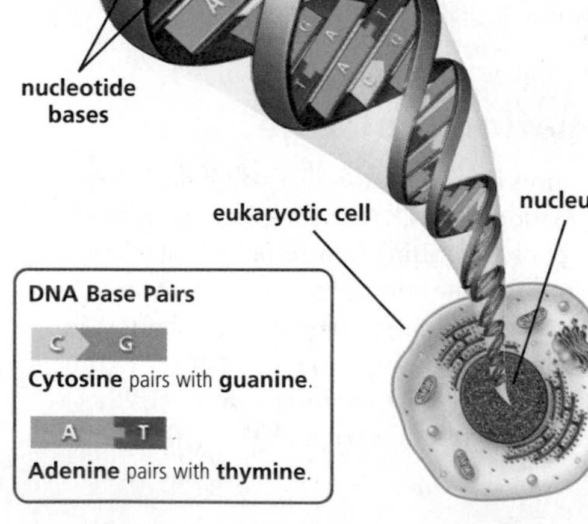

DNA Base Pairs

Cytosine pairs with **guanine**.

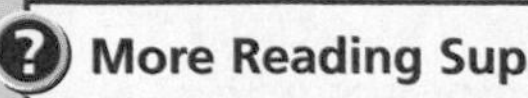

Adenine pairs with **thymine**.

DIFFERENTIATE INSTRUCTION

More Reading Support

A What is the shape of the DNA molecule? *a double-stranded spiral*

B In DNA, which nucleotide base always pairs with adenine? *thymine* With cytosine? *guanine*

English Learners Several questions in this section's review ask students to answer questions "based on what [they] have read." The word "base" may be confusing after studying acids and bases. Explain the difference between the two uses of *base*.

It is the sequence—the order—of bases in a strand of DNA that forms the code for making proteins. Like a list of ingredients in a recipe book, a set of bases specifies the amino acids needed to form a particular protein. The cookbook uses just 4 bases—A, T, G, and C—to code for 20 amino acids. A code of 2 bases to 1 amino acid gives only 16 possible combinations. However, a code of 3 bases to 1 amino acid gives 64 possible combinations.

T-C-T
(DNA triplet)

codes for

arginine
(amino acid)

The genetic code is, in fact, a triplet code. A specific sequence of 3 nucleotide bases codes for 1 amino acid. For example, the triplet T-C-T on a strand of DNA codes for the amino acid arginine. Some amino acids have two different codes. Others have three, and some have four. A gene is the entire sequence of the bases that codes for all the amino acids in a protein. Each gene is made up of a sequence of bases at a particular location on the DNA.

Replication

When a cell divides into two cells, each daughter cell receives an identical copy of the DNA. Before a cell divides, all of its DNA is copied, a process referred to as **replication.** Let's follow the process through for one DNA molecule. First, the two strands of DNA separate, almost like two threads in a string being unwound. Nucleotides in the area around the DNA match up, base by base, with the nucleotides on each DNA strand. C matches up with G, and A matches up with T. When replication is complete, there are two identical DNA molecules. Each molecule has one strand of old DNA and one strand of new DNA.

(C) (D)

READING TIP

Replicate includes the root word meaning "to repeat."

Replication

Replication produces two identical molecules of DNA.

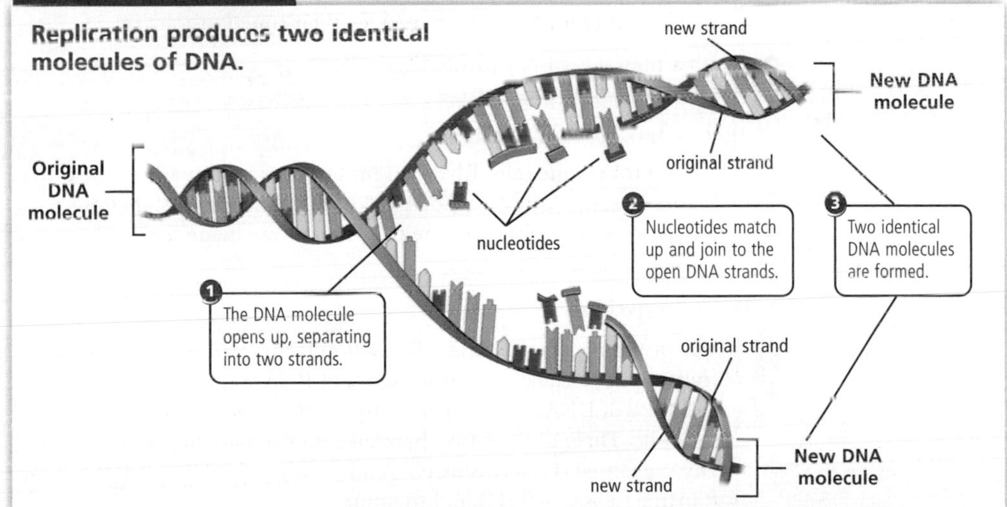

Address Misconceptions

IDENTIFY Ask students to describe the difference among DNA, genes, and chromosomes. Many students do not understand the relationship among them.

CORRECT Ask students to recall what they learned about genes and chromosomes in Chapters 3 and 4. After students read p. 137, review the following definitions:

DNA—molecule that stores information

gene—unit of heredity; located in DNA

chromosome—form DNA takes when a cell divides

REASSESS Ask students to draw a diagram showing the relationship among these three terms. *Diagrams should show a gene as a small segment. That segment is part of a long string of DNA. The DNA coils into a chromosome.*

Technology Resources

Visit **ClassZone.com** for background on common student misconceptions.

MISCONCEPTION DATABASE

Teach from Visuals

To help students interpret the diagram of DNA replication, ask:

- How are two DNA molecules formed during replication? *The DNA separates into two strands. Free nucleotides match up to and join the open strands.*
- When does DNA replication take place? *before a cell divides*

Ongoing Assessment

Describe how the structure of DNA stores information the cell needs.

Ask: What forms the code for making proteins in the DNA molecule? *The sequence, or order, of the nucleotide bases in a strand of DNA.*

DIFFERENTIATE INSTRUCTION

More Reading Support

C What is the process in which DNA is copied? *replication*

D What nucleotides always match up? *C with G; A with T*

English Learners Have students use matching pairs of colored papers (representing the four nucleotides) taped to two pipe cleaners to make a model of DNA. Students can use the models to show how the double strand replicates.

Teach from Visuals

To help students understand how templates work in DNA replication, ask:

- What does each DNA template strand make a copy of? *the other strand*
- How do the two new strands produced compare? *They are exact copies of each other.*
- How many templates are used in replication? *two*

Teacher Demo

Make a human model of DNA. Have students stand in two lines that spiral like a DNA molecule. Each line should hold string. Students should hold cards labeled A, T, C, or G to represent the nucleotide pairs. Have the two lines move away from each other to model how the DNA molecule separates into two strands. Have free standing students pair up with matching A, T, C, or G cards to show how the open strands replicate. As students perform this activity, point out that it is one concrete example of how models can be similar to yet different from the natural occurrences they represent.

History of Science

In 1952 British scientist Rosalind Franklin studied the structure of the DNA molecule using a new technology called x-ray diffraction. Her work contributed to the work of Watson and Crick, when in 1953, they demonstrated and modeled the double helix structure of the DNA molecule based on the patterns in Franklin's x-rays.

Ongoing Assessment

Explain how DNA is copied.

Ask: How do two open strands of DNA form two identical DNA molecules? *Free nucleotides are paired with their matching base on the open strands.*

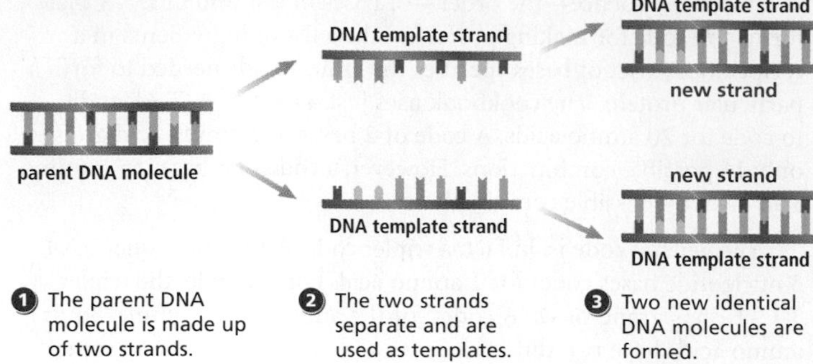

1 The parent DNA molecule is made up of two strands.

2 The two strands separate and are used as templates.

3 Two new identical DNA molecules are formed.

During replication, each strand of DNA is used as a template to produce a copy of the other strand. A template is a pattern or shape that produces a matching, or complementary, product. If you've ever made a plaster model of your hand, you've worked with a template. You press your hand into a soft material that leaves a mold of your hand. You then pour liquid plaster into the mold to produce a copy of your hand. The mold is a template. Its shape allows you to make a complementary shape that matches your hand.

READING TIP

Complementary has a root that means "to complete."

RNA is needed to make proteins.

VOCABULARY

Remember to choose strategies from an earlier chapter or some of your own to take notes on the term *RNA*.

E

DNA is not used to make proteins directly. Translating the genetic code of DNA involves another type of molecule, RNA. **RNA,** or ribonucleic acid, carries the information from DNA to a ribosome, where the amino acids are brought together to form a protein. DNA actually codes for RNA. Three different types of RNA are involved in making proteins. They are named for their functions:

- messenger RNA (mRNA)
- ribosomal RNA (rRNA)
- transfer RNA (tRNA)

In prokaryotic cells, RNA and proteins are both made in the cytoplasm. In eukaryotic cells, DNA is copied in the nucleus, then RNA moves to the cytoplasm, where the proteins are made.

Transcription

F

The process of transferring information from DNA to RNA is called transcription. The chemical structure of RNA is quite similar to the structure of DNA. Both are made up of four types of nucleotide subunits. Three of the bases that make up RNA are the same as in DNA: guanine (G), cytosine (C), and adenine (A). However, the fourth base is uracil (U), not thymine.

DIFFERENTIATE INSTRUCTION

More Reading Support

E What are the three kinds of RNA? *messenger, ribosomal, transfer*

F What is the process of transferring code from DNA to RNA? *transcription*

Below Level To reinforce the concept of coding, provide students with a copy of the Morse Code. Have them use the code to decode a message written in Morse Code. Ask them how Morse Code is similar to the pairing of nucleotides in DNA and RNA. They should understand that mRNA is similar to the key that matches dots and dashes to letters. The translation of the code into words is comparable to translation of mRNA by tRNA and ribosomes.

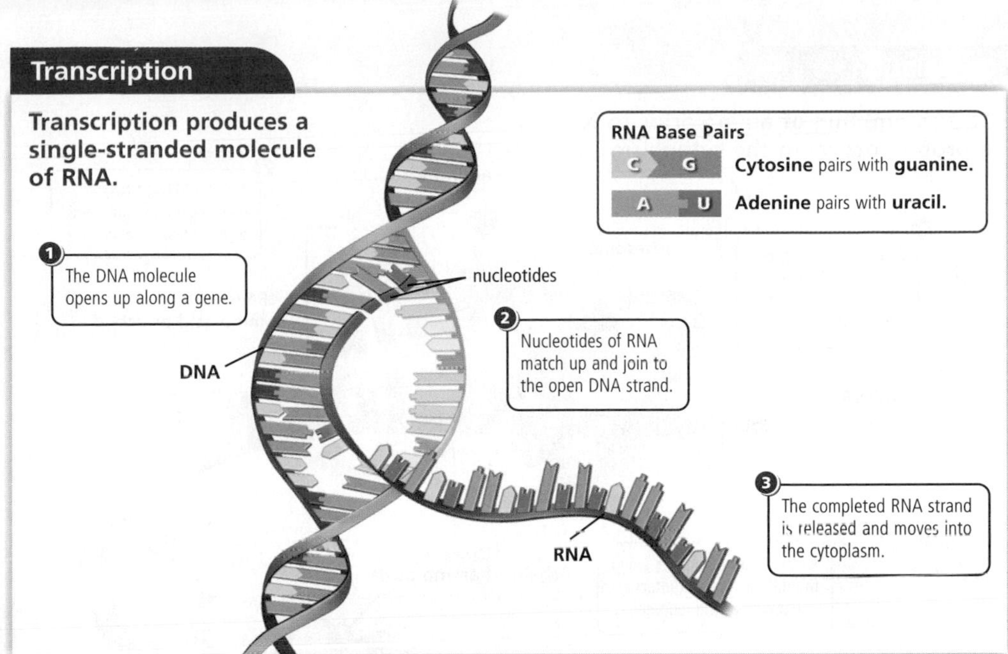

During transcription, DNA is again used as a template, this time to make a complementary strand of RNA. Only individual genes are transcribed, not a whole DNA molecule. The DNA again opens up, just where the gene is located. As shown in the diagram above, RNA bases match up to complementary bases on the DNA template. Adenine pairs with uracil (A-U) and cytosine pairs with guanine (C-G).

REMINDER
DNA base pairs:
C-G, A-T
RNA base pairs:
C-G, A-U

Transcription is different from replication in some important ways. Only one strand of DNA is transcribed, which means just a single strand of RNA is produced. When transcription is complete, the RNA is released, it does not stay attached to DNA. This means that many copies of RNA can be made from the same gene in a short period of time. At the end of transcription, the DNA molecule closes.

G

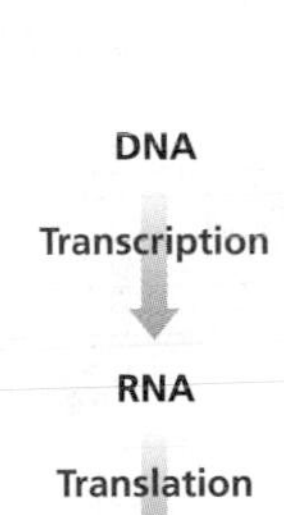

Translation

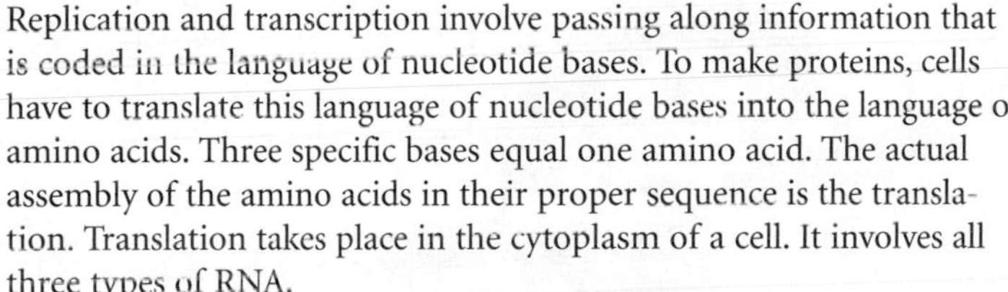

Replication and transcription involve passing along information that is coded in the language of nucleotide bases. To make proteins, cells have to translate this language of nucleotide bases into the language of amino acids. Three specific bases equal one amino acid. The actual assembly of the amino acids in their proper sequence is the translation. Translation takes place in the cytoplasm of a cell. It involves all three types of RNA.

H

Teach from Visuals

To help students interpret the diagram of transcription, ask:

- What takes place during transcription? *One strand of a DNA molecule is used to make a single-strand molecule of RNA.*
- What attaches to the open DNA strand? *nucleotides*
- What is the sequence of events in the production of protein? *transcription, then translation*

Teach Difficult Concepts

Many students may confuse DNA and RNA. Ask:

- How do the bases differ in RNA from DNA? *RNA has the base uracil instead of thymine.*
- How does the structure of the RNA molecule differ from the DNA molecule? *It is made up of one strand instead of two.*

Develop Critical Thinking

COMPARE AND CONTRAST To help students understand the difference between transcription and translation, Ask.

- What happens during transcription? *Information in DNA is transferred to RNA.*
- How does transcription begin? *It starts with the separating of one strand of DNA.*
- What happens during translation? *The code picked up by mRNA from DNA must be translated from the "language" of nucleotide bases into the "language" of amino acids. This is done by tRNA and ribosomes, which assemble amino acids into their proper sequence to form a protein.*

DIFFERENTIATE INSTRUCTION

More Reading Support

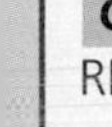

G What happens to RNA when transcription is complete? *It is released.*

H What is assembly of amino acids in sequence called? *translation*

Below Level Have students create a flow chart to show the process of transcription. Students should include the following terms in their charts: *DNA, mRNA, nucleus, cytoplasm,* and *nucleotides*. As they complete Section 5.1, students can add the processes of translation and protein synthesis to their flow charts of transcription. They should include the terms *tRNA, ribosome, triplet, amino acid,* and *protein.*

Teach from Visuals

To help students interpret the diagram of protein synthesis, have them read the steps of the process on p. 141 as they study the diagram. Then ask:

- What process begins when the mRNA molecule attaches to the ribosome? *Translation begins.*
- What is the job of transfer RNA? *Transfer RNA carries specific amino acids to the ribosomes.*
- What is the job of the triplet code? *It signals for a specific amino acid to be added to the protein.*
- How does the protein molecule continue to be built? *The tRNA molecules bring more amino acids to the ribosome, where they are linked together.*

The "Translation" visual is also available as T38 in the Unit Transparency Book.

History of Science

In 1869 Swiss scientist Johann Friedrich Miescher was the first to isolate DNA. Miescher studied white blood cells, which are abundant in pus, and were readily available in bandages from a hospital near his university. Miescher isolated a material from the cell and called it nuclein. Five years later, he isolated nuclein in a purer form, and renamed it nucleic acid in recognition of its acidic properties.

Teaching with Technology

Have students use slideshow software to create a multimedia presentation of the concepts in this section. Students can use the slide show software to show the steps in replication, translation, transcription, and protein synthesis.

Translation

The assembling of amino acids to form a protein occurs in the cytoplasm.

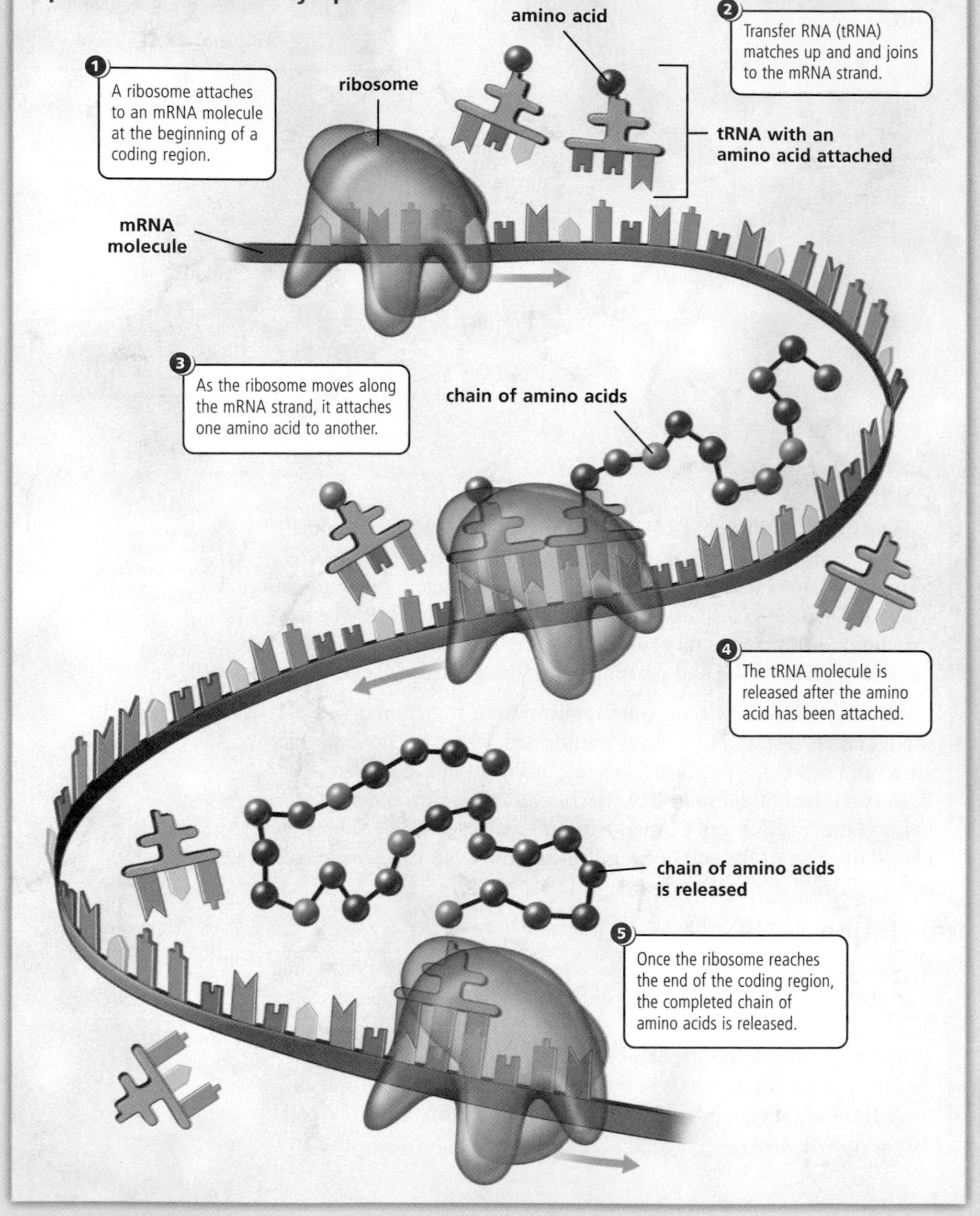

1 A ribosome attaches to an mRNA molecule at the beginning of a coding region.

2 Transfer RNA (tRNA) matches up and and joins to the mRNA strand.

amino acid

ribosome

tRNA with an amino acid attached

mRNA molecule

3 As the ribosome moves along the mRNA strand, it attaches one amino acid to another.

chain of amino acids

4 The tRNA molecule is released after the amino acid has been attached.

chain of amino acids is released

5 Once the ribosome reaches the end of the coding region, the completed chain of amino acids is released.

DIFFERENTIATE INSTRUCTION

Advanced Encourage students to create a timeline about the scientists that led to the discovery of the role of DNA in genetic inheritance. Scientists to highlight in their timelines might include Oswald Avery, Alfred Hershey, Martha Chase, Rosalind Franklin, James Watson, and Francis Crick.

Challenge and Extension, p. 258

Proteins are made on ribosomes, structures that are made up of ribosomal RNA and proteins. If you think of DNA as a cookbook for making different proteins, and mRNA as a recipe for making a protein, then the ribosome is the place where the cooking gets done. In this analogy, tRNA gathers the ingredients, which are amino acids.

A tRNA molecule is shaped in such a way that one end of it can attach to a specific amino acid. The other end of tRNA has a triplet of bases that is complementary to a triplet of bases on mRNA. Transfer RNA does the actual translation of bases to amino acid when it matches up with mRNA. The diagram on page 140 shows the whole process.

Refer to the diagram on page 140 as you read the text. The numbers in the text match the numbers in the diagram.

1. Translation begins when a ribosome attaches to the beginning end of an mRNA molecule.
2. A tRNA molecule carrying an amino acid matches up to a complementary triplet on mRNA on the ribosome.
3. The ribosome attaches one amino acid to another as it moves along the mRNA molecule.
4. The tRNA molecules are released after the amino acids they carry are attached to the growing chain of amino acids.
5. The ribosome completes the translation when it reaches the end of the mRNA strand. The newly made protein molecule, in the form of a chain of amino acids, is released.

CHECK YOUR READING Describe how the three different types of RNA work together in protein synthesis.

Watch an animation of how proteins are made.

The process of making proteins is basically the same in all cells. The flow of information in a cell goes from DNA to RNA to protein.

5.1 Review

KEY CONCEPTS

1. Describe the shape of the DNA molecule and how nucleotide bases fit into that structure.
2. What is a protein and what is it made up of?
3. Identify three types of RNA involved in protein synthesis and briefly describe what they do.

CRITICAL THINKING

4. **Infer** What might happen if the wrong amino acid is put on a tRNA molecule?
5. **Apply** Copy the following sequence of DNA bases: A-T-C-A-G-G. Write the complementary mRNA and tRNA sequences for this.

CHALLENGE

6. **Synthesize** Study the sequences you wrote for question 5. How does the tRNA sequence compare to the original DNA sequence?

ANSWERS

1. DNA is a double spiral strand. The strands are held together by specific pairs of nucleotides.

2. Proteins are large molecules that are made up of chains of amino acids.

3. mRNA picks up the code for making proteins from DNA; tRNA translates the code into amino acids; RNA in the ribosome brings together mRNA and tRNA and links the amino acids into their proper sequence to form a protein.

4. An incorrect amino acid would change the sequence of amino acids in the protein.

5. mRNA: U-A-G-U-C-C, tRNA: A-U-C-A-G-G

6. It is the same, except with U instead of T.

Ongoing Assessment

Explain how RNA uses the information from DNA to make proteins.

Ask: What determines the sequence of the amino acids in a protein? *the sequence of nucleotides of mRNA*

CHECK YOUR READING *Answer: First, mRNA is produced using a strand of DNA as a code. The mRNA moves to the cytoplasm and attaches to a ribosome, which includes RNA. There, the three nucleotides of the bases of mRNA match up with the tRNA carrying a specific amino acid. The ribosome brings together mRNA and tRNA, linking together the amino acids. The ribosome assembles the amino acids into their proper sequence to form a protein.*

Reinforce the BIG idea

Have students relate the section to the Big Idea.

 Reinforcing Key Concepts, p. 259

5.1 ASSESS & RETEACH

Assess

A Section 5.1 Quiz, p. 79

Reteach

Have students use their flow charts (see p. 139) to review the process of transcription, translation, and making proteins. As you review the process, have them add to or revise the information in their charts.

Technology Resources

Have students visit **ClassZone.com** for reteaching of Key Concepts.

 CONTENT REVIEW

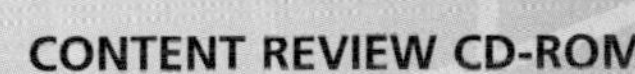

CHAPTER INVESTIGATION

Focus

PURPOSE To extract and observe DNA

OVERVIEW Students will use simple chemicals that break down the membranes of a cell to extract DNA from raw wheat germ. Students will then:

- examine properties of extracted DNA.
- compare observations with prior knowledge about DNA structure.

Lab Preparation

- Isopropyl alcohol and distilled water are available at local drugstores.
- The detergent solution should be 25% detergent to 75% distilled water.
- The salt solution should be 8% salt to 92% distilled water.
- For homework, have students read through the investigation and set up their data tables. Or, you may wish to copy and distribute datasheets and rubrics.

 UNIT RESOURCE BOOK, pp. 288–296

 SCIENCE TOOLKIT, F15

Lab Management

- Provide small beakers of alcohol for students to pour from the test tubes.
- Students can let their test tubes stand in a rack after pouring the alcohol.
- For best results, keep the alcohol in an ice bath before it is poured into the mixture.
- You may wish to distribute hand lenses for closer observation.
- Arrange for proper disposal of the DNA extractions.

SAFETY Caution students not to inhale or sniff fumes from the alcohol. Make sure students wear safety goggles and wash their hands thoroughly after completion of the lab. Review proper handling of glass and proper disposal of broken glass. Be sure that students work in groups of one or two and minimize movement.

INCLUSION Arrange to demonstrate the procedure prior to the investigation. You may perform the investigation with plastic rather than glass vessels.

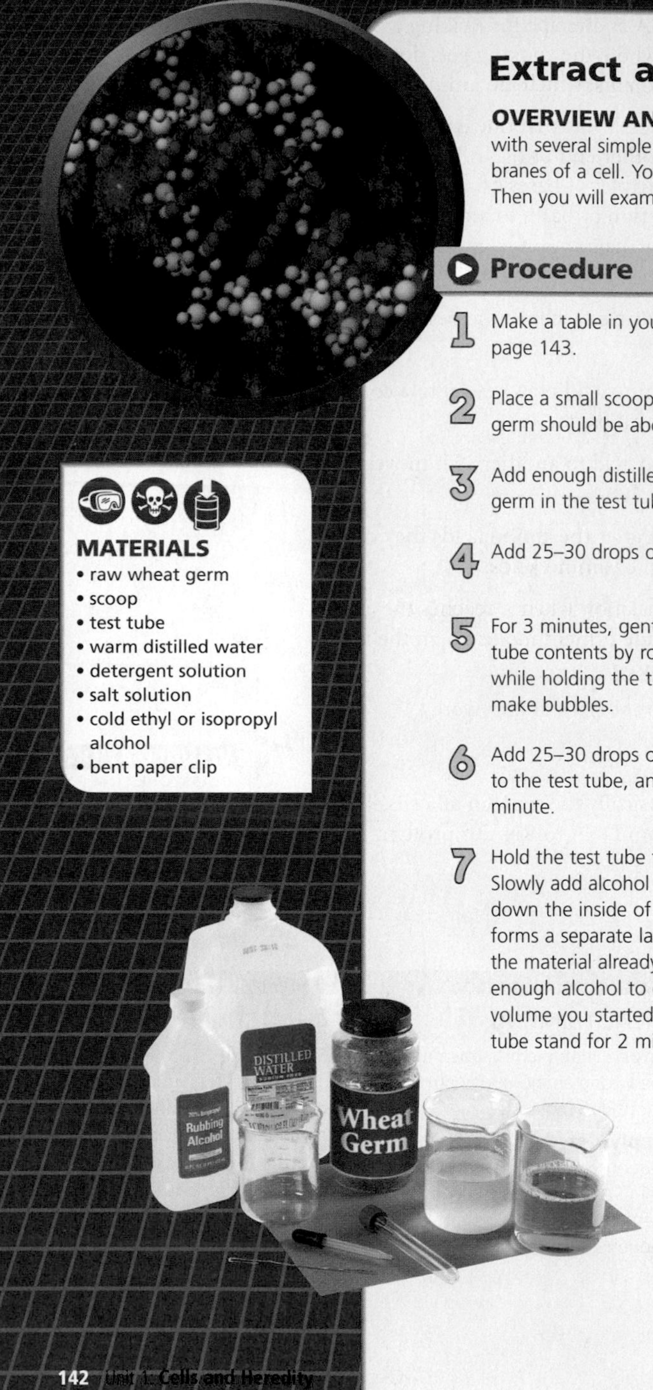

Extract and Observe DNA

OVERVIEW AND PURPOSE In this activity, you will work with several simple chemicals that can break down the membranes of a cell. You will extract DNA from raw wheat germ. Then you will examine the properties of the extracted DNA.

Procedure

1. Make a table in your **Science Notebook** like the one shown on page 143.
2. Place a small scoop of wheat germ in a test tube. The wheat germ should be about 1 cm high in the test tube.
3. Add enough distilled water to wet and cover all of the wheat germ in the test tube.
4. Add 25–30 drops of detergent solution to the test tube.
5. For 3 minutes, gently swirl the test tube contents by rotating your wrist while holding the tube. Try not to make bubbles.
6. Add 25–30 drops of the salt solution to the test tube, and swirl for 1 more minute.
7. Hold the test tube tilted at an angle. Slowly add alcohol so that it runs down the inside of the test tube and forms a separate layer on top of the the material already in the tube. Add enough alcohol to double the total volume you started with. Let the test tube stand for 2 minutes.

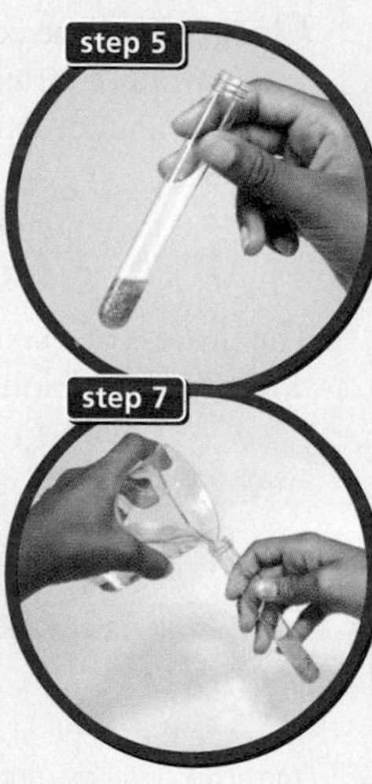

INVESTIGATION RESOURCES

 CHAPTER INVESTIGATION, Extract and Observe DNA
- Level A, pp. 288–291
- Level B, pp. 292–295
- Level C, p. 296

Advanced students should complete Levels B & C.

 Writing a Lab Report, D12–13

Technology Resources

Customize this student lab as needed or look for an alternative. Print rubrics to assess student lab reports.

 **Lab Generator CD-ROM**

8 Watch for stringy, cloudy material to rise up from the bottom layer into the alcohol layer. This is the DNA.

9 Use the bent paper clip to remove some DNA. Be careful to probe only the alcohol layer and not disturb the material at the bottom of the test tube.

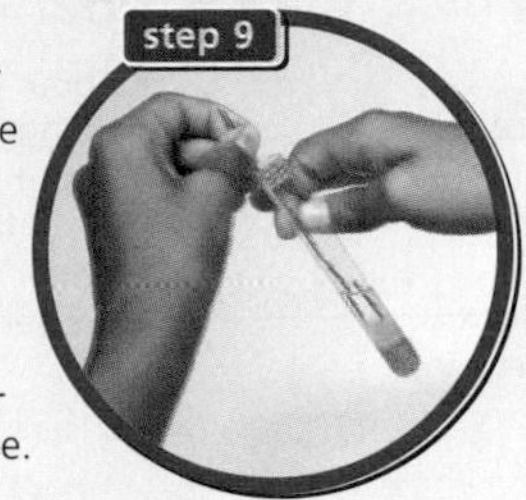

10 Wash your hands after working with the chemicals.

Observe and Analyze 

1. **OBSERVE** How do your observations of the DNA you just extracted compare with what you know about DNA. Record these comparisons in your notebook in a table similar to the one shown.
2. **INFER** What type of organism is wheat? Where is the DNA located in a wheat germ cell?
3. **INFER** What do you think was the purpose of using detergent in this experiment? Hint: How does soap work on greasy dishes?
4. **IDENTIFY LIMITS** What might happen if the wheat germ were not mixed properly with the detergent solution?

Conclude 

1. **INFER** If you had used cooked or toasted wheat germ in this experiment, you would not have gotten good results. Why do you think this is the case?
2. **INFER** Would this experiment work with cells from other organisms, such as bananas, onions, or cells from your own cheek? Why or why not?
3. **INFER** Would DNA from a single cell be visible to the naked eye?
4. **APPLY** The procedure that you performed today is used by many people to obtain DNA for further study. Give some examples of how DNA information is used in the world today.

INVESTIGATE Further

CHALLENGE Repeat the experiment replacing the alcohol with water in step 7. Compare the results with the results you obtained using alcohol.

Extract and Observe DNA

Table 1. Properties and Observations

Properties of DNA	Observations

Observe and Analyze 

1. *Responses will probably mention that the stringiness of the material is similar to the strandlike nature of DNA.*
2. *Wheat is a plant. Its DNA is found in the nuclei of its cells.*
3. *Detergent breaks apart fats and grease. The detergent helped break apart the lipid-based cell membranes of the wheat cells.*
4. *The wheat cells might not have broken down and it would not have been possible to extract the DNA.*

Conclude 

1. *Cooked wheat germ would have different properties—for example, the soap might not have been able to break down the lipids in the cell membranes. Also the DNA in cooked cells may not have been intact.*
2. *yes, because all cells have lipid membranes*
3. *no, because cells are so small*
4. *DNA is used to identify individuals. It is used in genetic engineering to modify organisms and give them desirable traits.*

INVESTIGATE Further

CHALLENGE Answers will likely mention an absence of strandlike material. Alcohol causes individual strands of DNA to unfold, and then all the strands come together in a single large clump of DNA. That is why the DNA is visible. Water has no such effect.

Teaching with Technology

Students might wish to use video cameras to record the steps of the investigation. A group of students could act as writers, recorders, and reporters, narrating the procedure and giving an analysis of the results.

Post-Lab Discussion

- Ask students why a salt solution was added to the wheat solution. *Salt would cause water to enter the cells, making them swell and burst.*
- Ask students to share any questions raised by their observations. Do their questions suggest any further investigation? How might they use a procedure similar to this one to test a hypothesis or to help answer a question?

5.2 FOCUS

Set Learning Goals

Students will

- Define mutations as any changes in DNA.
- Describe the possible effects of mutations.
- Describe pedigrees and explain how they are used.
- Make a model of neutral genetic mutations.

3-Minute Warm-Up

Display Transparency 36 or copy this exercise on the board:

Match the definitions to the terms.

Definitions

1. process in which DNA is copied *c*
2. a molecule that stores information *d*
3. the information in DNA to make proteins *a*

Terms

a. genetic code	d. DNA
b. translation	e. transcription
c. replication	

 3-Minute Warm-Up, p. T36

5.2 MOTIVATE

EXPLORE Codes

PURPOSE To explore the concept of coding

TIP *15 min.* Have students compare their sentences after they insert the extra letter.

WHAT DO YOU THINK? *No, the extra letter changed the words that followed into words that did not make sense.*

Inclusion

Write the individual words of the sentence, "One day the cat ate the rat." on slips of paper. Students can move pieces of paper to change the meaning.

KEY CONCEPT

5.2 Changes in DNA can produce variation.

BEFORE, you learned

- DNA contains information in the form of a sequence of bases
- Genes code for RNA and proteins
- DNA is transcribed into RNA, which is used to make proteins

NOW, you will learn

- About mutations, any changes in DNA
- About the possible effects of mutations
- About pedigrees and how they are used

VOCABULARY

mutation p. 145
pedigree p. 147

EXPLORE Codes

What happens to a code if small changes occur?

PROCEDURE

1. Language is a type of code. Look at the English sentence below.

   One day the cat ate the rat.

2. Insert an extra *a* into the word *cat* in the sentence above, but keep the spacing the same. That is, keep a space after every third letter.

WHAT DO YOU THINK?

- Does the sentence still make sense? How were the rest of the words affected?
- How would other small changes affect the meaning of the sentence? Try substituting, removing, and switching letters.

MATERIALS

- pencil
- paper

DNA sequences can change.

SUPPORTING MAIN IDEAS
In your notebook, organize information that supports this main idea: *DNA sequences can change.*

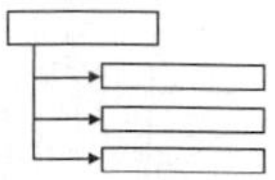

Differences, or variations, in DNA are what make one organism different from another. The number of differences in the DNA sequences between two species is large. Each human cell, with its 46 chromosomes, contains an astounding 3 billion base pairs in its DNA. A yeast cell, by comparison, has 12 million base pairs in its DNA.

The number of differences between any two individuals of the same species is small. For example, about 99.9 percent of the DNA in the cells of two different humans is the same. Just 0.1 percent variation in DNA makes you the unique person you are. That averages out to one base in a thousand.

RESOURCES FOR DIFFERENTIATED INSTRUCTION

Below Level

UNIT RESOURCE BOOK

- Reading Study Guide A, pp. 262–263
- Decoding Support, p. 285

AUDIO CDS

Advanced

UNIT RESOURCE BOOK

Challenge and Extension, p. 268

English Learners

UNIT RESOURCE BOOK

Spanish Reading Study Guide, pp. 266–267

 **AUDIO CDS**

- Audio Readings in Spanish
- Audio Readings (English)

How can there be such great variety among people if their DNA is so similar? The reason is that of the 6 billion base pairs in human DNA, only 5 percent are in the genes that code for RNA and proteins. As you learned in Chapter 4, genes and their interaction with the environment are what determine the traits of a person.

Many traits, including skin tones, are affected by genes.

Differences in genes affect the height of people or the color of their eyes, hair, or skin. Genes produce variation because the type or amount of the proteins they code for can vary from person to person. For example, skin color comes from a protein called melanin. The amount of melanin an individual produces affects the color of their skin.

Given the huge number of base pairs in the DNA of any organism, it is not surprising that errors occur when DNA is copied. DNA is also affected by the environment. For example, exposure to ultraviolet radiation or x-rays can damage DNA. Both natural and human-made toxins, which are harmful chemicals, can also damage DNA.

A

VOCABULARY
Remember to choose a strategy from an earlier chapter or use one of your own to take notes on *mutation.*

Any change in DNA is called a **mutation.** Cells have different ways to repair mistakes in a DNA sequence. Certain enzymes actually proofread DNA, for example correcting mismatched base pairs. Other enzymes enable damaged DNA to be fixed.

CHECK YOUR READING What is a mutation?

When a mutation occurs in a gene, the coding region of DNA, the wrong amino acid might be placed in the amino acid chain. If this happens, there are three possible outcomes.

1. **The mutation causes no effect.** Since some amino acids have more than one code, a mutation may not change the resulting protein. Also, since each cell has two sets of DNA, even if one gene is not working, enough protein may be produced.

2. **The effect of a mutation is minor.** A change in the genes that control the amount of melanin produced could affect not only how light or dark a person's skin is, it could also affect eye or hair color. The change, in this case, is a change in appearance.

3. **The effect of a mutation is great.** The effect can be good, such as a plant having an increased resistance to disease. Or the effect can be bad, causing a genetic disorder or disease.

B

RESOURCE CENTER CLASSZONE.COM

Find out more about mutations.

Remember, only 5 percent of human DNA is in genes. If a mutation occurs in a noncoding region of DNA, then chances are that the mutation will have no effect. Such a mutation is neutral.

DIFFERENTIATE INSTRUCTION

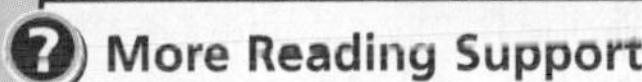

More Reading Support

A What are some things that can damage DNA? *ultraviolet radiation, x-rays, toxic chemicals*

B What harmful effects can a mutation cause? *disease*

Advanced Have students find out about the work of Hugo De Vries, a Dutch botanist whose work with primrose plants led to an understanding of mutations. They should present a sequence chart of important discoveries and what led up to them.

R Challenge and Extension, p. 268

5.2 INSTRUCT

Teach Difficult Concepts

To help students understand the relationship between DNA and mutations, ask:

- What percentage of DNA in a person's cells is genes? *only 5 percent*
- How do mutations occur? *An error can happen when DNA is copied. Also, exposure to harmful chemicals, x-rays, or UV radiation can damage DNA.*
- Are all mutations harmful? Explain. *No, some mutations have no effect on an individual. Other mutations may benefit the individual.*

Real World Example

Scientists have noticed an increase in the number of mutations occurring in frogs worldwide. Mutated frogs are born with either extra legs, or no legs at all. Scientists believe that the mutations are a result of pesticides and parasitic infections. Chemical pesticides seep into aquatic environments, contaminating the food supply. The frog's natural defenses are harmed by the pesticides, making them more susceptible to infection from flatworms known as trematodes. Mutated frogs have been spotted in at least 43 states.

Ongoing Assessment

Define mutations as any changes in DNA.

Ask: Why are chances small that a change in human DNA will have a noticeable effect? *95 percent of human DNA is noncoding DNA*

Ask: What does it mean that DNA is noncoding? *The DNA is not part of a gene. It does not make RNA or proteins.*

Ask: In what type of cell would a mutation to a gene have the greatest effect? *in an egg or sperm cell, because that mutation would affect all cells*

CHECK YOUR READING *Answer: A mutation is any change in DNA.*

INVESTIGATE Neutral Mutations

PURPOSE To model the probability of neutral mutations

TIP *15 min.* Select newspaper pages that are composed mostly of news articles and have limited advertisements or photographs.

WHAT DO YOU THINK? *Students will find that only a few of the "mutations" affected the gene sequences. Students should conclude that most mutations are neutral.*

CHALLENGE *Sample answer: Students should increase the number of circled words, or they could increase the number of paper-punch circles.*

 Datasheet, Neutral Mutations, p. 269

Technology Resources

Customize this student lab as needed or look for an alternative. Print rubrics to assess student lab reports.

 **Lab Generator CD-ROM**

Develop Critical Thinking

CONNECT To help students understand the concepts in "Investigate Neutral Mutations," ask students to give examples of the word *neutral* used in other situations. *neutral colors, neutral countries, neutral party, etc.* Then ask: What does it mean that most mutations are neutral? *Neutral mutations are those that have no effect on the organism.*

Ongoing Assessment

Describe the possible effects of mutations.

Ask: What are some genetic disorders that arise from mutations? *Tay-Sachs disease, cystic fibrosis, sickle cell disease, albinism*

 *Answer: a disease or condition that results from mutations that affect the normal functioning of the cells*

INVESTIGATE Neutral Mutations

How does a large number of noncoding sequences affect mutations?

SKILL FOCUS
Making models

MATERIALS
- newspaper
- pen
- paper-punch circles

TIME
15 minutes

PROCEDURE

1. Circle ten words on the page of a newspaper to represent genes. Place the newspaper on your desk.
2. Use a handful of paper-punch circles to represent mutations and scatter them onto the newspaper.
3. Count the number of paper-punch "mutations" that landed on "genes" and those that did not.

WHAT DO YOU THINK?

- What percentage of "mutations" affected gene sequences?
- What does this model suggest about the probability of mutations affecting genes that are only a small part of a DNA sequence?

CHALLENGE Most of the sequences in bacterial DNA are genes. How could you use the same model to evaluate the effect of mutations on bacterial DNA?

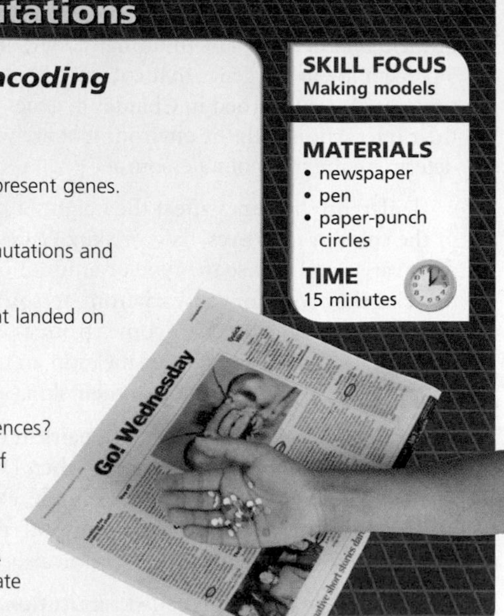

Mutations can cause genetic disorders.

A genetic disorder is a disease or condition that results from mutations that affect the normal functioning of a cell. Sometimes these disorders are inherited, passed on from parent to offspring. Examples of inherited disorders include Tay-Sachs disease, cystic fibrosis, sickle cell disease, and albinism. Other genetic disorders result from mutations that occur during a person's lifetime. Most cancers fall into this category.

CHECK YOUR READING What is a genetic disorder?

Sometimes a person carries a tendency for a disease, such as diabetes, glaucoma, Alzheimer's disease, or emphysema. In some cases, a person's behavior can help prevent the disease. Cigarette smoke is a leading cause of lung cancer. Smoke also greatly increases the risk of people with a genetic tendency for emphysema to develop that disease.

Sickle cell disease is an interesting example of how a mutation can have more than one effect. The mutation occurs in one of the genes that code for hemoglobin. Hemoglobin is a protein that carries oxygen in red blood cells. The mutation causes one amino acid to be replaced with another.

normal hemoglobin (protein)

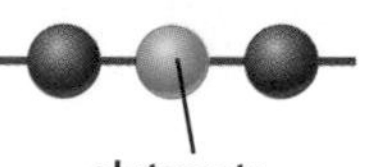

glutamate (amino acid)

sickle cell hemoglobin (protein)

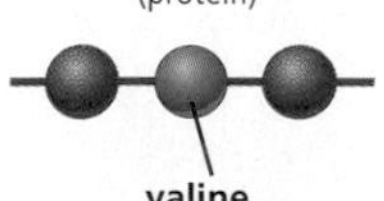

valine (amino acid)

DIFFERENTIATE INSTRUCTION

More Reading Support

C What is an example of a disease caused by a mutation during a person's lifetime? *cancer*

English Learners Read the Challenge in "Investigate Neutral Mutations," p. 146. Notice the phrases "How could you change this model . . ." and "How would your results change . . ." The words *would* and *could* are not universal in all languages. Help English learners understand that the questions refer to hypothetical situations. Students should use logic and what they have already learned to answer the questions.

Sickle cell disease is a recessive disorder. Only people who carry two recessive alleles are affected. Recall that an allele is one form of a gene. Because of the amino acid change, some red blood cells can take on a sickle shape. See the photograph at the right. The pedigree below shows the pattern of inheritance of the sickle cell allele through three generations of a family. A **pedigree** is a diagram of family relationships that includes two or more generations.

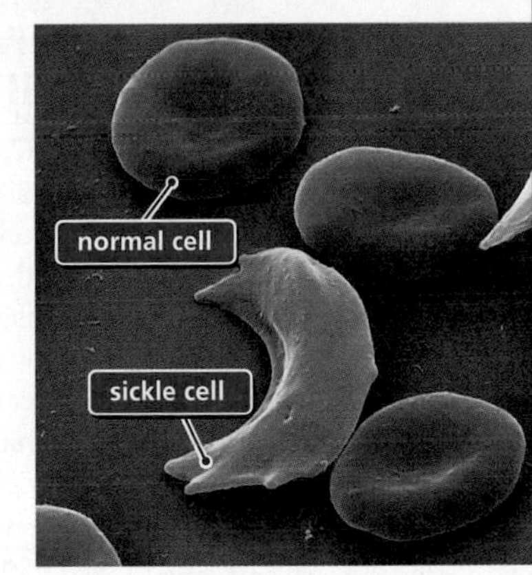

Sickle cell disease is a severe disease. Sickled red blood cells tend to break more easily than normal red blood cells. People with sickle cell disease do not get enough oxygen delivered to their body tissues, and the tissues become damaged. The disease is common in Africa and parts of India and the Middle East.

What is interesting about the sickle cell allele is that it provides protection against dying of malaria. Malaria is a severe disease, also common in Africa, India, and the Middle East. It is caused by microscopic organisms that reproduce in red blood cells. Scientists do not yet completely understand why people with the sickle cell allele are better able to survive malaria. However the effect of this protection is that the sickle allele remains common in populations that live in regions where malaria is common.

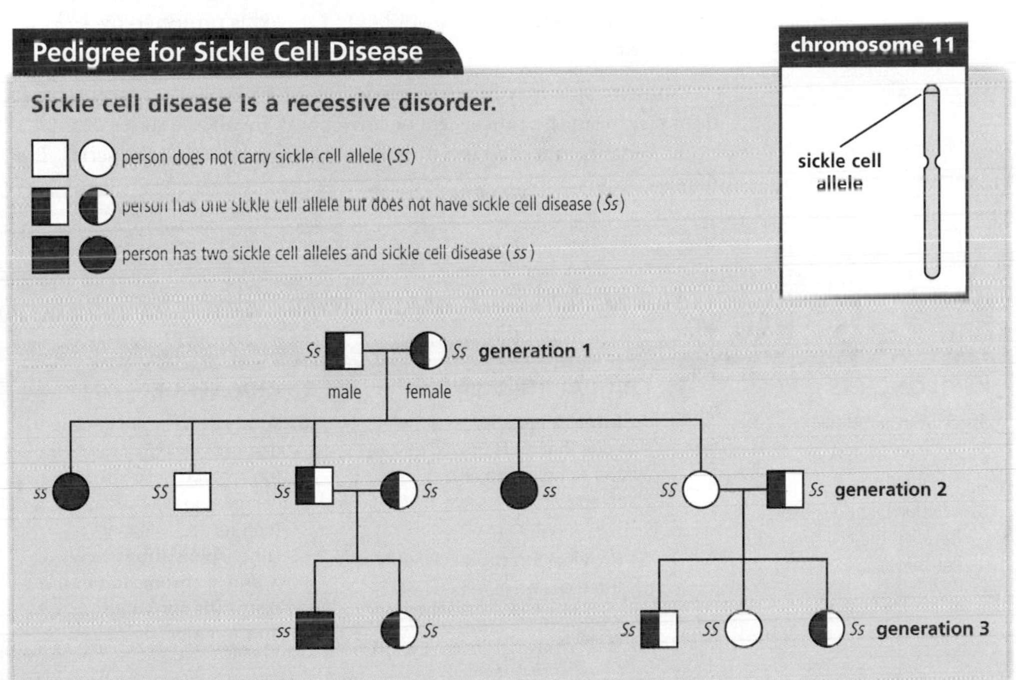

Real World Example

While having a sickle cell allele can protect people from dying from malaria, sickle cell disease remains debilitating. People with sickle cell disease have chronic anemia caused by the destruction of red blood cells, shortness of breath, fever, and severe pain in the abdomen, bones, and muscles. Prior to the development of effective treatments in the mid-1990s, the average life span of persons who had this disease was about 45 years. It is estimated that one in 12 African Americans are carriers of the sickle cell allele. Sickle cell disease is recessive. A person must have two alleles for the disease to occur. However, only one allele is needed to protect against dying from malaria.

Teach from Visuals

To help students interpret the pedigree chart, ask:

- How can you tell the difference between carriers of the disease and those who do not carry the disease? *Open circles and squares represent men and women who do not carry a gene for the disease. Half-shaded circles and squares represent people who have (carry) one sickle cell allele but do not have the disease.*
- What do the horizontal lines connecting males and females represent? *sexual reproduction between the two*
- How many people in the second generation have the disease? How is this shown? *two females, indicated by two fully shaded circles*
- How many people in the pedigree have some protection from malaria? Explain. *eleven, the number of people who have at least one sickle cell allele*

DIFFERENTIATE INSTRUCTION

More Reading Support

D What diagram shows information about family relationships? *pedigree*

E From which disease does a sickle cell allele give some protection? *malaria*

Below Level To reinforce the concept of a pedigree chart, invite students to invent a family and draw a pedigree chart showing the relationship among grandparents, parents, aunts, uncles, and siblings. Students should use circles to represent females and squares to represent males. A pedigree is not necessarily used to show the inheritance of a disease or trait. This is just how some scientists use pedigrees.

Ongoing Assessment

Describe pedigrees and explain how they can be used in genetics.

Ask: How are pedigrees used to follow a genetic disease through a family? *If the genotypes of the people in the family are known, then the pedigree can be used to show who has the disease or carries the allele for the disease.*

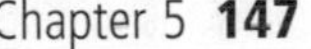

Ongoing Assessment

CHECK YOUR READING *Answer: All cancers are characterized by uncontrolled division of cells.*

Reinforce the BIG idea

Have students relate the section to the Big Idea.

 Reinforcing Key Concepts, p. 270

5.2 ASSESS & RETEACH

Assess

 Section 5.2 Quiz, p. 80

Reteach

Discuss each concept. Have students name examples from the text.

- Changes in the sequence of DNA can cause different types of mutations.
- Mutations can be caused by environmental factors and harmful chemicals.
- Mutations can cause genetic disorders.

To help students remember the difference among the different types of genetic disorders, have them create a chart listing the disorders discussed in the chapter. Students should label each disorder as inherited, tendency, or environmental.

Technology Resources

Have students visit **ClassZone.com** for reteaching of Key Concepts.

 **CONTENT REVIEW**

 **CONTENT REVIEW CD-ROM**

Cancer is a genetic disorder that affects the cell cycle.

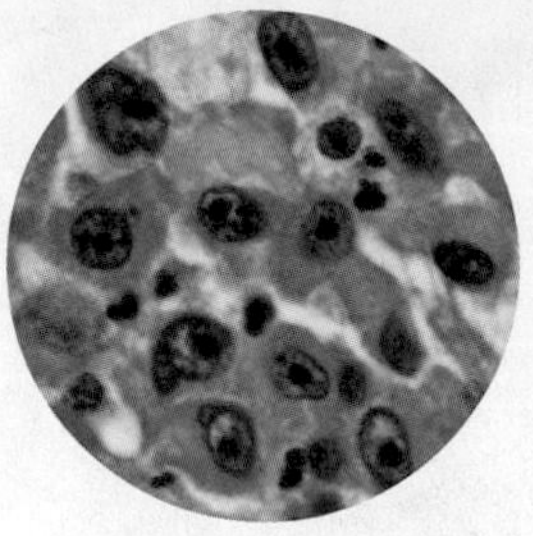

Cancer cells, such as the ones shown here, have abnormal shapes. Cancer cells reproduce uncontrollably and crowd out normal cells.

Cancer is not a single genetic disorder; but rather it is a group of disorders. All cancers are characterized by the uncontrolled division of cells. Normally, cells in a multicellular organism function to maintain the health of an organism. Cell division is controlled so that an organism has the number of cells it needs to function. Cancer cells are, in a way, "selfish" cells. Where normal cells stay within the same tissue, cancer cells spread quickly and can invade other tissues. A normal cell has a definite life span. Cancerous cells become "immortal"—they divide indefinitely.

CHECK YOUR READING What is a characteristic of all cancers?

Most cancers are caused by mutations to DNA that happen during a person's lifetime. Some mutations come from mistakes made during replication. But many are caused by harmful chemicals often referred to as *carcinogens* (kahr-SIHN-uh-juhnz). Many plants naturally produce carcinogens in their tissues. Nicotine is a carcinogen naturally found in tobacco leaves. There are other carcinogens in tobacco.

Ultraviolet and nuclear radiation as well as x-rays can also cause cancer. That is why, if you get an x-ray at the doctor's or dentist's office, the part of your body not being x-rayed is protected by a lead apron.

Some people may inherit a tendency for a particular cancer. That does not mean the cancer will occur. Cancer involves a series of mutations. What is inherited is a mutation that is one step in the series. The disease occurs only if other mutations come into play.

5.2 Review

KEY CONCEPTS

1. What is a mutation?
2. How do mutations affect an organism?
3. What effect does cancer have on the cell cycle of a cancerous cell?

CRITICAL THINKING

4. **Infer** A mutation in a triplet code that ends up coding for the same amino acid is referred to as a silent mutation. In what sense is it silent?
5. **Provide Examples** Identify three causes of genetic disorders and give an example of each.

CHALLENGE

6. **Analyze** Why are genetic diseases carried by genes on the X chromosome more common in male offspring than female offspring? Hint: Think about how X and Y chromosomes are distributed in males and females.

ANSWERS

1. A mutation is a change in the DNA of a cell.

2. Mutations can be neutral, harmful, or beneficial.

3. Cancer causes cells to divide continuously, upsetting the normal life cycle of the cell.

4. It is silent because it has no effect on the protein that is produced. The cell still functions normally.

5. inherited: sickle cell disease; tendency: diabetes; environmental: cancer, a disorder caused by mutations during a person's lifetime and can be caused by environmental factors.

6. A male has only one X chromosome and will have the disease if he has the disease gene. A female has two X chromosomes; even if one X chromosome has the disease gene, the other may not.

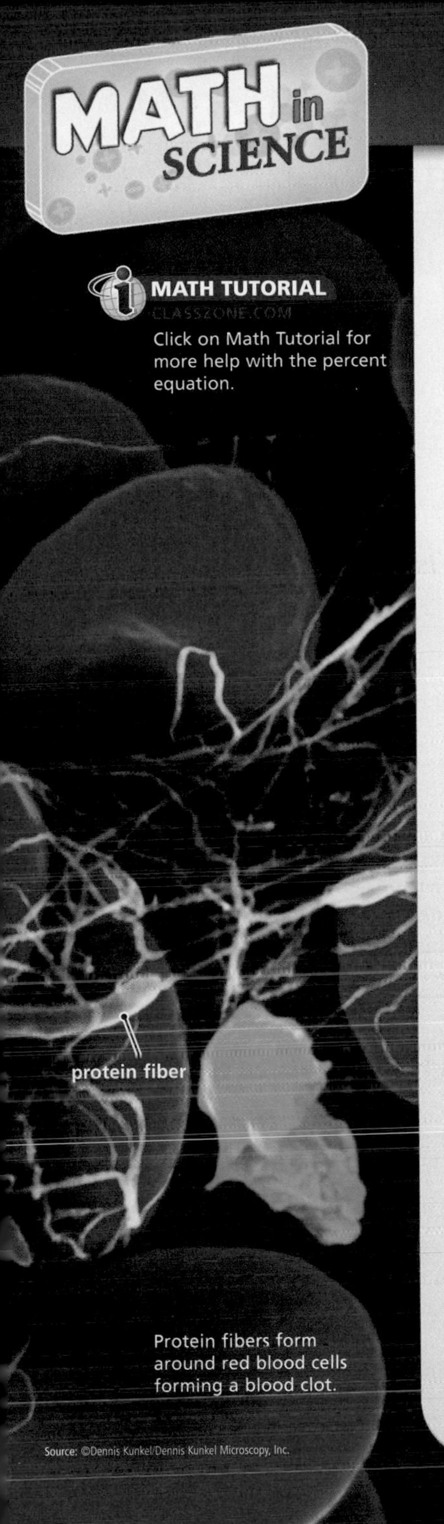

MATH TUTORIAL
CLASSZONE.COM
Click on Math Tutorial for more help with the percent equation.

Protein fibers form around red blood cells forming a blood clot.

Source: ©Dennis Kunkel/Dennis Kunkel Microscopy, Inc.

SKILL: FINDING PERCENT OF A WHOLE

Percents and Populations

Hemophilia is a genetic disorder in which blood does not clot properly. In any group of people who have hemophilia, approximately 80 percent have type A, which is caused by a mutation in one gene. Usually about 12 percent have type B, a different gene mutation.

To express what part of a population carries a gene mutation, scientists can use percentages. Once you know the percentage of a population, you can find out how many individuals that percent represents.

Example

Suppose a doctor is treating a group of people who have the disease hemophilia. The group has 400 people. About how many individuals would you expect to have hemophilia A?

(1) Write the percent as a decimal.

80% = 0.80

(2) Multiply the decimal number by the total population.

0.80 • 400 = 320.00

(3) Be sure the answer has the same number of decimal places as the total number of decimal places in the original factors.

0.80 • 400 = 320.00
(2 decimal places)

ANSWER There are probably about 320 people with hemophilia A.

Answer the following questions for a group of 400 hemophilia patients.

1. How many patients are likely to have hemophilia B?
2. Suppose a new doctor begins treatment of 20 percent of the hemophilia A patients. How many individuals is that?
3. In as many as 30 percent of cases of hemophilia, there is no family history of the disorder. In the group of 400, how many individuals probably did not have a family history of hemophilia?

CHALLENGE Write a fraction in simplest terms equal to each percentage: 80 percent, 30 percent, 12 percent, 3 percent. When you multiply these fractions by 400, do you get the same or different results as when you multiply 400 by the percentages? Explain why the results may be different.

ANSWERS

1. 0.12 · 400 = 48; 48 patients

2. 0.20 · 320 = 64; 64 patients

3. 0.30 · 400 = 120; 120 individuals

CHALLENGE *The results are the same. Multiplying by fractions in simplest terms is like multiplying by equivalent fractions, so the results would not change.*

MATH IN SCIENCE
Math Skills Practice for Science

Set Learning Goal

To find what part of a population carries a gene mutation by using percentages

Present the Science

Hemophilia is a sex-linked genetic disorder that is passed on to offspring by a recessive allele on the X chromosome. In order for the disorder to be expressed, two alleles must be passed onto the offspring. Because males have XY chromosomes, males are more likely to have the disorder because there are no matching alleles on the Y chromosome to mask the disorder.

Develop Percent Skills

A percent is a ratio that compares a number to 100; the ratio is expressed with a percent symbol (%). Remind students that a decimal is another way to write a percent, so 80% is the same as 0.80. 80% can also be written as a fraction, 80/100. To find the percent of a number, multiply the percent by the whole number.

DIFFERENTIATION TIP Write the steps for finding the percent of a number on an index card for students to use as a handy reference.

Close

Ask: What purpose might scientists have for finding the percentage of a population that has a genetic disorder? *Scientists might be better able to predict who is at risk of inheriting a genetic disease if percentages are known.*

- Math Support, p. 286
- Math Practice, p. 287

Technology Resources

Students can visit **ClassZone.com** to practice percentage skills.

 **MATH TUTORIAL**

5.3 FOCUS

Set Learning Goals

Students will

- Describe how scientists can change organisms by changing DNA.
- Describe some applications of DNA technology.
- Discuss some of the issues surrounding the use of DNA technology.

3-Minute Warm-Up

Display Transparency 37 or copy this exercise on the board:

Decide if these statements are true. If not true, correct them.

1. Mutations are always harmful. *Mutations can be harmful, neutral, or they can be beneficial.*
2. Mutations can only be caused by environmental factors. *Mutations can be caused by both environmental factors and by random changes in DNA during replication.*
3. The sickle-cell allele is a mutation that is both harmful and beneficial. *true*

5.3 MOTIVATE

THINK ABOUT

PURPOSE To make inferences about the genetic background of an animal

DISCUSS Have students describe a dog they have known or seen. Elicit from students that dogs have varied traits and the genetic backgrounds of different breeds. All dogs, however, are the same species. The characteristics of the animal in the picture suggest that its genes came from two different species; it is part goat and part sheep.

Ongoing Assessment

Explain how organisms change over time.

Ask: How is the genetic diversity of natural populations increased over time? *by random mutations*

KEY CONCEPT

Modern genetics uses DNA technology.

BEFORE, you learned

- Mutations are changes to DNA
- Not all mutations have an effect on an organism
- Mutations can lead to genetic disorders

NOW, you will learn

- How scientists can change organisms by changing DNA
- About some applications of DNA technology
- About some issues surrounding the use of DNA technology

VOCABULARY

selective breeding p. 151
genetic engineering p. 151
genome p. 154
cloning p. 154

THINK ABOUT

What type of animal is this?

Look at the photograph of the animal to the right. The cells in this animal contain DNA from two different species. For a long time humans have been able to mix genes by breeding together animals of different but similar species. Now scientists have the technology to mix together genes from two very different species by inserting genes from one organism into the cells of another. What do the characteristics of this animal suggest about the source of its genes?

SUPPORTING MAIN IDEAS
Begin a chart of information to support this main idea: *Changes in DNA can change an organism.*

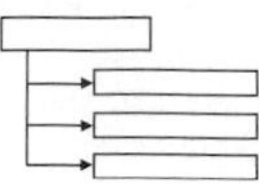

Changes in DNA can change an organism.

Organisms change over time. Changes come about because of mutations in DNA. Random changes in DNA may introduce new traits into an organism. Over time, certain traits may become more common in one group of organisms as they interact with the environment and each other.

Are all changes in a group of organisms random? There are dogs, such as bloodhounds, that are particularly well suited to tracking. There are cows that give large quantities of milk and crops that produce large quantities of grain. Changes such as these are not random, but result from careful breeding directed by humans.

150 Unit 1: Cells and Heredity

RESOURCES FOR DIFFERENTIATED INSTRUCTION

Below Level

UNIT RESOURCE BOOK

- Reading Study Guide A, pp. 273–274
- Decoding Support, p. 285

AUDIO CDS

Additional INVESTIGATION,
DNA Fingerprinting Simulation, A, B, & C, pp. 297–305; Teacher Instructions, pp. 308–309

Advanced

UNIT RESOURCE BOOK

- Challenge and Extension, p. 279
- Challenge Reading, pp. 281–282

English Learners

UNIT RESOURCE BOOK
Spanish Reading Study Guide, pp. 277–278

- Audio Readings in Spanish
- Audio Readings (English)

Selective Breeding

For thousands of years, humans have been carefully selecting and breeding certain plants and animals that have desirable traits. As the years have passed, horses have gotten faster, pigs have gotten leaner, and corn has become sweeter. **Selective breeding** is the process of selecting and breeding parent organisms to pass on particular traits to the offspring.

Bloodhounds, with their strong sense of smell, are used in police work for tracking.

Selective breeding can be successful as long as the desirable traits are controlled by genes. In fact, what these early farmers were actually selecting were alleles, particular versions of a gene. The alleles were already present in some members of the population. People were not changing DNA, but they were causing certain alleles to become more common in a particular breed. The different dog breeds are a good example of this. All dogs share a common ancestor, the wolf. However, thousands of years of selective breeding have produced dogs with a variety of characteristics.

CHECK YOUR READING How does selective breeding affect DNA?

Genetic Engineering

A Within the last fifty years it has become possible to directly change the DNA of an organism. **Genetic engineering** is the process in which a sequence of DNA from an organism is first isolated, then inserted into the DNA of another organism, changing that organism's DNA. The DNA that is engineered often codes for some particular trait of interest. Using technology, scientists can take a gene from one species and transfer it into the DNA of an organism from another species. The resulting organisms are referred to as genetically modified (GM), or transgenic.

READING TIP The root *trans* means "across." *Transgenic* refers to the movement of genes across species.

CHECK YOUR READING What are three steps involved in genetic engineering?

B One application of genetic engineering across species involves making plants more insect-resistant. Genetic engineers have isolated genes in microorganisms that produce natural insect-killing chemicals, or pesticides. They have succeeded in transferring these genes into the DNA of crop plants, such as corn and soybeans. The cells of the genetically modified plants then produce their own pesticide, reducing the amount of chemical pesticide farmers need to use on their fields.

5.3 INSTRUCT

Teach Difficult Concepts

To help students understand the similarities and differences between selective breeding and genetic engineering, point out that the DNA in selective breeding does not change, whereas in genetic engineering the DNA is modified to obtain a certain result. Ask:

- How does selective breeding produce dogs with different characteristics? *People breed dogs by selecting dogs with desirable characteristics (and alleles).*
- What are the advantages of both selective breeding and genetic engineering? *Both have the goal of producing species with desirable traits.*

EXPLORE the BIG idea

Revisit "What Vegetable Is That?" on p. 133. Explain that the broccoflower is a hybrid, a mix of two species. Discuss the difference between genetic engineering—which combines genes by isolating and transferring them—and hybridization, which combines the genes of two species through controlled reproduction and growth. Point out that many uses of genetic engineering are modifications rather than combinations. Ask students for examples. *A plant may be given pest resistance or a cow the ability to give more milk.*

Ongoing Assessment

Describe how scientists can change organisms by changing DNA.

Ask: What is a transgenic organism? *It is an organism that has been genetically modified.*

CHECK YOUR READING *Answer: Selective breeding causes certain alleles to become more common in a particular breed.*

CHECK YOUR READING *Answer: Genetic engineering involves isolating a segment of DNA from an organism and inserting the DNA into the DNA of another organism, thus changing that organism's DNA.*

DIFFERENTIATE INSTRUCTION

More Reading Support

A What is changed by genetic engineering? *DNA*

B Name an application of genetic engineering. *insect-resistant plants*

Additional Investigation To reinforce Section 5.3 learning goals, use the following full-period investigation:

R **Additional INVESTIGATION,** DNA Fingerprinting Simulation, A, B, & C, pp. 297–305, 308–309 (Advanced students should complete Levels B and C.)

English Learners Help students recognize when sentences indicate cause-and-effect relationships. For example, "When crops can be grown in more places, the yield of food increases." Even though the word *then* is missing from the second part of the sentence, it is implied.

Develop Critical Thinking

APPLY Ask students to brainstorm a list of ways that plants can be genetically altered to increase the production of food. *Sample answers: Food can be engineered to taste better, keep longer, resist disease, grow in different climates and temperatures, produce hardier varieties, and produce varieties that produce more fruit.*

Real World Example

In 1994 the FDA approved the Flavr Savr tomato, the first genetically modified food available for sale. These tomatoes are modified to stay firm after harvest, allowing them to be left on the vine for a longer period of time before shipping. The FDA did not mandate labeling the tomatoes to indicate the modification.

History of Science

In 1997, researchers at the Roslin Institute in Scotland announced the birth of the first mammal cloned from an adult cell. They had used somatic cell nuclear transfer, inserting the fertilized egg into the womb of a surrogate mother sheep. The result was a lamb named Dolly, who was genetically identical to the sheep who provided the original cell nucleus. Dolly lived six years, which is half as long as normal; however, there was no evidence that her health was in any way impaired by being a clone. For more information on Dolly and cloning, see p. 154.

Ongoing Assessment

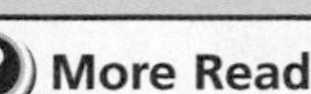

CHECK YOUR READING *Answer: risks: unknown effects on humans and ecosystems; benefits: greater amounts of food produced, more nutritious food produced, food produced with less environmental damage*

These tomatoes have been genetically modified to grow in conditions that would not support naturally occurring tomatoes.

Genetic engineering can address very specific needs. For example, in many parts of the world, soils are poor in nutrients. Or the soil may contain salts. Such soil is not good for growing food crops. Genetic engineers have inserted a gene from a salt-tolerant cabbage into tomatoes. The salt-tolerant tomatoes can grow in soil that natural tomatoes cannot grow in. These tomatoes can also be grown using brackish water, which is water with a higher salt content than fresh water.

There are risks and benefits associated with genetic engineering.

C

Genetic engineering offers potential benefits to society, but also carries potential risks. Probably most people in the United States have eaten foods made from genetically modified corn or soybeans. The plants have bacterial genes that make them more resistant to plant-eating insects. This increases food production and reduces the amount of chemical pesticides needed. Less chemical pesticide on the ground reduces the risk of environmental pollution.

However, many people worry that the natural pesticides produced by a genetically modified plant might have some effect on humans. What if genetically modified plants cross-breed with other plants, and give protection to plants that are considered weeds? There is also the question of how to let people know if the food they eat is genetically modified. Many people think that such food should be labeled.

CHECK YOUR READING What are some risks and benefits associated with using genetic engineering in food crops?

DIFFERENTIATE INSTRUCTION

More Reading Support

C How have corn and soybeans been genetically modified? *They are more resistant to plant-eating insects.*

Advanced Have students learn more about the issues that surround genetically engineered foods. Have students form their own opinions and hold a debate. It should address the potential benefits and dangers of genetically engineered food as well as the issue of whether these foods should be closely regulated by the government and how.

Challenge and Extension, p. 279

There is uncertainty about how the DNA of genetically modified organisms might affect natural populations. For example, scientists are working with salmon that are genetically modified to grow more quickly. Fish are an important food source, and natural fish populations are decreasing. However, the salmon are raised in pens set in rivers or the sea. If the fish escape, they may breed with fish from wild populations. Government officials have yet to decide whether the benefit of having these fast-growing fish is worth the risk to wild populations.

ANALYZE How would the genetic material of wild salmon change if they were to breed with genetically modified salmon?

DNA technology has many applications.

DNA technology is used in many different ways. It can be used to add nutrients to foods to make them more nutritious. It can be used to produce new and better drugs for treating disease. DNA technology can also be used to determine whether a particular drug might cause side effects in an individual. And it can be used to screen for and perhaps treat genetic disorders.

DNA Identification

You may have seen news stories about how DNA evidence is used to solve a crime. Law enforcement specialists gather as much DNA evidence as they can from a crime scene—for example, skin, hair, or blood. In a laboratory, they scan about ten regions of the DNA that are known to vary from individual to individual. They use this information to produce a DNA profile—a DNA fingerprint. This fingerprint is unique to a person, unless that person has an identical twin. If DNA analysis of tissue found at the crime scene matches the DNA fingerprint of a suspect, then police know the suspect was at the scene.

The more matches found between crime-scene DNA and the suspect's DNA, the higher the probability that the suspect is guilty. Experts currently recommend that at least four to six DNA regions be matched to establish a person's guilt. The chances are very small that another person would have exactly the same DNA profile for all the DNA regions tested. Of course, the courts also take other forms of evidence into account before an individual is convicted of a crime.

Learn more about DNA technology.

DIFFERENTIATE INSTRUCTION

More Reading Support

D How many regions of DNA are used to make a DNA fingerprint? *ten*

E Who is the only person who could match an individual's DNA fingerprint? *an identical twin*

Below Level Have students take on the roles of forensic scientists testifying at a trial in which DNA fingerprinting is to be used as evidence of a crime. Have students write a short paper explaining to a jury why DNA fingerprinting is reliable evidence for identifying a person.

Advanced Have students who are interested in genetic engineering read the following article:

 Challenge Reading, pp. 281–282

Integrate the Sciences

Forensic science applies the knowledge and tools of science to criminal investigations in order to provide evidence to solve criminal cases. Fields of forensic science include pathology, toxicology, anthropology, and odontology. Forensic pathology involves determining the cause of death through autopsy. Toxicology is concerned with the presence of poisons or drugs that may be present in a victim's body. Anthropology deals with the identification of skeletal remains, and odontology is related to bite-mark impressions. A separate field known as criminalistics deals with the gathering of evidence at a scene, such as blood, hair, fibers, and fingerprints.

EXPLORE the BIG idea

Revisit "Internet Activity: Human Genome" on p. 133. Have students share their observations.

Real World Example

Like identical twins, clones are two organisms that are genetically identical. One way to produce clones is artificial twinning. This process manually separates an early embryo into individual cells, which then divide and develop on their own. Another way to produce clones is somatic cell nuclear transfer. Researchers take out the nucleus of a cell that has a full complement of chromosomes (any cell but an egg or a sperm). They then insert this nucleus into an egg cell.

Ongoing Assessment

Describe some applications of DNA technology.

Ask: Why is DNA fingerprinting a reliable method of identifying a person? *The DNA fingerprint is unique to an individual.*

Develop Critical Thinking

EVALUATE Students can use p. 154 as a springboard for debate and discussion. Ask:

- What are the benefits of cloning? What are the risks?
- What are some ethical concerns of cloning?

Ongoing Assessment

Analyze the issues surrounding the use of DNA technology.

Ask: What are some of the benefits of cloning? *It has been used to produce proteins and drugs that fight disease.*

Reinforce 

Have students relate the section to the Big Idea.

 Reinforcing Key Concepts, p. 280

5.3 ASSESS & RETEACH

Assess

 Section 5.3 Quiz, p. 81

Reteach

Have students give an example of each concept:

- selective breeding *(Sample: McIntosh apples, Chihuahua dogs, merino sheep)*
- genetic engineering *(Sample: "Flavr Savr" tomatoes)*
- DNA technology *(Sample: tests used in forensics and paleontology)*
- cloning *(Sample: Dolly the sheep, the first cloned mammal)*

Technology Resources

Have students visit **ClassZone.com** for reteaching of Key Concepts.

 CONTENT REVIEW

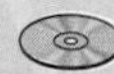 CONTENT REVIEW CD-ROM

Studying Genomes

VOCABULARY
Don't forget to choose a strategy to take notes on the term *genome*.

One of the most challenging scientific projects ever undertaken was the Human Genome Project. A **genome** is all the genetic material in an organism. The primary goal of the project was to sequence the 3 billion nucleotide pairs in a single set of human chromosomes. The initial sequence was published in 2001. Scientists are now working to identify the approximately 30,000 genes within the human genome.

Scientists have completed sequencing the genomes of many organisms. These organisms, often referred to as model organisms, enable scientists to compare DNA across species. Many of the genes found in model organisms, such as the fruit fly and mouse, are also found in the human genome.

Dolly was the first successful clone of a mammal.

Scientists are aware that there are many ethical, legal, and social issues that arise from the ability to change DNA. We as a society have to decide when it is acceptable to change DNA and how to use the technology we have. **Cloning** is a technique that uses technology to make copies. It can be applied to a segment of DNA or to a whole organism. Cloning has been used in bacteria to produce proteins and drugs that help fight disease. Human insulin, which is used to treat people with a certain form of diabetes, is now produced in large quantities as the result of cloning techniques.

The same technology, which is so helpful in one application, can be a cause of concern when applied in a different way. In 1996, scientists produced the first clone of a mammal, a sheep named Dolly. All of Dolly's DNA came from a single body cell of another sheep. The ability to clone such a complex animal raised many concerns about future uses of cloning. This, as well as many other possible applications of technology, makes it important that people understand the science of genetics. Only then can they make informed decisions about how and when the technology should be used.

5.3 Review

KEY CONCEPTS

1. What is a genetically modified organism?
2. What is the Human Genome Project?
3. List three different applications of DNA technology.

CRITICAL THINKING

4. **Compare and Contrast** How is selective breeding different from genetic engineering? How is it the same?
5. **Analyze** Do you think a genetically modified trait in an organism can be undone? Why or why not?

CHALLENGE

6. **Analyze** Why might a genetically engineered drug, such as insulin, be better for treatment of disease than a drug that is manufactured chemically?

154 Unit 1: **Cells and Heredity**

ANSWERS

1. A GM organism has had a gene from another species transferred to its DNA.

2. sequencing the 3 billion nucleotide pairs in human DNA

3. Sample answers: add nutrients to foods, produce new and better drugs, increase food production, and screen for genetic disorders

4. selective breeding—selecting parent organisms to pass on traits to offspring; genetic engineering—isolating specific DNA, inserting it into another organism; both—producing organisms with desirable traits

5. no, because the trait is now coded for in all the organism's cells

6. Sample answer: because it comes from a more natural source, or a source more similar to that of a healthy human

DNA OF EXTINCT ANIMALS

Modern Genetics Meets the Dodo and the Solitaire

Hunted to Extinction

The dodo bird was first sighted around 1600 by Portuguese sailors arriving on the shores of the island of Mauritius in the Indian Ocean. Portuguese sailors hunted the dodo, which was unable to fly, and used its meat for food. The bird, never having had contact with humans, did not run away. Only a mere 80 years later, the dodo was extinct.

DNA Evidence

Few bone specimens of the dodo bird remain today. Scientists collected and analyzed genetic material from preserved dodo specimens and specimens of another, similar extinct bird called the solitaire bird. The DNA evidence was compared with the genetic material of about 35 species of living pigeons and doves.

The model shows a solitaire bird, a close relative of the dodo.

The DNA had a story to tell. Evidence suggests that the dodo and solitaire bird were close relatives. Their nearest living relative is a species of pigeon found in nearby southeast Asia. From this evidence, scientists hypothesize that the dodo and solitaire birds species became separate almost 25 million years ago. In the geographic location of the island of Mauritius, the dodo developed its distinct characteristics, which eventually led to its extinction.

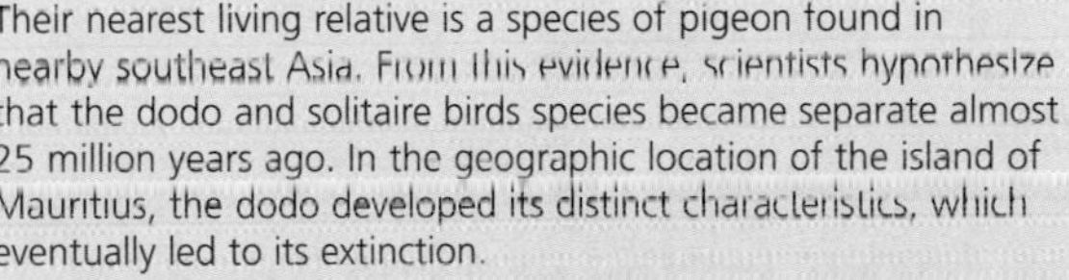

EXPLORE

1. **MAKE INFERENCES** How can scientists use what they know from analyzing dodo bones to help them form conclusions about the physical characteristics of the bird?
2. **CHALLENGE** Several factors contributed to the extinction of the dodo bird. Look online to find out more about these factors. How can learning about what happened to the dodo help save today's endangered species from extinction?

EXPLORE

1. *MAKE INFERENCES The bones would give some indication of the bird's size. Using DNA evidence, scientists can look for modern relatives that might give clues to the bird's physical characteristics and appearance.*
2. *CHALLENGE The dodo's inability to fly made it difficult for it to escape predators. Destruction of the dodo's environment led to a decrease in its food supply. Animals such as dogs, cats, and pigs were introduced into the environment by the sailors, and proceeded to destroy the dodo nests. Learning about past mistakes will help people avoid those mistakes in the future.*

EXTREME SCIENCE

Fun and Motivating Science

Set Learning Goal

To understand how scientists use DNA to solve mysteries about extinct species

Present the Science

Scientists hypothesize that the dodo evolved from a bird capable of flying, a bird similar to a pigeon. They think that an ancestor of the dodo may have landed on the island of Mauritius, where the abundant food supply and lack of predators allowed the species to evolve over many generations into the flightless dodo. Flying is an activity that requires a lot of energy. Being able to fly did not provide the birds with any advantage.

Discussion Questions

Ask: How were scientists able to determine that the dodo and solitaire birds were close relatives? *They extracted and compared the DNA.*

Many species of birds live on the island of Mauritius. Ask: How is it that one species evolved in a way that is distinctly different from the rest, and what does this have to do with the genetic makeup of the species? *Species can adapt to conditions in their environment. It is possible a mutation occurred in ancestors of the dodo that resulted in a group of birds that could not fly. Because of the particular conditions on the island (abundant food, lack of predators), these ancestral birds were able to survive and reproduce, at least until those conditions changed.*

Close

Ask: What difficulties do you think scientists might encounter in trying to establish common ancestry between living organisms and extinct species? *DNA evidence may not always be available for extinct species.*

BACK TO

the BIG idea

Have students look back at the photograph on pp. 132–133. Have them summarize what they have learned about the structure of DNA. How does the pairing of bases in the molecule enable DNA to make proteins? *DNA is made up of a sequence of nucleotides that form a code for making proteins.*

KEY CONCEPTS SUMMARY

SECTION 5.1
Ask students to describe the role of mRNA and tRNA in forming proteins. *The assembly of amino acids in their proper sequence begins when a ribosome attaches to an mRNA molecule. tRNA molecules carry specific amino acids to the ribosomes, matching them up with triplets on the mRNA molecule.*

SECTION 5.2
Ask students to give an example of a mutation that is beneficial and a mutation that is harmful. *Beneficial mutations might include a mutation that makes an organism more resistant to disease. Harmful mutations are those that result in genetic disorders such as cystic fibrosis.*

SECTION 5.3
Ask: What are some risks involved with genetic engineering when plants or animals are modified? *Plants that are modified to become resistant to insects might cross breed with plants that are undesirable such as weeds. Fish that are genetically modified to grow more quickly in fish farms could escape and breed with the natural population, possibly limiting genetic diversity.*

Review Concepts

- Big Idea Flow Chart, p. T33
- Chapter Outline, pp. T39–T40

5 Chapter Review

the BIG idea

DNA is a set of instructions for making cell parts.

KEY CONCEPTS SUMMARY

DNA and RNA are required to make proteins.

DNA contains a code that enables a cell to make RNA and proteins. Replication copies the code before a cell divides.

- DNA's triplet code enables a cell to code for proteins
- mRNA, tRNA, and ribosomes translate the code into a sequence of amino acids.
- The amino acids form a protein needed for cell function.

VOCABULARY
replication p. 137
RNA p. 138

Changes in DNA can produce variation.

Differences in DNA produce variations. Any change to DNA is a mutation. Many mutations have little or no effect. However, some mutations can change the way a cell works—sometimes helping an organism, sometimes hurting it.

Genetic disorders are caused by mutations in DNA. Some are inherited and can be followed through different generations of a family by using a pedigree. Other genetic disorders, such as cancer, are caused by mutations that occur during a person's lifetime.

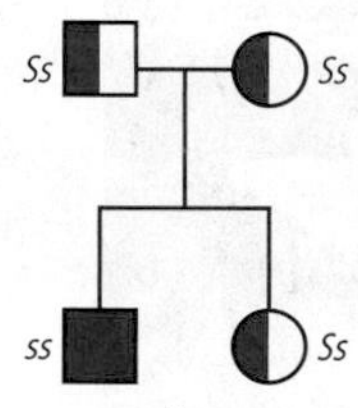
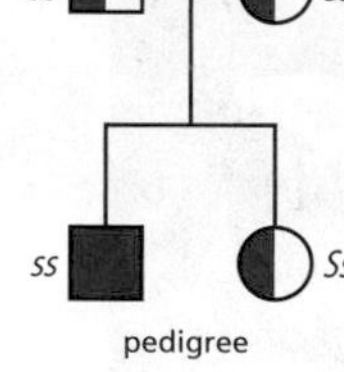

pedigree

VOCABULARY
mutation p. 145
pedigree p. 147

Modern genetics uses DNA technology.

Changes in DNA can change an organism. Selective breeding changes organisms by choosing desired traits already coded for by DNA.

Genetic engineering introduces changes to the DNA of an organism. It can be used to

- introduce new traits into an organism
- produce medicines and other products
- identify individuals
- clone genes as well as organisms
- sequence the genome of an organism

DNA technology raises important issues for society.

Dolly was the first clone of a mammal.

VOCABULARY
selective breeding p. 151
genetic engineering p. 151
genome p. 154
cloning p. 154

156 Unit 1: Cells and Heredity

Technology Resources

Have students visit **ClassZone.com** or use the CD-ROM for a cumulative review of concepts.

 **CONTENT REVIEW**

 **CONTENT REVIEW CD-ROM**

Engage students in a whole-class interactive review of Key Concepts. Edit content as you wish.

 **POWER PRESENTATIONS**

Reviewing Vocabulary

Copy the chart below and write the definition for each word. Use the meaning of the word's root to help you.

Term	Root Meaning	Definition
1. replication	to repeat	
2. mutation	to change	
3. genome	relating to offspring	
4. cloning	to branch off	

Reviewing Key Concepts

Multiple Choice *Choose the letter of the best answer.*

5. Genes are sequences of DNA, which are made up of
a. nucleotides **c.** phosphates
b. chromosomes **d.** ribosomes

6. What happens during replication?
a. DNA is copied.
b. RNA is copied.
c. Ribosomes are made.
d. Proteins are made.

7. Which base is found only in RNA?
a. thymine
b. guanine
c. adenine
d. uracil

8. The main function of mRNA in protein synthesis is to
a. transfer amino acids to a ribosome
b. carry proteins to the ribosome
c. transcribe genes from DNA
d. connect nucleotides together

9. Proteins are made up of a sequence of
a. chromosomes **c.** nucleotides
b. amino acids **d.** base pairs

10. Mutations are changes in
a. DNA **c.** tRNA
b. the cell cycle **d.** proteins

11. Which is a known cause of genetic mutations?
a. poor nutrition
b. malaria
c. ultraviolet radiation
d. cancer

12. A pedigree shows
a. how proteins are synthesized
b. how genes are inherited in a family
c. where mutations are located in a sequence of DNA
d. which triplet of bases matches up with a particular amino acid

13. The main goal of the Human Genome Project was to
a. find cures for genetic diseases
b. find all mutations in human DNA
c. count the number of genes in human DNA
d. sequence all DNA on human chromosomes

14. Genetic engineering involves
a. inserting changed DNA into an organism
b. cross-breeding plants
c. testing new medicines for genetic diseases
d. using x rays to change DNA

Short Answer *Write a short answer to each question.*

15. DNA is described as the information molecule. What is the information that DNA carries?

16. What is the difference between selective breeding and genetic engineering?

17. List three applications of DNA technology and how these uses benefit humans.

ASSESSMENT RESOURCES

UNIT ASSESSMENT BOOK
- Chapter Test, Level A, pp. 82–85
- Chapter Test, Level B, pp. 86–89
- Chapter Test, Level C, pp. 90–93
- Alternative Assessment, pp. 94–95
- Unit Test, A, B, & C, pp. 96–107

SPANISH ASSESSMENT BOOK
- Spanish Chapter Test, pp. 17–20
- Spanish Unit Test, pp. 21–24

Technology Resources

Edit test items and answer choices.

 **Test Generator CD ROM**

Visit **ClassZone.com** to extend test practice.

 **Test Practice**

Reviewing Vocabulary

Sample answers:

1. the process in which DNA is copied

2. a change in the DNA of a cell

3. all the genetic material in an organism—genes being units of heredity

4. technology that makes copies of DNA from living cells

Reviewing Key Concepts

5. a
6. a
7. d
8. c
9. b
10. a
11. c
12. b
13. d
14. a

15. DNA carries instructions for making proteins.

16. Selective breeding involves selecting species with desirable traits to produce a variety that always has those traits. Genetic engineering involves changing the DNA of an organism to produce desirable traits.

17. Scientists use genetic engineering to alter plants and animals to make them produce more food, to produce drugs for treating disease, and to screen for genetic disorders.

(Answers to items that appear on p. 158)

Thinking Critically

18. The mRNA strand will have the matching pairs of the DNA template strand—guanine and cytosine pair together, while uracil replaces thymine on the mRNA strand in pairing with adenine.

19. Messenger RNA contains the DNA code. Transfer RNA carries specific amino acids to the ribosomes and matches them up with the triplets on mRNA. Ribosomal RNA makes up the ribosomes, which links together the amino acids.

(Answers for items 18–19 appear on p. 157.)

Thinking Critically

20. *There are 3 bases per amino acid, so 393.*
21. *The gene on the other molecule of DNA will not necessarily be mutated.*
22. *The code translates to too few and incorrect amino acids.*
23. *The DNA molecule opens up, and one strand is transcribed into mRNA. The mRNA moves into the cytoplasm, where a ribosome (made of rRNA and proteins) attaches to it. Then tRNA molecules bring amino acids to the ribosome, which attaches them in the sequence coded on the mRNA. The completed protein is released.*
24. *Some genetic disorders are recessive, so they can be masked by a normal gene on the matching chromosome.*
25. *They might extract the DNA and look for changes in the sequence.*
26. *Brown spots would make it difficult for the hare to blend in with the arctic environment. The hare might become easy prey because it would not be camouflaged as well with brown spots.*
27. *If even one cancer cell is left, it will continue to divide in an uncontrolled manner, causing the cancer to spread.*
28. *The same DNA is being passed on to offspring over and over again, allowing for little genetic variety.*
29. *The scientist might infer that the cells function similarly, using similar proteins.*

the BIG idea

30. *Answers should mention the complementary pairing of bases on two strands, with the sequence forming a code.*
31. *Students' positions should be supported with concepts or examples presented in the chapter.*

UNIT PROJECTS

Have students present their projects. Use appropriate rubrics to evaluate work.

 Unit Projects, pp. 5–10

Thinking Critically

Use the diagram to answer the next three questions.

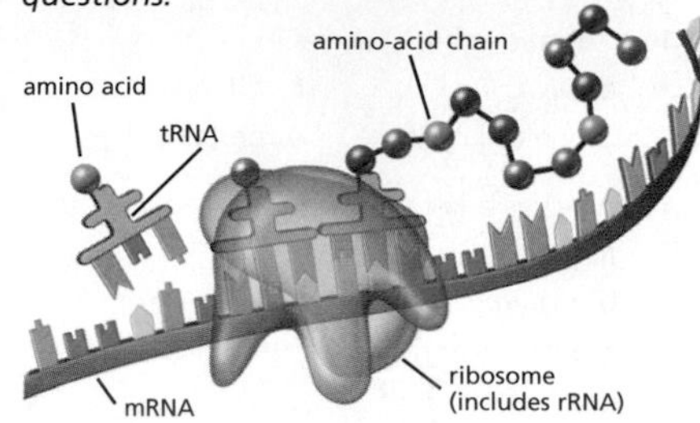

18. **ANALYZE** How does the mRNA strand above compare with the DNA template that produced it? Use the words *guanine, cytosine, thymine, adenine, and uracil* in your answer.
19. **SUMMARIZE** Three types of RNA are needed for protein synthesis. What are the three types and what is the function of each?
20. **APPLY** A protein contains 131 amino acids. How many bases will there be on the mRNA strand corresponding to these amino acids and how do you know?
21. **ANALYZE** A cell contains two sets of DNA. If the gene on one molecule of DNA has a mutation, how will that affect the gene on the other molecule of DNA?
22. **SYNTHESIZE** A mutation occurs during DNA replication. The following sequence

    A-T-T-A-C-A-G-G-G

    is copied as,

    A-T-A-C-A-G-G-G

    with one base missing. How does that affect the triplet code?
23. **SEQUENCE** List the steps in making a protein. Start with a gene on a DNA molecule. Include the chemical subunits involved in each step.
24. **EVALUATE** A person who carries a gene for a genetic disorder may not get the disorder. How can that be?
25. **INFER** How might a scientist determine if a neutral mutation has occurred in an organism?
26. **PREDICT** A mutation in an Arctic hare causes brown spots to appear on normally white fur. Explain how the mutation might affect the ability of the hare to survive.
27. **EVALUATE** Doctors can sometimes cure cancer by removing cancerous cells from a person's body. Why is it important for the doctors to remove all the cells?
28. **EVALUATE** How might selective breeding of a type of animal limit genetic diversity within the breed?
29. **EVALUATE** If a scientist compares the genome of a mouse to that of a human and discovers that the two organisms have many of the same genes, what can the scientist infer about how the cells in the two organisms function?

the BIG idea

30. **DRAWING CONCLUSIONS** Look again at the photograph on pages 132–133. How have models helped scientists understand the function of DNA?
31. **CONNECT** A local newspaper has written an editorial against the use of genetic engineering. The writer argues that humans should never change the DNA in an organism, even though they have the technology to do so. Write a response to the editorial, stating whether you think the benefits humans get from genetic engineering are worth the risks.

UNIT PROJECTS

Evaluate all the data, results, and information from your project folder. Prepare to present your project. Be ready to answer questions posed by your classmates about your results.

MONITOR AND RETEACH

If students are having trouble applying the concepts in Chapter Review items 18, 19, and 22, suggest that they review the illustrations of replication on p. 137, transcription on p. 139, and translation on p. 140. Then have students create a flow chart showing the sequence of events for each process.

Students may benefit from summarizing one or more sections of the chapter.

 Summarizing the Chapter, pp. 306–307

Standardized Test Practice

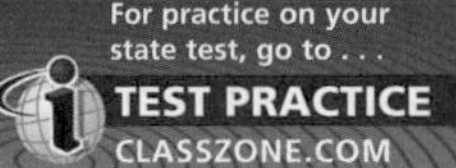

Analyzing Data

Use the following information and the pedigree chart to answer the questions.

Red-green colorblindness is one of the most common genetic conditions in the human population. About 5 percent of males are red-green colorblind. A male receives just one allele for this trait, on the X chromosome he inherits from his mother. If he receives the allele for red-green colorblindness, he will be colorblind. His genotype will be cb/Y.

Females inherit two alleles for the trait. Colorblindness (cb) is recessive and the allele for regular color vision (Cb) is dominant. A female with both the recessive allele and the dominant allele will have normal color vision. Her genotype would be Cb/cb. However, if the female has a male child, her child may be colorblind. The pedigree chart shows colorblindness in three generations.

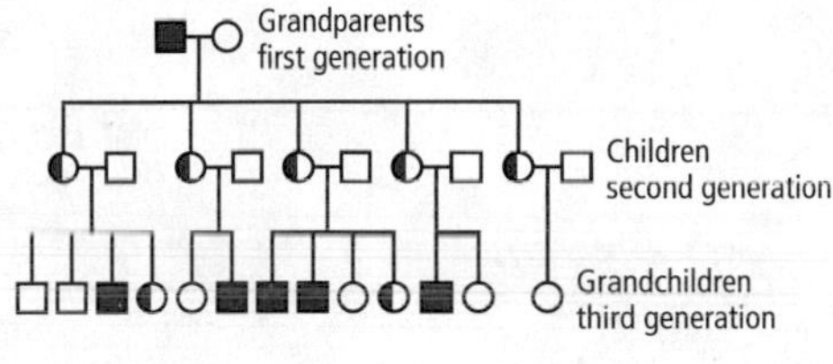

1. How many individuals in the first generation are colorblind?
   a. two
   b. one
   c. none
   d. three
2. How many individuals in the second generation are female?
   a. none
   b. one
   c. two
   d. five
3. Which statement describes the pattern of inheritance for colorblindness?
   a. Grandmother and granddaughter are both colorblind.
   b. Grandmother and son are both colorblind.
   c. Grandfather and granddaughter are both colorblind.
   d. Grandfather and grandson are both colorblind.
4. What are the genotypes of the males in the third generation?
   a. Cb/Y, Cb/Y, Cb/Y, cb/Y, cb/Y, cb/Y, cb/Y
   b. cb/Y, cb/Y, cb/Y, cb/Y, cb/Y, cb/Y, cb/Y
   c. Cb/Y, Cb/Y, Cb/Y, Cb/Y, Cb/Y, Cb/Y, CbY
   d. Cb/Y, Cb/Y, cb/Y, cb/y, cb/y ,cb/Y, cb/Y

Extended Response

5. Write a paragraph explaining why a color-blind man who has three daughters and one son with normal color vision might have two grandsons who are color-blind. Use the terms in the vocabulary box in your answer. Underline each term.

genotype	phenotype	allele
recessive	dominant	generation

6. The same color-blind man has four granddaughters. Would you predict the granddaughters to be colorblind? Explain why or why not. Use the terms in the vocabulary box.

METACOGNITIVE ACTIVITY

Have students answer the following questions in their **Science Notebook:**

1. What questions do you still have about DNA, how proteins are made, and how DNA is used to modify organisms through technology?
2. What did you learn about in this unit that surprised you? Explain.
3. While researching your unit project, where did your best research come from?

Analyzing Data

1. b *2. d* *3. d* *4. d*

Extended Response

5. RUBRIC

4 points for a response that correctly answers the question and includes at least four of the following terms:

- genotype
- recessive
- phenotype
- dominant
- allele
- generation

Sample answer: Because the man is colorblind, the daughters will inherit the recessive allele for the trait, but will not express the phenotype for colorblindness. These daughters are carriers of the trait. The sons of the next generation may be colorblind if they inherit the recessive allele from their mother.

3 points correctly answers the question and includes at least three of the terms listed

2 points correctly answers the question and includes at least two of the terms listed

1 point correctly answers the question and includes at least one of the terms listed

6. RUBRIC

4 points for a response that correctly answers the question and includes at least four of the terms.

Sample answer: The granddaughters may inherit the recessive allele for the trait from their mother, in which case they would have a genotype of Cb/cb. Because they can only inherit the dominant allele, Cb, from their father, the trait would not be expressed in the phenotype.

3 points correctly answers the question and includes at least three of the terms listed

2 points correctly answers the question and includes at least two of the terms listed

1 point correctly answers the question and includes at least one of the terms listed

McDougal Littell Science

Life Over Time

classification

FOSSIL

species

preserved remains

Life Over Time
Contents Overview

Unit Features

VIDEO SUMMARY

SCIENTIFIC AMERICAN FRONTIERS

"Noah's Snowball" is a segment of the *Scientific American Frontiers* series that aired on PBS stations. The video presents what geologists Paul Hoffman and Daniel Schrag of Harvard University call the "Snowball Earth" hypothesis.

They suggest that a slight temperature change about 700 million years ago caused the polar ice caps to cover Earth. Erupting volcanoes eventually raised the temperature enough to melt the ice. Within a hundred million years, they hypothesize, multicelled life forms developed in a "biological big bang."

Up to this time, life on Earth had consisted entirely of microbes. Paleontologists in China are shown in the video, excavating fossils that may represent the earliest known complex animals.

National Science Education Standards

A.1–8 Abilities Necessary to Do Scientific Inquiry

A.9.a–b, A.9.d–g Understandings About Scientific Inquiry

F.5.e Science and Technology in Society

G.1.a–b Science as a Human Endeavor

G.2.a, G.2.c Nature of Science

FRONTIERS in Science

Life By Degrees

What happens when Earth's climate changes? Scientists are studying how climate change has influenced the evolution of life on Earth.

SCIENTIFIC AMERICAN FRONTIERS

Learn about how climate change affected life on Earth. See the video "Noah's Snowball."

ADDITIONAL RESOURCES

Technology Resources

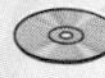

Scientific American Frontiers Video: *Noah's Snowball:* 11-minute video segment that introduces the unit.

ClassZone.com
CAREER LINK, Paleontologist

Guide student viewing and comprehension of the video:

Video Teaching Guide, pp. 1–2; Video Viewing Guide, p. 3; Video Wrap-Up, p. 4

Scientific American Frontiers Video Guide, pp. 3–6

Unit projects procedures and rubrics:

Unit Projects, pp. 5–10

Climate and Life

Throughout its history, Earth's climate has changed many times. Often the changes are gradual. They may seem small. However, an average global temperature change of just a few degrees can have a large impact on climate. Small changes in climate then cause big changes for plants and animals.

Before there were humans to record events, Earth recorded its changes in its rocks and fossils. For example, scientists get a sense for Earth's climate at different times in the distant past by looking at fossils, the remains and traces of living things. If scientists find fossils of tropical plants in places near the arctic circle, then they may conclude that the climate in those places was different in the past. **?** A

Scientists have found that warmer climates lead to a greater diversity of organisms. One researcher examined fossils of tiny organisms called phytoplankton (FY-toh-PLANK-tuhn). During cooler climate periods, there were fewer types of phytoplankton than during warmer periods. The same is true for other organisms. Peter Wilf and Conrad Labandeira studied fossil plants. They were especially interested in the marks they found on the plants. The marks were left by plant-eating animals who bit the leaves. The warmer the climate was, the more types of plants there were—and the more kinds of animals were eating the plants. **?** B

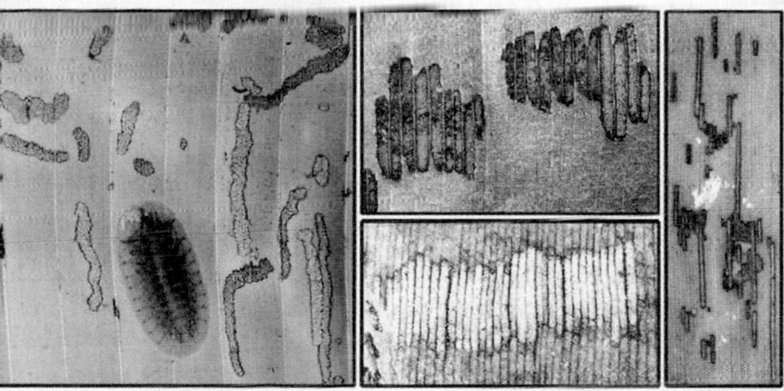

SOURCE: Images © 2000 AAAS

The chew marks of the hispine beetle larva on living ginger in Panama (left) look similar to fossilized chew marks found in Wyoming (three photos right).

DIFFERENTIATE INSTRUCTION

? **More Reading Support**

A What do you call the preserved remains of living things? *fossils*

B What climates lead to more diversity of life? *warm climates*

Advanced Have students research the climate history of the area in which you live. Have them include what species of plants and animals are hypothesized to have lived there in earlier eras.

FOCUS

Set Learning Goals

Students will

- Observe the relationship of climate to life on Earth.
- Analyze possible causes and results of mass extinctions.
- Analyze extinction and learn about extinct species.

Remind students that frontiers are places where limits are pushed back. Point out that the "Noah's Snowball" video shows real scientists gathering evidence and forming hypotheses to push back the limits surrounding knowledge of Earth before recorded history. Ask what such limits might be. Point out that, unlike people who study history—events recorded in words—scientists study fossils to gather unwritten evidence of life during Earth's prehistory.

INSTRUCT

Scientific Process

Ask students to identify some skills scientists use when constructing theories to explain how climate change millions of years ago affected life on Earth. *forming a hypothesis, making observations, collecting data, making inferences* Point out that forming a hypothesis requires careful gathering and study of fossil evidence that may be incomplete or open to misinterpretation. Note that to avoid misinterpretation, scientists may corroborate fossil evidence with evidence gained from studying modern living things.

Integrate the Sciences

When Peter Ward studied the sedimentary rocks of South African rivers, he found that large, meandering rivers changed during the Permian period, becoming braided. Geologists often compare present geological forms to earlier times and reason that similar processes caused them. Because some rivers have similar form then and now, it is reasonable to think the older rivers are in areas where plant devastation led to massive erosion.

Scientific Process

To understand the evidence recorded in fossils and rocks, paleontologists must understand how forces such as water, wind, and ice work on Earth's surface. Ask: Why does this make sharing results especially important? *Interpreting the evidence may require data gathered by scientists working in a variety of disciplines.*

Technology Design

Because the collision of an asteroid or comet with Earth would cause great destruction, NASA is trying to locate large asteroids that pose a risk to Earth. Making a massive, ordered patrol of the sky requires many hours of work. Robotic telescopes automatically point and focus, and record their findings on digital pictures, which computers can analyze.

Before and after photographs of the sky show that distinct bands appeared due to dust and ash from the 1991 volcanic eruption of Mt. Pinatubo.

Mass Extinction

Several times in Earth's past, many kinds of animals and plants have disappeared in a relatively short time. These events are called mass extinctions. While we don't know for sure what causes them, most scientists think climate change plays a role in mass extinctions.

? C

The largest mass extinction in Earth's history happened at the end of the Permian (PER-mee-uhn) Period about 248 million years ago. Scientists estimate that 90–95 percent of animal species that lived in the water died out. About three quarters of the vertebrates, or animals with backbones, living on land died out too.

Turn of Events

What caused this extinction? Using fossils, scientists have concluded that Earth's climate became cooler. Material from erupting volcanoes may have blocked sunlight long enough to cool the Earth. The cool temperatures and lack of sunlight may have killed plants and animals.

? D

Scientist Peter Ward has been studying the Permian extinction. He looked at ancient African rivers and found evidence that rivers had became clogged with soil. Plants normally holding soil in place may have been wiped out, causing the soil on the riverbanks to loosen. The plant extinction would also have led to animal extinction.

View the "Noah's Snowball" segment of your Scientific American Frontiers video to learn about another theory of how climate change affected life on Earth.

IN THIS SCENE FROM THE VIDEO **Fossil hunters examine evidence of early life in China.**

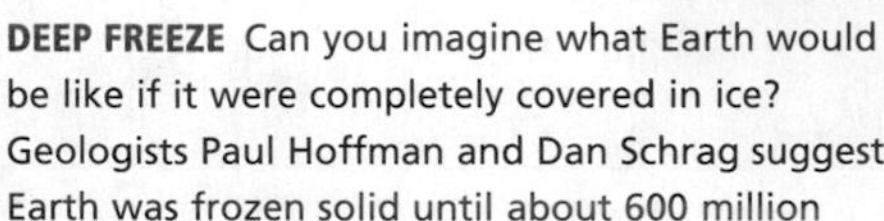

DEEP FREEZE Can you imagine what Earth would be like if it were completely covered in ice? Geologists Paul Hoffman and Dan Schrag suggest Earth was frozen solid until about 600 million years ago. They think Earth's climate changed by just a few degrees, but it was enough to make the ice caps cover the planet. The only life that survived was bacteria that were kept warm by volcanoes. And it was the volcanoes that changed the climate again, say Hoffman and Schrag. Suddenly eruptions melted the ice. Ocean levels rose. The scientists think this change might have taken only a hundred years. Not everyone agrees with the snowball hypothesis, but it could explain why new forms of life began to appear.

DIFFERENTIATE INSTRUCTION

More Reading Support

C What is a mass extinction? *when many species become extinct*

D What may have caused the largest mass extinction? *climate change*

Below Level Help students distinguish between the short-term climate changes that occur with the changing seasons of the year and the long-term climate changes being discussed here. Have them make a chart with events at each scale. *Sample answer: short-term: leaves fall from trees, animals grow thicker fur, snow falls and melts, we wear warm clothes or bathing suits; long-term: whole species become extinct, ice may cover a tropical area; less sunlight reaches Earth's surface and it is dark for many years*

What Hit Them?

Not all scientists agree about what caused the Permian extinction. If an asteroid hit Earth, it would push massive amounts of dirt and dust into the air. This could block sunlight and create a cooler climate. An increase in volcanic eruptions is another possible cause.

The most famous extinction of all took place at the end of the Cretaceous Period. The extended winter that may have followed a meteor impact caused many large land animals—including dinosaurs—to become extinct.

In a new climate some species thrive and survive. They spread out and, over time, evolve to fill empty niches or unique roles in the environment. For example, before the Cretaceous extinction, the only mammals were small. After the dinosaurs became extinct, large mammals could fill the roles of large plant-eaters and meat-eaters.

Even today, climate change continues. Earth's average temperature rose about half a degree Celsius in the twentieth century. Studying how past climate changes shaped life helps scientists predict how it may affect us in the future.

A large plant-eating mammal, *Chalicotherium grande*, roamed Asia millions of years ago.

UNANSWERED Questions

Scientists have learned a lot about climate change and mass extinctions by studying fossils. There are many questions still to be answered.

- What caused changes in Earth's climate?
- What else might have caused mass extinctions?
- How might climate change affect life on Earth in the future?

UNIT PROJECTS

As you study this unit, work alone or with a group on one of the projects listed below. Use the bulleted steps to guide your project.

Museum Display

What organisms survived the Permian extinction? What organisms went extinct?

- Create a museum display using art and text.
- Use visuals to show the organisms and the modern relatives that have close connections to them.

Design a Robot

Often, scientists design robots to study dangerous or distant locations.

- Design an artificial robot that would be well-adapted to survive an event that causes a mass extinction.
- Explain why the design would help the robot remain in operation.

Species over Time

Find out more about species that have gone extinct during recorded history.

- Choose one species that is now extinct.
- Present a timeline giving a history of that species.
- Describe what some of its ancestors and surviving related organisms are.
- Describe when it was last seen. Include some of the possible reasons for why it died out.

CAREER CENTER
CLASSZONE.COM

Learn more about careers in paleontology.

DIFFERENTIATE INSTRUCTION

More Reading Support

E Which species filled the niches left by dinosaurs? *large mammals*

Differentiate Unit Projects Projects are appropriate for varying abilities. Allow students to choose the ones that interest them most and let them vary their product. Encourage below level students to give visual or oral presentations or to record audio presentations about their topic.

Below Level Encourage students to try "Species over Time."

Advanced Challenge students to complete "Design a Robot."

UNANSWERED Questions

Have students read the questions and think of some of their own. Remind them that scientists always end up with more questions—that inquiry is the driving force of science.

- With the class, generate on the board a list of new questions.
- Students can add to the list after they watch the *Scientific American Frontiers* Video.
- Students can use the list of questions as a springboard for choosing their unit projects.

UNIT PROJECTS

Encourage students to pick the project that most appeals to them. Point out that each is long-term and will take several weeks to complete. You might group or pair students to work on projects and in some cases guide student choice. Some of the projects have student choice built into them. Each project has two worksheet pages, including a rubric. Use the pages to guide students through criteria, process, and schedule.

 Unit Projects, pp. 5–10

REVISIT concepts introduced in this article:

Chapter 6
- Fossils provide evidence of earlier life, pp. 169–171
- Earth's history includes mass extinctions, pp. 174–175
- Species change over time, pp. 177–187

Chapter 8
- Populations respond to pressures, pp. 250–257

CHAPTER

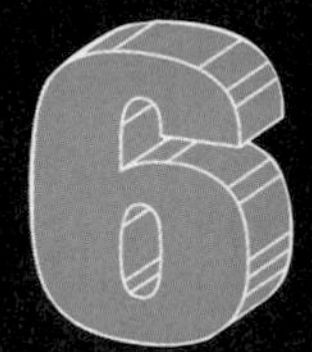

The History of Life on Earth

Life Science UNIFYING PRINCIPLES

PRINCIPLE 1
All living things share common characteristics.

PRINCIPLE 2
All living things share common needs.

PRINCIPLE 3
Living things meet their needs through interactions with the environment.

PRINCIPLE 4
The types and numbers of living things change over time.

Unit 2: Life Over Time BIG IDEAS

CHAPTER 6
The History of Life on Earth
Living things, like Earth itself, change over time.

CHAPTER 7
Classification of Living Things
Scientists have developed a system for classifying the great diversity of living things.

CHAPTER 8
Population Dynamics
Populations are shaped by interactions between organisms and the environment.

CHAPTER 6 KEY CONCEPTS

SECTION 1

Earth has been home to living things for about 3.8 billion years.

1. Fossils provide evidence of earlier life.
2. More complex organisms developed over time.
3. Earth's history includes mass extinctions.

SECTION 2

Species change over time.

1. Scientists explore the concept of evolution.
2. Natural selection explains how living things evolve.
3. New species develop from earlier species.

SECTION 3

Many types of evidence support evolution.

1. Observations provide evidence for theories.
2. Fossil evidence supports evolution.
3. Biological evidence supports evolution.
4. Genetic evidence supports evolution.

T The Big Idea Flow Chart is available on p. T1 in the **UNIT TRANSPARENCY BOOK.**

Previewing Content

SECTION

Earth has been home to living things for about 3.8 billion years. pp. 169–176

1. Fossils provide evidence of earlier life.

- **Fossils** are the remains of organisms preserved in the Earth. Fossils can consist of bones, bone fragments, imprints, and preserved remains.
- Absolute age of a fossil is determined by radioactive dating. The relative age of fossils is found by comparing the age of one fossil with another.
- The fossil record allows scientists to determine when species lived and died during Earth's geologic history.

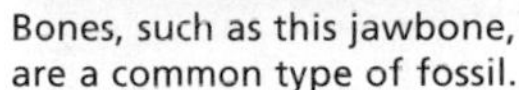

Bones, such as this jawbone, are a common type of fossil.

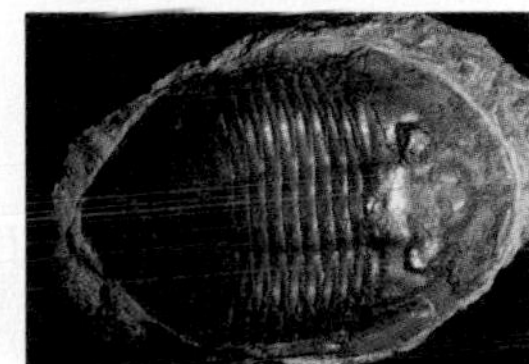

This fossil trilobite formed as minerals replaced the remains of the organism.

2. More complex organisms developed over time.
Unicellular organisms appeared on Earth about 3.8 billion years ago. Over millions of years, the cells became more complex, when, about 1.2 billion years ago, **multicellular organisms** appeared. These early organisms lived in the ocean for almost three billion years, finally making the move to land about 500 million years ago. These first land dwelling organisms were simple plants and fungi.

3. Earth's history includes mass extinctions.
Mass extinctions occur when large numbers of species die or become extinct in a short period of time. Two notable mass extinctions are the Permian Extinction, in which 90 percent of ocean-dwelling species became extinct, and the Cretaceous Extinction, in which dinosaurs became extinct.

SECTION

Species change over time. pp. 177–187

1. Scientists explore the concept of evolution.

- In the early 1800s, Jean-Baptiste de Lamarck proposed that organisms acquired traits during their lifetimes, then passed these traits on to their offspring.
- During a five-year voyage aboard the *Beagle*, Charles Darwin made observations that would form the basis of his theory of **evolution.** While visiting the Galapagos Islands, Darwin noticed differences in the species of tortoises and finches on the various islands. Darwin proposed that the species evolved differently due to different geographic locations.

Variations in finch beaks helped shape Darwin's theory of evolution.

2. Natural selection explains how living things evolve.

- Darwin based his theory of **natural selection** on his observations and his knowledge of artificial selection.
- Traits that appear in populations due to genetic variation may help a population survive. After many generations, the variation leads to an **adaptation,** an inherited trait that gives an organism an advantage in its environment. This advantage over other members of the population allows the population to evolve through natural selection.

3. New species develop from earlier species.
Speciation, the evolution of new species from existing species, occurs when a population of species becomes isolated from other members of their species. Isolation can be geographic, reproductive, or behavioral.

Common Misconceptions

MISCONCEPTION DATABASE
CLASSZONE.COM Background on student misconceptions

MASS EXTINCTIONS Many students think extinctions happen quickly, even mass extinctions caused by sudden events. Similar confusion arises over the "emergence" of a new species. In fact, both the extinction and emergence of species occur over periods of hundreds or thousands of years. Extinctions are ongoing and are most often caused by gradual geologic changes.

TE This misconception is addressed in Teach from Visuals, pp. 172, 173.

ADAPTATION AND EVOLUTION Many students think that organisms are able to change body structure to best exploit their habitats, or that organisms respond to a changed environment by leaving to seek a better one. Students also often think that adaptations result from a purpose or design, or as a conscious process.

TE This misconception is addressed on p. 182.

INHERITED AND ACQUIRED TRAITS Elementary and middle-school students tend to confuse non-inherited adaptations, developments, and changes acquired during an individual's lifetime with adaptive features that are inherited in a population.

TE This misconception is addressed on p. 183.

Previewing Content

SECTION

Many types of evidence support evolution. pp. 188–195

1. Observations provide evidence for theories.
A scientific theory is a widely accepted statement based on scientific evidence that helps explain and predict natural phenomena. The diagram on the right shows the three main sources of evidence on which the theory of evolution has been built.

2. Fossil evidence supports evolution.
Fossil evidence shows that two species with a common **ancestor** can develop differently.

3. Biological evidence supports evolution.
- Biological evidence includes the structure and development of living things. Structural evidence includes **vestigial organs** and similar structures with different functions.
- Vestigial organs are physical structures that are no longer useful to a living organism, but may have existed as fully developed similar structures useful to a common ancestor.
- Different species share many **similar structures,** but these have different functions, such as the forelimbs of a bat, gecko lizard, or manatee.
- Similarities in **embryonic development** also indicate common ancestry.

4. Genetic evidence supports evolution.
- Similar organisms have very similar **genes;** less closely related organisms have genes that are easy to tell apart.
- Organisms with similar **patterns of DNA** also share common ancestors.

Evidence: information from observations and experiments

Evidence for evolution

fossil

biological

genetic

Theory: a widely accepted statement based on scientific evidence that helps explain a group of facts

Common Misconceptions

MISCONCEPTION DATABASE
CLASSZONE.COM Background on student misconceptions

MODELS OF THE NATURAL WORLD Most middle-school students have some confusion about the accuracy of the various models that scientists use to represent the natural world—from models of molecules and cells, to models of weather patterns and populations. There is never a one-to-one correspondence with the model and that which is represented. There are always attributes that differ between the two.

This misconception is addressed in the Chapter Investigation, pp. 186–187.

THEORIES AND EVIDENCE Middle-school students persistently confuse the term *theory* with the term *hypothesis*. They think that theories are ideas that have not yet been proven and are not founded on scientific evidence. In fact theories are scientific principles that are widely used and upheld by evidence. As further evidence amasses, it refines understanding of the theory.

This misconception is addressed in Teach Difficult Concepts, p. 189.

Previewing Labs

EXPLORE the BIG idea

What Can Rocks Show About Earth's History? p. 167 Students observe rock samples to gather evidence about Earth's history.	**TIME** 10 minutes **MATERIALS** 2 rock samples
Which One of These Things Is Not Like the Others? p. 167 Students analyze variation in string beans to begin thinking about variety within a species.	**TIME** 10 minutes **MATERIALS** handful of various fresh raw string beans in pods
Internet Activity: Matching Finch Beaks, p. 167 Students match finch beaks to the foods the birds eat to learn that adaptations can have functions.	**TIME** 20 minutes **MATERIALS** computer with Internet access

SECTION 1	**EXPLORE Fossils,** p. 169 Students model fossil formation to infer how fossils are formed.	**TIME** 15 minutes **MATERIALS** clay, petri dish, small bone, shell, or hard plant part
	INVESTIGATE Fossil Records, p. 171 Students model how scientists interpret the fossil record by putting together the pieces of a puzzle.	**TIME** 15 minutes **MATERIALS** puzzle pieces from an ordinary jigsaw puzzle
SECTION 2	**CHAPTER INVESTIGATION** **Modeling Natural Selection,** pp. 186–187 Students play a game to model effects of natural selection in the environment.	**TIME** 40 minutes **MATERIALS** pair of number cubes, 16 red paper clips, 16 blue paper clips, 16 yellow paper clips
SECTION 3	**EXPLORE Evidence,** p. 188 Students demonstrate how observations can supply evidence.	**TIME** 15 minutes **MATERIALS** notebook
	INVESTIGATE Genes, p. 193 Students rearrange letters to model how sequencing can effect communication.	**TIME** 10 minutes **MATERIALS** 4 cards (or square sticky notes) with the letters *A, D, E,* and *R* written one to a card

R **Additional INVESTIGATION,** Virtual Fossil Hunt, A, B, & C, pp. 59–67; Teacher Instructions, pp. 188–189

Previewing Chapter Resources

	INTEGRATED TECHNOLOGY	LABS AND ACTIVITIES
CHAPTER 1 **The History of Life on Earth**	 **CLASSZONE.COM** • eEdition Plus • EasyPlanner Plus • Misconception Database • Content Review • Test Practice • Resource Centers • Internet Activity: Matching Finch Beaks • Math Tutorial  **SCILINKS.ORG** SCILINKS 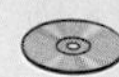 **CD-ROMS** • eEdition • EasyPlanner • Power Presentations • Content Review • Lab Generator • Test Generator 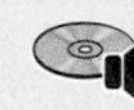 **AUDIO CDS** • Audio Readings • Audio Readings in Spanish	 EXPLORE the Big Idea, p. 167 • What Can Rocks Show About Earth's History? • Which One of These Things Is Not Like the Others? • Internet Activity: Matching Finch Beaks  **UNIT RESOURCE BOOK** • Family Letter, p. vii • Spanish Family Letter, p. viii • Unit Projects, pp. 5–10  **Lab Generator CD-ROM** Generate customized labs.
SECTION 1 **Earth has been home to living things for about 3.8 billion years.** pp. 169–176 Time: 2 periods (1 block)  Lesson Plan, pp. 11–12	 • **RESOURCE CENTER,** Mass Extinctions • **MATH TUTORIAL**  **UNIT TRANSPARENCY BOOK** • Big Idea Flow Chart, p. T1 • Daily Vocabulary Scaffolding, p. T2 • Note-Taking Model, p. T3 • 3-Minute Warm-Up, p. T4	 • EXPLORE Fossils, p. 169 • INVESTIGATE Fossil Records, p. 171 • Math and Science, p. 176  **UNIT RESOURCE BOOK** • Datasheet, Fossil Records, p. 20 • Math Support, p. 48 • Math Practice, p. 49 • Additional INVESTIGATION, Virtual Fossil Hunt, A, B, & C, pp. 59–67
SECTION  **Species change over time.** pp. 177–187 Time: 3 periods (1.5 blocks) Lesson Plan, pp. 22–23	 **RESOURCE CENTER,** Natural Selection **UNIT TRANSPARENCY BOOK** • Daily Vocabulary Scaffolding, p. T2 • 3-Minute Warm-Up, p. T4 • "Natural Selection" Visual, p. T6	CHAPTER INVESTIGATION, Modeling Natural Selection, pp. 186–187  **UNIT RESOURCE BOOK** CHAPTER INVESTIGATION, Modeling Natural Selection, A, B, & C, pp. 50–58
SECTION  **Many types of evidence support evolution.** pp. 188–195 Time: 3 periods (1.5 blocks) Lesson Plan, pp. 32–33	 **RESOURCE CENTER,** Evidence to Support Evolution  **UNIT TRANSPARENCY BOOK** • Big Idea Flow Chart, p. T1 • Daily Vocabulary Scaffolding, p. T2 • 3-Minute Warm-Up, p. T5 • Chapter Outline, pp. T7–T8	 • EXPLORE Evidence, p. 188 • INVESTIGATE Genes, p. 193 • THINK Science, p. 195  **UNIT RESOURCE BOOK** Datasheet, Genes, p. 41

KEY TO ICONS  CD/CD-ROM  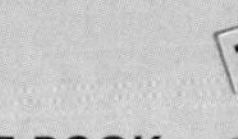 Teacher Edition 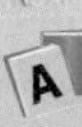 UNIT TRANSPARENCY BOOK 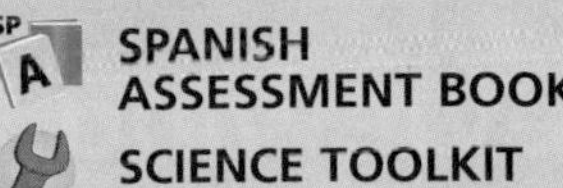 SPANISH ASSESSMENT BOOK

 INTERNET Pupil Edition 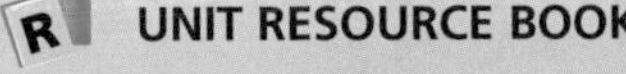 UNIT RESOURCE BOOK UNIT ASSESSMENT BOOK  SCIENCE TOOLKIT

READING AND REINFORCEMENT | ASSESSMENT | STANDARDS

Reading and Reinforcement

- Frame Game, B26–27
- Main Idea and Detail Notes, C37
- Daily Vocabulary Scaffolding, H1–8

UNIT RESOURCE BOOK
- Vocabulary Practice, pp. 45–46
- Decoding Support, p. 47
- Summarizing the Chapter, pp. 68–69

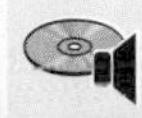

Audio Readings CD
Listen to Pupil Edition.

Audio Readings in Spanish CD
Listen to Pupil Edition in Spanish.

Assessment

- Chapter Review, pp. 197–198
- Standardized Test Practice, p. 199

UNIT ASSESSMENT BOOK
- Diagnostic Test, pp. 1–2
- Chapter Test, A, B, & C, pp. 6–17
- Alternative Assessment, pp. 18–19

Spanish Chapter Test, pp. 25–28

Test Generator CD-ROM
Generate customized tests.

Lab Generator CD-ROM
Rubrics for Labs

Standards

National Standards
A.1–8, A.9.a–c, A.9.e–g, C.3.d, C.5.a–c, D.2.b, G.1.b

See p. 166 for the standards.

UNIT RESOURCE BOOK
- Reading Study Guide, A & B, pp. 13–16
- Spanish Reading Study Guide, pp. 17–18
- Challenge and Extension, p. 19
- Reinforcing Key Concepts, p. 21
- Challenge Reading, pp. 43–44

Ongoing Assessment, pp. 170–171, 173–175

Section 6.1 Review, p. 175

UNIT ASSESSMENT BOOK
Section 6.1 Quiz, p. 3

National Standards
A.2–8, A.9.a–c, A.9.e–f, C.3.d, C.5.a–c, D.2.b, G.1.b

UNIT RESOURCE BOOK
- Reading Study Guide, A & B, pp. 24–27
- Spanish Reading Study Guide, pp. 28–29
- Challenge and Extension, p. 30
- Reinforcing Key Concepts, p. 31

Ongoing Assessment, pp. 177–178, 181, 183, 185

Section 6.2 Review, p. 185

UNIT ASSESSMENT BOOK
Section 6.2 Quiz, p. 4

National Standards
A.1–7, A.9.a–b, A.9.e–g, C.3.d, C.5.a–c, G.1.b

UNIT RESOURCE BOOK
- Reading Study Guide, A & B, pp. 34–37
- Spanish Reading Study Guide, pp. 38–39
- Challenge and Extension, p. 40
- Reinforcing Key Concepts, p. 42

Ongoing Assessment, pp. 189–190, 192–193

Section 6.3 Review, p. 194

UNIT ASSESSMENT BOOK
Section 6.3 Quiz, p. 5

National Standards
A.2–7, A.9.a–b, A.9.e–f, C.3.d, C.5.a–c, G.1.b

Previewing Resources for Differentiated Instruction

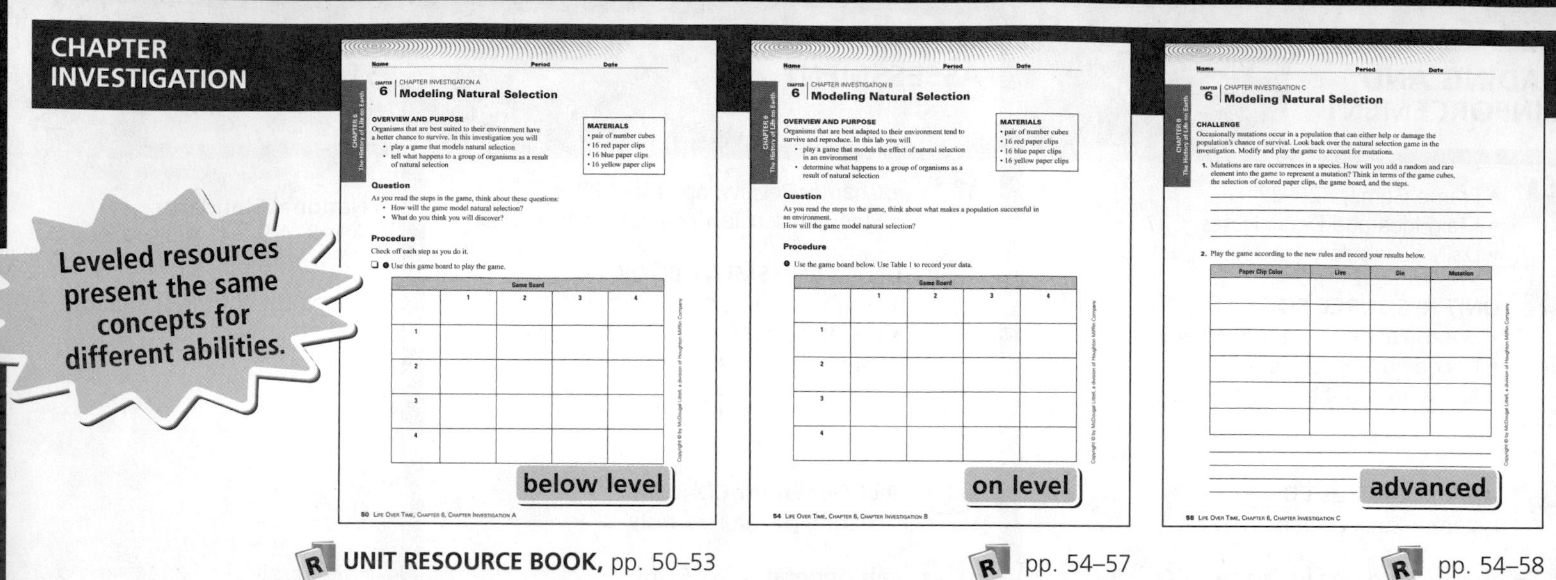

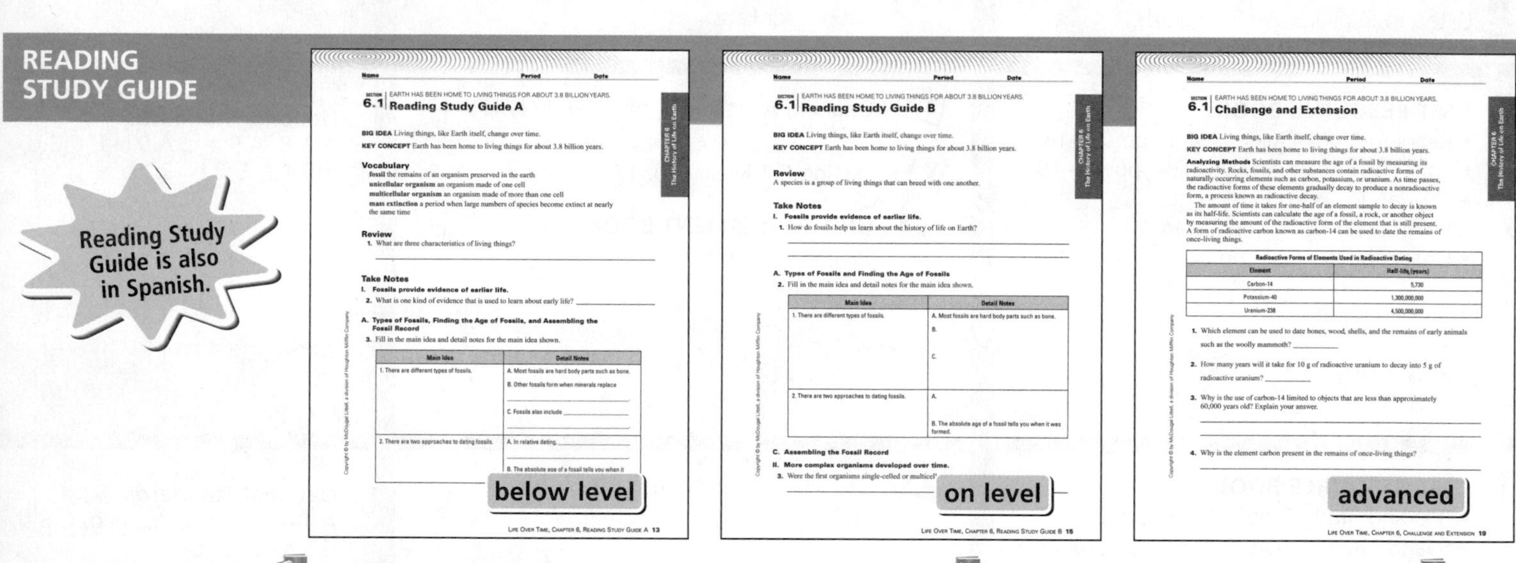

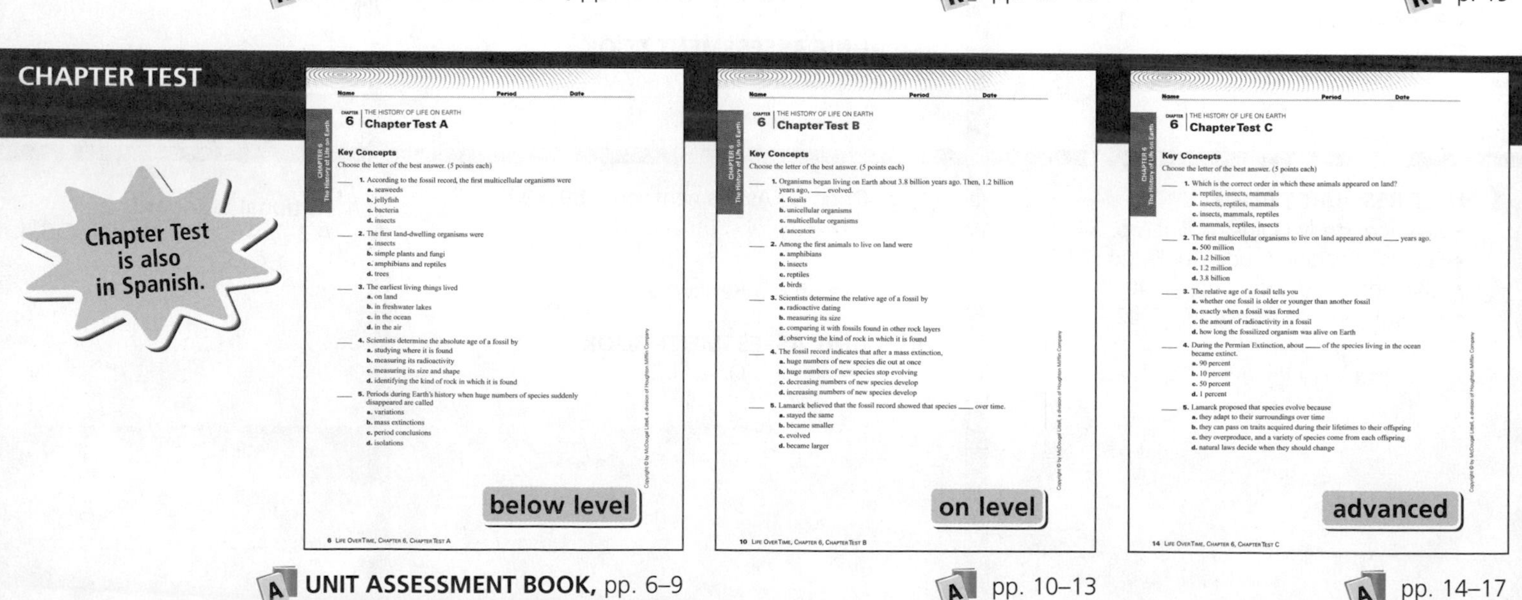

TECHNOLOGY

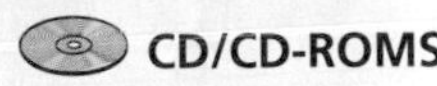

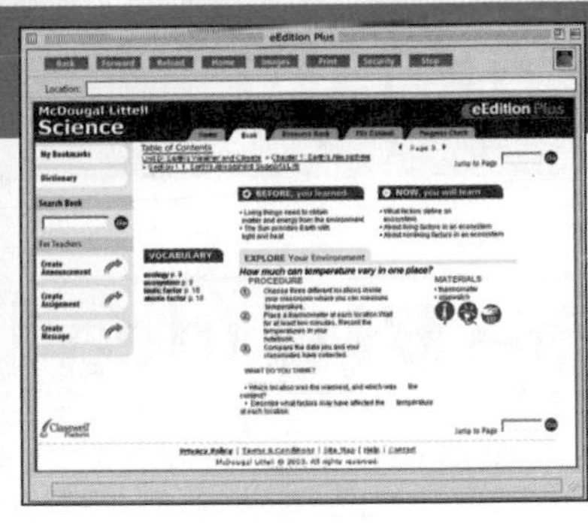

VISUAL CONTENT

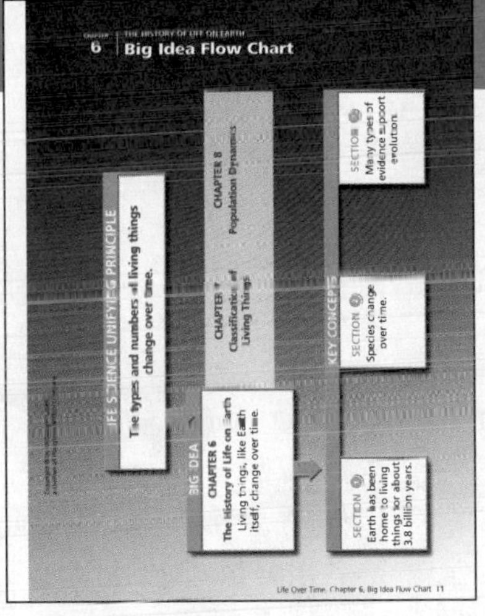

UNIT TRANSPARENCY BOOK, p. T1

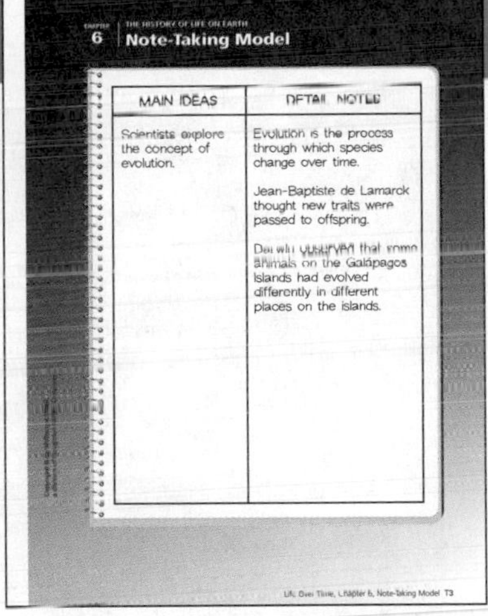

p. T3

p. T6

MORE SUPPORT

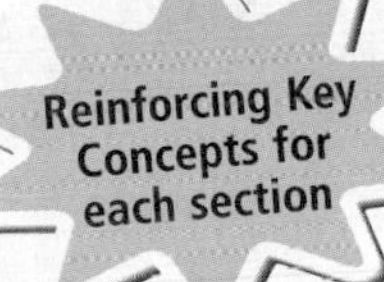

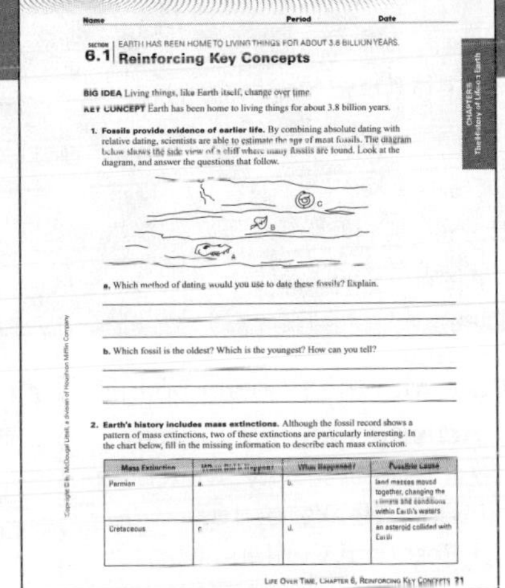

6.1 Reinforcing Key Concepts

UNIT RESOURCE BOOK, p. 21

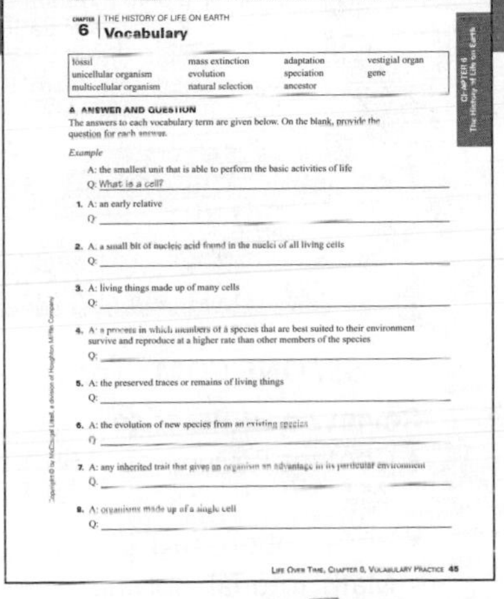

6 Vocabulary

pp. 45–46

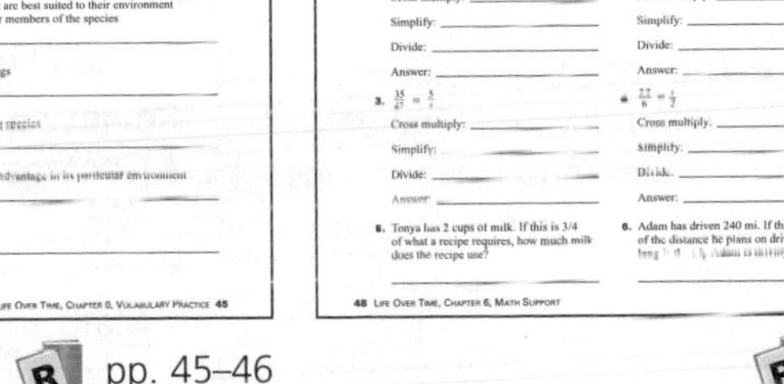

6 Math Support

p. 48

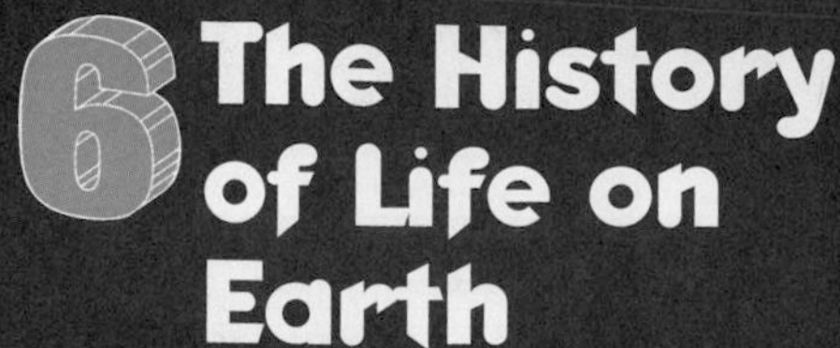

CHAPTER 6 The History of Life on Earth

INTRODUCE

the BIG idea

Have students view the photograph of the fossil dig. Discuss the question in the box.

- Ask: How are the scientists in the pictures like detectives?
- Brainstorm a list of items that scientists might find in a dig.

National Science Education Standards

Content

C.1.b Most organisms are single cells; other organisms are multicellular.

C.5.a Relationships among organisms can be found by looking at structures, processes, and common ancestry.

C.5.b Biological evolution has led to greater species diversity over time.

C.5.c Species may become extinct if they cannot survive changes.

D.2.b Fossils provide evidence of how life and the environment have changed.

Process

A.1–8 Identify questions that can be answered through scientific investigations; design and conduct an investigation; use tools to gather and interpret data; use evidence to describe, predict, explain, model; think critically to make relationships between evidence and explanations; recognize different explanations and predictions; communicate scientific procedures and explanations; use mathematics.

A.9.a–c, A.9.e–g Understand scientific inquiry by using different investigations, methods, mathematics, and explanations based on logic, evidence, and skepticism. Data often results in new investigations.

G.1.b Science requires different abilities.

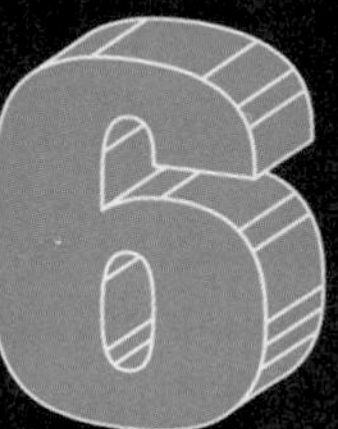

CHAPTER 6 The History of Life on Earth

the BIG idea

Living things, like Earth itself, change over time.

Key Concepts

SECTION 1 **Earth has been home to living things for about 3.8 billion years.** Learn how fossils help explain the development of life on Earth.

SECTION 2 **Species change over time.** Learn how species develop and change.

SECTION 3 **Many types of evidence support evolution.** Learn about the evidence scientists use to support evolution.

How do scientists learn about the history of life on Earth?

Internet Preview

CLASSZONE.COM

Chapter 6 online resources: Content Review, Simulation, Visualization, three Resource Centers, Math Tutorial, Test Practice

INTERNET PREVIEW

CLASSZONE.COM For student use with the following pages:

Review and Practice

- Content Review, pp. 168, 196
- Visualization, p. 170
- Math Tutorial: Solving Proportions, p. 176
- Test Practice, p. 199

Activities and Resources

- Internet Activity: Matching Finch Beaks, p. 167
- Resource Centers: Mass Extinctions, p. 174; Natural Selection, p. 181; Evidence to Support Evolution, p. 189

The Fossil Record
Code: MDL036

EXPLORE the BIG idea

What Can Rocks Show About Earth's History?

Look closely at two rocks from different places or at the two rocks below. What are the characteristics of each rock? Can you see evidence of living things in one of them?

Observe and Think
How could the evidence you gathered from your observations help you describe Earth's history?

Which One of These Things Is Not Like the Others?

Observe a handful of beans. Measure the length of each bean, observe the color, and note how many seeds are in each bean.

Observe and Think
What variety do you observe in the beans?

Investigate Activity: Matching Finch Beaks

Go to **Classzone.com** to match different finch beaks with the foods they eat. Learn how each type of beak functions.

Observe and Think
Can you think of any other beak types birds may have and how they relate to the food they eat?

NSTA scilinks.org SCILINKS
The Fossil Record **Code: MDL036**

EXPLORE the BIG idea

These inquiry-based activities are appropriate for use at home or as a supplement to classroom instruction.

What Can Rocks Show About Earth's History?

PURPOSE To look at physical evidence for indications of change.

TIP *10 min.* If possible, one rock in each sample should include a fossil or fossils. (The reddish rock pictured at left is fossilized wood.)

Sample answer: The various particles, layers, and forms in each rock are a record of its past, and thus hold clues to the past of the Earth around it.

REVISIT after p. 171.

Which One of These Things Is Not Like the Others?

PURPOSE To begin thinking about variety within a species.

TIP *10 min.* Try to include green beans with obvious variations in color and size. They should all be from one species, however.

Sample answer: Some beans were shorter, some longer. Some held more seeds. Some were darker, or were brownish or yellowish.

REVISIT after p. 183.

Internet Activity: Matching Finch Beaks

PURPOSE To learn that adaptations can have functions.

TIP *20 min.* If computer access is limited, print out images and laminate them.

Sample answer: Pelicans have scoop-shaped beaks for catching fish. Robins have small tweezer-like beaks for small fruits and insects. Raptors have hooked beaks for tearing meat.

REVISIT after p. 180.

TEACHING WITH TECHNOLOGY

Video Camera Students could use a video camera to record the procedure of the Chapter Investigation on pp. 186–187. Have a student videotape and narrate what is happening as a group of students completes the procedure. Students then give a synopsis of their observations, analysis, and conclusions on tape.

Timeline Software If timeline software is available, it can be used to model the periods in Earth's history. Students can use it to create study aids for pp. 174–175, or for the "Math in Science" activity on p. 176.

Desktop Publishing Have students use desktop publishing software to create a newspaper outlining the history of mass extinctions while studying the topic on pp. 174–175.

Prepare

CONCEPT REVIEW

Activate Prior Knowledge

- Ask students to describe the evidence scientists use to determine that Earth changes over time. *fossils, rock layers*
- Have students give an example of how Earth has changed over time. *Sample answer: formation of a land mass or extinction of an animal that no longer exists.*

TAKING NOTES

Main Idea and Details

Students can use the blue and red headings in the text as a basis for main ideas. Details to support the main idea may come from the text and visuals, such as photographs and diagrams.

Vocabulary Strategy

The frame game helps students understand vocabulary terms in context of related ideas, images, or concepts. The relationship may be one of example, description, part-to-whole, or other association. Students gain a full picture of the concept by relating it to other ideas.

Vocabulary and Note-Taking Resources

- Vocabulary Practice, pp. 45–46
- Decoding Support, p. 47

- Daily Vocabulary Scaffolding, pp. T2
- Note-Taking Model, p. T3

- Frame Game, B26–27
- Main Idea and Details, C37
- Daily Vocabulary Scaffolding, H1–8

CHAPTER 6

Getting Ready to Learn

CONCEPT REVIEW

- Earth was formed over 4 billion years ago.
- Living things interact with their environment.

VOCABULARY REVIEW

See Glossary for definitions.

cell **organism**
DNA **species**
genetic material **theory**

CONTENT REVIEW
CLASSZONE.COM
Review concepts and vocabulary.

TAKING NOTES

MAIN IDEA AND DETAILS

Make a two-column chart. Write the main ideas, such as those in the blue headings, in the column on the left. Write details about each of those main ideas in the column on the right.

VOCABULARY STRATEGY

Write each new vocabulary term in the center of a **frame game** diagram. Decide what information to frame it with. Use examples, descriptions, and parts of sentences that use the term in context or pictures. You can change the frame to fit each item.

See the Note-Taking Handbook on pages R45–R51.

SCIENCE NOTEBOOK

MAIN IDEAS	DETAILS
1. Fossils provide evidence of earlier life	1. Bones, prints, minerals 1. Relative dating compares fossils 1. Absolute dating uses the level of radioactivity

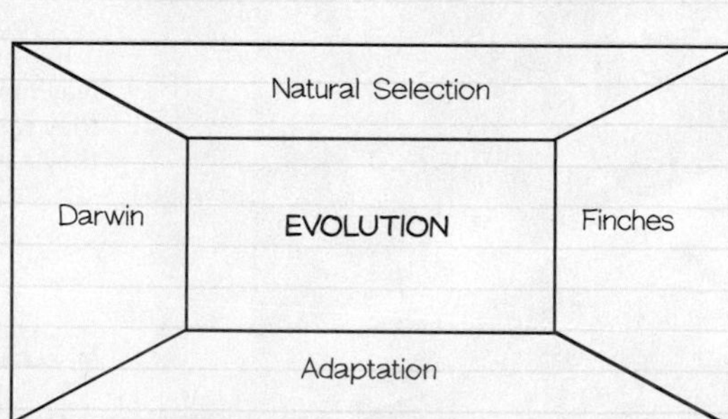

168 Unit 2: Life Over Time

CHECK READINESS

Administer the Diagnostic Test to determine students' readiness for new science content and their mastery of requisite math skills.

 Diagnostic Test, pp. 1–2

Technology Resources

Students needing content and math skills should visit **ClassZone.com**.

- **CONTENT REVIEW**
- **MATH TUTORIAL**

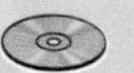 **CONTENT REVIEW CD-ROM**

KEY CONCEPT

Earth has been home to living things for about 3.8 billion years.

BEFORE, you learned
- Living things are diverse
- Living things share common characteristics
- A species is a group of living things that can breed with one another

NOW, you will learn
- How scientists use fossils to learn about the history of life
- About patterns in the fossil record
- About mass extinctions

VOCABULARY
fossil p. 169
unicellular organism p. 172
multicellular organism p. 173
mass extinction p. 174

EXPLORE Fossils

What can you infer from the marks an object leaves behind?

PROCEDURE
1. Press a layer of clay into the petri dish.
2. Choose a small object and press it into the clay to make an imprint of your object.
3. Remove the object carefully and trade your imprint with a classmate.

MATERIALS
- clay
- petri dish
- small object

WHAT DO YOU THINK?
- What object made the imprint?
- What do your observations indicate to you about how the imprint was formed?

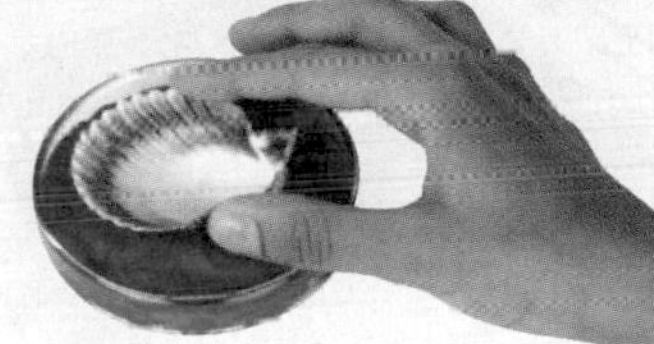

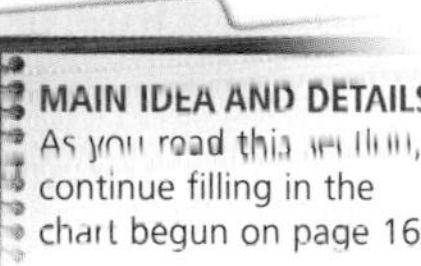

MAIN IDEA AND DETAILS As you read this section, continue filling in the chart begun on page 168.

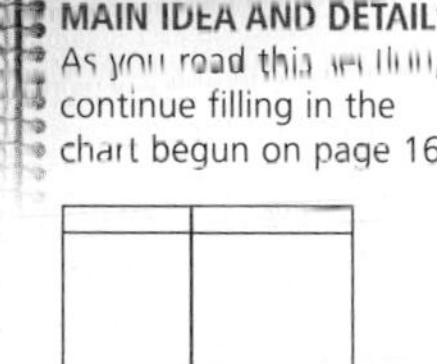

Fossils provide evidence of earlier life.

Imagine watching a movie about the history of life on Earth. The beginning of the movie is set 3.8 billion years ago. At that time, the ocean would have been the setting. All living things lived in the sea. The end of the movie would show Earth today—a planet that is home to millions of species living on land as well as in water and air.

Of course, learning about the history of life isn't as easy as watching a movie. Modern ideas about life's history involve careful observation of the available evidence. Much of this evidence is provided by fossils. **Fossils** are the remains of organisms preserved in the earth. Fossils provide a glimpse of a very long story. In some ways, observing a fossil is like hitting the pause button on your video machine or looking at a snapshot of another time.

6.1 FOCUS

Set Learning Goals

Students will
- Explain how scientists use fossils to learn about the history of life.
- Describe patterns in the fossil record.
- Explain what mass extinctions are and when they occurred.
- Model how scientists analyze the fossil record.

3-Minute Warm-Up

Display Transparency 4 or copy this exercise on the board:

Decide which of these statements are true. If not true, correct them.

1. All living things are organized into units called cells. *true*
2. All eukaryotic cells contain a nucleus. *true*
3. When living things die, their remains break down into nothing. *When living things die, their remains break down, and may become part of other living things or parts of rocks or soil.*

 3-Minute Warm-Up, p. T4

6.1 MOTIVATE

EXPLORE Fossils

PURPOSE To model fossil formation to infer how fossils are formed

TIP *15 min.* Students should keep secret the identity of the object they use to make the fossil imprint.

WHAT DO YOU THINK? *Students' answers will vary depending on the objects used to make the imprints. Students should note that the imprints are formed by the surfaces of the objects.*

RESOURCES FOR DIFFERENTIATED INSTRUCTION

Below Level

UNIT RESOURCE BOOK
- Reading Study Guide A, pp. 13–14
- Decoding Support, p. 47

AUDIO CDS

Additional INVESTIGATION, Virtual Fossil Hunt, A, B, & C, pp. 59–67; Teacher Instructions, pp. 188–189

Advanced

UNIT RESOURCE BOOK
- Challenge and Extension, p. 19
- Challenge Reading, pp. 43–44

English Learners

UNIT RESOURCE BOOK
Spanish Reading Study Guide, pp. 17–18

AUDIO CDS
- Audio Readings in Spanish
- Audio Readings (English)

6.1 INSTRUCT

Teach from Visuals

To help students interpret the photographs of fossils, ask:

- How are the fossils in the photographs similar? *All of these fossils show the remains of a once-living organism.*
- How are they different? Explain. *They differ in the way that they were formed and the type of remains. One shows a bone, one an imprint, and one the remains of a whole organism.*

Teacher Demo

Use everyday objects to model the concept of relative age—the idea that different layers of Earth are different ages. Prior to the demonstration, gather some everyday objects such as buttons, erasers, and pieces of crayons or chalk. Obtain several sheets of colored construction paper. Place one sheet on the bottom of a tray and tape several objects in place. Repeat, using three or four layers of paper with objects taped in place. Present the "layers of objects" to the class. Have volunteers remove each layer one at a time and record the objects in a chart in order from top (youngest) to bottom (oldest). Point out that objects in the bottom layer were placed there before others, and so have been there the longest, just as rocks and fossils at deeper levels of Earth have usually been formed, or deposited, earlier than those at Earth's surface.

Integrate the Sciences

In science, a rock is a naturally formed solid, usually made of one or more types of minerals. A rock can be as small as a grain of sand, or as large as a mountain face. Rocks form in many ways, including heating and cooling, chemical interactions that crystallize dissolved minerals, or the compacting of materials under pressure.

Ongoing Assessment

CHECK YOUR READING *Answer: Scientists date fossils by relative dating and absolute dating.*

Fossils

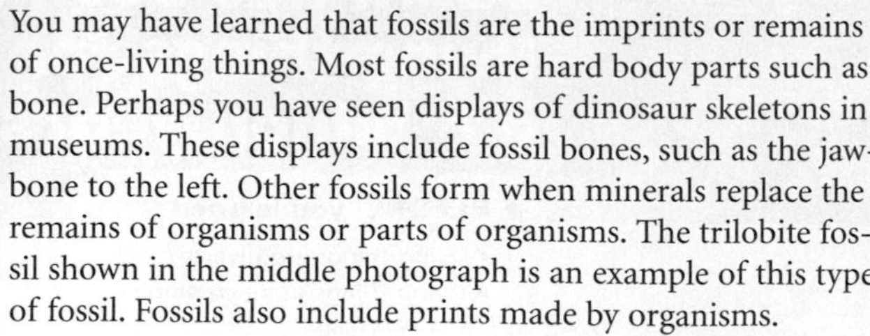

Bones, such as this jawbone, are a common type of fossil.

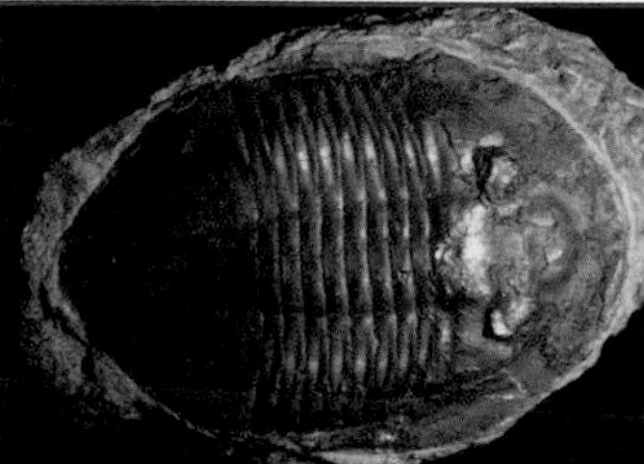

This fossil trilobite formed as minerals replaced the remains of the organism.

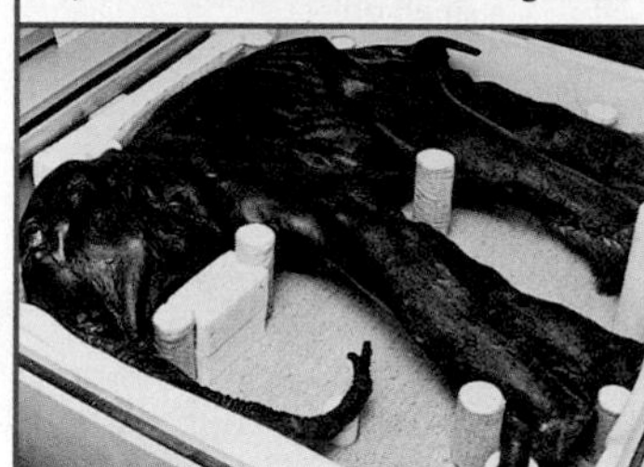

The preserved remains of ancient mammals, like the woolly mammoth, are rare.

Types of Fossils

You may have learned that fossils are the imprints or remains of once-living things. Most fossils are hard body parts such as bone. Perhaps you have seen displays of dinosaur skeletons in museums. These displays include fossil bones, such as the jawbone to the left. Other fossils form when minerals replace the remains of organisms or parts of organisms. The trilobite fossil shown in the middle photograph is an example of this type of fossil. Fossils also include prints made by organisms. **? A**

Very rarely, people find fossils that are the original remains of entire organisms. Explorers have found the frozen bodies of animals called woolly mammoths that lived about 10,000 years ago. The bodies of insects can be preserved in sap from plants.

Finding the Age of Fossils

How can scientists tell that the first organisms lived in oceans, or that dinosaurs lived on land and that they disappeared 65 million years ago? These questions and others can be addressed by determining the age of fossils. There are two approaches to dating fossils—relative dating and absolute dating. In relative dating, one fossil is compared with another fossil. The relative age tells you whether a fossil formed before or after another fossil.

The places where fossils are discovered provide information about their relative ages. Much of Earth's crust is rock, and rock forms over long periods of time. Understanding when and how rock forms gives scientists information about the sequence of events in Earth's history.

Materials such as sand and mud may settle to the bottom of a body of water. Over many millions of years, layers harden into rock. Shells and other remains of organisms can be trapped in those layers, forming fossils. Newer fossils are usually found in the top layers of rock, while older fossils are in the lower layers.

VISUALIZATION CLASSZONE.COM

Explore how a fossil can form.

The absolute age of a fossil tells you when it was formed. To find the absolute age, scientists study the radioactive elements found in rocks and fossils. Some of these elements, such as uranium, decay at a very precise rate into more stable elements, such as lead. Thus, by measuring the amount of uranium and the amount of lead in an object, scientists can determine the object's age. The more lead it has, the older it is. **? B**

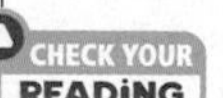

CHECK YOUR READING What are the two ways scientists can determine the age of fossils?

170 Unit 2: Life Over Time

DIFFERENTIATE INSTRUCTION

More Reading Support

A What do most fossils consist of? *hard body parts, such as bones*

B How do scientists find the absolute age of a fossil? *by measuring its radioactivity*

English Learners English learners may be challenged by comparative adverbs. Have students look at the sentence from "Investigate Fossil Records," p. 171.

"Was it easier or more difficult to study the record with more 'scientists' in your group?"

Explain that some words that compare can add an *-er* ending (easy, easier). Other words—usually those with three or more syllables—need the word *more* placed before them. List adverbs and adjectives and have students decide if the words take the *-er* ending or have *more* placed before them.

INVESTIGATE Fossil Records

How do scientists interpret fossil evidence?

SKILL FOCUS
Analyzing

MATERIALS
puzzle pieces

TIME
15 minutes

PROCEDURE

1. Individually examine each of your group's puzzle pieces. Consider the shape and size of each piece.
2. Arrange the pieces so that they fit together in the best possible way.
3. On the basis of your pieces, try to interpret what the overall puzzle picture may be.
4. Combine your puzzle pieces with another group's. Repeat steps 2 and 3.

WHAT DO YOU THINK?

- How did your interpretation of the puzzle picture change once you had more pieces to work with?
- Explain whether the gaps in the puzzle picture influenced your interpretation.
- Was it easier or more difficult to study the record with more "scientists" in your group?

CHALLENGE Brainstorm other ways scientists could learn about early life on Earth.

Assembling the Fossil Record

C

By combining absolute dating with relative dating, scientists can estimate the age of most fossils. The information about the fossils found in a particular location is called the fossil record. By assembling a fossil record, scientists can identify the periods of time during which different species lived and died. Scientists have used the fossil record to develop an overview of Earth's history.

READING TIP

A species is a group of organisms with similar characteristics that can interbreed.

Information from fossils helps scientists and artists describe wooly mammoths.

INVESTIGATE Fossil Records

PURPOSE To model how scientists analyze the fossil record

TIPS *15 min.* Prior to the activity, obtain a small jigsaw puzzle. It should have no more than 500 and no less than 100 pieces. Divide the puzzle pieces into groups and place them in envelopes, making sure that some pieces fit together while others do not.

INCLUSION You can use puzzles with larger and fewer pieces to make the activity easier.

WHAT DO YOU THINK? *Answers should mention that students are better able to visualize the puzzle picture with more pieces. Most students will answer that more "scientists" made it easier.*

CHALLENGE *Answers may include studying rock formations and how the shape of the land has changed.*

 Datasheet, Fossil Records, p. 20

Technology Resources

Customize this student lab as needed or look for an alternative. Print rubrics to assess student lab reports.

 **Lab Generator CD-ROM**

EXPLORE the BIG idea

Revisit "What Can Rocks Show About Earth's History?" on p. 167. Have students explain what types of evidence of the distant past can be found in some rocks.

Ongoing Assessment

Explain how scientists use fossils to learn about the history of life.

Ask: How does knowing the relative and absolute age of fossils help scientists assemble the fossil record? *Scientists are able to identify the periods of time during which fossil species lived.*

DIFFERENTIATE INSTRUCTION

More Reading Support

C What is the fossil record? *information about fossils in a particular location*

Below Level Have students construct models of fossil layers, using layers of different colored modeling clay. Students can gather and bury objects in the layers such as shells and rocks. When students have finished their models, slice the layers vertically to observe and discuss the relative ages of the "fossils." Have students explain how the model represents Earth's layers, which layers would be oldest and why. They can display their slices with a caption explaining "ages" of the layers.

Develop Critical Thinking

ANALYZE Remind students that all organisms are made up of basic units of life called cells. Ask: Why would unicellular organisms be able to survive in the early stages of Earth's history? *Unicellular organisms are single cells and all cells are able to carry on the processes necessary for life.*

Teach from Visuals

To help students interpret the diagram of Denver's past, ask:

- What is the earliest time period shown in the diagram? What type of life existed at that time? *250 million years ago; unicellular organisms lived in salty water*
- How many millions of years pass before sharks, marine lizards, and birds inhabit the land? *about 180 million years*
- The oldest layer can be found where in the diagram? *on the bottom layer in each illustration* When was it formed? *250 million years ago*

Integrate the Sciences

Earth's atmosphere is a blanket of gases that envelopes the planet. The blanket has many layers and is mainly composed of water vapor, nitrogen, carbon dioxide, and oxygen. As part of the carbon dioxide-oxygen cycle, plants use the atmosphere's carbon dioxide as well as oxygen and release mostly oxygen; animals breathe in and use mostly oxygen and exhale great amounts of carbon dioxide.

More complex organisms developed over time.

D

One of the most striking patterns that scientists find when they study the fossil record involves the development of more complex organisms. Below you will see how scientists have reconstructed the history of a modern city to show how life has developed over time. Recall that the first organisms were made up of single cells. Most organisms living today are single-celled. However, more and more species have developed more and more complex cells and structures over time.

Unicellular Organisms

READING TIP
Uni- means "single" and *multi-* means "several" or "many."

Unicellular organisms are organisms made up of a single cell. The organisms in the ocean 3.8 billion years ago were made of simple, single cells. Some of these organisms are responsible for the oxygen that now makes up our atmosphere. The early atmosphere did not contain as much oxygen as it now does. As the atmosphere changed, so did life on Earth.

Different types of single cells developed over time. Over millions of years the cells of organisms became more complex. Today, there are different species of life that include organisms made up of many cells.

Reconstructing the Past

Digging deep into the city of Denver, scientists have been able to reconstruct the ancient past.

55 million years ago The seas have been replaced by a tropical rain forest. The Rocky Mountains have been part of the landscape for over 10 million years.

70 million years ago Colorado is still flat and is now under a shallow sea. Sharks and marine lizards inhabit the water, and large reptiles fly overhead.

250 million years ago The area has no mountains and is covered in shallow, salty water. Unicellular organisms grow abundantly in the water.

DIFFERENTIATE INSTRUCTION

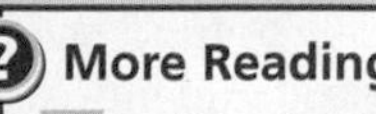
More Reading Support

D What were the first organisms on Earth? *single-celled (unicellular) organisms*

Advanced The Burgess Shale, in the Canadian Rockies, contains fossils of more than 100 marine invertebrate species. It documents the explosion of life at the middle of the Cambrian Period. Invite students to find out about the types of fossils found there and to report their findings in a series of labeled sketches.

Challenge and Extension, p. 19

Multicellular Organisms

Around 1.2 billion years ago, organisms made up of many cells began to live in Earth's oceans. **Multicellular organisms** are living things made up of many cells. Individual cells within multicellular organisms often perform specific tasks. For example, some cells may capture energy. Other cells might store materials. Still others might carry materials from one part of the organism to another. The most complex species of multicellular organisms have cells that are organized into tissues, organs, and systems.

Recall that all organisms have similar needs for energy, water, materials, and living space. For almost 3 billion years, these needs were met only in oceans. According to fossil records, the earliest multicellular organisms were tiny seaweeds. The earliest animals were similar to today's jellyfish.

CHECK YOUR READING Explain how unicellular and multicellular organisms differ.

Scientists learn about early life by studying different layers of rock

Life on Land

Consider the importance of water. Without it, you and most other living things would not be able to live. About 500 million years ago, the first multicellular organisms moved from water to land.

37 million years ago A volcanic eruption covers Colorado in a layer of hot ash, smothering plant and animal life.

16,000 years ago The plains look similar to what we see today—except that camels and mammoths roam the area.

Present day Buildings and highways cover the land. Humans have the technology to dig through layers of rock and reconstruct the past.

History of Science

Scientists did not recognize that Earth is millions of years old until 1859, when Charles Darwin realized that millions of years were necessary for evolution to take place. Prior to that, in the mid-17th century, Irish clergyman Bishop James Ussher concluded that the Earth was created in 4004 B.C., according to the Book of Genesis. In the 18th century, the age of the Earth was estimated at 75,000 years by French scientist Georges Louis Leclerc.

Teach from Visuals

To help students interpret the diagram of life on land, ask: How do you suppose the volcano 37 million years ago might have affected life on Earth at that time? *The volcano may have changed the atmosphere in the surrounding area. Some forms of life may not have been able to survive and became extinct.*

Ongoing Assessment

CHECK YOUR READING *Answer: Unicellular organisms are made up of one cell. Multicellular organisms are made up of many cells that each perform a specific task.*

DIFFERENTIATE INSTRUCTION

More Reading Support

E When did multicellular organisms appear? *about 1.2 billion years ago*

F How are cells of multicellular organisms grouped? *tissues, organs, systems*

English Learners Have students write the definitions for *fossil record, unicellular organism, multicellular organism, preserved, relative dating, atmosphere, meteorite,* and *mass extinction* in their Science Word Dictionaries. Encourage them to sketch an illustration or to clip pictures from natural history magazines to illustrate each term.

Have students who are interested in the fossil record read the following article:

Challenge Reading, pp. 43–44

Integrate the Sciences

Geologic time is the interval of time occupied by Earth's geologic history. The geologic time scale was developed in the 19th century from the fossil record. The time scale consists of four major intervals of time, called eras—Precambrian, Paleozoic, Mesozoic, and Cenozoic. These eras are further subdivided into periods. The present era, the Cenozoic era, is further subdivided into epochs.

Metacognitive Strategy

Have students make a series of icons to represent the organisms in the order in which they transitioned from water to land habitats.

Develop Critical Thinking

HYPOTHESIZE Have students brainstorm a list of reasons why the dinosaurs may have become extinct. Then ask: Why do you think a meteorite might have caused the extinction of dinosaurs? *Accept all reasonable responses. One theory is that a large meteorite could have created a huge cloud of dust that surrounded Earth. This cloud would have prevented sunlight from entering the atmosphere, killing off plant life. Without a food supply, many dinosaurs would not have been able to survive.*

Teaching with Technology

Students might use timeline software to create study aids or presentations of the periods of Earth's history covered in their texts, pp. 174–176. They can use the software for the Advanced activity, p. 174, or for the Math in Science activity, p. 176.

Ongoing Assessment

Describe patterns in the fossil record.

Ask: How are mass extinctions indicated in the fossil record? *In fossils of a certain age, huge numbers of species are shown, while those same species are absent in slightly younger fossils.*

Find out more about mass extinctions.

In order to survive, these living things needed structures to help them get water. The first land-dwelling organisms were simple plants and fungi. Plants were able to obtain water from the soil through structures called roots. Fungi absorbed water from plants as well as from the soil. Insects were also probably among the first living things to inhabit land. Plants provided insects with food and shelter. After insects, animals such as amphibians and reptiles began living on land. They were followed by birds and mammals.

Earth's history includes mass extinctions.

VOCABULARY
Remember to make a frame game for the term *mass extinction*.

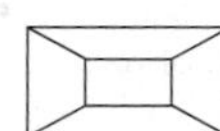

About 10,000 years ago, the last woolly mammoth died without any offspring. At that time, the species became extinct, which means it disappeared. The only way that we know that some species, such as woolly mammoths, ever existed is through the fossil record. During Earth's history, there have been several periods when huge numbers of species have died or become extinct in a very short time. These events are called **mass extinctions.**

Although the fossil record shows a pattern of mass extinctions, two of these extinctions are particularly interesting. These are the Permian Extinction and the Cretaceous Extinction. The causes of these mass extinctions are not fully known.

Permian Extinction

The largest mass extinction, the Permian Extinction, affected many different living things but it was the most devastating to organisms that lived in oceans.

About 250 million years ago, approximately 90 percent of the species living in the ocean became extinct. At the same time, many land-dwelling animals disappeared. Scientists who have studied Earth's history think that Earth's landmasses joined together, forming one enormous continent. This event would have changed the climate on land and the conditions within Earth's waters.

Cretaceous Extinction

Fossils show that around 140 million years ago, animals called dinosaurs lived all over the planet. However, the fossil record for dinosaurs ends about 65 million years ago. At the same time, more than half of the other species living on Earth became extinct.

How do scientists explain the extinction of so many species? One possibility is that a very large meteorite from space collided with Earth. The collision and its aftereffects wiped out most of the existing species. The remains of such a collision, the Chicxulub crater, can be found off the coast of Mexico. The computer graphic on page 175 shows the area of impact.

DIFFERENTIATE INSTRUCTION

More Reading Support

G What might have caused the Permian Extinction? *Earth's landmasses joined together, forming one continent.*

Advanced Have students research and present the Geologic Time Scale in a graphic display. Encourage students to include pictures, or descriptions of organisms that appeared during each of the geologic periods. Help them to connect geologic changes with the emergence of or extinction of plants, animals, and other organisms. Use the presentation to reinforce for other students how slow and gradual the shifts from period to period really are.

174 Unit 2: Life Over Time

The pattern in the fossil record shows that mass extinctions were followed by periods during which increasing numbers of new species developed. There may be a connection between the extinction of one species and the development of new species. For example, the extinction of dinosaurs may have made it possible for new species of mammals to develop.

 What do scientists think caused the most recent mass extinction?

6.1 Review

KEY CONCEPTS

1. How do fossils help scientists understand the history of life?
2. How do scientists know that the first organisms were simple, unicellular organisms?
3. What is extinction? Give an example of a mass extinction and its results.

CRITICAL THINKING

4. **Synthesize** How do absolute dating and relative dating help scientists assemble a fossil record for an area?
5. **Sequence** Draw a timeline showing the sequence of three major events in the history of life. Include the following terms on your timeline: *unicellular, multicellular, ocean, land.*

CHALLENGE

6. **Predict** Using the Denver reconstruction as your model, explain how you would reconstruct the history of the environment in your town.

ANSWERS

1. Fossils show signs of life as it existed millions of years ago.

2. Unicellular organisms contributed to Earth's atmosphere, which did not always contain the oxygen it does now.

3. Extinction occurs when the last member of a species dies. Permian Extinction—90 percent of ocean life became extinct; Cretaceous Extinction—the dinosaurs died

4. Absolute dating tells when fossils were formed. Relative dating compares the ages of fossils. Absolute dating cannot be used on all fossils, so the two methods combined give an accurate picture.

5. Students' timelines should show the progression of life on Earth—unicellular organisms, multicellular organisms, life in the oceans, and life moving to land.

6. Answers should reflect an understanding of the concepts presented in the Denver diagram.

Teaching with Technology

Encourage students to use desktop publishing software to create a newspaper with feature articles outlining the history of mass extinctions.

Ongoing Assessment

Explain what mass extinctions are and when they occurred.

Ask: Why are mass extinctions considered a pattern in the fossil record? *There have been several periods of mass extinctions throughout Earth's history.*

 *Answer: a meteorite*

Reinforce the BIG idea

Have students relate the section to the Big Idea.

 Reinforcing Key Concepts, p. 21

6.1 ASSESS & RETEACH

Assess

 Section 6.1 Quiz, p. 3

Reteach

Have small groups of students complete the graphic organizer by reviewing section 6.1. In each group, assign a reader, a recorder, a leader, and a reporter.

Types of Fossils	*bones, imprints, whole organisms*
Methods of Finding the Age of Fossils	*relative dating, absolute dating*
Knowledge Gained from Fossil Record	*types of organisms, ages of Earth's layers, mass extinctions*

Technology Resources

Have students visit **ClassZone.com** for reteaching of Key Concepts.

 CONTENT REVIEW

 CONTENT REVIEW CD-ROM

MATH IN SCIENCE
Math Skills Practice for Science

Set Learning Goal
To label a timeline by using proportions

Present the Science
Scientists use the Geologic Time Scale to mark the geologic events of Earth and the life forms that appear along the way. The first period of geologic time is Precambrian Time, which ended about 540 million years ago. The remaining history of Earth from that time is divided into eras, periods, and epochs.

Develop Proportion Skills
Ratios are used to compare two quantities and can be written as a fraction, for example, 2/4. This ratio shows a comparison of two out of total of four. A proportion is an equation that shows that two ratios are equal, for example, 2/4 = 4/8.

DIFFERENTIATION TIP Remind students that one meter = 100 centimeters and that 10 millimeters = one centimeter.

Close
Ask students why writing proportions is useful to scientists. *Proportions help scientists make comparisons about quantities.*

- Math Support, p. 48
- Math Practice, p. 49

Technology Resources

Students can visit **ClassZone.com** to practice proportion skills.

MATH TUTORIAL

MATH TUTORIAL
CLASSZONE.COM
Click on Math Tutorial for more help writing and solving proportions.

This fossil is very similar to the modern snail shown above.

SKILL: USING PROPORTIONS

A Span of Time

The history of planet Earth spans from the present to about 5 billion years back. By comparison, the history of life on the planet spans about 4/5 of that time. Such a comparison is called a proportion.

Example

To compare time spans in the history of Earth, you could make a meter-long timeline. Follow these steps:

(1) Measure and cut a piece of paper longer than 1 meter. Draw a straight line that is 1 meter long on your paper.

(2) Mark "0" at the far left to show the present day. Mark "5,000,000,000" at the right to show 5 billion years.

(3) Mark each centimeter along the line with a short stroke.

(4) Make a longer stroke at every 10 pencil marks. Your 5-billion-year span is now divided into 500-million-year sections. Each section is 1/10 in proportion to the total.

0   5,000,000,000

Label the timeline by answering the questions below.

1. Each short pencil stroke, or tick, represents 1/100 of the total span. How many years will each centimeter represent?
2. Each of the 10 long pencil marks should have its own label for the amount of time before the present day. The label for the first long pencil mark should be "500 million years." What numbers should label the others?
3. What fractions of the total span do the numbers in Question 2 represent?

CHALLENGE Copy and complete the table.

Event	Years Before Present Time	Number of cm from 0	Fraction of Total Time Span
Life appears on Earth.	3,800,000,000		
Multicellular life appears.	1,500,000,000		
First animals appear on land.	420,000,000		

176 Unit 2: Life Over Time

ANSWERS

1. 50,000,000 years (50 million years)

2. 1 billion, 1.5 billion, 2 billion, 2.5 billion, 3 billion, 3.5 billion, 4 billion, 4.5 billion, 5 billion

3. 1/10

***CHALLENGE** Life appears on Earth: 76 cm; 19/25; Multicellular life appears: 30 cm; 3/10; First animals appear on land: 8.4 cm; 21/250*

KEY CONCEPT

Species change over time.

BEFORE, you learned

- Fossils are evidence of earlier life
- More complex organisms have developed over time
- Mass extinctions contributed to the development of Earth's history

NOW, you will learn

- About early ideas and observations on evolution
- How Darwin developed his theory of natural selection
- How new species arise from older species

VOCABULARY

evolution p. 177
natural selection p. 181
adaptation p. 182
speciation p. 184

THINK ABOUT

How have telephones changed over time?

Today people across the world can communicate in many different ways. One of the most common ways is over the telephone. Looking at the two pictures, can you describe how this form of communication has changed over time?

Scientists explore the concept of evolution.

MAIN IDEA AND DETAILS
Make a chart for the main idea *scientists explore the concept of evolution.* Include details about scientists' observations.

In a general sense, evolution involves a change over time. You could say that the way humans communicate has evolved. Certainly telephones have changed over time. The first telephones were the size of a shoebox. Today a telephone can fit in the palm of your hand and can send images as well as sound.

In biology, **evolution** refers to the process though which species change over time. The change results from a change in the genetic material of an organism and is passed from one generation to the next.

CHECK YOUR READING What is evolution?

RESOURCES FOR DIFFERENTIATED INSTRUCTION

Below Level

UNIT RESOURCE BOOK
- Reading Study Guide A, pp. 24–25
- Decoding Support, p. 47

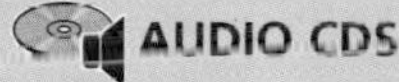
AUDIO CDS

Advanced

UNIT RESOURCE BOOK
- Challenge and Extension, p. 30

English Learners

UNIT RESOURCE BOOK
Spanish Reading Study Guide, pp. 28–29

AUDIO CDS

- Audio Readings in Spanish
- Audio Readings (English)

6.2 FOCUS

Set Learning Goals

Students will

- Describe early ideas and observations on evolution.
- Explain how Darwin developed his theory of natural selection.
- Describe how new species arise from older species.
- Model the effects of natural selection in the environment.

3-Minute Warm-Up

Display Transparency 4 or copy this exercise on the board:

Complete the graphic organizer.

Main Idea: Scientists use evidence to learn about the history of Earth.	
Detail: Fossil evidence	*bones, imprints, preserved remains*
Detail: Patterns in the fossil record	*mass extinctions occur several times in the fossil record*

3-Minute Warm-up, p. T4

6.2 MOTIVATE

THINK ABOUT

PURPOSE To discuss how telephones have changed over time

DISCUSS Have students compare the physical features of the two telephones. Then have them compare how communicating with the two phones is similar and different from each other. Ask students to discuss why they think that phones have changed over time. *As people's needs change, the phones changed to meet these needs.*

Ongoing Assessment

CHECK YOUR READING *Answer: Evolution refers to the process through which species change over time.*

6.2 INSTRUCT

Real World Example

Display a world map and have students locate the Galápagos Islands. Point out that these are a group of volcanic islands in the Pacific Ocean located off the coast of South America. Locate and review the names of the continents with students.

Teach from Visuals

To help students interpret the illustration of Darwin's voyage, ask:

- Where did Darwin's voyage begin? *England*
- What was the path of Darwin's voyage? *He sailed from England to South America; around the tip of South America to the Galápagos Islands; across the Pacific to Australia; then past the Cape of Good Hope on the southern tip of Africa; then back to England.*

Geography Connection

Students can make their own maps of Darwin's voyage on the *Beagle* and can provide a set of question-and-answer cards to accompany their maps. To begin, ask students to identify the continents Darwin's voyage included. *Europe, South America, Australia, Africa*

Ongoing Assessment

Describe early ideas and observations on evolution.

Who was the first scientist to propose a theory about how life evolves? *Jean-Baptiste de Lamarck*

CHECK YOUR READING *Answer: Lamarck believed that animals acquired traits and passed them on to their offspring.*

READING TIP

The word *acquire* comes from the root meaning "to add to." Acquired traits are those that are "added" after an organism is born.

Early Ideas

In the early 1800s, a French scientist named Jean Baptiste de Lamarck was the first scientist to propose a model of how life evolves. He became convinced that the fossil record showed that species had changed over time. He proposed an explanation for evolution based on the idea that an individual organism can acquire a new trait during its lifetime and then pass that trait on to its offspring. For example, Lamarck suggested that when giraffes stretched their necks to reach the leaves of tall trees, they passed the result of this stretching—a longer neck—to the next generation. Lamarck was a highly respected scientist, but he was unable to provide any evidence to support his idea. A

CHECK YOUR READING How did Lamarck explain the process of evolution?

Darwin's Voyage

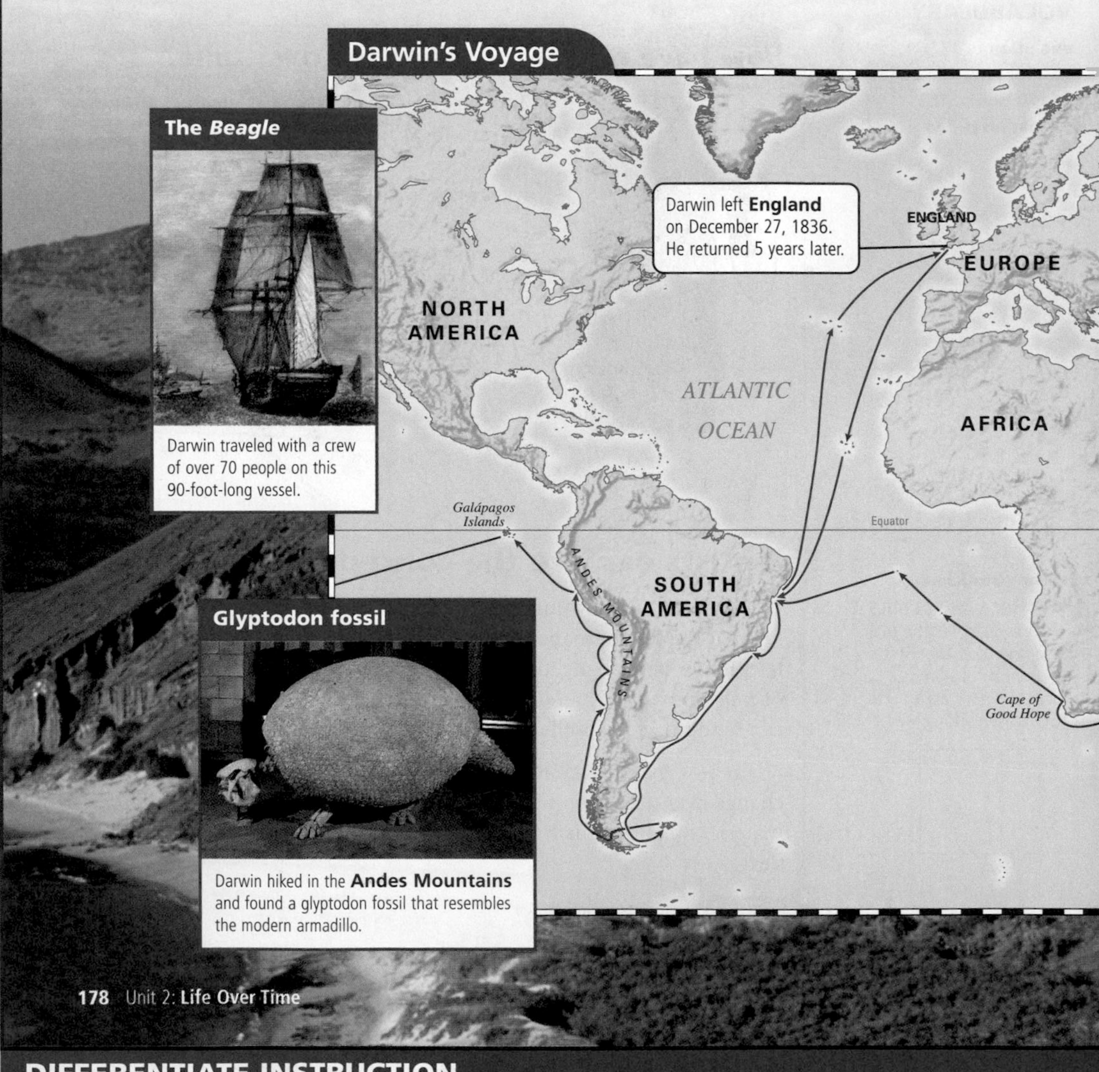

The *Beagle*

Darwin traveled with a crew of over 70 people on this 90-foot-long vessel.

Glyptodon fossil

Darwin hiked in the **Andes Mountains** and found a glyptodon fossil that resembles the modern armadillo.

DIFFERENTIATE INSTRUCTION

More Reading Support

A What did Lamarck observe about the fossil record? *that species change over time*

English Learners Place the terms *evolution, natural selection, adaptation,* and *speciation* on the classroom's Science Word Wall with brief definitions of each.

This section has a variety of introductory clauses and phrases that indicate time. For example, "In the early 1800s, a French scientist named Jean-Baptiste de Lamark was the first scientist to . . . " Have students write their own sentences with such time-locating introductory clauses as a method of reviewing each section in the chapter.

Darwin's Observations

About 50 years after Lamarck, the British naturalist Charles Darwin published what would become the basis of the modern theory of evolution. As a young adult, Darwin spent 5 years as a naturalist aboard the *Beagle,* a ship in the British navy. The map below shows the route Darwin traveled. As he sailed along the coast of South America, he studied rock formations and collected fossils. He also began to compare the new animals he was seeing with ones from his own country.

?
B

The differences he saw in animals became more obvious when he visited the Galápagos Islands, a chain of volcanic islands about 950 kilometers (600 mi) off the South American coast. On the 178 Galápagos Islands, plants and animals not only differed from those he saw on the mainland, but some differed from island to island.

Darwin was only 20 in 1831 when he joined H.M.S. *Beagle.*

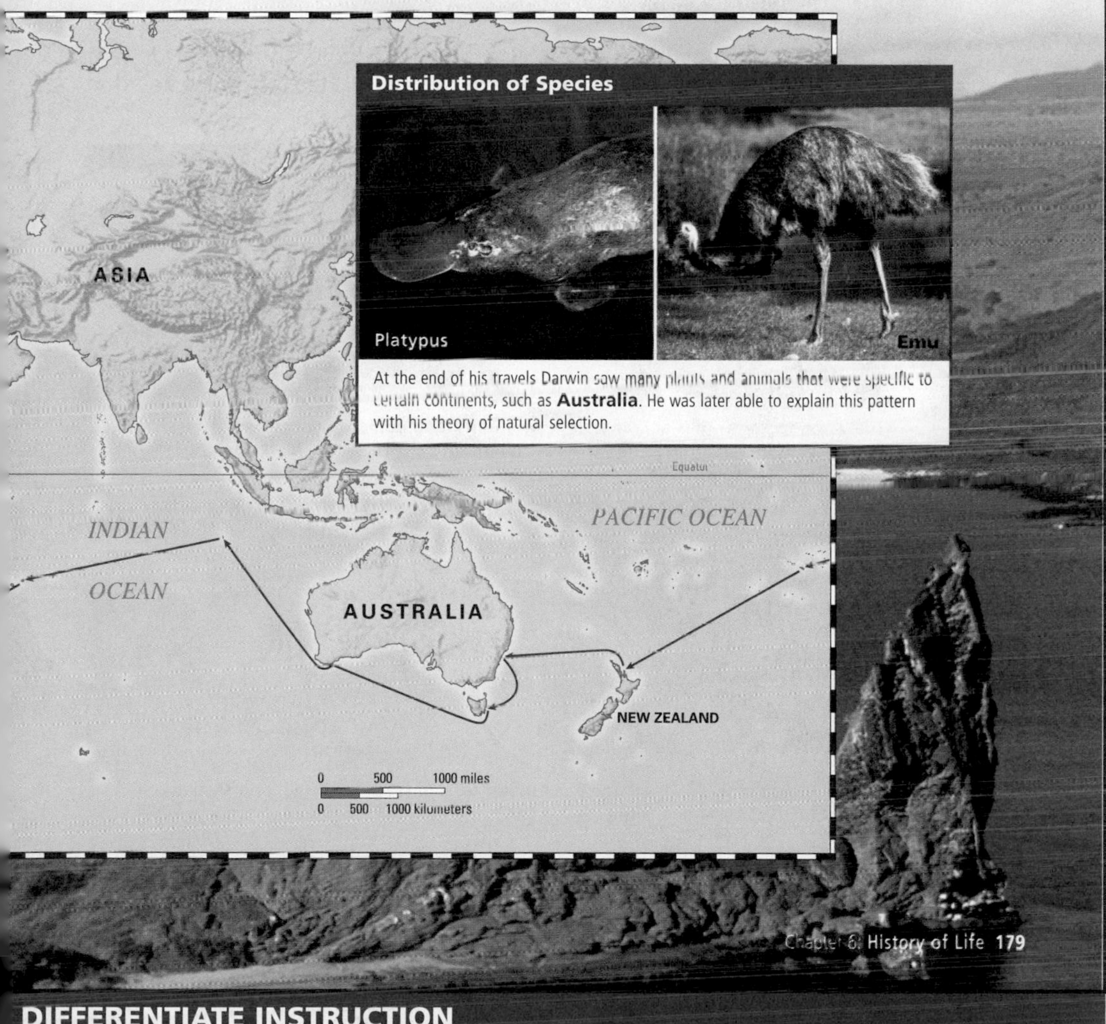

Distribution of Species

At the end of his travels Darwin saw many plants and animals that were specific to certain continents, such as **Australia**. He was later able to explain this pattern with his theory of natural selection.

History of Science

Although many people associate the theory of evolution with Charles Darwin, Darwin based his work on his observations as well as the work of other scientists of his time. Naturalist Alfred Russel Wallace proposed similar ideas, sending them in a paper to Darwin in 1858. Geologist Charles Lyell proposed that Earth was formed through a gradual, slow-moving process in 1830. This idea led Darwin to believe that living things might also evolve through a slow process. English economist Thomas Malthus made observations about human population growth that also contributed to Darwin's ideas.

Teach from Visuals

To help students interpret the photographs of animals and the map, ask: Why might Darwin's observations of these animals lead him to wonder about how life changes on Earth? *The animals that Darwin observed were not familiar to him and were not found in England.*

DIFFERENTIATE INSTRUCTION

More Reading Support

B What did Darwin do as he sailed the coast of South America? *He studied rock formations, collected fossils, and observed living things.*

Advanced Provide students with a copy of Darwin's *The Voyage of the Beagle.* Have them find excerpts that describe what Darwin observed in the Galápagos Islands.

R Challenge and Extension, p. 30

Teacher Demo

Model finch beaks by picking up different items using different utensils: tweezers, chopsticks, toothpicks, and tongs. Relate these tools to the finch beaks and how different beaks are useful to different tasks. Ask: Why would the finches in the Galápagos Islands have evolved different shaped beaks? *They needed different shaped beaks to eat different kinds of food.*

Teach from Visuals

To help students interpret the photographs of Darwin's finches, ask:

- How does the woodpecker's finch differ from the vegetarian finch? *The woodpecker finch's beak is longer and more pointed.*
- Of these two, which beak is more suitable for eating seeds and berries? *the vegetarian finch's beak*

Develop Critical Thinking

INFER Remind students that a theory is a well-tested explanation based on a broad range of facts and observations. Theories are not proven, but are generally accepted to be true. Ask students on what facts Darwin based his theory of evolution. *He based his theory on the similarities and differences he observed among the finches and other wildlife he observed in the Galápagos Islands.*

EXPLORE the BIG idea

Revisit "Internet Activity: Matching Finch Beaks" on p. 167. Have students explain how the activity of matching finch beaks provides evidence to support the theory of evolution.

C

Darwin observed several types of tortoises on the islands. Tortoises with short necks were living in damp areas with abundant plant life that grew close to the ground. Longer-necked tortoises were living in dry areas with cacti. He considered whether the length of their necks made it possible for the tortoises to live in different environments.

Darwin also found many different types of birds called finches living on the islands. Some finches were common in the treetops, while others lived in the lower shrubs of a neighboring island. Among the different islands he noticed a variety of beak shapes and sizes. Some finches had heavy, short beaks useful for pecking trees or seeds, while others had small, thin beaks that could be used for capturing insects. These observations caused Darwin to wonder if the birds had evolved from similar species.

Darwin's Finches

On the Galápagos Islands, Darwin observed similar-looking birds with very different beaks. These birds are closely related finch species that are suited to different habitats on the island.

The woodpecker finch is able to hold a twig in its long pointed beak, which it uses to pull the larvas of insects from a tree. The vegetarian finch has a curved beak, ideal for taking large berries from a branch.

The large ground finch has a large beak that it uses to crack open the hard shells of the seeds it feeds on. The cactus finch has a narrow beak that it uses to cut into a cactus and eat the tissue inside.

DIFFERENTIATE INSTRUCTION

More Reading Support

C What is a difference Darwin observed among the tortoises of the Galápagos Islands? *the lengths of their necks*

Advanced Have students research some of the ideas that influenced Darwin's ideas about evolution. Among them are the theories proposed by James Hutton, Thomas Malthus, Charles Lyell, and Alfred Wallace. Have students choose one scientist to research and explain how that person's ideas contributed to Darwin's theory. Then have students create a timeline based on their research.

Natural selection explains how living things evolve.

Learn more about natural selection.

After Darwin returned home to England in 1836, he spent several years analyzing the observations and specimens he had collected on his voyage. He struggled to develop an explanation that would account for the amazing diversity of species he saw and for the relationships between them. By 1844 he had developed a hypothesis based in part on an insight from one of his hobbies—breeding pigeons.

Darwin knew from personal experience that breeders can produce new varieties of an animal over time. The process breeders use is called artificial selection. For example, breeders produce a new breed of dog by selecting dogs that have certain desired traits and then allowing only those individuals to mate. From the resulting litters, they again selectively breed only the individual dogs with the desired traits. By repeating this process generation after generation, a new breed is produced.

What is artificial selection?

COMPARE AND CONTRAST These dogs are all terriers, but they have been bred through artificial selection to show very specific traits. How are the dogs similar? How are they different?

Darwin's insight was that a similar process might be going on in nature. He proposed that, through a process he called **natural selection,** members of a species that are best suited to their environment survive and reproduce at a higher rate than other members of the species. Darwin based this idea on a few key principles. These are overproduction, variation, adaptation, and selection.

DIFFERENTIATE INSTRUCTION

D What might occur when members of a species are more suited to survive than other members of the same species? *natural selection*

Below Level Provide pictures of several common animals such as a deer, a fish, a cat, a turtle, and so on. For each animal, have students make a list of adaptations that allow the animal to thrive in its environment.

Teach from Visuals

To help students interpret the photographs of the dogs, have them describe the similarities and differences among the traits of each dog pictured. Ask students: How might you account for the differences in these traits? *Dogs inherit different traits through genes from their parents. (Often artificial selection plays a role.)* For more information, see the Cells and Heredity unit.

Develop Critical Thinking

COMPARE AND CONTRAST To help students understand the difference between artificial selection and natural selection, point out that both have similar results: desired results are passed from one generation to the next. The differences occur in that humans control one process and the other is a result of natural processes.

Ongoing Assessment

Explain how Darwin developed his theory of natural selection.

Ask: What observations led Darwin to propose his theory of natural selection? *his observations of the differences in animals of the Galápagos Islands and his knowledge of the process of artificial selection in domestic breeding of animals*

CHECK YOUR READING *Answer: Artificial selection occurs when breeders produce a new breed of animal over a period of time by selecting animals that have certain desired traits and breeding them.*

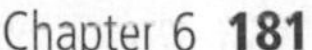

Address Misconceptions

IDENTIFY Ask students to describe how adaptations in organisms occur. If students say that individual organisms can adapt to a changing environment, they may hold the misconception that individual organisms are able to effect changes in bodily structure to exploit a particular habitat. Or they may think that an organism may respond to a changed environment by seeking a more favorable environment.

CORRECT As a class activity, create a two-column Main Idea and Details chart outlining the key ideas on pp. 182–183. For "Main Ideas," use the concepts and definitions for the following terms:

- overproduction
- variation
- adaptation
- selection

REASSESS Ask students to describe how the environment of a species selects an adaptive trait.

Technology Resources

Visit **ClassZone.com** for background on common student misconceptions.

MISCONCEPTION DATABASE

Teach Difficult Concepts

Students may confuse the differences among *variation, adaptation,* and *selection.* Use a flow chart for the salmon shown on p. 183 to illustrate how a variation becomes an adaptation. Point out that variation of a trait can lead to an adaptation. Adaptations, in turn, lead to natural selection.

Curved Tail Flow Chart

Variation
One or some fish have it.

↓

Adaptation
Those that have it use it to survive.

↓

Selection
Those that survive reproduce. Others die off early.

Overproduction

Take a look at how Darwin's ideas are useful for the study of salmon. When a plant or an animal reproduces, it usually makes more offspring than the environment can support, as you can see in the diagram on page 183. A female salmon may lay several thousand fertile eggs, but not all of them will hatch. Only a few hundred of the salmon that hatch from the eggs will survive disease and avoid fish-eating predators. Several dozen of these survivors will live to adulthood. An even smaller number will successfully reproduce.

Variation

READING TIP As you read about the principles of natural selection, refer to the diagrams on page 183.

Within a species there are natural differences, or variations, in traits. For example, if you looked very closely at thousands of salmon, you might see slight differences among individuals. Some might have larger fins. Others might have distinct patterns of spots on their scales. Many of the differences among individuals result from differences in the genetic material of the fish.

Sometimes the genetic material itself changes, causing a new variation to come about. A change in the genetic material is referred to as a mutation. As the fish with the new variation reproduces, the trait gets passed on to its offspring. Therefore, genetic variations are passed on from one generation to the next.

Adaptation

E

Sometimes a mutation occurs that makes an individual better able to survive than other members of the group. An **adaptation** is any inherited trait that gives an organism an advantage in its particular environment. For example, a slight change in the shape of a tail fin may increase a fish's chance of survival by helping it swim faster and avoid predators.

Selection

Darwin reasoned that individual organisms with a particular adaptation are most likely to survive long enough to reproduce. As a result, the adaptation becomes more common in the next generation of offspring. As this process repeats from generation to generation, more members of a species show the adaptation. Consider the shape of the salmon. If a change in the tail fin makes the salmon better able to move upstream and lay eggs, scientists say this trait has been selected for in this environment. In other words, the species is evolving through natural selection.

182 Unit 2: **Life Over Time**

DIFFERENTIATE INSTRUCTION

More Reading Support

E What term describes an inherited trait that gives an organism an advantage in its environment? *adaptation*

English Learners Have students work in pairs with advanced students to write their own easily remembered or easily understood definitions of *overproduction, variation, adaptation,* and *natural selection.* Then have them use the terms to create a flow chart showing how the process of natural selection occurs.

Natural Selection

Certain traits become more common in a group of organisms through the process of natural selection.

Overproduction

A fish may lay hundreds of eggs, but only a small number will survive to reach adulthood.

Variation

A mutation may cause a slight curve to develop in a fish's tail.

Adaptation

The fish with the curved tail is able to swim more quickly and so escapes predators. The fish reproduces.

Selection

With each generation, more fish with a curved tail survive to reproduce. Over time, they make up a larger part of the group.

READING VISUALS How does natural selection occur for an individual salmon?

DIFFERENTIATE INSTRUCTION

Advanced Challenge students to devise a board game called "Survival of the Fittest." In their game, students should apply the concepts of adaptation and natural selection by choosing examples of organisms (real or hypothetical) and their respective environments.

Teach from Visuals

To help students interpret the natural selection diagram, ask.

- What causes the variation? *a mutation*
- How does the adaptation enable the salmon to survive better than others? *It can swim faster, so it escapes predators and can spawn.*
- How does the adaptation become common in the next generation? *Salmon with the adaptation reproduce.*

The visual "Natural Selection" is available as T6 in the Unit Transparency Book.

Address Misconceptions

IDENTIFY Ask students to describe how genetic variations affect individuals. If students say that they are always beneficial, they may hold the misconception that genetic variation always helps individuals adapt to their environment.

CORRECT Provide an example to show that some adaptations have drawbacks; e.g., a curved tail may enable a fish to swim faster but may require more energy.

REASSESS Ask students to describe how a variation in a fish's tail would affect how it reacts to its environment.

Technology Resources

Visit **ClassZone.com** for background on common student misconceptions.

MISCONCEPTION DATABASE

EXPLORE the BIG idea

Revisit "Which One of These Things Is Not Like the Others?" on. p. 167. Have students explain what they observed in the string beans. What features were traits? variations? adaptations?

Ongoing Assessment

Answer: Salmon with curved tails have advantages that enable them to survive; other salmon do not. The variation is "selected" by the environment and passed on to new generations.

Real World Example

Geographic isolation is not always required for speciation to occur. Some species may inhabit the same environment, but do not interbreed because they have different mating habits. The mating song of the Eastern Meadowlark, for example, differs from that of the Western Meadowlark. Because of this, Eastern Meadowlarks only respond to the song of other Eastern Meadowlarks and vice versa.

Teach from Visuals

To help students interpret the illustration of speciation, have them compare and contrast the features of the three cichlids. Then ask:

- What happens to species A as the lake levels falling? *The fish gradually spread out into other habitats.*
- What happens as a result of the lake levels rising? *The species become isolated geographically and no interbreeding takes place.*
- What happens as a result of the geographic isolation? *New species evolve from species A over time.*

New species develop from earlier species.

Darwin's personal observations and the work of another scientist, Alfred Wallace, led Darwin to write about this new concept of evolution. In 1859, after more than twenty years of work, Darwin published his ideas in his book *On the Origin of Species.* This work led the way for our modern understanding of how new species arise.

Speciation

F

Speciation is the evolution of new species from an existing species. Speciation may occur when the environment changes dramatically, or when the environment changes gradually. The Galápagos finch populations Darwin studied showed evidence of speciation.

Isolation

Darwin's trip to the Galápagos Islands showed him an important point about speciation. Many new species had evolved after populations were separated from the mainland and were not able to breed with their mainland relatives. Darwin reasoned that isolation of populations by geographical or other barriers could contribute to the process of speciation. A species of fish called cichlids shows how a physical barrier contributes to speciation.

Speciation

In this African lake, new species of cichlids have evolved.

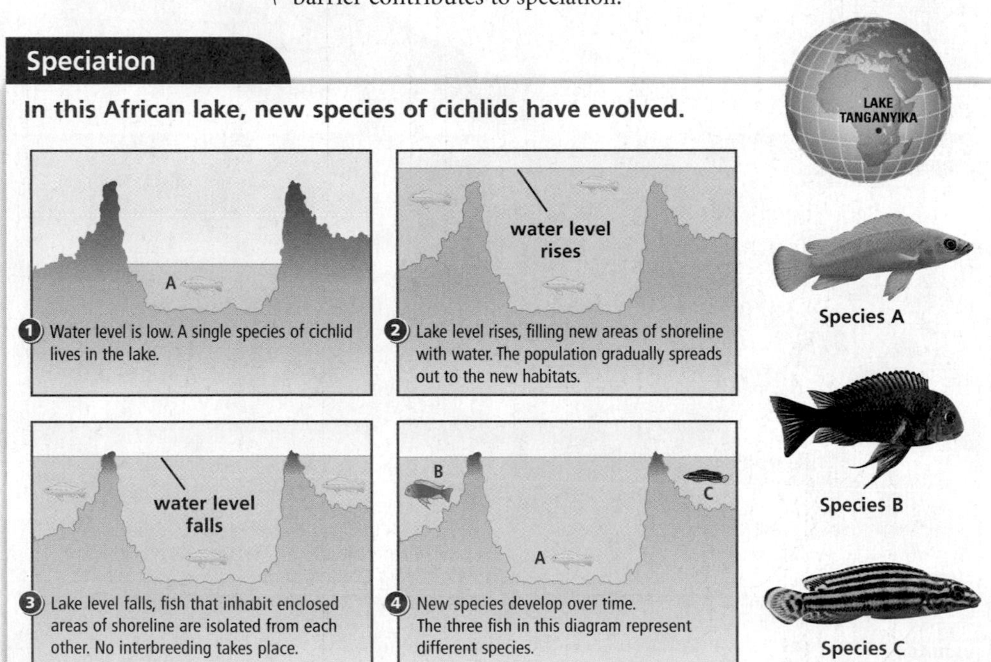

1. Water level is low. A single species of cichlid lives in the lake.
2. Lake level rises, filling new areas of shoreline with water. The population gradually spreads out to the new habitats.
3. Lake level falls, fish that inhabit enclosed areas of shoreline are isolated from each other. No interbreeding takes place.
4. New species develop over time. The three fish in this diagram represent different species.

184 Unit 2: **Life Over Time**

DIFFERENTIATE INSTRUCTION

More Reading Support

F What term describes the evolution of a new species from an existing species? *speciation*

Advanced Have pairs of students choose a species and make a chart similar to the one on p. 184 to show how isolation may lead to speciation. Students should name and describe the variation that might occur in the hypothetical new species that would thus evolve from the original in response to the condition of isolation.

In Lake Tanganyika, one of the largest lakes in the world, there are over 150 species of cichlids. Members of one particular genus, *tropheus*, originally lived along the rocky shore and couldn't cross the open water. The climate and geology of the area caused the lake's water level to rise and fall many times over thousands of years. As the water level changed, a new, rocky habitat was formed, and some populations of cichlids became isolated from each other.

The isolated populations were unable to interact with each other because they couldn't cross open waters. As a result, genetic differences began to add up in these populations. The cichlid populations now represent distinct species. They have developed unique characteristics and cannot breed with each other. See diagram on page 184.

Today scientists understand that isolation is essential to speciation. For a species to separate, two populations must be prevented from reproducing with each other. A geographic boundary like an ocean or mountain range can result in isolation. Two populations of a species can also be isolated if they feed on different things or reproduce at different times of the year.

As the cichlids in Lake Tanganyika show, the mutations in one isolated group may differ from another. Two or more populations may evolve differently from each other. The result is speciation, which has contributed to the biodiversity on Earth.

CHECK YOUR READING What is a key factor that can lead to speciation?

The Rocky Mountains are an example of a barrier that can isolate populations.

6.2 Review

KEY CONCEPTS

1. How did Lamarck's ideas differ from Darwin's?
2. What did Darwin observe in the finch populations that supported his idea of natural selection?
3. Explain how isolation helps speciation.

CRITICAL THINKING

4. **Hypothesize** Two species of grasses are separated by a tall mountain range. A third species of grass shares some characteristics with each of the other two species. It inhabits a small valley, surrounded on all sides by mountains. Form a hypothesis for the origin of the third species

CHALLENGE

5. **Predict** The Arctic hare lives in snow-covered mountains in Canada. The hare is hunted by foxes, wolves, and owls. Which trait is more likely to be inherited by new generations of hares: white fur or black fur?

ANSWERS

1. Lamarck believed an individual organism passed traits on to its offspring. He lacked support for his ideas. Darwin showed how traits could be passed on by natural selection.

2. Darwin noticed that beak shapes and sizes differed among the finches. This led him to believe that the finches evolved differently.

3. Isolation stops populations from interbreeding so new species evolve.

4. The third species most likely evolved from one of the two other species. Isolated by mountains, it began to develop its own unique characteristics.

5. White fur; it will help the hare blend in, escaping predators.

Ongoing Assessment

Describe how new species arise from older species.

Ask: How do new species develop from older species? *When a genetically different group within a species survives better than others, its traits are passed on to its offspring. If the differences become great, as when a population is isolated, the unique traits make the species unique.*

 *Answer: isolation by geographical or other barriers*

Reinforce the BIG idea

Have students relate the section to the Big Idea.

 Reinforcing Key Concepts, p. 31

6.2 ASSESS & RETEACH

Assess

 Section 6.2 Quiz, p. 4

Reteach

Write the following terms on the board: *overproduction, variation, adaptation,* and *selection.* Have students describe each process and how it leads to natural selection. Then have students give an example that they learned about from the text.

Technology Resources

Have students visit **ClassZone.com** for reteaching of Key Concepts.

 CONTENT REVIEW

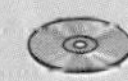 CONTENT REVIEW CD-ROM

CHAPTER INVESTIGATION

Focus

PURPOSE To model the effects of natural selection in the environment

OVERVIEW Students play a game that models natural selection. Students then use their observations to:

- record their results to show patterns in a population.
- determine what happens to a group of organism as a result of natural selection.

Lab Preparation

- If colored paper clips are not available, use beads, buttons, or dried beans. Coins, such as pennies, nickels, and dimes, will also work well on the game board.
- Prior to the investigation, have students read the investigations and prepare their own game boards (p. 186) and data tables (p. 187). Or you may wish to copy and distribute datasheets and rubrics.

UNIT RESOURCE BOOK, pp. 50–58

SCIENCE TOOLKIT, F15

Lab Management

INCLUSION Provide each student with an index card summarizing how to play the game, beginning with the number of paper clips to put on the board and how to roll. Read the card aloud as often as necessary, or encourage players to do so. Model Steps 4 through 6 for students before they begin.

Teaching with Technology

If video cameras are available, have students create videotapes of the game as students play. Students can narrate game play and then give a synopsis of the "Observe," "Analyze," and "Conclude" results. Encourage them to prepare a script ahead of time and to tape in segments to allow some preparation for each segment.

CHAPTER INVESTIGATION

Modeling Natural Selection

OVERVIEW AND PURPOSE Organisms that are best adapted to their environment tend to survive and reproduce. In this lab you will

- play a game that models the effect of natural selection in an environment
- determine what happens to a group of organisms as a result of natural selection

Question

As you read the steps to the game, think about what makes a population successful in an environment. How will the game model natural selection?

MATERIALS
- pair of number cubes
- 16 red paper clips
- 16 blue paper clips
- 16 yellow paper clips

Procedure

1. Make a game board like the one shown below. In your **Science Notebook** make a table like the one on page 187 to record your data.

	1	2	3	4
1				
2				
3				
4				

2. Count out 10 red paper clips, 4 blue paper clips, and 2 yellow paper clips. Randomly place the paper clips on the board. Keep the rest of the paper clips in a reserve pile.

INVESTIGATION RESOURCES

CHAPTER INVESTIGATION, Modeling Natural Selection
- Level A, pp. 50–53
- Level B, pp. 54–57
- Level C, p. 58

Advanced students should complete Levels B & C.

Writing a Lab Report, D12–13

Technology Resources

Customize this student lab as needed or look for an alternative. Print rubrics to assess student lab reports.

Lab Generator CD-ROM

3 Each color represents a different population of a single species. The board represents the environment. Roll the number cubes to determine which paper clips "live," or remain on the board, and which paper clips "die," or are removed from the board. Predict which color paper clip you think will be the last remaining color. Write down your prediction.

4 Roll the number cubes to determine which square, or part of the environment, will be affected. For example, 2,3 indicates the paper clip in column 2, row 3. If the numbers 5 or 6 come up, roll again until you have a number between 1 and 4 for each cube.

5 Now roll one cube to see what will happen to the paper clip or organism in that square. Use the chart below to determine if the paper clip "lives" or "dies." If the paper clip lives, repeat steps 4 and 5 until one paper clip dies, or is removed from the board. In your table, record which colors live and die.

Red	Remove if you roll a 1, 2, 3, 4, or 5.
Blue	Remove if you roll a 1, 2, or 3.
Yellow	Remove if you roll a 1 or 2.

6 Now that a paper clip has been removed, you need to see what population will reproduce to fill that space. Roll both cubes to choose another square. The color of the paper clip in that square represents the population that will "reproduce." Pick the same color paper clip from your reserve pile and place it on the empty square. All squares on the board should always have a paper clip.

7 Continue playing the game by repeating steps 4–6 until all the paper clips on the board are the same color.

Observe and Analyze

1. **OBSERVE** Which color paper clip filled the board at the end of the game?
2. **PREDICT** Compare the results with your prediction. Do the results support your prediction?

Conclude

1. **INFER** What does the random selection by rolling both number cubes represent? Explain.
2. **INFER** If the individual paper clips represent different members of a single species, then what might the different colors represent?
3. **LIMITATIONS** What problems or sources of error exist in this model? Give examples.
4. **APPLY** How does this game model natural selection?

INVESTIGATE Further

CHALLENGE Occasionally mutations occur in a population that can either help or damage the population's chance of survival. Add another step to the game that would account for mutations.

Modeling Natural Selection

Table 1. Patterns in a Population

Paper Clip Color	Live	Die

Observe and Analyze

1. *The red clips will not necessarily be the only color left on the board. They start out with more, but are removed more frequently. Other colors are equally likely to "win" the game.*
2. *Answers will depend on students' predictions.*

Conclude

1. *The roll represents natural selection. The rolls determine which square will be chosen for the single die roll.*
2. *Colors could represent the variations within a single species such as color, size, or other physical characteristics.*
3. *The model does not represent all of the factors that exist in a natural environment such as mutations and changes in populations due to environmental changes.*
4. *The remaining paper clip color must have been the one best adapted to survive in the environment.*

INVESTIGATE Further

CHALLENGE Possible answer: A "6" rolled on the die could indicate a mutation. The color of another clip, such as the clips with the fewest on the board, may be placed on the board.

Post-Lab Discussion

- Ask students to identify any new questions raised. How might these questions be tested within a real ecosystem?
- Tell students the clips represent fish. Have them assign traits to the colors such as red for large fins, blue for small size. What would the outcome say about the populations of fish? ***Sample answer: If fish that are small in size survive, then small fish would be suited for that environment.***

6.3 FOCUS

Set Learning Goals

Students will

- Explain how scientists develop theories.
- Describe the evidence Darwin used to support evolution.
- Describe the evidence scientists use today to support evolution.
- Model how sequencing affects communication.

3-Minute Warm-Up

Display Transparency 5 or copy this exercise on the board:

Fill in the boxes of the flow chart by completing each sentence.

Snowshoe Hare

Variation
White fur . . . *develops in a hare.*

↓

Adaptation
White fur . . . *improves the hare's survival in a white environment.*

↓

Selection
White fur . . . *is passed on to a new generation by the surviving hares.*

 3-Minute Warm-Up, p. T5

6.3 MOTIVATE

EXPLORE Evidence

PURPOSE To understand how observations can supply evidence

TIP *15 min.* Review the meaning of *observation* with students. Remind them that observations are made by using the senses. The information gathered through observation is known as *data*.

WHAT DO YOU THINK? *drops of water on cars, clouds, people with umbrellas. Some observations, such as clouds, do not support the statement.*

KEY CONCEPT

Many types of evidence support evolution.

BEFORE, you learned

- Natural selection explains part of the process of evolution
- New species develop from earlier species

NOW, you will learn

- How scientists develop theories
- About the evidence Darwin used to support evolution
- About additional evidence most scientists use today

VOCABULARY

ancestor p. 189
vestigial organ p. 190
gene p. 193

EXPLORE Evidence

How can observations supply evidence?

PROCEDURE

1. Consider the following statement: It rained last night.
2. Look at the following observations and determine which pieces of evidence support the statement.
   - There are puddles on the ground.
   - The weather report says there will be scattered showers today.
   - Your sister tells you there was a rain delay during last night's tennis match.

MATERIALS

- paper
- pencil

WHAT DO YOU THINK?

- What other observations can you come up with that would supply evidence for the first statement?
- Could any of the evidence be misleading?

MAIN IDEA AND DETAILS Don't forget to make a chart of details supporting the main idea that observations provide evidence for theories. Include a definition of *theory* in your chart.

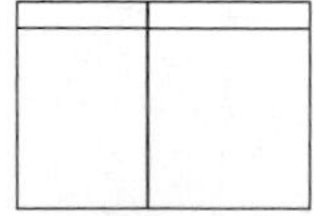

Observations provide evidence for theories.

In this chapter, you've learned about important observations that scientists have used to understand the history of living things. These observations provided Darwin with information he used to describe his ideas about evolution.

Darwin, like all good scientists, was skeptical about his observations and conclusions. Although the historic trip on the *Beagle* took place between 1831 and 1836, Darwin didn't publish the book explaining his theory until 1859. In order to understand the importance of Darwin's work, it is also important to understand the meaning of the term *theory.*

RESOURCES FOR DIFFERENTIATED INSTRUCTION

Below Level

UNIT RESOURCE BOOK

- Reading Study Guide A, pp. 34–35
- Decoding Support, p. 47

AUDIO CDS

Advanced

UNIT RESOURCE BOOK

Challenge and Extension, p. 40

English Learners

UNIT RESOURCE BOOK

Spanish Reading Study Guide, pp. 38–39

- Audio Readings in Spanish
- Audio Readings (English)

Evidence: information from observations and experiments

Evidence for evolution

fossil

biological

genetic

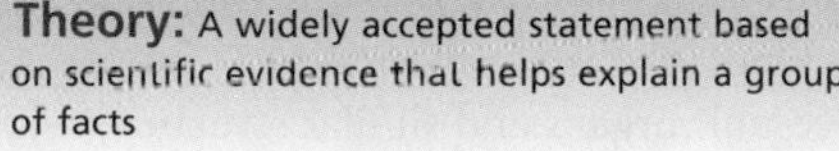

Theory: A widely accepted statement based on scientific evidence that helps explain a group of facts

Examine evidence to support evolution.

A scientific theory is a statement based on observation and experiment. If continued observation and experiment support the statement, it may become widely accepted. A theory that has been widely accepted is used to explain and predict natural phenomena. The chart above will help give you an idea of how a theory works and what evidence has been used to support evolution and the theory of natural selection.

How do scientists support theories?

Fossil evidence supports evolution.

You have read that Darwin collected many specimens of fossils on his trip. These specimens provided evidence that species existing in the past were very similar to species living during Darwin's time. For example, the fossil of an extinct animal called the glyptodon resembles the modern armadillo, an animal found today in South America.

The geographic information about many fossils provides evidence that two species with a common ancestor can develop differently in different locations. An **ancestor** is an early form of an organism from which later forms descend. The idea of common ancestors is important to the theory of natural selection and to the evidence that supports the theory. Scientists comparing modern plants and modern algae to fossil algae can tell that they all share a common ancestor.

What is a common ancestor?

6.3 INSTRUCT

Teach Difficult Concepts

Many students may think that theories are fact. Others may think that because something is a theory, it has little credibility. Point out that evidence is documentation or proof in the form of observations and data that support a theoretical statement. Make sure students understand that theories can change as new evidence is discovered.

Teach from Visuals

To help students interpret the information in the evidence diagram have them read the definition of a theory. Then ask: What evidence do scientists have that support the theory of evolution? *fossil, biological, and genetic evidence*

Teacher Demo

Show students pictures of fossils of both extinct organisms and their living relatives. Ask students to explain why scientists consider the fossils to be evidence of evolution. *The fossils demonstrate how these extinct organisms and their living relatives are related and how they have changed over time.*

Ongoing Assessment

Explain how scientists develop theories.

Why are theories widely accepted by scientists? *Theories are backed up by evidence.*

CHECK YOUR READING *Answer: Scientists support theories by observations and experiments.*

CHECK YOUR READING *Answer: an early form of an organism from which several later forms have descended*

DIFFERENTIATE INSTRUCTION

More Reading Support

A What term describes an early relative of a living species? *ancestor*

Inclusion Students with various learning disabilities, including those with Asperger's syndrome, may read words literally. For example, "evidence that supports the theory" does not mean the evidence physically holds up the theory. Also, "specimens provided evidence" does not mean literally that a specimen physically or intentionally gave the evidence to a scientist. Help students recognize and understand these phrases by rewording them so that a human is actively doing something, e.g., "Scientists find evidence by looking at specimens. Scientists form theories by collecting evidence that makes sense within the theory."

Real World Example

Ask students if they know of the common surgical operation whereby someone has their appendix removed. Point out that the appendix, unlike most other organs in the body, has no important purpose or use for humans. In other species of mammals, the appendix may play a role in digestion. The appendix is a vestigial structure in humans that might have had a more important role in the ancestors of modern humans.

Teach Difficult Concepts

Some students might confuse the difference between vestigial organs and similar structures. To help them, have students create a chart that answers the following questions:

- Are these physical structures?
- Do these structures serve a purpose for the organism? What is the purpose?
- Is the structure unused?

Ongoing Assessment

CHECK YOUR READING *Answer: vestigial organs and similar structures with different functions*

Biological evidence supports evolution.

Today scientists continue to study fossil evidence as well as biological evidence to support the concept of evolution. They have even returned to the Galápagos to further investigate Darwin's work. What they have found gives strength to the theory he proposed nearly 150 years ago. Returning year after year, these scientists are able to follow and record evolutionary changes as they are unfolding. The biological evidence they study includes the structure and the development of living things. This work has helped scientists identify relationships between organisms that exist today. In addition, their observations suggest how modern organisms are related to earlier species.

Similarities in Structure

Evidence for evolution can be observed within the physical structures of adult organisms. Scientists who study evolution and development consider two types of structural evidence. They are vestigial (veh-STIHJ-ee-uhl) organs and similar structures with different functions.

What are two types of structural evidence?

READING TIP

The root of the word vestigial means "footprint." A vestige refers to visible evidence that is left behind—such as a footprint.

Vestigial organs are physical structures that were fully developed and functional in an ancestral group of organisms but are reduced and unused in the later species. In the bodies of whales there are small leg bones that are vestigial. The skeletons of snakes also have traces of leglike structures that are not used. These vestigial organs help researchers see how some modern organisms are related to ancestors that had similar structures.

Similar structures with different functions Scientists studying the anatomy of living things have also noticed that many different species share similar structures. But these structures are used differently by each species. For example, lizards, bats, and manatees have forelimbs that have a similar bone structure. As you can see from the diagram on page 191, there is one short bone and one long bone that go from a shoulder structure to a wrist structure. But obviously, a lizard, a bat, and a manatee use this structure in different ways.

This similarity in structure indicates that these organisms shared a common ancestor. The process of natural selection caused the variations in form and function that can be observed today. These organisms lived in different environments and so were under different pressures. For lizards the environment was land, for bats it was the air, and for manatees the water. The environment influenced the selection of traits.

DIFFERENTIATE INSTRUCTION

Below Level Show students pictures of some familiar animals such as a moose, deer, zebra, duck, hawk, and robin. Have students group the animals according to their similarities. Most students would group the moose, deer, and zebra in one group, and the duck, hawk, and robin in another. Ask students what structures are similar in each group of animals (example: fur or hooves in one; feathers or beaks in the other). Then have them look at structures such as the vertebrae, ribs, limbs, or skull that are common yet differently formed in all the animals you have shown.

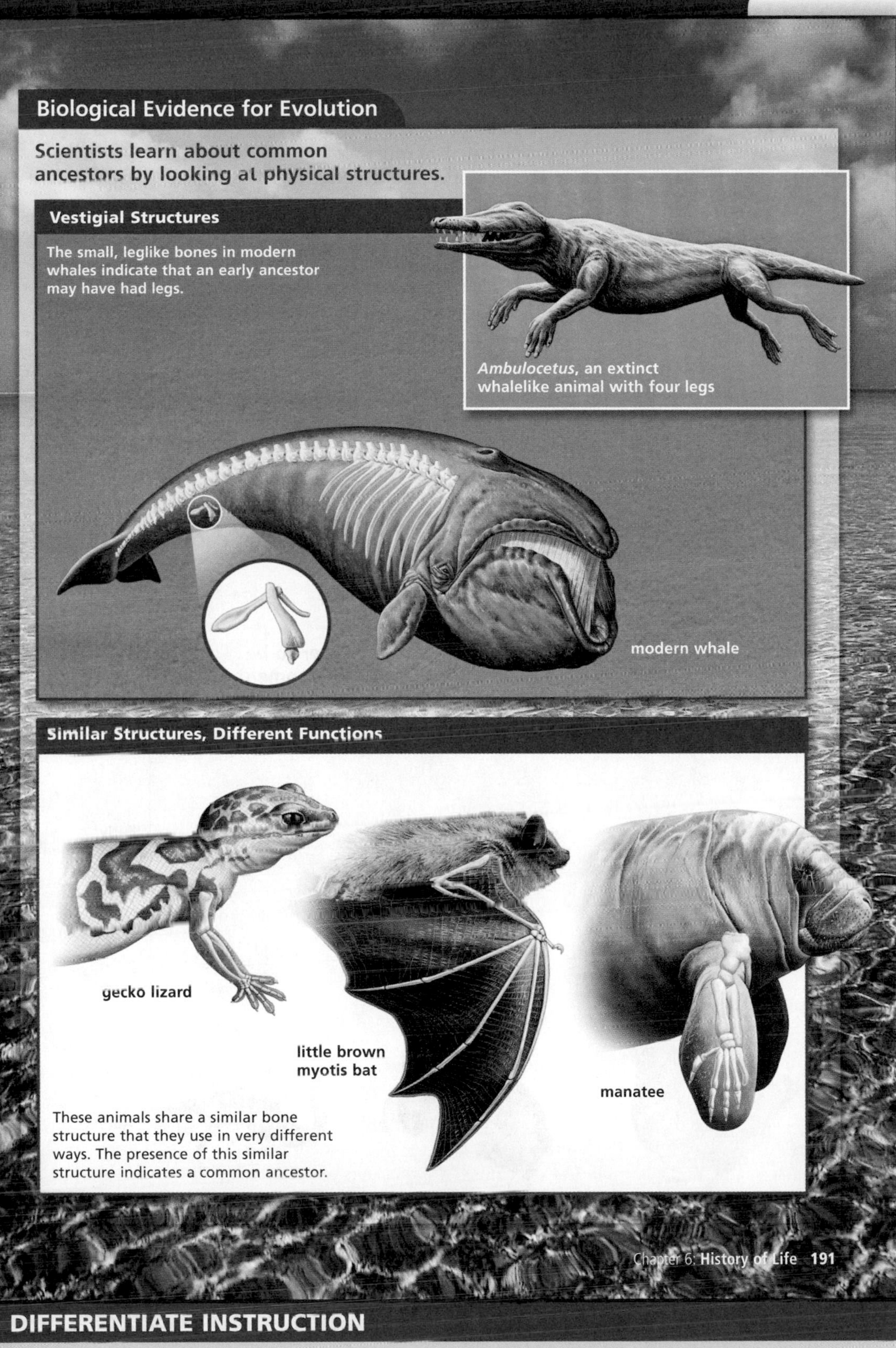

DIFFERENTIATE INSTRUCTION

Advanced Have students find pictures of skeletal structures of fish, birds, amphibians, reptiles, and mammals in reference books. Ask them to choose one similar structure and sketch it as it appears for a variety of animals. Then ask them to write what evidence indicates that all of these animals share a common ancestor.

R Challenge and Extension, p. 40

Teach from Visuals

To help students interpret the illustration of biological evidence for evolution, ask:

- Why is the small, leg-like bone in modern whales considered a vestigial structure? *It is an unused structure in modern whales.*
- What are the structures that are similar among the lizard, bat, and manatee? *the bones of their forelimbs*
- How do each of these animals use their forelimbs? *The gecko uses them to walk, the bat uses them to fly, and the manatee uses them to swim.*
- Why are these structures considered to be similar and not vestigial? *They are useful organs with different functions in different animals. They are similar in structure.*

Teach Difficult Concepts

Some students may think that structures such as wings in birds and butterflies are considered similar structures. Point out that similar structures have different functions as shown in the illustration. Structures in birds and butterflies have the same function—to help the animal fly—but do not necessarily indicate a common ancestor.

Teach from Visuals

To help students interpret the diagram of similarities in development, remind them that an embryo is a developing organism after fertilization has occurred. Then ask:

- How are these embryos similar? How are they different? *Similarities may include the shape of the head and body and the presence of a tail in the chicken and rabbit embryo. Differences include the shape and lack of a tail in the salamander embryo.*
- Based on the similarities and differences in the embryos, would you conclude that chickens are more closely related to rabbits or to salamanders? *rabbits*

Ongoing Assessment

Describe the evidence Darwin used to support evolution.

Ask: How do similarities in embryonic development support Darwin's theory of evolution? *Similarities show that certain organisms share a common ancestor.*

Similarities in Development

As you read about the development of a chicken, rabbit, and salamander, study the diagram below.

Scientists in the 1700s were fascinated by the fact that various animals looked similar in their earliest stages of life. They noted that as the organisms developed, they became less and less alike. Today's scientists continue to compare the developmental stages of different species.

The adult stages of many species do not look similar. For example, a rabbit does not look anything like a chicken. However, study reveals that the early life stages of a chicken and a rabbit are similar. An organism that is in an early stage of development is called an embryo.

In the diagram below, notice the development of three different species: a chicken, a rabbit, and a salamander. In the early stages of development, the embryos of all three organisms look similar. As they continue to develop, they begin to take on distinct characteristics. The chicken has a structure that starts to resemble a beak. The salamander begins to look as if it is adapted for life near water. In their adult stages, these three species no longer look similar.

Similarities in Development

The study of embryos shows that animals that appear to be very different as adults are similar during early development.

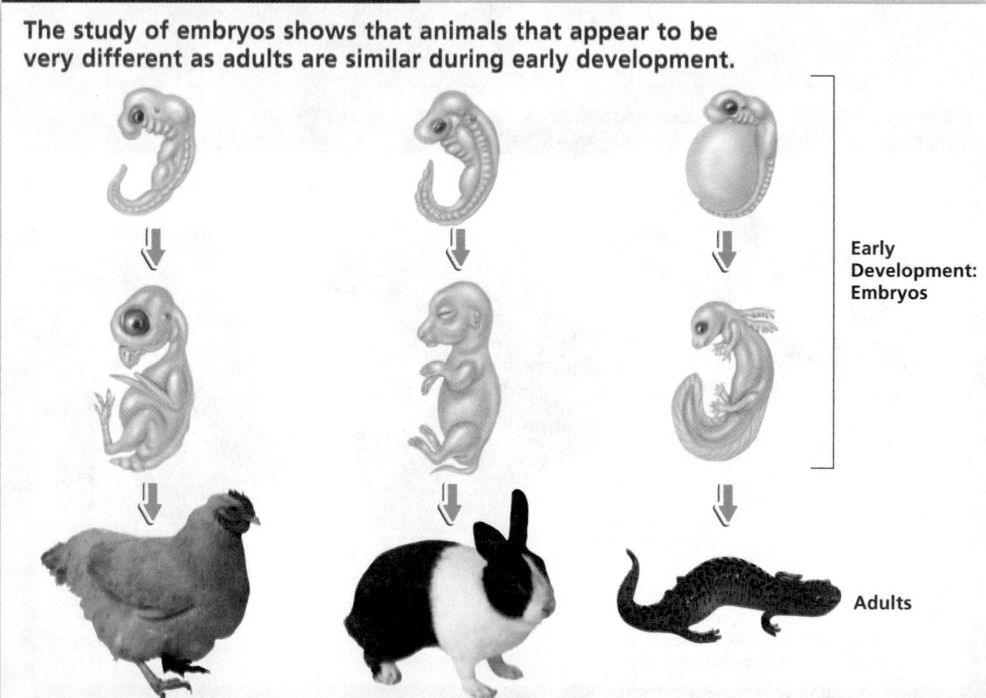

DIFFERENTIATE INSTRUCTION

More Reading Support

B What is the earliest stage of an organism's life? *embryo*

C What happens in later stages of different species? *They develop differently.*

English Learners Have students write definitions for *ancestor*, *vestigial organ*, and *gene* in their Science Word Dictionaries. Use the Chapter Summary page to help students focus on key concepts and vocabulary.

INVESTIGATE Genes

How can a sequence communicate information?

SKILL FOCUS
Sequencing

MATERIALS
letter cards

TIME
20 minutes

PROCEDURE

1. From your pile of letters (A, D, E, R), spell out the word RED.
2. Working with a partner, use the letters to spell two more words having three letters.

WHAT DO YOU THINK?

How does rearranging the letters change the meaning of the words?

CHALLENGE Cut out words from a newspaper. Arrange these words to form different phrases. How do these phrases communicate different messages?

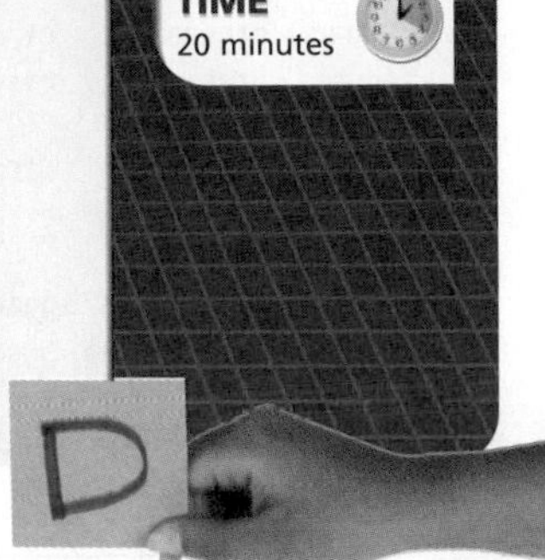

Genetic evidence supports evolution.

The key to understanding how traits are passed from one generation to the next lies in the study of DNA, the genetic material found in all organisms. DNA contains the information all organisms need to grow and to maintain themselves. When organisms reproduce, they pass on their genetic material to their offspring.

DNA contains a code that a cell uses to put together all the materials it needs to function properly. The code is made up of four different chemical subunits called bases. The bases are symbolized by the four letters A, T, C, and G. Located within DNA are individual genes. A **gene** is a segment of DNA that relates to a specific trait or function of an organism. Each gene has a particular sequence of bases. The cell takes this sequence and translates it into the chemicals and structures the organism needs.

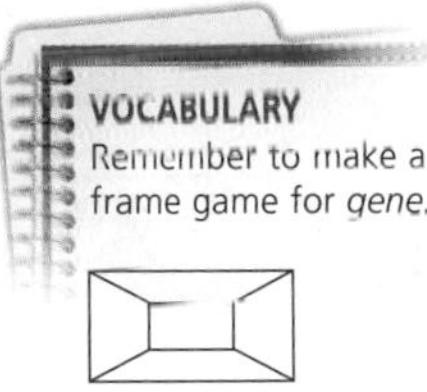

VOCABULARY
Remember to make a frame game for *gene*.

Scientists studying genes have identified a gene called the clock gene in many mammals. This particular gene relates to the function of sleeping and waking. As scientists learn more they can identify patterns of behavior in different organisms. The chart on page 194 compares the DNA sequence of part of the clock gene in both humans and mice.

CHECK YOUR READING What is a gene?

INVESTIGATE Genes

PURPOSE To model how a sequence can affect communication

TIPS *20 min.* Prior to the investigation, prepare letter cards. Each group of students should have letter cards *A, D, E,* and *R*. Students can extend the activity by working with other sets of cards, such as *O, P, S, T,* or *A, C, S, T*. They should make 4-letter words with these sets. For below-level students, these sets may be easier.

WHAT DO YOU THINK? *Students should spell out the words* ear, are, *or* era. *The sequence of letters changes the meaning of a word just as the sequence of DNA changes the information in the gene.*

CHALLENGE *The phrases communicate different messages because the letters form different words.*

 Datasheet, Genes, p. 41

Technology Resources

Customize this student lab as needed or look for an alternative. Print rubrics to assess student lab reports.

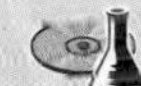 **Lab Generator CD-ROM**

Metacognitive Strategy

Have students create a mnemonic device or other study aid for remembering the types of evidence for evolution.

Integrate the Sciences

British researchers Maurice Wilkins and Rosalind Franklin used x-ray diffraction techniques in 1951 to create images of the patterns created when the DNA molecule is exposed to x-rays. Using this data, American scientist James D. Watson and British scientist Francis H. Crick determined the double-helix structure of DNA.

DIFFERENTIATE INSTRUCTION

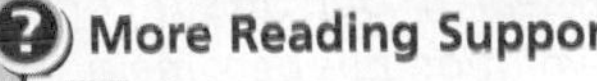

More Reading Support

D What does DNA contain? *information all organisms need to grow and maintain themselves*

Advanced Invite students to investigate examples of animals in which DNA evidence shows different conclusions about the ancestry of these animals than earlier believed. Animals to investigate include the giant panda and the elephant shrew.

Ongoing Assessment

CHECK YOUR READING *Answer: A gene is a segment of DNA that relates to a specific trait or function of an organism.*

Ongoing Assessment

Describe the evidence scientists use today to support evolution.

Ask: What technique, unavailable to Darwin, do today's scientists use to see relationships among species? *DNA sequencing*

Reinforce the BIG idea

Have students relate the section to the Big Idea.

Reinforcing Key Concepts, p. 42

6.3 ASSESS & RETEACH

Assess

Section 6.3 Quiz, p. 5

Reteach

Write the following concept map on the board. Ask volunteers to give one detail or characteristic about each type of evidence for evolution.

Evidence for Evolution		
Fossil Details	Biological Details	Genetic Details

Technology Resources

Have students visit **ClassZone.com** for reteaching of Key Concepts.

CONTENT REVIEW

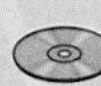
CONTENT REVIEW CD-ROM

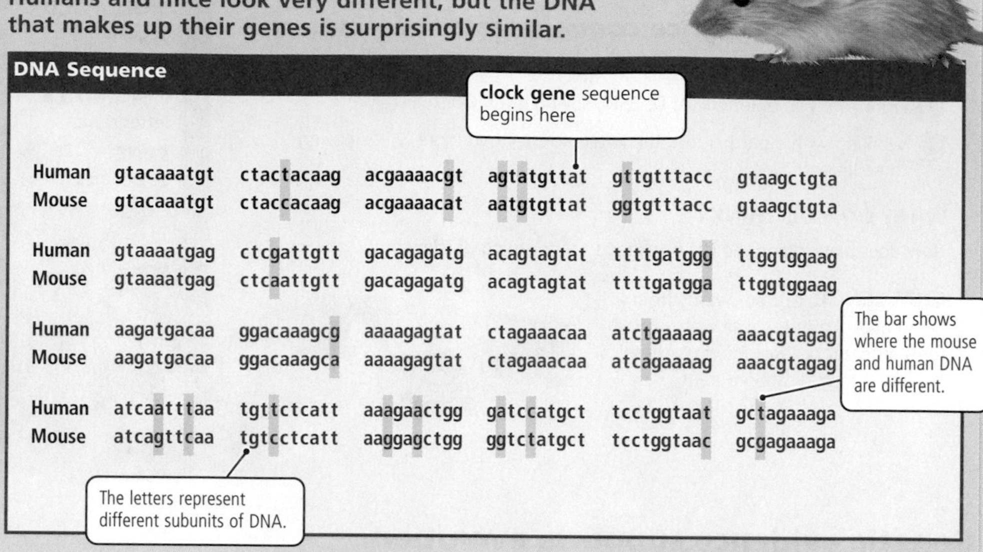

Scientists can tell how closely organisms are related by comparing their DNA. The more matches there are in the sequence of bases between two organisms, the more closely related they are. For example, almost all the genes found in a mouse are also found in a human. Even though the two organisms appear so different, much of the functioning of their cells is similar.

6.3 Review

KEY CONCEPTS

1. Describe in your own words how scientists use the word *theory*.
2. What type of evidence did Darwin use to support his theory of evolution?
3. Identify three different types of evidence that today's scientists use to support the theory of evolution.

CRITICAL THINKING

4. **Analyze** Describe three characteristics of a scientific theory. Explain how Darwin's theory of evolution is an example of a scientific theory.

CHALLENGE

5. **Predict** If you were looking at the sequence within the genes of two species, how would you predict that the two species are related?

ANSWERS

1. Possible answer: A theory is based on observations and testing.

2. Darwin used fossil evidence to support his theory of evolution.

3. Three types of evidence are fossil evidence, biological evidence, and genetic evidence.

4. A scientific theory is based on scientific evidence. It is a widely accepted statement. It is used to predict and explain natural phenomena. Based on his research, Darwin's theory of evolution has become a widely accepted statement.

5. The two species would most likely be related if they shared a similar sequence of bases.

SKILL: EVALUATING HYPOTHESES

How Did the Deep-Sea Angler Get Its Glow?

A fish that uses a fishing pole to catch food might seem odd. However, anglerfish do just that. The fish have a modified spine that extends from their head, almost like a fishing pole. At the end is a small piece of tissue that is similar in shape to a small worm. The tissue functions like a lure that a fisherman uses to catch fish. The anglerfish wiggles its "lure" to attract prey. If the prey fish moves in close enough, the anglerfish opens its mouth and swallows the prey whole. The "fishing poles" of abyssal anglerfish, anglerfish that live in the deep sea, have an interesting adaptation. The "lure" actually glows in the dark—it is bioluminescent.

Observations

From laboratory research and field studies, scientists made these observations.

- There are more than 200 species of anglerfish. Many of these live in deep water.
- Shallow-water species do not have glow-in-the-dark "lures."
- Only female abyssal anglerfish have a "pole." They do not have pelvic fins and are not strong swimmers.
- Other deep-sea organisms, including bacteria, jellyfish, even some squid, are bioluminescent.

Hypotheses

Consider these hypotheses.

- The ancestors of abyssal anglerfish lived in shallow waters. Some of these fish drifted into deep waters. A bioluminescent lure helped some survive.
- Light does not reach down to the bottom of the deep sea. Bioluminescence provides an advantage for the anglerfish because it makes its lure noticeable.
- A bioluminescent lure is more valuable to a female abyssal anglerfish than the ability to swim.

Evaluate Each Hypothesis

On Your Own For each hypothesis, think about whether all the observations support it. Some facts may rule out some hypotheses. Others may support them.

As a Group Decide which hypothesis is the most reasonable. Discuss your thinking and conclusions in a small group and see if the group can agree.

ANSWERS

Hypothesis 1 Reasonable. Observations 1 and 2 support this hypothesis since there is a great variety of anglerfish species and there are anglerfish that live in shallow water. There are no observations that rule it out.
Hypothesis 2 Most reasonable. All of the observations support this statement.
Hypothesis 3 Least reasonable. Only observation 3 supports this hypothesis, but there are no observations to rule it out.

THINK SCIENCE
Scientific Methods of Thinking

Set Learning Goal

To evaluate hypotheses based on observations that support or rule out each one

Present the Science

Anglerfish are named for their method of fishing for their prey. Deep-sea anglers generally inhabit the sea bottom, from depths of 500 to 2000 m (1640 to 6560 ft).

Guide the Activity

- Remind students that hypotheses must be supported by observations and data collected from experiments. Students should decide whether each hypothesis is supported by the observations.
- Remind students that *to evaluate* means to judge a statement based on criteria, such as observations.

COOPERATIVE LEARNING STRATEGY

Divide the class into groups of five. Assign a role to each student, such as group leader, note taker, and presenter. Assign each group one hypothesis to evaluate. The group leader makes sure that every group member has some input. The presenter discusses the groups' conclusions with the class. One student can read the text to the group. One might serve as timekeeper.

Close

Ask: Why is it important to check each hypothesis against each observation? *One observation may disprove a hypothesis.*

BACK TO the BIG idea

Have students explain why the words *change* and *over time* are important in the Big Idea statement. *Life has become more diverse through change, but the changes do not happen quickly. They take many generations.*

KEY CONCEPTS SUMMARY

SECTION 6.1
Ask students to describe the type of evidence that can be found in fossils as layers of Earth are uncovered. *Fossils provide information about the size and kind of organisms that once lived. Fossils are formed by hardened bones, imprints, and preserved remains. The age of a fossil tells scientists about the time period in which an organism lived and how it may have changed over time.*

SECTION 6.2
Ask: How do variation and adaptation lead to selection? *Organisms may have a genetic variation. The variation may then help them survive, so over time it may become an adaptation. As these adapted organisms survive and reproduce, their adaptations are passed on over many generations and are selected by the environment. This gives the species an advantage in its environment over other species.*

SECTION 6.3
Ask: How does biological evidence support evolution? *Biological evidence shows that certain embryos are similar in their development, indicating that those animals share a common ancestor. Similar structures with different functions and vestigial organs also indicate a common ancestor.*

Review Concepts

- Big Idea Flow Chart, p. T1
- Chapter Outline, pp. T7–T8

6 Chapter Review

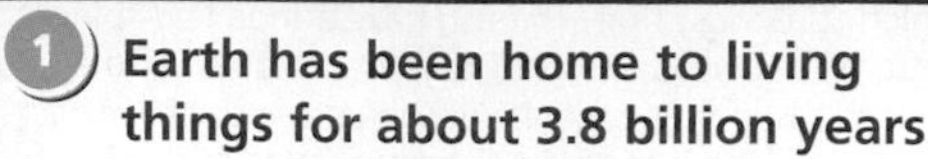

the BIG idea

Living things, like Earth itself, change over time.

KEY CONCEPTS SUMMARY

1 Earth has been home to living things for about 3.8 billion years.

Fossil records inform humans about the development of life on Earth. Information from fossils can help scientists reconstruct Earth's history.

VOCABULARY
fossil p. 169
unicellular organism p. 172
multicellular organism p. 173
mass extinction p. 174

2 Species change over time.

Darwin's theory of natural selection explains evolution.

Four principles of natural selection
- overproduction
- variation
- adaptation
- selection

The beak of this cactus finch provides an example of an adaptation.

VOCABULARY
evolution p. 177
natural selection p. 181
adaptation p. 182
speciation p. 184

3 Many types of evidence support evolution.

Three different types of evidence provide a bigger picture of evolution

fossil

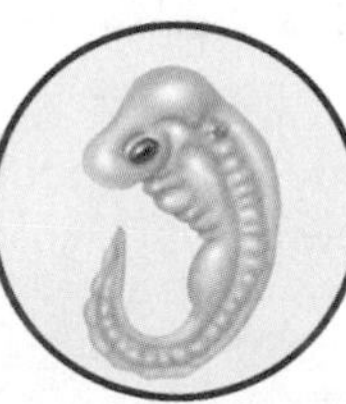

biological

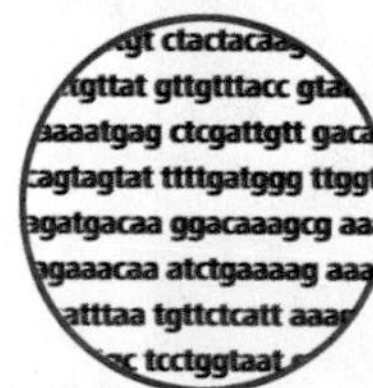

genetic

VOCABULARY
ancestor p. 189
vestigial organ p. 190
gene p. 193

Technology Resources

Have students visit **ClassZone.com** or use the CD-ROM for a cumulative review of concepts.

CONTENT REVIEW

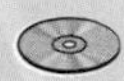
CONTENT REVIEW CD-ROM

Engage students in a whole-class interactive review of Key Concepts. Edit content as you wish.

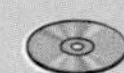
POWER PRESENTATIONS

Reviewing Vocabulary

Draw a triangle for each of the terms below. On the wide bottom of the triangle, write the term and your own definition of it. Above that, write a sentence in which you use the term correctly. At the top of the triangle, draw a small picture to show what the term looks like.

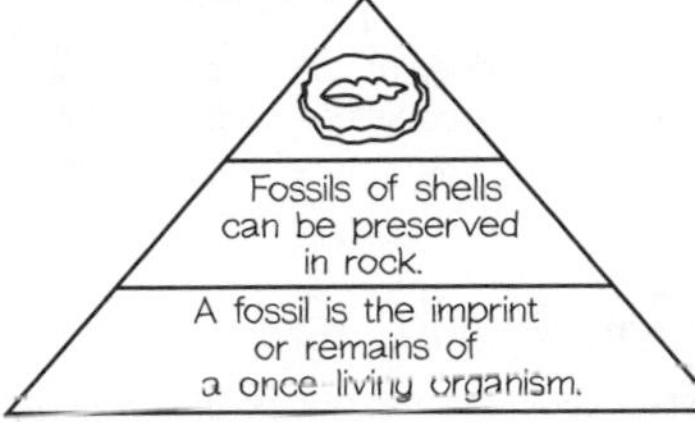

1. unicellular organism
2. multicellular organism
3. adaptation
4. vestigial structure

Reviewing Key Concepts

Multiple Choice *Choose the letter of the best answer.*

5. Which is *not* part of the fossil record?
   - a. fossil bones
   - b. preserved remains
   - c. living unicellular organisms
   - d. imprints
6. Whether a fossil formed before or after another fossil is described by its
   - a. relative age
   - b. absolute age
   - c. fossil record
   - d. radioactive age
7. The earliest multicellular organisms were
   - a. jellyfish
   - b. simple plants
   - c. fungi
   - d. tiny seaweeds
8. Which is a possible explanation for mass extinctions?
   - a. Earth had no water.
   - b. A meteorite collided with Earth.
   - c. The continents separated.
   - d. Woolly mammoths left no offspring.
9. Darwin's theory that species develop new traits and change over time is known as
   - a. natural selection
   - c. speciation
   - b. evolution
   - d. adaptation
10. Which describes Lamarck's explanation for changes in the fossil record?
    - a. Species best suited to their environments survive better than others.
    - b. Variation within a species can be passed on to offspring.
    - c. Acquired traits are passed on from one generation to another.
    - d. Giraffes adapted to their environment.
11. A slight change in a rabbit's ability to hear its predators better and help it survive is
    - a. an adaptation
    - b. a vestigial structure
    - c. an aquired trait
    - d. an isolation
12. Which is necessary for speciation to occur?
    - a. adaptation
    - b. mass extinction
    - c. isolation
    - d. acquired traits
13. Which of the following statements explain why the theory of evolution is widely accepted by the scientific community?
    - a. It has been proven by experiments.
    - b. The fossil record is complete.
    - c. It is supported by genetic evidence.
    - d. Lamarck's theory was correct.
14. Genetic evidence is based on the study of
    - a. embryonic development
    - b. mutations
    - c. common ancestors
    - d. DNA sequences

ASSESSMENT RESOURCES

UNIT ASSESSMENT BOOK
- Chapter Test, Level A, pp. 6–9
- Chapter Test, Level B, pp. 10–13
- Chapter Test, Level C, pp. 14–17
- Alternative Assessment, pp. 18–19

SPANISH ASSESSMENT BOOK
Spanish Chapter Test, pp. 25–28

Technology Resources

Edit test items and answer choices.

Test Generator CD-ROM

Visit **ClassZone.com** to extend test practice.

Test Practice

Reviewing Vocabulary

Drawings will vary. Sample answers:

1. A unicellular organism is made up of one cell. Unicellular organisms were the first organisms to inhabit Earth.

2. A multicellular organism is made up of many cells. Many multicellular organisms are made up of specialized groups of cells called tissues.

3. An adaptation is an inherited trait that gives an organism an advantage in its environment. Long necks are an adaptation in giraffes that help them better survive in their environment.

4. Vestigial structures are physical structures in organisms that are no longer useful. Whales have vestigial structures that look like small useless leg bones.

Reviewing Key Concepts

5. c
6. a
7. d
8. b
9. b
10. c
11. a
12. c
13. c
14. d

(Answers to items that appear on p. 198)

Thinking Critically

15. b

16. Older fossils are usually found in lower layers of rock.

17. Breeders use artificial selection to produce new varieties of species. In natural selection, the varieties are produced by nature.

18. Two species with a common ancestor may have developed different traits in different locations.

(Answers to items 15–18 appear on p. 197.)

Thinking Critically

19. *They learned about extinct organisms: what they looked like, how they lived, when they lived and died.*
20. *Overproduction occurs when a species produces more offspring than can survive. It ensures that at least some of the population reach reproductive age. Salmon are an example.*
21. *When dinosaurs became extinct, mammals no longer had to compete with them for food or space.*
22. *Giraffes with longer necks fed on taller trees and had a better chance of survival than short-necked giraffes. Long-necked giraffes passed on their genes to offspring. Over many generations, natural selection enabled these giraffes to evolve.*
23. *Over many generations variations in individuals may lead to the inheritance of a trait or adaptation. This makes an individual more able to survive so the species evolve by natural selection. Example: tail shape of a fish that helps it swim better*
24. *Rising water level gave cichlid population room to reproduce. Development of a new species might interrupt food chain in lake.*
25. *Isolation prevents two populations from reproducing. These populations evolve independently and natural selection allows different traits to evolve in each species.*
26. *genetic evidence*
27. *Organisms share a common ancestor.*

the BIG idea

28. *Sample: Fossils provide clues as to how organisms evolved.*
29. *Lamarck: Birds stretched beaks to fit inside flowers; passed acquired traits to offspring. Darwin: Birds with longer, thin beaks were better adapted to survive in certain environments through natural selection.*

UNIT PROJECTS

Give students Unit Projects worksheets. Directions and rubrics provide a guide.

 Unit Projects, pp. 5–10

15. Genetic information that cells use to control the production of new cells is located in
    - **a.** embryos
    - **b.** genes
    - **c.** the environment
    - **d.** vestigial structures

Short Answer *Write a short answer to each question.*

16. Describe how the relative age of a fossil is determined by studying layers of rock.
17. Explain the difference between artificial selection and natural selection.
18. How does common ancestry between two species support evolution?

Thinking Critically

19. **COMMUNICATE** What have scientists learned about past life on Earth from the fossil record?
20. **PROVIDE EXAMPLES** Explain the principle of overproduction. Give an example.
21. **SYNTHESIZE** How might the mass extinction of dinosaurs enable many new species of mammals to develop?
22. **EVALUATE** How would natural selection have led to the development of giraffes with long necks as opposed to giraffes with short necks?
23. **PROVIDE EXAMPLES** How are variation and adaptations related to natural selection? Give an example.
24. **PREDICT** In Africa's Lake Tanganyika different populations of cichlids became isolated from each other. Based on what you already learned, predict how the changing water level helped the cichlid population to change. How do you think the development of new cichlid species affected other living things in the lake?

25. **ANALYZE** How is geographic isolation related to the formation of a new species?
26. **EVALUATE** Pandas were once considered to be closely related to raccoons and red pandas because of their physical similarities. Today, scientists have learned that pandas are more closely related to bears than to raccoons and red pandas. What evidence might scientists have used to draw this conclusion? Explain.
27. **INFER** What does the presence of similar structures in two organisms—such as a dolphin's flipper and a lizard's forelimb—indicate?

the BIG idea

28. **INFER** Look again at the picture on pages 166–167. Now that you have finished the chapter, how would you change or add details to your answer to the question on the photograph?
29. **SYNTHESIZE** The beaks of hummingbirds are adapted to fit into long, thin flowers. Hummingbirds can feed on the nectar inside the flower. Write an explanation for this adaptation that Lamarck might have proposed. Then write an explanation for this adaptation based on Darwin's ideas. Use the terms acquired traits and natural selection in your answer.

UNIT PROJECTS

If you are doing a unit project, make a folder for your project. Include in your folder a list of the resources you will need, the date on which the project is due, and a schedule to track your progress. Begin gathering data.

198 Unit 2: **Life Over Time**

MONITOR AND RETEACH

If students are having trouble applying the concepts in Chapter Review items 22, 23, and 24, suggest that they review the illustration of the process of natural selection on p. 183. Then have students create a flow chart illustrating the process.

Students may benefit from summarizing one or more sections of the chapter.

 Summarizing the Chapter, pp. 68–69

Standardized Test Practice

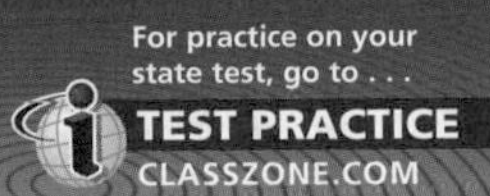

Interpreting Diagrams

Choose the letter of the best answer.

This diagram shows how groups of carnivores are related to one another. Each Y in the diagram indicates a common ancestor.

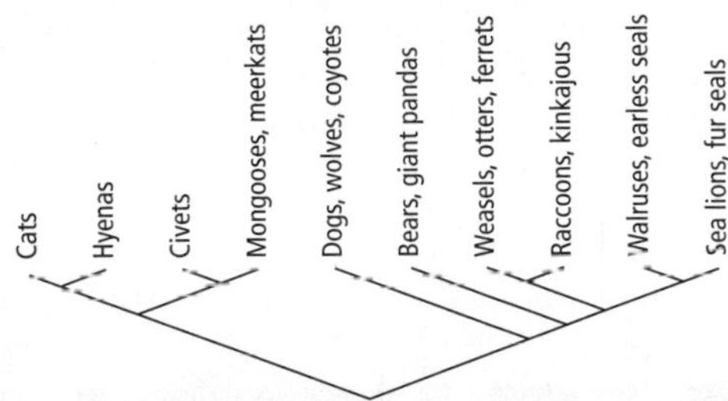

1. Hyenas are most closely related to which group?
- **a.** cats
- **b.** civets
- **c.** mongooses and meerkats
- **d.** raccoons and kinkajous

2. Weasels, otters, and ferrets are most closely related to
- **a.** bears and giant pandas
- **b.** sea lions and fur seals
- **c.** raccoons and kinkajous
- **d.** mongooses and meerkats

3. Sea lions and fur seals share their closest common ancestor with
- **a.** walruses and earless seals
- **b.** raccoons and kinkajous
- **c.** mongoose and muskrats
- **d.** civets

4. Which statement is true based on the information in the diagram?
- **a.** Dogs, wolves, and coyotes do not share a common ancestor with any of the groups.
- **b.** Raccoons are more closely related to weasels than they are to giant pandas.
- **c.** None of the groups shown in the diagram share a common ancestor.
- **d.** Mongooses and meerkats are the same as civets.

5. The branches on the diagram indicate where
- **a.** mass extinctions might have occurred
- **b.** speciation took place
- **c.** groups acquired traits and passed them onto their offspring
- **d.** there are gaps in the line of evolution

Extended Response

6. A scientist has discovered a new type of animal in the tundra area near the North Pole. Write a paragraph describing the type of evidence the scientist might use to classify the animal by its evolutionary history in the chart shown. Use these terms in your paragraph. Underline each term in your answer.

embryo	DNA sequences
vestigial structures	common ancestor

7. Write a paragraph in which you describe the traits of one of the animals named in the diagram. Choose several traits and describe how these traits might help the animal survive. Then describe how these might have been the result of adaptations and natural selection.

METACOGNITIVE ACTIVITY

Have students answer the following questions in their **Science Notebook:**

1. What did you find most surprising about the way that species evolve?
2. What questions do you still have about the processes of variation, adaptation, and natural selection, and the evidence that supports evolution?
3. How did your unit project help you gain a better understanding of the concepts studied in this chapter?

Interpreting Diagrams

1. a *2. c* *3. a* *4. b* *5. b*

Extended Response

6. RUBRIC

4 points for a response that correctly answers the question and uses the following terms accurately:

- embryo
- vestigial structures
- DNA sequences
- common ancestor

Sample answer: The scientist can compare the animal with fossils of early carnivores to determine a common ancestor. The scientist can also observe similarities in how the embryos develop with the other groups in the diagram. Similarities in structure such as the presence of vestigial structures might also link the animal to a common ancestor. The scientist can also study the DNA sequence of the animal to determine which group of animals on the chart it is most closely related to.

3 points correctly answers the question and uses three terms accurately
2 points correctly answers the question and uses two terms accurately
1 point correctly answers the question and uses one term accurately

7. RUBRIC

4 points for a response that correctly answers the question and discusses at least four traits that help the animal survive.

Sample answer: Cats have a keen sense of sight and hearing that enables them to stalk prey in the dark. Cats have claws for fending off predators. Their teeth consist of sharp canines that are adapted for tearing meat. They have powerful hind legs for jumping and running, which help them overrun and catch prey. Early cats with these traits would have been more likely to survive and so pass on the traits to offspring.

3 points response discusses three traits that help the animal survive
2 points response discusses two traits that help the animal survive
1 point response discusses one trait that helps the animal survive

CHAPTER

Classification of Living Things

Life Science
UNIFYING PRINCIPLES

PRINCIPLE 1
All living things share common characteristics.

PRINCIPLE 2
All living things share common needs.

PRINCIPLE 3
Living things meet their needs through interactions with the environment.

PRINCIPLE 4
The types and numbers of living things change over time.

Unit 2:
Life Over Time
BIG IDEAS

CHAPTER 6
The History of Life on Earth
Living things, like Earth itself, change over time.

CHAPTER 7
Classification of Living Things
Scientists have developed a system for classifying the great diversity of living things.

CHAPTER 8
Population Dynamics
Populations are shaped by interactions between organisms and the environment.

CHAPTER 7
KEY CONCEPTS

SECTION 1

Scientists develop systems for classifying living things.

1. Scientists classify millions of species.
2. Taxonomists study biological relationships.

SECTION 2

Biologists use seven levels of classification.

1. Linnaeus named about 4000 species.
2. Organisms can be classified into seven levels.
3. Dichotomous keys and field guides help people identify organisms.

SECTION 3

Classification systems change as scientists learn more.

1. Taxonomy changes as scientists make discoveries.
2. The two most familiar kingdoms are plants and animals.
3. Other organisms make up four more kingdoms.
4. Species and environments change.

T The Big Idea Flow Chart is available on p. T9 in the **UNIT TRANSPARENCY BOOK.**

Previewing Content

SECTION

Scientists develop systems for classifying living things. pp. 203–210

1. Scientists classify millions of species.
Classification is the scientific process of arranging organisms into groups based on similarities. **Taxonomy** is the science of naming and classifying organisms. A good system of taxonomy allows scientists to communicate about organisms without confusion. To classify organisms, scientists use physical similarities and differences as well as DNA.

2. Taxonomists study biological relationships.
- Scientists compare physical **traits** and evolutionary ancestry to determine how closely species are related.
- Fossils help scientists determine the evolutionary history of a species.
- DNA evidence can support physical evidence in determining how species are related. For example, DNA evidence suggests that the Giant panda is more closely related to the spectacled bears than the red panda, as previously believed.

SECTION

Biologists use seven levels of classification. pp. 211–219

1. Linnaeus named about 4000 species.
Linnaeus developed a system of **binomial nomenclature** for naming species and organizing them into groups. A species scientific name is made up of two parts—the first part is the **genus** name and the second part is the species name. Most scientific names are in Latin.

2. Organisms can be classified into seven levels.
The seven levels that identify a species are, in order from highest to most specific: kingdom, phylum, class, order, family, genus, and species. The classifications of the spotted turtle and the common house cat are shown in the table.

Classification Hierarchy

	Spotted turtle	Cat
Kingdom	Animalia	Animalia
Phylum	Chordata	Chordata
Class	Reptilia	Mammalia
Order	Testudines	Carnivora
Family	Emydidae	Felidae
Genus	*Clemmys*	*Felis*
Species	*guttata*	*catus*

3. Dichotomous keys and field guides help people identify organisms.
- A dichotomous key is a tool that helps scientists identify an organism by asking a series of paired questions about physical traits. The answer to each question either identifies the organism or leads to the next question.
- Field guides use paintings or photos of organisms and include scientific names, range maps, and descriptions.

Common Misconceptions

CLASSIFICATION OF ORGANISMS Many students misunderstand the concept of the scientific classification of organisms. They may group organisms according to their status, for example, placing them into groups of flying organisms or organisms that live in water. Or they may group organisms according to traits, such as possession of scales or wings, or according to concepts, such as endangered status or domesticity. They often do not understand the hierarchical nature of scientific classification.

This misconception is addressed on p. 207.

MISCONCEPTION DATABASE
CLASSZONE.COM Background on student misconceptions

Previewing Content

SECTION

Classification systems change as scientists learn more. pp. 220–229

1. Taxonomy changes as scientists make discoveries.

- As information about an organism's evolutionary history becomes available, taxonomists change their systems of classification.
- The six kingdoms are arranged into larger groups called **domains: Bacteria, Archaea,** and **Eukarya** based on cell type, cell number, and how organisms get their energy.
- Organisms in Archaea and Bacteria domains are made up of unicellular prokaryotic cells. They differ in cell chemistry. Archaea can survive extreme temperatures.
- The domain Eukarya is made up of the kingdoms **Protista, Fungi, Plantae,** and **Animalia**. These organisms are mostly multicellular. Organisms in the Protista, Fungi, Plantae, and Animalia kingdoms are all made up of eukaryotic cells such as the one shown.

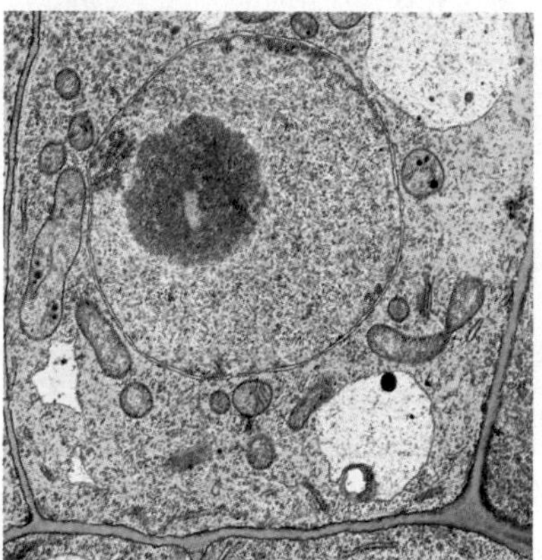

Eukaryotic cells each have a nucleus.

2. The two most familiar kingdoms are plants and animals.

Plants differ from animals in that their cells have cell walls and chloroplasts. Plants are producers that take in air and the Sun's energy and synthesize sugars. Animals are consumers—they need to eat other organisms for food.

3. Other organisms make up four more kingdoms.

- The kingdom Protista includes unicellular and multicellular organisms such as seaweeds. The multicellular organisms have structures that are too simple to be classified in the other groups.
- Fungi include mushrooms, yeasts, and molds. Fungi obtain their energy by breaking down dead or decaying materials.
- Archaea and Bacteria were once classified in the same group, but their differences led to a separate kingdom for each group. For these two kingdoms, the kingdom name and domain name are the same.

4. Species and environments change.

Species evolve over time and are affected by changes in their surroundings.

Common Misconceptions

MISCONCEPTION DATABASE

CLASSZONE.COM Background on student misconceptions

ABSOLUTE KNOWLEDGE Middle-school students may think that science as a discipline involves a collection of absolute knowledge—accurate facts that cannot be disputed. Scientific knowledge is a collective pursuit that rests on rigorous skepticism and the demand for evidence. However, the knowledge held by scientists is ever-changing and is often based on interpretation. New evidence, new perspectives, new ideas, and new questions continuously shape scientific understanding.

This misconception is addressed in the Ongoing Assessment on p. 220.

ANIMALS Many elementary and middle-school students have a limited concept of the term *animal*. These students do not understand that an animal is any living thing that belongs to the kingdom Animalia. They may use traits such as number of legs, body covering (hair or fur), ability to move, or habitat to decide whether living things are animals. When asked to name some animals, they may list only mammals, or only animals commonly found on farms or in zoos. They may also have trouble grasping that an organism can be classified within two sets, for example, as both a bird and an animal.

This misconception is addressed on p. 224.

Previewing Labs

EXPLORE the BIG idea

Lab	Time / Materials
How Are Fingerprints Different? p. 201 Students compare and contrast thumbprint traits of students.	**TIME** 10 minutes **MATERIALS** inkpads, paper
How Would You Sort Pennies? p. 201 Students create a set of classification characteristics for pennies.	**TIME** 15 minutes **MATERIALS** 20 pennies, paper or plastic cup
Internet Activity: Linnaeus, p. 201 Students determine the evidence Linnaeus used to create his system of scientific classification.	**TIME** 20 minutes **MATERIALS** computer with Internet access

Section	Lab	Time / Materials
SECTION 1	**INVESTIGATE Classifying Leaves,** p. 206 Students develop a taxonomy to classify leaves to understand how scientists' classification schemes work.	**TIME** 20 minutes **MATERIALS** assortment of leaves, hand lens, large newsprint or butcher paper
SECTION 2	**EXPLORE Classification,** p. 211 Students determine the importance of using characteristics to identify organisms.	**TIME** 15 minutes **MATERIALS** notebook
	INVESTIGATE Binomial Nomenclature, p. 212 Students develop a two-part naming system for everyday objects, using a dictionary.	**TIME** 30 minutes **MATERIALS** assorted common objects, dictionary, 10 index cards
SECTION 3	**CHAPTER INVESTIGATION Making a Field Guide,** pp. 228–229 Students observe and classify leaves to make a field guide.	**TIME** 40 minutes **MATERIALS** plastic gloves, shoebox, pencil, paper, crayons, hand lens, field guides for plants, assorted leaves, tracing paper

R **Additional INVESTIGATION,** Make a Dichotomous Key, A, B, & C, pp. 118–126; Teacher Instructions, pp. 188–189

Previewing Chapter Resources

CHAPTER 7
Classification of Living Things

INTEGRATED TECHNOLOGY

CLASSZONE.COM
- eEdition Plus
- EasyPlanner Plus
- Misconception Database
- Content Review
- Test Practice
- Simulation
- Resource Centers
- Internet Activity: Linnaeus
- Math Tutorial

SCILINKS.ORG

SCI LINKS

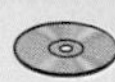

CD-ROMS
- eEdition
- EasyPlanner
- Power Presentations
- Content Review
- Lab Generator
- Test Generator

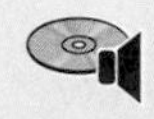

AUDIO CDS
- Audio Readings
- Audio Readings in Spanish

LABS AND ACTIVITIES

EXPLORE the Big Idea, p. 201
- How Are Fingerprints Different?
- How Would You Sort Pennies?
- Internet Activity: Linnaeus

UNIT RESOURCE BOOK
Unit Projects, pp. 5–10

Lab Generator CD-ROM
Generate customized labs.

SECTION

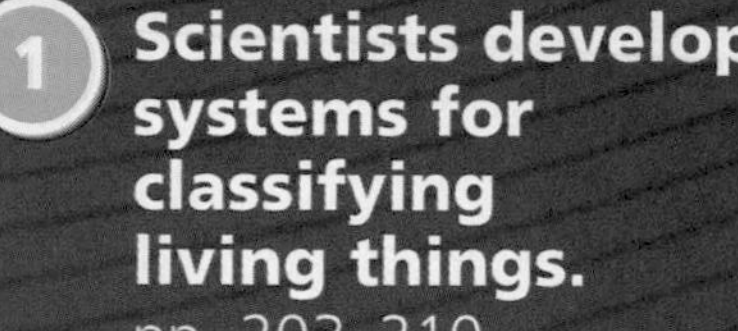

1 Scientists develop systems for classifying living things.
pp. 203–210

Time: 2 periods (1 block)

Lesson Plan, pp. 70–71

- **RESOURCE CENTER,** Taxonomy
- **MATH TUTORIAL**

UNIT TRANSPARENCY BOOK
- Big Idea Flow Chart, p. T9
- Daily Vocabulary Scaffolding, T10
- Note-Taking Model, p. T11
- 3-Minute Warm-Up, p. T12

- INVESTIGATE Classifying Leaves, p. 206
- Math in Science, p. 210

UNIT RESOURCE BOOK
- Datasheet, Classifying Leaves, p. 79
- Math Support, p. 107
- Math Practice, p. 108

SECTION

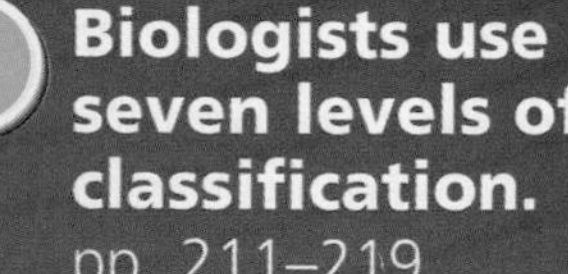

2 Biologists use seven levels of classification.
pp. 211–219

Time: 2 periods (1 block)

Lesson Plan, pp. 81–82

- **SIMULATION,** Dichotomous Key
- **RESOURCE CENTER,** New Insect Species
- **MATH TUTORIAL**

UNIT TRANSPARENCY BOOK
- Daily Vocabulary Scaffolding, p. T10
- 3-Minute Warm-Up, p. T12

- EXPLORE Classification, p. 211
- INVESTIGATE Binomial Nomenclature, p. 212
- Extreme Science, p. 219

UNIT RESOURCE BOOK
- Datasheet, Binomial Nomenclature, p. 90
- Additional INVESTIGATION, Make a Dichotomous Key, Levels A, B, & C, pp. 118–126

SECTION

3 Classification systems change as scientists learn more.
pp. 220–229

Time: 4 periods (2 blocks)

Lesson Plan, pp. 92–93

RESOURCE CENTER, Modern Classification

UNIT TRANSPARENCY BOOK
- Big Idea Flow Chart, p. T9
- Daily Vocabulary Scaffolding, p. T10
- 3-Minute Warm-Up, p. T13
- Chapter Outline, pp. T23–T24
- "Six Kingdoms" Visual, p. T14

CHAPTER INVESTIGATION Making a Field Guide, pp. 228–229

UNIT RESOURCE BOOK
- CHAPTER INVESTIGATION Making a Field Guide, Levels A, B, & C, pp. 109–117

KEY TO ICONS  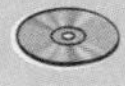 CD/CD-ROM  Teacher Edition  UNIT TRANSPARENCY BOOK 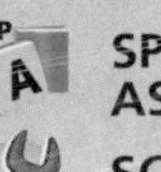 SPANISH ASSESSMENT BOOK

INTERNET · Pupil Edition · UNIT RESOURCE BOOK · UNIT ASSESSMENT BOOK · SCIENCE TOOLKIT

READING AND REINFORCEMENT	ASSESSMENT	STANDARDS
 • Description Wheel, B20–21 • Supporting Main Ideas, C42 • Daily Vocabulary Scaffolding, H1–8  **UNIT RESOURCE BOOK** • Vocabulary Practice, pp. 104–105 • Decoding Support, p. 106 • Summarizing the Chapter, pp. 127–128  **Audio Readings CD** Listen to Pupil Edition.  **Audio Readings in Spanish CD** Listen to Pupil Edition in Spanish.	 • Chapter Review, pp. 231–232 • Standardized Test Practice, p. 233  **UNIT ASSESSMENT BOOK** • Diagnostic Test, pp. 20–21 • Chapter Test, A, B, & C, pp. 25–36 • Alternative Assessment, pp. 37–38  **SPANISH ASSESSMENT BOOK** Spanish Chapter Test, pp. 29–32 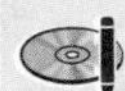 **Test Generator CD-ROM** Generate customized tests.  **Lab Generator CD-ROM** Rubrics for Labs	National Standards A.2–8, A.9.a–c, A.9.e–f, C.5.a, E.2–5, G.1.b See p. 200 for the standards.
 **UNIT RESOURCE BOOK** • Reading Study Guide, A & B, pp. 72–75 • Spanish Reading Study Guide, pp. 76–77 • Challenge and Extension, p. 78 • Reinforcing Key Concepts, p. 80	 Ongoing Assessment, pp. 204–209  Section 7.1 Review, p. 209  **UNIT ASSESSMENT BOOK** Section 7.1 Quiz, p. 22	National Standards A.2–8, A.9.a–c, A.9.e–f, C.5.a, E.2–5, G.1.b
 **UNIT RESOURCE BOOK** • Reading Study Guide, A & B, pp. 83–86 • Spanish Reading Study Guide, pp. 87–88 • Challenge and Extension, p. 89 • Reinforcing Key Concepts, p. 91	 Ongoing Assessment, pp. 213, 215–218  Section 7.2 Review, p. 218  **UNIT ASSESSMENT BOOK** Section 7.2 Quiz, p. 23	National Standards A.2–7, A.9.a–b, A.9.e–f, C.5.a, E.2–5, G.1.b
 **UNIT RESOURCE BOOK** • Reading Study Guide, A & B, pp. 94–97 • Spanish Reading Study Guide, pp. 98–99 • Challenge and Extension, p. 100 • Reinforcing Key Concepts, p. 101 • Challenge Reading, pp. 102–103	 Ongoing Assessment, pp. 220–221, 223–226  Section 7.3 Review, p. 227  **UNIT ASSESSMENT BOOK** Section 7.3 Quiz, p. 24	National Standards A.2–7, A.9.a–b, A.9.e–f, C.5.a, G.1.b

Previewing Resources for Differentiated Instruction

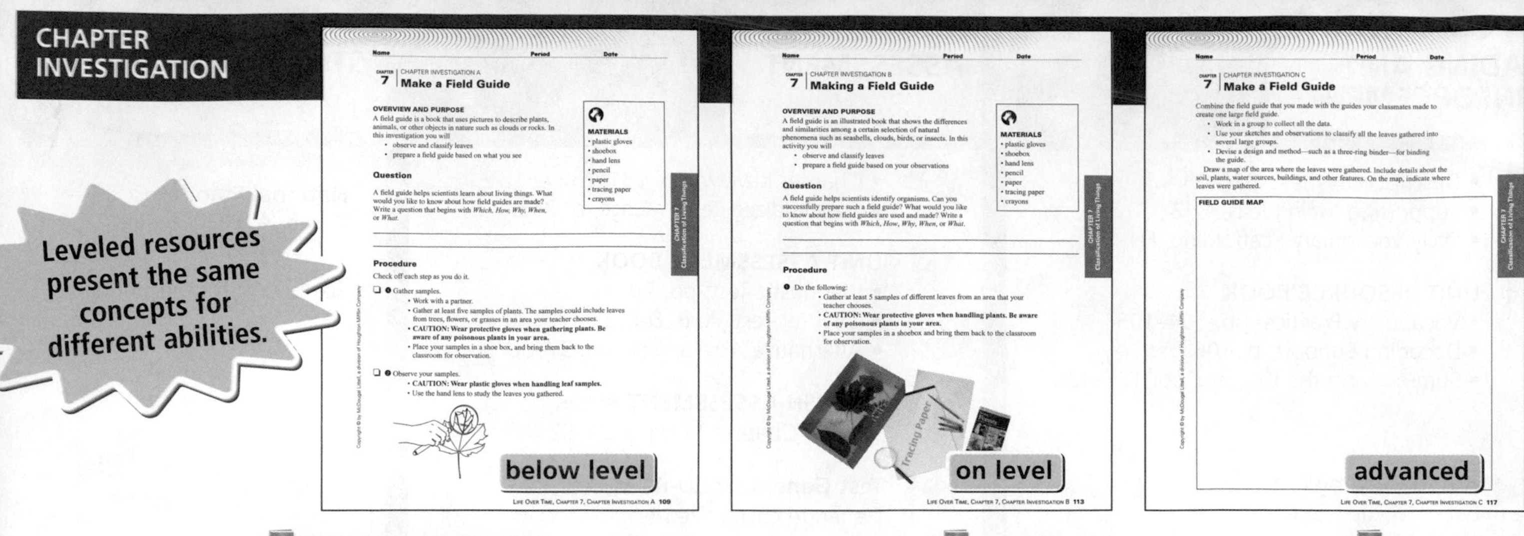

R UNIT RESOURCE BOOK, pp. 109–112 — R pp. 113–116 — R pp. 113–117

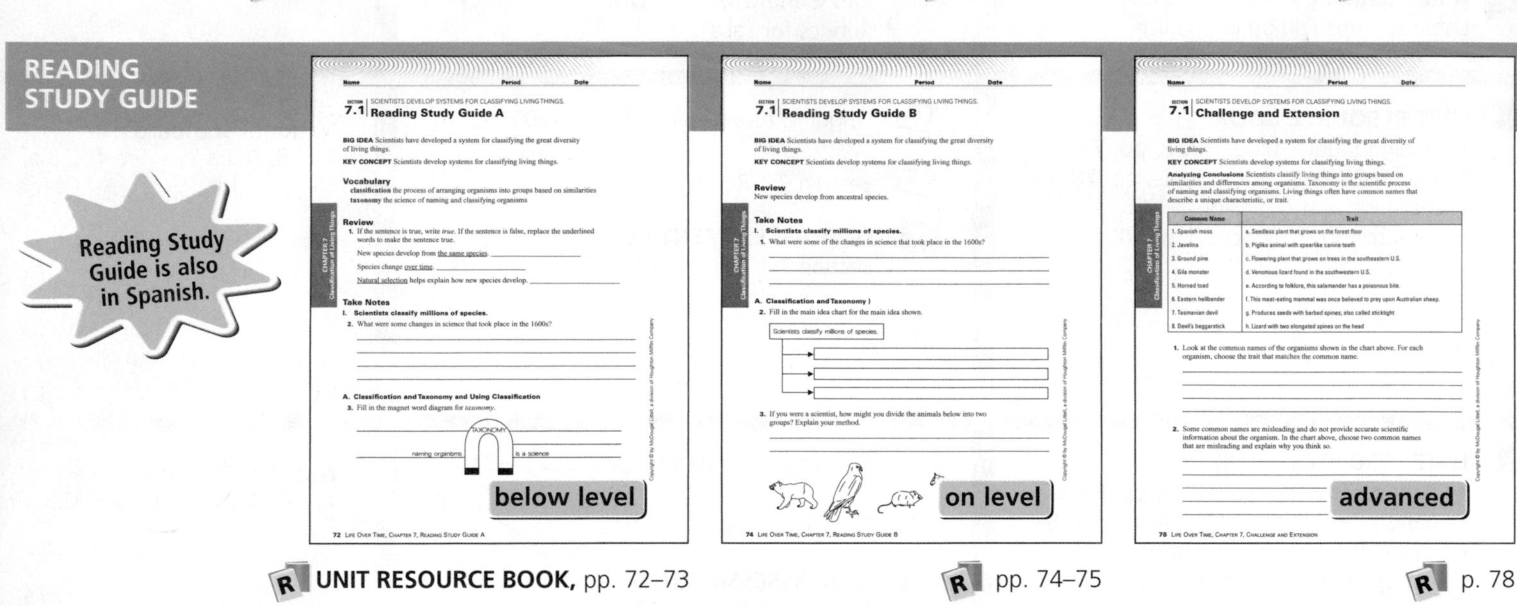

R UNIT RESOURCE BOOK, pp. 72–73 — R pp. 74–75 — R p. 78

CHAPTER TEST

Chapter Test is also in Spanish.

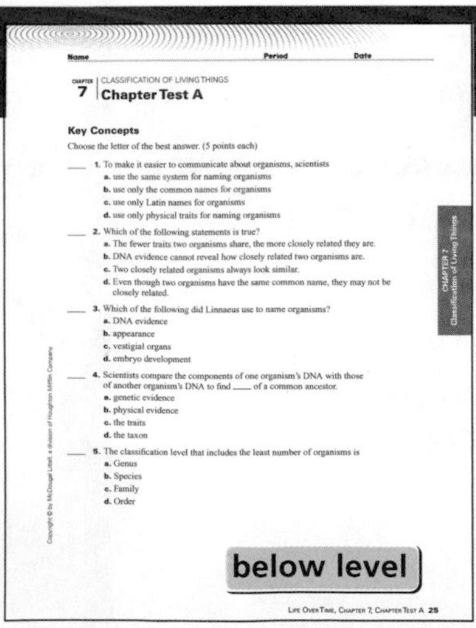

Chapter 7 Chapter Test A	Chapter 7 Chapter Test B	Chapter 7 Chapter Test C
below level	on level	advanced

A UNIT ASSESSMENT BOOK, pp. 25–28 — A pp. 29–32 — A pp. 33–36

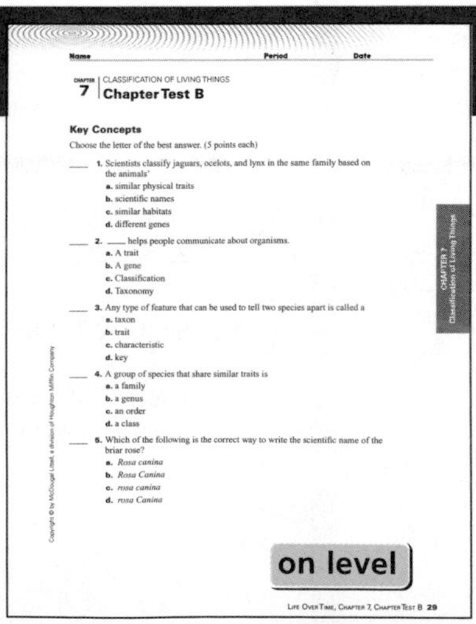

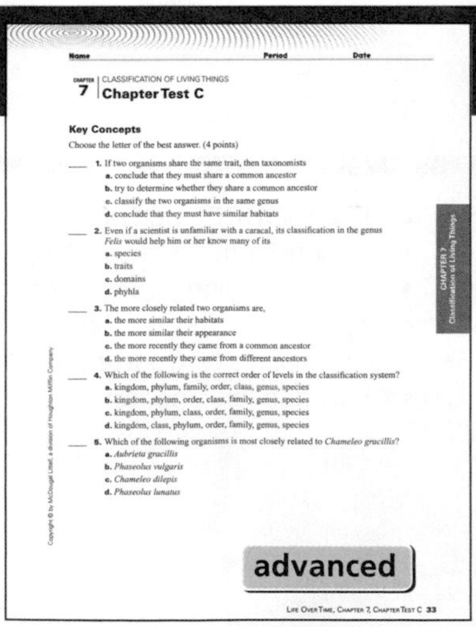

TECHNOLOGY

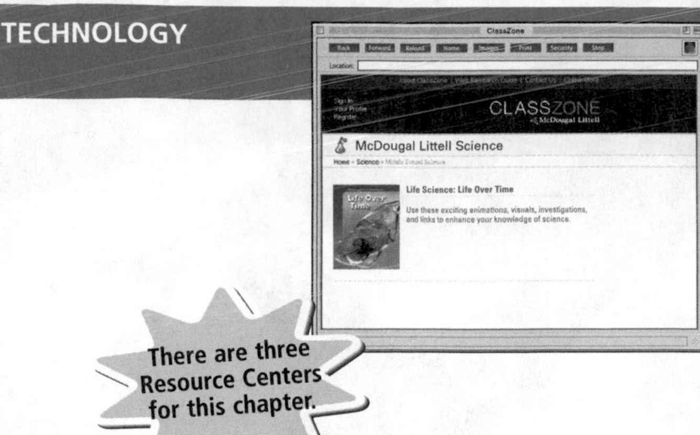

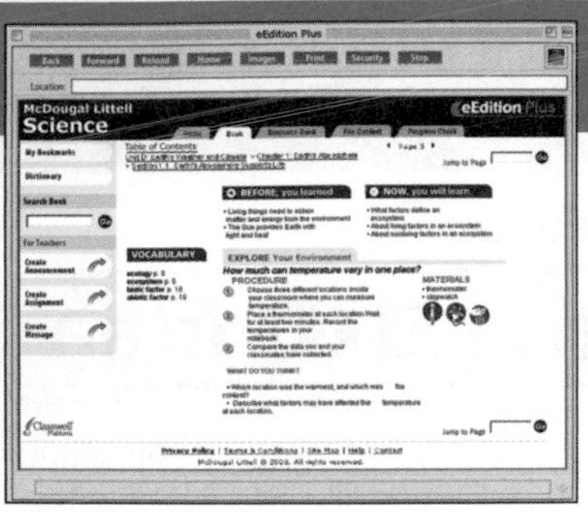

CLASSZONE.COM

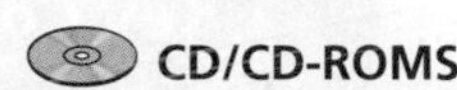
CD/CD-ROMS

CLASSZONE.COM

VISUAL CONTENT

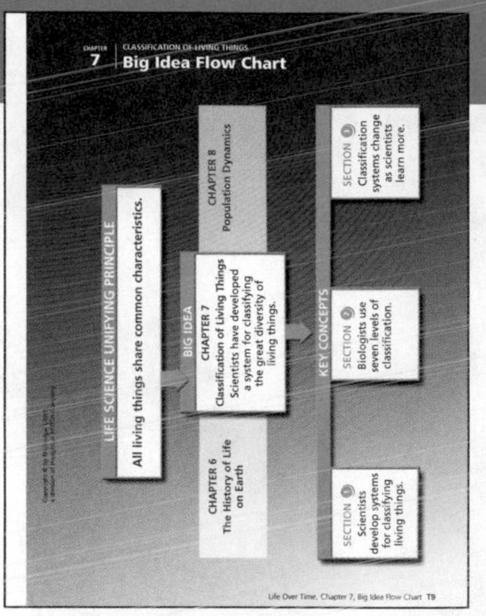

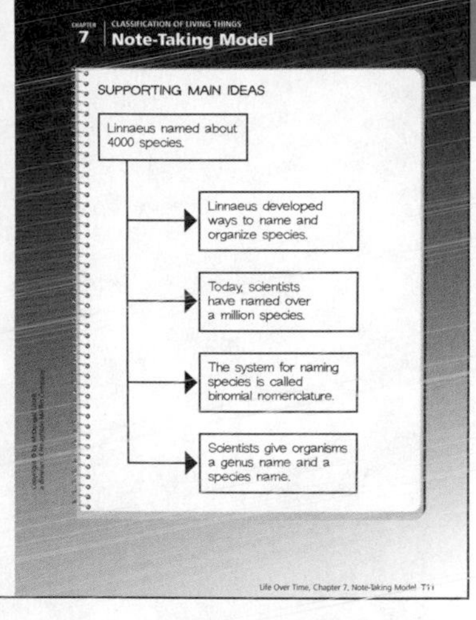

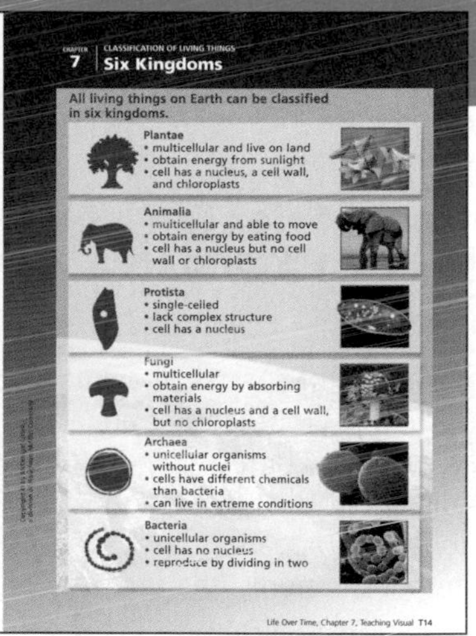

UNIT TRANSPARENCY BOOK, p. T9

p. T11

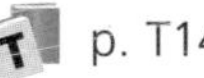
p. T14

MORE SUPPORT

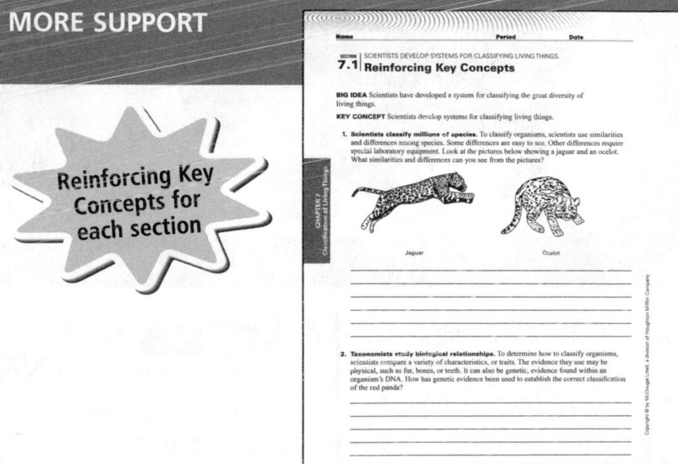

Name Period Date

SECTION 7.1 SCIENTISTS DEVELOP SYSTEMS FOR CLASSIFYING LIVING THINGS
Reinforcing Key Concepts

BIG IDEA Scientists have developed a system for classifying the great diversity of living things.

KEY CONCEPT Scientists develop systems for classifying living things.

1. **Scientists classify millions of species.** To classify organisms, scientists use similarities and differences among species. Some differences are easy to see. Other differences require special laboratory equipment. Look at the pictures below showing a jaguar and an ocelot. What similarities and differences can you see from the pictures?

Jaguar Ocelot

2. **Taxonomists study biological relationships.** To determine how to classify organisms, scientists compare a variety of characteristics, or traits. The evidence they use may be physical, such as fur, bones, or teeth. It can also be genetic, evidence found within an organism's DNA. How has genetic evidence been used to establish the correct classification of the red panda?

80 Life Over Time, Chapter 7, Reinforcing Key Concepts

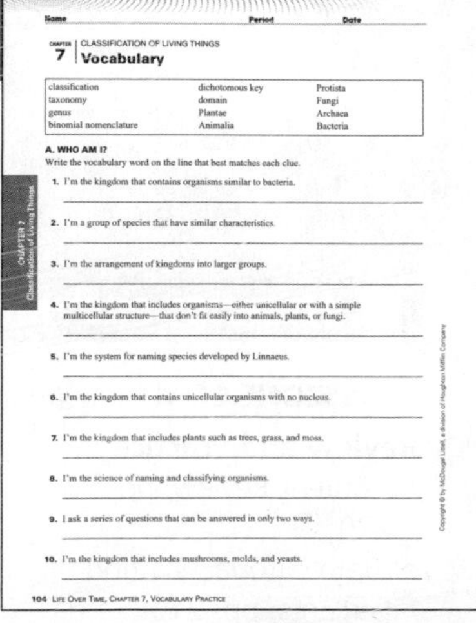
Name Period Date

CHAPTER 7 CLASSIFICATION OF LIVING THINGS
Vocabulary

classification	dichotomous key	Protista
taxonomy	domain	Fungi
genus	Plantae	Archaea
binomial nomenclature	Animalia	Bacteria

A. WHO AM I?
Write the vocabulary word on the line that best matches each clue.

1. I'm the kingdom that contains organisms similar to bacteria.
2. I'm a group of species that have similar characteristics.
3. I'm the arrangement of kingdoms into larger groups.
4. I'm the kingdom that includes organisms—either unicellular or with a simple multicellular structure—that don't fit easily into animals, plants, or fungi.
5. I'm the system for naming species developed by Linnaeus.
6. I'm the kingdom that contains unicellular organisms with no nucleus.
7. I'm the kingdom that includes plants such as trees, grass, and moss.
8. I'm the science of naming and classifying organisms.
9. I ask a series of questions that can be answered in only two ways.
10. I'm the kingdom that includes mushrooms, molds, and yeasts.

104 Life Over Time, Chapter 7, Vocabulary Practice

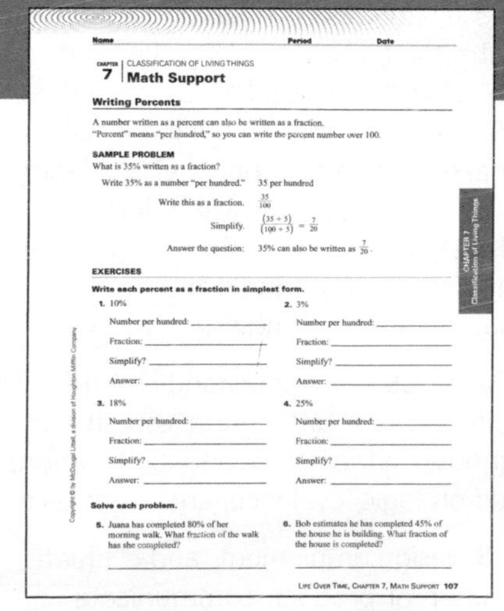
Name Period Date

CHAPTER 7 CLASSIFICATION OF LIVING THINGS
Math Support

Writing Percents

A number written as a percent can also be written as a fraction. "Percent" means "per hundred," so you can write the percent number over 100.

SAMPLE PROBLEM
What is 35% written as a fraction?

Write 35% as a number "per hundred." 35 per hundred

Write this as a fraction. $\frac{35}{100}$

Simplify. $\frac{(35 \div 5)}{(100 \div 5)} = \frac{7}{20}$

Answer the question: 35% can also be written as $\frac{7}{20}$.

EXERCISES

Write each percent as a fraction in simplest form.

1. 10% Number per hundred: Fraction: Simplify? Answer:
2. 3% Number per hundred: Fraction: Simplify? Answer:
3. 18% Number per hundred: Fraction: Simplify? Answer:
4. 25% Number per hundred: Fraction: Simplify? Answer:

Solve each problem.

5. Juana has completed 80% of her morning walk. What fraction of the walk has she completed?
6. Bob estimates he has completed 45% of the house he is building. What fraction of the house is completed?

Life Over Time, Chapter 7, Math Support 107

UNIT RESOURCE BOOK, p. 80

pp. 104–105

p. 107

CHAPTER 7

Classification of Living Things

INTRODUCE

the BIG idea

Have students look at the photograph of insect specimens and discuss how the question in the box links to the Big Idea:

- Ask: What are some of the ways that people classify or categorize everyday items?
- Have students think about some of the household pets that they have. Ask them to brainstorm a list of ways that the pets are similar and different. Write their list on the board as a starting point for discussing categories.

National Science Education Standards

Content

C.5.a Millions of species of animals, plants, and microorganisms are alive today. Although different species might look dissimilar, the unity among organisms becomes apparent from an analysis of internal structures, the similarity of their chemical processes, and the evidence of common ancestry.

Process

A.2–8 Design and conduct a scientific investigation; use tools to gather and interpret data; use evidence to describe, predict, explain, model; think critically to make relationships between evidence and explanation; recognize different explanations and predictions; communicate scientific procedures and explanations; use mathematics.

A.9.a–c, A.9.e–f Understand scientific inquiry by using different investigations, methods, mathematics, and explanations based on logic, evidence, and skepticism.

E.2–5 Design, implement, and evaluate a solution or product; communicate technological design.

G.1.b Science requires different abilities.

CHAPTER

Classification of Living Things

the BIG idea

Scientists have developed a system for classifying the great diversity of living things.

Key Concepts

SECTION

Scientists develop systems for classifying living things.
Learn about why scientists classify living things and about taxonomy.

SECTION

Biologists use seven levels of classification.
Learn about scientific names, how to classify organisms in seven levels, and dichotomous keys.

SECTION

Classification systems change as scientists learn more.
Learn how classification systems have changed based on features of cells.

Internet Preview

CLASSZONE.COM

Chapter 7 online resources: Content Review, Simulation, 3 Resource Centers, Math Tutorial, Test Practice

200 Unit 2: Life Over Time

How many different types of organisms do you see and how would you group them?

INTERNET PREVIEW

CLASSZONE.COM For student use with the following pages:

Review and Practice
- Content Review, pp. 202, 230
- Math Tutorial, Writing Percents, pp. 210
- Test Practice, p. 233

Activities and Resources
- Internet Activity: Linnaeus, p. 233
- Resource Centers: Taxonomy, p. 204; New Insect Species, p. 219; Modern Classification, p. 221
- Simulation: Dichotomous Key, p. 216

Classification Systems
Code: MDL037

EXPLORE the BIG idea

How Are Fingerprints Different?

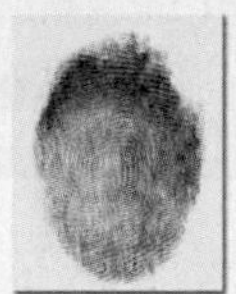

Make fingerprints of your thumb and the thumbs of several classmates on separate index cards.

Observe and Think What traits do all fingerprints have in common? What traits of fingerprints allow you to tell them apart?

How Would You Sort Pennies?

Place 20 pennies in a plastic cup. Place your hand over the cup and shake it. Gently pour the pennies onto a table. Without flipping the pennies over, use one trait of the pennies to sort them into groups A and B. Again, without flipping them over, use a second trait to sort the pennies in group A into groups A1 and A2.

Observe and Think What traits do the pennies in each group share? Which group has the largest numbers of pennies?

Internet Activity: Linnaeus

Go to Classzone.com to learn more about Carolus Linnaeus, who, over 200 years ago, laid the groundwork for how today's scientists classify things.

Observe and Think What evidence did Linnaeus use to classify organisms?

Classification Systems **Code: MDL037**

TEACHING WITH TECHNOLOGY

Web-Based Field Guides Students can use electronic field guides to inventory and study examples of local trees and their scientific names while studying the classification of leaves on p. 206. They might use digital cameras to document local finds. Digital photography can also help them in "Making a Field Guide," p. 228.

Microscopes Set up microscope stations where students can view slides of protists, bacteria, and archaea while studying these kingdoms on pp. 225–227.

Spreadsheet and Slide-Show Software Students can use a slide-show program, such as PowerPoint, or a spreadsheet to present the classification by attributes that they create in the investigations on pp. 206, 212.

EXPLORE the BIG idea

These inquiry-based activities are appropriate for use at home or as a supplement to classroom instruction.

How Are Fingerprints Different?

PURPOSE To determine differences among thumbprints.

TIPS *10 min.* Fingerprints come in three basic patterns: arches, loops, and whorls. Provide students with examples of the three types of fingerprints to help them classify their own thumbprints. Caution students to roll up sleeves and work slowly to avoid ink stains.

Answer: All fingerprints have a pattern of ridges. Fingerprints have three distinct patterns that set them apart.

REVISIT after p. 207.

How Would You Sort Pennies?

PURPOSE To create a set of classification characteristics for pennies.

TIPS *15 min.* Have students work in pairs or small groups. Write their criteria for classification on the board.

Answer: Students might classify pennies according to heads/tails, date, shininess, initial of mint, weight, or color.

REVISIT after p. 214.

Internet Activity: Linnaeus

PURPOSE To determine the criteria Linnaeus used to classify organisms.

TIP *20 min.* You may wish to have students predict what kind of criteria Linnaeus used to classify organisms.

Answer: Linnaeus used appearance to classify organisms.

REVISIT after p. 212.

PREPARE

CONCEPT REVIEW

Activate Prior Knowledge

- Ask students to describe the evidence scientists use to determine that species change over time. *fossils, genetic evidence, biological observation*
- Have students give an example of an animal that has changed over time and describe how it has changed. *Sample answer: Whales had ancestors with four legs.*

TAKING NOTES

Supporting Main Ideas

Students can rely on the blue headings in the text as a basis for main ideas. Red headings can aid students in locating topics and supporting information. Remind students that details to support the main idea may come from visuals such as photographs and diagrams or might come from their own prior knowledge or experience.

Vocabulary Strategy

The description wheel helps students understand vocabulary terms in a systematic manner. Students can include a brief definition of the term, descriptions, characteristics, and examples, if possible, of the term.

Vocabulary and Note-Taking Resources

- Vocabulary Practice, pp. 104–105
- Decoding Support, p. 106

- Daily Vocabulary Scaffolding, p. T10
- Note-Taking Model, p. T11

- Description Wheel, B20–21
- Supporting Main Ideas, C42
- Daily Vocabulary Scaffolding, H1–8

CHAPTER 7

Getting Ready to Learn

CONCEPT REVIEW

- Species change over time.
- Fossils and other evidence show that species change.
- New species develop from ancestral species.

VOCABULARY REVIEW

evolution p. 177
ancestor p. 189

See Glossary for definitions.

species, trait, DNA

CONTENT REVIEW
CLASSZONE.COM
Review concepts and vocabulary.

TAKING NOTES

SUPPORTING MAIN IDEAS

Make a chart to show main ideas and the information that supports them. Copy each blue heading. Below each heading, add supporting information, such as reasons, explanations, and examples.

VOCABULARY STRATEGY

Place each vocabulary term at the center of a **description wheel** diagram. Write some words describing it on the spokes.

SCIENCE NOTEBOOK

Scientists classify millions of species.
- Taxonomy is the science of classifying and naming organisms.
- Classification is the process of arranging organisms in groups.
- To classify organisms, scientists compare their characteristics.

CLASSIFICATION
organisms
seven levels
arrange into groups
Linnaeus
similar trait
systems can change

See the Note-Taking Handbook on pages R45–R51.

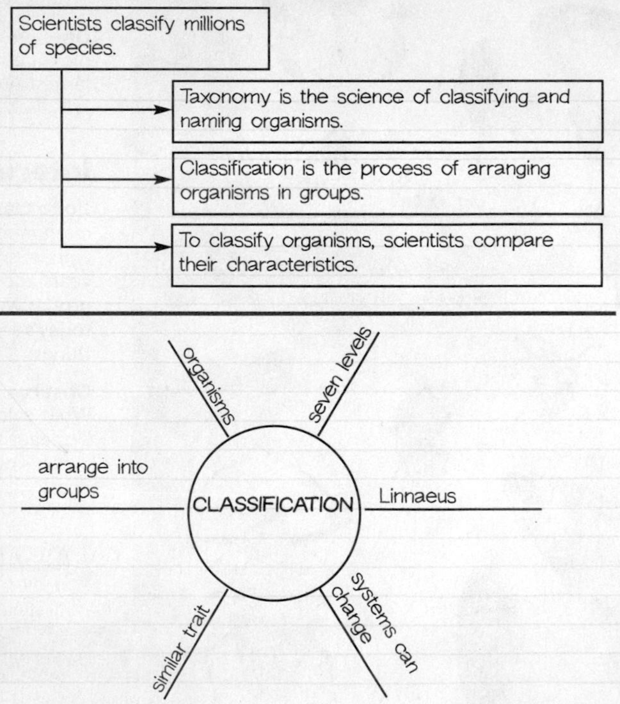

CHECK READINESS

Administer the Diagnostic Test to determine students' readiness for new science content and their mastery of requisite math skills.

 Diagnostic Test, pp. 20–21

Technology Resources

Students needing content and math skills should visit **ClassZone.com**.

- **CONTENT REVIEW**
- **MATH TUTORIAL**

 **CONTENT REVIEW CD-ROM**

KEY CONCEPT

Scientists develop systems for classifying living things.

BEFORE, you learned
- Natural selection helps explain how new species develop
- Evidence indicates that species change over time
- New species develop from ancestral species

NOW, you will learn
- Why scientists classify living things
- That taxonomists study biological relationships
- About evidence used to classify organisms

VOCABULARY
classification p. 204
taxonomy p. 204

THINK ABOUT

How are these organisms similar?

Both a worm and a caterpillar share many characteristics. Both have long, skinny bodies that are divided into segments. But an earthworm moves underground, has no legs or eyes, and can grow back segments that are lost. A caterpillar crawls aboveground and is just one part of a butterfly's life cycle. As you read this chapter, think about whether you would classify these animals together or separately.

Scientists classify millions of species.

About 400 years ago, scientists who studied insects classified them based upon their appearance and behavior. If animals looked alike, researchers concluded that they were related. In the last few centuries scientists have realized that appearances can suggest false connections. Although caterpillars look like worms, they are actually an earlier stage of a butterfly's life.

For some people, the world seemed to grow larger during the 1600s. Travelers sailed to distant lands and oceans. Scientists went on many of these trips, observing and collecting samples of living things they had never seen before. In addition, the microscope allowed scientists to see tiny organisms that had been invisible before. But how could scientists organize and talk about this wonderful new knowledge?

7.1 FOCUS

Set Learning Goals

Students will
- Explain why scientists classify living things.
- Understand that taxonomists study biological relationships to classify organisms.
- Describe the evidence scientists use to classify organisms.
- Develop a taxonomy for classifying leaves, based on a systematic set of traits.

3-Minute Warm-Up

Display Transparency 12 or copy this exercise on the board:

Decide if these statements are true. If not true, correct them.

1. In natural selection, a species that is better adapted to its environment is most likely to survive. *true*
2. Fossils that are found in the lower-most layers of Earth are the most recent. *Fossils found in the upper-most layers of Earth are the most recent.*
3. Most of what scientists know about extinct species is based on how animals have changed in the last hundred years. *Most of what scientists know about extinct species comes from the fossil record.*

 3-Minute Warm-Up, p. T12

7.1 MOTIVATE

THINK ABOUT

PURPOSE To decide how two organisms might be classified

DISCUSS Brainstorm a list of characteristics that might be used to classify an organism. Write students' suggestions on the board to use as a reference as they read through the chapter. Students may add to or revise the list as they read.

RESOURCES FOR DIFFERENTIATED INSTRUCTION

Below Level

UNIT RESOURCE BOOK
- Reading Study Guide A, pp. 72–73
- Decoding Support, p. 106

AUDIO CDS

Advanced

UNIT RESOURCE BOOK
- Challenge and Extension, p. 78

English Learners

UNIT RESOURCE BOOK
Spanish Reading Study Guide, pp. 76–77

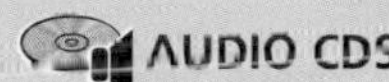

- Audio Readings in Spanish
- Audio Readings (English)

7.1 INSTRUCT

Teacher Demo

Collect and display several pictures of organisms such as a house cat, lion, wolf, dolphin, goldfish, frog, bird, bat, and snake. Discuss with students how the organisms are similar. Then ask students how the animals might be placed into two different groups. Then have students subdivide the two groups further. Post the classifications on the bulletin board for reference. Students may revise how they classified the animals as they read the chapter.

Teach from Visuals

To help students interpret the photographs of daddy longlegs, ask:

- Do these daddy longlegs have similar features? What are they? *Both have long legs.*
- How are they different? *The British daddy longlegs has a long body, wings, and six legs. The American daddy longlegs has eight legs and a central body.*
- Why might it be confusing to scientists to have the same name for two different organisms? *Scientists would not know for sure which organism is being referred to.*

Ongoing Assessment

CHECK YOUR READING *Answer: Classification is the process of organizing living things into groups based on similarities. Taxonomy is the science of naming and classifying organisms.*

VOCABULARY
Add a description wheel for *classification* to your notebook. Include the word *group* in your diagram.

Classification and Taxonomy

Two scientific processes deal with classifying and naming living things. **Classification** is the process of arranging organisms into groups based on similarities. **Taxonomy** is the science of naming and classifying organisms. A good system of classification allows you to organize a large amount of information so that it is easy to find and to understand. The system should provide a tool for comparing very large groups of organisms as well as smaller groups. Large groups might include all animals. Smaller groups might include birds, reptiles, or mammals.

A good system of taxonomy allows people to communicate about organisms. Before the 1700s, scientists had not agreed on a system of naming and grouping organisms. Take, for example, the common wild briar rose. Some scientists called it *Rosa sylvestris inodora seu canina* (odorless woodland dog rose). Others used the name *Rosa sylvestris alba cum rubore, folio glabro* (pinkish-white woodland rose with hairless leaves). Plus, any scientist studying a species could change the name.

These long Latin names may sound confusing, but even common names can be confusing. In England the bird called a robin—Britain's national bird—is only distantly related to the bird called a robin in the United States, even though they both have red feathers on their chests. A daddy longlegs could be either a long-legged relative of spiders (in the United States) or a long-legged relative of mosquitoes (in England).

British Daddy Longlegs

American Daddy Longlegs

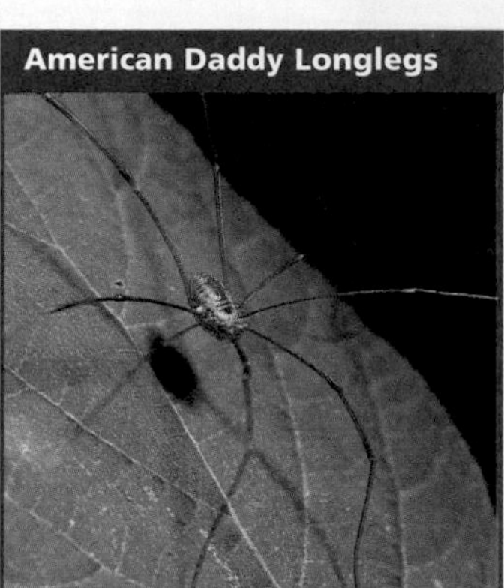

RESOURCE CENTER
CLASSZONE.COM
Find out more about taxonomy.

Clearly, biologists need both a system for organizing and a system for naming. Each name should refer to one specific type of organism. That way, scientists can use the species name and be sure that everybody knows exactly which organism they are talking about.

CHECK YOUR READING What is the difference between classification and taxonomy?

DIFFERENTIATE INSTRUCTION

More Reading Support

A Which process allows scientific grouping? *classification*

B Which process allows scientific naming? *taxonomy*

English Learners Have students write the definitions for the terms *species, biologist, characteristic, classification, taxonomy,* and *trait* in their Science Word Dictionaries. Have students list ten animals. Then, have students who speak a language other than English give the names for the listed animals in their languages. Discuss how many variations there are for each name. Ask: Why is taxonomy important in life science? *Scientists all over the world can have the same information about living things and can share ideas about them.*

Using Classification

To classify organisms, scientists use similarities and differences among species. Sometimes these differences are easy to see, such as whether an animal has fur, feathers, or scales. Other times, seeing the differences requires special laboratory equipment, such as equipment to study DNA.

A classification system can help you identify unfamiliar organisms. For example, if you had never heard of a caracal but were told that it was a kind of cat, you already would know many things about it. It has fur, fangs, and sharp claws. It's a meat eater, not a plant eater. You would know these things because the caracal shares those characteristics with all of the members of the cat family.

If you looked up *caracal* in an encyclopedia, you'd find that your guesses were right. The caracal is a small wildcat native to Africa, the Middle East, and India. It weighs about 13 to 19 kilograms (29 to 42 pounds). The name *caracal* comes from a Turkish word meaning "black-eared."

The more characteristics two organisms share, the more similar their names should be in the classification system. The caracal, a pet cat, and all the cats below are different in size, habitat, and other characteristics. But they also have many similarities, and all belong to the cat family, Felidae.

Like other cats, a caracal has fur, sharp fangs, and is a meat eater.

READING VISUALS COMPARE/CONTRAST: What traits do these cats have in common?

Teach from Visuals

To help students interpret the illustration of wild cats, ask: Why would a taxonomist classify all of these animals into one family? *All the cats have similar features, or characteristics.*

Develop Critical Thinking

CLASSIFY To illustrate the concept of how organisms are classified, try this activity. Ask all students to stand and note what kind of shirt they are wearing. Have students sit down as you read through the following characteristics: pullover shirt, button-down shirt, shirt with a collar, solid color shirt, striped shirt, print shirt, long-sleeve shirt, and short-sleeved shirt. (If necessary, add categories, such as one-piece dress, or sweater.) As you go through the list, most students should be sitting by the end of the activity. Point out that all the items you are classifying are shirts, but there are differences among them.

Ongoing Assessment

Explain why scientists classify living things.

Ask: How does grouping organisms based on shared characteristics make it easier for scientists to study them? *Classification systems provide rules for arranging organisms into groups. The similarities and differences become easy to see.*

READING VISUALS *Answer: All have spots, fur, paws, four legs, teeth, triangle-shaped noses, two eyes, whiskers.*

DIFFERENTIATE INSTRUCTION

More Reading Support

C What is used to classify organisms in the laboratory? *DNA*

Below Level To reinforce the concepts in the text, have students complete this classification activity. Provide students with a selection of buttons in various sizes, shapes, and colors. Have students create a classification system for the buttons. Ask students to explain their choices. You can further simplify the activity by using a deck of playing cards. Have students examine the variety of ways in which they might sort these cards (by suits, by colors, by numbers, pictures vs. numbers, etc.).

Integrate the Sciences

Geologists use geological relationships to classify minerals by several methods, including: physical observation, optical methods, and x-ray diffraction. Physical observations include classification of attributes such as luster, cleavage and hardness, fluorescence, and magnetism. Optical methods measure the refractive index. X-ray diffraction identifies characteristic crystalline patterns. Minerals are basically classified by chemical composition.

INVESTIGATE Classifying Leaves

PURPOSE To develop a taxonomy for classifying leaves; to understand how scientific classification and naming work

TIPS *20 min.* For best results, include both simple and complex leaves and as much diversity as possible. Be aware of allergies and toxic plants. Provide large newsprint or other paper for students to write on. Groups should exchange their schemes and try to use them. A dictionary may be useful for naming.

WHAT DO YOU THINK? *Answers can include grouping by size, shape, color, texture, vein patterns, or other traits. Students may or may not use similar methods. They should list similarities as well as any differences.*

CHALLENGE *does not include ancestry or genetic information*

 Datasheet, Classifying Leaves, p. 79

Technology Resources

Customize this student lab as needed or look for an alternative. Print rubrics to assess student lab reports.

Lab Generator CD-ROM

Teaching with Technology

Have students use electronic field guides. They might also use slide-show software to present their classifications.

Ongoing Assessment

 *Answer: Taxonomists group species that share common ancestors closer together than species that do not.*

Taxonomists study biological relationships.

READING TIP: *Taxonomy, taxonomist,* and *taxon* all share the same root.

Scientists need a simple, standard way of arranging all of the different species. The science of taxonomy is related to the Greek word *taxis,* which means "arrangement." Taxonomists are the scientists who classify and name organisms based on their similarities and differences. A taxon is a group of organisms that share certain traits. Taxons can be broad, like animals and plants, or more specific, like cats and roses.

As you learned in Chapter 6, living things evolve over time. A single species found in a fossil record might be the ancestor of many different species found on Earth today. Taxonomists study the relationships between species, trying to discover how one species evolved as compared with another species. Species that share ancestors are grouped together.

To determine how to classify organisms, scientists compare a variety of characteristics, or traits. A trait is a characteristic or behavior that can be used to tell two species apart, such as size or bone structure. If two organisms share a trait, taxonomists try to determine if they share the trait because they share an ancestor.

 How do taxonomists use biological relationships to classify organisms?

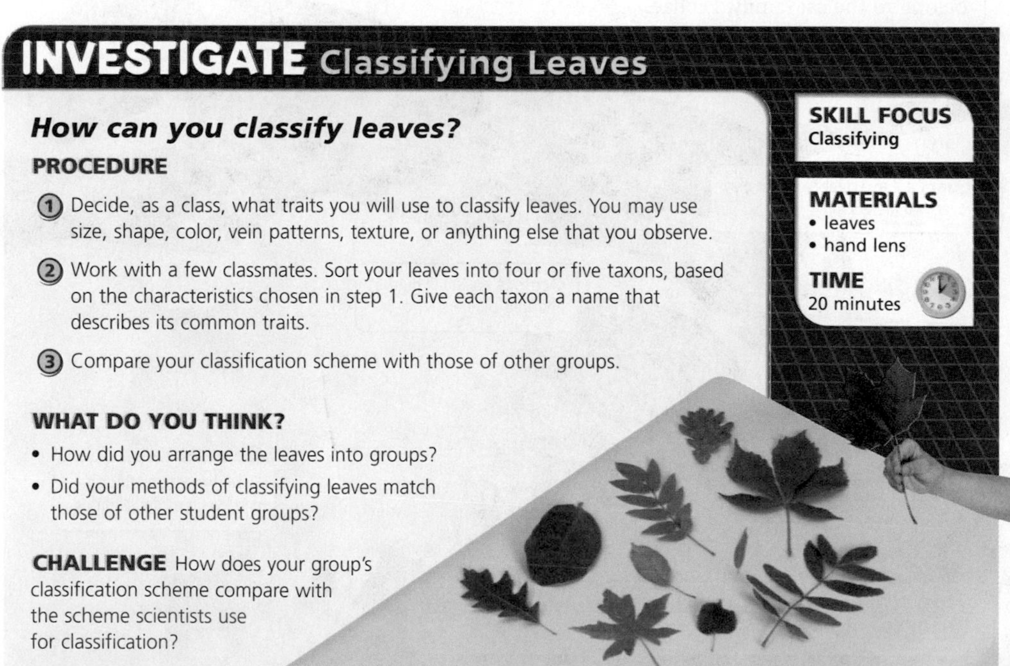

INVESTIGATE Classifying Leaves

How can you classify leaves?

SKILL FOCUS Classifying

MATERIALS
- leaves
- hand lens

TIME 20 minutes

PROCEDURE

1. Decide, as a class, what traits you will use to classify leaves. You may use size, shape, color, vein patterns, texture, or anything else that you observe.
2. Work with a few classmates. Sort your leaves into four or five taxons, based on the characteristics chosen in step 1. Give each taxon a name that describes its common traits.
3. Compare your classification scheme with those of other groups.

WHAT DO YOU THINK?

- How did you arrange the leaves into groups?
- Did your methods of classifying leaves match those of other student groups?

CHALLENGE How does your group's classification scheme compare with the scheme scientists use for classification?

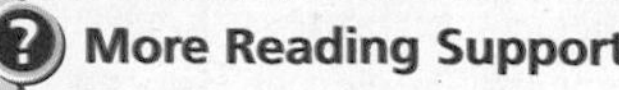

DIFFERENTIATE INSTRUCTION

More Reading Support

D What is the meaning of the Greek word *taxis? arrangement*

E What is an example of a trait? *size or bone structure*

Advanced Have students each present a chart or poster to show the methods of organization for various systems. Have them brainstorm a list of the different ways that we use classification systems around us. For example, libraries, grocery and department stores, and newspapers all use different methods of organization.

 Challenge and Extension, p. 78

Biological Relationships

Look at the photographs and try to determine to which organism a leafy sea dragon is more closely related. The leafy sea dragon shares traits with all of the other organisms pictured. For example, the sea dragon and the sargassum seaweed look similar, with greenish wavy fronds. But the sea dragon is an animal that moves, gets food from other organisms, and breathes oxygen. The sargassum seaweed is not an animal, it is a type of algae.

The sargassum fish shares more traits with the sea dragon, but its body is a much different shape and has scales. In fact, the leafy sea dragon is an animal that is closely related to a sea horse. Both have heads and bodies with similar shapes, and neither has scales. The sea horse shares more traits with the leafy sea dragon than with the other two organisms.

Taxonomists take evidence and try to reconstruct the evolution of a species. Then they place the species in the classification system. Scientists use physical evidence, such as fur, bones, and teeth. They also use genetic evidence, which is found within an organism's DNA.

DIFFERENTIATE INSTRUCTION

More Reading Support

F What trait do the sea dragon and sargassum seaweed share? *leafy fronds*

Inclusion Students who have a visual disability can use manipulatives such as pattern blocks or small plastic animals to practice sorting and classifying by various criteria and traits. Working with sets of manipulatives can also simplify the concepts of classification and taxonomy for students with learning disabilities, by making the concepts more concrete.

Teach from Visuals

To help students interpret the illustration of biological relationships, ask:

Why might scientists use the term sargassum to describe both a fish and a seaweed? *Both the sargassum fish and sargassum seaweed have similar traits.*

Address Misconceptions

IDENTIFY Ask students how they think scientists determine groupings of organisms. Some students may hold the misconception that organisms are classified by criteria such as ability to fly or habitation in the same area. Many students use mutually exclusive groups, rather than a hierarchy of groups.

CORRECT Point out that animals may share a common trait and not be grouped together scientifically. Example: jaguar and sargassum fish. Both have spots but are not in a group of "spotted animals." Ask students to study the photographs on p. 207 and make a chart comparing the traits of various organisms.

REASSESS Ask students to present charts and explain why organisms with similar traits should or should not be grouped together biologically as "relatives." *Organisms with similar traits are not necessarily biologically similar or related.*

Technology Resources

Visit **ClassZone.com** for background on common student misconceptions.

 **MISCONCEPTION DATABASE**

EXPLORE the BIG idea

Revisit "How Are Fingerprints Different?" on p. 201. Ask students how fingerprint classification is similar to the way they classified leaves. *both classified according to similarities and differences*

Ongoing Assessment

Understand that taxonomists study biological relationships to classify organisms.

Ask: What evidence besides physical traits do taxonomists use to classify organisms? *genetic evidence; evolution of species*

Teach from Visuals

To help students interpret the illustration of the birds, ask:

Why would a species' habitat be important evidence to use in classification? *Habitats vary, so the species that live in them would be adapted to certain environmental conditions. The adaptations would account for some physical differences between similar species.*

Develop Critical Thinking

ANALYZE Have students imagine that they have discovered a new organism. Ask them to consider the following questions for discussion: How would you classify the organism? How would you determine what other organisms it is related to? How would you plan your research?

History of Science

In 1953 Francis Crick and James D. Watson determined the molecular structure of the DNA molecule. By using x-ray diffraction pictures, Watson and Crick determined the chemical structure of DNA and made a model of it to show its double helix arrangement. They shared the 1962 Nobel Prize for physiology or medicine with Maurice Wilkins.

Ongoing Assessment

CHECK YOUR READING *Answer: If the modern and fossilized animal bones are similar then they may be related. If they are closely related then they shared a more recent ancestor.*

Physical Evidence

Steller's Jay
- Lives only west of the Rocky Mountains
- Has a solid black head and neck and almost no white feathers

Blue Jay
- Lives mostly east of the Rocky Mountains
- Has blue, black, and white feathers on its wings and neck

Physical Evidence

The primary tools early scientists used for taxonomy were their eyes and measuring devices. They collected examples of organisms and noted characteristics, such as color, size, weight, and how groups of organisms obtain energy. Scientists who studied animals observed the internal structure, as well as outward appearances. These physical features are still important today.

Individuals of two species, such as the two jays shown to the left, can have many similarities as well as some differences. One obvious difference is the color pattern. Another is the area of the world in which they live. Blue jays live east of the Rocky Mountains, and steller's jays live west of the Rockies. The common names and the scientific names reflect the differences and the common ancestor: blue jay, *Cyanocitta cristata* and steller's jay, *Cyanocitta stelleri.*

Skeletons, shells, and other hard parts of organisms become fossilized more easily than soft parts do. Scientists can observe and measure fossilized bones or pieces of bones and compare them with each other. They can also compare bones of species that are extinct with bones of modern species. From such studies, scientists can determine many things about the organism. Physical evidence provides clues about how an organism may have lived, how it moved, or what type of food it ate.

All of this physical evidence helps scientists see that all living organisms are related by evolution. Some are more closely related than others. This means they share a more recent ancestor.

How could comparing fossilized bones with a modern animal's bones help you see the modern animal's evolutionary history?

Genetic Evidence

In the early 20th century scientists discovered that organisms inherit their traits through structures called genes. In the mid-1950s they observed that genes are made of DNA and that DNA stores coded information.

Today scientists can use laboratory machines to catalog each component of an organism's DNA. With that information stored on a computer, scientists can compare the components of a gene from one organism with the components of the same gene from another organism.

Genetic evidence usually supports physical evidence, but not always. Consider the example shown on page 209. For years, taxonomists argued about how to classify this small, reddish animal from China. Its scientific name is *Ailurus fulgens*, and the common name is red panda.

DIFFERENTIATE INSTRUCTION

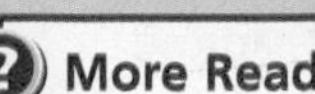

More Reading Support

G How do scientists classify organisms? *color, size, weight*

H How is DNA used to classify animals? *Scientists compare the genes of organisms.*

Advanced Explain that cladograms are diagrams that show evolutionary relationships among groups of organisms. Challenge students to find examples of cladograms and explain how the various organisms in each cladogram are related.

English Learners English learners may have trouble with abstract questions. The commands "suppose" and "explain" may be confusing. Provide a model answer to help students approach such questions in the review, p. 209.

Genetic Evidence

Both of these pandas live in the same habitat, have similar faces, and eat bamboo. But genetic evidence shows that red pandas and giant pandas are only distant relatives.

Red Panda

Red pandas have more DNA in common with **raccoons.**

Racoon

Giant Panda

Giant pandas have more DNA in common with **spectacled bears.**

Spectacled Bear

Later, scientists discovered a larger, bearlike animal in China, which they called the giant panda. Both pandas ate only bamboo, shared a common name, and their faces looked similar. Scientists concluded they were related to each other and to raccoons. However, molecular evidence has shown that the red panda is more closely related to raccoons and the giant panda is more closely related to bears.

7.1 Review

KEY CONCEPTS

1. Describe the benefits of classifying species.
2. Why do taxonomists study biological relationships?
3. How do scientists use genetic evidence when classifying organisms?

CRITICAL THINKING

4. **Analyze** Why do people need a universal system of naming organisms?
5. **Predict** The animal called a marbled godwit is a bird. What traits would you predict it has?

CHALLENGE

6. **Synthesize** Suppose you found two species of cave-dwelling lizards without eyes living on opposite sides of the world. Explain how you would try to determine if the two species were closely related.

ANSWERS

1. Classification allows taxonomists to organize a lot of data so that it is easy to find and understand.

2. Taxonomists study biological relationships to discover how one species evolved as compared with another species.

3. Scientists look at DNA and compare genes of organisms.

4. Having a universal naming system allows people speaking different languages to refer to all organisms the same way.

5. A marbled godwit would have marbled feathers, wings, feet, a beak.

6. Compare physical traits, such as color, size, weight, and how they get energy; analyze bones; compare to fossils; compare DNA.

Ongoing Assessment

Describe the evidence scientists use to classify organisms.

Ask: Why is molecular evidence so helpful to taxonomists? *Genetic evidence shows relationships among organisms that are not obvious by just observing physical traits.*

Reinforce the BIG idea

Have students relate the section to the Big Idea.

 Reinforcing Key Concepts, p. 80

7.1 ASSESS & RETEACH

Assess

 Section 7.1 Quiz, p. 22

Reteach

Return to the bulletin board of organisms that students classified at the beginning of the section. Ask if students would like to revise their classification system. Ask them what additional criteria they would use for classifying the organisms. *Additional criteria might include physical evidence, habitats, biological relationships, and molecular evidence such as DNA.*

Ask students whether some of their criteria are less scientific than others to use for grouping. Look for examples, such as organisms that compete, or that have similar abilities such as swimming, which would lead to unscientific groupings.

Technology Resources

Have students visit **ClassZone.com** for reteaching of Key Concepts.

 **CONTENT REVIEW**

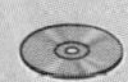 **CONTENT REVIEW CD-ROM**

MATH IN SCIENCE
Math Skills Practice for Science

Set Learning Goal
To determine ratios in populations by writing percents and fractions

Present the Science
All DNA is made up of a sequence of bases: adenine, thymine, guanine, and cytosine. It is the difference in the sequence of these bases that determines the type of protein molecule that will be produced.

Develop Percent Skills
Percent means "per hundred." Fifty percent means 50 per 100, or fifty out of one hundred. In addition, percents can be expressed as equivalent fractions or decimals. So, 50 percent is the same as 1/2 or 0.5. Percents, fractions, and decimals are different ways to express parts of a whole, or 100. Remind students that 40/100 and 2/5 are equivalent fractions and therefore express the same amount.

DIFFERENTIATION TIP To help students practice writing equivalent fractions, use fraction bars divided into equivalents such as 3/4, 6/8, and 9/12. Shade the area on the fractions bars to show equivalency.

Close
Ask students why writing amounts in percents is useful to scientists. *Percents help scientists make comparisons about two or more organisms and their characteristics.*

- Math Support, p. 107
- Math Practice, p. 108

Technology Resources
Students can visit **ClassZone.com** to practice fraction and percent skills.

MATH TUTORIAL

SKILL: WRITING PERCENTS

CLASSZONE.COM

Click on Math Tutorial for more help with percents and fractions.

Differences Between Species

Does it surprise you to learn that roughly 50 percent of the DNA in your cells is nearly identical to the DNA in the cells of a banana? You probably know from experience that 50 percent is the same as one half. But you can also convert any percent to a fraction by using the number 100 to represent the whole. Fifty parts out of 100 is the same as one half. Another example is shown below.

Example
Comparing the cells of two species, scientists find 40 percent of the DNA is identical. How can you show what fraction that is?

(1) Rewrite the percent as a numerator with a denominator of 100.
$\frac{40}{100}$

(2) Reduce the fraction. Use the greatest common factor (GCF) to write the numerator and the denominator as products.
$\frac{40}{100} = \frac{2 \cdot 20}{5 \cdot 20}$

(3) Divide the GCF by itself to get $\frac{1}{1}$, or 1.
$\frac{2}{5} \cdot \frac{20}{20} = \frac{2}{5} \cdot 1 = \frac{2}{5}$

ANSWER: 40 percent $= \frac{2}{5}$

Rewrite each sentence, changing the percent to a fraction.

1. About 85 percent of the DNA in human cells is similar to the DNA in mouse cells.
2. The tooth of a modern great white shark can be 34 percent of the length of a fossil tooth from a prehistoric shark.
3. There are about 20 percent as many penguin species as there are pine tree species in the world today.
4. There are about 8 percent as many bear species as pine tree species.

CHALLENGE Choose one example or exercise on this page. Tell whether the comparison works better as a fraction or a percent. Explain why.

ANSWERS

1. $\frac{85}{100} = \frac{5 \cdot 17}{5 \cdot 20} = \frac{17}{20}$
2. $\frac{34}{100} = \frac{2 \cdot 17}{2 \cdot 50} = \frac{17}{50}$
3. $\frac{20}{100} = \frac{20}{5 \cdot 20} = \frac{1}{5}$
4. $\frac{8}{100} = \frac{4 \cdot 2}{4 \cdot 25} = \frac{2}{25}$

CHALLENGE Answers will vary depending on the example chosen. Possible answer: 85% works better than 17/20 because 85% is easier to visualize.

KEY CONCEPT

Biologists use seven levels of classification.

BEFORE, you learned
- Classification is a system of organization
- Evidence is used to classify organisms

NOW, you will learn
- About scientific names
- About seven levels of classification
- How to use a dichotomous key

VOCABULARY
genus p. 212
binomial nomenclature p. 212
dichotomous key p. 216

EXPLORE Classification

What data do you need to identify objects?

PROCEDURE

1. Have one student in your group think of a secret object. The student should then tell the group one characteristic (shape, color, size, type, and so on) of that object.
2. The rest of the group guesses the object's identity. Each time someone guesses incorrectly, another characteristic of the object should be given. Record the characteristics and guesses as you go.
3. When the secret object is guessed correctly, begin again with a different student picking a different secret object.

WHAT DO YOU THINK?
- How many characteristics did it usually take to guess an object's identity?
- How does this exercise relate to identifying organisms?

Linnaeus named about 4000 species.

SUPPORTING MAIN IDEAS
Make a chart to show information that supports the first main idea presented: *Linnaeus named about 4000 species.*

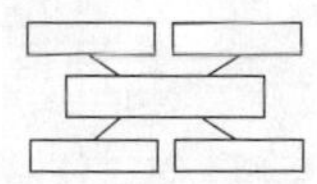

Scientists name species and arrange them into groups. One scientist named Carolus Linnaeus developed systems for both naming species and organizing them into groups. All 4000 species that Linnaeus named were plants or animals. Today, scientists have named over a million species. Linnaeus used appearance to group species. As you have read, modern scientists also use appearance, along with other types of evidence, to arrange species into groups.

7.2 FOCUS

Set Learning Goals

Students will
- Explain how scientific names are determined.
- Use the seven levels of classification.
- Analyze how to use a dichotomous key.
- Develop a two-part naming system for classifying everyday objects.

3-Minute Warm-Up

Display Transparency 12 or copy this exercise on the board:

Complete the graphic organizer.

Main Idea: Scientists use different evidence to classify organisms.		
Detail: Fossil evidence	**Detail:** Physical evidence	**Detail:** Genetic evidence
Shows how species evolved.	*Traits help tell species apart.*	*DNA supports physical evidence.*

 3-Minute Warm-Up, p. T12

7.2 MOTIVATE

EXPLORE Classification

PURPOSE To determine the importance of using characteristics to identify organisms

TIP *15 min.* Have each group record their guesses. At the end of the activity, compile their notes on the board. Discuss the similarities in the types of characteristics used to determine the identity of the object.

WHAT DO YOU THINK? *Number of characteristics used to guess the object will vary. Students should discover that it helps to start with the larger categories and work to the smaller ones.*

RESOURCES FOR DIFFERENTIATED INSTRUCTION

Below Level

UNIT RESOURCE BOOK
- Reading Study Guide A, pp. 83–84
- Decoding Support, p. 106

 AUDIO CDS

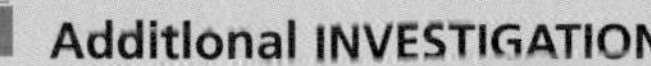 **Additional INVESTIGATION,** Make a Dichotomous Key, A, B, & C, pp. 118–126; Teacher Instructions, pp. 188–189

Advanced

UNIT RESOURCE BOOK
Challenge and Extension, p. 89

English Learners

UNIT RESOURCE BOOK
Spanish Reading Study Guide, pp. 87–88

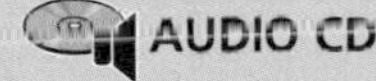 AUDIO CDS

- Audio Readings in Spanish
- Audio Readings (English)

7.2 INSTRUCT

INVESTIGATE Binomial Nomenclature

PURPOSE To develop a two-part naming system, using a dictionary, for classifying everyday objects

TIPS *30 min.* Prior to the activity, gather a number of everyday objects for students to choose from. Or, you may ask each student to bring one or two objects to class. Also, review using a dictionary to find word roots and Latin meanings. Model naming one object before students begin. Be sure to explain that when scientists name living things, they follow stricter guidelines so that all names work within a system.

WHAT DO YOU THINK? *Students' arrangement of objects will vary. It is important to be descriptive with names to avoid confusion between two or more objects or duplication.*

CHALLENGE *Sample answer: It is easy because the object can be named quickly, but if there are similar objects, then it will be hard to distinguish them and it is possible to run out of names.*

Datasheet, Binomial Nomenclature, p. 90

Technology Resources

Customize this student lab as needed or look for an alternative. Print rubrics to assess student lab reports.

Lab Generator CD-ROM

Teaching with Technology

Have students use spreadsheet or slide-show software to present their two-part naming system.

EXPLORE the BIG idea

Revisit "Internet Activity: Linnaeus" on p. 201. Ask students how Linnaeus' system of classification and naming organisms is similar to the system they used in the Investigation.

Naming Species

Sometimes using only one word to name an organism isn't specific enough. If you are telling a friend about your favorite writer, you might name Mary Oliver or Mary Whitebird or Mary Shelley. Using only "Mary" won't help your friend know the author you name, so you use two words. In a similar way, scientists use two words to name organisms.

A **genus** (JEE-nuhs) is a group of species that have similar characteristics. For example, the genus *Ursus* groups all of the animals known as bears. Included in this genus are *Ursus arctos* (grizzly bears), and *Ursus maritimus* (polar bears). Members of the same genus are closely related.

The system for naming species developed by Linnaeus is the basis of modern taxonomy. We call this system **binomial nomenclature** (by-NOH-mee-uhl NOH-muhn-KLAY-chuhr). *Binomial* means "two names" and *nomenclature* means "list of names." So binomial nomenclature describes a system of naming something using two names, or words. Most scientific names are Latin terms.

INVESTIGATE Binomial Nomenclature

How do you assign names?

SKILL FOCUS
Classifying

MATERIALS
- objects
- dictionary
- 10 index cards

TIME
30 minutes

PROCEDURE

1. Place ten objects on a table where everybody in the class can see them.
2. Give each object a genus name. Use a dictionary to come up with names that sound scientific. You may use only three genus names for the ten objects, so some names must apply to more than one objects.
3. Give each object a species name, using the dictionary again if you wish.
4. Write each object's full scientific name on an index card.
5. Trade your index cards with those of another group. Try to match their cards with the ten objects.

WHAT DO YOU THINK?

- How did the other group arrange the objects into genus names? How was their arrangement different from your group's?
- Why is it important for the names to be as descriptive as possible?

CHALLENGE Repeat the exercise, but now give each object a one-word name. Does this limitation make coming up with names easier or harder?

DIFFERENTIATE INSTRUCTION

More Reading Support

A What term describes a group of species with similar characteristics? *genus*

B What is binomial nomenclature? *a two-part system of naming*

English Learners This section contains a variety of introductory clauses and phrases. For example, "In a similar way, scientists use two words to name organisms." Have English learners find the comma that separates the introductory clause or phrase from the rest of the sentence. Then help them locate the subject of the sentence.

Binomial Nomenclature

All organisms are given a unique two-part name. Some organisms have the same species names: *gracilis* means "slender" or "graceful." Without the genus name, the species name is unclear.

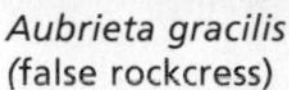

Aubrieta gracilis
(false rockcress)

Chameleo gracilis
(gracile chameleon)

Mammillaria gracilis
(thimble cactus)

Using Scientific Names

Linnaeus's system of binomial nomenclature made communication about certain species much easier. When naming an organism, the use of a genus name as well as a species name is necessary.

If the genus name is not included in the scientific name, the identity of a species can be a mystery. For example, the species name of the three different species shown above is *gracilis*. The word *gracilis* means "graceful" or "slender" in Latin.

- *Aubrieta gracilis* is a type of flower found in a rock garden.
- *Chameleo gracilis* is a type of lizard called a chameleon.
- *Mammillaria gracilis* is a type of cactus.

People follow certain rules when they write scientific names. The genus name comes first; the first letter is capitalized and the entire name is in italics. The species name is also written in italics, it follows the genus name, and the first letter is lowercased.

CHECK YOUR READING What is the difference between a genus and a species?

In addition to species and genus, the classification system includes several larger groups. Each larger group includes one or more smaller groups. Turn to page 214 to read about the larger groups in our modern system of classification.

Teach from Visuals

To help students interpret the three photographs and captions showing binomial nomenclature, ask:

- What is the species name used for all of these organisms? What does it mean? gracilis, *which means "slender" or "graceful"*
- How do you know that each organism shown belongs to a different genus? *The genus name comes first, and all of the genus names for these organisms are different.*

Teacher Demo

Display a picture of a mountain lion and ask students to write its name. Make a list of names on the board. Mountain lions are also known by the common names puma and cougar. Tell students that the scientific name of the animal is *Felis concolor.* Ask: How does knowing the scientific name of the animal help avoid confusion? *Scientists can be sure that they are all referring to the same animal.*

Develop Critical Thinking

ANALYZE Write the following names on the board: *Felis concolor, Felis onca,* and *Felis catus.* Remind students that *Felis concolor* is the scientific name for the mountain lion. Ask: What do you know about the other two animals? *They are all types of cats because they all belong to the same genus,* Felis.

Ongoing Assessment

Explain how scientific names are determined.

Ask: What are the two parts of a scientific name? *genus and species*

CHECK YOUR READING *Answer: A genus is a group of species that have similar characteristics. One or more species make up a genus.*

DIFFERENTIATE INSTRUCTION

More Reading Support

C Which name of a scientific name comes second? *the species name*

Below Level To reinforce the concept of binomial nomenclature, ask volunteers to write their first and last names on the board. Point out that a person's first name is like the species, or individual's, name. The last name is like the genus name and tells what family a person belongs to.

Develop Critical Thinking

ANALYZE Write *kingdom* on the board. Show a group of pictures of animals and ask students if the pictures illustrate a kingdom. How can they tell? Repeat the activity for phylum, class, order, family, genus, and species.

Next, ask students to choose three animals such as a mountain lion, wolf, dog, and shark and have students determine how to classify each one. Name the animals that belong to the same kingdom, phylum, class, and so on.

History of Science

Aristotle developed the first classification system in the fourth century B.C. He grouped organisms according to whether they were plants or animals. He also classified animals into invertebrate groups and recognized that whales, dolphins, and porpoises are not fish and have characteristics of other mammals. Organisms were ranked from simple to complex, but did not follow evolutionary lines of development. Aristotle's method of classification was used for almost 2000 years.

EXPLORE the BIG idea

Revisit "How Would You Sort Pennies?" on p. 201. Ask students if there are any similarities with the way they sorted the pennies to the levels of classification discussed in the text.

Organisms can be classified into seven levels.

SUPPORTING MAIN IDEAS Make a chart to show information that supports the main idea that *organisms can be classified into seven levels.*

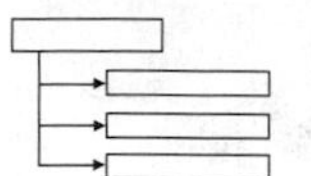

D

You've read about species and genus, the most specific levels of the classification system most scientists use today. There are seven levels that describe a species. The largest level is the kingdom, the group containing the most species. The seven levels of classification for a spotted turtle and a housecat are listed below.

1. Kingdom (Animalia—the animals)
2. Phylum (Chordata—animals with backbones)
3. Class (Mammalia—mammals, or furry animals that nurse their young)
4. Order (Carnivora—carnivores, or animals that kill and eat other animals)
5. Family (Felidae—the cat family)
6. Genus (*Felis*—housecats, cougars, and many others)
7. Species (*catus*—all housecats, no matter what their breed)

E

READING TIP *Phyla* is the plural form of *phylum.*

Like the cat, the turtle is also classified into seven levels. However, only the two largest levels, Animalia and Chordata, are the same as the classification for a housecat. The more names an organism shares with another organism, the more closely related the two organisms are. Cats and turtles are both animals with backbones, but are otherwise different. Spotted turtles have more traits in common with snakes and lizards than with cats. Lizards, snakes, and turtles all belong in the class Reptilia. Phyla are more specific than kingdoms, classes are more specific than phyla, and so on. The illustration on page 215 shows how kingdom is the broadest grouping of organisms, and species is the most specific.

Classification Hierarchy

	Spotted turtle	Cat
Kingdom	Animalia	Animalia
Phylum	Chordata	Chordata
Class	Reptilia	Mammalia
Order	Testudines	Carnivora
Family	Emydidae	Felidae
Genus	*Clemmys*	*Felis*
Species	*guttata*	*catus*

Clemmys guttata

Felis catus

DIFFERENTIATE INSTRUCTION

More Reading Support

D What is the highest level of classification? *kingdom*

E Which is the most specific level of classification? *species*

Advanced Provide students with a group of photographs of various organisms. Challenge students to classify the organisms according to the seven levels of organization. Students can use dictionaries or biology books to find the genus and species names. Challenge students to find two other organisms in the same family, genus, and species for each organism that they classify.

Challenge and Extension, p. 89

Teach from Visuals

To help students interpret the diagram of classifying organisms, have them think of the turtle as the guide and that they are to compare the turtle to the other organisms in each level to find similarities and differences. Ask:

- Which of the organisms in the first level belong to the animal kingdom? *all of them*
- Which animals were eliminated from the level of reptiles? *bird, frog, and monkey*
- Which animals were eliminated at the order level because they are not turtles? *alligator and snake*
- Are all of the turtles in the family level the same kind of turtle? Explain. *No, they can be further subdivided.*
- As the animals get closer to the species level, do they share more or fewer characteristics? *They share more characteristics.*

Teach Difficult Concepts

Some students confuse reptiles with amphibians and do not always recognize them as vertebrates. Point out that vertebrates include mammals, birds, reptiles, amphibians, and fish. Reptiles generally have scaly skin and live entirely on land. Amphibians begin their life in the water and develop lungs later on. They generally have moist, smooth skin.

Ongoing Assessment

Use the seven levels of classification.

Ask: What levels of classification do the housecat and turtle have in common? *kingdom and phylum*

DIFFERENTIATE INSTRUCTION

Additional Investigation To reinforce Section 7.2 learning goals, use the following full-period investigation:

R **Additional INVESTIGATION,** Make a Dichotomous Key, A, B, & C, pp. 118–126, 188–189 (Advanced students should complete Levels B and C.)

English Learners Place the terms *genus*, *binomial nomenclature*, and *dichotomous key* on the classroom's Science Word Wall with brief definitions of each. These terms are also difficult to pronounce. Help English learners by pronouncing them aloud as well.

Metacognitive Strategy

Have students create and share memory aids for remembering the order of the seven levels of classification. Post students' memory aids on a bulletin board for reference.

Mathematics Connection

The binary system is a numeration system that is based on the number 2. The numeration system that we are most familiar with, the decimal, or base 10, system, builds numbers in groups of 10. In contrast, the binary, or base 2, system builds numbers in groups of 2. For example, the number 10 in the binary system is equal to the number 2 in the decimal system. The *1* on the left means that there is 1 group of 2, and the *0* on the right means that there are no groups of 1.

Computers and other electronic devices work by coding data, such as numbers, letters, and many other types of information, into binary numbers. Then the numbers are converted into electrical charges in microprocessors, or chips, that contain many electronic circuits. A 1 means that a circuit is on, or is allowing current to flow through it. A 0 means that a circuit is off. Electronic devices are able to use patterns of on-off electrical signals to carry out highly complex tasks.

Real World Examples

Bring in copies of dichotomous keys for various groups of organisms such as birds, reptiles, insects, and plants. Have students choose one of the organisms in the key and make a list of characteristics used to classify the organism.

Ongoing Assessment

Answer: kingdom

Scientists can compare very broad categories of organisms, such as kingdoms and phyla. Or they can compare very specific categories, such as species. If scientists wish to compare all the different types of turtles to one another, then they will compare the organisms in the order Testudines. But if scientists want to compare turtles that live in or near water, then they will compare only organisms in the family Emydidae.

You can remember the classification levels and their order with this memory aid: Kings Play Chess On Fat Green Stools. The first letter of each word is the same as the first letter in each level of classification: *kingdom, phylum, class, order, family, genus,* and *species.* A complete classification of humans goes like this: kingdom Animalia, phylum Chordata, class Mammalia, order Primates, family Hominidae, genus *Homo,* species *sapiens.*

CHECK YOUR READING Which level of classification in the seven-level system includes the most species?

Dichotomous keys and field guides help people identify organisms.

With millions of organisms on Earth, how could a specific one be identified? Even if you know some of the larger categories, it can be difficult to find the species, genus, or even family name of many organisms from a long list of possibilities.

Take a beetle, for example. Even if you knew that it is in the kingdom Animalia, phylum Arthropoda (animals with jointed legs), class Insecta (insects), and order Coleoptera (hard-winged insects), you'd still have to choose among 300,000 known species of beetles that have been discovered around the world.

READING TIP The prefix *di-*means "two."

Taxonomists have come up with a tool to identify organisms such as this beetle. A **dichotomous key** (dy-KAHT-uh-muhs) asks a series of questions that can be answered in only two ways. Your answer to each question leads you to another question with only two choices. After a number of such questions, you will identify the organism. One example of a dichotomous key for trees is shown on page 217. G

Use an interactive dichotomous key.

The questions in a dichotomous key gradually narrow down the list of possible organisms. The questions can ask about any trait. The idea is simply to make identifying an organism as easy as possible. The dichotomous key for trees, for example, asks a set of questions that only ask about the traits of the leaves. Leaves are usually easy to get from a tree that needs to be identified, and they include many characteristics that can be used to tell different trees apart.

DIFFERENTIATE INSTRUCTION

More Reading Support

F What is the genus and species name for humans? *Homo sapiens*

G How does a dichotomous key work? *It offers two choices.*

Below Level Provide students with flash cards showing a variety of plant and animal life, including insects and other invertebrates, fish, amphibians, reptiles, birds, and mammals. Students can work in pairs to group the organisms according to kingdom, phylum, and class. Ask students to describe the species that are similar and those that are different in their classifications.

Dichotomous Key

Use the dichotomous key below to discover on what tree the circled leaf is found.

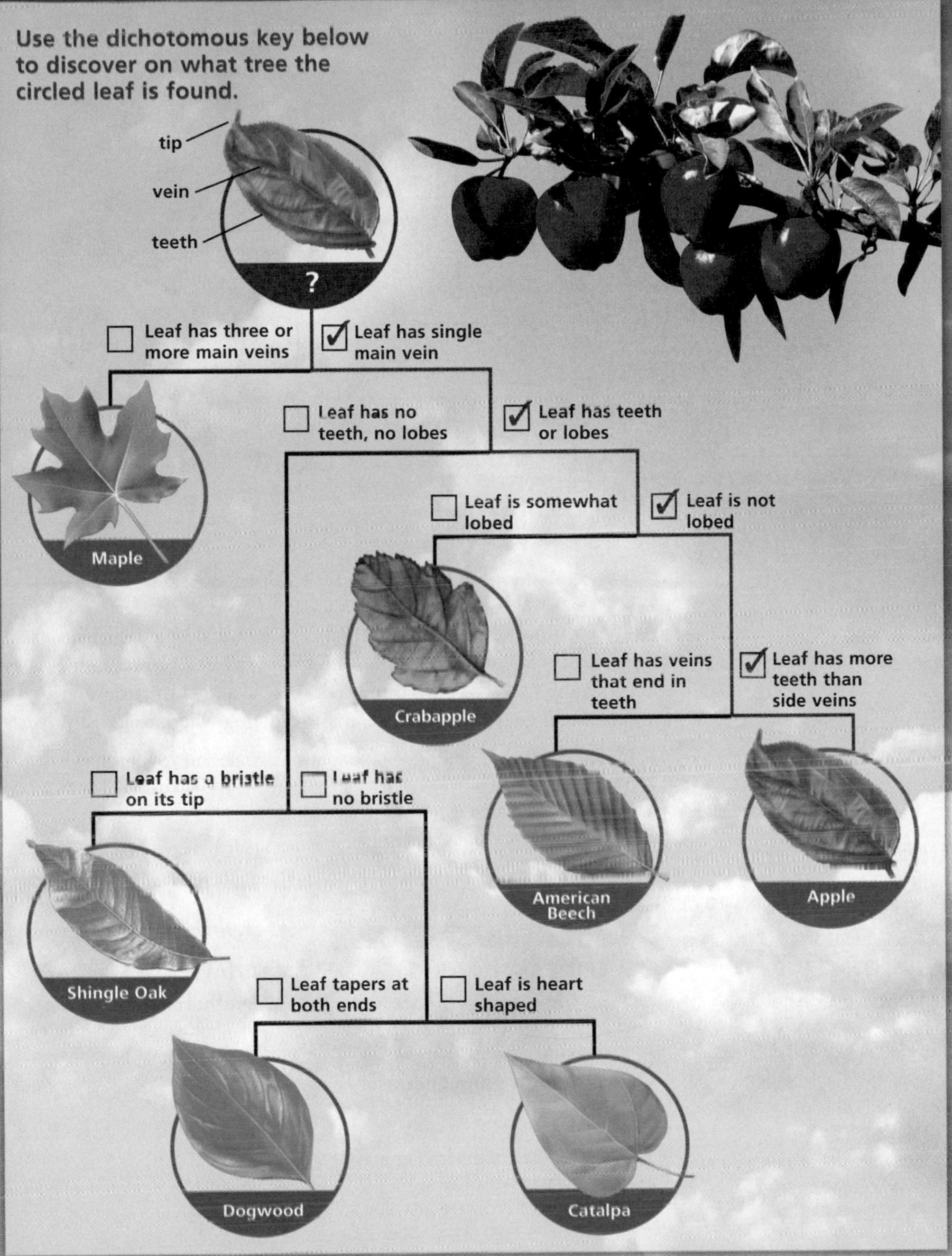

DIFFERENTIATE INSTRUCTION

Advanced Challenge students to devise a dichotomous key that could help identify a piece of fruit such as a banana, orange, strawberry, blueberry, peach, or apple. Student should construct a key similar to the one on the page. Have students compare keys to see if there are any similarities in the pairs of questions. Challenge interested students to create a Basic computer program that works as a dichotomous key.

Below Level Have students use the keys created in the Advanced activity to classify a given piece of fruit.

Teach from Visuals

To help students interpret the diagram of the dichotomous key, ask:

- How many choices are you given for each characteristic? *two*
- What characteristics in the key are used to identify the tree? *number of veins on the leaf, teeth or lobes, bristle or no bristle on the leaf tip, shape of leaf, veins that end in teeth, or more teeth than side veins*
- What is the identify of the tree shown in the picture? How do you know? *apple; all of the questions answered directed you to the apple leaf on the key.*

Teach Difficult Concepts

Explain to students that a dichotomous key is like a flow chart, and, at each point there is a question to answer. Guide students through the levels. As students work through the key, ask them yes or no questions at each point. For example, ask: Does the leaf have three or more main veins?

Ongoing Assessment

Analyze how to use a dichotomous key.

Ask: How would a dichotomous key help you to identify an organism such as a flower you might find? *The key asks a series of questions that can only be answered in two choices. After answering the questions, the genus and species of the organism should be identified.*

Ongoing Assessment

 *Answer: a dichotomous key and field guides*

Reinforce 

Have students relate the section to the Big Idea.

 Reinforcing Key Concepts, p. 91

7.2 ASSESS & RETEACH

Assess

 Section 7.2 Quiz, p. 23

Reteach

Make a four-column chart of "Tools Used to Identify and Classify Organisms."

- Label the columns: *Tools, Descriptions, Features, Help.*
- Then add a row for each of the following: *Binomial Nomenclature, Levels of Classification, Dichotomous Key.*
- Elicit help from students in filling in the remaining cells of the chart: *Sample: Binomial Nomenclature—two-part naming system; gives genus and species; identifies an organism; Levels of Classification—a hierarchy, categories; seven levels; organizes all organisms in one system; Dichotomous Key—a flow chart of questions; yes-or-no answers; pinpoints identity with a system.*

Technology Resources

Have students visit **ClassZone.com** for reteaching of Key Concepts.

 CONTENT REVIEW

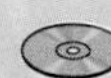 CONTENT REVIEW CD-ROM

Another tool for identifying organisms is a field guide. Field guides include paintings or photographs of familiar species. Flower guides may start with the flower's color. Bird guides are arranged by orders and families. Field guides also include maps showing where organisms live.

 What two tools have taxonomists developed to identify organisms?

7.2 Review

KEY CONCEPTS

1. What is binomial nomenclature?
2. Write the names of the seven levels of classification. Which level contains the most organisms?
3. What makes a dichotomous key easy to use?

CRITICAL THINKING

4. **Summarize** What were Carolus Linnaeus's main contributions to taxonomy?
5. **Compare and Contrast** Compare a dichotomous key with a typical field guide. What are the strengths and weaknesses of each?

CHALLENGE

6. **Synthesize** Predict what differences you might find among organisms in the same species.

ANSWERS

1. the naming system that uses the genus and species of an organism

2. kingdom, phylum, class, order, family, genus, species; kingdom level

3. Each question has only two choices. This eventually leads to the identification.

4. He developed systems for both naming species and organizing them into groups.

5. A dichotomous key is a series of questions with two possible answers for each question. A field guide has pictures of animals or plants. It can help determine visual similarities, but may be incomplete. A dichotomous key can help narrow down possible organisms, but may be time consuming.

6. size, coloration, age

EXTREME SCIENCE

NEW INSECT SPECIES

The Undiscovered

Everyone agrees that insects are the largest group of animals on Earth, but nobody knows exactly how many insect species exist. Some estimates predict that there are as many as 30 million. However, only about 900,000 have been classified. Twenty-nine million insect species may be waiting to be discovered!

Where in the World?

Many of the new insect species are found in tropical forests of South America and Asia. But plenty may be hiding close to your own home.

- The most massive bug in Southern California went undiscovered until April 4, 2002. This wingless relative of the Jerusalem cricket looks something like a puffed up 3-inch-long ant.
- While studying for her graduate degree, Christina Sandoval captured insects in Santa Barbara, California. She caught an unidentified species of walking stick insect, which she named after herself: *Timema cristinae.*
- The Hanford Nuclear Reservation, in Washington state, was closed to the public for about 50 years. After it opened for cleanup, the Nature Conservancy found 27 new insect species in just 4 years, including a new micromoth less than 1/8 inch long.

Scientists think that over one third of the estimated 164,000 insect species in the United States have yet to be discovered and named. Start looking. Who knows where they'll be!

A Whole New Order

In March 2002, for the first time in 87 years, a whole new order of insects was discovered. Insects in this order look like a cross between stick insects, praying mantises, and grasshoppers. Upon its discovery, the order was nicknamed *gladiators.* Now called *Mantophasmatodea,* the "gladiator bugs" raised the total number of insect orders to 31.

RESOURCE CENTER
CLASSZONE.COM
Learn more about newly discovered insects.

EXPLORE

1. **ANALYZE** List some things about an insect that could be included in its species name. Tell why each is important.
2. **CHALLENGE** Scientists recently discovered a new centipede in New York's Central Park, the first new species in the park in over 100 years. Centipedes are related to insects. Find out what centipedes and insects have in common and how they differ.

An adult Jerusalem cricket can reach 2 inches in length.

EXPLORE

1. ***ANALYZE*** *Possible answers: the size, shape, and features such as number of wings, how the insect gets its food, where it is found, or how it moves. The features help distinguish the insect from others.*

2. ***CHALLENGE*** *Centipedes have pairs of legs that are attached to segments along the body. They are not classified as insects because they do not have three distinct body parts, but both insects and centipedes are arthropods.*

EXTREME SCIENCE
Fun and Motivating Science

Set Learning Goal

To understand the incredible diversity of insects and the process of discovering new species

Present the Science

Insects outnumber all other animal groups and plant groups, accounting for nearly three-quarters of all living species on Earth. (For comparison, about 5 percent of all species are vertebrates.) Why are there so many insects? Both the large populations and large diversity of insects are due in part to insects' small size, high rates of reproduction, and plentiful food supplies, such as plants and decayed matter.

Discussion Questions

This page has two focuses: the variety of insects and the sheer number of insects including those species yet undiscovered.

Ask: Why do you think that most of the new insect species are found in tropical forests of South America and Asia? *Most of these forests are rainforests and have large areas that are yet to be explored by humans.*

Ask: What do you think accounts for the success and variety of insects on Earth? *their size, their numbers*

Close

Ask: What difficulties do you think scientists might encounter in trying to name and classify insects? *There are so many insects that it would be difficult to know if a certain insect is known or not.*

Technology Resources

Students can visit **ClassZone.com** for more links about new insects.

 **RESOURCE CENTER**

7.3 FOCUS

Set Learning Goals

Students will

- Analyze the connection between new discoveries and taxonomy.
- Describe the three domains.
- Describe the six kingdoms of living organisms.
- Observe and classify leaves to make a field guide.

3-Minute Warm-Up

Display Transparency 13 or copy this exercise on the board:

Match each definition with the terms.

Definitions

1. a group of species with similar traits *b*
2. the highest level of organization *c*
3. the most specific level of classification *e*

Terms

a. binomial nomenclature
b. genus
c. kingdom
d. phylum
e. species

 3-Minute Warm-Up, p. T13

7.3 MOTIVATE

THINK ABOUT

PURPOSE To understand why scientists group organisms

DISCUSS Brainstorm a list of the characteristics of living things. Write responses on the board. Go through the list and check characteristics that apply to the sea urchin, tiger, alligator, and humans. *Sample answer: gets food for energy, moves about, breathes, grows, reproduces*

Ongoing Assessment

Analyze the connection between new discoveries and taxonomy.

Ask: How do discoveries about evolution affect classification? *Organisms may be reclassified based on new information.*

KEY CONCEPT

7.3 Classification systems change as scientists learn more.

BEFORE, you learned

- Scientists give each species a unique scientific name
- There are seven levels of classification
- Dichotomous keys help us identify organisms

NOW, you will learn

- About the connection between new discoveries and taxonomy
- About three domains
- About six kingdoms

VOCABULARY

domain p. 221
Plantae p. 223
Animalia p. 223
Protista p. 223
Fungi p. 223
Archaea p. 223
Bacteria p. 223

THINK ABOUT

How do scientists define kingdoms?

Look at this photograph of a sea urchin. It lives its life buried in or slowly moving across the ocean floor. The sea urchin's mouth is located on its underside. It feeds on food particles that settle on or are buried in the ocean floor. The sea urchin doesn't appear to have much in common with a tiger, an alligator, even a human. Yet all of these organisms belong in the same kingdom, called Animalia. Why do you think scientists would group these organisms together?

Taxonomy changes as scientists make discoveries.

The list of species continues to grow as scientists discover new species. In addition, taxonomists are learning more about the evolutionary history of species. As you read in Section 7.1, new knowledge resulted in the reclassification of species such as the giant panda. Both the names of species and the groups into which they are arranged may change as a result of discoveries about the evolution of these species.

Early scientists described two large groups of organisms—plants and animals. Plants were described as green and nonmoving. Animals moved. Most scientists today use a system that includes six kingdoms. In addition, taxonomists have added a level of organization above the kingdom level.

RESOURCES FOR DIFFERENTIATED INSTRUCTION

Below Level

UNIT RESOURCE BOOK
- Reading Study Guide A, pp. 94–95
- Decoding Support, p. 106

Advanced

UNIT RESOURCE BOOK
- Challenge and Extension, p. 100
- Challenge Reading, pp. 102–103

English Learners

UNIT RESOURCE BOOK
Spanish Reading Study Guide, pp. 98–99

- Audio Readings in Spanish
- Audio Readings (English)

Three Domains

Microscopes and other advances in technology have allowed scientists to observe that there are three fundamentally different types of cells. On the basis of this observation, scientists have arranged kingdoms into larger groups called **domains.** For example, the domain Eukarya contains the protists, fungi, plants, and animals.

A

The table below summarizes the relationships among the six kingdoms and the three domains. You will learn more about kingdoms in the rest of this section.

RESOURCE CENTER
CLASSZONE.COM
Find out more about modern classification.

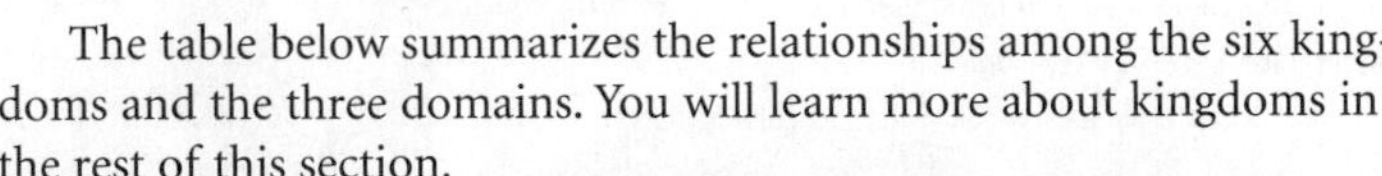

Domains and Kingdoms

Domain	Bacteria	Archaea	Eukarya			
Kingdom	Bacteria	Archaea	Protista	Fungi	Plantae	Animalia
Cell type	No nucleus	No nucleus	With nucleus	With nucleus	With nucleus	With nucleus
Cell number	Unicellular	Unicellular	Unicellular	Mostly multicellular	Multicellular	Multicellular
How organisms get energy	Varies	Varies	Varies	Absorbs materials	Uses sunlight	Consumes food

The photographs below show examples of cells from each domain. One of the traits that distinguishes cells of Eukarya from cells of Bacteria and Archaea is the presence of a nucleus. Cells that contain a nucleus are called eukaryotic cells, and cells that do not contain a nucleus are called prokaryotic cells. The domains Bacteria and Archaea include only organisms with prokaryotic cells. The domain Eukarya includes only organisms with eukaryotic cells.

B

CHECK YOUR READING How are prokaryotic cells different from eukaryotic cells?

Bacteria

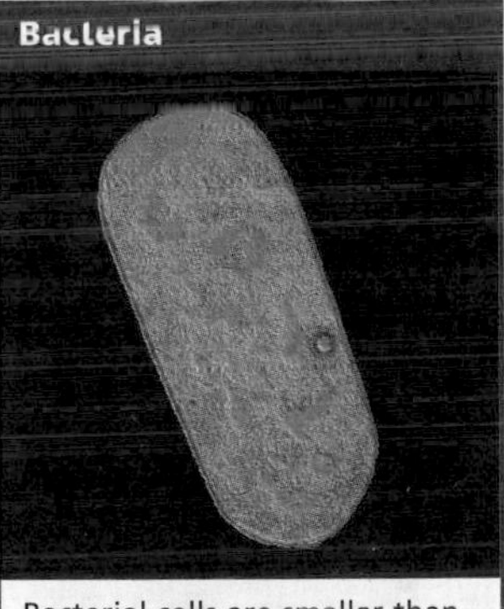

Bacterial cells are smaller than Eukarya cells and have no nucleus.

Archaea

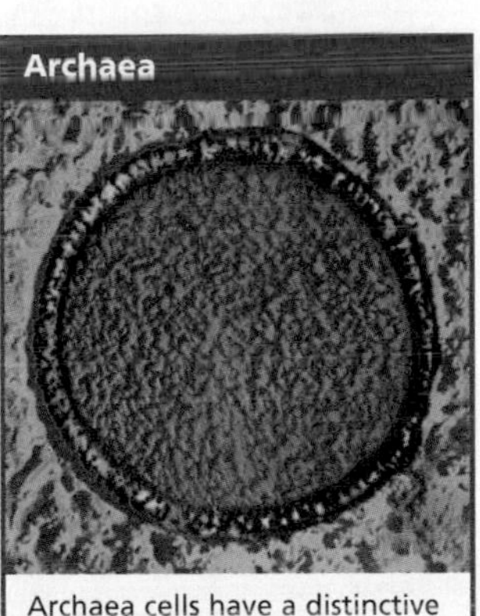

Archaea cells have a distinctive chemistry and can survive extreme environments.

Eukarya

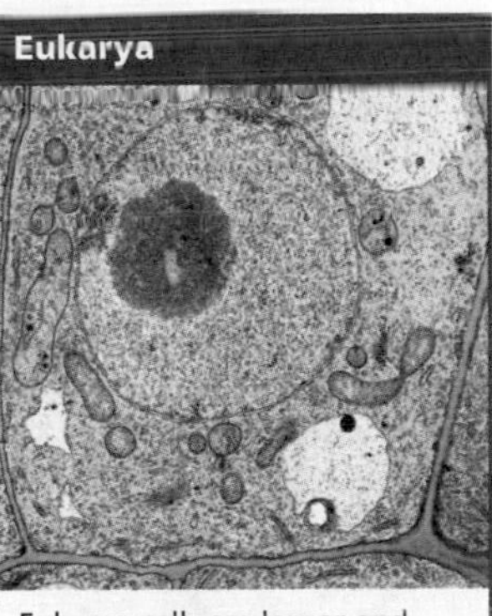

Eukarya cells are larger and contain more complex structures.

7.3 INSTRUCT

Teach Difficult Concepts

Students might confuse the differences among domains, kingdoms, and the seven levels of classification. Call attention to the chart and point out that kingdoms are a subgroup of the three domains. Each kingdom is then further divided into the seven levels of organization. Challenge students to draw a Venn diagram to illustrate this relationship.

Teach from Visuals

To help students interpret the information in the chart, the text, and the photographs of the domains, ask:

- Which two domains are made up of organisms with prokaryotic cells? *Bacteria and Archaea*
- How many kingdoms are in the domain Bacteria? What is it? *There is one kingdom called Bacteria.*
- Which domain is made up of organisms with eukaryotic cells? *Eukarya*
- How many kingdoms are in the domain Eukarya? What are they? *four: Protista, Fungi, Plantae, Animalia*

Ongoing Assessment

Describe the three domains of living organisms.

Ask: What are the three domains? *Bacteria, Archaea, Eukarya*

CHECK YOUR READING *Answer: Prokaryotic cells have no nucleus. Eukaryotic cells have a nucleus.*

DIFFERENTIATE INSTRUCTION

More Reading Support

A What groups do kingdoms fall within? *domains*

B What term describes cells that contain a nucleus? *eukaryotic*

English Learners Make a colorful poster for the Science Word Wall with the six kingdoms: *Plantae, Animalia, Protista, Fungi, Archaea,* and *Bacteria.* Next to each term place two or three diverse examples of the kingdom. For example, next to Animalia show a dog, a lizard, and a bird. Remind students that the common names for each kingdom can be found in the Latin name, e.g., *plant* in *Plantae, animal* in *Animalia,* and so on. Post the common names as well.

Teach from Visuals

To help students interpret the diagram of the six kingdoms, ask:

- All life on Earth is divided into how many kingdoms? *six*
- Which kingdoms contain multicellular organisms? *Plantae, Animalia, Protista, and Fungi*
- Which kingdoms contain organisms with cell walls? *Plantae and Fungi*
- How are the kingdoms of Archaea and Bacteria similar? *Both are unicellular; both lack nuclei.*

The "Six Kingdoms" visual is also available as T14 in the Unit Transparency Book.

Metacognitive Strategy

Have students play "What Am I?" to help them compare the six kingdoms. For example, a student might say, "I am unicellular. I live in extreme environments. What am I?" *Archaea*

Teach Difficult Concepts

Some students may be confused about the difference between the Protista, Archaea, and Bacteria groups. To help students, have them create a chart that answers the following questions for each group:

- Are the organisms unicellular? *Archaea and Bacteria are unicellular; some Protista are unicellular.*
- Are some of the organisms multicellular? *some in the Protista kingdom*
- Do the organisms have nuclei? *Protista have nuclei; Archaea and Bacteria do not.*
- Which of the organisms can survive extreme environments? *Archaea*

Six Kingdoms

All living things on Earth can be classified in six kingdoms.

Plantae
- Plants are multicellular and live on land.
- Plants obtain energy from sunlight.
- A plant cell has a nucleus, a cell wall, and chloroplasts.

Animalia
- Animals are multicellular and able to move.
- Animals obtain energy by eating food.
- An animal cell has a nucleus but no cell wall or chloroplasts.

Protista
- Most protists are single-celled.
- Multicellular protists lack complex structure.
- A protist cell has a nucleus.

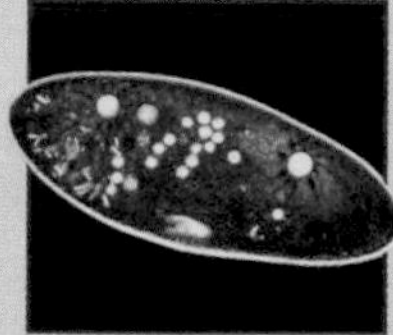

Fungi
- All fungi except yeasts are multicellular.
- Fungi obtain energy by absorbing materials.
- A fungus cell has a nucleus and a cell wall, but no chloroplasts.

Archaea
- Archaea are unicellular organisms without nuclei.
- Archaea cells have different chemicals than bacteria.
- Archaea can live in extreme conditions.

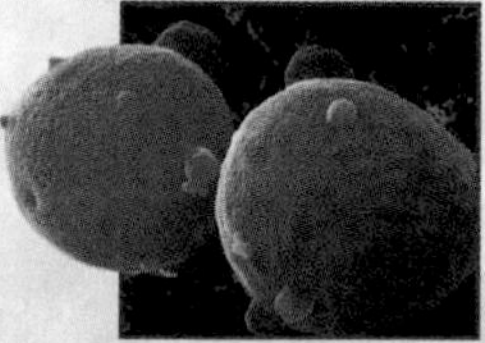

Bacteria
- Bacteria are unicellular organisms.
- A bacterial cell has no nucleus.
- Bacteria reproduce by dividing in two.

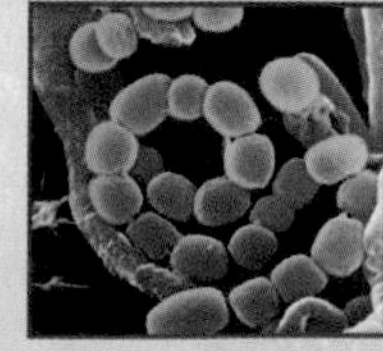

222

DIFFERENTIATE INSTRUCTION

Below Level To reinforce classification skills, have students work in groups. Each group chooses one kingdom. Then each student chooses one organism that is found in that kingdom. For each organism, have students classify it according to the seven levels of organization and find out its scientific name. Students should present their work on posters and display them for the class.

Six Kingdoms

The classification system that many scientists use today has six kingdoms. Every known species on Earth is included in one of these six kingdoms.

- Kingdom **Plantae** (PLAN-TEE) includes plants such as trees, grass, and moss.
- Kingdom **Animalia** (AN-uh-MAL-yuh) includes animals, from lions and tigers and bears to bugs and multicellular microbes.
- Kingdom **Protista** (pruh-TIHS-tuh) includes organisms that don't fit easily into animals, plants, or fungi. They are either unicellular organisms or have a simple multicellular structure.
- Kingdom **Fungi** (FUHN-jy) includes mushrooms, molds, and yeasts.
- Kingdom **Archaea** (AHR-kee-uh) contains organisms that are similar to bacteria, but have a cell structure that is so different that scientists separate them into their own kingdom.
- Kingdom **Bacteria** (bak-TIHR-ee-uh) are unicellular organisms with no nucleus.

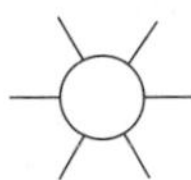

VOCABULARY
Add description wheels for *Plantae, Animalia, Protista, Fungi, Archaea,* and *Bacteria* to your notebook. You may want to add to your diagrams as you read the section.

This system may change as scientists learn more about the species in each kingdom. Before 1990, most scientists preferred a five-kingdom system that combined Archaea and Bacteria into a single kingdom. However, as scientists learned of chemical differences between the cells of the species, they arranged them into two kingdoms. Today, some scientists suggest that the kingdom Protista should be arranged into smaller kingdoms because of the many differences among its species. Many scientists agree on a three domain and six kingdom system similar to the one summarized on pages 221–223.

CHECK YOUR READING Which of the six kingdoms include unicellular organisms?

The two most familiar kingdoms are plants and animals.

Carolus Linnaeus divided all of the species he identified into two large groups: plants and animals. People still use these groups to describe most living things today. But these two kingdoms also include unfamiliar organisms.

It might seem odd that living things that are so different from each other—humans, elephants, termites, ducks, fish, worms—are all part of the same group. However, all of these organisms share some general traits, just as all plants share another set of general traits.

Develop Critical Thinking

CLASSIFY Display several pictures of organisms such as a green plant, a mushroom, an insect, a crayfish, a coral, a turtle, a deer, a snake, an amoeba, and a bacteria cell. Have students classify the organisms into each of the kingdoms. Ask students to give reasons for their classifications based on information from the text. Remind students that Linnaeus classified all organisms into two groups, plants and animals. Ask: Why do you think that this is not a good classification system? *There are many organisms that do not fit into either of those categories.*

Arts Connection

Allow students to prepare a poster of the six kingdoms. Students can highlight the names of the six kingdoms in red. They should give details about the kingdoms in blue. Then they can write examples of organisms for each kingdom in green. Encourage students to draw examples of organisms that represent each kingdom. Students can do a Web Quest to find reference photographs.

Ongoing Assessment

Describe the six kingdoms of living organisms.

Ask: Which kingdoms are made up of organisms that are only multicellular? *Plantae and Animalia*

CHECK YOUR READING *Answer: Protista, Fungi, Archaea, and Bacteria are kingdoms that include unicellular organisms.*

DIFFERENTIATE INSTRUCTION

More Reading Support

C Why did scientists decide to split Archaea and Bacteria into two kingdoms? *There are chemical differences between the two groups.*

Alternative Assessment Have students complete the following concept map, adding three details about each domain.

Domain		
Archaea	Bacteria	Eukarya
Details: 1. 2. 3.	Details: 1. 2. 3.	Details: 1. 2. 3.

Address Misconceptions

IDENTIFY Ask students to name some animal organisms. If students include only mammals or vertebrates in their list, then they might hold the misconception that animals do not include organisms such as fish, amphibians, reptiles or invertebrates. Many students will limit their classification of animals to land mammals commonly found in the home, farm, or zoo. Students might also have difficulty classifying an organism as both a bird and an animal.

CORRECT Have students create an idea map showing examples of animals by categorizing them according to body parts (segments, wings, antennae, number of legs, fins, claws, spines, scales, tentacles, and so on). Students may also list animals by categories such as method of movement, environment, and size.

REASSESS Ask students to describe the characteristics of animals. Then have them describe why animals are different from plants or fungi.

Technology Resources

Visit **ClassZone.com** for background on common student misconceptions.

MISCONCEPTION DATABASE

Teach from Visuals

To help students interpret the photographs of animals, ask: What do all of these organisms have in common? *They are all animals. They all move about and get their energy by eating other organisms.*

Ongoing Assessment

CHECK YOUR READING *Answer: Insects are the most abundant species in the animal kingdom.*

Clematis viticella
(Italian clematis)

Plantae

About 250,000 plant species live on Earth. They range from tiny mosses to the largest organisms on the planet, giant sequoia trees. The oldest living organism on our planet is a plant called the bristlecone pine. Some living bristlecone pines were growing when the Egyptians built the pyramids, about 4000 years ago.

All plants are multicellular and are eukaryotes, which means their DNA is stored in the nucleus of their cells. All plants are able to make sugars using the Sun's energy. Plants cannot move from place to place, but they can grow around objects, turn toward light, and grow upward. Plant cells are different from animal cells, because plant cells have tough walls outside their cell membranes.

Animalia

Scientists have already named a million species in the kingdom Animalia. Many different types of animals inhabit the planet, but more than 90 percent of the named species are insects. The animal kingdom also includes familiar animals such as whales, sharks, humans, bears, dogs, and fish.

All animals get their energy by eating other organisms or by eating food made by other organisms. Animals have the ability to move around for at least part of their life. Most animals have mouths and some type of nervous system. Plant and animal cells are both eukaryotic, but animal cells have no cell walls.

CHECK YOUR READING What is the most abundant type of species in the animal kingdom?

Abracadabrella birdsville
(jumping spider)

Giraffa camelopardalis
(giraffe)

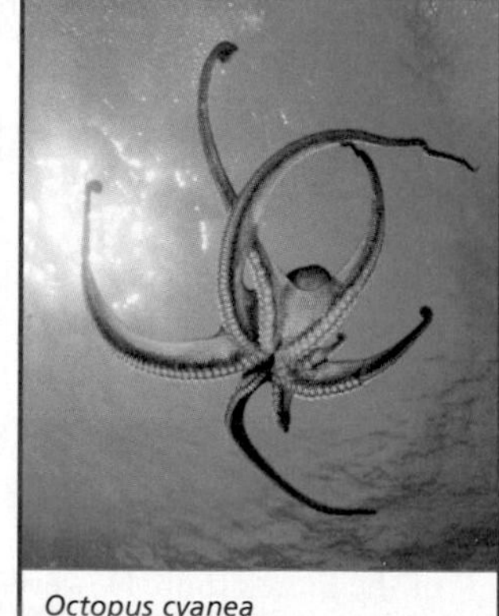
Octopus cyanea
(day octopus)

DIFFERENTIATE INSTRUCTION

More Reading Support

D What are the largest living organisms on Earth? *giant sequoia trees*

E How are animal cells different from plant cells? *They have no cell walls.*

Below Level To help students better understand the concept of kingdoms and classification among kingdoms that is the concept of hierarchy (rather than exclusive sets) in classification, have them practice group-subgroup-individual classification with a familiar example of food groups.

Other organisms make up four more kingdoms.

Carolus Linnaeus's classification systems included the organisms he knew about in the late 1700s. Some of the organisms Linnaeus called plants—the mushrooms, molds, and their relatives—turned out to have some characteristics very different from those of plants. Biologists now put fungi in a kingdom of their own.

Three other kingdoms consist mainly of microscopic organisms. These are Protista, Archaea, and Bacteria. Most organisms on Earth are classified as bacteria or archaea. These are prokaryotic organisms, which have small, simple cells and no nuclei.

CHECK YOUR READING What are the four kingdoms besides Plantae and Animalia?

Protista

The kingdom Protista includes a wide variety of organisms. Most protists are unicellular. Protists that are multicellular have structures that are too simple to be classified as animals, plants, or fungi. All protists have large, complex cells with a true nucleus (eukaryotes). Some eat other organisms as animals do; some get energy from sunlight as plants do. Some protists resemble fungi. However, protists that are multicellular do not have as many specialized cells or structures as plants, animals, and fungi.

Many protists live in pond water or sea water. The largest of the unicellular species are barely visible without a microscope. However, large organisms such as seaweeds are also classified as Protista. Some seaweeds can grow hundreds of feet in a single year.

Different groups of protists evolved from different ancestors. Scientists still debate whether kingdom Protista should be classified as one kingdom or should be split into several kingdoms.

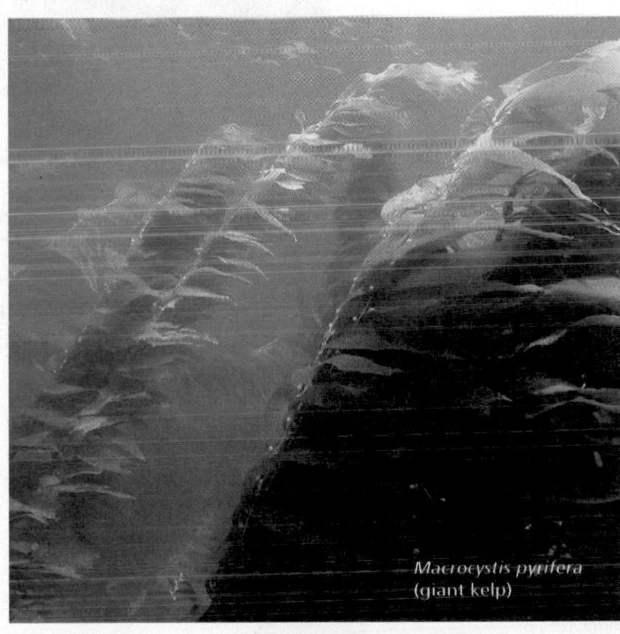

Macrocystis pyrifera (giant kelp)

History of Science

Anton van Leeuwenhoek was a Dutch amateur scientist and microscopist who, in 1674, was the first to observe bacteria and protozoa. He took samples of rainwater, pond, and well water and described his early observations as *animalcules.* He also observed red blood cells in humans and other animals, as well as spermatozoa of insects, dogs, and humans. Leeuwenhoek made many drawings of his observations, which he sent in his letters to the Royal Society of England. During his lifetime, Leeuwenhoek made over 400 simple microscopes, some of which still exist today.

Teaching with Technology

If microscopes are available, have students observe prepared slides of protozoa. Or you may wish to prepare wet mounts of pond water for students to observe as they work through Section 7.3. Caution students not to touch the pond water.

Ongoing Assessment

CHECK YOUR READING *Answer: Besides Plantae and Animalia, there are Protista, Fungi, Archaea, and Bacteria.*

DIFFERENTIATE INSTRUCTION

More Reading Support

F What are examples of large multicellular protists? ***seaweed***

Advanced Invite students to investigate the different classification schemes of protists proposed by scientists. Ask students why scientists would want to classify protists into different groups.

R Challenge and Extension, p. 100

Have students who are interested in the discovery of new species read the following article:

R Challenge Reading, pp. 102–103

Real World Examples

Mold, which is a type of fungi, is the source of penicillin and other antibiotics. In 1928 Alexander Fleming first observed the effects of penicillin on bacteria. Since then many antibiotics have been derived from living organisms such as bacteria and molds. Other types of fungi used commercially include the use of yeasts in baking bread and producing cheese. Industrial uses of bacteria include its use in the production of cheeses, yogurt, buttermilk, vinegar, and sauerkraut.

Integrate the Sciences

Methanobacterium, a member of the kingdom Archaea, are a form of archaebacteria that produce methane gas as an end product of metabolism. These organisms live in oxygen-free environments such as mud or the digestive tracts of animals.

Teacher Demo

Have students grow bread molds by placing slices of bread in re-sealable plastic bags and placing them in a warm place for several days. Students can observe the molds with a hand lens. Caution students to wear protective gloves when observing the molds and to wash their hands thoroughly after the activity. Have students sketch their observations. For further study, prepare wet mounts of the bread molds so students can see the structure of the fungi.

Ongoing Assessment

CHECK YOUR READING *Answer: Archaea do not have nuclei and their cell structure is different from bacteria. In addition, they also live in extreme environments.*

Fungi

Every time a loaf of bread is baked, a fungus is responsible for the rising dough. One group of fungi called yeasts makes it possible for us to make bread and many other food products. Another type of fungi that people eat includes some mushrooms. A mushroom grows in thin threads underground, and only the small cap breaks above the ground.

READING TIP: *Fungi* is the plural form of *fungus*.

G Fungi are usually divided into three categories: mushrooms, molds, and yeasts. The trait that separates fungi from other organisms is that fungi take in nutrients from their surroundings instead of eating other organisms or using sunlight. Both plants and fungi remain rooted in one place. Most fungi have cell walls similar to the cell walls of plants. H Unlike plants, however, many fungi act as decomposers, breaking down dead or decaying material into simpler parts that can be absorbed or recycled by other organisms.

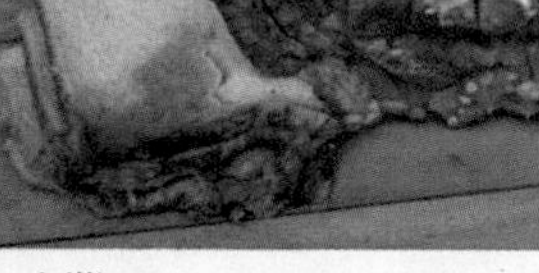

Penicillium (bread mold)

Lepiota procera (parasol mushroom)

Archaea

In the mid-1990s a researcher studying the genes of some bacteria discovered that although they resembled bacteria in size and cell type, some species had very specific genetic differences. After more study, scientists decided to call these organisms archaea. They differ so much that scientists now classify archaea in the separate kingdom or domain of Archaea.

In some ways, archaea appear to be more related to eukaryotes—organisms with complex cells containing nuclei—than to bacteria. Archaea do not have nuclei, but their cell structure is different from that of bacteria. Like bacteria, archaea live in many environments, especially in the ocean. But they also live in some very extreme environments, such as boiling mud near geysers, hot vents at the bottom of the ocean, salty ponds, and deep under the sand.

Methanococcoides burtonii

CHECK YOUR READING: Which traits classify an organism as part of the kingdom Archaea?

DIFFERENTIATE INSTRUCTION

More Reading Support

G What three groups of organisms make up fungi? *molds, yeasts, mushrooms*

H How do fungi take in nutrients? *by breaking down dead or decaying materials*

English Learners The use of dashes in writing may be confusing to English learners. Don't let students confuse the function of the dash with the function of commas or parentheses. The dash is used to interject an idea into a sentence. For example, "Archaea appear to be more related to eukaryotes—organisms with complex cells containing nuclei—than to bacteria." Show students that the sentence would still be complete if the words inside the dashes were not there.

Bacteria

Bacteria live nearly everywhere on Earth. This kingdom includes organisms that cause human disease and spoil food, but most of these organisms are helpful members of biological communities.

All bacteria are unicellular organisms. They have small, simple cells without a nucleus. Most bacteria have a cell wall outside the cell membrane, but this wall is not the same as the cell wall of plants. Bacteria reproduce by dividing in two, and can produce many new generations in a short period of time.

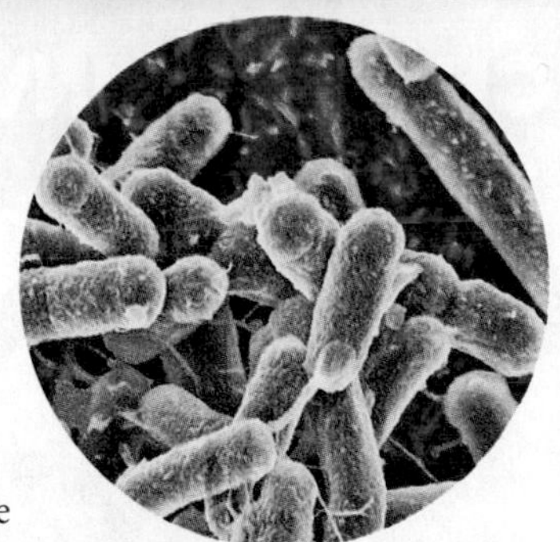

Escherichia coli (E. coli)

Species and environments change.

In the last chapter you read about the ways species change over time. You have also read how the evolutionary history of species helps scientists classify living things.

Scientists have named over a million species and placed them into six kingdoms. In addition, scientists estimate that there are millions—maybe tens of millions—more species that haven't been discovered. Scientists have also discovered forms of life preserved in the fossil record. Some of those organisms are the ancestors of organisms that live today.

Species evolve over time as individual organisms and environments change. Individual organisms are faced with many other pressures that affect daily lives. These pressures may come from changes in their living space, in the availability of food or other resources, or from other organisms. In the next chapter, you will read about how groups of species are affected by changes in their surroundings.

7.3 Review

KEY CONCEPTS

1. What are the names of the six kingdoms used in the classification system?
2. How are species sorted into the various kingdoms?

CRITICAL THINKING

3. **Communicate** Make a table with columns headed Characteristics, Animalia, and Plantae. Using as many rows as needed, list characteristics that differ between these two kingdoms.
4. **Analyze** Explain how fungi differ from plants.

CHALLENGE

5. **Analyze** One bacterium has a membrane surrounding its DNA. Should this organism be classified with the eukaryotes? Why or why not?

ANSWERS

1. Plantae, Animalia, Protista, Fungi, Bacteria, Archaea

2. Organisms are sorted according to general traits.

3. Plantae: store DNA in nucleus of cell, use Sun's energy and air to make sugars, cannot move from place to place, can grow upwards, around objects and turn toward light. Cell membranes have tough walls. Animalia: get energy from consuming organisms, can move around, most have mouths and some kind of nervous systems, do not have cell walls.

4. Plants use the Sun's energy and air to make sugars; fungi take in nutrients from their surroundings.

5. Most students will say no, because the organism does not have a nucleus. Some will say yes, the membrane and DNA are like a nucleus.

Teach from Visuals

To help students interpret the photographs of *E. coli* bacteria, point out that this bacteria is a harmful bacteria found in foods that can make humans ill.

Reinforce 

Have students relate the section to the Big Idea.

 Reinforcing Key Concepts, p. 101

7.3 ASSESS & RETEACH

Assess

 Section 7.3 Quiz, p. 24

Reteach

Create a diagram of the three domains and the six kingdoms. Ask volunteers to give one detail or characteristic about the kingdoms and domains. As you fill in the chart, ask students compare and contrast questions about the kingdoms such as:

- What sets apart the fungi kingdom from the others? *Fungi obtain energy by absorbing materials.*
- Which two kingdoms have no nuclei in their cells? *Bacteria and Archaea*
- Which kingdoms are made up of both unicellular and multicellular organisms? *Protista and Fungi*

Technology Resources

Have students visit **ClassZone.com** for reteaching of Key Concepts.

 **CONTENT REVIEW**

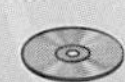 **CONTENT REVIEW CD-ROM**

CHAPTER INVESTIGATION

Focus

PURPOSE To observe and classify leaves in order to make a field guide

OVERVIEW Students will gather samples of leaves and use a hands lens to make observations about the leaves. Students will rely on their observations to:

- classify the leaves
- prepare a field guide based on their observations

Lab Preparation

- Students can use leaves they collect, or you may wish to provide students with samples.
- If students gather their own samples, provide them with a handout of the poisonous plants in your area.
- Prior to the investigation have students read through the investigation and prepare their data tables. Or you may wish to copy and distribute datasheets and rubrics.

 UNIT RESOURCE BOOK, pp. 109–117

 SCIENCE TOOLKIT, F15

Lab Management

- Caution students to wear gloves when handling leaves and make sure they wash their hands with soap and water after completing the activity.
- Inspect students' leaves before beginning. Ensure they have not gathered any poisonous leaves.
- Students may make leaf rubbings by using charcoal sticks or crayons that they can place on an edge.

INCLUSION Prepare examples of leaves showing each characteristic in the data chart on p. 229. Students with attention disorders or learning disabilities can compare their leaves with examples on the chart.

Teaching with Technology

Students might use digital cameras to photograph leaves for their guides.

Making a Field Guide

OVERVIEW AND PURPOSE A field guide is an illustrated book that shows the differences and similarities among plant or animal organisms. In this activity you will

- observe and classify leaves
- prepare a field guide based on your observations

Question

A field guide helps scientists identify organisms. Can you successfully prepare such a field guide? What would you like to know about how field guides are used and made? Write a question that begins with *Which, How, Why, When,* or *What.*

MATERIALS
- plastic gloves
- shoebox
- hand lens
- pencil
- paper
- tracing paper
- crayons

Procedure

1. Make 5 or more tables like the one shown on the sample science notebook on page 229. Gather at least 5 samples of different leaves from an area that your teacher chooses. **CAUTION: Wear protective gloves when handling plants. Be aware of any poisonous plants in your area. Place your samples in a shoebox and bring them back to the classroom for observation.**

2. **CAUTION: Wear plastic gloves when handling leaf samples.** Use the hand lens to study the leaves that you gathered. Make a sketch of each of the leaves. Create leaf rubbings by placing each leaf between two sheets of tracing paper and rubbing the top paper with the side of a pencil or crayon. Record your observations about each leaf in one of the data tables.

INVESTIGATION RESOURCES

 CHAPTER INVESTIGATION, Make a Field Guide
- Level A, pp. 109–112
- Level B, pp. 113–116
- Level C, p. 117

Advanced students should complete Levels B & C.

 Writing a Lab Report, D12–13

Technology Resources

Customize this student lab as needed or look for an alternative. Print rubrics to assess student lab reports.

 **Lab Generator CD-ROM**

3. Use the information in your table to prepare your field guide. Start by dividing your leaves into two groups on the basis of one of the characteristics you observed. Then compare the leaves in each group. How are they similar or different? Continue to observe and divide the samples in each group until each leaf is in a classification by itself.

4. Use scientific field guides or other sources to identify your sample leaves. Find out the common and scientific name for each leaf and add that information to your table.

5. Describe the location of each sample and what effect the plant it represents has on its environment. For example, does the plant provide food or shelter for animals? Does it have a commercial use, or is it an important part of the environment?

6. Use your data tables, sketches, and leaf rubbings to prepare your field guide for the chosen area.

Observe and Analyze

Write It Up

1. **CLASSIFY** What characteristics did you choose for classifying your leaf samples? Explain why you grouped the leaves the way you did.
2. **ANALYZE** Which characteristics of the leaves you gathered were most useful in finding their scientific names and in identifying them?

Conclude

1. **INFER** Could you use the same characteristics you used to group your samples to classify leaves of other species?
2. **LIMITATIONS** Were there any leaves you could not classify? What would help you classify them?
3. **APPLY** How are field guides useful to scientists working on environmental studies? How are field guides useful to tourists or others who are exploring an environment?

INVESTIGATE Further

CHALLENGE Combine your field guide with those made by all the other members of your class to make one large field guide. Use all the sketches and observations to classify leaves into several large groups.

Making a Field Guide: Leaf 1

Characteristic	Observations
Simple leaf or several leaflets	
Number of lobes	
Texture	
Leaf edge	
Vein patterns	

Common name ______________________

Scientific name ______________________

Location where found ______________________

Uses/role in environment ______________________

____

Chapter 7: **Classification of Living Things** 229

Observe and Analyze

1. *Students will most likely group leaves according to the data in the table.*
2. *Sample answer: size, shape, edges, veins*

Conclude

1. *Yes, most leaves will have similar characteristics such as simple or compound leaf structure, vein patterns, and so on.*
2. *a longer stem, more leaves, a newer leaf*
3. *Field guides can help scientists quickly identify leaves in their area. Tourists may also find the guides useful in observing plants that they are not familiar with and those that are native to the area.*

INVESTIGATE Further

CHALLENGE Students will devise ways to assemble their guides. They should demonstrate using the guide to identify real specimens You may wish to display the field guide and invite students to add to it.

Post-Lab Discussion

- Ask students how to create a dichotomous key using their leaves and data. *Create a series of questions with yes-or-no answers based on the characteristics of the leaves they observed. By answering the questions, the key would help identify each leaf.*
- Ask: What specific characteristics did you use to classify the leaves? *where the leaf attaches to the stem, tip shape, veining, edges*

BACK TO

the BIG idea

Have students look at the photograph on pp. 200–201. Ask them to write a short dichotomous key to separate the insects into five or six groups. *Students' keys should focus on visible characteristics that separate insects into biologically relevant groups.*

KEY CONCEPTS SUMMARY

SECTION 7.1

Ask: You are given 100 seashells to group by their relatedness. Is this task called classification or taxonomy? *classification*

SECTION 7.2

Ask: What is the binomial nomenclature for this animal? *Clemmys guttata*

Ask: At what level of classification can you distinguish this animal from a lizard? *order*

SECTION 7.3

Ask: What do Archaea and Bacteria have in common that distinguishes them from Eukarya? *single cells with no nucleus*

Review Concepts

- Big Idea Flow Chart, p. T9
- Chapter Outline, pp. T15–T16

7 Chapter Review

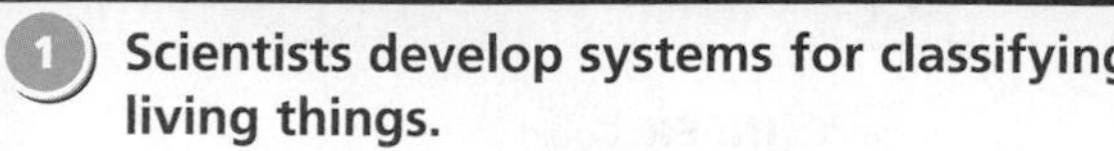

the BIG idea

Scientists have developed a system for classifying the great diversity of living things.

KEY CONCEPTS SUMMARY

1 Scientists develop systems for classifying living things.

- Living things are arranged in groups based on similarities.
- Classification is the process of arranging organisms into groups.
- Taxonomy involves classifying as well as naming species.

VOCABULARY
classification p. 204
taxonomy p. 204

2 Biologists use seven levels of classification.

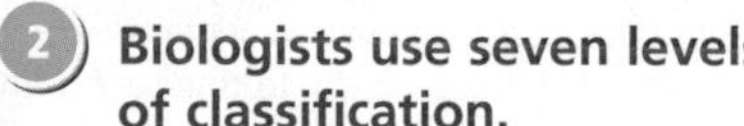

Spotted turtle
Clemmys guttata

Classification: Spotted turtle	
Kingdom	Animalia
Phylum	Chordata
Class	Reptilia
Order	Testudines
Family	Emydidae
Genus	*Clemmys*
Species	*guttata*

VOCABULARY
genus p. 212
binomial nomenclature p. 212
dichotomous key p. 216

3 Classification systems change as scientists learn more.

The most popular system of classification in use today is a three-domain system that includes six kingdoms of organisms.

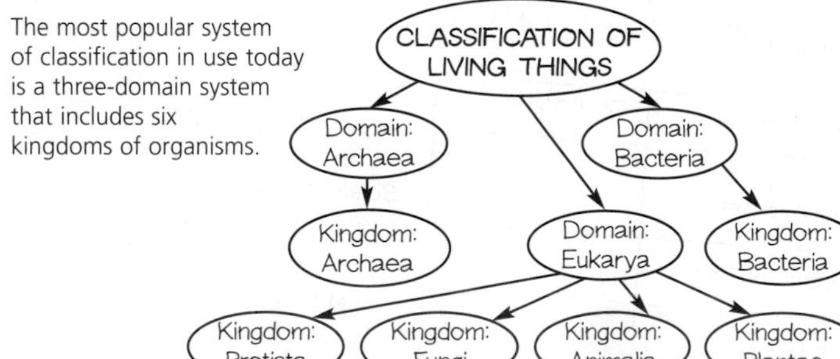

VOCABULARY
domain p. 221
Plantae p. 223
Animalia p. 223
Protista p. 223
Fungi p. 223
Archaea p. 223
Bacteria p. 223

230 Unit 2: Life Over Time

Technology Resources

Have students visit **ClassZone.com** or use the CD-ROM for a cumulative review of concepts.

CONTENT REVIEW

CONTENT REVIEW CD-ROM

Engage students in a whole-class interactive review of Key Concepts. Edit content as you wish.

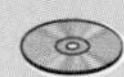
POWER PRESENTATIONS

Reviewing Vocabulary

Make a frame like the one shown for each vocabulary word listed below. Write the word in the center. Decide what information to frame it with. Use definitions, examples, descriptions, parts, or pictures.

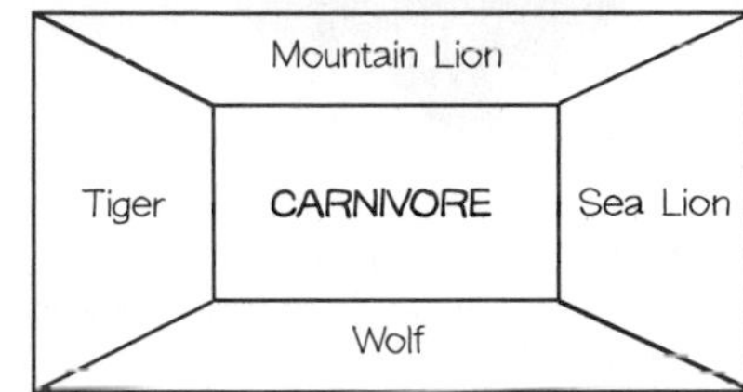

1. Plantae
2. Animalia
3. Protista
4. Fungi

Reviewing Key Concepts

Multiple Choice *Choose the letter of the best answer.*

5. The scientific process of arranging organisms into groups based on similarities is
   - **a.** observation
   - **b.** classification
   - **c.** binomial nomenclature
   - **d.** dichotomy
6. The system of naming organisms developed by Carolus Linnaeus is called
   - **a.** binomial nomenclature
   - **b.** taxonomy
   - **c.** dichotomous nomenclature
   - **d.** classification
7. Which group includes the most species?
   - **a.** kingdom
   - **b.** family
   - **c.** domain
   - **d.** phylum
8. The science of taxonomy allows scientists to
   - **a.** identify unfamiliar organisms
   - **b.** classify and name organisms
   - **c.** refer to one specific type of organism
   - **d.** determine similar traits of organisms
9. Which allows scientists to use genetic information to classify organisms?
   - **a.** physical traits
   - **b.** DNA
   - **c.** fossil evidence
   - **d.** habitats
10. A dichotomous key contains a series of questions that people use to
    - **a.** find similar organisms
    - **b.** identify organisms
    - **c.** name organisms
    - **d.** describe organisms
11. What are the names of the three domains?
    - **a.** Plantae, Animalia, Protista
    - **b.** Bacteria, Protista, Fungi
    - **c.** Bacteria, Archaea, Eukarya
    - **d.** Protista, Archaea, Eukarya
12. Which is an example of a trait?
    - **a.** bone structure
    - **b.** DNA information
    - **c.** fossil records
    - **d.** habitat
13. A group of species that have similar characteristics is called
    - **a.** an order
    - **b.** a family
    - **c.** a phylum
    - **d.** a genus
14. Which characteristic is common to animals, plants, protists, and fungi?
    - **a.** ability to make their own food
    - **b.** eukaryotic cells
    - **c.** ability to move
    - **d.** multicellular structure

Reviewing Vocabulary

Sample answers:

1. Plantae: (examples) cactus, maple, bluegrass, dandelion

2. Animalia: (descriptions) cannot make food; can move; cells have a nucleus, most are insects

3. Protista: (descriptions) mostly one-celled, seaweed, often live in water, cells have a nucleus

4. Fungi: (examples) mold, yeast, mushrooms, penicillin

Reviewing Key Concepts

5. b
6. a
7. a
8. b
9. b
10. b
11. c
12. a
13. d
14. b

(Answers to items that appear on p. 232)

Thinking Critically

15. It should refer to one specific type of organism.

16. Field guides help you to identify an organism, using pictures, descriptions, and range maps. A dichotomous key leads you to identify a species using questions.

17. Microscopes and other technology let scientists observe three fundamentally different types of cell.

ASSESSMENT RESOURCES

UNIT ASSESSMENT BOOK
- Chapter Test A, pp. 25–28
- Chapter Test B, pp. 29–32
- Chapter Test C, pp. 33–36
- Alternative Assessment, pp. 37–38

SPANISH ASSESSMENT BOOK
Spanish Chapter Test, pp. 29–32

Technology Resources

Edit test items and answer choices.

Test Generator CD-ROM

Visit **ClassZone.com** to extend test practice.

Test Practice

(Answers for items 15–17 appear on p. 231.)

Thinking Critically

18. Fossils show ancestral species that may be intermediates between existing species. They help show what species are biologically related, so they can be grouped together.
19. They can compare the DNA of vultures, falcons, and storks to see which groups are most like the American vulture.
20. Felis catus and Felis concolor; they are in the same genus.
21. The Ursus species are closely related, for they are in the same genus. Tremarctos is less closely related to any of the Ursus species than they are to each other.
22. They share characteristics that define the large group (class) but differ in characteristics that define the smaller group.
23. A phylum is more broadly described so it generally has more groups of organisms than family.
24. Read both choices at a decision point, take the branch that leads to next set of choices. Continue until key gives you organism's name.
25. Technology has shown taxonomists fundamental differences among organisms, so that they cannot be grouped with plants or animals.
26. Protista; Characteristics describe protists, but not other kingdoms.

the BIG idea

27. Answers will depend on students' original discussions.
28. Animalia: heterotroph, no cell wall, moves; Plantae: cell wall, chloroplasts, don't move; both: multicellular, cells with nucleus

UNIT PROJECTS

Students should have begun designing their models or presentations by this time. Remind them to continue researching as needed. Encourage them to try different solutions to the problems they encounter.

R Unit Projects, pp. 5–10

Short Answer *Write a short answer to each question.*

15. What are the rules for creating a scientific name for an organism?
16. How is a field guide different from a dichotomous key?
17. What types of information caused scientists to add the level of domain to the system of classification?

Thinking Critically

18. **ANALYZE** How do scientists use fossils to classify organisms?
19. **APPLY** Scientists once classified American vultures and African vultures together in the falcon family. Now, scientists know that American vultures are more closely related to storks. What type of evidence might scientists have used to come to this conclusion? Explain your answer.
20. **EVALUATE** Which two of these species are more closely related: *Felis catus, Felis concolor, Picea concolor?* How do you know?
21. **INFER** A scientist is studying the following organisms. What conclusions can you draw about the organisms based on their scientific names?
    - *Ursus americanus*
    - *Ursus arctos*
    - *Ursus maritimus*
22. **ANALYZE** Two organisms you are studying are in the same class, but in a different order. What does this information tell you about the two organisms?
23. **RANK** Which of these have more groups of organisms: phylum or family? Explain your answer.
24. **SUMMARIZE** Describe how you would use a dichotomous key to identify this leaf.

25. **SYNTHESIZE** Why was it necessary for scientists to create groups for classifying organisms other than the groups of plants and animals described by Linnaeus?
26. **CLASSIFY** Suppose you discover a new organism that is single celled, has a nucleus, lives in the water, and uses sunlight to produce its energy. In which kingdom would you classify this organism? Explain.

the BIG idea

27. **INFER** Look again at the picture on pages 200–201. Now that you have finished the chapter, how would you change or add details to your answer to the question on the photograph?
28. **PROVIDE EXAMPLES** Imagine that you are a scientist studying a variety of organisms in a South American rain forest. You have classified one organism in the kingdom Animalia and another organism in the kingdom Plantae. Give examples of the characteristics that would enable you to classify each organism in those kingdoms.

UNIT PROJECTS

Check your schedule for your unit project. How are you doing? Be sure that you've placed data or notes from your research in your project folder.

MONITOR AND RETEACH

If students have trouble with the concepts in items 18–21, have them review the chart on p. 215. Have them describe how the collection of animals changes at each level, starting at the top or the bottom. Ask for an example of what common characteristics the animals have in each level and what differences eliminate some animals at the next level.

Students may benefit from summarizing one or more sections of the chapter.

Summarizing the Chapter, pp. 127–128

Standardized Test Practice

For practice on your state test, go to . . .

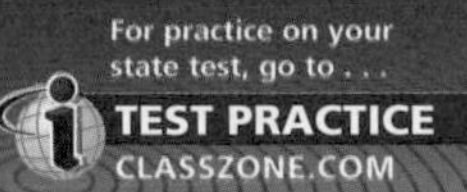

Analyzing Graphics

Choose the letter of the best response.

By following the steps in this chart, it is possible to find the type of tree to which a leaf belongs.

Step 1
1a) Leaves are needlelike..................Go to step 2
1b) Leaves are flat and scalelike.........Go to step 5
Step 2
2a) Needles are clustered...................Go to step 3
2b) Needles are not clustered..............Go to step 4
Step 3
3a) Clusters of 2–5 needles.............. Pine
3b) Clusters greater than 10.............Go to step 4
Step 4
4a) Needles soft..............................Larch
4b) Needles stiff...............................True cedar
Step 5
5a) Needles are short and sharp........Giant sequoia
5b) Some needles are not sharp..........Go to Step 6

1. Which has leaves with clusters of 2–5 needles?
a. pine tree
b. larch tree
c. true cedar tree
d. giant sequoia

2. If a tree has clusters of needles greater than 10, you would go to
a. step 1
b. step 2
c. step 3
d. step 4

3. Each step on the key compares two
a. species
b. animals
c. traits
d. trees

4. A tree with soft needles that are not clustered is most likely a
a. pine tree
b. larch tree
c. true cedar tree
d. giant sequoia

5. Which statement best describes the characteristics of a giant sequoia?
a. flat, scalelike needles that are short and sharp
b. flat, scalelike needles that are stiff
c. clustered needles that are soft
d. clustered needles that are short and sharp

Extended Response

6. A biologist has discovered and collected a number of unknown plant species from a rain-forest environment. Explain what type of evidence a biologist would rely on to determine if the plant species were new. Give specific examples of what a biologist would look for. What process would scientists go through to name the new species?

7. As you learned in the chapter, there are scientists who classify and name organisms. Explain why it is important for these taxonomists to study biological relationships. What may these relationships indicate about early life and modern life?

METACOGNITIVE ACTIVITY

Have students answer the following questions in their **Science Notebook:**

1. Why do you think it is important for you to learn about classification of organisms?
2. Which of our relatives in Eukarya would you like to learn more about?
3. Does knowing an organism's name make it seem more familiar or more strange to you? Why?

Analyzing Graphics

1. a *3. c* *5. a*
2. d *4. b*

Extended Response

6. RUBRIC

4 points for a response that describes a logical sequence to follow to classify and name a species and includes an appropriate list of characteristics to look for in a plant.

Sample answer: The biologist might use a dichotomous key to find out if the plant is new. He or she would look at leaves, fruit, and flowers to see what other plants are like it, and would try to place it in a genus. If the plant is new, a taxonomist would describe it and give it a species name.

3 points for a response that describes part of the process above and includes an appropriate list of characteristics to look for in a plant

2 points for a response that demonstrates little understanding of the process above and includes an appropriate list of characteristics to look for in a plant

1 point for a response that demonstrates no understanding of the process above and gives one or two characteristics to look for in a plant

7. RUBRIC

4 points for a response that correctly answers the question and demonstrates an understanding of biology's relation to taxonomy.

Sample answer: Taxonomists base classification on biological relatedness of organisms. The classification should reflect how organisms function, their structure, and their relationship to other species. Their place in the classification may show how species evolved.

3 points for a response that correctly answers the question and demonstrates partial understanding of biology's relation to taxonomy

2 points for a response that correctly answers the question but demonstrates little understanding of biology's relation to taxonomy

1 point for a response that does not correctly answer the question and demonstrates little understanding of biology's relation to taxonomy

FOCUS

Set Learning Goals

Students will

- Examine historical events that have contributed to our understanding of the history of life on Earth.
- Learn about some of the technology used to date and classify fossils.
- Write a proposal to fund a fossil excavation.

National Science Education Standards

A.9.a–g Understandings About Scientific Inquiry

E.6.a–c Understandings About Science and Technology

F.5.a–e, F.5.g Science and Technology in Society

G.1.a–b Science as a Human Endeavor

G.2.a Nature of Science

G.3.a–c History of Science

INSTRUCT

Point out that the top half of the timeline shows major discoveries in the history of life on Earth. The bottom half of the timeline illustrates technology and its application to the study of fossils. The gap between 1820 and 1900 represents 80 years.

Technology

REMOVING FOSSILS Discuss the low-tech approach to fossil collecting. Ask: Why do you think fossils need special care, beyond careful removal? *Small details can provide big clues to scientists. The smallest of chips or scratches might alter the evidence.* Explain to students that the same reasoning accounts for the use of low-tech hand tools and slow process for excavation.

TIMELINES in Science

LIFE Unearthed

How do scientists know about life on Earth millions of years ago? They dig, scratch, and hunt. The best clues they find are hidden in layers of rock. The rock-locked clues, called fossils, are traces or remains of living things from long ago. Some fossils show the actual bodies of organisms, while others, such as footprints, reveal behavior.

Before 1820, most fossil finds revealed the bodies of ocean life. Then large bones of lizardlike walking animals began turning up, and pictures of a new "terrible lizard," or dinosaur, took shape. Later, discoveries of tracks and nests showed behaviors such as flocking and caring for young. Even today, discoveries of "living fossils," modern relatives of prehistoric species, have offered us a rare glimpse of the activity of early life.

1824

Giant Lizards from Fragments

William Buckland describes *Megalosaurus,* a giant crocodilelike animal he studies from only a few bits of jaw, teeth, ribs, pelvis, and one leg. A year later Gideon Mantell assembles *Iguanodon,* a similar animal, from fossil bones.

EVENTS

1800 1810 1820

APPLICATIONS AND TECHNOLOGY

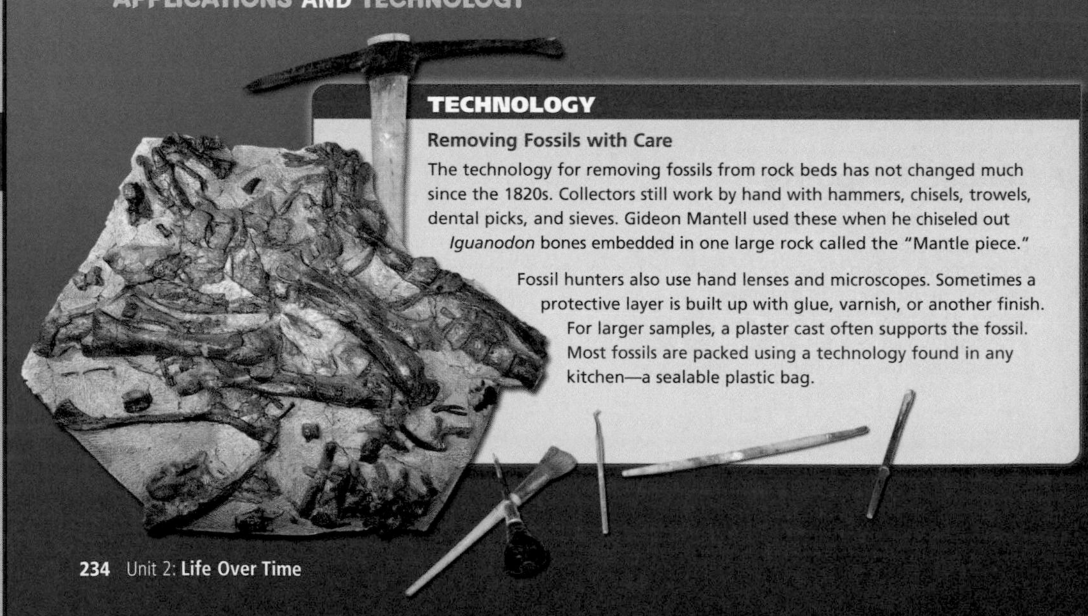

TECHNOLOGY

Removing Fossils with Care

The technology for removing fossils from rock beds has not changed much since the 1820s. Collectors still work by hand with hammers, chisels, trowels, dental picks, and sieves. Gideon Mantell used these when he chiseled out *Iguanodon* bones embedded in one large rock called the "Mantle piece."

Fossil hunters also use hand lenses and microscopes. Sometimes a protective layer is built up with glue, varnish, or another finish. For larger samples, a plaster cast often supports the fossil. Most fossils are packed using a technology found in any kitchen—a sealable plastic bag.

DIFFERENTIATE INSTRUCTION

Below Level Help students understand the timeline by having them construct a paper-clip chain, with each clip corresponding to ten years. They can tape the chain to posterboard and hang cards detailing items from the timeline suspended from the chain. They can leave gaps or fill the gaps depending on space.

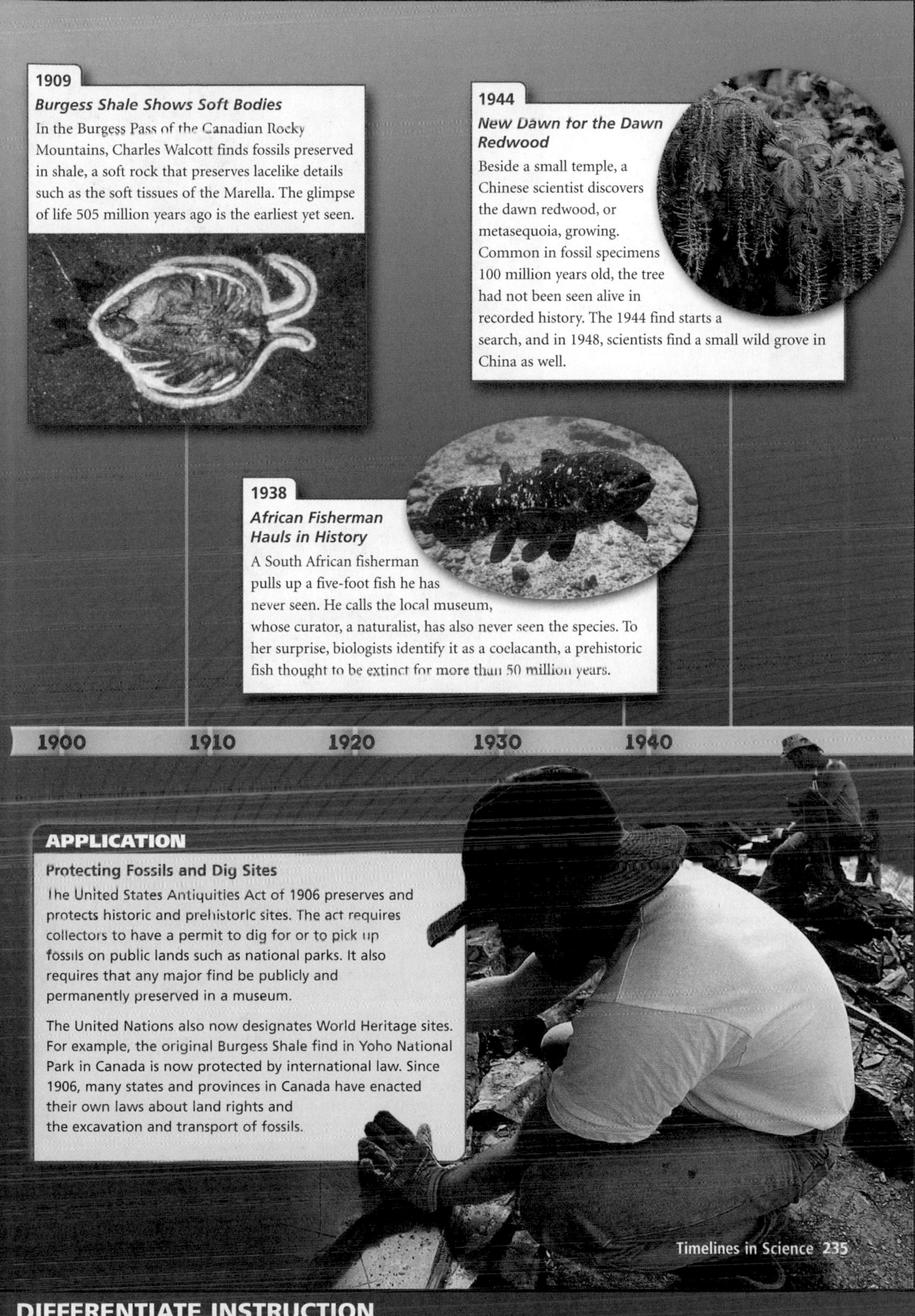

1909
Burgess Shale Shows Soft Bodies

In the Burgess Pass of the Canadian Rocky Mountains, Charles Walcott finds fossils preserved in shale, a soft rock that preserves lacelike details such as the soft tissues of the Marella. The glimpse of life 505 million years ago is the earliest yet seen.

1944
New Dawn for the Dawn Redwood

Beside a small temple, a Chinese scientist discovers the dawn redwood, or metasequoia, growing. Common in fossil specimens 100 million years old, the tree had not been seen alive in recorded history. The 1944 find starts a search, and in 1948, scientists find a small wild grove in China as well.

1938
African Fisherman Hauls in History

A South African fisherman pulls up a five-foot fish he has never seen. He calls the local museum, whose curator, a naturalist, has also never seen the species. To her surprise, biologists identify it as a coelacanth, a prehistoric fish thought to be extinct for more than 50 million years.

APPLICATION

Protecting Fossils and Dig Sites

The United States Antiquities Act of 1906 preserves and protects historic and prehistoric sites. The act requires collectors to have a permit to dig for or to pick up fossils on public lands such as national parks. It also requires that any major find be publicly and permanently preserved in a museum.

The United Nations also now designates World Heritage sites. For example, the original Burgess Shale find in Yoho National Park in Canada is now protected by international law. Since 1906, many states and provinces in Canada have enacted their own laws about land rights and the excavation and transport of fossils.

Scientific Process

When studying either living things or fossils, preserving the evidence is crucial. Coelacanths average five feet in length, and when the first one was caught in 1938, the available refrigerator was too small to hold it. A local taxidermist preserved the fish as much as possible, but its internal organs were destroyed. The fish could not be closely studied until another one was caught, 14 years later.

Application

1944 The dawn redwood has become a very popular tree, with millions planted in China each year. Many of the trees planted in 1948 are now over a meter in diameter. Due to this high growth rate, the species may become useful for timber production.

Application

PROTECTING FOSSILS China is a rich source of fossils, particularly of birds and dinosaur eggs. All fossils are the property of the Chinese government but many fossils are sold illegally. Many farmers in China are poor, and they can sell high-quality fossils for high prices to private collectors who subvert the law. Chinese law is still evolving to deal with this problem.

DIFFERENTIATE INSTRUCTION

Advanced Have students research the story behind the discovery of the coelacanth. They should start with writing a question each for the five words *Who, How, Where, When, What*. Then challenge them to create a dramatic news story reporting the event the day it happened.

Scientific Process

Johanson's discoveries in Ethiopia provoked great controversy in the scientific world, especially after he concluded that Lucy represented a new species, *Australopithecus afarensis*. The conflict raged for ten years, because Ethiopia was so politically turbulent that Johanson could not return to search for more evidence. He was finally able to return in 1990, and in 1992 found a large portion of a skull that silenced most of his critics.

Technology

AGE OF FOSSILS Radiometric dating relies on a constant rate of radioactive decay. Volcanic materials are dated by studying the breakdown of radioactive potassium-40 isotope into an inert gas, argon-40. When a volcano erupts, it expels its argon gas. Potassium-40, which naturally occurs in lava, breaks down over time into argon-40. Using the amount of argon found in lava and the rate at which potassium-40 decays into argon-40, scientists can determine the age of the lava.

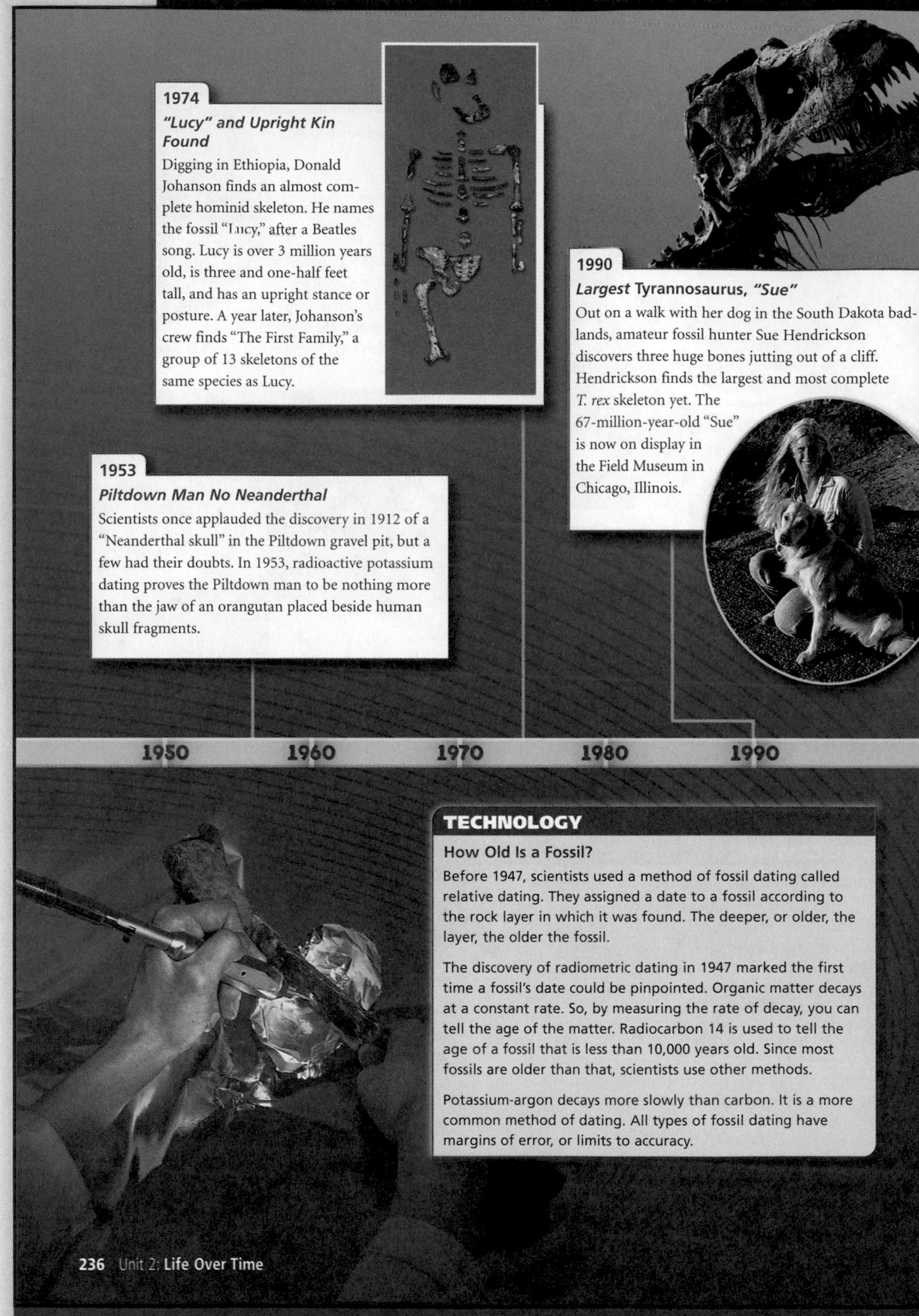

DIFFERENTIATE INSTRUCTION

Below Level Use plaster of Paris or modeling clay to have students construct their own models of fossils. Have each student create a specimen artifact giving evidence of a living thing such as a leaf, seashell, insect, or dried fish. Students should keep the source a secret. Assign students numbers to scratch on the underside of the specimen. Lay all the specimens out and have students try to identify what they see.

1993

Oldest Fossils Are Too Small to See

Fossils discovered up to this point date back about 550 million years, to the dawn of the Cambrian Period. J. William Schopf identifies fossils of microorganisms scientifically dated to 3.4 billion years ago. This startling find near Australia's Marble Bar opens up a vast period of time and once again reshapes theories about life's beginnings.

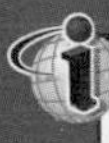

RESOURCE CENTER
CLASSZONE.COM
Discover more about the latest fossil and living-fossil finds.

2000

TECHNOLOGY

Fossil Classification and DNA

There are many ways to classify fossils. Scientists look at bone structure, body posture, evidence of behavior, and environment. Microscopes are used to identify organisms too small for the eye to see. Study of DNA molecules helps to identify species when soft tissues remain intact, such as in fossils formed in amber or crystallized tree sap. In 1985, polymerase chain reaction (PCR) became the simplest method to study the DNA extracted from fossils. In PCR, parts of DNA can be copied billions of times in a few hours.

INTO THE FUTURE

Technology is sure to play a role in future fossil finds. Scientists can communicate via laptop computers and satellites, which allow the public to follow excavations as they occur.

Computer modeling helps scientists determine what incomplete skeletons looked like. It also helps them determine how dinosaurs and other living things once moved. Fossil finds can be combined with digitized information about modern living organisms and about environmental conditions. The model can test hypotheses or even help to formulate them.

Another area of technology that may become increasingly applied to fossils is DNA testing to identify and help date fossils. This is more complicated in fossilized bone, as the genetic material can be fragmented. But with time, scientists may discover new techniques to extract better genetic information. DNA is also the basis for cloning, which as yet can only be applied to living organisms. Perhaps in the future it can be applied to preserved remains.

ACTIVITIES

Writing About Science: Film Script

Write your own version of the story of life on Earth. Include drawings, photographs, or video clips to illustrate your story.

Reliving History

Think about the equipment archaeologists and paleontologists use on excavations. Think about their goals. Write a proposal to a local university or museum asking them to fund your excavation.

DIFFERENTIATE INSTRUCTION

Advanced Students could request copies of actual grant proposals from a local university or library to see what types of information need to be included. They might also form a review board to judge the proposals they wrote and decide which should get funding.

Scientific Process

Recent experiments have produced another interpretation of the "oldest fossils." Tell students that these fossil-like structures could have formed inorganically. Silica-coated carbonate crystals can form long filaments via self-assembly in the right circumstances. They can produce structures that closely resemble bacterial fossils. Ask: Do you think it will be possible to confirm either hypothesis? Why? *Possible answer: Yes, scientists will eventually develop technology that can distinguish organically produced structures from inorganic ones.*

INTO THE FUTURE

Ask: What would you like to know about life in the past? Have students speculate on how the information could help them in their lives, or help humankind in general. A movie with prehistoric humans and animals at its center could be used to spark discussion.

ACTIVITIES

Writing About Science: Film Script

Suggest that students write a script for a travelogue that tells about finding living fossils such as cockroaches, the armadillo, garfish, crocodiles, and cycads. Their scripts should entertain as well as inform.

Reliving History

Remind students that proposals usually include an itemized budget. The proposal must justify the expenditure. Proposals should include detailed information on why the dig is important.

Technology Resources

Students can visit **ClassZone.com** for current news on fossil hunting.

CHAPTER

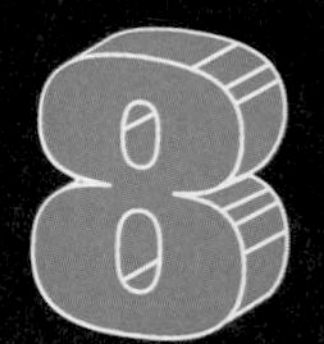

Population Dynamics

Life Science
UNIFYING PRINCIPLES

PRINCIPLE 1
All living things share common characteristics.

PRINCIPLE 2
All living things share common needs.

PRINCIPLE 3
Living things meet their needs through interactions with the environment.

PRINCIPLE 4
The types and numbers of living things change over time.

Unit 2: Life Over Time
BIG IDEAS

CHAPTER 6
The History of Life on Earth
Living things, like Earth itself, change over time.

CHAPTER 7
Classification of Living Things
Scientists have developed a system for classifying the great diversity of living things.

CHAPTER 8
Population Dynamics
Populations are shaped by interactions between organisms and the environment.

CHAPTER 8
KEY CONCEPTS

SECTION 1

Populations have many characteristics.

1. Populations go through three stages.
2. Four characteristics define a population.
3. Scientists can predict population change.

SECTION 2

Populations respond to pressures.

1. Population growth is limited.
2. Populations have distinct reproductive survival strategies.

SECTION 3

Human populations have unique responses to change.

1. Human populations differ from populations of other species.
2. Human populations are growing.
3. Human population growth affects the environment.

The Big Idea Flow Chart is available on p. T17 in the **UNIT TRANSPARENCY BOOK.**

Previewing Content

SECTION

Populations have many characteristics. pp. 241–249

1. Populations go through three stages.

- **Population dynamics** is the study of why populations change and what causes them to change.
- All populations go through stages of growth, stability, and decline and follow two patterns of growth: rapid growth and gradual growth. The maximum number of individuals an area can support is its **carrying capacity.**

2. Four characteristics define a population.

- Population size is the number of individuals in a population at a given time. Population sizes vary from one habitat to another and within single habitats.
- **Population density** is a measure of the number of individuals in a certain space at a particular time. Population densities may vary over a population range.
- Population spacing describes how individuals in a population arrange themselves. Three patterns of spacing include clumping, uniform, and random.
- Age structure divides a population into groups based on age: pre-reproductive, reproductive, and post-reproductive.

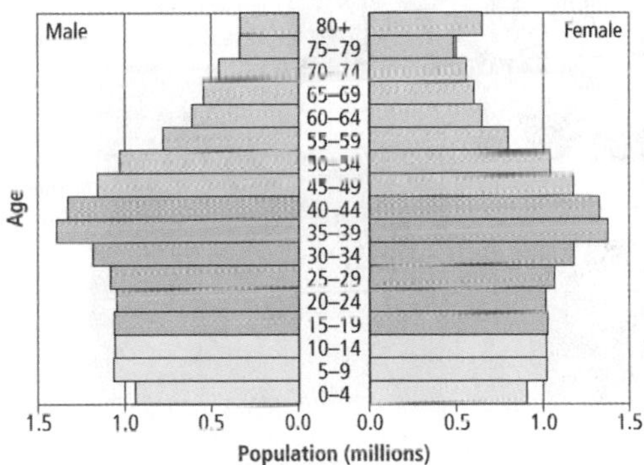

3. Scientists can predict population change.
Scientists use the four factors of a population to describe a population and predict how it may change.

SECTION

Populations respond to pressures. pp. 250–257

1. Population growth is limited.

- Birth and **immigration** lead to population growth while death and **emigration** lead to population decline.
- **Limiting factors** prevent the continued growth of a population in an ecosystem.
- Density-dependent limiting factors include competition, disease, parasitism, and predation.
- Density-independent limiting factors include storms, floods, droughts, and fires. Density-independent factors can affect populations with both high and low densities.

2. Populations have distinct reproductive strategies.

- **Opportunists** have adaptations that allow them to reproduce rapidly if their populations fall below carrying capacity.
- **Competitors** have adaptations that allow them to remain at carrying capacity for sustained periods. Competitors differ from opportunists in that they generally live longer and have fewer offspring.

Wolves, elephants, and other large mammals are generally competitors in terms of reproductive strategy.

Common Misconceptions

MISCONCEPTION DATABASE
CLASSZONE.COM Background on student misconceptions

NEEDS OF POPULATIONS Many students in middle school have trouble thinking of organisms in terms of populations. They more easily think of the needs of individual organisms rather than the needs of populations, and will substitute or confuse the two concepts. The study of populations puts organisms in the larger context of living systems. It is often necessary to expand student conceptions to this bigger picture.

This misconception is addressed on p. 247

Previewing Content

SECTION

Human populations have unique responses to change. pp. 258–267

1. Human populations differ from populations of other species.
- Humans are able to shape their environment through habitat expansion and technology.
- Habitat expansion allows humans to live comfortably in extreme environments by controlling indoor temperatures.
- Technology has increased life expectancy through improved sanitation and medicine.

2. Human populations are growing.
- Human population has increased rapidly in the past 300 years due to availability of resources, lack of predation, and survival of offspring to reproductive age.
- Population projections forecast how a population will change based on present size and age structure.
- Other factors, such as life expectancy, health, and the age of individuals that are having children also affect the growth of a population.

3. Human population growth affects the environment.
- As the human population grows, it has contributed to the decline and extinction of other populations through introduction of new species, overfishing, and **pollution.**
- New species introduced in an environment can upset the balance of nature in that environment by competing with native species for food and space.
- Pollution can add harmful substances to the environment such as chemical dumping, pesticides, and animal wastes.
- Overfishing depletes fish populations and may prevent them from reproducing to maintain their numbers.

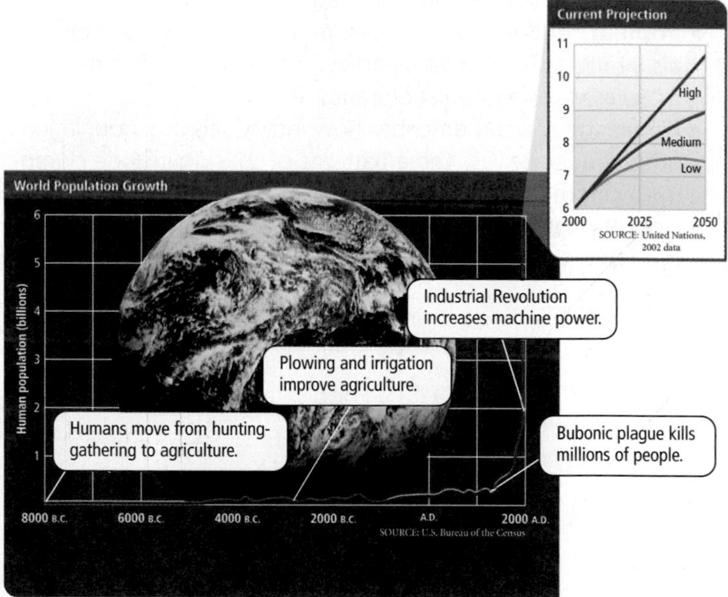

Common Misconceptions

MISCONCEPTION DATABASE
CLASSZONE.COM Background on student misconceptions

HUMAN POPULATION EFFECTS Many students seem unable to think of organisms and their environments without human involvement. Younger students often think that all organisms are fed or cared for by humans. Older elementary school and middle school students may hold the reverse misconception—that populations and ecosystems are unaffected by much of human activity.

 This misconception is addressed on p. 263.

POLLUTION Some younger students regard pollution as something that is sensed by people and affects people and other animals. They do not consider harm to plants as an environmental problem. Other pollution misconceptions include:
- Anything natural is not pollution.
- Biodegradable materials are not pollution.
- Solid waste in dumps is safe.
- The human race is indestructible as a species.

TE This misconception is addressed on p. 264.

Previewing Labs

Lab Generator CD-ROM
Edit these Pupil Edition labs and generate alternative labs.

EXPLORE the BIG idea

How Does Population Grow? p. 239 Students use a bucket and water to model the ratio of births and deaths in human population.	**TIME** 10 minutes **MATERIALS** bucket, water, one-cup measure
How Do Populations Differ? p. 239 Students model the effects of chance events on populations that vary in size.	**TIME** 10 minutes **MATERIALS** 40 marbles, 2 bowls
Internet Activity: Population Dynamics, p. 239 Students study the effects on a population of changing a factor describing that population.	**TIME** 20 minutes **MATERIALS** computer with Internet access

SECTION 2

EXPLORE Population Density, p. 250 Students observe student populations at different school locations to understand that population density varies.	**TIME** 15 minutes **MATERIALS** stopwatch, notebook
INVESTIGATE Limiting Factors, p. 254 Students design an experiment to test limiting factors on a plant population.	**TIME** 20 minutes **MATERIALS** 6 paper cups, potting soil, bean seeds, water

SECTION 3

EXPLORE Population Change, p. 258 Students draw line graphs to predict human population growth.	**TIME** 15 minutes **MATERIALS** graph paper, colored pencils
INVESTIGATE Population, p. 262 Students plot line graphs to investigate population growth in their area.	**TIME** 30 minutes **MATERIALS** graph paper, census data, 2 colored pencils
CHAPTER INVESTIGATION **Sustainable Resource Management,** pp. 266–267 Students model the population of trees in a forest and simulate the harvesting of these trees.	**TIME** 40 minutes **MATERIALS** coffee can with 120 craft sticks, bundle of 32 craft sticks, stopwatch or watch with second hand

R **Additional INVESTIGATION,** Introduced Species and Population Dynamics, A, B, & C, pp. 177–185; Teacher Instructions, pp. 188–189

Previewing Chapter Resources

CHAPTER 8 Population Dynamics

INTEGRATED TECHNOLOGY

CLASSZONE.COM
- eEdition Plus
- EasyPlanner Plus
- Misconception Database
- Content Review
- Test Practice
- Visualization
- Resource Centers
- Internet Activity
- Math Tutorial

SCILINKS.ORG
SCiLINKS

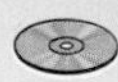
CD-ROMS
- eEdition
- EasyPlanner
- Power Presentations
- Content Review
- Lab Generator
- Test Generator

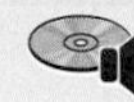
AUDIO CDS
- Audio Readings
- Audio Readings in Spanish

LABS AND ACTIVITIES

EXPLORE the Big Idea, p. 239
- How Does Population Grow?
- How Do Populations Differ?
- Internet Activity: Population Dynamics

UNIT RESOURCE BOOK
Unit Projects, pp. 5–10

Lab Generator CD-ROM
Generate customized labs.

SECTION 1 Populations have many characteristics.

pp. 241–249

Time: 2 periods (1 block)

 Lesson Plan, pp. 129–130

INTEGRATED TECHNOLOGY

- **MATH TUTORIAL**
- **VISUALIZATION,** Effects of Environmental Change

UNIT TRANSPARENCY BOOK
- Big Idea Flow Chart, p. T17
- Daily Vocabulary Scaffolding, p. T18
- Note-Taking Model, p. T19
- 3-Minute Warm-Up, p. T20
- "Population Spacing" Visual, p. T22

LABS AND ACTIVITIES

Math in Science, p. 242

UNIT RESOURCE BOOK
- Math Support, p. 166
- Math Practice, p. 167

SECTION 2 Populations respond to pressures.

pp. 250–257

Time: 2 periods (1 block)

 Lesson Plan, pp. 139–140

INTEGRATED TECHNOLOGY

UNIT TRANSPARENCY BOOK
- Daily Vocabulary Scaffolding, p. T18
- 3-Minute Warm-Up, p. T20

LABS AND ACTIVITIES

- EXPLORE Population Density, p. 250
- INVESTIGATE Limiting Factors, p. 254
- Science on the Job, p. 257

UNIT RESOURCE BOOK
Datasheet, Limiting Factors, p. 148

SECTION 3 Human populations have unique responses to change.

pp. 258–267

Time: 4 periods (2 blocks)

Lesson Plan, pp. 150–151

INTEGRATED TECHNOLOGY

RESOURCE CENTERS, Worldwide Population Growth, Introduced Species in United States

UNIT TRANSPARENCY BOOK
- Big Idea Flow Chart, p. T17
- Daily Vocabulary Scaffolding, p. T18
- 3-Minute Warm-Up, p. T21
- Chapter Outline, pp. T23–T24

LABS AND ACTIVITIES

- EXPLORE Population Change, p. 258
- INVESTIGATE Population, p. 262
- CHAPTER INVESTIGATION, Sustainable Resource Management, pp. 266–267

UNIT RESOURCE BOOK
- Datasheet, Population, p. 159
- CHAPTER INVESTIGATION Sustainable Resource Management, A, B, & C, pp. 168–176
- Additional INVESTIGATION, Introduced Species and Population Dynamics, A, B, & C, pp. 177–185

KEY TO ICONS  CD/CD-ROM  Teacher Edition UNIT TRANSPARENCY BOOK 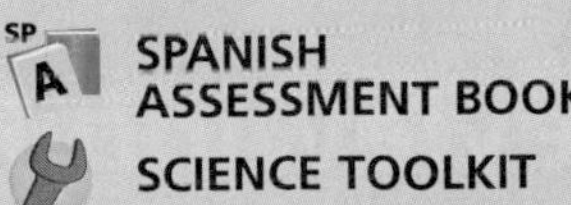 SPANISH ASSESSMENT BOOK

 INTERNET 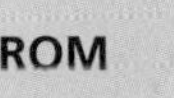 Pupil Edition  UNIT RESOURCE BOOK  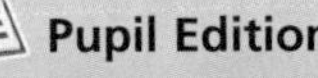  UNIT ASSESSMENT BOOK SCIENCE TOOLKIT

READING AND REINFORCEMENT	ASSESSMENT	STANDARDS
 • Magnet Word, B24–25 • Choose Your Own Strategy, C35–44 • Daily Vocabulary Scaffolding, H1–8  **UNIT RESOURCE BOOK** • Vocabulary Practice, pp. 163–164 • Decoding Support, p. 165 • Summarizing the Chapter, pp. 186–187  **Audio Readings CD** Listen to Pupil Edition.  **Audio Readings in Spanish CD** Listen to Pupil Edition in Spanish.	 • Chapter Review, pp. 269–270 • Standardized Test Practice, p. 271  **UNIT ASSESSMENT BOOK** • Diagnostic Test, pp. 39–40 • Chapter Test, A, B, & C, pp. 44–55 • Alternative Assessment, pp. 56–57 • Unit Test, A, B, & C, pp. 58–69  • Spanish Chapter Test, pp. 29–32 • Spanish Unit Test, pp. 37–40  **Test Generator CD-ROM** Generate customized tests.  **Lab Generator CD-ROM** Rubrics for Labs	National Standards A.1–8, A.9.a–c, A.9.e–g, C.4.a, C.4.d, F.2.a–b, G.1.b See p. 238 for the standards.
 **UNIT RESOURCE BOOK** • Reading Study Guide, A & B, pp. 131–134 • Spanish Reading Study Guide, pp. 135–136 • Challenge and Extension, p. 137 • Reinforcing Key Concepts, p. 138 • Challenge Reading, pp. 161–162	Ongoing Assessment, pp. 241–243, 245, 247–248 Section 8.1 Review, p. 248 **UNIT ASSESSMENT BOOK** Section 8.1 Quiz, p. 41	National Standards A.2.8, A.9.c, C.4.a, C.4.d, F.2.a–b, G.1.b
 **UNIT RESOURCE BOOK** • Reading Study Guide, A & B, pp. 141–144 • Spanish Reading Study Guide, pp. 145–146 • Challenge and Extension, p. 147 • Reinforcing Key Concepts, p. 149	 Ongoing Assessment, pp. 251–254, 256  Section 8.2 Review, p. 256 **UNIT ASSESSMENT BOOK** Section 8.2 Quiz, p. 42	National Standards A.2–7, A.9.a–b, A.9.e–f, C.4.a, C.4.d, F.2.a–b, G.1.b
 **UNIT RESOURCE BOOK** • Reading Study Guide, A & B, pp. 152–155 • Spanish Reading Study Guide, pp. 156–157 • Challenge and Extension, p. 158 • Reinforcing Key Concepts, p. 160	 Ongoing Assessment, pp. 259–261, 265  Section 8.3 Review, p. 265  **UNIT ASSESSMENT BOOK** Section 8.3 Quiz, p. 43	National Standards A.1–8, A.9.a–c, A.9.e–g, C.4.a, C.4.d, F.2.a–b, G.1.b

Previewing Resources for Differentiated Instruction

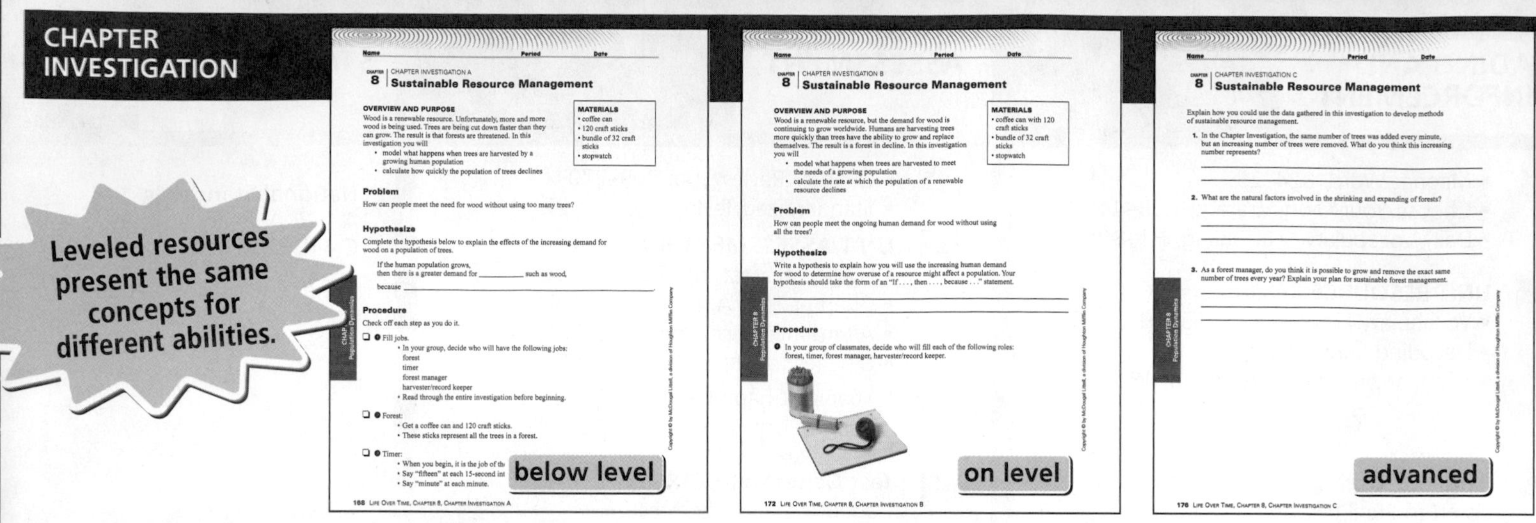

UNIT RESOURCE BOOK, pp. 168–171

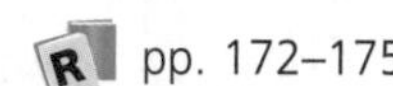

pp. 172–175

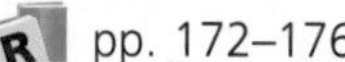

pp. 172–176

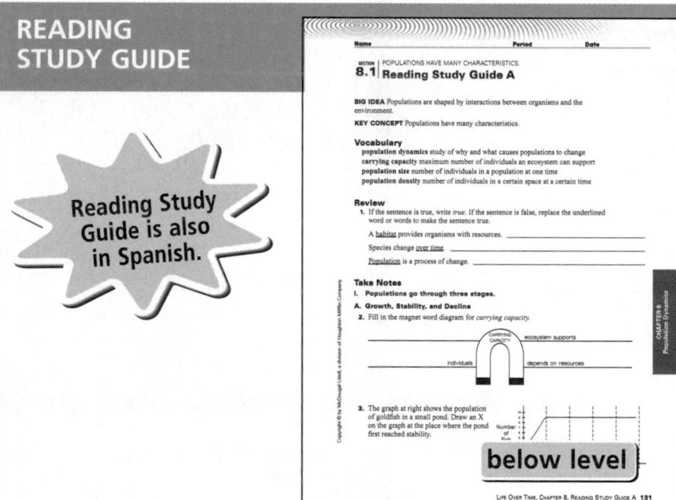

UNIT RESOURCE BOOK, pp. 131–132

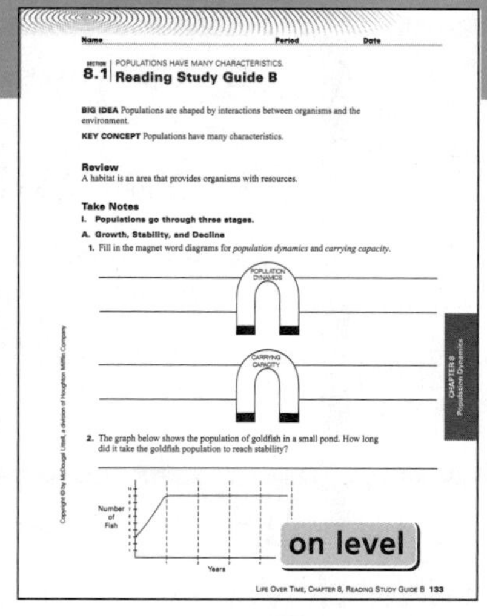

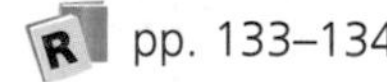

pp. 133–134

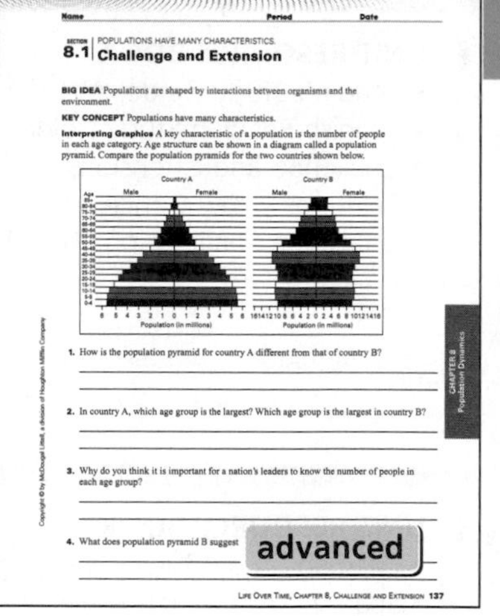

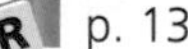

p. 137

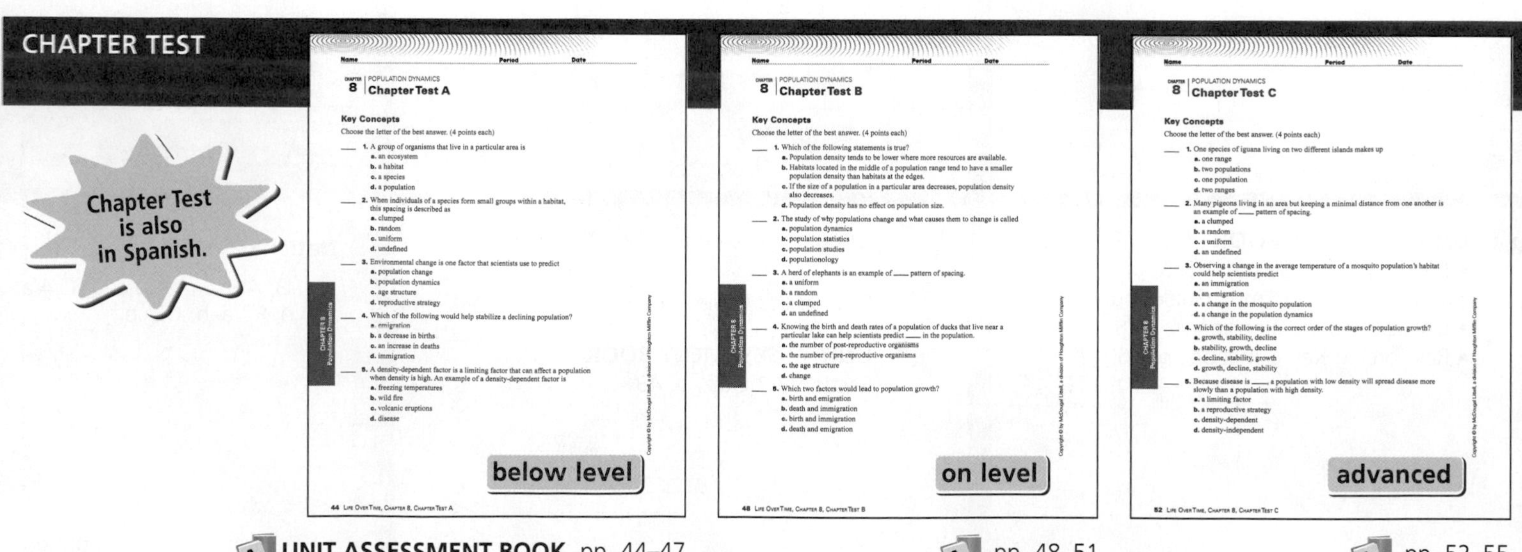

UNIT ASSESSMENT BOOK, pp. 44–47 pp. 48–51 pp. 52–55

TECHNOLOGY

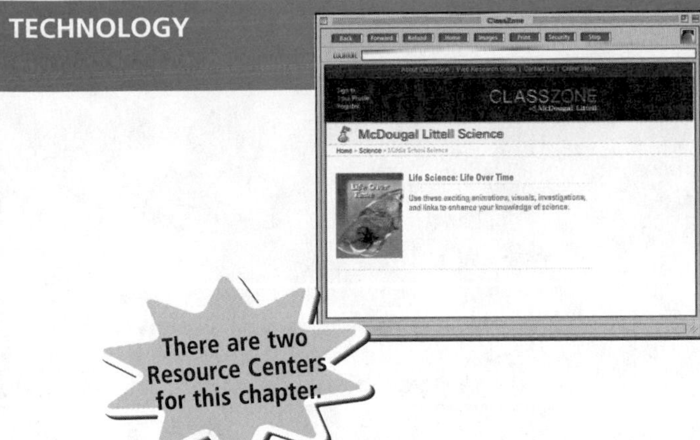

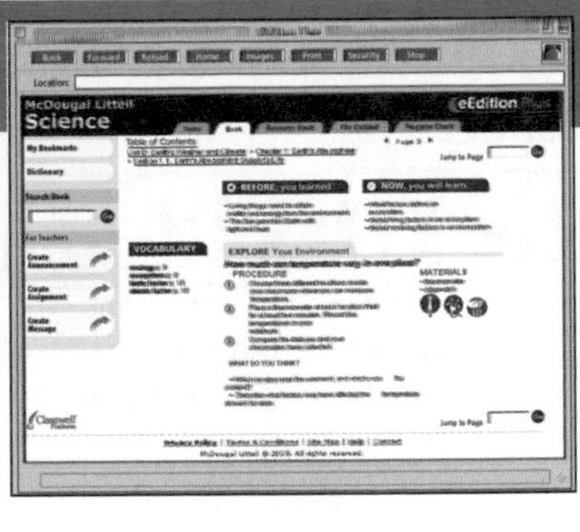

VISUAL CONTENT

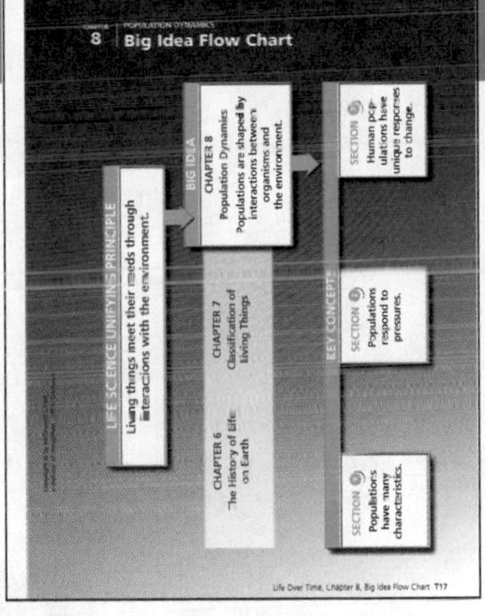

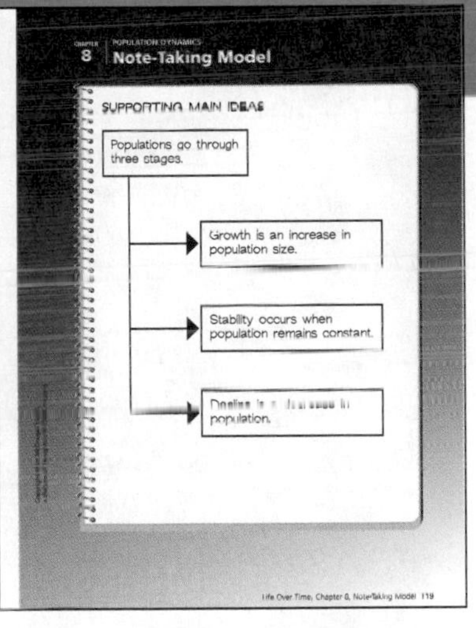

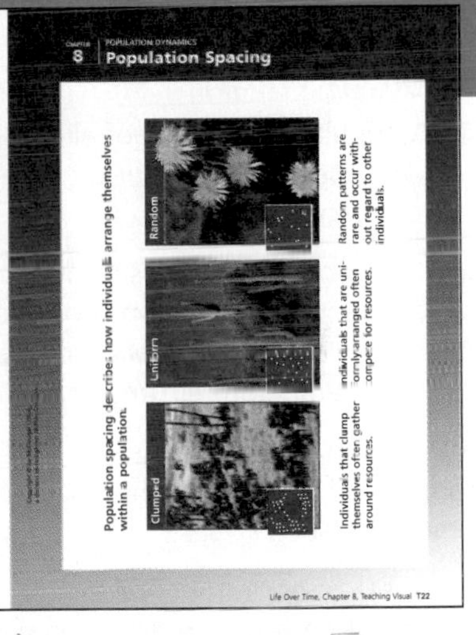

UNIT TRANSPARENCY BOOK, p. T17

p. T19

p. T22

MORE SUPPORT

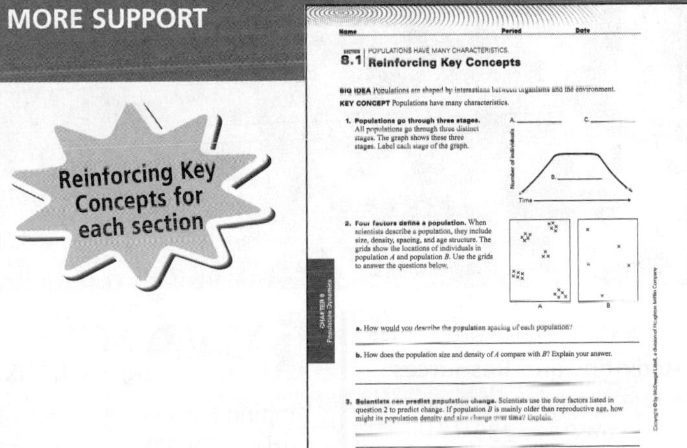

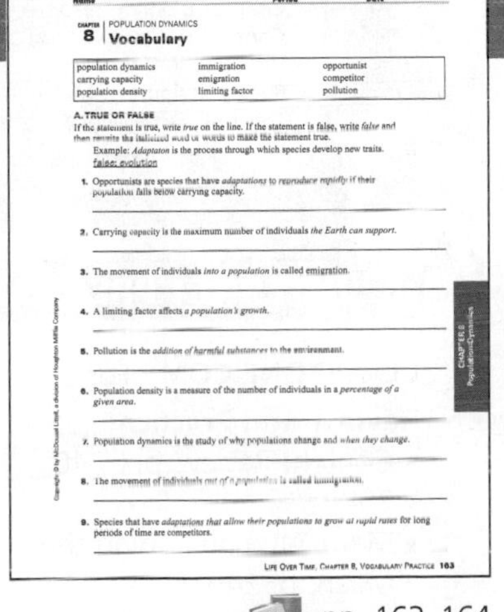

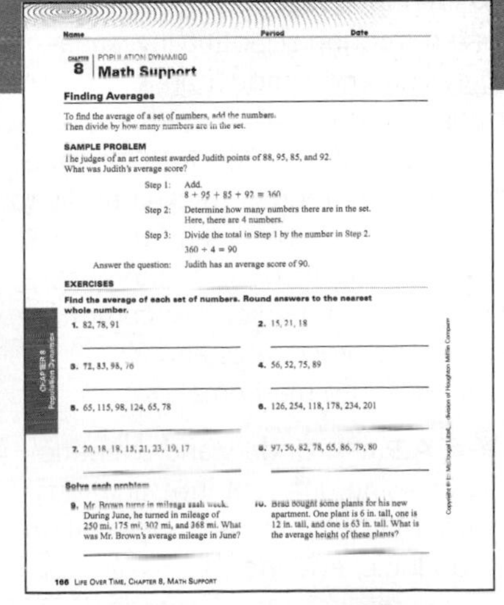

UNIT RESOURCE BOOK, p. 138

pp. 163–164

p. 166

CHAPTER 8 Population Dynamics

INTRODUCE

the BIG idea

Have students look at the satellite image. Discuss how the question in the box links to the Big Idea:

- Ask: What evidence of human populations do you see in the image? plant populations?
- Brainstorm a class list of statements about human population.

National Science Education Standards

Content

C.4.a A population consists of all individuals of a species that occur together at a given place and time.

C.4.d The number of organisms an ecosystem can support depends on the resources available and factors such as light, water, temperatures, and soil.

F.2.a When an area becomes overpopulated, the environment becomes degraded.

F.2.b Causes of environmental degradation and resource depletion vary.

Process

A.1–8 Identify questions that can be answered through scientific investigations; design and conduct an investigation; use tools to gather and interpret data; use evidence to describe, predict, explain, model; think critically to make relationships between evidence and explanation; recognize different explanations and predictions; communicate scientific procedures and explanations; use mathematics.

A.9.a–c, A.9.e–g Understand scientific inquiry by using different investigations, methods, mathematics, and explanations based on logic, evidence, and skepticism. Data often results in new investigations.

G.1.b Science requires different abilities.

CHAPTER

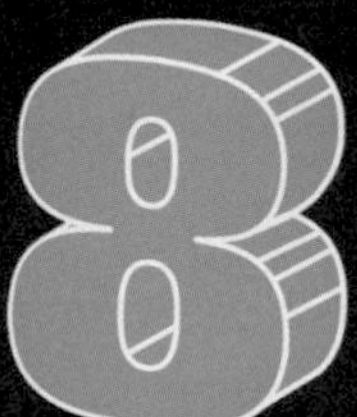

Population Dynamics

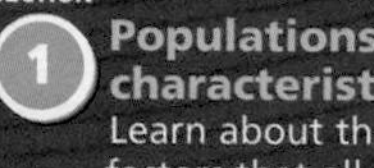

the BIG idea

Populations are shaped by interactions between organisms and the environment.

Key Concepts

SECTION 1
Populations have many characteristics.
Learn about the stages and factors that all populations have in common.

SECTION 2
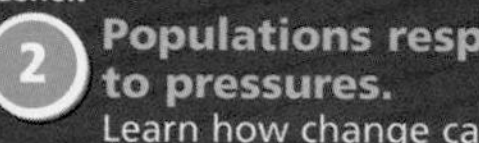
Populations respond to pressures.
Learn how change can affect populations.

SECTION 3

Human populations have unique responses to change.
Learn how the responses of human populations are different from responses of other populations.

Internet Preview

CLASSZONE.COM

Chapter 8 online resources: Content Review, Visualization, three Resource Centers, Math Tutorial, Test Practice

This image was created by combining satellite shots of parts of Earth. What does it suggest about Earth's populations?

INTERNET PREVIEW

CLASSZONE.COM For student use with the following pages:

Review and Practice
- Content Review, pp. 240, 268
- Math Tutorial: Finding the Mean, p. 249
- Test Practice, p. 271

Activities and Resources
- Internet Activity: Population Dynamics, p. 239
- Visualization: Environmental Change, p. 248
- Resource Centers: Population Growth, p. 261; Introduced Species, p. 263

Limiting Factors
Code: MDL038

EXPLORE the BIG idea

How Does Population Grow?

For every three human births there is one death. Use a bucket and water to represent the human population. For every 3 cups of water you add to the bucket, take away one cup.

Observe and Think How did the water level rise—quickly, slowly, or steadily?

How Do Populations Differ?

Put about 40 marbles in a bowl. Remove any 10 marbles from the bowl and put them in another dish. Each dish of marbles represents a population.

Observe and Think How would a chance event such as a fire affect these two populations differently?

Internet Activity: Population Dynamics

Go to ClassZone.com to learn more about the factors that describe a population. Find out how change in each of the factors can affect the population.

Observe and Think How would a change in one factor affect the dynamics of a population?

NSTA scilinks.org SCILINKS

Limiting Factors Code: MDL038

EXPLORE the BIG idea

These inquiry-based activities are appropriate for use at home or as a supplement to classroom instruction.

How Does Population Grow?

PURPOSE To model the ratio of births and deaths in human population.

TIP *10 min.* Have students predict what they think will happen to the water level in the bucket.

Answer: The water in the bucket will rise at a steady rate until the bucket overflows. If a population continues to grow at an unchecked rate, at some point, there will no longer be room in the environment for the whole population.

REVISIT after p. 242.

How Do Populations Differ?

PURPOSE To look at how limiting factors affect different sized populations.

TIP *10 min.* Have students describe each "population" in terms of size and density.

Answer: The greater the population size, the greater chance of its survival.

REVISIT after p. 252.

Internet Activity: Population Dynamics

PURPOSE To explore factors that affect population dynamics.

TIP *20 min.* Students can work in pairs to share ideas and present them to the class.

Answer: Change depends on the factor. The dynamics will not necessarily be drastic, but they will shift.

REVISIT after p. 260.

TEACHING WITH TECHNOLOGY

Digital Cameras Students can use digital cameras to photograph the progress of the bean plants each day in the Investigation on p. 254. A sequence of photographs will help them analyze the results.

Graphing Software Have students use graphing software to set up their graph while doing the Investigation on p. 262.

PREPARE

CONCEPT REVIEW

Activate Prior Knowledge

- Ask students to describe factors that enable living things to change over time. *genetic variation and adaptation*
- Have students give examples of what might cause a species to become extinct. *geologic changes such as those in temperature and light, lack of food, predation*

TAKING NOTES

Choose Your Own Strategy

Encourage students to start by discussing which note-taking strategies have helped them the most in earlier chapters. Then have them use the strategy which they find most comfortable, familiar, and useful. Alternatively, you might challenge some students to try a method new to them after listening to opinions of their classmates.

Vocabulary Strategy

Students can include as many details as they wish in a magnet word diagram. Words and phrases, descriptions, and definitions that are associated with the topic are useful in building understanding.

Vocabulary and Note-Taking Resources

- Vocabulary Practice, pp. 163–164
- Decoding Support, p. 165

- Daily Vocabulary Scaffolding, p. T18
- Note-Taking Model, p. T19

- Magnet Word, B24–25
- Choose Your Own Strategy, C35–44
- Daily Vocabulary Scaffolding, H1–8

CHAPTER 8

Getting Ready to Learn

CONCEPT REVIEW

- Living things change over time.
- Species adapt to their environment or become extinct.

VOCABULARY REVIEW

See Glossary for definition.

species

CONTENT REVIEW
CLASSZONE.COM
Review concepts and vocabulary.

TAKING NOTES

CHOOSE YOUR OWN STRATEGY

Take notes using one or more strategies from earlier chapters—**main idea and details** or **supporting main ideas.** You can also use other note-taking strategies that you might already know.

VOCABULARY STRATEGY

Think about a vocabulary term as a **magnet word** diagram. Write the other terms or ideas related to that term around it.

See the Note-Taking Handbook on pages R45–R51.

SCIENCE NOTEBOOK

CHECK READINESS

Administer the Diagnostic Test to determine students' readiness for new science content and their mastery of requisite math skills.

 Diagnostic Test, pp. 39–40

Technology Resources

Students needing content and math skills should visit **ClassZone.com**.

- CONTENT REVIEW
- MATH TUTORIAL

 CONTENT REVIEW CD-ROM

KEY CONCEPT

Populations have many characteristics.

BEFORE, you learned
- Species change over time
- Evolution is a process of change
- A habitat is an area that provides organisms with resources

NOW, you will learn
- About stages in population dynamics
- About variables that define a population
- About changes that affect populations

VOCABULARY

population dynamics p. 241
carrying capacity p. 242
population size p. 244
population density p. 245

THINK ABOUT

How fast can a population grow?

How big can a population grow? Suppose you started with a pair of fruit flies. That single pair can produce 200 eggs. In three weeks, each pair from that batch could produce 200 flies of its own—producing up to 20,000 flies. Assume all eggs hatch—an event highly unlikely in the real world. After three weeks, 2 million fruit flies would be buzzing around the area. After just 17 generations, given ideal conditions (for the fruit fly, that is), the mass of fruit flies would exceed the mass of planet Earth.

Populations go through three stages.

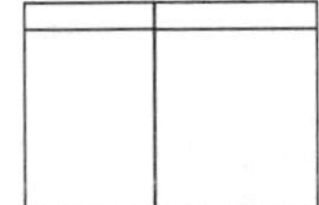

CHOOSE YOUR OWN STRATEGY
Begin taking notes on the three stages of populations. Use a strategy from an earlier chapter or one that you already know.

Look closely at the fruit flies above. As a group of the same species living together in a particular area, they represent a population. The particular area in which a scientist studies a population may be as large as a mountain range or as small as a puddle. Scientists study how populations of organisms change as they interact with each other and the environment. Over time, the number of individuals in a population changes by increasing or decreasing. **Population dynamics** is the study of why populations change and what causes them to change. In this chapter you will learn about some of the important observations scientists have made about populations.

CHECK YOUR READING What is population dynamics?

RESOURCES FOR DIFFERENTIATED INSTRUCTION

Below Level
UNIT RESOURCE BOOK
- Reading Study Guide A, pp. 131–132
- Decoding Support, p. 165

AUDIO CDS

Advanced
UNIT RESOURCE BOOK
- Challenge and Extension, p. 137
- Challenge Reading, pp. 161–162

English Learners
UNIT RESOURCE BOOK
Spanish Reading Study Guide, pp. 135–136

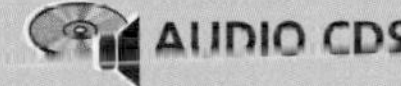

- Audio Readings in Spanish
- Audio Readings (English)

8.1 FOCUS

Set Learning Goals

Students will
- Understand the stages of population dynamics.
- Describe the variables that define a population.
- Explain the changes that affect a population.

3-Minute Warm-Up

Display Transparency 20 or copy this exercise on the board:

Match the definitions to the terms.

Definitions

1. a system for naming species *a*
2. the science of naming and classifying organisms *b*
3. a group of species with similar characteristics *d*

Terms

a. binomial nomenclature
b. taxonomy
c. dichotomous key
d. genus
e. domain

 3-Minute Warm-Up, p. T20

8.1 MOTIVATE

THINK ABOUT

PURPOSE To understand the meaning of exponential (rapid) growth

DISCUSS Ask students to write a definition of rapid growth based on the example. Then brainstorm a list of factors that might stop a population of fruit flies from growing exponentially. Write students' ideas on the board to use as a reference as they read the chapter. Students may add to or revise the list as they read.

Ongoing Assessment

 *Answer: Population dynamics is the study of why populations change and what causes them to change.*

8.1 INSTRUCT

Teach Difficult Concepts

Some students may not understand how one species can have more than one population. Point out that humans all belong to the same species. Yet, populations of humans live in many different cities of the world. The same applies to other species of living things in different environments.

Teach from Visuals

To help students interpret the diagram of population change, ask:

- What is the first stage? What happens during this stage? *Growth—populations increase in size as there are more births than deaths.*
- When does a population reach stability? *when the number of births equals the number of deaths*
- What happens when the number of deaths is greater that the number of births? *The population declines.*

EXPLORE the BIG idea

Revisit "How Does Population Grow?" on p. 239. Ask:

- What is the stage of the population represented by the water? *It is in the growth stage.*
- When does the bucket reach carrying capacity? *when it is full*

Ongoing Assessment

READING VISUALS *Answer: The population increases, becomes stable, then decreases.*

One species of iguana may have several populations living on different islands. As a result, these iguana populations don't interact with each other. Yet there may be other populations of iguanas living on the islands made up of a different species.

Growth, Stability, and Decline

READING TIP As you read about growth, stability, and decline, refer to the explanations on the graph.

A As different as populations may be—whether cacti, finches, dragonflies, or iguanas—all populations go through the same three stages of change: growth, stability, and decline.

All living things need resources such as water, energy, and living space. Populations get their resources from the environment. However, the area a population occupies can support only so many individuals. B **Carrying capacity** is the maximum number of individuals an ecosystem can support.

When a habitat contains enough resources to meet the needs of a population, the population grows rapidly. This growth stage of a population tends to be brief. On a graph, it looks like a sharp rise. The growth stage is followed by a period of stability, when the size of a population remains constant. For most populations, the stability stage is the longest stage of a population's existence. The stability stage is often followed by a decline in population size.

Population Change

The graph shows three stages of population change.

READING VISUALS How is the number of individuals changing over time?

DIFFERENTIATE INSTRUCTION

More Reading Support

A What are the three population stages? *growth, stability, decline*

B What is the maximum number of individuals that an ecosystem can support? *carrying capacity*

English Learners Students may be familiar with the basic *"If . . . , then . . . "* sentence structure. But variations of the structure are common and may confuse English learners. Sometimes *then* is omitted. For example, "If the birth rate does not match the death rate, a population could decline." Another variation to the *"If . . . , then . . . "* structure is the use of *when* instead of *if*. For example, "When a habitat contains enough resources to meet the needs of a population, the population grows rapidly."

During the growth stage, populations can increase according to two general patterns. One pattern is rapid growth, which increases at a greater and greater rate. Another pattern is gradual growth, which increases at a fairly steady rate. The two graphs below show the two different types of growth.

Population Growth

The graphs show two patterns of population growth.

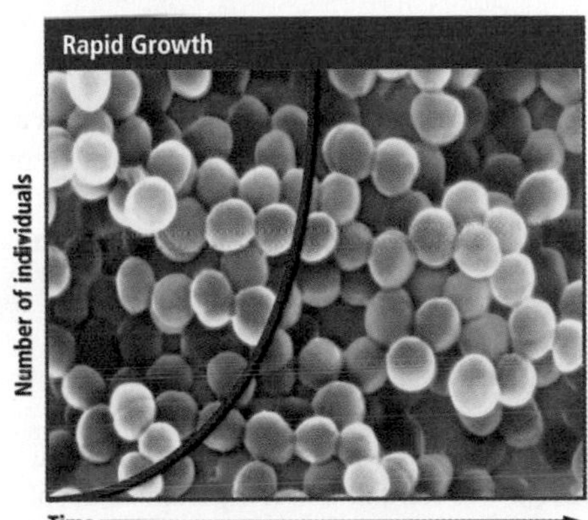

Darwin's Observations of Population Growth

In Chapter 6 you read about the observations and conclusions made by the naturalist Charles Darwin. In his book *On the Origin of Species* Darwin included important observations about population growth.

- All populations are able to grow rapidly.
- Populations tend to remain constant in size.
- There are limits to natural resources.
- Within a given population there is genetic variation.

REMINDER

A species that is no longer living is considered extinct.

Darwin recognized that organisms in most species have the ability to produce more than two surviving offspring. He knew that if there were no limits to growth, then populations would grow rapidly. However, Darwin also observed that in the real world there are natural limits to growth, so populations tend to stabilize. In order for a species to continue, individuals must be replaced as they die. This means that, on average, one member of a population must produce one surviving offspring. If the birth rate doesn't match the death rate, a population can decline until it becomes extinct.

Teach Difficult Concepts

Some students may not understand the meaning of *rapid growth*. Explain that when the individuals in a population reproduce at a steady rate, rapid growth occurs. Have them recall the Big Idea activity, "How does population grow?" Point out that each time, the water in the bucket increases by two cups. Ask: Does this demonstrate rapid growth? Explain. *Yes, because the water in the bucket increases at a steady rate.*

Teach from Visuals

To help students interpret the illustration of population growth, have them compare the curve of the lines in each graph. Then ask: Which graph illustrates exponential growth? Explain. *The first graph shows exponential growth because it shows a steady rate of growth that increases as the population gets larger.*

Ongoing Assessment

Understand the stages of population dynamics.

Ask: What did Darwin observe about the size of populations? *He observed that all populations are able to grow rapidly and that populations then tend to remain constant in size. He observed that all populations are limited by factors in their environment, and that within a population, there is genetic variation.*

DIFFERENTIATE INSTRUCTION

More Reading Support

C Which population growth pattern increases at a steady rate? *gradual growth*

Below Level To reinforce the concepts in the text, present this data to students:

Generation	Number of Fruit Flies
1	10
2	30
3	90
4	270
5	270

Ask: Which type of growth pattern is shown by the fruit fly population? *rapid growth*

When does the population reach carrying capacity? *at 270*

Develop Critical Thinking

ANALYZE Display the two bowls of marbles from the "Explore the Big Idea" activity at the beginning of the chapter.

Ask: If the marbles in the bowls represent two populations, then what does the number of marbles in each bowl represent? *the size of the population*

Teach Difficult Concepts

Some students may not think that plants can constitute a population. Direct attention to the photograph on p. 244. Point out that the cactus plants in the desert make up a population that is influenced by the same factors as animal populations. Plant populations also undergo growth patterns similar to animal populations.

Four characteristics define a population.

When scientists think about population dynamics, they consider four major characteristics. These characteristics include population size, population density, population spacing, and age structure.

Population Size

D

Population size is the number of individuals in a population at a given time. Even when the population size appears to be stable over time, changes can occur from year to year or from place to place. Population size varies from one habitat to another. It also varies within a single habitat.

An area where the summers are hot and the winters are cold is a good place to observe how population size might change at different times of year. For example, the population sizes of many insects change within a year. Mosquitoes that are all around you on warm summer evenings are nowhere in sight when the temperatures fall below freezing.

The size of plant populations can also change during the year. In the spring and summer you can see flowering plants across the deserts, woods, and mountains of North America. However, by fall and early winter, when there is less rainfall and temperatures drop, many of these plants die. Below is a picture of a southwestern desert in full bloom. During the springtime months of March through May, many deserts in the United States experience a change. There is a period of rapid growth as a variety of wildflowers begins to bloom.

When there is little rainfall a desert seems empty. After a rain, there is a brief time when plants bloom.

DIFFERENTIATE INSTRUCTION

More Reading Support

D What term describes the number of individuals in a population at a given time? *population size*

Advanced Have students research how the population of your town or city has changed over five years. Students can present their data in a graph. Ask students to hypothesize why the size of the population may have varied.

R Challenge and Extension, p. 137

The availability of resources, such as water, increases plant growth. By summer the change in season brings higher temperatures and less rainfall. As a result, desert wildflowers experience a rapid decline in their population size.

CHECK YOUR READING What are two factors that affect population size?

Population Density

Population density is a measure of the number of individuals in a certain space at a particular time. Population density is related to population size. If a population's size increases and all of the individuals remain in the same area, then population density increases, too. There are more individuals living in the same amount of space. If the size of a population in a particular area decreases, density also decreases. Some species, such as bumblebees or mice, live in populations with high densities. Other species, such as blue herons or wolves, live in populations with low densities.

? E

CHECK YOUR READING What is the difference between low density and high density?

Population Density

Density can change over time and over the entire area of the population.

Herons are usually found alone or in pairs in marshy areas. Herons are an example of a low-density population.

Bees in a beehive are an example of a high-density population—many individuals are packed into a small area.

READING VISUALS COMPARE How does the number of herons in an area compare with the number of bees?

Teach Difficult Concepts

Students may not understand the difference between population density and population size. To help with this concept, once again display the bowls of marbles. Try putting identical quantities of marbles in varying sizes of bowls. Point out that in one bowl the marbles are together in a small space while in another, the same sized "population" has more room or space per marble.

Point out that the size of the population is the same, but the density of the population differs.

Teacher Demo

To further reinforce the concept, have volunteers model population density. Use tape to block off a 6 ft × 6 ft square. Place two students inside the square to represent low density. Then tape off another 6 ft × 6 ft area and put enough students in the square to fill it tightly so that no students are touching. This represents high density.

Teach from Visuals

To help students interpret the photographs of population density, ask:

Why is the heron population an example of low population density? *because there is a small number of individuals in a certain space*

Ongoing Assessment

CHECK YOUR READING *Answer: Two factors that affect population size are temperature and rainfall.*

CHECK YOUR READING *Answer: Populations with low densities have few individuals in a certain space. Populations with high densities have many individuals in a certain space.*

READING VISUALS *Answer: There are fewer herons than bees in the given area, as shown by the blue dots in the inset boxes.*

DIFFERENTIATE INSTRUCTION

? More Reading Support

E If a population's size increases and all of the individuals remain in that area, what happens to its density? *It increases.*

Advanced Write the following formula for population density on the chalkboard:

$$\text{Population density} = \frac{\text{\# of individuals unit}}{\text{area}}$$

Then pose the following problem: Suppose there are 120 herons in an area that covers 4 sq km. What is the population density? *30 heron per sq km* Challenge students to make up their own problems and share them with classmates.

Develop Critical Thinking

COMPARE AND CONTRAST Have students describe the difference between population density and population range. Ask: What does the area of the classroom represent in the your class population? *the habitat* What does your school represent for your class population? *range*

Next, have students describe the difference between population range and population spacing. Encourage students to use the bowls of marbles (p. 239) to demonstrate examples of clumping, uniform, and randomly spaced populations.

Teach from Visuals

To help students interpret the photographs of population spacing, ask:

- What are the three types of population spacing? *clumped, uniform, and random*
- Why do members of a clumped population form small groups within a habitat? *so they can gather around resources*
- What do the white dots represent on the inset boxes? *members of a population* What does the blue in the inset boxes represent? *a population's range*

 The "Population Spacing" visual is also available as T22 in the Unit Transparency Book.

Ongoing Assessment

CHECK YOUR READING *Answer: The population density tends to be higher where more resources are available.*

READING VISUALS *Answer: Alike: Populations are spaced according to resources; Different: Populations can be clumped, uniform, or random*

 F

The distribution of a population across a large geographic area is its range. Within that range, population density may vary. For example, there may be more grasshoppers in the middle of a prairie than there are at the edges. The population density tends to be higher where more resources are available. Habitats located in the middle of a population range tend to have a greater population density than habitats located at the edges.

 How might population density vary within a range?

Population Spacing

Take a look around you as you walk through a local park. You might notice many flowers growing in open, sunny spots but few beneath the shade of large trees. The pattern in which the flowers grow is an example of population spacing. Scientists have observed three distinct patterns of spacing: clumped, uniform, and random.

In clumped spacing, individuals form small groups within a habitat. Animals like elephants clump because of their social nature. Clumping can also result from the way resources are distributed throughout a habitat. Salamanders that prefer moist, rotten logs may be clumped where logs have fallen in their habitat.

Population Spacing

Population spacing describes how individuals arrange themselves within a population.

Individuals that clump themselves often gather around resources.

Individuals that are uniformly arranged often compete for resources.

Random patterns are rare and occur without regard to other individuals.

 Compare and contrast the way populations are spaced.

DIFFERENTIATE INSTRUCTION

 **More Reading Support**

F Does population density tend to be higher or lower where there are more resources available? *higher*

Below Level Have students choose one animal population in your area. Have them research its range, population density, and population spacing and prepare a poster illustrating their research. Encourage students to use graphs, photographs, and diagrams in their posters.

Some individuals live at a distance from each other. These individuals are uniformly spaced. Many plants that grow too close together become evenly spaced as individuals die out. Uniform spacing can protect saguaro cacti from competing for important resources in the desert. Individuals that aren't uniform or clumped space themselves randomly. Dandelions, for instance, grow no matter where other dandelions are growing.

Age Structure

Scientists divide a population into three groups based on age.

- postreproductive: organisms can no longer reproduce
- reproductive: organisms capable of reproduction
- prereproductive: organisms not yet able to reproduce

The age structure of a population affects how much it can grow. On the graph below, the postreproductive age range for humans is over 45, reproductive is 14 to 44 years of age, and prereproductive is 0 to 14.

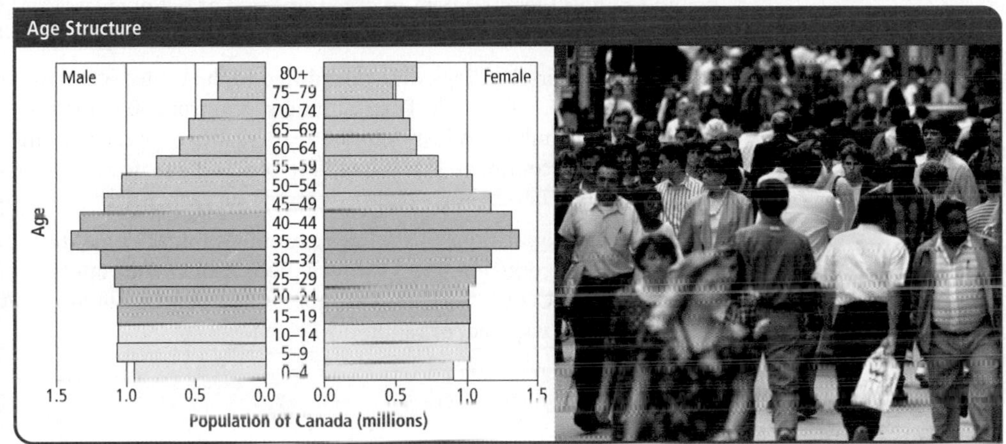

Scientists can predict population change.

Scientists use these four factors—size, density, spacing, and age structure—to describe a population and to predict how it might change over time. Sometimes a population changes when a particular factor changes.

A population can change in response to its surroundings. Suppose a population of frogs is living in a pond where the water becomes saltier. Only those frogs that can survive in an environment with more salt will survive. Thus the population size of frogs will probably decrease as a result of the changing conditions. By looking at population size, scientists can predict how changes affect the population.

DIFFERENTIATE INSTRUCTION

More Reading Support

G What term describes the spacing of a population in which members live at a distance from each other? *uniform spacing*

Advanced Have students research animals in your community that are over-populated or under-populated. Have them give reasons for the population sizes. Students should present data about the animal populations showing several characteristics. Encourage them to use one graph for each characteristic.

Have students who are interested in the characteristics of populations read the following article:

R Challenge Reading, pp. 161–162

Teach from Visuals

To help students interpret the graph of age structure, ask:

- What are the pre-reproductive ages in this population? *ages 0 to 14*
- What are the reproductive ages in this population? *ages 15 to 44*
- What might you predict about the growth of population represented by this age structure over the next 50 years? *The population will most likely have slow, steady growth.*

Address Misconceptions

IDENTIFY Ask students: How might a starling population be affected by increasing a factor such as size or density? If students answers begin with "A starling will," or "The starling will," then they are confusing the concepts of an individual organism's need and the needs of populations.

CORRECT Draw a "Living Systems" diagram of concentric circles on the board, starting with just one tiny dot, labeled *cell,* then *tissue, organ,* and *organ system.* Have student volunteers help you draw the next circles: *organism* and *population.* Add circles for *community* and *ecosystem.* Discuss with students why each level of organization is considered a system. Use the glossary if necessary.

REASSESS Ask students to describe why scientists can use factors such as density to predict changes in populations. *A population's needs differ depending on factors such as size or age. The population characteristics will change based on availability of resources as well as natural life cycles.*

Technology Resources

Visit **ClassZone.com** for background on common student misconceptions.

MISCONCEPTION DATABASE

Ongoing Assessment

Describe the variables that define a population.

Ask: What four factors do scientists use to predict changes in populations? *population size, density, spacing, and age structure*

Teach from Visuals

To help students interpret the map of the U.S. starling population, ask:

About how many years passed before the starling population made its way to Canada from New York? *about 65 years*

Reinforce the BIG idea

Have students relate the section to the Big Idea.

 Reinforcing Key Concepts, p. 138

8.1 ASSESS & RETEACH

Assess

 Section 8.1 Quiz, p. 41

Reteach

Have students begin a booklet that explains each of the vocabulary terms in this chapter. Students should include the following terms in their booklets:

- population dynamics
- carrying capacity
- population size
- population density

Technology Resources

Have students visit **ClassZone.com** for reteaching of Key Concepts.

 **CONTENT REVIEW**

 **CONTENT REVIEW CD-ROM**

Starling Population

1955 CANADA UNITED STATES 1950 1940 1930 1920 1910 1905 MEXICO

1890s European starlings are released in Central Park in New York City.

1940s Starling populations expand rapidly, especially in cool, wet habitats.

1950s Starling populations are found throughout Canada, the United States, and Mexico.

Scientists can also predict change by looking at the distribution of population. The story of the European starling provides a dramatic example of how the movement of organisms into or out of an area affects a population.

In 1890, the first starlings were introduced to the United States in New York City's Central Park. Their numbers went from 60 individuals to about 200 million in just over 100 years as they expanded on the North American continent. The population of starlings rose as starlings moved into new habitats that had the resources they needed.

Today large populations of starlings can still be found across the North American continent. Even within a given habitat, the population can vary. In Central Park, for example, you can find starlings in clumps, uniformly spaced, or randomly spaced.

VISUALIZATION CLASSZONE.COM

Watch how a change in the environment can affect a population.

8.1 Review

KEY CONCEPTS

1. Describe the three stages of population growth.
2. Make a chart showing the four factors that affect population dynamics and an example of each.
3. Give an example of how a shift in age distribution can affect population growth.

CRITICAL THINKING

4. **Apply** Choose a population in your neighborhood. Describe its population spacing. Is it clumped, uniformly spaced, or randomly spaced?
5. **Compare/Contrast** How is population size related to population density? Your answer should mention area.

CHALLENGE

6. **Predict** Explain how a heavy thunderstorm might affect the population density of birds living in the area.

ANSWERS

1. The three stages are growth, stability, and decline.

2. Charts should be labeled and titled to show each of the four factors: population size, density, spacing, and age structure.

3. A shift in age distribution to individuals that are reproductive age will likely increase the population.

4. Answers should demonstrate an understanding of the concept of population spacing.

5. Population size is the number of individuals in a population at a given time. Density measures the number of individuals that occupy a certain area.

6. Sample answer: A heavy thunderstorm may fell trees, destroying birds' habitat, resulting in decreased reproduction.

SKILL: FINDING AVERAGES

Making Sense of Samples

In a pond study, a biologist takes samples of water from four locations in one pond every three months. Using a microscope, she examines the samples and calculates the protist population for each location. The data table shows the number of protists found per milliliter in each sample of pond water.

Data Table: Number of protists per milliliter (mL) of pond water

Location	Fall	Winter	Spring	Summer
Under the pier	150	50	120	410
Among the water lilies	200	80	180	500
Shallow area	220	90	200	360
Deepest area	80	60	100	390
Seasonal Average				

Example

Suppose you want to find the average number of protists per milliliter of pond water for that fall.

Step 1. Find the sum of all the data given above for "Fall."

$$150 + 200 + 220 + 80 = 650$$

Step 2. Divide this total by the number of data entries for "Fall."

$$650 \div 4 = 162.5$$

Step 3. Round to nearest whole number.

$$162.5 \rightarrow 163$$

ANSWER 163 protists per mL of pond water

For each season or location give the average number of protists.

1. Winter
2. Spring
3. Summer
4. Under the pier
5. Among the water lilies
6. Shallow area
7. Deepest area
8. Whole pond, yearlong

CHALLENGE Suppose the biologist only took samples from three areas in the pond. Which missing area would throw off the averages the most?

MATH IN SCIENCE
Math Skills Practice for Science

Set Learning Goal

To find averages of sample data for protist populations

Present the Science

In cases where populations are very large or spread out over a wide range, sampling is a method used to count populations by estimating. One method involves counting the organisms in a small area, and then multiplying that number to find the population of a larger area.

Develop Sampling Skills

An average is found by adding all the values of a set of data and dividing by the number of data in the set. Average is also referred to as the *mean* in mathematics.

DIFFERENTIATION TIP Review rounding to whole numbers. Remind students that any decimal or fraction that is equal to or greater than one half is counted as the next whole number. Some students will benefit from a few practice numbers, such as *6 1/4 round to 6, 82.6 round to 83*, and so on.

Close

Ask students how taking samples of different areas in populations helps scientists learn more about their population size and density. *Sampling helps scientists make estimates to population size and is helpful when scientists cannot count whole populations.*

- Math Support, p. 166
- Math Practice, p. 167

Technology Resources

Students can visit **ClassZone.com** to practice finding averages.

 **MATH TUTORIAL**

ANSWERS

1. 50 + 80 + 90 + 60 = 270; 270 ÷ 4 = 70; 70 per mL
2. 120 + 180 + 200 + 100 = 270; 600 ÷ 4 = 150; 150 per mL
3. 410 + 500 + 360 + 390 = 1660; 1660 ÷ 4 = 415; 415 per mL
4. 150 + 50 + 120 + 410 = 730; 730 ÷ 4 = 182.5; 183 per mL
5. 200 + 80 + 180 + 500 = 960; 960 ÷ 4 = 240; 240 per mL
6. 220 + 90 + 200 + 360 = 870; 870 ÷ 4 = 217.5; 218 per mL
7. 80 + 60 + 100 + 390 = 630; 630 ÷ 4 = 157.5; 158 per mL
8. 163 + 70 + 150 + 415 = 798; 798 ÷ 4 = 199.5; 200 per mL
***CHALLENGE** The deepest area would throw off the averages the most.*

8.2 FOCUS

Set Learning Goals

Students will

- Describe the various limits to population growth.
- Explain how population density affects limiting factors.
- Describe two reproductive strategies found within populations.
- Design an experiment to test limiting factors for plant growth.

3-Minute Warm-Up

Display Transparency 20 or copy this exercise on the board:

Complete the graphic organizer.

Main Idea: Four factors affect the dynamics of a population	
Factors	**Details**
Size	*Number of individuals at a certain time*
Density	*Number of individuals in a certain space*
Spacing	*How individuals in a population are arranged*
Age structure	*Affects how much a population can grow*

3-Minute Warm-Up, p. T20

8.2 MOTIVATE

EXPLORE Population Density

PURPOSE To observe student populations at different school locations to understand that population density varies

TIPS *15 min.* Assign various locations around the school to each group. Record the findings of each group in a chart on the chalkboard.

WHAT DO YOU THINK? *Students might find that the number of people was the lowest in the hallways during class periods and the highest in places like the hallway between classes or in the cafeteria during lunchtime.*

KEY CONCEPT

8.2 Populations respond to pressures.

BEFORE, you learned

- Four characteristics are used to describe a population
- Scientists study these four characteristics to predict population change

NOW, you will learn

- About limits to population growth
- How population density affects limiting factors
- About two reproductive strategies found within populations

VOCABULARY

immigration p. 251
emigration p. 251
limiting factor p. 252
opportunist p. 255
competitor p. 256

EXPLORE Population Density

How does population density vary?

PROCEDURE

1. Choose three different locations in your school where you can observe how many people enter and leave an area during a specific time period.
2. Position three people at each location a counter, a timekeeper, and a recorder.
3. Count the number of people who pass through the area for at least 2 minutes. Record the number.
4. Compare your data with the data collected by other groups.

WHAT DO YOU THINK?

- Where was the number of people the highest? the lowest?
- Explain what may have affected population density at each location.

MATERIALS

- stopwatch
- notebook

CHOOSE YOUR OWN STRATEGY

Use a strategy from an earlier chapter or one of your own to take notes on the main idea: *Population growth is limited.*

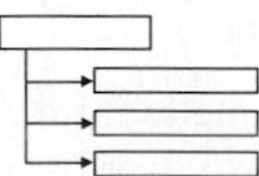

Population growth is limited.

No population can grow forever. Every population has a limit to its growth. For example, the cockroach has been around for more than 300 million years. This insect has outlived the dinosaurs and may persist long after humans have become extinct. Yet even if cockroaches became the only species on the planet, several factors would limit their population size.

RESOURCES FOR DIFFERENTIATED INSTRUCTION

Below Level

UNIT RESOURCE BOOK

- Reading Study Guide A, pp. 141–142
- Decoding Support, p. 165

Advanced

UNIT RESOURCE BOOK

Challenge and Extension, p. 147

English Learners

UNIT RESOURCE BOOK

Spanish Reading Study Guide, pp. 145–146

- Audio Readings in Spanish
- Audio Readings (English)

Birth, Death, Immigration, and Emigration

When scientists study how a population changes, they must consider four things: birth, death, immigration, and emigration. There is even a simple formula to help scientists track population change.

Population change = (birth + immigration) − (death + emigration)

It is too simple to say that a high birth rate means population growth, or that many deaths mean population decline. **Immigration** is the movement of individuals into a population. For example, if a strong wind blows the seeds of a plant from one area into another, the new plant would be said to immigrate into the new area. Immigration can increase a population or help stabilize a declining population. Birth and immigration introduce individuals into a population.

A

Emigration is the movement of individuals out of a population. If resources become scarce within a habitat, some of the individuals might move to areas with greater supplies. Others may even die. Death and emigration remove individuals from a population.

CHECK YOUR READING List two factors that lead to population growth and two that lead to population decline.

Consider, for example, a flock of seagulls that flies inland during a storm. They stop at a city dump, where food is plentiful. These incoming seagulls become part of the seagull population that is already living at the dump. A raccoon population living in the same area has been eating the seagulls' eggs, causing the number of seagull births to decrease. If enough seagulls immigrate to the dump, the seagull population would increase, making up for the decrease in births. Immigration would help keep the population stable. The seagull population would also increase if part of the raccoon population moved away.

251

8.2 INSTRUCT

Social Studies Connection

Human beings emigrate from one population, such as a country, to another population for many reasons. Some people desire better employment circumstances and a new way of life. Sometimes people search for cultural change. Others seek religious or political opportunities. A person's immigration from one country to another country creates population change in both countries.

History of Science

In 1798, Thomas Malthus published *An Essay on the Principle of Population* in which he predicted that the human population will grow faster than the food or space needed to support it. Malthus observed that the only thing to check the growth rate of the human population was famine, disease, and war. In 1803 Malthus published a revised edition of his work in which he theorized that late marriage might be an additional factor for limiting population growth.

Ongoing Assessment

CHECK YOUR READING *Answer: Birth and immigration contribute to population growth. Death and emigration contribute to population decline.*

DIFFERENTIATE INSTRUCTION

More Reading Support

A What are the effects of a population immigrating into an area? *It can increase or stabilize the population and reduce the amount of resources.*

English Learners Have students write the definitions for the terms *immigration, emigration, opportunists,* and *competitors* in their Science Word Dictionaries. Distinguishing between *immigration* and *emigration* may be confusing for English learners. Here is a helpful device:

Immigration begins with an *i*—*i* is for *in*. Individuals move *into* a population.

Emigration begins with an *e*—*e* is for *exit*. Individuals *exit* or move out of a population.

Teach from Visuals

To help students interpret the photographs exemplifying limiting factors on pp. 252 and 253, point out that limiting factors include both density-dependent factors and density-independent factors. Then ask:

- What is the difference between the two factors? *Density-dependent factors usually affect a high-density population. Density-independent factors affect a population no matter what its density.*
- What types of things might individuals in a population compete for? *food, space, water, shelter*

Develop Critical Thinking

COMPARE AND CONTRAST Review the density-dependent factors for the deer shown in the photograph (competition, disease, parasitism, predation). Ask: Are the density-dependent factors in a population the same for plants as they are for animals? Give examples. *Some of the factors are different. For example, plants make their own food so they do not compete for food. Plants are also not subject to predation by other plants. Plants can, however, be susceptible to disease and parasitism, and predation from animals.*

EXPLORE 

Have students revisit "How Do Populations Differ?" on p. 239. Ask them to explain the limiting factors that might affect their model populations.

Ongoing Assessment

CHECK YOUR READING *Sample answers: availability of air, light, and water, and other living things*

Limiting Factors

When a population is growing at a rapid rate, the birth rate is much higher than the death rate. That means that more individuals are being born than are dying during a particular time period. There are plenty of resources available, and the population size is increasing rapidly. Eventually, however, the population will stop growing, because a habitat can support only a limited number of organisms.

A **limiting factor** is a factor that prevents the continuing growth of a population in an ecosystem. Abiotic, or nonliving, limiting factors include air, light, and water. Other limiting factors can be living things, such as other organisms in the same population or individuals belonging to different species within the same area.

What are two limiting factors?

Competition can occur between different populations sharing the same habitat. Competition can also occur among individuals of the same population. Suppose, for example, that a population of deer in a forest preserve were to increase, either through births or immigration. Population density at the forest preserve would go up. More and more deer in that area would be competing for the same amount of food.

Density-Dependent Factors

DIFFERENTIATE INSTRUCTION

More Reading Support

B Why does a population stop growing? *Its habitat can only support a limited number of organisms.*

Advanced Give students these problems: Suppose a deer population is 1600 at the beginning of a year and 1850 at the end. What is the growth rate of the population? *250/1600* Suppose 75 older deer died that year. What is the population's growth rate? *175/1600* Suppose a disease killed 300 young deer the same year. What would the growth rate be then? *–125/1600*

 Challenge and Extension, p. 147

Effects of Population Density

In the situation described above, the seagull population could decrease as a result of competition for food. Competition is an example of a density-dependent factor—that is, a limiting factor that affects a population when density is high. Disease is another density-dependent factor. The more crowded an area becomes, the easier it is for disease to spread, so more individuals are affected. If population density is low, there is less contact between individuals, which means that disease will spread more slowly. Density-dependent factors have a greater effect on the population as it grows. They can bring a population under control, because they apply more pressure to a growing population.

There are also density-independent factors. These limiting factors have the same effect on a population, whether it has a high density or a low density. Freezing temperatures could be considered a density-independent factor. A freeze might kill all of the flowering plants in an area, whether or not the population density is high. A natural event such as a wildfire is another example of a density-independent factor. When a wildfire occurs in a forest, it can wipe out an entire ecosystem.

CHECK YOUR READING How are limiting factors that are density-dependent different from limiting factors that are density-independent?

DIFFERENTIATE INSTRUCTION

More Reading Support

C What type of limiting factor are competition and disease? *density-dependent*

Below Level Have students choose one of the limiting factors shown on pp. 252 and 253. Ask them to research a notable event in your area or state, such as a major drought, forest fire, or invasion of a destructive insect, and describe how the event affected the wildlife population in the area. Encourage students to present their research on posters and display them in the classroom.

Metacognitive Strategy

Challenge students to devise a strategy or memory device that will help them remember both density-dependent factors and density-independent factors.

Integrate the Sciences

Droughts are periods of unusually dry weather characterized by sustained lack of precipitation, causing an imbalance in the water cycle. The results of drought are water shortages, loss of crops, decreased groundwater sources, and soil that is devoid of moisture. Droughts are more severe than dry spells and can last for longer than 14 days. Droughts are classified according to the type of climate—there are permanent droughts, seasonal droughts, and unpredictable droughts where normal amounts of rainfall fail to occur.

Real World Example

Severe droughts occurred in the Dust Bowl, the area of the United States that includes Oklahoma, and parts of Texas, Colorado, New Mexico, and Kansas from 1934 to 1939. The root systems of the grasses were destroyed, and much of the soil was picked up by winds, resulting in severe dust storms that buried homes and roads. Thousands emigrated out of the area, and after emigration and deaths, only about one-quarter of the population remained.

Develop Critical Thinking

CAUSE AND EFFECT Have students brainstorm a list of the results of density-independent factors for each one listed in the illustration on p. 253. Students should include the effects on the land as well as on wildlife.

Ongoing Assessment

Describe the various limits to population growth.

Ask: What are some density-independent factors that limit the growth of populations? *Sample answers: drought, tornado, hurricanes, fires, and floods*

CHECK YOUR READING *Answer: They have a greater effect on a high-density population.*

INVESTIGATE Limiting Factors

PURPOSE To design an experiment about limiting factors and to identify variables

TIPS *20 min.* Prior to the activity, you may wish to soak the beans overnight in water to soften them. Rinse in tap water and drain. Remind students that they will need a control factor for each experimental setup. Be sure that all light sources are controlled.

WHAT DO YOU THINK? *Possible variables may include: amount of water, sunlight, type of soil, or temperature. Students should say that they expect to see some plants growing well, some poorly, or not at all. (Students should specify the factor that would cause the difference.)*

CHALLENGE Allow students class time each day to record their observations. Compile their data in a chart on the board for review and conclusions.

 Datasheet, Limiting Factors, p. 148

Technology Resources

Customize this student lab as needed or look for an alternative. Print rubrics to assess student lab reports.

 **Lab Generator CD-ROM**

Teaching with Technology

Have students use digital cameras to record pictures of their bean plants each day as they make and record observations.

Ongoing Assessment

Explain how population density affects limiting factors.

Ask: Would a highly dense population be affected by disease? Explain. *Yes, the closer members of the population are, the more likely they are to contract the disease.*

CHECK YOUR READING *Answer: Limiting factors such as famine can cause a population to decline.*

 D

Limiting factors include nonliving factors in the environment and natural events such as earthquakes, fires, and storms. During times of drought, there may not be enough food to meet the needs of all the organisms in an area. The quality of the food declines as well. For example, a lack of water may cause a population of trees to produce fewer pieces of fruit, and the fruit itself may be smaller. If there is little food available, a condition called famine arises. If the famine is severe, and if death rates exceed birth rates, then the population size will fall dramatically.

E

 How do limiting factors affect populations? Remember: a summary includes only the most important information.

Limiting factors affect human populations as well. However, humans have found different ways to help overcome many of these limits. In Section 8.3 you will read about how the human response to limits differs from that of other biological populations.

INVESTIGATE Limiting Factors

What limiting factors determine plant growth?

DESIGN — YOUR OWN — EXPERIMENT

Using the materials below, design an experiment to test how limiting factors such as sunlight or water can determine how well a plant population will grow.

SKILL FOCUS
Designing experiments

PROCEDURE

1. Decide how to use the beans, soil, and water.
2. Write up your experimental procedure. Include any safety tips.

WHAT DO YOU THINK?

- What variables did you use in your experiment?
- What evidence do you expect to see to support the goal of your experiment?

CHALLENGE Conduct your experiment. Be sure to observe your beans daily and note which ones are most healthy. Make a chart and record your observations. The beans should grow for at least two weeks before you make your conclusion.

MATERIALS
- 6 paper cups
- potting soil
- beans
- water

TIME
20 minutes

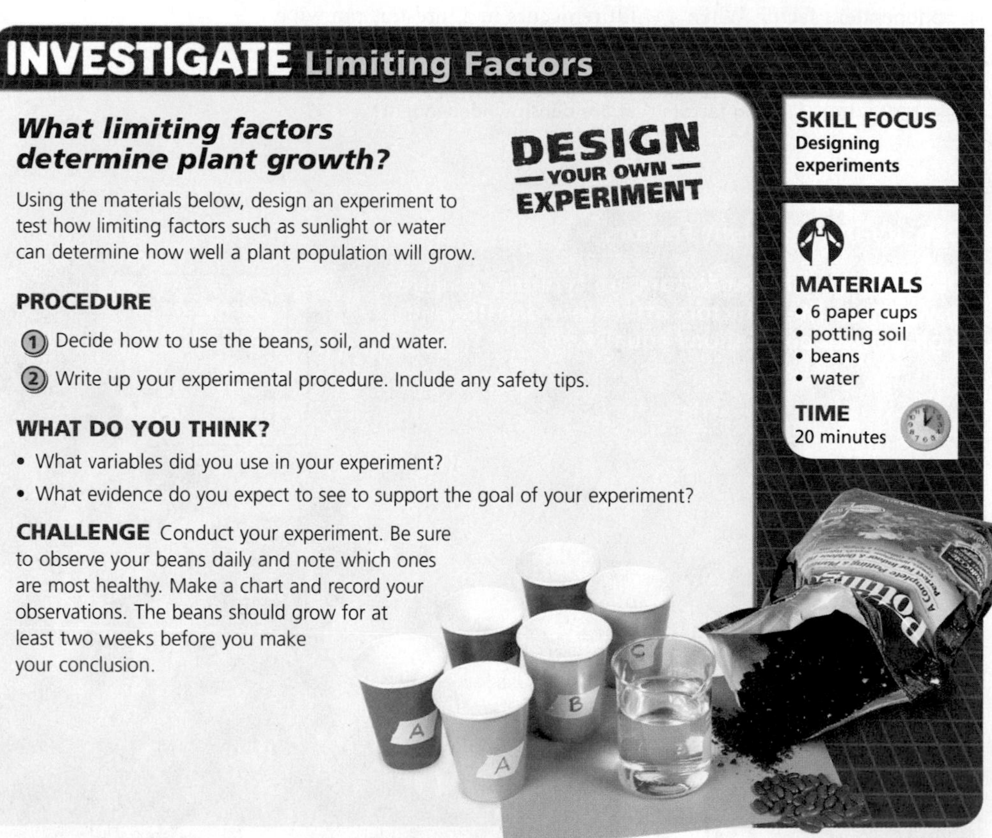

DIFFERENTIATE INSTRUCTION

More Reading Support

D What limiting factors are natural events? *earthquakes, fires, storms*

E What might happen if little food is available? *famine*

Below Level Have students choose an ecosystem such as a forest, desert, prairie, or grassland. Have them research wildlife in the ecosystem and draw a picture. Students should label the wildlife as opportunists or competitors.

Populations have distinct reproductive survival strategies.

Although reproduction of offspring is not necessary for the survival of an individual organism, it is necessary for the survival of a species. Scientists studying populations observe patterns in the reproductive strategies used among species. There are two main strategies that many species use. There are also many species whose strategies fit somewhere in between.

Strategies of Opportunists

F **Opportunists** are species that reproduce rapidly if their population falls below carrying capacity. They share many characteristics, including a short life span and the ability to reproduce large quantities of offspring. Their population size tends to change often, and opportunists live across many areas. Opportunists include algae, dandelions, bacteria, and insects. These species can reproduce and move across an area quickly. In addition, they can adapt quickly to environmental changes. Populations of opportunists often grow rapidly.

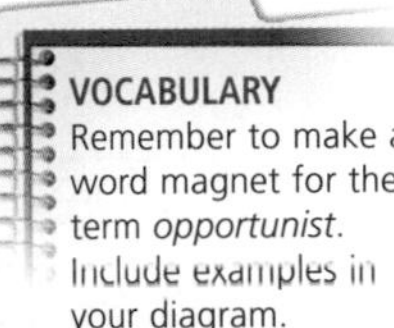

VOCABULARY
Remember to make a word magnet for the term *opportunist*. Include examples in your diagram.

Opportunists

Pine trees are opportunists that can spread across an area quickly.

Pine cones release huge amounts of pollen into the air.

Develop Critical Thinking

COMPARE AND CONTRAST Have students make a chart comparing and contrasting opportunists and competitors as they read pp. 255 and 256. Ask: What type of reproductive strategy do humans have? Explain. *Humans are most likely competitors. They live long and have fewer offspring that take a long time to develop. Most offspring usually survive to reproductive age.*

Teach from Visuals

To help students interpret the photograph showing pine pollen, ask:

What characteristics of pine cones and pollen qualify them as an opportunists? *Pine cones produce pollen, reproducing rapidly and moving quickly across an area.*

DIFFERENTIATE INSTRUCTION

More Reading Support

F How frequently does the population size of opportunists change? *often*

English Learners English learners may have trouble with hypothetical questions. For example, the Synthesize question on p. 256 in this section's Review gives a detailed hypothetical situation. Point out to students that although the situation does not exist, they can use logic and what they have already learned to answer the question.

Ongoing Assessment

Describe two reproductive strategies found within populations.

Which type of reproductive strategy allows a population to remain near carrying capacity? Give an example. *competitors; elephants and saguaro cacti*

Reinforce

Have students relate the section to the Big Idea.

Reinforcing Key Concepts, p. 149

8.2 ASSESS & RETEACH

Assess

Section 8.2 Quiz, p. 42

Reteach

Write the following terms on the board. For each term have students tell whether it is a density-dependent factor, or a density-independent factor. Then have them describe the difference between the two and how limiting factors affect a population.

- disease *density-dependent*
- competition *density-dependent*
- drought *density-independent*
- storms *density-independent*
- predation *density-dependent*
- fire *density-independent*
- parasitism *density-dependent*
- flood *density-independent*

Technology Resources

Have students visit **ClassZone.com** for reteaching of Key Concepts.

CONTENT REVIEW

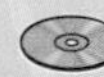
CONTENT REVIEW CD-ROM

Competitors

Wolves are examples of competitor species. These cubs will be cared for by adults until they are able to hunt.

Strategies of Competitors

You might be familiar with the term *competitor* as meaning an organism that struggles with another to get resources. Scientists who study population growth use the term *competitor* in another way. **Competitors** are species with adaptations that allow them to remain at or near their carrying capacity for long periods of time. Competitors have many characteristics that differ from those of opportunists.

Species that have a competitive reproductive strategy often live longer and have fewer offspring. Elephants and saguaro cacti are two examples of competitors. The offspring of competitors take longer to develop than those of opportunists. Also, animals with this strategy tend to take care of their young for a longer period of time. Competitors are not distributed across areas as widely as opportunists, but greater numbers of their offspring survive to reproductive age.

8.2 Review

KEY CONCEPTS

1. What four factors do scientists consider when they measure population change?
2. Give two examples of density-dependent factors and two examples of density-independent factors.
3. Other than life span, how do opportunists and competitors differ?

CRITICAL THINKING

4. **Analyze** Why would it be a mistake to predict population growth based on birth rate alone?
5. **Apply** Give an example of a factor that limits a population near you.

CHALLENGE

6. **Synthesize** There has been an oil spill along a waterway famous for its populations of seals, dolphins, and sea birds. Six months later, all populations show a decline. Explain what factors might have caused such a change and whether the oil spill was a density-dependent or density-independent factor or both.

ANSWERS

1. Scientists look at birth, death, immigration, and emigration.

2. density-dependent: disease and competition; density-independent: temperature changes, natural events

3. Opportunists produce large numbers of offspring and reproduce rapidly if they fall below carrying capacity. They have a wide range. Competitors remain at or near carrying capacity. They produce fewer offspring and take longer to develop. A greater number of competitors reach reproductive age.

4. A habitat can only support a limited number; populations may immigrate or emigrate.

5. Answers should demonstrate an understanding of limiting factors.

6. loss of habitat and polluted water; density-independent

FISHING BOAT CAPTAIN

Studying the Schools

There's a lot more to catching fish than putting a net or a line into the ocean. More and more these days, finding fish means looking at the big and changing picture of fish populations. Once you start fishing, you need to know when to stop fishing, as well as how to protect the other organisms in the ocean environment.

Density

If there are too few fish of a particular species in one area, it is best to leave them and look for a place with greater population density. By using the most suitable gear, the captain avoids killing or injuring fish and other animals that shouldn't be part of the catch.

Distribution

Some fish live alone, and some live in big groups, called schools. Some, called ground fish, stay on the bottom, while others swim near the surface. One way to see the distribution of fish is with sonar. An image made from sonar shows that a school of hake swims at a depth of about 320 meters (1050 ft).

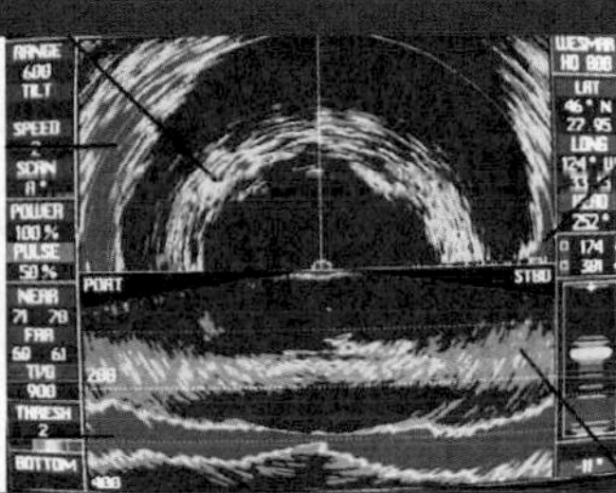

Partners in Research

Many boat captains set up partnerships with researchers to study fish and to help them to thrive. Sonar equipment is a tool shared by scientists and commercial fishers. Images are made by sending sound waves through the water and receiving the patterns of sound waves that bounce, or echo, back.

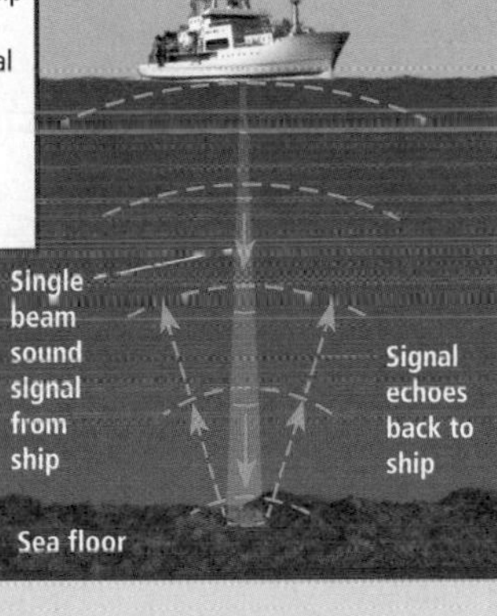

EXPLORE

1. **INFER** Boat captains talk to each other about how many fish they catch and where and when they catch them. What are three reasons why this would be important?
2. **CHALLENGE** Suppose a fishing boat captain overfishes an organism that is a source of food for another organism. Describe what may happen to the other organism.

EXPLORE

1. ***INFER*** *Sample answers: boat captains know where to find the most fish, how to avoid injuring fish, and how to help fish thrive, preventing overfishing*
2. ***CHALLENGE*** *Students' food chains may vary. Overfishing of an organism in the middle of the food chain will upset the balance of the food chain—fish that feed on the overfished organism may begin to die off without a sufficient food supply.*

SCIENCE ON THE JOB

Relevance of Science to Non-science Jobs

Set Learning Goal

To understand why fishing boat captains need knowledge of population dynamics

Present the Science

Ask students to recall what they learned about population size, density, and spacing. Ask them how these population dynamics might apply to fishing boat captains.

DENSITY The basic fishing vessel is the trawler, which has diesel engines and a variety of equipment for finding, capturing and storing fish. Fish are caught using nets, hooked lines, or traps.

DISTRIBUTION Different types of nets are used for different populations of fish, depending on whether the fish are bottom dwellers or swim near the surface. Bag or gill nets are most often used for fish near the surface. Dragged nets are used mostly for shellfish.

PARTNERS IN RESEARCH
Echosounders and sonar can track the presence of fish in water at depths of up to 730 m (2394 ft). In addition to sonar, airplanes are used to detect fish that swim near the surface.

Discussion Question

Ask: How has technology improved the success of fishing boat captains? *Devices such as sonar help captains locate fish populations.*

Close

Ask: Why do fishing boat captains need knowledge of science and modern fishing technologies? *It improves the chances that they will have a good catch. Technologies may also help captains from overfishing and reducing fish populations.*

8.3 FOCUS

Set Learning Goals

Students will

- Explain how human populations differ from other populations.
- Describe how humans adapt to the environment.
- Describe how human populations affect the environment.
- Graph data for local population growth.

3-Minute Warm-Up

Display Transparency 21 or copy this exercise on the board:

Match the definitions to the terms.

Definitions

1. movement of individuals out of an area *b*
2. species with adaptations that allow them to remain at carrying capacity *d*
3. natural events that prevent continued population growth *c*

Terms

a. immigration c. limiting factors
b. emigration d. competitors

3-Minute Warm-Up, p. T21

8.3 MOTIVATE

EXPLORE Population Change

PURPOSE To predict human population growth

TIP *15 min.* Review the meaning of immigration and emigration.

INCLUSION For students who have visual impairments, provide large copies of the graph on graph paper prior to the activity.

WHAT DO YOU THINK? *Sample answer: The population will stabilize or decrease with no immigration. Immigration will likely increase population size but does not necessarily affect the birth rate, a ratio of the number of births to the total population.*

KEY CONCEPT

8.3 Human populations have unique responses to change.

BEFORE, you learned

- Over time, all populations stop growing
- All populations are affected by limiting factors
- Reproductive strategies include opportunism and competition

NOW, you will learn

- How human populations differ from other populations
- How humans adapt to the environment
- How human populations affect the environment

VOCABULARY

pollution p. 264

EXPLORE Population Change

How can you predict human population growth?

PROCEDURE

1. Copy the graph on the right. The graph shows population growth expected in the United States with an increase in both birth and death rates and with steady immigration.
2. The graph shows a medium rate of growth. Draw another line to show what low population growth might look like. Label it.
3. Explain the patterns of birth rates, death rates, and immigration that might be likely to result in low population growth.

MATERIALS

- graph paper
- colored pencils

WHAT DO YOU THINK?

- How would the projected U.S. population size change if there were no immigration?
- How might an increase in immigration affect expected birth rates?

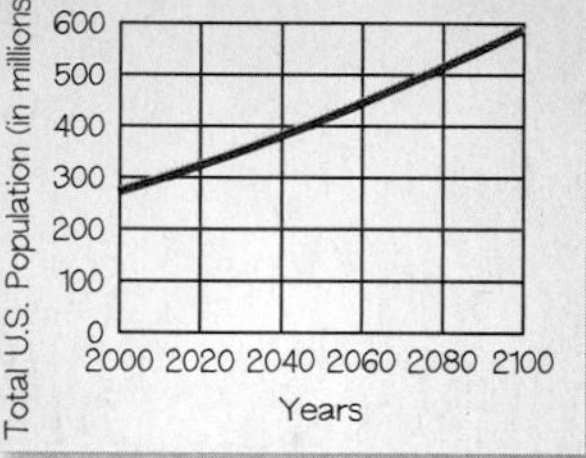

Human populations differ from populations of other species.

CHOOSE YOUR OWN STRATEGY
Begin taking notes on the differences between human populations and populations of other species.

Humans are not the fastest or the largest organisms on Earth. They must get food from other organisms. Humans have a limited sense of smell, and the vision of a human is inferior to that of a hawk. However, the human population now dominates our planet. Why? Humans are able to shape their environment. Humans are also able to determine their own biological reproduction. Because humans can control many factors that limit growth, Earth's carrying capacity for humans has increased. Two key factors that have increased Earth's carrying capacity for humans are habitat expansion and technology.

RESOURCES FOR DIFFERENTIATED INSTRUCTION

Below Level

UNIT RESOURCE BOOK

- Reading Study Guide A, pp. 152–153
- Decoding Support, p. 165

AUDIO CDS

Advanced

UNIT RESOURCE BOOK

Challenge and Extension, p. 158

English Learners

UNIT RESOURCE BOOK

Spanish Reading Study Guide, pp. 156–157

AUDIO CDS

- Audio Readings in Spanish
- Audio Readings (English)

Additional INVESTIGATION,
Introduced Species and Population Dynamics, A, B, & C, pp. 177–185; Teacher Instructions, pp. 188–189

Habitat Expansion

Individuals who study the history of ancient peoples know that populations of humans have spread throughout the world. Discoveries of ancient human tools and skeletons indicate that the first human populations lived on the continent now known as Africa. Over time, human populations have spread over nearly the entire planet.

The word *habitat* refers to a place where an organism can live. Humans have expanded their habitats, and thus the population has grown. Humans can survive in many different environments by adding air conditioning or heat to regulate indoor temperature. They can design and build shelters that protect them from harsh environments.

Adapting to Climate

Humans have designed buildings that allow them to survive in different climates.

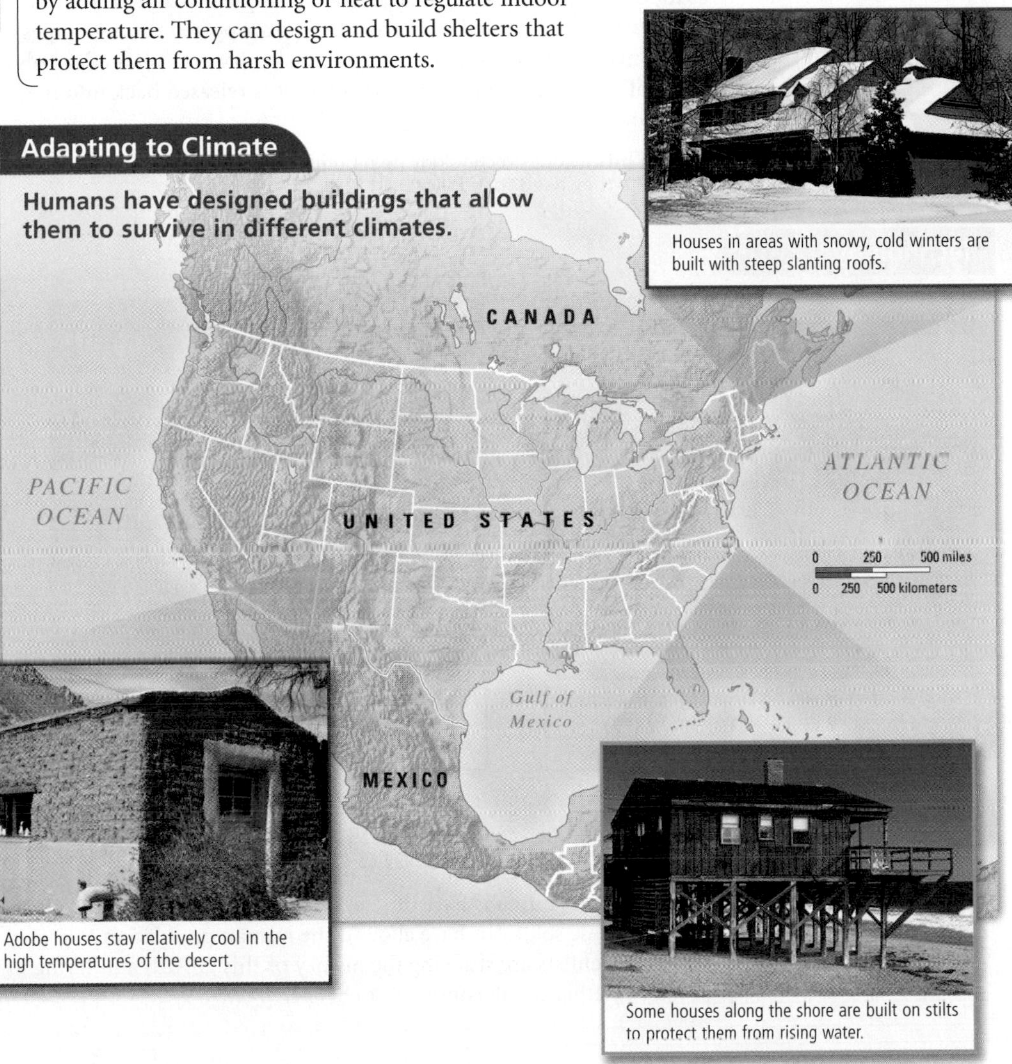

Houses in areas with snowy, cold winters are built with steep slanting roofs.

Adobe houses stay relatively cool in the high temperatures of the desert.

Some houses along the shore are built on stilts to protect them from rising water.

8.3 INSTRUCT

Integrate the Sciences

The earliest humans appeared on Earth near the end of the Pliocene Epoch, about two to three million years ago. The earliest true hominid is most likely Australopithecus. Fossils from several sites in Africa represent this early human, where it existed from 5.5 million to one million years ago. Australopithecus shares hominid characteristics in that it walked upright and had teeth similar to humans'. Australopithecus had a brain similar to that of most large apes. Fossil evidence supports three separate species of Australopithecus—the earliest and smallest was most likely an ancestor to both humans and later species of Australopithecus.

Teach from Visuals

To help students interpret the map and photographs depicting climate adaptations, ask:

- What types of climates are represented by the photographs and the map? *cold climate; hot, dry climates; and coastal climates*
- How do each of these shelters protect humans and enable them to live in each type of climate? *Shelters protect humans from snow and provide warmth. Adobe protects humans from the heat, keeping the home cool. The stilts of the beach house prevent the home from becoming flooded.*
- What is the relationship between population growth and habitat expansion? *As the population increases, the expansion of habitats increases, resulting in a loss of land space.*

DIFFERENTIATE INSTRUCTION

More Reading Support

A Where on Earth did the first humans appear? *in Africa*

B How do humans regulate indoor temperature? *by adding heat or air conditioning*

English Learners The "Explore Population Change" activity on p. 258 uses the imperative. The subject "you" is eliminated from the directions. For example, "Copy the graph on the right" is understood as "You copy the graph on the right." Make sure English learners understand how to read and follow these directions.

Ongoing Assessment

Describe how human populations differ from other populations.

Ask: What are two key factors that have increased Earth's carrying capacity for humans? *habitat expansion and technology*

Teach from Visuals

To help students interpret the photographs depicting technology, ask:

- How do these two types of technology differ? *One distributes water across farms to help crop growth. The other purifies water for human consumption.*
- How might these technologies be used together? *The water used on crops might be purified before it is transported.*

Develop Critical Thinking

PROVIDE EXAMPLES Ask students to give some specific examples of technology that have contributed to increased carrying capacity for humans. *Sample answers: discovery of antibiotics, improved surgical techniques, improved methods of sanitizing water supplies in the form of water treatment facilities, and improved methods of preparing and preserving food such as USDA inspections*

EXPLORE the BIG idea

Have students revisit "Internet Activity: Population Dynamics" on p. 239. Ask them to describe any human technologies that affected the populations they studied.

Ongoing Assessment

Describe how humans adapt to the environment.

Ask: What are two ways humans have adapted to their environment? *Sample answer: designing shelters for harsh conditions, inventing means of transportation*

CHECK YOUR READING *Sample answer: Food and shelter are manufactured and shipped throughout the world. Water is transported through pipes and dams. Water can also be purified for drinking.*

Technology

C

Limited resources and environmental conditions such as climate do not affect human population growth the way they do the growth of other biological populations. Humans have found ways to fit themselves into almost every climate by altering their clothing, shelter, diet, and means of transportation.

Scientific discoveries and the advances of technology—such as improved sanitation and medical care—have increased the standard of living and the life expectancy of many humans. Important goods such as food and shelter are manufactured and shipped around the world. Water, which is a limited resource, can be transported through pipes and dams to irrigate fields or reach normally dry areas. Water can also be purified for drinking or treated before it is released back into the environment.

CHECK YOUR READING How does technology help humans get resources they need for survival?

Technology

Transporting Water

Food is often grown on large farms. Humans have developed irrigation systems to carry water to the fields.

Purifying Water

Water that has been used by humans contains wastes that can be removed at large watertreatment plants.

Human populations are growing.

As you've read, humans have developed solutions to many limits on growth. These solutions have allowed the human population to grow rapidly. Scientists are studying the history of this growth and trying to predict whether it will continue or change.

DIFFERENTIATE INSTRUCTION

More Reading Support

C What types of things do humans alter in order to fit into every type of climate? *clothing, shelter, diet, transportation*

Below Level Have students compare and contrast the population changes of some countries of their choice in Europe, Asia, South America, and Africa. Have them note whether the populations have increased or decreased during the past 10 to 20 years. Have them note what caused the change in population.

History of Human Population Growth

Learn more about world-wide human population growth.

Until about 300 years ago, the human population grew slowly. Disease, climate, and the availability of resources limited population size. Most offspring did not survive to adulthood. Even though birthrates were high, death rates were also high.

Notice the human population on the graph below. Many historical events have affected its growth. For example, the development of agriculture provided humans with a more stable food source. This in turn helped support human population growth. Today, populations across many parts of the world are increasing rapidly. Scientists identify three conditions that allow for rapid growth: the availability of resources, lack of predators, and survival of offspring to reproductive age. As these conditions change, so does the population.

D

Population Projections

To help prepare for the future, scientists make predictions called population projections. Population projections forecast how a population will change, based on its present size and age structure. Population projections provide a picture of what the future might look like. Using population projections, government agencies, resource managers, and economists can plan to meet the future needs of a population.

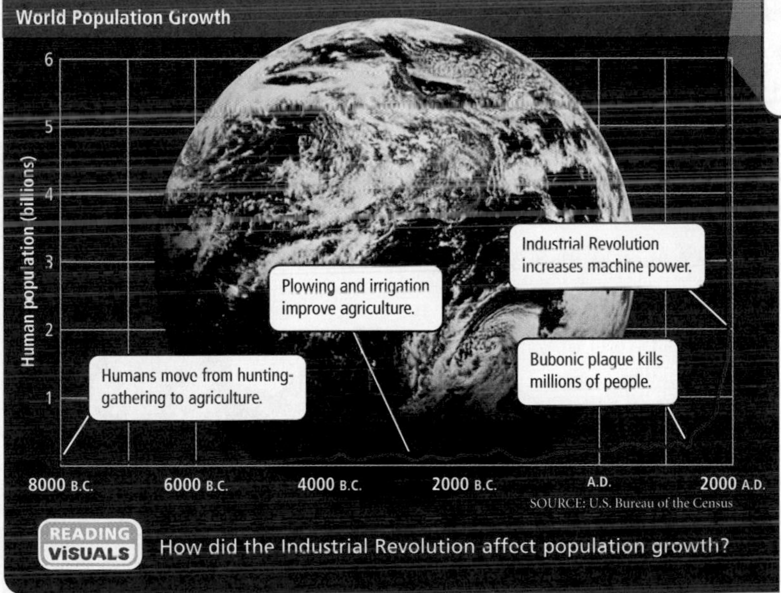

READING VISUALS How did the Industrial Revolution affect population growth?

Current Projection

High
Medium
Low
2000 2025 2050
SOURCE: United Nations, 2002 data

The blowout of the graph shows three projections for the human population size. Experts disagree about the rate at which the population will grow.

History of Science

The Industrial Revolution began in Great Britain during the late 1700s. It was the beginning of the transformation of traditional agricultural societies into industrial-based economies. The industrial revolution continues today in countries that are in early stages of industrial development. The invention of the flying shuttle, the steam engine, and the spinning jenny transformed cities into industrial centers.

Teacher Demo

Demonstrate the concept of one billion. Display a ream of 500 pages of paper. Ask students to predict how tall a stack of reams would be if it were made up of one billion pages. Write their predictions on the board. *A ream of paper is about 2 inches deep. A stack of one billion pages would reach a height of about 63 miles, more than 10 times the height of Mount Everest.*

Teach from Visuals

To help students interpret the diagram of world population growth, ask:

- At what point in human population growth did it reach rapid growth? *after the Industrial Revolution*
- What is the world population at the present time? *between 5 and 6 billion people*

Ongoing Assessment

READING VISUALS *Answer: The Industrial Revolution led to rapid increase in population growth.*

DIFFERENTIATE INSTRUCTION

More Reading Support

D What three conditions allow for rapid growth of human populations? *available resources, lack of predators, survival of offspring*

Advanced Challenge students to find the current population of the United States and the five most populated countries in the world. Then have them research population projections. Ask:

- What are three concerns about population growth?
- How does population growth in other countries affect us?
- What effects will another billion people have?

R Challenge and Extension, p. 158

INVESTIGATE Population

PURPOSE To investigate population growth in your area

TIPS *30 min.* Population figures can be obtained from the United States Census bureau at www.census.gov. Your town may also have a website that provides demographic information. You may substitute data for a larger or neighboring area if it is more readily available. Point out that the scale of numbers along the *y*-axis should reflect the population size of your community.

INCLUSION Provide large graph paper in poster size for students to work with. Show the *x*- and *y*-axes with colored markers. You may also wish to provide the scale of numbers in matching colors for both axes on a separate sheet of paper. Guide students in filling in the numerical information along each axis on the graph.

WHAT DO YOU THINK? *Answers will be based on the population changes in your community. Students should mention that a change in birthrate or age structure, and/or a change in immigration to the area or emigration from it, caused the change in population size.*

CHALLENGE *Student predictions may include rapid growth. They should reflect the concepts of population growth in this chapter.*

 Datasheet, Population, p. 159

Technology Resources

Customize this student lab as needed or look for an alternative. Print rubrics to assess student lab reports.

 **Lab Generator CD-ROM**

Teaching with Technology

Have students use graphing software to set up their graphs.

CHECK YOUR READING *population size, age structure, ages of individuals having children, average number of offspring produced by an individual, life expectancy, health*

In addition to population size and age structure, scientists making population projections consider other factors. These factors include the ages of individuals having children. The average number of offspring produced by an individual also affects projections. In addition, life expectancy and health in a particular population affect population growth.

The factors affecting population growth vary from society to society. The human population in the African country Botswana provides an example of how disease and health can affect population growth.

E F In some African countries, death rates due to HIV/AIDS have lowered population projections for the year 2015 by almost 18 percent. Botswana's population will decline, because more than 30 percent of adults are infected with HIV/AIDS. So many people in Botswana have already died of HIV/AIDS that the average life expectancy has dropped from 63 years of age in the late 1980s to 32 years in 2003. Consider the impact this will have on the population's age structure. Because many people who die from HIV/AIDS are in their reproductive years, the long-term effects on population growth will be significant.

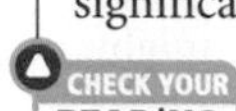 What factors do scientists consider when they make population projections?

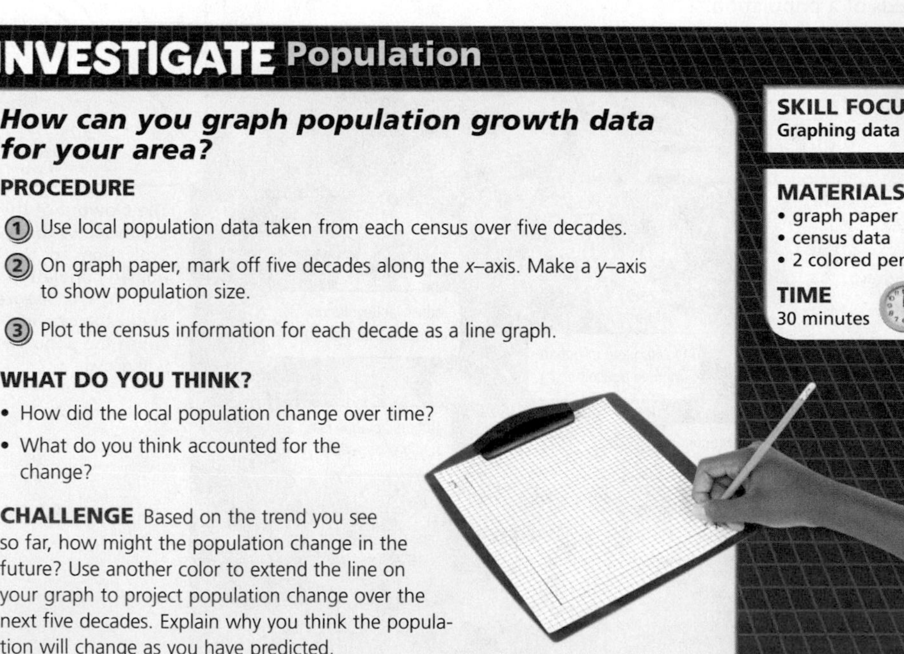

INVESTIGATE Population

How can you graph population growth data for your area?

PROCEDURE

1. Use local population data taken from each census over five decades.
2. On graph paper, mark off five decades along the *x*–axis. Make a *y*–axis to show population size.
3. Plot the census information for each decade as a line graph.

WHAT DO YOU THINK?

- How did the local population change over time?
- What do you think accounted for the change?

CHALLENGE Based on the trend you see so far, how might the population change in the future? Use another color to extend the line on your graph to project population change over the next five decades. Explain why you think the population will change as you have predicted.

SKILL FOCUS
Graphing data

MATERIALS
- graph paper
- census data
- 2 colored pencils

TIME
30 minutes

DIFFERENTIATE INSTRUCTION

More Reading Support

E Why will Botswana's population decline? *More than 30 percent of adults have HIV/AIDS.*

F What was the life expectancy in Botswana, 2003? *32 years*

Advanced Have students choose one country in Africa and use Internet resources to research the country's demographics. Students should find out the current population and age structure of the country. Challenge students to construct an age structure diagram based on their research. They can then make predictions about population growth or decline based on their diagrams.

Human population growth affects the environment.

You have read that extinction of species is a part of the history of life on Earth. The ways a population uses and disposes of resources have a great impact on local and global environments. As the human population continues to grow and use more resources, it contributes to the decline and extinction of other populations.

Some scientists estimate that over 99 percent of the species that have ever existed on Earth are now extinct. Most of these species vanished long before humans came on the scene. However, some experts are concerned that human activity is causing other species to become extinct at a much higher rate than they would naturally. Human populations put pressure on the environment in many ways, including

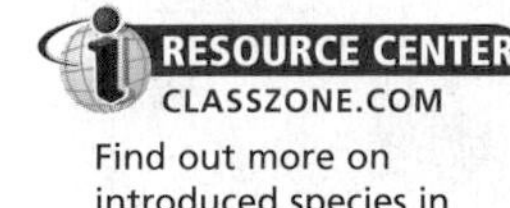

RESOURCE CENTER
CLASSZONE.COM
Find out more on introduced species in the United States.

G
- introduction of new species
- pollution
- overfishing

Introduction of New Species

Travelers have introduced new species to areas both on purpose and by accident. Many species introduced to an area provide benefits, such as food or beauty. Some species, however, cause harm to ecosystems. One example of an introduced species is the zebra mussel. An ocean vessel accidentally released zebra mussels from Europe into the Great Lakes region of the United States. With no natural predators that consume them, the mussels have reproduced quickly, invading all of the Great Lakes, the Mississippi River, and the Hudson River. The mussels compete with native species for food and affect water quality, endangering the ecosystem.

Kudzu is another introduced species. In the 1930s, kudzu was used in the southeastern United States to keep soil from being washed away. The plants, which have beautiful purple flowers, were imported from Japan. Starch made from kudzu is also a popular ingredient in some Asian recipes. However, populations of the kudzu vines planted in the United States have grown too far and too fast. Kudzu grows as much as 0.3 meters (about a foot) per day, killing trees and other plants living in the same area.

The kudzu plant, though at one time considered beautiful, is threatening other species.

263

Address Misconceptions

IDENTIFY Ask students to list some ways that humans affect the environment. Some students might hold the misconception that humans interact directly with all organisms. Other students might think only in terms of the needs of individual organisms rather than populations.

CORRECT Have students reread the end of the chapter. Have them note how humans interact with other organisms and if human actions affect individuals, populations as a whole, or both.

REASSESS Ask students to revise or add to their list of ways that humans affect the environment.

Technology Resources

Visit **ClassZone.com** for background on common student misconceptions.

MISCONCEPTION DATABASE

Real World Example

The Africanized honeybee was introduced into the United States when it was accidentally released from research hives in Brazil in 1956. The bees were originally brought to Brazil from Africa with the intention of genetically improving European bees to make them more suitable to South America. The Africanized honey bees interbred with European honey bees in the wild, and their strains reproduced more rapidly. Since 1956 the bees have swarmed over South and Central America through Mexico. They made their way into the United States in 1990 and are currently found in Arizona and parts of New Mexico and California.

DIFFERENTIATE INSTRUCTION

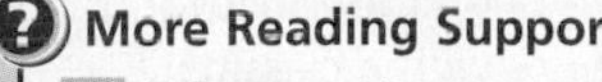

More Reading Support

G What are three ways that humans affect the environment? *introduction of new species, overfishing, pollution*

Additional Investigation To reinforce Section 8.3 learning goals, use the following full-period investigation:

R **Additional INVESTIGATION,** Introduced Species and Population Dynamics, A, B, & C, pp. 177–185, 188–189 (Advanced students should complete Levels B and C.)

Advanced Have students choose an invasive species and research where the species originated, how it came to the U.S., and its impact on the environment. Students may choose the species to research or find information at www.invasive species.gov.

Address Misconceptions

IDENTIFY Ask students to name some of the harmful affects of pollution. Students may hold several misconceptions regarding pollution. Many students do not think that harm to plants constitutes an environmental problem. Other misconceptions include:

- Anything natural is not pollution.
- Biodegradable materials are not pollutants.
- Oceans are a limitless resource.
- Solid waste dumps are safe.
- The human race is indestructible as a species.

CORRECT Have students make a list of the harmful effects of pollution and overfishing.

REASSESS Ask students to revise or add to the lists they made after they have had a chance to view each other's lists. They should think of ways that pollution affects plants, animals, and natural resources in the environment.

Technology Resources

Visit **ClassZone.com** for background on common student misconceptions.

MISCONCEPTION DATABASE

Teach from Visuals

To help students interpret the photograph of the Salton Sea, ask:

How does the Salton Sea become polluted by farms and industries that are miles away? *Used water drains off the land through rivers and into the ground from storms and flooding. Pipes also transport the used water from irrigation drains to the Salton Sea.*

Pollution

While human activities might cause some populations to decline, they can also cause other populations to grow. Sometimes this population growth causes pollution and habitat disturbance. **Pollution** is the addition of harmful substances to the environment. One example of such an activity is large-scale hog farming.

Large-scale hog farms affect water, soil, and air quality.

Human demands for pork combined with a growing human population have caused the hog farming industry to expand. Between 1987 and 2001, the hog population in North Carolina grew from 2.6 million to 10 million. These 10 million hogs produced more than 50,000 tons of waste each day. Wastes from large populations of hogs affect water supplies, soil, and air quality.  H

Pollution has also affected the Salton Sea in southeastern California. The growing demand for goods and agriculture has led to chemical dumping from industries and pesticide runoff from nearby farms. The rivers that run into the lake carry high levels of harmful chemicals such as DDT. Local birds that live and feed in this area have weakened shells that cannot support baby birds. Pollution has also caused fish to become deformed.

Pollution

The Salton Sea in California is surrounded by farm fields and industries that contribute to pollution.

DIFFERENTIATE INSTRUCTION

More Reading Support

H What three things in the environment were affected by hog waste? *water supply, soil, air quality*

Below Level Have students choose one of the following activities. Ask students to share their work with a classmate.

- Make a list of 10 things that you can do to reduce pollution and waste.
- Identify an endangered or threatened species in your state. In what ways did population growth and habitat expansion lead to the species endangerment? What is being done to protect the species?

Overfishing

Fish and crustaceans such as shrimp and lobsters have long been an important food source for many people. In the 1900s, the techniques and equipment that fishers used allowed them to catch so many fish that fish populations began to decrease. As the human population has continued to grow, so has the demand for fish. However, if fish do not survive long enough in the wild, they do not have the chance to reproduce. Many species have been so overfished that their populations may not recover.

Lobster fishing in particular has supported coastal communities in the northeastern United States for generations. But the demand for this food source has caused populations to decline. Areas that fishers trapped for years may now have only a small population of lobsters. And the lobsters fishers are catching may not be as large as those from earlier decades.

In order to help lobster populations recover, laws have been enforced to protect their life cycle and reproduction. Today, people who trap lobsters are required to release females with eggs. They are also allowed to keep only mature lobsters. Younger lobsters are returned to the waters to mature and reproduce. Efforts like these help protect the lobster population and secure the jobs of fishers by helping fish populations remain stable.

Fishers harvesting lobster measure the tails of the animals they catch. A lobster that is too small is returned to the sea to allow it to grow.

 Describe how overfishing would affect resources.

8.3 Review

KEY CONCEPTS

1. What factors—other than birth, death, immigration, and emigration—must scientists consider when making projections of human population?
2. Give an example of how Earth's carrying capacity for humans has increased.
3. What are three ways that humans affect other populations?

CRITICAL THINKING

4. **Infer** Consider the effect of HIV/AIDS on Botswana's human population. How might age structure affect Botswana's population growth?
5. **Analyze** Do you think it is possible to predict the maximum number of humans that Earth can support? Why or why not?

CHALLENGE

6. **Apply** Identify a challenge faced by the human population in your state. Explain how the challenge is related to pollution, introduction of new species, habitat disturbance, or overfishing.

ANSWERS

1. Scientists must also consider the age structure of a population and whether factors such as disease affect health and age expectancy.

2. Humans have shaped their environment—mostly through technology and habitat expansion.

3. Introduction of new species, overfishing and pollution, contribute to the decline and extinction of other species.

4. If people are dying at a younger age, many may not survive to reproduce. The population will most likely decline.

5. Students may suggest that maximum population can be calculated by comparing the land mass with the number of people it can support.

6. Answers should reflect the concepts in this chapter.

Ongoing Assessment

Describe how human populations affect the environment.

Ask: How do laws protect the lobster population from being overfished? *Fishers must return females with eggs back into the water and can only keep mature lobsters.*

 *Answer: Fish populations may not recover.*

Reinforce the BIG idea

Have students relate the section to the Big Idea.

 Reinforcing Key Concepts, p. 160

8.3 ASSESS & RETEACH

Assess

A Section 8.3 Quiz, p. 43

Reteach

Write the following concepts on the board. Ask volunteers to give one detail or fact about each concept. Write their responses below each concept.

- Human population is expanding. *Sample answer: The population is experiencing rapid growth.*
- Scientists make predictions using population projections. *Sample answer: Characteristics such as age structure allow scientists to predict changes to the birth rate and death rate.*
- Human population growth affects the environment. *Sample answer: Land development destroys habitats. Humans use resources and kill some populations, such as salmon and lobster, for food.*

Technology Resources

Have students visit **ClassZone.com** for reteaching of Key Concepts.

 CONTENT REVIEW

 CONTENT REVIEW CD-ROM

CHAPTER INVESTIGATION

Focus

PURPOSE To model sustainable resource management

OVERVIEW Students will use craft sticks to model the population of trees in a forest and simulate the harvesting of these trees. Students then use their observations to:

- conclude what happens when trees are harvested to meet the needs of population growth.
- calculate the rate of depletion of a renewable resource.

Lab Preparation

- Prior to the investigation, ask students to bring to class empty coffee cans from home. Ask volunteers to count and place 120 craft sticks into each container and to wrap bundles of 32 sticks with rubberbands.
- If craft sticks are unavailable, toothpicks may be used instead.
- Prior to the investigation, have students read through the investigation and prepare their data tables. Or you may wish to copy and distribute datasheets and rubrics.

UNIT RESOURCE BOOK, pp. 168–176

SCIENCE TOOLKIT, F14

Lab Management

- Make sure students have assigned each member of the group one of the roles described under the Procedure.
- Be sure to demonstrate, or have a volunteer demonstrate, proper use of the stopwatch before the lab.
- Watches with a minute hand can be used in place of stopwatches.

INCLUSION Prepare charts as shown on the student page with headings in different colors for easy reference.

CHAPTER INVESTIGATION

Sustainable Resource Management

OVERVIEW AND PURPOSE Wood is a renewable resource, but the demand for wood is continuing to grow worldwide. Humans are harvesting trees more quickly than trees have the ability to grow and replace themselves. The result is a forest in decline. In this activity you will

- model what happens when trees are harvested to meet the needs of a growing population
- calculate the rate at which the population of a renewable resource declines

MATERIALS
- coffee can with 120 craft sticks
- bundle of 32 craft sticks
- stopwatch

Question

Write It Up

How can people meet the ongoing human demand for wood without using all the trees? You will use the increasing human demand for wood to determine how overuse of a resource might affect a population. What would you like to discover about resource management? Write a question that begins with *Which, How, Why, When,* or *What.*

Procedure

1. Copy the data table on page 267 into your **Science Notebook.**
2. In your group of classmates, decide who will fill each of the following roles: forest, timer, forest manager, harvester/record keeper.
3. **Forest:** Get a coffee can of 120 craft sticks. These sticks represent the available tree supply.
4. **Timer:** Sound off each 15-second interval and each minute.

INVESTIGATION RESOURCES

CHAPTER INVESTIGATION, Sustainable Resource Management
- Level A, pp. 168–171
- Level B, pp. 172–175
- Level C, p. 176

Advanced students should complete Levels B & C.

Writing a Lab Report, D12–13

Technology Resources

Customize this student lab as needed or look for an alternative. Print rubrics to assess student lab reports.

Lab Generator CD-ROM

5 **Forest Manager:** Get 32 sticks from the teacher. You will add 1 new tree every 15 seconds by putting a stick in the coffee can.

6 **Harvester:** At the end of the first minute, cut down 1 tree by removing 1 stick from the coffee can. At the end of the second minute, cut down 2 trees; at the end of the third, cut down 4 trees. At the end of each additional minute cut down twice as many trees as you did before. This represents the doubling of the demand for trees based on human population growth.

Observe and Analyze

Write It Up

1. **CALCULATE** At the end of each minute, add 4 trees, but subtract twice as many trees as you subtracted the minute before.
2. **RECORD AND CALCULATE** Complete the chart. How many trees are left in the forest after 8 minutes of harvesting?

Conclude

1. **INFER** What effect does increasing human population growth have on forests?
2. **EVALUATE** Was the forest always shrinking?
3. **EVALUATE** How does this investigation help you to answer or change your question about resource management?
4. **IDENTIFY LIMITS** What aspects of this investigation fail to model the natural habitat?
5. **APPLY** What other renewable resources need sustainable management?

INVESTIGATE Further

CHALLENGE Explain how you could use the data gathered in this investigation to develop methods of sustainable resource management.

Sustainable Resource Management

Table 1. Rate of Harvest

Minutes	Number of Trees at Start of Minute	Number of New Trees	Number of Trees Harvested	Number of Trees at End of Minute
1	120	+4	−1	123
2				
3				
4				
5				
6				
7				
8				

Observe and Analyze

1. *Student should add a total of 28 new trees and subtract a total of 127 trees.*
2. *Sample answer: 21 trees will be left.*

Conclude

1. *Increasing human population is depleting forest resources.*
2. *No, the forest was not always shrinking.*
3. *Answers will vary depending on student questions.*
4. *The model does not take any of the many limiting factors in ecosystems—such as light, water, space, competition for resources, and so on—into account.*
5. *Possible answers: fresh water, ocean resources, land, and air*

INVESTIGATE Further

CHALLENGE Answers should show an understanding of the concept of sustainable management. For example, students can replace a greater number of trees every 15 seconds to compensate for the loss of trees.

Post-Lab Discussion

- Ask students what questions about sustainable resource management have been raised by developing their models. How is the model different from managing a real forest? How would they design a test for the effects of harvesting rates in a real managed forest?
- What are some ways that humans can apply sustainable use practices to other renewable resources? *Sample answer: People can care for soil in a way that does not deplete it.*

BACK TO

the BIG idea

Have students look back at the photograph on pp. 238 and 239. Have them summarize what they have learned about the factors that affect population growth. *Students should include a discussion of population dynamics, limiting factors, and what makes human population unique.*

KEY CONCEPTS SUMMARY

SECTION 8.1

Ask students to describe what happens in each stage of population growth. *In the growth stage, the population increases. In the stability stage, the population maintains a constant level. In the decline stage, the population decreases.*

SECTION 8.2

Which factors lead to population growth? Which lead to population decline? *Birth and immigration lead to growth. Death and emigration lead to decline.*

SECTION 8.3

What are two factors that humans control, which might normally limit a biological population? *They can regulate temperatures with heat and air conditioning and build shelters that protect them from the environment.*

Review Concepts

- Big Idea Flow Chart, p. T17
- Chapter Outline, pp. T23–T24

8 Chapter Review

the BIG idea

Populations are shaped by interactions between organisms and the environment.

KEY CONCEPTS SUMMARY

1 Populations have many characteristics.

- Populations go through three stages:
  growth
  stability
  decline
- Four characteristics define a population:
  size
  density
  spacing
  age structure
- Scientists can predict population changes.

VOCABULARY
population dynamics p. 241
carrying capacity p. 242
population size p. 244
population density p. 245

2 Populations respond to pressures.

Populations change as they respond to pressures from limiting factors.

Two types of limiting factors are density dependent and density independent.

VOCABULARY
immigration p. 251
emigration p. 251
limiting factor p. 252
opportunist p. 255
competitor p. 256

3 Human populations have unique responses to change.

Humans can control many factors that limit most biological populations.

VOCABULARY
pollution p. 264

Technology Resources

Have students visit **ClassZone.com** or use the CD-ROM for a cumulative review of concepts.

 **CONTENT REVIEW**

 **CONTENT REVIEW CD-ROM**

Engage students in a whole-class interactive review of Key Concepts. Edit content as you wish.

 **POWER PRESENTATIONS**

Reviewing Vocabulary

Describe how the vocabulary terms in the following pairs are related to each other. Explain the relationship in a one- or two-sentence answer. Underline each vocabulary term in your answers.

1. population dynamics and carrying capacity
2. immigration and emigration
3. limiting factor and population density
4. opportunists and competitors

Reviewing Key Concepts

Multiple Choice *Choose the letter of the best answer.*

5. The study of changes in a population over time and the factors that affect these changes is called population
   - **a.** stability
   - **b.** dynamics
   - **c.** spacing
   - **d.** density
6. A population that has reached its maximum size in a given area is said to have reached its
   - **a.** population range
   - **b.** gradual growth
   - **c.** carrying capacity
   - **d.** population projection
7. Assuming there is no immigration or emigration, a population size will remain constant if
   - **a.** the birth rate equals the death rate
   - **b.** the birth rate exceeds the death rate
   - **c.** the death rate exceeds the birth rate
   - **d.** the birth rate increases constantly
8. Distinct patterns in a population such as clumped, uniform, or random populations are examples of population
   - **a.** density
   - **b.** spacing
   - **c.** growth
   - **d.** dynamics
9. Which factors affect the size and growth of a population?
   - **a.** number of births and deaths
   - **b.** emigration and immigration
   - **c.** competition between populations
   - **d.** all of the above
10. A limiting factor that depends on the size of the population in a given area is a
    - **a.** density-dependent factor
    - **b.** density-independent factor
    - **c.** reproduction survival strategy
    - **d.** carrying capacity
11. Density-independent limiting factors include
    - **a.** predators
    - **b.** parasites
    - **c.** floods
    - **d.** competition
12. Which are abiotic factors in an environment?
    - **a.** disease and parasites
    - **b.** air, light, and water
    - **c.** pollution and overfishing
    - **d.** competition and predators
13. Which is an example of competition for resources?
    - **a.** individuals in a population feeding on the same food sources
    - **b.** movement of seagulls into a population of other seagulls
    - **c.** an increase in the population of raccoons in a particular environment at a steady rate
    - **d.** a population of fruit trees producing less fruit because of drought
14. Two factors that have increased Earth's carrying capacity for humans are habitat expansion, and
    - **a.** habitat disturbance
    - **b.** strategies of competitors
    - **c.** strategies of opportunists
    - **d.** technology

Reviewing Vocabulary

1. *<u>Population dynamics</u> influence the carrying capacity. Population dynamics is the study of why and how populations change. <u>Carrying capacity</u> refers to the greatest number of organisms (within a population) an ecosystem can support.*
2. *Both are movement of populations. <u>Immigration</u> is the movement of individuals into an ecosystem, while <u>emigration</u> is the movement of individuals out of an ecosystem.*
3. *Some <u>limiting factors</u> are based on <u>population density</u>. Population density is the number of individuals within a given area. A limiting factor affects the growth of a population.*
4. *<u>Opportunists</u> include species that have short life spans and reproduce at large rates. <u>Competitors</u> are the opposite—they have shortened life spans and fewer offspring.*

Reviewing Key Concepts

5. b
6. c
7. a
8. b
9. d
10. a
11. c
12. b
13. a
14. d

(Answers to items that appear on p. 270)

Thinking Critically

15. *When more resources are available, a population tends to be denser.*
16. *the proportion of each age group within a population; post-reproductive, reproductive, and pre-reproductive*
17. *availability of resources, few predators, and survival of offspring to reproductive age*

ASSESSMENT RESOURCES

UNIT ASSESSMENT BOOK
- Chapter Test, Level A, pp. 44–47
- Chapter Test, Level B, pp. 48–51
- Chapter Test, Level C, pp. 52–55
- Alternative Assessment, pp. 56–57
- Unit Test, A, B, & C, pp. 58–69

SPANISH ASSESSMENT BOOK
- Spanish Chapter Test, pp. 29–32
- Spanish Unit Test, pp. 37–40

Technology Resources

Edit test items and answer choices.

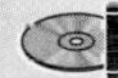 **Test Generator CD-ROM**

Visit **ClassZone.com** to extend test practice.

 **Test Practice**

(Answers for items 15–17 appear on p. 269.)

Thinking Critically

18. Gradual growth occurs after a period of rapid population growth. It can also occur after a period of immigration or emigration.
19. All populations are able to grow rapidly. Populations tend to remain constant in size. There are limits to natural resources. A population can have genetic variation.
20. about 60,000 individuals; it is following a pattern of rapid growth.
21. The population would likely increase because a large percentage of individuals are at the pre-reproductive and reproductive stages.
22. Sample answer: competition, disease, or a natural disaster; in all cases, the populations would likely decrease.
23. Sample answer: The increase of HIV/AIDS infected persons has affected the population of several African countries. Countries such as Botswana show a decrease in population due to AIDS.
24. most likely a decline in the wolf population; most likely due to disease, since the wolves could not have emigrated
25. Growth rates differ because of disease, food supply, and advanced technologies.
26. Sample answers: introduction of new species, overkill of populations, pollution and habitat disturbance. Students may suggest that people monitor consumption, development, and population growth.

the BIG idea

27. Answers will be based on students' original answers.
28. Answers should include concepts and terms from the chapter.

UNIT PROJECTS

Have students present their projects. Use rubrics to evaluate the work.

Unit Projects, pp. 5–10

Short Answer *Write a short answer to each question.*

15. What factors might affect the density of a population?
16. What is the age structure of a population?
17. Describe three factors that account for the rapid growth of the human population during the past 500 years.

Thinking Critically

18. **ANALYZE** Under what conditions does gradual growth in a population occur?
19. **COMMUNICATE** Describe four observations that Darwin made about population growth.
20. **PREDICT** The graph below shows the exponential growth rate of a colony of unicellular organisms. If the population continues to grow at the same rate during the next 2 hours, what will the population be after 10 hours? Explain your answer.

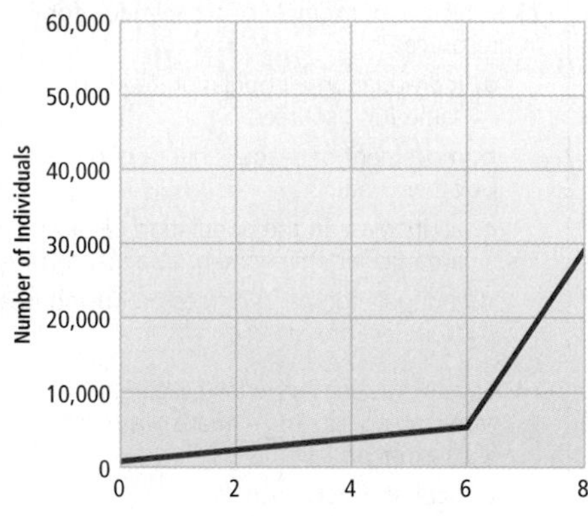

21. **PREDICT** In a certain population 35 percent of the individuals are under the age of 20. What predictions might you make about the size of the population in 10 years?
22. **PROVIDE EXAMPLES** What limiting factors might cause the carrying capacity of a population to change? Provide at least three examples. Describe how the population might change.
23. **SYNTHESIZE** What is an example of a density-independent factor that has affected a human population? Describe how this factor changed the population.
24. **INFER** Wolves are the natural predators of moose. Both populations are found on an island in the middle of Lake Superior. During one season, the population of moose increased dramatically. What could have caused the increase in the moose population?
25. **EVALUATE** Why do you suppose that the growth rate of human populations differs dramatically in different countries?
26. **SYNTHESIZE** Human activity has resulted in the decline of many populations of other species. Choose one example of how humans have put pressure on species around the world and describe ways that humans can avoid causing continued decreases in these populations.

the BIG idea

27. **INFER** Look again at the picture on pages 238–239. Now that you have finished the chapter, how would you change or add details to your answer to the question on the photograph?
28. **SUMMARIZE** Write one or more paragraphs describing the factors that affect population size, density, and age structure. Use the following terms in your descriptions.

immigration	density-dependent factors
emigration	density-independent factors
limiting factors	

UNIT PROJECTS

If you need to do an experiment for your unit project, gather the materials. Be sure to allow enough time to observe results before the project is due.

MONITOR AND RETEACH

If students are having trouble applying the concepts in Chapter Review items 23, 24, and 25, suggest that they review the illustrations of the limiting factors on pp. 252 and 253. Then have students create a concept map of density-dependent and density-independent factors.

Students may benefit from summarizing one or more sections of the chapter.

 Summarizing the Chapter, pp. 186–187

Standardized Test Practice

For practice on your state test, go to . . . TEST PRACTICE CLASSZONE.COM

Analyzing Data

The graph below is an example of a population growth curve.

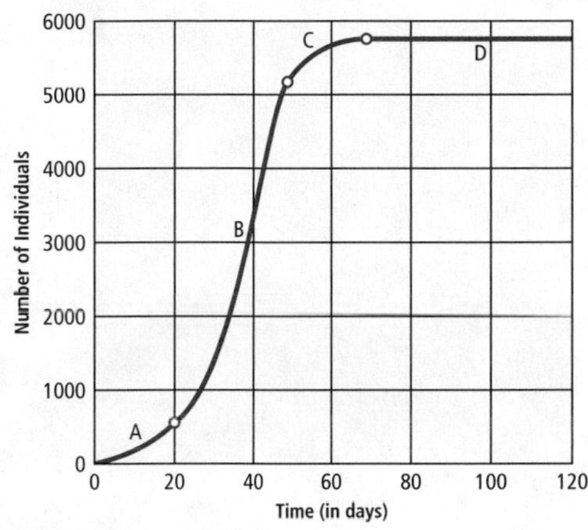

Use the graph to answer the questions below.

1. What does the time interval marked *D* represent?
   - **a.** Population is decreasing.
   - **b.** Carrying capacity has been reached.
   - **c.** Birth rates exceed death rates.
   - **d.** Population is growing.

2. Which time interval on the graph represents gradual growth?
   - **a.** interval A and interval B
   - **b.** interval C and interval D
   - **c.** interval C only
   - **d.** interval D only

3. During which time interval do limiting factors in a population begin to have an effect on the population growth?
   - **a.** interval A only
   - **b.** interval B only
   - **c.** interval C only
   - **d.** interval C and interval D

4. This graph represents a typical
   - **a.** gradual curve
   - **b.** rapid curve
   - **c.** slow curve
   - **d.** flat curve

5. What conclusion can you draw from the information in the graph?
   - **a.** Density-dependent factors have had no effect on the population shown on the graph.
   - **b.** The graph indicates an absence of disease and a supply of unlimited resources.
   - **c.** Resources have become more available, so the population continues to increase exponentially.
   - **d.** As resources become less available, the population rate slows or stops.

Extended Response

6. What part of the graph above shows the growth of the human population during the last 500 years? Explain. What are some factors that might allow the human population to reach its carrying capacity?

7. Choose a population of organisms in your area. Describe the limiting factors that may affect the growth of that population. Make sure you include both density-dependent and density-independent factors in your discussion.

METACOGNITIVE ACTIVITY

Have students answer the following questions in their **Science Notebook:**

1. What questions do you still have about population dynamics?
2. What helped you best to understand how human populations differ from other biological populations?
3. What might you change about the way you approached your unit project that would help you find and present information more efficiently?

Analyzing Data

1. b *3. d* *5. d*

2. c *4. a*

Extended Response

6. RUBRIC

4 points for a response that correctly answers the question and gives four examples of factors that allow a population to reach its carrying capacity.

Sample answer: Time interval B, which shows exponential growth, shows the growth rate of the human population during the past 500 years. Factors that could contribute to its reaching its carrying capacity are famine, wars, natural disasters that occur on a worldwide basis, diseases that have no cure and spread rapidly, depletion of natural resources on a worldwide scale, and loss of space for suitable habitats.

3 points correctly answers the question and gives examples of three factors

2 points correctly answers the question and gives examples of two factors

1 point correctly answers the question and gives an example of one factor

7. RUBRIC

4 points for a response that correctly answers the question and includes at least two of the following limiting factors:

- density-dependent: competition, predation, disease, parasitism
- density-independent: storms, floods, fires, drought

Sample answer: As a population of deer increases, they may be limited by competition for resources as well as disease. The more densely populated the area, the more likely it is for these factors to limit the deer herd. However, natural events, such as storms or forest fires, will occur regardless of the population size.

3 points response includes two density-dependent factors and one density-independent factor or vice versa

2 points response includes one density-dependent factor and one density-independent factor

1 point response includes either one density-dependent factor or one density-independent factor

McDougal Littell Science

Diversity of Living Things

ANIMALS

fungi

adaptations

PLANTS

Diversity of Living Things Contents Overview

Unit Features

FRONTIERS in Science

VIDEO SUMMARY

SCIENTIFIC AMERICAN FRONTIERS

"Frozen Alive," a segment of the *Scientific American Frontiers* series that aired on PBS, explores animal species that can survive freezing temperatures. Scientists hope that understanding the adaptations of these animals might lead to new technologies. It might be possible to freeze donated human organs and tissues. If the organs could be frozen safely without destroying their functions, they could be preserved until needed.

The two animals featured in the video are the flounder and the wood frog. When the days shorten, a flounder's body begins to produce a protein that acts like antifreeze in the bloodstream. This keeps the fish's blood from freezing at low temperatures. Similarly, when temperatures drop, wood frogs dig into the ground, and fluids in their bodies freeze solid. Extra glucose in the frog's liver lowers the freezing point, preserves the organs, and later promotes simultaneous thawing throughout the body. By studying these natural responses to extreme conditions, scientists hope to save more human lives.

National Science Education Standards

A.1–8 Abilities Necessary to Do Scientific Inquiry

A.9.a–b, A.9.d–g Understandings About Scientific Inquiry

F.5.e Science and Technology in Society

G.1.a–b Science as a Human Endeavor

G.2.a, G.2.c Nature of Science

FRONTIERS in Science

Chilling Changes

How do organisms survive in this chilly Arctic landscape? Scientists are studying how organisms have adapted to the extreme cold of Earth's northern climates.

SCIENTIFIC AMERICAN FRONTIERS

Learn more about how living things respond to freezing temperatures in the video "Frozen Alive."

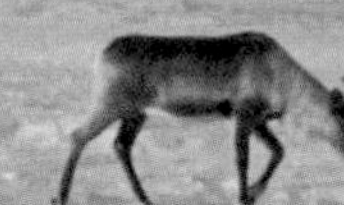

Caribou search for lichen and small plants to eat in northern Alaska.

274 Unit 3: Diversity of Living Things

ADDITIONAL RESOURCES

Technology Resources

Scientific American Frontiers Video: *Frozen Alive:* 11-minute video segment that introduces the unit.

ClassZone.com
CAREER LINK, Zoologist

Guide student viewing and comprehension of the video:

Video Teaching Guide, pp. 1–2; Video Viewing Guide, p. 3; Video Wrap-Up, p. 4

Scientific American Frontiers Video Guide, pp. 7–10

Unit projects procedures and rubrics:

Unit Projects, pp. 5–10

Lichen find materials and living space on rocks in frozen environments.

When Life Chills Out

When faced with the approach of winter, some animals hurry up, and some slow down. You may have seen animals getting a move on, migrating to warmer places. Other animals stay alive at home by hibernating, or entering a sleep-like state. Hibernation conserves energy until spring by slowing down many body processes. But what happens when an organism's body temperature dips below freezing?

Ice formation inside an organism's body is one of the most serious, and potentially damaging, threats to winter survival. If ice forms inside cells, it can damage the cell's operation and tear holes in the cell membrane, almost certainly leading to death.

An arctic ground squirrel peers above snow-covered ground in Alaska.

Some animals and plants take cold weather survival to an extreme. Some frogs and insects can allow their bodies to freeze solid. Some fish have fluids in their bodies that can *cool* below the freezing point of water and still flow. How do they do it?

Scientists studying survivors of extreme cold are not just learning about the ways organisms respond in the wild. Research on cold weather survival helps scientists understand problems faced by human society. Growing crops year-round and using bacteria to clean up pollution in a frozen environment are two examples. There are two main responses that allow living things to live in a subfreezing world.

DIFFERENTIATE INSTRUCTION

More Reading Support

A What do you call passing the winter in a sleeplike state? *hibernation*

B What happens if ice forms inside a cell? *The cell dies.*

Advanced Lichens are composite organisms of fungi in symbiosis with algae or cyanobacteria or both. Have students research lichens, focusing on how the symbiosis enables lichens to grow in extreme climates. Students could present their findings on a poster.

FOCUS

Set Learning Goals

Students will

- Analyze the harmful effects of very cold temperatures.
- Examine ways that animals and plants survive in extreme cold.
- Explore how various organisms respond to changes in their environment.

Point out that extremely cold environments are geographic frontiers as well as scientific ones. In order to study them, scientists have to first develop equipment and techniques for survival. Ask: Where are the extremely cold climates on Earth? *the Arctic, Antarctica, winter in temperate forests, ocean depths, mountaintops*

INSTRUCT

Scientific Process

Emphasize that, to determine how organisms survive in extreme cold, scientists must make very close, thorough observations. Also, observations of wildlife must sometimes take place for an extended time, requiring patience and accurate monitoring and recording of detail.

Technology Design

Learning how an animal's body changes in response to heat requires technologies that allow scientists to observe body processes without harming the animal or changing the course of the process that is being observed. In response to this challenge, scientists make use of noninvasive medical imaging tools such as CAT scans and MRIs.

Scientific Process

When Ken Storey began studying wood frogs, he theorized that they thaw in the same way objects do, warming from the outside in. Once he was able to scan frogs that were thawing, however, he had to reject that hypothesis. His observation showed that the internal organs, such as the heart and liver, are the first to thaw.

Integrate the Sciences

For a long time, scientists thought that life could survive only on Earth. Now, because researchers have found that microorganisms can live under extreme conditions, scientists have revised their knowledge about life and the conditions that can support it. In early 2004 *Spirit*, a NASA rover, looked for signs of water on Mars. Water is one need of all living things.

Determining What Is Known

Ask: How could scientists use what they know about human reactions to cold to learn about other types of organisms? *Knowing how cold affects humans gives scientists a basis for comparing those responses to the responses of animals and other living things.*

Arctic woolly bear caterpillars may take many years to grow to full size.

When the caterpillar reaches full size, it forms a cocoon and changes into a moth.

Avoid Ice, or Tolerate It

Organisms can either avoid the forming of ice or tolerate it. Some animals, like a fish called a flounder, produce antifreeze proteins in their bodies. The proteins keep ice from forming in the blood and other fluids. The fluids thicken but still flow. They never turn to ice crystals. Scientists call this response freeze-avoidance. C

Other organisms—including some frogs, many types of insects, and some trees—do allow ice to form inside their bodies. In these organisms, ice forms, but only in the spaces outside the cells. Freeze-tolerant organisms pump fluid out of their cells. Specialized proteins located outside of the cells encourage ice to form there, rather than inside the cells.

Perhaps the champion of freeze tolerance is a small Arctic insect called the Arctic woolly bear caterpillar. It is only active for a few weeks out of the year, during the brief Arctic summer. It can take this caterpillar up to fifteen years to mature into a moth!

D

Temperatures during Arctic winters often fall as low as −70°C. Because the ground is frozen year-round, the caterpillars cannot burrow. Instead, their bodies freeze solid in winter, shutting down nearly all of their cellular activity and

View the "Frozen Alive" segment of your Scientific American Frontiers video to see how scientists studying fish and frogs have begun to solve the mysteries of life surviving a freeze.

IN THIS SCENE FROM THE VIDEO **How do the frog's systems start up again, after being shut down during freezing?**

WHAT BRINGS ON THE THAW? Ken Storey collects wood frogs. The frogs have an automatic response to cold temperatures, which allows Ken and his team to keep them in a freezer without killing them. Storey and his team know the "what" of freeze tolerance. They want to learn the "how." How does the frog stay alive during and after shutdown? Storey expects that the thawing process works in the usual way, that the frogs will begin to warm from the outside in. Instead he finds that internal organs begin the thaw. The liver is the first organ to activate. It produces glucose or sugar, which then gets other cells, those in the heart, to begin their work.

DIFFERENTIATE INSTRUCTION

More Reading Support

C What is one animal that avoids freezing? *Sample answer: flounder*

D What is one animal that tolerates freezing? *Sample answer: Arctic woolly caterpillar*

Below Level Have students construct a chart to organize information about cold-weather adaptations. The chart might include different animals and plants, the conditions in which they live, and the behavioral and physical adaptations that suit them to a cold environment. Point out that what seems like a "difficult environment" to us may be the best possible environment for an organism such as the Arctic wooly caterpillar. Discuss why this so.

expending almost no energy. Scientists have known for centuries that some insects can freeze over the winter, but only recently have they begun to understand exactly how insects' bodies change to allow them to freeze and thaw.

Scientist Ken Storey has discovered a set of genes that turn on, like a switch, in response to freezing temperatures. These genes are called master control genes, because they have the ability to turn other genes in the body on or off. In the case of freeze-tolerant animals, master control genes first turn off nearly all the genes in the body. Arctic woolly bear caterpillars have many thousands of genes, but during the winter most of those genes are turned off. Keeping genes turned off is an adaptation that helps the caterpillar conserve energy throughout the winter.

Is It Really Extreme?

Organisms have adapted to a wide variety of environments. The Arctic woolly bear caterpillar is suited to life near the Arctic Circle. Some organisms must be able to survive in the exact opposite—the extreme heat of deserts. Others thrive in extremely salty conditions. Some plants and bacteria can even live in places with dangerously high levels of poisonous chemicals.

An environment doesn't have to be extreme to present challenges to the organisms that live there. Animals in a forest or meadow still need to find food and shelter, avoid predators, and respond to changes. The organisms living in any environment face a unique set of challenges.

UNANSWERED Questions

As scientists learn more about how animals survive in extremely cold climates, they also uncover additional questions:

- Do animals respond to temperature or a lack of light?
- How do cellular processes that halt during the winter get started up again?
- Can scientists grow freeze resistant crops?

UNIT PROJECTS

As you study this unit, work alone or in a group on one of the projects listed below. Use the bulleted steps to guide your project.

Museum Exhibit

Plan a museum exhibit showing different ways in which animals respond to extreme environments.

- Research three to five types of organisms and find out what kind of environmental changes these organisms face.
- Design, make visuals, and write text to accompany your exhibit.

Grow a Fast Plant

Observe the entire life cycle of a plant in less than six weeks. Record your observations in a journal.

- Gather information and any materials necessary to grow and care for fast plants. Obtain fast plant seeds and plant them.
- Observe the plant for a few minutes every day. Make notes in your journal, and write weekly summaries.

Local Field Study

Report on organisms that live in your local area.

- Identify three organisms you see on a regular basis and learn more about how they survive throughout the year.
- Pick one plant or animal and observe it for a few minutes once a week in the morning and in the late afternoon. How does it change over time?

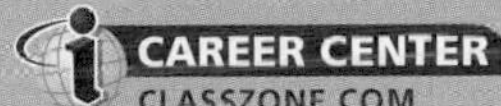

Learn more about careers in zoology.

UNANSWERED Questions

Have students read the questions and think of some of their own. Remind them that scientists always end up with more questions—that inquiry is the driving force of science.

- With the class, generate on the board a list of new questions.
- Students can add to the list after they watch the *Scientific American Frontiers* Video.
- Students can use the list as a springboard for choosing their Unit Projects.

UNIT PROJECTS

Encourage students to pick the project that most appeals to them. Point out that each is long-term and will take several weeks to complete. You might group or pair students to work on projects and in some cases guide student choice. Some of the projects have student choice built into them. Each project has two worksheet pages, including a rubric. Use the pages to guide students through criteria, process, and schedule.

 Unit Projects, pp. 5–10

REVISIT concepts introduced in this article:

Chapter 9
- Single-celled organisms have all the characteristics of living things, pp. 281–287
- Bacteria and Archaea are found in many environments, pp. 290–291

Chapter 10
- Multicellular organisms meet their needs in different ways, pp. 315–321
- Animals interact with the environment; animals respond to seasonal changes, pp. 334–336

Chapter 12
- Insects undergo metamorphosis, p. 418

Chapter 13
- Mammals are endotherms, pp. 455–456

DIFFERENTIATE INSTRUCTION

More Reading Support

E What types of environments present challenges for living things? *all environments*

Differentiate Unit Projects Projects are appropriate for varying abilities. Allow students to choose the ones that interest them most and let them vary their product. Encourage below level students to give visual or oral presentations or to record audio presentations about their topic.

Below Level Encourage students to try "Grow a Fast Plant."

Advanced Challenge students to complete "Local Field Study."

CHAPTER

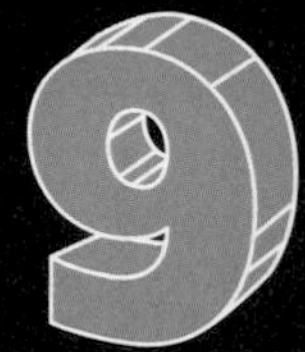

Single-Celled Organisms and Viruses

Life Science
UNIFYING PRINCIPLES

PRINCIPLE 1
All living things share common characteristics.

PRINCIPLE 2
All living things share common needs.

PRINCIPLE 3
Living things meet their needs through interactions with the environment.

PRINCIPLE 4
The types and numbers of living things change over time.

Unit 3: Diversity of Living Things
BIG IDEAS

CHAPTER 9
Single-Celled Organisms and Viruses
Bacteria and protists have the characteristics of living things, while viruses are not alive.

CHAPTER 10
Introduction to Multicellular Organisms
Multicellular organisms live in and get energy from a variety of environments.

CHAPTER 11
Plants
Plants are a diverse group of organisms that live in many land environments.

CHAPTER 12
Invertebrate Animals
Invertebrate animals have a variety of body plans and adaptations.

CHAPTER 13
Vertebrate Animals
Vertebrate animals live in most of Earth's environments.

CHAPTER 9
KEY CONCEPTS

SECTION 1

Single-celled organisms have all the characteristics of living things.
1. Living things come in many shapes and sizes.
2. Living things share common characteristics.
3. Living things need energy, materials, and living space.
4. Viruses are not alive.

SECTION 2

Bacteria are single-celled organisms without nuclei.
1. Bacteria and archaea are the smallest living things.
2. Archaea and bacteria are found in many environments.
3. Bacteria may help or harm other organisms.

SECTION 3

Viruses are not alive but affect living things.
1. Viruses share some characteristics with living things.
2. Viruses multiply inside living cells.
3. Viruses may harm host cells.

SECTION 4

Protists are a diverse group of organisms.
1. Most protists are single-celled.
2. Protists obtain their energy in three ways.

The Big Idea Flow Chart is available on p. T1 in the **UNIT TRANSPARENCY BOOK.**

Previewing Content

SECTION

Single-celled organisms have all the characteristics of living things.

pp. 281–287

1. Living things come in many shapes and sizes.
Living things range in size from the enormous honey mushroom fungus that is more than 5 kilometers wide to microorganisms that can be seen only with a microscope. This diversity of life is divided into six **kingdoms.**

- Archaea
- Bacteria
- Protists
- Animals
- Fungi
- Plants

2. Living things share common characteristics.
Certain characteristics are shared by all living things.

- Living things are organized into cells. Organisms that have only one cell have all the structures they need to survive.
- All living things grow. They consume food, build structures, and repair or replace worn-out structures.
- All living things reproduce, making more organisms like themselves. Single-celled organisms reproduce by **binary fission.**
- All living things respond to changes in their environment.

3. Living things need energy, materials, and living space.
Food supplies an organism with the energy it needs to move, grow, and develop. Organisms also need water and other materials.

- Water is an ingredient in many cellular reactions, it provides structure, and it makes the watery environment that cells need.
- Most organisms require oxygen from the air.

4. Viruses are not alive.
A **virus** contains genetic material enclosed in a protein shell. However, viruses are not as complex as living cells. For example, viruses do not grow or respond to the environment.

SECTION

Bacteria are single-celled organisms without nuclei. pp. 288–295

1. Bacteria and archaea are the smallest living things.
Bacteria are the simplest kind of life.

- A bacterial cell contains all the structures needed for survival. Its cell wall, cell membrane, DNA, and cytoplasm can all be seen below.

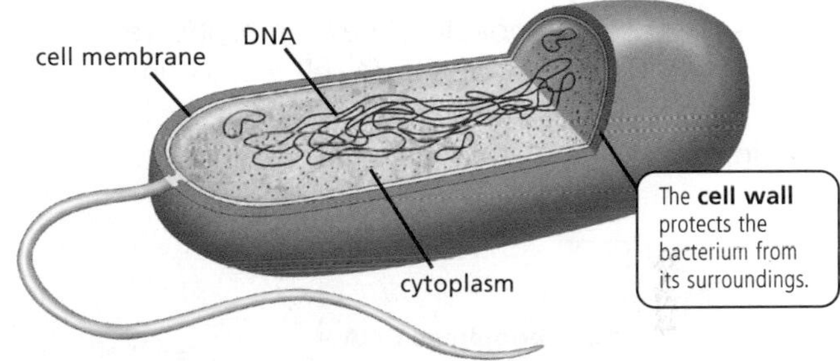

- Bacteria are often classified by their shape. They may be spirals, rods, or spheres.

2. Archaea and bacteria are found in many environments.
Archaea and bacteria are both single-celled with no nuclei, but are sufficiently different chemically to be in separate kingdoms.
Archaea can survive in a number of extreme environments.

- Methanogens produce methane and die if exposed to O_2.
- Halophiles must live in very salty water.
- Thermophiles live in either extreme heat or cold.

Bacteria are found almost everywhere.

- Some, called **producers,** use sunlight as an energy source.
- Others, **decomposers,** get energy from dead organic matter.
- **Parasites** get energy by living on or inside living organisms.

3. Bacteria may help or harm other organisms.
Helpful bacteria break down organic matter in soil and sewage. They also fix nitrogen, making it available to plants. They often are an essential part of animal digestive systems. Harmful bacteria cause disease in plants and animals by invading body parts or by poisoning the host organism with chemicals they release or with their cells.

Common Misconceptions

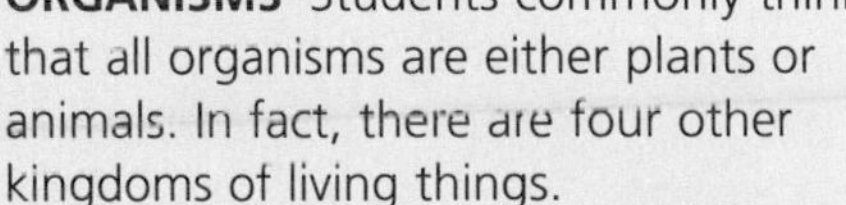

MISCONCEPTION DATABASE
CLASSZONE.COM Background on student misconceptions

ORGANISMS Students commonly think that all organisms are either plants or animals. In fact, there are four other kingdoms of living things.

 This misconception is addressed on p. 283.

BACTERIA Many students think that bacteria are not living things. They are, in fact, alive, and have all the characteristics of living things.

 This misconception is addressed on p. 289.

HELPFUL BACTERIA Students may hold the misconception that all bacteria cause disease and are bad. In reality, many bacteria are helpful. Some help produce food, some produce oxygen, some decompose waste material, and some fix nitrogen.

 This misconception is addressed on p. 292.

Previewing Content

SECTION

Viruses are not alive but affect living things. pp. 296–301

1. Viruses share some characteristics with living things.
Viruses are tiny infectious particles that consist of genetic material surrounded by a protein coat called a **capsid.** Viruses are not alive and do not grow or respond to the environment.

2. Viruses multiply inside living cells.
Although viruses are not alive, they can **replicate** by taking over the cell machinery of a **host cell** and forcing it to make more viruses. In the diagram below, a bacteriophage, a virus that infects bacteria, attaches to a bacterium.

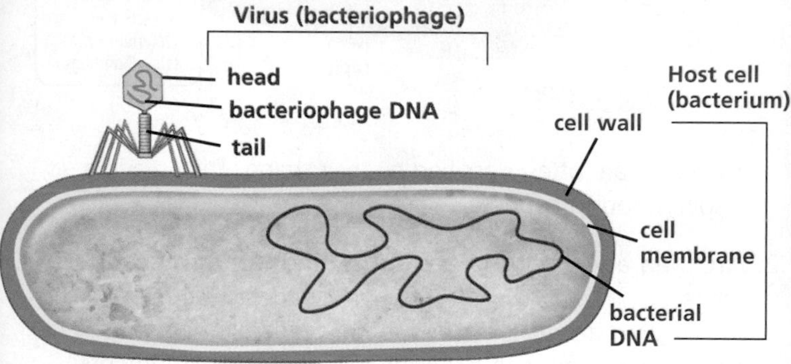

The viral DNA is injected into the cell, where it uses the host machinery to make more viral DNA and capsids. The viral parts are assembled into new viruses and released when the host cell bursts open.

3. Viruses may harm host cells.
Viruses use a host cell's material, energy, and cell processes to make more viruses. This reproductive process usually kills host cells and thus causes disease that may kill the organism. Scientists are currently trying to find ways to use viruses in positive ways, such as in gene therapy.

SECTION

Protists are a diverse group of organisms. pp. 302–307

1. Most protists are single-celled.
Protists include all organisms whose cells have nuclei and that are not plants, animals, or fungi. Most protists are single-celled. Some protists are producers and provide oxygen, some are parasites that cause disease, and some are decomposers.

2. Protists obtain their energy in three ways.
Protists can be classified by the way they get energy.

- **Algae** capture sunlight and convert it to chemical energy. They have chlorophyll and photosynthesize, releasing oxygen gas into the air. Thus, algae are producers. Seaweed, euglenas, diatoms, volvox, and the *Chlamydomonas* pictured below are algae.

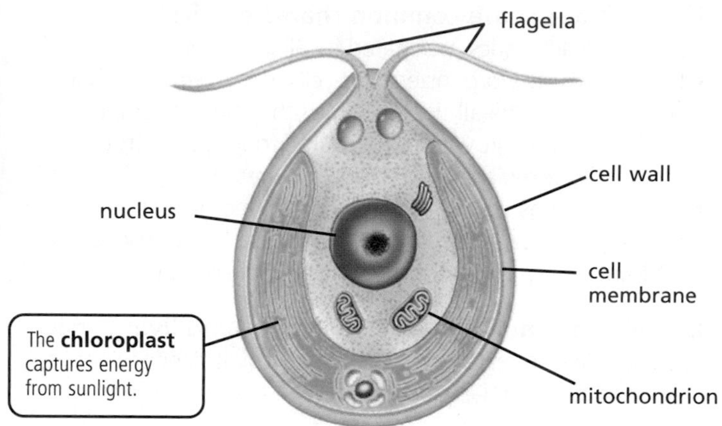

- **Protozoa** get their energy by eating other organisms. They are all single-celled, and most move about with cilia or flagella to search for food. Some protozoa are parasites and cause disease. Paramecia and the organism that causes malaria are protozoa.
- Other protists absorb materials that contain stored energy. Cellular slime molds, plasmodial slime molds, and water molds are members of this group.

Common Misconceptions

MISCONCEPTION DATABASE
CLASSZONE.COM Background on student misconceptions

CATCHING COLDS Many people think that you catch a cold by becoming chilled, going out without a coat, or going out in the rain without boots. The common cold is caused by viruses, which must infect body cells to produce the symptoms of a cold.

This misconception is addressed on p. 298.

Previewing Labs

EXPLORE the BIG idea

Where Can You Find Microscopic Life? p. 279 Students look for microscopic life, using a hand lens or microscope.	**TIME** 20 minutes **MATERIALS** hand lens or microscope
How Quickly Do Bacteria Multiply? p. 279 Students use beans to model binary fission and exponential growth.	**TIME** 10 minutes **MATERIALS** funnel, 2-L bottle, duct tape, beans, clock or stopwatch
Internet Activity: Microscopic Life and You, p. 279 Students investigate the microscopic life that lives on, in, and around people.	**TIME** 20 minutes **MATERIALS** computer with Internet access

SECTION 1	**EXPLORE Organisms,** p. 281 Students list living things found in a classroom.	**TIME** 10 minutes **MATERIALS** paper, pencil
	INVESTIGATE Microorganisms, p. 285 Students observe the responses of hydra and daphnia to their environment.	**TIME** 30 minutes **MATERIALS** microscope, slide, hydra culture, cover slip, daphnia culture, warm water
SECTION 2	**CHAPTER INVESTIGATION** **Bacteria,** pp. 294–295 Students sample bacteria that live on their hands and in the environment to determine how widespread bacteria are.	**TIME** 40 minutes **MATERIALS** 3 covered petri dishes with sterile nutrient agar, marker, tape, 3 sterile cotton swabs, small object (such as a coin or eraser), hand lens (for Challenge: 1 additional covered petri dish with agar, sterile swabs)
SECTION 3	**EXPLORE Viruses,** p. 296 Students model the way viruses were discovered, by passing a mixture through a filter.	**TIME** 10 minutes **MATERIALS** small kitchen sieve, paper plate, table salt, sesame seeds, small container, hand lens
	INVESTIGATE Viruses, p. 297 Students use a model to analyze how infections spread.	**TIME** 30 minutes **MATERIALS** class set of paper cups, water, baking soda, phenolphthalein (solution A), and 0.1 M dilute hydrochloric acid (solution B), 2 droppers, measuring spoons
SECTION 4	**INVESTIGATE Protists,** p. 303 Students observe the movement and behavior of protists in pond water.	**TIME** 40 minutes **MATERIALS** pond water, microscope, hand lens, dropper, slide, cover slip

R **Additional INVESTIGATION,** Growth of Algae, A, B, & C, pp. 70–78; Teacher Instructions, pp. 360–361

Previewing Chapter Resources

CHAPTER 9
Single-Celled Organisms and Viruses

INTEGRATED TECHNOLOGY

CLASSZONE.COM
- eEdition Plus
- EasyPlanner Plus
- Misconception Database
- Content Review
- Test Practice
- Visualizations
- Resource Centers
- Internet Activity: Microscopic Life and You
- Math Tutorial

SCILINKS.ORG

SCILINKS

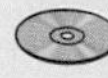

CD-ROMS
- eEdition
- EasyPlanner
- Power Presentations
- Content Review
- Lab Generator
- Test Generator

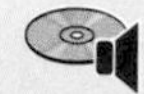

AUDIO CDS
- Audio Readings
- Audio Readings in Spanish

LABS AND ACTIVITIES

EXPLORE the Big Idea, p. 279
- Where Can You Find Microscopic Life?
- How Quickly Do Bacteria Multiply?
- Internet Activity: Microscopic Life and You

UNIT RESOURCE BOOK
- Family Letter, p. ix
- Spanish Family Letter, p. x
- Unit Projects, pp. 5–10

Lab Generator CD-ROM
Generate customized labs.

SECTION

1 Single-celled organisms have all the characteristics of living things.
pp. 281–287

Time: 2 periods (1 block)

 Lesson Plan, pp. 11–12

Integrated Technology

- **VISUALIZATION,** Binary Fission
- **MATH TUTORIAL**

UNIT TRANSPARENCY BOOK
- Big Idea Flow Chart, p. T1
- Daily Vocabulary Scaffolding, p. T2
- Note-Taking Model, p. T3
- 3-Minute Warm-Up, p. T4

Labs and Activities

- EXPLORE Organisms, p. 281
- INVESTIGATE Microorganisms, p. 285
- Math in Science, p. 287

UNIT RESOURCE BOOK
- Datasheet, Microorganisms, p. 20
- Math Support, p. 59
- Math Practice, p. 60

SECTION

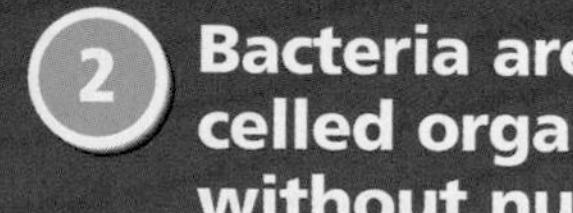

2 Bacteria are single-celled organisms without nuclei.
pp. 288–295

Time: 3 periods (1.5 blocks)

 Lesson Plan, pp. 22–23

Integrated Technology

RESOURCE CENTER, Bacteria

UNIT TRANSPARENCY BOOK
- Daily Vocabulary Scaffolding, p. T2
- 3-Minute Warm-Up, p. T4

Labs and Activities

CHAPTER INVESTIGATION, Bacteria, pp. 294–295

UNIT RESOURCE BOOK
CHAPTER INVESTIGATION, Bacteria, A, B, & C, pp. 61–69

SECTION

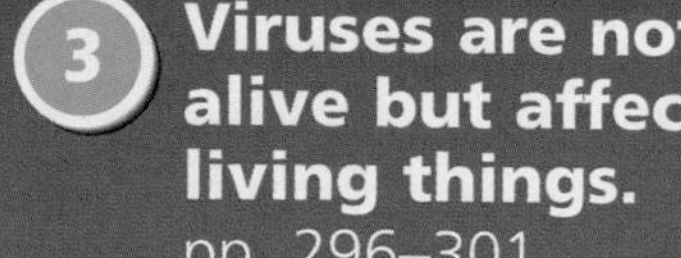

3 Viruses are not alive but affect living things.
pp. 296–301

Time: 2 periods (1 block)

 Lesson Plan, pp. 32–33

Integrated Technology

- **RESOURCE CENTER,** Viruses
- **VISUALIZATION,** Virus Replication

UNIT TRANSPARENCY BOOK
- Daily Vocabulary Scaffolding, p. T2
- 3-Minute Warm-Up, p. T5
- "Making New Viruses" Visual, p. T6

Labs and Activities

- EXPLORE Viruses, p. 296
- INVESTIGATE Viruses, p. 297
- Extreme Science, p. 301

UNIT RESOURCE BOOK
Datasheet, Viruses, p. 41

SECTION

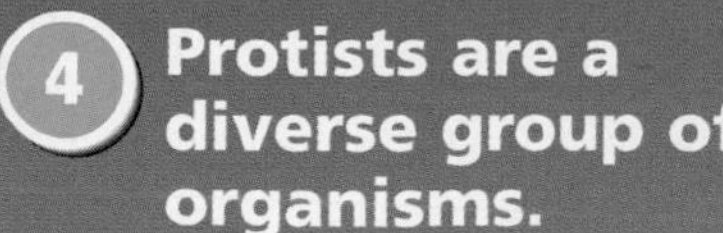

4 Protists are a diverse group of organisms.
pp. 302–307

Time: 3 periods (1.5 blocks)

Lesson Plan, pp. 43–44

Integrated Technology

UNIT TRANSPARENCY BOOK
- Big Idea Flow Chart, p. T1
- Daily Vocabulary Scaffolding, p. T2
- 3-Minute Warm-Up, p. T5
- Chapter Outline, pp. T7–T8

Labs and Activities

INVESTIGATE Protists, p. 303

UNIT RESOURCE BOOK
- Datasheet, Protists, p. 52
- Additional INVESTIGATION, Growth of Algae, A, B, & C, pp. 70–78

KEY TO ICONS 

 CD/CD-ROM
 Teacher Edition
 UNIT TRANSPARENCY BOOK
 SPANISH ASSESSMENT BOOK
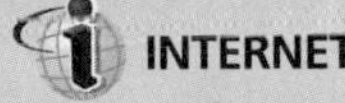 INTERNET
 Pupil Edition
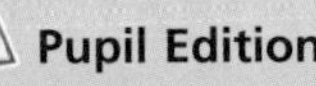
 UNIT RESOURCE BOOK
 UNIT ASSESSMENT BOOK
SCIENCE TOOLKIT

READING AND REINFORCEMENT	ASSESSMENT	STANDARDS
 • Description Wheel, B20–21 • Main Idea Web, C38–39 • Daily Vocabulary Scaffolding, H1–8  **UNIT RESOURCE BOOK** • Vocabulary Practice, pp. 56–57 • Decoding Support, p. 58 • Summarizing the Chapter, pp. 79–80 **Audio Readings CD** Listen to Pupil Edition. **Audio Readings in Spanish CD** Listen to Pupil Edition in Spanish.	 • Chapter Review, pp. 309–310 • Standardized Test Practice, p. 311  **UNIT ASSESSMENT BOOK** • Diagnostic Test, pp. 1–2 • Chapter Test, A, B, & C, pp. 7–18 • Alternative Assessment, pp. 19–20 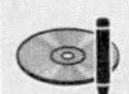 Spanish Chapter Test, pp. 41–44  **Test Generator CD-ROM** Generate customized tests. **Lab Generator CD-ROM** Rubrics for Labs	National Standards A.2–8, A.9.a–c, A.9.e–f, C.1.a–b, G.1.b See p. 278 for the standards.
UNIT RESOURCE BOOK • Reading Study Guide, A & B, pp. 13–16 • Spanish Reading Study Guide, pp. 17–18 • Challenge and Extension, p. 19 • Reinforcing Key Concepts, p. 21 • Challenge Reading, pp. 54–55	 Ongoing Assessment, pp. 282–284, 286  Section 9.1 Review, p. 286  **UNIT ASSESSMENT BOOK** Section 9.1 Quiz, p. 3	National Standards A.2–8, A.9.a–c, A.9.e–f, C.1.a–b, G.1.b
 **UNIT RESOURCE BOOK** • Reading Study Guide, A & B, pp. 24–27 • Spanish Reading Study Guide, pp. 28–29 • Challenge and Extension, p. 30 • Reinforcing Key Concepts, p. 31	 Ongoing Assessment, pp. 288–291, 293  Section 9.2 Review, p. 293 **UNIT ASSESSMENT BOOK** Section 9.2 Quiz, p. 4	National Standards A.2–7, A.9.a–b, A.9.e–f, C.1.a–b, G.1.b
 **UNIT RESOURCE BOOK** • Reading Study Guide, A & B, pp. 34–37 • Spanish Reading Study Guide, pp. 38–39 • Challenge and Extension, p. 40 • Reinforcing Key Concepts, p. 42	 Ongoing Assessment, pp. 297–299  Section 9.3 Review, p. 300 **UNIT ASSESSMENT BOOK** Section 9.3 Quiz, p. 5	National Standards A.2–7, A.9.a–b, A.9.e–f, C.1.a–b, G.1.a–b
 **UNIT RESOURCE BOOK** • Reading Study Guide, A & B, pp. 45–48 • Spanish Reading Study Guide, pp. 49–50 • Challenge and Extension, p. 51 • Reinforcing Key Concepts, p. 53	 Ongoing Assessment, pp. 303–304, 306–307  Section 9.4 Review, p. 307  **UNIT ASSESSMENT BOOK** Section 9.4 Quiz, p. 6	National Standards A.2–7, A.9.a–b, A.9.e–f, C.1.a–b, G.1.a–b

Previewing Resources for Differentiated Instruction

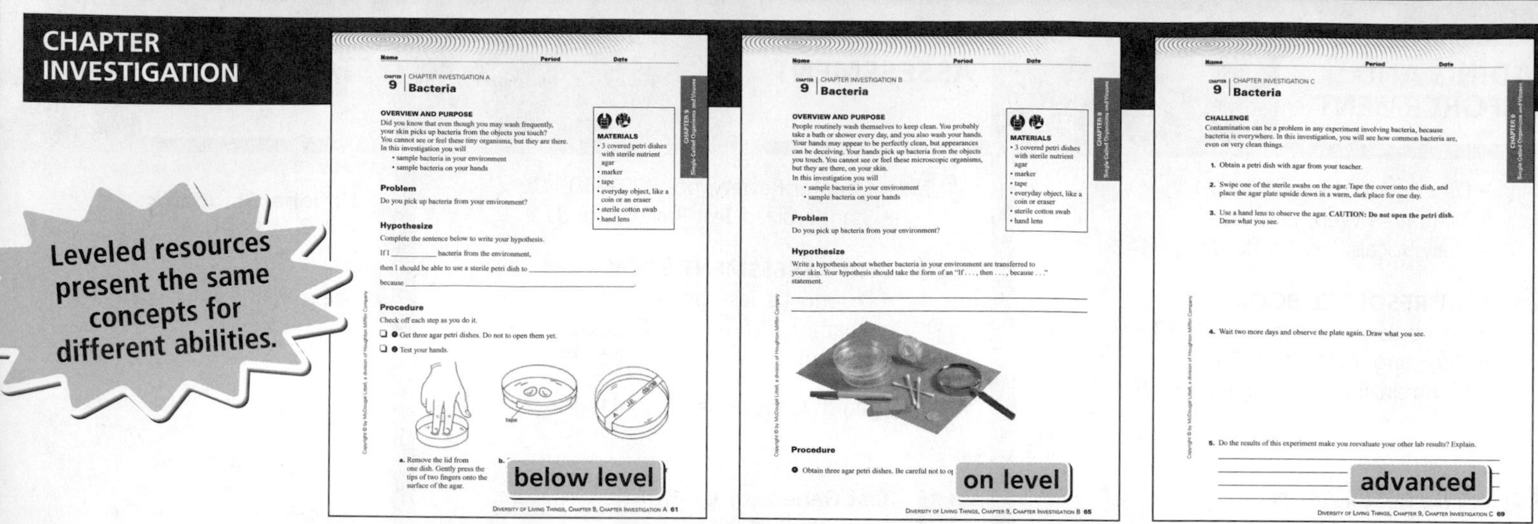

UNIT RESOURCE BOOK, pp. 61–64 pp. 65–68 pp. 65–69

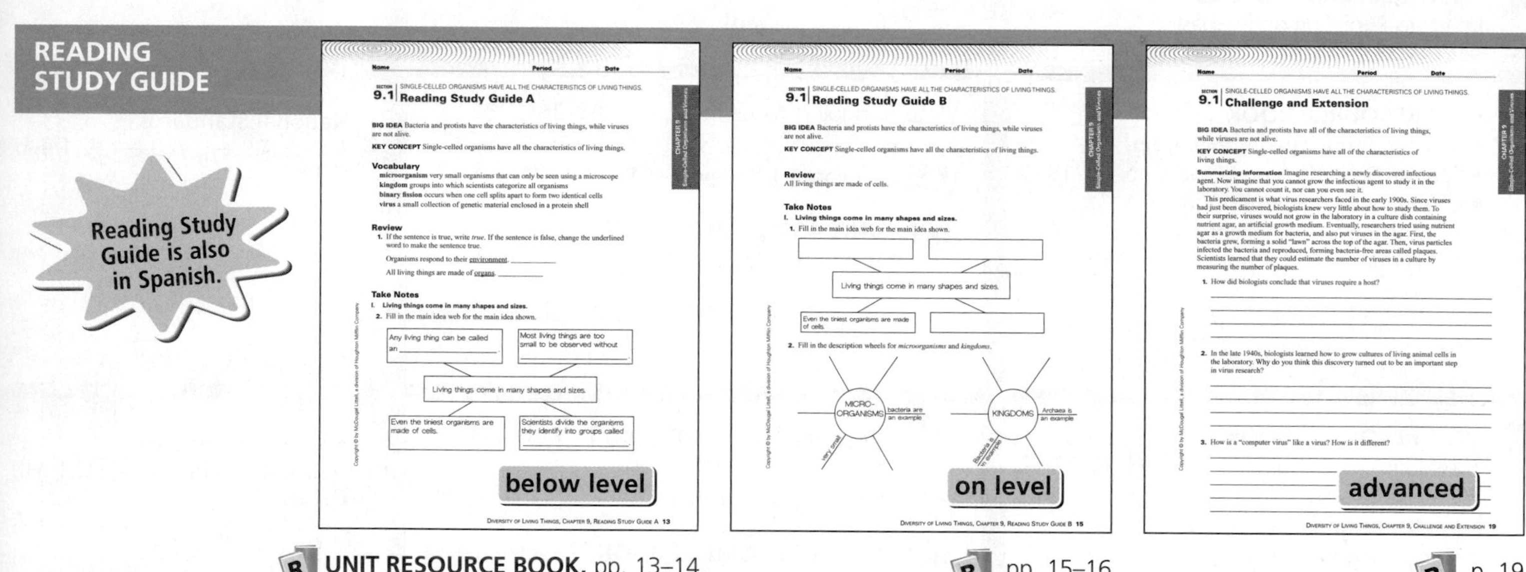

UNIT RESOURCE BOOK, pp. 13–14 pp. 15–16 p. 19

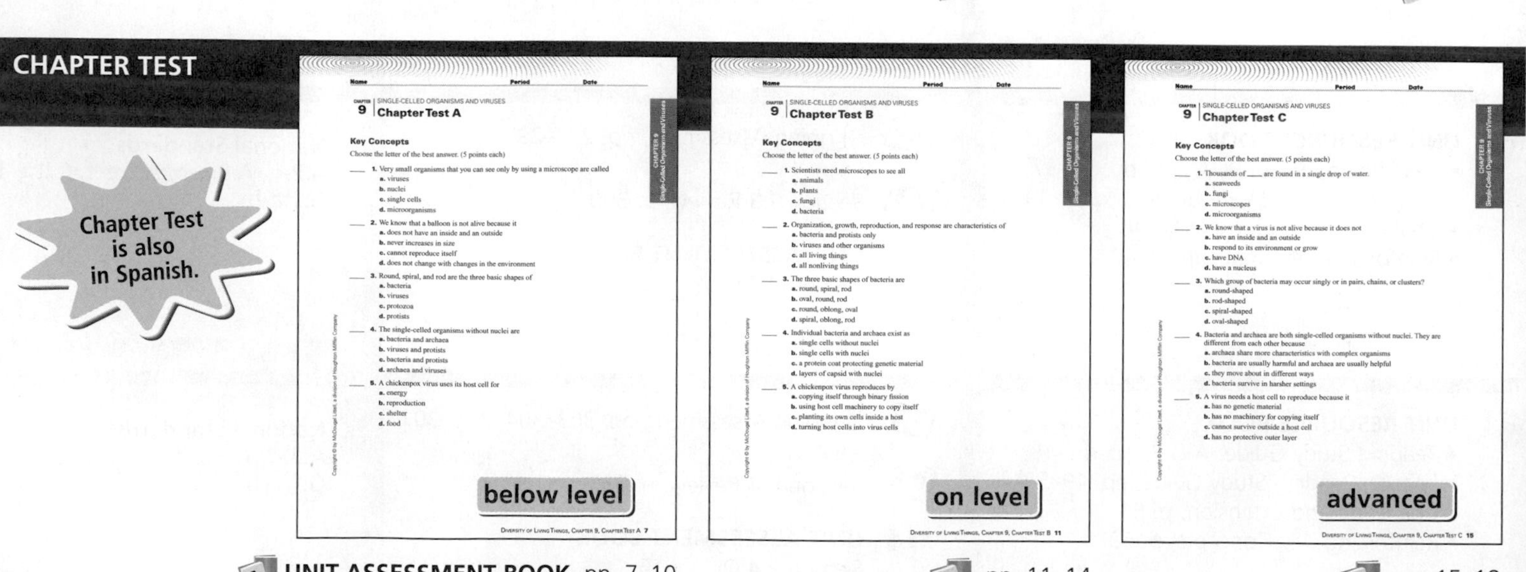

UNIT ASSESSMENT BOOK, pp. 7–10 pp. 11–14 pp. 15–18

TECHNOLOGY

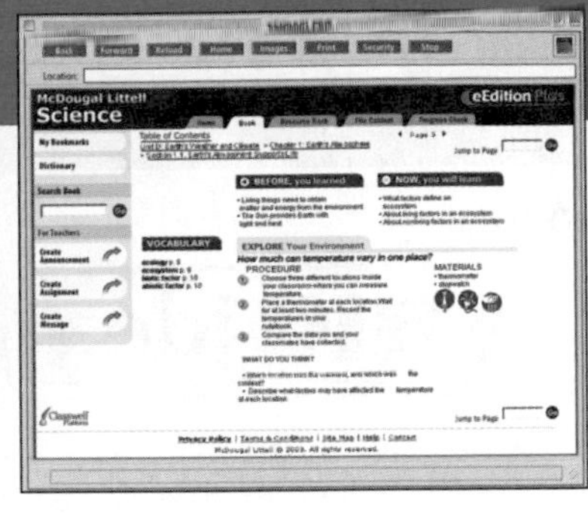

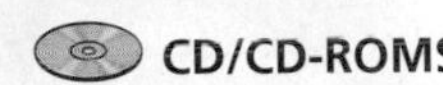

VISUAL CONTENT

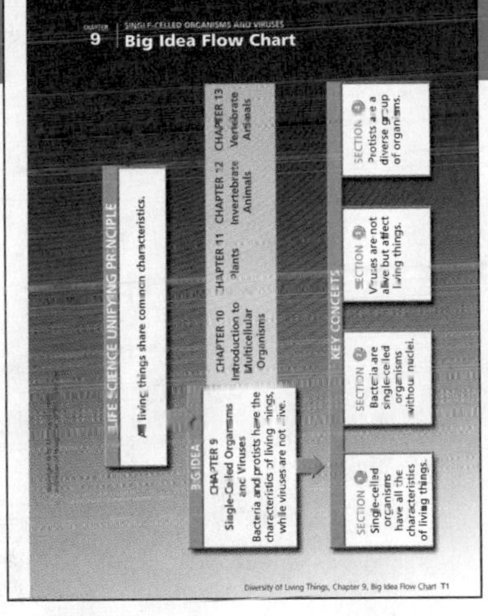

UNIT TRANSPARENCY BOOK, p. T1

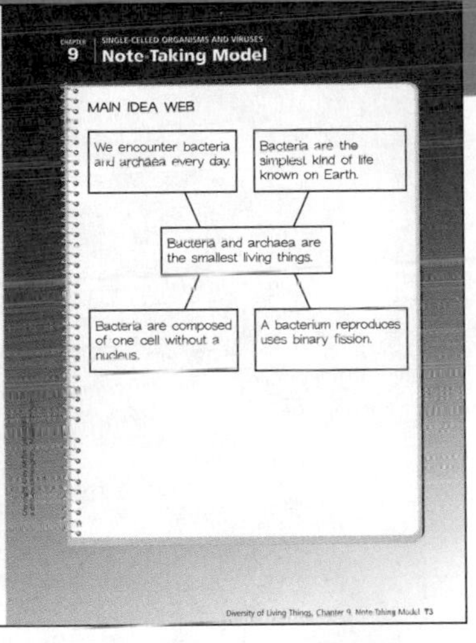

p. T3

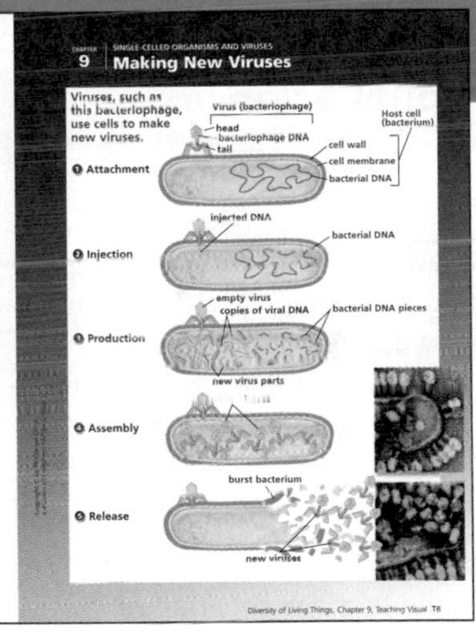

p. T6

MORE SUPPORT

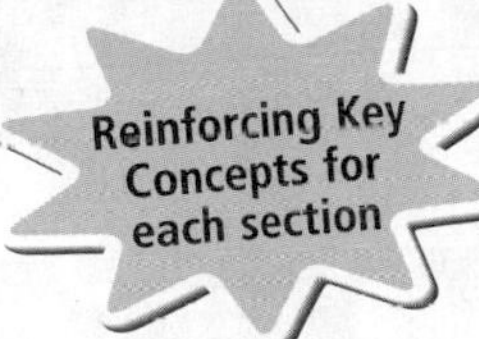

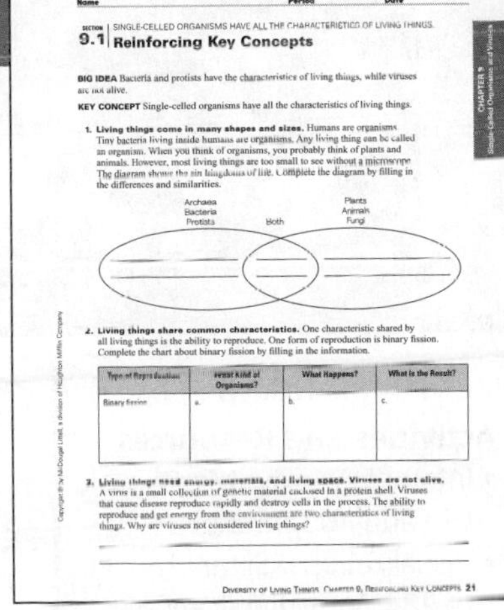

UNIT RESOURCE BOOK, p. 21

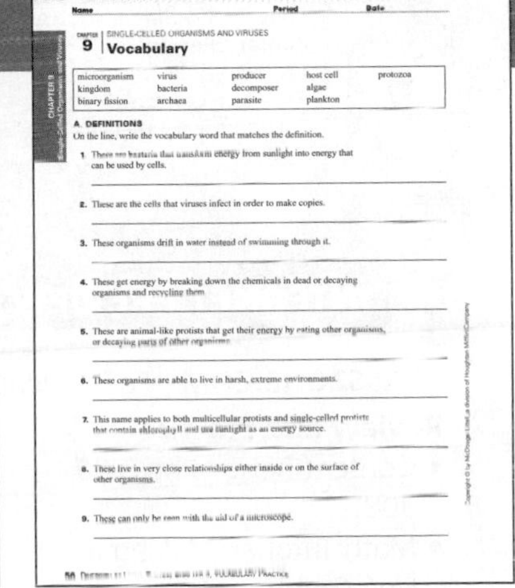

pp. 56–57

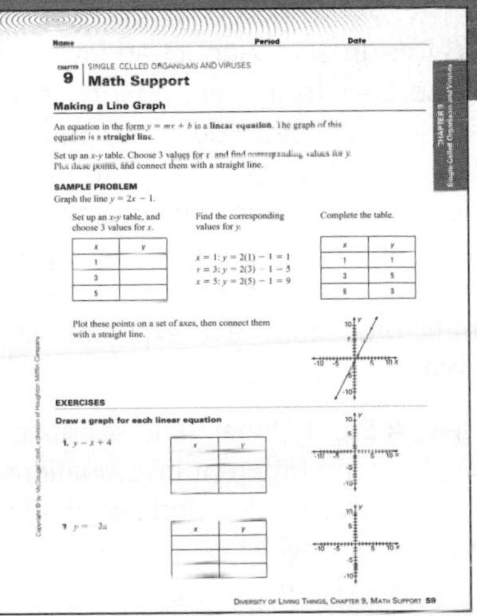

p. 59

INTRODUCE

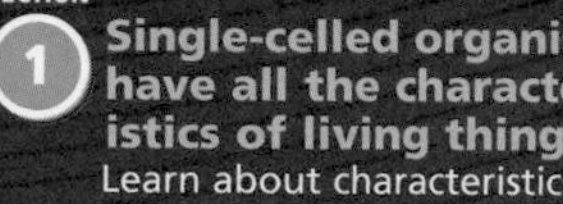

Have students look at the microscopic structures in the photograph and discuss how the question in the box links to the Big Idea:

- Do the structures in the photograph look like they are alive? Why or why not?
- How do you think you could determine if the structures are alive?

National Science Education Standards

Content

C.1.a Living systems at all levels of organization demonstrate the complementary nature of structure and function. Important levels of organization for structure and function include cells, organs, tissues, organ systems, whole organisms, and ecosystems.

C.1.b All organisms are composed of cells—the fundamental unit of life. Most organisms are single cells; other organisms, including humans, are multicellular.

Process

A.2–8 Design and conduct an investigation; use tools to gather and interpret data; use evidence to describe, predict, explain, model; think critically to make relationships between evidence and explanation; recognize different explanations and predictions; communicate scientific procedures and explanations; use mathematics.

A.9.a–c, A.9.e–f Understand scientific inquiry by using different investigations, methods, mathematics, and explanations based on logic, evidence, and skepticism.

G.1.b Science requires different abilities.

CHAPTER

Single-Celled Organisms and Viruses

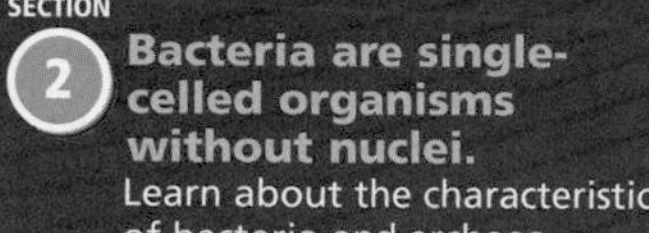

Bacteria and protists have the characteristics of living things, while viruses are not alive.

Key Concepts

SECTION 1
Single-celled organisms have all the characteristics of living things.
Learn about characteristics shared by all living things.

SECTION 2
Bacteria are single-celled organisms without nuclei.
Learn about the characteristics of bacteria and archaea.

SECTION 3
Viruses are not alive but affect living things.
Learn about the structure of viruses and how they affect cells.

SECTION 4
Protists are a diverse group of organisms.
Learn about protists and how they affect the environment.

Internet Preview

CLASSZONE.COM

Chapter 9 online resources: Content Review, two Visualizations, three Resource Centers, Math Tutorial, Test Practice.

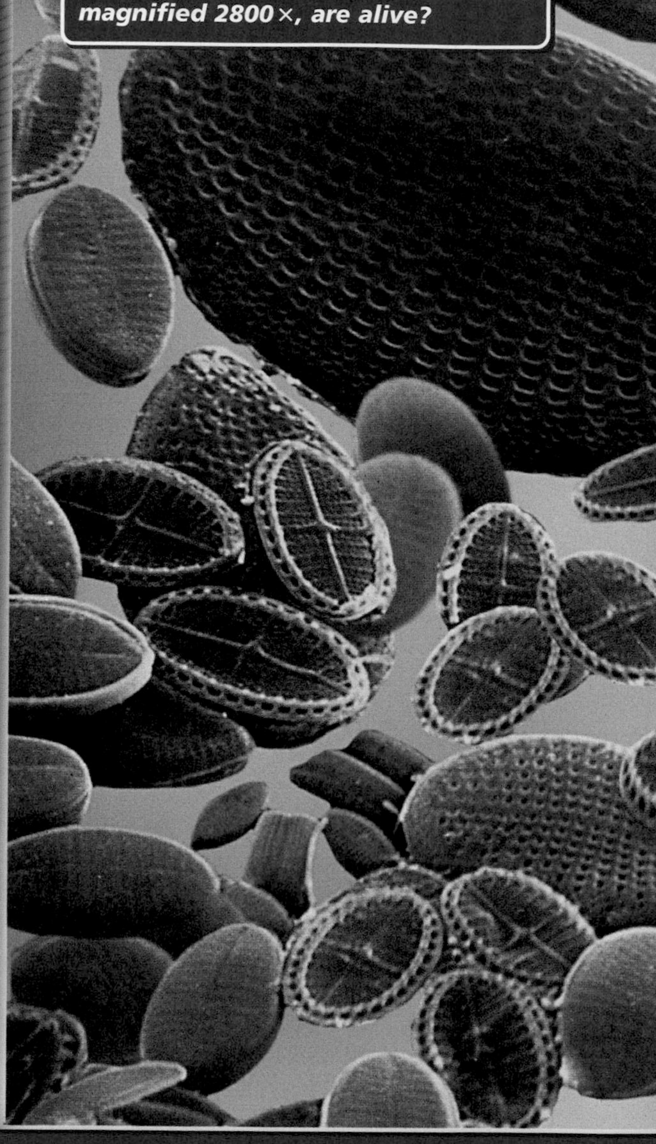

How can you tell if these structures, magnified 2800×, are alive?

INTERNET PREVIEW

CLASSZONE.COM For student use with the following pages:

Review and Practice
- Content Review, pp. 280, 308
- Math Tutorial: Making a Line Graph, p. 287
- Test Practice, p. 311

Activities and Resources
- Internet Activity: Microscopic Life and You, p. 279
- Visualizations: Binary Fission, p. 284; Virus Replication, p. 298
- Resource Centers: Bacteria, p. 290; Viruses, p. 297

Kingdom Protista
Code: MDL039

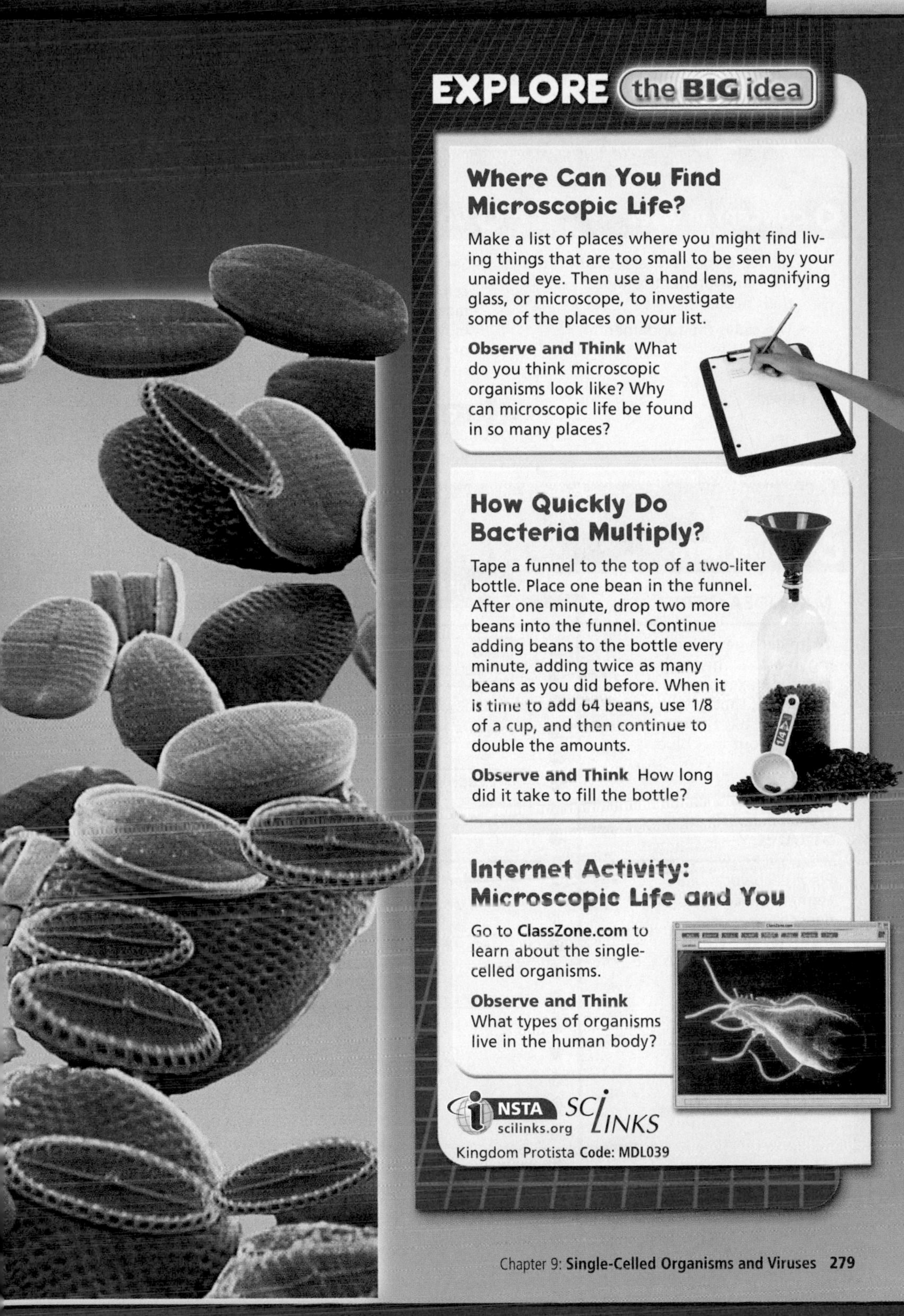

EXPLORE the BIG idea

Where Can You Find Microscopic Life?

Make a list of places where you might find living things that are too small to be seen by your unaided eye. Then use a hand lens, magnifying glass, or microscope, to investigate some of the places on your list.

Observe and Think What do you think microscopic organisms look like? Why can microscopic life be found in so many places?

How Quickly Do Bacteria Multiply?

Tape a funnel to the top of a two-liter bottle. Place one bean in the funnel. After one minute, drop two more beans into the funnel. Continue adding beans to the bottle every minute, adding twice as many beans as you did before. When it is time to add 64 beans, use 1/8 of a cup, and then continue to double the amounts.

Observe and Think How long did it take to fill the bottle?

Internet Activity: Microscopic Life and You

Go to **ClassZone.com** to learn about the single-celled organisms.

Observe and Think What types of organisms live in the human body?

NSTA scilinks.org SCILINKS

Kingdom Protista **Code: MDL039**

TEACHING WITH TECHNOLOGY

PC Microscopes or Microscopes with Cameras If computer microscopes are available, use them for the investigations on pp. 285 and 303 to view microscopic organisms on a computer screen. Save screen-grabs on the PC capturing magnified images of the organisms. If a microscope with attached camera is available, take photographs of these microorganisms for later identification.

EXPLORE the BIG idea

These inquiry-based activities are appropriate for use at home or as a supplement to classroom instruction.

Where Can You Find Microscopic Life?

PURPOSE To look at microscopic life using a hand lens or microscope.

TIP *20 min.* Have groups of students brainstorm to make their lists.

Answer: Microscopic organisms have diverse sizes and shape, although most have only one cell. They can survive in a large range of environments.

REVISIT after p. 282.

How Quickly Do Bacteria Multiply?

PURPOSE To model how quickly bacteria reproduce.

TIP *10 min.* Students should add large quantities of beans slowly, so the funnel does not clog.

Answer: The bottle should fill up in the 12th minute, when 4 cups of beans are added.

REVISIT after p. 284.

Internet Activity: Microscopic Life and You

PURPOSE To investigate the microscopic life that lives on, in, and around people.

TIP *20 min.* Have students list the places in the body where the organisms they read about are found.

Answer: Helpful bacteria live in many parts of the body. Harmful bacteria, fungi spores, and small insects can harm a human host.

REVISIT after p. 291.

PREPARE

CONCEPT REVIEW

Activate Prior Knowledge

- Have students reproduce Robert Hooke's discovery of cells by examining a small slice of real cork under a microscope. They should see empty cells, since cork is composed of dead tissue.
- Ask: In what ways does a single-celled organism interact with its environment to meet its needs? *It may search for and take in food; react to light, temperature, or touch; and avoid enemies.*

TAKING NOTES

Main Idea Web

A main idea web focuses students' attention as they read the text. The web is similar to an outline but allows a more random, less linear organization. Details can be added easily upon second and third reads of text portions, or as questions arise.

Vocabulary Strategy

A description wheel can include as much information as the student wants to add. By filling in their own words around the center term, students personalize their understanding of the term and retain its meaning.

Vocabulary and Note-Taking Resources

- Vocabulary Practice, pp. 56–57
- Decoding Support, p. 58

- Daily Vocabulary Scaffolding, T2
- Note-Taking Model, T3

- Description Wheel, B20–21
- Main Idea Web, C38–39
- Daily Vocabulary Scaffolding, H1–8

CHAPTER 9

Getting Ready to Learn

CONCEPT REVIEW

- All living things interact with their environment to meet their needs.
- The cell is the fundamental unit of life.

VOCABULARY REVIEW

See Glossary for definitions.

cell
matter
molecule
organism
species

CONTENT REVIEW
CLASSZONE.COM
Review concepts and vocabulary.

TAKING NOTES

MAIN IDEA WEB

Write each new blue heading in a box. Then write notes in boxes around the center box that give important terms and details about that blue heading.

VOCABULARY STRATEGY

Place each vocabulary term at the center of a **description wheel diagram.** Write some words describing it on the spokes.

See the Note-Taking Handbook on pages R45–R51.

SCIENCE NOTEBOOK

They are organized, with an outside and an inside.
They increase in size.
Living things share common characteristics.
They reproduce and form other organisms like themselves.
They respond to changes in the environment.

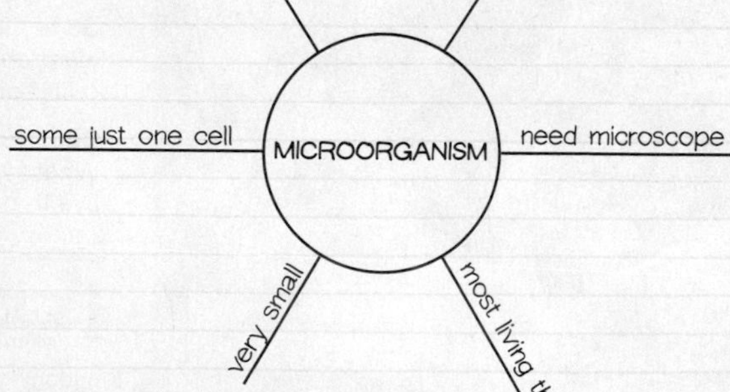

CHECK READINESS

Administer the Diagnostic Test to determine students' readiness for new science content and their mastery of requisite math skills.

 Diagnostic Test, pp. 1–2

Technology Resources

Students needing content and math skills should visit **ClassZone.com**.

- **CONTENT REVIEW**
- **MATH TUTORIAL**

 **CONTENT REVIEW CD-ROM**

KEY CONCEPT

Single-celled organisms have all the characteristics of living things.

BEFORE, you learned
- All living things are made of cells
- Organisms respond to their environment
- Species change over time

NOW, you will learn
- About the various sizes of organisms
- About characteristics that are shared by all living things
- About needs shared by all organisms

VOCABULARY

microorganism p. 282
kingdom p. 283
binary fission p. 284
virus p. 286

EXPLORE Organisms

What living things are in the room with you?

PROCEDURE

1. Make a list of all the living things that are in your classroom.
2. Compare your list with the lists of your classmates. Make one list containing all the living things your class has identified.

MATERIALS
- paper
- pencil

WHAT DO YOU THINK?
- How did you identify something as living?
- Were you and your classmates able to see all the living things on your list?

Living things come in many shapes and sizes.

MAIN IDEA WEB
Make a web of the important terms and details about the main idea: *Living things come in many shapes and sizes.*

You can spot mushrooms in many places while walking through a forest. Scientists have discovered mushrooms that come from the same individual fungus more than 5 kilometers (3 miles) apart in an Oregon forest. Most of this honey mushroom fungus is below ground, stretching over an area covering more than 1600 football fields. This mushroom is one of the largest known living things on Earth.

Many other living things share the soil in the Oregon forest. Earthworms, insects, and many other organisms that are too small to be seen with a naked eye, also live there. For every living thing that is large enough to be seen, there are often countless numbers of smaller living things that share the same living space.

9.1 FOCUS

Set Learning Goals

Students will
- Recognize that some organisms are too small to see.
- Identify the characteristics shared by all living things.
- State how living things are classified.
- Observe how organisms respond to their environment.

3-Minute Warm-Up

Display Transparency 4 or copy this exercise on the board:

Draw a simple diagram representing a cell. Give your diagram a title that tells what kind of a cell you have drawn. Label the most important organelles. *A eukaryotic cell has a nucleus, plasma membrane, mitochondria, Golgi apparatus, ribosomes, and endoplasmic reticulum. Plant cells have a cell wall and chloroplasts, in addition to the other organelles.*

3-Minute Warm-Up, p. T4

9.1 MOTIVATE

EXPLORE Organisms

PURPOSE To list living things found in a classroom

TIP *10 min.* Students will probably not include microorganisms on their lists. Remind them to "think small."

WHAT DO YOU THINK? *A living thing must be able to grow, have an organized system, and be able to reproduce.*

RESOURCES FOR DIFFERENTIATED INSTRUCTION

Below Level

UNIT RESOURCE BOOK
- Reading Study Guide A, pp. 13–14
- Decoding Support, p. 58

Advanced

UNIT RESOURCE BOOK
- Challenge and Extension, p. 19
- Challenge Reading, pp. 54–55

English Learners

UNIT RESOURCE BOOK
Spanish Reading Study Guide, pp. 17–18

- Audio Readings in Spanish
- Audio Readings (English)

9.1 INSTRUCT

Teach from Visuals

To help students interpret the visual of organisms in a mangrove swamp, ask:

- What types of organisms in the photograph are able to be seen? *plants and animals*
- What types of organisms in the photograph are unable to be seen? *Archaea, bacteria, protists, and fungi; the amoeba is a protist.*

EXPLORE the BIG idea

Revisit "Where Can You Find Microscopic Life?" on p. 279. Have students explain why there might be many microscopic organisms in the environment shown in the photograph on p. 282.

Arts Connection

Flemish artists of the 17th century often painted pictures of the living world as it was known at that time. Many of these paintings can be found on the Internet and printed. Show students a copy of one of these paintings, such as *Paradise* by Jan Brueghel the Younger. Point out that all of the organisms shown are either plants or animals.

Ongoing Assessment

Recognize that some organisms are too small to see.

Ask: How can you be sure that microscopic organisms are present in an environment such as a swamp? *You must use a microscope.*

CHECK YOUR READING *Answer: An organism is any living thing. Microorganisms are living things, but they are too small to be seen without a microscope.*

The honey mushroom fungus is one example of an organism. You, too, are an organism, and tiny bacteria living inside your body are also organisms. In fact, any living thing can be called an organism. **A**

When you think of living things, you probably begin with those you can observe—plants, animals, and fungi such as mushrooms. However, most living things are too small to observe without a microscope. Even the tiniest organisms are made of cells. Very small organisms are called **microorganisms.** Many microorganisms are made of just one cell. **B**

READING TIP The prefix *micro-* means "very small." Therefore, *microscope* means "very small scope" and *microorganism* means "very small organism."

CHECK YOUR READING Compare and contrast the words *microorganism* and *organism.*

A visitor to a mangrove swamp forest can find an amazing variety of organisms. The mangrove trees themselves are the most obvious organisms. Roots from these trees grow above and below the muddy bottom of the forest. Other organisms live in almost every part of the mangrove tree.

Six Kingdoms of Life

All organisms are divided into six groups called kingdoms.

Mostly Microscopic Kingdoms	Mostly Multicellular Kingdoms
• archaea • bacteria • protists	• animals • fungi • plants

DIFFERENTIATE INSTRUCTION

More Reading Support

A What is an organism? *any living thing*

B What do you call an organism that cannot be seen with the naked eye? *a microorganism*

English Learners Have English learners write the definitions for *microorganism, kingdom, binary fission,* and *virus* in their Science Word Dictionaries. Have students look up the definition for the prefix *micro-* in the dictionary. Then have them list other words that begin with *micro-* (microscope, microwave, microphone), and explain the meaning of the prefix. *very small*

A single drop of water from a mangrove swamp may be living space for many microorganisms. The circled photograph on page 282 was taken using a microscope, and shows an amoeba that may be found in the water of the swamp. Larger organisms, such as manatees and fish, swim around the roots of mangrove trees. Birds, such as tri-colored herons and roseate spoonbills, use the branches.

VOCABULARY
Add a description wheel for *kingdom* to your notebook. The spokes of your wheel should include examples from the six kingdoms.

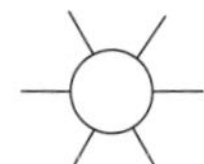

Scientists divide the organisms they identify into groups called **kingdoms.** This unit will cover all of the kingdoms of life, listed in the table on page 282. You are already familiar with plants and animals. Fungi are another kingdom. Fungi include mushrooms found in a forest. The other three kingdoms are composed of mostly microscopic life. You will learn more about microscopic organisms later in this chapter.

? C

Living things share common characteristics.

All living things—from the microorganisms living in a mangrove swamp to the giant organisms living in the open ocean—share similar characteristics. Living things are organized, grow, reproduce, and respond to the environment.

READING TIP
As you read about the four characteristics of all living things, note the examples of how single-celled organisms meet these four standards.

Organization

Cells are the basic unit of all living things. Cells, like all living things, have an inside and an outside. The boundary separating the inside from the outside of an individual cell is called the cell membrane. Within some cells, another structure called the nucleus is also surrounded by a membrane.

In this chapter, you will read about organisms made of a single cell. Some types of single-celled organisms contain a nucleus and some do not. All single-celled organisms contain everything they need to survive within their one cell. These cells are able to get energy from complex molecules, to move, and to sense their environment. The ability to perform these and other functions is part of their organization.

? D

Growth

Living things increase in size. Organisms made of one cell do not grow as large as organisms made of many cells. But all living things need to get energy. All living things also need to obtain materials to build new structures inside cells or replace worn-out cell parts. As a result, individual cells grow larger over time.

DIFFERENTIATE INSTRUCTION

More Reading Support

C What 3 kingdoms have organisms large enough to see? *fungi, plants, animals*

D How can an organism survive with only one cell? *It has all the structures needed in the cell.*

Below Level Demonstrate classification by having students separate a group of everyday items into categories according to their characteristics. Use items such as shoes or writing implements. Ask volunteers to explain why classifying is helpful when thinking about living things.

Address Misconceptions

IDENTIFY Show students pictures cut from magazines of living things from all six kingdoms, as well as some nonliving items such as a pile of sand, a lump of clay, and a rock. Then ask students to look at all the pictures and sort them into living and nonliving things. If students include only plants and animals as living, they may hold the misconception that all organisms are either plants or animals.

CORRECT Ask students to list living things that are not plants or animals. Lists should contain at least a few organisms from the Protista and Fungi kingdoms. Circle these items and lead a discussion about what makes them living things. *grow, respond, reproduce, take in air, food, water, and so on*

REASSESS Ask students to reconsider their definition of an organism and to write a definition in their own words that includes what they have learned. Ask that their definitions include diverse examples.

Technology Resources

Visit **ClassZone.com** for background on common student misconceptions.

MISCONCEPTION DATABASE

Develop Critical Thinking

APPLY Show students a photograph of a biome—a desert is a good example. Have them name what is living and what is not living in the picture. Ask them to apply their knowledge of the characteristics of life by telling what reasons they had for deciding what is living and what is not.

Metacognitive Strategy

Ask students to write a short paragraph describing how they remember the characteristics of living things.

Ongoing Assessment

State how living things are classified.

Ask: What characteristics are used to classify organisms? *They are classified based on characteristics such as cell structure, means of getting energy, and physical or body structure.*

Teach from Visuals

To help students interpret the photograph of binary fission, ask:

- What must happen before a single-celled organism can divide? *Its DNA must first be copied.*
- What would happen if a single-celled organism divided before it had two copies of its DNA? *Only one of the two resulting cells would contain DNA. The other cell could not survive.*

Teach Difficult Concepts

The concept of binary fission is difficult because students are used to thinking of linear relationships. Making a graph of an exponential increase might help illustrate how an unchecked population could grow. You might also use manipulatives, as in the Teacher Demo, below.

Teacher Demo

Using beans, demonstrate how bacteria divide by binary fission. Start by placing one bean on the table. Call the bean the "parent" bean. Have a student place two beans next to the parent bean. Toothpicks can be used to connect the parent bean to the offspring beans. Have another student provide the next generation by placing four beans on the table. Have other students add further generations.

EXPLORE (the BIG idea)

Revisit "How Quickly Do Bacteria Multiply?" on p. 279. Have students describe how fast the beans "reproduced," and why this is a good model of binary fission.

Ongoing Assessment

CHECK YOUR READING *Answer: Single-celled organisms have all the structures they need in one cell. They grow by increasing in size. They reproduce by binary fission, in which the organism divides into two organisms.*

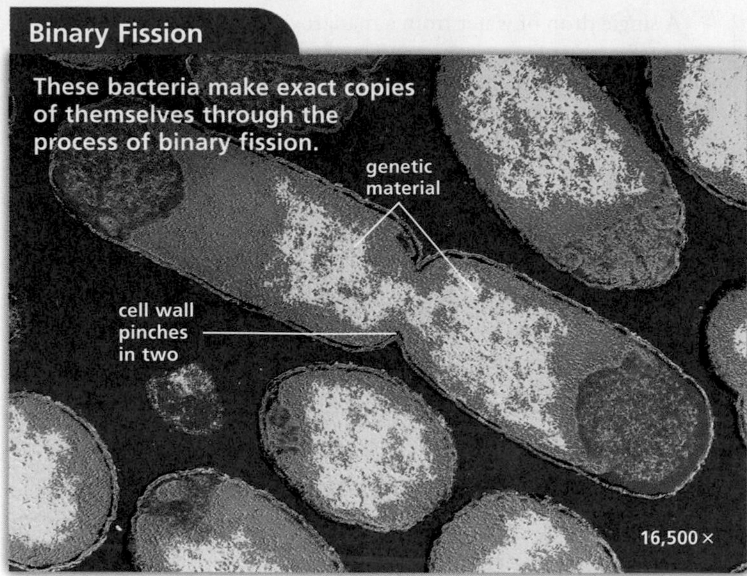

Reproduction

E Living things reproduce, forming other organisms like themselves. Every organism contains genetic material, which is a code contained in a special molecule called DNA. The code contains characteristics of the individual organism. In order to reproduce, an organism must make a copy of this material, which is passed on to its offspring.

F Some single-celled organisms reproduce by a process called **binary fission.** In binary fission, material from one cell separates into two cells. The genetic material of the original cell first doubles so that each daughter cell has an exact copy of the DNA of the original cell. You might say that single-celled organisms multiply by dividing. One cell divides into 2 cells, 2 cells divide into 4, 4 into 8, 16, 32, 64, and so on. In some cells, binary fission can take place as often as every 20 minutes.

VISUALIZATION CLASSZONE.COM
Observe the process of binary fission.

CHECK YOUR READING Describe how a single-celled organism is organized, grows, and reproduces.

Response

Organisms respond to changes in the environment. Even microscopic organisms respond to conditions such as light, temperature, and touch. The ability to respond allows organisms to find food, avoid being eaten, or perform other tasks necessary to survive.

DIFFERENTIATE INSTRUCTION

More Reading Support

E What molecule contains the cell's genetic material? *DNA*

F What process do single-celled organisms use to reproduce? *binary fission*

English Learners The activity on p. 285 uses the imperative. The word "you" in the directions is understood, or implied. For example, "Add a drop of the daphnia culture," really means "*You* add a drop of the daphnia culture." Make sure English learners understand how to read and follow these directions. You may wish to model the procedure for them, or have an advanced student do so.

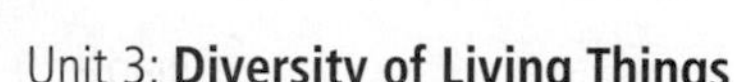

INVESTIGATE Microorganisms

SKILL FOCUS
Observing

MATERIALS
- microscope
- slide
- hydra culture
- daphnia culture
- water

TIME
30 minutes

How do these organisms respond to their environment?

PROCEDURE

1. Place a drop of the hydra culture on a microscope slide. Using the microscope, find a hydra under medium power and sketch what you see.
2. Add a drop of warm water to the culture on the slide. How does the hydra respond? Record your observations.
3. Add a drop of the daphnia culture. Record your observations.

WHAT DO YOU THINK?

- Which observations, if any, indicate that hydras respond to their environment?
- Daphnia are organisms. What is the relationship between hydra and daphnia?

CHALLENGE What other experiments could you do to observe the responses of hydra or daphnia to their environment?

Living things need energy, materials, and living space.

Have you ever wondered why you need to eat food, breathe air, and drink water? All living things need energy and materials. For most organisms, water and air are materials necessary for life.

G Food supplies you with energy. You—like all living things—need energy to move, grow, and develop. All animals have systems for breaking down food into usable forms of energy and materials. Plants have structures that enable them to transform sunlight into usable energy. Some microorganisms transform sunlight, while others need to use other organisms as sources of energy.

H Most of the activities of living things take place in water. Water is also an ingredient for many of the reactions that take place in cells. In addition, water helps support an organism's body. If you add water to the soil around a wilted plant, you will probably see the plant straighten up as water moves into its cells.

Materials in the air include gases such as carbon dioxide and oxygen. Many of the processes that capture and release energy involve these gases. Some organisms—such as those found around hydrothermal vents—use other chemicals to capture and release energy.

DIFFERENTIATE INSTRUCTION

More Reading Support

G Where do living things get energy? *food and sunlight*

H Why is water so important to living things? *Most activities take place in water.*

Advanced Have students learn more about the processes of cellular respiration and photosynthesis. Ask them to draw the cycle of energy in the environment, including cellular respiration and photosynthesis.

 Challenge and Extension, p. 19

Have students who are interested in the lives of single-celled organisms read the following article:

 Challenge Reading, pp. 54–55

INVESTIGATE Microorganisms

PURPOSE To observe the responses of hydra and daphnia to their environment

TIPS *30 min.* Warm water—between 25°C and 30°C—will give the best response. Students can best view the activity by using cover slips on the slides. Suggest that students record observations by drawing field of view circles and sketching within them. Assist students with disabilities by setting up pre-focused stations. Note that about 50 percent of hydra may show no response.

WHAT DO YOU THINK? *Hydras should move away from the warm water. They should capture daphnia with their tentacles and stuff them into their mouths. Both behaviors are responses to the environment. The daphnia may also try to get away from the hydra. The daphnia are food for the hydra.*

CHALLENGE *Answers may include testing the organisms' responses to light, darkness, various chemicals, and cold.*

 Datasheet, Microorganisms, p. 20

Technology Resources

Customize this student lab as needed or look for an alternative. Print rubrics to assess student lab reports.

 **Lab Generator CD-ROM**

Teaching with Technology

If a PC microscope is available, show the organisms on a computer screen. If a microscope fitted with a camera is available, photograph hydra and daphnia in action.

Integrate the Sciences

All organisms that use oxygen get energy through a complex series of chemical reactions known as cellular respiration. In this process, glucose breaks down, releasing the energy stored in its chemical bonds. The energy is then packaged in small quantities that the cell can use.

Teach from Visuals

To help students compare the photographs of the rotavirus, and the animal cell, ask them to make a table listing the two items on the left side and the four characteristics of life across the top. Have students check each characteristic of life that applies to the items.

Ongoing Assessment

Identify the characteristics shared by all living things.

Ask students to explain the difference between growth and reproduction. *Growth occurs when an organism increases in size. Reproduction makes more organisms.*

Reinforce the BIG idea

Have students relate the section to the Big Idea.

 Reinforcing Key Concepts, p. 21

9.1 ASSESS & RETEACH

Assess

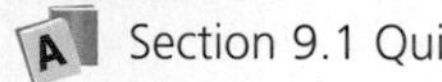

Reteach

Stage a "characteristics of life" scavenger hunt for students. Have the students work in teams with checklists and/or clipboards. The teams should list within 5 minutes for each "hunt":

- As many examples as possible of organisms growing.
- As many examples as they can find of organisms with structures.
- . . . of organisms reproducing.
- . . . of organisms responding to the environment.

Technology Resources

Have students visit **ClassZone.com** for reteaching of Key Concepts.

 CONTENT REVIEW

 CONTENT REVIEW CD-ROM

Viruses are not alive.

Sometimes it's not easy to tell the difference between a living and a nonliving thing. A **virus** has genetic material enclosed in a protein shell. Viruses have many of the characteristics of living things, including genetic material. However, a virus is not nearly as complex as a cell and is not considered a living thing.

Rotavirus

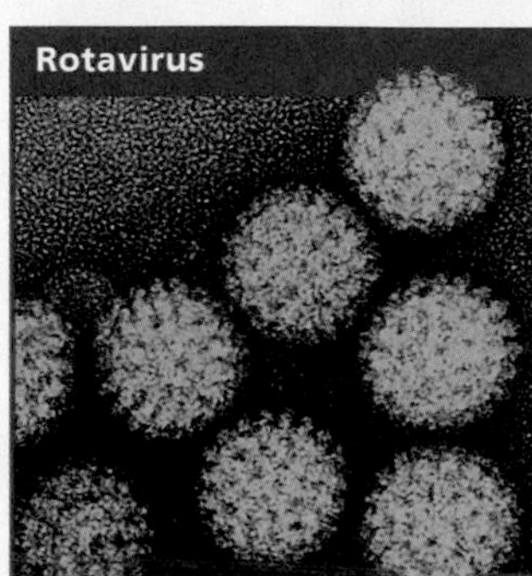

These viruses contain DNA but do not grow or respond to their environment. 570,000×

Animal Cell

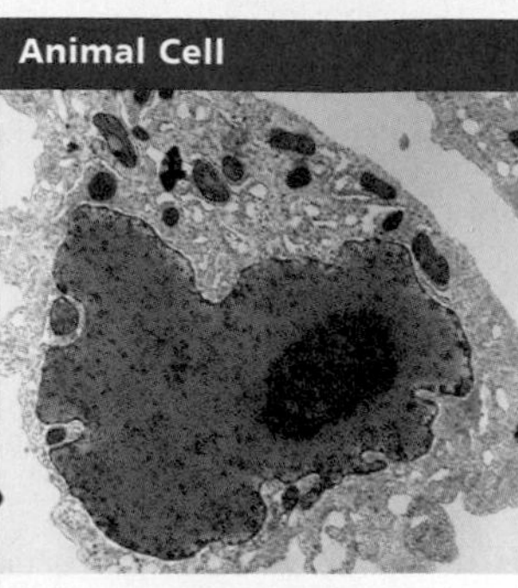

Animal cells grow, reproduce, and respond to external conditions. 4800×

For example, animal cells have structures that allow them to get materials or energy from their environment. Virus particles do not grow once they have formed, and they do not take in any energy. Animal cells can make copies of their genetic material and reproduce by dividing in two. Viruses are able to reproduce only by "taking over" a cell and using that cell to make new viruses. Animal cells also have many more internal structures than viruses. Viruses usually contain nothing more than their genetic material and a protein coat.

9.1 Review

KEY CONCEPTS

1. Give examples of organisms that are very large and organisms that are very small.
2. Name four characteristics that all living things share.
3. Name three things that living things must obtain to survive.

CRITICAL THINKING

4. **Synthesize** Give examples of how a common animal, such as a dog, is organized, grows, responds, and reproduces.
5. **Predict** In a certain lake, would you expect there to be more organisms that are large enough to see or more organisms that are too small for you to see? Why?

CHALLENGE

6. **Design** Try to imagine the different structures that a single-celled organism needs to survive in pond water. Then use your ideas to design your own single-celled organism.

ANSWERS

1. very large organism: huge fungus; very small organism: single-celled bacteria

2. growth, reproduction, organization, and response to environment

3. energy, materials, and living space

4. A dog is made of cells that perform specific functions. It starts as a puppy. As its cells reproduce, it grows to a full-sized dog. Male and female dogs reproduce sexually to create more puppies. Dogs bark at, run at, or run from different things they sense.

5. There is room in a lake for many billions of microscopic organisms but not for nearly as many larger organisms.

6. Examine students' designs for creativity and understanding of the characteristics and needs of life.

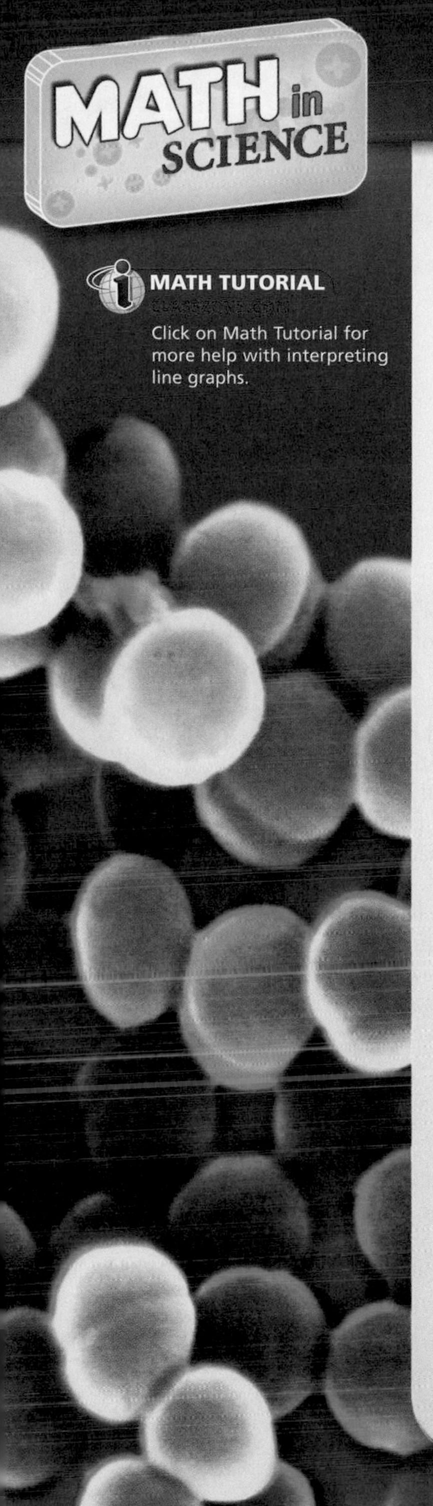

Click on Math Tutorial for more help with interpreting line graphs.

SKILL: MAKING A LINE GRAPH

Graphing Growth

If you hold marbles in your hand and drop them into a bowl one at a time, each drop into the bowl adds the same amount. If you plot this growth on a line graph, you will have a straight line.

By contrast, a bacterial colony's growth expands exponentially as it grows. All the bacteria divide in two. Every time all the bacteria divide, the colony doubles in size.

EXAMPLE

Compare the two types of growth on a graph.

Graph 1. Suppose the marble collection begins with one marble, and after every hour, one marble is added.

The graph shows: $x + 1 = y$
The slope of the line stays the same at each interval.

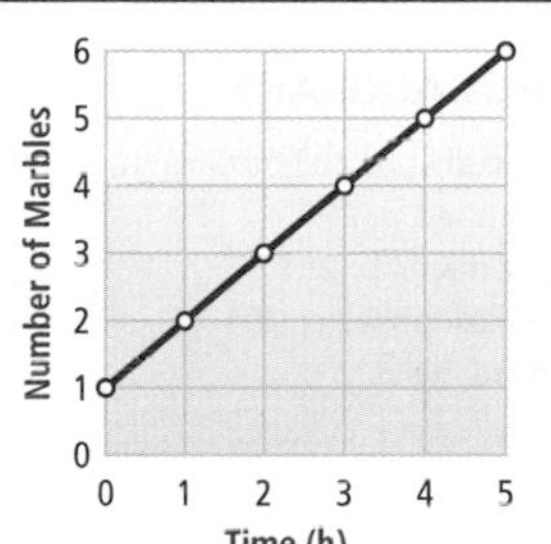

Graph 2. Suppose a bacterial colony begins with one bacterium, and every hour, a bacterial cell divides, forming two bacteria.

The graph shows: $2^x = y$
The slope gets steeper at each interval.

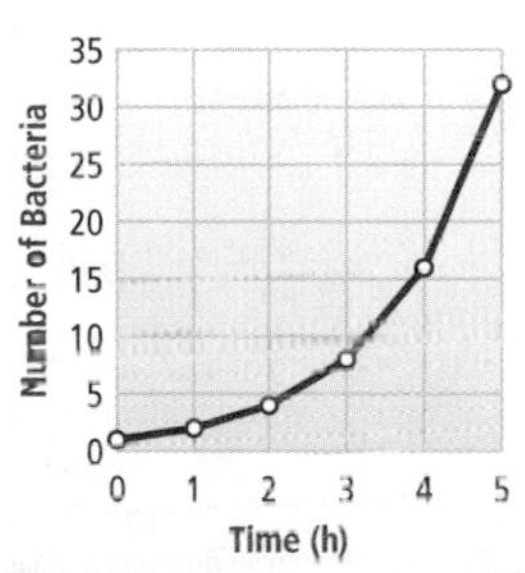

Examine the graphs and answer the questions.

1. How many marbles are in the collection after 3 h? How many bacteria are in the colony after 3 h?
2. After 7 h, what number of marbles would show in graph 1? Name the coordinates for this point. What number of bacteria would be shown in graph 2? Name the coordinates.
3. Copy the two graphs on graph paper. Extend each graph to 10 h. Plot the growth according to the pattern or formula given.

CHALLENGE Suppose each bacterium lives for 10 h. How many bacteria will be in the colony after 20 h?

287

ANSWERS

1. 4 marbles; 8 bacteria

2. 8 marbles; (7, 8); 128 bacteria; (7, 128)

3. Graph 1 will continue to be a straight line. Graph 2 will be a steep curved line.

***CHALLENGE** about 1,000,000 ($2^{20} = 1{,}048{,}576$). Since each bacteria divides ten times before it dies, the lifespan limitation does not significantly affect the size of the colony.*

MATH IN SCIENCE

Math Skills Practice for Science

Set Learning Goal

To compare line graphs of linear and exponential growth

Present the Science

When a diluted sample of bacteria is spread on a nutrient agar surface, the individual bacterial cells begin to divide. In 24 to 48 hours, they form bacterial colonies that can be seen with the naked eye. Each colony contains many generations of bacteria that arose from a single cell.

Develop Graphing Skills

- Remind students that the independent variable is plotted along the x-axis and the dependent variable is plotted on the y-axis.
- In both graphs, time is the independent variable. Number of bacteria and number of marbles are the dependent variables.
- Discuss the meaning of x and y in the equations.

DIFFERENTIATION TIP Review the concept of variables with students who need extra help.

Close

Ask: How are the two growth patterns similar at the beginning of growth? After growth has occurred for several minutes? *Graph 2 starts increasing similar to graph 1, but numbers of bacteria soon exceed the number of marbles.*

- Math Support, p. 59
- Math Practice, p. 60

Technology Resources

Students can visit **ClassZone.com** for practice making a line graph.

MATH TUTORIAL

9.2 FOCUS

Set Learning Goals

Students will

- Give reasons that bacteria are the simplest living things.
- Identify two groups of single-celled organisms.
- Recognize that bacteria may help or harm other organisms.

3-Minute Warm-Up

Display Transparency 4 or copy this exercise on the board:

Decide if these statements are true. If not true, correct them.

1. If an object cannot grow, it is not alive. *true*
2. Viruses are alive because they can reproduce. *Viruses are not alive because they reproduce only within host cells.*
3. Living things are divided into three kingdoms. *Living things are divided into six kingdoms.*

3-Minute Warm-Up, p. T4

9.2 MOTIVATE

THINK ABOUT

PURPOSE To examine the idea that bacteria live everywhere

DEMONSTRATE Show students the well-known electron micrograph of bacteria on the point of a pin, which can be found in many biology texts. See if students can identify what it shows. Ask why a pinprick can become infected.

Ongoing Assessment

Give reasons that bacteria are the simplest living things.

Ask: Why are bacteria thought to be simple? *They are one cell and have no nucleus.*

KEY CONCEPT

9.2 Bacteria are single-celled organisms without nuclei.

BEFORE, you learned

- Organisms come in all shapes and sizes
- All living things share common characteristics
- Living things may be divided into six kingdoms

NOW, you will learn

- About the simplest living things
- About bacteria and archaea
- That bacteria may help or harm other organisms

VOCABULARY

bacteria p. 288
archaea p. 290
producer p. 291
decomposer p. 291
parasite p. 291

THINK ABOUT

Where are bacteria?

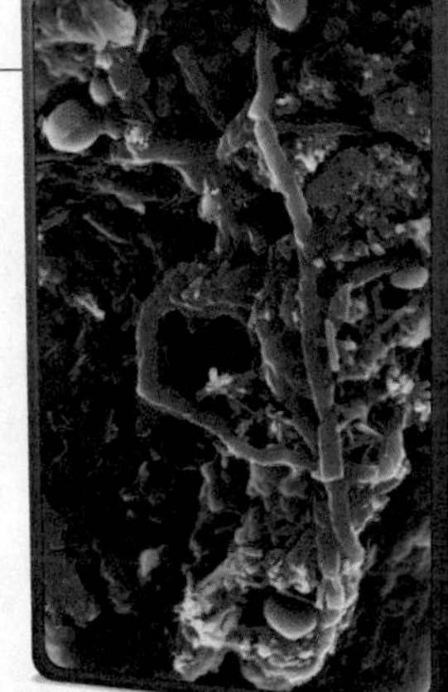

Bacteria are the simplest form of life. But that doesn't mean they're not important or numerous. As you look about the room you're sitting in, try to think of places where you might find bacteria. In fact, bacteria are on the walls, in the air, on the floor, and on your skin. It's hard to think of a place where you wouldn't find bacteria. The photograph shows a magnification of bacteria living on a sponge. The bacteria are magnified 580 ×. There are hundreds of millions of bacteria on your skin right now. There are trillions of bacteria that live inside your intestines and help you digest food.

Bacteria and archaea are the smallest living things.

MAIN IDEA WEB
Make a web of the important terms and details about the main idea: *Bacteria and archaea are the smallest living things.* Be sure to include how bacteria are classified.

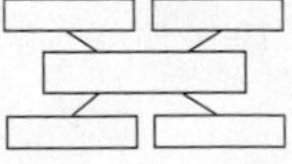

The names of the organisms belonging in the kingdoms Archaea and Bacteria are probably unfamiliar. Yet you actually encounter these organisms every day. Bacteria are everywhere: on your skin, in the ground, in puddles and ponds, in the soil, and in the sea. About 300 species of bacteria are living in your mouth right now.

Bacteria are the simplest kind of life known on Earth. All bacteria are composed of just one cell without a nucleus. Their genetic material is contained in loops within the cell. A bacterium reproduces using binary fission.

RESOURCES FOR DIFFERENTIATED INSTRUCTION

Below Level

UNIT RESOURCE BOOK

- Reading Study Guide A, pp. 24–25
- Decoding Support, p. 58

AUDIO CDS

Advanced

UNIT RESOURCE BOOK

Challenge and Extension, p. 30

English Learners

UNIT RESOURCE BOOK

Spanish Reading Study Guide, pp. 28–29

AUDIO CDS

- Audio Readings in Spanish
- Audio Readings (English)

Bacteria

All bacteria are single cells without nuclei.

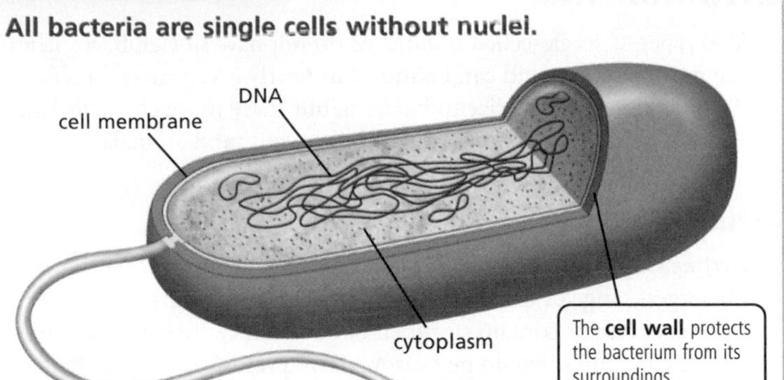

 A

Bacterial cells are different from the cells of other organisms. A bacterial cell is about 1/10 to 1/20 the size of a typical cell from organisms such as animals, plants, fungi, or protists. These four groups include organisms made up of cells with true nuclei. The nucleus is a structure that is enclosed by a membrane and that holds the genetic material.

READING TIP The plural of *bacterium* is *bacteria*, and the plural of *nucleus* is *nuclei*.

B

Despite their small size, bacteria are simple only when compared with more complex cells. Bacteria are much more complex than viruses, because they have many internal structures that viruses do not have. For example, one important feature of most bacteria is a covering called a cell wall, which surrounds and protects the soft cell membrane like a rain jacket. Bacterial cells contain many large molecules and structures that are not found in viruses.

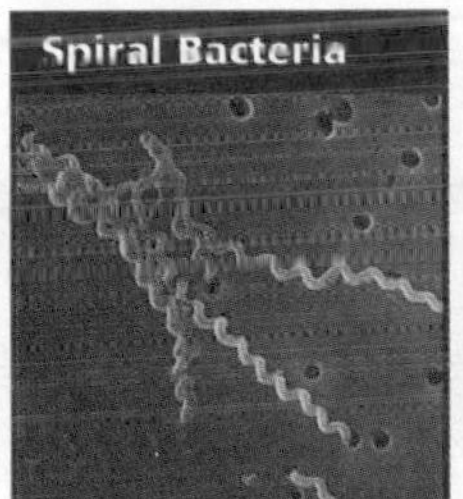
Spiral Bacteria

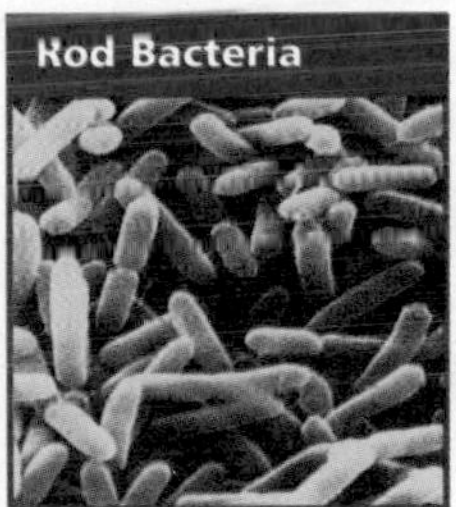
Rod Bacteria

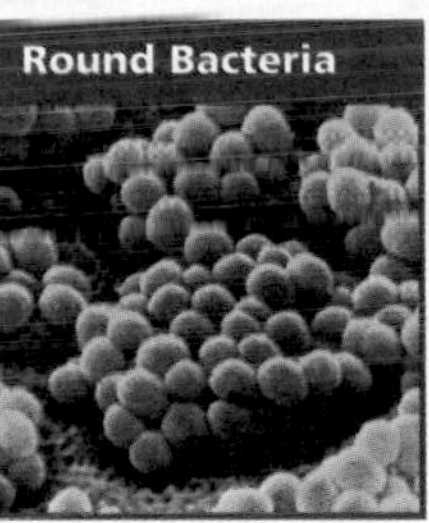
Round Bacteria

Scientists often classify bacteria by their external shapes.

- Spiral-shaped bacteria occur in single strands.
- Rod-shaped bacteria may occur singly or in chains.
- Round-shaped bacteria may occur singly or in pairs, chains, or clusters.

 Name two features that all bacteria share.

9.2 INSTRUCT

Teach from Visuals

To help students interpret the diagram of bacterial structure, ask:

- Where is the bacterium's DNA located? *in the cytoplasm*
- Why do you think a bacterial cell needs both a cell wall and a cell membrane? *The cell wall protects the cell from injury. The cell membrane regulates what materials move in and out of the cell.*

Address Misconceptions

IDENTIFY Ask: What do bacteria do? Students may answer that bacteria cause illness or help other organisms. If students do not mention growing, breathing, eating, reproducing, or other functions characteristic of life, they may think that bacteria are not alive.

CORRECT Have students list the characteristics of living things and determine how bacteria fulfill each of them. Have reference books available for student use.

REASSESS Ask: How do bacteria get food? *Some bacteria make their own food. Others get nutrients from their environment.*

Technology Resources

Visit **ClassZone.com** for background on common student misconceptions.

 **MISCONCEPTION DATABASE**

Ongoing Assessment

Recognize that bacteria come in three basic shapes.

Ask: What three shapes can bacteria have? *spirals, rods, and spheres*

 *Answer: Bacteria are single-celled and have no nuclei.*

DIFFERENTIATE INSTRUCTION

 **More Reading Support**

A How does a bacterial cell compare in size with other cells? *Bacterial cells are much smaller.*

B Are bacteria more or less complex than viruses? *more*

English Learners Place the words *producer, decomposer,* and *parasite* on the classroom's Science Word Wall with brief definitions of each. Have students draw and label their own models of bacteria as shown above. They can choose to draw the spiral, rod, or round bacteria shapes. They should label the *cell membrane, DNA, cytoplasm,* and *cell wall.*

Teach from Visuals

To help students interpret the photographs of archaea, ask: What do the environments of the organisms in the three photographs have in common? *They all have extreme conditions that most organisms cannot tolerate.*

Integrate the Sciences

In general, archaea are more similar to the rest of the living world than to true bacteria. For this reason, it is thought that archaea are the ancestors of all living things except true bacteria. Most of the differences between true bacteria and archaea are chemical. Bacterial cell walls contain peptidoglycan; archaea cell walls do not. The lipids in bacterial cell membranes are all unbranched hydrocarbons; archaea cell membranes contain some branched hydrocarbons. True bacteria are affected by certain antibiotics that do not affect archaea.

Real World Example

Until recently, scientists thought archaea were found only in extreme environments. In the past 10 years, however, many members of the kingdom Archaea have been found living with other organisms in the more moderate habitats of the oceans. It is now thought that archaea may be as ubiquitous as true bacteria.

Ongoing Assessment

Identify two groups of single-celled organisms.

Ask: What two groups of organisms are single-celled and have no nuclei? *bacteria and archaea*

Archaea and bacteria are found in many environments.

Find out more about the many different types of bacteria.

Two types of single-celled organisms do not have nuclei. Bacteria are the most common and can be found in nearly every environment. Archaea are similar in size to bacteria, but share more characteristics with the cells of complex organisms like plants and animals.

Archaea

Archaea (AHR-kee-uh) are single-celled organisms that can survive in the largest range of environments. These environments may be very hot, very cold, or contain so much of a substance such as salt that most living things would be poisoned. As a result, scientists often group archaea according to where they live.

Methanogens take their name from methane, the natural gas they produce. These archaea die if they are exposed to oxygen. They may live in the dense mud of swamps and marshes, and in the guts of animals such as cows and termites.

READING TIP

The word halophile is formed using the root word *halo-* which means "salt," and the suffix *–phile* which means "love." Therefore, a *halophile* is a "salt lover."

Halophiles live in very salty lakes and ponds. Some halophiles die if their water is not salty enough. When a salty pond dries up, so do the halophiles. They can survive drying and begin dividing again when water returns to the pond. C

Thermophiles are archaea that thrive in extreme heat or cold. They may live in hot environments such as hot springs, near hot vents deep under the sea, or buried many meters deep in the ice. D

Archaea

Archaea are organisms that can live in extreme environments.

Methanogens

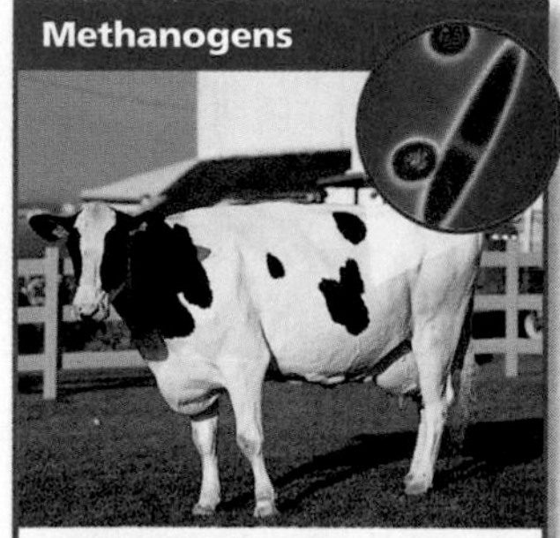

Methanogens may be found in a cow's stomach where they help with digestion.

Halophiles

Halophiles can be found in extremely salty bodies of water such as the Dead Sea.

Thermophiles

Thermophiles may be found in hot geysers such as this one in Yellowstone National Park.

DIFFERENTIATE INSTRUCTION

More Reading Support

C Where do halophiles live? *in very salty lakes and ponds*

D Where do thermophiles live? *in extreme heat or cold*

English Learners This section has a variety of introductory clauses and phrases. For example, "When a salty pond dries up, so do the halophiles." Have students find the comma that separates the introductory clause or phrase from the rest of the sentence. Then, help them locate the subject of the sentence.

Bacteria

Most single-celled organisms without a nucleus are classified as bacteria. Bacteria are found in almost every environment and perform a variety of tasks. Some bacteria contain chlorophyll. Using sunlight for energy, these bacteria are an important food source in oceans. These bacteria also release oxygen gas, which animals need to breathe.

What are some common traits of bacteria and archaea?

Bacteria without chlorophyll perform different tasks. Some bacteria break down parts of dead plants and animals to help recycle matter. Some bacteria release chemicals into the environment, providing a food source for other organisms. Scientists often group bacteria by the roles they play in the environment. Three of the most common roles are listed below.

E Bacteria that transform energy from sunlight into energy that can be used by cells are called **producers.** These bacteria are a food source for organisms that cannot make their own food.

Decomposers get energy by breaking down materials in dead or decaying organisms. Decomposers help other organisms reuse materials found in decaying matter.

F Some bacteria live in a very close relationship either inside or on the surface of other organisms. Some of these bacteria may have no effect on their host organisms or host cells. Some bacteria help their hosts. Other bacteria are **parasites,** organisms that harm their hosts.

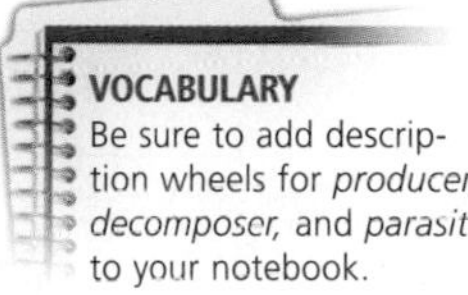

VOCABULARY
Be sure to add description wheels for *producer, decomposer,* and *parasite* to your notebook.

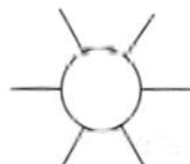

Bacteria

Three roles bacteria play in the environment are shown below.

Producers

Cyanobacteria in Earth's oceans provide oxygen for animals to breathe.

Decomposers

Some bacteria break down dead wood into materials used by other organisms.

Parasites

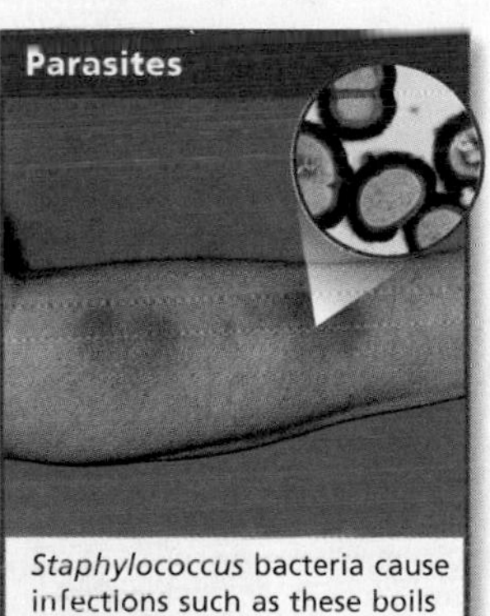

Staphylococcus bacteria cause infections such as these boils in humans.

Teach from Visuals

To help students interpret the photographs showing the roles that bacteria play, ask:

- How would our environment be different if cyanobacteria did not exist? *There probably would not be enough oxygen in the atmosphere for animals to breathe.*
- How would our environment be different if bacteria did not decompose materials? *Plants, insects, and fungus might not grow for lack of food and space.*
- How would our lives be different if no bacteria were parasites? *There would be no diseases caused by bacteria. Diseases caused by viruses would still exist, however.*

EXPLORE the BIG idea

Revisit "Internet Activity: Microscopic Life and You" on p. 279. Have students describe what they have learned about microscopic life.

Teacher Demo

Set up a microscope so students can observe *Lactobacillus,* the bacteria that is used to make yogurt. Use distilled water to thin some yogurt containing live bacteria. Put a drop of diluted yogurt on a microscope slide. Add a cover slip. Have students observe the bacteria under the highest power of the microscope.

Ongoing Assessment

CHECK YOUR READING *Answer: Archaea and bacteria are both single-celled and have no nuclei.*

DIFFERENTIATE INSTRUCTION

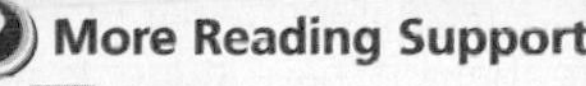

More Reading Support

E How do producers get energy? *from sunlight*

F Where do bacterial parasites live? *inside or on other organisms*

Advanced Have students research the organisms usually found in a compost pile. What conditions are there, and what is the source of the bacteria? Students can set up a small compost pile in a plastic or glass container.

R Challenge and Extension, p. 30

Below Level Have students use a Venn diagram to compare archaea and bacteria

Teach from Visuals

To help students interpret the photograph of helpful bacteria, ask:

- Where does the nitrogen gas that bacteria fix come from? *from the air*
- Why do plants need bacteria to fix nitrogen? *Plants cannot use nitrogen gas to make proteins. The nitrogen must be converted into a form that the plants can use.*

Address Misconceptions

IDENTIFY Ask students what a "germ" is and whether all bacteria are germs. If students respond that germs cause disease and that all bacteria are germs, they probably hold the misconception that all bacteria are harmful.

CORRECT Have students list the ways bacteria are helpful to other organisms or to the environment. *They release oxygen; fix nitrogen; break down dead organisms into chemicals that living things can use; clean up sewage, water, and oil spills; and aid in digestion.* Have students explain how each of the listed activities is helpful to other organisms. For example, bacteria that release oxygen help animals to breathe. Use a two-column chart such as the one below:

Bacteria's Action	How Helpful
O_2 release	animals breathe
fix nitrogen	nutrient for plants

REASSESS Ask: Why do you think people have this misconception that all bacteria are bad? *People think they are more affected by disease organisms than by helpful bacteria.*

Technology Resources

Visit **ClassZone.com** for background on common student misconceptions.

 **MISCONCEPTION DATABASE**

Real World Example

Bacteria help produce sauerkraut, pickles, vinegar, yogurt, cheese, sour cream, and other foods. Our diets would be limited without the help of bacteria.

Bacteria may help or harm other organisms.

Some bacteria, such as producers and decomposers, are helpful to other organisms. But other bacteria can be harmful. These bacteria can cause diseases in animals and plants.

Helpful Bacteria

One shovelful of ordinary soil contains trillions of bacteria, and every fallen leaf or dead animal is covered with bacteria. These bacteria break down the matter in dead bodies and waste materials. These broken-down materials are then available for other organisms to build their bodies.

Cities use bacteria to break down sewage. Bacteria in sewage-treatment plants live on the material dissolved in liquid sewage. These bacteria help make the water clean enough to be released into rivers or oceans. Other bacteria are used to clean up oil spills by decomposing oil suspended on the ocean's surface.

Bacteria can also change materials that do not come from living things and make them available for other organisms. For example, some bacteria can convert nitrogen gas to nitrogen compounds. This process, called nitrogen fixation, makes nitrogen available to plants in a form that is useful to them. Plants use this nitrogen in making proteins, which are an important part of every cell.

Helpful Bacteria

Bacteria inside the root nodules of soybean plants convert nitrogen into a form the plant can use.

DIFFERENTIATE INSTRUCTION

More Reading Support

G What do you call the conversion of nitrogen gas into nitrogen compounds by bacteria? *nitrogen fixation*

Alternative Assessment Invite a restaurant owner or manager to visit your classroom. Before the visit, have students write questions about the precautions the restaurant takes to prevent the growth of bacteria in food. Have students discuss with the restaurant owner general practices to ensure food safety.

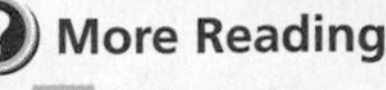

Like bacteria, certain types of archaea are helpful to other organisms. Animals that eat plants such as grass often depend on archaea. Methanogens help break down the cellulose in cell walls. Termites and cows are two examples of animals that can digest cellulose because of the archaea in their stomachs.

Name two helpful roles that bacteria can play in the environment.

Harmful Bacteria

Not all bacteria are helpful to other organisms. Scientists first discovered that bacteria cause some diseases in the late 1800s. Much of the scientific research into harmful bacteria developed because bacteria cause disease in humans. Tuberculosis, cholera, and infant diarrhea are examples of disease caused by bacteria. Bacteria also may cause disease in many other animals and in plants.

Bacteria can cause the symptoms of disease in three ways.

- They can invade parts of the body, multiplying in body tissues and dissolving cells.
- They can poison the body with chemicals they produce and release.
- They can poison the body with chemicals that are part of the bacteria themselves.

One way to fight bacterial disease is with vaccinations. Vaccines help individual organisms prepare to fight diseases they might encounter in the future. Humans, as well as cats and dogs, get vaccinations for bacterial diseases.

Bacterial wilt caused disease in this pumpkin.

9.2 Review

KEY CONCEPTS

1. Explain why bacteria are classified as living cells but viruses are not.
2. Name two main groups of bacteria.
3. Describe three ways that bacteria affect other organisms.

CRITICAL THINKING

4. **Visualize** Draw a diagram of a bacterium. Label the parts of the cell.
5. **Predict** Where in your neighborhood would you find most of the bacteria that cause decomposition?

CHALLENGE

6. **Analyze** Parasitic bacteria do not usually kill their hosts, at least not quickly. For a parasite, why is it better not to kill the host?

ANSWERS

1. Bacteria can grow, reproduce, and get nutrients from their environment. Viruses do not have structures that allow them to do these things.

2. bacteria and archaea

3. Producers provide oxygen and energy. Decomposers break down dead organisms. Parasites can cause disease in other organisms.

4. Diagrams should include the cell membrane, DNA, cytoplasm, and a cell wall. They should be spiral, round, or rod-shaped.

5. Sample answer: in soil and in a garbage can

6. If parasites kill their hosts, they cannot continue to grow and multiply in them and must find another host.

History of Science

Until the middle of the 19th century, many people died from bacterial infections after surgery or childbirth. Ignaz Philipp Semmelweis, a physician working in Vienna, demonstrated that the infection rate decreased when physicians washed their hands before treating patients. Later, Joseph Lister and Louis Pasteur confirmed Semmelweis's observations and identified the bacteria that caused many of the infections, thus proving the germ theory of disease.

Ongoing Assessment

Answer: decompose organic matter, fix nitrogen

Reinforce the BIG idea

Have students relate the section to the Big Idea.

Reinforcing Key Concepts, p. 31

9.2 ASSESS & RETEACH

Assess

Section 9.2 Quiz, p. 4

Reteach

Provide various materials that students can use to make models of bacterial and archaea cells. Yarn or string can represent DNA and a flagellum, gelatin can represent cytoplasm, a cross-section of a ball or tube can represent the cell wall.

Technology Resources

Have students visit **ClassZone.com** for reteaching of Key Concepts.

CONTENT REVIEW

CONTENT REVIEW CD-ROM

CHAPTER INVESTIGATION

Focus

PURPOSE To take samples and determine quantities of bacteria that live on hands and in the environment

OVERVIEW Students will touch their fingers, a common object, and a swab of an area of their environment to petri dishes containing sterile nutrient agar. They will examine the petri dishes after they have incubated to see whether bacterial colonies have grown. Students will find the following:

- Their hands harbor bacteria.
- Common objects harbor bacteria.
- Bacteria are in all areas of the environment.

Lab Preparation

- Sterile nutrient agar petri dishes can be purchased from a biological supply house or can be made in your own lab following careful instructions.
- Sterile cotton swabs can be purchased in a drug store.
- Arrange to borrow an incubator if a dark, warm area is not available.
- Prior to the investigation, have students read through it. Have them prepare data tables. Or, distribute datasheets and rubrics.

 UNIT RESOURCE BOOK, pp. 61–69

 SCIENCE TOOLKIT, F14

Lab Management

- In steps 3–6, remind students to close lids immediately after adding fingerprints to or swabbing the agar.
- Remind students that each bacterial colony represents many generations of bacteria that arose from a single cell that was deposited on the agar.
- Note that any fuzzy growth in the petri dishes are molds (fungi), not bacteria.

SAFETY Remind students to wash their hands after handling the bacterial cultures.

CHAPTER INVESTIGATION

Bacteria

OVERVIEW AND PURPOSE People routinely wash themselves to keep clean. You probably take a bath or shower every day, and you also wash your hands. Your hands may appear to be perfectly clean, but appearances can be deceiving. Your hands pick up bacteria from the objects you touch. You cannot see or feel these microscopic organisms, but they are there, on your skin. In this activity you will

- sample bacteria in your environment
- sample bacteria on your hands

Problem

Write It Up

Do you pick up bacteria from your environment?

Hypothesize

Write It Up

Write a hypothesis about whether bacteria in your environment are transferred to your skin. Your hypothesis should take the form of an "If . . . , then . . . , because . . ." statement.

MATERIALS
- 3 covered petri dishes with sterile nutrient agar
- marker
- tape
- everyday object, like a coin or eraser
- sterile cotton swab
- hand lens

for Challenge:
- 1 covered petri dish with sterile nutrient agar
- sterile swab

Procedure

1. Make a data table in your **Science Notebook** like the one shown on page 295.
2. Obtain three agar petri dishes. Be careful not to accidentally open the dishes.
3. Remove the lid from one dish and gently press two fingers onto the surface of the agar. Close the lid immediately. Tape the dish closed. Mark the tape with the letter A. Include your initials and the date. Mark your hand as the source in Table 1. Wash your hands.

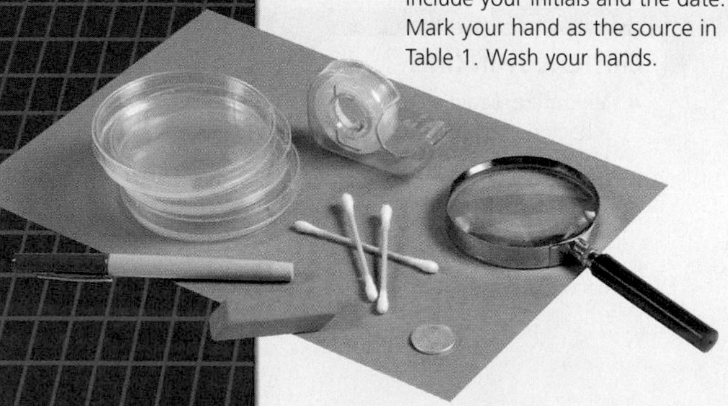

step 3

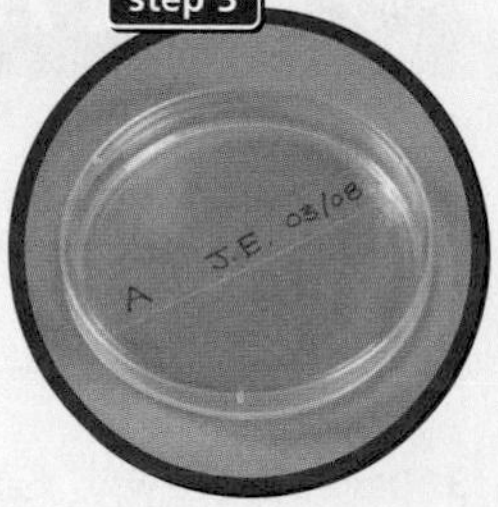

INVESTIGATION RESOURCES

 CHAPTER INVESTIGATION, Bacteria
- Level A, pp. 61–64
- Level B, pp. 65–68
- Level C, p. 69

Advanced students should complete Levels B & C.

 Writing a Lab Report, D12–13

Technology Resources

Customize this student lab as needed or look for an alternative. Print rubrics to assess student lab reports.

 Lab Generator CD-ROM

4 Choose a small object you handle every day, such as a coin or an eraser. Remove the lid from the second petri dish and swipe the object across the agar. You can instead use a sterile swab to rub on the object, and then swipe the swab across the agar. Close the lid immediately. Tape and mark the dish B, as in step 3. Include the source in Table 1.

5 Choose an area of the classroom you have regular contact with, for example, the top of your desk or the classroom door. Use a clean swab to rub the area and then swipe the swab across the agar of the third petri dish. Tape and mark the dish as C, following the instructions in step 3. Dispose of the swab according to your teacher's instructions.

step 5

6 Place the agar plates upside down in a dark, warm place for two to three days. **CAUTION: Do not open the dishes. Wash your hands when you have finished.**

Observe and Analyze

Write It Up

1. **OBSERVE** Observe the dishes with the hand lens. You may want to pull the tape aside, but do not remove the covers. Include a description of the bacteria in Table 1. Are the bacteria in one dish different from the others?
2. **OBSERVE** Observe the amounts of bacterial growth in each dish and record your observations in Table 1. Describe the amount of growth in relative terms, using words such as *most, least,* or *moderate.* Which dish has the most bacterial growth? the least growth?
3. Return the petri dishes to your teacher for disposal. **CAUTION: Do not open the dishes. Wash your hands thoroughly with warm water and soap when you have finished.**

Conclude

1. **INFER** Why is it necessary for the agar to be sterile before you begin the experiment?
2. **INFER** What function does the agar serve?
3. **INTERPRET** Compare your results with your hypothesis. Do your observations support your hypothesis?
4. **IDENTIFY LIMITS** What limits are there in making a connection between the bacteria in dish A and those in dishes B and C?
5. **EVALUATE** Why is it important to keep the petri dishes covered?
6. **APPLY** Why is it important to use separate petri dishes for each sample?

INVESTIGATE Further

CHALLENGE Contamination can be a problem in any experiment involving bacteria, because bacteria are everywhere. Obtain a petri dish from your teacher. Swipe a sterile swab on the agar and place the agar plate upside down in a dark, warm place for two to three days. Do the results of this test make you reevaluate your other lab results?

Bacteria

Table 1. Observations of Bacteria

Petri Dish	Source	Description of Bacteria	Amount of Bacteria
A	hand		
B			
C			

Observe and Analyze

1. *The colonies in different dishes may look alike, although they may be different bacteria. Most likely they will be different.*
2. *Results will depend on which surface has been cleaned most recently. The least growth will likely be in dish A or dish C. The greatest might be in any of A, B, or C.*

Conclude

1. *You need to be sure that the bacteria growing on the agar came from your sample and not from the agar itself.*
2. *It offers food and living space to the bacteria.*
3. *Answers should give any evidence that supported the hypothesis, or evidence that did not support it.*
4. *You cannot say definitely that an object or location is the source of the bacteria on your hands because bacteria are everywhere.*
5. *to prevent bacteria in the air from falling on the agar*
6. *to prevent cross-contamination*

INVESTIGATE Further

CHALLENGE This petri dish serves as a control. If bacterial colonies grow on this agar dish, you can infer that these bacteria came from the air or from the swab. If there is no growth on this dish, you can have confidence that most or all of the bacteria in dishes A–C came from the sample.

Post-Lab Discussion

- Ask: Why was it important to place the petri dishes in a warm place? *If the temperature was too low, bacteria might not grow.*
- Ask: Why do you think it was necessary to store the petri dishes upside down? *Water usually condenses on the inside of the petri dishes. This water might drip on the agar surface and spread the bacteria to other areas of the agar.*
- Ask: If bacteria are everywhere, how can you avoid getting sick? *Not all bacteria cause disease; wash your hands, keep hands away from face.*

9.3 FOCUS

Set Learning Goals

Students will

- Recognize that viruses consist of only genes and a protein coat.
- Describe how viruses harm host cells.
- Summarize how viruses use a cell's machinery to reproduce.
- Use a model to analyze how viral infections spread.

3-Minute Warm-Up

Display Transparency 5 or copy this exercise on the board:

Match the definition to the correct term.

Definitions

1. a very small living thing *d*
2. living thing that lives in or on another organism *c*
3. nonliving infectious particle *a*

Terms

a. virus
b. binary fission
c. parasite
d. microorganism
e. host cell

 3-Minute Warm-Up, p. T5

9.3 MOTIVATE

EXPLORE Viruses

PURPOSE To model the way viruses were discovered

TIP *10 min.* The sieves must have a fine enough mesh to prevent sesame seeds from falling through. Make sure that there are no tear holes in the mesh.

WHAT DO YOU THINK? *Particle size; make the mesh finer or add a second type of filter such as a piece of filter paper.*

KEY CONCEPT

Viruses are not alive but affect living things.

BEFORE, you learned

- Most organisms are made of a single cell
- Living things share common characteristics
- Viruses are not living things

NOW, you will learn

- About the structure of viruses
- How viruses use a cell's machinery to reproduce
- How viruses affect host cells

VOCABULARY

host cell p. 298

EXPLORE Viruses

How were viruses discovered?

PROCEDURE

1. Fill a small container with mixed sesame seeds and salt.
2. Holding the sieve over the paper plate, pour the mixture into the sieve.
3. Gently shake the sieve until nothing more falls through.
4. Using a hand lens, examine the material that fell through the sieve and the material that stayed in the sieve.

MATERIALS

- small container
- sesame seeds
- table salt
- small kitchen sieve
- paper plate
- hand lens

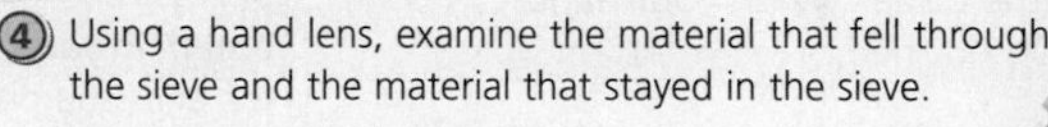

WHAT DO YOU THINK?

- What is the most important difference between the particles that got through the sieve and the particles that remained behind?
- How could you change your sieve to make it not let through both kinds of particles?

Viruses share some characteristics with living things.

MAIN IDEA WEB
Remember to make a web of the important terms and details about the main idea: *Viruses share some characteristics with living things.*

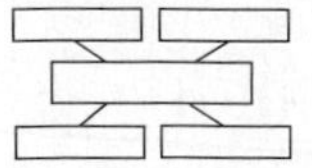

In the late 1800s, scientists such as Louis Pasteur showed that some small organisms can spoil food and cause disease. Once the cause was found, scientists looked for ways to prevent spoilage and disease. One method of prevention they found was removing these harmful organisms from liquids.

Bacteria may be removed from liquids by pouring the liquid through a filter, like a coffee filter or a sieve. To remove bacteria, a filter must have holes smaller than one millionth of a meter in diameter.

RESOURCES FOR DIFFERENTIATED INSTRUCTION

Below Level

UNIT RESOURCE BOOK

- Reading Study Guide A, pp. 34–35
- Decoding Support, p. 58

AUDIO CDS

Advanced

UNIT RESOURCE BOOK

Challenge and Extension, p. 40

English Learners

UNIT RESOURCE BOOK

Spanish Reading Study Guide, pp. 38–39

- Audio Readings in Spanish
- Audio Readings (English)

INSTRUCT

INVESTIGATE Viruses

INVESTIGATE Viruses

How do infections spread?

SKILL FOCUS
Analyzing

MATERIALS
- paper cup
- sample liquid
- solution A
- solution B

TIME
30 minutes

PROCEDURE

1. Get a cup of sample liquid from your teacher. Pour half the liquid from your cup into the cup of a classmate, then pour the same amount back into the original cup. Your cup should then contain a mixture of the liquids from both cups.
2. Repeat step 1 with at least two other classmates.
3. Drop one drop of solution A into your paper cup. If it changes color, you are "infected." If you were "infected," add drops of solution B until your liquid turns clear again. Count how many drops it takes to "cure" you.

WHAT DO YOU THINK?

- If you were "infected," can you figure out who "infected" you?
- If you were not "infected," is it possible for anyone who poured liquid into your cup to be "infected"?

CHALLENGE Only one person in your class started out with an "infection." Try to figure out who it was.

When a filter had removed all of the harmful organisms from a liquid, the liquid no longer caused any illnesses. This method worked when there was only bacteria in the liquid. Sometimes filtering did not prevent disease. Something much smaller than bacteria was in the liquid. Scientists called these disease-causing particles viruses, from the Latin word for "slimy liquid" or "poison."

RESOURCE CENTER
CLASSZONE.COM

Learn more about viruses.

CHECK YOUR READING How does the size of viruses compare with the size of bacteria?

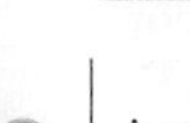

Scientists have learned much about viruses, and can even make images of them with specialized microscopes. Viruses consist of genetic material contained inside a protective protein coat called a capsid. The protein coat may be a simple tube, such as the coat of an ebola virus, or have many layers, such as the smallpox virus shown on page 298.

Viruses may come in many shapes and sizes, but all viruses consist of a capsid and genetic material. Viruses are able to use living cells to get their DNA copied and so can produce new viruses, a characteristic that makes them similar to living things. Also the protein coat is similar to a cell's outer membrane. But viruses do not grow, and viruses do not respond to changes in their environment. Therefore, viruses are not living organisms.

PURPOSE Use a model to analyze how viral infections spread

TIPS *30 min.* Give each student a cup of water, and one student a cup filled with a mixture of baking soda and water (1000 mg per 100 mL). You may need 2 or 3 drops of solution *A* (phenolphthalein) to get a pink color for "infected" students. Tap water may also turn pink, so use distilled water if possible. If students repeat step 1 two more times, about eight people will be infected.

WHAT DO YOU THINK? *You could narrow down the possibilities but you couldn't figure out for sure who infected you. It is not possible for anyone who poured liquid into your cup to be infected if you are not.*

CHALLENGE *Students who were uninfected at the end can rule out all the people they shared liquid with. Students who were infected at the end will have trouble ruling out anyone they shared liquid with.*

 Datasheet, Viruses, p. 41

Technology Resources

Customize this student lab as needed or look for an alternative. Print rubrics to assess student lab reports.

 **Lab Generator CD-ROM**

DIFFERENTIATE INSTRUCTION

More Reading Support

A How can viruses be seen? *with specialized microscopes*

English Learners In "Investigate Viruses" on p. 297, the repeated use of quotation marks around the word *infected* may be confusing to English learners. Explain that because the activity really is a model, no one is being infected. The quotes indicate that the infection is happening in thought only, or in an imagined situation.

Metacognitive Strategy

Have students write a short paragraph explaining any difficulties or particular interest they found while doing the Challenge analysis of "Investigate Viruses." Ask: How does this type of analysis apply to the real world? *Sample answer: Epidemiologists use surveys about recent contact to track down the origins of outbreaks.*

Ongoing Assessment

CHECK YOUR READING *Answer: Viruses are much smaller than bacteria.*

Teach from Visuals

To help students interpret the visual of the structure of a virus, ask:

- Where is the virus's genetic material? *inside the virus*
- What part of the virus attaches to the host cell? *the capsid*

Address Misconceptions

IDENTIFY Ask: Why might it be a bad idea to go without a coat in cold or rainy weather? If students say it causes a cold or flu, they may hold misconceptions about how viruses infect living things.

CORRECT Have students review the process of virus infection (steps 1–5 on p. 298). Discuss whether the infectious process can be affected by cold or rainy weather.

REASSESS Have students write a short paragraph explaining why going without a coat in cold or rainy weather cannot give you a cold.

Technology Resources

Visit **ClassZone.com** for background on common student misconceptions.

MISCONCEPTION DATABASE

Teach Difficult Concepts

To help students understand how virus genetic material can take over the machinery of the host cell, ask:

- How can a long molecule of host DNA be destroyed? *It can be chopped up so no intact genes are left.*
- How can virus genes take over the cell? *They can copy themselves and code only for virus proteins.*

Ongoing Assessment

Recognize that viruses consist of only genes and a protein coat.

Ask: What is the function of the protein coat of a virus? *It protects the genes inside the virus.*

Describe how viruses harm host cells.

Ask: What happens to the host cell after the virus reproduces? *It usually bursts open and dies.*

Virus

All viruses, including this smallpox virus, contain genetic material surrounded by a capsid.

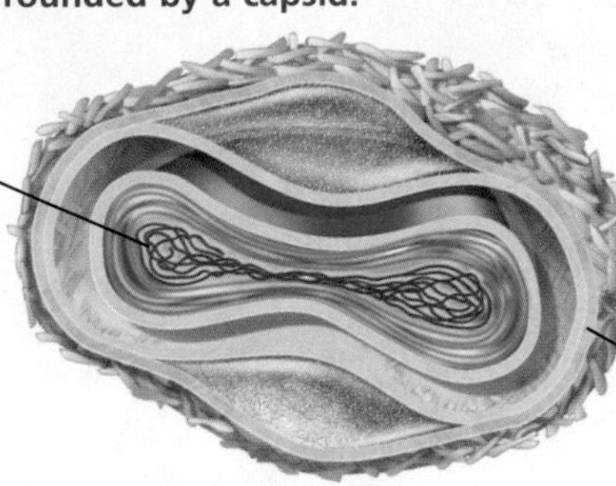

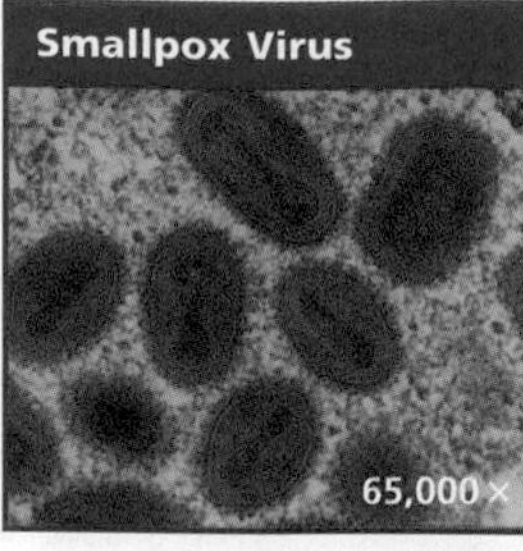

Viruses multiply inside living cells.

VISUALIZATION CLASSZONE.COM

See how viruses infect and multiply within bacteria.

Remember that all living things reproduce. Viruses cannot reproduce by themselves, which is one of the ways they are different from living things. However, viruses can use materials within living cells to make copies of themselves. The cells that viruses infect in order to make copies are called **host cells**. Despite their tiny size, viruses have the ability to cause a lot of damage to cells of other organisms.

B

One of the best studied viruses infects bacteria. It's called a bacteriophage (bak-TEER-ee-uh-FAYJ), which comes from the Latin for "bacteria eater." Some of the steps that a bacteriophage goes through to multiply are shown in the illustration on page 299.

1. **Attachment** The virus attaches to the surface of a bacterium.
2. **Injection** The virus injects its DNA into the bacterium.
3. **Production** Using the same machinery used by the host cell for copying its own DNA, the host cell makes copies of the viral DNA.
4. **Assembly** New viruses assemble from the parts that have been created.
5. **Release** The cell bursts open, releasing 100 or more new viruses.

C

Viruses have proteins on their surfaces that look like the proteins that the host cell normally needs. The virus attaches itself to special sites on the host that are usually reserved for these proteins.

Not every virus makes copies in exactly the same way as the bacteriophage. Some viruses stay inside their host cells. Others use the host cell as a factory that produces new viruses one at a time. These viruses may not be as harmful to the infected organism because the host cell is not destroyed.

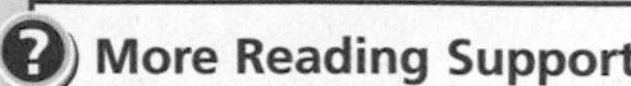
DIFFERENTIATE INSTRUCTION

More Reading Support

B What are host cells? *cells that are infected by viruses*

C How does virus DNA get into the host cell? *It is injected.*

Below Level Have students make a poster showing the steps of virus reproduction. They can use the poster for a class presentation, describing each of the five steps.

Making New Viruses

Viruses, such as this bacteriophage, use cells to make new viruses.

Virus (bacteriophage)
head
bacteriophage DNA
tail
cell wall
cell membrane
bacterial DNA
Host cell (bacterium)

1 Attachment The bacteriophage virus attaches to a bacterium.

injected DNA
bacterial DNA

2 Injection The virus injects its DNA into the host cell.

empty virus
copies of viral DNA
bacterial DNA pieces
new virus parts

3 Production The viral DNA uses the host cell's machinery to break down the host cell's DNA and produce the parts of new viruses.

new viruses

4 Assembly The parts assemble into new viruses.

burst bacterium
new viruses

5 Release The host cell breaks apart and new viruses that are able to infect other host cells are released.

DIFFERENTIATE INSTRUCTION

Below Level Students can make a model of a bacteriophage using a large bolt, two nuts, and three pieces of wire. Screw the nuts onto the bolt so they touch the bolt head. Wrap the wires around the bottom of the bolt. Ask: What do the bolt head and nuts represent? *the head of the bacteriophage* The wires? *the tail fibers of the bacteriophage*

Advanced Have students find out how scientists study viruses. Ask them to assess whether it's possible to study them in the classroom.

R Challenge and Extension, p. 40

Teach from Visuals

To help students interpret the diagram of virus replication, ask:

- How does the bacteriophage in the diagram attach to the host cell? *Its tail attaches to special sites on the host.*
- What parts of the virus does the host cell's machinery make? *tails and DNA*
- How are new viruses assembled? *New virus DNA is inserted inside new capsids.*
- What happens to the host cell when the new viruses are released? *It bursts and dies.*

The visual "Making New Viruses" is available as T6 in the Unit Transparency Book.

Teacher Demo

To demonstrate how easily viruses can spread from person to person, place some glitter on various classroom surfaces. Throughout the day, have students observe where the glitter has traveled. They will find glitter on their hands, clothing, and anything else they touch.

Develop Critical Thinking

COMPARE Have students compare computer viruses and the viruses they have been studying in this lesson. Discuss whether *virus* is an appropriate name for a computer virus. Ask: How does the method of "infection" of computer viruses compare with that of the viruses you are studying? *They can attach themselves to programs and destroy the program after reproducing themselves.*

Ongoing Assessment

Summarize how viruses use a cell's machinery to reproduce.

Ask: How does the virus disable the host cell's DNA? *The virus breaks up the DNA into pieces so that it can no longer function.*

History of Science

In 1967, the World Health Organization (WHO) began an international effort to eradicate smallpox. In 1980, WHO certified that smallpox had been eradicated worldwide. It has been estimated that if the eradication effort had not been made, 350 million additional victims and 40 million deaths would have occurred worldwide from 1980 to 2000.

Reinforce the BIG idea

Have students relate the section to the Big Idea.

 Reinforcing Key Concepts, p. 42

Assess

 Section 9.3 Quiz, p. 5

Reteach

Have students make a flipbook showing virus replication. They should make a title page and five labeled pages showing each step: attachment, injection, production, assembly, release. To draw the steps, they can refer to the diagram on p. 299. You might wish to have students create four to six "in between" sketches between each of the five "extreme" or "key" frames in their flipbooks.

Technology Resources

Have students visit **ClassZone.com** for reteaching of Key Concepts.

 CONTENT REVIEW

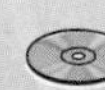 CONTENT REVIEW CD-ROM

Rows of hospital beds are filled with Massachusetts influenza patients in 1918.

Viruses may harm host cells.

A host cell does not often benefit from providing living space for a virus. The virus uses the cell's material, energy, and processes. In many cases, after a virus has made many copies of itself, the new viruses burst out of the host cell and destroy it.

Harmful viruses cause huge problems. Viruses that cause diseases such as polio, smallpox, diphtheria, or AIDS have had a major impact on human history. About 25 million people died of influenza in an outbreak that occurred just after World War I.

In the photograph, nurses work to ease the symptoms of infected patients. The most infectious patients were enclosed in tents. Others were made as comfortable as possible on beds outside. Since viruses such as influenza can spread quickly, the camp was isolated from the rest of the community.

Plant viruses can stunt plant growth and kill plants. When plant viruses invade crop plants, they can cause much economic damage, decreasing food production. Plants, animals, bacteria, and all other living things are capable of being infected by viruses.

Today, scientists are discovering ways to use viruses in a positive way. Scientists use viruses to insert certain pieces of genetic material into living cells. For example, the portion of genetic material that allows some marine organisms to produce a chemical that glows can be inserted into tissue samples to help scientists study the samples.

9.3 Review

KEY CONCEPTS

1. What are the two parts that every virus has?
2. Why are viruses not considered to be living things?
3. Explain how copies of viruses are produced.

CRITICAL THINKING

4. **Compare and Contrast** What features do viruses and cells have in common? How are they different?
5. **Explain** Summarize the steps by which a bacteriophage makes new viruses.

CHALLENGE

6. **Synthesize** What characteristics of viruses can make them so dangerous to humans and other living organisms?

ANSWERS

1. genetic material and a capsid

2. They cannot grow, respond, or reproduce outside a host cell.

3. Viruses invade host cells and use them as a factory to make new viruses.

4. Both contain genetic material. A viral capsid is like a cell wall. Cells have structures that grow and respond.

5. The bacteriophage attaches to the host cell and injects DNA into the cell. The genetic material takes over the cell's machinery to make new virus parts, which are assembled into new viruses. The new viruses escape when the host cell bursts.

6. Viruses easily spread from one living thing to another.

Patterns in these tulips are part of the genetic make-up of the flowers.

TULIPOMANIA

The Virus and the Tulip

The people of Holland around the 1620s were trading fortunes and farmland for one beautiful flower. Tulips had arrived from Turkey by way of Vienna, and interest in the flower spread through Holland like a fever. In a frenzy called "tulipomania," collectors paid as much as 5400 guilders, the price of a city house, for just one tulip bulb—but not any ordinary tulip.

Broken Flower Bulbs

Tulip traders searched for tulips with patterns, stripes, or feathery petals. These plants were called broken bulbs. Within a field of colored tulips, suddenly an odd or patterned flower grew. Once a color break showed up, it stayed with that flower's line into each new generation, until the line died off. And die off it did. The patterned petals were caused by a virus inside the plant, and the virus caused the flowers to weaken. The blooms got smaller in each generation.

The Mystery Source

While the trade in tulips rose, growers tried many tricks to produce the crazy patterns. Still, the broken bulbs grew rarely and randomly, or so it seemed. Viruses weren't discovered until 300 years later. Scientists then figured out that a virus had caused the broken bulbs.

A small leaf-eating insect called an aphid had carried the virus from plant to plant.

©Dennis Kunkel/Dennis Kunkel Microscopy, Inc.

Back Down to the Ground

Like any goldrush, tulipomania crashed. People lost fortunes and fought over claims. In 1637, the government stopped all trading. Today, tulips with striped and feathery patterns grow around the world, but the patterns observed are not caused by viruses. Still, every now and then, a strange looking bulb appears. Instead of prizing it, growers remove it. They don't want a field of virus-infested, weakened plants.

EXPLORE

1. **OBSERVE** Look at tulips in a garden catalog, and find breeds with patterns. Observe the tulip closely. Draw or paint the modern flower and label its name.
2. **CHALLENGE** Viruses can produce sickness, but they have other effects too. Do research on viruses to list some effects of viruses that have value to scientists, doctors, or other people.

EXPLORE

1. ***OBSERVE*** *Check students' drawings to be sure they are detailed and labeled.*

2. ***CHALLENGE*** *Viruses are currently being used in gene therapy and other forms of DNA technology. Some harmless viruses are used to make vaccines against serious diseases.*

EXTREME SCIENCE
Fun and Motivating Science

Set Learning Goal

To read independently to learn about one impact on history viruses have had

Present the Science

Tulips first appeared in western and central Asia, primarily in Armenia and Persia. From there, the tulip spread into areas along the Black Sea, the Mediterranean, and eastward into China. The Turks were growing tulips over a thousand years ago.

Discussion Questions

- Show students a map of the Netherlands. Ask them why they think that country became such a large commercial grower of tulips. *central location, port location for trading*
- Ask students how they think aphids carried the virus from plant to plant. *Aphids punch holes in plants with their mouthparts so they can suck the plant sap. When they puncture the leaves of an infected plant, they pick up virus particles on their mouthparts. When they bite another plant, they inject viruses into the plant.*

DIFFERENTIATION TIP This "Extreme Science" independent activity can be done in cooperative groups. Have groups of four students act as "Reader," "Recorder," "Leader," and "Reporter" to read the feature together, answer the questions, and present answers to the class.

Close

Ask: Do you think tulip collectors in the 17th century were wise to spend so much money on a rare tulip? Why or why not?

9.4 FOCUS

Set Learning Goals

Students will

- Recognize that most protists are single-celled.
- Recognize that all protists have cells with nuclei.
- Summarize how protists get energy in three different ways.
- Observe microscopic organisms in pond water.

3-Minute Warm-Up

Display Transparency 5 or copy this exercise on the board:

A student examines a drop of pond water under a microscope and notices a single-celled organism he has never seen before. The organism does not have a nucleus, but it has a cell wall and cell membrane. It swims around in the water. Can you conclude that this organism is a bacterium or a protist? Draw and label a diagram of this organism, based on your conclusion. *It is a bacterium.*

 3-Minute Warm-Up, p. T5

9.4 MOTIVATE

THINK ABOUT

PURPOSE To think about how limestone originated from ancient microorganisms

DISCUSS Have students suggest ways that limestone could have formed from protist shells. *The shells could have been greatly compacted under the weight of water and of other shells and debris on the ocean floor.*

KEY CONCEPT

Protists are a diverse group of organisms.

BEFORE, you learned
- Organisms are grouped into six kingdoms
- Bacteria are single-celled organisms without a nucleus
- Viruses are not living things

NOW, you will learn
- About characteristics of protists
- About the cell structure of protists
- How protists get their energy

VOCABULARY
algae p. 303
plankton p. 305
protozoa p. 306

THINK ABOUT

Where can protists be found?

Protists include the most complex single-celled organisms found on Earth. Fifty million years ago, a spiral-shelled protist called a nummulitid was common in some oceans. Even though its shell was the size of a coin, the organism inside was microscopic and single celled. When the organism died, the shells accumulated on the ocean floor. Over millions of years, the shells were changed into the rock called limestone. This limestone was used to build the great pyramids of Egypt. Some of the most monumental structures on Earth would not exist without organisms made of just a single cell.

Most protists are single celled.

When Anton van Leeuwenhoek began using one of the world's first microscopes, he looked at pond water, among other things. He described, in his words, many "very little animalcules." Some of the organisms he saw probably were animals—microscopic but multicellular animals. However, many of the organisms Leeuwenhoek saw moving through the pond water had only a single cell. Today, more than 300 years later, scientists call these single-celled organisms protists.

Protists include all organisms with cells having nuclei and not belonging to the animal, plant, or fungi kingdoms. In other words, protists may be considered a collection of leftover organisms. As a result, protists are the most diverse of all the kingdoms.

RESOURCES FOR DIFFERENTIATED INSTRUCTION

Below Level

UNIT RESOURCE BOOK
- Reading Study Guide A, pp. 45–46
- Decoding Support, p. 58

AUDIO CDS

Additional INVESTIGATION, Growth of Algae, A, B, & C, pp. 70–78; Teacher Instructions, pp. 360–361

Advanced

UNIT RESOURCE BOOK
Challenge and Extension, p. 51

English Learners

UNIT RESOURCE BOOK
Spanish Reading Study Guide, pp. 49–50

AUDIO CDS
- Audio Readings in Spanish
- Audio Readings (English)

INVESTIGATE Protists

What lives in pond water?

SKILL FOCUS
Observing

MATERIALS
- dropper
- pond water
- slide
- cover slip
- hand lenses
- microscope

TIME
40 minutes

PROCEDURE

1. Using a dropper, place one small drop of pond water in the center of a slide. Try to include some of the material from the bottom of the container.
2. Gently place a cover slip on the drop of water.
3. Observe the slide with a hand lens first.
4. Starting with low power, observe the slide with a microscope. Be sure to follow microscope safety procedures as outlined by your teacher. Carefully focus up and down on the water. If you see moving organisms, try to follow them by gently moving the slide.

WHAT DO YOU THINK?
- Describe and draw what you could see with the hand lens.
- Describe and draw what you could see with the microscope.
- Compare your observations with those of other students.

CHALLENGE Choose one organism that moves and observe it for some time. Describe its behavior.

A Most protists are single-celled, microscopic organisms that live in water. However, protists also include some organisms with many cells. These many-celled organisms have simpler structures than animals, plants, or fungi. They also have fewer types of cells in their bodies.

CHECK YOUR READING Why are protists considered the most diverse group of organisms?

The group of protists you're probably most familiar with is seaweeds. At first glance, seaweed looks like a plant. On closer inspection scientists see that it has a simpler structure. Some seaweeds called kelp can grow 100 meters long.

B The name **algae** applies to both multicellular protists and single-celled protists that use sunlight as an energy source. Both seaweed and diatoms are types of algae. Slime molds are another type of multicellular protist.

VOCABULARY
Be sure to make a description wheel for *algae* and add to it as you read this section.

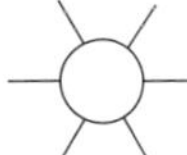

Given the many different types of organisms grouped together as protists, it is no surprise that protists play many roles in their environments. Algae are producers. They obtain energy from sunlight. Their cells provide food for many other organisms. These protists also produce oxygen, which is beneficial to many other organisms. Both of these roles are similar to those played by plants. Other protists act as parasites and can cause disease in many organisms, including humans.

DIFFERENTIATE INSTRUCTION

More Reading Support

A Where do most protists live? *in water*

B What are algae? *protists that use sunlight for energy*

English Learners The words *should, would,* and *could* are not universal in all languages but are common in academic English. Help students understand sentences that contain these words. For example, "Some of the most monumental structures on Earth would not exist without organisms made of just a single cell."

9.4 INSTRUCT

INVESTIGATE Protists

PURPOSE To observe the movement and behavior of protists in pond water

TIPS *40 min.* Students can add a drop of methyl cellulose to their wet mounts to slow down the movement of rapidly swimming protists. Try modeling use of the microscope before students begin. Field of view circles may be used to aid viewing.

WHAT DO YOU THINK? *Students may see multicellular algae; many ciliates and flagellates moving rapidly, some green, others transparent; and amoebae moving slowly by extending. Students will see images more clearly and in greater detail with the microscope. Students should note new details after comparing observations.*

CHALLENGE *Students could see a paramecium, which moves rapidly. When it bumps into anything, it stops, backs away, and changes direction.*

 Datasheet, Protists, p. 52

Technology Resources

Customize this student lab as needed or look for an alternative. Print rubrics to assess student lab reports.

 **Lab Generator CD-ROM**

Teaching with Technology

If a PC microscope is available, students can observe the organisms on a computer screen. If a microscope fitted with a camera is available, photograph the protists.

Ongoing Assessment

Recognize that most protists are single-celled.

Ask: Are all protists single-celled? Explain. *No; some are multicellular.*

 *Answer: Protists include all organisms that don't fit into the other kingdoms.*

Teach from Visuals

To help students interpret the photographs of protists, ask:

- Which of the three protists in the photographs can move itself? *the euglena*
- How do you know? *It has a flagellum.*
- What is unusual about the shape of diatoms? *They are quite varied.*

Social Studies Connection

Seaweed and products derived from seaweed are important to the food processing industry and thus to the general economy. Large quantities of seaweed are cooked and eaten in Japan, China, Wales, and other countries. It is an excellent source of iron. A seaweed called nori is dried into sheets and used to make sushi. Red algae are a source of a gumlike substance called carrageenan, which is used to thicken marshmallows and ice cream and other dairy products.

Develop Critical Thinking

SYNTHESIZE Have students describe the different ways that protists move. After researching the topic, students can demonstrate how protists with flagella and cilia move and compare their movements with amoeboid movement, which is quite different. Have students make class presentations of their discoveries.

Ongoing Assessment

Recognize that all protists have cells with nuclei.

Ask: Is the structure of protist cells more similar to the cells of bacteria or plants and animals? Why? *plants and animals; all have nuclei*

CHECK YOUR READING *Answer: All three organisms capture the energy in sunlight and convert it to chemical energy. All three are green (contain chlorophyll).*

Diversity of Protists

Protists come in a variety of shapes and sizes.

Euglena

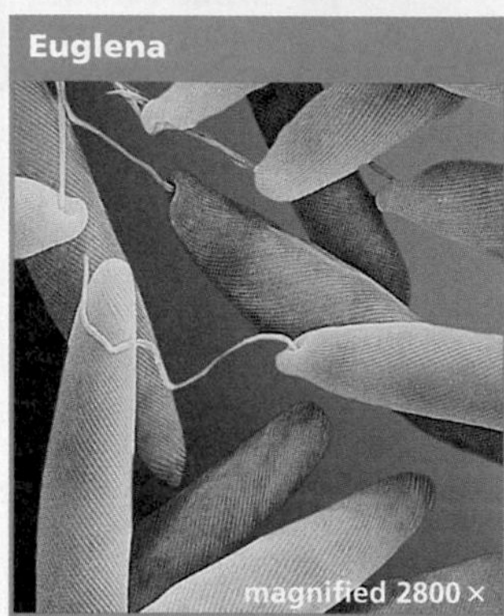

Diatoms

Seaweed

Protists live in any moist environment, including both freshwater and saltwater, and on the forest floor. Some protists move around in the water, some simply float in place, and some stick to surfaces. The photographs above show a small sample of the large variety of organisms that are called protists.

MAIN IDEA WEB
Remember to make a web of the important terms and details about the main idea: *Protists obtain their energy in three ways.* Include examples of each method of obtaining energy.

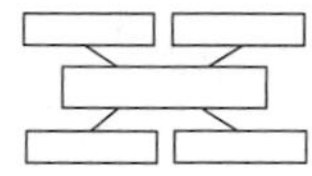

Seaweed is a multicellular protist that floats in the water and can be found washed up on beaches. Slime molds are organisms that attach to surfaces, absorbing nutrients from them. Diatoms are single-celled algae that float in water and are covered by hard shells. Euglena are single-celled organisms that can move like animals but also get energy from sunlight. C

Protists obtain their energy in three ways.

D Protists can be classified by their way of getting energy. Some protists capture sunlight and convert it to usable energy. Another group of protists gets its energy from eating other organisms. A third group gets energy by absorbing materials and nutrients from its environment.

Some protists, such as the euglena in the upper left photograph, can even switch from one mode of life to another. They swim rapidly through pond water like animals. If they receive enough sunlight, they look green and make their own food like plants. But if they are left in the dark long enough, they absorb nutrients from their environment like fungi.

CHECK YOUR READING Explain how the organisms in the photographs above get their energy.

DIFFERENTIATE INSTRUCTION

More Reading Support

C What is seaweed? *a multicellular protist that lives in the ocean*

D What is one way protists can be classified? *by the way they get energy*

Inclusion Have students make models of a euglena and a paramecium so that students can easily differentiate between flagella and cilia. A piece of string taped to a "euglena" made of clay can represent a flagellum. Shag carpeting, fake fur, or Velcro can represent cilia on a "paramecium."

Advanced Have students design an experiment to test a hypothesis about protists or pond water.

Challenge and Extension, p. 51

Algae

E

Plantlike protists, called algae, get energy from sunlight. Like plants, they use the Sun's energy, water, and carbon dioxide from the air or water. Algae contain chlorophyll, a green pigment that they use to capture the Sun's energy. In the process of transforming energy from sunlight, algae release oxygen gas into the air. This important process, which is called photosynthesis, also takes place in plants and some bacteria. Organisms that perform photosynthesis also supply much of the food for other organisms.

Diatoms are examples of single-celled algae. Like all algae, a diatom contains a nucleus which holds its genetic material. Diatoms also have chloroplasts, which are the energy-producing centers that contain chlorophyll.

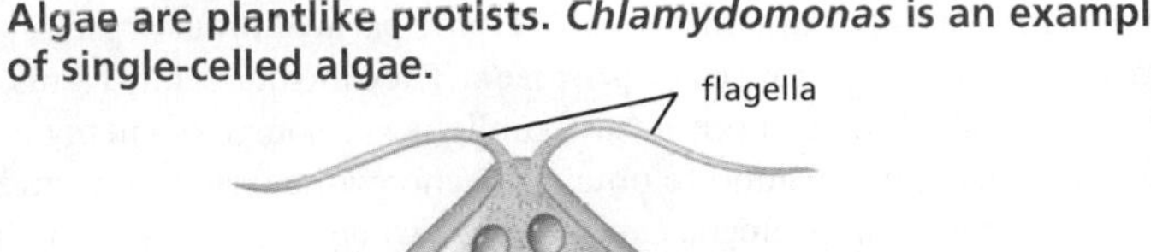

Algae

Algae are plantlike protists. *Chlamydomonas* is an example of single-celled algae.

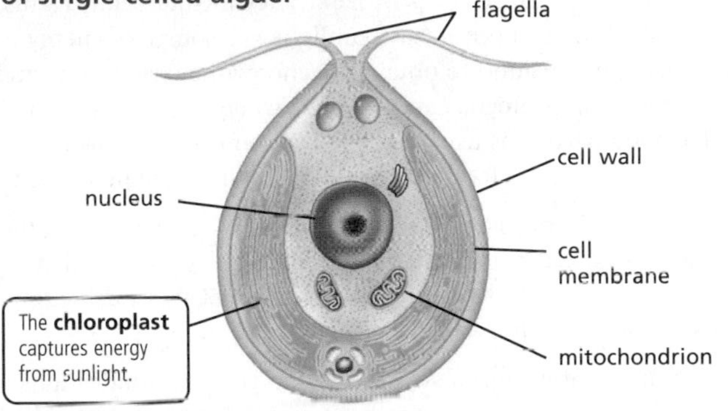

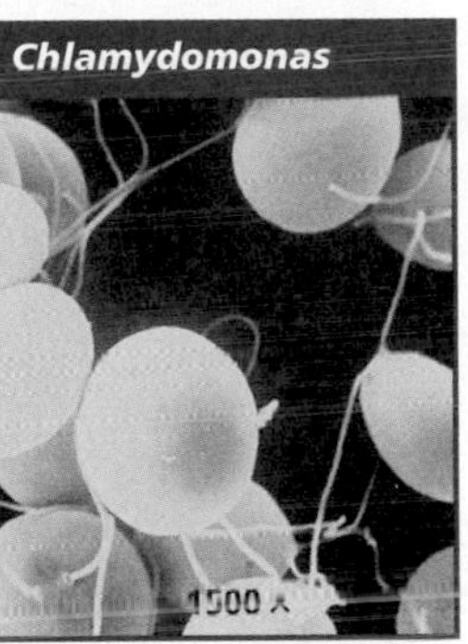

Another type of algae, called volvox, are microscopic colonies of nearly identical cells. These cells, arranged in a hollow ball, look like some single-celled algae. Sometimes cells break off from the hollow ball to form new colonies. The new colonies will eventually escape the parent colony. Colonial organisms such as volvox are the simplest kind of multicellular organisms. Seaweed is another example of multicellular algae.

F

All organisms that drift in water are called **plankton.** Plankton include the young of many animals and some adult animals, as well as protists. Plankton that perform photosynthesis are called phytoplankton (plantlike plankton). Phytoplankton include algae and the cyanobacteria you learned about earlier. Phytoplankton live in all of the world's oceans and produce most of the oxygen animals breathe.

Teach from Visuals

To help students interpret the diagram of *Chlamydomonas* structure, ask:

- How does *Chlamydomonas* move? *using two flagella*
- Why is *Chlamydomonas* green? *Its chloroplast contains chlorophyll.*
- What is the function of the mitochondrion in the *Chlamydomonas* cell? *energy conversion*

Teacher Demo

Set up several microscopes around the room so students can observe a variety of protists. Show prepared slides of diatoms and wet mounts of volvox and amoebae.

Teach Difficult Concepts

Students may have trouble understanding that plankton is not a specific kind of organism. Tell students that *plankton* is a general term used to describe any organism that drifts in water currents. Many plankton organisms are single celled bacteria and protists, but others are more complex multicellular plants and animals. Ask: Why is plankton so important to the environment? *It produces most of the oxygen that organisms breathe, and it is food for many marine animals.*

Arts Connection

Have students create an "underwater" drawing, painting, or model of pond life. An underwater effect can be made using oil pastels or crayons and washing over them with watercolor paint, or by simply using colored pencils and a watercolor wash. Their model or artwork should be based on sketching at an actual pond or from source materials, such as field guides. They should include at least one example each of algae and protozoa, as well as any animals or decaying matter found in the pond. *These works can be to scale or at an enlarged scale, but should specify the scale.*

DIFFERENTIATE INSTRUCTION

More Reading Support

E Where do algae get energy? *from sunlight*

F What are plankton? *tiny organisms that drift in water*

Additional Investigation To reinforce Section 9.4 learning goals, use the following full-period investigation:

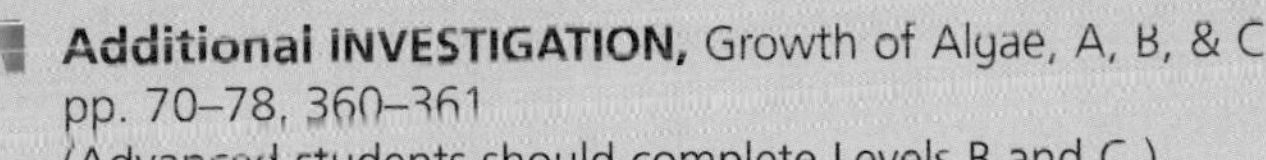

Additional INVESTIGATION, Growth of Algae, A, B, & C, pp. 70–78, 360–361
(Advanced students should complete Levels B and C.)

Below Level Give students a diagram of an alga like the one on this page. Have students label the parts of the organism.

Teach from Visuals

To help students interpret the diagram of paramecium structure, ask:

- How do you think food enters the oral groove? *Cilia sweep the food particles into the groove.*
- What clue in the photograph leads you to suspect that paramecia can move very rapidly? *The paramecium has thousands of cilia.*

History of Science

Anton van Leeuwenhoek was able to observe "little animalcules" with a microscope that he made himself. Although it had only a single lens, compared to the two or more lenses found in modern compound microscopes, the lens was very finely made, and van Leeuwenhoek could see many details. He spent many hours examining the life swimming in a drop of pond water. He kept a careful record of his observations, which still make interesting reading today.

Ongoing Assessment

CHECK YOUR READING *Answer: Protozoa eat other organisms and get energy from the nutrients in the organisms they eat. Algae get energy from sunlight.*

Protozoa

Protozoa, such as this *Paramecium*, are animal-like protists.

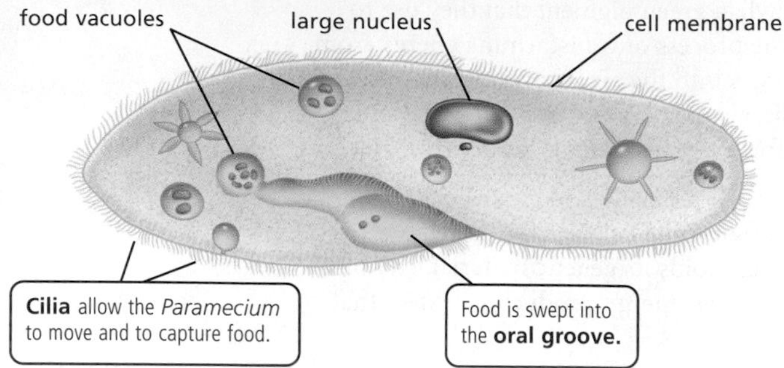

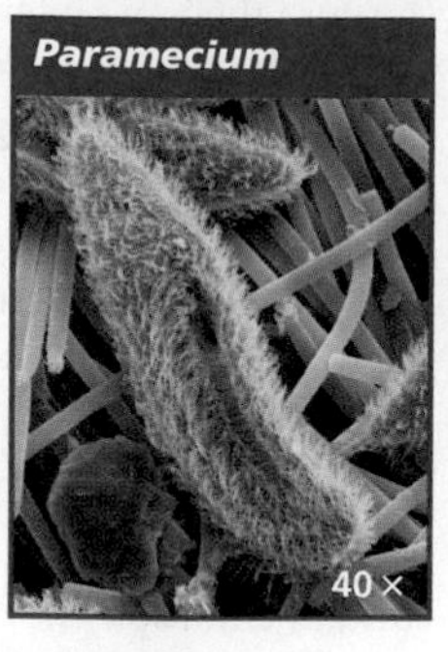

Protozoa

 G

Protists that eat other organisms, or decaying parts of other organisms, are animal-like protists, or **protozoa.** They include many forms, all single-celled. Protozoa cannot use sunlight as a source of energy and they must move around to obtain the energy they need to survive. Certain chemicals in protozoa can recognize when a particle of food is nearby. The food particle is usually another organism or a part of one. The protozoan ingests the food and breaks it down to obtain energy.

Some animal-like protists swim rapidly, sweeping bacteria or other protists into a groove that looks like a mouth. One example, called a paramecium, is shown above. A paramecium moves about using thousands of short wavy strands called cilia.

Another group of protozoa swim with one or more long whiplike structures called flagella. A third group of protozoa has very flexible cells. Organisms such as the amoeba oozes along surfaces. When it encounters prey, the amoeba spreads out and wraps around its food.

REMINDER: A parasite is an organism that lives inside or on another organism and causes the organism harm.

? H

A number of protists live as parasites, some of which cause disease in animals, including humans. One of the world's most significant human diseases, malaria, is caused by a protist. A mosquito carries the parasite from human to human. When the mosquito bites an infected human, it sucks up some of the parasite in the blood. When that same mosquito bites another human, it passes on some of the parasite. Within a human host, the parasite goes through a complex life cycle, eventually destroying red blood cells.

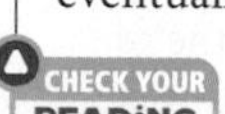 How do protozoa and algae differ in the way they obtain energy?

DIFFERENTIATE INSTRUCTION

 **More Reading Support**

G What are protozoa? *animal-like protists that eat other organisms*

H What causes the disease malaria? *a protist that is carried by mosquitoes*

Advanced Have students design an experiment that will demonstrate that euglenas can switch the way they obtain energy from capturing sunlight to absorbing nutrients from their food.

Decomposers

Protists that absorb food from their environment can be called funguslike protists. These protists take in materials from the soil or from other organisms and break materials down in order to obtain energy. They are called decomposers.

The term *mold* refers to many organisms that produce a fuzzy-looking growth. Most of the molds you might be familiar with, like bread mold, are fungi. But three groups of protists are also called molds. These molds have structures that are too simple to be called fungi, and they are single celled for a portion of their lives. One example of a funguslike protist is water mold, which forms a fuzzy growth on food. This food may be decaying animal or plant tissue or living organisms. Water molds live mainly in fresh water.

Slime molds live on decaying plants on the forest floor. One kind of slime mold consists of microscopic single cells that ooze around, eating bacteria. When their food is scarce, however, many of the cells group together to produce a multicellular colony. The colony eventually produces a reproductive structure to release spores. Wind can carry spores about, and they sprout where they land.

A walk in a moist forest might give you a chance to see a third kind of mold. This organism looks like a fine net, like lace, several centimeters across, on rotting logs. These slime molds are not multicellular, but instead one giant cell with many nuclei. They are the plasmodial slime molds.

Plasmodial slime mold may grow on decaying wood after a period of rainy weather.

How do funguslike protists get energy?

9.4 Review

KEY CONCEPTS

1. What are two characteristics of protists?
2. What feature do all protists have in common?
3. What are the three different types of protists?

CRITICAL THINKING

4. **Provide Examples** Some protists are dependent on other organisms and cannot live independently. Other protists are independent and have organisms that depend on them. Give an example of each.

CHALLENGE

5. **Hypothesize** Scientists are considering reclassifying protists into many kingdoms. How might they decide how many kingdoms to use and how to place organisms within these kingdoms?

ANSWERS

1. Most protists are single-celled; all protist cells have nuclei.

2. All protist cells have nuclei.

3. animal-like protists, plant-like protists, and funguslike protists

4. A parasite such as the malaria-causing protist is dependent on its host. Free-swimming algae are independent, but provide oxygen for other organisms.

5. Students are likely to choose a classification scheme with three parts, based on energy sources, but other classifications are reasonable

Real World Example

Many slime molds have very descriptive common names. Scrambled egg slime, toothpaste slime, wolf's milk slime, dog vomit slime, and troll butter are all slime molds that grow on damp rotted wood or garden mulch.

Ongoing Assessment

Summarize how protists get energy in three different ways.

Ask: In what three ways do protists get energy? *They capture energy from sunlight, get energy from other organisms, or absorb materials that contain stored energy.*

CHECK YOUR READING *Answer: Funguslike protists are decomposers that break down dead organisms and other organic matter to get energy.*

Reinforce the BIG idea

Have students relate the section to the Big Idea.

Reinforcing Key Concepts, p. 53

9.4 ASSESS & RETEACH

Assess

Section 9.4 Quiz, p. 6

Reteach

Have students make a chart summarizing the different groups of protists, if and how they move, how they get energy, and whether they are single-celled or multicellular.

Technology Resources

Have students visit **ClassZone.com** for reteaching of Key Concepts.

CONTENT REVIEW

CONTENT REVIEW CD-ROM

BACK TO

the BIG idea

Ask: What tests could scientists do to determine whether a microscopic object discovered on a plant is alive? *They could observe the object to see if it grows or reproduces. They could change the light and temperature conditions to see if it responds. They could examine it under a microscope to see if it has cellular organization.*

KEY CONCEPTS SUMMARY

SECTION 9.1
Ask: How are organisms grouped? *All living things are divided into six kingdoms according to their different characteristics.*

Ask: Are all organisms totally different from each other? *All living things share certain characteristics such as growth, organization, and reproduction.*

SECTION 9.2
Ask: How would you classify the bacteria shown in the photograph? *round bacteria that live in clusters*

Ask: What are three tasks bacteria perform in the environment? *producer, decomposer, parasite*

SECTION 9.3
Ask: What materials in the host cell does this virus use to make copies of itself? *host-cell machinery and DNA*

SECTION 9.4
Ask: In what way do algae, protozoans, and slime molds get energy? *Algae get energy from sunlight, protozoans get energy by eating other organisms, and slime molds get energy from the decomposed food they absorb.*

Review Concepts

- Big Idea Flow Chart, p. T1
- Chapter Outline, pp. T7–T8

9 Chapter Review

the BIG idea

Bacteria and protists have the characteristics of living things, while viruses are not alive.

KEY CONCEPTS SUMMARY

Single-celled organisms have all the characteristics of living things.

Scientists divide organisms into six **kingdoms.** All living things, including **microorganisms,** are organized, grow, reproduce, and respond to the environment.

Plants Animals Protists Fungi Archaea Bacteria

VOCABULARY
microorganism p. 282
kingdom p. 283
binary fission p. 284
virus p. 286

Bacteria are single-celled organisms without nuclei.

- Bacteria and archaea are the smallest living things.
- Archaea and bacteria are found in many environments.
- Bacteria may help or harm other organisms.

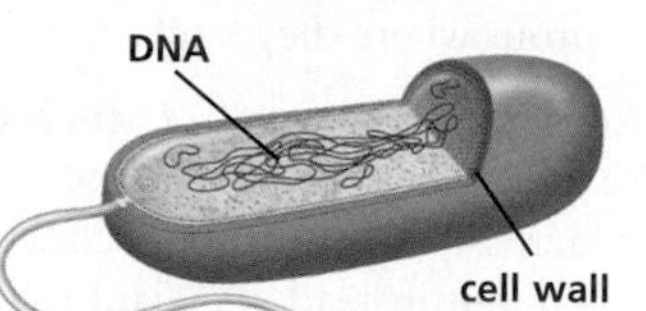

VOCABULARY
bacteria p. 288
archaea p. 290
producer p. 291
decomposer p. 291
parasite p. 291

Viruses are not alive but affect living things.

A virus consists of genetic material enclosed in a protein coat. Viruses cannot reproduce on their own, but they use materials within living cells to make copies of themselves.

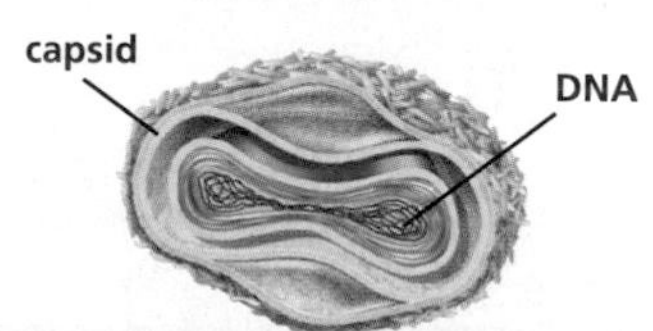

VOCABULARY
host cell p. 298

4 Protists are a diverse group of organisms.

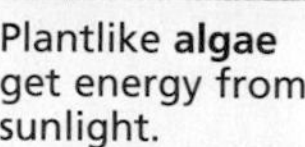
Plantlike **algae** get energy from sunlight.

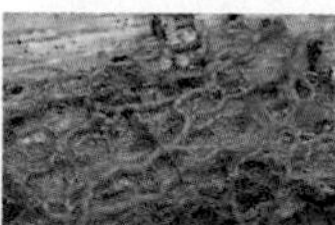
Funguslike protists are decomposers.

Protozoa, or animal-like protists, eat other organisms.

VOCABULARY
algae p. 303
plankton p. 305
protozoa p. 306

Technology Resources

Have students visit **ClassZone.com** or use the CD-ROM for a cumulative review of concepts.

CONTENT REVIEW

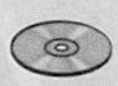
CONTENT REVIEW CD-ROM

Engage students in a whole-class interactive review of Key Concepts. Edit content as you wish.

POWER PRESENTATIONS

Reviewing Vocabulary

Draw a triangle for each of the terms listed below. Define the term, use it in a sentence, and draw a picture to help you remember the term. An example is completed for you.

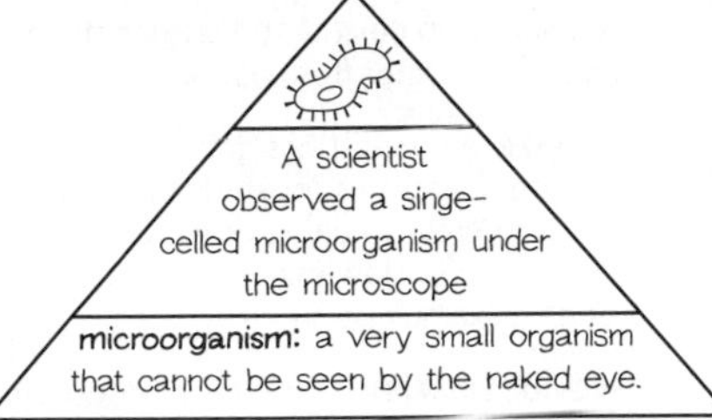

1. binary fission
2. producer
3. virus
4. host cell

Describe how the vocabulary terms in the following pairs of words are related to each other. Explain the relationship in a one- or two-sentence answer. Underline each vocabulary term in your answers.

5. archaea, bacteria
6. microorganism, organism
7. decomposers, parasite
8. protists, algae

Reviewing Key Concepts

Multiple Choice *Choose the letter of the best answer.*

9. Which group is *not* a microscopic kingdom?
   a. fungi
   b. bacteria
   c. archaea
   d. protists

10. What happens in binary fission?
    a. DNA is combined into one cell.
    b. The daughter cells differ from the parent cell.
    c. Material from one cell is divided into two cells.
    d. One cell divides into four exact cells.

11. Which is a characteristic of a virus?
    a. obtains energy from sunlight
    b. responds to light and temperature
    c. doesn't contain DNA
    d. reproduces only within cells

12. Which is the simplest type of organism on Earth?
    a. protists
    b. bacteria
    c. viruses
    d. parasites

13. Which statement about bacteria is *not* true?
    a. Bacteria reproduce using binary fission.
    b. Bacteria do not have a nucleus.
    c. Bacteria do not contain genetic material.
    d. Bacteria are either rod-, round-, or spiral-shaped.

14. Archaea that can survive only in extreme temperatures are the
    a. methanogens
    b. halophiles
    c. thermophiles
    d. bacteria

15. A fluid containing weakened disease-causing viruses or bacteria is
    a. a filter
    b. a diatom
    c. a bacteriophage
    d. a vaccine

16. Which group of protists are decomposers?
    a. diatoms
    b. molds
    c. protozoa
    d. plankton

Reviewing Vocabulary

1. *Binary fission is a method of reproduction in single-celled organisms. Bacteria reproduce by a process called binary fission.*
2. *A producer is a type of bacteria that transforms energy from sunlight into energy that is used by the cell. Producers in Earth's oceans provide oxygen for animals to breathe.*
3. *A virus is a particle that contains genetic material surrounded by a capsid. Viruses cause diseases such as smallpox and polio.*
4. *Host cells are cells infected by a virus. Bacteria are host cells for bacteriophages.*
5. *Archaea and bacteria are both single-celled organisms without nuclei. Archaea are more similar to plant and animal cells and can survive in extreme environments.*
6. *A microorganism is a type of organism that is very small and can be seen only with a microscope.*
7. *Decomposers get energy by breaking down dead or decaying material. Parasites get energy from a living cell.*
8. *Protists include all organisms with nuclei that are not plants, animals, or fungi. Algae are protists that use sunlight as an energy source.*

Reviewing Key Concepts

9. *a*
10. *c*
11. *d*
12. *b*
13. *c*
14. *c*
15. *d*
16. *b*

ASSESSMENT RESOURCES

UNIT ASSESSMENT BOOK
- Chapter Test A, pp. 7–10
- Chapter Test B, pp. 11–14
- Chapter Test C, pp. 15–18
- Alternative Assessment, pp. 19–20

SPANISH ASSESSMENT BOOK
Spanish Chapter Test, pp. 41–44

Technology Resources

Edit test items and answer choices.

Test Generator CD ROM

Visit **ClassZone.com** to extend test practice.

Test Practice

17. a
18. cellular organization, grow, reproduce, respond to their environment
19. Some bacteria cause disease.
20. protists and tiny animals that drift in the water

Thinking Critically

21. It would have organization, ability to grow and reproduce, respond to its environment.
22. Binary fission; cell duplicates its own DNA into two sides. Cell wall pinches in, forming two new cells.
23. Archaea may survive in extreme conditions. Their cells are more similar to other cells than bacteria.
24. They get energy by breaking down dead or decaying materials and recycling these materials.
25. 2^{10} bacteria. The bacteria double in number each hour.
26. less growth from washed finger than from unwashed finger
27. Viruses do not have the cell structures of bacteria, do not obtain energy from their environment, and cannot reproduce on their own.
28. provide living cells as hosts for virus reproduction
29. Algae act as producers and provide food for other organisms, including people. These release oxygen into the air for other organisms to use. Harmful protists such as some protozoa cause disease.

the BIG idea

30. Test structures to see if they meet the characteristics of life: organization, growth, response, reproduction. They are diatoms, single-celled algae protected by hard plates.

UNIT PROJECTS

Give students the appropriate Unit Project worksheets. Both directions and rubrics can be used as a guide.

 Unit Projects, pp. 5–10

---

17. Which obtains energy by feeding on other organisms?
    - a. amoeba
    - b. algae
    - c. phytoplankton
    - d. mushroom

Short Answer *Write a short answer to each question.*

18. Briefly describe the characteristics that all living things share.
19. How are some bacteria harmful to humans?
20. What are plankton?

Thinking Critically

21. **APPLY** Imagine you are a scientist on location in a rain forest in Brazil. You discover what you think might be a living organism. How would you be able to tell if the discovery is a living thing?
22. **COMMUNICATE** What process is shown in this photograph? Describe the sequence of events in the process shown.

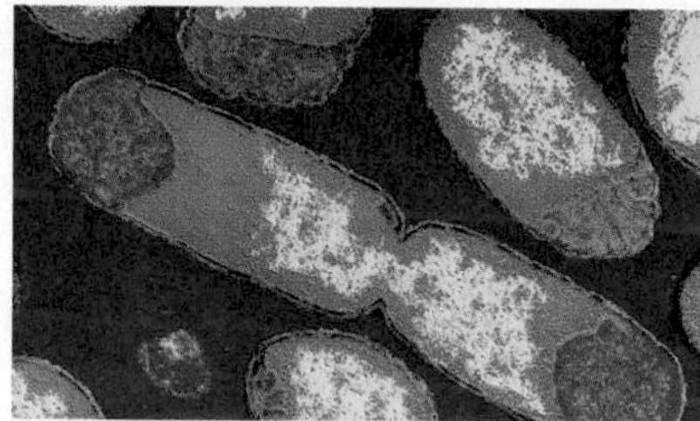

23. **CLASSIFY** Why are archaea classified in a separate kingdom from bacteria?
24. **ANALYZE** Why are some bacteria considered "nature's recyclers"? Explain the role that these bacteria play in the environment.
25. **CALCULATE** A bacterium reproduces every hour. Assuming the bacteria continue to reproduce at that rate, how many bacteria will there be after 10 hours? Explain how you know.
26. **HYPOTHESIZE** A student conducts an experiment to determine the effectiveness of washing hands on bacteria. He rubs an unwashed finger across an agar plate, then washes his hands and rubs the same finger across a second plate. What hypothesis might the student make for this experiment? Explain.
27. **COMPARE AND CONTRAST** Describe three ways that viruses differ from bacteria.
28. **ANALYZE** A scientist has grown cultures of bacteria on agar plates for study. Now the scientist wants to grow a culture of viruses in a laboratory for study. How might this be possible? Give an example.
29. **PROVIDE EXAMPLES** How are protists both helpful and harmful to humans? Give examples in your answer.

the BIG idea

30. **INFER** Look again at the picture on pages 278–279. Now that you have finished the chapter, how would you change or add details to your answer to the question on the photograph?

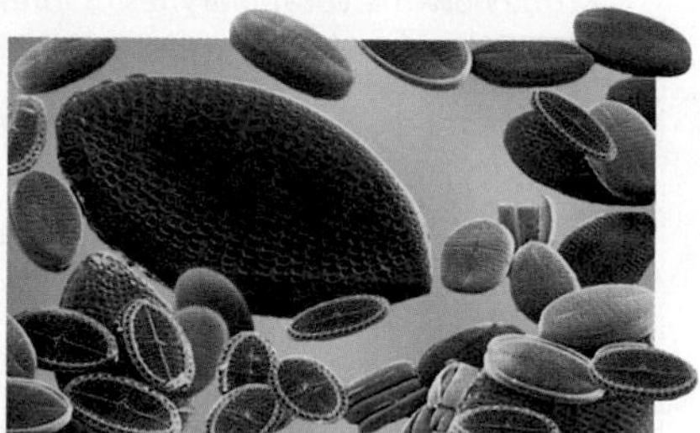

UNIT PROJECTS

If you are doing a unit project, make a folder for your project. Include in your folder a list of resources you will need, the date on which the project is due, and a schedule to track your progress. Begin gathering data.

MONITOR AND RETEACH

If students have trouble applying the concepts in items 22 and 25, review the process of binary fission. Have students draw a series of diagrams showing binary fission. The first diagram should show the cell's DNA being duplicated. The second diagram should show the cell's contents separating. The third diagram should show the cell wall pinching in to form two cells.

Students may benefit from summarizing one or more sections of the chapter.

 Summarizing the Chapter, pp. 79–80

Standardized Test Practice

For practice on your state test, go to . . . TEST PRACTICE CLASSZONE.COM

Analyzing Data

The graph below shows growth rates of bacteria at different temperatures.

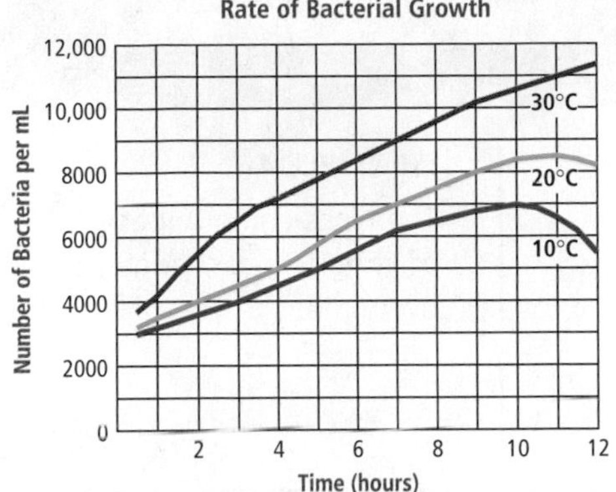

Choose the letter of the best answer.

1. At which temperature did growth of bacteria occur at the greatest rate?
   a. 0°C
   b. 10°C
   c. 20°C
   d. 30°C
2. Which statement is true about the growth rate of bacteria at 10°C?
   a. Bacteria grew rapidly at first, then declined after 6 hours.
   b. Bacteria growth increased at a steady rate.
   c. Bacteria grew slowly, then declined rapidly after 10 hours.
   d. Bacteria showed neither an increase nor decrease in growth rate.
3. What is the concentration of bacteria at a temperature of 20°C after 4 hours?
   a. about 5000 per mL
   b. about 6000 per mL
   c. about 7000 per mL
   d. about 8000 per mL
4. During which hour was the concentration of bacteria at 20°C the greatest?
   a. hour 2
   b. hour 4
   c. hour 8
   d. hour 10
5. Which conclusion can be drawn from the data in the graph?
   a. The rate of bacterial growth is the greatest at the highest temperature.
   b. The rate of bacterial growth is the least at the highest temperature.
   c. The rate of bacterial growth is the greatest at the lowest temperature.
   d. The rate of bacterial growth does not change depending on temperature.
6. How much did the rate of bacterial growth increase between 2 hours and 8 hours at 30°C?
   a. 2000 per mL
   b. 4000 per mL
   c. 6000 per mL
   d. 8000 per mL

Extended Response

7. A scientist wants to test the effect of temperature on the same bacteria shown in the graph at higher temperatures. The scientist tests the growth rate of bacteria at 50°C, 75°C, and 100°C. Based on the information in the graph and your knowledge of bacteria, what results might the scientist get? Explain your reasoning.
8. Antibiotics are drugs that are used to inhibit the growth of bacterial infections. A scientist wants to test the ability of three different antibiotics to control the growth of a certain type of bacteria. The scientist has isolated the bacteria in test tubes. Each antibiotic is prepared in a tablet form. Design an experiment that will test the effectiveness of the antibiotic tablets on the bacteria. Your experiment should include a hypothesis, a list of materials, a procedure, and a method of recording data.

METACOGNITIVE ACTIVITY

Have students answer the following questions in their **Science Notebook:**

1. What misconceptions about bacteria and viruses did you have? How have your ideas changed?
2. Which topics in this chapter would you like to study further? Why?
3. Have any of the concepts in this chapter made you want to change your behavior or everyday activities? What changes would you make?

Analyzing Data

1. d *3. a* *5. a*
2. c *4. d* *6. b*

Extended Response

7. RUBRIC

4 points for a response that correctly answers question and demonstrates an understanding of growth requirements of bacteria.

Sample answer: The bacterial population would most likely increase at 50°C since the trend in the graph indicates a better rate of growth at higher temperatures. However, many bacteria might not be able to survive at extremely high temperatures, such as 100°C, since that is the temperature of boiling water. Some archaea might be able to survive at such extreme temperatures.

3 points correctly answers question and demonstrates partial understanding of growth requirements of bacteria
2 points correctly answers question but demonstrates little understanding of growth requirements of bacteria
1 point incorrectly answers question and demonstrates little understanding of growth requirements of bacteria

8. RUBRIC

4 points for a response that demonstrates complete understanding of problem and includes an appropriate hypothesis, materials list, procedure, and method of recording data.

Sample answer: hypothesis: one of antibiotic samples will be more effective in controlling bacterial growth; materials: three petri dishes, agar, bacteria, antibiotic tablets; procedure: prepare petri dishes with agar, place bacteria in each dish, introduce a different antibiotic into each dish, observe rate of bacterial growth; data: record in a table observations about bacterial growth in each dish on succeeding days

3 points demonstrates partial understanding of problem and includes all requirements of the task as listed above
2 points demonstrates little understanding of problem. Some requirements of the task are missing.
1 point demonstrates minimal understanding of problem. Most requirements of the task are missing.

CHAPTER

Introduction to Multicellular Organisms

Life Science
UNIFYING PRINCIPLES

PRINCIPLE 1
All living things share common characteristics.

PRINCIPLE 2
All living things share common needs.

PRINCIPLE 3
Living things meet their needs through interactions with the environment.

PRINCIPLE 4
The types and numbers of living things change over time.

Unit 3:
Diversity of Living Things
BIG IDEAS

CHAPTER 9
Single-Celled Organisms and Viruses
Bacteria and protists have all of the characteristics of living things, while viruses are not alive.

CHAPTER 10
Introduction to Multicellular Organisms
Multicellular organisms live in and get energy from a variety of environments.

CHAPTER 11
Plants
Plants are a diverse group of organisms that live in many land environments.

CHAPTER 12
Invertebrate Animals
Invertebrate animals have a variety of body plans and adaptations.

CHAPTER 13
Vertebrate Animals
Vertebrate animals live in most of Earth's environments.

CHAPTER 10
KEY CONCEPTS

SECTION 

Multicellular organisms meet their needs in different ways.
1. Multicellular organisms have cells that are specialized.
2. Multicellular organisms are adapted to live in different environments.
3. Sexual reproduction leads to diversity.

SECTION 2

Plants are producers.
1. Plants capture energy from the Sun.
2. Plants are adapted to different environments.
3. Plants respond to their environment.
4. Plants respond to seasonal changes.

SECTION 

Animals are consumers.
1. Animals obtain energy and materials from food.
2. Animals interact with the environment and with other organisms.
3. Animals respond to seasonal changes.

SECTION 

Most fungi are decomposers.
1. Fungi absorb materials from the environment.
2. Fungi include mushrooms, molds, and yeasts.
3. Fungi can be helpful or harmful to other organisms.

 The Big Idea Flow Chart is available on p. T9 in the **UNIT TRANSPARENCY BOOK.**

Previewing Content

SECTION

Multicellular organisms meet their needs in different ways. pp. 315–322

1. **Multicellular organisms have cells that are specialized.**
   In multicellular organisms, different cells have different jobs.
   - Cells that work together to carry out a job are organized into **tissue.**
   - Tissues are organized into **organs.** Each organ has a particular function.
   - Organs are part of different organ systems that meet specific needs of the organism.

2. **Multicellular organisms are adapted to live in different environments.**
   All organisms have characteristics called adaptations that allow them to survive in their environment. An adaptation may relate to how an organism gets energy, it may relate to the organism's shape or structure, or it may be a type of behavior. Adaptations are the result of differences in genetic material.

3. **Sexual reproduction leads to diversity.**
   In asexual reproduction, only one parent is involved and the offspring are identical to the parent. Most multicellular organisms reproduce sexually.
   In **sexual reproduction,** the genetic material of two parents comes together to form an offspring.
   - The first part of sexual reproduction is **meiosis.** Meiosis forms egg and sperm cells that contain half the amount of genetic material that body cells contain.
   - The second part is **fertilization,** the union of a sperm and an egg, as seen in the diagram below.

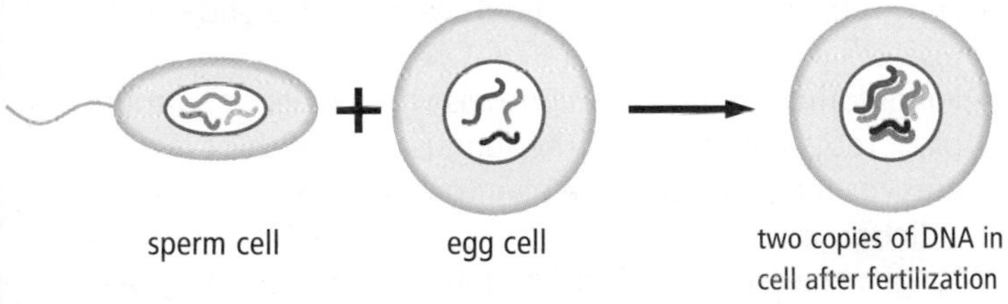

   - The offspring differs genetically from both parents.

SECTION

Plants are producers. pp. 323–329

1. **Plants capture energy from the Sun.**
   The Sun provides the energy almost all organisms need to live. Plants capture the Sun's energy and convert it to chemical energy during **photosynthesis.**
   - During photosynthesis, carbon dioxide and water convert to sugars and oxygen.
   - Plant cells store the sugars as granules of starch.
   - When the plant needs energy, it breaks down starch into sugars.
   - Plants are called **autotrophs** because they don't need to consume food; instead, they produce food for the rest of the ecosystem.
   - Plants can convert stored energy back into usable energy through **cellular respiration.**

2. **Plants are adapted to different environments.**
   Plants have developed many adaptations that allow them to live in a variety of environments.
   - Grasses have deep roots and produce seeds quickly so they can survive in areas with a wide range of temperatures and precipitation.
   - Trees need more water than grasses. Conifers can grow in colder climates than deciduous trees.
   - Reproductive adaptations, such as rapid life cycles, allow some plants to live in deserts or in other extreme climates.

3. **Plants respond to their environment.**
   Plants respond to several **stimuli** in their environment.
   - All plants respond to gravity. Their roots grow down, and their stems grow up.
   - Many plants produce tendrils that wrap around an object that they touch.
   - Plants respond to light by bending toward a light source. This response is due to the action of a hormone called auxin, which makes cells grow rapidly. The unequal growth of cells on opposite sides of a stem makes the stem bend.

4. **Plants respond to seasonal changes.**
   Shorter periods of daylight cause some plants to become dormant in autumn. They temporarily stop growing, lose their leaves, and require less energy.

Common Misconceptions

PLANTS' ORGANS Students often think that only animals have organs and organ systems. In this chapter students learn that plant structures such as leaves and roots are organs.

 This misconception is addressed on p. 317.

MISCONCEPTION DATABASE
CLASSZONE.COM Background on student misconceptions

PLANTS AS PRODUCERS Many students hold the misconception that carbon dioxide, water, and soil are food that plants eat. In fact, plants are producers and make carbon-containing compounds from carbon dioxide and water, using the energy from sunlight.

 This misconception is addressed on p. 325.

SECTION

Animals are consumers. pp. 330–337

1. Animals obtain energy and materials from food.
Animals are **heterotrophs**—they feed on other organisms. Animals consume the energy found in other organisms.

- Animals digest their food. Digestion breaks down large chunks of food into small compounds, including sugars, that can be taken into cells.
- Cellular respiration breaks the bonds in sugars and releases the energy stored in the bonds. Cellular respiration requires oxygen. Animals have specialized structures for taking oxygen into their bodies.

2. Animals interact with the environment and with other organisms.
Animals have many adaptations that allow them to interact with their environment. Animals respond to stimuli such as temperature changes, hunger and thirst, and other animals. These responses are called **behavior.** Behavior can be inherited or learned.
Some adaptive behaviors are interactions between animals of different species. **Predators** are animals that hunt other animals for food. **Prey** are the animals that are hunted. Other adaptive behaviors work for the benefit of both animals.

3. Animals respond to seasonal changes.
Some animals, such as the monarch butterfly, respond to seasonal changes by **migrating**. They spend the winter months in warmer climates, then return to their northern breeding grounds in the spring. Some animals, such as bears and frogs, hibernate in the cold months by slowing down their body systems to conserve energy.

SECTION

Most fungi are decomposers. pp. 338–345

1. Fungi absorb materials from the environment.
Fungi bodies are composed of threadlike **hyphae.** A mass of hyphae is a mycelium.

- The cells in the hyphae release digestive enzymes into the environment. Organic material is digested, and the cells absorb the nutrients that they need.
- Many fungi are decomposers. In the soil, simple compounds left over from fungal digestion are taken up by plant roots and recycled through the biosphere.

Fungi reproduce by forming **spores** that are released into the air and spread by wind. Spores can survive for many years. They begin to grow only when water and food are available.

2. Fungi include mushrooms, molds, and yeasts.
Fungi commonly have one of three forms.

- Mushrooms are the reproductive bodies of a fungus that grows on trees or soil. They are filled with hyphae. Spores are produced in the cap of a mushroom.
- Molds form a fuzzy growth on food and other substrates. This growth is a mass of hyphae. Some hyphae produce spores. Many molds cause diseases, such as Dutch elm disease. Other molds are of use to humans because they produce antibiotics such as penicillin.
- Yeasts are single-celled fungi. Some yeasts cause disease. Others are very useful in making food, such as bread.

3. Fungi can be helpful or harmful to other organisms.
Hyphae can grow into any material made by another organism. For this reason, fungi can be either helpful or harmful.

- Fungi produce harmful chemicals called toxins and can cause diseases in food crops and trees.
- Fungi form beneficial relationships with plants by surrounding plant roots with hyphae. The fungus provides digested nutrients for the plant, and the plant provides food for the fungus.
- A **lichen** is a relationship between single-celled algae and fungi. As seen in the diagram, the algae are held in place by a mass of hyphae. Lichens can live where neither organism alone can live.

Common Misconceptions

CELLULAR RESPIRATION Students may hold the misconception that only animals undergo cellular respiration. Actually, almost all organisms undergo cellular respiration and, thus, require oxygen.

This misconception is addressed on p. 333.

MISCONCEPTION DATABASE
CLASSZONE.COM Background on student misconceptions

DECOMPOSERS Students often hold misconceptions about the role of decomposers in the environment. They may not consider decomposers as part of feeding relationships, or may think of decomposers as the "bottom" of a chain or hierarchy. Decomposers are responsible for recycling nutrients in the biosphere.

This misconception is addressed on p. 342.

Previewing Labs

Lab Generator CD-ROM
Edit these Pupil Edition labs and generate alternative labs.

EXPLORE the BIG idea

Lab	Time and Materials
Where Does It Come From? p. 313 Students examine everyday objects to identify the sources of materials.	**TIME** 10 minutes **MATERIALS** 3 common objects, 3 index cards
How Can Multicellular Organisms Reproduce? p. 313 Students explore asexual reproduction by sprouting potato halves.	**TIME** 10 minutes (planting), 2 weeks (wait time), 5 minutes (observation) **MATERIALS** old potato with eyes, knife, 2 pots, soil, water
Internet Activity: Bee Dance, p. 313 Students explore how bees communicate.	**TIME** 20 minutes **MATERIALS** computer with Internet access
SECTION 1 **INVESTIGATE Specialization,** p. 316 Students model cell specialization and explore its advantages and disadvantages.	**TIME** 10 minutes **MATERIALS** 2 boxes, 40 paper clips, 4 pieces of paper, 2 pencils, watch with second hand
SECTION 2 **EXPLORE Stored Energy,** p. 323 Students test potatoes, celery, and pears with iodine, to see if they contain starch.	**TIME** 10 minutes **MATERIALS** pieces of potato, celery, and pears; 3 plastic cups; iodine solution; dropper
INVESTIGATE What Plants Need to Grow, p. 324 Students design an experiment that will test the hypothesis that plants grow by absorbing material from soil.	**TIME** 30 minutes **MATERIALS** potting soil, pots or paper cups, bean seedlings or beans, triple-beam balance, water
SECTION 3 **INVESTIGATE Owl Pellets,** p. 332 Students infer what an owl eats and how well it digests its food by examining an owl pellet.	**TIME** 30 minutes **MATERIALS** owl pellet, toothpick or dissecting needle, tweezers, tray, (for Challenge: bone identification key—available when ordering owl pellets)
SECTION 4 **EXPLORE Mushrooms,** p. 338 Students make spore prints to examine spores in mushroom caps.	**TIME** 10 minutes on 2 different days **MATERIALS** fresh store-bought mushrooms, sharp knife, clear plastic cup, white paper, hand lens
CHAPTER INVESTIGATION **Effect of Yeast on Bread Dough,** pp. 344–345 Students grow yeast on different substances to draw conclusions about how sugar, salt, and sweetener affect the growth of yeast.	**TIME** 40 minutes **MATERIALS** 4 sheets of notebook paper; baking sheet; 1 cup flour; measuring cups, 1 cup and 1/4 cup; measuring spoons, 1 tsp and 1/4 tsp; 3 teaspoons of sugar; 3 teaspoons of sweetener; 3 teaspoons of salt; 1 teaspoon of quick-rise yeast; warm water; metric ruler; marker; masking tape; 8 clear plastic straws; 8 clothespins

R **Additional INVESTIGATION,** Plant Growth and Light Conditions, A, B, & C, pp. 140–148; Teacher Instructions, pp. 360–361

Previewing Chapter Resources

CHAPTER 10

Introduction to Multicellular Organisms

INTEGRATED TECHNOLOGY

CLASSZONE.COM
- eEdition Plus
- EasyPlanner Plus
- Misconception Database
- Content Review
- Test Practice
- Visualization
- Resource Centers
- Internet Activity: Bee Dance
- Math Tutorial

SCILINKS.ORG

SCI LINKS

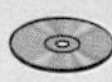
CD-ROMS
- eEdition
- EasyPlanner
- Power Presentations
- Content Review
- Lab Generator
- Test Generator

AUDIO CDS
- Audio Readings
- Audio Readings in Spanish

LABS AND ACTIVITIES

EXPLORE the Big Idea, p. 313
- Where Does It Come From?
- How Can a Multicellular Organism Reproduce on Its Own?
- Internet Activity: Bee Dance

UNIT RESOURCE BOOK
Unit Projects, pp. 5–10

Lab Generator CD-ROM
Generate customized labs.

SECTION 1

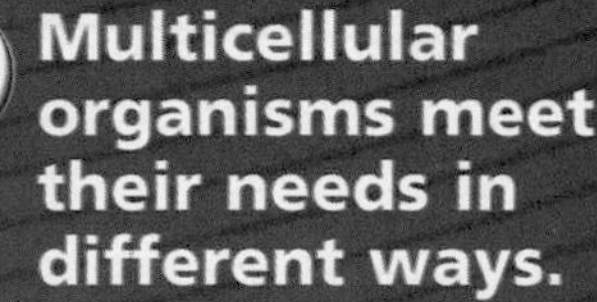
Multicellular organisms meet their needs in different ways.
pp. 315–322

Time: 2 periods (1 block)

 Lesson Plan, pp. 81–82

MATH TUTORIAL

UNIT TRANSPARENCY BOOK
- Big Idea Flow Chart, p. T9
- Daily Vocabulary Scaffolding, p. T10
- Note-Taking Model, p. T11
- 3-Minute Warm-Up, p. T12
- "Adaptations in Different Environments" Visual, p. T14

- INVESTIGATE Specialization, p. 316
- Math in Science, p. 322

UNIT RESOURCE BOOK
- Datasheet, Specialization, p. 90
- Math Support, p. 129
- Math Practice, p. 130

SECTION

Plants are producers.
pp. 323–329

Time: 2 periods (1 block)

 Lesson Plan, pp. 92–93

RESOURCE CENTER, Plant Adaptations

UNIT TRANSPARENCY BOOK
- Daily Vocabulary Scaffolding, p. T10
- 3-Minute Warm-Up, p. T12

- EXPLORE Stored Energy, p. 323
- INVESTIGATE What Plants Need to Grow, p. 324

UNIT RESOURCE BOOK
- Datasheet, What Plants Need to Grow, p. 101
- Additional INVESTIGATION, Plant Growth and Light Conditions, A, B, & C, pp. 140–148

SECTION

Animals are consumers.
pp. 330–337

Time: 2 periods (1 block)

Lesson Plan, pp. 103–104

- **RESOURCE CENTER,** Animal Adaptations
- **VISUALIZATION,** How Bees Communicate

UNIT TRANSPARENCY BOOK
- Daily Vocabulary Scaffolding, p. T10
- 3-Minute Warm-Up, p. T13

- INVESTIGATE Owl Pellets, p. 332
- Science on the Job, p. 337

UNIT RESOURCE BOOK
Datasheet, Owl Pellets, p. 112

SECTION

Most fungi are decomposers.
pp. 338–345

Time: 4 periods (2 blocks)

Lesson Plan, pp. 114–115

RESOURCE CENTER, Fungi

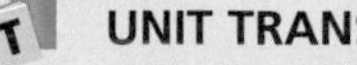
UNIT TRANSPARENCY BOOK
- Big Idea Flow Chart, p. T9
- Daily Vocabulary Scaffolding, p. T10
- 3-Minute Warm-Up, p. T13
- Chapter Outline, pp. T15–T16

- EXPLORE Mushrooms, p. 338
- CHAPTER INVESTIGATION, What Do Yeast Cells Use for Energy?, pp. 344–345

UNIT RESOURCE BOOK
CHAPTER INVESTIGATION, What Do Yeast Cells Use for Energy?, A, B, & C, pp. 131–139

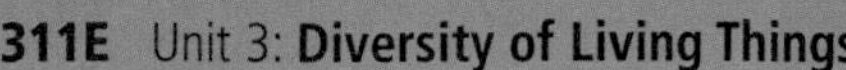

KEY TO ICONS  INTERNET 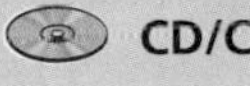 CD/CD-ROM  Pupil Edition · Teacher Edition · UNIT RESOURCE BOOK  UNIT TRANSPARENCY BOOK · UNIT ASSESSMENT BOOK 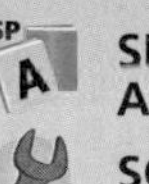 SPANISH ASSESSMENT BOOK · SCIENCE TOOLKIT

READING AND REINFORCEMENT

- Four Square, B22–23
- Main Idea and Detail Notes, C37
- Daily Vocabulary Scaffolding, H1–8

UNIT RESOURCE BOOK
- Vocabulary Practice, pp. 126–127
- Decoding Support, p. 128
- Summarizing the Chapter, pp. 149–150

Audio Readings CD
Listen to Pupil Edition.

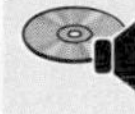

Audio Readings in Spanish CD
Listen to Pupil Edition in Spanish.

ASSESSMENT

- Chapter Review, pp. 347–348
- Standardized Test Practice, p. 349

UNIT ASSESSMENT BOOK
- Diagnostic Test, pp. 21–22
- Chapter Test, A, B, & C, pp. 27–38
- Alternative Assessment, pp. 39–40

Spanish Chapter Test, pp. 45–48

Test Generator CD-ROM
Generate customized tests.

Lab Generator CD-ROM
Rubrics for Labs

STANDARDS

National Standards
A.1–8, A.9.a–c, A.9.e–g, C.1.a, C.3.c, F.1.e, G.1.b

See p. 312 for the standards.

UNIT RESOURCE BOOK
- Reading Study Guide, A & B, pp. 83–86
- Spanish Reading Study Guide, pp. 87–88
- Challenge and Extension, p. 89
- Reinforcing Key Concepts, p. 90

Ongoing Assessment, pp. 315, 317–321

Section 10.1 Review, p. 321

UNIT ASSESSMENT BOOK
Section 10.1 Quiz, p. 23

National Standards
A.2–8, A.9.a–c, A.9.e–f, C.1.a, F.1.e, G.1.b

UNIT RESOURCE BOOK
- Reading Study Guide, A & B, pp. 94–97
- Spanish Reading Study Guide, pp. 98–99
- Challenge and Extension, p. 100
- Reinforcing Key Concepts, p. 102

Ongoing Assessment, pp. 324–326, 328–329

Section 10.2 Review, p. 329

UNIT ASSESSMENT BOOK
Section 10.2 Quiz, p. 24

National Standards
A.2–7, A.9.a–b, A.9.e–f, F.1.e, G.1.b

UNIT RESOURCE BOOK
- Reading Study Guide, A & B, pp. 105–108
- Spanish Reading Study Guide, pp. 109–110
- Challenge and Extension, p. 111
- Reinforcing Key Concepts, p. 113
- Challenge Reading, pp. 124–125

Ongoing Assessment, pp. 331–335

Section 10.3 Review, p. 336

UNIT ASSESSMENT BOOK
Section 10.3 Quiz, p. 25

National Standards
A.2–7, A.9.a–b, A.9.e–f, C.3.c, F.1.e, G.1.b

UNIT RESOURCE BOOK
- Reading Study Guide, A & B, pp. 116–119
- Spanish Reading Study Guide, pp. 120–121
- Challenge and Extension, p. 122
- Reinforcing Key Concepts, p. 123

Ongoing Assessment, pp. 339–343

Section 10.4 Review, p. 343

UNIT ASSESSMENT BOOK
Section 10.4 Quiz, p. 26

National Standards
A.1–7, A.9.a–b, A.9.e–g, C.3.c, F.1.e, G.1.b

Previewing Resources for Differentiated Instruction

CHAPTER INVESTIGATION

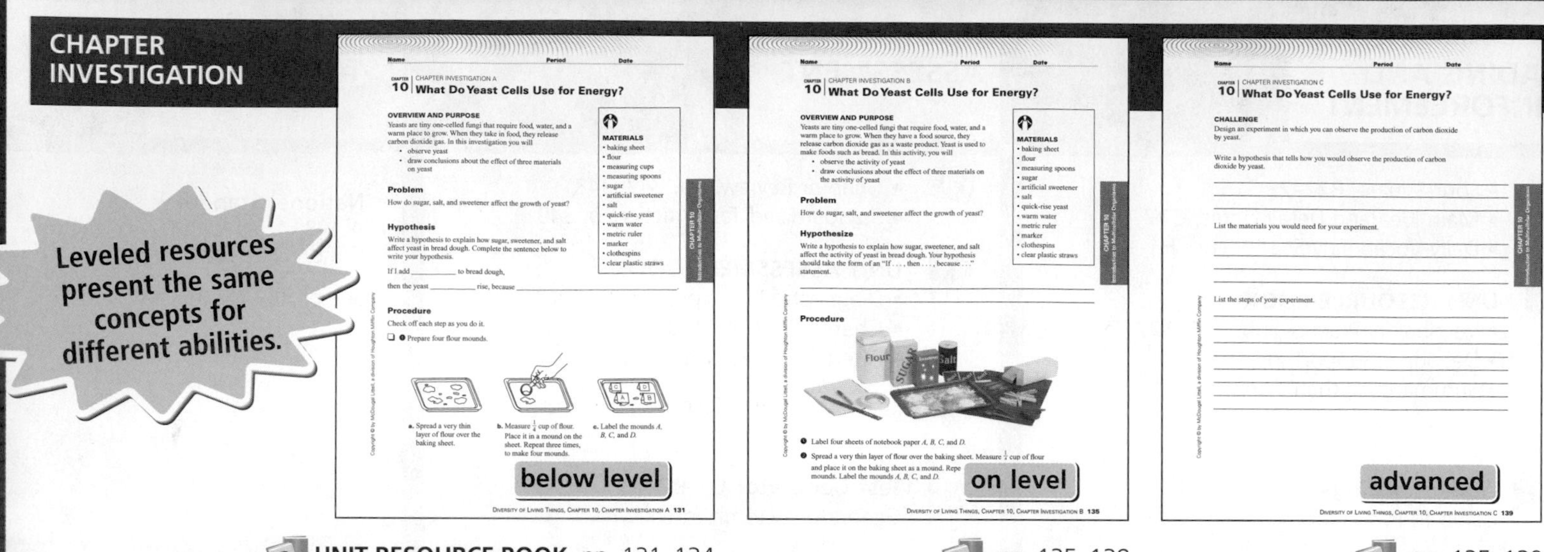

UNIT RESOURCE BOOK, pp. 131–134 | pp. 135–138 | pp. 135–139

READING STUDY GUIDE

Reading Study Guide is also in Spanish.

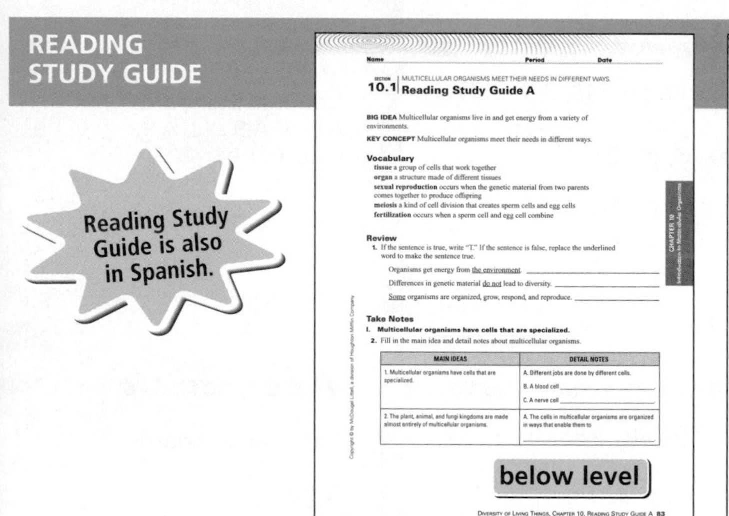

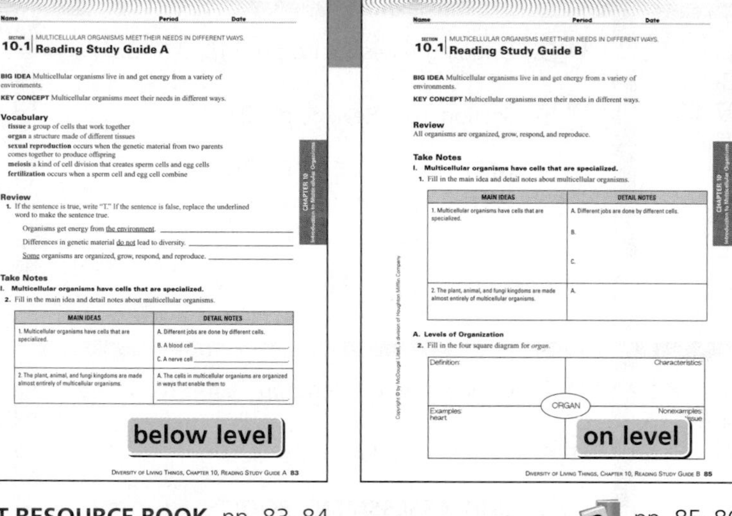

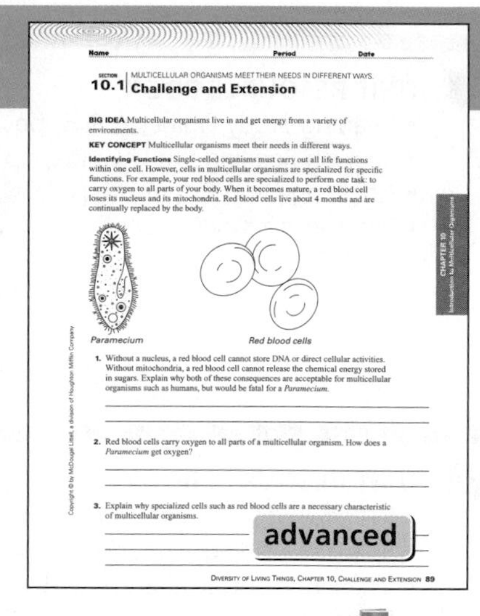

UNIT RESOURCE BOOK, pp. 83–84 | pp. 85–86 | p. 89

CHAPTER TEST

Chapter Test is also in Spanish.

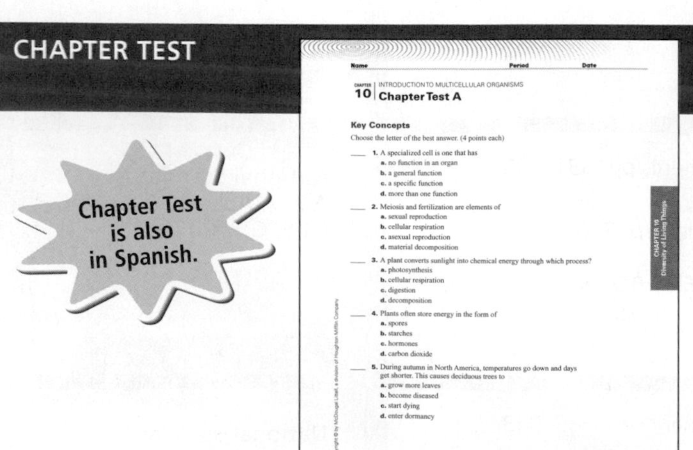

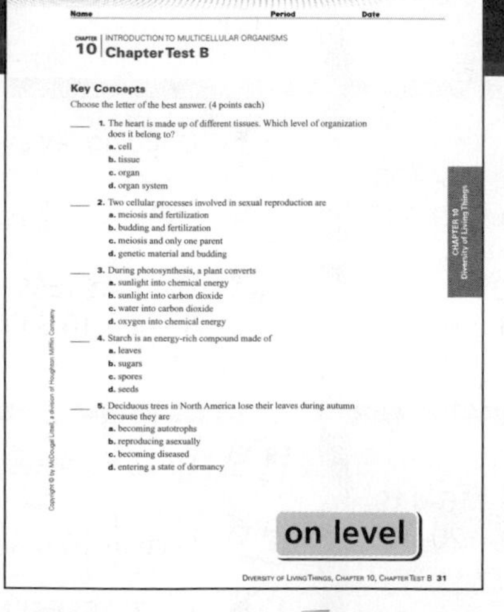

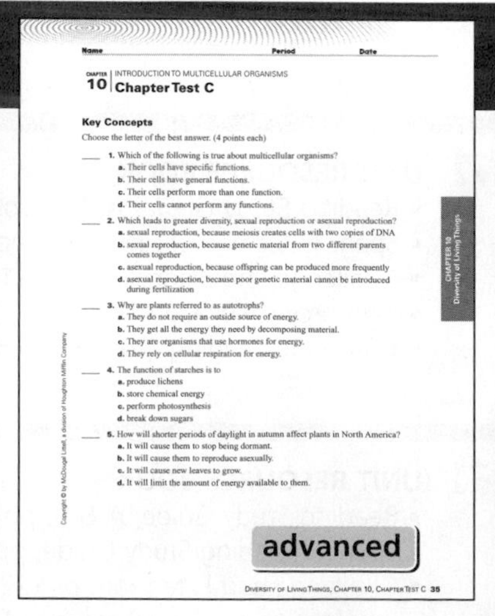

UNIT ASSESSMENT BOOK, pp. 27–30 | pp. 31–34 | pp. 35–38

TECHNOLOGY

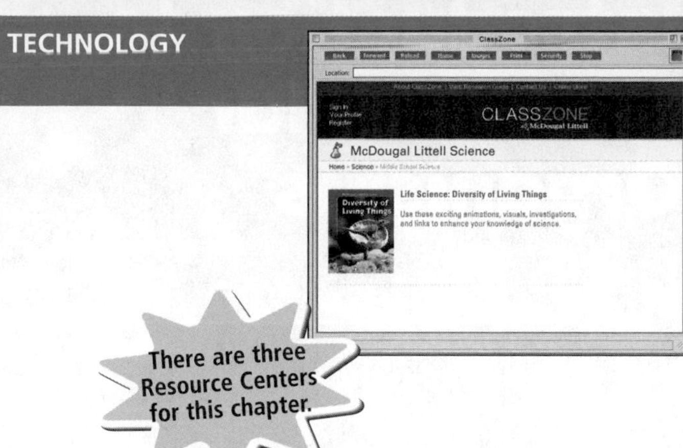

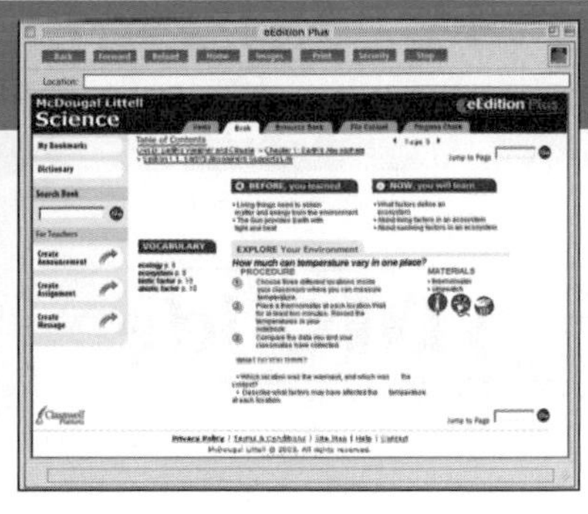

CLASSZONE.COM

CD/CD-ROMS

CLASSZONE.COM

VISUAL CONTENT

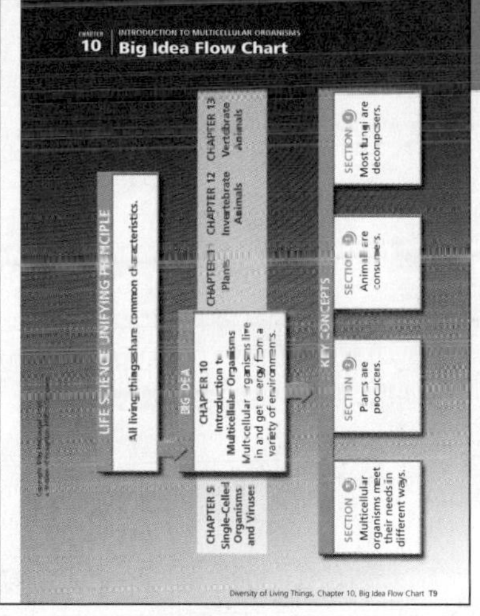

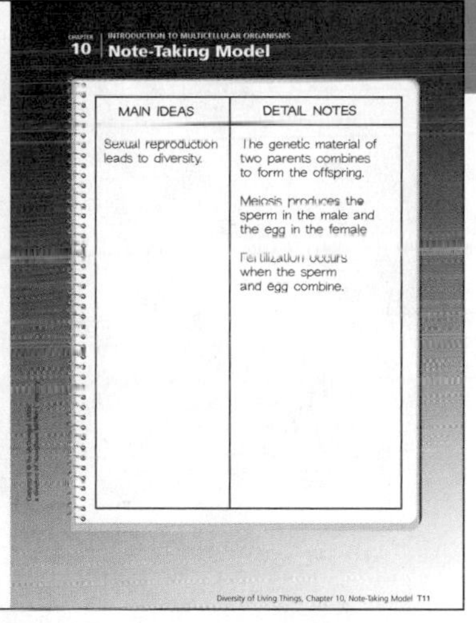

UNIT TRANSPARENCY BOOK, p. T9

p. T11

p. T14

MORE SUPPORT

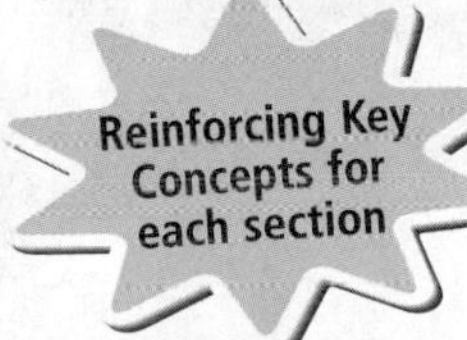

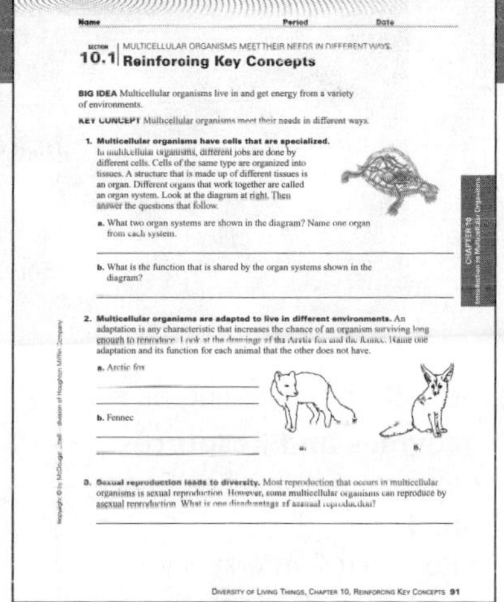

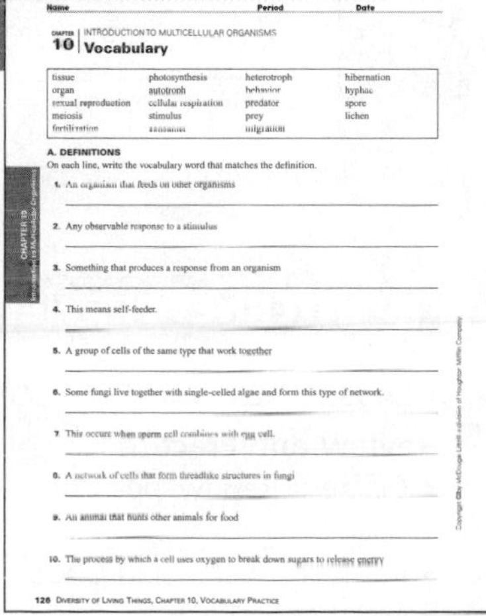

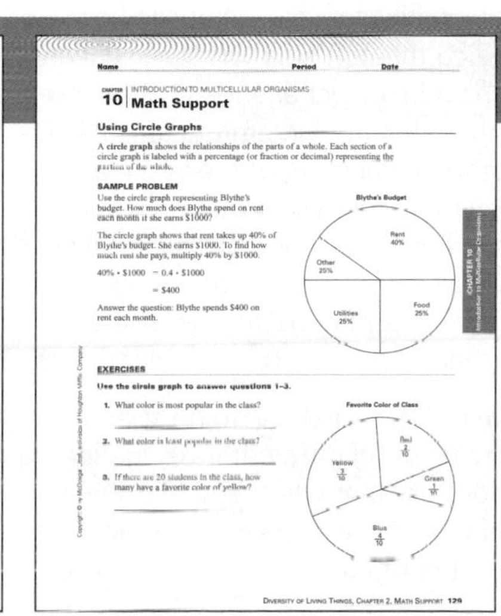

UNIT RESOURCE BOOK, p. 91

pp. 126–127

p. 129

CHAPTER 10

Introduction to Multicellular Organisms

INTRODUCE

the BIG idea

Have students look at the organisms in the photograph and discuss how the question in the box links to the Big Idea:

- Ask: How do you think the chipmunk gets energy?
- Ask: How do you think the mushroom gets energy?

National Science Education Standards

Content

C.1.a Important levels of organization for structure and function include cells, organs, tissues, organ systems, whole organisms, and ecosystems.

C.3.c Behavior is one response an organism can make to a stimulus. A behavioral response requires coordination and communication at many levels.

F.1.e Food provides energy and nutrients for growth and development. Nutrition requirements vary.

Process

A.1–8 Identify questions that can be answered through scientific investigations; design and conduct an investigation; use tools to gather and interpret data; use evidence to describe, predict, explain, and model; think critically to make relationships between evidence and explanation; recognize different explanations and predictions; communicate scientific procedures and explanations; use mathematics.

A.9.a–c, A.9.e–g Understand scientific inquiry by using different investigations, methods, mathematics, and explanations based on logic, evidence, and skepticism. Data often result in new investigations.

G.1.b Science requires different abilities.

CHAPTER

Introduction to Multicellular Organisms

the BIG idea

Multicellular organisms live in and get energy from a variety of environments.

Key Concepts

SECTION

Multicellular organisms meet their needs in different ways.
Learn about specialized cells, tissues, and organs.

SECTION

Plants are producers.
Learn how plants get energy and respond to the environment.

SECTION

Animals are consumers.
Learn how animals get energy and how they interact with the environment.

SECTION

Most fungi are decomposers.
Learn about fungi and how they get energy.

Internet Preview

CLASSZONE.COM

Chapter 10 online resources: Content Review, Visualization, four Resource Centers, Math Tutorial, Test Practice

312 Unit 3: Diversity of Living Things

How does an organism get energy and materials from its environment?

INTERNET PREVIEW

CLASSZONE.COM For student use with the following pages:

Review and Practice

- Content Review, pp. 314, 346
- Math Tutorial: Using Circle Graphs, p. 322
- Test Practice, p. 349

Activities and Resources

- Internet Activity: Bee Dance, p. 313
- Resource Centers: Plant and Animal Adaptations, pp. 326, 332; Fungi, p. 340
- Visualization, p. 328

Animal Behavior
Code: MDL040

EXPLORE the BIG idea

Where Does It Come From?

Think about the things you use every day. Just like any other organism, you depend on the environment to meet your needs. The food you eat comes from plants and animals. Also, much of what you use is made of materials processed from living matter.

Observe and Think Identify three nonfood items you come into contact with every day. Where does the material for these products come from?

How Can a Multicellular Organism Reproduce on Its Own?

Take an old potato and cut it in half, making sure that there are eyes on both halves. Plant each half in a pot of soil. Water the pots once a day. After two weeks, remove the potato halves from the pots and examine.

Observe and Think What happened to the potato halves?

Internet Activity: Bee Dance

Go to **ClassZone.com** to explore how bees communicate.

Observe and Think What type of information can a bee communicate to other bees in a hive?

NSTA scilinks.org SCILINKS
Animal Behavior **Code: MDL040**

EXPLORE the BIG idea

These inquiry-based activities are appropriate for use at home or as a supplement to classroom instruction.

Where Does It Come From?

PURPOSE To identify the sources of materials in everyday objects.

TIP *10 min.* Have groups of students brainstorm to name materials that come from plants. Suggest objects that are made in part from plant or animal matter.

Answers depend on objects chosen. Sample answers: cotton, wood, and paper from plants; silk and leather from animals

REVISIT after p. 329.

How Can Multicellular Organisms Reproduce?

PURPOSE To explore asexual reproduction. Students sprout potato halves in soil.

TIP *2 weeks* Position the potatoes in the soil with an eye at the top.

Answer: The eyes sprouted, and a new plant developed from each eye. This ability allows potatoes to reproduce asexually.

REVISIT after p. 321.

Internet Activity: Bee Dance

PURPOSE To explore how bees communicate with each other.

TIP *20 min.* Prompt students to discuss what kinds of information are important for a bee to know and communicate.

Answer: Bees communicate about the location of food.

REVISIT after p. 335.

TEACHING WITH TECHNOLOGY

Digital Camera Students can make a visual record of the materials they find in an owl pellet in the investigation on p. 332. If a tape recorder is available, they can record a narration to accompany the photographs.

CBL and Probeware Students can use a carbon dioxide probe stuck into a ball of dough to measure yeast fermentation activity in the Chapter Investigation on pp. 344–345. The probe replaces the straw apparatus.

PREPARE

CONCEPT REVIEW

Activate Prior Knowledge

Have students list the four characteristics of living things and draw a picture depicting each characteristic. *Drawings should portray organization, growth, response, and reproduction.*

TAKING NOTES

Main Idea and Detail Notes

Writing each new blue heading will emphasize the main ideas in each section. Students will probably fill the details column with the red headings. Blue and red headings form an outline that links the ideas of the section. Encourage students to use their charts as study tools.

Vocabulary Strategy

A four square diagram can include as much information as the student wants to add. By writing their own words around the center term, students personalize their understanding of the term and retain its meaning longer.

Vocabulary and Note-Taking Resources

- Vocabulary Practice, pp. 126–127
- Decoding Support, p. 128

- Daily Vocabulary Scaffolding, pp. T10
- Note-Taking Model, p. T11

- Four Square, B22–23
- Main Idea and Detail Notes, C37
- Daily Vocabulary Scaffolding, H1–8

CHAPTER 10

Getting Ready to Learn

CONCEPT REVIEW

- Living things are organized, grow, respond, and reproduce.
- Protists get energy in three different ways.
- Single-celled organisms reproduce when the cell divides.

VOCABULARY REVIEW

kingdom p. 283
producer p. 291
decomposer p. 291
See Glossary for definitions.

adaptation, DNA, genetic material

CONTENT REVIEW
CLASSZONE.COM
Review concepts and vocabulary.

TAKING NOTES

MAIN IDEA AND DETAILS

Make a two-column chart. Write the main ideas, such as those in the blue headings, in the column on the left. Write details about each of those main ideas in the column on the right.

VOCABULARY STRATEGY

Write each new vocabulary term in the center of a **four square** diagram. Write notes in the squares around each term. Include a definition, some characteristics, and some examples of the term. If possible, write some things that are not examples of the term.

See the Note-Taking Handbook on pages R45–R51.

SCIENCE NOTEBOOK

MAIN IDEAS	DETAILS
Plants respond to their environment.	1. Plants respond to different stimuli. 2. A stimulus is something that produces a response.

Definition	Characteristics
Group of same type of cells performing similar functions	Cells are similar. Different tissues do different jobs.
TISSUE	
Examples	**Nonexamples**
skin tissue nerve tissue muscle tissue	a simple cell

CHECK READINESS

Administer the Diagnostic Test to determine students' readiness for new science content and their mastery of requisite math skills.

 Diagnostic Test, pp. 21–22

Technology Resources

Students needing content and math skills should visit **ClassZone.com**.

- CONTENT REVIEW
- MATH TUTORIAL

 CONTENT REVIEW CD-ROM

KEY CONCEPT

Multicellular organisms meet their needs in different ways.

BEFORE, you learned
- Organisms get energy and materials from the environment
- All organisms are organized, grow, respond, and reproduce
- Differences in genetic material lead to diversity

NOW, you will learn
- About the functions of cells in multicellular organisms
- How multicellular organisms are adapted to different environments
- About sexual reproduction

VOCABULARY
tissue p. 316
organ p. 316
sexual reproduction p. 320
meiosis p. 320
fertilization p. 320

THINK ABOUT

Why is teamwork important?

For any team to be successful, it is important for people to work well together. Within a team, each person has a different role. For example, the team in this restaurant includes people to greet diners and seat them, people to buy and cook the food, and people to take food orders and serve the food. By dividing different jobs among different people, a restaurant can serve more customers at the same time. What would happen in a large restaurant if the diners were seated, cooked for, and served by the same person?

Multicellular organisms have cells that are specialized.

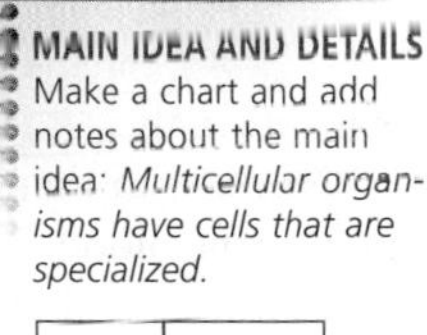

MAIN IDEA AND DETAILS Make a chart and add notes about the main idea: *Multicellular organisms have cells that are specialized.*

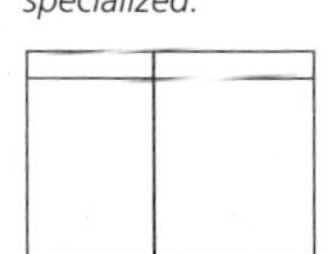

In single-celled organisms, all the functions of life are performed by one cell. These functions include getting energy and materials, removing wastes, and responding to changes in the environment. In multicellular organisms, however, different jobs are done by different cells—the cells are specialized. A blood cell carries oxygen. A nerve cell sends and receives signals. Just as the different jobs of running a restaurant are divided among different people, in multicellular organisms different functions are divided among different cells.

In this chapter, you will read about plants, animals, and fungi. These three kingdoms are made up almost entirely of multicellular organisms. The cells in multicellular organisms are organized in ways that enable them to survive and reproduce.

10.1 FOCUS

Set Learning Goals

Students will
- Explain the functions of cells in multicellular organisms.
- Describe how multicellular organisms are adapted to different environments.
- Summarize sexual reproduction.
- Model specialization in organisms.

3-Minute Warm-Up

Display Transparency 12 or copy this exercise on the board:

Imagine that a bacterium begins to divide by binary fission. Each generation of daughter cells also divides, and soon there are millions of bacteria. How do you think the newest bacterium compares to the original cell? Explain. *The cells are identical. Binary fission produces daughter cells that are each identical to the parent cell.*

 3-Minute Warm Up, p. T12

10.1 MOTIVATE

THINK ABOUT

PURPOSE To consider how task specialization helps a team

DISCUSS Have students discuss what a large restaurant with one employee would be like. Ask: How could the employee improve the situation without hiring additional people? *Sample answer: improve efficiency, do lots of prep work, have customers get their own food and clean up their places*

Ongoing Assessment

Explain the functions of cells in multicellular organisms.

Ask: How are multicellular organisms like the staff of a restaurant? *Like the different staff members, each type of cell has a different job that it does, and the cells work together.*

RESOURCES FOR DIFFERENTIATED INSTRUCTION

Below Level
UNIT RESOURCE BOOK
- Reading Study Guide A, pp. 83–84
- Decoding Support, p. 128

AUDIO CDS

Advanced
UNIT RESOURCE BOOK
Challenge and Extension, p. 89

English Learners
UNIT RESOURCE BOOK
Spanish Reading Study Guide, pp. 87–88

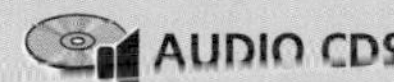

- Audio Readings in Spanish
- Audio Readings (English)

10.1 INSTRUCT

INVESTIGATE Specialization

PURPOSE To model cell specialization and explore its advantages and disadvantages

TIP *10 min.* Each group of five students should designate one "single-celled organism," one "multicellular organism," and a timekeeper.

WHAT DO YOU THINK? *It takes less time to do all three tasks, and those members with special skills can do a special job quicker and better. Cells need to get materials (water, oxygen, food) quickly or they will die.*

CHALLENGE *The group could not survive unless all members were present and functioning.*

 Datasheet, Specialization, p. 90

Technology Resources

Customize this student lab as needed or look for an alternative. Print rubrics to assess student lab reports.

 **Lab Generator CD-ROM**

History of Science

In 1838, almost 200 years after Robert Hooke first described cells, the German botanist Matthias Schleiden made careful studies of plant tissues and announced that cells are the fundamental unit of life in plants. A year later, the German physiologist Theodor Schwann made the same announcement about animals. These two discoveries are combined in the statement that all living things consist of cells. This generalization forms the basis of the cell theory, one of the foundations of biology.

INVESTIGATE Specialization

What are some advantages of specialization?

MATERIALS
- two boxes, each containing 20 paper clips, 2 pieces of paper, and 1 pencil

TIME
10 minutes

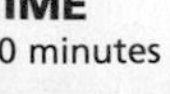

PROCEDURE

1. Form into two teams,each representing an organism. The single-celled team will be made up of just one person; the multicellular team will be made up of three. Each team obtains a box of materials from the teacher.
2. Each team must do the following tasks as quickly as possible: make a paper-clip chain, write the alphabet on both sides of one piece of paper, and make a paper airplane from the second piece of paper. The members of the three-person team must specialize, each person doing one task only.

WHAT DO YOU THINK?

- What are some advantages to having each person on the three-person team specialize in doing a different job?
- Why might efficiency be a factor in the activities done by cells in a multicellular organism?

CHALLENGE Suppose the "life" of the multicellular team depended on the ability of one person to make a paper airplane. How would specialization be a disadvantage if that person were not at school?

Levels of Organization

For any multicellular organism to survive, different cells must work together. The right type of cell must be in the right place to do the work that needs to be done.

Organization starts with the cell. Cells in multicellular organisms are specialized for a specific function. In animals, skin cells provide protection, nerve cells carry signals, and muscle cells produce movement. Cells of the same type are organized into **tissue,** a group of cells that work together. For example, what you think of as muscle is muscle tissue, made up of many muscle cells. **A**

VOCABULARY
Remember to add a four square for *tissue* and *organ* to your notebook.

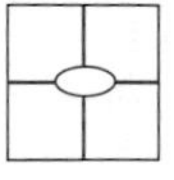

A structure that is made up of different tissues is called an **organ.** Organs have particular functions. The heart is an organ that functions as a pump. It has muscle tissue, which pumps the blood, and nerve tissue, which signals when to pump. Different organs that work together and have a common function are called an organ system. A heart and blood vessels are different organs that are both part of a circulatory system. These organs work together to deliver blood to all parts of a body. Together, cells, tissues, organs, and organ systems form an organism. **B**

DIFFERENTIATE INSTRUCTION

More Reading Support

A What are tissues made of? *cells*

B What is an organ made of? *tissues*

English Learners English learners may have trouble with abstract or hypothetical questions. For example, in "Investigate Specialization," p. 316, "Suppose the 'life' of the multicellular team depended on the ability of one person to make a paper airplane." Help English learners by explaining that words such as *suppose, imagine,* and *assume* may be used to set up a hypothetical or "imagined" situation.

Organ Systems and the Organism

In almost all multicellular organisms, different organ systems take care of specific needs. Here are a few examples of organ systems found in many animals:

- nervous system enables a response to changing conditions
- muscular system produces movement and supplies heat
- respiratory system takes in oxygen and releases carbon dioxide
- circulatory system delivers oxygen and removes carbon dioxide
- digestive system breaks down food into a usable form

Organ systems allow multicellular organisms to obtain large amounts of energy, process large amounts of materials, respond to changes in the environment, and reproduce.

REMINDER
A system is a group of objects that interact, sharing energy and matter.

How are the functions of organ systems related to the needs of an organism? Give an example.

Different organ systems work together. For example, the respiratory system works with the circulatory system to deliver oxygen and remove carbon dioxide. When an animal such as a turtle breathes in, oxygen is brought into the lungs. Blood from the circulatory system picks up the oxygen, and the heart pumps the oxygen-rich blood out to the cells of the body. As oxygen is delivered, waste carbon dioxide is picked up. The blood is pumped back to the lungs. The carbon dioxide is released when the turtle breathes out. More oxygen is picked up when the turtle breathes in.

Organ Systems

Organ systems work together to meet the needs of an organism.

Blood vessels called **veins** return oxygen-poor blood to the lungs.

Each **lung** fills with air containing oxygen.

Blood vessels called **arteries** carry oxygen rich blood to the body.

The **heart** pumps blood to the lungs.

DIFFERENTIATE INSTRUCTION

More Reading Support

C Why does a multicellular organism have several organ systems? *to take care of all its needs*

Below Level Have students draw a flow chart diagramming the path of oxygen into a turtle's body, through the blood, and into the cells. A second part of the flow chart can show the path of carbon dioxide away from the cells and out of the body.

Address Misconceptions

IDENTIFY Ask students what types of living things have organs. If students omit plants, or do not answer "multicellular organisms," they may hold the misconception that only animals have organs.

CORRECT Ask students to define an organ. *a structure made of different tissues* Display some leaves and have students examine them. Ask: Does a leaf fit this definition? What are the tissues in a leaf? *yes; the layers in the blade, veins (vascular tissue)*

REASSESS Ask students to list other organs that a plant has. *roots, flowers*

Technology Resources

Visit **ClassZone.com** for background on common student misconceptions.

MISCONCEPTION DATABASE

Teach from Visuals

To help students interpret the diagram of a turtle's circulatory system, ask:

- Why are some of the blood vessels red and others blue? *Red signifies blood that moves away from the heart and lungs. Blue indicates blood that returns to the heart.*
- What parts of the circulatory system are shown? *blood, arteries, veins, heart*
- What parts of the respiratory system are shown? *lungs*

Ongoing Assessment

Answer: Each organ system takes care of a specific need. Together, the organ systems meet all the needs of the organism. For example, the organism's cells need oxygen, which is taken in by the respiratory system and delivered to the cells by the circulatory system.

Teacher Demo

To demonstrate the advantages of color camouflage as an adaptation, use a hole punch to make a number of dots from different-colored construction paper. Spread out a square of colorful fabric and a square of plain white fabric on a desktop. Have students sprinkle the dots on each square and identify the background on which the dots are more visible. Ask students to apply this demo to how camouflage strategies work outdoors.

Ongoing Assessment

Describe how multicellular organisms are adapted to different environments.

Ask: Give an example of an adaptation an animal can have to cold climates. *Sample answer: thick fur*

CHECK YOUR READING *Answer: the way an organism gets energy or processes materials, how its body is shaped, and its behavior*

PHOTO CAPTION Answer: Flies are plant pollinators. The plant needs flies to reproduce.

Multicellular organisms are adapted to live in different environments.

READING TIP

Offspring is a word used to describe the new organisms produced by reproduction in any organism. Think of it as meaning "to spring off."

All organisms have characteristics that allow them to survive in their environment. An adaptation is any inherited characteristic that increases the chance of an organism's surviving and producing offspring that also reproduce. An adaptation may have to do with the way an organism gets its energy or processes materials. An adaptation may relate to the shape or structure of an organism's body. An adaptation can even be a form of behavior. ? D

The text above mentions different types of adaptations. Name three.

When most multicellular organisms reproduce, the offspring are not exact copies of the parents. There are differences. If a particular difference gives an organism an advantage over other members in its group, then that difference is referred to as an adaptation. Over time, the organism and its offspring do better and reproduce more.

You are probably familiar with the furry animal called a fox. Different species of fox have different adaptations that enable them to survive in different environments. Here are three examples:

- **Fennec** The fennec is a desert fox. Its large ears are an adaptation that helps the fox keep cool in the hot desert. As blood flows through the vessels in each ear, heat is released. Another adaptation is the color of its fur, which blends in with the desert sand.
- **Arctic fox** The Arctic fox lives in the cold north. Its small ears, legs, and nose are adaptations that reduce the loss of heat from its body. Its bluish-gray summer fur is replaced by a thick coat of white fur as winter approaches. Its winter coat keeps the fox warm and enables it to blend in with the snow.
- **Red fox** The red fox is found in grasslands and woodlands. Its ears aren't as large as those of the fennec or as small as those of the Arctic fox. Its body fur is reddish brown tipped in white and black, coloring that helps it blend into its environment.

INFER The strong odor of the rafflesia flower attracts flies into the plant. How might this adaptation benefit the plant?

The diversity of life on Earth is due to the wide range of adaptations that have occurred in different species. An elephant has a trunk for grasping and sensing. A female kangaroo carries its young in a pouch. The largest flower in the world, the rafflesia flower, is almost a meter wide, blooms for just a few days, and smells like rotting meat.

Adaptations are the result of differences that can occur in genetic material. The way multicellular organisms reproduce allows for a mixing of genetic material. You will read about that next.

DIFFERENTIATE INSTRUCTION

More Reading Support

D What is an adaptation? *inherited characteristic that increases survival chances*

E How do adaptations arise? *differences in genes*

English Learners Help students with the numerous word forms they may encounter. For example, *adaptation* and *adapt*. Have students write a sentence using the noun *adaptation*. Then have them write another sentence using the verb *adapt*. Encourage them to verbally explain the difference between the two words.

318 Unit 3: Diversity of Living Things

Adaptations in Different Environments

READING VISUALS Foxes are hunters that feed on small animals. How might the coat color of each fox contribute to its survival?

Teach from Visuals

To help students interpret the visual of adaptations in different environments, ask:

- Why would having white fur in summer be a disadvantage for an arctic fox? *In summer there is no snow. The environment is a brownish color. White fur would make the fox more visible to both prey and predators.*
- What might trigger an arctic fox's body to grow white fur? *cold temperatures or shorter daylight hours*

 The "Adaptations in Different Environments" visual is available as T14 in the Unit Transparency Book.

Develop Critical Thinking

SYNTHESIZE Have students design an animal that lives in a hot, rainy tropical rainforest. Their designs should show adaptations that will keep the animal cool and dry, protect it against enemies that live in the trees, and enable it to capture insects for food. Adaptations can be structural or behavioral. Have students draw pictures of their animal or build a model.

Metacognitive Strategy

Ask students to explain which was a better tool for them: the visual and its captions on p. 319 or the text on p. 318. Which could help them review or study?

Ongoing Assessment

READING VISUALS *Answer: Camouflage makes them less likely to be seen by the animals hunting them and less likely to be seen by the animals they are hunting.*

DIFFERENTIATE INSTRUCTION

Advanced Have students design an experiment to demonstrate that coat color in foxes can contribute to their survival. The experiment should be feasible as a field study in the wild. Students should choose one species of fox and one environment when designing their experiment. They should consider any needs of the foxes that would be compromised by research, and avoid such compromise.

 Challenge and Extension, p. 89

Teach from Visuals

To help students interpret the diagrams of cells, explain that the colored squiggles represent chromosomes, a component of DNA. Normal cells, such as the cell on the bottom right, have pairs of matching chromosomes. Sperm cells and egg cells only receive half of the chromosomes during meiosis. Ask: What kind of cell division yields cells with two copies of DNA? *mitosis*

Teacher Demo

To help students understand the differences between sexual and asexual reproduction, try the following demo.

Root an African violet *leaf* in moist sand. When roots form, plant the new violet in soil. Show students the African violet and a flower. Point out the female part (pistil) and male parts (stamens) of the flower. Explain that fertilization takes place inside the female part and eventually produces seeds. Ask:

- Is the flower a site for sexual or asexual reproduction? *sexual*
- How about the African violet? *asexual*
- How many parents does the African violet have? *one*
- If the flower is pollinated and produces a seed, how many parents does the seed have? *two*

Ongoing Assessment

Summarize sexual reproduction.

Ask: Why is it necessary for meiosis to come before fertilization? *If meiosis did not cut the number of chromosomes in half before fertilization, the chromosome number would double in each offspring.*

Sexual reproduction leads to diversity.

F

Most multicellular organisms reproduce sexually. In **sexual reproduction,** the genetic material of two parents comes together, and the resulting offspring have genetic material from both. Sexual reproduction leads to diversity because the DNA in the offspring is different from the DNA in the parents.

G

One copy of DNA in cell after meiosis

Two different cellular processes are involved in sexual reproduction. The first is **meiosis** (my-OH-sihs), a special form of cell division that produces sperm cells in a male and egg cells in a female. Each sperm or egg cell contains only one copy of DNA, the genetic material. Most cells contain two copies of DNA.

The second process in sexual reproduction is **fertilization.** Fertilization occurs when the sperm cell from the male parent combines with the egg cell from the female parent. A fertilized egg is a single cell with DNA from both parents. Once the egg is fertilized, it divides. One cell becomes two, two cells become four, and so on. As the cells divide, they start to specialize, and different tissues and organs form.

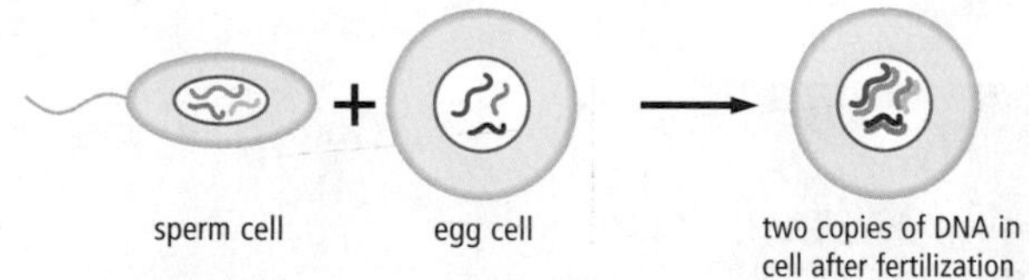

Differences in genetic material and in the environment produce differences in offspring. Whether a tulip flower is red or yellow depends on the genetic material in its cells. How well the tulip grows depends on conditions in the environment as well as genetic materials.

320 Unit 3: Diversity of Living Things

DIFFERENTIATE INSTRUCTION

More Reading Support

F How many parents take part in sexual reproduction? *two*

G What two processes are involved in sexual reproduction? *meiosis and fertilization*

Inclusion Model the genetics of sexual reproduction for students with visual impairments. Cut out cells from sandpaper. Make chromosomes with different textures of yarn, twine, string, or rope. Lay the chromosomes on cell bases, in pairs and singly.

Sexual Reproduction The fertilized eggs of a salamander contain genetic material from two parents.

Asexual Reproduction The buds of a sea coral have the same genetic material as the parent.

Most reproduction that occurs in multicellular organisms is sexual reproduction. However, many multicellular organisms can reproduce by asexual reproduction. With asexual reproduction, a single parent produces offspring.

Budding is a form of asexual reproduction. In budding, a second organism grows off, or buds, from another. Organisms that reproduce asexually can reproduce more often. Asexual reproduction limits genetic diversity within a group because offspring have the same genetic material as the parent.

How do offspring produced by sexual reproduction compare with offspring produced by asexual reproduction?

With sexual reproduction, there is an opportunity for new combinations of characteristics to occur in the offspring. Perhaps these organisms process food more efficiently or reproduce more quickly. Or perhaps they have adaptations that allow them to survive a change in their environment. In the next three sections, you will read how plants, animals, and fungi have adapted to similar environments in very different ways.

10.1 Review

KEY CONCEPTS

1. How do specialized cells relate to the different levels of organization in a multicellular organism?
2. What is an adaptation? Give an example.
3. What two cellular processes are involved in sexual reproduction?

CRITICAL THINKING

4. **Compare and Contrast** How does the genetic diversity of the offspring differ in sexual reproduction versus asexual reproduction?
5. **Predict** If fertilization occurred without meiosis, how many copies of DNA would be in the cells of the offspring?

CHALLENGE

6. **Synthesize** Do you consider the different levels of organization in a multicellular organism an adaptation? Explain your reasoning.

ANSWERS

1. Specialized cells make up different tissues.

2. An adaptation is a characteristic that helps an organism survive. Examples may include structures, behaviors, or processes.

3. meiosis and fertilization

4. Offspring of sexual reproduction have a combination of characteristics from two parents, increasing the species' diversity. Asexual reproduction produces identical offspring more often and with less energy.

5. four

6. The different levels of organization can be considered an adaptation. They help the organism survive by performing tasks more efficiently.

EXPLORE (the BIG idea)

Revisit "How Can Multicellular Organisms Reproduce?" on p. 313. Ask students what kind of reproduction their potatoes accomplished.

Develop Critical Thinking

INFER Ask students to give an example of when asexual reproduction might have advantages over sexual reproduction. *An organism would save energy and could reproduce more frequently.*

Ongoing Assessment

CHECK YOUR READING *Answer: An offspring produced by sexual reproduction has genetic material from two parents, so it has characteristics from each parent. An offspring produced asexually has identical genetic material and characteristics of the parent.*

Reinforce (the BIG idea)

Have students relate the section to the Big Idea.

 Reinforcing Key Concepts, p. 91

10.1 ASSESS & RETEACH

Assess

 Section 10.1 Quiz, p. 23

Reteach

Have students review pp. 316–317. Ask them to name an organ system in their body and list an organ, a tissue, and a type of cell in that system. *Sample answer: circulatory system, heart, muscle tissue, muscle cell*

Technology Resources

Have students visit **ClassZone.com** for reteaching of Key Concepts.

 CONTENT REVIEW

 CONTENT REVIEW CD-ROM

MATH IN SCIENCE

Math Skills Practice for Science

Set Learning Goal

To display part-to-whole relationships in a circle graph to present data about animal sightings

Present the Science

Counting the number of animals at a waterhole is a way to sample the total diversity of animals in the area.

Develop Graphing Skills

- Remind students that the bar in a fraction can be read as "out of" or "divided by."
- Review how to read a circle graph: Count up how many total parts there are (10), then determine how many parts are in the first shaded wedge (3). The shaded parts are numerators and the total number of parts is the denominator.

DIFFERENTIATION TIP Review fractions. Remind students that a fraction has two parts, a numerator (top number) and a denominator (bottom number).

Close

Ask: Why might a researcher want to count the number of animals at a waterhole each month for a year? *Sample answer: because animals migrate seasonally and may not be around each month of the year*

- Math Support, p. 129
- Math Practice, p. 130

Technology Resources

Students can visit **ClassZone.com** for practice using circle graphs.

 **MATH TUTORIAL**

SKILL: USING CIRCLE GRAPHS

MATH TUTORIAL
CLASSZONE.COM
Click on Math Tutorial for more help interpreting circle graphs.

Making Data Visual

A circle graph is a good way to see part-to-whole relationships. To use data presented in a circle graph, do the following:

Example

Suppose, at a waterhole in a game preserve, researchers observed ten animals throughout the day. What fraction of the sightings were giraffes?

(1) The circle graph shows the data for the sightings. The whole circle represents the total sightings, 10.

(2) 3 of the 10 equal parts are shaded for giraffes.

(3) Write "3 out of 10" as a fraction $\frac{3}{10}$.

ANSWER Giraffes = $\frac{3}{10}$ of the sightings.

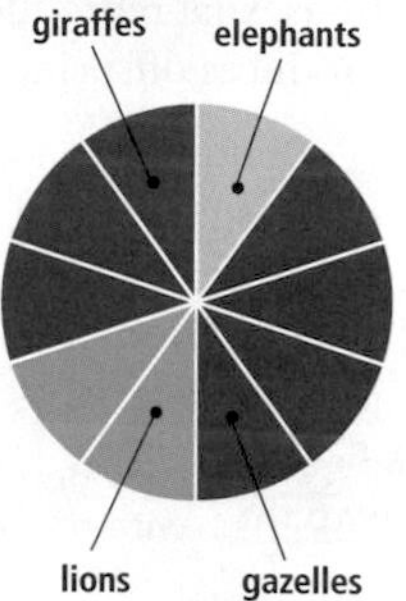

Answer the following questions.

1. What fraction of the sightings were lions?
2. What fraction of the sightings were gazelles?
3. Which animal did the researchers observe in greatest number?
4. Which animal did they observe in the least number? How many sightings occurred for that animal?
5. What fraction of the total does that animal represent?
6. If the researchers had seen one hundred animals, and the graph looked the same as it does, how many giraffe sightings would their graph represent?

CHALLENGE You also record the nighttime visitors: first, 2 young elephants; then a lioness with 2 thirsty cubs; then a giraffe, followed by a hyena and 3 gazelles. Calculate the fraction of the night's population that is represented by each type of animal. Use the fractions to draw a circle graph of the data on "Night Sightings at the Waterhole." Shade and label the graph with the types of animals.

ANSWERS

1. $\frac{2}{10}$ *or* $\frac{1}{5}$

2. $\frac{4}{10}$ *or* $\frac{2}{5}$

3. gazelles

4. elephants, 1

5. $\frac{1}{10}$

6. 30

CHALLENGE elephants: $\frac{2}{10}$*; lions:* $\frac{3}{10}$*; giraffe:* $\frac{1}{10}$*; hyena:* $\frac{1}{10}$*; gazelles:* $\frac{3}{10}$

KEY CONCEPT

10.2 Plants are producers.

BEFORE, you learned
- Multicellular organisms have tissues, organs, and systems
- Organisms have adaptations that can make them suited to their environment
- Sexual reproduction leads to genetic diversity

NOW, you will learn
- How plants obtain energy
- How plants store energy
- How plants respond to their environment

VOCABULARY

photosynthesis p. 324
autotroph p. 324
cellular respiration p. 325
stimulus p. 327

EXPLORE Stored Energy

In what form does a plant store energy?

PROCEDURE

1. Obtain pieces of potato, celery, and pear that have been placed in small plastic cups.
2. Place a few drops of the iodine solution onto the plant material in each cup. The iodine solution will turn dark blue in the presence of starch. It does not change color in the presence of sugar.

MATERIALS
- pieces of potato, celery, and pear
- 3 plastic cups
- iodine solution
- eye dropper

WHAT DO YOU THINK?
- Observing each sample, describe what happened to the color of the iodine solution after a few minutes.
- Starch and sugars are a source of energy for a plant. What do your observations suggest about how different plants store energy?

Plants capture energy from the Sun.

MAIN IDEA AND DETAILS Add the main idea *plants capture energy from the Sun* to your notebook and fill in details on photosynthesis and stored energy.

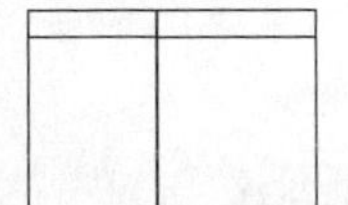

If you stand outside on a warm, sunny day, you may see and feel energy from the Sun. Without the Sun's energy, Earth would be a cold, dark planet. The Sun's heat and light provide the energy almost all organisms need to live.

However, energy from the Sun cannot drive cell processes directly. Light energy must be changed into chemical energy. Chemical energy is the form of energy all organisms use to carry out the functions of life. Plants are an important part of the energy story because plants capture energy from the Sun and convert it to chemical energy.

RESOURCES FOR DIFFERENTIATED INSTRUCTION

Below Level

UNIT RESOURCE BOOK
- Reading Study Guide A, pp. 94–95
- Decoding Support, p. 128

AUDIO CDS

Advanced

UNIT RESOURCE BOOK
Challenge and Extension, p. 100

English Learners

UNIT RESOURCE BOOK
Spanish Reading Study Guide, pp. 98–99

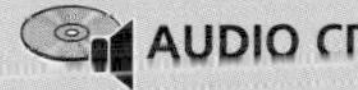
AUDIO CDS
- Audio Readings in Spanish
- Audio Readings (English)

Additional INVESTIGATION, Plant Growth and Light Conditions, A, B, & C, pp. 140–148; Teacher Instructions, pp. 360–361

10.2 FOCUS

Set Learning Goals

Students will
- Describe how plants obtain energy.
- Describe how plants store energy.
- Identify how plants respond to their environment.
- Design an experiment to see if plants grow by absorbing material from soil.

3-Minute Warm-Up

Display Transparency 12 or copy this exercise on the board:

Match the definitions to the correct terms.

Definitions
1. sperm or eggs are created *c*
2. a sperm and an egg join *d*
3. a group of cells that work together *a*

Terms
a. tissue
b. organ
c. meiosis
d. fertilization
e. sexual reproduction

3-Minute Warm-Up, p. T12

10.2 MOTIVATE

EXPLORE Stored Energy

PURPOSE To determine whether potatoes, celery, and pears contain starch

TIPS *10 min.* Choose pears carefully. The starch content of a pear decreases as it ripens. Iodine Solution is available in drug stores in the appropriate concentration. Be sure students do not ingest it. Review guidelines for safe handling.

WHAT DO YOU THINK? *The potato turns blue black, and the celery does not change color. Ripe pears do not turn blue black, but unripe pears do. Tubers and unripe fruits store energy in starch. Celery stems do not store energy in starch.*

10.2 INSTRUCT

INVESTIGATE What Plants Need to Grow

PURPOSE To design an experiment to test whether plants grow by absorbing material from soil

TIPS *30 min.* Discuss what experimental variables are. Make sure students understand that they are not testing the hypothesis that plants need *only* soil to grow. To test this hypothesis, plants would have to be grown in a vacuum and could not be watered. Other types of plants may be used.

WHAT DO YOU THINK? *Sample answer: the masses of the plant and the soil it grows in*

CHALLENGE *Sample answer: The dependent variable—the mass of the soil—should be measured at the beginning and at the end of the experiment by removing the plant, wiping all the soil from the roots into the pot, and weighing the soil on the balance.*

 Datasheet, What Plants Need to Grow, p. 101

Technology Resources

Customize this student lab as needed or look for an alternative. Print rubrics to assess student lab reports.

 **Lab Generator CD-ROM**

Ongoing Assessment

Describe how plants obtain energy.

Ask: What energy conversion takes place during photosynthesis? *The energy in sunlight changes to chemical energy.*

CHECK YOUR READING *Answer: Photosynthesis produces sugars and oxygen. The plant uses sugars for energy and as raw materials for growth.*

Producing Sugars

READING TIP
The roots for *photosynthesis* are *photo-*, which means "light," and *synthesis*, which means "to put together." Together they mean "put together by light."

Plants capture energy from sunlight and convert it to chemical energy through the process of **photosynthesis.** The plant takes in water and carbon dioxide from the environment and uses these simple materials to produce sugar, an energy-rich compound that contains carbon. Oxygen is also produced. Plants are referred to as producers because they produce energy-rich carbon compounds using the Sun's energy. 

The cells, tissues, and organ systems in a plant work together to supply the materials needed for photosynthesis. Most photosynthesis takes place in the leaves. The leaves take in carbon dioxide from the air, and the stems support the leaves and hold them up toward the Sun. The roots of the plant anchor it in the soil and supply water. The sugars produced are used by the plant for energy and as materials for growth.

 What is the product of photosynthesis?

 Another name for a plant is **autotroph** (AW-tuh-TRAHF). Autotroph means self-feeder. Plants do not require food from other organisms. Plants will grow if they have energy from the Sun, carbon dioxide from the air, and water and nutrients from the soil.

INVESTIGATE What Plants Need to Grow

Where does the material for plant growth come from?

DESIGN — YOUR OWN — EXPERIMENT

Until about 400 years ago, people thought that plants get everything they need from soil. Design an experiment to test this hypothesis: "If a plant grows by taking in material from soil, then the mass of the soil will decrease over time because soil material is taken into the plant."

PROCEDURE

1. Design an experiment, choosing from the materials listed.
2. Use the lab handbook, pages R28–32, to help you write your experimental procedure. Identify the variables and constants.

WHAT DO YOU THINK?
Measurement can be an important part of an experiment. What types of measurement do you use?

CHALLENGE An operational definition is a description of how you will measure the dependent variable. Give an operational definition for your experiment.

SKILL FOCUS
Designing experiments

MATERIALS
- potting soil
- pots or paper cups
- bean seedlings or beans
- triple beam balance
- water

TIME
30 minutes 

DIFFERENTIATE INSTRUCTION

More Reading Support

A What are the raw materials of photosynthesis? *water and CO_2*

B What do you call an organism that does not consume food? *an autotroph*

Additional Investigation To reinforce Section 10.2 learning goals, use the following full-period investigation:

Additional INVESTIGATION, Plant Growth and Light Conditions, A, B, & C, pp. 140–148, 360–361 (Advanced students should complete Levels B and C.)

English Learners Have students write the definitions for *autotroph, photosynthesis,* and *stimuli* in their Science Word Dictionaries. Pronounce these words for students.

Storing and Releasing Energy

Plants are not the only organisms that capture energy through photosynthesis. Algae and certain bacteria and protists also use photosynthesis. Plants are different from single-celled producers, however. Plants are multicellular organisms with parts of their bodies specialized for storing energy-rich material. Single-celled producers can store very little energy.

Only part of the energy captured by a plant is used as fuel for cellular processes. Some of the sugar produced is used as building material, enabling the plant to grow. The remaining sugar is stored. Often the sugars are stored as starches. Starch is an energy-rich compound made of many sugars. Starches can store a lot of chemical energy. When a plant needs energy, the starches are broken back down into sugars and energy is released. **Cellular respiration** is the process by which a cell uses oxygen to break down sugars to release the energy they hold.

D Some plants, such as carrots and beets, store starch in their roots. Other plants, including rhubarb, have stems adapted for storing starch. A potato is a swollen, underground stem called a tuber. Tubers have buds—the eyes of the potato—that can sprout into new plants. The starch stored in the tuber helps the new sprouts survive.

CHECK YOUR READING What is the original source of a plant's stored energy?

Plants are adapted to different environments.

Almost everywhere you look on land, you'll see plants. Leaves, stems, and roots are adaptations that enable plants, as producers, to live on land. Not all plants, however, look the same. Just as there are many different types of land environments, there are many different types of plants that have adapted to these environments.

Grasses are an example of plants that grow in several environments. Many grasses have deep roots, produce seeds quickly, and can grow in areas with a wide range of temperatures and different amounts of precipitation. Grasses can survive drought, fires, freezing temperatures, and grazing. As long as the roots of the plant survive, the grasses will grow again. Grasses are found in the Arctic tundra, as well as in temperate and tropical climates.

Teach from Visuals

To help students interpret the photograph of a potato plant, ask:

- Where are the plant's stems? *Some are aboveground, producing leaves. Some are underground, swollen structures that we call potatoes.*
- Where are the plant's roots? *underground*

Address Misconceptions

IDENTIFY Ask: How do plants get nutrients? If students' responses indicate that plants are consumers rather than producers, students may hold the misconception that carbon dioxide, water, and soil are food that plants eat.

CORRECT Ask students to define *food. stored energy* Have them explain why carbon dioxide, water, and soil are not food sources for plants. *They do not provide energy. The plants need to capture the sunlight to get their energy.*

REASSESS Ask: Why don't plants need food? *They get energy from sunlight and store it in the chemical bonds of sugars that they synthesize.*

Technology Resources

Visit **ClassZone.com** for background on common student misconceptions.

MISCONCEPTION DATABASE

Ongoing Assessment

Describe how plants store energy.

Ask: In what form do plants store the food they produce? *as sugar and starch*

CHECK YOUR READING *Answer: sunlight*

DIFFERENTIATE INSTRUCTION

More Reading Support

C What organisms other than plants use photosynthesis? *algae, some bacteria, and some protists*

D Where do plants store starch? *roots, stems, tubers*

Inclusion Bring in a small section of turf (lawn grasses) and a growing plant that has deep roots, such as most house plants. Let students who are visually impaired or who have cognitive disabilities examine the root systems of the plants and discover for themselves how shallow grass roots are compared with the roots of other plants.

Real World Example

Carnivorous plants usually grow in acid bogs that have little nitrogen. Although these plants make sugars by photosynthesis, they get the nitrogen and minerals they need by digesting insects. Pitcher plants attract insects with their bright colors. Once the insect enters the plant, it can only move down a long, water-filled tube. The insect drowns and is digested by enzymes that the plant secretes into the water. Sundews, which are found in temperate forests, secrete a sticky glue that traps insects on the leaves, where they are digested. Bladderworts are aquatic plants that trap insects in bladders, using a trapdoor that snaps shut like a spring. Enzymes digest the insect.

Teach from Visuals

To help students interpret the photographs of a Venus flytrap,

- Point out that the Venus flytrap has tiny hairs on the inner surfaces of the leaves. When an insect touches these hairs, the leaf snaps closed and traps the insect.
- Ask: Would you expect to find Venus flytraps growing in rich garden soil? Explain. *No; they grow in soil that lacks certain minerals. The digested insects supply these minerals.*

Ongoing Assessment

CHECK YOUR READING *Answer: reproductive adaptations such as the ability to produce seeds quickly, and protective adaptations such as thorns or odors*

PHOTO CAPTION Answer: Yes; it still produces sugars by photosynthesis; it is green because of chlorophyll. It gets its energy from sunlight absorbed by chlorophyll.

E

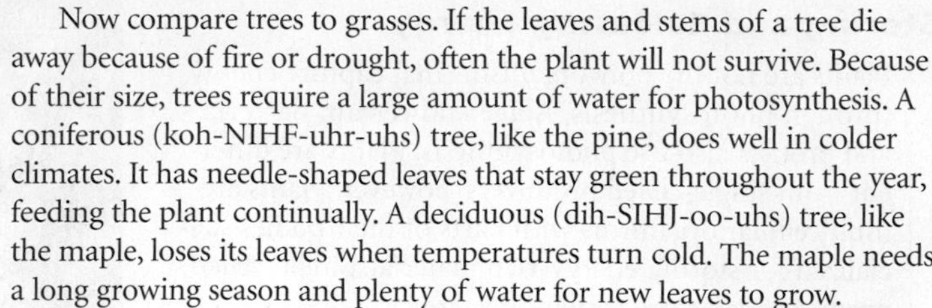

Now compare trees to grasses. If the leaves and stems of a tree die away because of fire or drought, often the plant will not survive. Because of their size, trees require a large amount of water for photosynthesis. A coniferous (koh-NIHF-uhr-uhs) tree, like the pine, does well in colder climates. It has needle-shaped leaves that stay green throughout the year, feeding the plant continually. A deciduous (dih-SIHJ-oo-uhs) tree, like the maple, loses its leaves when temperatures turn cold. The maple needs a long growing season and plenty of water for new leaves to grow.

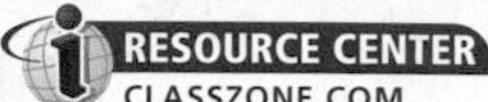
RESOURCE CENTER
CLASSZONE.COM

Learn more about plant adaptations.

Plants have reproductive adaptations. It may surprise you to learn that flowering plants living on cold, snowy mountaintops have something in common with desert plants. When rain falls in the desert, wildflower seeds sprout very quickly. Within a few weeks, the plants grow, flower, and produce new seeds that will be ready to sprout with the next rainy season. The same thing happens in the mountains, where the snow may thaw for only a few weeks every summer. Seeds sprout, flowers grow, and new seeds are produced—all before the snow returns. You will read more about plant reproduction in Chapter 11.

F

Some plants have adaptations that protect them. Plants in the mustard family give off odors that keep many plant-eating insects away. Other plants, such as poison ivy and poison oak, produce harmful chemicals. The nicotine in a tobacco plant is a poison that helps to keep the plant from being eaten.

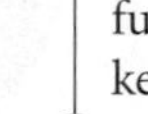
CHECK YOUR READING Name two different types of adaptations plants have.

Some adaptations plants have relate to very specific needs. For example, the Venus flytrap is a plant that grows in areas where the soil lacks certain materials. The leaves of the Venus flytrap fold in the middle and have long teeth all around the edges. When an insect lands on an open leaf, the two sides of the leaf fold together. The teeth form a trap that prevents the captured insect from escaping. Fluids given off by the leaf digest the insect's body, providing materials the plant can't get from the soil.

ANALYZE An insect provides nutrients that this Venus flytrap cannot get from the soil. Is this plant still a producer? Ask yourself where the plant gets its energy.

DIFFERENTIATE INSTRUCTION

More Reading Support

E Do trees or grasses need more water? *trees*

F Name a protective adaptation. *Sample answer: odors*

Below Level Have students research the many adaptations of cactus plants to their dry environment and prepare a poster in the style of the diagram for adaptation, p. 319.

Plant roots always grow downward and stems always grow upward. All plants respond to gravity as a stimulus.

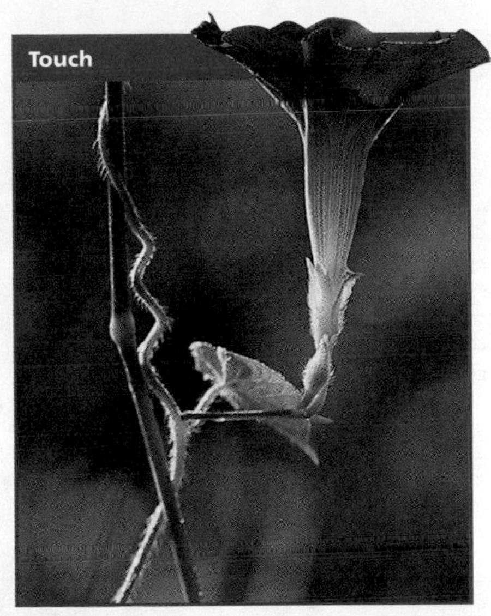

The tendril of a climbing plant grows around a nearby object. The plant responds to touch as a stimulus.

Plants respond to their environment.

During a hot afternoon, parts of the flower known as the Mexican bird of paradise close. As the Sun goes down, the flower reopens. The plant is responding to a stimulus, in this case, sunlight. A **stimulus** is something that produces a response from an organism. Plants, like all organisms, respond to stimuli in their environment. This ability helps them to survive and grow.

G

VOCABULARY Make a four square for the term *stimulus* in your science notebook.

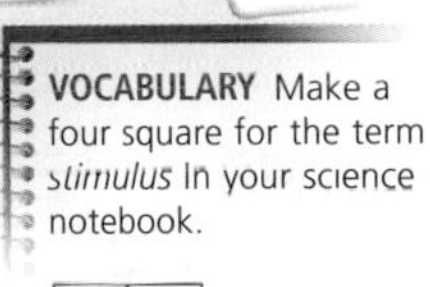

Gravity

Gravity is the force that keeps you bound to Earth and gives you a sense of up and down. All plants respond to gravity. They also have a sense of up and down—roots grow down and stems grow up. Suppose you place a young seedling on its side, so that its roots and stems stretch out to the side. In a very short time, the tip of the root will begin to turn down, and the tip of the stem will turn up.

H

Touch

Many plants also respond to touch as a stimulus. Peas, morning glories, tropical vines, and other climbing plants have special stems called tendrils. Tendrils respond to the touch of a nearby object. As the tendrils grow, they wrap around the object. The twining of tendrils around a fence or another plant helps raise a plant into the sunlight.

Teach from Visuals

To help students interpret the photographs of plant responses, ask:

- What is the advantage to a plant to have its roots grow down and its stems grow up? *Roots must take in water, usually found in soil. Leaves on stems must collect sunlight to photosynthesize.*
- What is the advantage of having tendrils? *Plants with weak stems can stretch above the shade of other plants, and get more sunlight.*

Teach Difficult Concepts

Students often have trouble understanding that stems respond to gravity by growing up, although the force of gravity is downward. Explain that roots exhibit a positive response to gravity when they grow down, and stems exhibit a negative response to gravity. You might also try the following demonstration.

Teacher Demo

Soak four corn seeds in water for 24 hours. Crumple up two wet paper towels and place them in the bottom of a petri dish. Arrange the seeds on the paper towels at the 12, 3, 6, and 9 o'clock positions. The pointed ends of the seeds should all face toward the center of the dish. Cover the petri dish, tape it closed, and mark an arrow on the cover. Stand the dish on its edge so the arrow points down. In about two days, the seeds will germinate. Roots will appear first, then green shoots. The roots will grow down, and the shoots will grow up.

DIFFERENTIATE INSTRUCTION

More Reading Support

G What produces a response from an organism? *a stimulus*

H How do plants respond to gravity? *Roots grow down; stems grow up.*

English Learners Have students look up words that have similar roots to *stimulus,* such as *stimulate* and *stimulation.* Have them look up the words *simulate* and *simulation.* Point out that these two groups of words have completely different meanings. Have students use the words in sentences.

Teach from Visuals

To help students interpret the diagram of how plants respond to light, ask:

- What do the dots in the cells in the circle represent? *auxin*
- Why do the cells on the left side of the stem have more auxin than the cells on the right side? *They are on the dark side of the stem.*
- Why does the stem bend to the right? *Because the cells on the left are longer, there is more surface area on the left side of the stem.*

History of Science

In the late 19th century, Charles Darwin and his son Francis conducted some of the first experiments on the response of plants to light. They observed that a grass seedling bends toward light only if the tip of the shoot is present. When they removed the tip or covered it with a tiny opaque cap, the seedling did not bend. They concluded that the tip of the shoot is responsible for sensing light. In 1926 Friedrich Went, a Dutch botanist, identified auxin, the chemical substance that causes plant stems to bend toward light.

Ongoing Assessment

Identify how plants respond to their environment.

Ask: Why do plants grow toward light? *The stimulus of light causes chemical changes that make the plant grow that way.*

Light

READING TIP The words *stimulus, stimuli,* and *stimulate* all have the same root, meaning "to provoke or encourage action."

Light is a powerful stimulus for plants. You can see that stems and leaves grow toward light by placing an indoor plant near a window. After several days, the tips of the stems start to bend toward the window. What happens if you turn the plant around so that those stems reach into the room? The stems will bend as they continue to grow, turning back toward the light.

Plants respond to light with the help of a hormone. A hormone is a chemical substance that is produced in one part of an organism and travels to a different part where it produces a reaction. Hormones act as chemical messengers. They allow an organism to respond to changes in its body or to changes in the environment around it.

Examine how plants respond to different stimuli.

Auxin (AWK-sihn), a plant hormone that stimulates cell growth, is produced at the tip of a plant stem. Auxin moves away from light. As a result, the cells on the darker side of a plant stem contain more auxin than those on the lighter side. Higher levels of auxin in plant cells on the darker side cause those cells to grow longer. The longer cells cause the plant stem to bend, moving the tip of the stem toward the light.

328 Unit 3: **Diversity of Living Things**

DIFFERENTIATE INSTRUCTION

More Reading Support

I What is the name of a plant hormone that stimulates cell growth? *auxin*

Alternative Assessment Have students answer the Check Your Reading question by drawing diagrams. Diagrams should include responses to each of the three stimuli.

Advanced Have students design experiments to test plant responses. They should choose one response to test, such as response to gravity, to touch, and so on. They should research the response in a particular plant variety, then write a hypothesis and procedure.

 Challenge and Extension, p. 100

Plants respond to seasonal changes.

Most regions of the world go through seasonal changes every year. For example, during the summer in North America, temperatures rise and the days get longer. As winter approaches, temperatures go down and the days become shorter. These types of seasonal changes have an effect on plants.

For plants, a shorter period of daylight will affect the amount of sunlight available for photosynthesis. Shorter days cause many plants to go into a state of dormancy. When plants are dormant, they temporarily stop growing and so require less energy.

In temperate climates, the approach of winter causes the leaves of deciduous trees to die and drop to the ground. The trees enter a state of dormancy during which their growth is slowed. Other plants, such as wild cornflowers, do not survive the change. New cornflowers will grow the following season, from seeds left behind.

What stimulus causes a deciduous plant to respond by dropping its leaves?

For many plants, reproduction is also affected by seasonal changes. For some plants, the amount of daylight is a factor. A few plants, such as rice and ragweed, produce flowers only in autumn or winter, when days are short. They are short-day plants. Long-day plants flower in late spring and summer, when days are long. Lettuce, spinach, and irises are long day-plants. You will read more about plants in Chapter 11.

10.2 Review

KEY CONCEPTS

1. What process makes a plant a producer, and what does a plant produce?
2. Name three stimuli that plants respond to, and give examples of how a plant responds.
3. How do seasonal changes affect plants? Give an example.

CRITICAL THINKING

4. **Give Examples** Give three examples of ways that plants are adapted to their environments. How do these adaptations benefit the plant?

CHALLENGE

5. **Apply** Some experiments suggest that the hormone auxin is involved in the twining of tendrils. Use what you know about auxin to explain how it might cause tendrils to twine around anything they touch. Draw a diagram.

ANSWERS

1. photosynthesis; sugar and starch

2. Light: plants grow toward the light; Touch: peas have tendrils that wrap around nearby objects; Gravity: stems grow up and roots grow down.

3. Some plants produce flowers only in autumn or winter. Shortened hours of daylight cause some trees to become dormant.

4. Sample answer: Rapid life cycle gives plants a better chance to reproduce. Odors protect plants from animals that want to eat them. Plants that grow in poor soil get nutrients from insects.

5. Answers should reflect an understanding that a higher level of auxin on one side of a tendril causes the tendril to bend toward the other side.

EXPLORE the BIG idea

Revisit "Where Does It Come From?" on p. 313. Have students explain how they decided each item's source.

Ongoing Assessment

Answer: fewer hours of daylight

Reinforce the BIG idea

Have students relate the section to the Big Idea.

 Reinforcing Key Concepts, p. 102

10.2 ASSESS & RETEACH

Assess

 Section 10.2 Quiz, p. 24

Reteach

Have students make a poster summarizing plant responses to light, gravity, and touch. Posters should include a drawing or a picture cut out of a magazine, and give the stimulus, the response, and the effect on the plant for each type of response.

Technology Resources

Have students visit **ClassZone.com** for reteaching of Key Concepts.

 CONTENT REVIEW

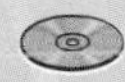 CONTENT REVIEW CD-ROM

10.3 FOCUS

Set Learning Goals

Students will

- Describe how animals obtain energy.
- Summarize how animals process food.
- Identify different ways animals respond to their environment.
- Infer what an owl eats and how well it digests its food.

3-Minute Warm-Up

Display Transparency 13 or copy this exercise on the board:

Decide if these statements are true. If not true, correct them.

1. Plant stems grow up and do not respond to gravity. *Plant stems grow up and do respond to gravity.*
2. Plants are producers because they make energy. *Plants are producers because they make sugar and starch.*
3. Carrot plants have roots that are adapted for storing energy-rich carbon compounds. *true*

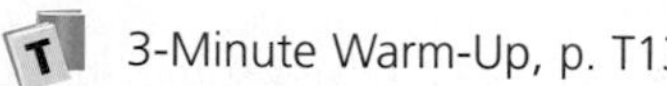
3-Minute Warm-Up, p. T13

10.3 MOTIVATE

THINK ABOUT

PURPOSE To understand that an animal's diet affects its teeth

DISCUSS Have students brainstorm what different shapes of teeth suggest about an animal's diet. Ask: Why do humans need four kinds of teeth? *We eat animals and plants, so we need teeth that can bite and chew both.*

KEY CONCEPT

10.3 Animals are consumers.

BEFORE, you learned

- Plants are producers
- Plants have adaptations for capturing and storing energy
- Plants respond to different stimuli

NOW, you will learn

- How animals obtain energy
- How animals process food
- About different ways animals respond to their environment

VOCABULARY

consumer p. 330
heterotroph p. 330
behavior p. 334
predator p. 335
prey p. 335
migration p. 336
hibernation p. 336

THINK ABOUT

What can you tell from teeth?

Many animals have teeth. Teeth bite, grind, crush, and chew. A fox's sharp biting teeth capture small animals that it hunts on the run. A horse's teeth are flat and strong—for breaking down the grasses it eats. Run your tongue over your own teeth. How many different shapes do you notice? What can the shape of teeth suggest about the food an animal eats?

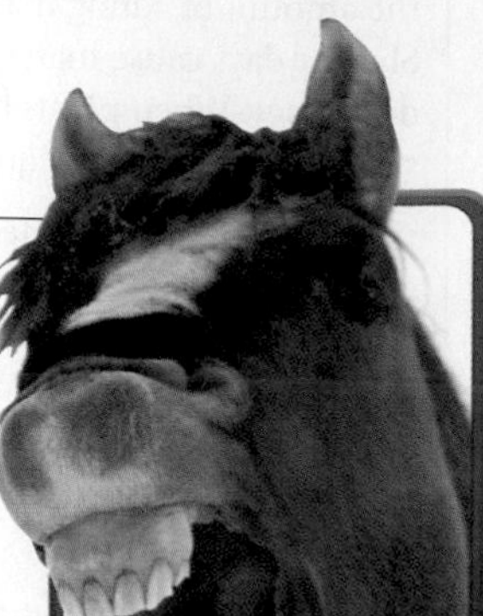

Animals obtain energy and materials from food.

You probably see nonhuman animals every day, whether you live in a rural area or a large city. If the animals are wild animals, not somebody's pet, then chances are that what you see these animals doing is moving about in search of food.

READING TIP

The meaning of *heterotroph* is opposite to that of *autotroph*. The root *hetero-* means "other." *Heterotroph* means "other-feeder," or "feeds on others."

Animals are consumers. A **consumer** is an organism that needs to get energy from another organism. Unlike plants, animals must consume food to get the energy and materials they need to survive. Animals are heterotrophs. A **heterotroph** (HEHT-uhr-uh-TRAHF) is an organism that feeds on, or consumes, other organisms. By definition, animals are, quite simply, multicellular organisms that have adaptations that allow them to take in and process food.

RESOURCES FOR DIFFERENTIATED INSTRUCTION

Below Level

UNIT RESOURCE BOOK

- Reading Study Guide A, pp. 105–106
- Decoding Support, p. 128

AUDIO CDS

Advanced

UNIT RESOURCE BOOK

- Challenge and Extension, p. 111
- Challenge Reading, pp. 124–125

English Learners

UNIT RESOURCE BOOK

Spanish Reading Study Guide, pp. 109–110

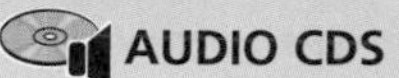
AUDIO CDS

- Audio Readings in Spanish
- Audio Readings (English)

Obtaining Food

Food is a source of energy and materials for animals.

Simple feeding Some animals, such as corals, can filter food from their environment.

Complex feeding Many animals, such as bats, actively search for and capture food.

Animals need food and have many different ways of getting it. For some animals, feeding is a relatively simple process. An adult coral simply filters food from the water as it moves through the coral's body. Most animals, however, must search for food. Grazing animals, such as horses, move along from one patch of grass to another. Other animals must capture food. Most bats use sound and hearing to detect the motion of insects flying at night. Its wings make the bat able to move through the air quickly and silently.

What Animals Eat

Just about any type of living or once-living material is a source of food for some animal. Animals can be grouped by the type of food they eat.

- Herbivores (HUR-buh-VAWRS) feed on plants or algae.
- Carnivores (KAHR-nuh-VAWRS) feed on other animals.
- Omnivores (AWM-nuh-VAWRS) feed on both plants and animals.

Another group are those animals that feed on the remains of once-living animals. Many insects do, as do some larger animals, such as vultures. Other animals, such as worms, act as decomposers.

CHECK YOUR READING Describe how herbivores, carnivores, and omnivores get their energy.

MAIN IDEA AND DETAILS Make a chart about the main idea: *Animals obtain energy and materials from food.* Include *herbivore, carnivore,* and *omnivore* in the details.

B

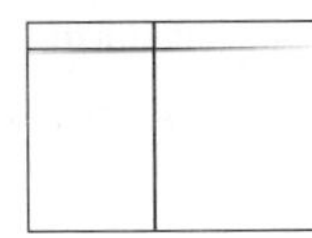

Different species of animals have adapted in different ways to take advantage of all the energy-rich material in the environment. To get energy and materials from food, all animals must first break the food down—that is, they must digest it.

10.3 INSTRUCT

Teach from Visuals

To help students interpret the photographs of animals obtaining food, ask:

- How do you think a coral filters food from the water? *Special cells filter tiny organisms out of the water as it flows through the sponge's body.*
- How do you think bats find insects at night? *They use sound and hearing.*

Metacognitive Strategy

Ask students to restate in their own words the definitions of the three groups of animals based on the type of food the animals eat.

Ongoing Assessment

Describe how animals obtain energy.

Ask: Where does an animal get the energy that it needs? *eating and digesting food*

CHECK YOUR READING *Answer: Herbivores feed on plants or algae, carnivores feed on other animals, and omnivores feed on both plants and animals.*

DIFFERENTIATE INSTRUCTION

More Reading Support

A What do herbivores eat? *plants or algae*

B What do carnivores eat? *other animals*

English Learners Place the terms *heterotroph, behavior, predator, prey, migration,* and *hibernation* on the classroom's Science Word Wall. Have students list as many animals as they know in five minutes. Then, have them go down their list and assign *herbivore, carnivore,* or *omnivore* to each animal. If they don't know what a certain animal eats, have them look it up in the encyclopedia.

INVESTIGATE Owl Pellets

PURPOSE To infer what an owl eats and how well it digests its food

TIPS *30 min.* Groupings of two or three students are ideal. Have diagrams of various small rodent skeletal systems available so students can identify the bones. Owl pellets can be ordered from biological supply catalogs. If you order owl pellets, they will come with a bone identification key. Remind students to use caution when handling the needle tool.

WHAT DO YOU THINK? *Students can infer that an owl is a carnivore because they will see fur and bones remaining. They can infer that an owl has no teeth and swallows its prey whole because bones are intact. Owls digest soft tissues but not fur and bones.*

CHALLENGE *Owls eat birds or small rodents such as mice.*

 Datasheet, Owl Pellets, p. 112

Technology Resources

Customize this student lab as needed or look for an alternative. Print rubrics to assess student lab reports.

 **Lab Generator CD-ROM**

Teaching with Technology

If digital cameras are available, students can take photographs of what they find in their owl pellets. If tape recorders are available, students could narrate what they find as they separate the materials in their pellet.

Ongoing Assessment

Summarize how animals process food.

Ask: Why does food have to be processed? *Large, complex compounds in food must be broken down into smaller compounds that a body's cells can use.*

Answer: It must be broken into smaller compounds.

Find out more about animal adaptations.

Processing Food

Energy is stored in complex carbon compounds in food. For the cells in an animal to make use of the energy and materials stored in this food, the large complex compounds must be broken back down into simpler compounds.

How must food be changed so an animal gets energy?

 C

Digestion is the process that breaks food down into pieces that are small enough to be absorbed by cells. A few animals, such as sponges, are able to take food particles directly into their cells. Most animals, however, take the food into an area of their body where the materials are broken down. Cells absorb the materials they need. Animals such as jellyfish have a single opening in their bodies where food is brought into a central cavity, or gut. The unused materials are released through the same opening.

A digestive system uses both physical and chemical activity to break down food. Many animals have a tubelike digestive system. Food is brought in at one end of the animal, the mouth, and waste is released at the other end. As food moves through the system, it is continually broken down, releasing necessary materials called nutrients to the cells.

What does an owl eat, and how well does it digest its food?

PROCEDURE

1. Get an owl pellet from your teacher. Open the foil and place the pellet in a tray.
2. Use a needle tool and tweezers to sort through the materials in the pellet and separate them.
3. When you have finished, dispose of the materials according to your teacher's instructions, and wash your hands.

WHAT DO YOU THINK?

- What can you tell about what an owl eats from looking at the remains in the pellet?
- What materials are not digested?

CHALLENGE Use the bone identification key to identify what the owl ate.

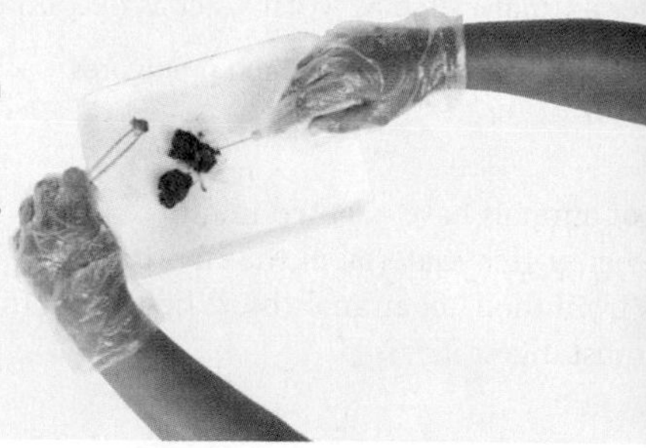

SKILL FOCUS
Inferring

MATERIALS
- owl pellet
- needle tool
- tweezers
- tray
- *for Challenge:* bone identification key

TIME
30 minutes

DIFFERENTIATE INSTRUCTION

 **More Reading Support**

C What is the process that breaks down food? *digestion*

Alternative Assessment Have students give an oral report to the class in which they describe how they made their inferences about what an owl eats and how well it digests its food. Have the class ask questions after the presentation.

Obtaining Oxygen

Animals need oxygen to release the energy in food.

Grasshopper

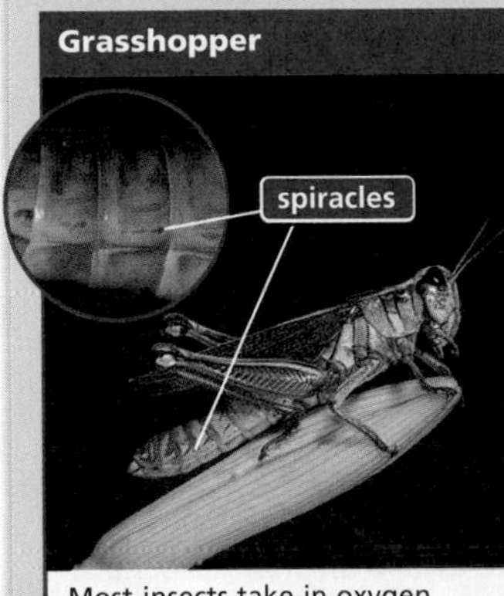

Most insects take in oxygen through body openings called spiracles.

Bass

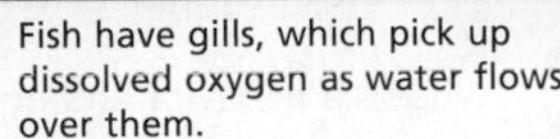

Fish have gills, which pick up dissolved oxygen as water flows over them.

Tiger

This yawning tiger, like many animals, gets oxygen by inhaling air into its lungs.

Releasing and Storing Energy

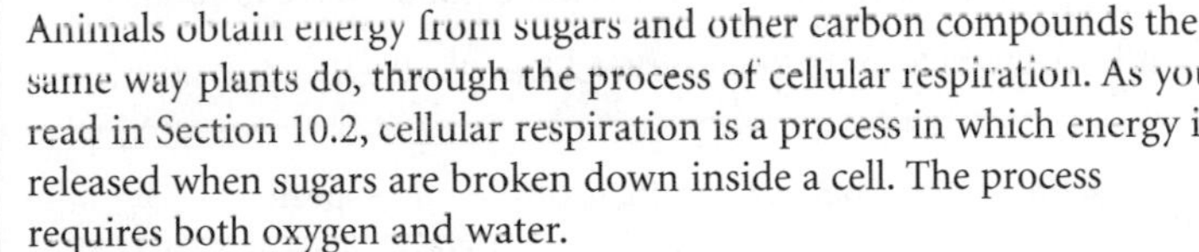

D Animals obtain energy from sugars and other carbon compounds the same way plants do, through the process of cellular respiration. As you read in Section 10.2, cellular respiration is a process in which energy is released when sugars are broken down inside a cell. The process requires both oxygen and water.

CHECK YOUR READING What is the function of cellular respiration?

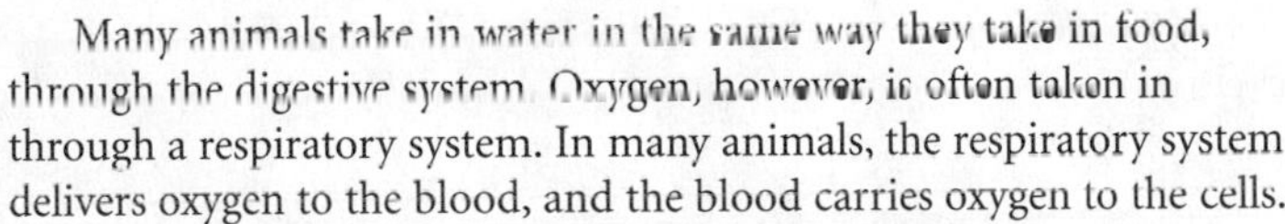

E Many animals take in water in the same way they take in food, through the digestive system. Oxygen, however, is often taken in through a respiratory system. In many animals, the respiratory system delivers oxygen to the blood, and the blood carries oxygen to the cells.

Animals have different structures for obtaining oxygen. Many insects take in oxygen through spiracles, tiny openings in their bodies. Fish have gills, structures that allow them to pick up oxygen dissolved in the water. Other air-breathing animals take in oxygen through organs called lungs.

Most animals do not feed continuously, so they need to be able to store materials from food in their tissues or organs. Many animals, including humans, take in large amounts of food at one time. This gives an animal time to do other activities, such as caring for young or looking for more food.

DIFFERENTIATE INSTRUCTION

More Reading Support

D What process releases energy for an organism? *cellular respiration*

E What does a respiratory system do? *It delivers oxygen to the blood.*

Below Level Have students draw a flow chart diagramming the path of food through an animal's body. *Teeth or structures in the mouth grind and cut up the food, which is then digested and absorbed. The processed food moves to cells, where it undergoes cellular respiration, releasing energy.*

Teach from Visuals

To help students interpret the photographs of how animals get oxygen, ask:

- Whose method of getting oxygen do you think provides the most oxygen for the animal? *the tiger's*
- Why do you think a larger animal might need more oxygen than a small one? *They need to use more energy to move and to maintain their body.*

Address Misconceptions

IDENTIFY Ask: How do plants and animals release energy? If students respond that different organisms use different processes, they may hold the misconception that only animals undergo cellular respiration.

CORRECT Demonstrate that plants respire. Put a sprig of *Elodea* in a test tube, cover it with water, and add one milliliter of bromthymol blue. Let the test tube stand for a few minutes. Small bubbles will come from the leaves, and the color will change from blue to green to yellow as the plant produces carbon dioxide during cellular respiration.

REASSESS Ask: What kinds of organisms undergo cellular respiration? *all organisms that use oxygen*

Technology Resources

Visit **ClassZone.com** for background on common student misconceptions.

MISCONCEPTION DATABASE

Ongoing Assessment

CHECK YOUR READING *Answer: to release the energy stored in sugars*

Develop Critical Thinking

CONNECT Have students give examples of inherited and learned behavior in humans. *An example of inherited behavior might be jerking one's hand away after touching a hot object. A learned behavior is tying one's shoes.*

Real World Example

Animal behaviorists used to think that birds instinctively knew how to sing the songs of their species. However, young sparrows reared away from other members of their species or in the presence only of other species sang incorrectly. When scientists reared young sparrows in soundproof incubators fitted with microphones and recording devices, the songs the birds sang when they matured were poorly developed. It is now believed that both genetics and learning are necessary if a bird is to sing the common songs of its species.

Ongoing Assessment

CHECK YOUR READING *Answer: A behavior is any observable response to a stimulus.*

Animals interact with the environment and with other organisms.

Animals, as consumers, must obtain food, as well as water, from their environment. An animal's body has many adaptations that allow it to process food. These can include digestive, respiratory, and circulatory systems. Also important are the systems that allow animals to interact with their environment to obtain food. In many animals, muscle and skeletal systems provide movement and support. A nervous system allows the animal to sense and respond to stimuli.

Animals respond to many different types of stimuli. They respond to sights, sounds, odors, light, or a change in temperature. They respond to hunger and thirst. They also respond to other animals. Any observable response to a stimulus is described as a **behavior.** A bird's drinking water from a puddle is a behavior. A lion's chasing an antelope is a behavior, just as the antelope's running to escape the lion is a behavior.

What is a behavior and how does it relate to a stimulus?

Some behaviors are inherited, which means they are present at birth. For example, a spider can weave a web without being shown. Other behaviors are learned. For example, the young lion in the photograph learns that a porcupine is not a good source of food.

All behaviors fall into one of three general categories:

- individual behaviors
- interactions between animals of the same species
- interactions between animals of different species

ANALYZE Do you consider the defensive behavior of a porcupine an adaptation?

334

DIFFERENTIATE INSTRUCTION

More Reading Support

F Is a spider's ability to make a web inherited or learned behavior? *inherited*

Advanced Spiders are predators. They have the adaptation of building webs to catch their prey. The size and design of spider webs can be affected by several factors. Have students each research one type of web-building spider and report on how various stimuli affect the web-building behaviors of the spider.

 Challenge and Extension, p. 111

Have students who are interested in animal behavior read the following article:

 Challenge Reading, pp. 124–125

For macaques, grooming is both an individual and a social behavior. Here a mother grooms her young.

Individual behaviors often involve meeting basic needs. Animals must find food, water, and shelter. They sleep. They groom themselves. Animals also respond to changes in their environment. A lizard may warm itself in the morning sunlight and then move into the shade when the Sun is high in the sky.

Interactions that occur between animals of the same species are often described as social behaviors. Basic social behaviors include those between parents and offspring and behaviors for attracting a mate. Within a group, animals of the same species may cooperate by working together. Wolves hunt in packs and bees maintain a hive. Behaviors among animals of the same species can also be competitive. Animals often compete for a mate or territory.

CHECK YOUR READING What are some ways that animals of the same species cooperate and compete?

G

Interactions that occur between animals of different species often involve the search for food. A **predator** is an animal that hunts other animals for food. Predators have behaviors that allow them to search for and capture other organisms. A cheetah first stalks an antelope, then chases it down, moving as fast as 110 kilometers per hour.

H

An animal that is hunted by another animal as a source of food is the **prey.** Behaviors of prey animals often allow them to escape a predator. An antelope may not be able to outrun a cheetah, but antelopes move in herds. This provides protection for the group since a cheetah will kill only one animal. Other animals, such as the pufferfish and porcupine, have defensive behaviors and structures.

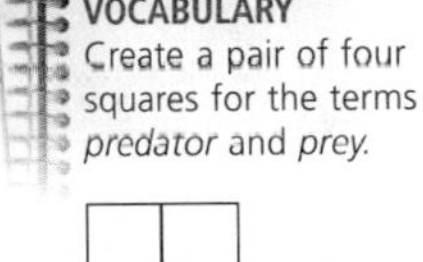

VOCABULARY
Create a pair of four squares for the terms *predator* and *prey*.

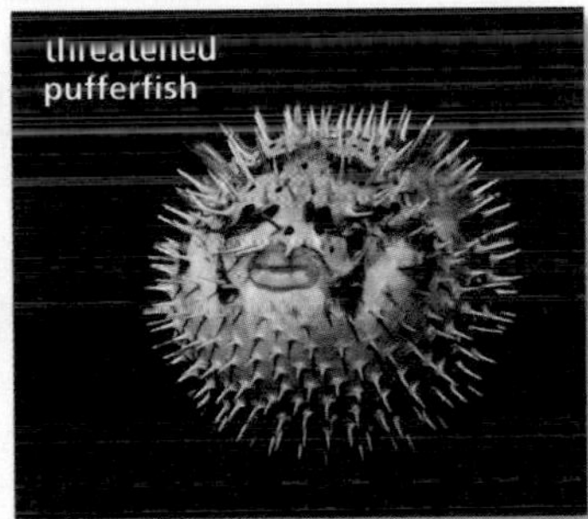

Animals of different species can also interact in cooperative ways. Tickbirds remove ticks from the skin of an impala. This behavior provides food for the bird and provides relief for the impala. Sometimes animals take advantage of the behavior of other animals. Many animals eat the remains of prey left over after a predator has finished feeding.

History of Science

Imprinting is the process of forming a social attachment between parents and offspring. The classic experiments in this field were conducted by Konrad Lorenz in the 1930s. Graylag goslings that hatched from eggs incubated with the mother goose followed and interacted with the mother. However, goslings that hatched from eggs that were isolated in an incubator spent their first few hours with Lorenz. These geese followed Lorenz around and showed no recognition of their mother or of other geese. They behaved as if Lorenz were their mother.

Teach Difficult Concepts

Students often confuse scavengers with decomposers. Decomposers, such as fungi and bacteria, are organisms that break down organic matter into small compounds so they can be taken up and recycled by plants. A scavenger is an animal that eats meat (a carnivore), but the meat it eats is from dead animals and may be decaying or rotted. Vultures, condors, jackals, hyenas, and coyotes are scavengers, as are certain types of insects.

EXPLORE the BIG idea

Revisit "Internet Activity: Bee Dance" on p. 313. Have students explain how bee communication is a type of behavior.

Ongoing Assessment

Identify different ways animals respond to their environment.

Ask: Give an example of cooperative behavior among animals of the same species and of different species. *social behavior in a bee hive, a bird cleaning insects from an impala*

CHECK YOUR READING *Answer: Animals of the same species may cooperate by hunting together or by working together like bees in a hive. They may compete for territory or for a mate.*

DIFFERENTIATE INSTRUCTION

More Reading Support

G What do you call an animal that hunts other animals for food? *a predator*

H What do you call animals that are hunted by others for food? *prey*

English Learners Have English learners write the definitions of *predator* and *prey* in their Science Word Dictionaries. Ask them to think of predator/prey relationships between animals found in their countries of origin or ancestry.

Integrate the Sciences

Many migrating birds navigate by detecting Earth's magnetic field. Studies have shown that placing a powerful magnet near the birds makes them change their direction.

Real World Example

Hibernation is just one example of how organisms escape harsh conditions. Many toads estivate, which means to spend the summer in a dormant state. Toads dig holes in the ground and bury themselves during hot, dry summers to protect themselves from heat and dehydration.

Reinforce (the BIG idea)

Have students relate the section to the Big Idea.

 Reinforcing Key Concepts, p. 113

10.3 ASSESS & RETEACH

Assess

 Section 10.3 Quiz, p. 25

Reteach

Share with students these sentences explaining the difference between cellular respiration and respiration, a term commonly used to mean breathing:

- Cellular respiration is a chemical process that takes place in cells.
- It involves the chemical breakdown of glucose, releasing energy.
- Respiration, or breathing, is a physical process of taking air into the body.

Then have students work in pairs to create a Venn diagram comparing the two processes. Point out that all multicellular organisms do cellular respiration, but that only animals do respiration.

Technology Resources

Have students visit **ClassZone.com** for reteaching of Key Concepts.

 CONTENT REVIEW

 CONTENT REVIEW CD-ROM

Monarch butterflies migrate each winter to California and Mexico.

Animals respond to seasonal changes.

monarch butterfly

Animals, like plants, are affected by seasonal changes in their environment. Certain types of food may not be available all year round. A region might go through periods of drought. Some animals do not do well in extreme heat or cold. Unlike plants, animals can respond to seasonal changes by changing their location. **Migration** is the movement of animals to a different region in response to changes in the environment.

Each spring, millions of monarch butterflies begin to fly north from Mexico and parts of southern California. They first migrate to the southern United States, where the females lay eggs on milkweed plants. The new generation will travel further north and then lay eggs, too. Summer monarchs live as butterflies for only three to five weeks. After three or four generations, the last generation reaches the northern United States and Canada. Monarchs cannot survive the winter temperatures of the north, so the last generation of butterflies makes the long journey back to Mexico and California in the fall. These butterflies will live eight or nine months. The fall migration route is shown on the map.

Not all animals migrate in response to seasonal changes. Many nonmigratory animals do change their behaviors, however. For example, when winter cold reduces the food supply, some animals hibernate. **Hibernation** is a sleeplike state that lasts for an extended time period. The body systems of a hibernating animal slow down, so the animal needs less energy to survive. Many animals, including frogs, turtles, fish, and some types of insects, hibernate. You will learn more about different types of animals in Chapters 12 and 13.

10.3 Review

KEY CONCEPTS

1. In what way are animals consumers?
2. Name three body systems that relate to how an animal gets its energy.
3. What is a behavior?

CRITICAL THINKING

4. **Give Examples** Identify three categories of animal behavior and give an example of each.
5. **Analyze** How is migration similar to hibernation? How is it different?

CHALLENGE

6. **Analyze** Scientists often look at feeding patterns as a flow of energy through the living parts of the environment. Describe the flow of energy as it relates to plants, herbivores, and carnivores.

ANSWERS

1. Animals must consume food to live.

2. digestive system, respiratory system, circulatory system

3. an observable response to a stimulus

4. individual: grooming, eating, sleeping; within species: parenting, mating, herding; between species: preying, scavenging

5. Migration and hibernation are both responses to changes in seasons. Migration involves moving between locations, while hibernation involves entering a dormant state.

6. Energy is captured by a plant, then captured by a herbivore that eats the plant, then captured by a carnivore that eats the herbivore. Energy flows from plant to herbivore to carnivore.

SCIENCE on the JOB

WILDLIFE PHOTOGRAPHER

An Animal's World

Have you ever watched a TV documentary, or flipped through the pages of a magazine and wondered, "How did the photographer ever get that picture?" For a wildlife photographer, understanding animal behavior is essential.

Behavior

To photograph an endangered species like the jaguar, a photographer must learn animal behavior. Steve Winter and a team of scientists used dogs with keen scent-tracking to find jaguars who are active mostly at night. They learned that jaguars have a favorite scratching tree—perfect photo opportunity!

Cover and Protection

Photographers use camera traps and blinds. A blind, made of branches, is built upwind of an animal gathering place. Steve Winter has built camera traps, where a hidden camera emits a beam of light when an animal steps into it.

Specialized Gear

Certain environments—such as snow and cold, swamp and mud, or sea water—present challenges to a person with a camera. Underwater photographers need to use scuba gear to swim with animals like the Caribbean reef shark.

EXPLORE

1. **OBSERVE** With or without a camera, find a spot where you are likely to find wildlife. Sit as still as possible and wait. What animals do you observe? What do they do?
2. **CHALLENGE** Interview a photographer about digital photography, and ask how technology is changing photography.

SCIENCE ON THE JOB

Relevance of Science to Non-science Jobs

Set Learning Goal

To learn how a wildlife photographer uses knowledge of animal biology

Present the Science

In addition to using scuba gear, underwater photographers use special cameras. Some cameras have all their openings and controls waterproofed by rubber rings. Other cameras are conventional and housed in waterproof cases. Underwater photographers also use strobe lights that must be waterproofed.

Discussion Questions

- Brainstorm what special qualifications or training a wildlife photographer might need.
- Ask: What other people might a wildlife photographer have to work with? *They might need guides who do not speak the same language. They might need to get special permits and government approval to visit certain areas.*
- Ask: What are some pros and cons to this kind of work? How might one person's pro (such as travel excitement, meeting new people) be another person's con (such as travel danger, being away from home and medical care)?

Close

Ask: What science might a wildlife photographer need to understand? *Sample answer: animal behavior, life cycles of various organisms, habitat requirements, optics, ecology, mechanics*

EXPLORE

1. ***OBSERVE*** *Many students will observe birds, especially if they set up a feeder or bird bath. Others will observe insects or small animals on the ground.*
2. ***CHALLENGE*** *In digital photography, the photographer has many more options for how the photographic image can be produced.*

10.4 FOCUS

Set Learning Goals

Students will

- Describe how fungi get energy and materials.
- Identify different types of fungi.
- Recognize how fungi interact with other organisms.
- Conduct an experiment to draw conclusions about how sugar, salt, and sweetener affect the growth of yeast.

3-Minute Warm-Up

Display Transparency 13 or copy this exercise on the board:

Make a chart outlining the relationships between predator and prey animals. Start with one animal (for example, a fly). Next, name a predator of that animal (for example, a frog). Continue your chart by naming an animal that eats the previously named animal. Your chart is finished when you can go no farther.

3-Minute Warm-Up, p. T13

10.4 MOTIVATE

EXPLORE Mushrooms

PURPOSE To examine mushroom spores

TIPS *10 min. on 2 different days*
Fresh mushrooms work better than old mushrooms or dried mushrooms. It may be easier to "pop" the mushroom stem off than to cut it off.

WHAT DO YOU THINK? *The mushroom cap has the same pattern as the print. Spores that were released from the cap made the print.*

KEY CONCEPT

10.4 Most fungi are decomposers.

BEFORE, you learned

- All organisms interact with the environment
- Plants transform sunlight into chemical energy
- Animals get energy by eating other organisms

NOW, you will learn

- How fungi get energy and materials
- About different types of fungi
- How fungi interact with other organisms

VOCABULARY
hyphae p. 339
spore p. 339
lichen p. 342

EXPLORE Mushrooms

What does a mushroom cap contain?

PROCEDURE

1. Carefully cut the stem away from the mushroom cap, as near the cap as possible.
2. Place the mushroom cap on white paper and cover it with a plastic cup. Leave overnight.
3. Carefully remove the cup and lift the mushroom cap straight up.
4. Use a hand lens to examine the mushroom cap and the print it leaves behind.

WHAT DO YOU THINK?

- How does the pattern in the mushroom cap compare with the mushroom print?
- What made the print?

MATERIALS

- fresh store-bought mushrooms
- sharp knife
- clear plastic cup
- paper
- hand lens

Fungi absorb materials from the environment.

MAIN IDEA AND DETAILS Don't forget to make a main idea chart with detail notes on the main idea: *Fungi absorb materials from the environment.*

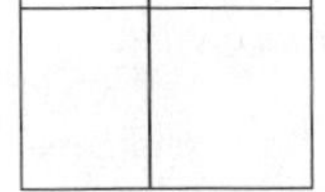

Plants are producers; they capture energy from the Sun and build complex carbon compounds. Animals are consumers; they take in complex carbon compounds and use them for energy and materials. Fungi (FUHN-jy), at least most fungi, are decomposers. Fungi break down, or decompose, the complex carbon compounds that are part of living matter. They absorb nutrients and leave behind simpler compounds.

Fungi are heterotrophs. They get their energy from living or once-living matter. They, along with bacteria, decompose the bodies of dead plants and animals. They also decompose materials left behind by organisms, such as fallen leaves, shed skin, and animal droppings.

RESOURCES FOR DIFFERENTIATED INSTRUCTION

Below Level

UNIT RESOURCE BOOK

- Reading Study Guide A, pp. 116–117
- Decoding Support, p. 128

AUDIO CDS

Advanced

UNIT RESOURCE BOOK
Challenge and Extension, p. 122

English Learners

UNIT RESOURCE BOOK
Spanish Reading Study Guide, pp. 120–121

AUDIO CDS

- Audio Readings in Spanish
- Audio Readings (English)

Characteristics of Fungi

Except for yeasts, most fungi are multicellular. The cells of a fungus have a nucleus and a thick cell wall, which provides support. Fungi are different from plants and animals in their organization. Plants and animals have specialized cells, which are usually organized into tissues and organs. Multicellular fungi don't have tissues or organs. Instead, a typical fungus is made up of a reproductive body and network of cells that form threadlike structures called **hyphae** (HY-fee).

A mass of hyphae, like the one shown in the diagram below, is called a mycelium (my-SEE-lee-uhm). The hyphae are just one cell thick. This means the cells in the mycelium are close to the soil or whatever substance the fungus is living in. The cells release chemicals that digest the materials around them, and then absorb the nutrients they need. As hyphae grow, openings can form between the older cells and the new ones. This allows nutrients to flow back to the older cells, resulting in what seems like one huge cell with many nuclei.

READING TIP

The root of the word *hyphae* means "web." Look at the diagram below to see their weblike appearance.

Reproduction

B

Fungi reproduce with spores, which can be produced either asexually or sexually. A **spore** is a single reproductive cell that is capable of growing into a new organism. The mushrooms that you buy at the store are the spore-producing structures of certain types of fungi. These spore-producing structures are reproductive bodies of mushrooms. A single mushroom can produce a billion spores.

Parts of a Fungus

The mycelium makes up a large part of a multicellular fungus.

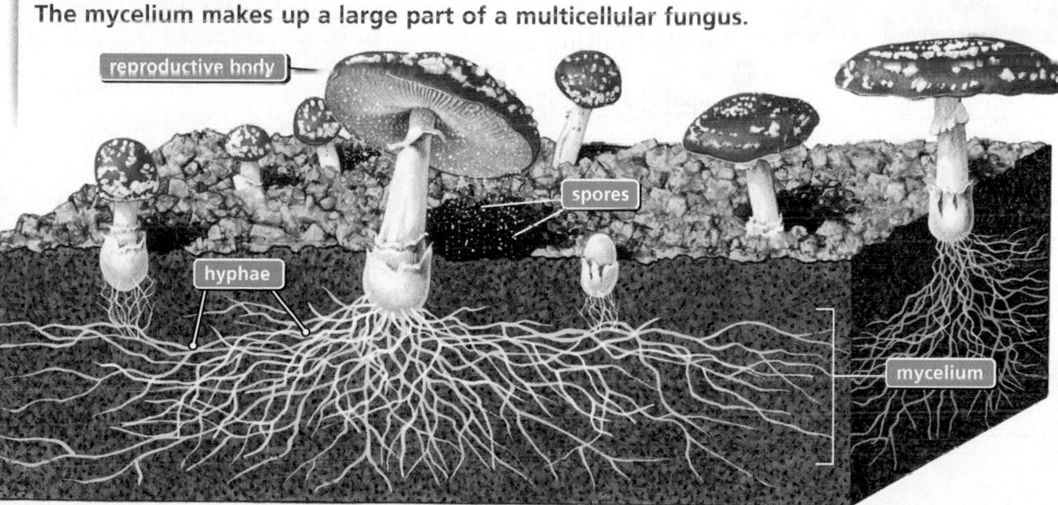

10.4 INSTRUCT

Teach Difficult Concepts

Students may have difficulty understanding how material is digested outside the body and then absorbed. Ask:

- How does digested material get into the fungus? *through the cell walls*
- Why can't a fungus take dead material into its cells? *Cell walls let only tiny things into the cell.*
- What happens to the digested material that the fungus does not need? *Plant roots and other living things absorb it.*

Teach from Visuals

To help students interpret the diagram of fungus growth, ask:

- What is the common name for the reproductive body of the fungus? *a mushroom or toadstool*
- Which comes first, the mycelium or the mushroom? *the mycelium*

Ongoing Assessment

Describe how fungi get energy and materials.

Ask: Where does fungal digestion take place? *in the substance surrounding the hyphae*

DIFFERENTIATE INSTRUCTION

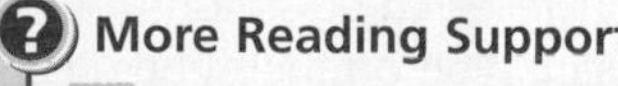

More Reading Support

A What are hyphae? *threadlike structures that make up a fungus*

B What are spores? *reproductive cells of a fungus*

English Learners Have students write the definitions for *hyphae, spore,* and *lichen* in their Science Word Dictionaries. Have English learners look up the words *hyphae* and *lichen* in a dictionary that provides phonetic spellings. Encourage them to look up words in the dictionary or to practice with an advanced student when they are unsure of pronunciation.

Teach from Visuals

To help students interpret the photograph of mushroom growth, ask:

- What is the mushrooms' food source? *organic matter in the tree trunk*
- Does the photograph show one organism or many organisms? *probably one organism connected by a single mycelium*

Teacher Demo

Demonstrate that fungi need moisture and a food supply to grow. You must use bread without preservatives for this demo. Place a piece of fresh bakery bread in a self-seal plastic bag. Moisten a second piece of the same bread and place it in a second bag. Trap air in the bags so the plastic does not touch the top of the bread, and seal the bags. Incubate the bags in a dark, warm place for several days. Mold will grow on the moistened bread but probably not on the dry bread. Have students examine the mold, but do not allow them to open the bags. Ask what the food source is for the mold.

Integrate the Sciences

There are very few truly poisonous mushrooms. The genus *Amanita* causes 90 percent of deaths by mushroom poisoning. Several members of this group contain amanitin, one of the deadliest poisons found in nature. One cap of a destroying angel mushroom, for example, can kill an adult human. The toxin causes irreparable liver and kidney damage.

Ongoing Assessment

Answer: The cap produces and holds the reproductive spores.

PHOTO CAPTION *Answer: inside the tree*

Learn more about different types of fungi.

Spores are released into the air and spread by the wind. Because they're so small and light, the wind can carry spores long distances. Scientists have found spores 160 kilometers above Earth's surface. Some spores have a tough outer covering that keeps the reproductive cell from drying out. Such spores can survive for many years. If the parent fungus dies, the spores may remain and grow when conditions are right.

Fungi reproduce in other ways. For example, a multicellular fungi can reproduce asexually when hyphae break off and form a new mycelium. Yeasts, which are single-celled fungi, reproduce asexually by simple cell division or by budding. Yeasts can also produce spores.

Fungi include mushrooms, molds, and yeasts.

A convenient and simple way to study fungi is to look at their forms. They are mushrooms, molds, and yeasts. You are probably familiar with all of them. The mushrooms on your pizza are a fungus. So is the mold that grows if you leave a piece of pizza too long in the refrigerator. The crust of the pizza itself rises because of the activity of yeast.

INFER Where is the mycelium of these mushrooms?

Mushrooms

What we call a mushroom is only a small part of a fungus. A single mushroom you buy in the store could have grown from a mycelium that fills an area 30 meters across. When you see a patch of mushrooms, they are probably all part of a single fungus.

For humans, some mushrooms are edible and some are poisonous. A toadstool is a poisonous mushroom. The cap of a mushroom is where the spores are produced. Both the cap and the stalk it grows on are filled with hyphae.

What is produced in a mushroom cap?

Molds

What we call mold, that fuzzy growth we sometimes see on food, is the spore-producing part of another form of fungus. The hyphae of the mold grow into the food, digesting it as they grow. Not all food molds are bad. Different species of the fungus *Penicillium* are used in the production of Brie, Camembert, and blue cheeses. Some species of the *Aspergillus* fungus are used to make soy sauce.

One interesting application of a mold is the use of the fungus *Trichoderma.* This mold grows in soil. The digestive chemicals it produces are used to give blue jeans a stonewashed look.

DIFFERENTIATE INSTRUCTION

More Reading Support

C How do fungi reproduce? *from spores, hyphae, and budding*

Advanced Have interested students research poisonous mushrooms and give a short class presentation on their findings.

340 Unit 3: Diversity of Living Things

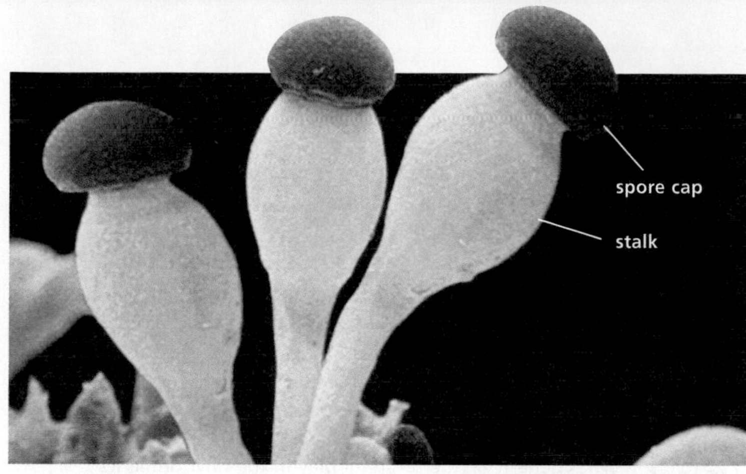

Pilobolus reacts to sunlight as a stimulus. The bend in the stalk will cause the spore cap to fly off.

Many molds cause disease. Fungal molds cause athlete's foot. Molds also affect plants. They are the cause of Dutch elm disease and the powdery white mildews that grow on plants. Compounds made from molds are also used to treat disease. Penicillin is an antibiotic that comes from the *Penicillium* fungus. It is used to fight bacterial diseases, such as pneumonia.

Molds reproduce with spores, which are typically carried by moving air. The "hat thrower" fungus *Pilobolus*, however, has an interesting adaptation for spreading spores. *Pilobolus* grows in animal droppings. It has a spore-containing cap—its hat—that grows on top of a stalk. The stalk responds to light as a stimulus and bends toward the Sun. As the stalk bends, water pressure builds up, causing the spore cap to shoot off, like a tiny cannonball. A spore cap can be thrown up to two meters away. If the spore caps land in grass, then cows and other grazing animals will eat the caps as they graze. A new cycle begins, with more *Pilobolus* being dispersed in the animal's droppings.

Yeasts

? D Yeasts are single-celled fungi. Some species of fungi exist in both yeast form and as multicellular hyphae. Yeasts grow in many moist environments, including the sap of plants and animal tissues. They also grow on moist surfaces, including shower curtains. Certain yeasts grow naturally on human skin. If the yeast begins to reproduce too rapidly, it can cause disease.

Yeasts are used in many food products. The activity of yeast cells breaking down sugars is what makes bread rise. The genetic material of the yeast *Saccharomyces cerevisiae* has been carefully studied by scientists. The study of this organism has helped scientists understand how genetic material controls the activities of a cell.

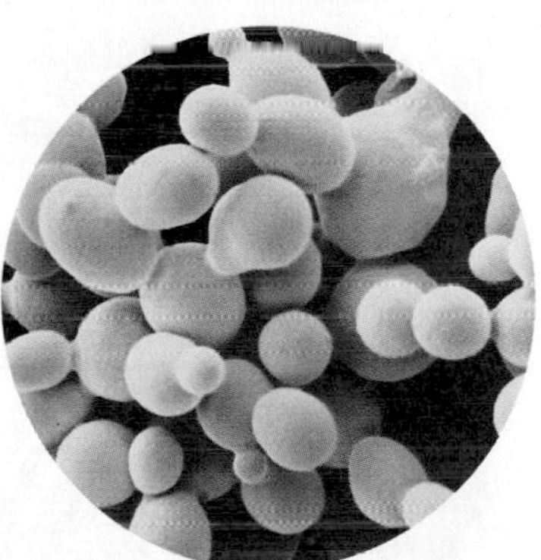

Yeasts are single-celled fungi.

Teach from Visuals

To help students interpret the photograph of *Pilobolus,* ask:

- What is the function of the stalk? *It holds up the spore cap and responds to sunlight.*
- What is the advantage of releasing spores far away from the fungus? *The new organisms that form will not compete with the parent organism for food and moisture.*

Teacher Demo

To demonstrate how yeast cells make bread rise, mix about half an envelope of dry yeast with some warm water in an uncovered jar or beaker. Add a teaspoon of granulated sugar and stir. Set the jar aside for a few minutes. The yeast will begin to ferment the sugar, producing carbon dioxide. The yeast suspension will get foamy and will increase in volume. It is this gas that makes bread dough rise.

Real World Example

Mold-infested office buildings, schools, and homes are being blamed for an increase in serious respiratory illnesses. Coughs, shortness of breath, sinus infections, dizziness, burning eyes, and asthma are common in certain airtight buildings that have water leakage problems. Carpeting and drywall may have to be replaced after the water problem is resolved.

Ongoing Assessment

Identify different types of fungi.

Ask: How are yeasts different from mushrooms and molds? *Yeasts are single-celled.*

DIFFERENTIATE INSTRUCTION

? More Reading Support

D What is yeast? *single-celled fungi*

Below Level The reproduction of yeasts can be modeled using modeling clay. Have students make a yeast cell out of clay. They can form a bud on the cell, then pinch it off to form a new yeast organism. This activity will also help students who have impaired vision.

Teach from Visuals

To help students interpret the diagram of a lichen, ask:

- How do the algae provide nutrients for themselves and the fungus? *Algae produce nutrients by photosynthesis.*
- How does the fungus hold the algae in place? *The hyphae wrap around the algae.*

Address Misconceptions

IDENTIFY Ask: What do decomposers decompose? If students cannot answer, they may not know the exact role of decomposers in the environment. If students answer "dead or decaying organic material," ask them where the material comes from and where it goes. If they do not say "from living organisms that die or produce wastes," and "to soil, air, and nutrients," they may hold the misconception that decomposers are the bottom of the food chain.

CORRECT Have students make a series of diagrams showing the steps of the decomposition process.

REASSESS Have students write a short paragraph explaining why decomposers are necessary in the environment. *Dead material would pile up if it were not decomposed. The living world would run out of nutrients if nothing were recycled.*

Technology Resources

Visit **ClassZone.com** for background on common student misconceptions.

MISCONCEPTION DATABASE

Ongoing Assessment

Recognize how fungi interact with other organisms.

Ask: Describe the relationship between algae and fungus in a lichen. *The algae produces food for the fungus, which provides a structure and protection.*

Answer: Fungi are decomposers.

Fungi can be helpful or harmful to other organisms.

Fungi have a close relationship to the environment and all living things in the environment. Fungi, along with bacteria, function as the main decomposers on Earth. The digestive chemicals that fungi release break down the complex compounds that come from living matter, dead matter, or the waste an organism leaves behind. A fungus absorbs what it needs to live and leaves behind simpler compounds and nutrients. These are then picked up again by plants, as producers, to start the cycle over again. Fungi also live in the sea, recycling materials for ocean-living organisms.

What beneficial role do fungi play in the environment?

The threadlike hyphae of a fungus can grow into and decompose the material produced by another organism. This means that fungi can be helpful, for example, by releasing the nutrients in a dead tree back into the soil. Or fungi can be harmful, for example, attacking the tissues of a plant, such as the Dutch elm.

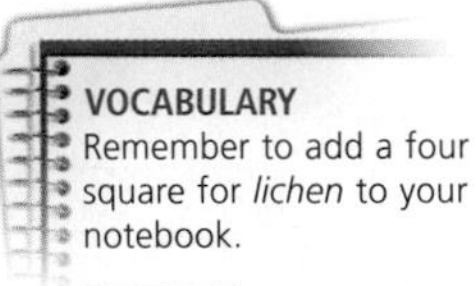

VOCABULARY
Remember to add a four square for *lichen* to your notebook.

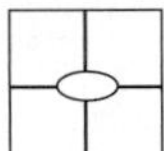

Most plants interact with fungi in a way that is helpful. The hyphae surround the plant roots, providing nutrients for the plant. The plant provides food for the fungus. Some fungi live together with single-celled algae, a network referred to as a **lichen** (LY-kuhn). The hyphae form almost a sandwich around the algae, which produce sugars and other nutrients the fungus needs.

Lichen

A lichen is formed by a close association between algae and fungi.

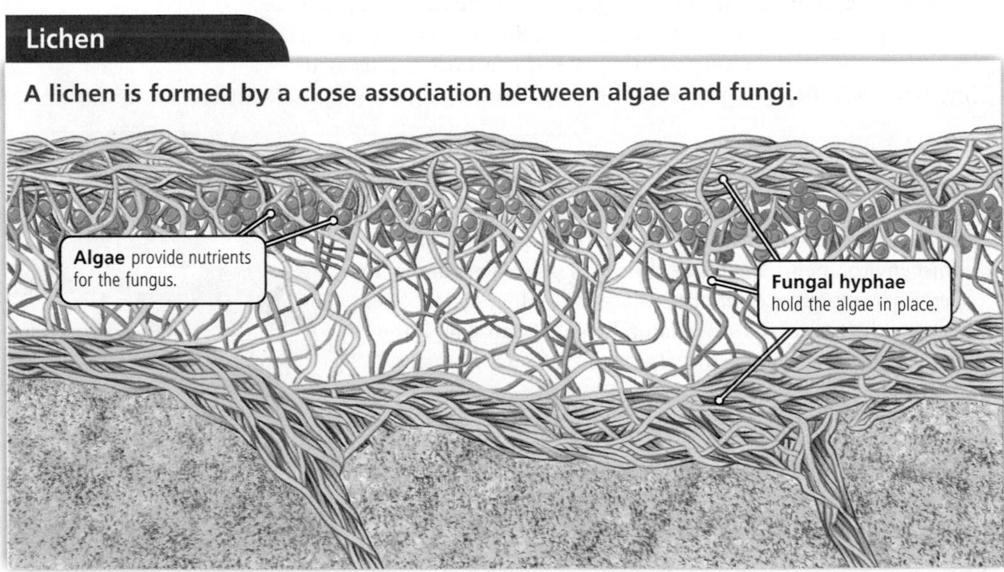

DIFFERENTIATE INSTRUCTION

More Reading Support

E What does algae provide for the fungus in a lichen? *food*

Alternative Assessment Have students make a poster showing the beneficial relationship between a plant and the mycorrhizal fungi that grow around the plant's roots. A small amount of research will give students additional information for their posters and for a class presentation.

Advanced Have students design an experiment to determine the best growing conditions for yeast.

Challenge and Extension, p. 122

Lichens can live just about anywhere. Lichens are found in the Arctic and in the desert. They can even grow on bare rock. The hyphae can break the rock down, slowly, and capture the particles of newly formed soil. This eventually prepares the ground for new plant growth.

On the harmful side, many fungi produce toxins, harmful chemicals. In 1845, a fungus infected Ireland's potato crop, causing the population of Ireland to drop from 8 million to about 4 million. Many people died from disease. Others died from starvation because of the loss of the important food crop. And hundreds of thousands of Irish left Ireland, many emigrating to the United States. Today, several fungal diseases are spreading through the world's banana crops.

CHECK YOUR READING Name some ways fungi can be harmful to organisms.

The toxic quality of a fungus can be put to good use, as in the case of the antibiotic penicillin. The photographs show what happens when a bacterium comes in contact with penicillin. The antibiotic prevents the bacterial cells from making new cell walls when they divide. This causes the cells to break open and the bacteria to die.

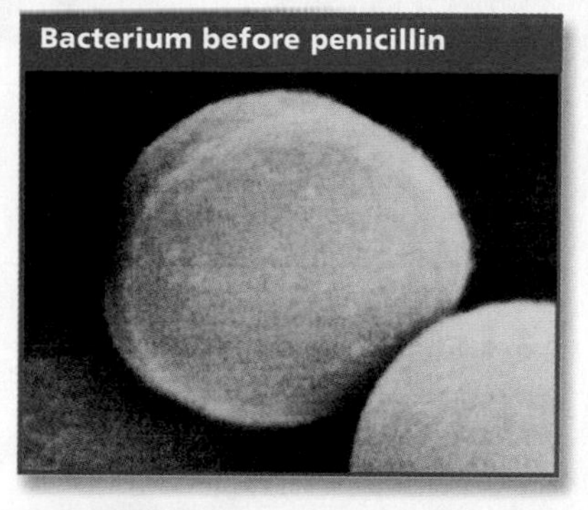

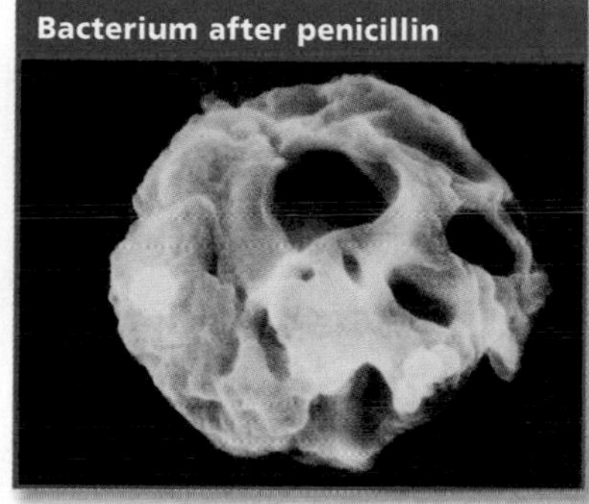

Penicillin is an antibiotic drug made from compounds taken from a species of the *Penicillium* fungus.

10.4 Review

KEY CONCEPTS

1. Describe the structure of a fungus.
2. How do fungi reproduce?
3. Describe two relationships between fungi and other organisms.

CRITICAL THINKING

4. **Analyze** Scientists used to classify fungi as plants. Today, scientists say that fungi are more like animals than plants. How are fungi like plants? How are they like animals?
5. **Predict** What might change in an environment where there were no fungi?

CHALLENGE

6. **Connect** Think of at least one way your life is affected by fungi in each of their three main forms: mushrooms, molds, and yeast. Are these effects beneficial or harmful to you?

ANSWERS

1. A fungus is a network of hyphae that forms reproductive structures above ground to produce spores.

2. from spores, by budding, or from pieces of hyphae

3. Fungi may cause disease, and they act as decomposers.

4. Fungi are like plants because they have a thick cell wall. Fungi are like animals because they get their energy from other organisms.

5. Fungi are decomposers. Without them, organic matter would not be recycled.

6. Sample answer: Eating mushrooms on pizza gives me energy and helps me grow (beneficial). Athlete's foot is a disease caused by a mold (harmful). Yeast makes bread rise for me to eat (beneficial).

History of Science

Penicillin was discovered by chance in 1928 after Alexander Fleming left a petri dish of bacteria uncovered in his lab for a few days. When he returned, the dish had been contaminated by a mold that inhibited bacterial growth. Fleming's discovery revolutionized the practice of medicine when the antibiotic penicillin from the *Penicillium* mold was used to treat infected wounds.

Ongoing Assessment

CHECK YOUR READING *Answer: Fungi spoil food, release toxins that cause disease, and attack food crops and trees.*

Reinforce 

Have students relate the section to the Big Idea.

 Reinforcing Key Concepts, p. 123

10.4 ASSESS & RETEACH

Assess

 Section 10.4 Quiz, p. 26

Reteach

Give pairs of students a fresh white mushroom. Have them use a toothpick to pull apart the hyphae that make up the mycelium in the mushroom. Students should also examine the gills on the underside of the cap. After they dissect the mushroom, have them draw it, label the parts, and label the type of organism and its way of feeding.

Technology Resources

Have students visit **ClassZone.com** for reteaching of Key Concepts.

 **CONTENT REVIEW**

 **CONTENT REVIEW CD-ROM**

CHAPTER INVESTIGATION

Focus

PURPOSE To investigate the ability of yeast to use different food sources

OVERVIEW Students will make dough using flour, water, and one of the following additives: sugar, salt, and sweetener. Students will measure how much each dough rises and determine which substances yeast can use as a food source. Students will find the following:

- Yeast use sugar for food and produce carbon dioxide.
- Yeast cannot use artificial sweetener or salt as a food source.

Lab Preparation

- Prior to the investigation, proof the yeast by mixing a sample with warm water and sugar and letting it sit for about 20 minutes. If the yeast is alive, bubbles will form.
- Clothespins must be the spring type to make a tight closure.
- Prior to the investigation, have students read through the investigation and prepare their data tables. Or you may wish to copy and distribute datasheets and rubrics.

UNIT RESOURCE BOOK, pp. 131–139

SCIENCE TOOLKIT, F14

Lab Management

- Have students use a clean spoon to mix each mound or wash their hands between kneading mounds to prevent contamination.
- Remind students not to eat the dough.
- Three teaspoons equals one tablespoon. A tablespoon can be used to measure the sugar, salt, and sweetener.

Teaching with Technology

If probeware is available, a carbon dioxide probe can be inserted into each ball of dough instead of using the straw apparatus.

CHAPTER INVESTIGATION

What Do Yeast Cells Use for Energy?

OVERVIEW AND PURPOSE Yeasts are tiny one-celled fungi that require food, water, and a warm place to grow. When they have a food source, they release carbon dioxide gas as a waste product. Yeast is used to make foods such as bread. In this activity, you will

- observe the activity of yeast
- draw conclusions about the effect of three materials on the activity of yeast

MATERIALS
- baking sheet
- flour
- measuring cups
- measuring spoons
- sugar
- artificial sweetener
- salt
- quick-rise yeast
- warm water
- metric ruler
- marker
- clothespins
- clear plastic straws

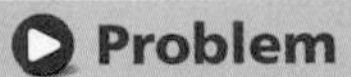

Problem

How do sugar, salt, and sweetener affect the growth of yeast?

Hypothesize

Write a hypothesis to explain how sugar, sweetener, and salt affect the activity of yeast in bread dough. Your hypothesis should take the form of an "If . . ., then . . ., because . . ." statement.

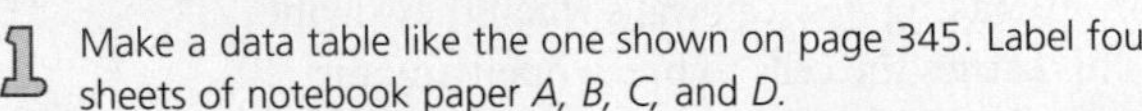

Procedure

1. Make a data table like the one shown on page 345. Label four sheets of notebook paper *A, B, C,* and *D.*

2. Spread a very thin layer of flour over the baking sheet. Measure $\frac{1}{4}$ cup of flour and place it on the baking sheet as a mound. Repeat three times, forming separate mounds. Label the mounds *A, B, C,* and *D.*

INVESTIGATION RESOURCES

CHAPTER INVESTIGATION, What Do Yeast Cells Use for Energy?
- Level A, pp. 131–134
- Level B, pp. 135–138
- Level C, p. 139

Advanced students should complete Levels B & C.

Writing a Lab Report, D12–13

Technology Resources

Customize this student lab as needed or look for an alternative. Print rubrics to assess student lab reports.

Lab Generator CD-ROM

3 Add 3 teaspoons of sugar to mound A. Add 3 tsp of sweetener to mound B. Add 3 tsp of salt to mound C. Add nothing to mound D.

4 Add $\frac{1}{4}$ tsp of the quick-rise yeast to each of the mounds. Slowly add 1 tsp of warm water to each mound to moisten the mixture. Spread a pinch of flour over your hands and knead the mounds by hand. Add water, 1 tsp at a time until the mixture has the consistency of dough. If the mixture gets too sticky, add more flour. Knead well and form each mound into a ball. Wash your hands thoroughly when you are finished. Do not taste or eat the dough.

5 Push 2 straws into each ball of dough, making sure the dough reaches at least 3 cm into the straws.

step 5

6 Squeeze the end of each straw to push the dough from the ends. Place a clothespin on the end of each straw closest to the dough. Fold and tape the other end. Mark both edges of the dough on the straw. Stand each straw upright on the appropriate piece of paper labeled *A*, *B*, *C*, or *D*.

step 6

7 Predict which mounds of dough will rise after 30 minutes. Write down your predictions in the data table.

8 After 30 minutes, measure the amount the dough has risen in each straw. Write down the results in the data table.

Observe and Analyze

1. **OBSERVE** In which mounds did the dough rise?
2. **OBSERVE** Did any of the remaining mounds of dough change? Explain.
3. **INFER** What was the purpose of using two straws for each of the mounds?

Conclude

1. **INTERPRET** Which is the most likely source of energy for yeast: salt, sugar, or sweetener? How do you know?
2. **INTERPRET** Compare your results with your hypothesis. How does your data support or disprove your hypothesis?
3. **LIMITATIONS** What limitations or sources of error could have affected your results?
4. **CONNECT** How would you account for the air spaces that are found in some breads?
5. **APPLY** Would you predict that breads made without yeast contain air spaces?

INVESTIGATE Further

CHALLENGE Design an experiment in which you can observe the production of carbon dioxide by yeast.

What Do Yeast Cells Use for Energy?

Table 1. Observations of Dough Rising

Mound	Prediction	Results
A. sugar and yeast		
B. sweetener and yeast		
C. salt and yeast		
D. yeast		

Observe and Analyze

1. The dough rose in the mixture containing sugar.

2. no

3. as duplicates to compare results

Conclude

1. Sugar; the yeast produced a lot of carbon dioxide in the dough with sugar.

2. Check student hypotheses. Students should provide evidence or explanation for describing whether their hypothesis is correct or incorrect.

3. Possible sources of error are contamination of mounds with sugar, and inactive yeast.

4. The air spaces are pockets of carbon dioxide produced by the yeast in the bread dough.

5. No, matzo and tortillas are not made with yeast, so they do not rise.

INVESTIGATE Further

CHALLENGE One way to observe carbon dioxide production by yeast is to grow yeast in a sugar solution in a test tube that is inverted in a dish containing water. The test tube must be full, with no trapped air pockets. As carbon dioxide is produced, it will rise to the top of the tube (the closed end), displacing some of the liquid.

Post-Lab Discussion

- Ask: What was the purpose of mound D, which did not have anything added except yeast? *It was a control.*
- Ask: Why might the yeast produce carbon dioxide in mound D if no food source was added? *Yeast used the starch in the flour.*
- Have students discuss any new questions that arose from the investigation.
- Have students plan an investigation where the results would help answer one of their questions.

BACK TO

the BIG idea

Ask: How do plants, animals, and fungi work together to maintain a healthy environment? *Plants use the Sun's energy to produce food consumed by animals and fungi. Animals' complex interactions with one another and their environment keep the environment in balance. Fungi act as decomposers.*

KEY CONCEPTS SUMMARY

SECTION 10.1
Ask: How does sexual reproduction contribute to a species' ability to adapt to its environment? *Offspring are genetically different from parents. They may have unique traits that allow them to survive more successfully than their parents.*

SECTION 10.2
Ask: How do types of leaves help plants adapt to different environments? *Leaves of conifers stay green and produce food for the plant in winter. Leaves of deciduous trees drop off in the fall, allowing the trees to rest during winter. Leaves of the Venus flytrap are specially adapted as traps for insects.*

SECTION 10.3
Ask: What function does digestion serve in an animal? *Digestion enables an animal to get energy from food.*

SECTION 10.4
Ask: How does fungi's role as decomposers benefit other organisms? *Fungi's digestive chemicals release useful compounds locked in dead matter and waste materials from living matter so that these compounds can be used again by living things. This process also removes waste from the environment.*

Review Concepts

- Big Idea Flow Chart, p. T9
- Chapter Outline, pp. T15–T16

10 Chapter Review

the BIG idea

Multicellular organisms live in and get energy from a variety of environments.

KEY CONCEPTS SUMMARY

1 Multicellular organisms have many ways of meeting their needs.

- The bodies of multicellular organisms have different levels of organization.
- Multicellular organisms have a wide range of adaptations.
- Multicellular organisms reproduce by sexual reproduction. Some also reproduce asexually.

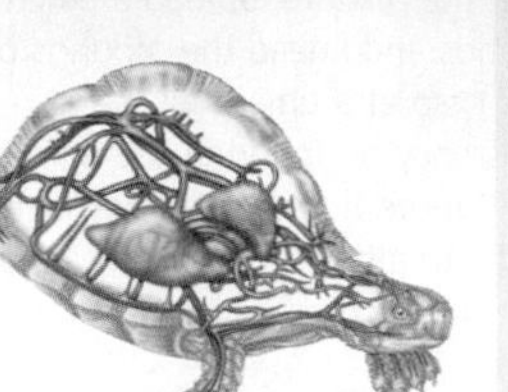

VOCABULARY
tissue p. 316
organ p. 316
sexual reproduction p. 320
meiosis p. 320
fertilization p. 320

2 Plants are producers.

Plants capture energy from the Sun and store it as sugar and starch. Plants are adapted to many environments. They respond to stimuli in the environment.

VOCABULARY
autotroph p. 324
photosynthesis p. 324
cellular respiration p. 325
stimulus p. 327

3 Animals are consumers.

Animals consume food to get energy and materials. Animals are adapted to many enviroments. They interact with the environment and with other organisms.

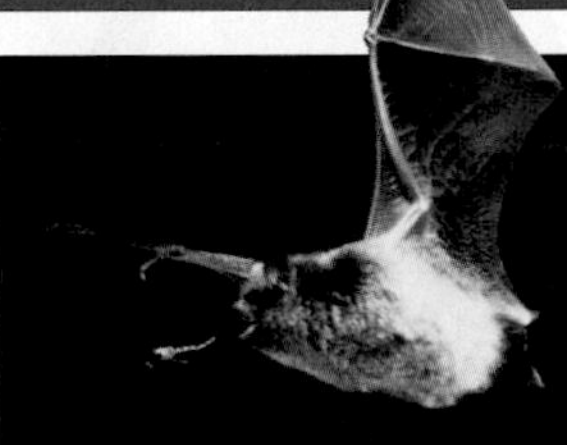

VOCABULARY
consumer p. 330
heterotroph p. 330
behavior p. 334
predator p. 335
prey p. 336
migration p. 336
hibernation p. 336

4 Most fungi are decomposers.

Fungi absorb energy from their surroundings. Fungi include mushrooms, molds, and yeasts. They affect people and other organisms in both helpful and harmful ways.

VOCABULARY
hyphae p. 339
spore p. 339
lichen p. 342

Technology Resources

Have students visit **ClassZone.com** or use the CD-ROM for a cumulative review of concepts.

 **CONTENT REVIEW**

 **CONTENT REVIEW CD-ROM**

Engage students in a whole-class interactive review of Key Concepts. Edit content as you wish.

 **POWER PRESENTATIONS**

Reviewing Vocabulary

Draw a Venn diagram for each pair of terms. Put at least one shared characteristic in the overlap area, and put at least one difference in the outer circles.

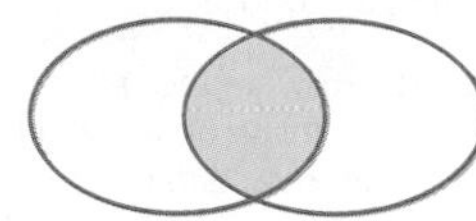

1. tissue, organ
2. autotroph, heterotroph
3. photosynthesis, cellular respiration
4. predator, prey
5. producer, consumer
6. migration, hibernation

Reviewing Key Concepts

Multiple Choice *Choose the letter of the best answer.*

7. Which body system transports materials such as nutrients and oxygen throughout an animal's body?
   - a. respiratory system
   - b. circulatory system
   - c. digestive system
   - d. nervous system

8. An example of an adaptation is
   - a. a change in climate that increases plant growth
   - b. the movement of a group of animals to an area that has more food and water
   - c. a change in location of a squirrel's nest
   - d. the ability of a plant to resist fungal disease better than other plants

9. Plants capture the Sun's energy through which process?
   - a. reproduction
   - b. cellular respiration
   - c. photosynthesis
   - d. digestion

10. Plants produce auxin in response to which stimulus?
    - a. light
    - b. gravity
    - c. temperature
    - d. touch

11. A plant is best described as
    - a. a herbivore
    - b. an omnivore
    - c. a carnivore
    - d. a producer

12. A carnivore is best described as an animal that
    - a. eats plants
    - b. eats plants and other animals
    - c. eats other animals
    - d. makes its own food

13. Mushrooms produce
    - a. spores
    - b. buds
    - c. mold
    - d. yeast

14. Fungi and algae together form
    - a. hyphae
    - b. mushrooms
    - c. lichen
    - d. mold

Short Answer *Write a short answer to each question.*

15. Write a short paragraph comparing sexual reproduction with asexual reproduction. How are they the same? How are they different?

16. Write a short paragraph to explain how the sugars and starches stored in plant tissue are important to the survival of animals.

17. Write a short paragraph to explain how fungi are dependent on plants and animals for their energy.

ASSESSMENT RESOURCES

UNIT ASSESSMENT BOOK
- Chapter Test A, pp. 27–30
- Chapter Test B, pp. 31–34
- Chapter Test C, pp. 35–38
- Alternative Assessment, pp. 39–40

SPANISH ASSESSMENT BOOK
Spanish Chapter Test, pp. 45–48

Technology Resources

Edit test items and answer choices.

Test Generator CD-ROM

Visit **ClassZone.com** to extend test practice.

Test Practice

Reviewing Vocabulary

Sample answers:

1. same: level of organization in body
tissue: made up of similar cells
organ: made up of different tissues

2. same: organisms
autotroph: gets energy from Sun
heterotroph: gets energy from food

3. same: cellular process
photosynthesis: captures energy
cellular respiration: releases energy

4. same: animal
predator: eats another animal
prey: is eaten

5. same: involves means of getting food
producer: makes own food
consumer: eats or absorbs food

6. same: type of behavior
migration: move with change in environment
hibernation: go into sleeplike state with change in environment

Reviewing Key Concepts

7. b	*11. d*
8. d	*12. c*
9. c	*13. a*
10. a	*14. c*

15. Reproduction is the process by which an organism produces offspring. Both single-celled and some multicellular organisms are capable of both sexual and asexual reproduction. Only one organism is involved in asexual reproduction, and the offspring have the same genetic material as the parent. In sexual reproduction, two parents are involved and the offspring have genetic material from both parents.

16. Most of the food that animals use comes either directly or indirectly from plants. Plants use energy from the Sun to put together complex carbon compounds into sugar and starch. Animals get energy from sugar and starch by eating plants.

17. Fungi absorb nutrients from living material. Many fungi get nutrients from the remains of dead plants and animals or the waste products of living plants and animals. Other fungi grow into the living tissue of organisms.

Thinking Critically

18. Sun; plants capture energy from Sun; organisms get energy from plants or animals that eat plants.
19. insect, worm, woodchuck, robin, owl
20. insect: herbivore; worm: decomposer; robin and owl: carnivores; woodchuck: omnivore
21. Yes; it has more options because if animal food is not available, it can eat both plants and animals.
22. It breaks down plant and animal matter and returns nutrients to soil.
23. In winter, less food is available. Some animals migrate; others hibernate.
24. Hibernation; it allows an animal to get through winter on little food.
25. yes; ensures that animals will survive to reproduce
26. Gravity establishes up/down for plants. Roots grow into soil; stems and leaves grow up. Touch allows stems and leaves to find support. Light provides energy.
27. All cells support life. Single-celled organisms: functions are done by single cell. Multicellular organisms: cells specialize to do certain jobs.
28. Fungal cells can multiply asexually very quickly.

the BIG idea

29. Plants capture energy from Sun. Animals get energy from food. Fungi break down complex carbon materials into simple materials.
30. Producers, such as plants, use sunlight to make sugar and starch through photosynthesis. Energy flows to consumers when they eat food. Decomposers take materials from living matter and break it down.

UNIT PROJECTS

Check to make sure students are working on their projects. Check schedules and work in progress.

 Unit Projects, pp. 5–10

Thinking Critically

The diagram below shows a woodland food web. Each arrow starts with a food source and points to a consumer. Use the diagram to answer the next six questions.

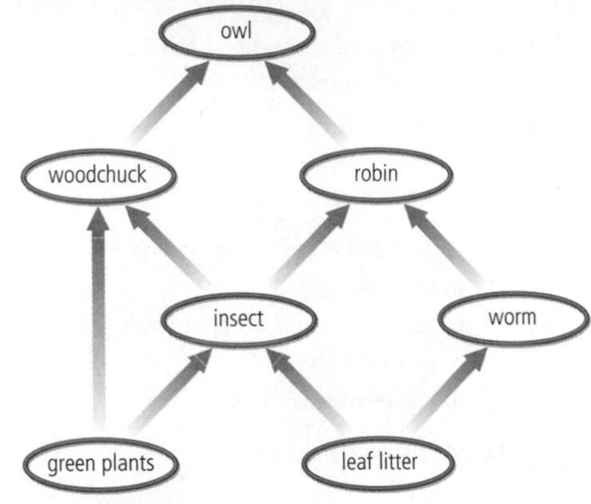

18. **ANALYZE** What is the original source of energy for all the animals in the food web? Explain your reasoning.
19. **CLASSIFY** Identify the consumers in this food web.
20. **CLASSIFY** Identify the animals in the food web as either herbivores, carnivores, omnivores, or decomposers.
21. **EVALUATE** Does an omnivore have an advantage over carnivores and herbivores in finding food?
22. **ANALYZE** What role does the worm play in the food web, and why it is important?
23. **PREDICT** How might this food web change over the course of a year, and how would that affect the feeding activity of animals in the food web?
24. **CONNECT** A woodchuck is sometimes referred to as a groundhog. Many people celebrate February 2 as groundhog day. The legend is that if a groundhog emerges from its burrow on this day and sees its shadow, then there will be six more weeks of winter. The groundhog is emerging from a long sleeplike state. What is this behavior, and how does it benefit the animal?
25. **ANALYZE** Do you think the defensive behavior of a porcupine or pufferfish is an adaptation? Explain your reasoning.
26. **SYNTHESIZE** A plant responds to gravity, touch, and light as stimuli. How does this relate to a plant being a producer?
27. **SYNTHESIZE** How are the cells of multicellular organisms like those of single-celled organisms? How are they different?
28. **ANALYZE** What quality of asexual reproduction makes a fungal disease spread so quickly.

the BIG idea

29. **SYNTHESIZE** Look again at the photograph on pages 312–313. Plants, animals, and fungi are pictured there. How do these organisms get energy and materials from the environment?
30. **SUMMARIZE** Write a short paragraph to describe how matter and energy move between members of the kingdoms of plants, animals, and fungi. Use the words in the box below. Underline the terms in your answer.

photosysnthesis	consumer
producer	decomposer

UNIT PROJECTS

By now you should have completed the following items for your unit project.

- questions that you have asked about the topic
- schedule showing when you will complete each step of your project
- list of resources including Web sites, print resources, and materials

MONITOR AND RETEACH

If students have trouble with the concepts in Chapter Review item 26, have them review pp. 327–329. Point out the three responses.

Students may benefit from summarizing one or more sections of the chapter.

 Summarizing the Chapter, pp. 149–150

Standardized Test Practice

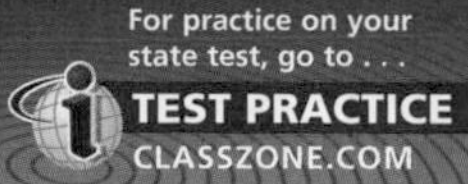

Interpreting Diagrams

The diagram shows the feeding relationships between certain animals and plants in a forest environment. The size of the bars represent the relative numbers of each organism. The arrow shows the flow of energy between these groups of organisms.

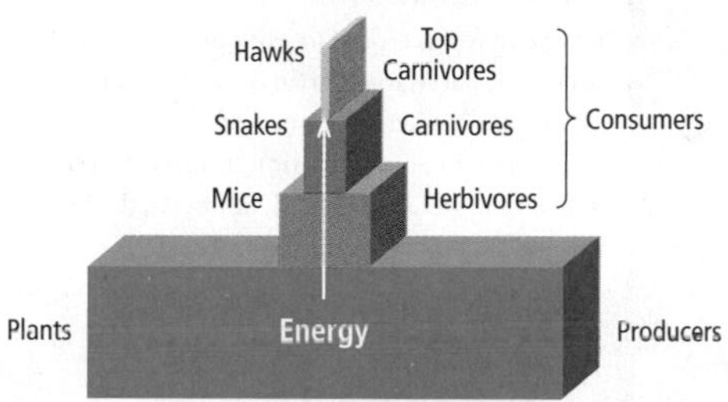

Feeding Relationships Among Plants and Animals

Use the diagram to answer the questions below.

1. Which is the largest group of organisms in the forest?
   a. plants
   b. mice
   c. snakes
   d. hawks

2. Most energy in the forest comes from
   a. top carnivores
   b. carnivores
   c. herbivores
   d. plants

3. Which description best fits the snake?
   a. a producer that feeds upon mice
   b. a consumer that is eaten by mice
   c. a consumer that feeds upon mice
   d. a consumer that feeds upon plants

4. A hawk is a top carnivore that feeds upon both snakes and mice. Which of the following best describes a top carnivore?
   a. a carnivore that feeds upon other carnivores
   b. a carnivore that feeds upon both carnivores and herbivores
   c. a consumer that gets its energy from producers
   d. a producer that supplies energy to consumers

5. Which statement best summarizes the diagram?
   a. The energy in a forest environment flows one way, from producers to consumers.
   b. Consumers don't need as much energy as producers.
   c. Energy in a forest environment goes from plants to animals and then back to plants.
   d. The number of producers depends on the number of consumers.

Extended Response

6 The diagram above shows the relative number of organisms at each level of a forest environment and the flow of energy from the producers to the consumers. Describe what happens to the amount of energy going from the producer level into the different levels of consumers. Not all the energy produced at a given level is available to organisms in the next level. What has happened to that energy? Use the words in the word box in your answer. Underline the words.

producer	energy
consumer	food

7. How would the number of plants, snakes, and hawks be affected if some disease were to reduce the numbers of mice in the forest?

METACOGNITIVE ACTIVITY

Have students answer the following questions in their **Science Notebook:**

1. What concepts about multicellular organisms are still confusing to you?
2. What did you learn about plants that surprised you?
3. How might working with a partner help you with your Unit Project?

Interpreting Diagrams

1. a   2. d   3. c   4. b   5. a

Extended Response

6. RUBRIC

4 points for a response that correctly answers the question and uses the following terms accurately:

- producer
- consumer
- energy
- food

Sample answer: The diagram starts out large at the base and then gets significantly smaller going from one level to the next. The most energy is with the producers. Consumers get energy from food; some is stored, but some is used by their bodies. Therefore, at each level, less energy is available. The less energy available in a level, the smaller the number of organisms in the level.

3 points correctly answers the question and uses three terms accurately
2 points correctly answers the question and uses two terms accurately
1 point correctly answers the question and uses one term accurately

7. RUBRIC

4 points for a response that correctly answers the question and demonstrates an understanding of a food web.

Sample answer: The numbers of plants might increase if there were fewer mice to feed on plants and plant seeds. The number of snakes and hawks might decrease because both these organisms rely on mice as a food source.

3 points correctly answers the question and demonstrates partial understanding of a food web
2 points correctly answers the question but demonstrates little understanding of a food web
1 point does not correctly answer the question and demonstrates little understanding of a food web

FOCUS

Set Learning Goals

Students will

- Examine historical events that contribute to our understanding of biodiversity.
- Learn about some of the technology that makes close observation of different species possible.
- Invent an animal classification system, using criteria such as habitat or diet.

National Science Education Standards

A.9.a–g Understandings About Scientific Inquiry

E.6.a–c Understandings About Science and Technology

F.5.a–g Science and Technology in Society

G.1.a–b Science as a Human Endeavor

G.2.a Nature of Science

G.3.a–c History of Science

INSTRUCT

Point out that the top half of the timeline depicts scientists' progress in understanding the many forms of life. The bottom half provides examples of technology and their application to the study of biodiversity. The gaps represent blocks of time omitted.

Technology

NAVIGATION Any location on Earth can be described using latitude and longitude. Lines of latitude circle Earth in horizontal slices. Lines of longitude divide Earth from pole to pole. Discuss why determining longitude was a harder problem than latitude: You can measure the angle of the Sun above the horizon at noon, to tell latitude. For longitude, you must also measure the time the Sun appeared highest. Keeping time was difficult at sea.

TIMELINES in Science

DISCOVERIES IN Biodiversity

Scientists have discovered new species in the treetops of tropical forests and in the crannies of coral reefs. The quest to catalog the types and numbers of living things, the biodiversity of Earth, began in the late 1600s. A wave of naturalists set sail from Europe to the Americas and to Africa to find specimens of living things.

In the late 19th century, biologists reached agreement on a system for naming and classifying each new species. The mid-20th century brought an understanding of DNA and how it could be used to compare one species with another. Now new organisms could be pinpointed with precision. To this day, millions of undiscovered species lie deep in the unexplored ocean, in tropical forests, and even in heavily trafficked U.S. cities. A large concentration of Earth's known species now live in named and protected biodiversity "hotspots."

1670

Merian Illustrates from Life

In her day, it was typical to work from preserved specimens, but Maria Merian draws from life. Shown below is her illustration of the Legu Lizard she observes in South America. In 1670, she publishes a richly illustrated book of insects, the first to describe the process of metamorphosis.

EVENTS

1670

APPLICATIONS AND TECHNOLOGY

TECHNOLOGY

Improvements in Navigation

Since the Age of Exploration in the 1500s and 1600s, European shipbuilding and sailing had boomed. Vast improvements had been made, especially in charting and mapping. Travel from Europe to Africa, Asia, and the Americas became an important part of business and science. Still, ships often lost their way or wrecked in raging storms. The invention by John Harrison in 1765 of the marine chronometer, a clock that could work at sea, changed navigation forever. Nobody expected a landlocked clockmaker to solve the puzzle, but the sea clock provided an accurate way to record sightings of stars and planets, and thus plot longitude at sea. The ocean remained a dangerous passage, but now, if tossed off course, a captain could still steer clear.

DIFFERENTIATE INSTRUCTION

Below Level Connect the events above the timeline with the technology below it. Ask how each technology helped people make discoveries. *Sample answer: Navigational improvement made it possible to find new places and identify where new organisms were found.*

350 Unit 3: Diversity of Living Things

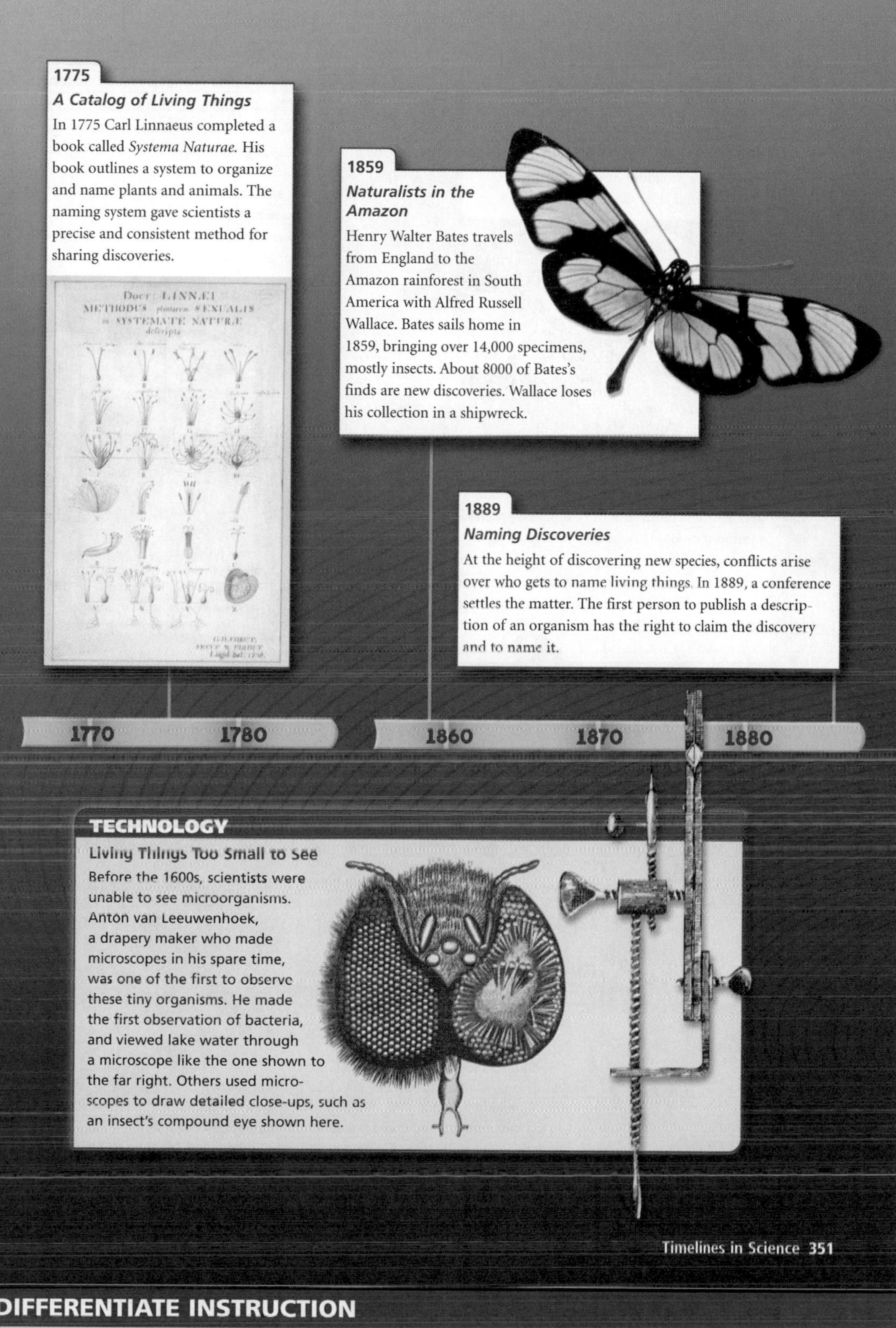

1775

A Catalog of Living Things

In 1775 Carl Linnaeus completed a book called *Systema Naturae.* His book outlines a system to organize and name plants and animals. The naming system gave scientists a precise and consistent method for sharing discoveries.

1859

Naturalists in the Amazon

Henry Walter Bates travels from England to the Amazon rainforest in South America with Alfred Russell Wallace. Bates sails home in 1859, bringing over 14,000 specimens, mostly insects. About 8000 of Bates's finds are new discoveries. Wallace loses his collection in a shipwreck.

1889

Naming Discoveries

At the height of discovering new species, conflicts arise over who gets to name living things. In 1889, a conference settles the matter. The first person to publish a description of an organism has the right to claim the discovery and to name it.

1770 1780 1860 1870 1880

TECHNOLOGY

Living Things Too Small to See

Before the 1600s, scientists were unable to see microorganisms. Anton van Leeuwenhoek, a drapery maker who made microscopes in his spare time, was one of the first to observe these tiny organisms. He made the first observation of bacteria, and viewed lake water through a microscope like the one shown to the far right. Others used microscopes to draw detailed close-ups, such as an insect's compound eye shown here.

Timelines in Science 351

DIFFERENTIATE INSTRUCTION

Advanced Have students choose some plants and animals for which they know the common names, and then research the scientific names. They should write a brief explanation of each name, tracing the name back to its Latin meaning.

Scientific Process

1859 Henry Walter Bates made detailed studies of butterflies, particularly their color patterns. His studies led to the understanding of what is called Batesian mimicry. Some nonpoisonous animals mimic the colors, shape, or behavior of poisonous animals. Bates concluded that the success of organisms with this adaptation was clear evidence for the theory of natural selection.

Technology

TOO SMALL TO SEE The microscope pictured, like all of Leeuwenhoek's microscopes, is a simple one, using only one lens. Though other researchers were using compound microscopes with more than one lens, Leeuwenhoek was so skilled at grinding lenses and adjusting lighting that his simple microscopes actually achieved greater magnification. Ask: Can you think of another example of a scientific tool where simpler is better? *Sample answer: A drawing may tell more than a photograph.*

Integrate the Sciences

1990 Boyle's Law states that the volume of a gas varies inversely with the pressure on it. When a diver goes underwater holding his or her breath, all the air-filled spaces in the body, such as the lungs and ears, will compress. If the diver goes too deep and the spaces compress too much, blood will leave the capillaries to try to fill in the spaces created, causing hemorrhage or ruptured membranes.

Scientific Process

1974 Discuss the practical problems involved in sampling canopy insects. Ask: Can you think of reasons that fogging might not be a good way to collect insects? *Sample answer: Some insects might not be susceptible, and birds might be killed. Also, a scientist might prefer to study living organisms, not dead ones.* Invite students to brainstorm other methods of collecting insects in the forest canopy.

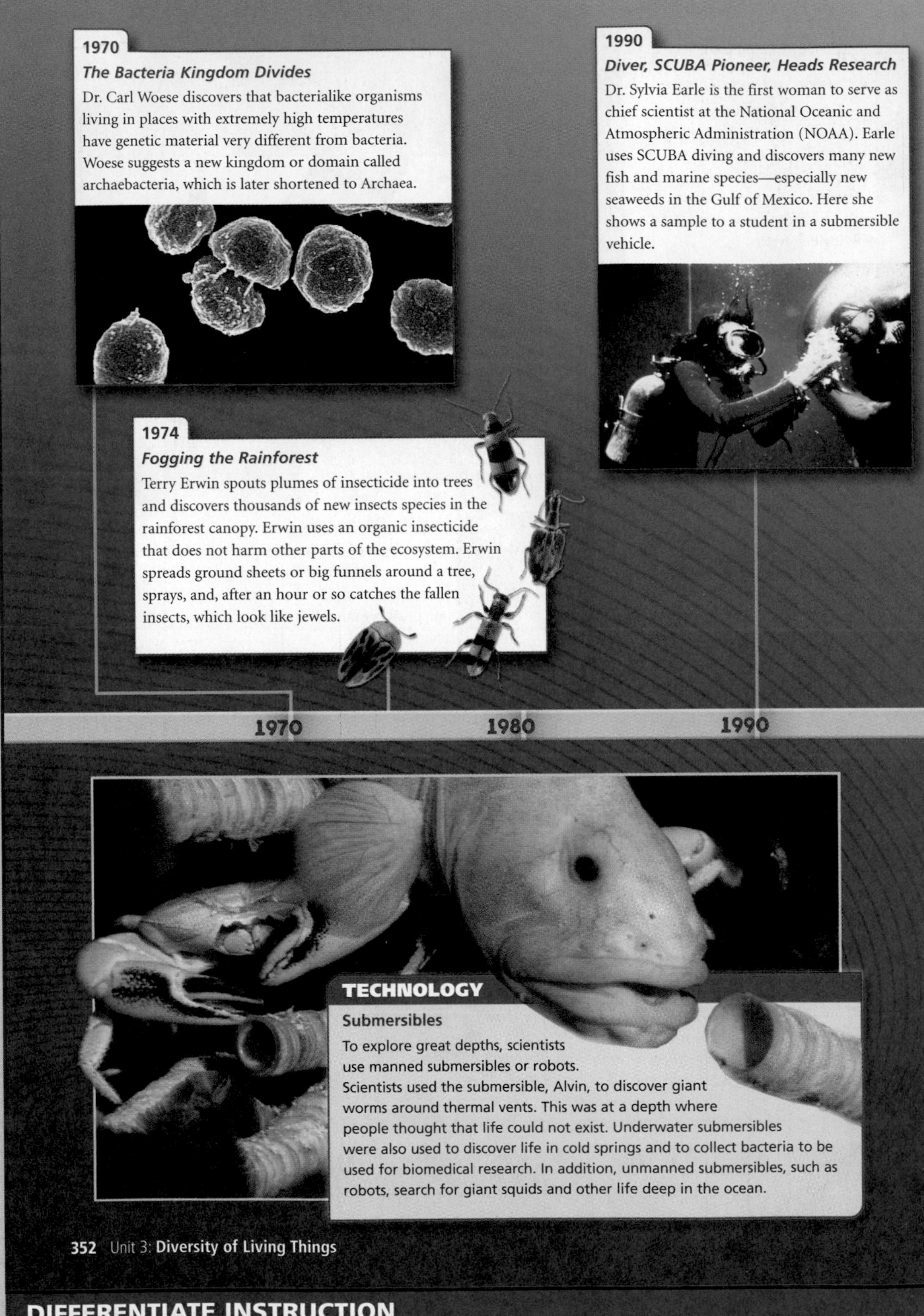

DIFFERENTIATE INSTRUCTION

Advanced Have students investigate organic insecticides such as the spray used by Terry Erwin. They can compare them to chemical insecticides used in agriculture in rain forests. They should present a detailed comparison of the effects—positive and negative—of each compound on the biodiversity of environments where it is used.

2002 to Present

New Plant Genera

Scientists who study plants and insects in tropical rain forests discover so many new species that they are sometimes backlogged in naming them. In the plant kingdom, it has been estimated that for every 1000 species discovered, one new genus will be found. In 2002 scientists found a new genus of ginger in the wild in Singapore. More and more, genera are identified in the laboratory using DNA.

RESOURCE CENTER
CLASSZONE.COM
Read about current biodiversity discoveries and research.

2000

APPLICATION

Biodiversity Hotspots

In 1988, British ecologist Norman Mike Myers creates a list of 18 areas that he calls biodiversity "hotspots." In 2000, Myers and others increase the number of hotspots to 25. How does an area get to be called a hotspot? It has to have a large number of species that exist only in that location and it has to be a region in great danger of habitat loss. Hotspots cover only 1.5 % of the Earth's surface yet they contain 44 percent of all species of higher plants and 35 percent of all land vertebrates. Scientists place most of their effort in discovering new species in these hotspots.

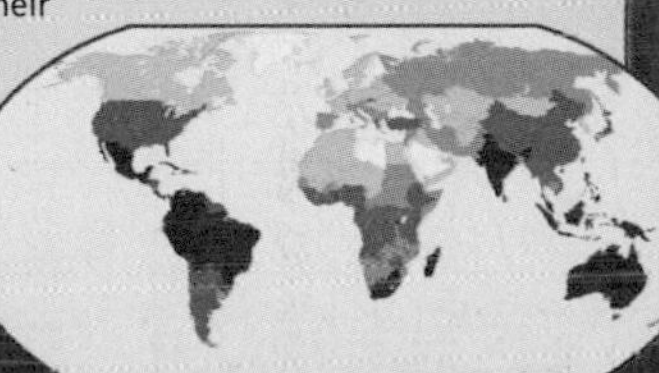

INTO THE FUTURE

Although scientists have explored most of the continents, little is known about what life is like in the more remote areas. Deep-sea exploration, for example, is only just beginning, and big surprises surface with each expedition. Technology will continue to delve deeper toward the floor of deep oceans with underwater robotics, manned submersibles, and better mapping and imaging systems.

Science will increasingly rely on organizing the growing data on biodiversity. Currently, scientists who study one area of life mostly share data with others in the same field. For example, scientists studying plants share their data with other botanists. An effort to create global databases to share information about all species is beginning to bring together this data. Databases that catalogue the genes of living things are being created. The better we know the genetic profile of various species, the better we can identify and compare them.

In addition, the attention to the health of biodiversity hotspots and ecosystems everywhere may help stop extinction, the dying off of a whole species. Extinction decreases the diversity of living things, and scientists have recognized that Earth's biodiversity plays a big role in keeping ecosystems healthy.

ACTIVITIES

Writing About Science: Documentary

Research one hotspot and report on the diverse species living there. Note any legal steps or other efforts to conserve biodiversity in that area.

Reliving History

Devise an animal classification system based on a criterion such as habitat, diet, or behavior. What are the strengths and weaknesses of your system?

DIFFERENTIATE INSTRUCTION

Below Level Have students choose a biodiversity hotspot and make a collage of some of the species that live there. They can use their own drawings and pictures cut from magazines to highlight as diverse a sample as possible of the types of organisms in each area.

Application

BIODIVERSITY HOTSPOTS Over 120 currently used pharmaceutical products are derived from plants. Indigenous people who have a long history of traditional medicine are rich sources of information about medically valuable plants. Ask: Where is a good source of medical plants that are relatively unexplored or unknown? *the rain forest*

INTO THE FUTURE

Have students brainstorm illnesses or problems that might be treated using species that have not yet been discovered. Discuss how to acknowledge and address the needs and rights of indigenous peoples living in biodiversity hotspots, and how to balance their needs with the need to preserve biodiversity.

ACTIVITIES

Writing About Science: Documentary

Have students put their findings into a letter to the editor asking for public support of policies to conserve biodiversity.

Reliving History

One type of classification might be based on diet. Such a classification might be used to analyze how nutrients move in a system.

Technology Resources

Students can visit **ClassZone.com** for current news on biodiversity preservation.

CHAPTER

Plants

Life Science UNIFYING PRINCIPLES

PRINCIPLE 1
All living things share common characteristics.

PRINCIPLE 2
All living things share common needs.

PRINCIPLE 3
Living things meet their needs through interactions with the environment.

PRINCIPLE 4
The types and numbers of living things change over time.

Unit 3: Diversity of Living Things BIG IDEAS

CHAPTER 9
Single-Celled Organisms and Viruses
Bacteria and protists have all of the characteristics of living things, while viruses are not alive.

CHAPTER 10
Introduction to Multicellular Organisms
Multicellular organisms live in and get energy from a variety of environments.

CHAPTER 11
Plants
Plants are a diverse group of organisms that live in many land environments.

CHAPTER 12
Invertebrate Animals
Invertebrate animals have a variety of body plans and adaptations.

CHAPTER 13
Vertebrate Animals
Vertebrate animals live in most of Earth's environments.

CHAPTER 11 KEY CONCEPTS

SECTION 1

Plants are adapted to living on land.
1. Plants are a diverse group of organisms.
2. Plants share common characteristics.
3. Plant parts have special functions.
4. Plants grow throughout their lifetimes.

SECTION 2

Most mosses and ferns live in moist environments.
1. Plant species adapted to life on land.
2. Mosses are nonvascular plants.
3. Mosses reproduce with spores.
4. Ferns are vascular plants.
5. Ferns reproduce with spores.

SECTION 3

Seeds and pollen are reproductive adaptations.
1. Seeds are an important adaptation.
2. Some plants reproduce with seeds.
3. Pine trees reproduce with pollen and seeds.
4. Gymnosperms are seed plants.

SECTION 4

Many plants reproduce with flowers and fruit.
1. Angiosperms have flowers and fruit.
2. Animals spread both pollen and seeds.
3. Humans depend on plants for their survival.

The Big Idea Flow Chart is available on p. T17 in the **UNIT TRANSPARENCY BOOK.**

Previewing Content

SECTION

Plants are adapted to living on land. pp. 357–363

1. Plants are a diverse group of organisms.
Plants come in a variety of sizes and shapes, and are found in all environments, from the icy arctic to the tropics.

2. Plants share common characteristics.
All plants are multicellular. Plant cells have a nucleus and cell wall. Plants are producers and have life cycles that are divided into two stages.

3. Plant parts have special functions.

- Plants have two systems—shoot systems that consist of stems and leaves, and root systems.
- **Vascular systems** in plants are made up of two kinds of tissues. Xylem tissue carries water and dissolved nutrients up from the roots. Phloem tissue transports energy-rich materials down from the leaves.
- All plants photosynthesize. Photosynthesis takes place in chloroplasts where sugars and oxygen are produced from the raw materials of carbon dioxide, water, and solar energy. In **transpiration** water vapor moves out of the plant. Stomata regulate the movement of gases and water in and out of the plant.

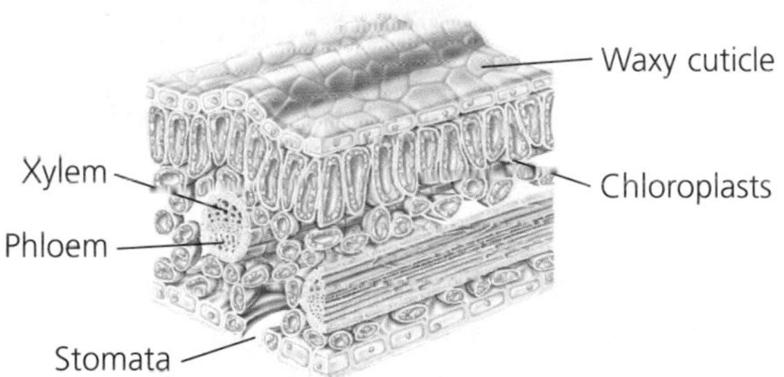

4. Plants grow throughout their lifetimes.
Plants with soft stems survive under the right conditions for growth and photosynthesis. Many of these plants are seasonal. Plants with woody stems have thick, tough stems formed from xylem. These plants survive from year to year.

SECTION

Most mosses and ferns live in moist environments. pp. 364–369

1. Plant species adapted to life on land.

- Plant life appeared on land about 475 million years ago. Early plants were much like green algae of today.
- As plants moved to land, they adapted structures for support and for taking in nutrients and water.
- The first land plants were similar to present-day mosses and ferns.

2. Mosses are nonvascular plants.
Mosses have simple roots, stems, and leaves, but lack vascular tissues. Mosses are able to reproduce both asexually and sexually.

3. Mosses reproduce with spores.

- In the first generation, moss plants grow from spores. These plants have male and female reproductive parts that can produce sperm and eggs. Fertilization occurs as sperm swim through water to the eggs.
- In the second generation, the fertilized egg grows into a stalk with a capsule. Through meiosis, thousands of spores are produced inside the capsule. The spores are released from the capsule and may grow into new moss plants.

4. Ferns are vascular plants.
The vascular tissues of ferns allow them to grow larger than mosses. Root systems can branch out more and water and nutrients are able to move more efficiently through the plant.

5. Ferns reproduce with spores.

- In the first generation, male and female structures produce eggs. Sperm swim to fertilize the eggs.
- In the second generation, the fertilized eggs grow structures that produce spores. The spores are found in clusters on leafy structures called fronds.

Common Misconceptions

PLANT NUTRITION Many studies have shown that students have the misconception that plants get food from the soil by sucking it up through their roots. In fact, plants use carbon dioxide from the air and combine it with the energy from sunlight to synthesize usable energy and materials they need to grow. Plants do not "make food" in photosynthesis, but rather store energy and materials which then become food for any organism that eats the plant.

 This misconception is addressed on p. 360.

MISCONCEPTION DATABASE
CLASSZONE.COM Background on student misconceptions

LIVING OR NONLIVING Many students do not classify plants, ferns, and mosses as living or alive. They also often think plant life to be very different than animal life and often do not recognize similarities.

 This misconception is addressed on p. 367.

Previewing Content

SECTION

Seeds and pollen are reproductive adaptations. pp. 370–378

1. Seeds are an important adaptation.
Seeds are young plants enclosed in protective coatings. Fertilization brings about the growth of the **embryo,** the immature form of the plant inside the seed. An embryo remains dormant until conditions are right for **germination.**

2. Some plants reproduce with seeds.
Seeds contain a food supply for the developing embryo. They can travel long distances, spread by wind, animals, or water. Sperm do not need water to reach the egg, so seed plants can reproduce in drier environments than mosses or ferns.

3. Pine trees reproduce with pollen and seeds.
In seed plants, meiosis and fertilization occur completely within the tissue of the mature plant. Gymnosperms such as pine trees have pollen, small multicellular structures that hold sperm cells. The diagram below summarizes the life cycle of a pine tree.

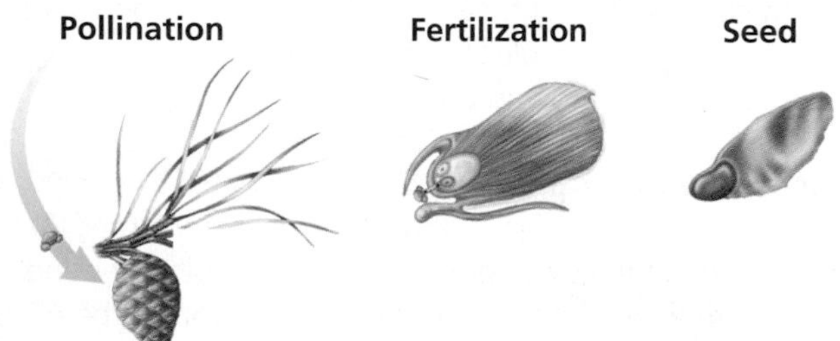

1. Reproductive structures are in pinecones.
2. Male cones: sperm cells are contained in pollen grains. Female cones: contain egg cells.
3. Pollination: pollen grains attach to female cone and release sperm. Fertilization: occurs inside the female structure.
4. Fertilized egg grows into embryo within a seed.

4. Gymnosperms are seed plants.
A gymnosperm is a plant that produces seeds that are not enclosed in flowers or fruit. Four kinds of gymnosperms on Earth today are: conifers, ginkgoes, cycads, and gnetophytes.

SECTION

Many plants reproduce with flowers and fruit. pp. 379–387

1. Angiosperms have flowers and fruit.
- Most plants on Earth today are angiosperms.
- Angiosperm reproductive cycles are similar to gymnosperms. In angiosperms the sperm and egg cells are contained in a **flower.** When fertilized eggs form seeds, the ovary wall thickens into a **fruit.**
- Male sperm cells are produced in the anther and are released in pollen grains. Female egg cells are produced in the ovary. Pollen grains, when released, attach to the pistil. Fertilization occurs after the pollen tube reaches the ovary and the sperm fertilizes the egg.
- Flowers vary in size, shape, color, and fragrance. The parts of the flower are shown in the diagram.

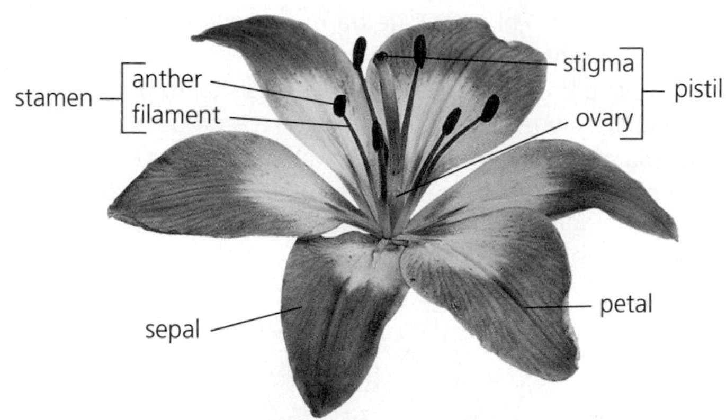

2. Animals spread both pollen and seeds.
- Animals such as bees and hummingbirds feed on the nectar of flowers. These animals pollinate flowers by brushing up against the pollen and carrying it to the reproductive parts of another flower.
- Seeds can be dispersed from fruits by wind, on the fur of animals, and in their digested waste.

3. Humans depend on plants for their survival.
Plants provide oxygen and energy sources for consumers in the form of plant food. Other resources from plants include natural gas, coal, and soil.

Common Misconceptions

SEEDS Only slightly more than half of students above the fourth-grade level classify embryos (seeds and eggs) as part of a living thing. Many students do not think a seed to be a plant. In fact, a seed is a stage in the life cycle of a plant.

MISCONCEPTION DATABASE
CLASSZONE.COM Background on student misconceptions

This misconception is addressed on p. 372.

Previewing Labs

Lab Generator CD-ROM
Edit these Pupil Edition labs and generate alternative labs.

EXPLORE the BIG idea

How Are Plants Alike, How Are They Different? p. 355 Students compare and contrast samples of plants to learn about the characteristics of plants.	**TIME** 15 minutes **MATERIALS** samples of local plants, hand lens, notebook
How Are Seeds Dispersed? p. 355 Students make a model of a seed with wing-like structures to examine dispersal by wind.	**TIME** 15 minutes **MATERIALS** paper, scissors, paper clip
Internet Activity: Sprouting Seeds, p. 355 Students learn about plant life cycles by observing seeds sprouting.	**TIME** 20 minutes **MATERIALS** computer with Internet access

SECTION 

EXPLORE Leaf Characteristics, p. 357 Students examine the characteristics of a leaf.	**TIME** 15 minutes **MATERIALS** assorted leaves, hand lens, (optional) colored pencils

SECTION 

EXPLORE Moss Plants, p. 364 Students observe the structures and distinct parts of moss plants.	**TIME** 20 minutes **MATERIALS** live moss plant, hand lens
INVESTIGATE Capturing the Sun's Energy, p. 366 Students measure how much sunlight reaches organisms living in water to learn the advantages for plants of living on land.	**TIME** 15 minutes **MATERIALS** white button, string, empty 1 L clear plastic bottle, water, ruler, kelp granules, tablespoon measure

SECTION 

INVESTIGATE Pinecones, p. 374 Students observe the structure of pinecones to learn about the reproductive structures of gymnosperms.	**TIME** 20 minutes **MATERIALS** dried, open pinecones; beaker of water; paper towels
CHAPTER INVESTIGATION, Which Seeds Will Grow? pp. 376–377 Students compare and contrast germination and growth patterns of various types of seeds.	**TIME** 40 minutes **MATERIALS** assorted seeds, potting soil, paper cups, water, paper towels, labels

SECTION 

EXPLORE Fruit, p. 379 Students explore the inside of different fruits to discover the structures of seeds in angiosperms.	**TIME** 15 minutes **MATERIALS** apple, paper towel, plastic knife, pea pod
INVESTIGATE Flower Parts, p. 383 Students identify the parts of a flower to learn more about the reproductive cycle of angiosperms.	**TIME** 15 minutes **MATERIALS** assorted flowers, hand lens

R **Additional INVESTIGATION,** Fertilization in Angiosperms, A, B, & C, pp. 210–218; Teacher Instructions, pp. 360–361

Previewing Chapter Resources

CHAPTER 11
Plants

INTEGRATED TECHNOLOGY

CLASSZONE.COM
- eEdition Plus
- EasyPlanner Plus
- Misconceptions
- Content Review
- Test Practice
- Simulation
- Resource Centers
- Internet Activity: Sprouting Seeds
- Math Tutorial

SCILINKS.ORG

SCILINKS

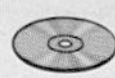
CD-ROMS
- eEdition
- EasyPlanner
- Power Presentations
- Content Review
- Lab Generator
- Test Generator

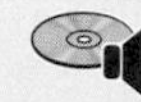
AUDIO CDS
- Audio Readings
- Audio Readings in Spanish

LABS AND ACTIVITIES

EXPLORE the Big Idea, p. 355
- How Are Plants Alike, How Are They Different?
- How Are Seeds Dispersed?
- Internet Activity: Sprouting Seeds

UNIT RESOURCE BOOK
Unit Projects, pp. 5–10

Lab Generator CD-ROM
Generate customized labs.

SECTION

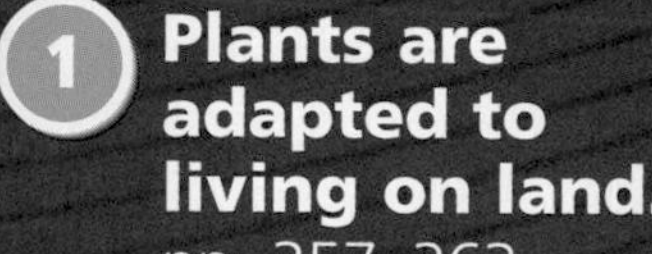

1 Plants are adapted to living on land.
pp. 357–363

Time: 2 periods (1 block)

 Lesson Plan, pp. 151–152

RESOURCE CENTER, Plant Systems

UNIT TRANSPARENCY BOOK
- Big Idea Flow Chart, p. T17
- Daily Vocabulary Scaffolding, p. T18
- Note-Taking Model, p. T19
- 3-Minute Warm-Up, p. T20

EXPLORE Leaf Characteristics, p. 357

SECTION

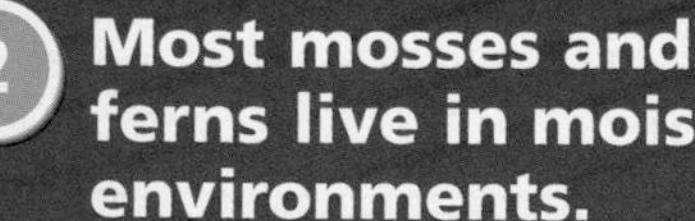

2 Most mosses and ferns live in moist environments.
pp. 364–369

Time: 2 periods (1 block)

 Lesson Plan, pp. 161–162

RESOURCE CENTER, Plant Evolution

UNIT TRANSPARENCY BOOK
- Daily Vocabulary Scaffolding, p. T18
- 3-Minute Warm-Up, p. T20

- EXPLORE Moss Plants, p. 364
- INVESTIGATE Capturing the Sun's Energy, p. 366

UNIT RESOURCE BOOK
Datasheet, Capturing the Sun's Energy, p. 170

SECTION

3 Seeds and pollen are reproductive adaptations.
pp. 370–378

Time: 3 periods (1.5 blocks)

 Lesson Plan, pp. 172–173

RESOURCE CENTER, Seeds, Extreme Seeds

UNIT TRANSPARENCY BOOK
- Daily Vocabulary Scaffolding, p. T18
- 3-Minute Warm-Up, p. T21
- "Life Cycle of a Pine Tree" Visual, p. T22

- INVESTIGATE Pinecones, p. 374
- CHAPTER INVESTIGATION, pp. 376–377
- Extreme Science, p. 378

UNIT RESOURCE BOOK
- Datasheet, Pinecones, p. 181
- CHAPTER INVESTIGATION, Which Seeds Will Grow? A, B, & C, pp. 201–209

SECTION

4 Many plants reproduce with flowers and fruit.
pp. 379–387

Time: 3 periods (1.5 blocks)

 Lesson Plan, pp. 183–184

- **SIMULATION,** Seed Dispersal
- **MATH TUTORIAL**

UNIT TRANSPARENCY BOOK
- Big Idea Flow Chart, p. T17
- Daily Vocabulary Scaffolding, p. T18
- 3-Minute Warm-Up, p. T21
- Chapter Outline, pp. T23–T24

- EXPLORE Fruit, p. 379
- INVESTIGATE Flower Parts, p. 383
- Math in Science, p. 387

UNIT RESOURCE BOOK
- Datasheet, Flower Parts, p. 193
- Math Support & Practice, pp. 199–200
- Additional INVESTIGATION, Fertilization in Angiosperms, A, B, & C, pp. 210–218

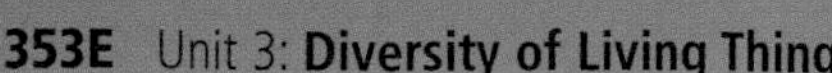

KEY TO ICONS 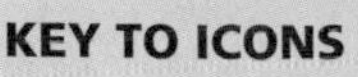

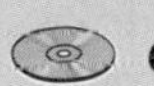 CD/CD-ROM

INTERNET

Pupil Edition

 Teacher Edition

UNIT RESOURCE BOOK

 UNIT TRANSPARENCY BOOK

UNIT ASSESSMENT BOOK

 SPANISH ASSESSMENT BOOK

SCIENCE TOOLKIT

READING AND REINFORCEMENT	ASSESSMENT	STANDARDS
 • Word Triangle, B18–19 • Mind Map, C40–41 • Daily Vocabulary Scaffolding, H1–8  **UNIT RESOURCE BOOK** • Vocabulary Practice, pp. 196–197 • Decoding Support, p. 198 • Summarizing the Chapter, pp. 219–220 **Audio Readings CD** Listen to Pupil Edition. **Audio Readings in Spanish CD** Listen to Pupil Edition in Spanish.	• Chapter Review, pp. 389–390 • Standardized Test Practice, p. 391 **UNIT ASSESSMENT BOOK** • Diagnostic Test, pp. 41–42 • Chapter Test, A, B, & C, pp. 47–58 • Alternative Assessment, pp. 59–60  Spanish Chapter Test, pp. 49–52  **Test Generator CD-ROM** Generate customized tests.  **Lab Generator CD-ROM** Rubrics for Labs	National Standards A.2–8, A.9.a–c, A.9.e–f, C.2.b, C.4.c, G.1.b See p. 354 for the standards.
 **UNIT RESOURCE BOOK** • Reading Study Guide, A & B, pp. 153–156 • Spanish Reading Study Guide, pp. 157–158 • Challenge and Extension, p. 159 • Reinforcing Key Concepts, p. 160 • Challenge Reading, pp. 194–195	 Ongoing Assessment, pp. 358–362  Section 11.1 Review, p. 363  **UNIT ASSESSMENT BOOK** Section 11.1 Quiz, p. 43	National Standards C.4.c, G.1.b
 **UNIT RESOURCE BOOK** • Reading Study Guide, A & B, pp. 163–166 • Spanish Reading Study Guide, pp. 167–168 • Challenge and Extension, p. 169 • Reinforcing Key Concepts, p. 171	Ongoing Assessment, pp. 365–369  Section 11.2 Review, p. 369  **UNIT ASSESSMENT BOOK** Section 11.2 Quiz, p. 44	National Standards A.2–7, A.9.a–b, A.9.e–f, C.2.b, C.4.c, G.1.b
 **UNIT RESOURCE BOOK** • Reading Study Guide, A & B, pp. 174–177 • Spanish Reading Study Guide, pp. 178–179 • Challenge and Extension, p. 180 • Reinforcing Key Concepts, p. 182	Ongoing Assessment, pp. 371–374  Section 11.3 Review, p. 375 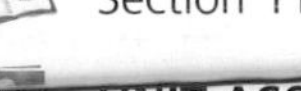 **UNIT ASSESSMENT BOOK** Section 11.3 Quiz, p. 45	National Standards A.2–7, A.9.a–b, A.9.e–f, C.4.c, G.1.b
 **UNIT RESOURCE BOOK** • Reading Study Guide, A & B, pp. 185–188 • Spanish Reading Study Guide, pp. 189–190 • Challenge and Extension, p. 191 • Reinforcing Key Concepts, p. 193	 Ongoing Assessment, pp. 380–385 Section 11.4 Review, p. 386  **UNIT ASSESSMENT BOOK** Section 11.4 Quiz, p. 46	National Standards A.2–8, A.9.a–c, A.9.e–f, C.4.c, G.1.b

Previewing Resources for Differentiated Instruction

CHAPTER INVESTIGATION

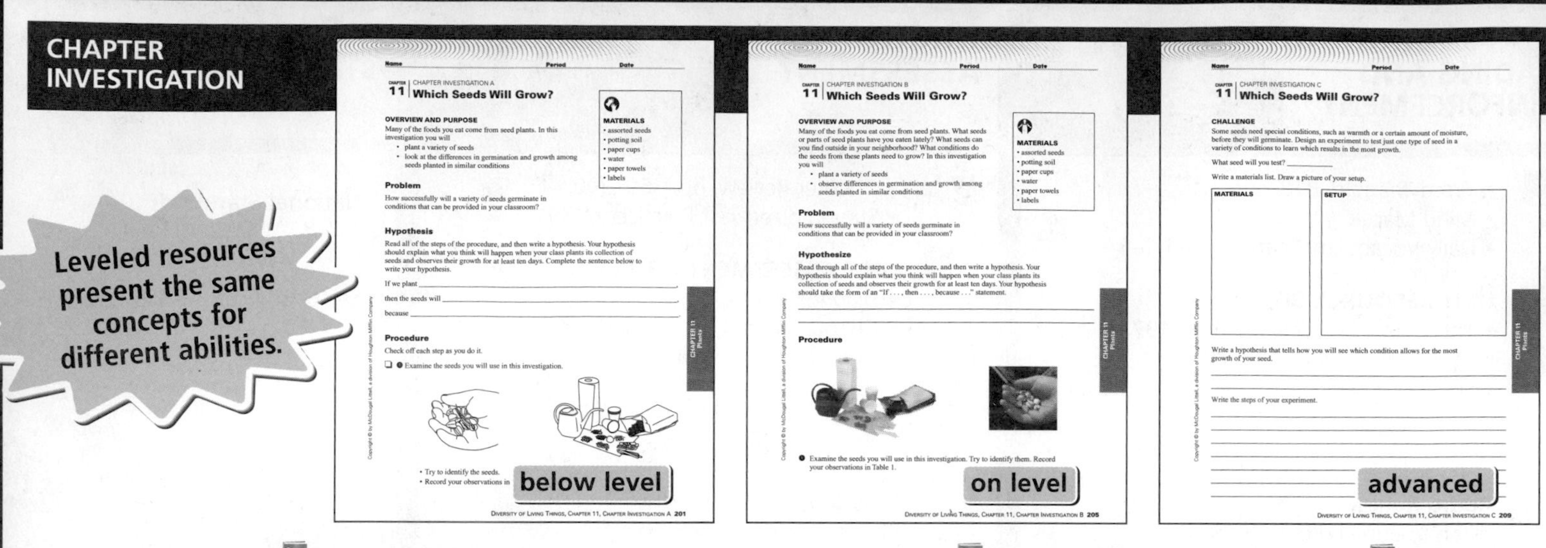

Name Period Date

CHAPTER 11 | CHAPTER INVESTIGATION A
Which Seeds Will Grow?

OVERVIEW AND PURPOSE
Many of the foods you eat come from seed plants. In this investigation you will
- plant a variety of seeds
- look at the differences in germination and growth among seeds planted in similar conditions

MATERIALS
- assorted seeds
- potting soil
- paper cups
- water
- paper towels
- labels

Problem
How successfully will a variety of seeds germinate in conditions that can be provided in your classroom?

Hypothesis
Read all of the steps of the procedure, and then write a hypothesis. Your hypothesis should explain what you think will happen when your class plants its collection of seeds and observes their growth for at least ten days. Complete the sentence below to write your hypothesis.

If we plant ______
then the seeds will ______
because ______

Procedure
Check off each step as you do it.
❑ ❶ Examine the seeds you will use in this investigation.
- Try to identify the seeds.
- Record your observations in ...

DIVERSITY OF LIVING THINGS, CHAPTER 11, CHAPTER INVESTIGATION A 201

Name Period Date

CHAPTER 11 | CHAPTER INVESTIGATION B
Which Seeds Will Grow?

OVERVIEW AND PURPOSE
Many of the foods you eat come from seed plants. What seeds or parts of seed plants have you eaten lately? What seeds can you find outside in your neighborhood? What conditions do the seeds from these plants need to grow? In this investigation you will
- plant a variety of seeds
- observe differences in germination and growth among seeds planted in similar conditions

MATERIALS
- assorted seeds
- potting soil
- paper cups
- water
- paper towels
- labels

Problem
How successfully will a variety of seeds germinate in conditions that can be provided in your classroom?

Hypothesize
Read through all of the steps of the procedure, and then write a hypothesis. Your hypothesis should explain what you think will happen when your class plants its collection of seeds and observes their growth for at least ten days. Your hypothesis should take the form of an "If . . . , then . . . , because . . ." statement.

Procedure
❶ Examine the seeds you will use in this investigation. Try to identify them. Record your observations in Table 1.

DIVERSITY OF LIVING THINGS, CHAPTER 11, CHAPTER INVESTIGATION B 205

Name Period Date

CHAPTER 11 | CHAPTER INVESTIGATION C
Which Seeds Will Grow?

CHALLENGE
Some seeds need special conditions, such as warmth or a certain amount of moisture, before they will germinate. Design an experiment to test just one type of seed in a variety of conditions to learn which results in the most growth.

What seed will you test? ______

Write a materials list. Draw a picture of your setup.

MATERIALS	SETUP

Write a hypothesis that tells how you will see which condition allows for the most growth of your seed.

Write the steps of your experiment.

DIVERSITY OF LIVING THINGS, CHAPTER 11, CHAPTER INVESTIGATION C 209

UNIT RESOURCE BOOK, pp. 201–204 | pp. 205–208 | pp. 205–209

READING STUDY GUIDE

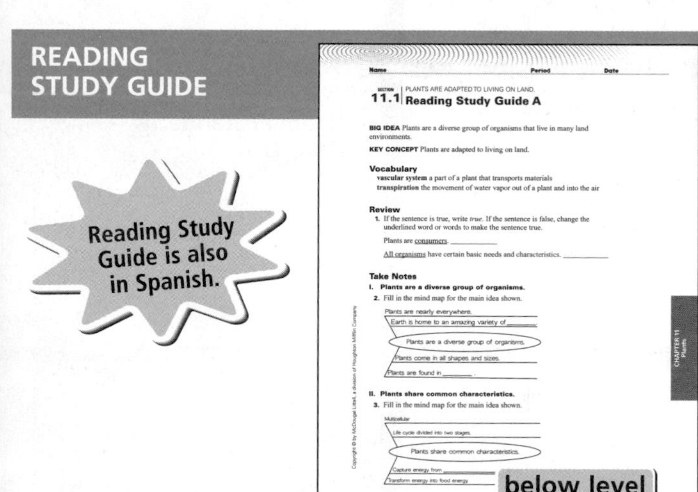

Name Period Date

SECTION 11.1 | PLANTS ARE ADAPTED TO LIVING ON LAND
Reading Study Guide A

BIG IDEA Plants are a diverse group of organisms that live in many land environments.
KEY CONCEPT Plants are adapted to living on land.

Vocabulary
vascular system a part of a plant that transports materials
transpiration the movement of water vapor out of a plant and into the air

Review
1. If the sentence is true, write *true*. If the sentence is false, change the underlined word or words to make the sentence true.
Plants are consumers. ______
All organisms have certain basic needs and characteristics. ______

Take Notes
I. Plants are a diverse group of organisms.
2. Fill in the mind map for the main idea shown.
Plants are nearly everywhere. / Earth is home to an amazing variety of ______ / Plants are a diverse group of organisms. / Plants come in all shapes and sizes. / Plants are found in ______

II. Plants share common characteristics.
3. Fill in the mind map for the main idea shown.
Multicellular / Life cycle divided into two stages / Plants share common characteristics. / Capture energy from ______ / Transform energy into food energy

DIVERSITY OF LIVING THINGS, CHAPTER 11, READING STUDY GUIDE A 153

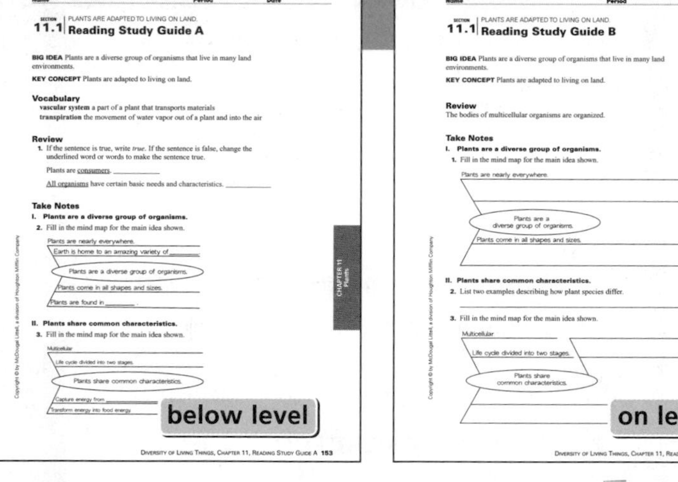

Name Period Date

SECTION 11.1 | PLANTS ARE ADAPTED TO LIVING ON LAND
Reading Study Guide B

BIG IDEA Plants are a diverse group of organisms that live in many land environments.
KEY CONCEPT Plants are adapted to living on land.

Review
The bodies of multicellular organisms are organized.

Take Notes
I. Plants are a diverse group of organisms.
1. Fill in the mind map for the main idea shown.
Plants are nearly everywhere. / Plants are a diverse group of organisms. / Plants come in all shapes and sizes.

II. Plants share common characteristics.
2. List two examples describing how plant species differ.
3. Fill in the mind map for the main idea shown.
Multicellular / Life cycle divided into two stages / Plants share common characteristics.

DIVERSITY OF LIVING THINGS, CHAPTER 11, READING STUDY GUIDE B 155

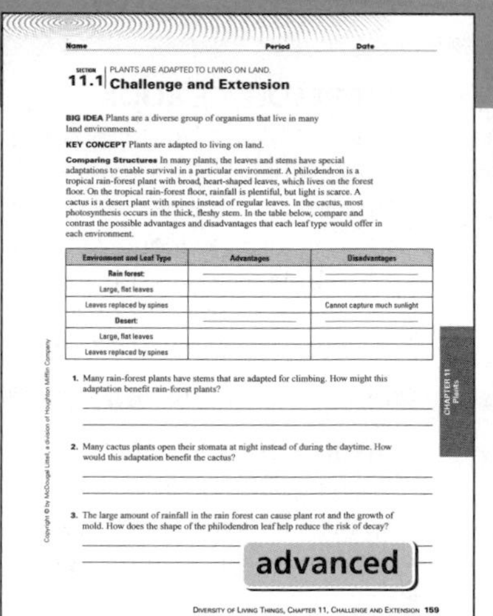

Name Period Date

SECTION 11.1 | PLANTS ARE ADAPTED TO LIVING ON LAND
Challenge and Extension

BIG IDEA Plants are a diverse group of organisms that live in many land environments.
KEY CONCEPT Plants are adapted to living on land.

Comparing Structures In many plants, the leaves and stems have special adaptations to enable survival in a particular environment. A philodendron is a tropical rain-forest plant with broad, heart-shaped leaves, which lives on the forest floor. On the tropical rain-forest floor, rainfall is plentiful, but light is scarce. A cactus is a desert plant with spines instead of regular leaves. In the cactus, most photosynthesis occurs in the thick, fleshy stem. In the table below, compare and contrast the possible advantages and disadvantages that each leaf type would offer in each environment.

Environment and Leaf Type	Advantages	Disadvantages
Rain forest:		
Large, flat leaves		
Leaves replaced by spines		Cannot capture much sunlight
Desert:		
Large, flat leaves		
Leaves replaced by spines		

1. Many rain-forest plants have stems that are adapted for climbing. How might this adaptation benefit rain-forest plants?
2. Many cactus plants open their stomata at night instead of during the daytime. How would this adaptation benefit the cactus?
3. The large amount of rainfall in the rain forest can cause plant rot and the growth of mold. How does the shape of the philodendron leaf help reduce the risk of decay?

DIVERSITY OF LIVING THINGS, CHAPTER 11, CHALLENGE AND EXTENSION 159

UNIT RESOURCE BOOK, pp. 153–154 | pp. 155–156 | p. 159

CHAPTER TEST

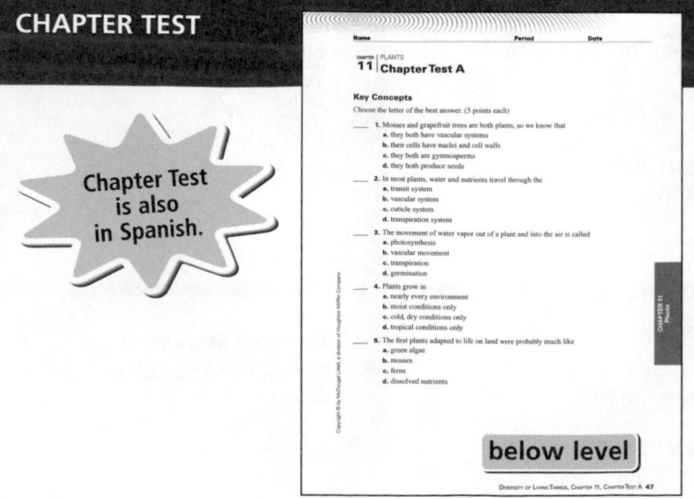

Name Period Date

CHAPTER 11 | PLANTS
Chapter Test A

Key Concepts
Choose the letter of the best answer. (5 points each)

___ 1. Mosses and grapefruit trees are both plants, so we know that
a. they both have vascular systems
b. their cells have nuclei and cell walls
c. they both are gymnosperms
d. they both produce seeds

___ 2. In most plants, water and nutrients travel through the
a. transit system
b. vascular system
c. cuticle system
d. transpiration system

___ 3. The movement of water vapor out of a plant and into the air is called
a. photosynthesis
b. vascular movement
c. transpiration
d. germination

___ 4. Plants grow in
a. nearly every environment
b. moist conditions only
c. cold, dry conditions only
d. tropical conditions only

___ 5. The first plants adapted to life on land were probably much like
a. green algae
b. mosses
c. ferns
d. dissolved nutrients

DIVERSITY OF LIVING THINGS, CHAPTER 11, CHAPTER TEST A 47

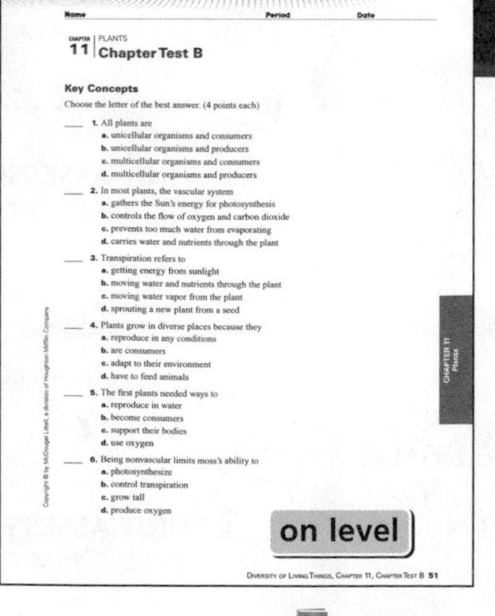

Name Period Date

CHAPTER 11 | PLANTS
Chapter Test B

Key Concepts
Choose the letter of the best answer. (4 points each)

___ 1. All plants are
a. unicellular organisms and consumers
b. unicellular organisms and producers
c. multicellular organisms and consumers
d. multicellular organisms and producers

___ 2. In most plants, the vascular system
a. gathers the Sun's energy for photosynthesis
b. controls the flow of oxygen and carbon dioxide
c. prevents too much water from evaporating
d. carries water and nutrients through the plant

___ 3. Transpiration refers to
a. getting energy from sunlight
b. moving water and nutrients through the plant
c. moving water vapor from the plant
d. sprouting a new plant from a seed

___ 4. Plants grow in diverse places because they
a. reproduce in any conditions
b. are consumers
c. adapt to their environment
d. have to feed animals

___ 5. The first plants needed ways to
a. reproduce in water
b. become consumers
c. support their bodies
d. use oxygen

___ 6. Being nonvascular limits moss's ability to
a. photosynthesize
b. control transpiration
c. grow tall
d. produce oxygen

DIVERSITY OF LIVING THINGS, CHAPTER 11, CHAPTER TEST B 51

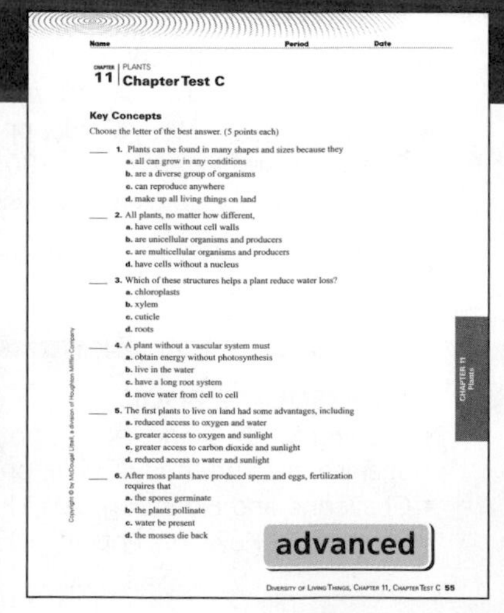

Name Period Date

CHAPTER 11 | PLANTS
Chapter Test C

Key Concepts
Choose the letter of the best answer. (5 points each)

___ 1. Plants can be found in many shapes and sizes because they
a. all can grow in any conditions
b. are a diverse group of organisms
c. can reproduce anywhere
d. make up all living things on land

___ 2. All plants, no matter how different,
a. have cells without cell walls
b. are unicellular organisms and producers
c. are multicellular organisms and producers
d. have cells without a nucleus

___ 3. Which of these structures helps a plant reduce water loss?
a. chloroplasts
b. xylem
c. cuticle
d. roots

___ 4. A plant without a vascular system must
a. obtain energy without photosynthesis
b. live in the water
c. have a long root system
d. move water from cell to cell

___ 5. The first plants to live on land had some advantages, including
a. reduced access to oxygen and water
b. greater access to oxygen and sunlight
c. greater access to carbon dioxide and sunlight
d. reduced access to water and sunlight

___ 6. After moss plants have produced sperm and eggs, fertilization requires that
a. the spores germinate
b. the plants pollinate
c. water be present
d. the mosses die back

DIVERSITY OF LIVING THINGS, CHAPTER 11, CHAPTER TEST C 55

UNIT ASSESSMENT BOOK, pp. 47–50 | pp. 51–54 | pp. 55–58

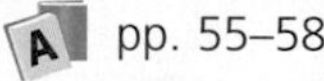

TECHNOLOGY

There are four Resource Centers for this chapter.

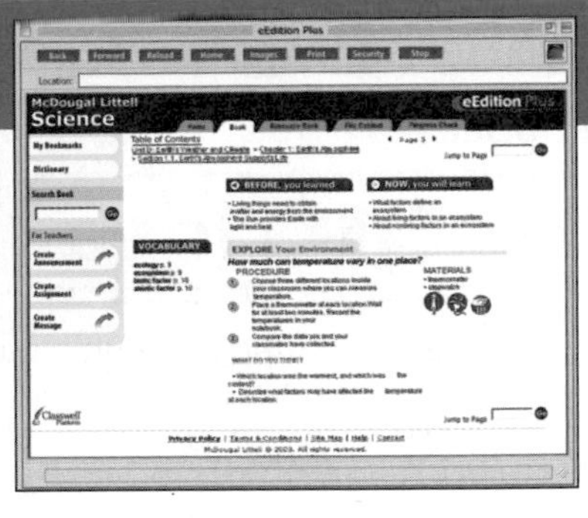

CLASSZONE.COM

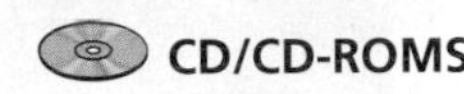
CD/CD-ROMS

CLASSZONE.COM

VISUAL CONTENT

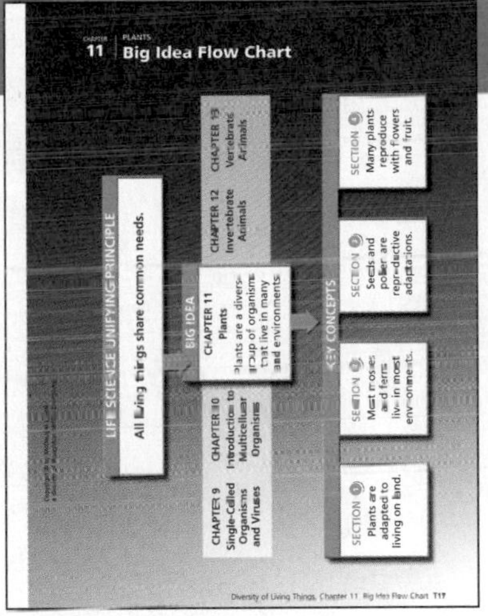

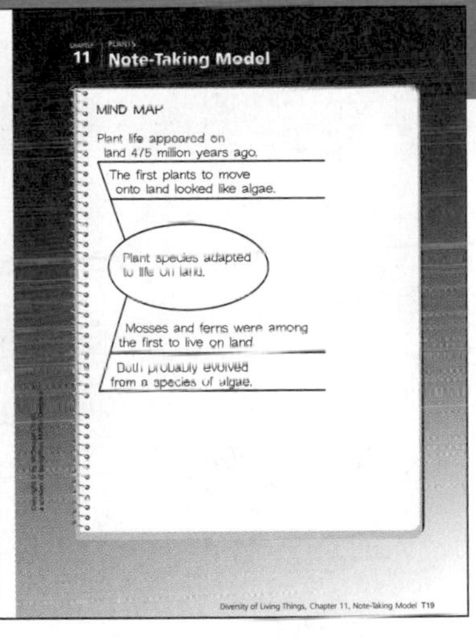

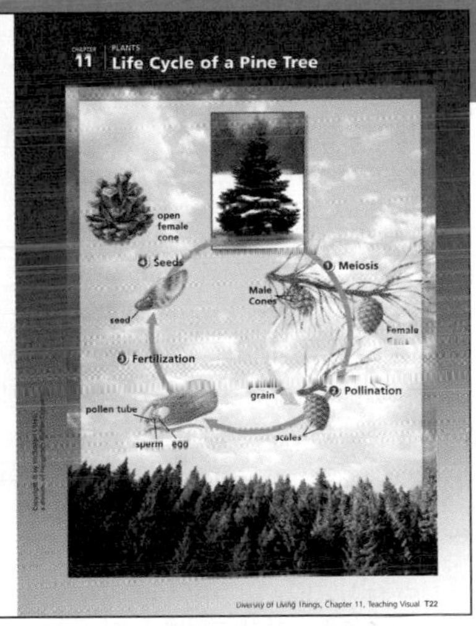

UNIT TRANSPARENCY BOOK, p. T17

p. T19

p. T22

MORE SUPPORT

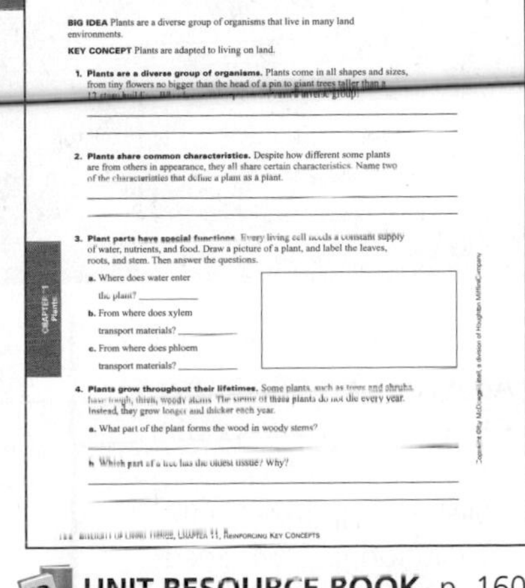

Reinforcing Key Concepts for each section

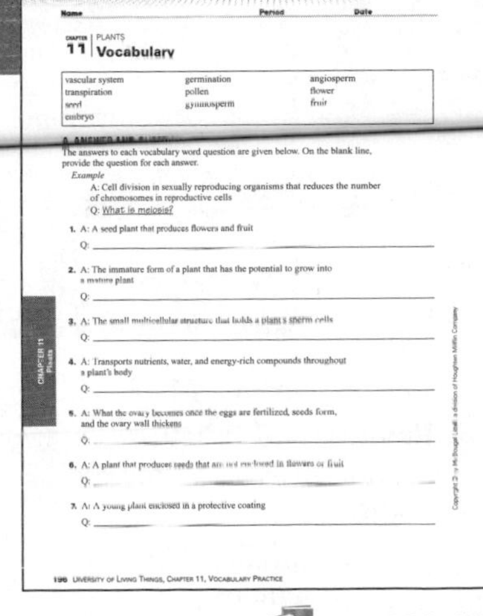

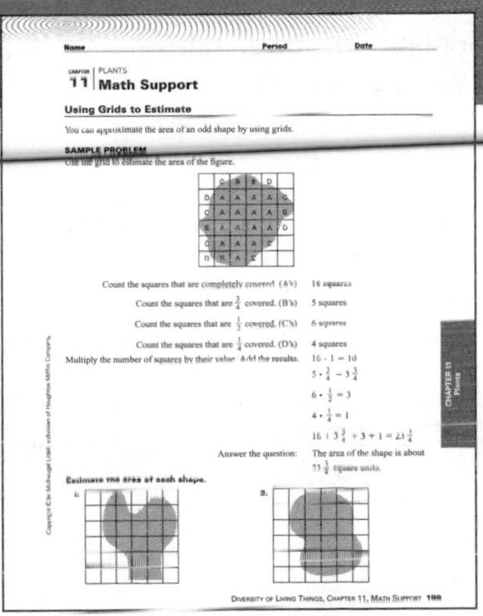

UNIT RESOURCE BOOK, p. 160

pp. 196–197

p. 199

CHAPTER 11 **Plants**

INTRODUCE

the BIG idea

Have students look at the photograph of plants and discuss how the question in the box links to the Big Idea:

- Why do some plants grow larger than others?
- Why can a tree grow larger and live longer than an animal?

National Science Education Standards

Content

C.2.b Plants reproduce sexually—the egg and sperm are produced in the flowers of flowering plants. An egg and sperm unite to begin development of a new individual.

C.4.c For ecosystems, the major source of energy is sunlight. Energy entering ecosystems as sunlight is transferred by producers into chemical energy through photosynthesis. That energy then passes from organism to organism in food webs.

Process

A.2–8 Design and conduct an investigation; use tools to gather and interpret data; use evidence to describe, predict, explain, model; think critically to make relationships between evidence and explanation; recognize different explanations and predictions; communicate scientific procedures and explanations; use mathematics.

A.9.a–c, A.9.e–f Understand scientific inquiry by using different investigations, methods, mathematics, and explanations based on logic, evidence, and skepticism.

G.1.b Science requires different abilities.

CHAPTER 11 Plants

the BIG idea

Plants are a diverse group of organisms that live in many land environments.

Key Concepts

SECTION

Plants are adapted to living on land.
Learn about plant characteristics and structures.

SECTION

Most mosses and ferns live in moist environments.
Learn about how mosses and ferns live and reproduce.

SECTION

Seeds and pollen are reproductive adaptations.
Learn about seeds, pollen, and gymnosperms.

SECTION

Many plants reproduce with flowers and fruit.
Learn about flowers, fruit, and angiosperms.

Internet Preview

CLASSZONE.COM

Chapter 11 online resources: Content Review, Simulation, Visualization, four Resource Centers, Math Tutorial, Test Practice

How does such a large tree get what it needs to survive?

INTERNET PREVIEW

CLASSZONE.COM For student use with the following pages:

Review and Practice
- Content Review, pp. 356, 388
- Math Tutorial: Using Grids to Estimate, p. 387
- Test Practice, p. 391

Activities and Resources
- Internet Activity: p. 355
- Resource Centers: Plant Systems, p. 362; Plant Evolution, p. 364; Seeds, p. 371; Extreme Seeds, p. 378
- Simulation: p. 384

Plant Kingdom
Code: MDL041

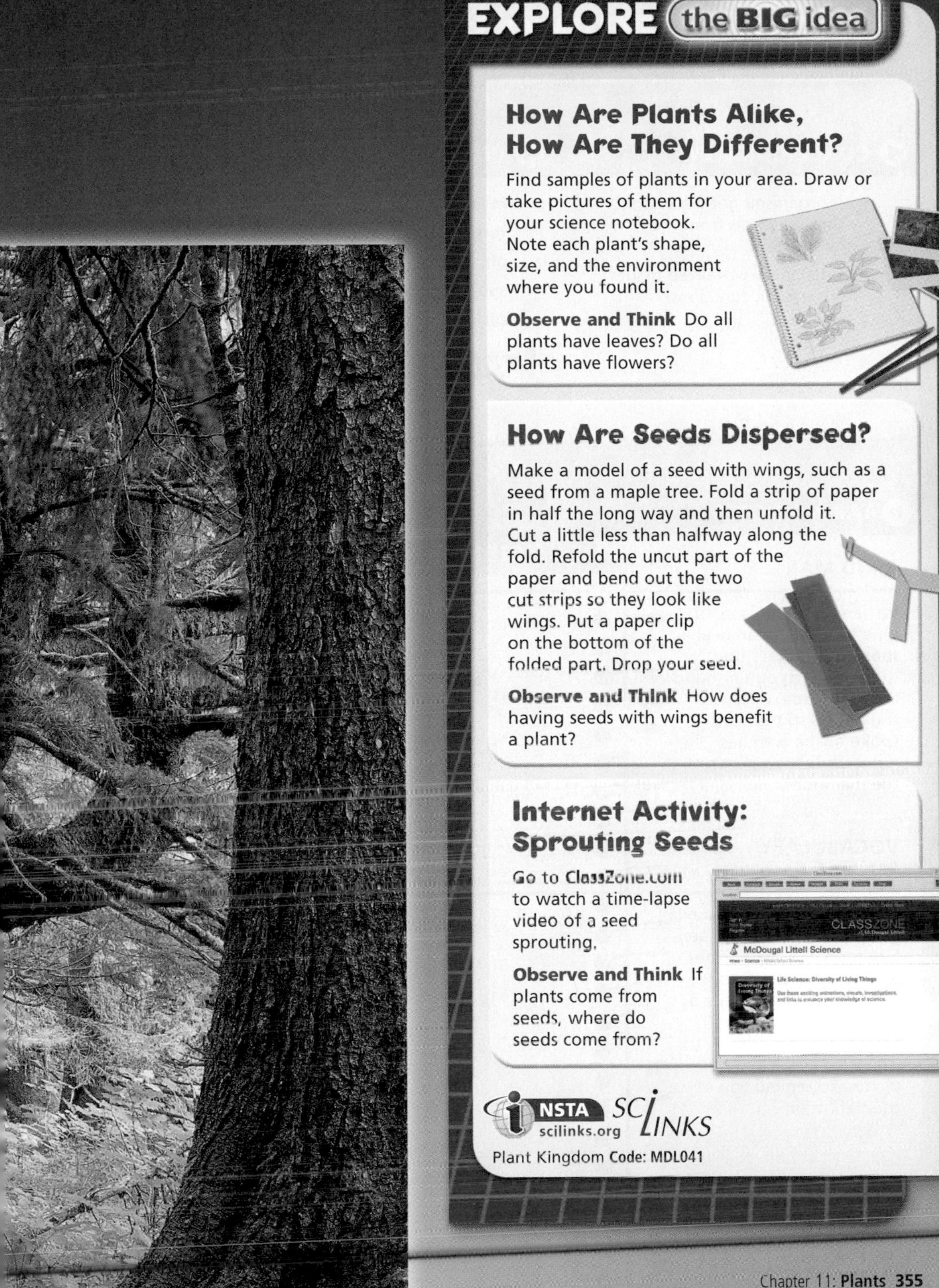

EXPLORE the BIG idea

How Are Plants Alike, How Are They Different?

Find samples of plants in your area. Draw or take pictures of them for your science notebook. Note each plant's shape, size, and the environment where you found it.

Observe and Think Do all plants have leaves? Do all plants have flowers?

How Are Seeds Dispersed?

Make a model of a seed with wings, such as a seed from a maple tree. Fold a strip of paper in half the long way and then unfold it. Cut a little less than halfway along the fold. Refold the uncut part of the paper and bend out the two cut strips so they look like wings. Put a paper clip on the bottom of the folded part. Drop your seed.

Observe and Think How does having seeds with wings benefit a plant?

Internet Activity: Sprouting Seeds

Go to **ClassZone.com** to watch a time-lapse video of a seed sprouting.

Observe and Think If plants come from seeds, where do seeds come from?

NSTA scilinks.org SCI LINKS

Plant Kingdom **Code: MDL041**

EXPLORE the BIG idea

These inquiry-based activities are appropriate for use at home or as a supplement to classroom instruction.

How Are Plants Alike, How Are They Different?

PURPOSE To compare and contrast samples of plants.

TIP *15 min.* Gather plants for students to examine. Use caution to avoid selecting poisonous plants.

Answer: Most plants have leaves, but they vary in shape and size. Most plants have flowers at some point in their life cycle, while some do not.

REVISIT after p. 358.

How Are Seeds Dispersed?

PURPOSE To make a model of a seed with wing-like structures.

TIP *15 min.* Make a sample model for students to follow. Ask students what the paper clip represents. *the seed* Encourage students to try dropping the "seeds" in various wind conditions, or from various heights. They might also experiment with types of paper.

Answer: Wing-like structures allow plants to spread seeds beyond the parent plant. This allows the young plants to grow without competition for sunlight, water, and nutrients.

REVISIT after p. 385.

Internet Activity: Sprouting Seeds

PURPOSE To observe how plants grow from seeds.

TIP *20 min.* Challenge students to create sketches of the sprouting seed.

Answer: Seeds come from the reproductive structures of plants, and are usually found in fruits or pinecones.

REVISIT after p. 371.

TEACHING WITH TECHNOLOGY

Digital Camera Students can use digital cameras to take daily photographs of the germinating seeds, while doing the Chapter Investigation on pp. 376–377. Have students include the photographs in their Science Notebooks.

CBL and Probeware Students might use a pressure sensor to study the movement of water within a plant while studying gas exchange and water loss in plants on p. 361. They could enter and plot the data on a graphing calculator.

PREPARE

CONCEPT REVIEW

Activate Prior Knowledge

- Ask students to name some of the common characteristics that all living organisms share. *All living organisms grow and reproduce and need energy, water, other materials, and living space.*
- What are some parts of plants you have seen? Can you name their function in the plant? *Sample answer: Roots take up water; seeds and flowers help the plant reproduce.*
- Ask students to give an example of an organism that could be called a "producer"—that is, one at the start of a food chain. *a plant or protist*

TAKING NOTES

Mind Map

Students may also use the red headings in the text to form the basis of some of the details in the Mind Map. The maps are useful as study tools when students review the chapter or organize their notes.

Vocabulary Strategy

The word triangle allows students to demonstrate understanding of nouns that can be illustrated with a visual. Illustrating terms and using them in meaningful sentences help students personalize and own the new concepts that challenge them.

Vocabulary and Note-Taking Resources

- Vocabulary Practice, pp. 196–197
- Decoding Support, p. 198

- Daily Vocabulary Scaffolding, p. T18
- Note-Taking Model, p. T19

- Word Triangle, B18–19
- Mind Map, C40–41
- Daily Vocabulary Scaffolding, H1–8

CHAPTER 11

Getting Ready to Learn

CONCEPT REVIEW

- All organisms get water and other materials from the environment.
- Plants have specialized tissues with specific functions.
- Plants are producers.

VOCABULARY REVIEW

meiosis p. 320
fertilization p. 320
photosynthesis p. 324
spore p. 339
cycle *See Glossary.*

CONTENT REVIEW
CLASSZONE.COM
Review concepts and vocabulary.

TAKING NOTES

MIND MAP

Write each main idea, or blue heading, in an oval; then write details that relate to each other and to the main idea. Organize the details so that each spoke of the web has notes about one part of the main idea.

VOCABULARY STRATEGY

Draw a **word triangle** diagram for each new vocabulary term. On the bottom line, write and define the term. Above that, write a sentence that uses the term correctly. At the top, draw a small picture to remind you of the definition.

See the Note-Taking Handbook on pages R45–R51.

SCIENCE NOTEBOOK

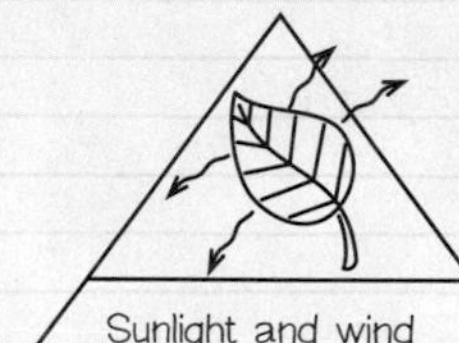

CHECK READINESS

Administer the Diagnostic Test to determine students' readiness for new science content and their mastery of requisite math skills.

 Diagnostic Test, pp. 41–42

Technology Resources

Students needing content and math skills should visit **ClassZone.com**.

- CONTENT REVIEW
- MATH TUTORIAL

 CONTENT REVIEW CD-ROM

KEY CONCEPT

Plants are adapted to living on land.

BEFORE, you learned
- All organisms have certain basic needs and characteristics
- The bodies of multicellular organisms are organized
- Plants are producers

NOW, you will learn
- About plant diversity
- About common characteristics of plants
- How the bodies of plants are organized

VOCABULARY
vascular system p. 359
transpiration p. 360

EXPLORE Leaf Characteristics

What is a leaf?

PROCEDURE

1. Examine the leaf your teacher gives you carefully. Try to notice as many details as you can.
2. Make a drawing of both sides of your leaf in your notebook. Label as many parts as you can and write down your ideas describing each part's function.
3. Compare your diagram and notes with those of your classmates.

MATERIALS
- assorted leaves
- hand lens

WHAT DO YOU THINK?
- What characteristics did most or all of your leaves have?
- How would you describe your leaf to someone who could not see it?

MIND MAP
Make a mind map for the first main idea: *Plants are a diverse group of organisms.*

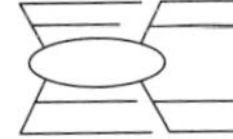

Plants are a diverse group of organisms.

Plants are nearly everywhere. Walk through a forest, and you're surrounded by trees, ferns, and moss. Drive along a country road, and you pass fields planted with crops like cotton or wheat. Even a busy city has tree-lined sidewalks, grass-covered lawns, and weeds growing in vacant lots or poking through cracks in the pavement.

Earth is home to an amazing variety of plant life. Plants come in all shapes and sizes, from tiny flowers no bigger than the head of a pin to giant trees taller than a 12-story building. Plants are found in all types of environments, from the icy Arctic to the steamy tropics.

RESOURCES FOR DIFFERENTIATED INSTRUCTION

Below Level

UNIT RESOURCE BOOK
- Reading Study Guide A, pp. 153–154
- Decoding Support, p. 198

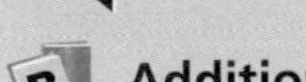 **AUDIO CDS**

Advanced

UNIT RESOURCE BOOK
- Challenge and Extension, p. 159
- Challenge Reading, pp. 194–195

English Learners

UNIT RESOURCE BOOK
Spanish Reading Study Guide, pp. 157–158

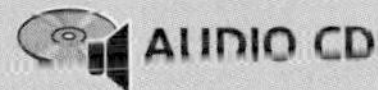

- Audio Readings in Spanish
- Audio Readings (English)

Additional INVESTIGATION, Fertilization in Angiosperms, A, B, & C, pp. 210–218; Teacher Instructions, pp. 360–361

11.1 FOCUS

Set Learning Goals

Students will
- Make observations about plant diversity.
- Identify common characteristics of plants.
- Describe how the bodies of plants are organized.

3-Minute Warm-Up

Display Transparency 20 or copy this exercise on the board:

Decide if these statements are true. If not true, correct them.

1. Living organisms need only water and air to survive. *Living organisms need to obtain energy, materials, water, and air to survive.*
2. Most multicellular organisms are organized into tissues and organs. *true*
3. Producers are organisms that feed off of other organisms. *Producers are organisms that capture energy to meet their needs.*

 3-Minute Warm-Up, p. T20

11.1 MOTIVATE

EXPLORE Leaf Characteristics

PURPOSE To explore the characteristics of a leaf

TIPS *15 min.* Use fallen leaves for this activity if you prefer not to remove leaves from living plants. Students may be able to see stomata on the undersides of certain types of leaves with the aid of a hand lens.

WHAT DO YOU THINK? *Sample answer: Most leaves are green and flat, have veins, are symmetrical, and have stems. Students may describe how big the leaves are and whether the leaves are round or pointed. Pine needles are, in fact, a type of modified leaf.*

11.1 INSTRUCT

Teach from Visuals

To help students interpret the photographs of plant diversity, ask:

- What structures of these plants are you able to observe? *leaves, flowers, stems, branches*
- What structures of these plants are you unable to see? *cells that make up the plants, roots, inside the layers of plant tissues*

EXPLORE the BIG idea

Revisit "How Are Plants Alike, How Are They Different?" on p. 355. Ask: What common features do the plants discussed on this page share with the plants you observed in the activity? *Students should now understand that despite unique or dissimilar appearances all plants are alike in four basic ways. Plants are multicellular, have a two-part life cycle, photosynthesize, and are made up of cells with nuclei and cell walls. They may also mention that the plants they have observed all have leaves, stems, and green color.*

Ongoing Assessment

Make observations about plant diversity.

Ask: What are some ways in which plants are diverse? *They vary in size, shape, color, and the environments in which they live.*

CHECK YOUR READING *Answer: 1) multicellular; 2) cell with nucleus and cell wall; 3) producers that get energy from the Sun; 4) two-part life cycle*

Diversity of Plants

Plant species live in a variety of environments and have a wide range of features.

Orchids

Seed pods of the vanilla orchid are used to flavor food.

Horsetails

Horsetails have a distinctive shape and texture.

Bristlecone Pine

Bristlecone pines are some of the oldest trees on Earth.

Plants share common characteristics.

Scientists estimate that at least 260,000 different species of plants live on Earth today. The photographs on this page show three examples of plants that are very different from one another.

Orchids are flowering plants that mostly grow in tropical rain forests. To get the sunlight they need, many orchids grow not in the soil but on the trunks of trees. Horsetails are plants that produce tiny grains of a very hard substance called silica. Sometimes called scouring rushes, these plants were once used to scrub clean, or scour, dishes and pots. Bristlecone pine trees live on high mountain slopes in North America, where there is little soil and often high winds. These trees grow very slowly and can live for several thousand years.

READING TIP

The word *species* comes from a root word meaning "kind" or "type." In science, *species* is a classification for a group of organisms that are so similar that members of the group can breed and produce offspring that can also reproduce. ? A

You can see from these three examples that plant species show great diversity. Despite how different an orchid is from a horsetail and a bristlecone pine, all three plants share certain characteristics. These are the characteristics that define a plant as a plant:

- Plants are multicellular organisms.
- A plant cell has a nucleus and is surrounded by a cell wall.
- Plants are producers. They capture energy from the Sun.
- Plant life cycles are divided into two stages, or generations.

CHECK YOUR READING What characteristics are shared by all plants?

358 Unit 3: **Diversity of Living Things**

DIFFERENTIATE INSTRUCTION

More Reading Support

A From where do plants obtain energy? *the Sun*

B What is common in all plant life cycles? *There are two stages or generations.*

English Learners Place the terms *vascular system* and *transpiration* on a classroom Science Word Wall with brief definitions of each. Pronounce these words for students.

English learners may not recognize that some words change their spellings when made plural. For example, in this section the words *leaf* and *leaves* are seen repeatedly. Point these out to students and give examples of other word pairs, such as *knife* and *knives*, or *hoof* and *hooves* that change when plural.

Plant parts have special functions.

You could say that a plant lives in two worlds. The roots anchor a plant in the ground. Aboveground, reaching toward the Sun, are stems and leaves. Together, stems and leaves make up a shoot system. These two systems work together to get a plant what it needs to survive.

REMINDER Plants, like animals, have several levels of oranization. The root system and shoot system are organ systems.

A plant's root system can be as extensive as the stems and leaves that you see aboveground. Roots absorb water and nutrients from the soil. These materials are transported to the leaves through the stems. The leaves use the materials, along with carbon dioxide from the air, to make sugars and carbohydrates. The stems then deliver these energy-rich compounds back to the rest of the plant.

? C

CHECK YOUR READING What are two plant systems, and what are their functions?

Transporting Water and Other Materials

Stems serve as the pathway for transporting water, nutrients, and energy-rich compounds from one part of a plant to another. In most plants, the materials move through a **vascular system** (VAS-kyuh-lur) that is made up of long, tubelike cells. These tissues are bundled together and run from the roots to the leaves. A vascular bundle from the stem of a buttercup plant is shown.

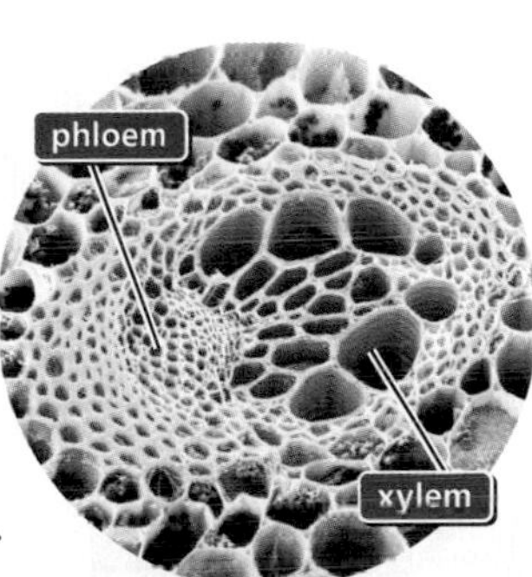

This vascular bundle has been magnified 113×.

? D

Transport is carried out by two types of tissue. Xylem (ZY-luhm) is a tissue that carries water and dissolved nutrients up from the roots. Phloem (FLOH-em) is a tissue that transports energy-rich materials down from the leaves. Xylem cells and phloem cells are long and hollow, like pipes. The xylem cells are a little larger than the phloem cells. Both tissues include long fibers that help support the plant body, as well as cells that can store extra carbohydrates for energy.

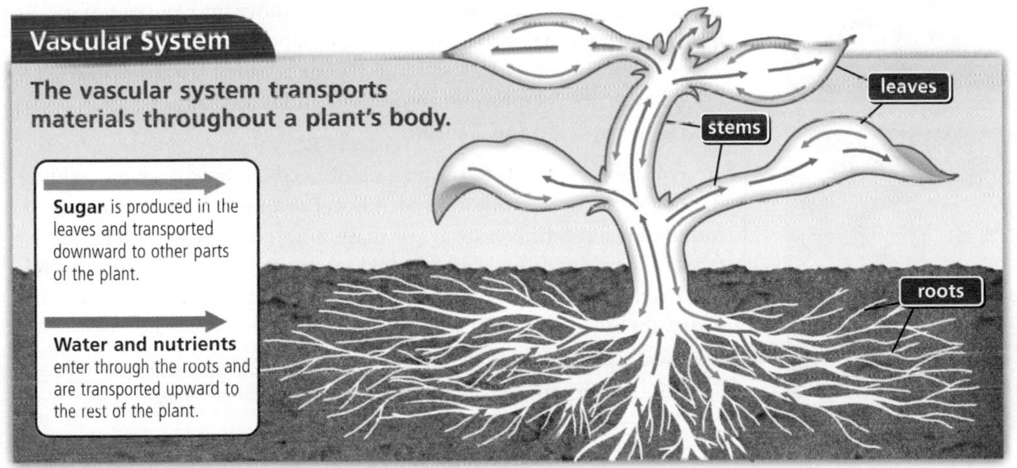

DIFFERENTIATE INSTRUCTION

More Reading Support

C What compounds are made in the leaves of plants? *sugars, carbohydrates*

D What tissues are in a plant's vascular system? *xylem, phloem*

Advanced Provide students with a sampling of leaves and a field guide for plants in your area. Challenge students to use the field guide to identify the plants. Ask students to describe the various criteria used to identify the plants.

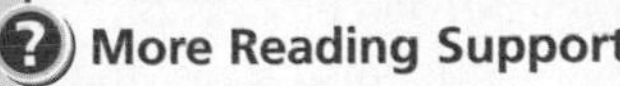

R Challenge and Extension, p. 159

Have students who are interested in how plants use water read the following article:

R Challenge Reading, pp. 194–195

Real World Example

The oldest trees on Earth are the bristlecone pines. Some bristlecones are over 4000 years old. The oldest known tree is nicknamed Methuselah, estimated to be over 4600 years old. The tree's exact location in the Inyo National Forest in California is kept secret by the U.S. Forest Service. The oldest trees are not necessarily the largest. Bristlecone pines grow very slowly. Their age can be determined by the number of growth rings they have.

Teach from Visuals

To help students interpret the diagram of vascular systems in plants, ask:

- In what parts of a plant are sugars made? *the green parts of a plant, its leaves and stems*
- Through which parts of a plant do water and some trace nutrients enter? *roots*

Teach Difficult Concepts

Tell students that plants need sugar for survival. Sugar, which is a molecule that contains carbon, is an essential nutrient for plant growth and function. Some other nutrients necessary for plants, such as nitrogen, enter through the roots. The bulk of material needed for a plant's growth is from water (absorbed from roots) and carbon dioxide (taken in from the air).

Ongoing Assessment

Identify common characteristics of plants.

Ask: What are two ways in which plant cells are all alike? *They each have a nucleus and a cell wall.*

CHECK YOUR READING *Answer: A root system brings in water and nutrients; a shoot system made up of leaves and stems makes energy-rich materials and moves material up and down through the plant.*

Address Misconceptions

IDENTIFY Ask students about where plants get sugars. Students may hold the misconception that plants get food from the soil.

CORRECT Ask students to study the formula for photosynthesis. Explain that the Sun provides energy for a series of chemical reactions that take place in plant cells. Plants do not eat "food," instead they make their own sugar. Ask students to name the raw materials and products of photosynthesis. *raw materials: carbon dioxide, water, and sunlight; products: sugars and oxygen*

REASSESS Sketch a tiny seedling and a tall tree on the board. Ask: Where did this plant get the materials to grow from so tiny to so big? *It absorbed water with its roots and used the Sun's energy to synthesize sugar in its leaves.*

Technology Resources

Visit **ClassZone.com** for background on common student misconceptions.

MISCONCEPTION DATABASE

History of Science

Many scientists have contributed to the understanding of how plants get the materials they need. It began in the mid 1600s. Belgian chemist Jan Baptista van Helmont grew a tree in a carefully measured amount of soil and gave it only water over a five-year period. Since the weight of the soil remained relatively unchanged, he concluded that plants do not "eat" soil.

Ongoing Assessment

CHECK YOUR READING *Answer: Photosynthesis is a series of chemical reactions that use energy from the Sun to produce sugars. It is important since this is how plants get their energy.*

Answer: The plant's cuticle and stomata keep it from drying out.

Making Sugars

Plants produce sugars through the process of photosynthesis. Photosynthesis is a series of chemical reactions that capture light energy from the Sun and convert it into chemical energy stored in sugar molecules. The starting materials needed are carbon dioxide, water, and light. The end products are sugars and oxygen. The chemical reactions for photosynthesis can be summarized like this:

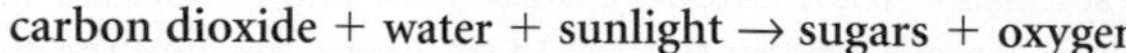
carbon dioxide + water + sunlight → sugars + oxygen

Photosynthesis takes place in chloroplasts, structures that contain chlorophyll. Chlorophyll absorbs the sunlight that the chloroplasts need to produce the reaction. Most chloroplasts in a plant are located in leaf cells. As you can see from the illustration on page 361, the structure of the leaf is specialized for capturing light energy and producing sugar.

What is photosynthesis, and why is it important?

The upper surface of the leaf, which is turned toward the Sun, has layers of cells filled with chloroplasts. Vascular tissue located toward the center of the leaf brings in water and nutrients and carries away sugars and other carbohydrates. Tiny openings at the bottom of the leaf, called stomata (STOH-muh-tuh), lead to a network of tiny spaces where gases are stored. The carbon dioxide gas needed for photosynthesis comes in through the stomata, and oxygen gas moves out. This process is called gas exchange.

Open Stomata

214×

Closed Stomata

Controlling Gas Exchange and Water Loss

For photosynthesis to occur, a plant must maintain the balance of carbon dioxide and water in its body. Carbon dioxide gas from the air surrounding a plant enters through the stomata in its leaves. Open stomata allow carbon dioxide and oxygen to move into and out of the leaf. These openings also allow water to evaporate. The movement of water vapor out of a plant and into the air is called **transpiration** (TRAN-spuh-RAY-shuhn). Both sunlight and wind cause water in leaves to evaporate and transpire.

For photosynthesis to occur, a plant needs to have enough carbon dioxide come in without too much water evaporating and moving out. Plants have different ways of maintaining this balance. The surfaces of leaves and stems are covered by a waxy protective layer, called a cuticle. The cuticle keeps water from evaporating. Also, when the air is dry, the stomata can close. This can help to prevent water loss.

What are two ways plants have to keep from losing too much water?

DIFFERENTIATE INSTRUCTION

More Reading Support

E Where does photosynthesis take place? *chloroplasts*

F Through which structures in the leaf do gases enter and leave the plant? *stomata*

Below Level To help students remember the process of photosynthesis, have them write a recipe. Students can list the "main ingredients" (carbon dioxide, water, and sunlight). Make sure students include process steps as well as ingredients in their recipe: the main ingredients are "combined," or "mixed," inside a chloroplast. The results yield sugars and oxygen.

Advanced Have a small group of advanced students design an experiment to recreate Priestley's experiment to show that plants release gas. They can perform the experiment with adult supervision.

DIFFERENTIATE INSTRUCTION

Below Level Ask students to describe in their own words the processes of photosynthesis and transpiration, using the main concepts presented in the visual.

English Learners Have students use a dictionary to find the origins of the word parts in *chloroplast* and *chlorophyll*. You might also write related words, such as *plastic, phyllo dough,* and *chlorine,* on the board. Chloro- *comes from a Greek word meaning* green; phyll- *comes from the Greek word for* leaf, *and* plast- *comes from the Greek word for* molded.

Teach from Visuals

To help students interpret the diagram of leaf structure, ask:

- Through which structure of the leaf does transpiration take place? *stomata*
- Where are most of the chloroplasts in the leaf located? Why do you think this is so? *In the upper layer; the chloroplasts need to be exposed to sunlight for photosynthesis to take place.*

Teaching with Technology

If pressure sensor probeware is available, have students use it to measure pressure in stems and leaves of a classroom plant. They can use a graphing calculator to show the data visually. Then ask them to use their data to infer which times had faster or slower transpiration rates.

Teacher Demo

Obtain two long balloons and inflate them. Use the balloons to demonstrate the opening and closing of stomata. Ask: Under what conditions do stomata open and close? *Stomata open to allow oxygen in and carbon dioxide and water vapor out; stomata close under dry conditions to prevent water loss.*

Language Arts Connection

Students can write or narrate the story of imaginary travel through the structure of a leaf. Have them describe what cells are at the surface, and what structures such as xylem, phloem, and stomata look like and do. Assign a choice of formats for the story such as poem, newscast, letters, diary, or comic strip.

Ongoing Assessment

Describe how the bodies of plants are organized.

Ask: Which tissue in a leaf transports sugars and runs through all parts of the plant? *phloem*

READING VISUALS *Answer: The top of a leaf has a waxy covering (cuticle) and more cells with chloroplasts; the bottom of the leaf has stomata.*

Develop Critical Thinking

INFER Direct attention to the photograph of the prickly pear cactus. Ask: How might the spines be a benefit to the cactus other than being a way to minimize water loss? *The spines keep it from being eaten by consumers.*

Integrate the Sciences

Colors of the visible spectrum include red, orange, yellow, green, blue, and violet. Most objects reflect some of the colors of the spectrum while they absorb other colors. When light strikes the leaves of a plant, the green waves of the spectrum are reflected, giving the leaves their green color. All of the other colors are absorbed.

Ongoing Assessment

CHECK YOUR READING *Answer: Plant stems can 1) store food; 2) provide support for the plant body; and 3) transport materials via the vascular system. Some plants, such as cacti, perform photosynthesis in their stems.*

APPLY Plant stems branch as they grow. Do cactus plants have branches?

The stomata are an adaptation that allows a plant to adjust to daily changes in its environment. Plants can respond to hot, dry weather by keeping their stomata closed. Stomata can be open during the night, when evaporation is less likely to occur. Most plants have stomata.

G

Some species of plants have special adaptations for survival in a particular environment. For example, a cactus plant has adaptations that allow it to survive in a desert. The spines of a cactus are actually modified leaves. A plant with regular leaves would lose too much water through transpiration. In cacti, most photosynthesis occurs in the thick fleshy stem, where the cactus also stores water and carbon dioxide gas.

Plants grow throughout their lifetimes.

Plants grow as long as they live. This is true for plants that live for only one season, such as sunflowers, and for plants that can live for many years, such as trees. Plants grow bigger when cells at the tips of their roots and stems divide and multiply more rapidly than other plant cells do. A plant's roots and stems can grow longer and thicker and can branch, or divide. However, only stems grow leaves. Leaves grow from buds produced by growth tissue in a plant's stems. The bud of an oak tree is shown on page 363.

Plant stems are structures with more than one function. You have read that a plant's stem includes its vascular system, which allows the plant to transport materials between its leaves and roots. Long stiff fibers in the tissues of the vascular system provide support and give the plant shape. Plant stems can also store the sugars produced by photosynthesis. Many plants, including broccoli, celery, and carrots, convert sugars into starch and then store this energy-rich material in their stems or roots.

What are three functions of plant stems?

Plants with Soft Stems

Learn more about plant systems.

The soft stems and leaves of many wildflowers, garden flowers, and vegetables die when the environment they live in becomes too cold or too dry. This type of plant survives by using the carbohydrates stored in its roots. Then, when the environment provides it with enough warmth, water, and sunlight, the plant will grow new, soft, green stems and leaves.

DIFFERENTIATE INSTRUCTION

More Reading Support

G Describe how stomata respond to hot, dry weather. *They stay closed during the day and may open at night when it is cooler.*

English Learners Pair students who are new to English with partners who are advanced. Have them use web sites, botany books, or field guides to prepare a booklet of Unusual Plant Adaptations. Encourage each pair to present a picture, diagram, or illustration of the plant's unusual structure(s). They should include a sentence on how the structure benefits the plant or suits it to its environment. Suggest students research one of the following plants to begin: staghorn, rafflesia, mangrove, Venus flytrap, and bristlecone pine.

Plant Growth

Plants, such as these oak trees, grow most when there is enough warmth, water, and sunlight.

Oak Bud

The tips of the shoots produce buds, which become new leaves and stems.

Plants with Woody Stems

Some plants, such as trees and shrubs, have tough, thick stems that do not die each year. These stems keep growing longer and thicker. As the stems grow, they develop a type of tough xylem tissue that is not found in soft stems. This tough xylem tissue is called wood. The growing tissues in woody stems are located near the outer surface of the stem, right under the bark. This means that, for a tree like one of the oaks in the photograph above, the center of the trunk is the oldest part of the plant.

11.1 Review

KEY CONCEPTS

1. What characteristics do all plants have in common?
2. How does the structure of a leaf relate to its function?
3. What tissues move materials throughout a plant?

CRITICAL THINKING

4. **Summarize** Describe how the structure of a leaf allows a plant to control the materials involved in photosynthesis.
5. **Analyze** Do you think the stems of soft-stemmed plants have chloroplasts? How about woody-stemmed plants? Explain your reasoning. Hint: Think about the color of each.

CHALLENGE

6. **Evaluate** Scientists who study the natural world say that there is unity in diversity. How does this idea apply to plants?

ANSWERS

1. Plants are multicellular with cells that have a nucleus and a cell wall. They are producers and have a two-stage life cycle.

2. A leaf is suited for photosynthesis, having cells with many chloroplasts at its surface. Xylem brings in water. Stomata let in carbon dioxide. The cuticle keeps water in. Phloem transports sugars.

3. xylem and phloem

4. Stomata regulate the amount of carbon dioxide, oxygen, and water vapor that enters and exits the plant.

5. Soft-stemmed plants have green stems, with cells that have chloroplasts. Woody stems are brown or grey; the cells do not have chloroplasts.

6. Plants differ in height. Some are soft-stemmed. Some are woody. They live in many different environments. Yet the basic structure is the same: roots, stems, leaves. All rely on photosynthesis to get needed energy and materials.

Reinforce (the BIG idea)

Have students relate the section to the Big Idea.

 Reinforcing Key Concepts, p. 160

11.1 ASSESS & RETEACH

Assess

 Section 11.1 Quiz, p. 43

Reteach

Have students create comic strips that describe the process of photosynthesis. Tell students to include in their comic strips the following key points, which can be provided before they begin:

- where photosynthesis occurs: *in chloroplasts*
- where raw materials come from: *sunlight and air*
- what the raw materials are: *carbon dioxide, water, and light energy*
- how the raw materials get into the leaf: *CO_2 through stomata, light absorbed by chloroplasts, water by roots*
- what the end products are: *sugar and oxygen*
- how the end products move from the leaf to other parts of the plant or out into the air: *Sugars are carried by phloem to all parts of plant; oxygen is released through stomata.*

Technology Resources

Have students visit **ClassZone.com** for reteaching of Key Concepts.

 CONTENT REVIEW

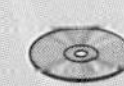 CONTENT REVIEW CD-ROM

11.2 FOCUS

Set Learning Goals

Students will

- Explain how plants are adapted to live on land.
- Describe the reproductive cycle of mosses.
- Describe the reproductive cycles of ferns.
- Measure distance to infer how much sunlight reaches an organism.

3-Minute Warm-Up

Display Transparency 20 or copy this exercise on the board:

Complete the chart to describe the characteristics of plants.

Plant Adaptations	
Characteristics	*multicellular, cell walls, nuclei, two-stage life cycles*
Functions	*photosynthesis, transpiration*
Structures	*roots, stems, leaves*

3-Minute Warm-Up, p. T20

11.2 MOTIVATE

EXPLORE Moss Plants

PURPOSE To observe the structures of moss plants

TIP *15 min.* Growing moss plants can be purchased from biological supply companies. If possible, obtain "sporulating" moss so that students can observe the spore-making stalk-and-capsule structures (sporophytes) as well as the more familiar leafy green parts (gametophytes).

WHAT DO YOU THINK? *Sample answer: Students observations may include noticing that typical moss has leaf-like structures that branch off a main stem. These structures are often arranged in a spiral around the central stem. Moss plants are not very tall and the plant bodies are only a few millimeters thick.*

KEY CONCEPT

11.2 Most mosses and ferns live in moist environments.

BEFORE, you learned

- All plants share common characteristics
- The body of a plant has specialized parts
- Plants grow throughout their lifetimes

NOW, you will learn

- About the first plants
- About reproduction in nonvascular plants, such as mosses
- About reproduction in vascular plants, such as ferns

EXPLORE Moss Plants

What do moss plants look like?

PROCEDURE

1. Use a hand lens to examine a moss plant. Look for different structures and parts you can identify.
2. Draw a diagram of the moss plant in your notebook. Label parts you identified and parts you would like to identify.
3. Write a brief description of each part's function.

MATERIALS

- live moss plant
- hand lens

WHAT DO YOU THINK?

- How would you describe a moss plant to someone who had never seen one?
- How does a moss plant compare with the other plants you are familiar with?

Plant species adapted to life on land.

Evidence indicates that life first appeared on Earth about 3.8 billion years ago. Tiny single-celled and multicellular organisms lived in watery environments such as warm shallow seas, deep ocean vents, and ponds. Fossil evidence suggests that plant life did not appear on land until about 475 million years ago. The ancestors of the first plants were among the first organisms to move onto land.

What did these plantlike organisms look like? Scientists think they looked much like the green algae you can find growing in watery ditches or shallow ponds today. Both green algae and plants are autotrophs, or producers. Their cells contain chloroplasts that enable them to convert the Sun's light energy into the chemical energy stored in sugars.

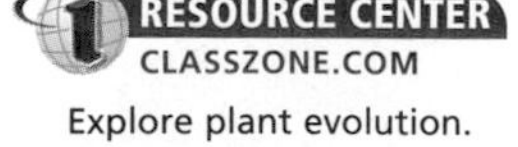

Explore plant evolution.

364 Unit 3: Diversity of Living Things

RESOURCES FOR DIFFERENTIATED INSTRUCTION

Below Level

UNIT RESOURCE BOOK

- Reading Study Guide A, pp. 163–164
- Decoding Support, p. 198

AUDIO CDS

Advanced

UNIT RESOURCE BOOK

Challenge and Extension, p. 169

English Learners

UNIT RESOURCE BOOK

Spanish Reading Study Guide, pp. 167–168

AUDIO CDS

- Audio Readings in Spanish
- Audio Readings (English)

The First Plants

Suppose that hundreds of millions of years ago, the area now occupied by your school was a shallow pond full of tiny, floating organisms that could photosynthesize. The Sun overhead provided energy. The pond water was full of dissolved nutrients. The organisms thrived and reproduced, and over time the pond became crowded. Some were pushed to the very edges of the water. Then, after a period of dry weather, the pond shrank. Some organisms at the edge were no longer in the water. The ones that were able to survive were now living on land.

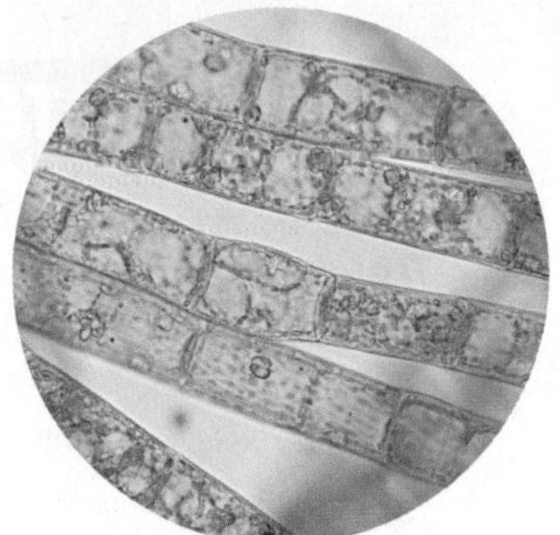

Scientists think the first plants shared a common ancestor with green algae, shown here magnified about 80×.

Scientists think that something like this took place in millions of watery environments over millions of years. Those few organisms that were stranded and were able to survive became ancestors to the first plants. Life on land is very different from life in water. The first plants needed to be able to get both nutrients and water from the land. There is no surrounding water to provide support for the body or to keep body tissues from drying out. However, for organisms that survived, life on land had many advantages. There is plenty of carbon dioxide in the air and plenty of direct sunlight.

CHECK YOUR READING Why is having plenty of sunlight and water an advantage for a plant? Your answer should mention photosynthesis.

Mosses and Ferns

Among the first plants to live on Earth were the ancestors of the mosses and ferns you see today. Both probably evolved from species of algae that lived in the sea and in freshwater. Mosses are simpler in structure than ferns. Mosses, and two closely related groups of plants known as liverworts and hornworts, are descended from the first plants to spread onto the bare rock and soil of Earth. Ferns and their relatives appeared later.

This diorama shows what a forest on Earth might have looked like about 350 million years ago.

DIFFERENTIATE INSTRUCTION

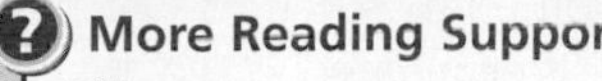

More Reading Support

A Which plants most likely first appeared on land? *mosses*

B Which plants appeared after mosses? *ferns*

Advanced Have students make their own dioramas similar to the Field Museum diorama of a swamp forest in the prehistoric Carboniferous Era shown on this page. They can work from the photographs on pp. 365–369 to plan materials that resemble the mosses, ferns, liverworts, and hornworts of 350 million years ago. They should add a caption to their display that summarizes their understanding of "Earth's First Plants."

R Challenge and Extension, p. 169

11.2 INSTRUCT

Integrate the Sciences

The first plants to invade the land probably appeared during the Ordovician Period of the Paleozoic Era (505 to 438 million years ago). The oldest fossil evidence of plants is of liverworts from the rocks of the Devonian Period, about 400 million years ago.

Teach from Visuals

To help students interpret the diorama of forests growing 350 million years ago, ask: How might an artist know what plants looked like millions of years ago? *Fossil evidence would tell scientists about the structure and size of plants.*

Real World Example

Point out that the illustration shows a diorama from the Field Museum of Natural History in Chicago. It is an artist's depiction of a swamp forest of the Carboniferous Era (about 350 million years ago). The plants that look like trees are giant club mosses, which are a type of fern. The plants in the foreground in front of the fallen log are ancestors of horsetails, similar to the ones in the photograph on p. 358.

Ongoing Assessment

Describe how the first plants appeared on land.

Ask: From which organisms did the first land plants evolve? *algae*

CHECK YOUR READING *Answer: The more sunlight and water available to the plant, the more energy-rich sugars the plant can produce through photosynthesis.*

INVESTIGATE Capturing the Sun's Energy

PURPOSE To explore how much sunlight reaches an organism in water

TIPS *20 min.* Before the investigation, attach the button to the string and lower it into the water. The button should not float. When the kelp granules are added, part of the water will be obscured. Explain that the kelp represents organisms floating in the ocean.

WHAT DO YOU THINK? *The second distance was shorter. On land, all organisms are "on the surface" of Earth and so have generally better access to sunlight.*

CHALLENGE *The kelp granules represent organisms for resources. On land, where there is generally better access to resources such as sunlight, there is less competition for such resources.*

Datasheet, Capturing the Sun's Energy, p. 170

Technology Resources

Customize this student lab as needed or look for an alternative. Print rubrics to assess student lab reports.

Lab Generator CD-ROM

Develop Critical Thinking

SYNTHESIS Write the term *osmosis* on the board and explain to students that this is the process by which water moves through a membrane such as a cell membrane. Ask: If there is a higher concentration of water molecules outside a cell membrane than on the inside of the cell membrane, what will happen? *The water will move through the membrane to the area of lesser concentration.* How does osmosis relate to nonvascular plants? *Nonvascular plants such as mosses transport water from one part of the plant to another by the process of osmosis.*

Ongoing Assessment

CHECK YOUR READING *Answer: Mosses are nonvascular plants. Water passes through their bodies cell by cell. This limits their size because their stems can be only a few cells thick.*

INVESTIGATE Capturing the Sun's Energy

SKILL FOCUS
Measuring

MATERIALS
- white button
- string
- empty clear plastic bottle
- water
- ruler
- kelp granules
- tablespoon

TIME
20 minutes

How much sunlight reaches an organism living in water?

PROCEDURE

1. Thread the string through the holes in the button so that the button hangs flat. Fill the empty bottle with clean water.
2. Look down through the top of the bottle. Lower the button into the water until it either disappears from view or reaches the bottom. Have a classmate measure how far the button is from the surface of the water.
3. Add two spoonfuls of kelp granules to the water. Repeat step 2.

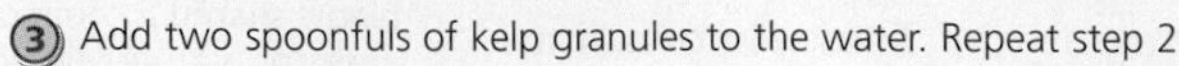

WHAT DO YOU THINK?
- How did the distance measured the second time compare with your first measurement?
- Why might a photosynthetic organism living on land get more sunlight than one living in water?

CHALLENGE What do the kelp granules in this experiment represent? What does that suggest about the advantages of living on land?

Mosses are nonvascular plants.

Moss plants have adaptations for life on land. For example, each moss cell, like all plant cells, is surrounded by a thick wall that provides it with support. Moss cells also have special storage areas for water and nutrients. Mosses do not grow very large, but they have simple structures that function like roots, stems, and leaves. These adaptations help moss plants survive on land, while algae survive only in water.

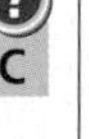

If you look closely at a clump of moss, you will see that it is actually made up of many tiny, dark green plants. Mosses belong to a group called nonvascular plants. Nonvascular plants do not have vascular tissue. Water and nutrients simply move through nonvascular plants' bodies cell by cell. A plant can get enough water this way as long as its body is no more than a few cells thick.

CHECK YOUR READING What limits the size of moss plants?

Water also plays a part in the reproductive cycle of a moss plant. In the first part of the cycle, the moss grows and maintains itself, producing the male and female structures needed for sexual reproduction. If conditions are right and there is enough water, the plant enters a spore-producing stage, the second part of the cycle.

DIFFERENTIATE INSTRUCTION

More Reading Support

C Why are mosses described as nonvascular plants? *They do not have vascular tissues.*

D Which reproduction involves male and female structures? *sexual*

English Learners The investigation on p. 366 uses imperative sentences. The word "you" is eliminated in the directions. Make sure English learners know how to read and follow these directions. For example, the direction "Look down through the top of the bottle," is to be understood as "You look down through the top of the bottle."

Mosses reproduce with spores.

Mosses, ferns, and fungi all reproduce with spores. Spores are an important adaptation that allowed the ancestors of these organisms to reproduce on land. A spore is a single reproductive cell that is protected by a hard, watertight covering. The covering prevents the cell from drying out. Spores are small and can be transported through the air. This means offspring from spores can grow in places that are distant from the parent organisms.

REMINDER

Sexual reproduction involves two processes: fertilization and meiosis.

The green moss plants you are familiar with have grown from spores. They represent the first generation. Within a clump of moss are both male and female reproductive structures. When conditions are right, these structures produce sperm and eggs. Fertilization can occur only if water is present because the tiny moss sperm move by swimming. A layer of water left by rain is one way sperm can move to the eggs on another part of the plant.

The fertilized egg grows into a stalk with a capsule on the end—the second generation of the plant. The stalk and capsule grow from the female moss plant. Inside the capsule, the process of meiosis produces thousands of tiny spores. When the spores are released, as shown in the photograph, the cycle can begin again.

Moss Releasing Spores

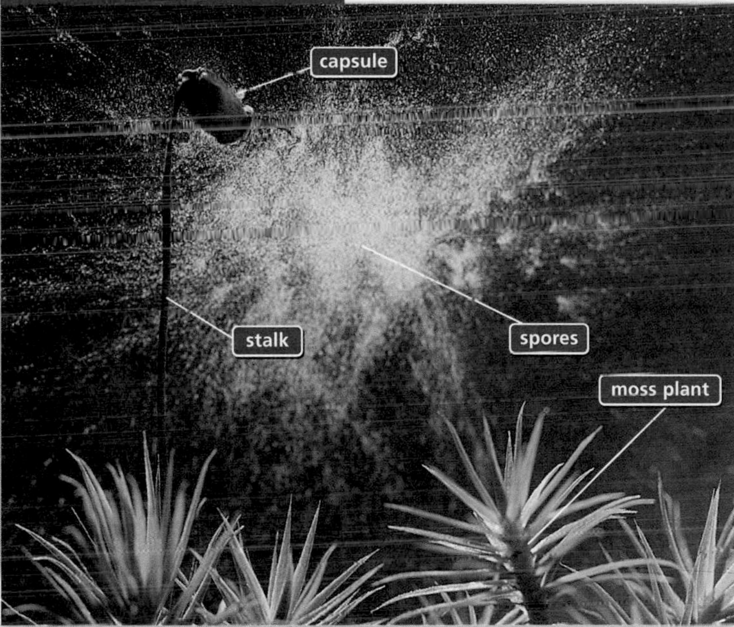

IDENTIFY Point out the two generations of the moss plant shown here.

Address Misconceptions

IDENTIFY Ask students if a moss is more like a rock or an animal. Students may hold the misconception that plants are not living things. They may say plants have more in common with a rock because neither can move around. However plants have much more in common with other living things, such as animals, than they do with nonliving things, such as rocks.

CORRECT Have students recall what characteristics and needs are shared by all living things. *characteristics: grow, reproduce, have an organized structure, use energy; needs: water, oxygen, nutrients, energy, living space*

REASSESS Ask students if mosses fit this description. *Mosses reproduce, grow, and need water and nutrients.*

Technology Resources

Visit **ClassZone.com** for background on common student misconceptions.

MISCONCEPTION DATABASE

Teach Difficult Concepts

Students may not understand the concept of two generations, the idea that a plant takes two different forms during its reproductive cycle. Ask:

- What does a moss plant grow from? *spores*
- How are spores produced? *Fertilization must occur in the moss plant, producing a stalk and capsule. Spores are produced by meiosis in the capsule.*
- What two forms does a moss take during its reproductive cycle? *moss plant and stalk with capsule*

DIFFERENTIATE INSTRUCTION

More Reading Support

E What do male moss plants produce in order to reproduce sexually? *sperm*

F What does the fertilized egg of a moss plant grow into? *a stalk with a capsule on the end*

Advanced Pair students to create a diagram to show the two-part life cycle of mosses. Students should label stages and identify the generation to which each stage belongs. They should use the last two paragraphs and photograph on p. 367 to break out steps of the cycle and relate them in a repeating sequence. *FIRST GENERATION: 1. Capsule releases spores. 2. Spores grow into green moss plant with male and female structures. 3. Sperm fertilizes egg. SECOND GENERATION. 4. Stalk and capsule grow from egg. 5. Inside capsule meiosis produces spores.*

Ongoing Assessment

PHOTO CAPTION *Answer: The green clumps are the first generation; the stalk and capsule are the second generation.*

Teacher Demo

You can demonstrate how mosses can grow by asexual reproduction. Take moss and crumble it in a blender. Mix 1 part moss to 2 parts buttermilk (for nutrients). Spread the mixture on some rocks in a terrarium and keep moist and shady (3–6 hours of sunlight per day). The moss cells in the mix will grow into new moss plants in about 8 weeks.

Develop Critical Thinking

INFER Direct attention to the photographs of nonvascular and vascular plants. Ask: What is different about the arrangement of cells in the fern compared to those in a moss? *The fern has vascular tissue, that is groups of cells working together to move nutrients and water throughout the plant. The moss does not.*

Teach from Visuals

To help students understand the photograph on p. 369 of the fern and its spores, ask: What part of the fern life cycle is shown? How do you know? *The second part of the life cycle is shown because the leafy frond has developed spore-producing clusters.*

Ongoing Assessment

Describe the function of vascular tissue.

Ask: What are two functions of vascular tissue that enable vascular plants to grow larger than nonvascular plants? *Vascular tissue moves nutrients and water more quickly and also provides support.*

CHECK YOUR READING *Answer: In sexual reproduction the genetic material from two parents comes together producing offspring with a mix of genetic material. In asexual reproduction, the genetic material of the offspring is the same as the parent's.*

READING VISUALS *Answer: The penny and the person in the photographs show the difference in scale between the two plants.*

G

Mosses, like other plants, can also reproduce asexually. A small piece of a moss plant can separate and can grow into a new plant, or new plants can branch off from old ones. Asexual reproduction allows plants to spread more easily than sexual reproduction. However, the genetic material of the new plants is the same as that of the parent. Sexual reproduction increases genetic diversity and the possibility of new adaptations.

Compare and contrast sexual and asexual reproduction. Your answer should mention *genetic material.*

Ferns are vascular plants.

H

Ferns, and two closely related groups of plants known as horsetails and club mosses, were the first plants on Earth with vascular systems. The tubelike tissue of a vascular system moves water through a plant's body quickly and effectively. Because of this transport system, vascular plants can grow much larger than nonvascular plants. Vascular tissue also provides support for the weight of a larger plant.

The presence of vascular tissue has an effect on the development of roots, stems, and leaves. The root system can branch out more, anchoring a larger plant as well as providing water and nutrients. Vascular tissue moves materials more efficiently and gives extra support. The stems can branch out and more leaves can grow. This results in more sugars and other materials needed for energy and growth.

Nonvascular

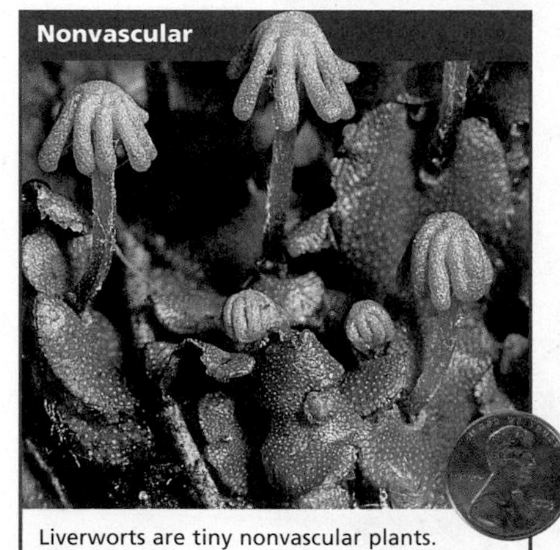

Liverworts are tiny nonvascular plants. The liverworts shown here are life-size.

Vascular

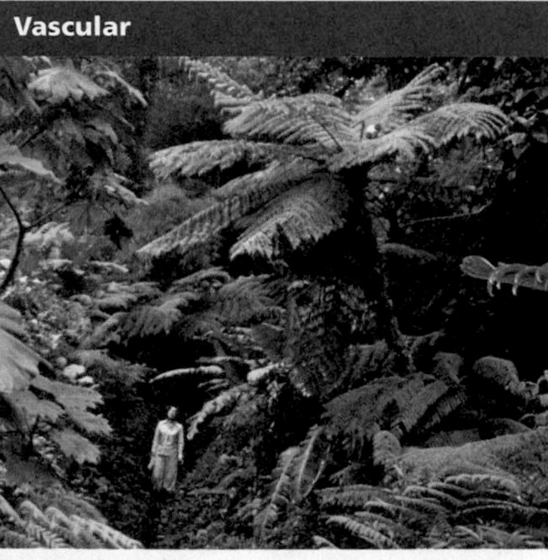

Ferns are vascular plants. Notice how tall a tree fern can grow.

READING VISUALS **COMPARE AND CONTRAST** How do the penny and the person help to show that the tree ferns are much larger than the liverworts?

368 Unit 3: Diversity of Living Things

DIFFERENTIATE INSTRUCTION

More Reading Support

G How are mosses able to reproduce? *asexually and sexually*

H What were the first plants with vascular systems? *ferns*

Below Level Have pairs of students create a two-column chart to compare mosses and ferns. Each student should complete one column of the chart for each plant. Students then highlight in red how the plants are similar. Then they highlight in blue how the plants are different.

Ferns reproduce with spores.

As fern fronds grow, they produce clusters of spores on the back of the fronds.

You may have seen ferns growing in the woods or in a garden. The leaves of ferns, called fronds, are often included in a flower bouquet. The next time you have a chance to look at a fern frond, take a look at the back. You will probably see many small clusters similar to those shown to the right. The clusters are full of spores.

Ferns, like mosses, have a two-part life cycle. In ferns, spores grow into tiny structures that lie very close to the ground. You would have to look closely to find these structures on the ground, for they are usually smaller than the size of your thumbnail. Within these structures are the sperm- and egg-producing parts of the fern plant. This is the first generation of the plant. Like mosses, the sperm of a fern plant need water to swim to the egg. So fertilization occurs only when plenty of moisture is present.

The second part of a fern life cycle is the plant with fronds that grows from the fertilized egg. As the fronds grow, the small egg-bearing part of the plant dies away. The fronds produce clusters, and cells within those clusters undergo meiosis and produce spores. The more the fern grows, the more clusters and spores it produces. The spores, when they are released, spread through the air. If conditions are right where the spores land, they grow into new fern plants and a new cycle begins. This is sexual reproduction. Ferns, like mosses, also reproduce asexually. New ferns branch off old ones, or pieces separate from the plant and grow.

CHECK YOUR READING Explain one way that sexual reproduction in ferns is similar to reproduction in mosses. Explain one way it is different.

11.2 Review

KEY CONCEPTS

1. For the ancestors of the first plants, what were some advantages to living on land?
2. What are three adaptations that make mosses able to live on land?
3. What are two characteristics you can observe that distinguish vascular plants from nonvascular plants?

CRITICAL THINKING

4. **Synthesize** Vascular plants such as ferns can grow bigger and taller than nonvascular plants such as mosses. Does this mean they can also capture more sunlight? Explain your answer.
5. **Compare** Make a chart that shows how the life cycles of mosses and ferns are different, and how they are similar.

CHALLENGE

6. **Evaluate** Consider the conditions that are needed for mosses and ferns to reproduce sexually. Sexual reproduction increases genetic diversity within a group of plants, while asexual reproduction does not. Explain why asexual reproduction is still important for both moss and fern plants.

ANSWERS

1. They had easier access to carbon dioxide and sunlight.

2. Mosses have simple roots, stems, leaves; can store water and nutrients; and produce spores.

3. Vascular plants can grow taller and have larger stems and leaves.

4. The larger the plant, the more chloroplasts it has to capture energy.

5. Differences: main moss plant produces eggs and sperm, main fern plant produces spores; similarities: two-part life cycle, have spores, need water

6. Asexual reproduction allows plants to spread more quickly. Plants can reproduce under conditions that are not favorable to sexual reproduction.

Ongoing Assessment

Describe the life cycles of ferns.

Ask: Where are the spore producing clusters found on ferns, and what do the spores do? *On the underside of the leafy part of the fern, known as a frond; the spores grow into tiny structures as one stage of the fern life cycle.*

CHECK YOUR READING *Sample answer: Similarities: two-part life cycles, sperm that swim through water, special spore making structures, spores grow into new plants. Difference: the fern's dominant stage is its spore-producing stage.*

Reinforce the BIG idea

Have students relate the section to the Big Idea.

 Reinforcing Key Concepts, p. 171

11.2 ASSESS & RETEACH

Assess

A Section 11.2 Quiz, p. 44

Reteach

Write the terms on the board. For each term, have students tell if it relates to moss reproduction, fern reproduction, or both. Then have them tell if the term occurs in the first or second generation.

1. spore *both, second generation*
2. sperm *both, first generation*
3. egg *both, first generation*
4. fertilization *both, first generation*
5. capsule *moss, second generation*
6. stalk *moss, second generation*
7. frond *fern, second generation*

Technology Resources

Have students visit ClassZone.com for reteaching of Key Concepts.

 CONTENT REVIEW

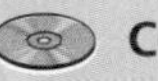 CONTENT REVIEW CD-ROM

11.3 FOCUS

Set Learning Goals

Students will

- Discuss the advantages that plants with pollen and seeds have over nonseed plants.
- Describe how some plants reproduce with pollen and seeds.
- Observe conditions that make a pinecone open.

3-Minute Warm-Up

Display Transparency 21 or copy this exercise on the board:

Predict what will happen:

A group of moss plants live in a moist area. The area experiences a period of drought. How does this affect the moss plants? Explain.

The moss plants will not be able to reproduce because the sperm need water in which to reach the eggs of the female plant. The plants may die.

3-Minute Warm-Up, p. T21

11.3 MOTIVATE

THINK ABOUT

PURPOSE To understand how seeds are adapted for survival and reproduction

DISCUSS Invite students to describe what they see in the photograph. Explain that the seed and the plant embryo it contains can become a living organism. The thousand-year-old lotus seeds were able to survive because the structure of the seed provides a protective coating and food for the embryo. This allows the embryo to remain dormant (capable of living but not growing or acting) until the conditions for growth or activity are right.

KEY CONCEPT

11.3 Seeds and pollen are reproductive adaptations.

BEFORE, you learned

- Plant species evolved from algaelike ancestors
- Mosses are nonvascular plants that reproduce with spores
- Ferns are vascular plants that reproduce with spores

NOW, you will learn

- How some plants reproduce with pollen and seeds
- About the advantages of pollen and seeds

VOCABULARY

seed p. 370
embryo p. 370
germination p. 371
pollen p. 372
gymnosperm p. 374

THINK ABOUT

Is a seed alive?

A lotus is a type of pond lily that is commonly found in water gardens. The plants take root in the bottom of a pond. A plant scientist in California experimented with lotus seeds from China that were over 1000 years old. The scientist made a small opening in the hard covering of each seed and planted the seeds in wet soil. Some of the seeds sprouted and grew. What made it possible for these seeds to survive for such a long time? Is a seed alive?

Seeds are an important adaptation.

Spores are one adaptation that made it possible for plants to reproduce on land. Seeds are another. A **seed** is a young plant that is enclosed in a protective coating. Within the coating are enough nutrients to enable the plant to grow. Seeds and spores can both withstand harsh conditions. Seed plants, however, have several survival advantages over seedless plants. These advantages make it possible for seed plants to spread into environments where seedless plants are less likely to survive.

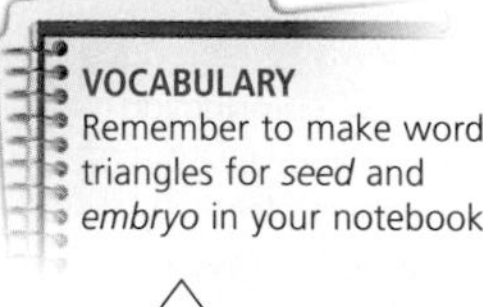

VOCABULARY
Remember to make word triangles for *seed* and *embryo* in your notebook.

In all plants, fertilization brings about the growth of the next generation of the plant, beginning with an embryo. An **embryo** (EHM-bree-OH) is the immature form of an organism that has the potential to grow and develop. In seed plants, the embryo is protected. The seed coat protects the immature plant until conditions are right for it to grow.

RESOURCES FOR DIFFERENTIATED INSTRUCTION

Below Level

UNIT RESOURCE BOOK

- Reading Study Guide A, pp. 174–175
- Decoding Support, p. 198

AUDIO CDS

Advanced

UNIT RESOURCE BOOK

Challenge and Extension, p. 180

English Learners

UNIT RESOURCE BOOK

Spanish Reading Study Guide, pp. 178–179

AUDIO CDS

- Audio Readings in Spanish
- Audio Readings (English)

An embryo can remain inside a seed for a long time without growing. When moisture, temperature, and other conditions are right, a seed will start to grow. **Germination** (JUR-muh-NAY-shuhn) is the beginning of growth of a new plant from a spore or a seed. If you've ever planted a seed that sprouted, you've observed germination.

What is germination?

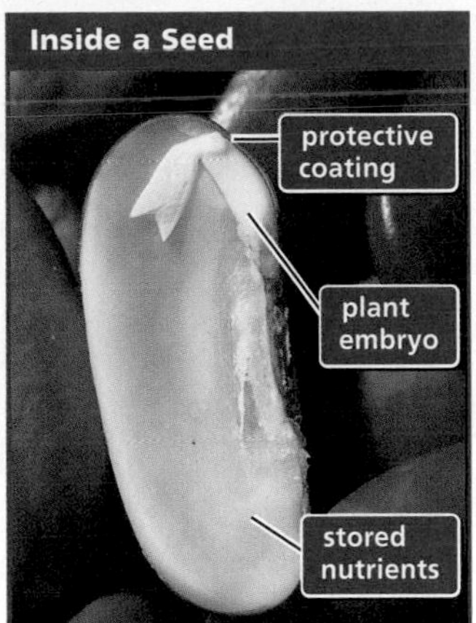

When a seed germinates, it takes in water from its surroundings. As the embryo begins to grow, it uses the stored nutrients in the seed for energy and materials. The nutrients need to last until the new plant's roots and shoots can start to function.

Some plants reproduce with seeds.

In most places, plants that reproduce with seeds are common and easy to see. Trees, bushes, flowers, and grasses are all seed plants. It's a bit harder to find plants that reproduce with spores, such as mosses or ferns. Why are there so many more seed plants in the world? The diagram below shows some of the differences and similarities between seeds and spores.

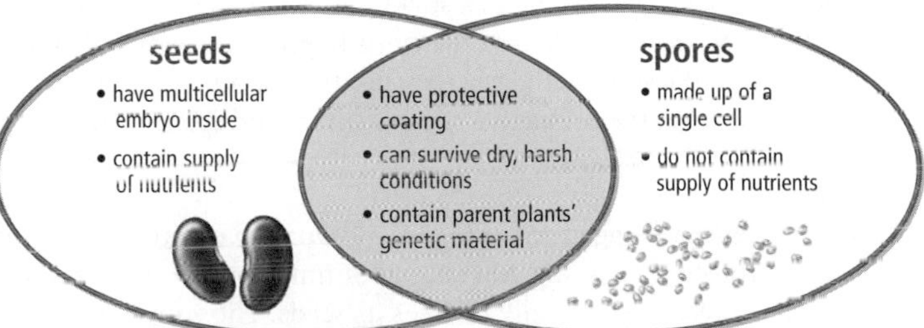

One important difference between a seed and a spore is that the seed contains a multicellular organism. If you look closely at the photograph above you can see the tiny leaves at the top of the embryo, with the root below. Spores are just a single cell. Seeds can be spread by wind, animals, or water. Spores are mostly carried by the wind. The sperm of seed plants, unlike the sperm of mosses and ferns, do not need water to reach the egg. One important similarity between a seed and a spore is that both can grow into a new plant.

Name three ways seeds are different from spores.

Learn more about seeds.

11.3 INSTRUCT

Teach from Visuals

To help students interpret both the photograph of the seed and the Venn diagram, ask the following questions that relate the visuals to the text:

- What is the function of the stored food supply? *to provide the growing embryo with nutrients*
- What is the function of the seed coat? *to protect the embryo from harsh conditions in the environment*
- What advantages do seeds have over spores? *Seeds have an embryo, a tiny plant ready to grow. Seeds also have a food supply for the plant once it starts to grow.*

EXPLORE the BIG idea

Revisit "Internet Activity: Sprouting Seeds" on p. 355. Ask students if their ideas of what seeds are have changed based on their observations and what they have learned from the text.

Ongoing Assessment

Discuss the advantages that plants with pollen and seeds have over nonseed plants.

Ask students to list two advantages that seeds provide in a plant life cycle. *Seeds provide a supply of nutrients to the developing plant. Seeds can be spread by wind, animals, or water.*

CHECK YOUR READING *Answer: Germination is the growth of a new plant from a seed or a spore under the right conditions of moisture and temperature.*

CHECK YOUR READING *Answer: Seeds contain a multicellular embryo; they have their own food supply; they can be transported by animals or water as well as by wind.*

DIFFERENTIATE INSTRUCTION

More Reading Support

A What does an embryo use stored nutrients for? *energy and materials*

B What are some examples of seed plants? *trees, bushes, flowers, and grasses*

English Learners Venn diagrams, such as the one on this page, can be especially helpful in summarizing content in a visual way. Be sure to explain the significance of each section of the diagram, especially the center. Have students make their own version of this Venn diagram. They should write in their own words the separate and the shared qualities of seeds and spores. You might simplify language for them as: Seeds—new plant inside, food supply; Both—protected, do not dry out, can grow into a new plant; Spores—one cell, no food supply.

Address Misconceptions

IDENTIFY Ask students if a seed is alive. Students may not realize that a seed is capable of becoming a living plant. A seed does not show the characteristics of a living thing until it germinates, when it begins to grow.

CORRECT Have students describe or sketch what happens to a plant as it grows: roots and shoots develop so a plant can get water and nutrients from its environment. (Remind them of the Internet Activity on p. 355.). Ask: What are the characteristics of life? *organization, growth, reproduction, and response*

REASSESS Ask students to draw a diagram of the life cycle of a pine tree. Remind them that the cycle should include two generations, and also pollen and seeds. Ask them to indicate where meiosis and fertilization occur.

Technology Resources

Visit **ClassZone.com** for background on common student misconceptions.

 **MISCONCEPTION DATABASE**

Metacognitive Strategy

Students can use the heads in the caption boxes in the illustration on p. 373 as a starting point to create memory aids for life cycles of pine trees. They could choose to write, draw, or create manipulative cards, or even to create a song. Ask them to explain why their strategies work well for remembering.

Ongoing Assessment

Describe how some plants reproduce with pollen and seeds.

Ask: What is pollen? What is pollination? *Pollen contains sperm cells. Pollination occurs when a pollen grain attaches to the part of the plant that holds the egg. The sperm are released.*

CHECK YOUR READING *Answer: Pollen grains contain sperm cells, and female cone scales contain egg cells.*

Pine trees reproduce with pollen and seeds.

 C

Seed plants, such as pine trees, do not have swimming sperm. Instead, they have pollen. A **pollen** grain is a small multicellular structure that holds a sperm cell. It has a hard outer covering to keep the sperm from drying out. Pollen grains can be carried from one plant to another by wind, water, or by animals such as insects, bats, or birds. The process of pollination is completed when a pollen grain attaches to the part of a plant that contains the egg and releases the sperm.

READING TIP: As you read the numbered paragraphs on this page, follow the numbers on the labels of the diagram on page 373.

The life cycle of a pine tree provides an example of how seed plants reproduce.

Pinecones release lots of pollen into the air.

1. The reproductive structures of a pine tree are the pinecones. Meiosis occurs in the pine cones, producing sperm and egg cells. Each tree has separate male and female cones.
2. In male cones, the sperm cells are contained in pollen grains, which are released into the air. In female cones, the egg cells are enclosed in protective compartments within the cone scales.
3. The female cone produces a sticky substance. When a pollen grain lands, it sticks. A pollen tube begins to grow from the pollen grain through the scale to the egg. Fertilization occurs when the pollen tube reaches the protective compartment and sperm travel through it to one of the eggs.
4. The fertilized egg grows into an embryo. The compartment, with its protective covering and supply of nutrients, becomes the seed. The pinecone eventually releases its seeds. The winged seeds can float through the air and may be carried long distances by the wind. If the seed lands on the ground and germinates, it can become a new pine tree.

In the life cycle of a pine tree, meiosis and fertilization occur completely within the tissue of the mature plant. Fertilization doesn't require an outside source of water. The sperm cells in a pollen grain and the egg cells in a cone scale represent the first generation of the plant. The seed and the tree that grows from the seed represent the second generation.

 What do pollen grains and cone scales contain?

DIFFERENTIATE INSTRUCTION

 **More Reading Support**

C How is pollen carried from plant to plant? *by wind, water, and animals*

Below Level Have pairs of students create a flow chart to illustrate the life cycle of the pine tree. Students should include the following terms in their flow charts: *meiosis, spore cells, pollen grains, sperm cells, egg cells, fertilization, embryo, seed.* Allow time for pairs to share their flow charts with other students and make necessary adjustments or changes.

Life Cycle of a Pine Tree

open female cone

① **Meiosis**

A mature pine tree has both male and female cones. Meiosis occurs inside the cones, producing sperm and egg cells.

Male Cones

Female Cone

② **Pollination**

Male cones release pollen into the air. A pollen grain sticks to the scales of a female cone, and a pollen tube begins to grow.

pollen grain

scales

③ **Fertilization**

Sperm move through the pollen tube to fertilize one of the egg cells at the base of the female cone scale.

pollen tube

sperm

egg

④ **Seeds**

Each fertilized egg becomes an embryo in a seed. A female cone can contain many seeds. The cone opens and the seeds are released.

seed

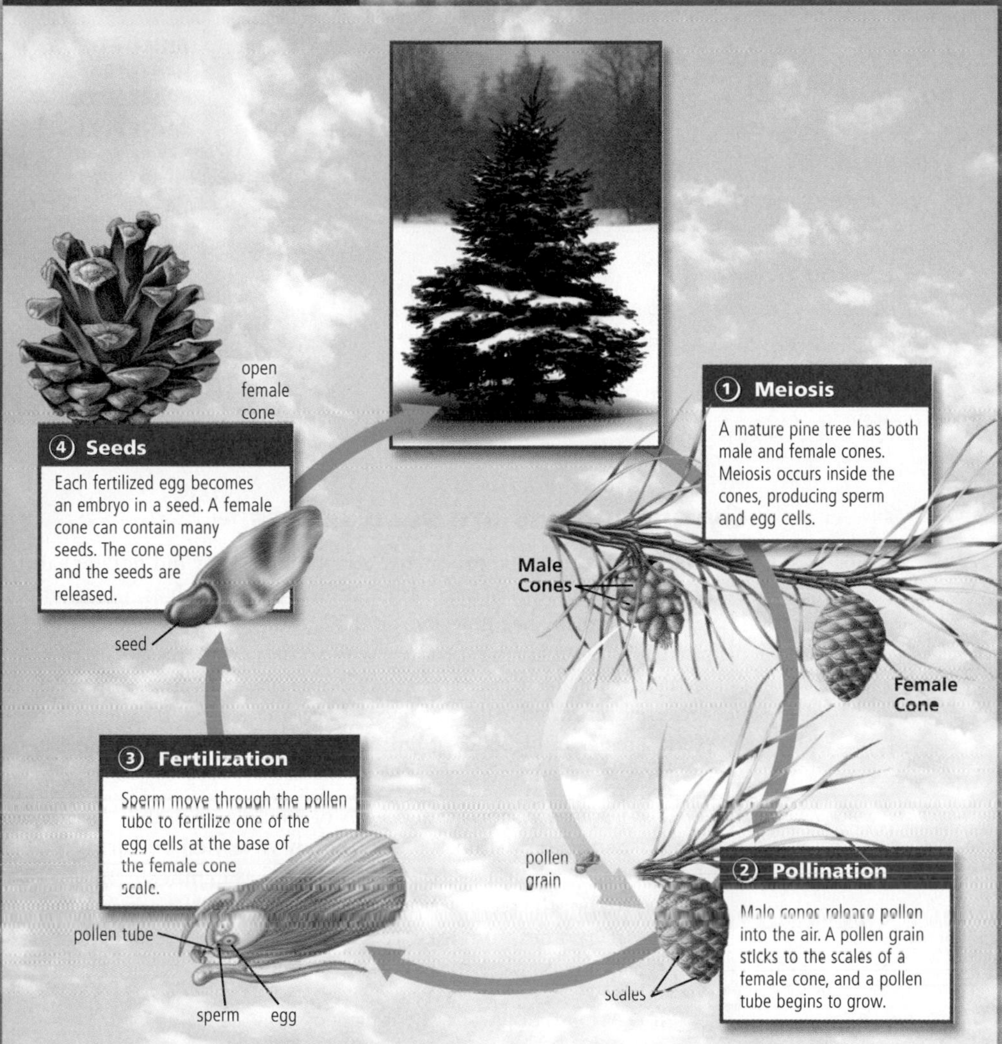

READING VISUALS Use the definition of a cycle to predict what happens after seeds are released from pinecones.

Chapter 11: Plants 373

DIFFERENTIATE INSTRUCTION

Below Level Invite students to bring in any pinecones they might have collected to share with the class. Have students note the various shapes and sizes of the cones. You may use the cones for the investigation on p. 374.

Advanced Challenge students to find pinecones or parts that match each of the stages and structures shown in the diagram. If pine trees are not local, have students find images of the parts and trace, draw, or clip-and-paste copies with captions.

Challenge and Extension, p. 180

Teach from Visuals

To help students interpret the diagram of the life cycle of pine trees, ask:

- Where are the reproductive structures of the tree found? *in the pinecones*
- What is produced by the male and female cones? *sperm and eggs*
- When does fertilization occur? *when the sperm reaches one of the egg cells inside the female cone scale*

The "Life Cycle of a Pine Tree" visual is also available as T22 in the Unit Transparency Book.

Develop Critical Thinking

ANALYZE Direct attention to the illustration of the pine seed. Ask: How do you think the shape of the seed affects how it travels? *The shape of the seed allows the wind to carry the seed and prevent it from falling directly under the tree.*

Real World Example

Because of the many uses of conifers, large forests are grown in many areas of the United States. A method called clearcutting is used to obtain the lumber in which all of the trees are cut down in a forest at once. An alternative method, called sustained yield, allows foresters to harvest lumber without destroying entire forests of trees. In this method, only a percentage of lumber is cut every year, allowing a constant supply of trees to be maintained in the forest.

Ongoing Assessment

READING VISUALS *Answer: The seed will be carried away by the wind, germinate if conditions are right, and grow into a pine tree similar to the one in the top picture, allowing the cycle to continue.*

INVESTIGATE Pinecones

PURPOSE To observe the structure of pinecones

TIPS *20 min.* Ask students to collect fallen pinecones and allow them to dry in the classroom. Cones fall from conifers at varying stages of ripeness, so students may find seeds inside the pinecones. You may wish to call "time" after 10 minutes in water to be sure students observe drying as well as moistening.

WHAT DO YOU THINK? *The cone floated in the water and gradually the scales closed. When the cone dried out, the cone opened up again.*

CHALLENGE *Students will likely have similar results with other pine species.*

 Datasheet, Pinecones, p. 181

Technology Resources

Customize this student lab as needed or look for an alternative. Print rubrics to assess student lab reports.

 **Lab Generator CD-ROM**

Social Studies Connection

Pine trees, or conifers, are a common lumber source for the papermaking industry. Students can do research into the current and past lumber harvesting practices for papermaking. Have them write a report that summarizes the arguments both for *and* against one of these practices, such as clearcutting, forced burning, or sustained yield harvesting.

Ongoing Assessment

 *Answer: Gymnosperm seeds are naked because they are not contained in fruit.*

INVESTIGATE Pinecones

What conditions make a pinecone open?

PROCEDURE

1. Place your pinecone in the beaker of water. Observe any changes that take place. Leave the cone in the water until the changes stop.
2. Remove the cone from the water and place it on a paper towel to dry. Observe any changes that take place as the cone dries.

WHAT DO YOU THINK?

- What did you observe when the cone was in the water?
- What happened when the cone dried out?

CHALLENGE Try this procedure on cones from different plant species.

SKILL FOCUS
Observing

MATERIALS
- dried, open pinecones
- beaker of water
- paper towels

TIME
20 minutes

Gymnosperms are seed plants.

Pollen and seeds are reproductive adaptations. They did not appear in plants until millions of years after seedless plants such as mosses and ferns had already begun to live on land. Today, however, most of the plant species on Earth reproduce with seeds, and many species of seedless plants have become extinct. Some scientists think this is because over time Earth's climate has become drier and cooler. Seed plants are generally better at reproducing in dry, cool environments than seedless plants are.

MIND MAP
Make a mind map for the main idea that *gymnosperms are seed plants.* Don't forget to include the definition of a gymnosperm in your mind map.

D

Fossil evidence shows that species of seed plants in the **gymnosperm** (JIHM-nuh-SPURM) group have existed on Earth for more than 250 million years. Plants classified as gymnosperms produce seeds, but the seeds are not enclosed in fruit. The word *gymnosperm* comes from the Greek words for "naked seed." There are four types of gymnosperms living on Earth today.

 What is distinctive about gymnosperm seeds?

Conifers

The conifers, or cone-bearing trees, are the type of gymnosperm you are probably most familiar with. The conifers include pine, fir, spruce, hemlock, cypress, and redwood trees. Many conifers are adapted for living in cold climates, where there is relatively little water available. Their leaves are needle-shaped and have a thick cuticle. This prevents the plant from losing much water to transpiration. Conifers can also keep their needles for several years, which means the plants can produce sugars all year.

DIFFERENTIATE INSTRUCTION

 **More Reading Support**

D Which kinds of seed plants do scientists think were the first to inhabit Earth? *gymnosperms*

E What are conifers? *cone-bearing trees*

Inclusion For students who have vision impairments, the "Investigate Pinecones" on this page can be adapted so that "observations" are based on touch rather than visual image. Students can place their fingers on the pinecone during the time it is in water, and again while it is drying. Time them for about 10 minutes for each step.

Ginkgo trees like this one are gymnosperms that do not produce cones. Their seeds are exposed to the environment.

Other Gymnosperms

The other types of living gymnosperms are cycads, gnetophytes (NEE-toh-fyts), and ginkgoes. These three types of gymnosperms appear to be quite different from one another. Cycads are palmlike plants that are found in tropical areas. They produce cones for seeds. Many cycads produce poisonous compounds. Gnetophytes are another type of tropical gymnosperm that produces cones. Chemicals taken from certain gnetophyte plants have been used to treat cold symptoms for thousands of years.

Ginkgoes are gymnosperms with fleshy seeds that hang from their branches. Ginkgoes are often grown in parks and along streets, but you will not often see them with seeds. People avoid putting male and female ginkgo trees together because the seed coat of a ginkgo produces a particularly foul smell.

11.3 Review

KEY CONCEPTS

1. How are seeds different from spores?
2. How does fertilization in seed plants differ from fertilization in seedless plants?
3. Seed plants are found in environments where seedless plants are not. List at least two reasons why.

CRITICAL THINKING

4. **Compare and Contrast** What is the difference between a spore and a pollen grain? In what ways are spores and pollen grains similar?
5. **Hypothesize** Gymnosperms produce a lot of pollen, and most of it blows away, never fertilizing an egg. Why might this characteristic help a plant species survive?

CHALLENGE

6. **Analyze** Like all plants, a pine tree has a two-part life cycle. Look again at the diagram on page 373, and then make a new version of it in your notebook. Your version should show where in the life cycle each generation begins and ends. Hint: reread the text on page 372.

ANSWERS

1. Seeds: multicellular embryo, food supply. Spores: single cells

2. The sperm of seed plants do not need water to carry them to the egg.

3. Fertilization does not require water. Seeds are spread by animals.

4. Spores are single cells that grow into plants that produce sperm and eggs. Pollen are multicellular and carry only sperm cells. Both are protected by a hard covering.

5. A lot of pollen increases the chances of a pollen grain reaching the female cone of another plant.

6. Diagrams should show that a new generation begins in the pinecones, with meiosis producing sperm and egg cells. The seed produced after fertilization represents the second generation, the pine tree.

Develop Critical Thinking

SYNTHESIZE Compare the needles of conifers with the leaves of deciduous trees (trees that lose their leaves in winter). Ask:

- How are conifer's needles adapted to surviving winter conditions? *The shape of the needles allows the tree to conserve water when little is available.*
- Since there is less surface area on the needles for photosynthesis to take place, how do you think these plants get energy and materials they need? *The needles have less surface area but they are green all year and do photosynthesize. There may be more needles than leaves. They keep the needles all year.*

Reinforce the BIG idea

Have students relate the section to the Big Idea.

 Reinforcing Key Concepts, p. 182

11.3 ASSESS & RETEACH

Assess

 Section 11.3 Quiz, p. 45

Reteach

Reproduce the photograph on p. 367 of Moss Releasing Spores and the illustration of the pine tree life cycle on p. 373. (Or use the transparency "Life Cycle of the Pine Tree," in the Unit Transparency Book.) Have student volunteers use these two diagrams to explain examples of the following concepts.

- Plants reproduce well on land.
- Pollen and seeds have made some plants spread out more than others.

Technology Resources

Have students visit **ClassZone.com** for reteaching of Key Concepts.

 CONTENT REVIEW

 CONTENT REVIEW CD-ROM

CHAPTER INVESTIGATION

Focus

PURPOSE To compare and contrast germination and growth patterns of various types of seeds

OVERVIEW Students will set up a classroom greenhouse and plant a variety of seeds. Students will determine:

- differences in germination.
- differences in growth patterns.

Lab Preparation

- Have students collect seeds ahead of time and make predictions as to which seeds will grow. They may use seeds they collect from the outdoors or from foods. Dried beans and mixed bird seed work. Popcorn, rice, and grocery-store fruit seeds are unlikely to grow.
- Point out that the data tables will vary, depending on the seeds used.
- Prior to the investigation have students read through the investigation and prepare their data tables. Or you may wish to copy and distribute datasheets and rubrics.

UNIT RESOURCE BOOK, pp. 201–209

SCIENCE TOOLKIT, F14

Lab Management

- Prompt students to control the following: containers, planting medium, the depth at which seeds are planted, the amounts of light and warmth, and the amount of water.

INCLUSION For students with attention disorders or learning disabilities, prepare a checklist of plant care. Have students use the checklist each day that they care for and observe their plants.

Teaching with Technology

If digital cameras or stop-frame video are available, students may make close-up photographs of their plants. They can use time-lapse slides or videos to show the pattern of growth.

CHAPTER INVESTIGATION

Which Seeds Will Grow?

OVERVIEW AND PURPOSE Many of the foods you eat come from seed plants. What seeds or parts of seed plants have you eaten lately? What seeds can you find outside in your neighborhood? What conditions do the seeds from these plants need to grow? In this investigation, you will

- plant a variety of seeds
- observe differences in germination and growth among seeds planted in similar conditions

MATERIALS
- assorted seeds
- potting soil
- paper cups
- water
- paper towels
- labels

Problem

Write It Up

How successfully will a variety of seeds germinate in conditions that can be provided in your classroom?

Hypothesize

Write It Up

Read through all of the steps of the procedure and then write a hypothesis. Your hypothesis should explain what you think will happen when your class plants its collection of seeds and observes their growth for at least ten days. Your hypothesis should take the form of an "If . . . , then . . . , because . . ." statement.

Procedure

1. Make a data table in your **Science Notebook** like the one shown on page 377.

2. Examine the seeds you will use in this investigation. Try to identify them. Record your observations in the data table.

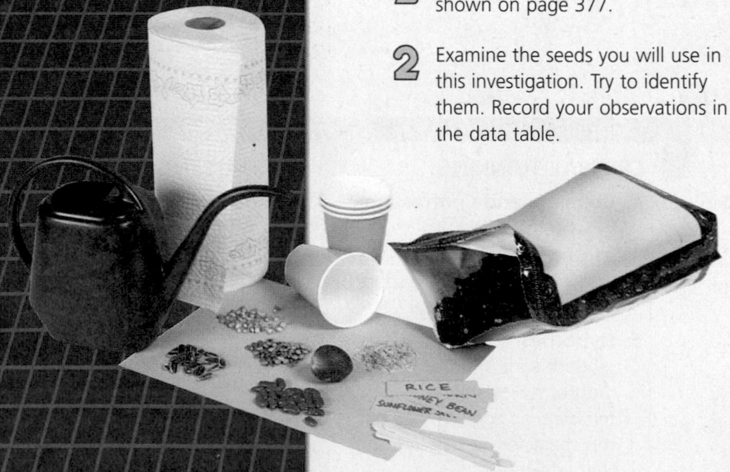

step 2

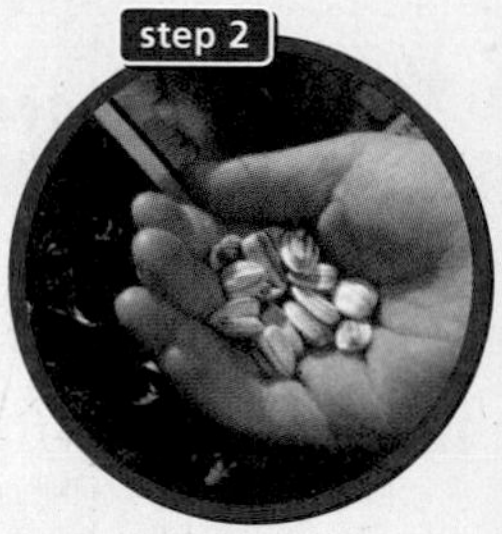

INVESTIGATION RESOURCES

CHAPTER INVESTIGATION, Which Seeds Will Grow?
- Level A, pp. 210–204
- Level B, pp. 205–208
- Level C, p. 209

Advanced students should complete Levels B & C.

Writing a Lab Report, D12–13

Technology Resources

Customize this student lab as needed or look for an alternative. Print rubrics to assess student lab reports.

Lab Generator CD-ROM

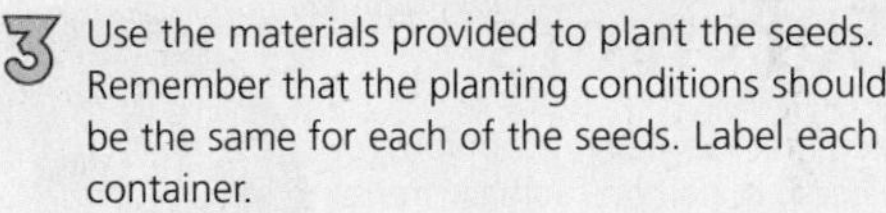

3. Use the materials provided to plant the seeds. Remember that the planting conditions should be the same for each of the seeds. Label each container.

4. Decide where you will keep your seeds while they are growing and how often you will check and water them. Be sure to keep the growing conditions for all of the seeds the same. Wash your hands.

5. Observe your seeds for at least ten days. Check and water them according to the plan you made.

Observe and Analyze

Write It Up

1. In your **Science Notebook**, draw and label a diagram showing how you planted the seeds, the materials you used, and the place where they are being kept.
2. Each time you check on your seeds, record your observations in your data table.
3. **IDENTIFY** Which seeds germinated? What differences in growth and development did you observe in the different types of seeds?

Conclude

1. **INTERPRET** Compare your results with your hypothesis. Did your data support your hypothesis?
2. **INFER** What patterns or similarities did you notice in the seeds that grew most successfully?
3. **IDENTIFY LIMITS** What unexpected factors or problems might have affected your results?
4. **APPLY** Use your experience to tell a young child how to grow a plant from a seed. What type of seeds would you suggest? Write directions for planting and caring for seeds that a younger child could understand.

INVESTIGATE Further

CHALLENGE Some seeds need special conditions, such as warmth or a certain amount of moisture, before they will germinate. Design an experiment in which you test just one type of seed in a variety of conditions to learn which results in the most growth. Include a hypothesis, a materials list, and a procedure when you write up your experiment.

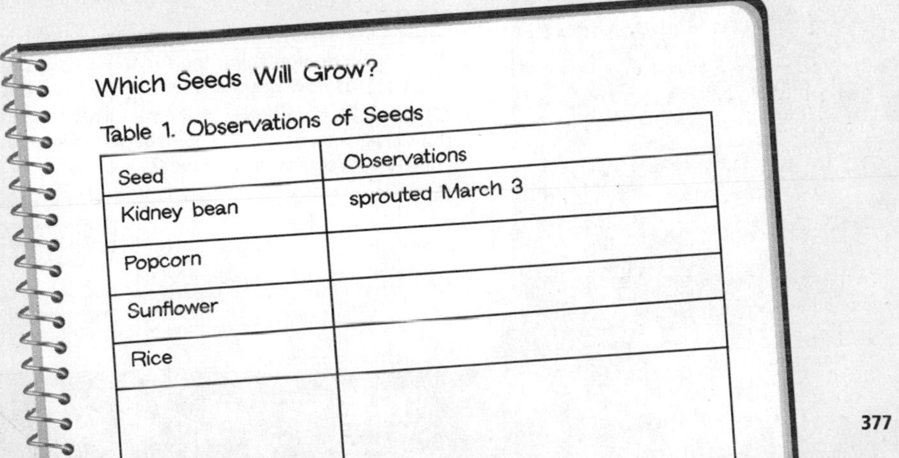

Which Seeds Will Grow?

Table 1. Observations of Seeds

Seed	Observations
Kidney bean	sprouted March 3
Popcorn	
Sunflower	
Rice	

377

Observe and Analyze

1. *Students should make sure that all plants are grown under the same conditions.*
2. *Check that students' data tables are complete and correspond to the actual seeds they chose to plant.*
3. *Answers will depend on the seeds selected for the lab.*

Conclude

1. *Students should provide evidence or explanation for describing whether their hypotheses are correct or incorrect.*
2. *Sample answer: Seeds that grew most successfully were planted near the top of the soil and not too close together.*
3. *Sample answers: environment of classroom, limitations of container, soil quality, type of seeds*
4. *Answers should be based on experience gained from this investigation.*

INVESTIGATE Further

CHALLENGE Collect student procedures. Procedures should allow student to test at least one variable (amount of water, temperature, soil type, soil depth, etc.) to determine what conditions are best for the seed.

Post-Lab Discussion

- Discuss why some of the seeds students planted grew better than others, or why some of the seeds did not grow. *Sample answer: Some seeds may take longer to germinate, or may require conditions that are not possible to duplicate in a classroom.*
- Why is it important to have all seeds grown under the same conditions? *If there is more than one variable, it will be difficult to draw conclusions related to the types of seeds.*

EXTREME SCIENCE
Fun and Motivating Science

Set Learning Goal
To understand the ability of seeds to survive under extreme conditions

Present the Science
Many seeds remain dormant, or inactive, after they have been dispersed. Under the right conditions of temperature, moisture, and oxygen, seeds will germinate. Seeds with thick or waxy coats may block the entry of water and oxygen. These seeds may remain dormant for extended periods of time. Most seeds, however, lose the ability to germinate within several years.

Discussion Questions
Review with students the various ways that seeds are dispersed.

Ask: By what methods were the seeds discussed on the page dispersed:

- Jackpine seeds? *were released by cones and spread through air*
- Sea rocket seed? *traveled by water*
- Calvaria seeds? *were spread through the wastes of an animal*

Close
Ask: Why do you think seeds are adapted to germinate under extreme conditions? *Without these adaptations, the seeds might not germinate and the plant species would be in danger of becoming extinct.*

Technology Resources

Students can visit **ClassZone.com** for more links about extreme seeds.

 RESOURCE CENTER

Forest Fires release jackpine seeds from their pinecones to sprout after the fire stops.

AMAZING SEEDS

Seed Survivors

Not only can seeds survive harsh conditions, but sometimes harsh conditions actually make it possible for seeds to grow into new plants.

Forest Fires
Jackpine seeds are locked inside pinecones by a sticky resin. The pinecones survive hot forest fires that melt the resin and release the seeds. In fact, without the high temperatures from fires, the seeds would never get the chance to germinate and grow into jackpine trees.

Bomb Damage
In 1940, during World War II, the British Museum was firebombed. People poured water over the burning museum and its contents. In the museum were silk-tree seeds collected in China and brought to the museum in 1793. After the firebombing 147 years later, the seeds sprouted.

Dodo Digestion
Seeds of Calvaria trees, which live on the island of Mauritius have very hard outer shells. The outer shell must be softened before the seeds can sprout. Hundreds of years ago, dodo birds ate the Calvaria fruits. Stones and acids in the birds' digestive tract helped soften the seed. After the dodo birds deposited them, the softened seeds would sprout. Dodo birds went extinct in 1681, and no young Calvaria trees grew. In 1975, only about 13 Calvaria trees remained. Recently, scientists have used artificial means to grind and break down the Calvaria seed cover and foster new tree growth.

EXPLORE

1. **INFER** Why do you think the silk tree seeds sprouted? Think about how the seeds' environment changed.
2. **CHALLENGE** If you were a scientist who wanted to help the Calvaria trees make a comeback, what methods might you try for softening the seeds?

RESOURCE CENTER
CLASSZONE.COM

Find out more about extreme seeds.

EXPLORE

1. ***INFER*** *Heat and water from the firebombing most likely gave the right conditions of moisture and temperature for the seeds to germinate.*
2. ***CHALLENGE*** *Accept all reasonable responses. Students might suggest soaking the seeds in a moist environment containing acids to simulate the digestive tract of the dodo birds.*

KEY CONCEPT

Many plants reproduce with flowers and fruit.

BEFORE, you learned
- Seed plants do not have swimming sperm
- Gymnosperms reproduce with pollen and seeds

NOW, you will learn
- About flowers and fruit
- About the relationship between animals and flowering plants
- How humans need plants

VOCABULARY

angiosperm p. 379
flower p. 380
fruit p. 380

EXPLORE Fruit

What do you find inside fruit?

PROCEDURE

1. Place the apple on a paper towel. Carefully cut the apple in half. Find the seeds.
2. Place the pea pod on a paper towel. Carefully split open the pea pod. Find the seeds.
3. Both the apple and the pea pod are examples of fruits. In your notebook, draw a diagram of the two fruits you examined. Label the fruit and the seeds.

WHAT DO YOU THINK?
- How many seeds did you find?
- What part of an apple do you eat? What part of a pea?

MATERIALS
- apple
- paper towel
- plastic knife
- pea pod

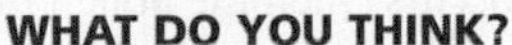

Angiosperms have flowers and fruit.

MIND MAP
Make a mind map diagram for the main idea: *Angiosperms have flowers and fruit.*

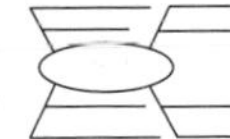

Have you ever eaten peanuts, grapes, strawberries, or squash? Do you like the way roses smell, or how spider plants look? All of these plants are angiosperms, or flowering plants. An **angiosperm** (AN-jee-uh-SPURM) is a seed plant that produces flowers and fruit. Most of the species of plants living now are angiosperms. The grasses at your local park are angiosperms. Most trees whose leaves change color in the fall are angiosperms.

The sperm of a flowering plant are protected in a pollen grain and do not need an outside source of water to reach the eggs. The eggs develop into embryos that are enclosed within seeds. Both generations of angiosperms and gymnosperms occur within a single plant.

RESOURCES FOR DIFFERENTIATED INSTRUCTION

Below Level

UNIT RESOURCE BOOK
- Reading Study Guide A, pp. 185–186
- Decoding Support, p. 198

AUDIO CDS

Additional INVESTIGATION, Fertilization in Angiosperms, A, B, & C, pp. 210–218; Teacher Instructions, pp. 360–361

Advanced

UNIT RESOURCE BOOK
Challenge and Extension, p. 191

English Learners

UNIT RESOURCE BOOK
Spanish Reading Study Guide, pp. 189–190

AUDIO CDS
- Audio Readings in Spanish
- Audio Readings (English)

11.4 FOCUS

Set Learning Goals

Students will
- Describe the characteristics of flowers and fruit.
- Analyze the relationship between animals and flowering plants.
- Discuss human uses of plants.
- Observe and identify parts of a flower.

3-Minute Warm-Up

Display Transparency 21 or copy this exercise on the board:

Match each definition with the correct term.

Definitions
1. the immature form of a plant that has the potential to grow and develop *b*
2. the multicellular structure that holds the sperm cell *e*
3. the beginning of growth from a spore or seed *c*

Terms

a. seed
b. embryo
c. germination
d. pollination
e. pollen

 3-Minute Warm-Up, p. T21

11.4 MOTIVATE

EXPLORE Fruit

PURPOSE To explore the inside of different fruits

TIPS *15 min.* Apples may be cut ahead of time. Put lemon juice on cut surfaces to reduce browning. Students may not think that foods such as pea pods are actually fruits. Encourage students to determine why these foods are considered fruits as they examine them.

WHAT DO YOU THINK? *Number of seeds found will vary, but students should find several in each fruit. In the apple, you would eat the fruit (the ripened ovary). In pea pods, you would eat the seeds, and in some cases, the fruit (pod) as well.*

11.4 INSTRUCT

Teach Difficult Concepts

Students may confuse angiosperms and gymnosperms and the differences in their life cycles. To help them understand the differences, discuss the following questions:

- Compare the reproductive structures of angiosperms with those of a pine tree. How are they different? *In angiosperms, the reproductive structures are in flowers. In pine trees, they are in pine cones.*
- How is pollination similar in both types of plants? *In both plants, the pollen grain goes through a pollen tube to reach the egg.*
- Compare the seeds of angiosperms with those of a pine tree. How are they different? *In pine trees, seeds are not enclosed inside a fruit, as in angiosperms.*

Language Arts Connection

Many of the structures and processes in an angiosperm life cycle are used in English as metaphors for ideas and human actions. Some such as seed, fruit, germ, and kernel have multiple definitions relating to plants or to ideas. Some may be used in poetry or a story to create similes (sprout like a weed, fresh as a flower) or metaphors, implied comparisons that do not use "like" or "as." Assign students an exercise of creating their own original similes and metaphors based on words describing angiosperm structures or processes.

Ongoing Assessment

Answer: Angiosperms have flowers and fruit.

Answer: Flowers produce egg and sperm cells. Once the egg in the ovary is fertilized, the seeds grow and the ovary becomes a fruit.

The reproductive cycles of angiosperms and gymnosperms are alike in many ways. Both angiosperms and gymnosperms have separate male and female reproductive structures. In some species, male and female parts grow on the same plant, but in others there are separate male and female plants.

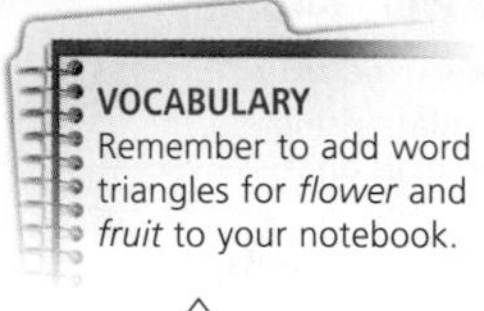

An important difference between angiosperms and gymnosperms is that in angiosperms, the sperm and egg cells are contained in a flower. The **flower** is the reproductive structure of an angiosperm. Egg cells develop in a part of the flower called an ovary. Once the eggs are fertilized and the seed or seeds form, the ovary wall thickens and the ovary becomes a **fruit.**

CHECK YOUR READING What reproductive structures do angiosperms have that gymnosperms do not?

The diagram on page 381 shows the life cycle of one type of angiosperm, a cherry tree. As you read the numbered paragraphs below, follow the numbers on the labels in the diagram.

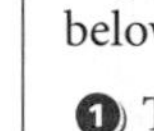

1. The reproductive structures of a cherry tree are its flowers. The anther is the male part. The pistil is the female part. Meiosis in the anther produces sperm cells enclosed within pollen grains. Meiosis in the ovary of the pistil produces egg cells.
2. The pollen grains are released. When a pollen grain is caught on the pistil of a flower, a pollen tube starts to grow. Within the ovary one of the egg cells matures.
3. Fertilization occurs when the pollen tube reaches the ovary and a sperm fertilizes the egg. The fertilized egg grows into an embryo and develops a seed coat. The ovary develops into a fruit.
4. The fruit may fall to the ground or it may be eaten by animals. If the seed inside lands in a place where it can germinate and survive, it will grow into a new cherry tree.

What is the flower's role in the sexual reproduction of an angiosperm?

Many flowering plants also reproduce asexually. New shoots can grow out from the parent plant. For example, strawberries and spider plants can reproduce by sending out shoots called runners. New plants grow from the runners, getting nutrients from the parent until the roots of the new plant are established. Plants can spread quickly this way. This form of asexual reproduction allows plants to reproduce even when conditions are not right for the germination of seeds.

380 Unit 3: Diversity of Living Things

DIFFERENTIATE INSTRUCTION

A Which structure of the flower develops into the fruit? *the ovary*

B Which part of the flower is the male part? The female part? *male—anther, female—pistil*

English Learners As students read the text and study the diagram on pp. 380–381, they will encounter many unfamiliar words, such as *anther, pistil, ovary,* and *angiosperm.* Encourage students to make a picture dictionary for "Flowering Plants" by defining unknown words and drawing pictures for as many examples as they can. Students new to English may have difficulty with words such as *shoots, grain, embryo, pollen, runners,* and *germinate,* all of which are important to the life cycle of flowering plants.

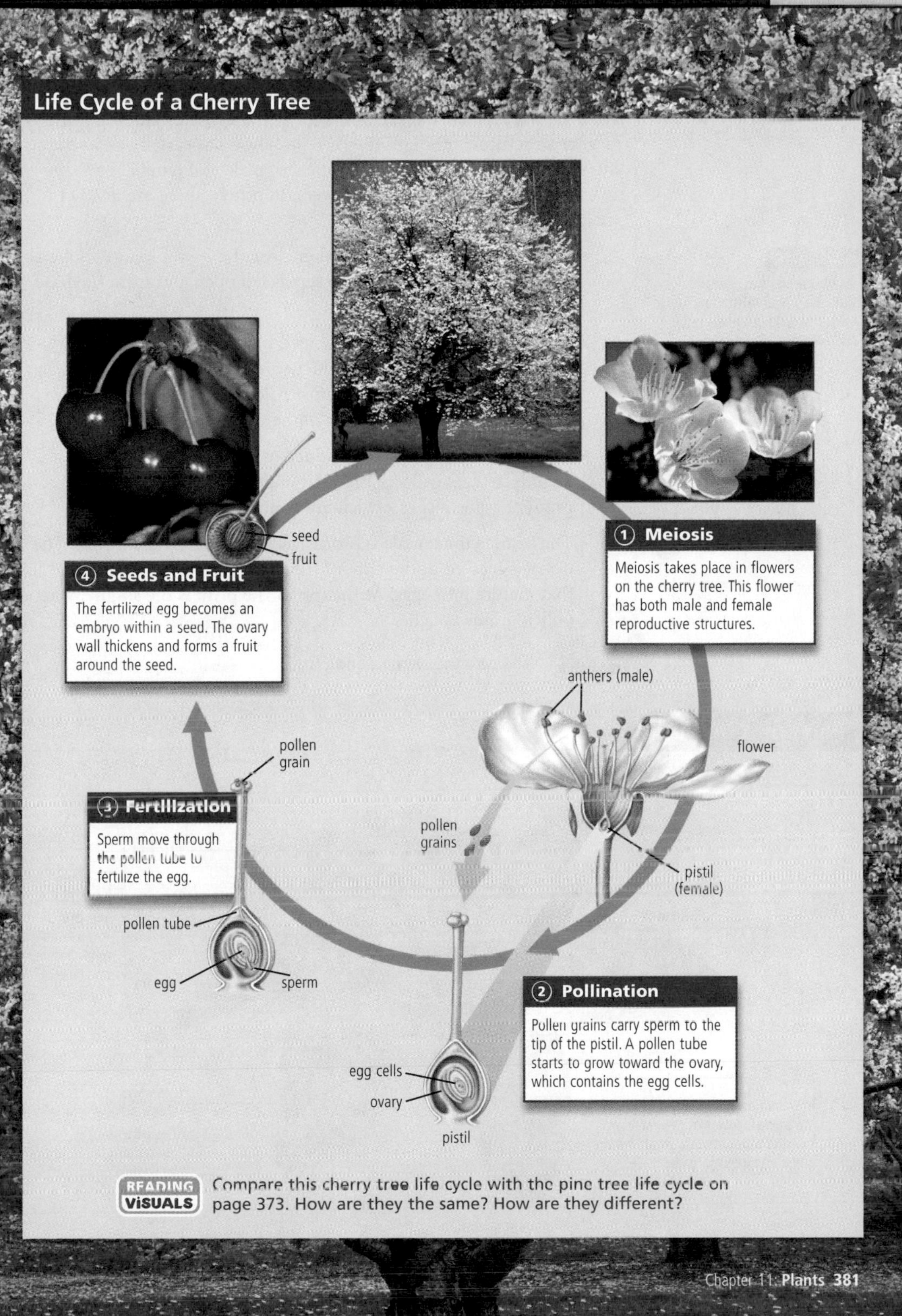

DIFFERENTIATE INSTRUCTION

Below Level Ask students to create a flow chart illustrating the stages for angiosperm reproduction. Students can compare the flow charts to the ones they made for pine tree reproduction in Section 11.3 (p. 372). Ask students to compare their flow charts and describe how they are alike and how they differ.

Teach from Visuals

To help students interpret the diagram of the life cycle of a cherry tree, ask:

- Where does meiosis occur? *in the flowers*
- What happens during pollination? *Pollen grains are released and land on the pistil.*
- Where does fertilization take place? *in the ovary*
- How do the pollen grains reach the ovary? *by producing a pollen tube*

Metacognitive Strategy

Ask students to restate the steps for the life cycle of a cherry tree to a partner or group using their own words. Encourage them to move in order from one stage to the next. Have them discuss which steps are easy or difficult to recall. Next have them imagine a vivid image for each step. They can discuss how this may or may not increase their ability to remember.

Arts Connection

Since flowers have been an inspiration to painters in nearly all cultures and in all periods of art history, the cherry blossom is a common motif. Display Japanese prints and watercolors, as well as Dutch still life paintings and Victorian botanical drawings. Students can apply their science learning to identifying structures of flowers in the artworks. They may also try sketching or painting their own likenesses of live, or cut, flowers.

Ongoing Assessment

READING VISUALS *Answer: Both diagrams show tree life cycles. Both life cycles have meiosis, pollen, pollination, and fertilization steps. Both result in seeds being produced. Differences include: angiosperms have male and female structures within a single flower, and an ovary that will become a fruit.*

Arts Connection

Allow students to create models of flowers, using materials they find at home or in the classroom. For example, they could use colorful wrapping paper or tissue paper for sepals and petals, toothpicks for filaments, clay for anthers, a pipe cleaner for the stigma, and a foam ball for the ovary. Allow students class time to share their models and identify the parts of the flower. They might also create a caption describing parts of the model.

Teach from Visuals

To help students interpret the diagram of flower parts, ask:

- Which two structures make up the stamen? *anther and filament*
- Which two structures make up the pistil? *stigma and ovary*

Ongoing Assessment

Describe the characteristics of flowers and fruit.

Ask: What part of a flower later becomes a fruit? What did that part contain in the flower, and what does it contain as it becomes fruit? *An ovary becomes a fruit. The ovary contained an egg which when fertilized became a seed in the fruit.*

CHECK YOUR READING *Answer: The stamen is the male reproductive structure of the plant. The pistil is the female reproductive structure.*

Flowers

Flowers vary in size, shape, color, and fragrance. They all have some similar structures, although they are not always as easy to see as in the lily pictured below. Also, in some species, male and female reproductive structures are on different flowers. In others, there are distinct male and female plants.

READING TIP As you read, match the bulleted items in the text with the colored labels on the photograph below.

- Sepals are leafy structures that enclose the flower before it opens. When the flower blooms, the sepals fall open and form the base of the flower.
- Petals are leafy structures arranged in a circle around the pistil. The petals open as the reproductive structures of the plant mature. Petals are often the most colorful part of a flower. The petals help to attract animal pollinators.
- C The stamen is the male reproductive structure of a flower. It includes a stalk called a filament and the anther. The anther produces sperm cells, which are contained in pollen grains.
- 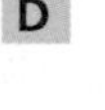 D The pistil is the female reproductive structure of the flower. The ovary is located at the base of the pistil and contains the egg cells that mature into eggs. At the top of the pistil is the stigma, where pollen grains attach.

CHECK YOUR READING What are the stamen and pistil?

Parts of a Flower

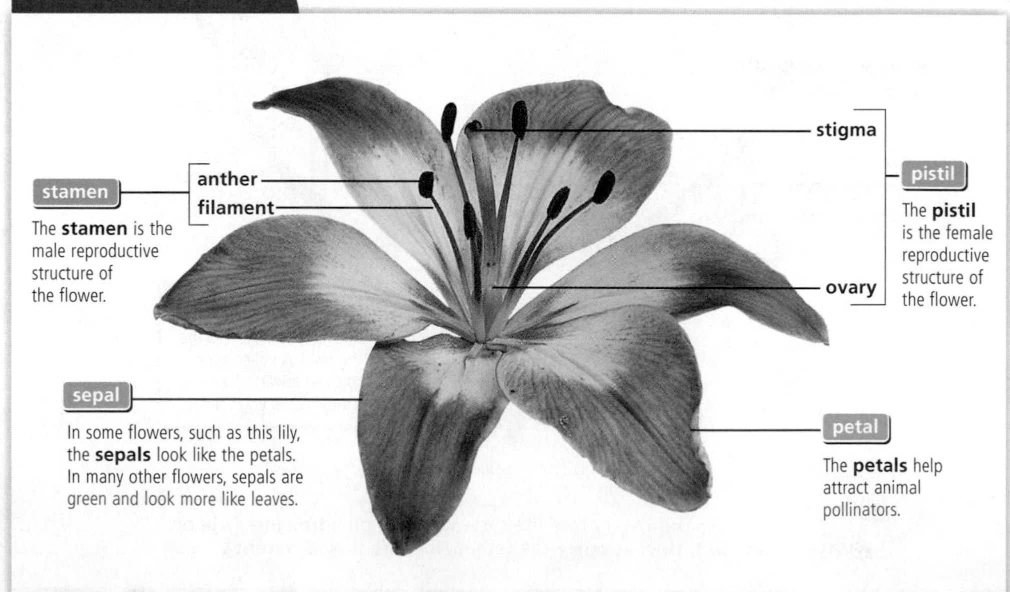

DIFFERENTIATE INSTRUCTION

More Reading Support

C Where in the stamen is the pollen produced? *in the anther*

D Where in the pistil are the eggs produced? *in the ovary*

Advanced Invite interested students to research and report on carnivorous plants, such as the Venus flytrap, pitcher plants, and sundew plants. Ask students to report on how the structure of the flowers and the plant are adapted to trap food.

 Challenge and Extension, p. 191

INVESTIGATE Flower Parts

What parts of a flower can you identify?

PROCEDURE

1. Examine the flower you are given. Try to notice as many details as you can. Draw a diagram of the flower in your notebook and label its parts.
2. Carefully take your flower apart. Sort the parts. Draw and label one example of each part in your notebook.

WHAT DO YOU THINK?

- Which of the parts of a flower labeled in the diagram on page 382 did you find in your flower?
- Based on your experience, what would you look for if you were trying to decide whether a structure on an unfamiliar plant was a flower?

SKILL FOCUS
Observing

MATERIALS
- assorted flowers
- hand lens

TIME
15 minutes

Fruit

E

A fruit is a ripened plant ovary. Some ovaries contain more than one seed, such as an apple. Some contain only one seed, like a cherry. Apples and cherries are called fleshy fruits, because they have juicy flesh. The corn you eat as corn on the cob is a fleshy fruit. There are also dry fruits. Peanuts, walnuts, and sunflowers are dry fruits. The shells of dry fruits help protect the seeds. Some dry fruits, like the winged fruit of a maple tree or the feathery tip of a dandelion seed, have structures that allow the seeds to be carried by the wind.

Animals spread both pollen and seeds.

Reproduction in many types of flowering plants includes interactions between plants and animals. The plants are a source of food for the animal. The animals provide a way to transport pollen and seeds. As they eat, animals move pollen from flower to flower and seeds from place to place.

F

Have you ever watched a honeybee collect nectar from a flower? Nectar is a sweet sugary liquid located at the bottom of the flower. As the bee crawls around in the flower, reaching down for the nectar, it rubs against the anthers and picks up pollen grains. When the bee travels to another flower, some of that pollen rubs off onto the pistil of the second flower.

CHECK YOUR READING How do bees benefit from the flowers they pollinate?

DIFFERENTIATE INSTRUCTION

More Reading Support

E Give an example of a fleshy fruit and a dry fruit. *Sample answer: cherry, peanut*

F What is the sugary liquid located at the bottom of a flower? *nectar*

Advanced Write the terms *monocot* and *dicot* on the board and tell students that angiosperms come in these two distinct types. Have students find out the characteristics of each and give examples of each. Encourage students to illustrate their findings with diagrams, photographs, and illustrations.

Inclusion "Investigate Flower Parts" can be tailored for students of differing abilities by providing flowers that are less challenging (such as a lily) or more challenging (such as a daisy or sunflower) to dissect and identify.

INVESTIGATE Flower Parts

PURPOSE To identify the parts of a flower

TIPS *15 min.* Flowers with anatomies that are easy to identify (both male and female parts) include lilies, tulips, and gladiolus. Flowers that are "daisy-like" will be more difficult to identify.

WHAT DO YOU THINK? *Part of the flower that students identify will vary depending on the selection of flowers. Students might say that they would look for brightly colored petal-like parts, pollen, parts that look like anthers, and stamens and pistils in the center of the bloom.*

 Datasheet, Flower Parts, p. 199

Technology Resources

Customize this student lab as needed or look for an alternative. Print rubrics to assess student lab reports.

 **Lab Generator CD-ROM**

Teacher Demo

Provide examples of fleshy and dry fruits for students to examine. (Dry fruits include acorns, walnuts, and other nuts; fleshy fruits include mangoes, oranges, pears, and many similar fruits.) Allow students time to examine the fruits with a hand lens and note the color, texture, and shape. Cut several of the fleshy fruits in half and have students observe the ovaries and seeds.

Ongoing Assessment

CHECK YOUR READING *Answer: Bees get energy and material from the nectar they drink.*

Integrate the Sciences

Scientists have discovered that honeybees can distinguish at least four different colors of the spectrum: yellow, blue green, blue, and ultraviolet. Their ability to see ultraviolet allows bees to follow ultraviolet patterns in flowers that are not visible to the human eye.

Bats, on the other hand, are able to locate sources of food, such as insects or flowers through echolocation. They emit high-frequency pulses of sound that are not audible to human ears and listen for the echoes that return. The echoes enable the bats to determine position and direction of food objects.

Teach Difficult Concepts

Some students think that pollination and fertilization are the same process. Point out that pollination is necessary for fertilization to occur. Refer students back to the "Life Cycle of a Cherry Tree" diagram on p. 381. Ask: What is the difference between pollination and fertilization? *Pollination moves sperm from the male part of the flower (anther) to the female part of the flower (stigma). Fertilization occurs when the egg and sperm are united (when sperm travels down a pollen tube to reach an egg in the ovary).*

Ongoing Assessment

Analyze the relationship between animals and flowering plants.

Ask: How do animals help plants grow and reproduce? *Animals pollinate plants by spreading pollen from one plant to another, and help plants grow by dispersing their seeds.*

CHECK YOUR READING *Answer: Animal pollinators move pollen from flower to flower, often of the same species. Wind blows pollen around and there is only a small chance it will land on the female part of a plant of the right species.*

READING TIP
The word *pollinate* means "to transfer pollen from an anther to a stigma." Note the differences in spelling between *pollen* and *pollinate, pollinator.*

An animal that pollinates a flower is called a pollinator. Bees and other insects are among the most important pollinators. Bees depend on nectar for food, and they collect pollen to feed their young. Bees recognize the colors, odors, and shapes of flowers. Thousands of species of plants are pollinated by bees, including sunflowers and lavender.

The relationship between angiosperms and their pollinators can be highly specialized. Sometimes the nectar is located in a tube-shaped flower. Only certain animals, for example hummingbirds with long, slender beaks, can pollinate those flowers. Some flowers bloom at night. These flowers attract moths and bats as pollinators. Night-blooming flowers are usually pale, which means they are visible at night. Also, they may give off a strong scent to attract animal pollinators.

The advantage of animal pollination is that the pollen goes to where it is needed most. The pollen collected by a bee has a much better chance of being brought to another flower. By comparison, pollen grains that are spread by the wind are blown in all directions. Each grain has only a small chance of landing on another flower. Wind-pollinated plants produce a lot more pollen than plants that are pollinated by animals.

CHECK YOUR READING What is the advantage of animal pollination over wind pollination?

SIMULATION CLASSZONE.COM
Compare the different ways seeds are dispersed.

The fruits produced by angiosperms help to spread the seeds they contain. Some seeds, like dandelion and maple seeds, are carried by the wind. Many seeds are scattered by fruit-eating animals. The seeds go through the animal's digestive system and are eventually deposited on the ground with the animal's waste. Wide scattering of seeds ensures that some seeds will land in an area with enough resources and room to grow.

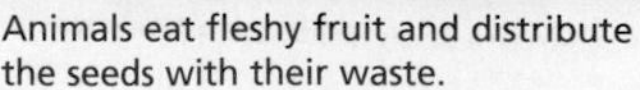

Animals eat fleshy fruit and distribute the seeds with their waste.

The burrs in this horse's mane are dry fruit that contain seeds.

DIFFERENTIATE INSTRUCTION

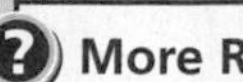

More Reading Support

G Nectar found in a long slender flower is likely pollinated by which animal? *hummingbird*

H How are dandelion seeds dispersed? *by wind*

Below Level Ask students to draw a comic strip of animals pollinating flowers or dispersing seeds. Students should include captions of the action in their strips to explain how the processes occur.

Additional Investigation To reinforce Section 11.4 learning goals, use the following full-period investigation:

R **Additional INVESTIGATION,** Fertilization in Angiosperms, A, B, & C; pp. 210–218; 360–361
(Advanced students should complete Levels B and C.)

Animals also help to scatter some types of dry fruits—not by eating them, but by catching them on their fur. Have you ever tried to pet a dog that has run through a grassy field? You might have noticed burrs stuck in the animal's fur. The seeds of many grasses and wildflowers produce dry fruits that are covered with spines or have pointed barbs. Seeds protected by these types of dry fruits stick to fur. The seeds travel along with the animal until the animal rubs them off.

Humans depend on plants for their survival.

Without plants, humans and all other animals would not be able to live on Earth. After plants adapted to life on land, it became possible for animals to live on land as well. Land animals rely on plants for food and oxygen. Many animals live in or near plants. Plants also supply materials humans use every day.

Food and Oxygen

All organisms must have energy to live. For animals, that energy comes from food. Plants, especially angiosperms, are the ultimate source of food for all land animals. Plants capture energy from the Sun to make sugars and other carbohydrates. Those same energy-rich materials are then consumed by animals as food. Even animals that eat other animals depend on plants for survival, because plants may provide food for the animals they eat.

Photosynthesis, the process that plants use to produce sugars and carbohydrates, also produces oxygen. The oxygen in the air you breathe is the product of the photosynthetic activity of plants and algae. Animals, including humans, need oxygen to release the energy stored in food.

Plants capture light energy from the Sun and store it in sugars and other carbohydrates.

Energy Resources and Soil

Plants are an important source of many natural resources. Natural gas and coal are energy resources that formed deep underground from the remains of plants and other organisms. Natural gas and coal are important fuels for many purposes, including the generation of electricity.

Even the soil under your feet is a natural resource associated with plants. Plant roots can break down rock into smaller and smaller particles to form soil. When plants die, their bodies decay and add richness to the soil.

History of Science

Humans began the transition from a hunter-gatherer society to cultivating the land and domestication of animals around 9000 B.C. to 7000 B.C. Scientists think that agricultural techniques developed somewhat simultaneously throughout the world. In the Middle East, people began to harvest types of grain and barley. The domestication of cattle and sheep allowed for the cultivation of crops. In China, millet and rice were both grown by 4000 B.C. The Americas saw cultivation of peppers, avocados, and amaranths around 7000 B.C. to 5000 B.C.

EXPLORE the BIG idea

Revisit "How Are Seeds Dispersed?" on p. 355. Ask: What features of seeds enable them to be dispersed by both animals and wind? *Sample answers: Seeds have burrs that stick to animals, seeds have wings that allow them to be blown in the wind. Animals eat the fruit surrounding seeds and deposit the seeds in wastes.*

Ongoing Assessment

Discuss human uses of plants.

Ask: Other than food, what are some resources for humans that come from plants? *Sample answer: gas and coal obtained from long-decayed plants, soil and fertilizer, oxygen in air, clothing fibers, paper, wood for building*

DIFFERENTIATE INSTRUCTION

More Reading Support

I What is the main source of food for land animals? *plants*

Alternative Assessment Ask students to create a mind map showing the importance of plants to human survival. Students should include subheads of food and oxygen and energy resources and soil in their graphics.

Teach from Visuals

To help students interpret the photographs of plants and products ask: About how many pounds of cotton are needed to produce a single pair of jeans? *about two and one-half pounds*

Reinforce the BIG idea

Have students relate the section to the Big Idea.

 Reinforcing Key Concepts, p. 193

11.4 ASSESS & RETEACH

Assess

 Section 11.4 Quiz, p. 46

Reteach

Ask students to identify an angiosperm they are familiar with. Prompt volunteers to discuss:

- parts of the plant and their functions.
- the stages the plant goes through when it reproduces.
- how pollen and seeds from the plant are dispersed.

As you guide them through their identification, students may wish to sketch or diagram the answers. Then pairs can review the notes. *Sample answer: A flower contains male and female structures: sperm cells are produced in anther and egg cells in ovary. Pollen grains with sperm cells are released and attach to pistil. When pollen tube reaches ovary, sperm can fertilize egg, seeds and fruit form. Pollen and seeds are spread by animals, wind, and water.*

Technology Resources

Have students visit **ClassZone.com** for reteaching of Key Concepts.

 CONTENT REVIEW

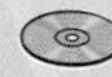 CONTENT REVIEW CD-ROM

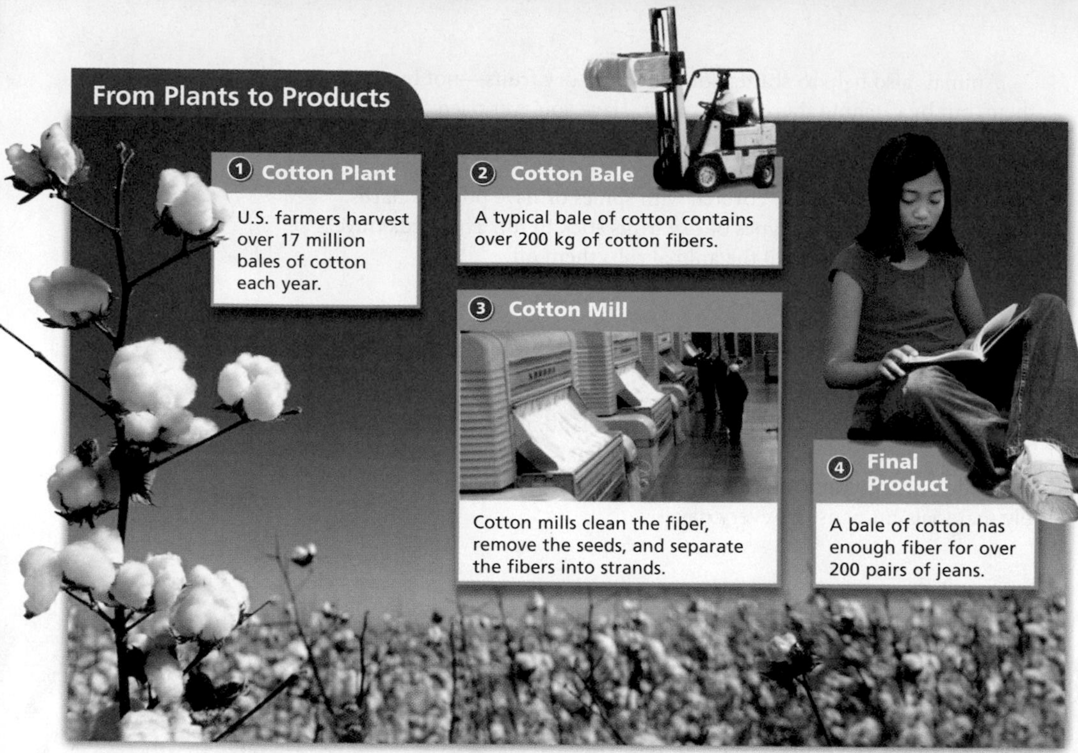

Other Products

Plant materials are part of many products people use every day. Plants provide the wood used to build houses and the wood pulp used to make paper for books like the one you are reading. The cotton in blue jeans comes from plants. So do many dyes that are used to add color to fabrics. Aspirin and many other medicines made by drug companies today are based on chemicals originally found in plants.

11.4 Review

KEY CONCEPTS

1. How do flowers relate to fruit?
2. How are animals involved in the life cycles of some flowering plants?
3. List three ways that humans depend upon plants.

CRITICAL THINKING

4. **Predict** If you observed three plants in a forest—a moss, a fern, and a flowering plant—which would have the most insects nearby? Why?
5. **Connect** Draw an apple like the one shown on page 379. Label three parts of the fruit and explain from which part of an apple flower each part grew.

CHALLENGE

6. **Synthesize** There are more species of flowering plants on Earth than species of mosses, ferns, or cone-bearing plants such as pine trees. How do you think the different ways spores, pollen, and seeds are spread affect the genetic diversity of different types of plants? Explain your reasoning.

ANSWERS

1. Ovary of flower becomes fruit.

2. Some animals feed on nectar, carrying pollen from flower to flower. Others eat fruit and disperse seeds as waste.

3. Sample answers: oxygen, food, material, coal and gas, wood, paper, fabric, medicine

4. flowering plants because insects feed on nectar and fruit

5. Upper part of pistil becomes stem, fertilized eggs become seeds, ovary becomes fruit.

6. Fruits enable plant species to spread seeds into different environments because seeds are spread more readily. This increases genetic diversity. Spores and pollen are more limited in ways they can spread.

SKILL: USING GRIDS TO ESTIMATE

Chloroplast Math

You can't count the number of chloroplasts in a leaf very easily, but you can estimate the number. For example, if you know the number of chloroplasts in a small area, you can estimate the number of chloroplasts in a whole leaf.

MATH TUTORIAL
CLASSZONE.COM
Click on Math Tutorial for more help with perimeter and area.

Example

Suppose you are studying how lilacs make food from sunlight. You read that there are 50 million chloroplasts for every square centimeter of a leaf. You want to know the number in a whole leaf.

(1) Cover the leaf with centimeter grid paper.

(2) Count the number of whole squares covering the leaf.
7

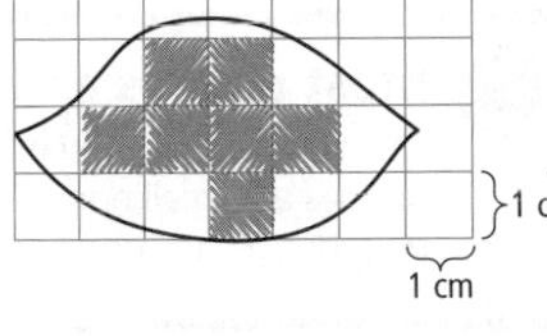

(3) Match pairs or sets of partly covered squares, that add up to a whole square.
$7 + 5 = 12$

(4) Add on any remaining 0.5 (half), 0.025 (quarter), or 0.75 (three-quarters) of a square.
$12 + .5 = 12.5$

(5) Finally, multiply the number of squares by the number of chloroplasts in one square.

ANSWER $50{,}000{,}000 \times 12.5 = 625{,}000{,}000.$

Give estimates for the following amounts.

1. Trace the beech leaf shown on this page onto a sheet of centimeter grid paper. What is the leaf's approximate area in cm^2?
2. About how many chloroplasts are in this beech leaf?
3. A eucalyptus leaf is long and thin. Suppose a healthy leaf is 1.5 centimeters wide and 6 centimeters long. Estimate its area. Hint: Make a sketch.
4. What is the approximate number of chloroplasts in the eucalyptus leaf described above?

CHALLENGE Collect two leaves. Trace the leaves on centimeter grid paper. Label each tracing with its name, estimated area, and its approximate number of chloroplasts.

ANSWERS

1. about 11 cm^2

2. about 550,000,000 chloroplasts ($11 \times 50{,}000{,}000 = 550{,}000\ 000$)

3. about $8\frac{1}{2}$ cm^2

4. about 425,000,000 chloroplasts ($8\frac{1}{2} \times 50{,}000{,}000 = 425{,}000\ 000$)

5. CHALLENGE Check students' leaf samples and sketches.

MATH IN SCIENCE
Math Skills Practice for Science

Set Learning Goal

To use area concepts to estimate the number of chloroplasts on a leaf

Present the Science

Chloroplasts are mostly found on the surface of the leaf where they are in full view of sunlight. A single leaf can contain millions of chloroplasts.

Develop Measurement Skills

Areas of irregular objects can be found by using a grid and estimating square units that cover the area.

As students work through the example, make sure they accurately combine parts of squares to equal one whole square. For example, combine 3/4 of a square with 1/4 to get a full square.

DIFFERENTIATION TIP Enlarge a copy of the leaf by about 60% and have students use one-inch grid paper to make their tracings.

Close

Ask students how using grids can help scientists study plants in other ways. *Sample answer: Scientists might estimate numbers of stomata, of cells, of xylem or phloem, etc., in leaves or stems.*

Point out that scientists can use grids for sampling purposes. If a square foot of a field contains a certain number of plants, scientists can estimate the number in the whole field.

- Math Support, p. 199
- Math Practice, p. 200

Technology Resources

Students can visit **ClassZone.com** to practice using grids to estimate.

MATH TUTORIAL

BACK TO

the BIG idea

Ask students to choose one of the groups of plants in Chapter 11 (mosses, ferns, gymnosperms, and angiosperms) and to name an adaptation that allows the plant to survive in its environment. *Sample answer: Ferns and mosses have sperm that swim through water, enabling them to reproduce. In gymnosperms, sperm are contained in pollen that travels through air. Angiosperms have seeds that are enclosed in fruits.*

KEY CONCEPTS SUMMARY

SECTION 11.1
Ask: How is the tree able to get essential water and nutrients from the soil to its leaves and energy from its leaves to the rest of tree? *Bundles of vascular tissues called* xylem *and* phloem *transport these materials.*

SECTION 11.2
Ask students to explain how water is transported throughout the bodies of mosses. *Mosses are nonvascular plants and do not have tissue for transporting water. Instead water travels from one cell to the next.*

SECTION 11.3
Ask students to describe the advantages gymnosperms have over mosses and ferns in reproduction. *Gymnosperm have seeds that contain food for the embryo; sperm does not need water to reach an egg.*

SECTION 11.4
Ask: What is the main difference between reproduction in angiosperms and gymnosperms? *Male and female reproductive parts are found in a flower in angiosperms. Seeds are surrounded by fruit.*

Review Concepts

- Big Idea Flow Chart, p. T17
- Chapter Outline, pp. T23–T24

11 Chapter Review

the BIG idea

Plants are a diverse group of organisms that live in many land environments.

CONTENT REVIEW
CLASSZONE.COM

KEY CONCEPTS SUMMARY

1 Plants are adapted to living on land.

All plants share common characteristics. The parts of a plant are specialized to get water and nutrients from the soil, gases from the air, and energy from the Sun. Plants have tissues, organs, and organ systems.

VOCABULARY
vascular system p. 359
transpiration p. 360

2 Most mosses and ferns live in moist environments.

The ancestors of present-day mosses and ferns were among the first land plants. Mosses are small nonvascular plants. Ferns are larger vascular plants. Both reproduce with spores and need moisture for a sperm to reach an egg.

3 Seeds and pollen are reproductive adaptations.

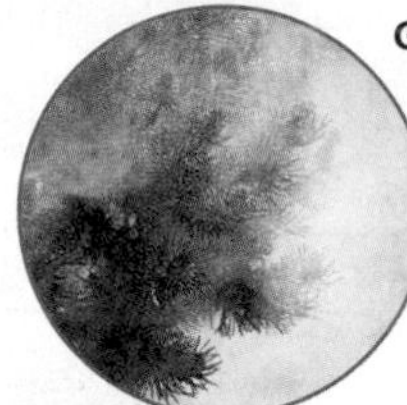

Gymnosperms, such as the pine tree, reproduce with **pollen** and seeds.

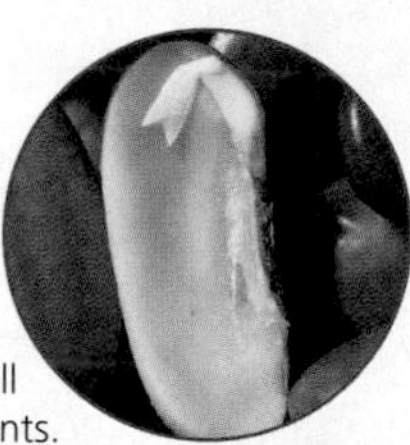

Seeds provide protection for the young plant as well as a supply of nutrients.

VOCABULARY
seed p. 370
embryo p. 370
germination p. 371
pollen p. 372
gymnosperm p. 374

4 Many plants reproduce with flowers and fruit.

Angiosperms use flowers and fruit to reproduce. **Flowers** produce pollen and contain the plant's reproductive structures.

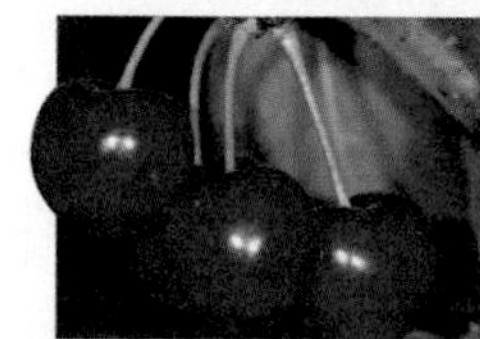

Fruit develops after pollination and contains seeds. Animals eat fruit and transport seeds to new locations.

VOCABULARY
angiosperm p. 379
flower p. 380
fruit p. 380

388 Unit 3: **Diversity of Living Things**

Technology Resources

Have students visit **ClassZone.com** or use the CD-ROM for a cumulative review of concepts.

CONTENT REVIEW

CONTENT REVIEW CD-ROM

Engage students in a whole-class interactive review of Key Concepts. Edit content as you wish.

POWER PRESENTATIONS

Reviewing Vocabulary

Write a statement describing how the terms in each pair are related to each other.

1. transpiration, cuticle
2. spores, seeds
3. seed, embryo
4. flower, fruit

The table below shows Greek (G.) and Latin (L.) words that are roots of words used in this chapter.

angeion (G.)	vessel or holder
gymnos (G.)	naked
sperma (G.)	seed
germinatus (L.)	sprout
pollen (L.)	fine flour

Describe how these word roots relate to the definitions of the following words.

5. angiosperm
6. gymnosperm
7. germination
8. pollen

Reviewing Key Concepts

Multiple Choice *Choose the letter of the best answer.*

9. Which of these is a characteristic of only some plants?
   a. They produce sugars.
   b. They are multicellular.
   c. They have a vascular system.
   d. They have a two-stage life cycle.
10. Which part of a plant anchors it in the soil?
   a. shoot system
   b. root system
   c. vascular system
   d. growth tissue
11. Which plant system transports water to different parts of the plant?
   a. vascular
   b. leaf
   c. stomata
   d. cuticle
12. Which part of a leaf does *not* allow transpiration?
   a. stomata
   b. cell wall
   c. stem
   d. cuticle
13. Which of these structures do mosses and ferns reproduce with?
   a. seeds
   b. growth tissue
   c. spores
   d. pollen
14. How are mosses different from ferns, pine trees, and flowering plants?
   a. Mosses reproduce through sexual reproduction.
   b. Mosses need moisture to reproduce.
   c. Mosses produce sugar through photosynthesis.
   d. Mosses have no vascular tissue.
15. What do seeds have that spores and pollen do not?
   a. a supply of nutrients
   b. a reproductive cell
   c. a protective covering
   d. a way to be transported

Short Answer *Write a short answer to each question.*

16. What are three ways plants are important to humans?
17. Explain how the bat in these photographs is interacting with the flower. How might the activity benefit the plant?

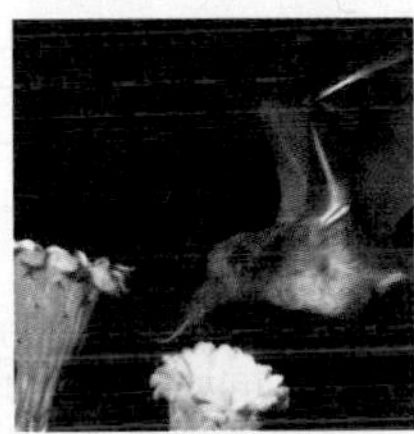

ASSESSMENT RESOURCES

UNIT ASSESSMENT BOOK
- Chapter Test, Level A, pp. 47–50
- Chapter Test, Level B, pp. 51–54
- Chapter Test, Level C, pp. 55–58
- Alternative Assessment, pp. 59–60

SPANISH ASSESSMENT BOOK
Spanish Chapter Test, pp. 49–52

Technology Resources

Edit test items and answer choices.

 **Test Generator CD-ROM**

Visit **ClassZone.com** to extend test practice.

 **Test Practice**

Reviewing Vocabulary

1. Transpiration is movement of water vapor out of a plant through the leaves. The cuticle is a waxy layer on the surface of leaves that limits transpiration.

2. Both grow into new plants. Spores are single cells released from a moss or fern. Seeds contain multi-celled embryos and are produced by angiosperms or gymnosperms.

3. The embryo is a new plant. It is contained in the seed, which provides protection and nutrients.

4. The flower is the reproductive part of the plant. Egg cells inside the flower are fertilized, forming seeds. The fruit grows around the seeds.

5. Angiosperms are plants with seeds enclosed in fruit. The fruit is like a vessel or holder for the seeds.

6. Gymnosperm seeds are not enclosed in fruit. In this way they are naked seeds.

7. Germination is the process by which a seed or spore begins to sprout into a plant.

8. Pollen is like fine flour in that it is made up of small particles.

Reviewing Key Concepts

9. c

10. b

11. a

12. d

13. c

14. d

15. a

16. Answers should mention three of the following: Plants supply oxygen, materials for shelter, food; contribute to energy resources; and are used to manufacture cloth, paper, medicines, and other products.

17. As the bat feeds on the nectar, it picks up pollen. The bat brings pollen to the next plant it visits. This enables the plant to be pollinated. It also increases genetic diversity in plants.

Thinking Critically

18. The cuticle is a waxy covering that keeps water needed for photosynthesis from evaporating.

19. Xylem and phloem are in the vascular system. Xylem brings water and nutrients in; phloem moves energy-rich materials out.

20. Stomata allow exchange of gases. When air is dry, the stomata close so water will not evaporate.

21. Chloroplasts produce sugars using energy from sunlight. More are in the upper leaf, where there is plenty of sunlight.

22. Photosynthesis is the main function. A large surface allows for a lot of energy from sunlight. Stomata allow CO_2 gas in and let O_2 gas out. Xylem brings water and nutrients in, phloem transports sugars out.

23. Pine trees—gymnosperms; cherry trees—angiosperms; angiosperms are more widespread.

24. A large amount of pollen increases the chances of fertilization.

25. egg: all; pollen and seed: pine tree, cherry tree; cone: pine tree; flower and fruit: cherry tree

26. Plants provide food, O_2, shelter. Animals transport pollen and seeds.

27. Plants can produce offshoots, such as runners. Plants can spread more quickly, but genetic material is the same as parent's.

the BIG idea

28. The tree has a large root system, a vascular system to move materials, and lots of leaves for photosynthesis.

29. Answers should refer to at least three different types of plants.

UNIT PROJECTS

Collect schedules, materials lists, and questions. Be sure dates and materials are obtainable, and questions are focused.

R Unit Projects, pp. 5–10

Thinking Critically

The next four questions refer to the labeled parts of the diagram of the leaf below.

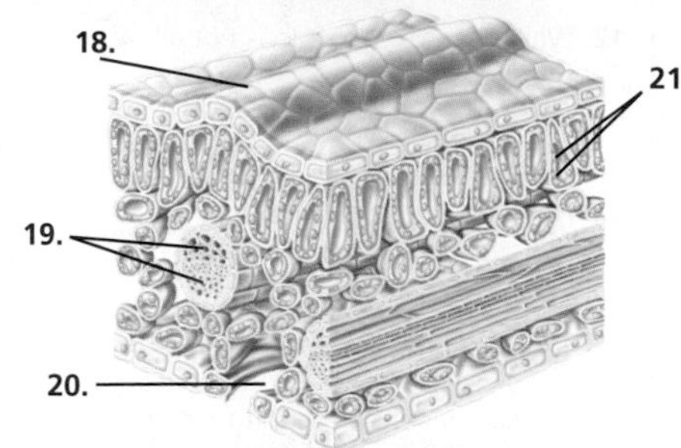

18. CLASSIFY Identify the layer that covers a leaf. What function does it serve, and why is that function important?

19. CLASSIFY What are the two tissues shown here, how do they function, and what system do they belong to?

20. PREDICT Identify the structure and predict what would happen to this structure if the air around the plant was very hot and dry.

21. ANALYZE What are these structures? What is their function? What are the advantages of having more of them at the top of the leaf than at the bottom?

22. COMMUNICATE A leaf is made up of different tissues and specialized cells. What is the main function of a leaf? How does the organization of tissues and cells in a leaf help it to carry out this function? Include the following terms in your answer: *sunlight, energy, oxygen gas, carbon dioxide gas, water,* and *sugar.*

23. CLASSIFY What is the name of the group of plants pine trees belong to? What group of plants do cherry trees belong to? Which of the two groups is more widespread?

24. CONNECT You or someone you know may be allergic to pollen that is in the air during some plants' growing seasons. What is the advantage of a plant producing so much pollen?

25. SUMMARIZE Copy and complete the table below, indicating which reproductive structures are part of the life cycles of mosses, ferns, pine trees, and cherry trees. The first row is done.

	moss	fern	pine tree	cherry tree
sperm	✓	✓	✓	✓
egg				
pollen				
seed				
cone				
flower				
fruit				

26. SYNTHESIZE Plants were among the first organisms to live on land. Name at least two ways that plants made land habitable for animals. In what way did animals help plants to spread farther onto the land?

27. INFER Describe how a plant might reproduce asexually. Explain one advantage and one disadvantage asexual reproduction might have for the plant you described.

the BIG idea

28. SUMMARIZE Look again at the photograph on pages 354–355. Now that you have finished the chapter, how would you change or add details to your answer to the question on the photograph?

29. SYNTHESIZE Think of three different types of plants that you have seen. Use what you know about those plants as supporting evidence in a paragraph you write on one of these topics:

Plants are a diverse group of organisms.

Plants share common characteristics.

UNIT PROJECTS

Check your schedule for your unit project. How are you doing? Be sure that you have placed data or notes from your research in your project folder.

MONITOR AND RETEACH

If students are having trouble applying the concepts in items 18–21, suggest that they review the visual on p. 361. Have them create a word frame diagram for each of the following words: *stomata, chloroplast, xylem, phloem, photosynthesis,* and *leaf.* Tell them to leave the center blank and write the word very small on the back of the page. They can then trade frames with a partner and guess the words.

Students may benefit from summarizing one or more sections of the chapter.

 Summarizing the Chapter, pp. 219–220

390 Unit 3: **Diversity of Living Things**

Standardized Test Practice

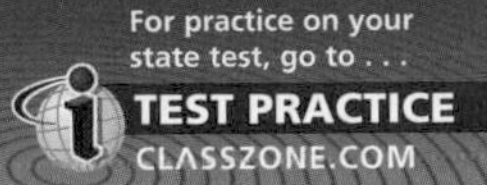

Analyzing Data

A pesticide is a material that kills pests, such as insects. A plant specialist wants to know if a new pesticide has any effect on the production of oranges. Grove A is planted using the same pesticide that was used in previous years. The new pesticide is used in grove B. Both groves have the same number of orange trees. The bar graph shows the data for one season.

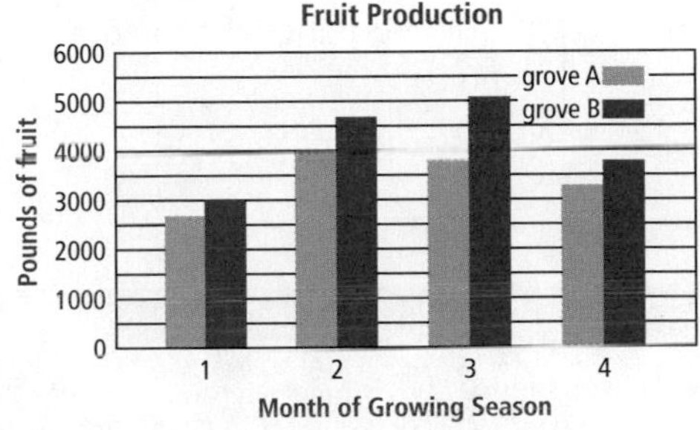

Choose the letter of the best response.

1. About how many pounds of fruit were grown in grove A during month 1 of the growing season?
   a. about 2000 lb
   b. about 2700 lb
   c. about 3000 lb
   d. about 3500 lb
2. During which month in the growing season was the most fruit produced?
   a. month 1
   b. month 2
   c. month 3
   d. month 4
3. About how many pounds of fruit were produced altogether by both groves in month 2?
   a. about 4000 lb
   b. about 4700 lb
   c. about 5000 lb
   d. about 8700 lb
4. Comparing the production in both groves, during which month was there the least amount of difference in the number of pounds of fruit produced?
   a. month 1
   b. month 2
   c. month 3
   d. month 4
5. Based on the data in the graph, what might the plant specialist conclude about the effectiveness of the new pesticide used in grove B?
   a. The pesticide is effective only after three months of growth.
   b. The pesticide does not have any effect on orange production.
   c. The pesticide used in grove A is more effective than the pesticide used in grove B.
   d. The pesticide increases the overall production of oranges throughout the growing season.

Extended Response

6. Pesticides are intended to kill insects that harm the growth of a plant. However, not all insects are harmful. Insects often pollinate the flowers of fruit trees. Pollination leads to fertilization of the flower, and fruit grows from the fertilized flower. Describe what might happen if a pesticide kills insects that are pollinators. What effect might such a pesticide have on the flowers of the plant and on its fruit?
7. Pesticides are only one factor that affect the growth of plants and the number of flowers or fruit the plant produces. Write a paragraph that names some other factors that may affect plant growth. Include environmental factors and factors that are controlled by humans.

Analyzing Data

1. b *3. d* *5. d*
2. c *4. a*

Extended Response

6. RUBRIC

4 points for a response that correctly identifies four ways that plants will be affected.

Sample answer: If the insecticide kills insects that pollinate the flowers, the flowers will still grow. With fewer pollinating insects around, there is less chance that the insects will feed on nectar and pollinate the flowers. If flowers are not pollinated, the eggs will not be fertilized and produce fruit. Fruit production will decline and the plant population will be in danger of declining as well.

3 points correctly identifies three ways that plants will be affected
2 points correctly identifies two ways that plants will be affected
1 point correctly identifies one way that plants will be affected

7. RUBRIC

4 points for a response that correctly describes environmental factors and those that are controlled by humans.

Sample answer: The amount of precipitation affects growth, either too little or too much. Temperature can also affect growth—too high and the plants dry out; too low and the plants freeze. The quality of soil is also a factor. Humans can alter the amount of water by irrigating fields. They can improve the quality of soil by fertilizing it. They can breed plants that are better able to grow and produce fruit.

3 points describes at least two effects of environment and one effect of humans
2 points describes at least one effect of environment and one effect of humans
1 point describes at least one effect of environment or one effect of humans

METACOGNITIVE ACTIVITY

Have students answer the following questions in their **Science Notebook:**

1. What plants were familiar to you before you read the chapter? What were some unfamiliar plants or new plants you learned about?
2. What most surprised you about the relationships between plants and animals, including humans?
3. What activity or question helped you most in learning about plants?

CHAPTER

Invertebrate Animals

Life Science
UNIFYING PRINCIPLES

PRINCIPLE 1
All living things share common characteristics.

PRINCIPLE 2
All living things share common needs.

PRINCIPLE 3
Living things meet their needs through interactions with the environment.

PRINCIPLE 4
The types and numbers of living things change over time.

Unit 3: Diversity of Living Things
BIG IDEAS

CHAPTER 9
Single-Celled Organisms and Viruses
Bacteria and protists have the characteristics of living things, while viruses are not alive.

CHAPTER 10
Introduction to Multicellular Organisms
Multicellular organisms live in and get energy from a variety of environments.

CHAPTER 11
Plants
Plants are a diverse group of organisms that live in many land environments.

CHAPTER 12
Invertebrate Animals
Invertebrate animals have a variety of body plans and adaptations.

CHAPTER 13
Vertebrate Animals
Vertebrate animals live in most of Earth's environments.

CHAPTER 12
KEY CONCEPTS

SECTION 1

Most animals are invertebrates.
1. Invertebrates are a diverse group of organisms.
2. Sponges are simple animals.

SECTION 2

Cnidarians and worms have different body plans.
1. Cnidarians have simple body systems.
2. Animals have different body plans.
3. Most worms have complex body systems.

SECTION 3

Most mollusks have shells, and echinoderms have spiny skeletons.
1. Mollusks are soft-bodied animals.
2. Mollusks show a range of adaptations.
3. Echinoderms have unusual adaptations.

SECTION 4

Arthropods have exoskeletons and joints.
1. Most invertebrates are arthropods.
2. Insects are six-legged arthropods.
3. Crustaceans live in water and on land.
4. Arachnids are eight-legged arthropods.
5. Millipedes and centipedes are arthropods.

T The Big Idea Flow Chart is available on p. T25 in the **UNIT TRANSPARENCY BOOK.**

Previewing Content

SECTION

Most animals are invertebrates. pp. 395–399

1. Invertebrates are a diverse group of organisms. Invertebrates include all groups of animals that do not have backbones. The six groups of **invertebrates** include sponges, cnidarians, worms, mollusks, echinoderms, and arthropods. Invertebrates live in a variety of environments on both land and in water.

2. Sponges are simple animals.

- A **sponge** is made up of a body wall with inner and outer layers.
- Flagella that line the body cavity of the sponge move water through the sponge, as shown. Specialized food cells digest plankton and other tiny organisms that sponges feed upon.

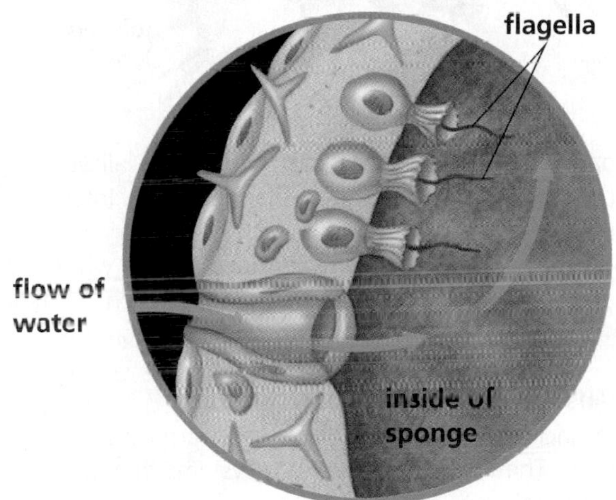

- Sponges reproduce asexually by budding. The new sponges are genetically identical to the parent sponge. Sponges also reproduce sexually by releasing sperm into the water. Sperm from one sponge then fertilizes the eggs of another sponge. **Immature** sponges, or **larvae,** are then released into the water where they attach to an underwater surface and remain **sessile.**

SECTION

Cnidarians and worms have different body plans. pp. 400–407

1. Cnidarians have simple body systems.

- **Cnidarians** include jellyfish, corals, sea anemones, and hydras. All cnidarians have **tentacles** with specialized stinging cells. These cells contain nematocysts, capsules that hold poisonous barbed filaments. Tissues in the cnidarians body include muscle and nerve cells that allow them to sense and respond to stimuli in the environment.
- Cnidarians reproduce both asexually and sexually. The jellyfish life cycle includes a polyp stage that is sessile and a medusa stage that is mobile. The polyps release disk-shaped buds, which grow into adult medusas.

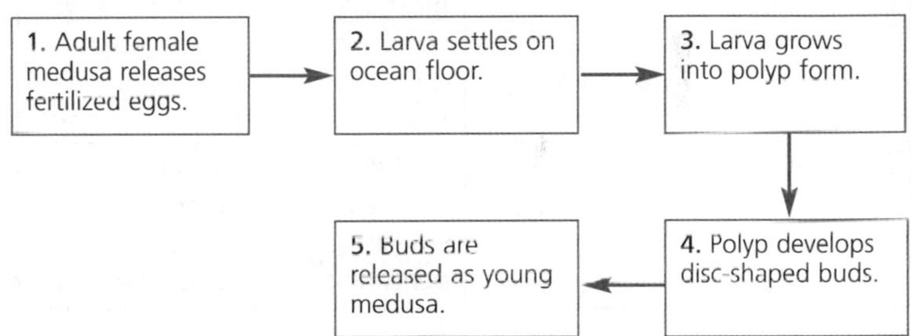

2. Animals have different body plans.

- A radial body plan is organized around a central point, usually a mouth that leads into a cavity where food is digested.
- A bilateral body plan has two mirror images of each other. Bilaterally shaped animals have front and back ends. The front end usually includes a head and mouth that consumes food, while the back end releases wastes.

3. Most worms have complex body systems.

- Segmented worms, called annelids, are divided into segments. Annelids have digestive, circulatory, muscular, and nervous systems. Annelids reproduce both asexually and sexually.
- Flatworms are the simplest worms, often living as parasites. Roundworms are more complex than flatworms.

Common Misconceptions

IS IT AN ANIMAL? Many studies have shown that students often think that animals only include large land animals, such as pets, farm animals, and those seen in zoos. When it comes to invertebrates, fewer than half of elementary students will identify an animal as such. In fact, any multicellular organism that does not photosynthesize and can move on its own is an animal.

This misconception is addressed on p. 396.

MISCONCEPTION DATABASE
CLASSZONE.COM Background on student misconceptions

REPRODUCTION Students commonly hold these misconceptions about reproduction: 1) Animals plan their reproductive strategies; 2) Sexual reproduction must involve a separate male and female organism; and 3) Sexual reproduction must involve mating. In fact, none of the above are necessarily true of all animals.

This misconception is addressed on p. 402.

Previewing Content

SECTION

Most mollusks have shells, and echinoderms have spiny skeletons. pp. 408–413

1. Mollusks are soft-bodied animals.
Mollusks include bivalves, gastropods, and cephalopods. Most mollusks have a hard, outer shell and relatively well-developed organ systems. They also have a muscular foot and a mantle, a layer of folded skin that protects internal organs. The table shows the mollusk groups and their characteristics.

Mollusks			
	Bivalves	**Gastropods**	**Cephalopods**
Characteristics	made up of two matching shell halves	most are protected by a spiral-shaped shell	most have eyes and tentacles for capturing prey
Examples	clams, scallops, mussels, oysters	snails, slugs, conches, whelks, periwinkles	squids, chambered nautiluses, octopuses

2. Mollusks show a range of adaptations.
The muscular foot is a feature that has been adapted to function differently for each group of mollusks.

3. Echinoderms have unusual adaptations.
- **Echinoderms** include radially symmetric sea stars, sea urchins, and sand dollars. These animals have mouths that are located in the center of the body and feed upon the ocean floor.
- Echinoderms have spines and internal skeletons. Water vascular systems and tube feet enable echinoderms to move and feed.

SECTION

Arthropods have exoskeletons and joints. pp. 414–421

1. Most invertebrates are arthropods.
Arthropods have a segmented body covered with an **exoskeleton,** an outer covering that is made up of chitin. This exoskeleton is shed as the animal grows in a process called **molting.** Arthropods have complex body systems. The three main groups of arthropods are insects, crustaceans, and arachnids.

2. Insects are six-legged arthropods.
- All adult **insects** have three distinct body segments and six legs.

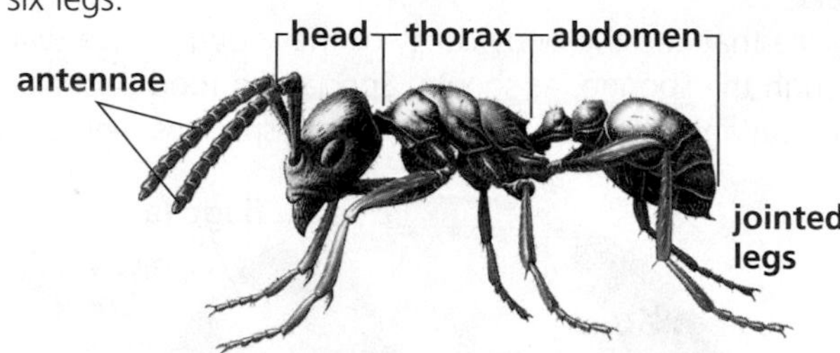

- Insects have a variety of adaptations such as specialized mouth parts, wings, and color and shape to blend into the environment.
- Insects undergo a process called **metamorphosis** in which the insect's appearance and body systems change at each life stage. Insects may go through simple or complete metamorphosis.

3. Crustaceans live in water and on land.
Crustaceans include lobsters, shrimp, crabs, barnacles, krill, and copepods. They have complex body systems that include a circulatory system.

4. Arachnids are eight-legged arthropods.
Arachnids include spiders, mites, ticks, and scorpions. They have two body segments as opposed to the three body segments in insects. Spiders have a unique adaptation for capturing prey by spinning webs made of silk.

5. Millipedes and centipedes are arthropods.
Millipedes have two pairs of walking legs on multiple body segments. Centipedes have one pair of walking legs per body segment.

Common Misconceptions

MISCONCEPTION DATABASE
CLASSZONE.COM Background on student misconceptions

ANIMAL TRAITS Among middle school students, reasons for identifying something as an animal commonly include: has four legs, makes sound, and has fur. Most of the animals in this chapter would not fit any of those criteria.

This misconception is addressed on p. 416.

Previewing Labs

Lab Generator CD-ROM
Edit these Pupil Edition labs and generate alternative labs.

EXPLORE the BIG idea

Worm-Watching, p. 393 Students observe worms in order to describe the worms' characteristics, activities, and behavior.	**TIME** 10 minutes **MATERIALS** notebook, outdoor area, hand lens
Insects and You, p. 393 Students list the types of insects seen during a week in order to discover diversity and characteristics.	**TIME** 10 minutes **MATERIALS** notebook, outdoor area, hand lens
Internet Activity: Invertebrate Diversity, p. 393 Students observe invertebrates to learn about the different types.	**TIME** 20 minutes **MATERIALS** computer with Internet access

SECTION 

INVESTIGATE Invertebrates, p. 396 Students make a potato trap to determine the kinds of invertebrates that live in local environments.	**TIME** 20 minutes **MATERIALS** potato, plastic knife, spoon, masking tape

SECTION 

EXPLORE Worm Movement, p. 400 Students observe a worm to explain how its body shape affects its movement.	**TIME** 20 minutes **MATERIALS** worm, tray, soil to cover bottom of tray, spray bottle filled with distilled water
CHAPTER INVESTIGATION, Worm Behavior, pp. 406–407 Students observe earthworm behavior and predict how they will respond to environmental stimuli.	**TIME** 40 minutes **MATERIALS** potting soil, coarse sand, aquarium, filter paper, spray bottle, small beaker, distilled water, 5 or more worms, 2 containers (one for untested worms and one for tested worms), stopwatch, (for Challenge: flashlight)

SECTION 

INVESTIGATE Mollusks and Echinoderms, p. 410 Students examine mollusk and echinoderm shells to compare and contrast their characteristics.	**TIME** 15 minutes **MATERIALS** selection of mollusk shells, sea stars, and sand dollars

SECTION 

EXPLORE Arthropods, p. 414 Students observe pillbugs to describe their characteristics.	**TIME** 20 minutes **MATERIALS** clear container, shoebox (half of cover removed), pillbugs, hand lens
INVESTIGATE Insect Metamorphosis, p. 418 Students observe mealworms to discover how often they molt.	**TIME** 20 minutes **MATERIALS** glass jar with lid with air holes, oat bran, potato, carrot, mealworms, (for Challenge: petri dish, tweezers)

 **Additional INVESTIGATION,** Exploring How a Squid Moves, A, B, & C, pp. 280–288; Teacher Instructions, pp. 360–361

Previewing Chapter Resources

CHAPTER 12

Invertebrate Animals

INTEGRATED TECHNOLOGY

CLASSZONE.COM
- eEdition Plus
- EasyPlanner Plus
- Misconception Database
- Content Review
- Test Practice
- Resource Centers
- Visualization
- Internet Activity
- Math Tutorial

SCILINKS.ORG

SCILINKS

CD-ROMS
- eEdition
- EasyPlanner Plus
- Power Presentations
- Content Review
- Lab Generator
- Test Generator

AUDIO CDS
- Audio Readings
- Audio Readings in Spanish

LABS AND ACTIVITIES

EXPLORE the Big Idea, p. 393
- Worm-Watching
- Insects and You
- Internet Activity: Invertebrate Diversity

UNIT RESOURCE BOOK

Unit Projects, pp. 5–10

Lab Generator CD-ROM

Generate customized labs.

SECTION

1 Most animals are invertebrates.

pp. 395–399

Time: 2 periods (1 block)

 Lesson Plan, pp. 221–222

Integrated Technology

- **MATH TUTORIAL**

UNIT TRANSPARENCY BOOK
- Big Idea Flow Chart, p. T25
- Daily Vocabulary Scaffolding, p. T26
- Note-Taking Model, p. T27
- 3-Minute Warm-Up, p. T28

Labs and Activities

- INVESTIGATE Invertebrates, p. 396
- Math in Science, p. 399

UNIT RESOURCE BOOK
- Datasheet, Invertebrates, p. 230
- Math Support, p. 269
- Math Practice, p. 270

SECTION

2 Cnidarians and worms have different body plans.

pp. 400–407

Time: 3 periods (1.5 blocks)

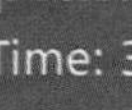 Lesson Plan, pp. 232–233

Integrated Technology

RESOURCE CENTER, Types of Worms

UNIT TRANSPARENCY BOOK
- Daily Vocabulary Scaffolding, p. T26
- 3-Minute Warm-Up, p. T28
- "Inside an Earthworm" Visual, p. T30

Labs and Activities

- EXPLORE Worm Movement, p. 400
- CHAPTER INVESTIGATION, Worm Behavior, pp. 406–407

UNIT RESOURCE BOOK

CHAPTER INVESTIGATION, Worm Behavior, A, B, & C, pp. 271–279

SECTION

3 Most mollusks have shells, and echinoderms have spiny skeletons.

pp. 408–413

Time: 2 periods (1 block)

 Lesson Plan, pp. 242–243

Integrated Technology

RESOURCE CENTER, Mollusks
VISUALIZATION, Cephalopods

UNIT TRANSPARENCY BOOK
- Daily Vocabulary Scaffolding, p. T26
- 3-Minute Warm-Up, p. T29

Labs and Activities

- INVESTIGATE Mollusks and Echinoderms, p. 410
- Think Science, p. 413

UNIT RESOURCE BOOK
- Datasheet, Mollusks and Echinoderms, p. 251
- Additional INVESTIGATION, Exploring How a Squid Moves, A, B, & C, pp. 280–288

SECTION

4 Arthropods have exoskeletons and joints.

pp. 414–421

Time: 3 periods (1.5 blocks)

Lesson Plan, pp. 253–254

Integrated Technology

RESOURCE CENTER, Diversity of Arthropods

UNIT TRANSPARENCY BOOK
- Big Idea Flow Chart, p. T25
- Daily Vocabulary Scaffolding, p. T26
- 3-Minute Warm-Up, p. T29
- Chapter Outline, pp. T31–T32

Labs and Activities

- EXPLORE Arthropods, p. 414
- INVESTIGATE Insect Metamorphosis, p. 418

UNIT RESOURCE BOOK

Datasheet, Insect Metamorphosis, p. 262

KEY TO ICONS

 CD/CD-ROM
 Teacher Edition
 UNIT TRANSPARENCY BOOK
 SPANISH ASSESSMENT BOOK
INTERNET
 Pupil Edition
 UNIT RESOURCE BOOK
 UNIT ASSESSMENT BOOK
SCIENCE TOOLKIT

READING AND REINFORCEMENT | ASSESSMENT | STANDARDS

Reading and Reinforcement

- Choose Your Own Strategy, B18–27
- Combination Notes, C36
- Daily Vocabulary Scaffolding, H1–8

 **UNIT RESOURCE BOOK**
- Vocabulary Practice, pp. 266–267
- Decoding Support, p. 268
- Summarizing the Chapter, pp. 289–290

 **Audio Readings CD**
Listen to Pupil Edition.

 **Audio Readings in Spanish CD**
Listen to Pupil Edition in Spanish.

Assessment

- Chapter Review, pp. 422–423
- Standardized Test Practice, p. 424

 **UNIT ASSESSMENT BOOK**
- Diagnostic Test, pp. 61–62
- Chapter Test, A, B, & C, pp. 67–78
- Alternative Assessment, pp. 79–80

 Spanish Chapter Test, pp. 53–56

 **Test Generator CD-ROM**
Generate customized tests.

 **Lab Generator CD-ROM**
Rubrics for Labs

Standards

National Standards
A.1–8, A.9.a–c, A.9.e–g, C.1.d, C.5.a, G.1.b

See p. 392 for the standards.

Reading and Reinforcement

 **UNIT RESOURCE BOOK**
- Reading Study Guide, A & B, pp. 223–226
- Spanish Reading Study Guide, pp. 227–228
- Challenge and Extension, p. 229
- Reinforcing Key Concepts, p. 231

Assessment

 Ongoing Assessment, pp. 395–397

 Section 12.1 Review, p. 398

 **UNIT ASSESSMENT BOOK**
Section 12.1 Quiz, p. 63

Standards

National Standards
A.2–8, A.9.a–c, A.9.e–f, C.1.d, C.5.a, G.1.b

Reading and Reinforcement

 **UNIT RESOURCE BOOK**
- Reading Study Guide, A & B, pp. 234–237
- Spanish Reading Study Guide, pp. 238–239
- Challenge and Extension, p. 240
- Reinforcing Key Concepts, p. 241
- Challenge Reading, pp. 264–265

Assessment

 Ongoing Assessment, pp. 401, 403–405

 Section 12.2 Review, p. 405

 **UNIT ASSESSMENT BOOK**
Section 12.2 Quiz, p. 64

Standards

National Standards
A.1–7, A.9.a–b, A.9.e–g, C.1.d, C.5.a, G.1.b

Reading and Reinforcement

 **UNIT RESOURCE BOOK**
- Reading Study Guide, A & B, pp. 244–247
- Spanish Reading Study Guide, pp. 248–249
- Challenge and Extension, p. 250
- Reinforcing Key Concepts, p. 252

Assessment

 Ongoing Assessment, pp. 409–412

 Section 12.3 Review, p. 412

 **UNIT ASSESSMENT BOOK**
Section 12.3 Quiz, p. 65

Standards

National Standards
A.2–7, A.9.a–b, A.9.e–f, C.1.d, C.5.a, G.1.b

Reading and Reinforcement

 **UNIT RESOURCE BOOK**
- Reading Study Guide, A & B, pp. 255–258
- Spanish Reading Study Guide, pp. 259–260
- Challenge and Extension, p. 261
- Reinforcing Key Concepts, p. 263

Assessment

Ongoing Assessment, pp. 414–421

 Section 12.4 Review, p. 421

 **UNIT ASSESSMENT BOOK**
Section 12.4 Quiz, p. 66

Standards

National Standards
A.2–7, A.9.a–b, A.9.e–f, C.1.d, C.5.a, G.1.b

Previewing Resources for Differentiated Instruction

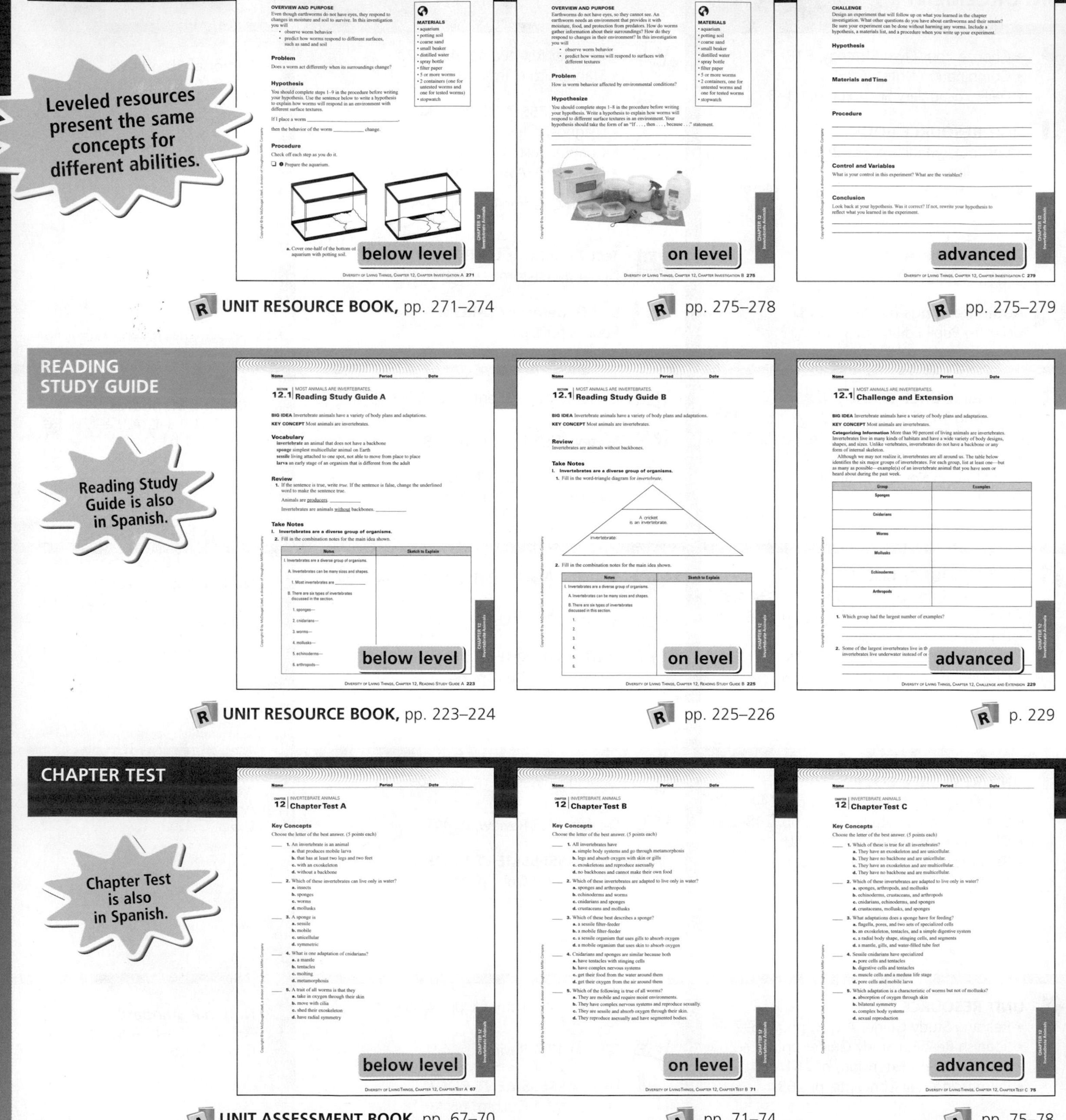

TECHNOLOGY

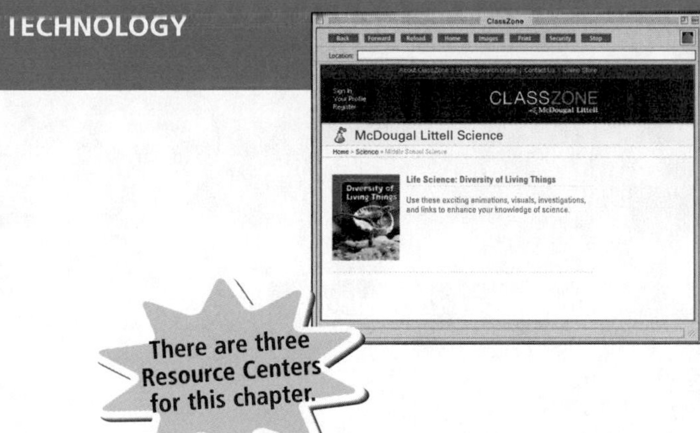

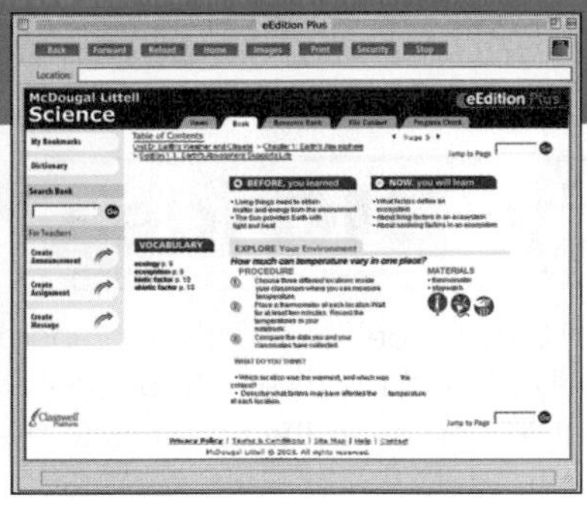

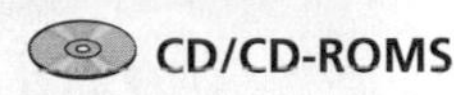

VISUAL CONTENT

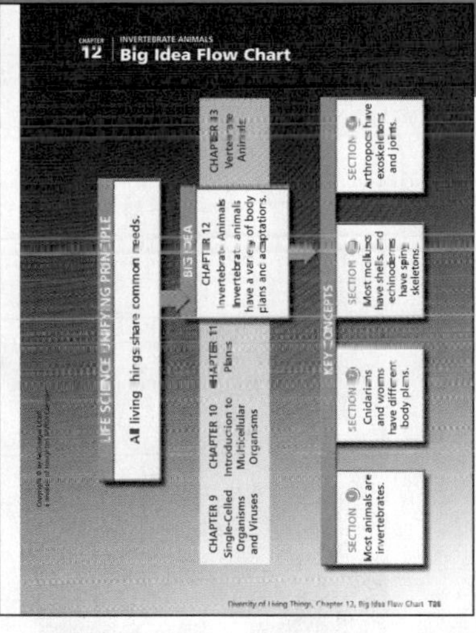

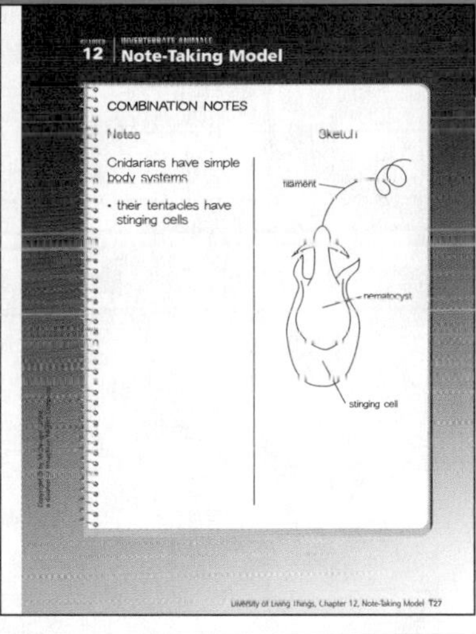

UNIT TRANSPARENCY BOOK, p. T25

p. T27

p. T30

MORE SUPPORT

Reinforcing Key Concepts for each section

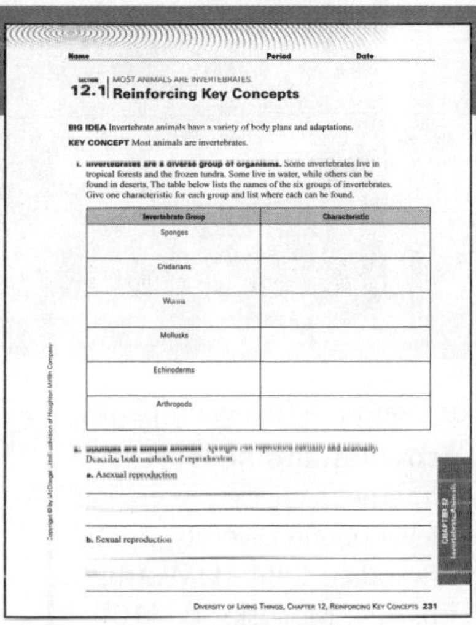

12.1 Reinforcing Key Concepts

BIG IDEA Invertebrate animals have a variety of body plans and adaptations.

KEY CONCEPT Most animals are invertebrates.

Invertebrate Group	Characteristic
Sponges	
Cnidarians	
Worms	
Mollusks	
Echinoderms	
Arthropods	

12 Vocabulary

invertebrate	cnidarian	gill	exoskeleton
sponge	tentacle	lung	molting
sessile	mobile	echinoderm	insect
larva	mollusk	arthropod	metamorphosis

A. WHO AM I?

Write the vocabulary word that best matches each clue.

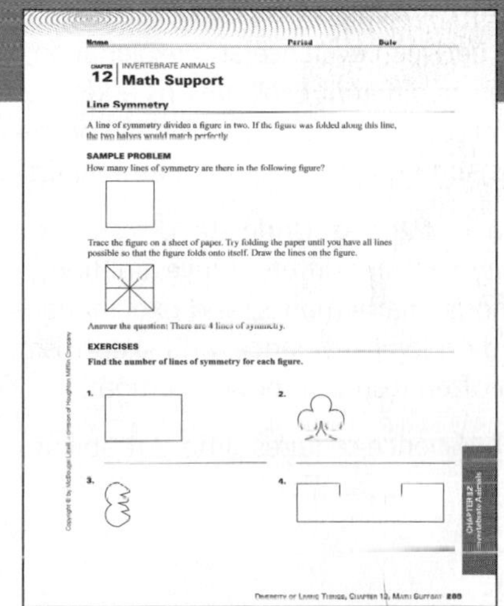

UNIT RESOURCE BOOK, p. 231

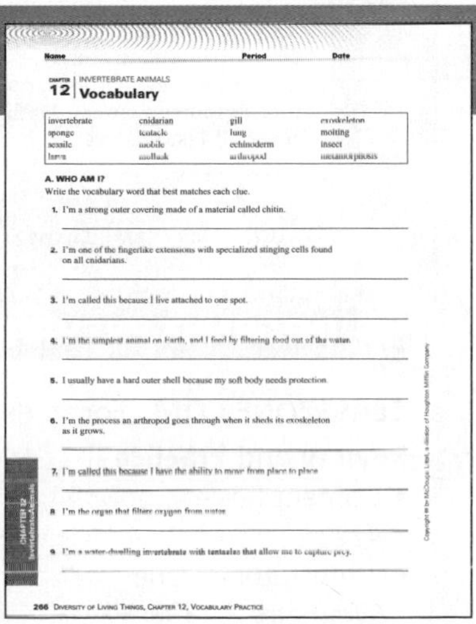

pp. 266–267

p. 269

INTRODUCE

the BIG idea

Have students look at the photograph of the jellyfish and the diver and discuss how the question in the box links to the Big Idea:

- How is the body of the jellyfish adapted to finding and eating food?
- How are our bodies adapted to taking in food?
- With students, brainstorm ways that organisms find and eat food.

National Science Education Standards

Content

C.1.d Specialized cells perform specialized functions in multicellular organisms.

C.5.a Although different species might look dissimilar, the unity among organisms becomes apparent from an analysis of internal structures.

Process

A.1–8 Identify questions that can be answered through scientific investigations; design and conduct an investigation; use tools to gather and interpret data; use evidence to describe, predict, explain, model; think critically to make relationships between evidence and explanation; recognize different explanations and predictions; communicate scientific procedures and explanations; use mathematics.

A.9.a–c, A.9.e–g Understand scientific inquiry by using different investigations, methods, mathematics, and explanations based on logic, evidence, and skepticism. Data often results in new investigations.

G.1.b Science requires different abilities.

CHAPTER 12 Invertebrate Animals

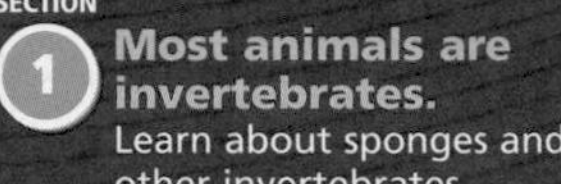

Invertebrate animals have a variety of body plans and adaptations.

Key Concepts

SECTION 1

Most animals are invertebrates.
Learn about sponges and other invertebrates.

SECTION 2

Cnidarians and worms have different body plans.
Learn how the body plans of cnidarians are different from those of worms.

SECTION 3

Most mollusks have shells, and echinoderms have spiny skeletons.
Learn about how mollusks and echinoderms meet their needs.

SECTION 4
Arthropods have exoskeletons and joints.
Learn about insects, crustaceans, and arachnids.

Internet Preview

CLASSZONE.COM
Chapter 12 online resources: Content Review, Visualization, four Resource Centers, Math Tutorial, Test Practice

INTERNET PREVIEW

CLASSZONE.COM For student use with the following pages:

Review and Practice
- Content Review, pp. 394, 422
- Math Tutorial: Line Symmetry, p. 399
- Test Practice, p. 425

Activities and Resources
- Internet Activity: Invertebrate Diversity, p. 393
- Resource Centers: Worms, p. 404; Mollusks, p. 410; Arthropods, p. 415
- Visualization: Cephalopods, p. 410

Sponges **Code: MDL042**

EXPLORE the BIG idea

Worm-Watching

Find a worm and observe it for a while in its natural environment. How much can you learn about how a worm meets its needs by watching it for a short time? Record your observations in your notebook.

Observe and Think What body parts can you identify on a worm? How would you describe a worm's activities and behavior?

Insects and You

Think about times when you have seen or noticed insects. Make a list of your experiences in your notebook. Then, start keeping a list of all the insects you see for the next week. How long do you think this list will be?

Observe and Think How many different types of insects did you see? Where did you see them? What characteristics do you think insects share?

Internet Activity: Invertebrate Diversity

Go to **ClassZone.com** to learn more about different types of invertebrates.

Observe and Think Of every 20 animal species on Earth, 19 are invertebrates. How many types of invertebrates can you name?

NSTA scilinks.org SCILINKS
Sponges Code: MDL042

Chapter 12: **Invertebrate Animals** 393

TEACHING WITH TECHNOLOGY

Electronic Encyclopedias Students can use electronic encyclopedias to investigate the body structures of echinoderms and mollusks, while doing the Investigation on p. 410. Have students print pictures and write their own captions to create a display.

Video Camera Students might want to use a video camera to record close-up observations of worms while investigating worm behavior on pp. 406–407.

Electronic Databases Students can compile a "Fun Facts" database about arthropods as they read about them on pp. 420–421. They can print or post the database to share it.

EXPLORE the BIG idea

These inquiry-based activities are appropriate for use at home or as a supplement to classroom instruction.

Worm-Watching

PURPOSE To observe how a worm meets its needs in its environment.

TIPS *10 min.* If worms are unavailable in an outdoor environment, set up a classroom observation tank with worms and moist soil. Remind students not to harm the worms. Students might gently move the worm they observe from pavement to a grassy area to observe in both environments.

Answer: Students might identify the "head," "mouth," and "tail." They might also notice body segmentation. Students will notice a variety of worm activities.

REVISIT after p. 404.

Insects and You

PURPOSE To discover the variety of insect characteristics.

TIP *10 min.* Some students may name animals that are not insects. Revisit the activity after discussing the characteristics of insects in section 12.4.

Sample answer: ten different types; students will observe most insects outdoors but in many places; common characteristics might include wings, legs, antennae.

REVISIT after p. 417.

Internet Activity: Invertebrate Diversity

PURPOSE To observe the variety of invertebrates.

TIP *20 min.* Challenge students to learn to recognize invertebrates, especially local species.

Answer: Have students make a classroom list of invertebrates and add to it as they study the chapter.

REVISIT after p. 421.

PREPARE

CONCEPT REVIEW

Activate Prior Knowledge

- Ask students to name some of the common characteristics that all living organisms share. *growth, response, reproduction, organization*
- Discuss how organisms meet their needs such as obtaining food, water, and oxygen. *Students will describe various methods, including respiration, eating, photosynthesis.*
- Ask students to name some invertebrate animals. *Students should not list fish, reptiles, amphibians, birds, or mammals, nor microorganisms.*

TAKING NOTES

Combination Notes

Combining a sketch with notes will help students to visualize a new concept and connect it with a concrete example. Later, they can fold the paper and study from the sketches, quizzing each other about written concepts.

Vocabulary Strategy

Allowing students to choose their own strategy helps them to assess their own learning styles and to tailor note-taking to their personal needs. Students might trade their description wheels, four squares, or word triangles with others when they are complete. They can use the diagrams as study aids.

Vocabulary and Note-Taking Resources

- Vocabulary Practice, pp. 266–267
- Decoding Support, p. 268

- Daily Vocabulary Scaffolding, p. T26
- Note-Taking Model, p. T27

- Choose Your Own Strategy, B18–27
- Combination Notes, C36
- Daily Vocabulary Scaffolding, H1–8

CHAPTER 12

Getting Ready to Learn

CONCEPT REVIEW

- All animals need energy, materials, and living space.
- Animals get energy and materials from food.
- Animals have different adaptations and behaviors for meeting their needs.

VOCABULARY REVIEW

predator p. 335

prey p. 335

adaptation *See Glossary.*

CONTENT REVIEW
CLASSZONE.COM
Review concepts and vocabulary.

TAKING NOTES

COMBINATION NOTES

To take notes about a new concept, first make an informal outline of the information. Then make a sketch of the concept and label it so you can study it later. Use arrows to connect parts of the concept when appropriate.

CHOOSE YOUR OWN STRATEGY

For each new vocabulary term, take notes by choosing one of the strategies from earlier chapters—**description wheel, four square,** or **word triangle.** You can also use other vocabulary strategies that you might already know.

See the Note-Taking Handbook on pages R45–R51.

SCIENCE NOTEBOOK

Notes

Sponges are simple animals

- no organs
- attached to one place
- remove food from water

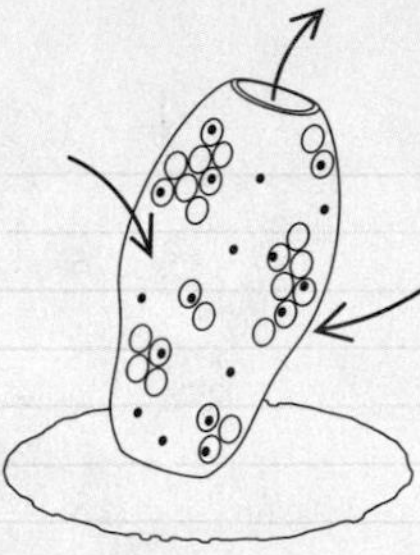

Description Wheel — feature, feature, feature, WORD, feature, feature

Four Square — Definition, Characteristics, TERM, Examples, Nonexamples

Word Triangle — sketch, sentence using the word, WORD: definition

394 Unit 3: Diversity of Living Things

CHECK READINESS

Administer the Diagnostic Test to determine students' readiness for new science content and their mastery of requisite math skills.

 Diagnostic Test, pp. 61–62

Technology Resources

Students needing content and math skills should visit **ClassZone.com**.

- **CONTENT REVIEW**
- **MATH TUTORIAL**

 **CONTENT REVIEW CD-ROM**

KEY CONCEPT

12.1 Most animals are invertebrates.

BEFORE, you learned

- Animals are consumers; they get food from the environment
- Most animals have body systems, including tissues and organs
- Animals interact with the environment and other animals

NOW, you will learn

- About the diversity of invertebrates
- About six groups of invertebrates
- How sponges get energy

VOCABULARY

invertebrate p. 395
sponge p. 397
sessile p. 397
larva p. 398

THINK ABOUT

What makes an animal an animal?

A sponge is an animal. It has no head, eyes, ears, arms, or legs. A sponge doesn't have a heart or a brain or a mouth. It doesn't move. Typically, it spends its life attached to the ocean floor. Many people used to think that sponges were plants that had adapted to life in the water. Scientists, however, classify them as animals. How might you decide if the organism in the photograph is an animal?

Invertebrates are a diverse group of organisms.

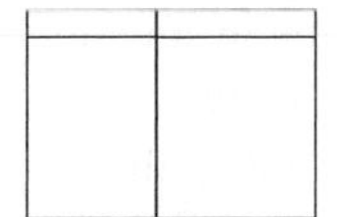

COMBINATION NOTES Make notes and diagrams for the first main idea: *Invertebrates are a diverse group of organisms.* Include a sketch of a member of each group.

About one million invertebrate species live on Earth. **Invertebrates** are animals that do not have backbones. In fact, invertebrates do not have any bone tissue at all. Invertebrates can be found just about everywhere, from frozen tundra to tropical forests. Some invertebrates live in water, while others survive in deserts where there is almost no water. Many invertebrates live inside other organisms.

Most invertebrate animals are small. Crickets, oysters, sea stars, earthworms, ants, and spiders are some examples of invertebrates. The fact that invertebrates do not have backbones for support tends to limit their size. However, some ocean-dwelling invertebrates can be quite large. For example, the giant squid can grow to 18 meters (59 ft) in length and can weigh over 450 kilograms (992 lb).

RESOURCES FOR DIFFERENTIATED INSTRUCTION

Below Level

UNIT RESOURCE BOOK

- Reading Study Guide A, pp. 223–224
- Decoding Support, p. 268

AUDIO CDS

Advanced

UNIT RESOURCE BOOK

Challenge and Extension, p. 229

English Learners

UNIT RESOURCE BOOK

Spanish Reading Study Guide, pp. 227–228

AUDIO CDS

- Audio Readings in Spanish
- Audio Readings (English)

12.1 FOCUS

Set Learning Goals

Students will

- Discuss the diversity of invertebrates.
- Describe the six groups of invertebrates.
- Explain how sponges get energy.
- Observe invertebrates that live in local environments.

3-Minute Warm-Up

Display Transparency 28 or copy this exercise on the board:

Decide which of these statements are true. If not true, correct them.

1. Invertebrates are animals that lack internal skeletons. *true*
2. Animals are producers; they make their own food through photosynthesis. *Animals are consumers; they must eat food.*
3. Tissues are made up of groups of similar organs. *Tissues are made up of groups of similar cells.*

3-Minute Warm-Up, p. T28

12.1 MOTIVATE

THINK ABOUT

PURPOSE To understand the characteristics of an animal

DISCUSS Brainstorm with students a list of characteristics of animals and write students' responses on the board.

Sample answer: Because the animal is not green and lives underwater, it is not a plant. You might observe if the organism consumes food. You could also take a cell sample and examine the cell for the presence of cell walls.

Ongoing Assessment

Discuss the diversity of invertebrates.

Ask: Give an example of how invertebrates are a diverse group of organisms. *Sample answer: They can range in size from an 18 m giant squid to a tiny ant.*

12.1 INSTRUCT

INVESTIGATE Invertebrates

PURPOSE Observe the kinds of invertebrates that live in local environments

TIPS *20 min.* Potato traps buried in moist soil will have the best results. If students bury traps in a variety of locations, they will collect a larger sample. The activity works best in warm weather.

WHAT DO YOU THINK? *Answers depend on location, season, climate.*

CHALLENGE *Students should note that they may find different types of invertebrates in the potato trap.*

 Datasheet, Invertebrates, p. 230

Technology Resources

Customize this student lab as needed or look for an alternative. Print rubrics to assess student lab reports.

 **Lab Generator CD-ROM**

Address Misconceptions

IDENTIFY Ask students for examples of animals. If students name only vertebrates, they may hold the misconception that animals include only large land animals.

CORRECT Have students make a chart of the six types of invertebrates. Include a drawing of an example for each type.

REASSESS Ask students to describe some invertebrate animals.

Technology Resources

Visit **ClassZone.com** for background on common student misconceptions.

 **MISCONCEPTION DATABASE**

Ongoing Assessment

Describe the six groups of invertebrates.

Ask: Which three groups of invertebrates contain animals that live on land?
worms, mollusks, and arthropods

INVESTIGATE Invertebrates

Which types of invertebrates live near you?

SKILL FOCUS
Observing

MATERIALS
- potato
- knife
- spoon
- masking tape

TIME
20 minutes

PROCEDURE

1. Cut the potato in half lengthwise. Scoop out a hole and carve a channel so it looks like the photograph below.
2. Put the two halves back together and wrap them with masking tape. Leave the channel uncovered. It is the entrance hole.
3. Take the potato trap outside and bury it upright in soil, with the entrance hole sticking out of the ground. Wash your hands.
4. Collect the potato the next day. Remove the masking tape and look inside.

WHAT DO YOU THINK?

- Observe the contents of the potato. Record your observations.
- Would you classify the contents of the potato as living or nonliving? Do you think they are animals or plants?

CHALLENGE Predict how your observations would be different if you buried the potato in a different place.

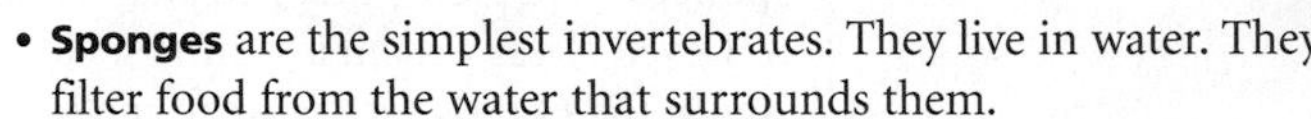

In this chapter, you will learn about six groups of invertebrates:

A
- **Sponges** are the simplest invertebrates. They live in water. They filter food from the water that surrounds them.
- **Cnidarians** also live in water. Animals in this group have a central opening surrounded by tentacles. They take in food and eliminate waste through this opening. Jellyfish, sea anemones, hydras, and corals are cnidarians.
- **Worms** are animals with soft, tube-shaped bodies and a distinct head. Some worms live inside other animals. Others live in the water or on land.

B
- **Mollusks** have a muscular foot that allows them to move and hunt for food. Some mollusks live on land. Others live in water. Clams, snails, and octopuses are mollusks.
- **Echinoderms** are water animals that have a central opening for taking in food. Sea stars and sand dollars are echinoderms.
- **Arthropods** are invertebrates that are found on land, in the water, and in the air. They have legs. Some have wings. Insects, spiders, crabs, and millipedes are arthropods.

DIFFERENTIATE INSTRUCTION

More Reading Support

A Which group of invertebrates are the simplest?
sponges

B What body structure allows mollusks to move?
a muscular foot

English Learners To better understand the process of filter feeding in sponges, let English learners who speak the same first language discuss it together in their common language. Encourage them to use the visual on p. 397 for help. Then, have each student write out or repeat aloud the process in English.

Below Level Have students write a song or a comedy sketch that introduces some sponges and their features to the class. Include details about how they get food, move, and reproduce, as well as behavior and environment.

Sponges are simple animals.

Sponges are the simplest multicellular animals on Earth. These invertebrates are **sessile** (SEHS-EEL) organisms, which means they live attached to one spot and do not move from place to place. Most live in the ocean, although some live in fresh water. Sponges have no tissues or organs. The body of a sponge is made up of a collection of cells. The cells are organized into a body wall, with an outside and an inside. Sponges are adapted to feed continuously. They feed on plankton and other tiny organisms that live in the water.

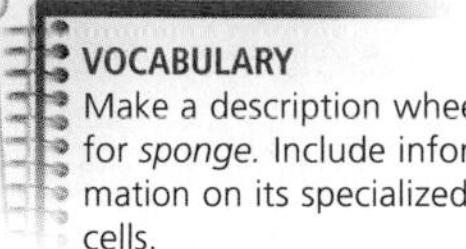

VOCABULARY
Make a description wheel for *sponge*. Include information on its specialized cells.

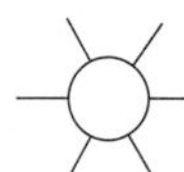

Specialized Cells

A sponge meets its needs with cells specialized for different functions. Pore cells along the body wall create tiny openings throughout the body. The pores lead into larger canals and sometimes a central opening, where cells with tiny hairs, or flagella, move water through the sponge. As water moves out, more water enters, as shown in the diagram below. Specialized cells filter out food particles and oxygen. Other specialized cells digest the food.

CHECK YOUR READING What adaptations does a sponge have for obtaining food?

Feeding in Sponges

Structures in a sponge's body function to remove food from water.

1. Water flows into the sponge through pores in the body wall.
2. Flagella along the inside of the sponge move water through the sponge.
3. Specialized cells pick up food particles as the water moves by.
4. Specialized cells digest the food particles.

flow of water

inside of sponge

pores

DIFFERENTIATE INSTRUCTION

More Reading Support

C What term describes how sponges are attached to one spot? *sessile*

D What do sponges feed on? *plankton, tiny water organisms*

Advanced Challenge students to design an experiment to see whether natural or common household sponges are more absorbent. Give the following guidelines:

- Always start with a dry sponge.
- Make sure the methods are scientifically sound.
- Use a graph to show your results.

R • Challenge and Extension, p. 229

Teacher Demo

Bring to class samples of natural sponges for students to examine. Provide a hand lens for students to observe the surface of the sponge and its pores. Explain that natural sponges are not the same as the synthetic sponges often used in the kitchen.

Language Arts Connection

Write the term *Porifera* on the board and tell students that this is the name of the phylum to which sponges belong. Ask students to use a dictionary to find out the derivation of the term. *Porifera comes from the Latin word* porus, *which means "pore."* A common word with this derivation is *porous,* meaning full of pores, or holes.

Teach from Visuals

To help students interpret the diagram of how sponges feed, ask:

- What structures help pump water and food particles through the body cavity of the sponge? *flagella*
- Why must the sponge depend on water flowing through its body to feed? *Sponges are attached to one spot and do not move.*

Ongoing Assessment

Explain how sponges get energy.

Ask: How do sponges feed and digest food? *Specialized cells pick up food particles as water flows through the sponge's body cavity. These cells digest the food particles.*

CHECK YOUR READING *Answer: The sponge has specialized cells for moving water as well as filtering food and digesting it. It also has a body shape adapted for moving water through it.*

Teach Difficult Concepts

In addition to spicules, the body walls of many sponges contain a substance called spongin, which makes them softer to touch than species that have a lot of spicules. Interlocking spicules of sponges can be considered a kind of exoskeleton, or outer skeleton. Ask students to identify the spicules in the diagram of the sponge on p. 397.

Reinforce (the BIG idea)

Have students relate the section to the Big Idea.

 Reinforcing Key Concepts, p. 231

12.1 ASSESS & RETEACH

Assess

 Section 12.1 Quiz, p. 63

Reteach

Ask students to explain why some people might think a sponge is a plant. *Sponges are attached to one spot.*

Then write the following on the board: *Characteristics of Sponges.* Encourage students to name facts about sponges that enable us to classify it as an animal. *Sample answers: It feeds on plankton and tiny organisms; it gets water from its environment; it reproduces asexually and sexually; it has a means of protecting itself.*

Technology Resources

Have students visit **ClassZone.com** for reteaching of Key Concepts.

 CONTENT REVIEW

 CONTENT REVIEW CD-ROM

Another adaptation sponges have are structures that make the body stiff. Most sponges have spicules (SPIHK-yoolz), which are needlelike spines made of hard minerals such as calcium or silicon. Spicules help give the sponge its shape and provide support. In some sponges, spicules stick out from the body. This may make the sponge less likely to become a source of food for other animals.

Reproduction

Sponges can reproduce asexually. Buds form alongside the parent sponge or the buds break off and float away. Tiny sponges can float quite a distance before they attach to the ocean floor or some underwater object and start to grow.

Sponges also reproduce sexually, as most multicellular organisms do. In sponges, sperm are released into the water. In some sponges, the eggs are released too. In this case, fertilization occurs in the water. In other sponges, the eggs are contained in specialized cells in the body wall. Sperm enter the sponge to fertilize the eggs.

A fertilized egg becomes a larva. A **larva** is an immature form—an early stage—of an organism that is different from the parent. Sponge larvae are able to swim. They move away from the parent and will grow into a sponge once they attach to some underwater surface. Then they become sessile, like their parents.

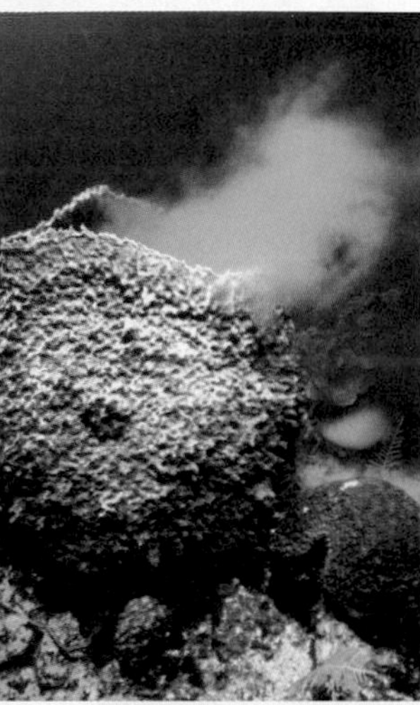

This basket sponge is releasing microscopic larvae into the water.

Sponges provide a good starting point for studying other invertebrates. There are many different types of invertebrates, with a wide range of body structures and behaviors. Invertebrates have adapted to many different environments. But the sponge is a simple organism that has changed very little over time. Sponges today look very similar to fossil sponges that are millions of years old.

12.1 Review

KEY CONCEPTS

1. Make a table with six columns. Write the name of an invertebrate group above each column. Fill in the table with a characteristic and an example for each group.
2. What does it mean that sponges are sessile?
3. How do sponges meet their need for energy?

CRITICAL THINKING

4. **Apply** Give two examples of how structure in a sponge relates to function. You should use the words *flagella* and *spicule* in your answer.
5. **Infer** How is water involved in the reproductive cycle of a sponge?

CHALLENGE

6. **Analyze** Sponges have lived on Earth for hundreds of millions of years. Sponges today look very similar to fossil sponges. What does this suggest about how well the simple structure of a sponge meets its needs? Do species always change over time?

ANSWERS

1. Check students' tables with the information given on p. 396.

2. Sessile means that sponges live their lives attached to one spot.

3. They filter food from the surrounding water.

4. The sponge's pores and flagella allow water to move into and around the sponge's body, where specialized cells pick up and digest food that floats in the water. Spicules are needlelike structures that provide protection from predators.

5. Water allows sperm to travel to eggs, and larvae or buds to float far away.

6. Sponges evolved everything they need to meet their needs millions of years ago and have not been forced to evolve since. No.

MATH TUTORIAL

Click on Math Tutorial for more help with line symmetry.

SKILL: LINE SYMMETRY

Mirror, Mirror

A pattern or shape that has *line symmetry* contains a mirror image of its parts on either side of a straight line. Think about the shapes of a sea star or a butterfly.

Example

If you were to cut these shapes out of flat paper, you could fold the paper along a line of symmetry. The two halves would match.

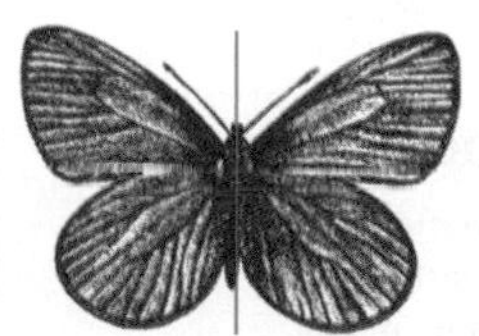

Some shapes have more than one line of symmetry. The shapes of most anemones and sea stars can fold along two, three, or more lines of symmetry.

Sketch each shape. Then draw any lines of symmetry. If there are none, write "zero."

1) 
2) 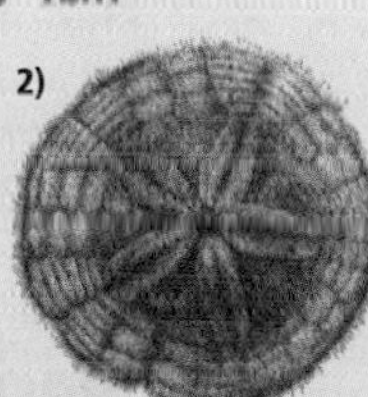
3) 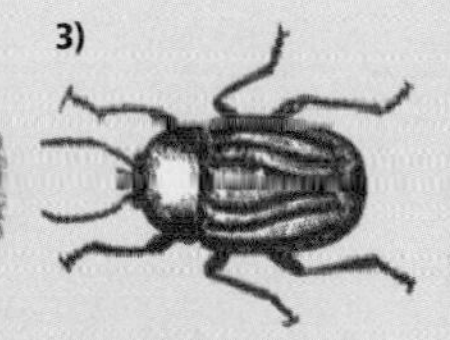
4) 
5) 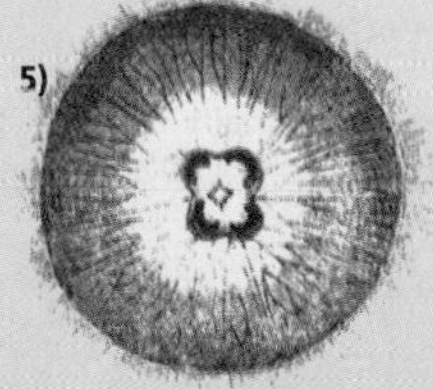

CHALLENGE Write out the uppercase letters of the alphabet *A* to *Z*. For each letter, write whether it has zero, one, or two lines of symmetry.

ANSWERS

1. one line of symmetry
2. five lines of symmetry
3. one line of symmetry
4. zero
5. four lines of symmetry

CHALLENGE zero: F, G, J, L, N, P, Q, R, S, Z; one: A, B, C, D, E, K, M, T, U, V, W, Y; two: H, I, O, X

MATH IN SCIENCE
Math Skills Practice for Science

Set Learning Goal

To apply the mathematics of line symmetry to the body plans of invertebrates

Present the Science

Organisms that have radial or bilateral body shapes are symmetric. That is, they have parts that form mirror images. An organism that has a radial body shape will have more than one line of symmetry. Some organisms with symmetrical body plans will appear asymmetrical (having no lines of symmetry) when viewed from different angles. The symmetry in nature is never an exact match, just as circles and squares in nature are never as exact as they are in a mathematical ideal.

Develop Geometry Skills

Review symmetry with students by drawing shapes of circles, squares, triangles, and irregular polygons on the board. Have students note which shapes have one line of symmetry, multiple lines of symmetry, or no lines of symmetry.

DIFFERENTIATION TIP Have students fold papers in half and cut out shapes along the folded parts. Students can unfold the shapes to see the line of symmetry.

Close

Ask students to discuss the difference between the symmetry of a flat shape on paper and symmetry in three dimensions. Why might the clam, shown in figure 4, have a symmetrical body plan, though it appears not to? *It has two shells that are identical. If held up so you see the line between the shells, it will present a symmetrical shape.*

- Math Support, p. 269
- Math Practice, p. 270

Technology Resources

Students can visit **ClassZone.com** to practice determining symmetry.

 **MATH TUTORIAL**

12.2 FOCUS

Set Learning Goals

Students will

- Describe the body systems of cnidarians.
- Analyze body symmetry and feeding patterns.
- Describe body systems in worms.

3-Minute Warm-Up

Display Transparency 28 or copy this exercise on the board:

Fill in the circles surrounding the word web to describe the characteristics of animals.

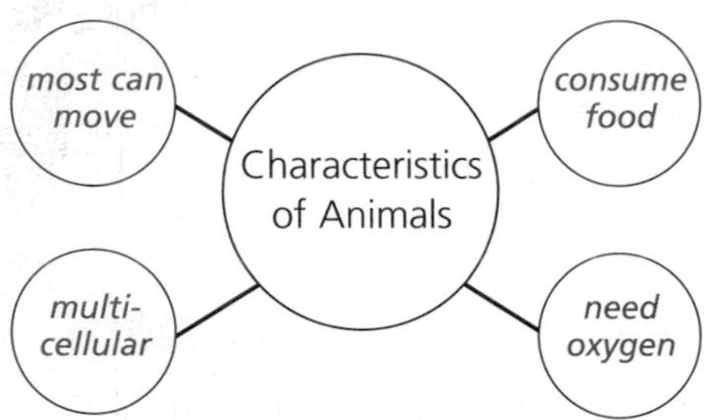

3-Minute Warm-Up, p. T28

12.2 MOTIVATE

EXPLORE Worm Movement

PURPOSE To understand how the body shape of a worm affects its movement

TIPS *20 min.* Ensure that all surfaces the worms will be contacting are kept moist; the worms will die if they dry out. Remind students to treat worms humanely, which means paying attention to what the worms need to thrive. See the notes for the Chapter Investigation, pp. 406–407, for more information on obtaining, handling, and caring for worms in the classroom.

WHAT DO YOU THINK? *Students should note that segmented worms move by contracting and relaxing their muscles. Worms also have very small bristles that anchor them in the soil.*

KEY CONCEPT

12.2 Cnidarians and worms have different body plans.

BEFORE, you learned

- Invertebrates are a diverse group of animals
- Sponges are sessile organisms
- Sponges meet their needs with simple bodies and specialized cells

NOW, you will learn

- About body systems in cnidarians
- About body symmetry and feeding patterns
- About body systems in worms

VOCABULARY

cnidarian p. 400
tentacle p. 400
mobile p. 402

EXPLORE Worm Movement

How does body shape affect movement?

PROCEDURE

1. Put a thin layer of soil on the tray and gently place the worm on it. Use the spray bottle to keep the soil and your hands moist.
2. Draw a sketch of the worm and try to identify the parts of its body.
3. Record your observations of its movement.
4. Follow your teacher's instructions in handling the worm and materials at the end of the lab. Wash your hands.

MATERIALS

- worm
- tray
- soil
- spray bottle filled with distilled water

WHAT DO YOU THINK?

- How does the shape of a worm's body affect its movement?
- How would you describe a worm to someone who has never seen one?

COMBINATION NOTES
Make notes and diagrams for the main idea: *Cnidarians have simple body systems.*

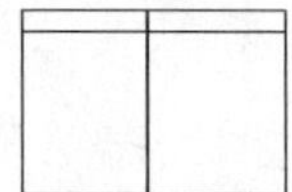

Cnidarians have simple body systems.

Cnidarians (ny-DAIR-ee-uhnz) are invertebrates. Like sponges, cnidarians are found only in water. This group includes jellyfish, corals, sea anemones, and small freshwater organisms called hydras. Most cnidarians feed on small plankton, fish, and clams. Many cnidarians are sessile for most of their lives. Like sponges, cnidarians have adaptations that allow them to pull food in from the water that surrounds them.

All cnidarians have **tentacles,** fingerlike extensions of their body that reach into the water. Other animals have tentacles, but the tentacles of cnidarians have specialized stinging cells. The tentacles, with their stinging cells, are an adaptation that enables cnidarians to capture prey.

RESOURCES FOR DIFFERENTIATED INSTRUCTION

Below Level

UNIT RESOURCE BOOK

- Reading Study Guide A, pp. 234–235
- Decoding Support, p. 268

AUDIO CDS

Advanced

UNIT RESOURCE BOOK

- Challenge and Extension, p. 240
- Challenge Reading, pp. 264–265

English Learners

UNIT RESOURCE BOOK

Spanish Reading Study Guide, pp. 238–239

AUDIO CDS

- Audio Readings in Spanish
- Audio Readings (English)

Stinging Cells in Cnidarians

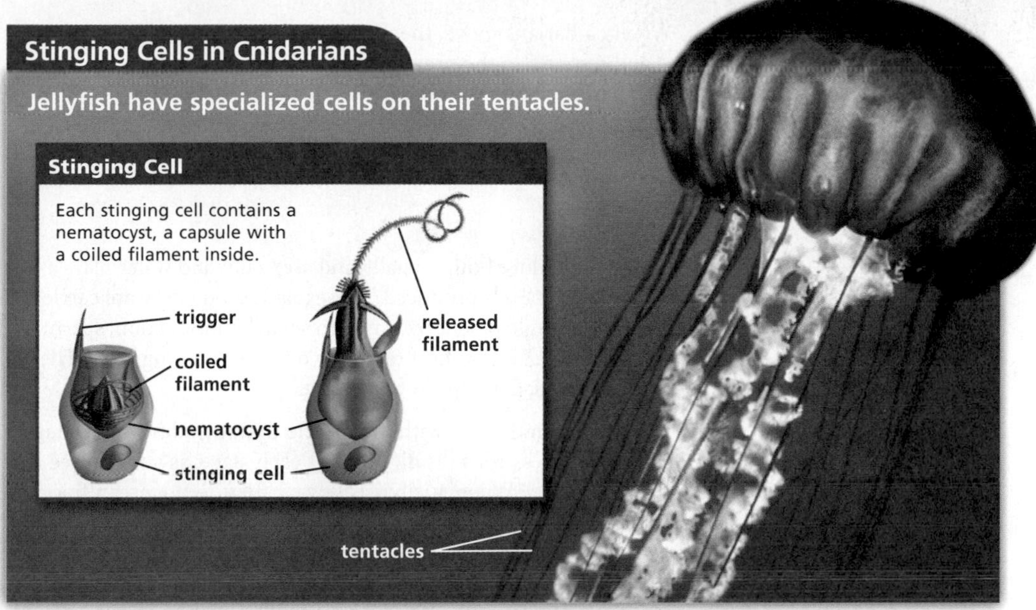

Each stinging cell has a nematocyst (NEHM-uh-tuh-SIHST), a capsule that holds a barbed filament. The filament is like a tiny hollow tube coiled up inside the capsule. When prey comes into contact with the stinger cell, the filament is released. Sometimes this stinger wraps itself around the prey. In most species of cnidarians, the stinger stabs the prey and releases a poison from its tip. These stingers are what produce the sting of a jellyfish. Stinging cells have a second function. They protect cnidarians from predators.

READING TIP Refer to the diagram above as you read the description of a nematocyst and its structure.

CHECK YOUR READING Describe how the structure of a nematocyst allows it to function in capturing food and providing protection.

Tissues and Body Systems

A cnidarian's body is made up of flexible layers of tissue. These tissues, along with specialized cells, make up its body systems. The tissues are organized around a central opening where food is taken in and wastes are released. The tentacles bring the prey into this opening. The opening leads into a cavity, a gut, where the food is digested.

Cnidarians have a simple muscle system for movement. Even though cnidarians are sessile during most of their lives, they still move their bodies. Cnidarians bend from side to side and extend their tentacles. Adult jellyfish swim. The movement is produced by muscle cells that run around and along the sides of its body. When the muscle cells shorten, or contract, they produce movement.

12.2 INSTRUCT

Teach from Visuals

To help students interpret the diagram of stinging cells in cnidarians, ask:

- What structure is found inside the stinging cell? *the nematocyst*
- What is a nematocyst? What is contained inside the nematocyst? *The nematocyst is a capsule that contains a coiled filament.*
- What is the purpose of the coiled filament? *It is a stinger that releases poison to capture prey or ward off predators.*

Integrate the Sciences

The Great Barrier Reef off the coast of Australia is the world's largest collection of coral reefs, shoals, and islets that extends for about 1,250 miles (2000 km) and has an area of 135,000 square miles (350,000 square km). The Great Barrier Reef is made up of corals dating back to the Miocene Epoch (23.7 to 5.3 million years ago). The reef is home to at least 300 species of coral, as well as anemones, sponges, worms, mollusks, arthropods, and a variety of fish. Reef-building coral are generally found in the tropical areas between the Tropic of Cancer and the Tropic of Capricorn.

Ongoing Assessment

Describe the body systems of cnidarians.

Ask: What body systems enable cnidarians to respond to their environment? *muscle cells that run along the side of the body and a network of nerve cells*

CHECK YOUR READING *Answer: When the trigger comes into contact with a prey, the nematocyst opens and a poisonous filament stabs the prey.*

DIFFERENTIATE INSTRUCTION

More Reading Support

A What happens when the trigger of the nematocyst comes in contact with prey? *Stinger is released.*

B How do cnidarians move? *by contracting cells in their bodies*

English Learners Point out that the "c" in *cnidarian* is silent. Pair English learners with native English speakers and have them create a list of words in which the first consonant is silent. Examples include: *know, knot, who, gnat, gnome, whose, psychology,* and *pseudonym.*

Address Misconceptions

IDENTIFY Ask students how reproduction occurs in cnidarians. If students respond that two cnidarians must find a mate to produce offspring, then they may hold the misconception that animal reproduction must involve separate male and female organisms, that it must involve mating, and/or that animal reproduction involves choice and planning.

CORRECT Have students create a flow chart that shows the jellyfish life cycle. Students should use the following terms in their flow charts: *larva, polyp,* and *medusa.* Ask student to indicate in their charts in which stages the jellyfish are sessile and in which stage they are mobile.

REASSESS Ask students to describe how water is involved in the reproduction of cnidarians. *Buds that are produced by a parent organism are carried away by water and form a new individual. Eggs are fertilized by sperm carried to them in water.*

Technology Resources

Visit **ClassZone.com** for background on common student misconceptions.

MISCONCEPTION DATABASE

Teach from Visuals

To help students understand the life cycle diagram of jellyfish, ask:

- During which stage of the life cycle are the organisms sessile? *during the polyp stage*
- During which stage of the life cycle are the jellyfish considered to be adults? *during the medusa stage*

Language Arts Connection

The term *medusa* is taken from Greek mythology. Have students read versions of the myth and give a short retelling to the class. Then ask: Why is the adult jellyfish named after this mythical being? *A ball shape with tentacles looks like a head with snakes for hair.*

When cnidarians move, they interact with the environment. They sense and respond to the prey that come in contact with their tentacles. This behavior is the result of a simple nervous system. Cnidarians have a network of nerve cells, a nerve net that extends throughout their bodies.

VOCABULARY
Choose a strategy from earlier chapters, such as a four square, or one of your own to take notes on the term *mobile.*

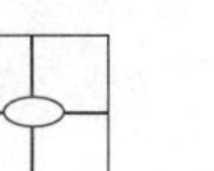

Reproduction

Cnidarians reproduce both sexually and asexually, and water plays a role in both processes. Buds produced by asexual reproduction are carried away from the sessile parent by water. In sexual reproduction, sperm are carried to the egg. Fertilization results in a free-swimming larva. The larva, if it survives, develops into an adult.

Jellyfish are cnidarians with a life cycle that includes several stages. A jellyfish's body, or form, is different at each stage, as you can see in the diagram below. When a jellyfish larva settles on the ocean floor, it grows into a form called a polyp. The polyp, which is sessile, develops disk-shaped buds that stack up like a pile of plates. The buds, once they are released, are called medusas. Each medusa is an adult jellyfish. In the medusa stage, jellyfish are **mobile,** which means they can move their bodies from place to place.

Jellyfish Life Cycle

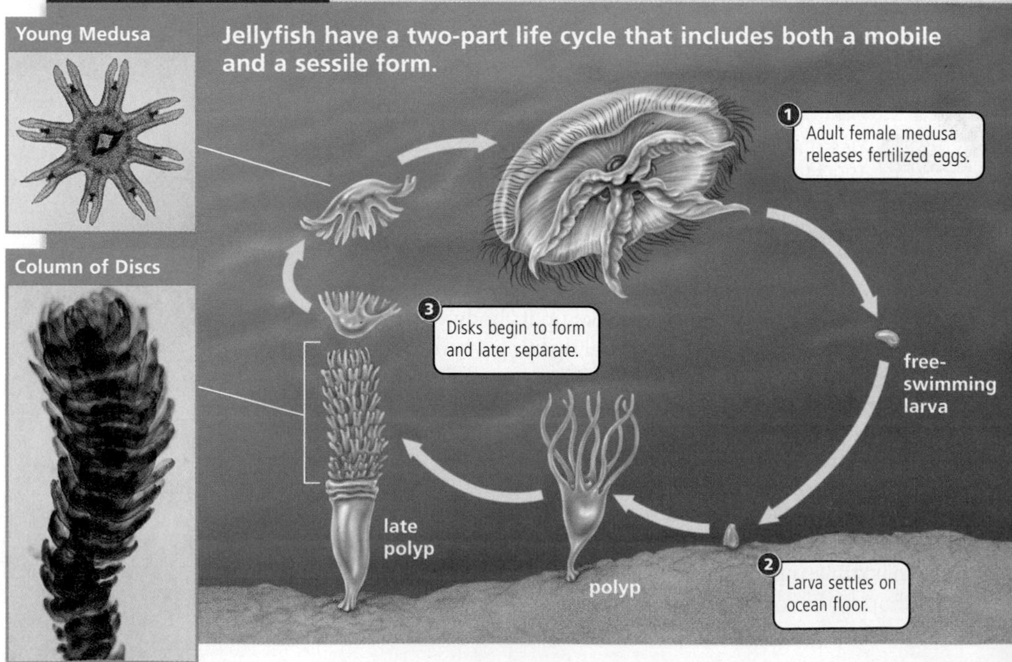

DIFFERENTIATE INSTRUCTION

More Reading Support

C What is the early stage of an organism called? *the larva*

D When buds are released from a polyp, what are they called? *medusas*

Below Level Have pairs of students work together to create a science fiction comic book story about a jellyfish. The details of the story should use scientifically accurate knowledge. Have them include facts about the jellyfish life cycle and habitat and how jellyfish move and feed.

Radial Symmetry

Animals with a circular body shape, such as this sea anemone, have radial symmetry.

Bilateral Symmetry

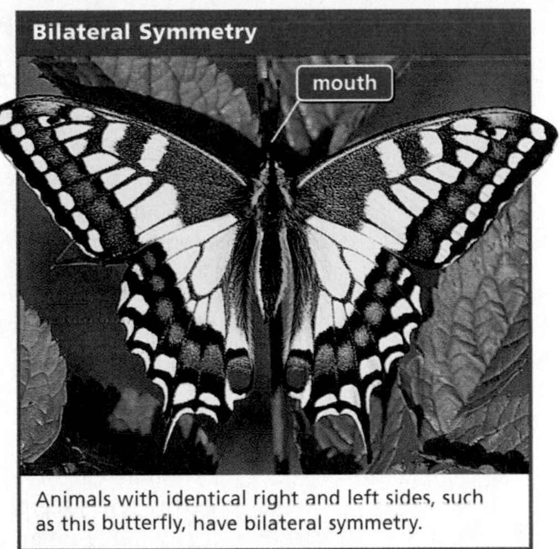

Animals with identical right and left sides, such as this butterfly, have bilateral symmetry.

Animals have different body plans.

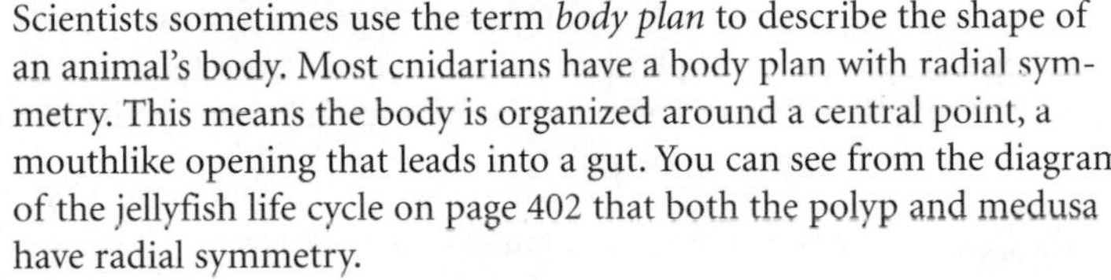

E Scientists sometimes use the term *body plan* to describe the shape of an animal's body. Most cnidarians have a body plan with radial symmetry. This means the body is organized around a central point, a mouthlike opening that leads into a gut. You can see from the diagram of the jellyfish life cycle on page 402 that both the polyp and medusa have radial symmetry.

A radial body plan allows a sessile organism, such as the sea anemone shown in the photograph above, to capture food from any direction. A radial body plan also affects how a mobile animal moves. A jellyfish medusa moves forward by pushing down on the water. It has to stop moving to change direction.

F Most animals, including worms, butterflies, birds, and humans, have a body plan with bilateral symmetry. One half looks just like the other, as you can see in the photograph of the butterfly above. You can recognize a bilaterally symmetrical shape because there is only one way to draw a line dividing it into two equal halves.

Animals with bilateral symmetry have a forward end where the mouth is located. This is the animal's head. The animal moves forward, head first, in search of food. A bilateral body shape works well in animals that are mobile. Food enters at one end, and is processed as it moves through the body. Once all the nutrients have been absorbed, the remaining wastes are released at the other end.

READING TIP

The root of the word *radial* means "ray," like the spoke of a wheel. The roots of the word *bilateral* are *bi-*, meaning "two," and *lateral*, meaning "side."

CHECK YOUR READING Describe how radial symmetry and bilateral symmetry affect an animal's feeding behaviors.

Teach from Visuals

To help students understand the concept of radial and bilateral body shape shown in the photographs, ask:

- What is different about the body shapes you see here from the body shape of a sponge? *A sponge does not have a regular shape; it does not have a mouth or other body structures such as antennae or wings.*
- Do you think that most animals have radial or bilateral symmetry? *bilateral*
- What are some examples of animals with bilateral symmetry? *Answers may include fish, frogs, turtles, snakes, birds, humans, insects, dogs, and so on.*

Teach Difficult Concepts

Students may not fully understand that some invertebrates do not have distinct digestive and excretory systems. Direct students' attention to the photograph of the sea anemone. Point out that organisms with radial symmetry often have only one body cavity. It is through this cavity that food is ingested and waste is excreted.

Ongoing Assessment

Analyze body symmetry and feeding patterns.

What is the difference between radial and bilateral body symmetry in relation to an animal's way of feeding? *In radial symmetry, the body is organized around a central point. The mouth is in the center. In bilateral symmetry, the body forms around a center line. The mouth is at one end of the line, and the other end is where the waste is released.*

CHECK YOUR READING *Answer: An animal with radial symmetry can capture food from any direction. An animal with bilateral symmetry has one end that is its front. The animal moves itself forward, in search of food.*

DIFFERENTIATE INSTRUCTION

More Reading Support

E Which type of body shape do cnidarians have? *radial symmetry*

F Which type of body shape do humans have? *bilateral symmetry*

Advanced Challenge students to choose a cnidarian not discussed in detail in the text, such as hydra, sea anemone, or coral and create a poster showing the body systems of the organism and how it reproduces and obtains food.

R Challenge and Extension, p. 240

Have students who are interested in venomous jellyfish read the following article:

R Challenge Reading, pp. 264–265

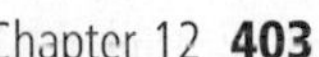

Teach Difficult Concepts

To help students understand the increasing complexity of organisms, have them compare the body systems of cnidarians with those of the more complex annelids. The body shapes of the less complex organisms tend to be radially symmetric as opposed to bilaterally symmetric.

EXPLORE the BIG idea

Revisit "Worm-Watching" on p. 393. Now that students have studied the body systems in worms, ask them if their understandings about worms have changed and if they would like to add to their observations.

Develop Critical Thinking

COMPARE AND CONTRAST Have students work together to create Venn diagrams to compare worms and jellyfish. Challenge teams of students to find as many similarities and as many differences as they can.

Teach from Visuals

To help students interpret the diagram of the internal structure of an earthworm, ask them to identify the body system of each of the organs labeled in the diagram. For example, the brain belongs to the nervous system.

 This visual is also available as T30 in the Unit Transparency Book.

Arts Connection

Ask students to stage a mock interview between an earthworm and a lifestyle reporter for a celebrity magazine or celebrity news show. The questions and answers should address how the worm moves and gets food as well as how it interacts with its environment.

Ongoing Assessment

CHECK YOUR READING *Sample answer: Two body systems found in worms are the digestive system and excretory system.*

Most worms have complex body systems.

Learn more about the many types of worms.

Some worms have simple bodies. Others have well-developed body systems. Worms have a tube-shaped body, with bilateral symmetry. In many worms, food enters at one end and is processed as it moves through a digestive tract. Worms take in oxygen, dissolved in water, through their skin. Because of this, worms must live in moist environments. Many live in water.

Segmented Worms

Segmented worms have bodies that are divided into individual compartments, or segments. These worms are referred to as annelids (AN-uh-lihdz), which means "ringed animals." One annelid you might be familiar with is the earthworm. As the diagram below shows, an earthworm's segments can be seen on the outside of its body.

An earthworm has organs that are organized into body systems. The digestive system of an earthworm includes organs for digestion and food storage. It connects to the excretory system, which removes waste. Earthworms pass soil through their digestive system. They digest decayed pieces of plant and animal matter from the soil and excrete what's left over. A worm's feeding and burrowing activity adds nutrients and oxygen to the soil.

Name two body systems found in earthworms.

Inside an Earthworm

An earthworm has organs and body systems.

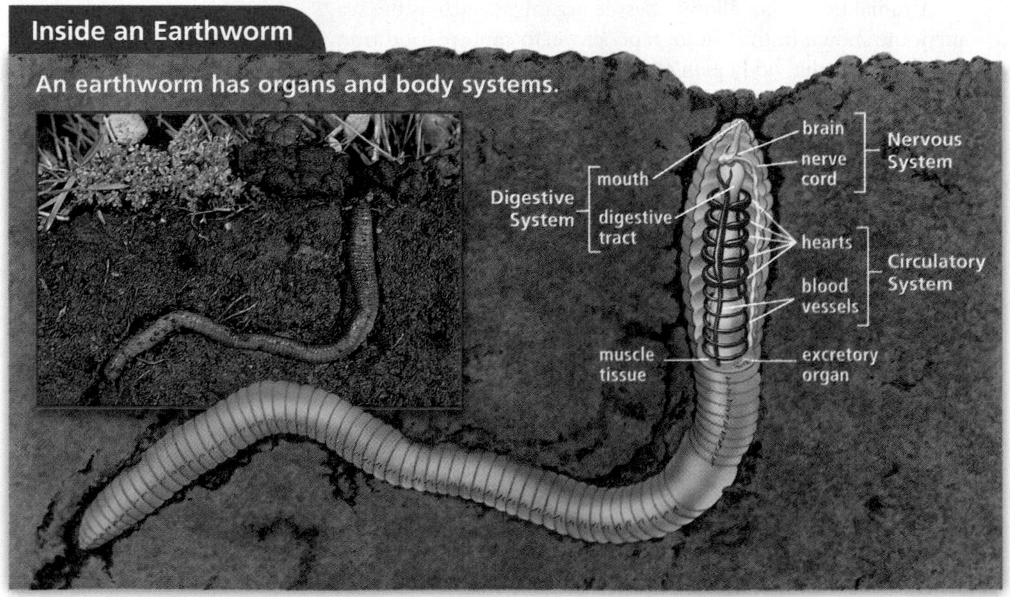

404 Unit 3: **Diversity of Living Things**

DIFFERENTIATE INSTRUCTION

G What term describes segmented worms? *annelids*

Advanced Have students observe the unsegmented section about one-third of the way down the earthworm's body in the illustration on p. 404. Explain that this structure is the *clitellum*, the reproductive structure of the worm. It encloses fertilized eggs and then slides off the worm's body. Young worms hatch in the resulting cocoon from eggs encased within it. Ask: How can you tell that earthworms reproduce sexually? *Two worms exchange sperm that fertilize the eggs inside the clitellum. Since sperm cells and egg cells are involved, it is sexual reproduction.*

Earthworms have several layers of muscle tissue in their body wall. Hairlike bristles on the segments help to anchor a worm in the soil as it moves. The nervous system includes a brain and a nerve cord that runs through the body. An earthworm can detect strong light and vibrations in the soil. These stimuli signal danger to a worm. An earthworm also has a circulatory system. It is made up of several hearts that pump blood through blood vessels.

Some annelids reproduce asexually, while others reproduce sexually. There are no distinct male or female worms. Earthworms, for example, carry both male and female reproductive structures. To reproduce, two worms exchange sperm. The sperm fertilize eggs the worms carry in their bodies. The eggs are laid and later hatch into larvae.

Flatworms and Roundworms

Flatworms are the worms with the simplest bodies. Some are so small and flat that they move with cilia, not muscles. These flatworms absorb nutrients directly through the skin. Many flatworms live as parasites, feeding off other organisms. For example, tapeworms are flatworms that infect humans and other animals. The tapeworm has no need for a digestive system because it gets digested nutrients from its host.

Roundworms are found just about everywhere on Earth. The bodies of roundworms are more complex than those of flatworms. They have muscles to move with, and a nervous system and digestive system. Some roundworms are important decomposers on land and in the water.

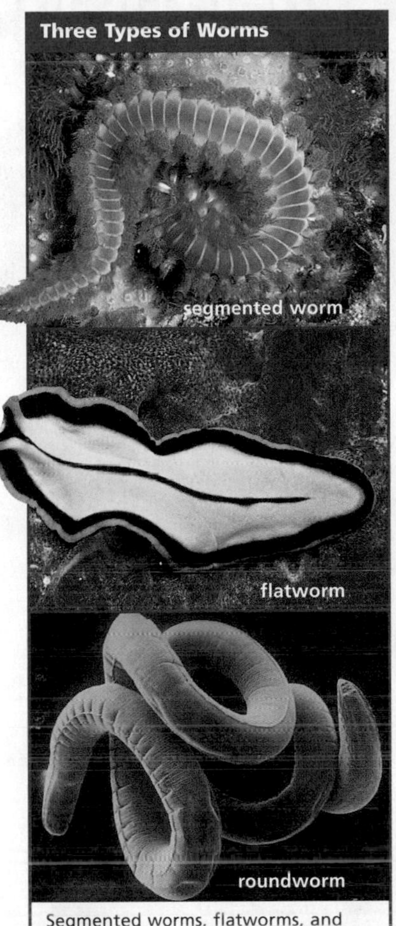

Segmented worms, flatworms, and roundworms are the most common worms on Earth.

12.2 Review

KEY CONCEPTS

1. What adaptation do cnidarians have for capturing prey?
2. What is the difference between radial symmetry and bilateral symmetry?
3. Pick two systems found in an earthworm and describe how they work together.

CRITICAL THINKING

4. **Predict** How might having sense organs located at the front end of the body benefit an animal?
5. **Infer** Would the food of a jellyfish medusa be different from the food of a polyp? Support your answer.

CHALLENGE

6. **Compare and Contrast** Describe how the different body symmetries of cnidarians and segmented worms affect their movement and feeding behaviors.

ANSWERS

1. tentacles with stinging cells

2. Radial symmetry is symmetry around a center; bilateral symmetry has two identical halves.

3. Sample answer: Wastes from digestion pass through the excretory system.

4. Sense organs allow an animal to collect information about the environment. Eyes located in the front allow an animal to seek out food and determine where to move.

5. No, both forms have tentacles and nematocysts. Medusas may eat larger prey since they are usually larger.

6. Cnidarians use the same opening for eating and propulsion. Annelids have a head and move forward toward food.

Ongoing Assessment

Describe body systems in worms.

Ask: How is the digestive system of the earthworm similar to that of humans? *The earthworm has organs that break down, digest, and store food. The food enters through a mouth and moves through the body out of the other end.*

Reinforce the BIG idea

Have students relate the section to the Big Idea.

 Reinforcing Key Concepts, p. 241

12.2 ASSESS & RETEACH

Assess

 Section 12.2 Quiz, p. 64

Reteach

Write the following organisms on the board: *jellyfish, sea anemone, earthworm, flatworm.* For each organism, have students tell if it is has radial body shape or bilateral body shape. Then have students name the body systems for each.

jellyfish and sea anemone: radial; nervous systems

earthworm and flatworm: bilateral; circulatory, digestive, nervous systems

For in-depth reteaching, have small groups of students develop larger-than-life models or diagrams for jellyfish and for earthworms and their environments. They should base the models on the text and on the illustrations on pp. 402 and 404.

Technology Resources

Have students visit **ClassZone.com** for reteaching of Key Concepts.

 CONTENT REVIEW

 CONTENT REVIEW CD-ROM

CHAPTER INVESTIGATION

Focus

PURPOSE To observe the behavior of worms and hypothesize about how worms will respond to stimuli, and to test hypotheses

OVERVIEW Students will create a worm farm, using different types of surfaces to test the following:

- how earthworms respond to sand and potting soil surfaces.
- how earthworms behave and respond to changes in their environment.

Lab Preparation

- This investigation can be done with earthworms collected from outdoors, or with worms from a kit available at biological supply houses.
- Vermiculite (worm composting) kits tend to use red "wiggler" worms *(Eisenia foetida)* rather than the familiar earthworm *(Lumbricus terrestrial)*. Both species are safe choices. Redworms are not native to the U.S. and should not be released.
- The set-up for the investigation can be prepared in advance.
- Explain how to distinguish between the anterior and posterior of a worm.
- Prior to the investigation, have students read through the investigation and prepare their data tables. Or you may wish to copy and distribute datasheets and rubrics.

UNIT RESOURCE BOOK, pp. 271–279

SCIENCE TOOLKIT, F14

Lab Management

- All surfaces that worms come in contact with should be moist.
- Students should care for and treat worms humanely, which also means knowing what conditions the animals need in order to thrive.

SAFETY Make sure students wash their hands thoroughly after the lab.

INCLUSION Students can draw pictures of their observations rather than write out results, or can share results in a discussion.

CHAPTER INVESTIGATION

Worm Behavior

OVERVIEW AND PURPOSE Earthworms do not have eyes, so they cannot see. An earthworm needs an environment that provides it with moisture, food, and protection from predators. How do worms gather information about their surroundings? How do they respond to changes in their environment? In this investigation you will

- observe worm behavior
- predict how worms will respond to surfaces with different textures

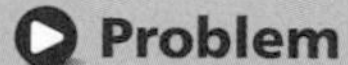

Problem

Write It Up

How is worm behavior affected by environmental conditions?

Hypothesize

Write It Up

You should complete steps 1–9 in the procedure before writing your hypothesis. Write a hypothesis to explain how worms will respond to different surface textures in an environment. Your hypothesis should take the form of an "If . . . , then . . . , because . . ." statement.

MATERIALS

- aquarium
- potting soil
- coarse sand
- small beaker
- distilled water
- spray bottle
- filter paper
- 5 or more worms
- 2 containers, one for untested worms and one for tested worms
- stopwatch
- *for Challenge* flashlight

Procedure

1. Make a data table in your **Science Notebook** like the one shown on page 407.
2. Cover one half of the bottom of the aquarium with potting soil and the other half with sand.
3. Fill the beaker with 250 mL of distilled water and use it to fill the spray bottle. Spray all the water over the potting soil so it is evenly moistened.

INVESTIGATION RESOURCES

CHAPTER INVESTIGATION, Title

- Level A, pp. 271–274
- Level B, pp. 275–278
- Level C, p. 279

Advanced students should complete Levels B & C.

Writing a Lab Report, D12–13

Technology Resources

Customize this student lab as needed or look for an alternative. Print rubrics to assess student lab reports.

Lab Generator CD-ROM

4. Repeat step 3, but this time moisten the sand. Refill the spray bottle.

5. Place a piece of filter paper in the middle of the aquarium so it is half on the soil and half on the sand, as shown.

step 5

6. Put on your gloves. Spray your hands with water. Gently remove one worm and observe it until you can tell which end is its head.

step 6

7. Start the stopwatch as you place the worm on the middle of the filter paper. Note which part of the aquarium the worm's head points toward.

8. Observe the worm's behavior for two minutes and then remove it carefully from the aquarium and place it in the container for tested worms.

9. Write your observations in your data table. State your hypothesis.

10. Fix the sand, soil, and paper in the aquarium so they are arranged as they were for the first worm. Then repeat steps 6–9 with at least four more worms.

11. Return the worms to their original living place. Wash your hands.

Observe and Analyze

Write It Up

1. **OBSERVE** What behaviors suggest that worms get information about their surroundings?
2. **OBSERVE** What evidence did you see to suggest that worms respond to information they get about their surroundings?
3. **INTERPRET DATA** What patterns did you notice in the behavior of the worms you tested?

Conclude

1. **INTERPRET** Compare your results with your hypothesis. Does your data support your hypothesis?
2. **IDENTIFY LIMITS** What sources of error could have affected your investigation?
3. **EVALUATE** Based on your observations and evidence, what conclusions can you draw about the connection between worm behavior and environmental conditions?

INVESTIGATE Further

CHALLENGE Worms respond to light as a stimulus. Design an experiment to test the reaction of worms to the presence of light.

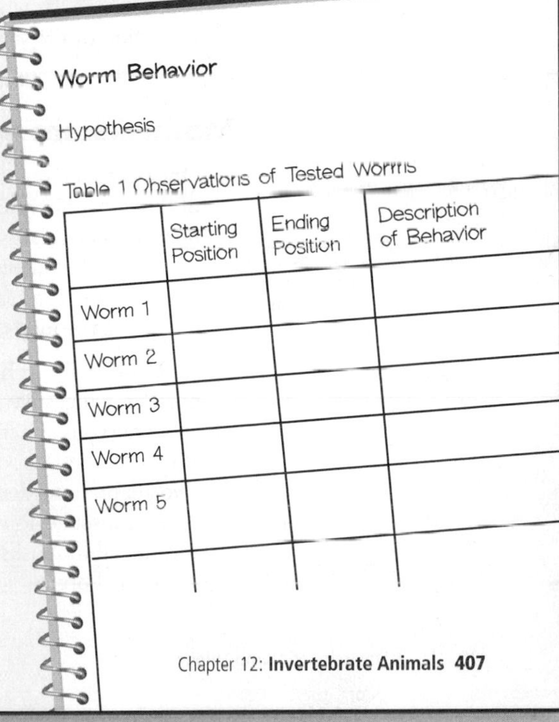

Worm Behavior

Hypothesis

Table 1 Observations of Tested Worms

	Starting Position	Ending Position	Description of Behavior
Worm 1			
Worm 2			
Worm 3			
Worm 4			
Worm 5			

Observe and Analyze

1. *The worms' behavior will vary depending on the conditions of the experimental setting. Worms generally proceed off the filter paper in whatever direction they are pointing until they encounter an obstacle such as the aquarium wall.*
2. *Sample answer: Worms turn in the direction they are pointing and hug the wall of the aquarium until they locate a surface to burrow into.*
3. *Sample answer: Some worms explore and reject certain environments depending on moisture and ability to burrow into the sand or potting soil.*

Conclude

1. *Answers should give evidence from results to support or to counter student hypotheses.*
2. *Sample answer: How the worms were placed, the type of soil and food used, and the condition of the worms could have affected the results.*
3. *Sample answer: Worms will usually move into environments more suitable to them: a moist, moderately cool area with food.*

INVESTIGATE Further

CHALLENGE Check student designs. Experiments should use a control and test only one variable (amount of light).

Teaching with Technology

If video cameras are available, students may make close-up video shots of their earthworm observations.

Post-Lab Discussion

- Discuss with students any new questions that arose from the investigation. What do their results suggest about their hypotheses? What new hypotheses might be inferred from their observations? How might they conduct a new experiment to test these ideas?
- Ask students to describe how a worm is able to move. *An earthworm moves by contracting muscles, then relaxing them.*

12.3 FOCUS

Set Learning Goals

Students will

- Describe different types of mollusks and their features.
- Describe different types of echinoderms and their features.
- Observe details of mollusk and echinoderm shells.

3-Minute Warm-Up

Display Transparency 29 or copy this exercise on the board:

Match the definitions to the terms.

Definitions

1. attached to one spot *a*
2. fingerlike extensions of the body *d*
3. early immature stage of an organism *e*

Terms

a. sessile
b. mobile
c. invertebrate
d. tentacle
e. larva

3-Minute Warm-Up, p. T29

12.3 MOTIVATE

THINK ABOUT

PURPOSE To understand how a snail uses its muscular foot to move itself

DISCUSS If possible, have students observe a snail through the glass of an aquarium. While observing the action of the snail's foot, students may also be able to see the snail's mouth and its radula. Discuss with students how the snail is adapted for life in an aquatic environment. *The snail glides along the glass surface through muscular contractions of its foot. It has a hard shell for protection, and gills to breathe underwater.*

KEY CONCEPT

12.3 Most mollusks have shells, and echinoderms have spiny skeletons.

BEFORE, you learned

- Body shape affects how animals move and behave
- Cnidarians have radial symmetry and simple body systems
- Worms have bilateral symmetry and segmented body systems

NOW, you will learn

- About different types of mollusks and their features
- About different types of echinoderms and their features

VOCABULARY

mollusk p. 408
gill p. 409
lung p. 409
echinoderm p. 411

THINK ABOUT

How does a snail move?

Snails belong to a group of mollusks called gastropods. The name means "belly foot." Snails are often put into aquariums to clean up the algae that can build up along the walls of the tank. If you get a chance, look at a snail moving along the glass walls of an aquarium, observe how it uses its foot to move. How would you describe the action of the snail's foot?

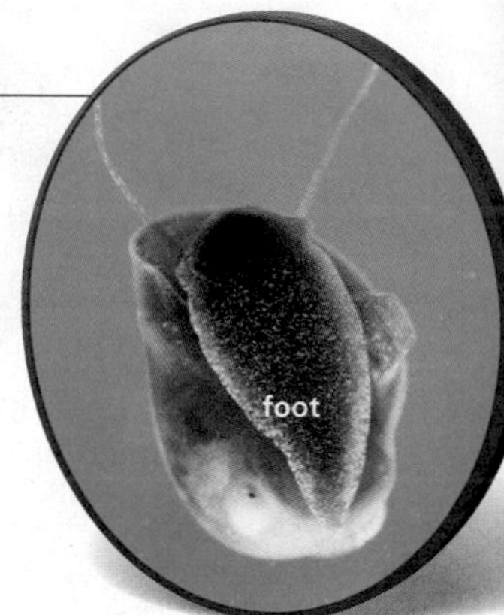

Mollusks are soft-bodied animals.

VOCABULARY
Choose a strategy from earlier chapters, such as a word triangle, or one of your own to take notes on the term *mollusk*.

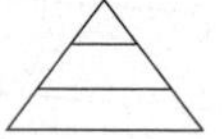

One characteristic that is shared by all **mollusks** is a soft body. Many of these invertebrate animals also have an outer shell to protect their body. Oysters, clams, snails, and mussels are all mollusks. So are octopuses, squids, and slugs. Mollusks live on land and in freshwater and saltwater environments. You will read about three groups of mollusks: bivalves, gastropods, and cephalopods.

Most mollusks have well-developed organ systems. They have muscles, a digestive system, a respiratory system, a circulatory system, and a nervous system with sensory organs. Mollusks reproduce sexually, and in most species there are distinct male and female organisms. Two adaptations distinguish mollusks as a group. First, all mollusks have a muscular foot. A mollusk's head is actually attached to its foot. Second, all mollusks have a mantle, a layer of folded skin that protects its internal organs.

RESOURCES FOR DIFFERENTIATED INSTRUCTION

Below Level

UNIT RESOURCE BOOK

- Reading Study Guide A, pp. 244–245
- Decoding Support, p. 268

Advanced

UNIT RESOURCE BOOK
Challenge and Extension, p. 250

English Learners

UNIT RESOURCE BOOK
Spanish Reading Study Guide, pp. 248–249

- Audio Readings in Spanish
- Audio Readings (English)

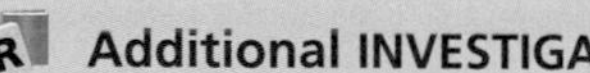
Exploring How a Squid Moves, A, B, & C, pp. 280–288; Teacher Instructions, pp. 360–361

Bivalves

Bivalve

Most of this blue-eyed scallop's body is inside its two-part shell.

Bivalves are named for a hard shell that is made up of two matching halves. Clams, mussels, scallops, and oysters are all bivalves. The shell, when it is closed, completely encloses the body. If you've ever seen a raw oyster, you know that a bivalve's body looks like a mass of tissue. Bivalves do not have a distinct head, but they do have a mouth and sensory organs. The scallop shown in the photograph has light-sensitive organs that look like tiny eyes.

Bivalves are filter feeders, they filter food from the surrounding water. To move, a bivalve balances upright, opens its shell, and extends its foot. The animal moves by pushing the foot in and out. The foot is also used for burrowing, digging down into the sand.

The invertebrates you've studied so far—sponges, cnidarians, and worms—take in oxygen all along the surface of their bodies. A bivalve takes in oxygen through a pair of gills. A **gill** is an organ that filters dissolved oxygen from water. The gill is an adaptation that allows an organism to take in a lot of oxygen in just one area of its body. It is made up of many folds of tissue that create a large surface area. Blood picks up the oxygen and moves it to the rest of the animal's body. In most bivalves, the gills also filter food from the water.

RESOURCE CENTER CLASSZONE.COM

Discover more about mollusks.

CHECK YOUR READING What are the two functions of gills and how do those functions relate to where bivalves live?

Gastropods

Gastropod

This brown-lipped snail extends most of its body out of its shell when it moves.

Gastropods are the most diverse group of mollusks. Some, such as snails and slugs, live on land. Many live in water, for example, conches, whelks, and periwinkles. Many gastropods are protected by a spiral-shaped shell. To protect itself, a gastropod withdraws into the shell.

The gastropod's head is located at the end of its foot. The head has eyes and specialized tentacles for sensing. Many gastropods have a cutting mouth part, called a radula, that shreds their food. Some gastropods eat animals, but most feed on plants and algae. Gastropods that live in water have gills. Some gastropods that live on land have lungs. A **lung** is an organ that absorbs oxygen from the air. Like gills, lungs have a large surface area.

12.3 INSTRUCT

Teach from Visuals

- To help students interpret the photographs of the bivalve and the gastropod, ask: What type of body symmetry do these organisms have? *bilateral*
- How do the shells of bivalves differ from those of the gastropods? *Bivalves have shells that are made up of two matching parts, while gastropods have one large domed shell that encloses the body.*

Develop Critical Thinking

APPLY Have students discuss the reasons why a large surface area in gills and lungs is an adaptation that is an advantage for mollusks. *The larger surface area enables more water or air to pass over the gills and lungs. Organisms with gills and lungs do not need to absorb oxygen through the cells of their bodies as do sponges and cnidarians.*

Real World Example

Mollusks such as mussels, oysters, squid, octopuses, and snails are considered a delicacy in the United States and around the world. Invite students to research the nutrients found in these foods and to make inferences about why certain nutrients are abundant.

Ongoing Assessment

CHECK YOUR READING *Answer: Bivalve gills filter oxygen and food from water. They are specialized to function in water.*

DIFFERENTIATE INSTRUCTION

More Reading Support

A What adaptations do gastropods have for taking in oxygen? *lungs and gills*

English Learners Have students write definitions and/or descriptions for *mollusk, clam, snail, octopus,* and *squid* in their Science Word Dictionaries. Students can draw pictures next to each description. As they read through section 12.3, they can add to their sketches with labels for body parts, such as *gill, radula, mantle, tentacle,* and so on.

INVESTIGATE Mollusks and Echinoderms

PURPOSE To observe details of mollusk and echinoderm shells

TIPS *15 min.* Invite students to bring in samples of mollusk shells, sand dollars, and sea stars that they may have collected from the beach. Samples may also be obtained through biological supply houses.

WHAT DO YOU THINK? *Answers will depend on the samples that students observe. Be sure that both similarities and differences are listed.*

CHALLENGE *Inferences should mention that the mollusks' bodies are inside their shells with a foot that could be extended or taken into the shell, while the echinoderms' bodies were once covered with a layer of skin, and that echinoderms' tube feet were on the outside of their bodies.*

 Datasheet, Mollusks and Echinoderms, p. 251

Technology Resources

Customize this student lab as needed or look for an alternative. Print rubrics to assess student lab reports.

 **Lab Generator CD-ROM**

Teaching with Technology

If computers and Internet access are available, have students use electronic encyclopedias to investigate the body structures of mollusks and echinoderms. Have students print out pictures and use them in conjunction with the investigation. They should caption the pictures using their own words and observations.

Ongoing Assessment

CHECK YOUR READING *Answer: Cephalopods have vision and tentacles adapted for hunting. They can move quickly because of a mantle that is adapted for producing a jet of water that moves the animal.*

INVESTIGATE Mollusks and Echinoderms

How do mollusk shells compare with echinoderm skeletons?

PROCEDURE

1. Closely observe the mollusk shells and skeletons of sea stars and sand dollars you are given.
2. Examine the shape and texture of each. Sort them by their characteristics.

WHAT DO YOU THINK?

How are the shells and skeletons the same? How are they different?

CHALLENGE Based on your observations, what can you infer about the bodies of living mollusks, sea stars, and sand dollars?

SKILL FOCUS
Observing

MATERIALS
Selection of mollusk shells, sea stars, and sand dollars

TIME
15 minutes

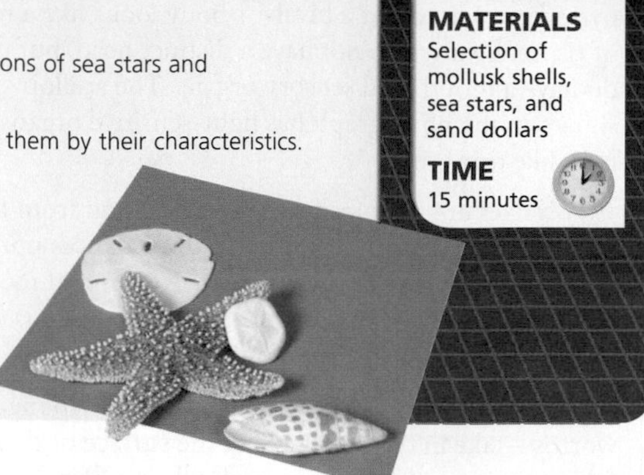

Cephalopods

Cephalopods (SEHF-uh-luh-PAHDZ) live in saltwater environments. Octopuses, squids, and chambered nautiluses are cephalopods. Among mollusks, cephalopods have the most well-developed body systems.

Cephalopods

This Maori octopus has a well-developed head attached to a foot with eight tentacles.

Cephalopods have a brain and well-developed nerves. They have a pair of eyes near their mouth. The foot, which surrounds the mouth, has tentacles for capturing prey. The mantle is adapted to push water forcefully through a tube-shaped structure called a siphon. This produces a jet of water that moves the animal. Gills take in oxygen, which is picked up by blood vessels and pumped through the body by three hearts. ? B

Octopuses and squids do not have protective shells. They do have protective behaviors, however. Some can change body color to match their surroundings. Some release dark clouds of inklike fluid into the water, to confuse their predators. The lack of a shell lets them move freely through the water.

The nautilus is the only cephalopod that has a shell. The shell is made up of separate compartments, or chambers. The nautilus itself lives in the outermost chamber. The inner chambers are filled with gas, which makes the animal better able to float. The chambered shell also provides the soft-bodied nautilus with protection from predators. ? C

VISUALIZATION CLASSZONE.COM

Watch how different cephalopods move.

 CHECK YOUR READING How is the foot of a cephalopod adapted for hunting?

DIFFERENTIATE INSTRUCTION

More Reading Support

B What two structures do cephalopods have that other bivalves do not? *gills and a siphon*

C Which cephalopod has an exterior shell? *the nautilus*

Below Level Use the table below to help students compare and contrast the differences among the three types of mollusks.

	Bivalves	Gastropods	Cephalopods
Outer covering	matching shells	spiral shells	none except nautilus
Body features	muscular foot	head, eyes, tentacles	siphon, gills, eyes, tentacles
Movement	muscular foot	muscular foot	mantle

Mollusks show a range of adaptations.

You might not think that a clam would belong to the same group as an octopus. These organisms look very different from one another. They also interact with the environment in different ways. The great variety of mollusks on Earth today provides a good example of how adaptations within a group can lead to great diversity. A good example of this is the range of adaptations shown in the shape and function of a mollusk's foot.

COMPARE How does the foot of this clam compare with the foot of an octopus?

The foot of the bivalve is a simple muscular structure that moves in and out of its shell. The foot allows a bivalve to crawl along the ocean floor and to bury itself in the sand. Gastropods have a head at the end of the foot, which runs the length of the body. Muscles in the foot produce ripples that allow the gastropod to glide over a surface as it searches for food. In cephalopods, the foot has tentacles to pull food into its mouth. The tentacles also help some cephalopods move along the ocean floor.

Echinoderms have unusual adaptations.

D **Echinoderms** are a group of invertebrates that live in the ocean. In their adult form, their bodies have radial symmetry. Sea stars, sea urchins, sea cucumbers, and sand dollars belong to this group. Echinoderms feed off the ocean floor as they move along. An echinoderm's mouth is located at the center of the body, on the underside. Some echinoderms, such as sea urchins and sand dollars, filter food from their surroundings. Others, such as sea stars, are active predators that feed on clams, snails, and even other echinoderms.

COMBINATION NOTES Remember to take notes and make sketches for the main idea: *Echinoderms have unusual adaptations.*

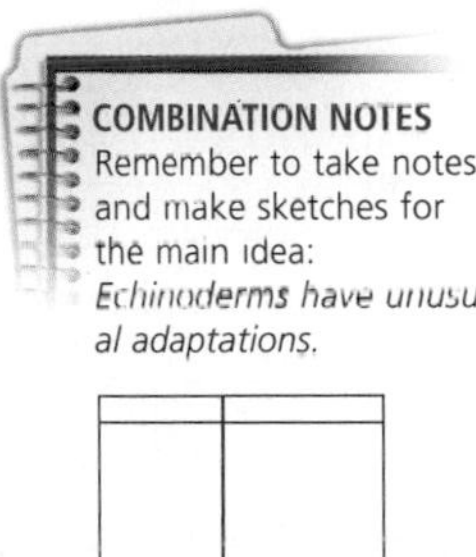

Spines and Skeletons

Echinoderm means "spiny-skinned." Some of the more familiar echinoderms have long, sharp spines, like the sea urchin in the photograph at the bottom of this page. However, some echinoderm species, such as sea cucumbers, have spines that are very small.

This purple sea urchin has very obvious spines.

E One unusual adaptation that echinoderms have is a type of skeleton. Remember that echinoderms are invertebrates, they have no bone tissue. The echinoderm skeleton is made up of a network of stiff, hard plates. The plates lie just under the surface of the echinoderm's skin. Some echinoderms, such as sea stars, have skeletons with loosely connected plates and flexible arms. In other echinoderms, such as sand dollars, the plates grow close together, so the skeleton does not allow for much flexibility.

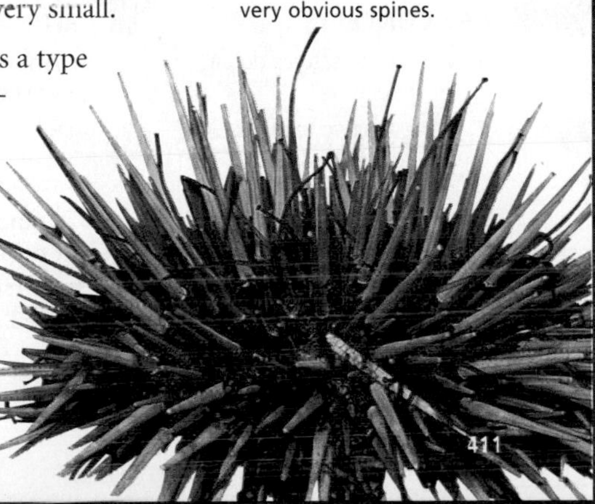

DIFFERENTIATE INSTRUCTION

More Reading Support

D Which type of body shape do echinoderms have? *radial symmetry*

E What makes up an echinoderm's skeleton? *stiff, hard plates*

Additional Investigation To reinforce Section 12.3 learning goals, use the following full period investigation:

R **Additional INVESTIGATION,** Exploring How a Squid Moves, A, B, & C, pp. 280–288, 360–361 (Advanced students should complete Levels B and C.)

Advanced Have students look up roots and origins of *cephalopod*, *gastropod*, *arthropod*, and *echinoderm*. Challenge them to find related words and write context sentences.

R Challenge and Extension, p. 250

Real World Example

A new species of deep sea squid has been spotted in the waters of the Gulf of Mexico, Pacific, Atlantic, and Indian Oceans at depths ranging from 1900 meters (6200 feet) to 4800 meters (16,000 feet). The newly discovered species has been spotted only eight times, with the first sighting in 1995. Unlike more familiar squids, this species has 10 long arm-like appendages, which radiate from the main axis of the body, and two large fins. Sizes of the squid are estimated from 1.5 to 7 meters (5 to 23 feet).

Develop Critical Thinking

INFER Direct attention to the photograph of the purple sea urchin, pointing out that you can see its tube feet among its spines. Ask: What do you think is the purpose of the spines? *to ward off predators*

Teacher Demo

Many grocery stores stock fresh, frozen, and dried octopus and squid. Since many students will not have seen these animals, you may wish to show them to students.

Language Arts Connection

Interested students might read *2000 Leagues Under the Sea,* by Jules Verne or read excerpts from it and create a two-column chart showing the "Scientifically Accurate" and "Scientifically Inaccurate" information about giant squids.

Ongoing Assessment

Describe different types of mollusks and their features.

Ask: What adaptations of echinoderms enable them to live in a water environment? *Echinoderms have mouths located on the underside of their bodies, enabling them to feed off ocean floors. Spines ward off predators. They have a skeleton.*

Teach from Visuals

To help students interpret the photograph of the sea stars, ask: How does a sea star use its tube feet to feed? *It spreads its arms over its prey and attaches its tube feet to the two shells. The suction tube feet gradually pull the shell open.*

Ongoing Assessment

Describe the different types of echinoderms and their features.

Ask: How does the water vascular system enable the sea star to move? *Tiny openings along the surface of the body allow water into the tubes of the system. When the openings close, suction is produced at the base of the tubes allowing the sea star to pull itself.*

Reinforce the BIG idea

Have students relate the section to the Big Idea.

 Reinforcing Key Concepts, p. 252

Assess

 Section 12.3 Quiz, p. 65

Reteach

Write the following terms on the board. Have students tell whether each is a mollusk or an echinoderm. Then have students describe a characteristic for each.

- bivalve *mollusk, two shells*
- gastropod *mollusk, spiral shell*
- cephalopod *mollusk, tentacles*
- sea urchin *echinoderm, spines*
- sea star *echinoderm, radial symmetry*

Technology Resources

Have students visit **ClassZone.com** for reteaching of Key Concepts.

 CONTENT REVIEW

 CONTENT REVIEW CD-ROM

This sea star has captured a bivalve and is using its tube feet to open the shell.

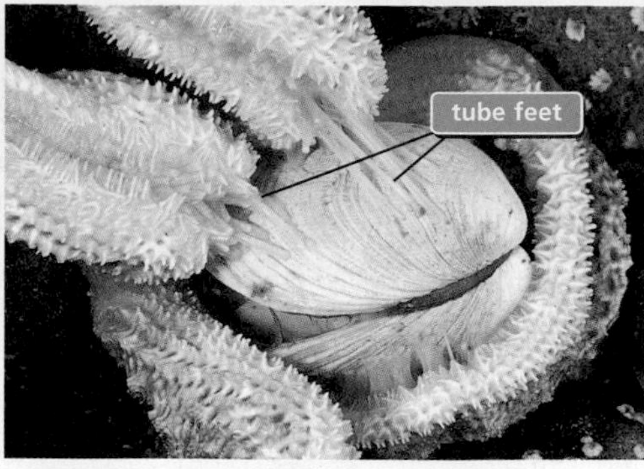

This sea star's arms have been pulled up to show how its tube feet are attached to the bivalve's shell.

Water Vascular System and Tube Feet

Another adaptation that is unique to echinoderms is a water vascular system. This system is made up of water-filled tubes that radiate out from the center of the echinoderm's body. Tiny openings along the upper surface of the echinoderm's body feed water into these tubes. At the base of the tubes is a series of tube feet.

Muscles attached to the top of each tube can close the tube off, producing suction at the base of the tube. The tube feet stick to the ocean floor, allowing the echinoderm to pull itself along. The tube feet can also be used for hunting prey. For example, a sea star can surround a clam or oyster with its body, as shown in the photograph on the left. The tube feet pull the shell open. Then, the sea star's stomach is pushed out through its mouth and into the bivalve's shell, where it begins to digest the bivalve's body. Not all echinoderms eat other animals. Some, like sea urchins, feed off algae on the ocean floor.

12.3 Review

KEY CONCEPTS

1. What two features do all mollusks have?
2. What are two features all echinoderms have?
3. What are two functions of tube feet in echinoderms?

CRITICAL THINKING

4. **Analyze** For mollusks and echinoderms, what are the advantages and disadvantages of having a shell or spiny skeleton?
5. **Compare and Contrast** Compare the foot of mollusks with the tube feet of echinoderms.

CHALLENGE

6. **Analyze** Animals with lungs or gills can be larger than animals that take in oxygen through their skin. What feature do both lungs and gills have that affect the amount of oxygen they can absorb? What role does the circulatory system play?

ANSWERS

1. muscular foot, mantle

2. spiny skeleton, water vascular system

3. movement, getting food

4. Shells and spiny skeletons provide protection from predators. Shells are heavy and not flexible. Spiny skeletons may inhibit movement and cannot protect tube feet.

5. Both use water. In cephalopods, water is drawn in and forcefully pushed out, moving the animal through the water. In echinoderms, the animals use water to create suction and move along the ocean floor.

6. Blood is able to move oxygen to different parts of the body quickly. Oxygen that enters the body across an outer surface must move into the body cell by cell.

Think SCIENCE

SKILL: EVALUATING CONCLUSIONS

Eating Well

Common sea stars have five arms. When one arm is missing, sea stars are, amazingly, able to grow another. Scientists interested in this amazing ability designed an experiment to see how having four arms instead of five affects a sea star's ability to consume prey. The sea stars use tube feet on each arm to pry open the shells of mussels and eat the animals' insides.

Scientists, working in 1999 and 2000, examined common sea stars caught in fishing gear. The study divided them into two groups: one group with five arms and one group with only four arms. Each sea star was tested to see how well it could open and eat a mussel.

Observations

Scientists made these observations:

a. Most of the sea stars with all five arms opened and ate a mussel.
b. Fewer than half of the sea stars with four arms opened and ate a mussel.
c. All the sea stars that opened a mussel took about 13 hours to finish eating it.

Conclusions

Here are some conclusions about sea stars eating mussels:

a. Common sea stars are most likely to feed successfully if they have all their arms.
b. A common sea star with only four arms will starve.
c. Common sea stars eat slowly regardless of how many arms they have.
d. Common sea stars with only four arms choose mussels that are difficult to open.

Evaluate the Conclusions

On Your Own Think about each observation that the scientists noted. Do they support the conclusions? Do some observations support one conclusion but not another? If a conclusion is not supported, what extra observations would you need to make?

With a Partner Compare your thinking with your partner's thinking. Do you both agree with the conclusions?

CHALLENGE Why do you think the sea stars with only four arms were less likely to open and eat a mussel?

The common sea star *(Asterias rubeus)* can regrow a missing arm. Its main prey is the mussel.

ANSWERS

Conclusion a: Reasonable. Observations a. and b. support this conclusion. Observation c. does not have any bearing on this conclusion.
Conclusion b: Not reasonable. Observation b. does not support this conclusion since some of the four-armed sea stars were able to open the mussels.
Conclusion c: Reasonable. Observation c. supports this conclusion.
Conclusion d: Not reasonable. Neither observations a., b., or c. support this conclusion as the difficulty of opening the mussels is not a factor.
CHALLENGE *These sea stars most likely have less strength and leverage than those with five arms.*

THINK SCIENCE

Scientific Methods of Thinking

Set Learning Goal

To evaluate conclusions by deciding whether or not they are based on observations and prior knowledge

Present the Science

Common sea stars have the ability to regenerate—to grow lost parts. A sea star can grow a new arm if it loses one. Some species of sea stars can regenerate completely from one arm and a piece of the central disc.

Guide the Activity

- Remind students that conclusions must be based upon observations and data collected from experiments.
- Students should check that each conclusion is supported by observations. Point out that the observations in the notebook are quantitative. That is, data can be counted, measured, or calculated.
- Remind students that to evaluate means to judge a statement based on criteria, such as observations.

COOPERATIVE LEARNING STRATEGY

- Group students in pairs to complete the activity.
- Have one student explain what makes each statement an "observation" that is listed as such.
- The other student can explain why each conclusion statement qualifies as a conclusion.
- Lastly, have partners work through the questions by discussing the validity of each conclusion.

Close

Ask: Why is it important to check each conclusion against each observation? *One observation may disprove a conclusion.*

12.4 FOCUS

Set Learning Goals

Students will

- Explore arthropods, the largest group of invertebrates.
- Recognize that all arthropods have exoskeletons.
- Describe the process of metamorphosis that insects undergo.
- Observe the development process of mealworms, including molting.

3-Minute Warm-Up

Display Transparency 29 or copy this exercise on the board:

Complete the Venn diagram. List unique features in the separate circles. Then list similarities in the overlap.

Mollusks	Both	Echinoderms
muscular foot *mantle*	*invertebrates* *gills or lungs*	*spiny skeleton* *water vascular system*

 3-Minute Warm-Up, p. T29

12.4 MOTIVATE

EXPLORE Arthropods

PURPOSE To describe some characteristics of a pill bug, a land invertebrate

TIP *20 min.* Allow students to share and discuss their sketches.

WHAT DO YOU THINK? *Features might include mouth, head, eyes, tentacles, antennae, and jointed legs or other appendages. Pill bugs have bilateral symmetry.*

Ongoing Assessment

Explore arthropods, the largest group of invertebrates.

Ask: What types of organisms are included in the group of arthropods? *insects, shrimp, and spiders*

KEY CONCEPT

12.4 Arthropods have exoskeletons and joints.

BEFORE, you learned

- Mollusks are invertebrates with soft bodies, some have shells
- Echinoderms have spiny skeletons
- Different species adapt to the same environment in different ways

NOW, you will learn

- About different groups of arthropods
- About exoskeletons in arthropods
- About metamorphosis in arthropods

VOCABULARY

arthropod p. 414
exoskeleton p. 415
molting p. 415
insect p. 417
metamorphosis p. 418

EXPLORE Arthropods

What are some characteristics of arthropods?

PROCEDURE

1. Observe the pillbugs in their container. Draw a sketch of a pillbug.
2. Gently remove the pillbugs from their container and place them in the open end of the box. Observe and make notes on their behavior for several minutes.
3. Return the pillbugs to their container.

WHAT DO YOU THINK?

- Describe some of the characteristics you noticed about pillbugs.
- Are pillbugs radially or bilaterally symmetrical?

MATERIALS

- clear container
- shoebox with half of cover removed
- pillbugs
- hand lens

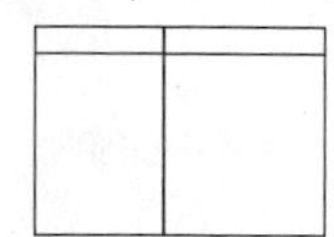

COMBINATION NOTES Make notes and diagrams for the main idea: *Most invertebrates are arthropods.*

Most invertebrates are arthropods.

There are more species of arthropods than there are any other type of invertebrate. In fact, of all the animal species classified by scientists, over three-quarters are arthropods. An **arthropod** is an invertebrate that has a segmented body covered with a hard outer skeleton. Arthropods can have many pairs of legs and other parts that extend from their body. Insects are arthropods, as are crustaceans such as the shrimp and arachnids such as the spider.

Fossil evidence shows that arthropods first appeared on land about 420 million years ago, around the same time as plants. Arthropods are active animals that feed on all types of food. Many arthropods live in water, but most live on land.

RESOURCES FOR DIFFERENTIATED INSTRUCTION

Below Level

UNIT RESOURCE BOOK

- Reading Study Guide A, pp. 255–256
- Decoding Support, p. 268

Advanced

UNIT RESOURCE BOOK

Challenge and Extension, p. 262

English Learners

UNIT RESOURCE BOOK

Spanish Reading Study Guide, pp. 259–260

- Audio Readings in Spanish
- Audio Readings (English)

RESOURCE CENTER
CLASSZONE.COM
Find out more about the diversity of arthropods.

The exoskeleton of this crayfish completely covers its body.

Exoskeletons and Jointed Parts

One adaptation that gives arthropods the ability to live in many different environments is the exoskeleton. An **exoskeleton** is a strong outer covering, made of a material called chitin. The exoskeleton completely covers the body of an arthropod. In a sense, an exoskeleton is like a suit of armor that protects the animal's soft body. For arthropods living on land, the exoskeleton keeps cells, tissues, and organs from drying out.

CHECK YOUR READING What are two functions of an exoskeleton?

A suit of armor is not much good unless you can move around in it. The arthropod's exoskeleton has joints, places where the exoskeleton is thin and flexible. There are joints along the different segments of the animal's body. An arthropod body typically has three sections: a head at one end, a thorax in the middle, and an abdomen at the other end. Legs are jointed, as are other parts attached to the body, such as antennae and claws. Muscles attach to the exoskeleton around the joints, enabling the arthropod to move. (A)

The exoskeleton is like a suit of armor in one other way. It doesn't grow. An arthropod must shed its exoskeleton as it grows. This process is called **molting.** For an arthropod, the times when it molts are dangerous because its soft body is exposed to predators. (B)

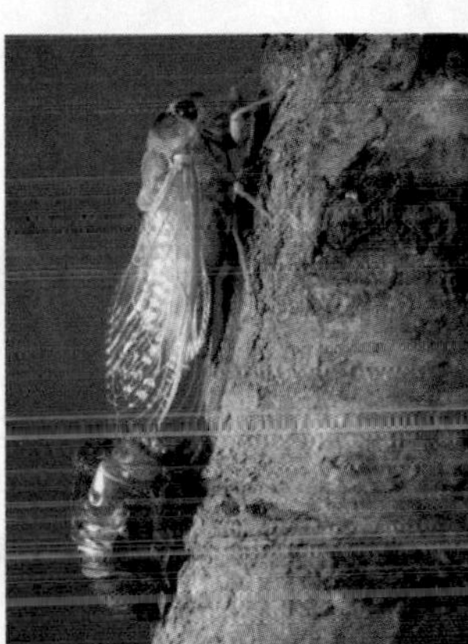

COMPARE How does the shape of this cicada's molted exoskeleton compare to the shape of its body?

Complex Body Systems

Arthropods have well-developed body systems. They have a nervous system with a brain and many different sensory organs. Their digestive system includes a stomach and intestines. Arthropods have an open circulatory system, which means the heart moves blood into the body directly. There are no blood vessels. Arthropods reproduce sexually. An arthropod has either a male or a female reproductive system.

12.4 INSTRUCT

Teach from Visuals

To help students interpret the photograph of the crayfish, ask: What body features of this arthropod help it to move around on land? *segmented body and jointed legs*

Integrate the Sciences

The fossil record shows that the most primitive insects lived during the Middle Devonian period about 350 million years ago. Most of the early insect fossils, however, are from the Carboniferous Period (about 360 to about 280 million years ago). There are many gaps in the insect fossil record, but there have been epochs of "explosive" evolution during which many species appeared. After arthropods became firmly established, fossil evidence indicates that many insects and plants co-evolved due to their interdependence.

Ongoing Assessment

Recognize that all arthropods have exoskeletons.

Ask: What is an exoskeleton? *It is a strong outer covering made of chitin, which completely covers the body of an arthropod.*

CHECK YOUR READING *Answer: The exoskeleton protects the animal and keeps land-dwelling arthropods from drying out.*

DIFFERENTIATE INSTRUCTION

More Reading Support

A How is the exoskeleton attached to the joints of the arthropod? *by muscles*

B What term describes the process of shedding an exoskeleton? *molting*

English Learners Have students write the definitions for the terms *exoskeleton, molting,* and *metamorphosis* in their Science Word Dictionaries. Pronounce these words for students. Use the Chapter Summary page to help students focus on key concepts and vocabulary.

Teach from Visuals

To help students compare the three photographs showing characteristics of the three major groups of arthropods, ask:

- How do arachnids differ from the insect and crustacean groups? *They have 4 pairs of legs instead of 3 pairs. They have no antennae.*
- How are the insect and arachnid groups alike? *Most live on land.*

Address Misconceptions

IDENTIFY Ask students which characteristics they would use to identify an organism as an animal. Many students will hold the misconception that animals have four legs, make sounds, and have fur. Most of the animals in this chapter would not fit any of those criteria.

CORRECT Construct a bulletin board with labels *Fur, Makes Sound,* and *Four Legs*. Have students put the names of invertebrate species on scraps of paper and tack them under one of the headings, or in a separate area.

REASSESS Based on the bulletin board above, ask students to re-think their criteria for characteristics of animals. Student answers should include the many characteristics of invertebrates.

Technology Resources

Visit **ClassZone.com** for background on common student misconceptions.

MISCONCEPTION DATABASE

Ongoing Assessment

READING VISUALS *Answer: All have legs and segmented bodies, eyes, and heads.*

Three Major Groups of Arthropods

Scientists have named at least ten groups of arthropods, but most arthropod species belong to one of three groups: insects, crustaceans, or arachnids.

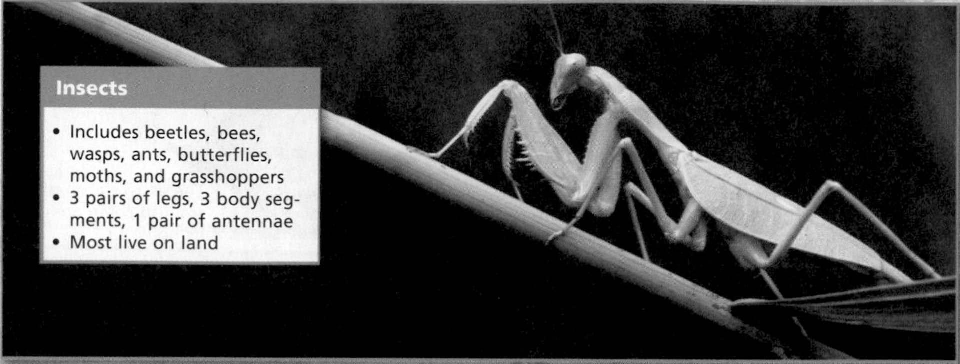

Insects

- Includes beetles, bees, wasps, ants, butterflies, moths, and grasshoppers
- 3 pairs of legs, 3 body segments, 1 pair of antennae
- Most live on land

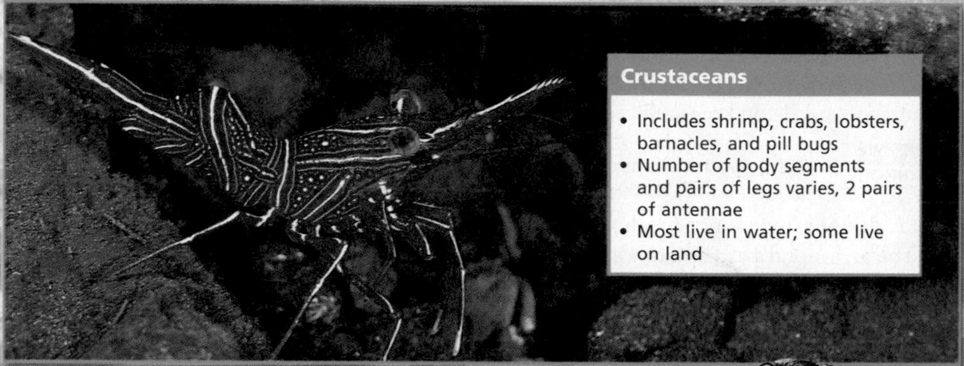

Crustaceans

- Includes shrimp, crabs, lobsters, barnacles, and pill bugs
- Number of body segments and pairs of legs varies, 2 pairs of antennae
- Most live in water; some live on land

Arachnids

- Includes spiders, ticks, mites, and scorpions
- 4 pairs of legs, 2 body segments, no antennae
- Most live on land

READING VISUALS What body features can you see that are shared by all of these arthropods?

416 Unit 3: Diversity of Living Things

DIFFERENTIATE INSTRUCTION

Below Level Provide students with close-up photographs obtained from nature magazines of the major groups of arthropods. Have students examine the photographs for structures such as number of pairs of legs, presence and number of antennae, and number of body segments. Have students fill in a chart with the characteristics pictured, then classify each arthropod as an insect, crustacean, or arachnid.

Advanced Challenge students to develop a classification key using "yes" and "no" questions to classify the major groups of arthropods.

Parts of an Insect's Body

Adult insects have three body segments and six jointed legs.

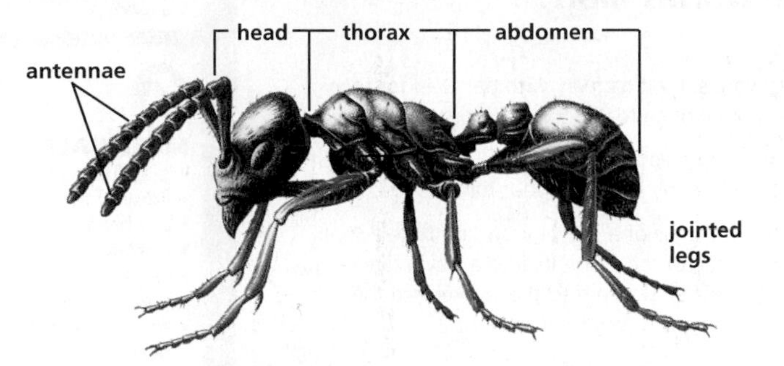

READING TIP
The word *insect* relates to its body being **in sect**ions. Note the three sections in the diagram of the ant.

Insects are six-legged arthropods.

Scientists have so far identified over 700,000 insect species. **Insects** are arthropods that as adults have three body segments, a pair of antennae, and six legs attached to the middle segment, the thorax. Insect species have adapted to all sorts of environments and live on every continent. Most insects live on land. These insects obtain oxygen through spiracles, small openings in their exoskeleton. C

VOCABULARY
Don't forget to take notes on the term *insect*, using a strategy from an earlier chapter or one that you already know.

CHECK YOUR READING What are two characteristics all adult insects share?

Insects show great diversity in appearance. Many species have adaptations in color and shape that allow them to blend into their environments. For example, a stick insect is the same color and shape as a twig. Insect bodies also have different adaptations. Many insects have compound eyes and antennae, which are sensory organs. Many insects fly, having one or two pairs of wings.

Many insects are herbivores. And many insect species have mouth parts adapted for feeding on specific plants. A butterfly, for example, has a tubelike mouth that can reach into a flower to get nectar. Insects that feed on flowers often help the plants reproduce because the insects carry pollen from flower to flower. Other insects harm the plants they feed on. A grasshopper has jawlike mouth parts that crush parts of a plant. Many plants have defensive adaptations, such as poisons in leaves and stems, to keep insects from eating them.

D Some insects, for example, ants, termites, and some bees, are social insects. They must live in groups in order to survive. Members of the group work together to gather food, maintain the nest, and care for the offspring. Often with social insects, just one female, called a queen, produces and lays eggs.

Develop Critical Thinking

COMPARE AND CONTRAST To help students understand the structure of the insect, ask: How are the segments of the insect's body different from those of an earthworm? *The insect has three distinct segments that are different from each other. The earthworm has segments that look the same.*

Teacher Demo

To demonstrate the importance of segmented joints, invite a volunteer to the front of the room. Place a rolled cardboard tube around the student's arm up to the shoulder. Challenge the student to write on the board, lift an object, or eat a cracker. Reinforce the concept that jointed appendages are an adaptation that enabled arthropods to live on land.

EXPLORE the BIG idea

Revisit "Insects and You" on p. 393. Ask students if their idea of insects has changed based on their observations and what they have learned from the text.

Ongoing Assessment

CHECK YOUR READING *Answer: Adult insects have three body segments, six jointed legs.*

DIFFERENTIATE INSTRUCTION

More Reading Support

C Through which structures do insects obtain oxygen? *spiracles*

D What term describes insects that live in groups? *social insects*

Advanced Invite interested students to choose one group of social insects, such as ants, termites, or bees. The dance of bees might be of particular interest, a dance of communication that informs other honeybees as to the type, quality, and location of nectar. Ask students to display their findings using illustrations, captions, and other graphics.

R Challenge and Extension, p. 261

INVESTIGATE Insect Metamorphosis

PURPOSE To observe the development of mealworms to discover how often they molt

TIPS *20 min.* Make holes in lids of jars prior to activity so mealworms will have enough air. They will not escape. The oats are the mealworms' food; the potato provides moisture they need. Purchase mealworms at pet stores or biological supply companies.

WHAT DO YOU THINK? *Eggs will be visible with a magnifying glass. Larva hatches from egg in one to two weeks. Larval stage lasts an average of ten weeks and includes several molts. Pupal stage lasts two to three weeks. Newly hatched adults have pale soft exoskeletons, which later harden and darken.*

CHALLENGE *There are approximately four to six molts during the larval stage, so students should find about four to six times the number of shed exoskeletons as living mealworms.*

Datasheet, Insect Metamorphosis, p. 262

Technology Resources

Customize this student lab as needed or look for an alternative. Print rubrics to assess student lab reports.

Lab Generator CD-ROM

Teach Difficult Concepts

Pupae, chrysalis, and eggs are among the stages of a life cycle. In each stage the organism may not be moving, but its cells continue to grow, feed, respond, and maintain internal conditions. The cells have not died and reanimated. They emerge from living cells that were their parents.

Ongoing Assessment

CHECK YOUR READING *Answer: During metamorphosis, an insect's body systems change dramatically in three stages. Larva: the insect eats; pupa: it develops in a protective casing. It emerges as an adult, capable of reproducing.*

INVESTIGATE Insect Metamorphosis

How often do mealworms molt?

PROCEDURE

1. Prepare the jar for the mealworms. Fill it halfway with oat bran for food. Place a slice of potato and a piece of carrot on top for moisture.
2. In your notebook, note how many mealworms you have. Carefully place the mealworms inside the jar and close the lid. Wash your hands.
3. Without opening the jar, look for signs of activity every day. Once a week, open the container and pour some of the contents into a tray. Examine this sample for molted exoskeletons. Then return it to the jar. Replace the vegetables and add new oats as needed. Wash your hands.

WHAT DO YOU THINK?

- What changes did you observe in the mealworms?
- Did you see any sign of other stages of development?

CHALLENGE Use tweezers and a petri dish to collect the molted exoskeletons. How do the number of molts compare to the number of worms? Estimate how often the worms molt.

SKILL FOCUS
Observing

MATERIALS
- glass jar
- lid with air holes
- oat bran
- potato
- carrot
- mealworms
- *for Challenge:* petri dish tweezers

TIME
20 minutes

All insects can reproduce sexually. Females lay eggs, often a large number of eggs. The queen honey bee can lay over a million eggs in her lifetime. Many insect eggs have a hard outer covering. This adaptation protects the egg from drying out and can allow hatching to be delayed until conditions are right.

READING TIP: The word *metamorphosis* means "many changes."

During their life cycle, insects undergo a process in which their appearance and body systems may change dramatically. This process is called **metamorphosis.** There are three stages to a complete metamorphosis. The first stage is the larva, which spends its time eating. The second stage is the pupa. During this stage, the insect body develops within a protective casing. The final stage is the adult, which is capable of going on to produce a new generation.

What happens to an insect during metamorphosis?

Not all insects go through complete metamorphosis. Some insects, such as grasshoppers, have a simple metamorphosis. When a young grasshopper hatches from an egg, its form is similar to an adult's, just smaller. A grasshopper grows and molts several times before reaching adult size.

DIFFERENTIATE INSTRUCTION

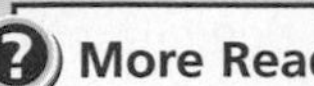

More Reading Support

E What term describes the changes in an insect's life? *metamorphosis*

F Give an example of an insect that undergoes simple metamorphosis. *Sample answer: grasshopper*

English Learners Allow English learners to draw their observations in the investigation, p. 418, or to narrate their observations to a partner or group.

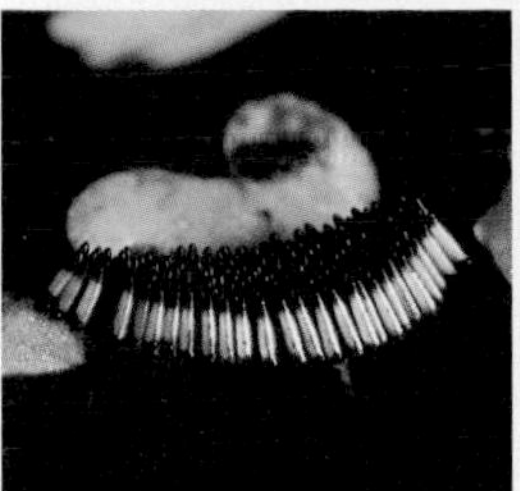

1. A female mosquito lays a mass of eggs on the surface of the water.

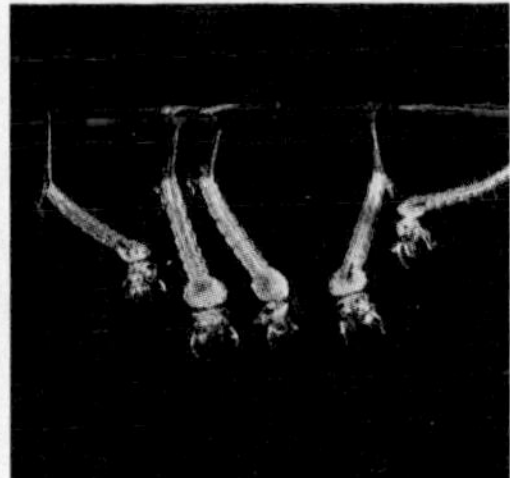

2. Each egg develops into a larva that swims head down, feeding on algae.

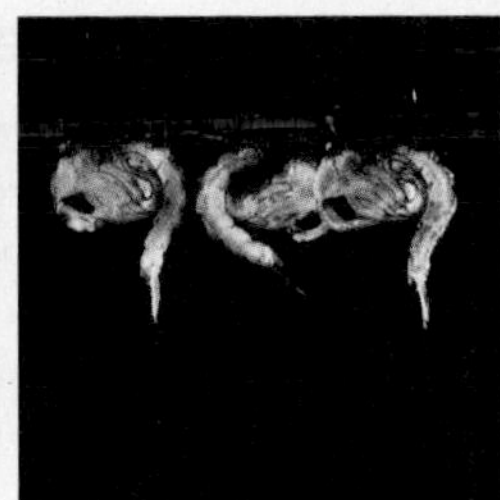

3. The larva develops into a pupa. Inside, the body of the insect matures.

4. At the adult stage, the mosquito leaves the water and flies away.

You have probably seen many insects in their larval form. A caterpillar is a larva; so is an inchworm. Often the larval form of an insect lives very differently from its adult form. A mosquito, for example, begins its life in the water. The larva swims about, feeding on algae. The pupa forms at the water's surface. The developing mosquito is encased in a protective covering. The adult form of the mosquito, the flying insect, leaves the water. The female is a parasite that feeds off the blood of other animals.

Crustaceans live in water and on land.

Most crustacean species live in the water. Several of these, including the Atlantic lobster and the Dungeness crab, are used by people as a source of food. Crustaceans are important to the ocean food web. Tiny crustaceans such as krill and copepods are a food source for many other animals, including other invertebrates, fish, and whales. Some species of crustaceans live in freshwater and a few, such as pill bugs, live on land.

CHECK YOUR READING Where do most crustaceans live?

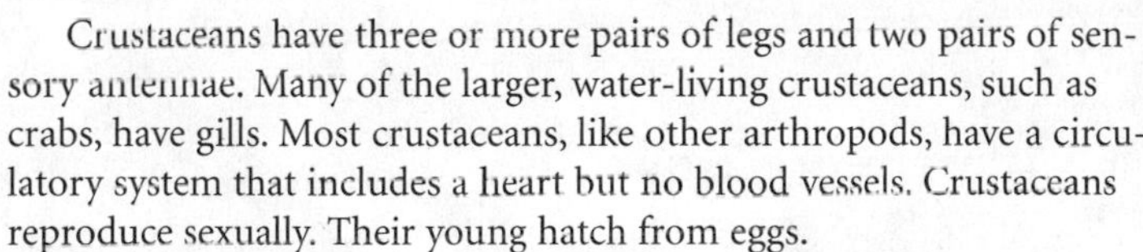

G Crustaceans have three or more pairs of legs and two pairs of sensory antennae. Many of the larger, water-living crustaceans, such as crabs, have gills. Most crustaceans, like other arthropods, have a circulatory system that includes a heart but no blood vessels. Crustaceans reproduce sexually. Their young hatch from eggs.

The eating habits of crustaceans vary. Lobsters and shrimp eat plants and small animals. Many crustaceans are scavengers, feeding off the remains of other organisms. Some, such as barnacles, are filter feeders. The larval form of a barnacle is free swimming. However, as an adult this arthropod attaches itself to a rock or another hard surface, such as a mollusk's shell or the hull of a ship. It uses its tentacles to capture food from the surrounding water.

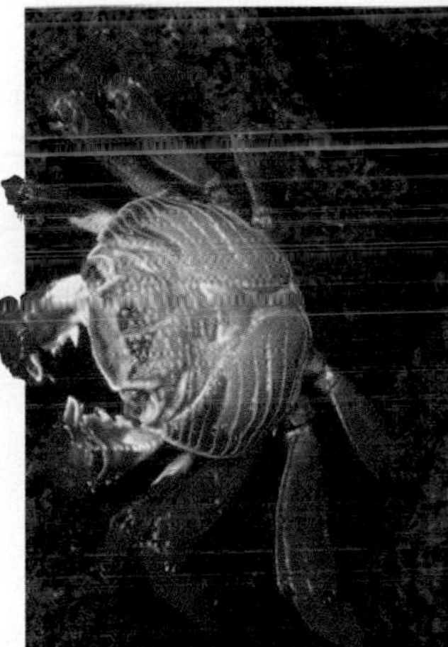

IDENTIFY How many pairs of legs does this crab have?

Teach from Visuals

To help students understand the photographs of mosquito metamorphosis, ask:

- What are the four stages of insect development? *egg, larva, pupa, adult*
- When is metamorphosis complete? *when the pupa becomes an adult*

History of Science

Some diseases, such as West Nile virus and malaria, are transmitted to humans by the bites of mosquitoes. Malaria has been documented as far back as 400 B.C. by Hippocrates. It most likely made its way to the Americas by import through Spanish explorers. It was not until 1880 that French army surgeon Alphonse Laveran became the first to recognize the malarial parasite. West Nile virus has been studied for several decades and has become an increasing public health concern in North America. It made its way to the United States in 1999 and spread into Canada and the Caribbean.

Mathematics Connection

To date, scientists recognize about 800,000 different species of insects. This represents about three-fourths of all known species on Earth. To help students visualize the vast numbers of insects that inhabit Earth, draw a circle graph on the board. Shade in three fourths of the circle, pointing out that this portion of the circle represents the number of insect species on Earth compared to all other animal species.

Ongoing Assessment

Describe the process of metamorphosis.

Ask students to compare the metamorphosis of a mosquito to that of a butterfly. *Each metamorphosis takes the insect from larval stage to a stage within a protective case (pupa) to a fully developed adult.*

CHECK YOUR READING *Answer: Most crustaceans live in water.*

***PHOTO CAPTION** Answer: It has ten jointed legs covered by an exoskeleton.*

DIFFERENTIATE INSTRUCTION

More Reading Support

G How many pairs of antennae do crustaceans have? *two pairs*

Below Level Have each student write a one-page story entitled "A Day in the Life of Insect X." Each story should include scientific information such as life cycle stages, how the insect moves, what the insect eats, and how the insect's body plan suits its environment. The story could end with the question: "Who am I?" and students can try to guess the identity of each other's subjects as they read them in a class book or display.

Real World Example

Commercial silk is produced by the cocoons of moth species known as silkworms. Silk weaving dates back to the 3rd millennium B.C. in China, where its production was a highly guarded secret. To produce silk, the larvae inside the cocoons of the silkworms are killed by steam or hot air. The strands of silk that make up the cocoons are unwrapped and twisted into yarn.

Language Arts Connection

The name *Arachnida* comes from the Greek mythological character Arachne, a peasant girl who challenged the weaving talent of the goddess Athena. Arachne was able to match Athena's talent in a competition, but succumbed in response to Athena's anger. Athena turned Arachne into a spider, allowing her to keep her weaving talent.

Teaching with Technology

Invite students to compile an electronic database of "Fascinating Facts" about arthropods. For example, some species of centipedes and millipedes can grow up to 8 inches long. Students can print their databases or post them on a school Web site.

Ongoing Assessment

CHECK YOUR READING *Answer: Some spiders weave webs, which are unusual because they are traps for prey.*

Arachnids are eight-legged arthropods.

Spiders, mites, ticks, and scorpions belong to a group called the arachnids. Like all arthropods, arachnids have an exoskeleton, jointed limbs, and segmented bodies. But the bodies of arachnids have some characteristics that distinguish them from other arthropods. Arachnids always have four pairs of legs and only two body segments. Arachnids do not have antennae.

Some arachnids, including ticks and chigger mites, are parasites. Other arachnids, such as spiders and scorpions, are predators. Recall that predators get their food by capturing and consuming other animals. Predatory arachnids kill their prey by stinging them, biting them, or injecting them with venom.

This mite is an arachnid that lives in dust. This micrograph shows it magnified 150×.

? H

The spiders are the largest group of arachnids. Many spiders have a unique adaptation for capturing their prey. They produce an extremely strong material, called silk, inside their bodies and use the silk to make webs for capturing food. The spider spins strands of silk out from tubes called spinnerets at the rear of its abdomen. It weaves the strands into a nearly invisible web. The web serves as a net for catching insects and other small organisms that the spider eats. This adaptation allows web-building spiders to wait for their prey to come to them. Other invertebrates, such as silkworms, produce silk, but they do not weave webs.

How is the way some spiders capture prey unusual?

Some arachnids obtain oxygen through spiracles, as insects do. However, certain species of spiders have a unique type of respiratory organ referred to as book lungs. Book lungs are like moist pockets with folds. They are located inside the animal's abdomen.

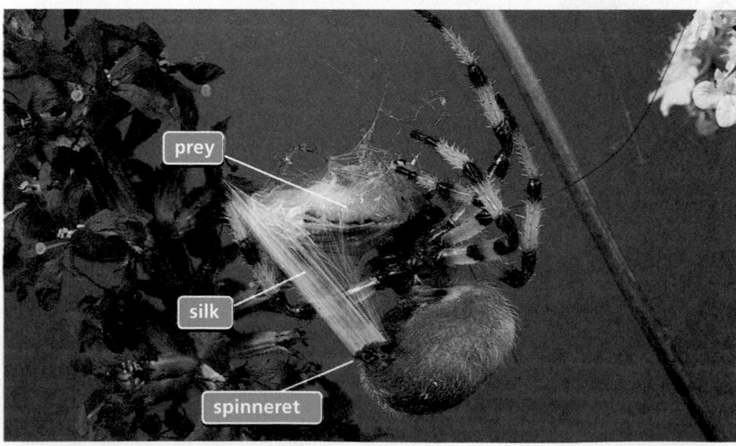

This spider has wrapped its prey in silk.

DIFFERENTIATE INSTRUCTION

More Reading Support

H What is the largest group of arachnids? *spiders*

Inclusion To help students learn the differences among insects, crustaceans, and arachnids, help them to build models using clay or pipe cleaners. Allow time for students to display and discuss their models with other students.

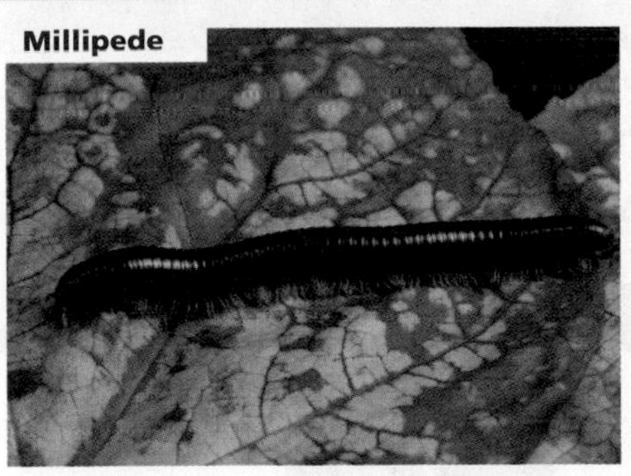
Millipede

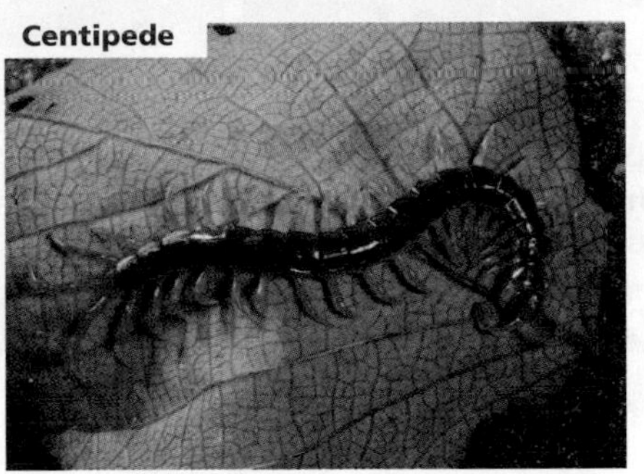
Centipede

READING VISUALS **COMPARE AND CONTRAST** With their long segmented bodies, a millipede and a centipede look very similar. How are they different?

Millipedes and centipedes are arthropods.

At first glance, the members of two other arthropod groups look similar. Both centipedes and millipedes have long, segmented bodies and many legs. However, animals from these groups differ in their body features and their behavior.

Millipedes are arthropods with two pairs of walking legs on each body segment. Millipedes move rather slowly and eat decaying leaves and plant matter. When disturbed, many millipedes emit a foul odor that can be harmful to predators.

Centipedes can move more quickly. They have one pair of walking legs per body segment. They have antennae and jawlike mouthparts. Many centipedes also have pincers on their rearmost segment. Centipedes are predators. They can use their jaws and pincers to paralyze prey and protect themselves from predators.

12.4 Review

KEY CONCEPTS

1. Describe the characteristics of insects, crustaceans, and arachnids.
2. What is molting and how does it relate to an exoskeleton?
3. Name three arthropods and the adaptations they have for feeding.

CRITICAL THINKING

4. **Analyze** How does the form of an exoskeleton relate to its function?
5. **Connect** Mosquitoes can spread disease, such as the West Nile virus. People are advised not to leave open containers of water in the yard. How does standing water contribute to an increase in the number of mosquitoes?

CHALLENGE

6. **Evaluate** Many plant-eating insects live less than a year. An adult will lay eggs in the fall and then die as winter comes. The eggs hatch the next spring. How does the life cycle of the insect fit in with the life cycle of plants? What role does the egg play in the survival of the insect species in this case?

ANSWERS

1. Insects have three segments, six legs, and one pair of antennae. Crustaceans have two pairs of antennae and specialized legs. Arachnids have two body segments, eight legs, and no antennae.

2. Molting is the shedding of an exoskeleton in order to grow a larger one.

3. Sample answer: Butterflies have tubelike mouths, barnacles have tentacles, and spiders make webs.

4. Exoskeletons are hard in order to protect the animal, and have joints that allow the animal to move.

5. Standing water gives the mosquitoes a place to breed.

6. Insect life cycles may be timed so they mature at same time plant is ready to be pollinated. Egg protects offspring during winter.

EXPLORE the BIG idea

Revisit "Internet Activity: Invertebrate Diversity" on p. 393. Now that students have studied the variety of invertebrates, ask them if their understandings about invertebrates have changed.

Ongoing Assessment

READING VISUALS *Answer: The centipede has fewer legs than the millipede, and appears to be longer and thicker. The centipede has curved structures at one end of its body. A millipede has more body segments than the centipede, and more legs per segment.*

Reinforce the BIG idea

Have students relate the section to the Big Idea.

 Reinforcing Key Concepts, p. 263

12.4 ASSESS & RETEACH

Assess

 Section 12.4 Quiz, p. 66

Reteach

Ask students to name a type of arthropod. Then have students tell whether it is an insect, crustacean, or arachnid. Ask for volunteers to describe some body characteristics about the organism such as number of body segments, presence of antennae, and the like. Students can then describe one fact about the organism, such as it lives in water, spins silk, or goes through metamorphosis.

Technology Resources

Have students visit **ClassZone.com** for reteaching of Key Concepts.

 CONTENT REVIEW

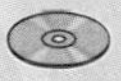 CONTENT REVIEW CD-ROM

BACK TO

the BIG idea

Have students name and describe two body plans and two adaptations of invertebrate animals. *Bilaterally symmetrical bodies have halves that are mirror images. Radially symmetric bodies are organized around a central point. Adaptations may include jointed appendages and an external skeleton.*

KEY CONCEPTS SUMMARY

SECTION 12.1
Ask students to describe how specialized cells in sponges enable them to feed on and digest food. *Specialized cells filter out food particles as water moves through the sponge. Other specialized cells digest food.*

SECTION 12.2
Ask students how the body plans of cnidarians and worms differ. *All cnidarians are radially symmetrical and have tentacles that surround a mouth cavity. Worms are bilaterally symmetrical and have organs that are organized into body systems.*

SECTION 12.3
Ask students to name two adaptations that distinguish mollusks as a group. *a mantle and a muscular foot* Then ask students to explain the purpose of the water vascular system in echinoderms. *Water-filled tubes end in a series of tube feet. As muscles close off the top of the tubes, suction is produced at the feet, enabling the animal to move and feed on prey.*

SECTION 12.4
Have students describe why the exoskeletons and jointed appendages are adaptations that allow arthropods to live on land. *They provide support, protection, and movement, allowing arthropods to live in many different environments.*

Review Concepts

- Big Idea Flow Chart, p. T25
- Chapter Outline, pp. T31–T32

12 Chapter Review

the BIG idea

Invertebrate animals have a variety of body plans and adaptations.

KEY CONCEPTS SUMMARY

1 Most animals are invertebrates.

Invertebrates are a diverse group of animals. Species of invertebrates live in almost every environment.

Sponges are simple invertebrates that have several types of specialized cells.

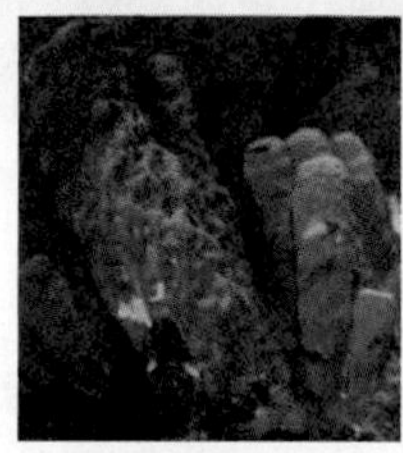

VOCABULARY
invertebrate p. 395
sponge p. 397
sessile p. 397
larva p. 398

2 Cnidarians and worms have different body plans.

Cnidarians have simple bodies with specialized cells and tissues.

Most **worms** have organs and complex body systems.

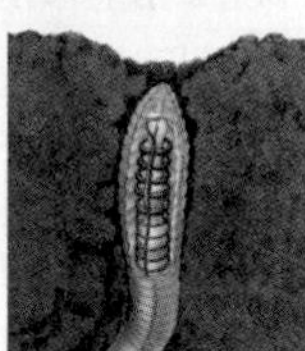

VOCABULARY
cnidarian p. 400
tentacle p. 400
mobile p. 402

3 Most mollusks have shells, and echinoderms have spiny skeletons.

Mollusks include bivalves, gastropods, and cephalopods.

Echinoderms have a water vascular system and tube feet.

VOCABULARY
mollusk p. 408
gill p. 409
lung p. 409
echinoderm p. 411

4 Arthropods have exoskeletons and joints.

Arthropods, which include insects, crustaceans, and arachnids, are the most abundant and diverse group of animals.

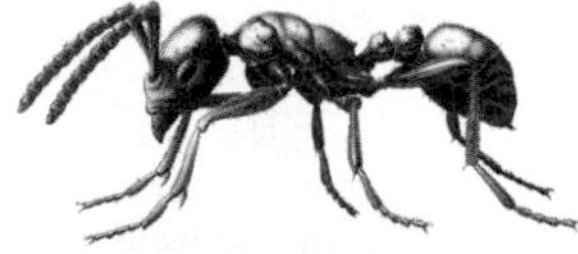

VOCABULARY
arthropod p. 414
exoskeleton p. 415
molting p. 415
insect p. 417
metamorphosis p. 418

422 Unit 3: Diversity of Living Things

Technology Resources

Have students visit **ClassZone.com** or use the CD-ROM for a cumulative review of concepts.

 **CONTENT REVIEW**

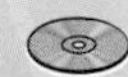 **CONTENT REVIEW CD-ROM**

Engage students in a whole-class interactive review of Key Concepts. Edit content as you wish.

 **POWER PRESENTATIONS**

Reviewing Vocabulary

Copy and complete the chart below.

Word	Definition	Example
1. mollusk		clam, snail, squid
2. arthropod	invertebrate with jointed legs, segmented body, and an exoskeleton	
3.	ocean-dwelling animal with spiny skeleton	sea star
4. sessile		sponge
5. larva		caterpillar
6. metamorphosis		caterpillar changing into a butterfly
7. molting	process by which an arthropod sheds its exoskeleton	
8.	arthropod with three body segments, one pair of antennae, and six legs	grasshopper, mosquito, beetle

Reviewing Key Concepts

Multiple Choice *Choose the letter of the best answer.*

9. Which of the following groups of animals is the most abundant?
- **a.** worms
- **b.** mollusks
- **c.** echinoderms
- **d.** arthropods

10. In what way are all invertebrates alike?
- **a.** They do not have backbones.
- **b.** They live in the ocean.
- **c.** They are predators.
- **d.** They have a closed circulatory system.

11. Sponges bring food into their bodies through a
- **a.** system of pores
- **b.** water vascular system
- **c.** mouth
- **d.** digestive tract

12. Which group of invertebrates has a mantle?
- **a.** echinoderms
- **b.** crustaceans
- **c.** cnidarians
- **d.** mollusks

13. Bivalves, cephalopods, and gastropods are all types of
- **a.** echinoderms
- **b.** mollusks
- **c.** crustaceans
- **d.** cnidarians

14. As they grow, arthropods shed their exoskeleton in a process called
- **a.** metamorphosis
- **b.** symmetry
- **c.** molting
- **d.** siphoning

15. Which invertebrate animals always have three body segments: a head, a thorax, and an abdomen?
- **a.** segmented worms
- **b.** adult insects
- **c.** arachnids
- **d.** echinoderms

16. Which group of invertebrates have a water vascular system and tube feet?
- **a.** echinoderms
- **b.** crustaceans
- **c.** cnidarians
- **d.** mollusks

Short Answer *Write a short answer to each question.*

17. Describe the stages in the life cycle of an insect that has complete metamorphosis.

18. Explain one advantage and one disadvantage an exoskeleton has for an organism.

19. Is a spider an insect? Explain.

ASSESSMENT RESOURCES

UNIT ASSESSMENT BOOK
- Chapter Test, Level A, pp. 67–70
- Chapter Test, Level B, pp. 71–74
- Chapter Test, Level C, pp. 75–78
- Alternative Assessment, pp. 79–80

SPANISH ASSESSMENT BOOK
Spanish Chapter Test, pp. 53–56

Technology Resources

Edit test items and answer choices.

Test Generator CD-ROM

Visit **ClassZone.com** to extend test practice.

Test Practice

Reviewing Vocabulary

1. invertebrate with a strong muscular foot and a mantle
2. sample answers: lobster, insect, spider
3. echinoderm
4. lives and grows while remaining in one place
5. an immature, or early, stage of life for an organism, in which it may look different from the adult form
6. process of physical transformation as an organism matures from one stage of life to the next
7. sample answers: mealworm, larva, softshell crabs, cicada
8. insect

Reviewing Key Concepts

9. d
10. a
11. a
12. d
13. b
14. c
15. b
16. a
17. The egg hatches into a larva. The larva eats, grows, and becomes a pupa. During the pupa stage, the animal may not move or eat. The final stage is the adult stage.
18. allows for attachment of muscles and provides animal with protection; can be heavy, impair movement, or cause periods of vulnerability when some animals move or grow and molt
19. A spider is an arachnid. Insects, arachnids, and crustaceans are examples of a larger group of invertebrates called arthropods.

(Answers to items that appear on p. 424)

Thinking Critically

20. Plantlike: A sponge is sessile, does not have a mouth, eyes, or legs, nor a symmetrical body plan. Animal: It consumes and digests food.
21. Sample answers: legs, wings, antennae for sensing, eyes for seeing
22. Food materials can be taken in at one tube end, be broken down and absorbed as they are moved through the tube, wastes excreted out the far end.

(Answers for items 20–22 appear on p. 423.)

Thinking Critically

23. Both start as larva. Jellyfish larvae develop into polyps, mosquito larvae into pupae. A jellyfish medusa is mobile; the polyp is not. Mosquito larvae swim; adults fly.

24. 86%

25. 14%

26. Shade the red slice to show what percentage of it are insects, crustaceans, and arachnids.

27. sea star: mouth in center, spreads its arms around prey, bringing it to the middle of its body; spider: mouth at front end, prey is brought in front

28. Insects, crustaceans, and arachnids all have exoskeletons, segmented bodies, paired legs, and distinct life stages. Crustaceans usually have 2 sets of antennae, insects 1, and arachnids none. Arachnids have 8 legs; insects 6.

29. A sponge's body has stiff spicules that provide support. The bivalve is surrounded by a shell; the body is inside. The insect has an exoskeleton that completely covers its body.

30. If insects became extinct, many plants and animals would die for lack of food. We would need a new way to pollinate plants. It would likely lead to extinction of most life.

the BIG idea

31. Jellyfish has a nerve net and tentacles that allow it to sense and respond. Some have tentacles and venom. It does not select what it stings. Its stinging cells are released as it brushes an object. The diver may be in danger of being stung.

32. Answers should relate body plan to environment and feeding method.

UNIT PROJECTS

Evaluate designs and drafts for students' models, visuals, or text. Encourage students to cite research sources.

R Unit Projects, pp. 5–10

Thinking Critically

20. **CLASSIFY** What characteristics does a sponge have that make it seem like a plant? What characteristic makes a sponge an animal?

21. **PROVIDE EXAMPLES** Arthropods are the most diverse and abundant group of animals on Earth. Give three examples of arthropod features that enable them to be active in their environment.

22. **INFER** Worms have a tube-shaped body with openings at either end. How does this body plan relate to the way a worm obtains its food and processes it?

23. **COMPARE** Jellyfish go through a life cycle that involves different stages of development. Insects also go through different stages of development in a process called metamorphosis. What are some similarities between metamorphosis in a mosquito, for example, and a jellyfish life cycle? Use the terms in the table below in your answer.

larva	polyp	medusa
pupa	adult	mobile
sessile		

Refer to the chart below as you answer the next three questions.

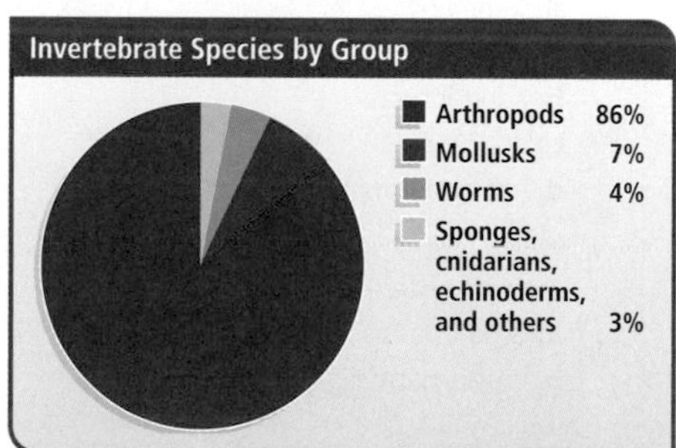

24. **APPLY** What percentage of invertebrate species are arthropods?

25. **CALCULATE** What is the combined percentage of all other invertebrate species, not including arthropods?

26. **APPLY** How could you modify this pie chart to show that insects, crustaceans, and arachnids are types of arthropods?

27. **APPLY** A sea star has a radial body plan. A spider has a bilateral body plan. How does the shape of these animal's bodies affect how they capture their food?

28. **COMPARE AND CONTRAST** How are the three main groups of arthropods similar? How are they different?

29. **SYNTHESIZE** Animal bodies need support as well as protection. What structures do the bodies of a sponge, a bivalve, and an insect have for protection and support? Use the terms in the table below in your answer.

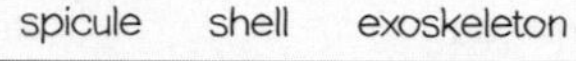

spicule	shell	exoskeleton

30. **PREDICT** Many people think of insects as pests, but some species of insects are important pollinators for many flowering plants. Also, many animals eat insects. What problems would humans face if Earth's insect species became extinct?

the BIG idea

31. **INFER** How does a cnidarian such as the jellyfish in the photograph on pages 392–393 respond to its environment? Is the diver in the photograph in danger? Explain your answer.

32. **COMPARE AND CONTRAST** Make a chart showing the key features of the body plans of three different invertebrate animal groups. For each group, identify one characteristic that is an adaptation.

UNIT PROJECTS

If you need to create graphs or other visuals for your project, be sure you have grid paper, poster board, markers, or other supplies.

424 Unit 3: **Diversity of Living Things**

MONITOR AND RETEACH

If students are having trouble applying the concepts in Chapter Review item 23, suggest that they review the illustration of Mosquito Metamorphosis on p. 419. Then have students create a flow chart to show the process.

Students may benefit from summarizing one or more sections of the chapter.

 Summarizing the Chapter, pp. 289–290

Standardized Test Practice

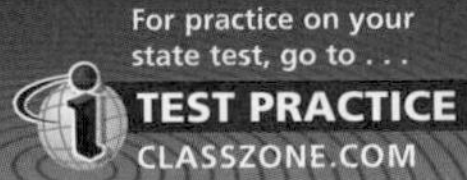

Analyzing Data

Reef-building corals are invertebrates that live in clear, warm ocean water. As a coral grows, it produces a hard external skeleton. If many generations of corals grow near each other over a long period of time, their accumulated skeletons form a structure called a reef. Many ocean life-forms live in and around coral reefs. This table shows the maximum growth rates of five species of reef-building corals.

Species	Rate of Growth (mm per year)	Number of Years to Grow a 1400-m Reef
A	143	9,790
B	99	14,100
C	120	11,700
D	100	14,000
E	226	6,190

Choose the letter of the best response

1. Which has the fastest rate of growth?
- **a.** Species C
- **b.** Species B
- **c.** Species D
- **d.** Species E

2. What is the growth rate for Species B ?
- **a.** 99 mm per year
- **b.** 120 mm per year
- **c.** 143 mm per year
- **d.** 14,100 mm per year

3. Which takes the shortest amount of time to grow to 1400 meters?
- **a.** Species B
- **b.** Species C
- **c.** Species D
- **d.** Species E

4. Which have about the same rate of growth?
- **a.** Species A and C
- **b.** Species B and D
- **c.** Species C and E
- **d.** Species D and E

5. How many years does it take Species A to grow into a 1400-m reef?
- **a.** 143
- **b.** 226
- **c.** 9790
- **d.** 14,000

6. Based on the information in the table, which statement is true?
- **a.** Coral species with the fastest growth rates take the greatest amount of time to grow.
- **b.** Coral species with the slowest growth rates take the least amount of time to grow.
- **c.** Coral species have different rates of growth that affect how long it takes them to grow.
- **d.** Coral species that grow more than 100 mm per year take the longest to grow.

Extended Response

7. Corals are cnidarians. They are sessile animals that live attached to one place. Other ocean-dwelling animals are mobile and can move about their environment. Crustaceans like the lobster are mobile, so are mollusks like the octopus. How does being sessile or mobile affect the feeding behaviors of an animal? Do you think the bodies and systems of sessile animals are going to be different from those of mobile animals? Use some of the terms in the word box in your answer.

digestive system	sessile	mobile
nervous system	filter	mouth
muscle tissue	food	sensory organs

Analyzing Data

1. d *2. a* *3. d* *4. b* *5. c* *6. c*

Extended Response

7. RUBRIC

4 points for a response that correctly answers the questions and includes at least five of the following terms:

- digestive system
- nervous system
- muscle tissue
- sessile
- filter
- food
- mobile
- mouth
- sensory organs

Sample: Because they are not mobile, sessile animals cannot chase prey. They need to have specialized mouths and sensory organs to allow them to filter food from the water or grab it as it passes by. Their nervous systems could be simpler because they do not need complex behaviors for finding and catching prey or escaping predators. Mobile animals need to have more developed muscle tissue for movement. The digestive systems of mobile and sessile animals differ because of their different eating habits.

3 points correctly answers the question and includes at least four of the terms shown

2 points correctly answers the question and includes at least three of the terms shown

1 point correctly answers the question and includes at least two terms shown

METACOGNITIVE ACTIVITY

Have students answer the following questions in their **Science Notebook:**

1. What seems most puzzling to you about invertebrate animals?
2. Did you learn anything about invertebrate animals that surprised you? Explain.
3. What strategies are you using to keep work on your Unit Project organized?

CHAPTER

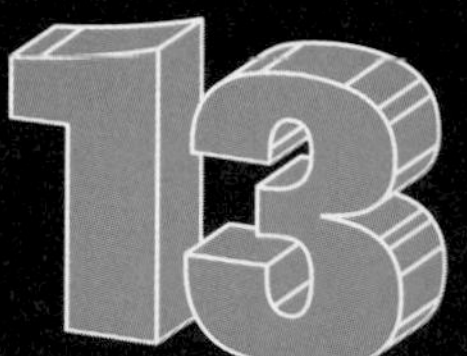

Vertebrate Animals

Life Science UNIFYING PRINCIPLES

PRINCIPLE 1
All living things share common characteristics.

PRINCIPLE 2
All living things share common needs.

PRINCIPLE 3
Living things meet their needs through interactions with the environment.

PRINCIPLE 4
The types and numbers of living things change over time.

Unit 3: Diversity of Living Things BIG IDEAS

CHAPTER 9
Single-Celled Organisms and Viruses
Bacteria and protists have the characteristics of living things, while viruses are not alive.

CHAPTER 10
Introduction to Multicellular Organisms
Multicellular organisms live in and get energy from a variety of environments.

CHAPTER 11
Plants
Plants are a diverse group of organisms that live in many land environments.

CHAPTER 12
Invertebrate Animals
Invertebrate animals have a variety of body plans and adaptations.

CHAPTER 13
Vertebrate Animals
Vertebrate animals live in most of Earth's environments.

CHAPTER 13 KEY CONCEPTS

SECTION 1

Vertebrates are animals with endoskeletons.

1. Vertebrate animals have backbones.
2. Most vertebrates are fish.
3. Fish can be classified in three groups.
4. Most young fish develop inside an egg.

SECTION 2

Amphibians and reptiles are adapted for life on land.

1. Vertebrates adapted to live on land.
2. Amphibians have moist skin and lay eggs without shells.
3. Reptiles have dry, scaly skin and lay eggs with shells.
4. The body temperatures of amphibians and reptiles change with the environment.

SECTION 3

Birds meet their needs on land, in water, and in the air.

1. Bird species live in most environments.
2. Birds can maintain body temperature.
3. Most birds can fly.
4. Birds lay eggs with hard shells.
5. Most birds take care of their offspring.

SECTION 4

Mammals live in many environments.

1. Mammals are a diverse group.
2. Mammals are endotherms.
3. Mammals have adapted to many environments.
4. Mammals have reproductive adaptations.

T The Big Idea Flow Chart is available on p. T33 in the **UNIT TRANSPARENCY BOOK.**

Previewing Content

SECTION

Vertebrates are animals with endoskeletons. pp. 429–435

1. Vertebrate animals have backbones.
About five percent of all animals are **vertebrates.** They are distinguished from other animals by an **endoskeleton.** Specialized bones called vertebrae form the backbone of these animals.

2. Most vertebrates are fish.

- Fish are the most diverse group of vertebrates. They are adapted to life in water.
- Fish breathe through gills. Most fish have a swim bladder that allows the fish to adjust the depth at which it floats. A lateral line is a sensory organ that allows the fish to sense objects and other organisms that are nearby.

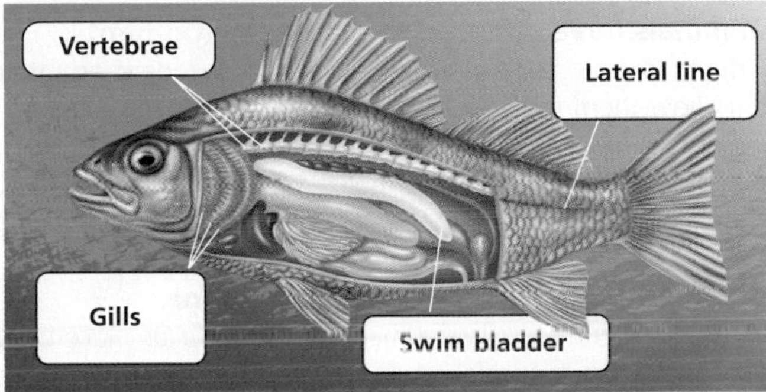

3. Fish can be classified in three groups.

- Jawless fish include lampreys and hagfish. This group is distinguished by tube-shaped bodies and jawless mouths.
- Cartilaginous fish include sharks, rays, and skates. They are distinguished by skeletons that are made of cartilage.
- Bony fish make up the largest group of fish. Most bony fish are covered with **scales.**

4. Most young fish develop inside an egg.
Female fish release eggs into the water where they are fertilized by sperm. Fish eggs get water and oxygen directly from the water. The eggs have a yolk that provides nutrients.

SECTION

Amphibians and reptiles are adapted for life on land. pp. 436–444

1. Vertebrates adapted to live on land.
The first vertebrates to live on land were **amphibians,** followed by **reptiles.** Some of the organisms in Earth's ancient seas developed limbs and lungs and made the move to land.

2. Amphibians have moist skin and lay eggs without shells.

- All amphibians share certain characteristics. Some of these are: they have two pairs of legs; they lay their eggs in water; and they obtain oxygen through their skin and as adults through lungs.
- The amphibian life cycle includes a larval stage. The flow chart shows the life cycle of a typical amphibian wood frog.

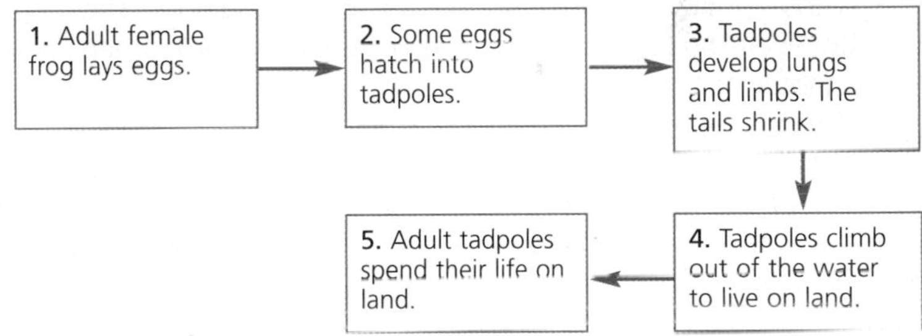

3. Reptiles have dry, scaly skin and lay eggs with shells.

- Most reptiles have two pairs of legs, breathe through lungs, and lay eggs with shells on land. Dry, scaly skin protects the reptile from predators and the environment.
- The reptilian egg is an adaptation that allows vertebrates to live completely on land. The egg has a shell to protect the embryo and a yolk to provide it with nutrients.

4. The body temperatures of amphibians and reptiles change with the environment.
Amphibians and reptiles are **ectotherms**—their body temperatures change with the temperature of the environment in which they live.

Common Misconceptions

MISCONCEPTION DATABASE
CLASSZONE.COM Background on student misconceptions

REPTILES AND AMPHIBIANS Many studies have shown that students at all levels correctly identify mammals and birds as vertebrates. Students often fail to classify amphibians and reptiles as vertebrates or even as animals. The misconceptions arise through students' preconceptions of external features of these organisms such as segmentation, body covering, and appendages. Some students classify vertebrates such as snakes and fish as invertebrates because they lack external segmentation and limbs. Certain invertebrates, such as grasshoppers, are misclassified as vertebrates because they have segmentation and appendages. Students also frequently classify amphibians as reptiles and vice versa.

 This misconception is addressed on pp. 437 and 441.

Previewing Content

SECTION

Birds meet their needs on land, in water, and in the air. pp. 445–453

1. **Bird species live in most environments.**
Bird species inhabit all environments. Birds are characterized by feathers and a beak, and a pair of legs and a pair of wings.

2. **Birds can maintain body temperature.**
Birds are **endotherms**—animals that maintain a constant body temperature. Down feathers insulate bird bodies against cold and contour feathers are water-resistant.

3. **Most birds can fly.**
   - A bird's body has external and internal structures that are adapted for flight.
   - Some bones of the endoskeleton are fused, or connected without joints. This makes the body strong and light. The bones of the legs and wings are hollow. Contour feathers are adapted for flight.
   - The respiratory system contains air sacs, which allow the bird to take in more oxygen. Instead of teeth, birds have a beak and an internal organ called a gizzard to grind food.
   - Many birds migrate to warmer climates in cold winter seasons.

Wings and feathers are structural adaptations for flight.

4. **Birds lay eggs with hard shells.**
Fertilization occurs internally. Hard shells allow the parent bird to **incubate** the eggs by sitting on top of them.

5. **Most birds take care of their offspring.**
In some bird species, both parents provide the young hatchlings with food, warmth, and protection.

SECTION

Mammals live in many environments. pp. 454–459

1. **Mammals are a diverse group.**
Mammals have characteristics that distinguish them, including:
   - All mammals have hair for some part of their lives.
   - Mammals have specialized teeth.
   - Mammals produce milk to feed their young.

2. **Mammals are endotherms.**
   - Hair allows mammals to keep warm or to protect them from extreme heat. Some hair is specialized, such as whiskers for sensing and quills for protection.
   - Mammals have a layer of body fat for maintaining body temperature. The body fat also stores energy for future use.

3. **Mammals have adapted to many environments.**
Some mammals, such as whales and dolphins, have adaptations that allow them to live in water. These adaptations include blowholes, flippers, tail flukes, and blubber. Other mammals, such as otters, monkeys, and moles, have adapted to completely different environments.

4. **Mammals have reproductive adaptations.**
   - In most mammals, development of young takes place using the **placenta,** a special organ that transports nutrients, water, and oxygen from the mother's blood to the growing embryo.
   - Some mammals, such as the duck-billed platypus, lay eggs. Marsupials are pouched mammals in which the young compete their **gestation** inside the mother's external pouch.

Mammary glands in females produce milk, allowing mammals to feed their young.

Common Misconceptions

MISCONCEPTION DATABASE
CLASSZONE.COM Background on student misconceptions

VERTEBRATES VS. MAMMALS Students assume that animal is synonymous with vertebrate, more specifically mammal. Mammals are often the prototypical animal followed by birds, reptiles, and fish in descending order of usage. Students also think that any animal in the water is a fish, including whales and other mammals.

 This misconception is addressed on p. 455.

Previewing Labs

Lab Generator CD-ROM
Edit these Pupil Edition labs and generate alternative labs.

EXPLORE the BIG idea

What Animals Live Near You? p. 427 Students consider the diversity of animals by listing organisms that live in their area and classifying them into groups.	**TIME** 10 minutes **MATERIALS** notebook, pencil
How Is a Bird Like a Frog? p. 427 Students compare vertebrate internal structures to learn about vertebrates.	**TIME** 10 minutes **MATERIALS** notebook, pencil
Internet Activity: Where in the World? p. 427 Students learn about U.S. wildlife by observing where different animals are found in North America.	**TIME** 20 minutes **MATERIALS** computer with Internet access

SECTION 1

EXPLORE Streamlined Shapes, p. 429 Students use a tub of water to explore how the shape of a fish helps it move.	**TIME** 10 minutes **MATERIALS** tub of water

SECTION 2

EXPLORE Moving on Land, p. 436 Students use a meter stick to calculate jumping distance.	**TIME** 15 minutes **MATERIALS** meter stick
INVESTIGATE Eggs, p. 442 Students examine a hard-boiled egg to determine the characteristics of eggs.	**TIME** 20 minutes **MATERIALS** hard-boiled egg, plastic knife

SECTION 3

EXPLORE Feathers, p. 445 Students explore bird feathers to learn how they differ.	**TIME** 15 minutes **MATERIALS** assorted bird feathers, including down and contour feathers
CHAPTER INVESTIGATION **Bird Beak Adaptations,** pp. 452–453 Students determine how different bird beaks are adapted for gathering and eating different types of food in order to learn how structure relates to function.	**TIME** 40 minutes **MATERIALS** tweezers, eyedropper, slotted spoon, pliers, test tubes in rack, water, dried pasta, millet seeds, jar of rubber bands, empty containers, stopwatch

SECTION 4

INVESTIGATE How Body Fat Insulates, p. 456 Students make a "blubber glove" to model how fat keeps a mammal warm.	**TIME** 15 minutes **MATERIALS** 3 zip-lip plastic bags, 1/2 gallon size; can of vegetable shortening; bowl of ice water

R **Additional INVESTIGATION,** Adaptations of a Frog's Tongue, A, B, & C, pp. 349–357; Teacher Instructions, pp. 360–361

Previewing Chapter Resources

CHAPTER 13
Vertebrate Animals

INTEGRATED TECHNOLOGY

CLASSZONE.COM
- eEdition Plus
- EasyPlanner Plus
- Misconception Database
- Content Review
- Test Practice
- Resource Centers
- Internet Activity: Where In the World?
- Math Tutorial

SCILINKS.ORG

CD-ROMS
- eEdition
- EasyPlanner Plus
- Power Presentations
- Content Review
- Lab Generator
- Test Generator

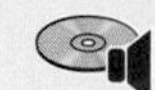
AUDIO CDS
- Audio Readings
- Audio Readings in Spanish

LABS AND ACTIVITIES

EXPLORE the Big Idea, p. 427
- What Animals Live Near You?
- How is a Frog Like a Bird?
- Internet Activity: Where in the World?

UNIT RESOURCE BOOK
Unit Projects, pp. 5–10

Lab Generator CD-ROM
Generate customized labs.

SECTION

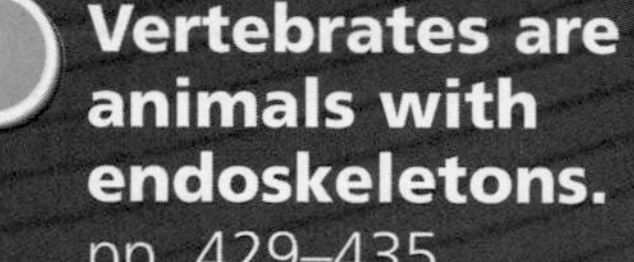

1 Vertebrates are animals with endoskeletons. pp. 429–435

Time: 2 periods (1 block)

 Lesson Plan, pp. 291–292

Integrated Technology

- **RESOURCE CENTER,** Fish
- **MATH TUTORIAL**

UNIT TRANSPARENCY BOOK
- Big Idea Flow Chart, p. T33
- Daily Vocabulary Scaffolding, p. T34
- Note-Taking Model, p. T35
- 3-Minute Warm-Up, p. T36

Labs and Activities

- EXPLORE Streamlined Shapes, p. 429
- Math in Science, p. 435

UNIT RESOURCE BOOK
- Math Support, p. 338
- Math Practice, p. 339

SECTION

2 Amphibians and reptiles are adapted for life on land. pp. 436–444

Time: 2 periods (1 block)

 Lesson Plan, pp. 301–302

Integrated Technology

- **RESOURCE CENTERS,** Amphibians, Reptiles

UNIT TRANSPARENCY BOOK
- Daily Vocabulary Scaffolding, p. T34
- 3-Minute Warm-Up, p. T36

Labs and Activities

- EXPLORE Moving on Land, p. 436
- INVESTIGATE Eggs, p. 442
- Connecting Sciences, p. 444

UNIT RESOURCE BOOK
- Datasheet, Eggs, p. 310
- Additional INVESTIGATION, Adaptations of a Frog's Tongue, Levels A, B, & C, pp. 349–357

SECTION

3 Birds meet their needs on land, in water, and in the air. pp. 445–453

Time: 3 periods (1.5 blocks)

Lesson Plan, pp. 312–313

Integrated Technology

UNIT TRANSPARENCY BOOK
- Daily Vocabulary Scaffolding, p. T34
- 3-Minute Warm-Up, p. T37
- "Adaptations for Flight" Visual, p. T38

Labs and Activities

- EXPLORE Feathers, p. 445
- CHAPTER INVESTIGATION, Bird Beak Adaptations, pp. 452–453

UNIT RESOURCE BOOK
CHAPTER INVESTIGATION Bird Beak Adaptations, Levels A, B, & C, pp. 340–348

4 Mammals live in many environments. pp. 454–459

Time: 3 periods (1.5 blocks)

Lesson Plan, pp. 322–333

Integrated Technology

RESOURCE CENTER, Mammals

UNIT TRANSPARENCY BOOK
- Big Idea Flow Chart, p. T33
- Daily Vocabulary Scaffolding, p. T34
- 3-Minute Warm-Up, p. T37
- Chapter Outline, pp. T39–T40

Labs and Activities

INVESTIGATE How Body Fat Insulates, p. 456

UNIT RESOURCE BOOK
Datasheet, How Body Fat Insulates, p. 331

 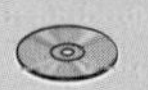    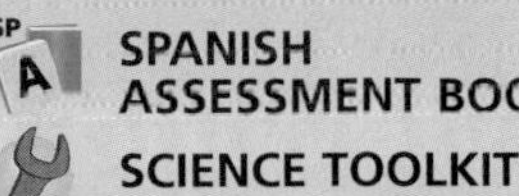

KEY TO ICONS CD/CD-ROM · Teacher Edition · UNIT TRANSPARENCY BOOK · SPANISH ASSESSMENT BOOK · INTERNET · Pupil Edition · UNIT RESOURCE BOOK · UNIT ASSESSMENT BOOK · SCIENCE TOOLKIT

READING AND REINFORCEMENT	ASSESSMENT	STANDARDS
 • Magnet Words, B24–25 • Choose Your Own Strategy, C35–44 • Daily Vocabulary Scaffolding, H1–8  **UNIT RESOURCE BOOK** • Vocabulary Practice, pp. 335–336 • Decoding Support, p. 337 • Summarizing the Chapter, pp. 358–359  **Audio Readings CD** Listen to Pupil Edition.  **Audio Readings in Spanish CD** Listen to Pupil Edition in Spanish.	 • Chapter Review, pp. 461–462 • Standardized Test Practice, p. 463  **UNIT ASSESSMENT BOOK** • Diagnostic Test, pp. 81–82 • Chapter Test, A, B, & C, pp. 87–98 • Alternative Assessment, pp. 99–100 • Unit Test, A, B, & C, pp. 101–112  • Spanish Chapter Test, pp. 57–60 • Spanish Unit Test, pp. 61–64 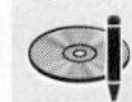 **Test Generator CD-ROM** Generate customized tests.  **Lab Generator CD-ROM** Rubrics for Labs	National Standards A.1–8, A.9.a–c, A.9.e–g, C.3.b, C.5.b, G.1.b See p. 426 for the standards.
 **UNIT RESOURCE BOOK** • Reading Study Guide, A & B, pp. 293–296 • Spanish Reading Study Guide, pp. 297–298 • Challenge and Extension, p. 299 • Reinforcing Key Concepts, p. 300	 Ongoing Assessment, pp. 429–434  Section 13.1 Review, p. 434  **UNIT ASSESSMENT BOOK** Section 13.1 Quiz, p. 83	National Standards A.2.8, A.9.c, C.3.b, C.5.b, G.1.b
 **UNIT RESOURCE BOOK** • Reading Study Guide, A & B, pp. 303–306 • Spanish Reading Study Guide, pp. 307–308 • Challenge and Extension, p. 309 • Reinforcing Key Concepts, p. 311	Ongoing Assessment, pp. 437–441, 443  Section 13.2 Review, p. 443  **UNIT ASSESSMENT BOOK** Section 13.2 Quiz, p. 84	National Standards A.2–7, A.9.a–b, A.9.c–f, C.3.b, C.5.b, G.1.b
 **UNIT RESOURCE BOOK** • Reading Study Guide, A & B, pp. 314–317 • Spanish Reading Study Guide, pp. 318–319 • Challenge and Extension, p. 320 • Reinforcing Key Concepts, p. 321	Ongoing Assessment, pp. 446, 448–450  Section 13.3 Review, p. 451  **UNIT ASSESSMENT BOOK** Section 13.3 Quiz, p. 85	National Standards A.1–7, A.9.a–b, A.9.e–g, C.3.b, C.5.b, G.1.b
 **UNIT RESOURCE BOOK** • Reading Study Guide, A & B, pp. 324–327 • Spanish Reading Study Guide, pp. 328–329 • Challenge and Extension, p. 330 • Reinforcing Key Concepts, p. 332 • Challenge Reading, pp. 333–334	 Ongoing Assessment, pp. 455–456, 458–459  Section 13.4 Review, p. 459  **UNIT ASSESSMENT BOOK** Section 13.4 Quiz, p. 86	National Standards A.2–7, A.9.a–b, A.9.e–f, C.3.b, C.5.b, G.1.b

Previewing Resources for Differentiated Instruction

CHAPTER INVESTIGATION

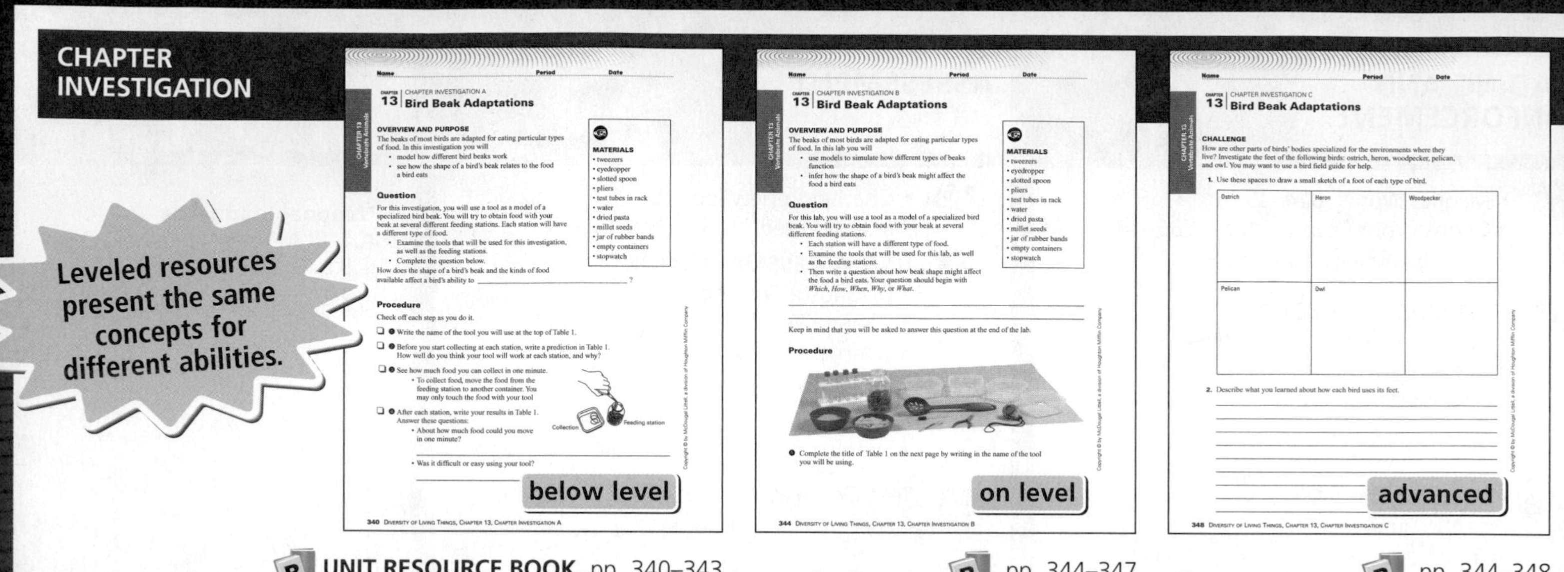

UNIT RESOURCE BOOK, pp. 340–343

pp. 344–347

pp. 344–348

READING STUDY GUIDE

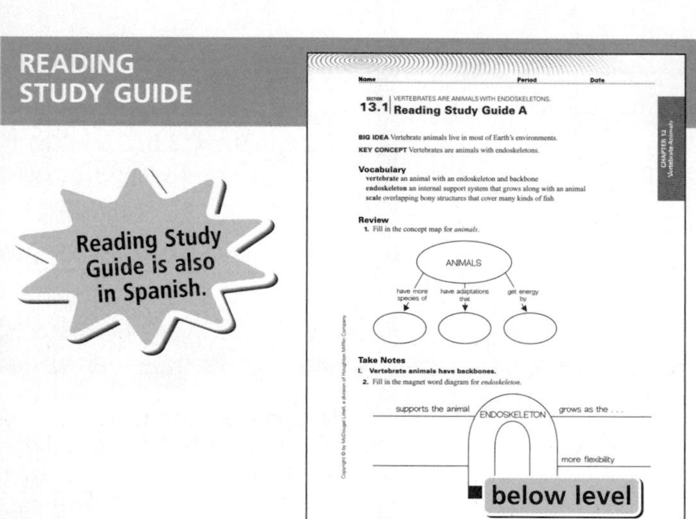

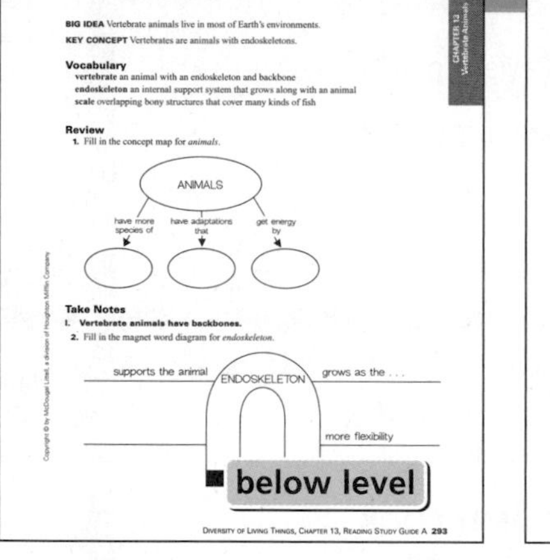

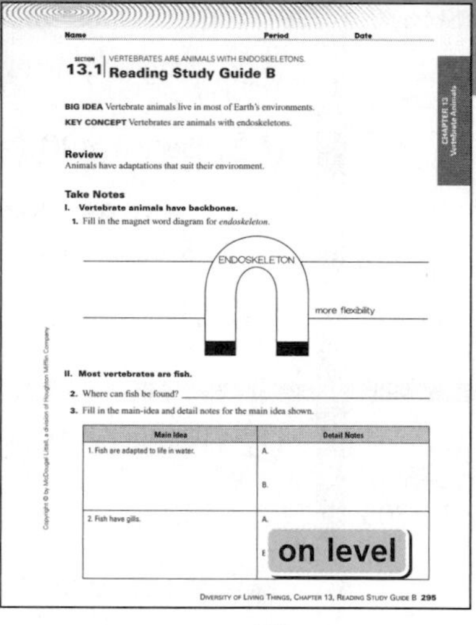

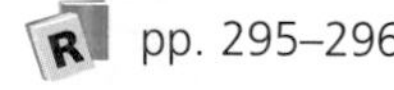

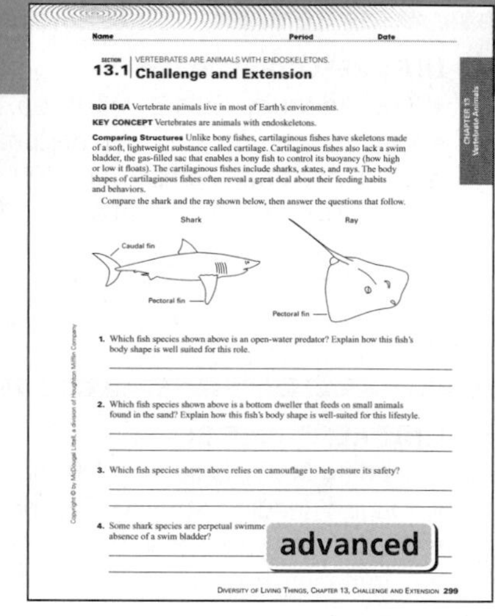

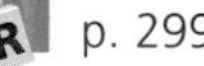

UNIT RESOURCE BOOK, pp. 293–294

pp. 295–296

p. 299

CHAPTER TEST

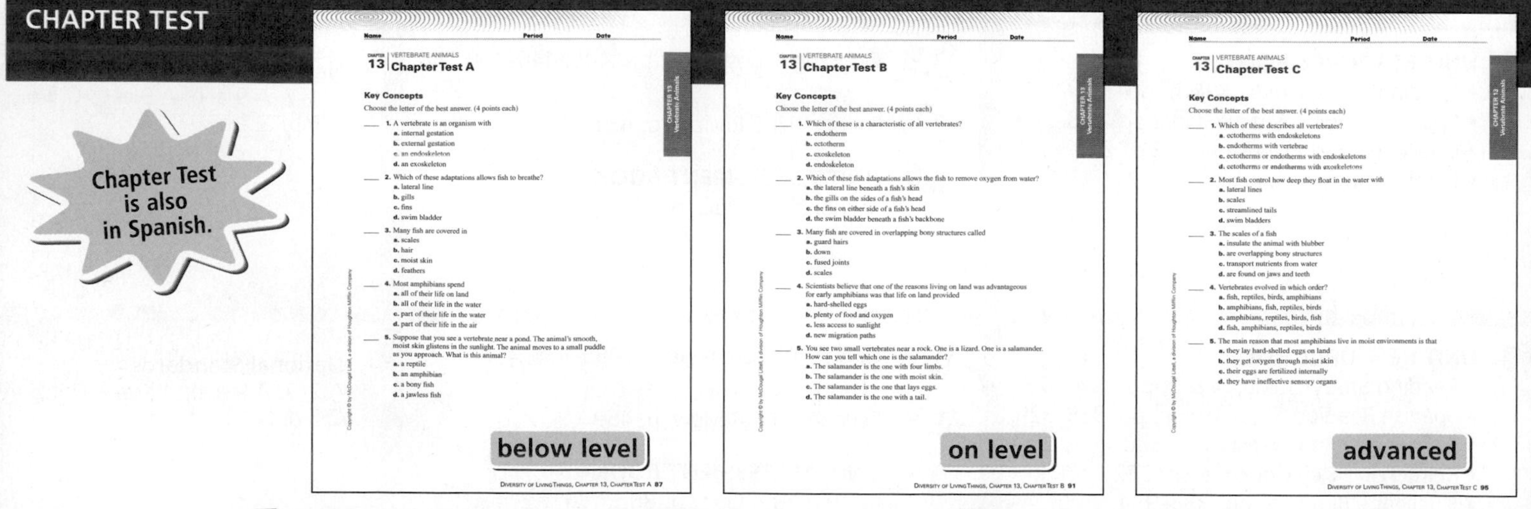

UNIT ASSESSMENT BOOK, pp. 87–90

pp. 91–94

pp. 95–98

TECHNOLOGY

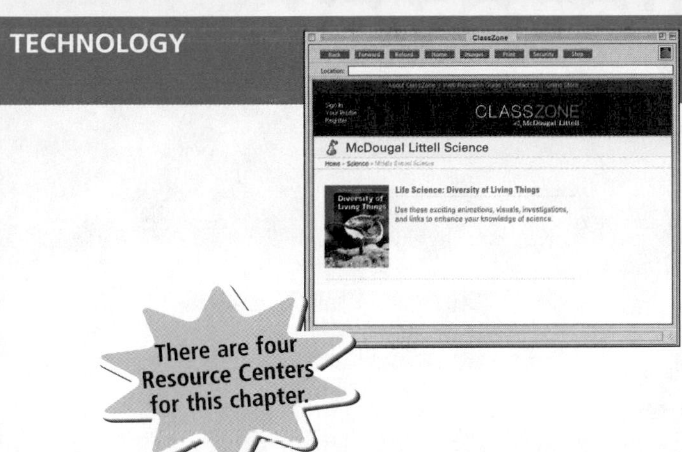

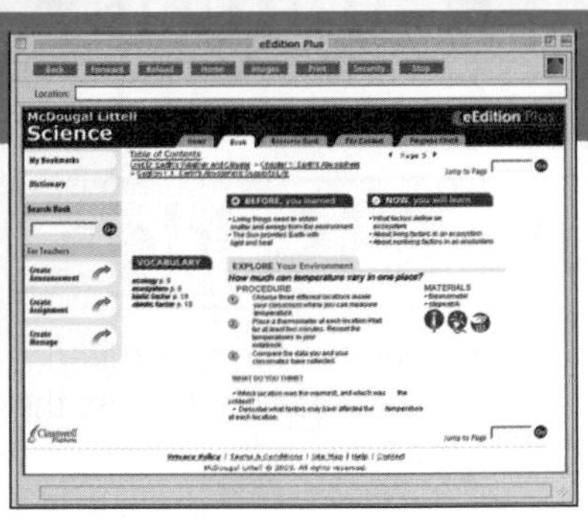

CLASSZONE.COM

CD/CD-ROMS

CLASSZONE.COM

VISUAL CONTENT

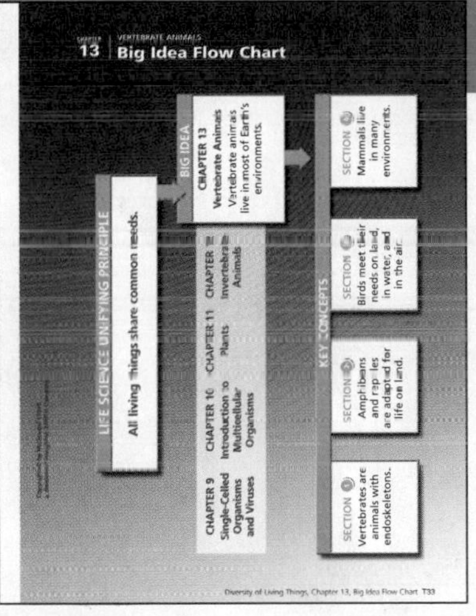

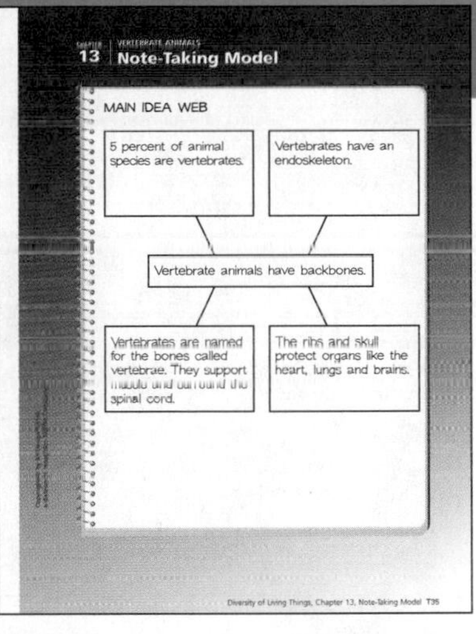

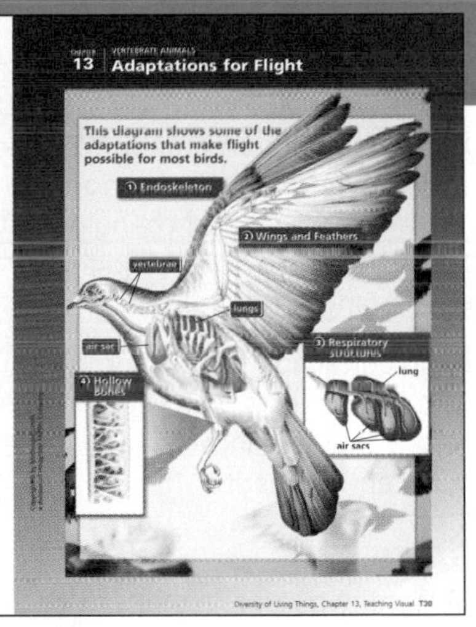

T UNIT TRANSPARENCY BOOK, p. T33

p. T35

p. T38

MORE SUPPORT

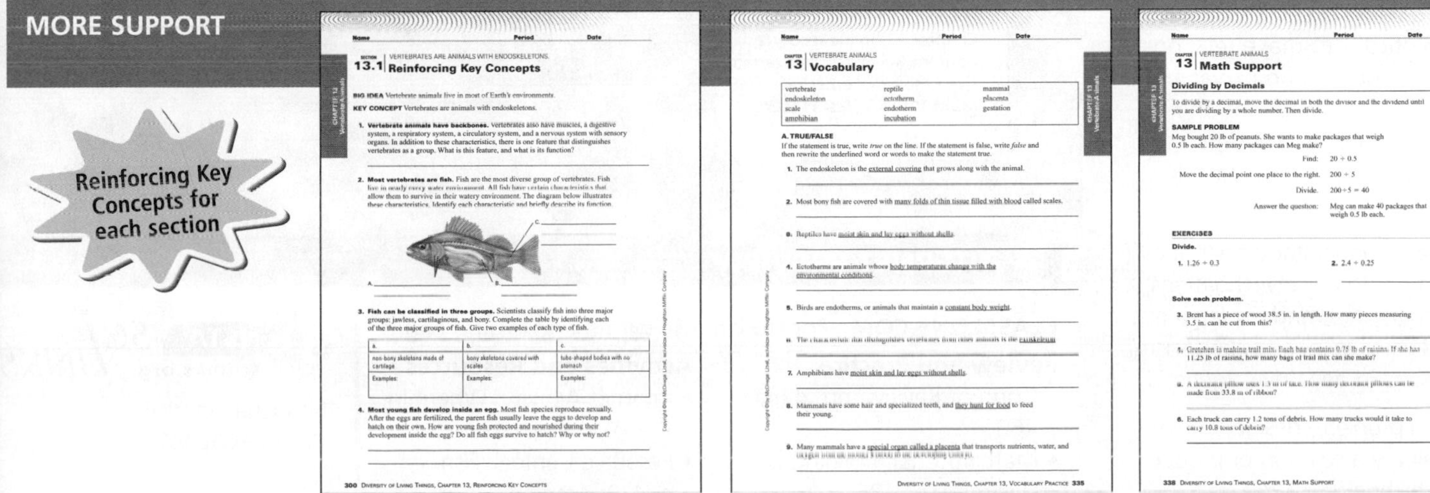

R UNIT RESOURCE BOOK, p. 300

R pp. 335–336

R p. 338

INTRODUCE

the BIG idea

Have students look at the photograph of penguins and a sea lion. Discuss the question in the box:

- Ask: In what type of environment do the penguin and the seal live?
- Ask: How are their bodies adapted to the cold and to the water?
- Brainstorm a list of environments in which vertebrate animals live.

National Science Education Standards

Content

C.3.b Regulation of an organism's internal environment involves sensing the internal environment and changing physiological activities to keep conditions within the range required to survive.

C.5.b Biological adaptations include changes in structures, behaviors, or physiology that enhance survival in a particular environment.

Process

A.1–8 Identify questions that can be answered by scientific investigations; design and conduct an investigation; use tools to gather and interpret data; use evidence to describe, predict, explain, model; think critically to make relationships between evidence and explanation; recognize different explanations and predictions; communicate scientific procedures and explanations; use mathematics.

A.9.a–c, A.9.e–g Understand scientific inquiry by using different investigations, methods, mathematics, and explanations based on logic, evidence, and skepticism. Data often results in new investigations.

E.1–5 Identify a problem; design, implement, and evaluate a solution or product; communicate technological design.

G.1.b Science requires different abilities.

CHAPTER

Vertebrate Animals

the BIG idea

Vertebrate animals live in most of Earth's environments.

Key Concepts

SECTION 1 **Vertebrates are animals with endoskeletons.** Learn how most of the vertebrates on Earth are fish.

SECTION 2 **Amphibians and reptiles are adapted for life on land.** Learn how most amphibians hatch in water and most reptiles hatch on land.

SECTION 3 **Birds meet their needs on land, in water, and in the air.** Learn how adaptations for flight affect how birds meet their needs.

SECTION 4 **Mammals live in many environments.** Learn about mammals' many adaptations.

Internet Preview

CLASSZONE.COM

Chapter 13 online resources: Content Review, Visualization, five Resource Centers, Math Tutorial, Test Practice.

What do these penguins have in common with this seal?

INTERNET PREVIEW

CLASSZONE.COM For student use with the following pages:

Review and Practice
- Content Review, pp. 428, 460
- Math Tutorial: Dividing by Decimals, p. 435
- Test Practice, p. 463

Activities and Resources
- Internet Activity: Where in the World?, p. 427
- Resource Centers: Fish, p. 432; Amphibians, p. 439; Reptiles, p. 441; Mammals, p. 455

Bird Characteristics
Code: MDL043

TEACHING WITH TECHNOLOGY

Electronic Encyclopedias Students can use electronic encyclopedias to investigate the body structures of vertebrate groups, beginning with the study of fish on p. 430. Have students print pictures and create a display.

Computer Dissections Students can use computer dissections to investigate the internal structures of vertebrates beginning with the internal structure of fish on p. 431.

EXPLORE the BIG idea

These inquiry-based activities are appropriate for use at home or as a supplement to classroom instruction.

What Animals Live Near You?

PURPOSE To list local animals and classify them into groups.

TIPS *10 min.* Have students work in groups. Compile their groupings of animals on a chart on the board.

Answers depend on the area in which you live and organisms that students listed. The most and widest variety of animals should be where there are the most resources.

REVISIT after p. 459.

How Is a Bird Like a Frog?

PURPOSE To compare vertebrate internal structures.

TIP *10 min.* Guide students to choose animals that belong in different classes.

Check student diagrams for realism. Help students research information of which they are unsure.

REVISIT after p. 430.

Internet Activity: Where in the World?

PURPOSE To observe where different animals are found in North America.

TIP *20 min.* Challenge students to learn to recognize vertebrates, especially local species.

Sample answers: North Pole: ways of keeping warm and getting water in freezing temperatures; Desert: ways of staying cool and getting water in an environment that is hot and dry during daylight hours.

REVISIT after p. 457.

PREPARE

CONCEPT REVIEW

Activate Prior Knowledge

- Ask students to name some of the common characteristics that all living organisms share. *organization, growth, reproduction, and response*
- Discuss how organisms meet their needs by obtaining food, water, and oxygen.
- Have students brainstorm a list of body structures that characterize vertebrate animals. *digestive systems, skeletal systems, circulatory systems, reproductive systems*

TAKING NOTES

Choose Your Own Strategy

Students can rely on the blue and red headings in the text as a basis for main ideas. Specific information from text and visuals can serve as details in the Main Idea Web, Main Idea and Details Notes, and the Mind Map. Encourage students to compare their choices in strategies.

Vocabulary Strategy

Students can include as many details as they wish in a magnet diagram. Words and phrases, descriptions, and definitions that are associated with the topic are useful study devices.

Vocabulary and Note-Taking Resources

- Vocabulary Practice, pp. 335–336
- Decoding Support, p. 337

- Daily Vocabulary Scaffolding, p. T34
- Note-Taking Model, p. T35

- Magnet Words, B24–25
- Choose Your Own Strategy, C35–44
- Daily Vocabulary Scaffolding, H1–8

CHAPTER 13

Getting Ready to Learn

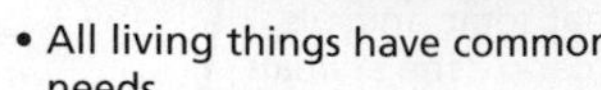

CONCEPTS REVIEW

- All living things have common needs.
- Plants and some invertebrates have adaptations for life on land.
- Most multicellular organisms can reproduce sexually.

VOCABULARY REVIEW

migration p. 336
embryo p. 370
gill p. 409
lung p. 409
exoskeleton p. 415

CONTENT REVIEW
CLASSZONE.COM
Review concepts and vocabulary.

TAKING NOTES

CHOOSE YOUR OWN STRATEGY

Take notes using one or more of the strategies from earlier chapters – **main idea webs, main idea and details, mind maps,** or **combination notes.** You can also use other note-taking strategies that you may already know.

VOCABULARY STRATEGY

Think about a vocabulary term as a **magnet word** diagram. Write other terms and ideas related to that term around it.

See the Note-Taking Handbook on pages R45–R51.

SCIENCE NOTEBOOK

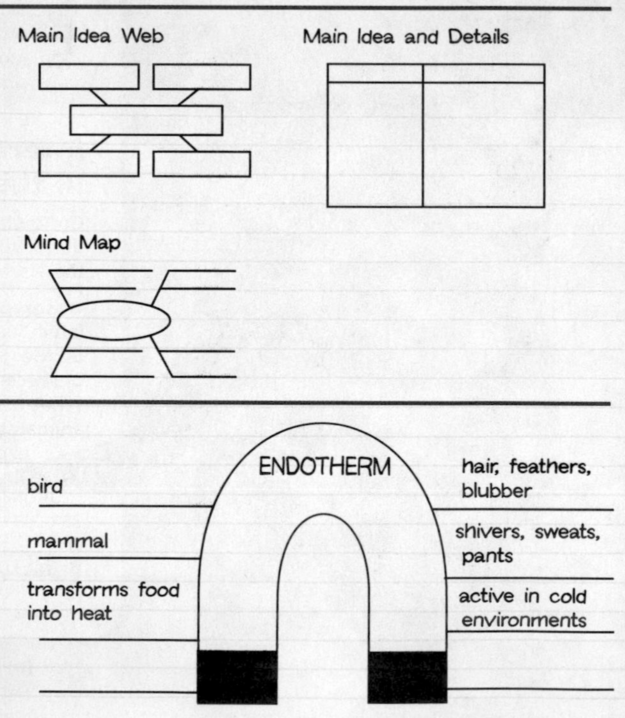

Main Idea Web

Main Idea and Details

Mind Map

ENDOTHERM
bird
mammal
transforms food into heat
hair, feathers, blubber
shivers, sweats, pants
active in cold environments

CHECK READINESS

Administer the Diagnostic Test to determine students' readiness for new science content and their mastery of requisite math skills.

 Diagnostic Test, pp. 81–82

Technology Resources

Students needing content and math skills should visit **ClassZone.com**.

- **CONTENT REVIEW**
- **MATH TUTORIAL**

 **CONTENT REVIEW CD-ROM**

KEY CONCEPT

Vertebrates are animals with endoskeletons.

BEFORE, you learned
- Most animals are invertebrates
- Animals have adaptations that suit their environment
- Animals get energy by consuming food

NOW, you will learn
- About the skeletons of vertebrate animals
- About the characteristics of fish
- About three groups of fish

VOCABULARY

vertebrate p. 429
endoskeleton p. 429
scale p. 433

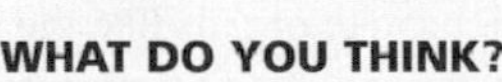

EXPLORE Streamlined Shapes

How does a fish's shape help it move?

PROCEDURE

1. Place your hand straight up and down in a tub of water. Keep your fingers together and your palm flat.
2. Move your hand from one side of the tub to the other, using your palm to push the water.
3. Move your hand across the tub again, this time using the edge of your hand as if you were cutting the water.

MATERIALS
tub of water

WHAT DO YOU THINK?
- In which position was the shape of your hand most like the shape of a fish's body?
- How might the shape of a fish's body affect its ability to move through water?

Vertebrate animals have backbones.

If you asked someone to name an animal, he or she would probably name a vertebrate. Fish, frogs, snakes, birds, dogs, and humans are all **vertebrates,** or animals with backbones. Even though only about 5 percent of animal species are vertebrates, they are among the most familiar and thoroughly studied organisms on Earth.

Vertebrate animals have muscles, a digestive system, a respiratory system, a circulatory system, and a nervous system with sensory organs. The characteristic that distinguishes vertebrates from other animals is the **endoskeleton,** an internal support system that grows along with the animal. Endoskeletons allow more flexibility and ways of moving than exoskeletons do.

VOCABULARY
Add magnet word diagrams for *vertebrate* and *endoskeleton* to your notebook.

RESOURCES FOR DIFFERENTIATED INSTRUCTION

Below Level

UNIT RESOURCE BOOK
- Reading Study Guide A, pp. 293–294
- Decoding Support, p. 337

AUDIO CDS

Advanced

UNIT RESOURCE BOOK
- Challenge and Extension, p. 299

English Learners

UNIT RESOURCE BOOK
Spanish Reading Study Guide, pp. 297–298

- Audio Readings in Spanish
- Audio Readings (English)

13.1 FOCUS

Set Learning Goals

Students will
- Explain that vertebrate animals have internal skeletons with backbones.
- Discuss how fish are adapted for life in water.
- Characterize the three main groups of fish.
- Explore how the shape of a fish helps it move.

3-Minute Warm-Up

Display Transparency 36 or copy this exercise on the board:

Decide which of these statements are true. If not true, correct them.

1. All invertebrate animals have external skeletons. *Arthropods have external skeletons.*
2. Sponges are the simplest invertebrates. *true*
3. Cephalopods are mollusks with two shells that are held together at a hinge. *Bivalves are mollusks that have two shells.*

3-Minute Warm-Up, p. T36

13.1 MOTIVATE

EXPLORE Streamlined Shapes

PURPOSE To explore how the shape of a fish helps it move

TIPS *10 min.* Note that students' hands appear larger when submerged in water. Students will be more comfortable if the water is warm.

WHAT DO YOU THINK? *The second hand position is most like the shape of a fish's body. A more streamlined body will move through water more efficiently.*

Ongoing Assessment

Explain that vertebrate animals have internal skeletons with backbones.

Ask: What is an endoskeleton? *an internal support system found in vertebrates that grows as the animal grows*

13.1 INSTRUCT

Teach from Visuals

To help students interpret the diagram of the cheetah's skeleton, ask:

- What structures aid in movement? *muscles attached to bones*
- What is the function of the cheetah's ribs? *protects organs like heart and lungs*

Teaching with Technology

If students have access to electronic encyclopedias, have them find and print pictures of the various vertebrate groups as they read through the chapter.

EXPLORE the BIG idea

Revisit "How Is a Bird Like a Frog?" on p. 427. Have students take another look at the sketches they made and be sure that backbones are included.

Ongoing Assessment

READING VISUALS *Answer: The cheetah's endoskeleton creates the shape of the cheetah.*

CHECK YOUR READING *Answer: The endoskeleton supports muscles and surrounds and protects the spinal cord.*

Vertebrate Skeleton and Muscles

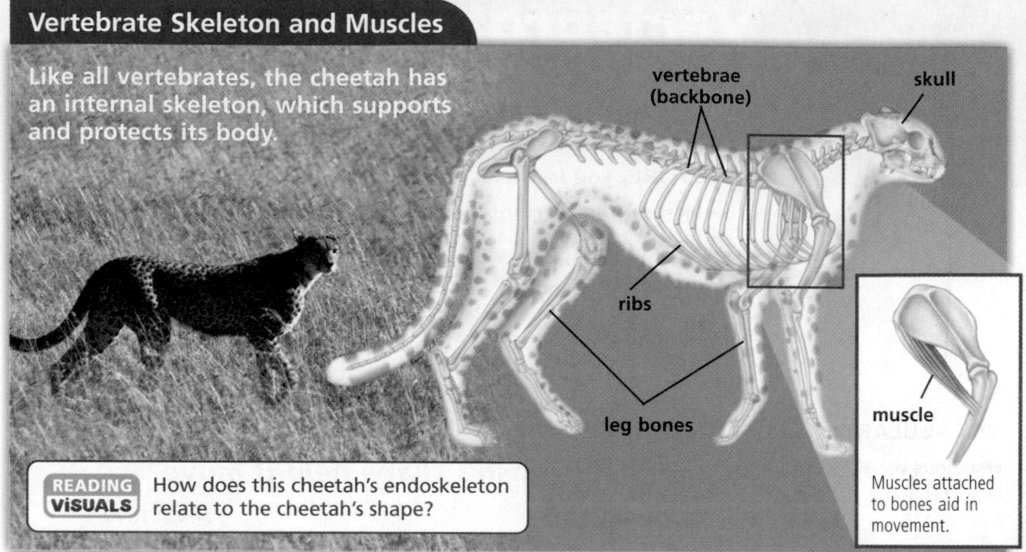

Vertebrates are named for specialized bones called vertebrae. These bones are located in the middle of each vertebrate animal's central body segment. Together, the vertebrae are sometimes called a backbone. The vertebrae support muscles and surround the spinal cord, which connects the animal's brain to its nerves. Other bones, such as the ribs and skull, protect organs like the heart, lungs, and brain.

CHECK YOUR READING What is one function of the endoskeleton for vertebrate animals?

NOTETAKING STRATEGY
Choose a strategy from an earlier chapter to take notes on the idea that most vertebrates are fish. Be sure to include information on adaptations to water.

Most vertebrates are fish.

Fish are the most diverse group of vertebrate animals. There are more than 20,000 species of fish, ranging in size from tiny minnows to huge whale sharks. Fish live in nearly every aquatic environment, from freshwater lakes to the bottom of the sea. Some fish even are able to survive below the ice in the Antarctic!

Fish are adapted for life in water. Like all living things, fish need to get materials from their environment. For example, fish must be able to get oxygen from water. Fish must also be able to move through water in order to find food. Fish that live in water where sunlight does not penetrate need special organs to help them find food.

Most fish move by using muscles and fins to push their streamlined bodies through water. These muscles allow fish to move more

DIFFERENTIATE INSTRUCTION

More Reading Support

A Together, what are vertebrae called? *a backbone*

B Which organ does the skull protect? *brain*

English Learners When introducing new vocabulary, encourage students to use all the information that a dictionary offers. For example, when learning *endoskeleton* and *exoskeleton*, have students look up the meanings of the prefixes *endo-* and *exo-*. Have students look up the term *vertebrate* in the dictionary. Ask them what the Latin meaning of the term—"having joints"—has to do with the definition.

quickly than most other vertebrates. Most fish also have an organ called a swim bladder, which allows them to control the depth at which they float.

Fish have sensory organs for taste, odor, and sound. Most fish species have eyes that allow them to see well underwater. Most fish also have a sensory system unlike that of other vertebrates. This system includes an organ called a lateral line, which allows fish to sense vibrations from objects nearby without touching or seeing them.

C Fish, like some invertebrates, remove oxygen from water with specialized respiratory organs called gills. You can locate most fishes' gills by looking for the openings, called gill slits, on the sides of their head. You can see what gills look like in the diagram of a fish below.

VISUALIZATION CLASSZONE.COM
Explore how fish breathe.

CHECK YOUR READING How are gills similar to lungs?

Fish gills are made up of many folds of tissue and are filled with blood. When a fish swims, it takes water in through its mouth and then pushes the water back over its gills. In the gills, oxygen dissolved in the water moves into the fish's blood. Carbon dioxide, a waste product of respiration, moves from the blood into the water. Then the water is forced out of the fish's body through its gill slits. The oxygen is transported to the fish's cells. It is a necessary material for releasing energy.

Inside a Fish

Fish are vertebrates that live in water.

Vertebrae make up part of the endoskeleton of this fish.

Lateral line is an organ in the sensory system that allows fish to sense objects and organisms that are nearby.

Gills remove oxygen from water and exchange it for carbon dioxide in the fish's blood.

Swim bladder allows the fish to adjust how high or low it floats.

READING VISUALS What is the function of the vertebrae on the fish's backbone?

Teaching with Technology

If computers are available, have students use them to perform computer dissections to study the internal organs of vertebrates.

Teacher Demo

Model the swim bladder of a fish with a partially inflated balloon and a weight in a tank of water. The weight should be attached to the balloon with string and the combination should be suspended motionless in the water.

Teach from Visuals

To help students interpret the diagram of the internal structure of the fish, ask:

- What structures enable the fish to breathe? *gills*
- How might the lateral line help protect the fish from possible predators? *The lateral line allows the fish to sense other fish that might be nearby.*

Ongoing Assessment

Explain how fish are adapted for life in water.

Ask: What are three adaptations that enable fish to live in water? Explain each one. *Gills enable fish to obtain oxygen from water. Swim bladders allow fish to control the depth at which they swim, and lateral lines enables fish to sense nearby organisms and objects.*

CHECK YOUR READING *Answer: Both gills and lungs transfer oxygen into blood.*

READING VISUALS *Answer: make up backbone*

DIFFERENTIATE INSTRUCTION

More Reading Support

C Where does the exchange of oxygen and carbon dioxide in fish take place? *gills*

Below Level Have students write mystery vertebrate riddles that mirror the following example: I have a backbone, moist skin, and I lay eggs. What am I? Answer: amphibian. Have students write two mystery questions for each type of vertebrate.

Teach from Visuals

To help students interpret the photographs of the fish, ask:

- Which fish is the least complex? Explain. *The jawless fish is the least complex because it lacks a jawbone.*
- What is the difference between cartilaginous fish and bony fish? *Cartilaginous fish have skeletons made of cartilage. Bony fish have skeletons made of bone and are covered with scales.*

Develop Critical Thinking

COMPARE AND CONTRAST Point out that vertebrate bones are made of bone tissue, a substance that is not the same as a mollusk's shell or an arthropod's exoskeleton, even though these structures have similar functions in supporting the animals' bodies. Have students complete this chart to help them compare and contrast the three kinds of fish.

Kind	Traits	Examples
Jawless	*tubelike shape, digestive system with no stomach*	*lampreys, hagfish*
Cartilaginous	*skeletons made of cartilage, feed on small animals*	*sharks, rays, skates*
Bony	*skeletons made of hard bone, covered with scales*	*tuna, flounder, goldfish, eels*

Ongoing Assessment

Answer: The fish all have mouths at the front (or head) end of their bodies. They have eyes and gill slits.

CHECK YOUR READING *Answer: They have tube-shaped bodies.*

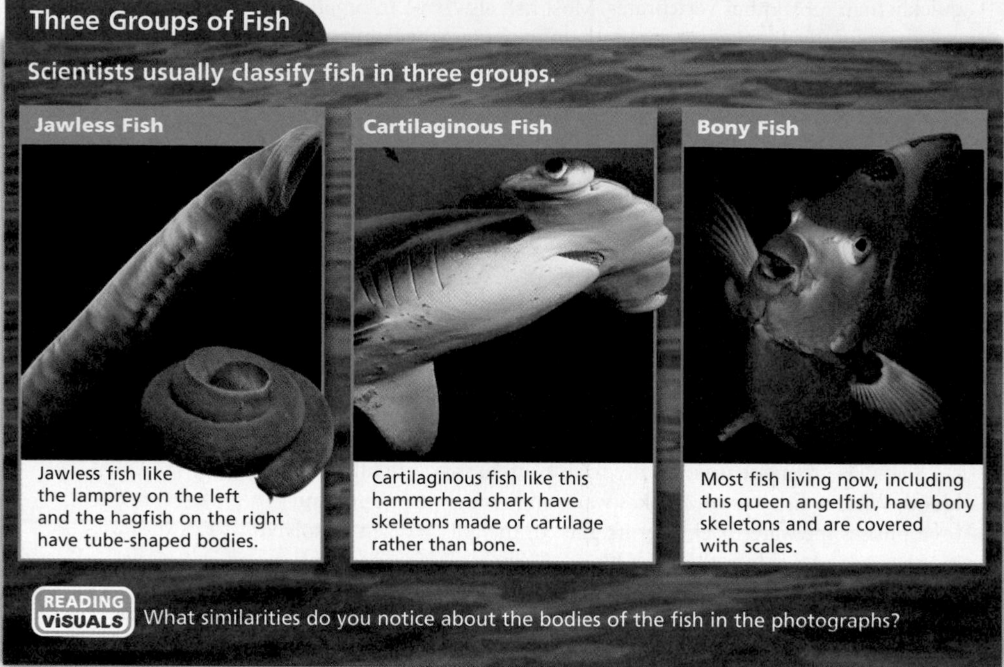

Fish can be classified in three groups.

Scientists classify fish into three major groups: jawless fish, cartilaginous fish, and bony fish. Each group is characterized by body features. As you read on and learn about each group of fish, look at the photographs above.

Jawless Fish

D

Scientists think that fish in this group, which includes lampreys and hagfish, are the living animals most similar to the first fish that lived on Earth. Jawless fish have simpler bodies than the other fish. They have a slender tubelike shape and a digestive system without a stomach.

As the name of the group implies, these fish do not have jaw bones. Although they do have teeth, they cannot chew. Most jawless fish eat by biting into another animal's body and then sucking out flesh and fluids. E

What is a characteristic of jawless fish?

RESOURCE CENTER CLASSZONE.COM
Learn more about fish.

DIFFERENTIATE INSTRUCTION

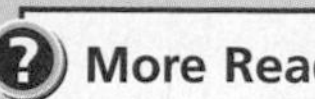

More Reading Support

D Which group of fish includes lampreys and hagfish? *jawless fish*

E How do jawless fish eat? *They bite into animals' bodies and suck out flesh and fluids.*

Advanced Offer the following challenge: Choose three animals: a fish, a mammal, and a reptile. Research what their skeletons look like. Draw a picture of each skeleton making sure to highlight the backbone. Explain how each species' structure affects how it moves. Include an explanation of how each structure is different from the other structures.

Challenge and Extension, p. 299

Cartilaginous Fish

This group includes sharks, rays, and skates. Their skeletons are not made of hard bone, but of a flexible tissue called cartilage (KAHR-tuhl-ihj). Some species of sharks are dangerous to humans, but most cartilaginous fish feed primarily on small animals such as mollusks and crustaceans. Whale sharks and basking sharks, which are the largest fish on Earth, feed by filtering small organisms from the water as they swim.

Rays are flat-bodied cartilaginous fish that live most of their lives on the ocean floor. Their mouths are on the underside of their bodies. Most rays eat by pulling small animals out of the sand. A ray's flat body has fins that extend on either side of its vertebrae like wings. When rays swim, these fins wave so it looks as if the fish is flying through the water.

CHECK YOUR READING Describe three ways cartilaginous fish species obtain food.

Bony Fish

Most fish species, including tuna, flounder, goldfish, and eels, are classified in this large, diverse group. Of the nearly 20,000 fish species, about 96 percent are bony fish. Bony fish have skeletons made of hard bone, much like the skeleton in your body. Most bony fish are covered with overlapping bony structures called **scales.** They have jaws and teeth and several pairs of fins.

The range of body shapes and behavior in bony fish shows how living things are adapted to their environments. Think of the bright colors and patterns of tropical fish in an aquarium. These eye-catching features are probably adaptations for survival in the fishes' natural environment. In a coral reef, for example, bright stripes and spots might provide camouflage or might advertise the fish's presence to other animals, including potential mates.

Most young fish develop inside an egg.

Most fish species reproduce sexually. The female produces eggs, and the male produces sperm. In many fish species, individual animals select a mate. For example, a female fish might release eggs into the water only when a certain male can fertilize them. After the eggs are fertilized, the parent fish usually leave the eggs to develop and hatch on their own. Most fish reproduce this way, but there are many exceptions.

REMINDER

In sexual reproduction the genetic material from two parents is combined in their offspring.

Integrate the Sciences

The first fish, which were the first vertebrates, appeared during the Cambrian Period about 510 million years ago. They were jawless fish that lived mainly in fresh water. Lampreys and hagfish are believed to have evolved from this early group of jawless fish. The first fish with jaws appeared in the late Silurian Period, about 410 million years ago. Modern bony fish did not appear until the late Silurian or early Devonian Period, about 395 million years ago.

Develop Critical Thinking

COMPARE AND CONTRAST Ask students why they think that marine animals such as starfish, crayfish, and sea anemones are not classified as fish. *Because fish are classified as vertebrates (animals with backbones) and these animals lack backbones.*

Ongoing Assessment

Characterize the three main groups of fish.

Ask: What differentiates, or defines, the three main types of fish? *jawless—have tube-shaped bodies; cartilaginous—have skeletons made of cartilage; bony—have bony skeletons and scales*

CHECK YOUR READING *Answer: biting with their jaws, filtering from water, pulling from sand*

DIFFERENTIATE INSTRUCTION

More Reading Support

F Which group of fish includes sharks, rays, and skates? *cartilaginous fish*

G What term describes the overlapping structures that cover the bodies of bony fish? *scales*

Below Level There is great diversity in how fish species reproduce, tend their eggs, and care for their young. There are fish that bury their eggs, fish that make nests, and a group called *mouthbrooders* that incubate eggs and protect offspring by keeping them in their mouths. Invite interested students to find out more about how fish reproduce and tend to their eggs. Have them create a bulletin board display of their findings.

Ongoing Assessment

CHECK YOUR READING *Answer: Fish eggs have a soft case. Water and other materials pass into the egg directly from the environment.*

Reinforce the BIG idea

Have students relate the section to the Big Idea.

 Reinforcing Key Concepts, p. 300

13.1 ASSESS & RETEACH

Assess

 Section 13.1 Quiz, p. 83

Reteach

Have students create trading cards for the different types of fish by observable traits. On one side they can draw a picture of the skeleton of the fish and on the other side they can write facts about the species including adaptations to the environment. They should divide the deck of trading cards into three "suits" for the three major types of fish. As a starting point, they might trace or sketch the fish pictured on p. 431, and list the adaptations explained in the captions of the photographs.

Technology Resources

Have students visit **ClassZone.com** for reteaching of Key Concepts.

 CONTENT REVIEW

 CONTENT REVIEW CD-ROM

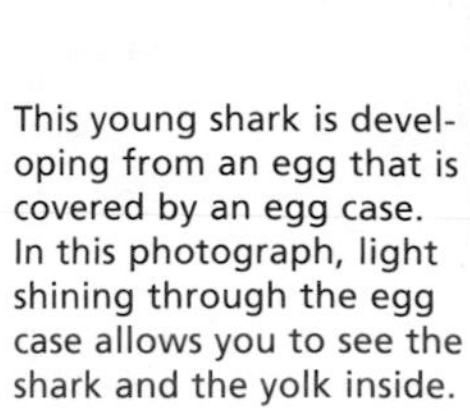

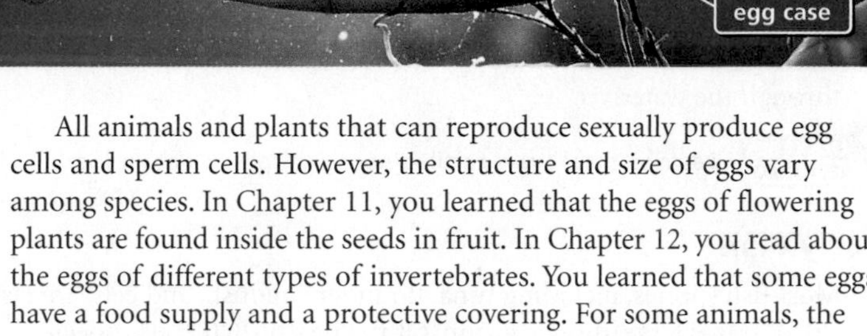

This young shark is developing from an egg that is covered by an egg case. In this photograph, light shining through the egg case allows you to see the shark and the yolk inside.

All animals and plants that can reproduce sexually produce egg cells and sperm cells. However, the structure and size of eggs vary among species. In Chapter 11, you learned that the eggs of flowering plants are found inside the seeds in fruit. In Chapter 12, you read about the eggs of different types of invertebrates. You learned that some eggs have a food supply and a protective covering. For some animals, the food supply is called yolk, and the covering is called an egg case.

REMINDER: An embryo is the immature form of an organism that has the potential to grow to maturity.

Most fish eggs are surrounded by a soft egg case that water can pass through. Since fish lay eggs in the water, this means that a fish embryo inside an egg gets the water and oxygen it needs directly from its surroundings. The egg's yolk provides the developing fish with food. Such eggs can develop on their own, without needing care from adults. However, many animals eat fish eggs. Fish often lay and fertilize many eggs, but few of them survive to maturity.

 **How are fish eggs different from invertebrate eggs?**

13.1 Review

KEY CONCEPTS

1. Why are fish classified as vertebrate animals?
2. What are three adaptations that suit fish for life in water?
3. Name a feature for fish from each of these groups: jawless, cartilaginous, and bony.

CRITICAL THINKING

4. **Apply** If you wanted to choose tropical fish that could live comfortably in the same tank, what body features or behaviors might you look for?
5. **Infer** Some fish do not lay eggs. Their eggs develop inside the female fish. How might the offspring of one of these fish differ from those of an egg-laying fish?

CHALLENGE

6. **Synthesize** Fossils indicate that species of fish with bodies very similar to today's sharks have lived in aquatic environments for hundreds of millions of years. What can you infer about the adaptations of sharks from this?

ANSWERS

1. because they have an endoskeleton that includes vertebrae, or a backbone

2. Sample answers: gills, a swim bladder, a lateral line, fins, streamlined body

3. jawless: no jaw, tube-shaped body; cartilaginous: skeleton made of cartilage; bony: skeleton made of bone, scales

4. Sample answers: similar coloration, body shapes, and similarities in behavior

5. A fish that retained the eggs inside its body would produce fewer eggs than one that laid its eggs in water. However, eggs protected inside the parent's body would be less vulnerable to predators.

6. Sharks are very well adapted to their environment and have been able to meet their needs without changing.

SKILL: DIVIDING BY DECIMALS

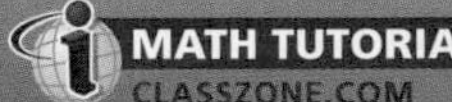

CLASSZONE.COM

Click on Math Tutorial for more help dividing by decimals.

Great Growth

The leatherback sea turtle is one of the largest reptiles alive. Full-grown, adult leatherbacks can weigh 880 kilograms. This huge turtle starts out life weighing just 44 grams.

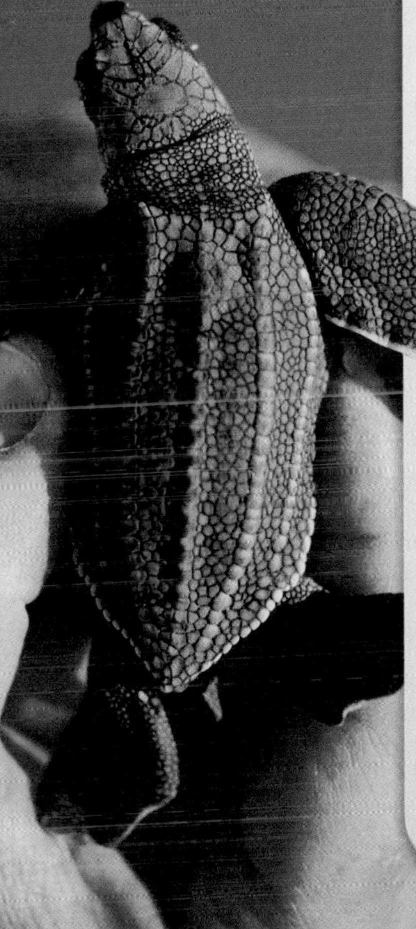

Example

How many times heavier is the 880 kg adult than the 44 g baby?

(1) Convert the units so they are all in kilograms.
44 g × 0.001 kg/g = 0.044 kg

(2) Divide 880 by 0.044 to get the answer.

(3) To divide by a decimal, multiply the divisor and the dividend by a multiple of 10. Since the decimal number is in thousandths, multiply by 1000.

$0.044\overline{)880000}$ $\quad$ $\begin{array}{r} 20{,}000 \\ 44\overline{)880000} \end{array}$

ANSWER The adult leatherback is 20,000 times heavier than the baby leatherback hatchling.

Answer the following questions.

1. An adult leatherback has been measured as 1.5 m from nose to tail. The same animal measured just 6 cm as a baby hatchling. How many times longer is the adult?
2. A typical box turtle grows to 12.5 cm long. How many times longer is the adult leatherback than the adult box turtle?
3. Suppose the box turtle hatched with a length of 2.5 cm. By how many times has its length grown at adulthood?
4. How many times longer is the leatherback hatchling than the box turtle hatchling?

CHALLENGE What fraction of its adult weight is the leatherback hatchling in the example?

ANSWERS

1. 150 ÷ 6 = 25 times

2. 150 ÷ 12.5 = 1500 ÷ 125 = 12 times

3. 12.5 ÷ 2.5 = 125 ÷ 25 = 5 times

4. 6 ÷ 2.5 = 60 ÷ 25 = 2.4 times

CHALLENGE $\frac{.044}{880} = \frac{1}{20{,}000}$

MATH IN SCIENCE
Math Skills Practice for Science

Set Learning Goal

To compare animal measurements by dividing by decimals

Present the Science

The leatherback turtle is the largest living species of turtle. The leatherback lives in the open sea, but goes ashore to lay its eggs. It is a threatened species worldwide because of over-hunting of its eggs, fishing, pollution, and a reduction of nesting sites.

Develop Measurement Skills

Review metric equivalents with students. Remind them that there are 1000 grams in one kilogram. So, 1 g = 1/1000 kg. To convert from grams to kilograms, multiply by 1/1000 or 0.001. Also remind students that 1 meter = 100 centimeters.

DIFFERENTIATION TIP Prepare a chart of metric conversions for students to use as a reference.

Close

Ask students why knowing how to compute with decimals is helpful to scientists. *Many scientific measurements involve the metric system. In order to convert measurements within the system, division with decimals is used.*

- Math Support, p. 338
- Math Practice, p. 339

Technology Resources

Students can visit **ClassZone.com** to practice measurement skills.

MATH TUTORIAL

13.2 FOCUS

Set Learning Goals

Students will

- Discuss the characteristics of amphibians, vertebrates that can live on land for part of their lives.
- Recognize the characteristics of reptiles, vertebrates that can live on land for their entire lives.
- Explain that amphibians and reptiles are *ectotherms.*
- Observe and describe characteristics of eggs.

3-Minute Warm-Up

Display Transparency 36 or copy this exercise on the board:

Complete the graphic organizer.

Main Idea: Fish are adapted to live in water.	
Adaptation	Function
Gills	*Allow fish to breathe*
Lateral line	*Allows fish to sense objects*
Swim bladder	*Adjusts how high or low fish float*

 3-Minute Warm-Up, p. T36

13.2 MOTIVATE

EXPLORE Moving on Land

PURPOSE To calculate jumping distance

TIP *15 min.* Have students convert their measurements to centimeters. (1 m = 100 cm)

WHAT DO YOU THINK? *Jumping ability might enable a frog to escape predators and to catch food whereas the human body is adapted to walk upright and use hands with thumbs.*

KEY CONCEPT

Amphibians and reptiles are adapted for life on land.

BEFORE, you learned

- Fish are vertebrates that live in water
- Fish gills remove oxygen from water
- Most young fish develop inside eggs laid in the water

NOW, you will learn

- About amphibians, vertebrates that can live on land for part of their lives
- About reptiles, vertebrates that can live on land for their whole lives
- About the body temperature of amphibians and reptiles

VOCABULARY

amphibian p. 439
reptile p. 440
ectotherm p. 442

EXPLORE Moving on Land

What good are legs?

PROCEDURE

1. Measure and record your height in meters.
2. Jump as far as you can, and have your partner record the distance.
3. Divide the distance you jumped by your height.
4. Some frogs can jump a distance that's equal to 10 times their body length.Calculate the distance you would be able to jump if you were a frog.

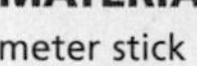

MATERIALS
meter stick

WHAT DO YOU THINK?
How might the ability to jump help a frog survive on land?

Vertebrates adapted to live on land.

Most of the groups of invertebrates and all of the vertebrates you have read about so far live in water. Organisms such as plants and insects became very diverse after adapting to live on land. Some vertebrate animals adapted to live on land as well. In this section you will learn about the first vertebrates to live on land, a group called the amphibians, and the group that came next, the reptiles.

Amphibians living today include frogs, toads, and salamanders. Reptiles include turtles, snakes, lizards, and crocodiles. Some people find it hard to tell animals from these two groups apart, but there are some important characteristics that distinguish them.

More than 350 million years ago, Earth was already inhabited by many species of vertebrate animals. All of them were fish. They

RESOURCES FOR DIFFERENTIATED INSTRUCTION

Below Level

UNIT RESOURCE BOOK

- Reading Study Guide A, pp. 303–304
- Decoding Support, p. 337

 **AUDIO CDS**

 **Additional INVESTIGATION,** Adaptations of a Frog's Tongue, A, B, & C, pp. 349–357; Teacher Instructions, pp. 360–361

Advanced

UNIT RESOURCE BOOK

Challenge and Extension, p. 309

English Learners

UNIT RESOURCE BOOK

Spanish Reading Study Guide, pp. 307–308

 **AUDIO CDS**

- Audio Readings in Spanish
- Audio Readings (English)

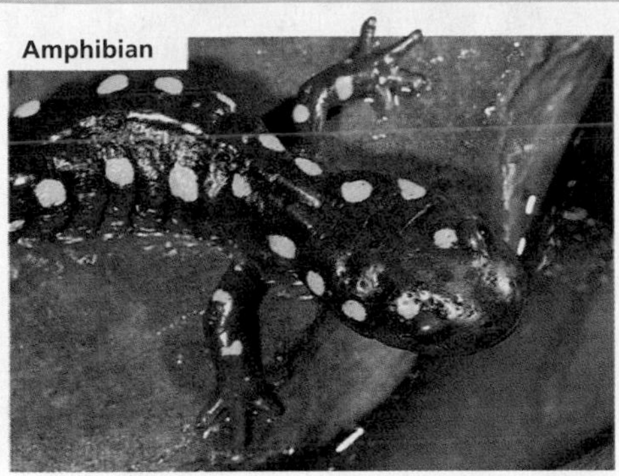
Amphibian

Reptile

READING VISUALS COMPARE AND CONTRAST Just by looking at these two animals, what physical differences can you see? What similarities do you see?

lived in salt water and fresh water, consumed other organisms as food, and obtained oxygen using specialized organs called gills.

Recall the pond you imagined in Chapter 11, when you learned that plants adapted to land. Now imagine the same pond a hundred million years later. The pond is crowded with invertebrates and fish, all competing for oxygen and food.

Suppose a period of dry weather makes the pond start to dry up. Many animals die, and food and oxygen become scarce. On the banks of the pond it might be less crowded. Invertebrates living there are sources of food. Air on land contains more oxygen than water does. Fish that could survive on land would be better off than the fish in the pond in this situation.

However, the gills of fish work only when they are wet. Fins can function to make a fish move through water, but they are not good for moving on land. Water provides more support for the body than air. Plus, fish sensory organs are specialized for detecting sounds and smells in water, not in air.

A It took millions of years and many generations before different adaptations occurred and amphibians became a distinct group. These early amphibians were able to survive on land. Today there are fish that can breathe air and fish that can walk for short distances on land. There are also some modern amphibian species that have adapted to life only in water.

CHECK YOUR READING How are amphibians different from fish?

NOTETAKING STRATEGY
Choose a strategy from an earlier chapter or use one of your own to take notes on how vertebrates adapted to life on land.

13.2 INSTRUCT

Address Misconceptions

IDENTIFY Ask students to make a list of some vertebrate animals. If students list snakes and turtles, they may hold the misconception that if an organism lacks obvious external segmentation and limbs, such as a snake, or if an organism contains an external shell, as a turtle does, that the organism must be an invertebrate.

CORRECT Ask students to create a comparison poster depicting two organisms as examples, and stating the main difference between invertebrates and vertebrates. *Vertebrates have backbones.*

REASSESS Ask students to explain why an amphibian is classified as a vertebrate. *Amphibians have backbones.*

Technology Resources

Visit **ClassZone.com** for background on common student misconceptions.

MISCONCEPTION DATABASE

Ongoing Assessment

READING VISUALS *Answer: The skin texture is different: the amphibian appears to have smooth skin, while the reptile appears to have bumpy- or rough-looking skin. Both animals have heads with eyes, mouths, jaws, and front limbs with toes.*

CHECK YOUR READING *Answer: Amphibians can live on land.*

DIFFERENTIATE INSTRUCTION

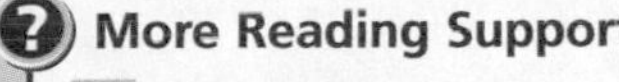
More Reading Support

A Which group of vertebrates evolved after fish? *amphibians*

English Learners Have students create a picture dictionary of amphibians and reptiles. Students can print or sketch pictures from electronic encyclopedias and label the pictures with the animal names in English and other languages.

Additional Investigation To reinforce Section 13.2 learning goals, use the following full-period investigation:

R **Additional INVESTIGATION,** Adaptations of a Frog's Tongue, A, B, & C, pp. 349–357, 360–361
(Advanced students should complete Levels B and C.)

Teach from Visuals

To help students interpret the wood frog life cycle, ask:

- Where do wood frogs begin their lives? *in water*
- How are tadpoles similar to fish? *They breathe with gills and swim and live in the water.*
- What physical developments occur in tadpoles that allow them to move onto land? *They develop legs and lungs.*

Real World Example

An adult wood frog is about two inches long. Each female lays a mass of 2,000 to 3,000 eggs. The transformation from tadpole to frog is completed quickly in wood frogs, which typically lay their eggs in fish-free ponds, puddles, or vernal pools. These habitats form as a result of snow melt and spring rain. They disappear quickly and so the young amphibians that hatch in them must complete their development and move to land before their ponds dry out.

Ongoing Assessment

READING VISUALS *Answer: The most obvious changes are the growth of legs (back pair first) and the shrinking tail. The shape of the frog's head also changes. Its eyes grow toward the top of the head, and its round mouth widens and develops an upper and lower jaw.*

DIFFERENTIATE INSTRUCTION

Alternative Assessment Have students work independently to create a flow chart to illustrate the life cycle of the wood frog. Students should include these terms in their charts: *eggs, tadpole, gills,* and *lungs.*

Advanced Have pairs of students work together to create a game about amphibians and reptiles. The game should include Q-and-A or pitfalls and opportunities that address the habitat, adaptations, and any threats to the animals' survival. As part of the game design, students might research the worldwide decline of frogs and amphibians and include suggestions about what can be done to address this problem.

Amphibians have moist skin and lay eggs without shells.

As adults, most **amphibians** have these characteristics:

- They have two pairs of legs, or a total of four limbs.
- They lay their eggs in water.
- They obtain oxygen through their smooth, moist skin. Many also have respiratory organs called lungs.
- Their sensory organs are adapted for sensing on land.

Most amphibians live in moist environments. Their skin is a respiratory organ that functions only when it is wet. Most species of amphibians live close to water or in damp places. Some are most active at night, when the ground is wet with dew. Others live mostly underground, beneath wet leaves, or under decaying trees.

Amphibians reproduce sexually. In most amphibian species, a female lays eggs in water, a male fertilizes them with sperm, and then the offspring develop and hatch on their own. Yolk inside the eggs provides developing embryos with nutrients. Like fish eggs, amphibian eggs do not have hard shells. This means developing amphibians can get water and oxygen directly from their surroundings.

CHECK YOUR READING How is the way most amphibians reproduce similar to the way most fish reproduce?

RESOURCE CENTER CLASSZONE.COM
Learn more about amphibians.

Amphibian Life Cycle

The diagram shows the life cycle of one amphibian, the wood frog. When a young amphibian hatches, it is a larva. In Chapter 12 you learned that a larva is an early stage that is very different from the animal's adult form. For example, the larvae of frogs and toads are called tadpoles. Tadpoles look and behave like small fish. They breathe with gills, eat mostly algae, and move by pushing against the water with their tails.

After a few weeks, a tadpole's body begins to change. Inside, the lungs develop and parts of the digestive system transform. The tadpole begins to have some of the external features of a frog. It develops legs, its tail shrinks, and its head changes shape.

As a young wood frog's body changes, its gills stop functioning, and it begins breathing air with its lungs. The frog starts using its tongue to capture and eat small animals. It leaves the water and begins using its legs to move around on land. Some amphibians, such as sirens and bullfrogs, remain in or near water for all of their lives. Others, like wood frogs, most toads, and some salamanders, live in moist land environments as adults.

READING TIP
As you read about the amphibian life cycle in these paragraphs, look at the diagram on page 438 to see what a wood frog looks like at each stage.

DIFFERENTIATE INSTRUCTION

More Reading Support

B What are two ways adult amphibians get oxygen? *skin and lungs*

C How do tadpoles move? *They push against water with tails.*

Advanced The three categories of amphibians are salamanders, frogs and toads, and caecilians. Caecilians live primarily in South America; there are no living species in the United States. There is considerable variety among amphibians. Invite students to research and produce single pages for a field guide on "Amazing Amphibians." They can include pictures, facts, and scientific names.

 Challenge and Extension, p. 309

Develop Critical Thinking

ANALYZE Have students study and interpret the list of amphibian characteristics. Ask:

- Why do most adult amphibians stay near the water throughout their lives? *They need to stay near water to keep their skin moist. They need to lay their eggs in a moist environment for the eggs to survive.*
- Would a tadpole be able to live on land? Explain. *No, a tadpole does not have legs to move around or lungs to breathe.*
- What invertebrate animal also breathes through its skin? *earthworms*

Metacognitive Strategy

Ask students to recall the stages of insect metamorphosis they studied in Chapter 12. Ask: How are the stages of a tadpole's metamorphosis similar to those of a butterfly? *Some insects, such as the butterfly begin as eggs and hatch into larva. The larva stages of both the butterfly and the tadpole look very different physically from the adult forms.*

Ongoing Assessment

Describe the characteristics of amphibians.

Ask: What adaptations do amphibians have that suit them to life in both water and land environments? *They lay eggs in water, have lungs as well as the ability to breathe through skin, have legs and webbed feet.*

CHECK YOUR READING *Answer: Similarities include soft eggs that are laid in water, eggs that are fertilized externally, and offspring that develop and hatch with little or no care from adults.*

Teach Difficult Concepts

Some students might think that the hard, outer coverings of some reptiles, such as turtles, are made of bone tissue. Point out that the shells are not made of bone, but are fused with the vertebrae so their backs are not flexible. Explain that the bone on the inside, including the vertebrae, is made up of bone tissue.

After reviewing the list of reptilian characteristics, point out that not all of the animals classified as reptiles have all of the characteristics listed. Snakes, for example, do not have visible legs, nor do legless lizards. Many reptilian species are aquatic and have adaptations for sensing and responding in water that complement or may even be better than their senses on land.

Ongoing Assessment

CHECK YOUR READING *Answer: Differences include tough, dry skin covered with scales; sensory organs adapted for sensing on land; eggs that have shells and are laid on land; only lungs for respiration.*

Reptiles have dry, scaly skin and lay eggs with shells.

VOCABULARY
Add a magnet word diagram for *reptile* to your notebook.

Reptiles evolved soon after amphibians and are closely related to them. However, animals in the reptile group have adaptations that allow them to survive in hotter, drier places than amphibians. For many millions of years they were the largest and most diverse vertebrate animal group living on land. Most of the animals classified as reptiles have these characteristics:

- They have two pairs of legs, for a total of four limbs.
- They have tough, dry skin covered by scales.
- D They obtain oxygen from air with respiratory organs called lungs.
- Their sensory organs are adapted for sensing on land.
- E They lay their eggs, which have shells, on land.

CHECK YOUR READING What characteristics of reptiles are different from the characteristics of amphibians listed on page 439?

Lungs

Reptiles do not get oxygen through their skin the way amphibians do. They are born with lungs that provide their bodies with all the oxygen they need. Lungs are internal organs made up of many small lobes of thin tissue filled with tiny blood vessels. When an animal with lungs inhales, it takes air in through its nostrils or mouth and moves the air into its lungs. There, oxygen is transported across the tissues and into the blood, and carbon dioxide is moved from the blood to the lungs and exhaled.

Reptiles like these garter snakes are covered with scales and breathe through their nostrils.

DIFFERENTIATE INSTRUCTION

More Reading Support

D How do reptiles obtain oxygen? *through lungs*

E Where do reptiles lay their eggs? *on land*

Below Level To help students understand the difference between reptiles and amphibians, have them complete this compare/contrast graphic organizer:

Trait	Amphibians	Reptiles
Number of limbs	*four*	*four*
Outer skin	*wet and smooth*	*dry with scales*
Way of getting oxygen	*moist skin*	*lungs*
Eggs	*in water*	*on land*

CONTRAST How does the egg this gecko hatched from differ from the wood frog eggs shown on page 438?

Dry, Scaly Skin

F

Reptile skin is hard, dry, and covered with scales made of keratin, a substance much like your fingernails. The thick, waterproof skin of reptiles protects them from the environment and from predators. However, this means that reptiles cannot obtain water through their skin.

Eggs with Shells

G

The reptile egg is an important adaptation that allows vertebrate animals to survive in hot, dry environments. The eggs of reptiles contain everything an embryo needs: water, nutrients, a system for gas exchange, and a place to store waste. Membranes separate the internal parts of the egg, which is covered by a protective shell.

Reptiles reproduce sexually. The egg cell of the female joins with the sperm cell of the male in the process of fertilization. After fertilization, a protective case, or shell, forms around each egg while it is still inside the female's body. The female selects a place to lay the eggs on land. Many species of reptiles build or dig nests. Some female reptiles, including alligators, guard their nests and care for their offspring after they hatch. Most reptiles, however, leave soon after the eggs are laid. As you can see in the photograph above, when young reptiles hatch, they look like small adults.

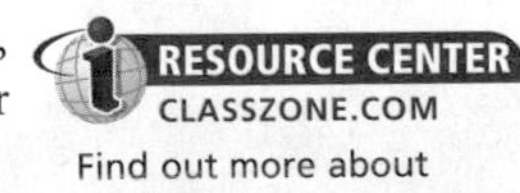
RESOURCE CENTER
CLASSZONE.COM
Find out more about reptiles.

Address Misconceptions

IDENTIFY Ask students to give some examples of reptiles and amphibians. Many students may hold the misconception that amphibians and reptiles are not vertebrates. Students also will frequently confuse the two classes or lump them together.

CORRECT Have students create a Venn diagram of the characteristics of amphibians and reptiles. In the intersecting section of the diagram they should note how the organisms are similar. For example, both have backbones, are vertebrates, and so on.

REASSESS Ask students to explain why a turtle or a snake is classified as a reptile. *Turtles lay eggs, have four legs, and their legs and heads are covered with dry, scaly skin. Snakes have more characteristics of reptiles than of other vertebrates, only lacking limbs.*

Technology Resources

Visit **ClassZone.com** for background on common student misconceptions.

MISCONCEPTION DATABASE

Real World Example

Aquatic reptiles, such as many species of sea turtles, have lungs and must come to the surface to breathe. These turtles are adapted to sea life with forelimbs that are modified into flippers for swimming. Most sea turtles only leave the sea during the breeding season when the females lay and bury their eggs on land. The hatchlings then make their journey from the nest to the sea.

Ongoing Assessment

Describe the characteristics of reptiles.

Ask: What characteristics make reptiles suited to life in a land environment? *eggs with shells; protective, thick skin; lungs and respiratory organs; legs; sensory organs*

PHOTO CAPTION Answer: The gecko egg is on land and has a shell that is hard and protective; the wood frog egg is in water and is soft.

DIFFERENTIATE INSTRUCTION

More Reading Support

F What are the scales of reptile skin made of? *keratin*

G Why is the reptile egg an important adaptation? *Reptiles may survive in hot, dry environments.*

Advanced Have students create a timeline showing the geological periods in which fish, amphibians, and reptiles made their appearances on Earth. They will need to do research in paleontology to complete the chart. Students can add to the timeline as they study birds and mammals later in Chapter 13. Encourage students to include pictures in their timelines of extinct and present-day species of animals.

INVESTIGATE Eggs

PURPOSE Students observe a hard-boiled egg to determine the characteristics of eggs

TIPS *20 min.* Make sure students handle their eggs with care to avoid dropping and breaking the eggs. Put down sheets of newspaper or plastic bags over work surfaces. Have students peel eggs directly over their work surfaces.

WHAT DO YOU THINK? *Eggs with shells have a shell, a protective membrane, an egg white, and a yolk. The shell protects the egg, the membrane regulates and holds the embryo's environment, the yolk provides nutrients.*

CHALLENGE *As the embryo develops, it consumes the yolk and grows. The membrane contains the embryo, and the egg white contains structures that help maintain the egg's internal environment.*

 Datasheet, Eggs, p. 310

Technology Resources

Customize this student lab as needed or look for an alternative. Print rubrics to assess student lab reports.

 **Lab Generator CD-ROM**

INVESTIGATE Eggs

What are some of the characteristics of eggs?

PROCEDURE

1. Carefully examine the outside of the hard-boiled egg. Try to notice as many details as you can. Write your observations in your notebook.
2. Gently crack the eggshell and remove it. Try to keep the shell in large pieces and the egg whole. Set the egg aside, and examine the pieces of shell. Look for details you could not see before. Write your observations in your notebook.
3. Examine the outside of the egg. Make notes about what you see. Include a sketch.
4. Use the knife to cut the egg in half. Take one half apart carefully, trying to notice as many parts as you can. Use the other half for comparison. Write up your observations.

WHAT DO YOU THINK?

- Reptiles, like birds, have eggs with hard shells. What structures does an egg with a shell contain?
- What might the function of each structure be?

CHALLENGE How might the egg's structures support a developing embryo?

SKILL FOCUS
Observing

MATERIALS
- hard-boiled egg
- plastic knife

TIME:
20 minutes

The body temperatures of amphibians and reptiles change with the environment.

Amphibians and reptiles are **ectotherms,** animals whose body temperatures change with environmental conditions. You are not an ectotherm. Whether the air temperature of your environment is −4°C (25°F) or 43°C (110°F), your body temperature remains around 37°C (99°F). A tortoise's body temperature changes with the temperature of the air or water surrounding it. On a cool day, a tortoise's body will be cooler than it is on a hot one.

Many ectothermic animals can move and respond more quickly when their bodies are warm. Many ectotherms warm themselves in sunlight. You may have seen turtles or snakes sunning themselves. Ectothermic animals transform most of the food they consume directly into energy. Some ectotherms, even large ones such as alligators, or the Galápagos tortoise in the photograph, can survive for a long time without consuming much food.

Develop Critical Thinking

ANALYZE Point out that ectothermic animals are sometimes referred to as "cold-blooded." Ask: Why do you think that this term is inaccurate? *An ectothermic animal that is in a hot environment would have a high body temperature.*

Real World Example

Most fish are considered ectotherms, but the general temperature in water environments does not vary as dramatically or change as rapidly as it does on land. Some fish, such as tuna, generate body heat and are considered endothermic. Other fish have anti-freeze proteins in the blood that allow them to remain active in extremely cold water.

DIFFERENTIATE INSTRUCTION

More Reading Support

H What term describes an animal whose body temperature changes with environmental conditions? *ectotherm*

Below Level Have students research what a herpatologist does. Ask them to find out about the different areas of studies, what kind of training is needed, and what kind of jobs are available.

Students might also find out about the needs of amphibians and reptiles that are kept as pets. They can write interview questions for a local pet store owner and then conduct the interview. They can then share their findings with the class.

This sand-diving lizard can reduce the amount of heat that transfers from the sand into its body by standing on two feet.

Although amphibians and reptiles do not have a constant body temperature, their bodies stop functioning well if they become too hot or too cold. Most amphibians and reptiles live in environments where the temperature of the surrounding air or water does not change too much. Others, like wood frogs and painted turtles, have adaptations that allow them to slow their body processes during the winter.

Amphibians and reptiles also have behaviors that allow them to adjust their body temperature in less extreme ways. The sand-diving lizard in the photograph above is able to control how much heat enters its body through the sand by standing on just two of its four feet. Many amphibians and reptiles live near water and use it to cool off their bodies.

13.2 Review

KEY CONCEPTS

1. What are three adaptations that allowed the first amphibians to survive on land?
2. What are two adaptations reptiles have that allow them to live their whole life on land?
3. A crocodile has been lying in the sun for hours. When it slides into the cool river, how will its body temperature change? Why?

CRITICAL THINKING

4. **Compare and Contrast** Make a diagram to show how amphibians and reptiles are different and how they are similar.
5. **Infer** Some reptiles, like sea turtles, live almost their whole lives in water. What differences would you expect to see between the bodies of a sea turtle and a land turtle?

CHALLENGE

6. **Hypothesize** For many millions of years, reptiles were the most diverse and successful vertebrate animals on land. Now many of these ancient reptiles are extinct. Give some reasons that might explain the extinction of these reptiles.

ANSWERS

1. limbs, lungs, sensory organs adapted for land

2. born with lungs, eggs have shells

3. Its body temperature should go down. The water will cool its body.

4. Diagrams should include adaptations, methods of reproduction, and how animals obtain oxygen.

5. Sample answer: a more streamlined body in sea turtle (for moving through water), webbing on feet of sea turtle, better underwater eyesight and other senses, and more lung capacity in sea turtle.

6. Answers should show understanding of how environmental factors affect survival rates. Sample answer: If climate changed and became significantly cooler, reptiles might be adversely affected.

Ongoing Assessment

Explain that reptiles and amphibians are ectotherms.

Ask: How might the body temperature of an ectotherm become hot? *The animal could warm itself in the Sun.*

Reinforce the BIG idea

Have students relate the section to the Big Idea.

 Reinforcing Key Concepts, p. 310

13.2 ASSESS & RETEACH

Assess

 Section 13.2 Quiz, p. 84

Reteach

Have students create a compare and contrast chart about amphibians and reptiles. Charts should include:

- body structures suited to environments
- how oxygen is obtained
- how the animal group reproduces

Technology Resources

Have students visit **ClassZone.com** for reteaching of Key Concepts.

 CONTENT REVIEW

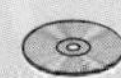 CONTENT REVIEW CD-ROM

CONNECTING SCIENCES
Integration of Sciences

Set Learning Goal

To understand how physics principles, such as the bonding of atoms, apply to a trait of certain reptiles

Present the Science

Geckos are nocturnal insect-eating lizards that are found in warm climates. There are about 700 species of geckos. Most are about four to six inches (10 cm to 15 cm) in length. The largest can grow to a length of 14 inches (35.5 cm). Feet of geckos vary. Some toes have claws, others, extensive webbing and climbing pads.

The explanation for why a gecko's spatulae help it stick to walls relies on physical science. When two atoms from different molecules get very close together, the movement of the electrons within each atom are forced to change. This produces electrical charges that fluctuate and move along the surface of each atom. The net result is a force that attracts the two atoms towards each other. This force, called the van der Waals force, can bond spatulae atoms to a wall's atoms.

Discussion Questions

Ask: How are the hairs in a gecko's foot arranged? *The hairs branch into hundreds of tiny hairs called* spatulae.

Ask: Why do you think the gecko's ability to stick to walls is called *dry adhesion*? *Adhesion occurs between two dry surfaces.*

Close

Ask: How does the gecko's ability to stick to surfaces rely on the physical activity of atoms? *The interaction between the atoms of the gecko's feet and the surface is based on one property of atoms that is the attraction of electrons to one another.*

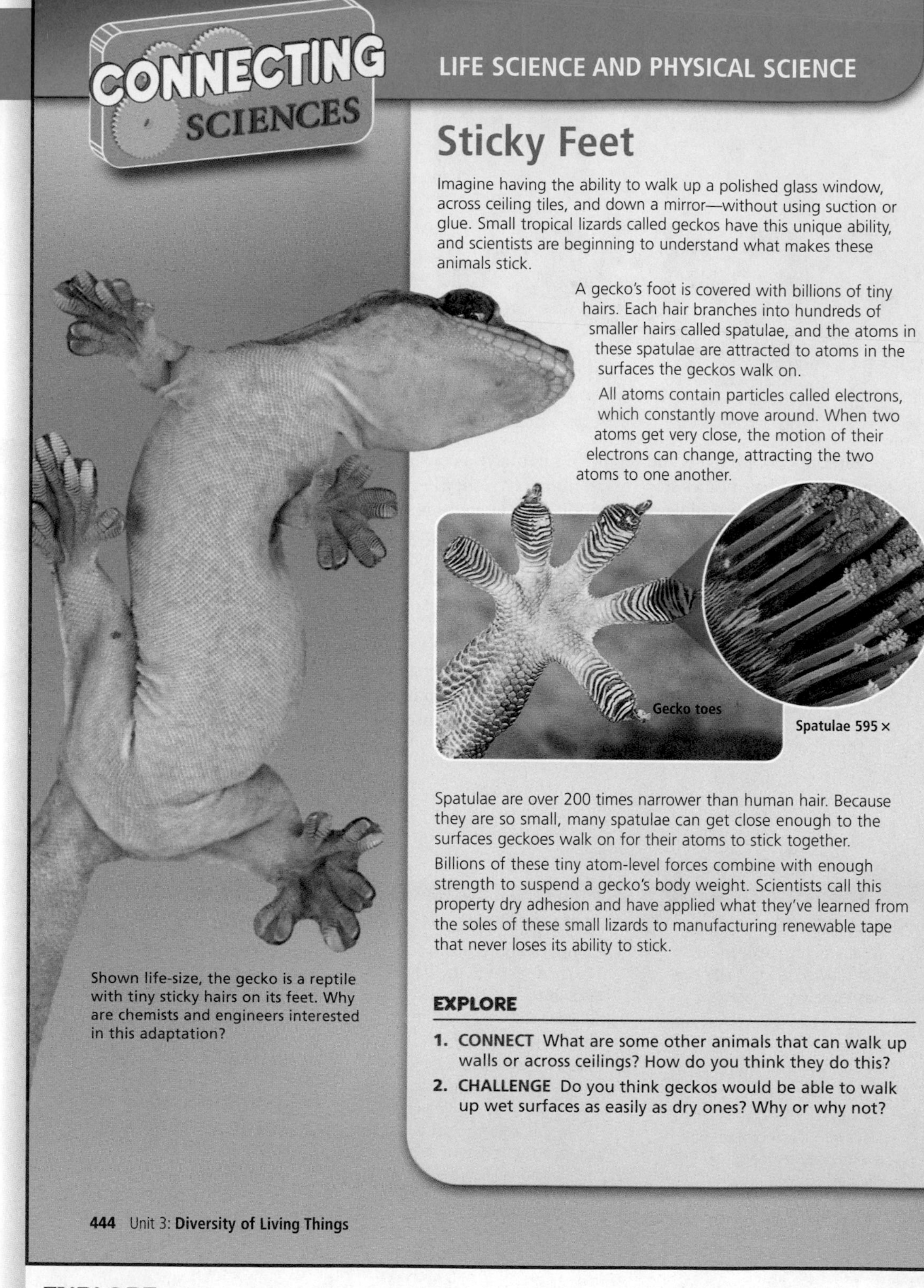

CONNECTING SCIENCES

LIFE SCIENCE AND PHYSICAL SCIENCE

Sticky Feet

Imagine having the ability to walk up a polished glass window, across ceiling tiles, and down a mirror—without using suction or glue. Small tropical lizards called geckos have this unique ability, and scientists are beginning to understand what makes these animals stick.

A gecko's foot is covered with billions of tiny hairs. Each hair branches into hundreds of smaller hairs called spatulae, and the atoms in these spatulae are attracted to atoms in the surfaces the geckos walk on.

All atoms contain particles called electrons, which constantly move around. When two atoms get very close, the motion of their electrons can change, attracting the two atoms to one another.

Gecko toes

Spatulae 595 ×

Spatulae are over 200 times narrower than human hair. Because they are so small, many spatulae can get close enough to the surfaces geckoes walk on for their atoms to stick together.

Billions of these tiny atom-level forces combine with enough strength to suspend a gecko's body weight. Scientists call this property dry adhesion and have applied what they've learned from the soles of these small lizards to manufacturing renewable tape that never loses its ability to stick.

Shown life-size, the gecko is a reptile with tiny sticky hairs on its feet. Why are chemists and engineers interested in this adaptation?

EXPLORE

1. **CONNECT** What are some other animals that can walk up walls or across ceilings? How do you think they do this?
2. **CHALLENGE** Do you think geckos would be able to walk up wet surfaces as easily as dry ones? Why or why not?

444 Unit 3: **Diversity of Living Things**

EXPLORE

1. ***CONNECT*** *Sample answers: insects, some reptiles such as lizards. Accept all reasonable responses.*
2. ***CHALLENGE*** *If the surface is wet, the spatulae will not be able to get as much suction on the surface. Therefore, the gecko will have more trouble walking up wet surfaces.*

KEY CONCEPT

Birds meet their needs on land, in water, and in the air.

BEFORE, you learned

- Vertebrate animals have endoskeletons with backbones
- Amphibians and reptiles have adaptations for life on land
- Ectotherms do not maintain a constant body temperature

NOW, you will learn

- About birds as endotherms
- How the adaptations of birds allow them to live in many environments
- About adaptations for flight

VOCABULARY

endotherm p. 446
incubation p. 451

EXPLORE Feathers

How do feathers differ?

PROCEDURE

1. Examine several feathers.
2. Make a list of ways some of your feathers differ from others.
3. Make a diagram of each feather, showing the characteristics you listed.
4. Compare your list and your diagram with those of your classmates.

MATERIALS
assorted feathers

WHAT DO YOU THINK?

- Of all the characteristics of feathers that you and your classmates listed, which do you think are the most important? Why?
- On the basis of your observations, what are some functions of feathers for birds?

NOTETAKING STRATEGY
Be sure to take notes on the main idea, *Bird species live in most environments.* Choose an earlier strategy or one of your own.

Bird species live in most environments.

Penguins live in Antarctica, and parrots inhabit the tropics. Pelicans scoop their food from the water, while cardinals crack open seeds and eat the insides. Swallows skim insects from above the surface of a pond. A soaring hawk swoops down, and a smaller animal becomes its prey. There are nearly 10,000 species of the vertebrate animals called birds. Their adaptations allow them to live all over the world.

Some bird species, such as pigeons, are adapted to live in a wide range of environments, while others have adaptations that limit them to living in one place. Many birds travel long distances during their lives. Some migrate as the seasons change, and others cover long distances while searching for food.

RESOURCES FOR DIFFERENTIATED INSTRUCTION

Below Level

UNIT RESOURCE BOOK

- Reading Study Guide A, pp. 314–315
- Decoding Support, p. 337

AUDIO CDS

Advanced

UNIT RESOURCE BOOK

Challenge and Extension, p. 320

English Learners

UNIT RESOURCE BOOK

Spanish Reading Study Guide, pp. 318–319

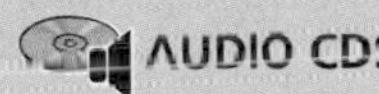

- Audio Readings in Spanish
- Audio Readings (English)

13.3 FOCUS

Set Learning Goals

Students will

- Recognize that birds are endotherms.
- Describe how birds' adaptations allow them to live in many environments.
- Explain the adaptations that enable most birds to fly.

3-Minute Warm-Up

Display Transparency 37 or copy this exercise on the board:

Write *reptile* or *amphibian* for each description.

Descriptions

1. begins life in water breathing through gills *amphibian*
2. lays eggs on land *reptile*
3. has moist skin for obtaining oxygen *amphibian*
4. has scales that are made up of keratin *reptile*

 3-Minute Warm-Up, p. T37

13.3 MOTIVATE

EXPLORE Feathers

PURPOSE To inquire about the structures and functions of bird feathers

TIPS *15 min.* Bags of feathers can be purchased at art supply or craft stores. The best sample will include naturally colored feathers of varying shapes and sizes that are all from the same species of bird. Examining feathers from different species will also work.

WHAT DO YOU THINK? *Students should note that birds have contour feathers of varying sizes and shapes, as well as down feathers. Color, shape, form, and function of the feathers vary depending on where the feather is located on the body. Most feathers have a central shaft. Smaller shafts project from the central shaft. Some feathers (not down) have barbs that knit the feathers together.*

13.3 INSTRUCT

Develop Critical Thinking

ANALYZE Explain that bird beaks and feathers are made of keratin as are the scales on their legs. Then ask:

- What other animal has body parts that are made of keratin? *Reptiles have scales made of keratin.*
- How are feathers like the scales of a reptile? *Both provide a covering for the body.*
- How do these features indicate that birds share common ancestors with reptiles? *Bird feathers are modified scales. Feathers may have evolved from reptilian scales showing that birds and reptiles have common ancestors.*

Ongoing Assessment

Recognize that birds are endotherms.

What are endotherms? *animals that maintain a constant body temperature*

CHECK YOUR READING *Answer: Endotherms generate more body heat than ectotherms. Endotherms have adaptations and behavior for conserving body heat so they can maintain a constant body temperature.*

It probably seems easy for you to recognize which animals are birds. Birds are distinguished by these characteristics:

A

- They have feathers and a beak.
- They have four limbs: a pair of scaly legs and a pair of wings.
- Their eggs have hard shells.

Birds can maintain body temperature.

In the last section, you learned that the body temperature of ectotherms, such as amphibians and reptiles, changes with their environment. Birds are **endotherms,** or animals that maintain a constant body temperature. Maintaining temperature allows endotherms to live in some places where frogs, turtles, and alligators cannot.

This chickadee is an endotherm. This means its body remains warm, even in very cold weather.

When an ectothermic animal's body is cool, its systems slow down and it becomes less active. A less active animal consumes little or no food and is unlikely to reproduce. It moves slowly or not at all and breathes less often. Its nervous system becomes less responsive, and its heart pumps more slowly. An ectothermic animal that stays cool for too long will die. Even if it has enough food, its body lacks the energy needed to digest the food.

All animals are affected by the air temperature of their environment and will die if they become too cold. However, birds and other endotherms can stay active in colder climates than ectotherms can. This is because endothermic animals have adaptations for generating more body heat and keeping it near their bodies. B

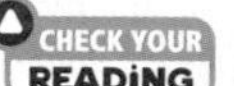
CHECK YOUR READING How can endotherms stay alive in colder climates than ectotherms?

Generating Heat

The energy birds produce as body heat comes from food. This means that birds and other endotherms need to eat a lot. An ectotherm such as a frog might be able to survive for days on the energy it gets from just one worm, while a bird on the same diet might starve. Also, the amount of food an endotherm needs is affected by climate. House sparrows and other birds that do not migrate need to eat more food and produce more energy to survive in winter than they do during warmer seasons.

DIFFERENTIATE INSTRUCTION

More Reading Support

A How many limbs do birds have? What are they? *two legs, two wings*

B What happens to an endotherm in cold weather? *It uses activity to generate body heat.*

English Learners Students new to English may add these words to their Science Notebooks: *endotherm, temperature, endoskeleton, migration,* and *incubation.* Compare the prefixes *endo-* in *endotherm* and *endoskeleton.* Tell students that *endo-* means "inner." Point out that *migration* and *incubation* are forms of the verbs *migrate* and *incubate.*

Insulating with Down

Just as warm air trapped between down feathers helps keep geese warm, feathers in a jacket keep a student warm.

Controlling Body Temperature

Birds have soft feathers, called down, that keep warm air close to their bodies. If you have ever slept with a down comforter or worn a down jacket, you know that these feathers are good insulation, even though they are not very heavy. Other feathers, called contour feathers, cover the down on birds. In most species, contour feathers are water-resistant and protect birds from getting wet. C

Birds shiver when they are cold, and this muscular movement generates heat. They also have ways of cooling their bodies down when the weather is hot. Birds do not sweat, but they can fluff their feathers out to release heat. D Birds, like other animals, have behaviors for maintaining body temperature, such as resting in a shady place during the hottest part of a summer day.

Most birds can fly.

Of all the animals on Earth today, only three groups have evolved adaptations for flight: insects, bats, and birds. Fossil evidence suggests that the first birds appeared on Earth about 150 million years ago and that they were reptiles with adaptations for flight. Scientists think that all birds are descended from these flying ancestors, even modern species such as ostriches and penguins, which cannot fly.

Teach from Visuals

To help students interpret the photograph, have them recall what they observed about down feathers in the explore activity on p. 445. Then ask: Why do you think down feathers are able to trap air? *Down feathers are soft, fluffy, and flexible. They have air pockets within the feathers, where the warm air is trapped in pockets.*

Integrate the Sciences

Materials that do not conduct heat well are insulators. Substances such as wool, wood, straw, cork, paper, and gases such as air are good insulators of heat. Materials such as metals are good conductors of heat. The heat travels quickly through the material. That is why a metal spoon will heat up and be hot to the touch when placed in hot water and a wooden spoon will still be cool to the touch. Insulators such as down feathers slow the transfer of heat away from a bird's body.

Teacher Demo

Demonstrate how feathers make good insulation. Display two plastic cups filled with warm water. Wrap aluminum foil around one cup. Fold a paper towel in half and fill it with down feathers. Wrap the other cup with the paper towel holding the feathers. Secure each wrapping with a rubber band. Place a thermometer in each cup. Have students note which cup retains its temperature over a period of time.

DIFFERENTIATE INSTRUCTION

More Reading Support

C Which bird feathers are water-resistant? *contour feathers*

D How do birds release heat from their bodies? *They fluff up their feathers.*

Below Level Encourage groups of interested students to find out what birds are in your school yard by creating a school bird feeder. A bird feeder can be as simple as dried bread spread with honey and seeds. Students can do a simple tally count of which birds visit the feeder. Provide field guides or an Internet field guide for them to identify the birds. Then have them prepare a bar graph or pictograph showing, by species, the birds who visited.

Develop Critical Thinking

ANALYZE Discuss the difference between sustained flight and what flying squirrels or flying foxes do, which is glide. Point out that many birds, such as ostriches and penguins do not have the ability to fly. Ask:

- Why do you think that these birds are unable to fly? *They are large and heavy in size and their wings would have to be much larger to compensate for their weight.*
- Do you think humans should be added to the list of animals that fly? *Accept all reasonable responses.*

Integrate the Sciences

Bernoulli's principle of lift helps explain why birds are able to fly. Bernoulli's principle states that the pressure exerted by a moving stream of air is less than pressure of the air surrounding it. As air moves over a bird's wings, the air pressure below the wings is less than the pressure above the wings. Because a bird's wings are curved, the air above the wing moves at a faster rate. This difference in pressure creates the upward lift, enabling the bird to fly.

Ongoing Assessment

Describe how bird adaptations allow them to live in many environments.

Ask: Why do you think birds may have been the first vertebrates adapted to live on islands? *Birds have wings that allow them to cross bodies of water as well as to live in high or low places.*

CHECK YOUR READING *Answer: Birds do not have teeth or strong jaws, so they cannot chew. Some parts of their skeletons are fused, making the trunk parts of their bodies less flexible.*

Adaptations for Flight

To lift its body into the air and fly, an animal's body has to be very strong, but also light. Many adaptations and many millions of years were needed before birds' body plans and systems became capable of flight. With these adaptations, birds lost the ability to do some things that other vertebrates can. As you read about birds' adaptations for flight, match the numbers with the diagram on the next page.

READING TIP As you read the numbered text on this page, find the matching number on page 449.

1. **Endoskeleton** Some of the bones in a bird's body are fused, or connected without joints. This makes those parts of a bird's skeleton light and strong, but not as flexible. A specialized bone supports the bird's powerful flight muscles.
2. **Wings and Feathers** Birds do not have hands or paws on their wings. Contour feathers along the wing are called flight feathers, and are specialized for lifting and gliding. Feathers are a strong and adjustable surface for pushing against air.
3. **Specialized Respiratory System** Flying takes a lot of energy, so birds need a lot of oxygen. They breathe using a system of air sacs and lungs. Air follows a path through this system that allows oxygen to move constantly through a bird's body.
4. **Hollow Bones** Many of the bones in a bird's skeleton are hollow. Inside, crisscrossing structures provide strength without adding much weight.

E

Other body systems within birds are more suited for flight than systems in other invertebrates. Instead of heavy jaws and teeth, an internal organ called a gizzard grinds up food. This adaptation makes a bird lighter in weight and makes flight easier. Birds also have highly developed senses of hearing and vision, senses which are important for flight. Their senses of taste and smell are not as well developed.

CHECK YOUR READING Give two examples of things that birds cannot do that relate to their adaptations for flight.

Benefits of Flight

Flight allows animals to get food from places where animals living on land or in water cannot. For example, some species of birds spend most of their lives flying over the ocean, hunting for fish. Also, a flying bird can search a large area for food more effectively than it could if it walked, ran, or swam.

F

For many species of birds, flight makes migration possible. In Chapter 10, you learned that some animals migrate to different living places in different seasons. Most migratory birds have two living places, one for the summer and one for the winter.

DIFFERENTIATE INSTRUCTION

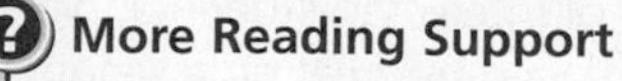
More Reading Support

E What is a gizzard? *an internal organ in birds that grinds food*

F What do birds having two living places do in different seasons? *They migrate.*

English Learners Have English learners draw their own pictures of a bird. Then, have them label the *endoskeleton, wings and feathers, hollow bones,* and *specialized respiratory system.* Students can compare their drawings and labels to the diagram on p. 449.

Adaptations for Flight

This diagram shows some of the adaptations that make flight possible for most birds.

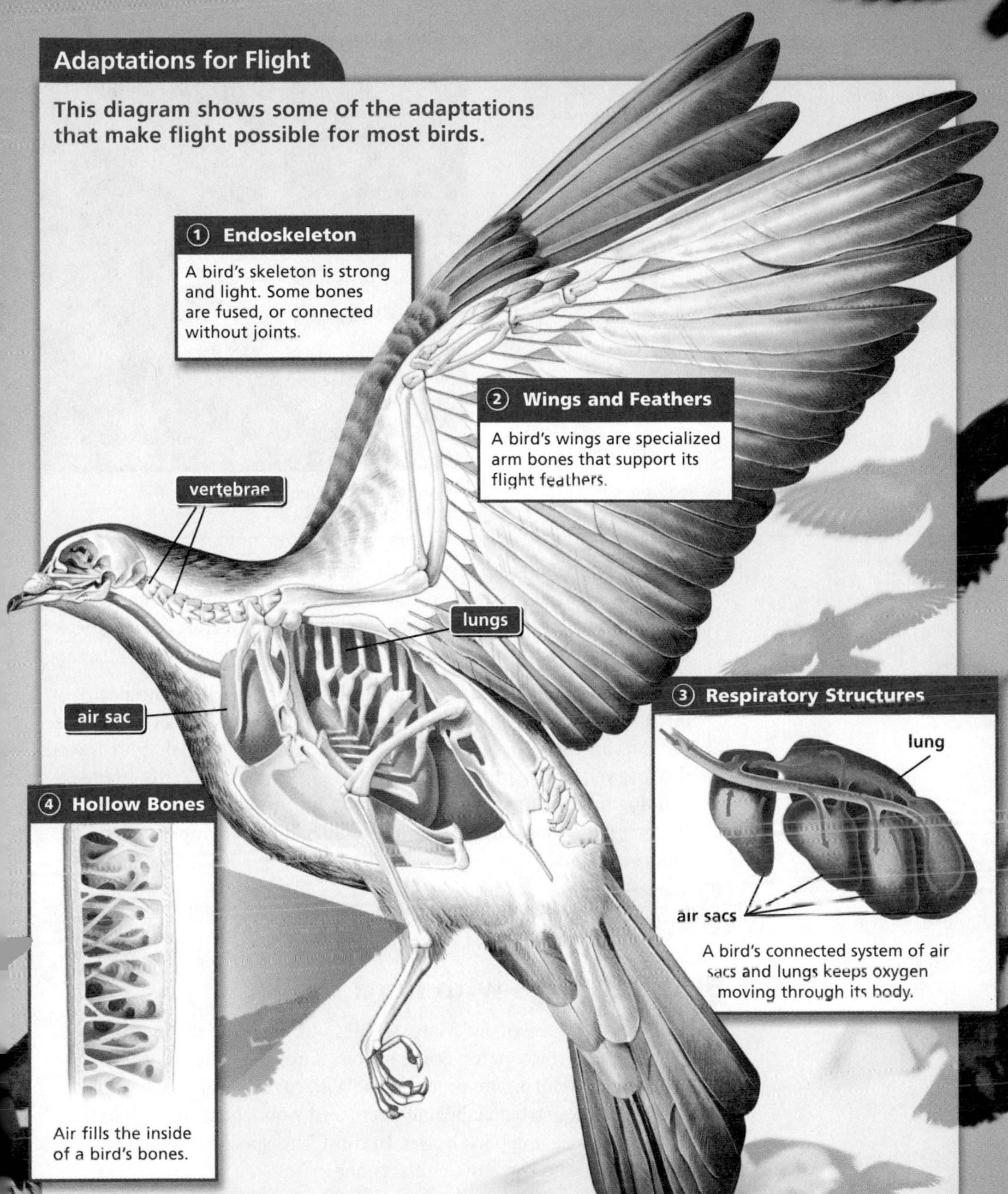

① Endoskeleton

A bird's skeleton is strong and light. Some bones are fused, or connected without joints.

② Wings and Feathers

A bird's wings are specialized arm bones that support its flight feathers.

vertebrae

lungs

air sac

③ Respiratory Structures

lung

air sacs

A bird's connected system of air sacs and lungs keeps oxygen moving through its body.

④ Hollow Bones

Air fills the inside of a bird's bones.

READING VISUALS Do you think any one of these adaptations is more important than the rest?

Teach from Visuals

To help students interpret the diagram illustrating adaptations for flight, ask:

- How might a flexible neck be beneficial to a bird? *A flexible neck allows a bird to catch food, clean itself, and increases the field of vision.*
- Why would a bird need powerful chest muscles? *The chest muscles are needed to enable the wings to fly for long periods of time.*
- How are the wings specialized for flight? *They are hollow; they have flight feathers attached to them.*
- What are two structures in the bird body that allow air inside? How is this beneficial to the bird? *Air sacs and hollow bones are filled with air. This makes the bird lighter and enables it to fly.*

This visual is also available as T38 in the Unit Transparency Book.

Ongoing Assessment

Explain the adaptations that enable most birds to fly.

Ask: How are hollow bones an adaptation for flight? *Hollow bones are lightweight.*

READING VISUALS *Sample answer: Adaptations to the skeleton are especially important. Many of the features described in the diagram are especially important.*

DIFFERENTIATE INSTRUCTION

Below Level Have students create models of wings and birds by using paper and other objects such as drinking straws and brass fasteners. Point out that a bird moves its wings in a circular motion when in flight, not up and down.

Teach from Visuals

To help students interpret the photographs showing flight, ask:

How is the osprey's body adapted for capturing prey? *The feet have strong talons, or claws, that enable the bird to capture its prey.*

History of Science

Many recent bird extinctions are due to the adverse effect of humans on the natural habitats of birds. One of the most notable extinctions was that of the dodo bird, once found on the island of Mauritius in the Indian Ocean. First encountered by Portuguese sailors in the early 1500s, the dodo was a flightless bird that did not have any natural predators. By 1681, the dodo was extinct. Sailors had hunted the dodo for food and had introduced dogs and swine, which ate dodo eggs and the young.

Ongoing Assessment

CHECK YOUR READING *Answer: Flight gives birds access to food in a larger area, access to food and living places that are not reachable on foot or by swimming. Flight allows birds to escape from predators and other dangers, and find safe places to raise their young.*

Escaping Danger

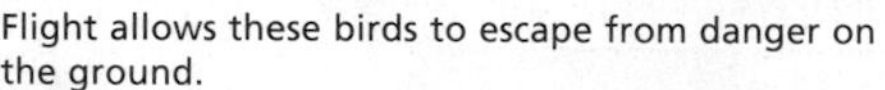

Flight allows these birds to escape from danger on the ground.

Catching Food

Flight allows this osprey to hunt for fish in bodies of water.

Some birds migrate very long distances. Ruby-throated hummingbirds, for example, migrate from Canada and the United States to Mexico and Central America each winter, flying nonstop 700 kilometers across the Gulf of Mexico.

By flying, birds can escape danger on the ground. Many species of birds are able to lay their eggs and raise their young in places that are difficult for predators to reach. Fossil evidence suggests that birds were the first vertebrate animal species to live on many of Earth's islands. Like the first organisms that adapted to live on land, birds that were the first vertebrates on an island usually had little competition for food, water, and living space.

CHECK YOUR READING How does flight benefit birds? Give three examples.

Birds lay eggs with hard shells.

Birds reproduce sexually. Many species of birds have distinctive ways of trying to attract mates. Some species sing, and others develop colorful feathers during mating season. Wild turkeys fight each other, bowerbirds construct elaborate nests, and woodcocks fly high in the air and then zig-zag back down. In most bird species, the male animals display and the female selects her mate.

The reproduction process for birds is similar to that of reptiles. After internal fertilization, a shell forms around each fertilized egg while it is still inside the female's body. Reptiles' eggs usually have flexible shells, but the shells of birds' eggs are hard.

450 Unit 3: **Diversity of Living Things**

DIFFERENTIATE INSTRUCTION

More Reading Support

G How do the shells of bird eggs differ from reptile's eggs? *Bird eggs are hard; reptile eggs are flexible.*

Advanced Invite students to investigate the different orders of birds and provide examples of the special adaptations that allow them to live in certain environments. Bird groups to investigate include perching birds, birds of prey, cavity-nesting birds, shore birds, diving birds, game birds, song birds, and ostriches and their relatives.

Challenge and Extension, p. 320

Usually the female bird chooses where to lay the eggs. Often this is a nest. In some bird species either the male or the female builds the nest, while in others, mated birds build a nest together. Bird eggs have to be kept at a constant, warm temperature or they will not develop. Nearly all birds use their body heat to keep the eggs warm. They sit on the eggs, which can support the adult bird's weight because the shells are hard. This process is called **incubation**. When the eggs hatch, the young birds are not yet able to fly. They must be cared for until they can meet their own needs.

These 3- to 8-day-old tanagers are being fed by both of their parents.

Most birds take care of their offspring.

In some bird species, male and female mates care for their offspring together. This is often the case for birds, such as the tanagers in the top photograph, whose young hatch before their eyes open or their feathers grow. It takes two adult birds to provide them with enough food, warmth, and protection.

The offspring of some species, like the ducks in the bottom photograph, hatch at a later state of development, with open eyes. They are already covered with down feathers and able to walk. In such species it's common for just one adult, usually the female, to incubate the eggs and care for the young.

These 7-day-old ducklings are able to find their own food while their mother watches over them.

13.3 Review

KEY CONCEPTS

1. What does an endothermic animal need to do in order to generate body heat?
2. What are two types of feathers, and what are their functions?
3. Describe three adaptations that make flight possible for birds.

CRITICAL THINKING

4. **Compare and Contrast** How is reproduction in birds similar to reproduction in reptiles? How does it different?
5. **Synthesize** Some flightless birds live on islands or in remote places where there are few predators. Explain why, in such an environment, flying birds' bodies might have adapted and become flightless.

CHALLENGE

6. **Hypothesize** Many species of birds begin migration while food is still plentiful in their current environment. Understanding what triggers migration in birds is an active area of scientific research. Develop a hypothesis about migration triggers in one species of bird. Describe how to test your hypothesis.

ANSWERS

1. Endotherms need to consume food to produce body heat.

2. Down feathers provide insulation. Contour feathers protect the body

3. Sample answers: feathers; fused bones and hollow bones; air sacs, crop and gizzard; and keen sight and hearing.

4. Both birds and reptiles lay eggs with shells. Bird eggs have hard shells while the shells of reptiles' eggs are flexible. Most reptiles do not incubate their eggs.

5. Flight requires a great deal of energy. If food was plentiful and there was little threat of predation, the birds may not need to fly.

6. Accept all reasonable hypotheses and tests.

Teacher Demo

To demonstrate the strength of eggs, bring in half of an egg carton and place four raw eggs in the corners. Ask students to predict what might happen if you place a heavy book on top of the eggs. The eggs should be strong enough to support a heavy dictionary.

Reinforce the BIG idea

Have students relate the section to the Big Idea.

 Reinforcing Key Concepts, p. 321

13.3 ASSESS & RETEACH

Assess

 Section 13.3 Quiz, p. 85

Reteach

Have students describe how each of these structures is an adaptation for flight.

- hollow bones
- air sacs
- contour features

Have students describe how each of these structures is an adaptation for a bird to live in different environments.

- down feathers
- wings
- hard-shelled eggs

Technology Resources

Have students visit **ClassZone.com** for reteaching of Key Concepts.

 **CONTENT REVIEW**

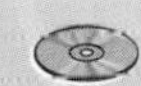 **CONTENT REVIEW CD-ROM**

CHAPTER INVESTIGATION

Focus

PURPOSE To determine how different bird beaks are adapted for gathering and eating different types of food

OVERVIEW Students will model bird beaks using everyday tools. They will:

- simulate how the different types of beaks are adapted for gathering food.
- make inferences about factors that influence how a bird meets its needs.

Lab Preparation

- Include tools that model beaks suited for significantly different foods, and "food" that can be collected with varying degrees of success.
- Prior to the investigation have students read through the investigation and prepare their data tables. Or you may wish to copy and distribute datasheets and rubrics.

 UNIT RESOURCE BOOK, pp. 340–348

 SCIENCE TOOLKIT, F15

Lab Management

Students can work in groups and rotate from station to station. Set up the feeding stations as follows:

- A rack of test tubes containing water simulates nectar in flowers.
- Dried pasta represents the diet of an omnivorous bird. Add "non-food" material such as rice that will filter through the slotted spoon.
- Millet seeds, spread in a thin layer over a flat surface, represent small seeds or insects consumed by a small bird. To make this task more challenging, bury the seeds under a layer of sand or dirt.
- Fill the jar halfway with rubber bands to simulate food for robins that pluck worms from beneath the ground.

INCLUSION Some students may have difficulty manipulating tools. Have them record observations while a partner performs the activities. Alternatively, station them at an area that is manageable.

CHAPTER INVESTIGATION

Bird Beak Adaptations

OVERVIEW AND PURPOSE The beaks of most birds are adapted for eating particular types of food. In this lab you will

- use models to simulate how different types of beaks function
- infer how the shape of a bird's beak might affect the food a bird eats

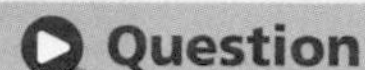

Question

For this lab, you will use a tool as a model of a specialized bird beak. You will try to obtain food with your beak at several different feeding stations. Each station will have a different type of food. Examine the tools that will be used for this lab, as well as the feeding stations. Then write a question about how beak shape might affect the food a bird eats. Your question should begin with *Which, How, When, Why,* or *What*. Keep in mind that you will be asked to answer this question at the end of the lab.

MATERIALS

- tweezers
- eyedropper
- slotted spoon
- pliers
- test tubes in rack
- water
- dried pasta
- millet seeds
- jar of rubber bands
- empty containers
- stopwatch

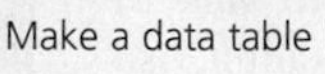

Procedure

1. Make a data table like the one shown on page 453.
2. Complete the title of your data table by writing in the name of the tool you will be using.
3. Before you start collecting food at one of the feeding stations, write a prediction in your data table. Predict how well you think the tool will function and why.

INVESTIGATION RESOURCES

 CHAPTER INVESTIGATION, Bird Beak Adaptations
- Level A, pp. 340–343
- Level B, pp. 344–347
- Level C, p. 348

Advanced students should complete Levels B & C.

 Writing a Lab Report, D12–13

Technology Resources

Customize this student lab as needed or look for an alternative. Print rubrics to assess student lab reports.

 **Lab Generator CD-ROM**

4 See how much food you can collect in one minute. To collect food, you must move it from the feeding station into a different container, and you may only touch the food with the tool.

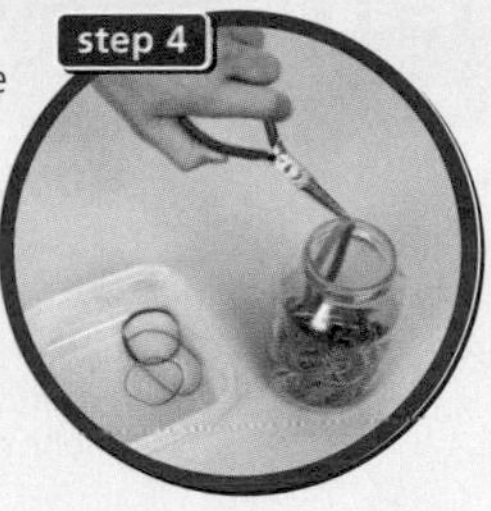

5 Describe your results in your data table.

6 Return the food you collected to the feeding station. Try to make it look just like it did when you started.

7 Repeat steps 3–6 at each of the other feeding stations.

Observe and Analyze

1. **INTERPRET DATA** At which feeding station did you have the best results? Why? Explain your answer.
2. **EVALUATE** How accurate were the predictions you made?
3. **APPLY** If you could visit each feeding station again, how would you change the way you used the tool to collect food? Explain your answer.
4. **SYNTHESIZE** What environmental and physical factors can a bird actually control when it is getting food?
5. **APPLY** Examine the beaks of the birds in the photographs below. Write a brief description of the shape of each bird's beak. Then, for each bird, name one type of food its beak might be suited for and one type of food each bird would probably not be able to eat.

Conclude

Write It Up

1. **INFER** What answers do you have for the question you wrote at the beginning of this lab?
2. **INFER** In what ways do you think the experience you had during this lab is similar to the ways real birds obtain food?
3. **IDENTIFY LIMITATIONS** What unexpected factors or problems might have affected your results?

INVESTIGATE Further

CHALLENGE How are other parts of birds' bodies specialized for the environments where they live? Investigate the feet of the following birds: ostrich, heron, woodpecker, pelican, and owl.

Bird Beak Adaptations

Question:

Table 1. Collecting Food with_______

Station	Prediction	Results
Water in test tubes		
Dried pasta		
Millet seeds		
Rubber bands in jar		

Post-Lab Discussion

- On the board, keep a tally of results. Students can infer why one tool worked better than others at the various stations.
- Ask students to describe the features of each "beak." Have them describe how each model bird beak compares with the real beak. *Sample answer: The eyedropper represents a beak that is long and narrow. This type of beak would feed from nectar in long, slender flowers.*
- Discuss any questions raised by the lab. How might students investigate or observe to find answers?

Observe and Analyze

1. *The eyedropper will be the best tool for gathering water from the test tubes. The forceps, spoon, and tweezers can collect this food from the pasta bowls in varying amounts. Tweezers will be most successful at gathering millet seed. The only tool that should easily reach the rubber bands is the forceps.*
2. *Accuracy will depend on original predictions. Answers should cite results as evidence of accuracy.*
3. *Accept all reasonable improvements upon feeding techniques.*

Conclude

1. *Answers depend on students' original questions. Check that they correlate.*
2. *Real birds have beaks adapted to allow them to get certain types of food successfully. A bird with a small, pointy beak cannot get much nourishment from an acorn.*
3. *Students might suggest different tools, designs for different feeding stations, or varying sizes and metabolic rates of birds.*
4. *A bird can choose the territory in which it searches for and obtains food. It can decide when to eat, and when to do other things. It can probably learn how to be a more effective food-obtainer by improving upon its "technique" for opening seeds, locating worms or insects.*
5. *Pictured birds are (left to right) hummingbird, parrot, and robin. Sample answer: hummingbird: needle shape, nectar; parrot: hook shape, hard seeds; robin: dart shape, worms, insects, small seeds*

INVESTIGATE Further

CHALLENGE Students should find that birds' feet are different sizes and shapes according to the environments in which they live and the needs of the birds. They may be adapted for running, wading in water, grabbing onto the sides of trees, and grabbing prey.

13.4 FOCUS

Set Learning Goals

Students will

- Recognize that mammals are endotherms.
- Describe the diversity of adaptations that are found in mammals.
- Explain that mammals produce milk, which is food for their young.
- Make models to show how fat keeps a mammal warm.

3-Minute Warm-Up

Display Transparency 37 or copy this exercise on the board:

Complete the Venn diagram to show how reptiles and birds are similar in the intersecting circles. In the outer circles, describe the features of each that differ.

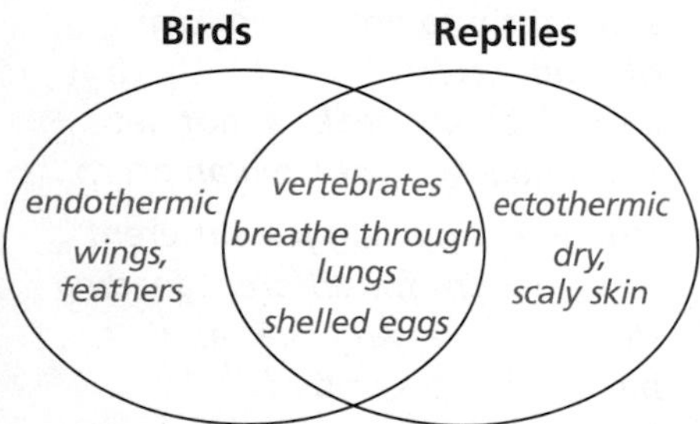

 3-Minute Warm-Up, p. T37

13.4 MOTIVATE

THINK ABOUT

PURPOSE To examine the diversity of mammals

DISCUSS Ask students what characteristics a tiny shrew, an elephant, and a polar bear have that make them suitable for different environments. *Shrews are very small and can live in small cracks and crevasses and escape the notice of predators; elephants have a trunk that can be used to drink large amounts of water and to grip things; polar bears have thick fur to keep them warm.*

KEY CONCEPT

13.4 Mammals live in many environments.

BEFORE, you learned

- Endotherms can stay active in cold environments
- Many bird adaptations are related to flight
- Birds lay hard-shelled eggs and usually take care of their young

NOW, you will learn

- About mammals as endotherms
- About the diversity of adaptations in mammals
- That mammals produce milk, which is food for their young

VOCABULARY

mammal p. 455
placenta p. 458
gestation p. 458

THINK ABOUT

How diverse are mammals?

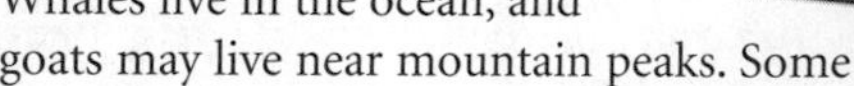

Mammals have adapted to survive in many environments and come in many shapes and sizes. Whales live in the ocean, and goats may live near mountain peaks. Some monkeys live in tropical forests, and polar bears survive in frozen areas. An elephant might not fit in your classroom, but the tiny shrew shown here could fit on your finger. As you read this chapter, think about the characteristics of mammals that help them to survive in such a variety of ways.

Mammals are a diverse group.

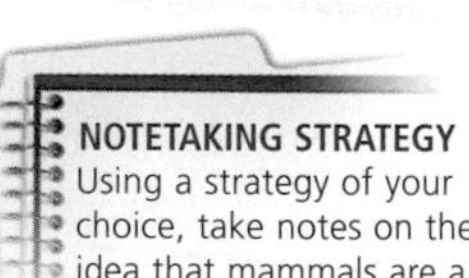

NOTETAKING STRATEGY
Using a strategy of your choice, take notes on the idea that mammals are a diverse group. Be sure to include mammal characteristics.

The group of vertebrates called mammals includes many familiar animals. Mice are mammals, and so are cows, elephants, and chimpanzees. You are a mammal, too. Bats are mammals that can fly. Some mammals, including whales, live in water.

Some mammal species, such as raccoons and skunks, have adapted to live in many sorts of environments, including cities. Others, such as cheetahs and polar bears, have adaptations for meeting their needs in just a few environments.

Mammals are a diverse animal group. Although there are less than 5000 species of mammals on Earth, mammal species come in many shapes and sizes, and have many different ways of moving, finding

454 Unit 3: **Diversity of Living Things**

RESOURCES FOR DIFFERENTIATED INSTRUCTION

Below Level

UNIT RESOURCE BOOK

- Reading Study Guide A, pp. 324–325
- Decoding Support, p. 337

 **AUDIO CDS**

Advanced

UNIT RESOURCE BOOK

- Challenge and Extension, p. 330
- Challenge Reading, pp. 333–334

English Learners

UNIT RESOURCE BOOK

Spanish Reading Study Guide, pp. 328–329

 **AUDIO CDS**

- Audio Readings in Spanish
- Audio Readings (English)

food, and eating. These are some of the characteristics that distinguish **mammals** from other animals:

- All mammals have hair during some part of their lives.
- Most mammal species have teeth specialized for consuming particular kinds of food.
- All mammal species produce milk, with which they feed their young.

Learn more about mammals.

Mammals are endotherms.

You have learned that endothermic animals are able to stay active in cold environments. This is because endotherms maintain a constant body temperature. Mammals are endotherms. This means that they use some of the food they consume to generate body heat. Mammals also have adaptations for controlling body temperature.

Hair

Many species of mammals have bodies covered with hair. Like birds' feathers, hair is an adaptation that allows mammals to have some control over the warmth or coldness of their bodies. Mammals that live in cold regions, like polar bears, have hair that keeps them warm. Desert mammals, such as camels, have hair that protects them from extreme heat.

Most mammals have at least two types of hair. Soft, fluffy underhairs keep heat close to their bodies, like the down feathers of birds. Water-resistant guard hairs cover the underhairs and give the animal's fur its color.

Some species of mammals also have specialized hairs. A specialized structure is one that performs a particular function. For example, whiskers are sensory hairs that are part of an animal's sense of touch. Porcupines' quills are hairs that function in self defense.

What are three functions of hair?

Colored guard hairs give this tiger its stripes. Its whiskers are specialized sensory hairs. It also has underhairs, which you cannot see.

This porcupine's quills are specialized guard hairs.

13.4 INSTRUCT

Address Misconceptions

IDENTIFY Ask students what characteristics they use to identify a vertebrate. Students might hold the misconception that animal is synonymous with vertebrate, more specifically mammal. Mammals are often the prototypical animal followed by birds, reptiles, and fish in descending order of usage.

CORRECT Construct a bulletin board with the main heading *Vertebrates* and subheadings *Backbones, Ectothermic, Endothermic.* Have students put the names of vertebrate species on scraps of paper and tack them under the appropriate headings.

REASSESS Based on the bulletin board activity above, ask students to re-evaluate their criteria for characteristics of vertebrates.

Technology Resources

Visit **ClassZone.com** for background on common student misconceptions.

MISCONCEPTION DATABASE

Teach from Visuals

To help students interpret the photographs showing animal hair, ask:

What are the specialized hairs found on these mammals? *whiskers; quills*

What are the hairs' functions? *sense of touch; self defense*

Ongoing Assessment

Recognize that mammals are endotherms.

Ask: What adaptation enables mammals to survive in cold climates? *Their bodies are insulated and they are endothermic.*

Sample answers: Hair controls heat loss (keeps heat in or lets it out); hair can be water-resistant; it provides color for camouflage; hairs can be sensory structures such as whiskers, or used for defense such as quills.

DIFFERENTIATE INSTRUCTION

More Reading Support

A How do all mammals feed their young? *They produce milk.*

B How are some mammals' hairs like down feathers? *They keep heat close to the body.*

English Learners Place the terms *mammal, placenta,* and *gestation* on a classroom Science Word Wall with brief definitions of each. Use the chapter summary on p. 460 to help students focus on key concepts and vocabulary.

Teach Difficult Concepts

Many students think that any animal living in water is a fish, including whales, dolphins, and other marine mammals. Ask students to describe the characteristics of mammals and compare them to those of fish. Then ask them to make a two-column chart of marine animals, with headings "Breathe with Gills" and "Breathe with Lungs." (The "Breathe with Lungs" list may include reptiles, amphibians, and mammals.) Remind students that animals are classified according to body characteristics, DNA evidence, and fossil histories, not where the animals live.

INVESTIGATE How Body Fat Insulates

PURPOSE To make a model of how well fat keeps a mammal warm

TIPS *15 min.* The "blubber gloves" can be made (following procedure step 1) prior to the lesson and reused. You may want to spread newspaper on work surfaces to control spills.

WHAT DO YOU THINK? *Students should find that the hand without the glove gets cold more quickly than the hand in the glove.*

CHALLENGE *A mammal that lives in a hot environment would not be as likely to have a thick layer of body fat. The animal would most likely have very little body fat.*

 Datasheet, How Body Fat Insulates, p. 331

Technology Resources

Customize this student lab as needed or look for an alternative. Print rubrics to assess student lab reports.

Lab Generator CD-ROM

Ongoing Assessment

 *Answer: Body fat insulates mammals and stores energy obtained from food.*

Body Fat

 C

Some mammal species that live in water, such as dolphins, have very little hair. These mammals have a layer of fat, called blubber, that plays an important role in maintaining body temperature. The blubber is located between the animal's skin and muscles, and provides its organs with insulation from heat and cold.

Body fat can also be a storage place for energy. When a mammal consumes more food than it needs, the extra energy may be stored in its fat cells. Later, if the animal needs energy but cannot find food, it can use the energy stored in the fat.

For example, animals that hibernate, such as woodchucks, may eat a lot more than they need to survive at times when plenty of food is available. This makes them fat. Then, while they are hibernating, they do not have to eat, because their body fat provides them with the energy they need.

 What are two ways that body fat functions in mammals?

INVESTIGATE How Body Fat Insulates

How well does fat keep a mammal warm?

A layer of body fat between the muscles and the skin allows some mammals to survive in very cold places. In this investigation, you will experience how well that adaptation works by making a blubber glove model.

SKILL FOCUS
Making models

MATERIALS
- 3 zip-lip plastic bags, 1/2-gallon size
- can of vegetable shortening
- bowl of ice water

TIME
15 minutes

PROCEDURE

1. Half fill one large, zip-lip plastic bag with vegetable shortening. Turn another bag inside out and place it inside the bag with the shortening. Zip the edges of the two bags together so that the shortening is sealed between them.
2. Place one hand inside this "blubber glove." Place the other hand inside the third bag. Then submerge both hands in a tub of ice water. Which hand stays warmer? For how long? Record your observations.

WHAT DO YOU THINK?

How well did the blubber glove insulate your hand?

CHALLENGE Would you expect an animal that lives in a very hot environment to have a thick layer of body fat?

DIFFERENTIATE INSTRUCTION

More Reading Support

C Where is a mammal's blubber located? *between skin and muscle*

Below Level Invite interested students to find out more about marine mammals. Students should make a chart listing the characteristics that help to classify these animals as mammals. Alternatively, they might draw the animals and label the characteristics, as in the diagram of the dolphin, p. 457.

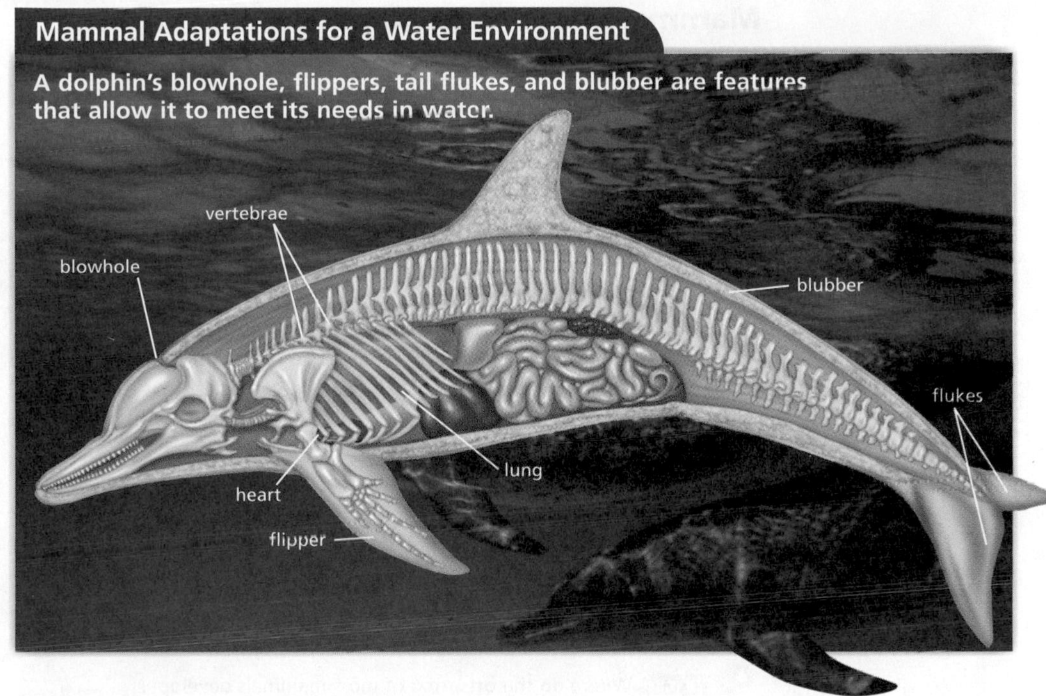

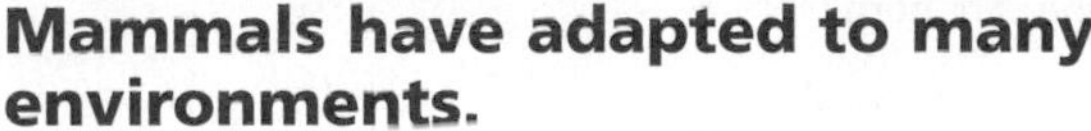

Mammals have adapted to many environments.

Scientists think mammals appeared on Earth about 200 million years ago. Fossil evidence suggests that the first mammals were small land vertebrates with four limbs, a tail, and specialized teeth. They probably had fur and were most active at night.

Over millions of years, those early mammals adapted to live in many different environments and became the diverse group of species they are today. Moles, for example, live almost entirely underground. They have strong limbs for digging and organs specialized for sensing invertebrate prey in the dark. Spider monkeys, on the other hand, live mostly in trees. A spider monkey can use all four of its long limbs and its flexible, grasping tail to move through a forest without touching the ground.

E The first mammals lived on land, but over time some species adapted to live in watery environments. Some of them, such as otters and walruses, live mostly in water but can also be found on land. Others, such as dolphins and whales, have bodies so completely adapted for life in the water that they no longer have a way of moving on land. If you look carefully at the diagram above, however, you will see that a dolphin's body plan differs in some important ways from that of a fish.

Teach from Visuals

To help students interpret the illustration of mammal adaptations for water, ask:

- Which features of marine mammals enable them to live in water? *blowhole, flippers, flukes, blubber*
- What is the purpose of the blowhole? *It allows the mammal to come to the surface of the water and breathe.*
- What do the bones inside the flipper resemble in other mammals? *forelimbs and fingers*

Integrate the Sciences

The first mammals appeared during the Triassic Period more than 190 million years ago. These early mammals evolved from mammal-like reptiles that dominated Earth about 280 million years ago during the Permian Period before dinosaurs appeared on Earth. The early mammals were as small as mice and most likely fed on insects. Mammals persisted during the reign of dinosaurs most likely because they were nocturnal, small, and inconspicuous. When dinosaurs became extinct about 65 million years ago, mammals flourished, due to lack of competition from the dinosaurs and the many adaptations that they had evolved over time. The Cenozoic Era, from 65 million years ago to the present is considered the Age of Mammals.

EXPLORE the BIG idea

Revisit "Internet Activity: Where in the World?" on p. 427. Ask students to compare the list of adaptations from the activity with those they have read about concerning mammals.

DIFFERENTIATE INSTRUCTION

More Reading Support

D When did mammals appear on Earth? *about 200 million years ago*

E Which land mammals spend most of their time in the water? *otters and walruses*

Advanced Have students change one feature of the skeleton of a mammal to design a fictional mammal species that is well suited to live in a real or fictional environment. Students should create a poster showing both the original and altered skeletons. On the altered skeleton, students should extrapolate the animal's behaviors or capabilities in relation to its environment.

- Challenge and Extension, p. 330
- Challenge Reading, pp. 333–334

Develop Critical Thinking

INFER Point out that the major difference among the three groups of mammals is the way in which they reproduce and give birth. Ask: What advantage do mammals with young that develop with help from placentas have over mammals that lay eggs and have young develop in pouches? *Eggs are less likely to be eaten by predators. Marsupial young might not make it into their mother's pouch right after they are born. Placental mammals are more developed when born.*

Teach from Visuals

To help students interpret the graph showing gestation, point out that this is a bar graph that is used to compare sets of data. Ask:

Which animal has the longest period of gestation? *The elephant—84–88 weeks.* How do you know? *The bar for elephant is the longest on the graph.*

History of Science

Domestication of mammals occurred gradually, perhaps before the development of agriculture. Domestication of goats and sheep occurred around 7000 B.C. Cattle and pigs followed around 4000 B.C. to 3000 B.C. The dog was most likely the first pet, dating back almost 10,000 years ago. Cats, revered in ancient Egypt, most likely appeared as pets 5000 years ago.

Ongoing Assessment

Answer: inside the mother's body

Mammals have reproductive adaptations.

Mammals reproduce sexually. Before a mammal can produce offspring, it finds a mate. Some mammals, such as lions, live in groups that include both males and females. However, most mammals live alone most of the time. They find a mate when they are ready to reproduce. Some mammal species breed only at certain times of the year. Others can reproduce throughout the year.

Development Before Birth

VOCABULARY
Remember to make a word magnet for the terms *placenta* and *gestation.*

? F

Fertilization occurs internally in mammals. In almost every species of mammal, the offspring develop inside the female's body. Many mammals have a special organ called a **placenta** that transports nutrients, water, and oxygen from the mother's blood to the developing embryo. The embryo's waste materials leave through the placenta and are transported out of the mother's body along with her waste.

? G

The time when a mammal is developing inside its mother is called **gestation**. As you can see in the diagram, the length of the gestation period is different for different species. Gestation ends when the young animal's body has grown and developed enough for it to survive outside the mother. Then it is born.

Where do the offspring of most mammals develop before they are born?

Length of Gestation

The length of gestation varies greatly in placental mammals.

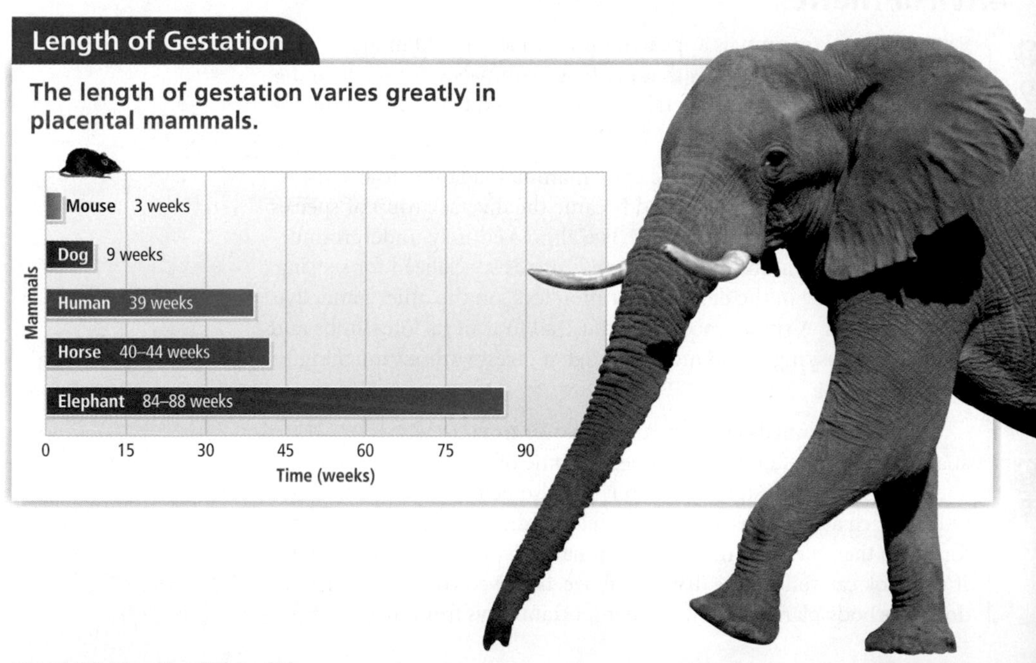

DIFFERENTIATE INSTRUCTION

More Reading Support

F What is the organ that provides a mammalian embryo with nutrients? *the placenta*

G When does gestation end? *when the mammal is born*

Below Level Invite interested students to find out about the gestation periods of other mammals and create a bar graph displaying their findings.

458 Unit 3: **Diversity of Living Things**

Not all mammals fully develop inside their mothers. The duck-billed platypus and two species of spiny anteaters have young that hatch from eggs. Mammals in a group called the marsupials (mahr-SOO-pee-uhlz), which includes kangaroos, develop inside the mother at first but are born when they are still extremely small. Right after birth, a young marsupial climbs across its mother to a special pouch on the outside of her body. It completes its development there. Only one marsupial, the opossum, lives in North America.

Raising Young

Milk, a high-energy liquid food full of proteins, fats, sugars, and other nutrients, is the first food young mammals consume. Each species' milk has a different combination of these ingredients.

This dog is feeding her puppies with milk.

Mammals' bodies have special glands for producing milk, called mammary glands. In almost all mammal species, only females' mammary glands function. This means that only female mammals can feed the young with milk. In most mammal species, females gestate and care for the offspring alone. However, in some mammal species, the male helps raise the young.

Different species of mammals are born at varying stages of development. Most mice are helpless, blind, and naked at birth, while giraffes can walk soon after they are born. The length of time a young mammal needs care from an adult varies. Some seals nurse their young for less than a month before leaving them to survive on their own. Some whales live alongside their young for a much longer time. However, humans may be the mammal species that takes care of their offspring for the longest time of all.

13.4 Review

KEY CONCEPTS

1. Why is a bat classified as a mammal instead of a bird? Why are whales classified as mammals and not fish?
2. Name two adaptations that allow mammals to have control over body temperature.
3. How does the way that mammals feed their young differ from the ways other animals feed their young?

CRITICAL THINKING

4. **Apply** One day on your way home from school, you see an animal that you have never seen before. What clues would you look for to tell you what type of animal it is?
5. **Synthesize** Make a Venn diagram that shows how the vertebrate animal groups you learned about in this chapter are similar and different.

CHALLENGE

6. **Evaluate** This section begins with the statement "mammals are a diverse group." Explain what this means and why it is a true statement. How does the diversity of mammals compare to the diversity of other living things, such as bacteria, plants, arthropods, or fish?

ANSWERS

1. Bats and whales are classified as mammals because they have body hair, body fat, and mammary glands.

2. hair and body fat

3. Young mammals consume milk that is produced by female mammals' bodies.

4. Student answers should reflect knowledge that physical features and behavior can be used to identify animals.

5. The best diagrams will show overlaps between the groups clearly and accurately.

6. Mammals have larger variety in size, shape, behavior, and environment than any other type of organisms. There are more species of arthropods, fish, etc., than mammals; however, they are limited to certain environments and body types.

Ongoing Assessment

Explain that mammals produce milk which is food for their young.

Ask: How does producing milk help mammals to care for their young? *Milk is a high-energy food which is easily taken in and digested by newborns. It provides young mammals with the nutrients they need.*

EXPLORE the BIG idea

Revisit "What Animals Live Near You?" on p. 427. Ask students if they would like to add to or revise their lists.

Reinforce the BIG idea

Have students relate the section to the Big Idea.

 Reinforcing Key Concepts, p. 332

13.4 ASSESS & RETEACH

Assess

 Section 13.4 Quiz, p. 86

Reteach

Ask students to describe each of the following characteristics of mammals and explain how each allows mammals to live in different environments.

- hair
- blubber
- specialized teeth
- placenta

Technology Resources

Have students visit **ClassZone.com** for reteaching of Key Concepts.

 CONTENT REVIEW

 CONTENT REVIEW CD-ROM

BACK TO

the BIG idea

Have students choose one of the vertebrate groups in the chapter and describe how the animals in this group are adapted to live in a variety of environments. *Students should give specific examples of body traits and characteristics.*

KEY CONCEPTS SUMMARY

SECTION 13.1
Ask students to explain why the endoskeleton is an important adaptation for vertebrate animals. *The endoskeleton provides support and grows as the animal grows, allowing vertebrates to become larger in size than invertebrates.*

SECTION 13.2
Which structures of amphibians and reptiles allow them to live on land? Explain. *They have lungs for breathing, limbs for movement; reptiles have eggs with shells and yolks that allow the enclosed embryos to develop on land.*

SECTION 13.3
How are bird bodies adapted for flight? *They have wings, contour feathers, hollow bones, and air sacs to increase the amount of oxygen in the body.*

SECTION 13.4
What are three ways in which mammals bear their young? *Monotremes lay eggs; marsupials give birth to live young that develop in pouches; the young of placental mammals develop fully inside placentas until they are born.*

Review Concepts

- Big Idea Flow Chart, p. T33
- Chapter Outline, pp. T39–T40

13 Chapter Review

the BIG idea

Vertebrate animals live in most of Earth's environments.

KEY CONCEPTS SUMMARY

1 Vertebrates are animals with endoskeletons.

All **vertebrate** animals have an **endoskeleton** which includes vertebrae, or backbones.

Most vertebrates are fish. Fish are adapted for life in a water environment.

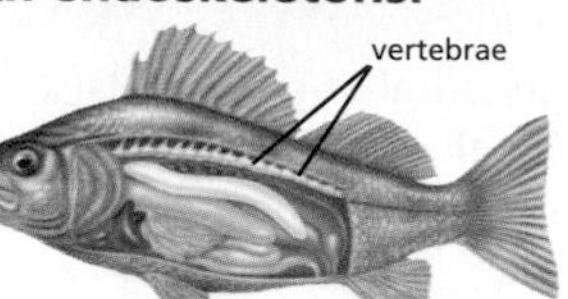

VOCABULARY
vertebrate p. 429
endoskeleton p. 429
scale p. 433

2 Amphibians and reptiles are adapted for life on land.

Amphibians and **reptiles** have adaptations for moving, getting food, and breathing on land.

Most amphibians live in moist places.

Many reptiles live in hot, dry places.

VOCABULARY
ectotherm p. 442
amphibian p. 439
reptile p. 440

3 Birds meet their needs on land, in water, and in the air.

Birds have adaptations that allow them to survive in many environments. Many of the features and behaviors of birds relate to flight.

VOCABULARY
endotherm p. 446
incubation p. 451

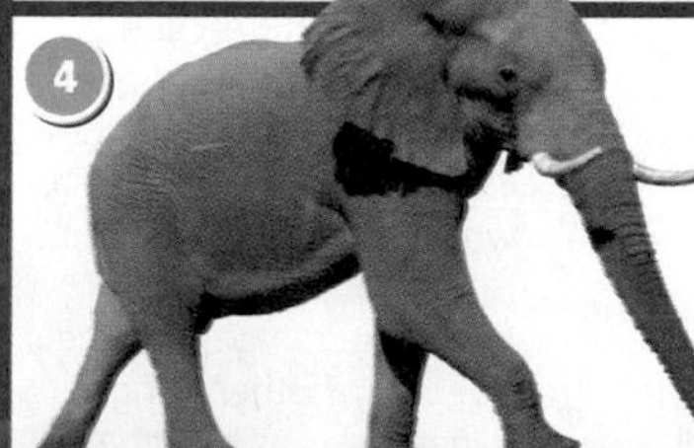

4 Mammals live in many environments.

Mammal species live in many environments. Mammals have adaptations that allow them to survive in cold places. They also have distinctive reproductive adaptations.

VOCABULARY
mammal p. 455
placenta p. 458
gestation p. 458

460 Unit 3: Diversity of Living Things

Technology Resources

Have students visit **ClassZone.com** or use the CD-ROM for a cumulative review of concepts.

 CONTENT REVIEW

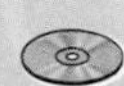 CONTENT REVIEW CD-ROM

Engage students in a whole-class interactive review of Key Concepts. Edit content as you wish.

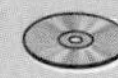 POWER PRESENTATIONS

Reviewing Vocabulary

Place each vocabulary term listed below at the center of a description wheel diagram. Write some words describing it on the spokes.

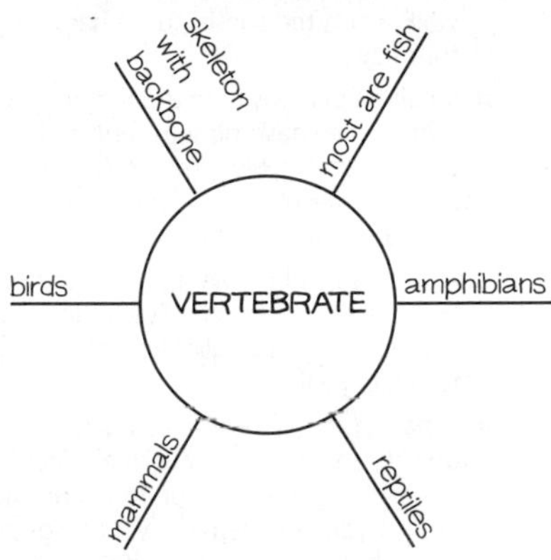

1. endotherm
2. migration
3. ectotherm
4. scale
5. incubation
6. gestation

Reviewing Key Concepts

Multiple Choice *Choose the letter of the best response.*

7. The vertebrate endoskeleton differs from an arthopod's exoskeleton because it
   a. supports muscles
   b. protects organs
   c. is inside the animal's body
   d. has joints

8. Most vertebrate species are
   a. fish
   b. amphibians
   c. birds
   d. mammals

9. Fish obtain oxygen from water with structures called
   a. vertebrae
   b. fins
   c. lungs
   d. gills

10. Down feathers provide insulation for a bird's body because they
    a. trap warm air between them
    b. are waterproof
    c. overlap each other
    d. are slightly oily

11. Which organ do both fish and amphibians have?
    a. lateral line
    b. lungs
    c. gills
    d. scaly skin

12. Mammals differ from other vertebrates because mammals
    a. can lay eggs
    b. can produce milk
    c. are endotherms
    d. are able to swim

13. The two types of vertebrates that lay their eggs in water are
    a. amphibians and birds
    b. reptiles and fish
    c. fish and amphibians
    d. mollusks and fish

14. Which statement is true?
    a. All birds are ectotherms.
    b. All birds can fly.
    c. All birds have two wings and two legs.
    d. All birds have teeth and beaks.

15. The organ that transports materials between a female mammal and the offspring developing inside her body is called a
    a. yolk
    b. placenta
    c. blubber
    d. vertebrae

Short Answer *Write a short answer to the questions below.*

16. Describe how you would determine if an animal was a salamander or a lizard.

17. Why do bird eggs have to be incubated?

Reviewing Vocabulary

1. *Sample answer: bird, mammal, survives cold, constant temperature, internal source of heat, needs lots of energy*
2. *Sample answer: birds, Monarch butterflies, seasonal, winter home, summer home, warmer weather*
3. *Sample answer: reptiles, amphibians, fish, changing temperature, can't survive cold, needs less energy*
4. *Sample answer: overlapping, bird's feet, reptile's skin, fish, bony fish, keratin*
5. *Sample answer: birds, monotremes, hard shells, marsupials, keeps warm, endotherms*
6. *Sample answer: mammals, live young, inside mother, mice: 3 weeks, elephants: 88 weeks, humans: 39 weeks*

Reviewing Key Concepts

7. *c*
8. *a*
9. *d*
10. *a*
11. *c*
12. *b*
13. *c*
14. *c*
15. *b*
16. *A salamander has smooth, moist, skin. A lizard has dry, scaly skin.*
17. *Bird eggs must be incubated because their body temperature must be maintained and kept warm by the parent bird.*

ASSESSMENT RESOURCES

UNIT ASSESSMENT BOOK
- Chapter Test, Level A, pp. 87–90
- Chapter Test, Level B, pp. 91–94
- Chapter Test, Level C, pp. 95–98
- Alternative Assessment, pp. 99–100
- Unit Test, A, B, & C, pp. 101–112

SPANISH ASSESSMENT BOOK
- Spanish Chapter Test, pp. 57–60
- Spanish Unit Test, pp. 61–64

Technology Resources

Edit test items and answer choices.

 **Test Generator CD-ROM**

Visit **ClassZone.com** to extend test practice.

 **Test Practice**

Thinking Critically

18. *The person in Mexico, because reptiles are ectotherms and more common in warmer, drier climates.*
19. *Polar bears should have more body fat because fat provides insulation from the cold.*
20. *The bird's skeleton provides support, a means of movement, and grows as the bird's body grows.*
21. *digestive system—has a gizzard that helps in digestion, circulatory system—heart*
22. *Answers may vary. Sample answers include the hypothesis that birds that do not migrate would have a more varied diet than migratory birds.*
23. *The salamander will be extinct by the year 2019. Divide 825 by 50 to get 16.5. Round to up 17, then add 2002 + 17. The sum is 2019.*
24. *a. reptile; b. amphibians; c. mammal; d. birds*

the BIG idea

25. *Penguins and seals are both vertebrates and endotherms. They have body coverings (feathers for penguin and hair for the seal) that help keep heat in. They burn food to create body heat, and they store excess food energy as fat.*
26. *Answers will vary depending on the animal that students chose.*

UNIT PROJECTS

Have students present their projects. Use appropriate rubrics from the Unit Resource Book to evaluate their work.

 Unit Projects, pp. 5–10

Thinking Critically

18. **PREDICT** Imagine that you live in Mexico and you have a pen pal who lives in Iceland. Both of you want to know about animals in the other person's country. Which of you will be more likely to have seen wild reptiles? Why?
19. **APPLY** Polar bears live in an arctic environment. Jaguars live in a rain forest environment. Which animal would you expect to have more body fat? Explain.

Refer to diagram below as you answer parts of the next two questions.

20. **COMPARE** Birds, like all vertebrates, have internal skeletons. What functions does a bird's skeleton have in common with all other vertebrates?
21. **INFER** This diagram shows only some of a bird's body systems. Name two systems that are not shown here, including organs that belong to them and their functions.
22. **HYPOTHESIZE** Not all birds migrate. Some birds, such as pigeons and house sparrows, stay in one living place through the winter. What do you think you would find if you compared the diets of birds that migrate with those of birds that do not?
23. **MATH AND SCIENCE** Scientists studying an endangered species of rainforest salamanders estimated that only 875 of these animals were still living in 2002. If this salamander population decreases by 50 animals per year, in what year will it become extinct? Explain how you found your answer.
24. **CLASSIFY** Imagine that you move to a new place and spend a year watching nearby animals. Read each description and identify each animal described below as a fish, amphibian, reptile, bird, or mammal.
    - **a.** A scaly animal warms itself on your sidewalk when the sun is out. It has dry skin, four legs, and a tail.
    - **b.** Small animals swim in a pond near your home. They have no legs, but they do have tails. As they grow older, their tails shrink and they develop four limbs. Then they disappear from the pond.
    - **c.** A furry animal chews a hole under your porch and seems to be living there. You later see it with smaller animals that appear to be its young.
    - **d.** A pair of flying, feathered animals collect objects and carry them into an opening under the gutter of your neighbor's house. At first you see them carrying twigs and grass, but later it looks as if they are carrying worms.

the BIG idea

25. **DRAW CONCLUSIONS** Look again at the picture on pages 426–427. What do penguins and seals have in common? What adaptations do some species of birds and mammals have that allow them to survive in cold environments like Antarctica?
26. **PROVIDE EXAMPLES** Think of an example of a species from each of the vertebrate animal groups you've learned about, and describe an adaptation that suits each to the environment where it lives. Explain your answers.

UNIT PROJECTS

Evaluate all the data, results, and information from your project folder. Prepare to present your project. Be ready to answer questions posed by your classmates about your results.

MONITOR AND RETEACH

If students are having trouble applying the concepts in Chapter Review items 20 and 21, suggest that they review the diagram of the bird on p. 449. Then have students create concept maps for the following:

- structures in the body that are adapted for flight
- structures in the skin that are characteristic of all birds

Students may benefit from summarizing one or more sections of the chapter.

 Summarizing the Chapter, pp. 358–359

Standardized Test Practice

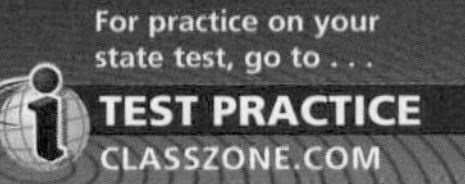

Analyzing Diagrams

Read the text and study the diagram, and then choose the best response for the questions that follow.

Vertebrates, such as birds, fish, and mammals, have endoskeletons. This internal skeleton is made up of a system of bones that extends throughout the body. Muscles can attach directly to the bones, around joints—the place where two bones meet. As shown in the generalized diagram below, at least two muscles are needed to produce movement. One of the muscles contracts, or shortens, pulling on the bone, while the other muscle extends, or is stretched.

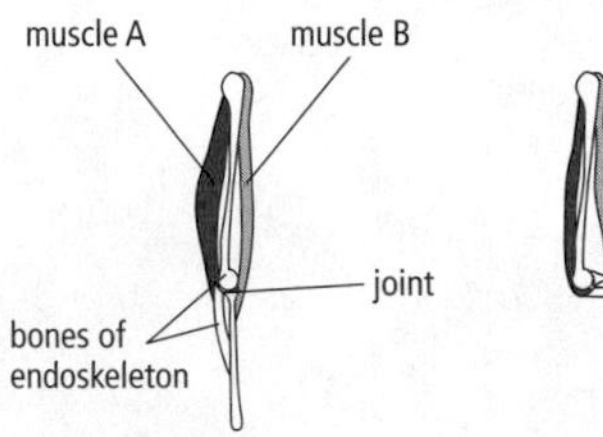

1. Endoskeletons are made up of
   a. contracting muscles
   b. extending muscles
   c. internal bones
   d. external bones
2. A muscle produces movement by
   a. pulling
   b. relaxing
   c. extending
   d. rotating
3. A joint is where
   a. one muscle connects to another
   b. one bone connects to another
   c. a muscle connects to a bone
   d. the bone ends
4. The leg in the diagram bends when
   a. muscle A contracts
   b. muscle A relaxes
   c. muscle B contracts
   d. muscles A and B contract
5. What is the main point of the diagram and the text above?
   a. Two muscles are needed to produce movement in vertebrates.
   b. Vertebrates have internal skeletons.
   c. When one muscle shortens, another muscle gets longer.
   d. Movement in vertebrates is the result of the interaction of muscles and bones.

Extended Response

Use terms from the word box to answer the next question. Underline each term you use in your answer.

6. Many fish go forward by moving their tails from side to side. Describe the action of the muscles on each side of the fish as the tail moves from one side to the other.

contract	pull
extend	muscle

7. Using what you know about joints and muscles and the diagram, describe what happens to muscles and bones as you bend your leg at the knee.

METACOGNITIVE ACTIVITY

Have students answer the following questions in their **Science Notebook:**

1. What are some strategies you used to learn about the similarities and differences among the various groups of vertebrates?
2. What questions do you still have about the characteristics of fish, amphibians, reptiles, birds, or mammals?
3. How did your unit project help you gain a better understanding of the vertebrates studied in this chapter?

Analyzing Diagrams

1. c *3. b* *5. d*
2. a *4. c*

Extended Response

6. RUBRIC

4 points for a response that correctly answers the question and uses the following terms accurately:

- contract
- pull
- extend
- muscle

Sample answer: The fish will have muscles on both sides of its body that attach to its tail. When muscles on one side contract they pull the tail to that side. When this happens the muscles on the other side are extended. For the tail to move to the other side, the extended muscles must contract, pulling the tail back to the other side. The muscles that were contracted are now relaxed.

3 points correctly answers the question and uses three terms accurately
2 points correctly answers the question and uses two terms accurately
1 point correctly answers the question and uses one term accurately

7. RUBRIC

4 points for a response that correctly answers the question and meets the following criteria:

- reflects that the knee is a joint
- describes accurately how the bones move
- understanding of how muscles contract to pull bones
- understanding how a pair of muscles works together

Sample answer: When the knee bends, the two bones that meet at the knee change from forming a straight line to forming an angle. The center of the angle is the joint where the two leg bones meet. One muscle contracts and forces one bone to swivel around the joint. At the same time, a second muscle relaxes to allow this movement. The second muscle must contract for the bones to move back to their original place.

3 points includes three of the above criteria
2 points includes two of the above criteria
1 point includes one of the above criteria

McDougal Littell Science

Ecology

symbiosis

Tickbird
(Buphagus erythrorhynchus)

Impala
(Aepyceros melampus)

Ecology Contents Overview

Unit Features

VIDEO SUMMARY

SCIENTIFIC AMERICAN FRONTIERS

"Prairie Comeback" is a segment of the Scientific American Frontiers series that aired on PBS stations. In this video, host Alan Alda visits the Tallgrass Prairie Preserve in northeastern Oklahoma. This is the location of an attempt to reconstruct an ecosystem that once covered more than a quarter of the continental United States. The Great Plains was once the largest grassland on Earth. Cultivation and the disappearance of wildlife, including buffalo herds, resulted in the prairie's disappearance. In 1989, the Nature Conservancy identified a large ranch that had never been farmed and therefore still had all the plants that grew on the original prairie. On 50 square miles of land, they have attempted to create a model of the prairie. They introduced a herd of buffalo to graze on the prairie plants. Today, a system based on controlled fires and grazing buffalo reproduces the life cycles of the original prairie.

National Science Education Standards

A.9.a–d Understandings about Scientific Inquiry

E.6.a–f Understandings about Science and Technology

F.5.a–e Science and Technology in Society

G.1.a–b Science as a Human Endeavor

G.2.a Nature of Science

FRONTIERS in Science

ECOSYSTEMS ON FIRE

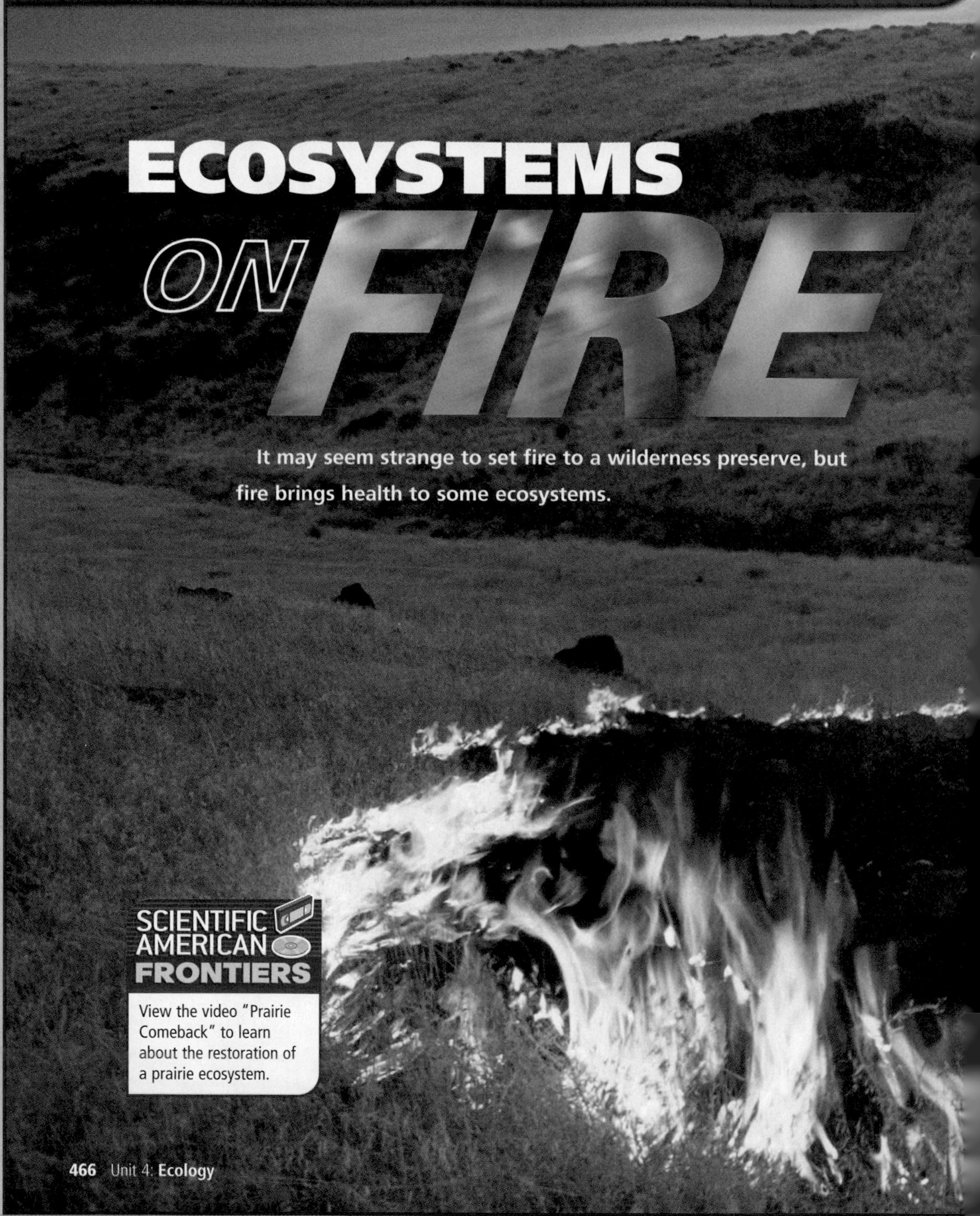

It may seem strange to set fire to a wilderness preserve, but fire brings health to some ecosystems.

SCIENTIFIC AMERICAN FRONTIERS

View the video "Prairie Comeback" to learn about the restoration of a prairie ecosystem.

ADDITIONAL RESOURCES

Technology Resources

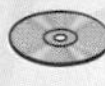
Scientific American Frontiers Video: *Ecosystems on Fire:* 8-minute video segment that introduces the unit.

ClassZone.com
CAREER LINK, Ecologist

Guide student viewing and comprehension of the video:

Video Teaching Guide, pp. 1–2; Video Viewing Guide, p. 3; Video Wrap-Up, p. 4

Scientific American Frontiers Video Guide, pp. 9–12

Unit projects procedures and rubrics:

Unit Projects, pp. 5–10

An astonishing variety of plants blooms in this prairie in Missouri.

Fire and Life

Intense heat, smoke, the crackling of burning grasses, the crashing of flaming trees—all these characteristics of fire seem threatening. In recent years, forest fires have burned huge areas of forest and have endangered people and property nearby. But even though fire can be destructive, it can also be an agent of life. In fact, scientists are actively using fire to manage ecosystems—areas that contain specific groups of living and nonliving things. Prairies, forests, and woodlands are examples of ecosystems. A

The fear of fire has led people to limit fires that are a natural part of some ecosystems. Preventing or putting out smaller fires in a forest ecosystem can mean trouble. Occasional small fires burn small amounts of material and cause only limited damage. Without these smaller fires, burnable materials may build up and lead to the outbreak of a catastrophic fire.

The species of living things in some ecosystems have adaptations that allow them to thrive on fire. B In North America trees such as lodgepole pine and jack pine depend upon flames to release seeds from their cones. Cape lilies lying under the forest floor blossom almost immediately after a forest fire. On prairies, flowers such as the rare coastal gayfeather in Texas or the fringed prairie orchid in Illinois benefit from prairie fires.

DIFFERENTIATE INSTRUCTION

More Reading Support

A What are scientists using fire to do? *manage ecosystems*

B Why do some species survive and even thrive in fires? *because they have adaptations*

Advanced Have students determine the locations of major forests, woodlands, and prairies in the United States. Ask them to indicate these locations on a blank map. Students may wish to look up statistics on occurrences of wildfires in the United States and draw a conclusion about the conditions of these forests and prairies.

FOCUS

Set Learning Goals

Students will

- Observe positive and negative effects of prairie fires.
- Examine unanswered questions concerning ecosystem restoration.
- Explore the parts of an ecosystem.

Remind students that frontiers are undeveloped fields for discovery or research, and that the "Ecosystems on Fire" video shows real scientists gathering and analyzing data to find answers or solve problems. Have students look at the photographs and title on pp. 466–467 and predict what questions the scientists are trying to answer.

INSTRUCT

Scientific Process

Emphasize to students that understanding the effects of fires on ecosystems requires that scientists learn as much as they can about the plants and animals that live in the ecosystem. Have students review the parts of the scientific process on pages xxiii–xxv and ask what part this step falls under. *Determine what is known.*

Integrate the Sciences

Executing a controlled burn in an ecosystem requires attention to many details. Besides knowing how plants and animals will react to the effects of the fire, what other knowledge, skills, or personnel should scientists have before attempting a controlled burn? *They should know how to start fires and how fires spread.*

Teach from Visuals

Have students look at the photos of the forest after the controlled burn and seven months after the burn. Ask students why the second photo shows a healthier ecosystem. *There is new, green vegetation and the trees have leaves in the second photo.*

Scientific Process

Ask students to identify the skill scientists use most in studying ecosystems. *observing*

Sharing Results

Ask students why it is even more crucial that scientists share what they learn from their observations of different ecosystems with other scientists. *The lives of people and animals depend upon the ecosystem. The better scientists understand an ecosystem, the better they help preserve the lives that depend on it.*

Social Studies Connection

The American bison, or buffalo, has had a troubled existence in the United States. Once it was a major source of food and clothing for many Native American tribes. However, increased settlement on the prairie brought increased hunting and near extinction for the buffalo as well as for the Native Americans that depended on them.

Seven months after a controlled burn, light shines on a new patch of wild hyacinth growing at the base of an oak tree.

Observing Patterns

C

Ecosystems include living things, such as plants and animals, and nonliving things, such as water and soil. Fires affect both the living and the nonliving. The photographs above show part of an oak woodland ecosystem. The photograph on the left shows a burn—a fire set deliberately by humans. The photograph on the right shows the same area seven months later.

Ashes left from fires add nutrients to the soil. Fire also opens space on the forest floor. Areas that were shaded by small trees, plants, and dead branches receive light. Over time, wild hyacinth and other new plants grow around the oak, and new insects and animals move into the area.

View the "Prairie Comeback" segment of your Scientific American Frontiers video to see how understanding ecosystems can help bring a prairie into bloom.

IN THIS SCENE FROM THE VIDEO a bison grazes on new growth that appears after the prairie is burned.

D

BRINGING BACK THE PRAIRIE At one time natural events, such as lightning, along with human activity caused regular patterns of fire on the prairie. Bison grazed on tender young plants that grew up after fires, and the plants that weren't eaten by the bison had room to grow. In 1989, an organization called The Nature Conservancy turned the Chapman-Barnard Cattle Ranch in Northeast Oklahoma into the Tall Grass Prairie Restoration Preserve.

Scientists at the preserve are using controlled fire and reintroducing bison to the area. Today there are more than 750 species of plants and animals growing in the preserve.

DIFFERENTIATE INSTRUCTION

More Reading Support

C What do ecosystems include? *living and nonliving things*

D Name one natural phenomenon that could start a prairie fire. *lightning*

Below Level Have students identify all of the words on this page that refer to protecting or safeguarding: *conservatory, restoration,* and *preserve.* Point out to students how the words *conservatory* and *preserve* share a stem, *–serve.* Have students think of another word that has this stem, like *reserve,* and ask if it has a similar meaning. *Yes. When you reserve something, you are protecting it in a way.*

In tall-grass prairie ecosystems, fire provides similar benefits. Fire burns away overgrown plants, enriches the soil, and clears the way for the growth of new plants. Bison prefer to graze on these new plants that appear after a fire.

A New Understanding

Although some of the benefits provided by ecosystems can't be measured, researchers are starting to measure the financial contributions of ecosystems. Ecosystems may help clean our water, balance gases in the atmosphere, and maintain temperature ranges.  E

Researchers today are studying these benefits. In fact, a new frontier in ecology, called ecosystem services, is emerging. This new study is gaining the attention of both scientists and economists.  F

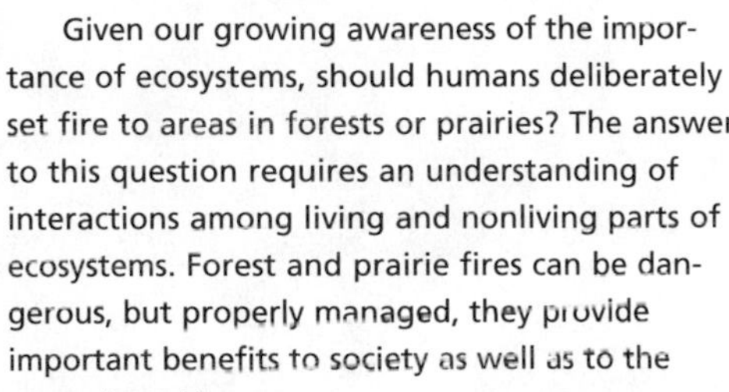

Given our growing awareness of the importance of ecosystems, should humans deliberately set fire to areas in forests or prairies? The answer to this question requires an understanding of interactions among living and nonliving parts of ecosystems. Forest and prairie fires can be dangerous, but properly managed, they provide important benefits to society as well as to the natural world.

UNANSWERED Questions

Understanding the connections within ecosystems raises more questions. In the coming years, people will need to analyze the costs and benefits of ecosystem restoration.

- How will humans balance the need to feed the human population with the cost of destroying ecosystems such as the prairie?
- How can scientists and wildlife managers protect people and property near forests while maintaining forest ecosystems?
- How do ecosystems protect natural resources, such as soil and water?

UNIT PROJECTS

As you study this unit, work alone or with a group on one of the projects listed below. Use the bulleted steps to guide your project.

Build an Ecosystem

Use an aquarium or other container to build an ecosystem.

- Set up your ecosystem. Observe it daily, and record your observations.
- Bring your ecosystem into your classroom, or take photographs and make diagrams of it. Present the record of your observations along with the visual displays.

Conservation Campaign

Find out how much water, paper, and energy are used in a month at your school.

- Describe a plan for conserving resources.
- Present your plan. You might make posters, write announcements, or perform a short skit.

Design a Park

You are part of a group that is planning a park near your school. Your group wants the park to include plants that lived in the area twenty-five years ago.

- Collect information from local museums, park districts, or botanic gardens. You can also visit Web sites sponsored by those organizations.
- Prepare a report and drawing of your park design.

CAREER CENTER
CLASSZONE.COM

Learn more about careers in ecology.

UNANSWERED Questions

Have students read the questions and think of some of their own. Remind them that scientists always end up with more questions—that inquiry is the driving force of science.

- With the class, generate on the board a list of new questions.
- Students can add to the list after they watch the *Scientific American Frontiers* Video.
- Students can use the list as a springboard for choosing their Unit Projects.

UNIT PROJECTS

Encourage students to pick the project that most appeals to them. Point out that each is long-term and will take several weeks to complete. You might group or pair students to work on projects and in some cases guide student choice. Each project has two worksheet pages, including a rubric to guide students through criteria, process, and schedule.

 Unit Projects, pp. 5–10

REVISIT concepts introduced in this article:

Chapter 14
- Ecosystems support life, pp. 473–479
- Living things depend on the environment, pp. 473–474
- All ecosystems need certain materials, p. 480

Chapter 15
- Groups of living things interact within ecosystems, pp. 509–515
- Ecosystems are always changing, pp. 527–533

Chapter 16
- Human activities affect the environment, pp. 553–561
- People are working to protect ecosystems, pp. 562–571

DIFFERENTIATE INSTRUCTION

More Reading Support

E Name one way ecosystems help us. *clean water, balance gases in the atmosphere*

F Who is interested in ecosystem services? *scientists and economists*

Differentiate Unit Projects Projects are appropriate for varying abilities. Allow students to choose the ones that interest them most and let them vary their product. Encourage below level students to give visual or oral presentations or to record audio presentations about their topic.

Below Level Encourage students to try "Build an Ecosystem."

Advanced Challenge students to complete "Design a Park."

CHAPTER

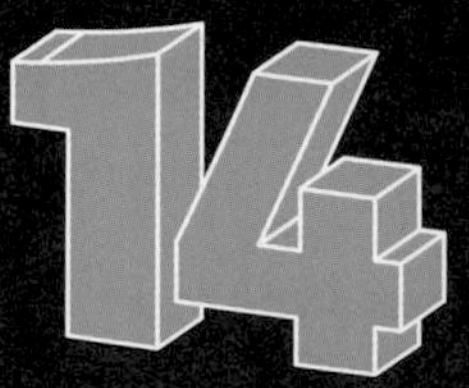

Ecosystems and Biomes

Life Science UNIFYING PRINCIPLES

PRINCIPLE 1
All living things share common characteristics.

PRINCIPLE 2
All living things share common needs.

PRINCIPLE 3
Living things meet their needs through interactions with the environment.

PRINCIPLE 4
The types and numbers of living things change over time.

Unit 4: Ecology BIG IDEAS

CHAPTER 14 Ecosystems and Biomes
Matter and energy together support life within an environment.

CHAPTER 15 Interactions within Ecosystems
Living things within an ecosystem interact with each other and the environment.

CHAPTER 16 Human Impact on Ecosystems
Humans and human population growth affect the environment.

CHAPTER 14 KEY CONCEPTS

SECTION 1

Ecosystems support life.
1. Living things depend on the environment.
2. Biotic factors interact with an ecosystem.
3. Many abiotic factors affect ecosystems.

SECTION 2

Matter cycles through ecosystems.
1. All ecosystems need certain materials.
2. Water cycles through ecosystems.
3. Carbon cycles through ecosystems.
4. Nitrogen cycles through ecosystems.

SECTION 3

Energy flows through ecosystems.
1. Living things capture and release energy.
2. Models help explain feeding relationships.
3. Available energy decreases as it moves through an ecosystem.

SECTION 4

Biomes contain many ecosystems.
1. Regions of Earth are classified into biomes.
2. Water covers most of Earth's surface.

T The Big Idea Flow Chart is available on p. T1 in the **UNIT TRANSPARENCY BOOK.**

Previewing Content

SECTION

Ecosystems support life. pp. 473–479

1. Living things depend on the environment.
An **ecosystem** comprises organisms and their physical environment. **Ecology** is the scientific study of how organisms interact with their environment and with other organisms.

- Natural ecosystems include water, air, and sunlight, as well as microorganisms, plants, and animals.
- **Biotic factors** are the living parts of an ecosystem.
- **Abiotic factors** are the nonliving parts.

2. Biotic factors interact with an ecosystem.
Every organism affects, and is affected by, other organisms in its ecosystem. Moles are a good example of this interrelatedness. They eat insects, worms, and grubs. They can severely damage plants, but moles help keep insect populations in check. Mole tunnels aerate soil, which is necessary for the growth of soil organisms and plant roots.

3. Many abiotic factors affect ecosystems.
Abiotic factors include any nonliving features of the environment, from soil fertility to climate characteristics—precipitation, temperature, air currents, and humidity. Here is a short list of the most influential factors.

- available water
- temperature
- available light
- soil content

The size of soil particles affects how much air and water the soil can hold.

SECTION

Matter cycles through ecosystems. pp. 480–485

1. All ecosystems need certain materials.
Living things need certain materials, or matter, to meet their needs. This matter remains in the ecosystem, moving through it in continuous **cycles,** in which the matter changes form, but is never created or destroyed.

2. Water cycles through ecosystems.
All substances on Earth, including water, are repeatedly recycled. Five processes make up the **water cycle.**

- Condensation: water vapor condenses to liquid in the atmosphere.
- Precipitation: water falls back to Earth.
- Transpiration: plants take up water in their roots and release it from their leaves.
- Respiration: animals release water vapor as they exhale.
- Evaporation: heat changes liquid water to gaseous water vapor, which rises into the atmosphere.

3. Carbon cycles through ecosystems.
Life on Earth is based on carbon compounds. The **carbon cycle** includes several different processes.

- Photosynthesis removes carbon from the air
- Animals obtain carbon by eating plants.
- Plants and animals release carbon dioxide during respiration.
- Carbon contained in fossil fuels and wood is released as carbon dioxide during combustion.

4. Nitrogen cycles through ecosystems.
Nitrogen is required for all life. Almost 78 percent of the air is nitrogen, but organisms cannot use nitrogen in gaseous form. In the **nitrogen cycle**, bacteria in soil and roots fix nitrogen by changing it from a gas to nitrate compounds that can be taken up by plants.

Common Misconceptions

MISCONCEPTION DATABASE
CLASSZONE.COM Background on student misconceptions

PHOTOSYNTHESIS Students generally think that plants absorb food from the soil rather than manufacturing it. Through photosynthesis, plants make food—sugars—from sunlight, carbon dioxide, and water from the environment.

 This misconception is addressed on p. 476.

WATER CYCLE Though students may be familiar with the water cycle, they often think that water gets added to the system from somewhere. Earth has a finite amount of water that cycles through living things and the environment continuously.

 This misconception is addressed on p. 481.

Previewing Content

SECTION

Energy flows through ecosystems.
pp. 486–493

1. Living things capture and release energy.
Energy and matter can move through an ecosystem as food.
- **Producers** capture energy from sunlight or, in a few cases, from chemicals in the deep sea.
- **Consumers** obtain food by eating producers or other consumers.
- **Decomposers** break down dead plant and animal matter into simpler compounds, returning them to the water or soil so that the matter may be used again.

2. Models help explain feeding relationships.
Food chains and food webs are models that show how energy and matter move through the organisms of an ecosystem.
- A **food chain** shows one path of energy movement through an ecosystem, from producer (e.g., grass) to herbivore or primary consumer (grasshopper), to a secondary consumer (robin), to a tertiary consumer (hawk).
- A **food web** shows many paths of energy movement through an ecosystem. It indicates that each organism eats and is eaten by several organisms.

3. Available energy decreases as it moves through an ecosystem.
An **energy pyramid** models the amount of energy available to producers and consumers in an ecosystem. At the bottom of the pyramid are the producers, which use the Sun's abundant energy to manufacture sugars. At the top of the pyramid are the tertiary consumers.
This model shows that the amount of available energy decreases with each succeeding layer.

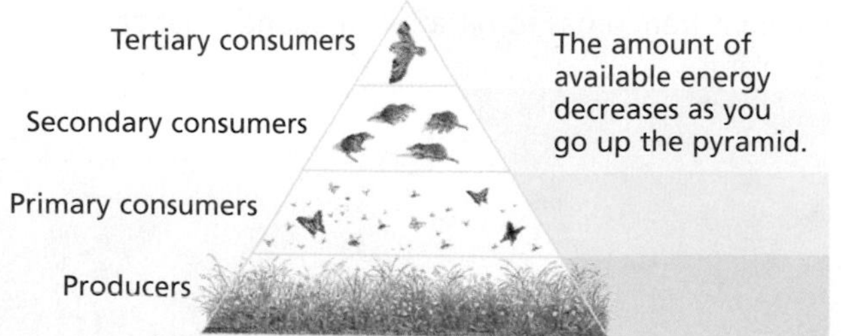

SECTION

Biomes contain many ecosystems.
pp. 494–501

1. Regions of Earth are classified into biomes.
Earth's six terrestrial **biomes** are regions made up of ecosystems with similar plant life and climate.
- Tundra has little precipitation and lowest temperatures of all land biomes. Typical vegetation is lichens and mosses.
- Taiga has cold winters and short, cool summers. It supports **coniferous** trees with needlelike leaves.
- Desert has little precipitation and can be hot or cold. Typical vegetation is cacti and small plants.
- Grassland has rich soil but supports few shrubs and trees.
- Temperate forest includes mostly **deciduous** trees.
- Tropical rain forest is consistently warm and wet. Typical vegetation is broadleaf evergreen trees, with a huge number of species.

2. Water covers most of Earth's surface.
Freshwater biomes include
- rivers and streams, with high oxygen levels; plants are limited to shorelines and slow-moving shallows.
- lakes and ponds, with middling to very low oxygen levels; plants grow along the shoreline or float in upper layers.
- wetlands, such as swamps and bogs, that are wet most or all of the year; waterlogged soils limit plant species.
- **estuaries,** which are mixed fresh and salt water, where river meets ocean; fertile ecosystems act as nurseries for fish and other sea animals.

Marine biomes include
- coastal ocean, or seashore areas; many ecosystems, from sandy beaches to mud flats to rocky shores.
- open ocean to depths where sunlight stops penetrating; the plankton here serve as the basis of the ocean food web.
- deep ocean, where sunlight does not reach.

Common Misconceptions

MISCONCEPTION DATABASE
CLASSZONE.COM Background on student misconceptions

FOOD CHAINS AND WEBS Students often think of feeding relationships as linear. They may misunderstand the food chain model in several ways: 1. They think arrows represent who eats whom rather than flow of energy; 2. They think organisms high up the chain eat everything that is lower on the chain; 3. They see only linear food chains as unconnected to a food web.

 This misconception is addressed on p. 490.

PYRAMID OF ENERGY Students commonly think that energy accumulates as it moves up a food chain or web. In reality, significant amounts of available energy are lost moving up a food chain or web. The least amount of energy is available and the fewest number of organisms are present at the top of an energy pyramid.

 This misconception is addressed in the reteach on p. 492.

Previewing Labs

Lab Generator CD-ROM
Edit these Pupil Edition labs and generate alternative labs.

EXPLORE the BIG idea

Lab	TIME	MATERIALS
How Do Plants React to Sunlight? p. 471 Students observe a plant's response to light.	10 minutes	potted plant
What Is Soil? p. 471 Students determine what materials make up soil.	10 minutes	garden soil, funnel, clear plastic bottle with cap, water
Internet Activity: A Prairie Ecosystem, p. 471 Students simulate a prairie ecosystem.	20 minutes	computer with Internet access

SECTION 1

Lab	TIME	MATERIALS
EXPLORE Your Environment, p. 473 Students measure the temperature in different places to discover variations in warmth.	10 minutes	thermometer, stopwatch
CHAPTER INVESTIGATION **Soil Samples,** pp. 478–479 Students investigate the characteristics of three soil types.	40 minutes	50 mL each of clay, coarse sand, loam; 3 pieces of paper; spoon; hand lens; toothpick; eyedropper; 3 pieces of filter paper; 3 plastic funnels; 3 large beakers; small beaker; dropper; water; stopwatch

SECTION 2

Lab	TIME	MATERIALS
EXPLORE The Water Cycle, p. 480 Students cover part of a plant and discover that plants give off water vapor.	10 minutes	1 small potted plant, 1 clear plastic bag, tape, water
INVESTIGATE Carbon, p. 483 Students observe how carbon is released in the ocean by adding vinegar to broken sea shells.	15 minutes	whole seashell or fragments, mortar and pestle, white vinegar, small beaker

SECTION 3

Lab	TIME	MATERIALS
EXPLORE Energy, p. 486 Students demonstrate energy conversion by using light to produce heat, which produces air movement.	10 minutes	paper, marker, scissors, thread, tape, desk lamp
INVESTIGATE Decomposers, p. 489 Students observe the effect of decomposers on plant matter.	30 minutes	clear soda bottle with cap, scissors, stones, garden soil, leaves, slices of fruit, masking tape, marker, water

SECTION 4

Lab	TIME	MATERIALS
INVESTIGATE Climate, p. 499 Students collect and graph climate data for their area.  Climate Graph, p. 52	20 minutes	graph data, 2 colored pencils, Climate Graph

 **Additional INVESTIGATION,** The Water Cycle, A, B, & C, pp. 71–79; Teacher Instructions, pp. 200–201

Previewing Chapter Resources

CHAPTER 14
Ecosystems and Biomes

INTEGRATED TECHNOLOGY

CLASSZONE.COM
- eEdition Plus
- EasyPlanner Plus
- Misconception Database
- Content Review
- Test Practice
- Visualizations
- Simulations
- Resource Centers
- Internet Activity: A Prairie Ecosystem
- Math Tutorial

SCILINKS.ORG
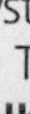
SCILINKS

CD-ROMS
- eEdition
- EasyPlanner
- Power Presentations
- Content Review
- Lab Generator
- Test Generator

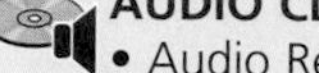
AUDIO CDS
- Audio Readings
- Audio Readings in Spanish

LABS AND ACTIVITIES

EXPLORE the Big Idea, p. 471
- How Do Plants React to Sunlight?
- What Is Soil?
- Internet Activity: A Prairie Ecosystem

UNIT RESOURCE BOOK
- Family Letter, p. vii
- Spanish Family Letter, p. viii
- Unit Projects, pp. 5–10

Lab Generator CD-ROM
Generate customized labs.

SECTION

Ecosystems support life.
pp. 473–479

Time: 3 periods (1.5 blocks)

Lesson Plan, pp. 11–12

INTEGRATED TECHNOLOGY

RESOURCE CENTER, Ecosystems

UNIT TRANSPARENCY BOOK
- Big Idea Flow Chart, p. T1
- Daily Vocabulary Scaffolding, p. T2
- Note-Taking Model, p. T3
- 3-Minute Warm-Up, p. T4

LABS AND ACTIVITIES

- EXPLORE Your Environment, p. 473
- CHAPTER INVESTIGATION Soil Samples, pp. 478–479

UNIT RESOURCE BOOK
CHAPTER INVESTIGATION, Soil Samples, A, B, & C, pp. 62–70

SECTION

Matter cycles through ecosystems.
pp. 480–485

Time: 2 periods (1 block)

Lesson Plan, pp. 21–22

INTEGRATED TECHNOLOGY

- **RESOURCE CENTER,** Cycles in Nature
- **VISUALIZATION,** Nitrogen Cycle
- **MATH TUTORIAL**

UNIT TRANSPARENCY BOOK
- Daily Vocabulary Scaffolding, p. T2
- 3-Minute Warm-Up, p. T4

LABS AND ACTIVITIES

- EXPLORE The Water Cycle, p. 480
- INVESTIGATE Carbon, p. 483
- Math in Science, p. 485

UNIT RESOURCE BOOK
- Datasheet, Carbon, p. 30
- Math Support and Practice, pp. 60–61
- Additional INVESTIGATION, The Water Cycle, A, B, & C, pp. 71–79

SECTION

Energy flows through ecosystems.
pp. 486–493

Time: 2 periods (1 block)
Lesson Plan, pp. 32–33

INTEGRATED TECHNOLOGY

UNIT TRANSPARENCY BOOK
- Daily Vocabulary Scaffolding, p. T2
- 3-Minute Warm-Up, p. T5
- "Energy Flows Through Ecosystems" Visual, p. T6

LABS AND ACTIVITIES

- EXPLORE Energy, p. 486
- INVESTIGATE Decomposers, p. 489
- Connecting Sciences, p. 493

UNIT RESOURCE BOOK
Datasheet, Decomposers, p. 41

SECTION

Biomes contain many ecosystems.
pp. 494–501

Time: 3 periods (1.5 blocks)
Lesson Plan, pp. 43–44

INTEGRATED TECHNOLOGY

RESOURCE CENTER, Land and Aquatic Biomes

UNIT TRANSPARENCY BOOK
- Big Idea Flow Chart, p. T1
- Daily Vocabulary Scaffolding, p. T2
- 3-Minute Warm-Up, p. T5
- Chapter Outline, pp. T7–T8

LABS AND ACTIVITIES

INVESTIGATE Climate, p. 499

UNIT RESOURCE BOOK
- Climate Graph, p. 52
- Datasheet, Climate, p. 53

KEY TO ICONS 

 CD/CD-ROM  INTERNET  Teacher Edition  UNIT TRANSPARENCY BOOK  SPANISH ASSESSMENT BOOK

Pupil Edition · UNIT RESOURCE BOOK · UNIT ASSESSMENT BOOK · SCIENCE TOOLKIT

READING AND REINFORCEMENT	ASSESSMENT	STANDARDS
 • Frame Game, B26–27 • Combination Notes, C40 • Daily Vocabulary Scaffolding, H1–8  **UNIT RESOURCE BOOK** • Vocabulary Practice, pp. 57–58 • Decoding Support, p. 59 • Summarizing the Chapter, pp. 80–81  **Audio Readings CD** Listen to Pupil Edition. 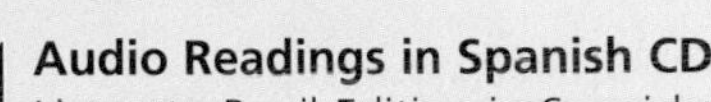 **Audio Readings in Spanish CD** Listen to Pupil Edition in Spanish.	• Chapter Review, pp. 503–504 • Standardized Test Practice, p. 505 **UNIT ASSESSMENT BOOK** • Diagnostic Test, pp. 1–2 • Chapter Test, A, B, & C, pp. 7–18 • Alternative Assessment, pp. 19–20 Spanish Chapter Test, pp. 61–64  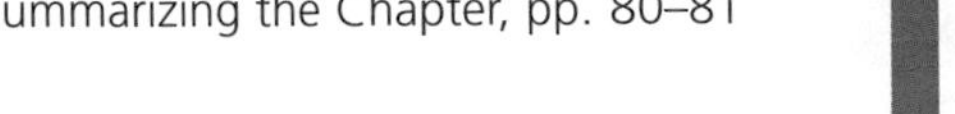 **Test Generator CD-ROM** Generate customized tests.  **Lab Generator CD-ROM** Rubrics for Labs	National Standards A.2–8, A.9.a–c, A.9.e–f, C.4.b–d, D.1.f See p. 470 for the standards.
UNIT RESOURCE BOOK • Reading Study Guide, A & B, pp. 13–16 • Spanish Reading Study Guide, pp. 17–18 • Challenge and Extension, p. 19 • Reinforcing Key Concepts, p. 20	 Ongoing Assessment, pp. 474–477  Section 14.1 Review, p. 477  **UNIT ASSESSMENT BOOK** Section 14.1 Quiz, p. 3	National Standards A.2–7, A.9.a–b, A.9.e–f, C.4.c
 **UNIT RESOURCE BOOK** • Reading Study Guide, A & B, pp. 23–26 • Spanish Reading Study Guide, pp. 27–28 • Challenge and Extension, p. 29 • Reinforcing Key Concepts, p. 31	 Ongoing Assessment, pp. 481–484  Section 14.2 Review, p. 484  **UNIT ASSESSMENT BOOK** Section 14.2 Quiz, p. 4	National Standards A.2–8, A.9.a–c, A.9.e–f, D.1.f
 **UNIT RESOURCE BOOK** • Reading Study Guide, A & B, pp. 34–37 • Spanish Reading Study Guide, pp. 38–39 • Challenge and Extension, p. 40 • Reinforcing Key Concepts, p. 42 • Challenge Reading, pp. 55–56	 Ongoing Assessment, pp. 487–491  Section 14.3 Review, p. 492  **UNIT ASSESSMENT BOOK** Section 14.3 Quiz, p. 5	National Standards A.2–7, A.9.a–b, A.9.e–f, C.4.b–c
 **UNIT RESOURCE BOOK** • Reading Study Guide, A & B, pp. 45–48 • Spanish Reading Study Guide, pp. 49–50 • Challenge and Extension, p. 51 • Reinforcing Key Concepts, p. 54	 Ongoing Assessment, pp. 496, 498, 500  Section 14.4 Review, p. 501  **UNIT ASSESSMENT BOOK** Section 14.4 Quiz, p. 6	National Standards A.2–8, A.9.a–c, A.9.e–f, C.4.d

Previewing Resources for Differentiated Instruction

CHAPTER INVESTIGATION

Leveled resources present the same concepts for different abilities.

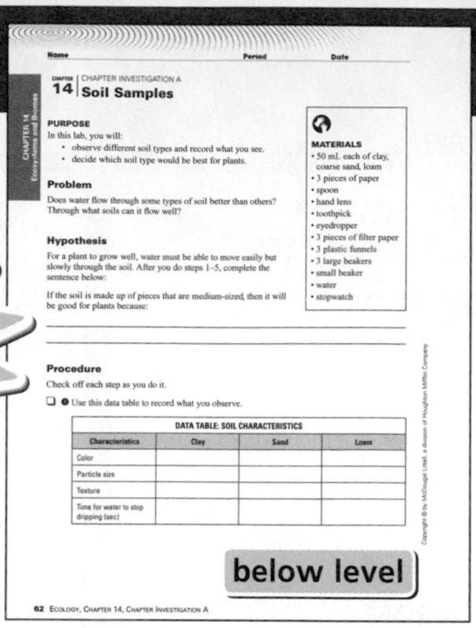

CHAPTER 14 | CHAPTER INVESTIGATION A
Soil Samples

below level

R **UNIT RESOURCE BOOK,** pp. 62–65

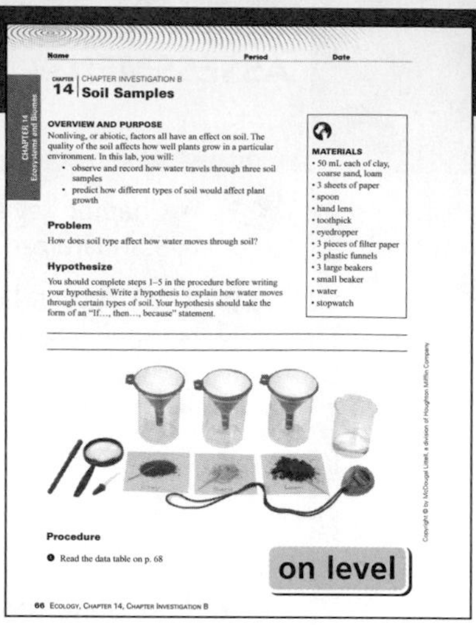

CHAPTER 14 | CHAPTER INVESTIGATION B
Soil Samples

on level

R pp. 66–69

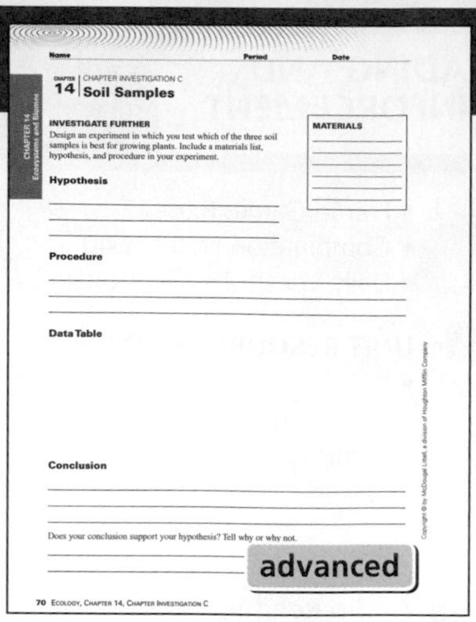

CHAPTER 14 | CHAPTER INVESTIGATION C
Soil Samples

advanced

R pp. 66–70

READING STUDY GUIDE

Reading Study Guide is also in Spanish.

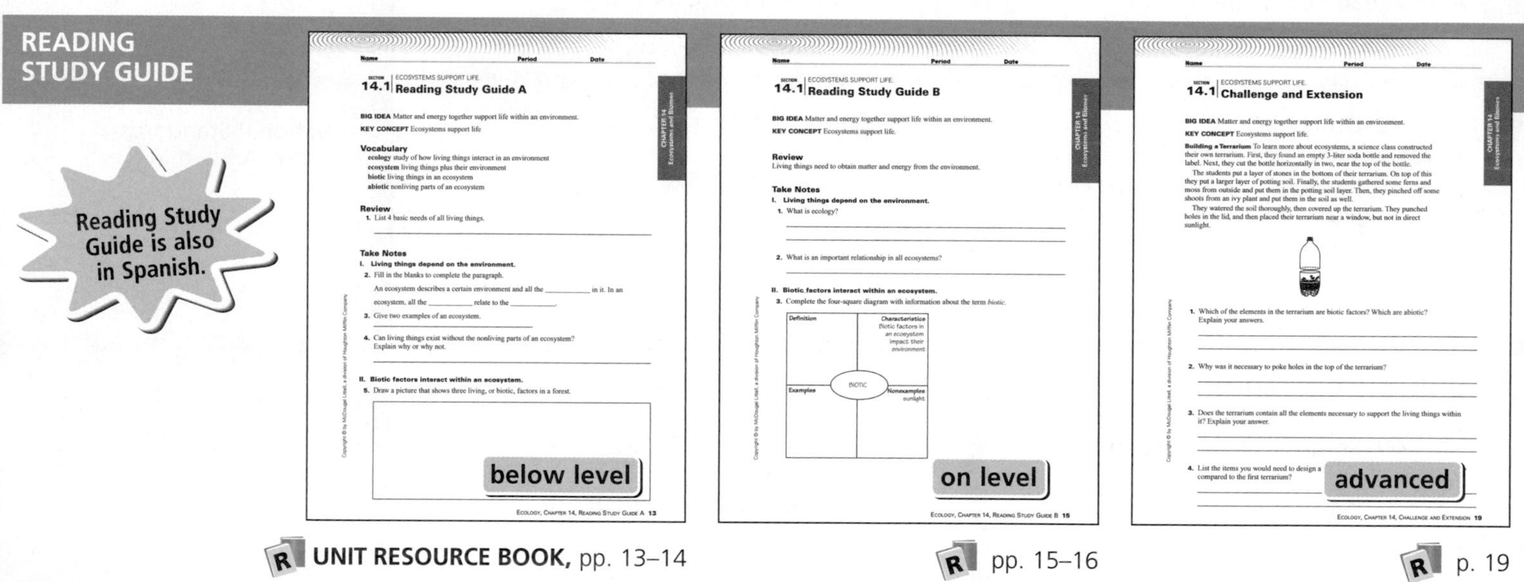

SECTION 14.1 | ECOSYSTEMS SUPPORT LIFE
Reading Study Guide A

below level

SECTION 14.1 | ECOSYSTEMS SUPPORT LIFE
Reading Study Guide B

on level

SECTION 14.1 | ECOSYSTEMS SUPPORT LIFE
Challenge and Extension

advanced

R **UNIT RESOURCE BOOK,** pp. 13–14

R pp. 15–16

R p. 19

CHAPTER TEST

Chapter Test is also in Spanish.

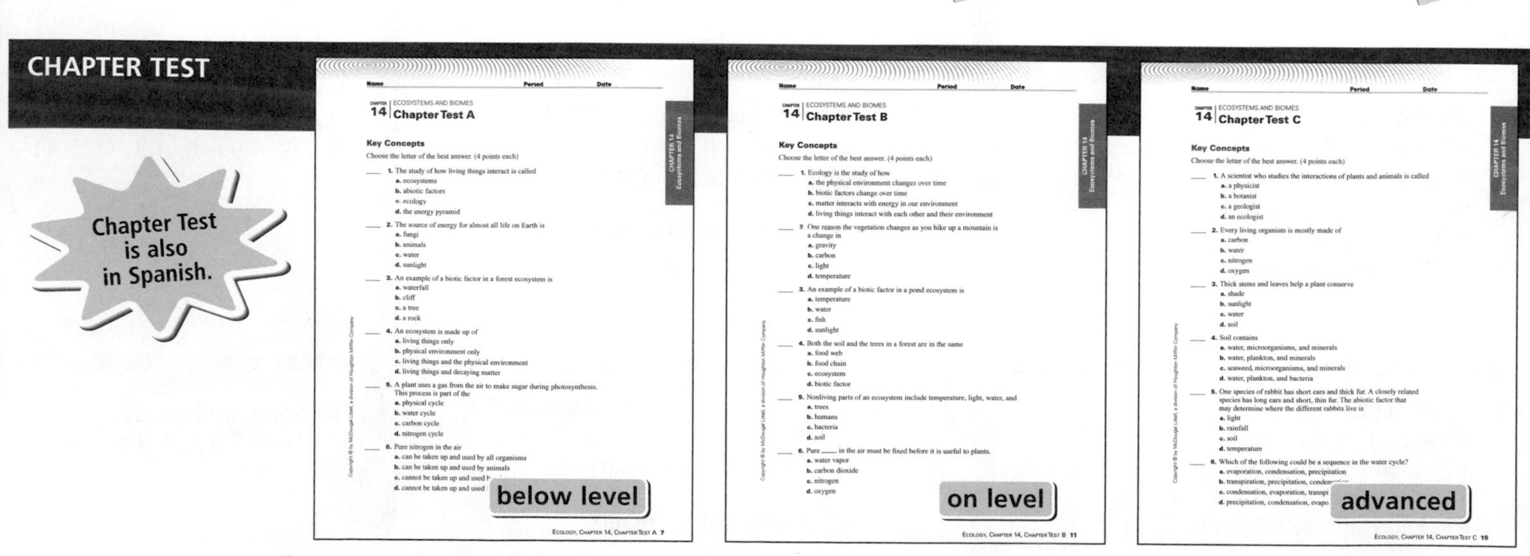

CHAPTER 14 | ECOSYSTEMS AND BIOMES
Chapter Test A

below level

CHAPTER 14 | ECOSYSTEMS AND BIOMES
Chapter Test B

on level

CHAPTER 14 | ECOSYSTEMS AND BIOMES
Chapter Test C

advanced

A **UNIT ASSESSMENT BOOK,** pp. 7–10

A pp. 11–14

A pp. 15–18

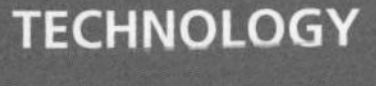

TECHNOLOGY

There are two Resource Centers and a Visualization for this chapter.

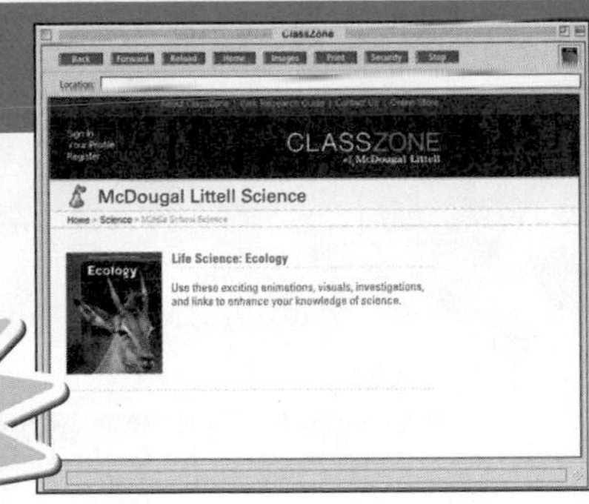

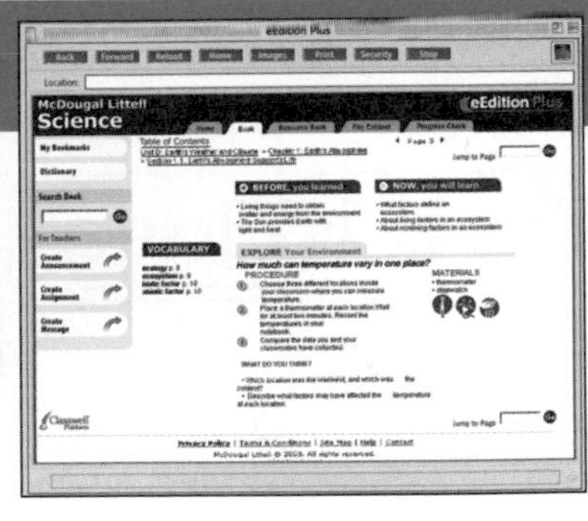

VISUAL CONTENT

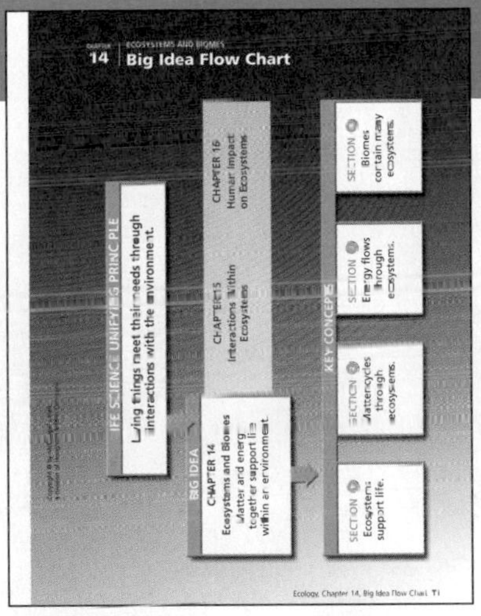

UNIT TRANSPARENCY BOOK, p. T1

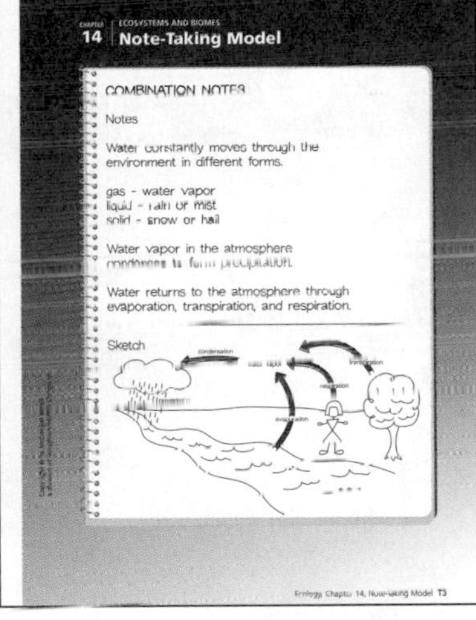

p. T3

p. T6

MORE SUPPORT

Reinforcing Key Concepts for each section

14.1 Reinforcing Key Concepts

UNIT RESOURCE BOOK, p. 20

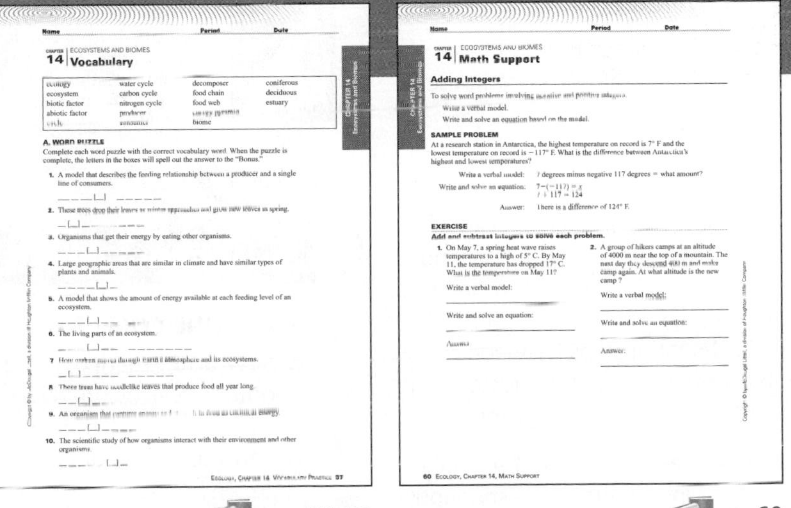

pp. 57–58

p. 60

CHAPTER 14 Ecosystems and Biomes

INTRODUCE

the BIG idea

Have students look at the photograph of Portage Lake, Alaska. Discuss how the question in the box relates to the Big Idea:

- What plants and animals are in the photograph?
- What might be keeping them alive?

National Science Education Standards

Content

C.4.b Populations of organisms can be categorized by the function they serve in an ecosystem. Plants and some microorganisms are producers. All animals are consumers. Decomposers consume waste materials and dead organisms for food. Food webs identify the relationships among producers, consumers, and decomposers in an ecosystem.

C.4.c Sunlight is transferred by producers into chemical energy through photosynthesis. That energy passes from organism to organism in food webs.

C.4.d The number of organisms an ecosystem can support depends on the resources available and abiotic factors.

D.1.f Water circulates through Earth's crust, oceans, and atmosphere in the "water cycle."

Process

A.2–8 Design and conduct a scientific investigation; use tools to gather and interpret data; use evidence to describe, predict, explain, model; use critical thinking to find relationships between results and interpretation; communicate results; use mathematics in investigations.

A.9.a–c, A.9.e–f Understand scientific inquiry by using different investigations, methods, mathematics, and explanations based on logic, evidence, and skepticism.

CHAPTER 14 Ecosystems and Biomes

the BIG idea

Matter and energy together support life within an environment.

Key Concepts

SECTION 1 **Ecosystems support life.** Learn about different factors that make up an ecosystem.

SECTION 2 **Matter cycles through ecosystems.** Learn about the water, carbon, and nitrogen cycles.

SECTION 3 **Energy flows through ecosystems.** Learn how energy moves through living things.

SECTION 4 **Biomes contain many ecosystems.** Learn about different land and water biomes.

Internet Preview

CLASSZONE.COM

Chapter 14 online resources: Content Review, Simulation, Visualization, three Resource Centers, Math Tutorial, Test Practice

How many living and nonliving things can you identify in this photograph?

INTERNET PREVIEW

CLASSZONE.COM For student use with the following pages:

Review and Practice

- Content Review, pp. 472, 502
- Math Tutorial: Adding Integers, p. 485
- Test Practice, p. 505

Activities and Resources

- Internet Activity: A Prairie Ecosystem, p. 471
- Resource Centers: Ecosystem, p. 474; Cycles, p. 480; Biomes, p. 500
- Visualization: Nitrogen, p. 484

Food Chains and Food Webs
Code: MDL001

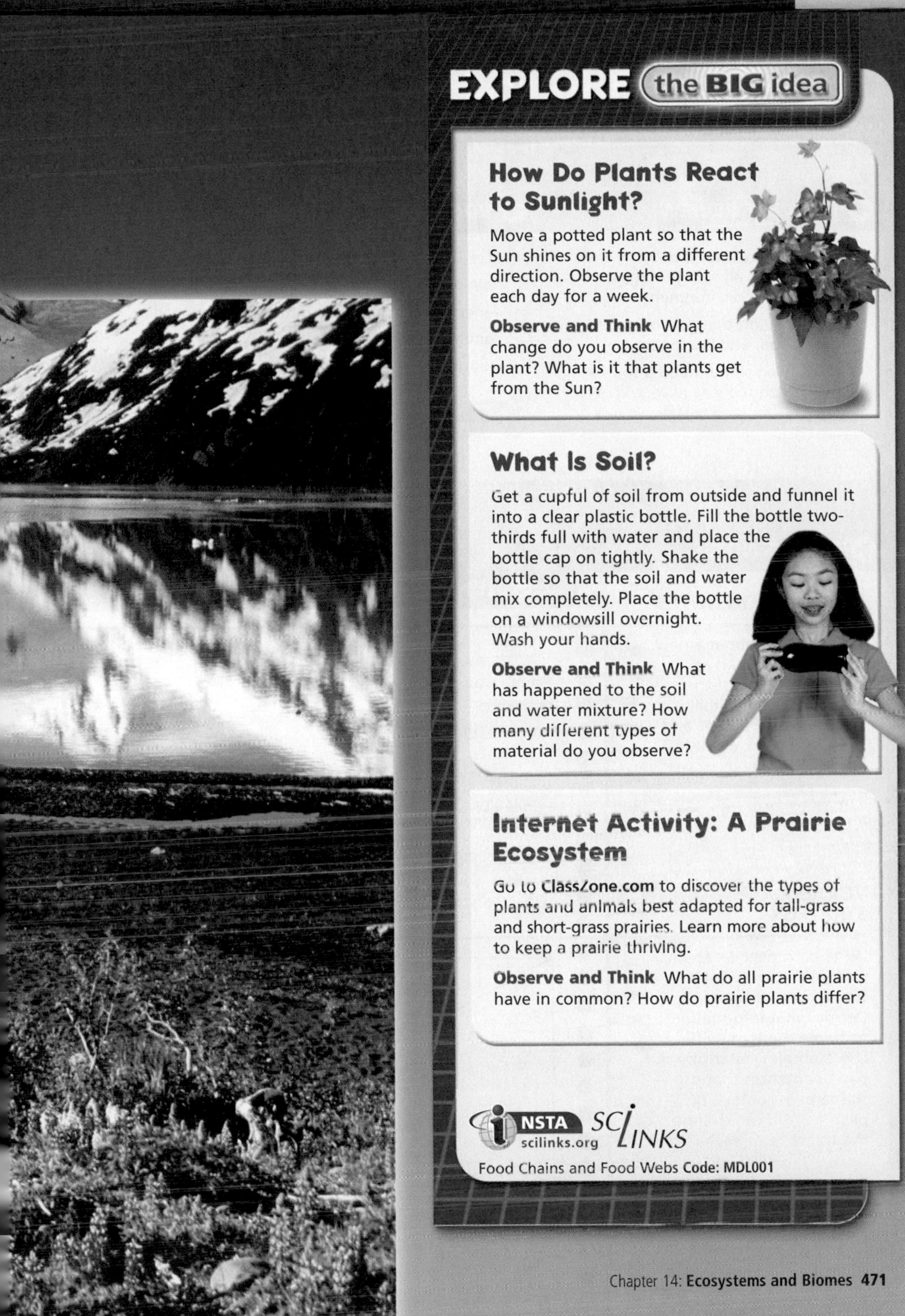

EXPLORE the BIG idea

How Do Plants React to Sunlight?

Move a potted plant so that the Sun shines on it from a different direction. Observe the plant each day for a week.

Observe and Think What change do you observe in the plant? What is it that plants get from the Sun?

What Is Soil?

Get a cupful of soil from outside and funnel it into a clear plastic bottle. Fill the bottle two-thirds full with water and place the bottle cap on tightly. Shake the bottle so that the soil and water mix completely. Place the bottle on a windowsill overnight. Wash your hands.

Observe and Think What has happened to the soil and water mixture? How many different types of material do you observe?

Internet Activity: A Prairie Ecosystem

Go to **ClassZone.com** to discover the types of plants and animals best adapted for tall-grass and short-grass prairies. Learn more about how to keep a prairie thriving.

Observe and Think What do all prairie plants have in common? How do prairie plants differ?

NSTA scilinks.org SCILINKS

Food Chains and Food Webs **Code: MDL001**

Chapter 14: **Ecosystems and Biomes** **471**

TEACHING WITH TECHNOLOGY

Digital Camera If a digital camera is available, students can photograph their potted plants (pp. 474, 480) each day. They can then assemble a series of still shots as a digital movie and dub sound over the image or add text screens to create a presentation.

Computer Microscope Have students use a computer microscope to examine particles in the Chapter Investigation on p. 478.

Spreadsheet Software Students can use graphing calculators or spreadsheet software to present their climate data on p. 499.

EXPLORE the BIG idea

These inquiry-based activities are appropriate for use at home or as a supplement to classroom instruction.

How Do Plants React to Sunlight?

PURPOSE To demonstrate that plants respond to the presence of sunlight.

TIP *10 min.* Use plants with flexible, leafy stems. Bean, radish, or other seedlings will move toward light in a short time period.

Answer: Leaves and stems moved toward the sunlight; energy.

REVISIT after p. 476.

What Is Soil?

PURPOSE To introduce students to soil, a mixture of materials that support life within an environment.

TIP *10 min.* Have students compare their soil samples with those of their classmates. They may observe that their region has more than one type of soil.

Answer: It has separated into layers. Number of types of material will vary depending on composition of soil used.

REVISIT after p. 477.

Internet Activity: A Prairie Ecosystem

PURPOSE To introduce students to factors that cause changes in an ecosystem.

TIP *20 min.* You might bring real samples of grasses into the classroom and compare them with the varieties on screen.

Answer: They are all grasses; some are low to ground, others tall.

REVISIT after p. 490.

PREPARE

CONCEPT REVIEW

Activate Prior Knowledge

- Ask students to come to the board and draw familiar plants and animals in their natural environment.
- Ask students to name the living organisms shown in the environment and to suggest ways in which the organisms might interact with each other.
- Ask students to suggest possible ways in which each organism finds water, energy, and living space.

TAKING NOTES

Combination Notes

Combining pictures with notes will help students connect abstract concepts with concrete examples. Later, students can fold over their two-column combination notes and quiz themselves based on thier pictures.

Vocabulary Strategy

Surrounding each term with a context helps students develop meaning.

Students can opt to use their frame game notes to create a guessing game with a partner. Partners fill in frames, but leave the "picture" or center-word blank, then trade with each other to "complete the picture."

Vocabulary and Note-Taking Resources

- Vocabulary Practice, pp. 57–58
- Decoding Support, p. 59

- Daily Vocabulary Scaffolding, p. T2
- Note-Taking Model, p. T3

- Frame Game, B26–27
- Combination Notes, C40
- Daily Vocabulary Scaffolding, H1–8

CHAPTER 14

Getting Ready to Learn

CONCEPT REVIEW

- The natural world that surrounds all living things is called the environment.
- Most living things need water, air, food, and living space.
- All living things need a source of energy to stay alive and grow.

VOCABULARY REVIEW

See Glossary for definitions.

biology	**nutrient**
energy	**photosynthesis**
environment	**respiration**
matter	**system**

CONTENT REVIEW
CLASSZONE.COM
Review concepts and vocabulary.

TAKING NOTES

COMBINATION NOTES

To take notes about a new concept, first make an informal outline of the information. Then make a sketch of the concept and label it so you can study it later.

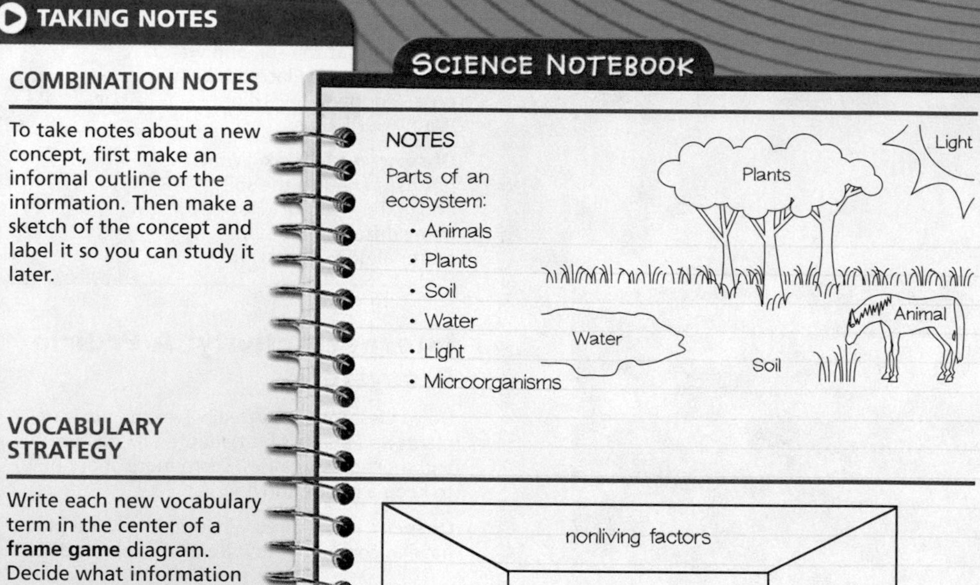

VOCABULARY STRATEGY

Write each new vocabulary term in the center of a **frame game** diagram. Decide what information to frame the term with. Use examples, descriptions, parts, sentences that use the term in context, or pictures. You can change the frame to fit each item.

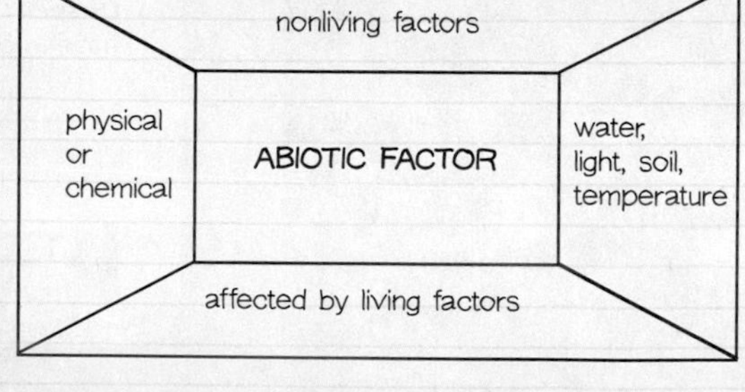

See the Note-Taking Handbook on pages R45–R51.

CHECK READINESS

Administer the Diagnostic Test to determine students' readiness for new science content and their mastery of requisite math skills.

 Diagnostic Test, pp. 1–2

Technology Resources

Students needing content and math skills should visit **ClassZone.com**.

- **CONTENT REVIEW**
- **MATH TUTORIAL**

 **CONTENT REVIEW CD-ROM**

KEY CONCEPT

Ecosystems support life.

BEFORE, you learned
- Living things need to obtain matter and energy from the environment
- The Sun provides Earth with light and heat

NOW, you will learn
- What factors define an ecosystem
- About living factors in an ecosystem
- About nonliving factors in an ecosystem

VOCABULARY

ecology p. 473
ecosystem p. 473
biotic factor p. 474
abiotic factor p. 474

EXPLORE Your Environment

How much can temperature vary in one place?

PROCEDURE

1. Choose three different locations inside your classroom where you can measure temperature.
2. Place a thermometer at each location. Wait for at least two minutes. Record the temperatures in your notebook.
3. Compare the data you and your classmates have collected.

WHAT DO YOU THINK?
- Which location was the warmest, and which was the coldest?
- Describe what factors may have affected the temperature at each location.

MATERIALS
- thermometer
- stopwatch

Living things depend on the environment.

You wouldn't find a kangaroo in the Arctic and you won't see a polar bear in Australia. Each of these organisms is suited to a certain environment. The kangaroo and the polar bear are able to survive despite the harsh conditions of their surroundings. **Ecology** is the scientific study of how organisms interact with their environment and all the other organisms that live in that environment.

Scientists use the word **ecosystem** to describe a particular environment and all the living things that are supported by it. An ecosystem can be as small as a pond or as large as a desert. What is important in an ecosystem is how the living parts of the ecosystem relate to the nonliving parts.

VOCABULARY
Add frame game diagrams for *ecology* and *ecosystem* to your notebook.

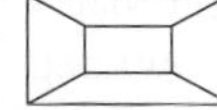

14.1 FOCUS

Set Learning Goals

Students will
- Explain what factors define an ecosystem.
- Describe the living factors in an ecosystem.
- Describe the nonliving factors in an ecosystem.
- Measure different temperatures to discover variations in warmth.

3-Minute Warm-Up

Display Transparency 4 or copy this exercise on the board:

Match the definitions to the correct terms.

Definitions
1. It surrounds all living things. *d*
2. All living organisms need it. *b*
3. It gives Earth most of its energy. *e*

Terms
a. organism
b. energy
c. the ocean
d. environment
e. the Sun

 3-Minute Warm-Up, p. T4

14.1 MOTIVATE

EXPLORE Your Environment

PURPOSE To demonstrate that microclimates with different characteristics differ in temperature

TIP *10 min.* Students should select three locations that receive different amounts of sunlight, air exchange with the outdoors, or heat or air conditioning from indoor sources.

WHAT DO YOU THINK? *Sample answer: The location with the most sunlight was warmest, proximity to windows, doors, heat sources, air conditioning vents, number of people in the area, open windows or doors.*

RESOURCES FOR DIFFERENTIATED INSTRUCTION

Below Level

UNIT RESOURCE BOOK
- Reading Study Guide A, pp. 13–14
- Decoding Support, p. 59

 AUDIO CDS

Advanced

UNIT RESOURCE BOOK

Challenge and Extension, p. 19

English Learners

UNIT RESOURCE BOOK

Spanish Reading Study Guide, pp. 17–18

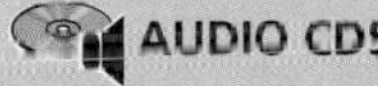 AUDIO CDS
- Audio Readings in Spanish
- Audio Readings (English)

14.1 INSTRUCT

Teach from Visuals

To help students interpret the photograph of the pond ecosystem, ask:

- How do the living factors in this ecosystem depend on one another? *They depend on each other for food and shelter.*
- How do nonliving factors affect the living factors in this ecosystem? *They provide nutrients and energy for organisms.*
- Are there any living or nonliving factors that might be in this ecosystem but are not visible in the photograph? *living factors: fish, insects, microorganisms; nonliving factors: nutrients, oxygen, carbon dioxide, rocks*

History of Science

Biosphere 2 was built in the late 1980s with the intention of creating a closed system similar enough to Earth to be self-sustaining. The initial experiment lasted two years and yielded valuable information, but the system was not self-sustaining and could not be kept closed. Today, Biosphere 2's ecosystems are used for education and research.

A project in Japan called Mini Earth is attempting to pick up where Biosphere 2 left off. About half the size of Biosphere 2, Mini Earth is housed in three large buildings linked by stainless steel passageways. Scheduled to launch in 2005, the project will involve two scientists sealed inside along with plants and animals. It is intended to be self-sustaining, with no need for oxygen to be supplied from the outside. Developers of the project hope that the technologies used in Mini Earth will help future space exploration.

Ongoing Assessment

Explain what factors define an ecosystem.

Ask: What is the definition of an ecosystem? *living things and the physical environment around them*

Learn more about ecosystems.

A

Let's take a look at a pond. A pond ecosystem is more than just water and fish. Plants grow in and around the water, and animals feed on these plants. A variety of tiny microorganisms in the water are food for fish and for each other. These are just a few of the living parts, or **biotic factors** (by-AHT-ihk), of a pond ecosystem. The nonliving parts, or **abiotic factors** (AY-by-AHT-ihk), include the air that supplies oxygen and carbon dioxide, the soil that provides nutrients, the water in the pond, and the sunlight that plants need to grow.

CLASSIFY Name three living and three nonliving factors that are part of this pond ecosystem.

Biotic factors interact with an ecosystem.

B

Living things depend upon an ecosystem for food, air, and water, as well as other things they need for survival. In turn, living things have an impact on the ecosystem in which they live. Plants, as a biotic factor in land ecosystems, affect other biotic and abiotic parts of ecosystems. Plants are an important source of food. The types of plants found in a particular ecosystem will determine the types of animals that can live there. Plants can affect temperature by blocking sunlight. Plant roots hold soil in place. Even the atmosphere is affected by plants taking in carbon dioxide and releasing oxygen.

Animals, as biotic factors, also affect an ecosystem. A beaver that builds a dam changes the flow of a river and so affects the surrounding landscape. Large herds of cattle can overgraze a grassland ecosystem and cause the soil to erode. In an ocean biome, corals form giant reefs that provide food and shelter for marine organisms.

DIFFERENTIATE INSTRUCTION

More Reading Support

A What two kinds of factors are in an ecosystem? *biotic and abiotic*

B Are plants abiotic or biotic factors? *biotic*

English Learners Have English learners write the definitions of *ecology* and *ecosystem* in their Science Word Dictionaries. Encourage students to look up *eco-* in the dictionary. Be certain that English learners understand the difference between *biotic factors* and *abiotic factors.* Ask them to list the different biotic and abiotic factors they see around them. Some biotic factors might be classmates, teachers, class pets, plants in the classroom or visible through a window. Abiotic factors might be desks, books, board, or lights.

Many abiotic factors affect ecosystems.

Abiotic factors include both the physical and chemical parts of an ecosystem. Physical factors are factors that you can see or feel, such as the temperature or the amount of water or sunlight. Important chemical factors include the minerals and compounds found in the soil and whether the ecosystem's water is fresh or salty. It is the combination of different abiotic factors that determines the types of organisms that an ecosystem will support.

READING TIP The word *biotic* means "living." The prefix *a-* in *abiotic* means "not," so *abiotic* means "not living."

CHECK YOUR READING List four different abiotic factors that can affect an ecosystem.

Temperature

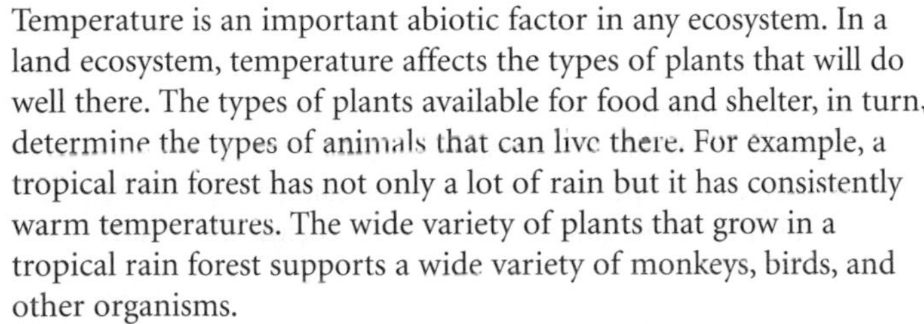

Temperature is an important abiotic factor in any ecosystem. In a land ecosystem, temperature affects the types of plants that will do well there. The types of plants available for food and shelter, in turn, determine the types of animals that can live there. For example, a tropical rain forest has not only a lot of rain but it has consistently warm temperatures. The wide variety of plants that grow in a tropical rain forest supports a wide variety of monkeys, birds, and other organisms.

Animals are as sensitive to temperature as plants are. Musk oxen with their thick coat of fur can survive in very cold environments, where temperatures of –40°C (–40°F) are normal. The water buffalo, with its light coat, is better suited to warm temperatures. The wild water buffalo lives where temperatures can reach 48°C (118°F).

This musk ox's thick fur keeps it warm in the cold temperatures of northern Canada.

A water buffalo cools itself in a shallow stream during a hot day in India.

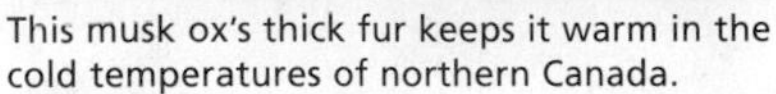

READING VISUALS **COMPARE AND CONTRAST** How are these animals alike? How are they different?

DIFFERENTIATE INSTRUCTION

More Reading Support

C What are physical abiotic factors? *light, temperature, amount of water*

D What determines the types of animals in an ecosystem? *plants*

Advanced Give students examples of three ecosystems of different sizes, such as an anthill, a one-acre meadow, and a continent. Have them describe the features that make each of these an ecosystem.

Teach from Visuals

Using the photographs, have students compare abiotic factors of the ecosystems in which musk oxen and water buffalo live. Ask:

- How does temperature affect the availability of water in each ecosystem? *Liquid water is present in the water buffalo's ecosystem, but water is often frozen in the musk ox's ecosystem.*
- How do temperature and water affect soil and plant life in each ecosystem? *Musk ox: Soil is often frozen, and vegetation is short and sparse. Water buffalo: Soil is often moist or muddy, and plant life is plentiful.*

Language Arts Connection

Help students understand the terms *ecology* and *ecosystem* by explaining the origin of the word root *ecos*, which means "house" or "place to live." Ecology then can be thought of as the study of places where organisms *live*; an ecosystem as the *system* of relationships among organisms and their *home* or surroundings.

Ongoing Assessment

Describe the living factors in an ecosystem.

Ask: Give some examples of the biotic factors in an ecosystem. *Sample answer: bacteria, insects, plants, algae, animals*

CHECK YOUR READING *Answer: light, temperature, soil, water, air*

READING VISUALS *Answer: They both have similar sizes, similar bodies, and horns. In a warm climate, the musk ox's fur would make the animal too hot. The water buffalo has no protection from the cold.*

Address Misconceptions

IDENTIFY Ask: Where do green plants get their food? If students answer "from the soil," they might hold the misconception that plants obtain food from the environment rather than capturing energy from sunlight, and combining it with the chemicals in air.

CORRECT On the board, write an equation for photosynthesis: water + carbon dioxide + light = sugar + oxygen. Remind students that photosynthesis takes place in leaf cells and that sugar is food for the plant.

REASSESS Ask students where each item in the equation comes from. *water from soil, carbon dioxide from air, light from the Sun, sugar from all three combined, oxygen is left over*

Technology Resources

Visit **ClassZone.com** for background on common student misconceptions.

 **MISCONCEPTION DATABASE**

EXPLORE the BIG idea

Revisit "How Do Plants React to Sunlight?" on p. 471. Have students explain their results.

Teach from Visuals

To help students interpret the soil visuals, explain the following interactions:

- Plant roots interact with soil. Roots take water from soil. Bacteria and fungi on plant roots help the roots absorb nutrients. Roots help hold soil in place.
- Air interacts with soil. Most soil organisms need air to survive. Their activity loosens soil, allowing air to circulate.
- Earthworms interact with soil. Worms digest organic matter, pass waste back into soil, and mix and aerate soil.

Ongoing Assessment

Describe the nonliving factors in an ecosystem.

Ask: What are some examples of abiotic factors in an ecosystem? *Sample answer: light, soil, water, temperature, minerals*

COMBINATION NOTES Remember to make notes and diagrams to show how abiotic factors affect biotic factors in an ecosystem.

Light

You can easily understand how abiotic factors work together when you think about sunlight and temperature. Sunlight warms Earth's surface and atmosphere. In addition, energy from sunlight supports all life on Earth. **E** The Sun provides the energy that plants capture and use to produce food in a process called photosynthesis. **F** The food produced by plants, and other photosynthetic organisms, feeds almost all the other living things found on Earth.

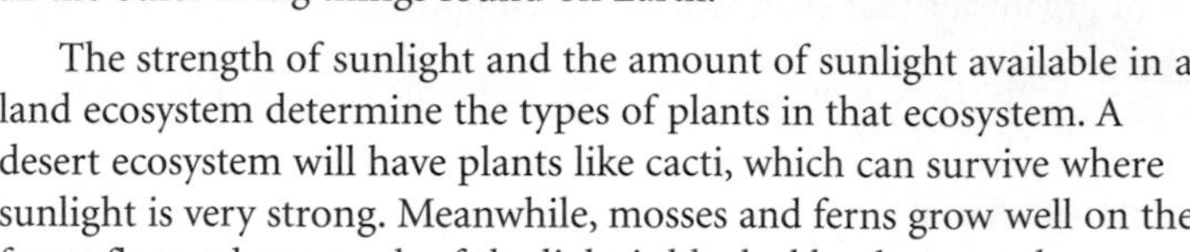

The strength of sunlight and the amount of sunlight available in a land ecosystem determine the types of plants in that ecosystem. A desert ecosystem will have plants like cacti, which can survive where sunlight is very strong. Meanwhile, mosses and ferns grow well on the forest floor, where much of the light is blocked by the trees above.

Light is a factor in ocean ecosystems as well. The deeper the water is, the less light there is available. In the shallow water near the shore, photosynthetic organisms can survive at the surface and on the ocean floor. In the open ocean, light is available for photosynthetic organisms only in the first hundred meters below the surface.

Soil

Soil, which is a mixture of small rock and mineral particles, is an important abiotic factor in land ecosystems. Organisms within the soil break down the remains of dead plants and animals. This process of decay provides important raw materials to the living plants and animals of an ecosystem.

The size of soil particles affects how much air and water the soil can hold.

DIFFERENTIATE INSTRUCTION

More Reading Support

E Ecosystems need energy to function. Where does this energy come from? *the Sun*

F How do plants get energy? *by photosynthesis*

Advanced Invite students to observe small soil samples using a hand lens or dissecting microscope. Have them draw and identify the organisms they see, and use their research skills to find out more about them.

 Challenge and Extension, p. 19

Different ecosystems have different types of soil. The characteristics of the soil in an ecosystem affect plant growth. Soils that have a lot of decaying, or organic, matter can hold water well and allow air to reach the plant roots. Sandy soils usually do not hold water well because the water flows through too easily. Clay soil, which has small, tightly packed particles, will not allow water to move through easily at all. Minerals in the soil also affect plant growth.

 Explain how soil can affect plant life in an ecosystem.

Water

Another important abiotic factor in land ecosystems is the amount of water available to support life. All living things need water to carry out life processes. Plants need water as well as sunlight for photosynthesis. Animals need water to digest food and release the energy stored in the food. Look at the photograph to see the effect that an underground water source has on an otherwise dry, desert ecosystem. Trees could not survive there without a plentiful supply of water.

INFER An oasis forms in the desert when underground water comes to the surface. How can you identify the boundary of this oasis?

Ecosystems that have a lot of water can support a large number of different types of plants. These different types of plants can then support a large number of different types of animals. Tropical rain forests, the wettest of all ecosystems on land, are also the most diverse. Desert ecosystems, which are the driest land ecosystems, have far fewer types of plants and animals. The types and number of living things in a land ecosystem will always be related to the amount of fresh water available for its inhabitants.

14.1 Review

KEY CONCEPTS

1. Draw a diagram of an ecosystem near where you live. Label the factors "biotic" or "abiotic."
2. Give two examples of how plants and animals affect their environment.
3. Describe how temperature, light, and soil affect an ecosystem.

CRITICAL THINKING

4. **Predict** Think of a forest ecosystem. Now imagine that a large volcanic eruption throws large amounts of dust and ash into the air, blocking out sunlight. How might the forest ecosystem be affected if the sunlight is blocked for a day? For a year?

CHALLENGE

5. **Apply** Think of how you fit into your local environment. List ways in which you interact with biotic and abiotic factors within your ecosystem.

ANSWERS

1. Diagrams should show awareness that biotic factors are organisms and abiotic factors are nonliving.

2. Sample answer: Plants produce oxygen and food. Coral reefs provide shelter.

3. They determine the types and abundance of plant life.

4. For a day: would have little effect on the ecosystem; for a year: much of the plant life would disappear, and the animal life that depends on it

5. Sample answer: biotic factors: eating plants and animals, being stung by an insect, feeding birds; abiotic factors: breathing air, drinking water, building with stone

Ongoing Assessment

 *Answer: The amount of water and nutrients in the soil affects what types of plants can survive.*

EXPLORE the BIG idea

Revisit "What Is Soil?" on p. 471. Have students analyze the soil materials they observed.

Reinforce the BIG idea

Have students relate the section to the Big Idea.

 Reinforcing Key Concepts, p. 20

14.1 ASSESS & RETEACH

Assess

 Section 14.1 Quiz, p. 3

Reteach

Choose one of these ecosystems: an artificial ecosystem such as a classroom aquarium or terrarium; an ecosystem shown in photographs from books or magazines; or a backyard, park, or a schoolyard ecosystem. Have students identify as many biotic and abiotic factors as they can. Ask them to write a paragraph describing how the abiotic factors influence the biotic factors in the chosen ecosystem.

Technology Resources

Have students visit **ClassZone.com** for reteaching of Key Concepts.

 CONTENT REVIEW

 CONTENT REVIEW CD-ROM

CHAPTER INVESTIGATION

Focus

PURPOSE To observe the water-related characteristics of different types of soil

OVERVIEW Students will measure the rate at which water flows through three types of soil. They will find that the rate increases as the particle size increases. Water passes most quickly through coarse sand and most slowly through clay.

Lab Preparation

- Use coarse sand for this activity. The particle size of fine sand will produce slow percolation, too similar to clay.
- Use clear drinking glasses or clear plastic cups instead of beakers if you prefer.
- For homework the night before, have students read the investigation and draw their data table. Or you may wish to copy and distribute datasheets and rubrics.

 UNIT RESOURCE BOOK, pp. 62–70

 SCIENCE TOOLKIT, F12

Lab Management

- Be sure students can demonstrate how to operate the stopwatch before they begin the lab.
- Tell students to take care not to poke holes in the filters, as this will affect percolation rate.
- Remind students to start the stopwatch when the water begins to flow out the bottom of the funnel, even if the flow begins before all the water has been poured into the funnel.

SAFETY Emphasize that students should wash their hands after step 5 and again at the end of the activity.

Teaching with Technology

Students could use a computer microscope to examine soil particles, take pictures, and prepare slides for presenting data.

CHAPTER INVESTIGATION

Soil Samples

OVERVIEW AND PURPOSE Nonliving, or abiotic, factors all have an effect on soil. The quality of the soil affects how well plants grow in a particular environment. In this investigation, you will

- observe and record how water travels through three soil samples
- predict how different types of soil would affect plant growth

MATERIALS
- 3 pieces of paper
- spoon
- 50 mL each of clay, coarse sand, loam
- hand lens
- toothpick
- eyedropper
- water
- 3 pieces of filter paper
- 3 plastic funnels
- 3 large beakers
- small beaker
- stopwatch

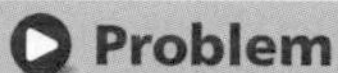

Problem

Write It Up

How does soil type affect how water moves through soil?

Hypothesize

Write It Up

You should complete steps 1–5 in the procedure before writing your hypothesis. Write a hypothesis to explain how water moves through certain types of soil. Your hypothesis should take the form of an "If . . . , then . . . , because . . ." statement.

Procedure

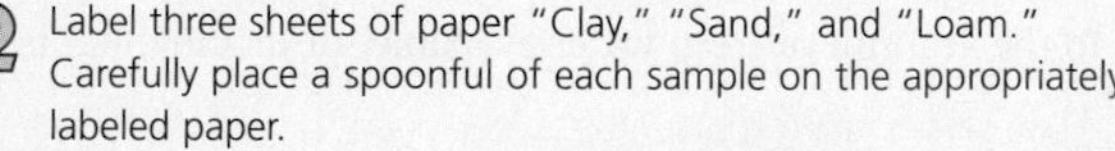

1. Make a data table in your **Science Notebook** like the one shown on page 479.
2. Label three sheets of paper "Clay," "Sand," and "Loam." Carefully place a spoonful of each sample on the appropriately labeled paper.
3. Carefully examine each of the soils, with and without the hand lens. Describe the color of each, and record the information in your data table.

478 Unit 4: Ecology

INVESTIGATION RESOURCES

 CHAPTER INVESTIGATION, Soil Samples
- Level A, pp. 62–65
- Level B, pp. 66–69
- Level C, p. 70

Advanced students should complete Levels B & C.

 Writing a Lab Report, D12–13

Technology Resources

Customize this student lab as needed or look for an alternative. Print rubrics to assess student lab reports.

 **Lab Generator CD-ROM**

4 Use a toothpick to separate the particles of each sample of soil. Record the size of the particles in the data table.

5 Put a small amount of each soil sample in the palm of your hand. Add a drop of water and mix the soil around with your finger. Write a description of the texture of each sample in your data table. Be sure to wash your hands after you finish. After you have recorded your observations, write your hypothesis.

6 Fold each piece of filter paper to form cones as shown in the diagram. Place one filter inside each funnel. Place one funnel in each large beaker. Measure 50 mL of each soil sample and place the sample in one of the funnels.

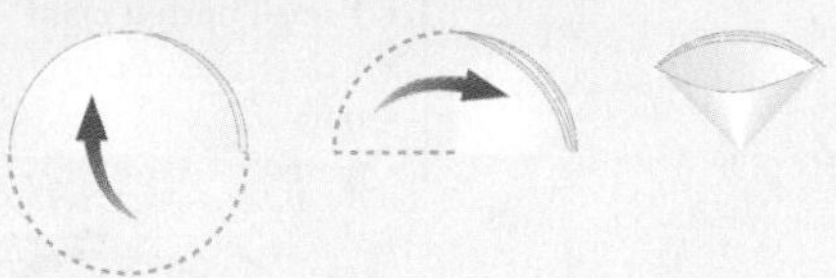

7 Measure 150 mL of water and pour it into the funnel containing the clay. Start the stopwatch when the water begins to drip out of the funnel. Stop the watch when the water stops dripping. Record the time in seconds in the data table.

8 Repeat step 7 for the sand and the loam. When you have finished with the activity, dispose of the materials according to your teacher's directions, and wash your hands.

Observe and Analyze

1. **INTERPRET DATA** Through which soil sample did the water move the fastest? The slowest?
2. **OBSERVE** What type of changes occurred in the soil as the water was added?

Conclude

Write It Up

1. **INTERPRET** Compare your results with your hypothesis. Does your data support your hypothesis?
2. **IDENTIFY LIMITS** What sources of error could have affected this investigation?
3. **EVALUATE** Based on your observations, what can account for the differences in the times recorded for the three soil samples?
4. **PREDICT** Based on your results, which of the soil samples would you expect to be the best type of soil in which to grow plants? Explain.

INVESTIGATE Further

CHALLENGE Design an experiment in which you test which of the three soil samples is best for growing plants. Include a materials list, hypothesis, and procedure for your experiment.

Soil Samples
Table 1. Soil Characteristics

Characteristics	Clay	Sand	Loam
Color			
Particle size			
Texture			
Time for water to stop dripping (sec)			

Observe and Analyze

SAMPLE DATA clay: grayish-brown, very fine, very soft; sand: light brown, coarse, rough; loam: black, fine, soft

1. *fastest: sand; slowest: clay*
2. *Sample answer: All soils got darker; clay became muddy; the particles of loam floated; wet sand became hard, like beach sand.*

Conclude

1. *Answers will vary depending on observations and results in the investigation. Students should provide evidence or explanation for describing whether their hypotheses are correct or incorrect.*
2. *Errors might include procedural errors, sample inconsistencies, or inaccurate measurement, starting the stopwatch a little before or after flow begins, and so on.*
3. *Sample answer: Some soil particles were closer together or stuck to each other more than others. Some soil contains more moisture than others. (Clay has most, then loam, then sand.) The moisture (water) in the soil helps hold water that enters it.*
4. *Loam; sand does not store enough water, clay is too tightly packed for roots to get water easily.*

INVESTIGATE Further

CHALLENGE Materials: plants, pots, soil, water, light source. Hypothesis should state which soil is best for plant growth. Procedure should include step-by-step instructions for setting up the experiment in such a way that the only variable is the soil and all other items (plant species, amount of water, soil, sunlight, air temperature, and so on) are constant.

Post-Lab Discussion

- On the board, make a chart correlating the three soil types with the characteristics students observed in steps 3–5. Have student teams write the flow rates from step 7 on the chart. Keep a tally from one class period to the next to show that larger data samples reveal more accurate trends.
- Discuss why permeability is an important property of soils. *Permeability affects plant growth.*

14.2 FOCUS

Set Learning Goals

Students will

- Explain how matter is exchanged between organisms and their environment.
- Describe the water, carbon, and nitrogen cycles.
- Observe carbon gas released from crushed seashells.

3-Minute Warm-Up

Display Transparency 4 or copy this exercise on the board:

Decide if these statements are true. If not true, correct them.

1. Organisms in soil are an example of abiotic factors. *Organisms in soil are an example of biotic factors.*
2. The amount of light available in an ecosystem affects the types and amount of plant life that will grow there. *true*
3. Plants use energy to make sugars through photosynthesis. *true*

3-Minute Warm-Up, p. T4

14.2 MOTIVATE

EXPLORE The Water Cycle

PURPOSE To introduce the concept that plants release water vapor (transpiration)

TIPS *10 min.* Put bags on a single stem to make them easier to seal. If possible, move the activity outdoors. Any lamp will work for this exploration.

SAFETY Have students place the lamp at a safe distance from the plant to avoid burning the leaves or melting the plastic bag.

WHAT DO YOU THINK? *Water condenses inside each bag. The plastic bag traps water vapor.*

Teaching with Technology

Students can use a digital camera as described on p. 471 to photograph plants.

KEY CONCEPT

Matter cycles through ecosystems.

BEFORE, you learned

- Ecosystems support life
- Living and nonliving factors interact in an ecosystem
- Temperature, light, soil, and water are important nonliving factors in ecosystems

NOW, you will learn

- How matter is exchanged between organisms and their environment
- About the water, carbon, and nitrogen cycles

VOCABULARY

cycle p. 480
water cycle p. 481
carbon cycle p. 482
nitrogen cycle p. 483

EXPLORE The Water Cycle

Do plants release water?

PROCEDURE

1. Cover a branch of the plant with a plastic bag. Tape the bag firmly around the stem.
2. Water the plant and place it in a sunny window or under a lamp. Wash your hands.
3. Check the plant after ten minutes, at the end of class, and again the next day.

MATERIALS

- 1 small potted plant
- 1 clear plastic bag
- tape
- water

WHAT DO YOU THINK?

- What do you see inside the plastic bag?
- What purpose does the plastic bag serve?

All ecosystems need certain materials.

RESOURCE CENTER CLASSZONE.COM
Explore cycles in nature.

Living things depend on their environment to meet their needs. You can think of those needs in terms of the material, or matter, required by all living things. For example, all organisms take in water and food in order to survive. All of the materials an organism takes in are returned to the ecosystem, while the organism lives or after it dies.

The movement of matter through the living and nonliving parts of an ecosystem is a continuous process, a cycle. A **cycle** is a series of events that happens over and over again. Matter in an ecosystem may change form, but it never leaves the ecosystem, so the matter is said to cycle through the ecosystem. Three of the most important cycles in ecosystems involve water, carbon, and nitrogen.

RESOURCES FOR DIFFERENTIATED INSTRUCTION

Below Level

UNIT RESOURCE BOOK

- Reading Study Guide A, pp. 23–24
- Decoding Support, p. 59

AUDIO CDS

Additional INVESTIGATION, The Water Cycle, A, B, & C, pp. 71–79; Teacher Instructions, pp. 200–201

Advanced

UNIT RESOURCE BOOK
Challenge and Extension, p. 29

English Learners

UNIT RESOURCE BOOK
Spanish Reading Study Guide, pp. 27–28

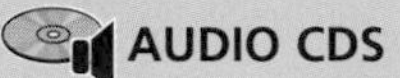
AUDIO CDS

- Audio Readings in Spanish
- Audio Readings (English)

Water Cycle

Different processes combine to move water through the environment.

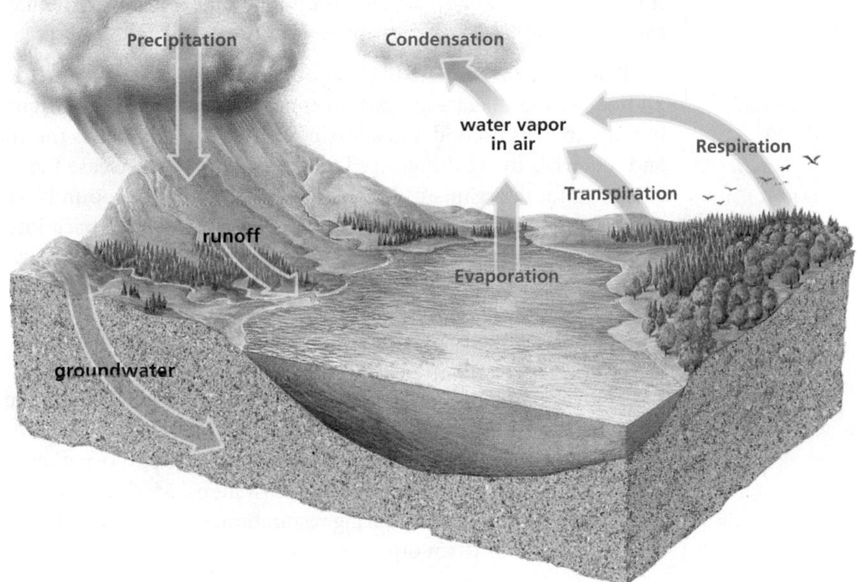

Water cycles through ecosystems.

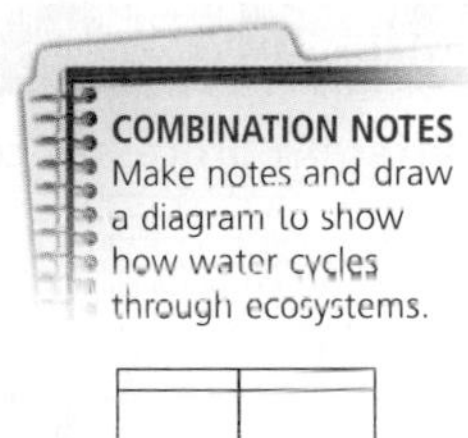

COMBINATION NOTES Make notes and draw a diagram to show how water cycles through ecosystems.

Water is stored on Earth's surface in lakes, rivers, and oceans. Water is found underground, filling the spaces between soil particles and cracks in rocks. Large amounts of water are stored in glaciers and polar ice sheets. Water is also part of the bodies of living things. But water is not just stored, it is constantly moving. The movement of water through the environment is called the **water cycle.**

A Water is made up of just two elements: oxygen and hydrogen. As water moves through an ecosystem, it changes in physical form, moving back and forth between gas, liquid, and solid. Water in the atmosphere is usually in gaseous form—water vapor. Water that falls to Earth's surface is referred to as precipitation. For precipitation to occur, water vapor must condense—it must change into a liquid or solid. This water can fall as rain, snow, sleet, mist, or hail.

 **CHECK YOUR READING** What are the three physical forms of water in the water cycle?

B Water returns to the atmosphere when heated, changing back into vapor, a process called evaporation. Living things also release water vapor. Animals release water vapor when they breathe, or respire. Plants release water vapor through a process called transpiration.

14.2 INSTRUCT

Teach from Visuals

Remind students that the arrows in the diagram of the water cycle represent the movement of water molecules. Ask:

- What happens during condensation? *Water vapor becomes liquid water.*
- What happens during transpiration? *Water vapor is released from tiny openings in plant leaves.*

Language Arts Connection

On the board, write the verb form of each process in the water cycle next to its root meaning.

- Evaporate: vapor: the gaseous form of a liquid
- Transpire; respire: spiritus (Latin): breath
- Condense: dense: crowded, thick, compact

Address Misconceptions

IDENTIFY Ask: Where does the water in Earth's water cycle come from? If students answer "oceans" or "atmosphere," they may think that water is added to or created within the water cycle.

CORRECT Create a demonstration using two beakers; fill one with water. Stopper the beakers and connect them with a rubber hose. Boil the water and have students observe as the water leaves one beaker and reappears in the other.

REASSESS Ask: Where did the water that appeared in the second beaker come from? *from the first beaker* How did it move? *Heating caused the water to change from liquid form into water vapor, which traveled through the hose. As water vapor cooled, it changed back into a liquid and collected in the second beaker.*

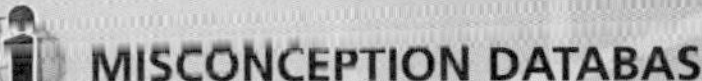

Technology Resources

Visit **ClassZone.com** for background on common student misconceptions.

MISCONCEPTION DATABASE

Ongoing Assessment

CHECK YOUR READING *Answer: gas, liquid, and solid*

DIFFERENTIATE INSTRUCTION

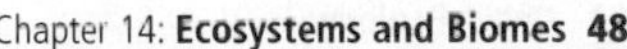

More Reading Support

A What is water made of? *oxygen and hydrogen*

B What process turns water to water vapor? *evaporation*

English Learners Place *water cycle, carbon cycle,* and *nitrogen cycle* on the Science Word Wall with abbreviated definitions. It may also be helpful for English learners to discuss each cycle with another English learner in their first language. Working out difficult concepts together in their first language can be beneficial to students. Encourage them to repeat or write down what they have learned in English afterwards.

Teach from Visuals

To help students interpret the diagram of the carbon cycle, ask:

- How does carbon move from the air into plants and animals? *Carbon moves into plants by photosynthesis, and into animals by eating plants or other animals.*
- How does carbon move into the air from plants and animals? *The cells of plants and animals use oxygen to release the energy stored in food molecules. This process is called respiration. Carbon dioxide is released as a by-product of respiration.*
- How does carbon move into the air from fossil fuels? *Carbon is released as carbon dioxide when fossil fuels burn.*

History of Science

Recently, groups of college graduates in science were asked where a plant's mass comes from. Almost all of them answered sunlight, water, or soil. Few understood that carbon in the air was responsible.

In the 1640s, Jan Baptista van Helmont conducted an experiment that proved most of a plant's mass does not come from soil. Setting out to bolster his theory that everything is made of water, he placed 200 pounds of soil in a pot in which he planted a 5-pound willow tree. He watered the tree regularly and protected it from dust, but added no soil.

In five years, the tree gained 164 pounds, but the soil weighed 199 pounds.

The experiment showed that little of the tree's weight came from soil. Van Helmont thought the increase of weight was from water; in fact, it came from carbon dioxide.

Ongoing Assessment

CHECK YOUR READING *Answers should include three of the following: plants take in CO_2, animals release CO_2, carbon is deposited on seafloor when an organism dies, decaying matter releases CO_2, carbon in dead plants and animals becomes fossil fuel.*

Carbon cycles through ecosystems.

C

Carbon is an element found in all living things. Carbon moves through Earth's ecosystems in a cycle referred to as the **carbon cycle.** It is through carbon dioxide gas found in Earth's atmosphere that carbon enters the living parts of an ecosystem.

READING TIP
Notice that photosynthesis is a process that brings carbon into living matter and respiration is a process that releases carbon.

Plants use carbon dioxide to produce sugar—a process called photosynthesis. Sugars are carbon compounds that are important building blocks in food and all living matter. Food supplies the energy and materials living things need to live and grow. To release the energy in food, organisms break down the carbon compounds—a process called respiration. Carbon is released and cycled back into the atmosphere as carbon dioxide. When living things die and decay, the rest of the carbon that makes up living matter is released.

CHECK YOUR READING Name three ways that living things are part of the carbon cycle.

Earth's oceans contain far more carbon than the air does. In water ecosystems—lakes, rivers, and oceans—carbon dioxide is dissolved in water. Algae and certain types of bacteria are the photosynthetic organisms that produce food in these ecosystems. Marine organisms, too, release carbon dioxide during respiration. Carbon is also deposited on the ocean floor when organisms die.

Carbon Cycle

Different processes combine to move carbon through the environment.

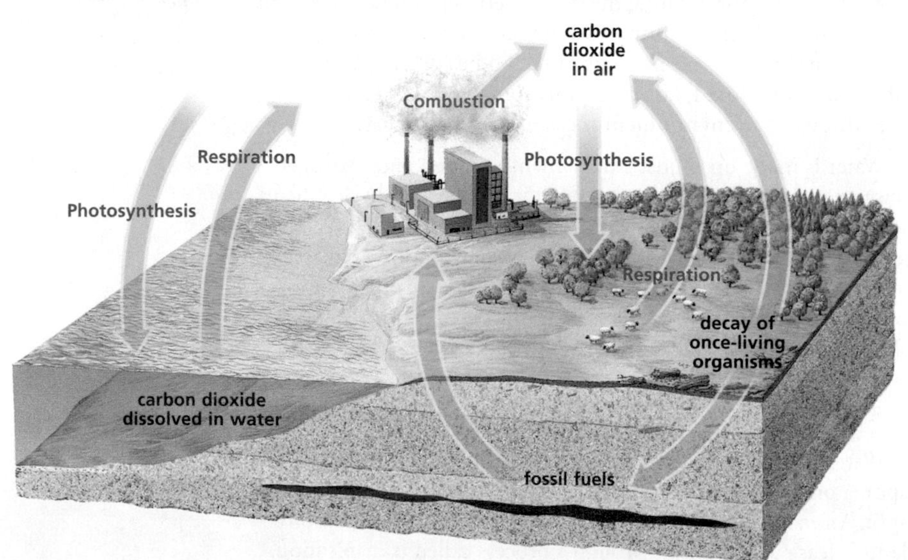

DIFFERENTIATE INSTRUCTION

More Reading Support

C All living things contain what chemical element? *carbon*

Below Level Encourage students to create their own color-coded diagrams of the carbon cycle. Have them use one color to represent carbon dioxide gas and another for solid carbon. Ask: Where is carbon dioxide gas found? *in the air and dissolved in oceans, lakes, streams* Ask: Where is solid carbon found? *in the bodies of plants and animals*

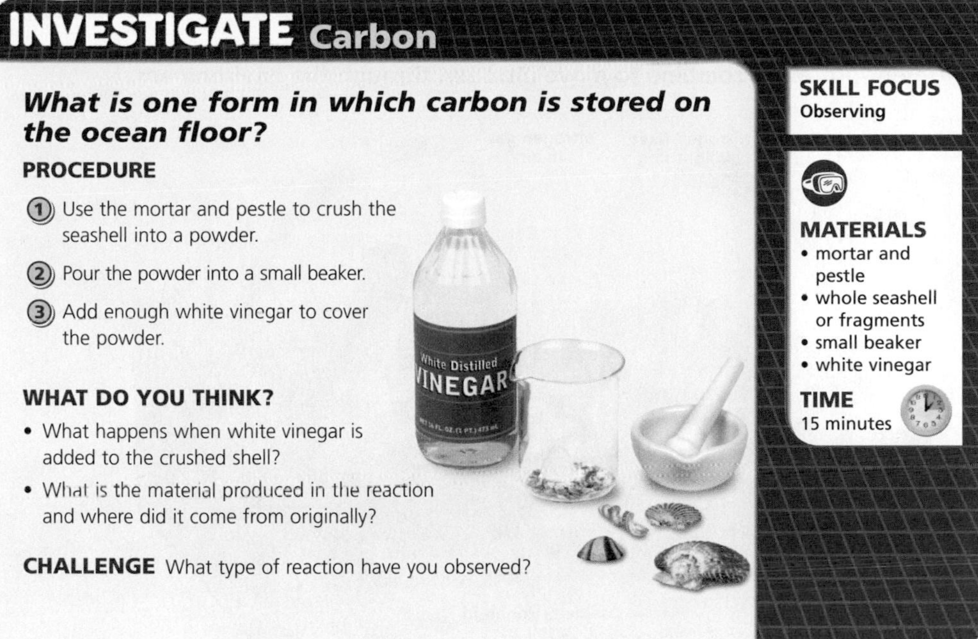

INVESTIGATE Carbon

What is one form in which carbon is stored on the ocean floor?

PROCEDURE

1. Use the mortar and pestle to crush the seashell into a powder.
2. Pour the powder into a small beaker.
3. Add enough white vinegar to cover the powder.

WHAT DO YOU THINK?

- What happens when white vinegar is added to the crushed shell?
- What is the material produced in the reaction and where did it come from originally?

CHALLENGE What type of reaction have you observed?

SKILL FOCUS
Observing

MATERIALS
- mortar and pestle
- whole seashell or fragments
- small beaker
- white vinegar

TIME
15 minutes

Large amounts of carbon are stored underground. The remains of plants and animals buried for millions of years decay slowly and change into fossil fuels, such as coal and oil. The carbon in fossil fuels returns to ecosystems in a process called combustion. As humans burn fossil fuels to release energy, dust particles and gases containing carbon are also released into the environment.

Nitrogen cycles through ecosystems.

Nitrogen is another element important to life that cycles through Earth in the **nitrogen cycle.** Almost four-fifths of the air you breathe is clear, colorless nitrogen gas. Yet, you cannot get the nitrogen you need to live from the air. All animals must get nitrogen from plants.

Plants cannot use pure nitrogen gas either. However, plants can absorb certain compounds of nitrogen. Plants take in these nitrogen compounds through their roots, along with water and other nutrients. So how does the nitrogen from the atmosphere get into the soil? One source is lightning. Every lightning strike breaks apart, or fixes, pure nitrogen, changing it into a form that plants can use. This form of nitrogen falls to the ground when it rains.

INVESTIGATE Carbon

PURPOSE To observe the release of carbon in water

TIPS *15 min.* Students should wear safety goggles or protective eyewear throughout the experiment. Calcium carbonate is also in the shells of birds' eggs. A similar test with an egg will have good results.

WHAT DO YOU THINK? *Answers: Gas bubbles form. CO_2 is produced; it originally came from the shells*

CHALLENGE *chemical*

 Datasheet, Carbon, p. 30

Technology Resources

Customize this student lab as needed or look for an alternative. Print rubrics to assess student lab reports.

 **Lab Generator CD-ROM**

Real World Example

All living things contain carbon. People get carbon compounds from food. In the oceans, living things get carbon from carbon dioxide dissolved in water. Clams and oysters, for example, use carbon to make the hard calcium carbonate in their shells. To find out if an element, such as carbon, is present, scientists use chemical tests. In the case of carbon, an acid, such as vinegar, reacts with calcium carbonate to produce carbon dioxide gas.

Integrate the Sciences

Living organisms are made up of chemical compounds: carbohydrates, fats, and proteins. All of these compounds contain carbon, hydrogen, and oxygen. Proteins contain nitrogen as well.

Ongoing Assessment

Explain how matter is exchanged between organisms and their environment.

Ask: How does matter cycle between organisms and their environment? *Organisms take in water, carbon, and nitrogen; use them for life processes; and release them.*

DIFFERENTIATE INSTRUCTION

More Reading Support

D Where do animals get nitrogen? *from plants*

E Where do plants get the nitrogen they need? *from the soil*

Additional Investigation

To reinforce Section 14.2 learning goals, use the following full-period investigation:

Additional INVESTIGATION, The Water Cycle, A, B, & C, pp. 71–79, 200–201 (Advanced students should complete Levels B and C.)

Alternative Assessment

Have students explain orally the findings of their investigation.

Challenge and Extension, p. 29

Ongoing Assessment

Describe the water, carbon, and nitrogen cycles.

Ask: How are the water, carbon, and nitrogen cycles alike? *Sample answer: All three pass into and out of the atmosphere, soil, and living organisms.*

Reinforce 

Have students relate the section to the Big Idea.

 Reinforcing Key Concepts, p. 31

14.2 ASSESS & RETEACH

Assess

 Section 14.2 Quiz, p. 4

Reteach

Draw or have volunteers draw simple versions of the three cycle diagrams in Section 14.2 on the board. Next, have students describe similarities and differences in the water, carbon, and nitrogen cycles. Ask:

- How does water enter the atmosphere? Carbon? Nitrogen? *Water evaporates, is transpired by plants, and is exhaled by animals during respiration. Carbon is released during respiration and decay. Nitrogen is converted into gas by bacteria.*
- How does water leave the atmosphere? Carbon? Nitrogen? *Water vapor condenses and falls to the ground as precipitation. Carbon is fixed by plants during photosynthesis. Nitrogen is fixed by bacteria or by lightning.*
- Where is water stored? Carbon? Nitrogen? *water: oceans, lakes, groundwater; carbon: plant and animal bodies, ocean floor; nitrogen: plant and animal bodies*

Technology Resources

Have students visit **ClassZone.com** for reteaching of Key Concepts.

 CONTENT REVIEW

 CONTENT REVIEW CD-ROM

Nitrogen Cycle

Different processes combine to move nitrogen through the environment.

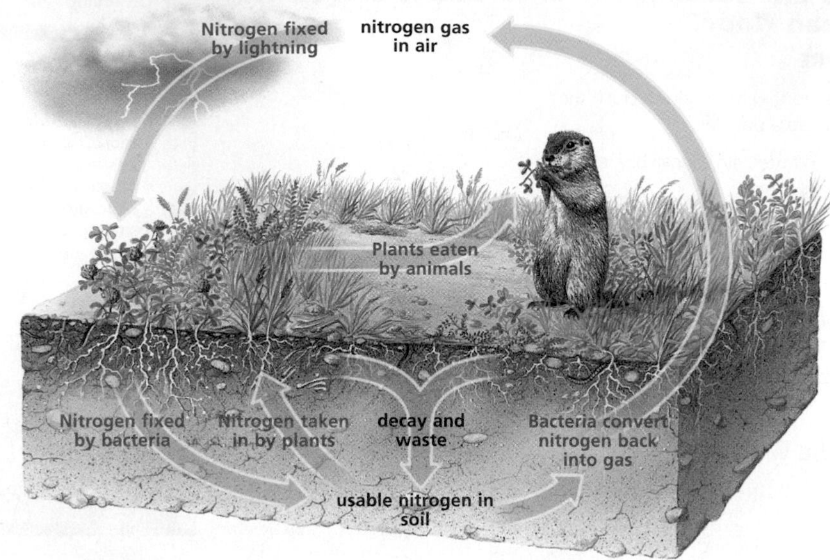

Watch the nitrogen cycle in action.

A far greater source of nitrogen is nitrogen-fixing bacteria. These bacteria live in the oceans as well as the soil. Some even attach themselves to the roots of certain plants, like alfalfa or soybeans. When organisms die, decomposers in the ocean or soil break them down. Nitrogen in the soil or water is used again by living things. A small amount is returned to the atmosphere by certain bacteria that can break down nitrogen compounds into nitrogen gas.

14.2 Review

KEY CONCEPTS

1. Draw a diagram of the water cycle. Show three ways in which water moves through the cycle.
2. Summarize the main parts of the carbon cycle.
3. Explain two ways that nitrogen gas in the atmosphere is changed into nitrogen compounds that plants can use.

CRITICAL THINKING

4. **Predict** When people burn fossil fuels, carbon dioxide gas is added to the atmosphere. How might increased carbon dioxide affect plant growth?
5. **Compare and Contrast** Review the nitrogen and carbon cycles. How are these two cycles similar and different?

CHALLENGE

6. **Apply** Draw a cycle diagram that shows how water is used in your household. Include activities that use water, sources of water, and ways that water leaves your house.

ANSWERS

1. Diagrams should include precipitation, evaporation, and condensation.

2. Green plants and algae remove CO_2 from air. Animals get carbon from food and release carbon as CO_2. The burning of fossil fuels, wood, or other organisms and decay release carbon.

3. Bacteria break down nitrogen compounds into nitrogen gas. Lightning breaks apart pure nitrogen in the atmosphere.

4. Plants might grow larger or increase in numbers.

5. Both have a gaseous form. Plants make both elements available to animals. Decay returns both elements to the atmosphere.

6. Diagrams should include activity, source, and exit route.

SKILL: ADDING INTEGERS

Temperature and the Water Cycle

MATH TUTORIAL
CLASSZONE.COM
Click on Math Tutorial for more help with adding integers.

Changes in temperature help water move through the environment. At freezing temperatures—below 32°F or 0°C for sea-level environments—water can begin to become solid ice. Ice starts to melt when the temperature rises above freezing, causing the water to become liquid again. Temperature change also causes water to become vapor, or gas, within the air.

This iceberg is made up of fresh water, which freezes at 0°C. The surrounding ocean is salt water, which doesn't freeze at 0°C.

Example

Suppose you are waiting for winter to come so you can skate on a small pond near your house. The weather turns cold. One day the temperature is 25°C, then the next day the air temperature drops by 35°C. What temperature is the air? If the air stays below 0°C, some of the water will begin to freeze.

(1) Write a verbal model:
25 degrees + a 35-degree drop = what temperature?

(2) Write an equation. Use negative and positive integers:
$25 + (-35) = ?$

(3) Solve the equation:
$25 - 35 = -10$

ANSWER −10°C.

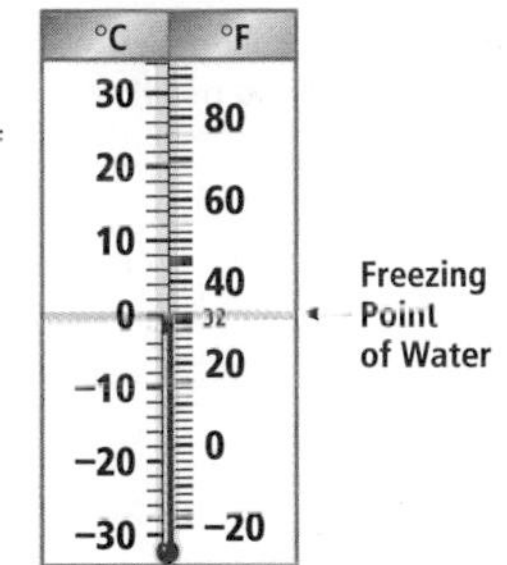

Answer the following questions.

1. A container of water is left out over night, when the temperature is −18°C. In the morning, the air temperature rises by 8°C. What temperature is the air? What will happen to the water?

2. An ice block sits in a field where the air is 0°C. The air temperature rises by 16°C, then it drops by 8°C. What temperature is the air in the field now? What will happen to the ice?

3. What happens to a block of ice after the temperature in the air follows this pattern: $-6 + 17 + 10 + 18 + (-5)$? What temperature has the air reached?

CHALLENGE Use a thermometer to measure the temperature of the air outside and indoors in degrees Celsius. Write two addition equations that show the temperature change between the two locations. One equation should show a rise, and one should show a drop.

ANSWERS

1. −18 + 8 = −10°C; the water will freeze.

2. 0 + 16 − 8 = 8°C; some of the ice block will melt.

3. It melts, 34°C

CHALLENGE Temperature figures should be recorded in degrees Celsius. The equations should show lower temperature + difference = higher temperature, and higher temperature + (− difference) = lower temperature.

MATH IN SCIENCE
Math Skills Practice for Science

Set Learning Goal
To add positive and negative integers in situations involving temperature

Present the Science
Read the explanation with students. Make sure they understand the freezing point and boiling point of fresh water, and that a temperature below zero is preceded by a minus sign. Remind students that saltwater freezes at a lower temperature. The term "water" in this exercise refers to fresh water only.

Develop Algebra Skills
Go through the sample question with students. Ask:

- Why is a negative number (−35) used for the equation in step 2? *The temperature decreases so a negative number is used.*
- How do you subtract a larger number from a smaller number? *You can subtract the smaller number from the larger one, and then add a negative sign: 35 − 25 = 10; 25 − 35 = −10*

DIFFERENTIATION TIP Suggest that students use a number line. Demonstrate how to use the number line to figure rise and fall in temperatures.

Close
Ask: Name another example in the sciences where adding positive and negative integers is used. *elevations below sea level, dates B.C. and A.D.*

- Math Support, p. 60
- Math Practice, p. 61

Technology Resources

Students can visit **ClassZone.com** for practice in adding integers.

MATH TUTORIAL

14.3 FOCUS

Set Learning Goals

Students will

- Explain how living organisms move energy through an ecosystem.
- Explain how feeding relationships are important in an ecosystem.
- Explain how the amount of energy changes as it flows through an ecosystem.
- Observe plants decomposing with the help of microorganisms.

3-Minute Warm-Up

Display Transparency 5 or copy this exercise on the board:

Serena puts a small amount of water in a saucer and leaves it on a sunny windowsill for several hours. What happens to the water? Why? *The water evaporates. Heat from the Sun changes liquid water into vapor, which escapes into the air. After several hours, the saucer may be completely dry.*

 3-Minute Warm-Up, p. T5

14.3 MOTIVATE

EXPLORE Energy

PURPOSE To demonstrate how energy changes form as it moves through an ecosystem

TIPS *10 min.* Cut spirals from circles or squares of paper about 8 centimeters square. Origami paper, construction paper, and Bristol board work well. As a control, hang one spiral in an area protected from air movement.

WHAT DO YOU THINK? *The spiral turned. Heat from the lamp is the energy source. It creates airflow.*

KEY CONCEPT

14.3 Energy flows through ecosystems.

BEFORE, you learned

- Matter cycles continuously through an ecosystem
- Living things are part of the water, carbon, and nitrogen cycles

NOW, you will learn

- How living things move energy through an ecosystem
- How feeding relationships are important in ecosystems
- How the amount of energy changes as it flows through an ecosystem

VOCABULARY

EXPLORE Energy

How can you observe energy changing form?

PROCEDURE

1. Mark and cut a spiral pattern in a square piece of paper.
2. Cut a 15-cm piece of thread and tape one end to the center of the spiral.
3. Adjust the lamp to shine straight at the ceiling. Turn the lamp on.
4. Hold the spiral by the thread and let it hang 10 cm above the light bulb. **CAUTION: Don't let the paper touch the bulb!**

WHAT DO YOU THINK?

- What do you see happen to the spiral?
- In what sense has the energy changed form?

MATERIALS

- paper
- marker
- scissors
- thread
- tape
- desk lamp

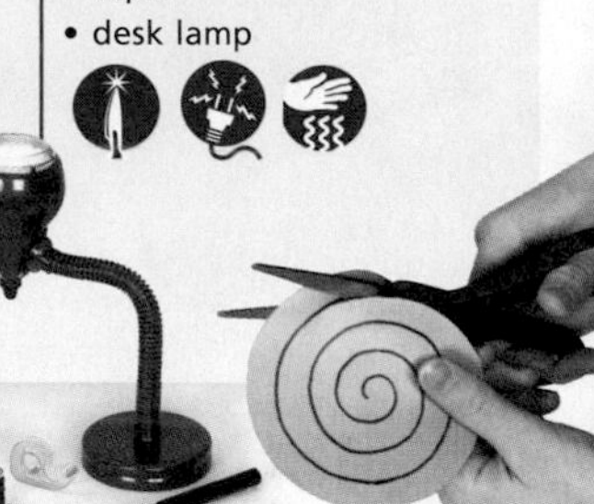

Living things capture and release energy.

Everything you do—running, reading, and working—requires energy. The energy you use is chemical energy, which comes from the food you eat. When you go for a run, you use up energy. Some of that energy is released to the environment as heat, as you sweat. Eventually, you will need to replace the energy you've used.

Energy is vital to all living things. Most of that energy comes either directly or indirectly from the Sun. To use the Sun's energy, living things must first capture that energy and store it in some usable form. Because energy is continuously used by the activities of living things, it must be continuously replaced in the ecosystem.

RESOURCES FOR DIFFERENTIATED INSTRUCTION

Below Level

UNIT RESOURCE BOOK

- Reading Study Guide A, pp. 34–35
- Decoding Support, p. 59

AUDIO CDS

Advanced

UNIT RESOURCE BOOK

- Challenge and Extension, p. 40
- Challenge Reading, pp. 55–56

English Learners

UNIT RESOURCE BOOK

Spanish Reading Study Guide, pp. 38–39

AUDIO CDS

- Audio Readings in Spanish
- Audio Readings (English)

Producers

All of these producers capture energy from sunlight.

Plants

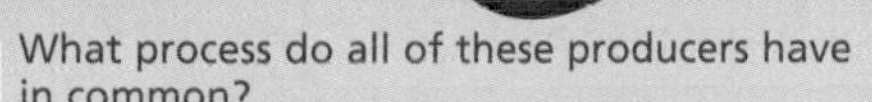

READING VISUALS What process do all of these producers have in common?

Seaweed

Seaweed is a producer found in Earth's oceans and coastal zones.

Phytoplankton

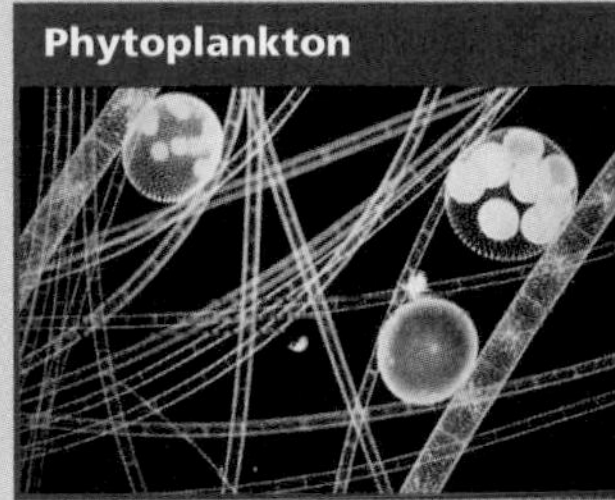

The most numerous producers are tiny organisms that live in water called phytoplankton.

Producers

A **producer** is an organism that captures energy and stores it in food as chemical energy. The producers of an ecosystem make energy available to all the other living parts of an ecosystem. Most energy enters ecosystems through photosynthesis. Plants, and other photosynthetic organisms, take water and carbon dioxide from their environment and use energy from the Sun to produce sugars. The chemical energy stored in sugars can be released when sugars are broken down.

VOCABULARY
Remember to add a frame game for *producers* to your notebook.

CHECK YOUR READING How does energy enter into the living parts of an ecosystem?

Plants are the most common producers found in land ecosystems. In water ecosystems, most food is produced by photosynthetic bacteria and algae. A few examples of producers that use photosynthesis are shown in the photographs above.

The Sun provides most of the energy that is stored in food. One exception is the unusual case of a type of bacteria that lives in the deep ocean, where there is no sunlight. These bacteria produce food using heated chemicals released from underwater vents. This process is called chemosynthesis. Whether producers use photosynthesis or chemosynthesis, they do just as their name suggests—they produce food for themselves and for the rest of the ecosystem.

DIFFERENTIATE INSTRUCTION

More Reading Support

A In an ecosystem, what do producers do? *make energy available*

B How does a producer use energy from the Sun? *It uses energy to produce sugars.*

English Learners Providing models is an effective way to help English learners produce work that is representative of their abilities. If a student is asked to write an explanatory paragraph, provide an appropriate model of one. For example, on p. 492 students are asked to draw a food chain and a food web. Refer students back to the examples on p. 491 for a model of each.

14.3 INSTRUCT

Teach from Visuals

To help students interpret the visual of producers:

- Tell students the photographs show three types of producers. One type is green plants. Ask: What are the other two? *seaweed and phytoplankton*
- Ask: Which of these producers do humans use for food? *green plants (and seaweed)*
- Ask: What form of energy do the producers use, and what form of energy do they produce? *Producers change light energy into chemical energy.*

Develop Critical Thinking

CLASSIFY Ask students to apply the concept of producers to the following ecosystems by identifying the producers in each list:

- forest: pine trees, birds, ferns, decaying logs, termites, earthworms, squirrels *trees, ferns*
- ocean: jellyfish, corals, phytoplankton, fish, crabs, seaweed *seaweed, phytoplankton*

Teacher Demo

Light a candle or a gas burner to demonstrate the conversion of chemical energy into heat and light energy. Point out that candle wax and natural gas are made from petroleum, which comes from the decayed bodies of ancient plants and animals. (Beeswax candles are made from plant material—pollen collected by bees—not petroleum.) Ask: What was the original source of this energy? *the Sun*

Ongoing Assessment

READING VISUALS *Answer: They perform photosynthesis.*

CHECK YOUR READING *Answer: through photosynthesis and chemical energy*

Teach from Visuals

To help students interpret the visual of consumers, ask:

- Why is the plant identified as the producer? *It is where photosynthesis takes place.*
- Why is the caterpillar identified as the primary consumer? *It eats the leaves of the plant (the producer).*
- Why is the bird identified as the secondary consumer? *The bird is second in the line of consumers—it eats a primary consumer.*

Develop Critical Thinking

CONNECT Have students discuss the transfer of energy and matter in the food chain represented in the illustration. Ask:

- Once the bird has eaten the caterpillar, what happens to the matter that made up the caterpillar and the energy that was stored in the caterpillar's cells? *It transfers to the body of the bird.*
- What kind of energy conversion is involved when a bird flies? *Chemical energy converts to mechanical energy.*

Integrate the Sciences

All matter on Earth is reused. Your body might contain carbon atoms that once were part of a dinosaur.

Energy cannot be recycled, but it is constantly converted from one form to another and transferred from place to place. For example, the Sun's radiation changes to heat energy as it shines on Earth. Chemical energy stored in wood changes to heat energy as it ignites and burns.

Ongoing Assessment

READING VISUALS *Answer: The bird eats the caterpillar, which ate the leaf. Energy and matter transfer from leaf to caterpillar to bird.*

CHECK YOUR READING *Answer: Producers transform the Sun's energy into sugars. Consumers take in this stored energy when they eat the producers.*

Consumers

A consumer is an organism that gets energy by eating producers or other consumers.

Primary consumer: caterpillar

Producer: tree

Secondary consumer: bird

READING VISUALS How does the energy inside the leaf get transferred to the bird?

Consumers

C

Organisms that cannot produce their own food must get their food from other sources. **Consumers** are organisms that get their energy by eating, or consuming, other organisms. To understand how energy flows through an ecosystem, you have to study feeding relationships. A feeding relationship starts with a producer, followed by one and often many more consumers.

CHECK YOUR READING Describe the producer-consumer relationship in terms of energy.

READING TIP *Primary* is a word that means "first in order," *secondary* means "second in order," and *tertiary* means "third in order."

Consumers are classified by their position in a feeding relationship. In a meadow ecosystem, animals such as antelopes and grasshoppers feed on grasses. They are primary consumers because they are the first link between the producers and the rest of the consumers in an ecosystem. The wolves that eat the antelopes and the meadowlarks that eat the grasshoppers are secondary consumers. There are also tertiary consumers, like the prairie falcon that eats the meadowlark. Ecosystems also have special consumers called scavengers, like the vulture, which is a consumer that feeds on dead animals.

D

In the photograph above, energy enters the ecosystem through the tree, which is the producer. The caterpillar that gets its energy by feeding on the leaves is the first, or primary, consumer. The bird that gets its energy by feeding on the caterpillar is a secondary consumer.

DIFFERENTIATE INSTRUCTION

More Reading Support

C What organisms get energy by eating other organisms? *consumers*

D What feed on dead animals? *scavengers*

Below Level Have students draw the organisms in the "Consumers" diagram as a food chain. Then have them draw a tertiary consumer, such as a fox or a hawk, in its appropriate place in the food chain.

Decomposers

If you've been for a hike through a forest, or a walk through a park, you have seen the interaction of producers and consumers. Tall trees and leafy shrubs are home to many insects and the birds that feed upon the insects. Also important to the maintenance of an ecosystem are decomposers, a group of organisms that often go unseen. **Decomposers** are organisms that break down dead plant and animal matter into simpler compounds.

? E

Fungi, such as these mushrooms, are decomposers.

You can think of decomposers as the clean-up crew of an ecosystem. In a forest, consumers such as deer and insects eat a tiny fraction of the leaves on trees and shrubs. The leaves that are left on the forest floor, as well as dead roots and branches, are eventually digested by fungi and bacteria living in the soil. Decomposers also break down animal remains, including waste materials. A pinch of soil may contain almost half a million fungi and billions of bacteria.

The energy within an ecosystem gets used up as it flows from organism to organism. Decomposers are the organisms that release the last bit of energy from once-living matter. Decomposers also return matter to soil or water where it may be used again and again.

INVESTIGATE Decomposers

Where do decomposers come from?

SKILL FOCUS
Observing

PROCEDURE

1. Carefully use scissors to cut an opening across the middle of the bottle.
2. Place a handful of stones in the bottom of the bottle for drainage, and add enough soil to make a layer 10 cm deep.
3. Place some leaves and fruit slices on top of the soil.
4. Seal the cut you made with tape. Mark the date on the tape.
5. Add water through the top of the bottle to moisten the soil, and put the cap on the bottle. Wash your hands.
6. Observe the fruit slices each day for two weeks. Record your observations. Keep the soil moist.

WHAT DO YOU THINK?

- What do you observe happening to the fruit slices?
- Where do the decomposers in your bottle come from?

CHALLENGE Predict what would happen if you used potting soil instead of soil from outside.

MATERIALS
- clear soda bottle with cap
- scissors
- stones
- garden soil
- leaves
- slices of fruit
- masking tape
- marker
- water

TIME
30 minutes

INVESTIGATE Decomposers

PURPOSE To observe the effect of decomposers on plant matter

TIP *30 min.* You might want to start with rotting fruit rather than fresh fruit in this activity. It will speed the process, and you will avoid wasting food.

WHAT DO YOU THINK? *Answers: The fruit slices turn brown and rot; the decomposers come from the garden soil.*

CHALLENGE *The fruit would take longer to decay and not break down as well because potting soil does not have as many decomposers as garden soil.*

 Datasheet, Decomposers, p. 41

Technology Resources

Customize this student lab as needed or look for an alternative. Print rubrics to assess student lab reports.

 **Lab Generator CD-ROM**

Ongoing Assessment

Explain how organisms move energy through an ecosystem.

Ask: How does the Sun's energy end up in the milk you drink at lunch? *Grasses (producers) convert the Sun's energy into food. Cows use matter and energy from grass to produce milk.*

DIFFERENTIATE INSTRUCTION

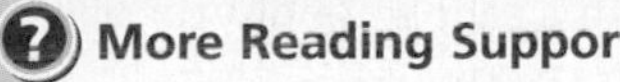

More Reading Support

E What kind of organism breaks down the bodies of dead plants and animals into simpler compounds? *decomposer*

Advanced Decomposers such as fungi and bacteria are continuously at work in ecosystems breaking down plant and animal wastes. Have students list and describe some specific processes of decomposition that benefit human beings.

Have students who are interested in ecosystem processes that benefit humans read the following article:

 Challenge Reading, pp. 55–56

Address Misconceptions

IDENTIFY Ask: What do the arrows in the food web on p. 491 mean? If students answer that the arrows point from the eater to the eaten, they may hold the misconception that a food web is a linear model showing only which organism eats which.

CORRECT Create a food web bulletin board for an ecosystem in your area, using pictures of producers and consumers linked by arrows. Explain that the arrows show the flow of energy from one organism to another. Therefore, the arrows point from the eaten to the eater. Arrange the arrows so that they point in the opposite direction from the way they should. Have students explain the error.

REASSESS Ask: In a food web, what does an arrow pointing from a frog to a stork mean? *It means that energy flows from the frog to the stork when the stork eats the frog.*

EXPLORE the BIG idea

Revisit "Internet Activity: A Prairie Ecosystem" on p. 471. Have students explain the feeding relationships and other factors moving energy and water through that ecosystem.

Ongoing Assessment

CHECK YOUR READING *Answer: A food chain shows only one set of feeding relationships in an ecosystem; a food web shows many different feeding relationships.*

COMBINATION NOTES Remember to take notes and draw a diagram for *food chain* and *food web.*

Models help explain feeding relationships.

You have learned how energy is captured by producers and moved through ecosystems by consumers and decomposers. Scientists use two different models to show the feeding relationships that transfer energy from organism to organism. These models are food chains and food webs.

Food Chain

A chain is made of links that are connected one by one. Scientists use the idea of links in a chain as a model for simple feeding relationships. A **food chain** describes the feeding relationship between a producer and a single chain of consumers in an ecosystem.

The illustration in the white box on page 491 shows a wetland food chain. The first link in the chain is a cattail, a primary producer that captures the Sun's energy and stores it in food. The second link is a caterpillar, a primary consumer of the cattail. The frog is the next link, a secondary consumer that eats the caterpillar. The final link is a heron, a tertiary consumer that eats the frog. Energy is captured and released at each link in the chain. The arrows represent the flow of energy from organism to organism. You can see that some of the energy captured by the cattail makes its way through a whole chain of other organisms in the ecosystem.

Food Web

A **food web** is a model of the feeding relationships between many different consumers and producers in an ecosystem. A food web is more like a spiderweb, with many overlapping and interconnected food chains. It is a better model for the complex feeding relationships in an ecosystem, which usually has many different producers, with many primary and secondary consumers.

The illustration on page 491 also shows a wetland food web. You can see that the feeding relationships can go in several directions. For example, the food web shows that ruddy ducks eat bulrushes, which are producers. That makes ruddy ducks primary consumers. Ruddy ducks are also secondary consumers because they eat snails. A food web shows how one consumer can play several roles in an ecosystem.

READING TIP Notice that the food chain described above is also a part of the food web described here. Follow the blue arrows in the diagram on page 491.

What is the difference between a food chain and a food web?

Both food chains and food webs show how different organisms receive their energy. They also show how different organisms depend on one another. If one organism is removed from the food web or food chain, it may affect many other organisms in the ecosystem.

DIFFERENTIATE INSTRUCTION

More Reading Support

F What are the links in a food chain or food web? *organisms and their feeding relationships*

G Which shows complex feeding relationships? *food web*

Below Level Have students create a simple food web with four to six organisms. Have them remove one of the organisms and explain some likely results for the rest of the organisms.

Inclusion Let students with cognitive disabilities use their bodies to represent the links in a food chain or food web. Have each student make and wear the name or picture of the organism he or she represents. Use yarn or string to show the links in the food web they are modeling.

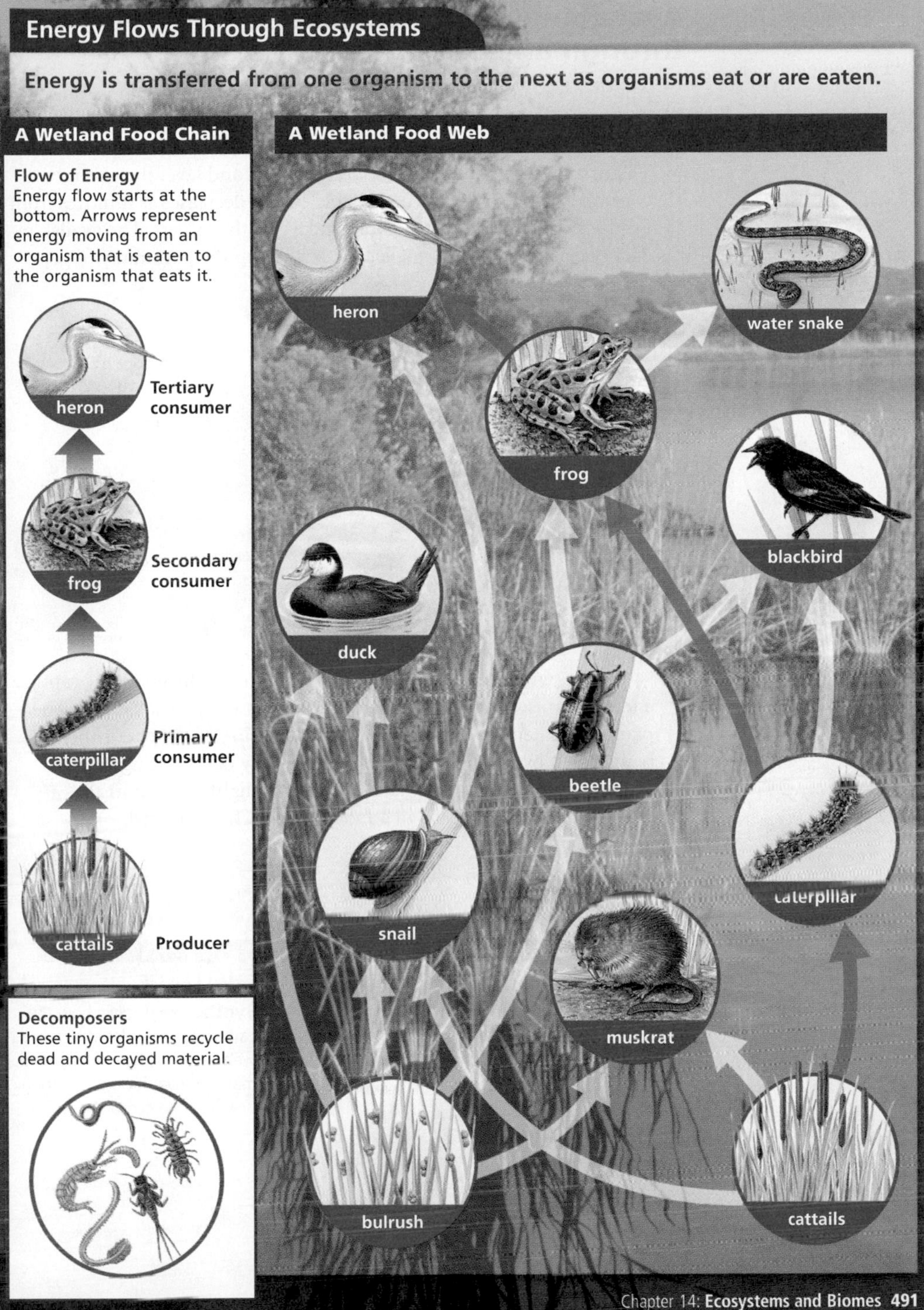

Energy Flows Through Ecosystems

Energy is transferred from one organism to the next as organisms eat or are eaten.

A Wetland Food Chain

Flow of Energy
Energy flow starts at the bottom. Arrows represent energy moving from an organism that is eaten to the organism that eats it.

heron — Tertiary consumer

frog — Secondary consumer

caterpillar — Primary consumer

cattails — Producer

Decomposers
These tiny organisms recycle dead and decayed material.

A Wetland Food Web

heron
water snake
frog
blackbird
duck
beetle
snail
caterpillar
muskrat
bulrush
cattails

Teach from Visuals

To help students interpret the visual of energy flowing through an ecosystem:

- Ask: Why are there no arrows pointing away from the heron or the water snake? *Answer: because they are the tertiary consumers and they are not eaten by any organism shown in this food web*
- Have students list three different food chains that you can find in the food web shown here. *bulrush, beetle, blackbird; cattails, snail, duck; bulrush, snail, heron; cattails, muskrat, water snake*

 The visual "Energy Flows Through Ecosystems" is available as T6 in the Unit Transparency Book.

Develop Critical Thinking

CONNECT Have students apply their knowledge of a food web by asking them to create a food web for familiar organisms they observe in a local ecosystem, such as a park, garden, backyard, vacant lot, or urban neighborhood. *Sample answer: Aphids, crickets, and other insects feed on leaves of plants. Pigeons and sparrows eat insects. Falcons and hawks eat sparrows and pigeons.*

Ongoing Assessment

Explain how feeding relationships are important in an ecosystem.

Ask: What would happen to secondary consumers, such as cats, if primary consumers were eliminated from a food web? *Secondary consumers would starve unless they could eat and use producers or find another primary consumer on which to feed.*

DIFFERENTIATE INSTRUCTION

Below Level Have students work in pairs to identify the different food chains in the food web in the illustration. Assign each pair of students one of the organisms, and have them draw all of the food chains associated with that organism.

Advanced Have students hypothesize what would happen to the wetland food chain if one organism were removed.

 Challenge and Extension, p. 40

Teach from Visuals

To help students interpret the energy pyramid, ask:

- Which layer of the pyramid contains the most energy? *producers*
- Which layer of the pyramid contains the least energy? *tertiary consumers*
- Why is there less energy in the primary consumers than there is in the producers? *The life processes of the producers use up some of the energy before primary consumers eat the producers.*

Reinforce the BIG idea

Have students relate the section to the Big Idea.

 Reinforcing Key Concepts, p. 42

14.3 ASSESS & RETEACH

Assess

 Section 14.3 Quiz, p. 5

Reteach

Have students draw a food chain for one or more foods they've eaten. Ask them to indicate how energy travels in the chain and how much there is at each step. Ask:

- Did all of the Sun's energy absorbed by the producer in your food chain end up in your body? Why or why not? *No; some of the energy was used by the plant before it was eaten.*
- Describe your place in the food chain. *Answer should be a primary or higher consumer.*
- What other animals might take your place in this food chain? *other high-level consumers*

Technology Resources

Have students visit **ClassZone.com** for reteaching of Key Concepts.

 CONTENT REVIEW

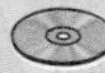 CONTENT REVIEW CD-ROM

Available energy decreases as it moves through an ecosystem.

Another way to picture the flow of energy in an ecosystem is to use an energy pyramid. An **energy pyramid** is a model that shows the amount of energy available at each feeding level of an ecosystem. The first level includes the producers, the second level the primary consumers, and so on. Because usable energy decreases as it moves from producers to consumers, the bottom level is the largest. The available energy gets smaller and smaller the farther up the pyramid you go.

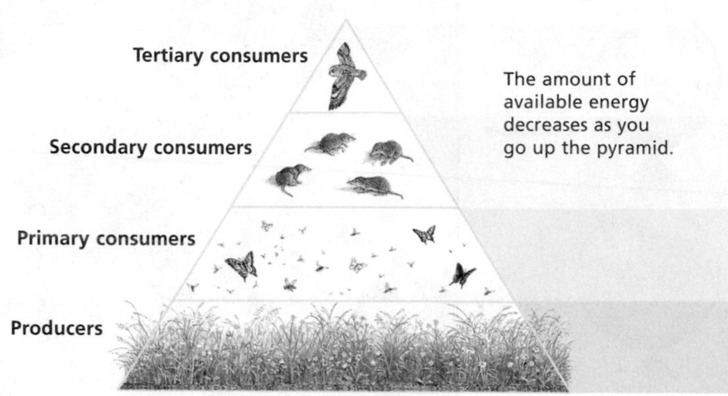

READING TIP
Refer to the diagram above as you read the text. It is because available energy decreases at each level that the diagram takes the shape of a pyramid.

In the pyramid shown here, plants are the producers. They capture energy from sunlight, use some of it, then store the rest as food. The plants are eaten by insects, which also use some of the energy before being eaten by shrews. The shrews use energy before being eaten by the owl. You can see that it takes a lot of sunlight to support the producers and consumers in a food web that feeds an owl.

14.3 Review

KEY CONCEPTS

1. Describe the role of producers, consumers, and decomposers in an ecosystem.
2. Explain why a food web provides a better model of an ecosystem than a food chain does.
3. Explain how the amount of available energy changes as energy moves up a food chain.

CRITICAL THINKING

4. **Apply** Draw a food chain and a food web for an ecosystem near your home.
5. **Predict** Imagine that muskrats are removed from a wetland ecosystem. Predict what would happen both to producers and to secondary consumers.

CHALLENGE

6. **Synthesize** Explain how the carbon cycle is related to a food web. Describe how energy and matter move through the food web and the carbon cycle.

ANSWERS

1. Producers make sugars using sunlight. Consumers eat other consumers and producers. Decomposers break down dead producers and consumers.

2. Food webs show that one organism can have more than one role in an ecosystem.

3. Available energy decreases.

4. Food chains should show one energy path. Webs should show multiple paths.

5. Secondary consumers would disappear without having muskrats to eat. Producers would get more plentiful without the muskrats eating them.

6. A food web shows movement of energy, but it also shows movement of matter. As consumers eat, carbon in plants and animals is transferred through the food web.

CONNECTING SCIENCES

LIFE SCIENCE AND PHYSICAL SCIENCE

Biomagnification

Matter moves through living things in an ecosystem. Some of it is used up, some of it is stored. Sometimes, a toxic, or poisonous, material can get into a food chain and be stored. Biomagnification is the process by which matter becomes concentrated in living things.

Moving up the Food Chain

DDT provides one example of the effects of biomagnification in an ecosystem. DDT is a chemical that was widely used to kill plant-eating insects. Some chemicals break down over time, but DDT does not. DDT collected in water and soil, was absorbed by living things, and moved up the food chain. The diagram shows how DDT became magnified in a wetland ecosystem. It entered through tiny organisms called zooplankton, which absorbed DDT from the water.

1. The concentration of DDT in zooplankton was about 800 times greater than in the environment.
2. Minnows fed on zooplankton. DDT was magnified 31 times, so the concentration of DDT in minnows was 24,800 times greater than in the environment: 800 x 31 = 24,800.
3. Trout ate minnows. DDT was magnified 1.7 times, so the concentration of DDT in trout was 42,160 times greater than in the environment.
4. Gulls ate trout. DDT was magnified 4.8 times, so the concentration of DDT in gulls was over 200,000 times greater than in the environment.

DDT is especially harmful to large birds such as osprey and eagles. The chemical made the shells of the eggs of these large birds so thin that the eggs did not survive long enough to hatch.

Moving up the Food Chain

This diagram shows how DDT moved up a food chain in Long Island Sound. The color in each circle below represents a certain level of DDT.

CHALLENGE Even though DDT was effective, some insects were not harmed by DDT. Predict what might happen to the numbers of those insects as a result of DDT use.

Chapter 14: Ecosystems and Biomes 493

EXPLORE

CHALLENGE Insects not affected by DDT might increase in numbers as living things that consume those insects might decrease in population.

CONNECTING SCIENCES

Connecting Life and Physical Sciences

Set Learning Goal

To understand how chemicals in the environment can accumulate in organisms that feed high on the food chain

Present the Science

DDT is stored in fatty tissues. Accumulations of DDT in the body may not lead to death, but its gradual buildup can affect an animal's health and ability to reproduce. Although DDT was banned in the United States in 1972, it lingers in the environment. It is still used in some countries, especially to control malaria-carrying mosquitoes.

Discussion Questions

Go through the steps of the biomagnification food chain. Ask:

- How does DDT get into the bodies of zooplankton? *Runoff washes DDT into waterways, where zooplankton absorb it from the water.*
- How does an organism's place on the food chain relate to the concentration of DDT in its body? *Organisms higher on the food chain have higher concentrations of DDT.*
- How does the biomagnification of DDT affect reproduction in birds of prey? *It causes thin eggshells that break before young birds have a chance to hatch.*

Close

Ask: How does the biomagnification of nonbiodegradable chemicals show that matter moves through a food chain? *DDT is not broken down or used at each step in the food chain, so increasing amounts accumulate in the bodies of organisms that are higher on the chain.*

14.4 FOCUS

Set Learning Goals

Students will

- Describe how biomes vary by region and how they are classified by the plant life they support.
- Explain that different ecosystems make up a biome.
- Describe different land and water biomes on Earth.
- Gather and graph local climate data.

3-Minute Warm-Up

Display Transparency 5 or copy the exercise on the board:

The organisms in a certain grassland ecosystem include grasses, insects, meadowlarks, mice, and owls. Draw a diagram that shows how these organisms depend on one another for food. Label each organism and use an arrow to show which organism(s) it feeds on.

Students should produce a simple food web with arrows from grasses to insects, insects to meadowlarks and mice, mice to owls.

 3-Minute Warm-Up, p. T5

14.4 MOTIVATE

THINK ABOUT

PURPOSE To understand how a plant's characteristics are important for survival

DISCUSS What adaptations do cacti have? *thick green stems and spines* What do they do for the plants? *reduce water loss, perform photosynthesis, protect plant from herbivores.*

Answers: tubular stems and oval-shaped growth off stems; it has spines instead of leaves; its pads are stems; it flowers; it must conserve water; the environment is dry.

KEY CONCEPT

Biomes contain many ecosystems.

BEFORE, you learned

- Feeding relationships describe how energy flows through ecosystems
- The amount of available energy decreases as it flows through ecosystems

NOW, you will learn

- How biomes vary by region and by the plant life they support
- How different ecosystems make up a biome
- About the different land and water biomes on Earth

VOCABULARY

biome p. 494
coniferous p. 496
deciduous p. 497
estuary p. 500

THINK ABOUT

What do this plant's characteristics suggest about its environment?

A plant's overall shape and form help it to survive in its environment. Look closely at this plant in the photograph. Describe its shape. Does it have leaves? a stem? flowers? Look at the surrounding area. What do your observations suggest about the environment in general?

COMBINATION NOTES
Remember to take notes and draw a diagram for each of the six land biomes described in the text.

Regions of Earth are classified into biomes.

If you could travel along the 30° latitude line, either north or south of the equator, you'd notice an interesting pattern. You would see deserts give way to grasslands and grasslands give way to forests. Across Earth, there are large geographic areas that are similar in climate and that have similar types of plants and animals. Each of these regions is classified as a **biome** (BY-OHM). There are six major land biomes on Earth, as shown on the map on page 495.

Climate is an important factor in land biomes. Climate describes the long-term weather patterns of a region, such as average yearly rainfall and temperature ranges. Climate also affects soil type. Available water, temperature, and soil are abiotic factors important in ecosystems. The fact that the abiotic factors of a particular biome are similar helps to explain why the ecosystems found in these biomes are similar. Biomes represent very large areas, which means that there will be many ecosystems within a biome.

RESOURCES FOR DIFFERENTIATED INSTRUCTION

Below Level

UNIT RESOURCE BOOK

- Reading Study Guide A, pp. 45–46
- Decoding Support, p. 59

AUDIO CDS

Advanced

UNIT RESOURCE BOOK

Challenge and Extension, p. 51

English Learners

UNIT RESOURCE BOOK

Spanish Reading Study Guide, pp. 49–50

 **AUDIO CDS**

- Audio Readings in Spanish
- Audio Readings (English)

Land Biomes

Each land biome is characterized by a particular climate, the quality of the soil, and the plant life found there.

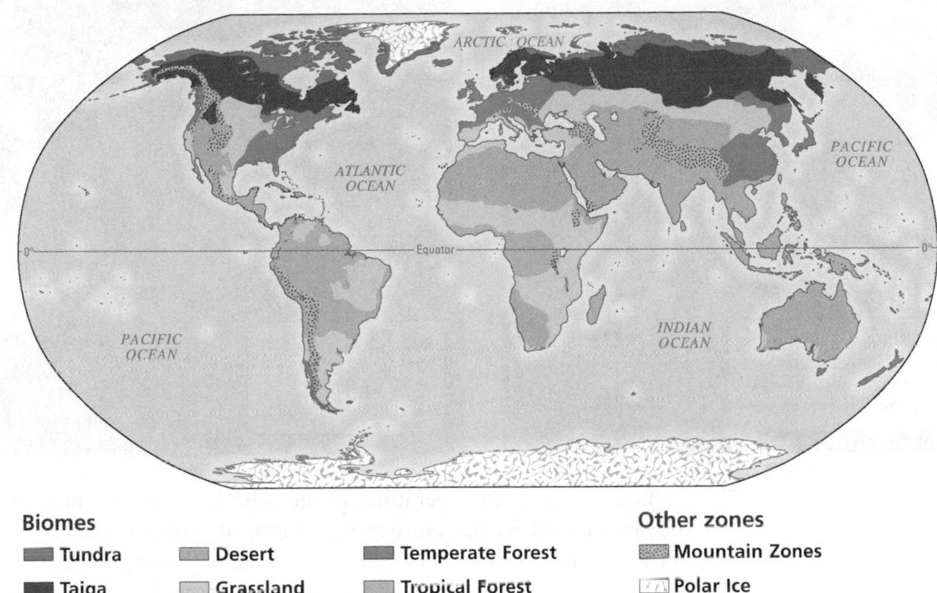

Taiga and Tundra

If you go to the northernmost regions of Earth, you will find two biomes—tundra and taiga—that are characterized by long cold winters and short cool summers. In the Arctic tundra, temperatures can go as low as –50°C, with a high of about 18°C. Temperature ranges in the taiga (TY-guh) are similar, –40°C to 20°C.

The tundra doesn't get much precipitation, less than 25 centimeters each year. Yet the area is wet because cold temperatures keep the water from evaporating. One of the important characteristics of tundra is permafrost, a deep layer of permanently frozen soil that lies just below the surface soil. Permafrost prevents trees from taking root in the tundra. Plants of the tundra are small and include mosses, grasses, and woody shrubs. Organisms called lichens also do well in the tundra.

The producers of tundra ecosystems support rodents, caribou, and musk oxen. Grizzly bears, white fox, and snowy owls are predators found there. Migrating birds come to nest in the tundra, feeding on insects that mature in summer.

snowy owl

14.4 INSTRUCT

Teach from Visuals

To help students interpret the map of land biomes, ask:

- How many of the six land biomes occur in North America? *all six*
- Which biomes occur in South America? *all except taiga and tundra*
- Which biome dominates Europe? *temperate forest*
- How do the biomes of Australia and southern Africa compare? *Both include desert and grassland and some tropical forest.*

Geography Connection

Remind students that latitude lines mark distance above and below the equator. Point out the location of the equator and the Arctic Circle on a world map or globe. Ask:

- In what latitudes does tundra occur? *around the Arctic Circle; in the Northern Hemisphere only*
- Why is there no tundra or taiga in the Southern Hemisphere? *No landmasses, other than the polar ice of Antarctica are close to the south pole.*
- Where do tropical forests occur on Earth? *near the equator, and spreading north and south*

DIFFERENTIATE INSTRUCTION

More Reading Support

A What two biomes are found in Earth's northernmost regions? *tundra and taiga*

B Which biome is drier than and nearly as cold as the taiga? *tundra*

English Learners Ask English learners to describe the climate, soil quality, and plant life found in their home country. Help them determine which type of biome they have described. Be certain that students understand that a country or region may have more than one type of biome. Have students write the definitions of *biome, coniferous, deciduous,* and *estuary* in their Science Word Dictionaries.

Teach from Visuals

To help students compare and contrast the photographs of tundra and taiga, ask:

- What differences do you notice between the taiga and tundra? *Taiga has tall trees and bushes; tundra has only low-growing plants.*
- What is a primary reason for these differences? *Permafrost prevents the growth of the large, deep root systems of large plants in the tundra.*

Teach Difficult Concepts

Students may have difficulty remembering differences between taiga and tundra. Point out that tundra can be considered a kind of cold desert because it is cold, windy, and dry. The taiga, by contrast, is thickly forested with tall trees. Taiga receives more precipitation than tundra (30 to 60 cm compared to less than 25 cm) and has trees and no permafrost.

Teacher Demo

Show students what permafrost is like. Use a sharp spade or trowel to collect a block of turf or other soil that measures about 15 cm square. Keep the block intact and place it in a shallow container in the freezer for several hours. Remove the container from the freezer a few minutes before class so that the upper portion will begin to thaw. Let students use disposable chopsticks or other probes to explore the texture of the frozen soil. Students may find it helpful to know that *permafrost* is short for "permanent frost."

Ongoing Assessment

Describe how biomes vary by region and are classified according to the plant life they support.

Ask: Where do you find taiga and how do you recognize it? *It is in northern latitudes, has long winters and short summers, and is often dominated by coniferous trees.*

Tundra Only small plants and lichens grow in the tundra because the soil below the surface is frozen.

Taiga Evergreen trees grow in the taiga, where the ground is cold but not frozen.

Even though the temperatures of the taiga are similar to those of the tundra, the taiga has more precipitation, 30 to 60 centimeters a year. The effect of this is that there is more snow on the ground, which insulates the soil below, keeping it from permanently freezing.

C

Taiga ecosystems are characterized by evergreen trees called **coniferous** (koh-NIHF-uhr-uhs) trees. These trees have needlelike leaves that produce food all year long. This is an advantage in taiga ecosystems because decomposers work slowly in the cold, so the soil is low in nutrients. The wood and leaves of these trees feed insects and their seeds feed birds and squirrels. Taiga ecosystems support deer, elk, snowshoe hares, and beavers. Predators include lynx, owls, bears, and wolves.

Desert and Grassland

collared lizard

Deserts and grasslands are biomes found toward the middle latitudes. You can see from the map on page 495 that a desert biome often leads into a grassland biome. What deserts and grasslands have in common is that they do not get enough precipitation to support trees.

? D

Some deserts are cold and some deserts are hot, but all deserts are characterized by their dry soil. Less than 25 centimeters of rain falls each year in a desert. Desert plants, like the cactus, and desert animals, like the collared lizard, can get by on very little water. Small burrowing animals like the kangaroo rat and ground squirrel are part of desert ecosystems. Desert predators include snakes, owls, and foxes.

DIFFERENTIATE INSTRUCTION

More Reading Support

C What are evergreens in taiga ecosystems called? *coniferous*

D Which biome is defined by dry soil? *desert*

Inclusion For students who are still at a concrete stage of learning, model the rainfall amounts in this section either by filling a clear beaker or by displaying vertical strips of varying lengths. Explain how each amount represents the water that would collect in a rain gauge from falling precipitation.

Grassland ecosystems develop in areas of moderate rainfall, generally from 50 to 90 centimeters each year. There is enough rain to support grasses, but too little rain to support forests. Periodic wildfires and droughts keep smaller shrubs and tree seedlings from growing. Summers in grassland ecosystems are warm, up to 30°C, but winters are cold.

E Grasses do well in large open areas. The more rain a grassland ecosystem gets, the higher the grasses grow. These ecosystems support seed-eating rodents that make their burrows in the grassland soil. There are also large grazing animals, like bison, wild horses, gazelle, and zebra. Predators include wolves, tigers, and lions.

Desert Plants of the desert are adapted to survive in dry soil. Many must also survive high daytime temperatures.

Grassland Grasslands receive enough rain to support grasses. Wildfires keep shrubs and trees from growing.

Temperate Forest and Tropical Forest

Trees need more water than smaller plants, shrubs, and grasses. So forest biomes are usually located in regions where more water is available. The taiga is a forest biome. There the coniferous trees survive on smaller amounts of precipitation because the cold weather limits evaporation. Across the middle latitudes, temperate forests grow where winters are short and 75 to 150 centimeters of precipitation fall each year. Near the equator, there are no winters. There, tropical forests grow where 200 to 450 centimeters of rain fall each year.

F Most temperate forests are made up of deciduous trees, sometimes referred to as broadleaf trees. **Deciduous** (dih-SIHJ-oo-uhs) trees drop their leaves as winter approaches and then grow new leaves in spring.

Teach from Visuals

To help students compare and contrast the photographs of deserts and grasslands, ask:

- What differences do you notice between the desert and grassland? *Desert has bare soil with rocks and cacti; grassland soil is covered with grasses and wildflowers.*
- What are some primary reasons for these differences? *Grasslands receive more rain and have richer soil than deserts do.*

Teacher Demo

Compare features of grasses and broad-leaved plants for students. Carefully wash the soil from the roots of a sample of lawn grass and an uprooted broad-leaved plant. Show students the intact plants, including root system. Ask: Why can grass plants survive grazing and fire? *New leaves grow from an underground part of the plant that usually escapes damage from grazing or fire.*

Develop Critical Thinking

SYNTHESIZE Have students choose one animal from the taiga and suggest adaptations that animal would need to survive in the tundra. Students might choose other animals from other biomes as well. For example, what would make it hard for a snowy owl to survive in a grassland? What adaptations could increase its survival?

DIFFERENTIATE INSTRUCTION

More Reading Support

E What kind of plant does well in large open areas? *grass*

F Which biome has trees that are bare of leaves in winter? *temperate forest*

Below Level Help students remember the differences among biomes by having them make flash cards. On one side of a card, have them write a biome name, and on the other side, one feature of that biome. Give students time to study their flash cards with the help of a partner.

Teach from Visuals

To help students compare and contrast the photographs of temperate and tropical forests, ask:

- What differences do you notice between the temperate and tropical forests? *Sample answer: more vines, greater number and variety of trees in the tropics*
- What do you notice about the variety of types of leaves in temperate and tropical forests? *A tropical forest has a greater variety of leaf types and sizes.*

Real World Example

The Alaskan forest contains cedar and spruce trees, salmon in rivers, sea lions, otters, and belugas in coastal waters. In 1989, the need to protect this bounty was magnified when the *Exxon Valdez* accidentally dumped 11 million gallons of oil on 15,000 miles of coastline. Wildlife like the otter, harbor seal, and harlequin duck still haven't recovered. Now the forest faces a greater threat: logging. Humans are leveling trees at a record rate. Some environmental groups are trying to preserve the rainforest. Oil-spill funds from the *Exxon Valdez* have added 66,000 acres of forest to the state-park system.

Ongoing Assessment

Explain that biomes are made up of several ecosystems.

Ask: What are some of the ecosystems in our biome? *Sample answer for temperate forest: deciduous forest, shrubland, marsh; grassland: meadow, field, banks of a stream*

CHECK YOUR READING *Answer: the greater the plant variety in a biome, the greater the variety of animals*

Temperate Forest
Temperate forests contain many trees with leaves that change color and fall as winter approaches.

Tropical Forest
Tropical forests are warm enough that trees stay green during the entire year.

The most common broadleaf trees in North American deciduous forests are oak, birch, beech, and maple. Temperate forests support a wide variety of animals. Animals like mice, chipmunks, squirrels, raccoons, and deer live off seeds, fruit, and insects. Predators include wolves, bobcats, foxes, and mountain lions.

G Most temperate forests in North America are deciduous. However, the wet winters and dry summers in the Pacific Northwest support forests made up mostly of coniferous trees—redwoods, spruce, and fir. These forests are referred to as temperate rain forests. The largest trees in the United States are found in these temperate rain forests.

H Tropical forests are located near the equator, where the weather is warm all year, around 25°C. The tropical rain forest is the wettest land biome, with a rainfall of 250 to 400 centimeters each year. The trees tend to have leaves year round. This provides an advantage because the soil is poor in nutrients. High temperatures cause materials to break down quickly, but there are so many plants the nutrients get used up just as quickly.

More types of animals, plants, and other organisms live in the tropical rain forest than anywhere else on Earth. The trees grow close together and support many tree-dwelling animals like monkeys, birds, insects, and snakes. There are even plants, like orchids and vines, that grow on top of the trees.

CHECK YOUR READING How does the variety of plants in a biome affect the variety of animals in a biome?

DIFFERENTIATE INSTRUCTION

More Reading Support

G Which biome includes forests that are deciduous? *temperate forest*

H What is the wettest biome on Earth? *tropical forest*

Advanced Tropical rain forests contain most of Earth's species, yet they are rapidly disappearing. Challenge students to brainstorm products we use that come from the rain forest and explain why we rely on the rain forest in everyday life. Ask them to infer why use of each product would either help or harm rain forest conservation.

Challenge and Extension, p. 51

INVESTIGATE Climate

How can you graph climate data for your area?

PROCEDURE

1. Gather local data on the average monthly precipitation and the average monthly temperature for a 12-month period.
2. On graph paper, mark off 12 months along the *x*-axis. Make a *y*-axis for each side of the graph, marking one "Temperature (°C)" and the other "Precipitation (mm)."
3. Plot the average precipitation for each month as a bar graph.
4. Plot the average temperature for each month as a line graph.

WHAT DO YOU THINK?

- How much precipitation did the area receive overall?
- What is the temperature range for the area?

CHALLENGE Collect data for the same location, going back 10, 20, and 30 years ago. Graph the data for each of these and compare these graphs to your original graph. Has the climate in your area changed? How might severe changes in climate affect the plant and animal life in your area?

SKILL FOCUS
Graphing data

MATERIALS
- graph data
- 2 colored pencils

TIME
20 minutes

Water covers most of Earth's surface.

Close to three-quarters of Earth's surface is covered by water. Water, or aquatic, biomes can be divided into two broad categories: freshwater biomes and saltwater biomes. Plants have a role as producers in the water biomes that are closely surrounded by land—in ponds and streams and wetlands, and in coastal areas. The food chains of deepwater ecosystems depend on tiny photosynthetic microorganisms called phytoplankton.

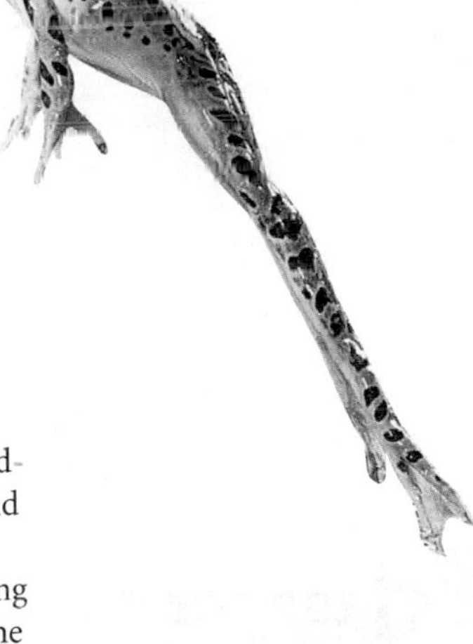

leopard frog

Freshwater Biomes

The ecosystems of freshwater biomes are affected by the qualities of the landscape in which they are found. For example, the running water of streams and rivers results from differences in elevation. In shallow rivers, green algae and plants grow in from the banks, providing food for insects and snails that feed fish, salamanders, turtles, and frogs. Plants in a freshwater biome, like a stream or river, may take root in the soil under the water if the water is not too deep or moving too fast. Phytoplankton are not part of river ecosystems because of the moving water.

INVESTIGATE Climate

PURPOSE To understand differences in precipitation and temperature over a 12-month period

TIP *20 min.* You may wish to have students work in pairs to create their graphs.

WHAT DO YOU THINK? *Sample answers should match climate in your region.*

CHALLENGE *Sample answers should match climatic change in your region. One example of severe climatic change is drought, which affects plant growth.*

- Climate Graph, p. 52
- Datasheet, Climate, p. 53

Technology Resources

Customize this student lab as needed or look for an alternative. Print rubrics to assess student lab reports.

Lab Generator CD-ROM

Teaching with Technology

Students may use spreadsheets or graphing software to organize data and create their graphs.

DIFFERENTIATE INSTRUCTION

More Reading Support

I What covers almost three-quarters of Earth's surface? *water*

Alternative Assessment Rather than asking students to write a formal report on the investigation, have student pairs explain the story that the data tell. Ask students to write a paragraph explaining how the lines on the graph describe the data.

Teach from Visuals

To help students understand the illustration and photographs of aquatic biomes, ask:

- What differences do you notice between the river and the lake or pond? *River has flowing water that travels a long way through the countryside. Ponds and lakes have still water that does not travel.*
- What differences do you notice between the estuary and the lake or pond? *There are no trees around the estuary. There is flowing water in the estuary. The pond is farther from the ocean.*

Integrating the Sciences

The biosphere is the part of Earth that supports life. It includes air, soil, and water. It extends from the bottom of the deepest ocean to high in the atmosphere, miles above Earth's surface. Just as biomes are made up of ecosystems, the biosphere is made up of biomes. In turn, the Earth as a system is made up of spheres. The spheres include the geosphere, the hydrosphere, the atmosphere, and the biosphere.

Ongoing Assessment

CHECK YOUR READING *Answer: any two: lakes, ponds, estuaries, and rivers*

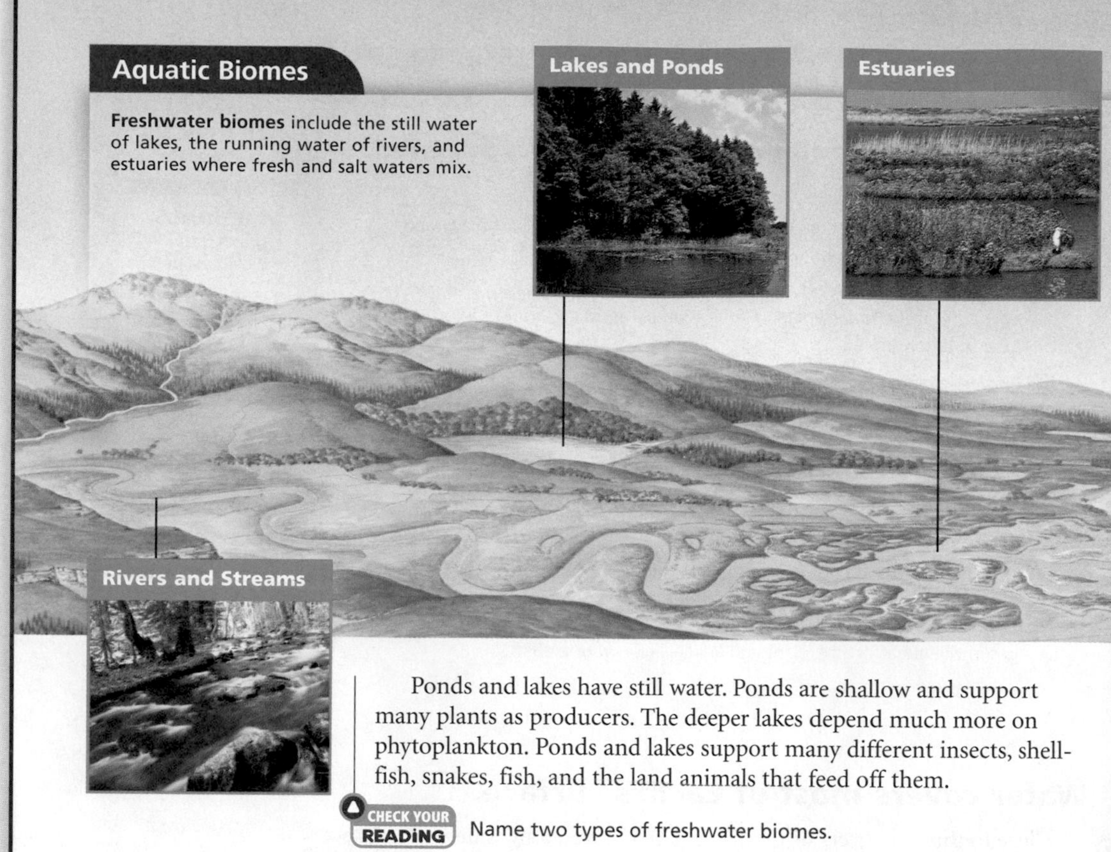

Freshwater biomes include the still water of lakes, the running water of rivers, and estuaries where fresh and salt waters mix.

Ponds and lakes have still water. Ponds are shallow and support many plants as producers. The deeper lakes depend much more on phytoplankton. Ponds and lakes support many different insects, shellfish, snakes, fish, and the land animals that feed off them.

CHECK YOUR READING Name two types of freshwater biomes.

Estuaries are water ecosystems that mark a transition between freshwater and saltwater biomes. An **estuary** is the lower end of a river that feeds into the ocean, where fresh water and salt water mix. Marshes and wetlands are two types of estuaries. Estuaries are sometimes referred to as the nurseries of the sea because so many marine animals travel into the calm waters of an estuary to reproduce. Seaweed, marsh grasses, shellfish, and birds all thrive in estuaries.

Marine Biomes

Marine biomes are saltwater biomes. The three general marine biomes are coastal ocean, open ocean, and deep ocean. Beaches are part of the coastal ocean biome. Tidal pools also form along the coast as the tide comes in and goes out and the conditions constantly change. Organisms like crabs and clams are able to survive the ever-changing conditions to thrive in coastal areas.

RESOURCE CENTER
CLASSZONE.COM
Find out more about land and aquatic biomes.

Organisms in the open ocean receive less sunlight than in the coastal ocean, and the temperatures are colder. Many types of fish and

DIFFERENTIATE INSTRUCTION

More Reading Support

J Which biome combines fresh and saltwater? *estuary*

K Which biomes are in the ocean? *marine biomes; coastal, open ocean, deep ocean*

Advanced Have students select freshwater or marine ecosystems and draw or paint an ecosystem in that biome. If possible, use a technique called "crayon resist." Students draw organisms with oil pastels or crayons, then paint the watery surrounding using water-color paint. Ask them to use their drawings to create a classroom display that shows how the ecosystems combine to form different aquatic biomes.

Coastal

Marine biomes include rocky and sandy shores as well as the open ocean and the deep waters below, where little or no light can reach.

Open Ocean

Deep Ocean

other marine animals and floating seaweed live in the upper ocean. There are no plants in the open ocean. The producers at the bottom of the food chain are different types of phytoplankton.

The deep-ocean regions are much colder and darker than the upper ocean. In the deep ocean there is no sunlight available for photosynthesis. The animals in the deep ocean either feed on each other or on material that falls down from upper levels of the ocean. Many organisms in deep ocean biomes can only be seen with a microscope.

14.4 Review

KEY CONCEPTS

1. In biomes located on land, abiotic factors are used to classify the different biome types. What are these abiotic factors?
2. Name a characteristic type of plant for each of the six land biomes.
3. Name six different aquatic biomes.

CRITICAL THINKING

4. **Predict** If an ecosystem in the grassland biome started to receive less and less rainfall every year, what new biome would be established?
5. **Infer** Name some abiotic factors that affect aquatic biomes and ecosystems.

CHALLENGE

6. **Apply** Use the map on page 495 to list the following four biomes in the order you would find them moving from the equator to the poles.
   - desert
   - taiga
   - tropical Forest
   - tundra

ANSWERS

1. available water, temperature, soil

2. tundra: mosses, lichens; taiga: coniferous trees; desert: cacti; grassland: grasses; temperate forest: deciduous trees; tropical forest: plants grow on top of each other

3. rivers and streams, lakes and ponds, estuaries, coastal ocean, open ocean, deep ocean

4. desert

5. sunlight, water depth, temperature, nutrients

6. tropical forest, desert, taiga, tundra

Teach from Visuals

To help students understand marine biomes, ask:

- How are the coastal ocean and open ocean similar? *Both receive sunlight.*
- How does the deep ocean differ from the coastal and open ocean? *It is dark and cold.*

Reinforce the BIG idea

Have students relate the section to the Big Idea.

 Reinforcing Key Concepts, p. 54

14.4 ASSESS & RETEACH

Assess

 Section 14.4 Quiz, p. 6

Reteach

Start by listing the six land biomes on the board. Then list aquatic biomes.

Next, show pictures of landscapes and ask students to identify what biome they could be from. Have students point to details that support their identification. Discuss any landscapes that are difficult to categorize.

Technology Resources

Have students visit **ClassZone.com** for reteaching of Key Concepts.

 **CONTENT REVIEW**

 **CONTENT REVIEW CD-ROM**

BACK TO

the BIG idea

Have students draw and label a diagram showing how matter and energy are both needed to support life in an ecosystem. *Drawings should show the movement of matter through an ecosystem and the movement of energy and matter through its food web.*

KEY CONCEPTS SUMMARY

SECTION 14.1

Ask: What abiotic features are pictured? *temperature, sunlight, soil, water*

Ask: What biotic features are pictured? *tree, horse*

SECTION 14.2

Ask: What are the three important processes that take place in the water cycle? *evaporation, condensation, precipitation*

Ask: How does carbon move from air to plants to animals? *Plants absorb carbon dioxide from air, and animals eat plants.*

Ask: How does nitrogen move from air to plants to animals in an ecosystem? *Bacteria fix nitrogen gas into a compound that is taken up by plants. Animals eat plants.*

SECTION 14.3

Ask: Name one path that matter and energy take as they move through the food web shown in the picture on p. 491. *Sample answer: bulrush, snail, heron*

Ask: Which organisms are at the top of this ecosystem's energy pyramid? *heron, water snake*

SECTION 14.4

Ask: What are the chief factors that define a biome? *plant life and climate*

Review Concepts

- Big Idea Flow Chart, p. T1
- Chapter Outline, pp. T7–T8

14 Chapter Review

the BIG idea

Matter and energy together support life within an environment.

KEY CONCEPTS SUMMARY

Ecosystems support life.

Ecosystems are made up of living things (biotic) and nonliving things (abiotic).

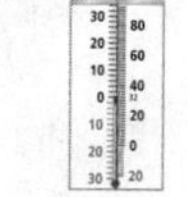
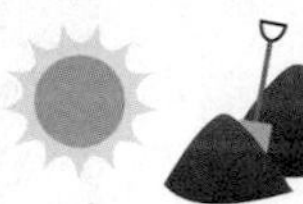

plants animals temperature Sun soil water

Biotic Factors **Abiotic Factors**

VOCABULARY
ecology p. 473
ecosystem p. 473
biotic factor p. 474
abiotic factor p. 474

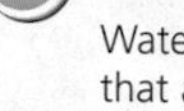

Matter cycles through ecosystems.

Water, carbon, and nitrogen are materials that are necessary for life. They move through ecosystems in continuous cycles.

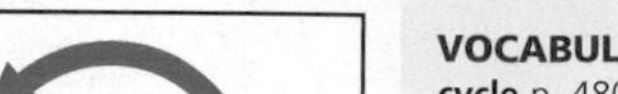

VOCABULARY
cycle p. 480
water cycle p. 481
carbon cycle p. 482
nitrogen cycle p. 483

Energy flows through ecosystems.

Producers are the basis of feeding relationships in ecosystems.

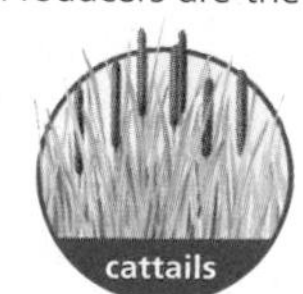

Producer

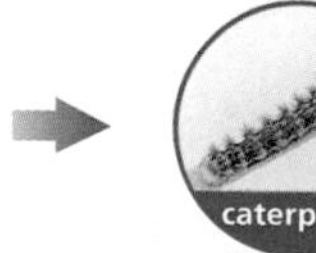

Primary consumer

Secondary consumer

Food chains and food webs help show how energy moves through living things.

VOCABULARY
producer p. 487
consumer p. 488
decomposer p. 489
food chain p. 490
food web p. 490
energy pyramid p. 492

4 Biomes contain many ecosystems.

Ecosystems of land biomes
- are affected by climate
- are affected by conditions of the soil
- are characterized by types of plants

Ecosystems of water biomes
- can be freshwater or saltwater
- are affected by landscape if freshwater
- are affected by depth if marine

VOCABULARY
biome p. 494
coniferous p. 496
deciduous p. 497
estuary p. 500

Technology Resources

Have students visit **ClassZone.com** or use the CD-ROM for a cumulative review of concepts.

CONTENT REVIEW

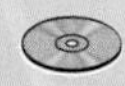
CONTENT REVIEW CD-ROM

Engage students in a whole-class interactive review of Key Concepts. Edit content as you wish.

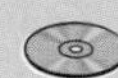
POWER PRESENTATIONS

Reviewing Vocabulary

Write a statement describing how the terms in each pair are similar and different.

1. biotic, abiotic
2. producer, consumer
3. food chain, food web

The table shows the meanings of word roots that are used in many science terms.

Root	Meaning
bio-	life
ecos-	house
-ogy	study of

Use the information in the table to write definitions for the following terms.

4. ecology
5. biome
6. ecosystem

Reviewing Key Concepts

Multiple Choice *Choose the letter of the best answer.*

7. Which best describes the components of an ecosystem?
   a. light, water, soil, and temperature
   b. autotrophs and heterotrophs
   c. biotic and abiotic factors
   d. producers, consumers, and decomposers
8. What is the primary source of energy for most ecosystems?
   a. water c. soil
   b. nitrogen d. sunlight
9. What is the process by which the water in rivers, lakes, and oceans is converted to a gas and moves into the atmosphere?
   a. precipitation c. condensation
   b. evaporation d. transpiration
10. The process called nitrogen fixation is essential for life on Earth. Which of the following is an example of nitrogen fixation?
    a. Plants take in nitrogen gas from the atmosphere.
    b. Animals take in nitrogen gas from the atmosphere.
    c. Water absorbs nitrogen.
    d. Bacteria convert nitrogen gas into a form that plants can use.
11. Which organism is a decomposer?
    a. vulture c. musk ox
    b. sunflower d. fungus
12. How are decomposers important in an ecosystem?
    a. They make atmospheric nitrogen available to plants in a usable form.
    b. They convert organic matter into more complex compounds.
    c. They are an important source of food for scavengers.
    d. They break down organic matter into simpler compounds.
13. What factor is least important in determining the plant life in a biome?
    a. average annual rainfall
    b. average annual temperature
    c. the type of soil
    d. the type of animals living there

Short Answer *Write a short answer to each question.*

14. Write a paragraph to describe how carbon dioxide gas in the atmosphere can become part of the carbon compounds found inside animals.
15. Write a paragraph to explain how the amount of available energy changes as you move from producers to consumers in a food web.
16. Write a paragraph to describe one important way in which the flow of energy through ecosystems is different from the cycling of matter.

ASSESSMENT RESOURCES

UNIT ASSESSMENT BOOK
- Chapter Test A, pp. 7–10
- Chapter Test B, pp. 11–14
- Chapter Test C, pp. 15–18
- Alternative Assessment, pp. 19–20

SPANISH ASSESSMENT BOOK
Spanish Chapter Test, pp. 65–68

Technology Resources

Edit test items and answer choices.

Test Generator CD-ROM

Visit **ClassZone.com** to extend test practice.

Test Practice

Reviewing Vocabulary

1. Both are parts of the ecosystem. Biotic are the living parts, and abiotic are the nonliving parts.

2. Producers and consumers are parts of the ecosystem. Consumers get their food from producers directly by eating them, or indirectly by eating other consumers that eat producers.

3. Both are feeding relationships. A food chain is a single relationship; food webs have many interconnected food chains in the same ecosystem.

4. ecology: from ecos– *meaning "house" and* –ology *meaning "study of"—the scientific study of how organisms interact with their environment and all the other organisms in that environment.*

5. biome: from bio– *meaning "life"—a region on Earth with similar types of plants and animals.*

6. ecosystem: from ecos– *meaning "house" and* system, *parts that work together—a particular environment and all the living things supported by it.*

Reviewing Key Concepts

7. c	*11. d*
8. d	*12. d*
9. b	*13. d*
10. d	

14. Plants use carbon dioxide in the air to produce sugars in a process called photosynthesis. Then animals eat the plants. The compounds in the plants become part of the animals.

15. Available energy decreases as you move from the bottom to the top of the energy pyramid. Each time energy moves from one level to the next, it changes form, and some energy is lost in that process. Some of the energy is also used by the organisms at each level.

16. Sample answers: Cycles involve movement of matter through the environment. A cycle happens over and over again. The flow of energy involves food webs in which energy and matter are transferred from one organism to the next as organisms eat and are eaten.

Thinking Critically

17. a food web; a model of the feeding relationships in an ecosystem

18. producer: cattails; primary: mosquito, slug; secondary: frog; tertiary: water snake

19. shrew next to salamander, arrow from slug to shrew, arrow from salamander to shrew, arrow from shrew to water snake

20. about one-thousandth

21. Decomposers do not produce food. They break down dead plant and animal matter for food.

22. desert, taiga, grassland, deciduous forest, tropical rain forest

23. Climate, temperature, rainfall, and available water determine type of plants that will grow. Some animals migrate to different biomes during the year. In theory, this makes plants a more reliable indicator of difference.

24. Diagrams should show correct relationships among various aquatic biomes; saltiness of water and amount of oxygen available in water differ among these biomes.

25. Answers might include a description of the living and nonliving things in a home, home climate, and that a home environment is a controlled environment.

26. Sample answer: a summer drought killed grasses and plant life, which were food for small animals.

the BIG idea

27. Sample answer: I would add organisms you can't see such as decomposers and plankton. I would mention soil, air, and sunlight as well.

28. Student answers should use the eight listed terms correctly in a paragraph(s).

UNIT PROJECTS

Give students the appropriate Unit Project worksheets from the Unit Resource Book for their projects. Both directions and rubrics can be used as a guide.

 Unit Projects, pp. 5–10

Thinking Critically

Use the diagram to answer the next four questions.

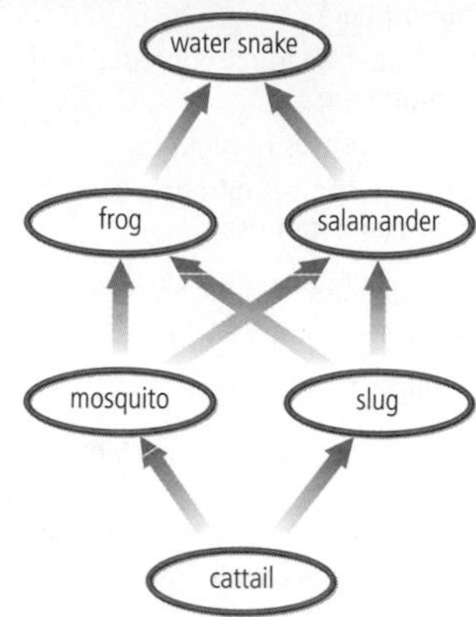

17. CONNECT What does the diagram above represent and how does it relate to energy in an ecosystem?

18. CLASSIFY Identify each of the animals in the diagram above as a producer, primary consumer, or secondary consumer or tertiary consumer.

19. APPLY Another animal that is found in many wetlands ecosystems is the shrew. The shrew eats salamanders and slugs and is eaten by water snakes. Copy the diagram above and show how you would add the shrew to the diagram.

20. CONNECT Use the diagram above to make an energy pyramid. If only one-tenth of the energy available at each level is passed on to the next higher level, how much of the energy in a cattail is transferred to a salamander?

21. SYNTHESIZE Why would it be difficult to show a decomposer as part of an energy pyramid?

22. RANK Arrange the following list of biomes according to the relative amounts of precipitation in each, going from the least amount to the most: grassland, desert, deciduous forest, taiga, tropical rain forest.

23. SYNTHESIZE Why are plants but not animals considered an important factor in classifying a land biome?

24. SUMMARIZE Draw a diagram that illustrates aquatic biomes. On your diagram label the following: freshwater river, freshwater lake, estuary, coastal zone, open ocean zone. How do abiotic factors differ among these biomes?

25. COMPARE AND CONTRAST In what ways is your home like an ecosystem? In what ways is it different?

26. APPLY Describe a change in an abiotic factor that affected living factors in an ecosystem near you.

the BIG idea

27. CLASSIFY Look again at the photograph on pages 470–471. Now that you have finished the chapter, how would you change or add details to your answer to the question on the photograph?

28. SYNTHESIZE Write one or more paragraphs describing how matter and energy together support life in an ecosystem. You may use examples from one specific ecosystem if you wish. In your description, use each of the following terms. Underline each term in your answer.

ecosystem	decomposer
food web	nitrogen cycle
producer	carbon cycle
primary consumer	secondary consumer

UNIT PROJECTS

If you are doing a unit project, make a folder for your project. Include in your folder a list of the resources you will need, the date on which the project is due, and a schedule to track your progress. Begin gathering data.

MONITOR AND RETEACH

If students have trouble with concepts in items 17–21, have them review the energy pyramid on p. 492, then make pie graphs with captions to show relative amount of energy available. Tell students the pie graphs are a visual memory device and the data is estimated.

Students may benefit from summarizing one or more sections of the chapter.

 Summarizing the Chapter, pp. 80–81

Standardized Test Practice

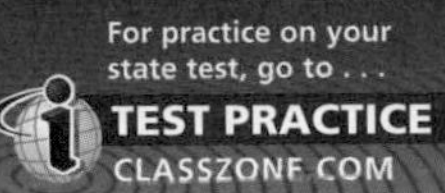

Interpreting Graphs

Choose the letter of the best response.

The graphs below show average monthly temperature and precipitation for one year in Staunton, Virginia, an area located in a temperate deciduous forest biome.

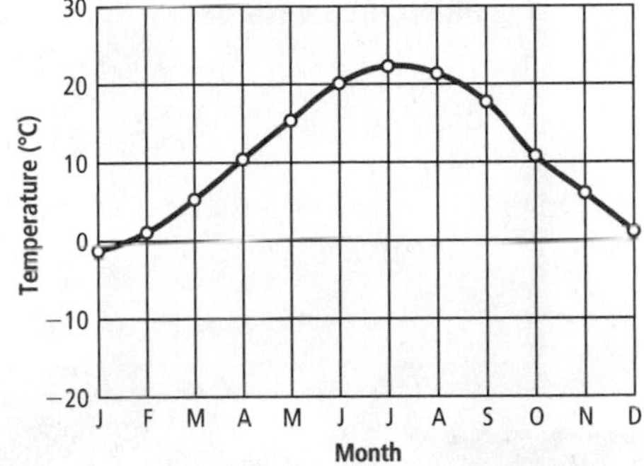

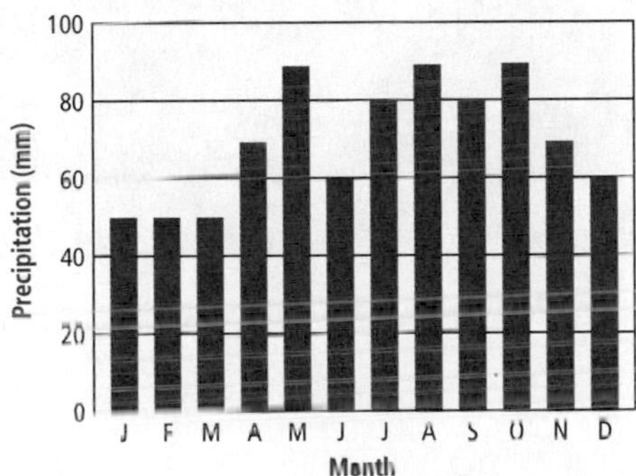

SOURCE: NASA

1. What was the average temperature during July?
   - a. 20°
   - b. 10°
   - c. 23°
   - d. 0°
2. Which months had the most precipitation?
   - a. January, February, March
   - b. May, August, October
   - c. July, August, September
   - d. December, January, February
3. What were conditions during May?
   - a. warm and moist
   - b. warm and dry
   - c. cool and moist
   - d. cool and dry
4. Which temperature is closest to the average temperature for the year shown?
   - a. about 16°
   - b. about 0°
   - c. about 20°
   - d. about 10°
5. How much precipitation would you estimate fell as snow in the year shown?
   - a. less than 50 mm
   - b. between 50 and 100 mm
   - c. between 100 and 200 mm
   - d. over 200 mm

Extended Response

6. Most of the United States is part of a temperate deciduous forest biome. The deciduous forest biome has four seasons. Trees in this biome lose their leaves yearly. Use this information, as well as the information in the graphs, to describe the seasons in the temperate deciduous forest biome.

7. Write a paragraph in which you describe a typical ecosystem in your city or town. In your answer include biotic factors such as plants, animals, and other organisms. Also include abiotic factors such as light, temperature, soil, and water. Finish your description by saying how you and other humans affect the ecosystem.

METACOGNITIVE ACTIVITY

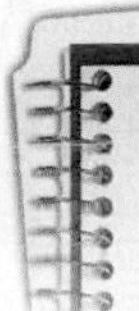

Have students answer the following questions in their **Science Notebook:**

1. What ecosystems and biomes were you already familiar with? What new things have you learned about those places?
2. How do you see yourself taking part in an ecosystem?
3. What goals have you set for your Unit Project? What is the next step you will complete?

Interpreting Graphs

1. c
2. b
3. a
4. d
5. b

Extended Response

6. RUBRIC

4 points for a response that includes complete sentences and temperature and precipitation information for a temperate deciduous forest and refers to information in both graphs:

Sample: This biome is characterized by trees that lose their leaves yearly. There are four seasons in this biome. Average precipitation is highest in the spring, summer, and autumn months, the months in which trees have their leaves. Average temperatures range from 20° C in summer months to around 0° C in winter.

3 points includes complete sentences and information about a temperate deciduous forest
2 points includes complete sentences and refers to information in the graphs
1 point attempts to accomplish the task, but does not meet the requirements

7. RUBRIC

4 points for a response that includes complete sentences and a description of biotic and abiotic factors, as well as human effects on the ecosystem:

Sample: In my town park there are ponds in the park that support fish, frogs, insects, and ducks. There are plants, shrubs, grass, and trees. Humans affect the ecosystem by walking on the grass and littering. Walking on the grass can kill the grass. Littering can affect the animals, plants, and water in the park. A piece of paper that is dropped can prevent a small plant from receiving enough light, and the plant may die.

3 points includes complete sentences and a description of biotic and abiotic factors
2 points includes complete sentences and human effect on the ecosystem
1 point attempts to accomplish the task, but does not meet the requirements

CHAPTER

Interactions Within Ecosystems

Life Science
UNIFYING PRINCIPLES

PRINCIPLE 1
All living things share common characteristics.

PRINCIPLE 2
All living things share common needs.

PRINCIPLE 3
Living things meet their needs through interactions with the environment.

PRINCIPLE 4
The types and numbers of living things change over time.

Unit 4: Ecology
BIG IDEAS

CHAPTER 14
Ecosystems and Biomes
Matter and energy together support life within a certain environment.

CHAPTER 15
Interactions Within Ecosystems
Living things within an ecosystem interact with each other and the environment.

CHAPTER 16
Human Impact on Ecosystems
Humans and human population growth affect the environment.

CHAPTER 15
KEY CONCEPTS

SECTION 1

Groups of living things interact within ecosystems.

1. Organisms occupy specific living areas.
2. The environment can be organized into five levels.
3. Patterns exist in populations.

SECTION 2

Organisms can interact in different ways.

1. Organisms interact in different ways.
2. The survival of one species might depend on another species.
3. Interactions in an ecosystem are complex.

SECTION 3

Ecosystems are always changing.

1. Populations change over time.
2. Ecosystems change over time.

T The Big Idea Flow Chart is available on p. T9 in the **UNIT TRANSPARENCY BOOK.**

Previewing Content

SECTION

Groups of living things interact within ecosystems. pp. 509–517

1. Organisms occupy specific living areas.
Organisms are members of the same **species** if they are similar to each other and produce offspring that can breed. Members of the same species who live in a particular **habitat** constitute a **population.** The habitat provides everything the population needs to survive.

Organisms perform roles, called **niches,** in the habitat. For instance, grasses on a prairie anchor the topsoil and provide food for grazing animals. Populations that live together and interact form a **community.**

2. The environment can be organized into five levels.
Beyond the community are higher levels of organization.

- Organisms and their local environments constitute an **ecosystem.**
- Places that are similar in terms of climate and vegetation are called **biomes.** These are broadly defined and have world-wide distribution.

The diagram shows the levels of organization at a glance.

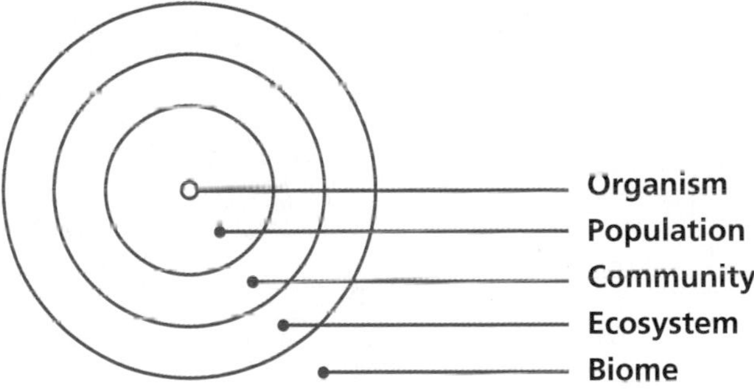

3. Patterns exist in populations.
The size of a population may change over time as a result of factors such as the change of seasons or interaction with another species. Spatial patterns of population distribution may result from the way organisms gather resources or from their need for mutual protection.

SECTION

Organisms can interact in different ways. pp. 518–526

1. Organisms interact in different ways.
A food chain is made up of producers and consumers, although the distinction between the two groups is not always clear-cut. An animal, for example, could be predator, prey, or both.

When more than one organism, whether of the same species or not, needs the same resources, the organisms will **compete.** Some organisms, such as ants or packs of hunters, **cooperate** to improve their survival.

2. The survival of one species might depend on another.
Individuals of two species may have a close relationship called **symbiosis.** Three kinds of symbiosis are commonly recognized.

- **Mutualism** occurs when both species in the symbiosis benefit from the interaction.
- **Commensalism** occurs if one species benefits while the other is unharmed and unaffected.
- **Parasitism** occurs when one species is harmed while the other benefits.

The table shows how the three symbiotic relationships can be beneficial (+), neutral (**0**), or harmful (−).

Symbiosis		
Relationship Between Species	**One Species**	**Other Species**
mutualism	+	+
commensalism	0	+
parasitism	−	+

3. Interactions in an ecosystem are complex.
Relationships and interactions do not exist in isolation. Any one species can have a range of symbiotic or predatory relationships with many other species.

Common Misconceptions

HUMANS IN AN ECOSYSTEM Students commonly think that they themselves are not part of ecosystems. Many children view the lives of humans as separate and different from those of plants, animals, and microorganisms. Each species of living thing is unique, yet all share common needs and characteristics. All species—including humans—live and interact in ecosystems.

This misconception is addressed on p. 513.

MISCONCEPTION DATABASE
CLASSZONE.COM Background on student misconceptions

Previewing Content

SECTION

Ecosystems are always changing.
pp. 527–533

1. **Populations change over time.**
Population size changes in response to food supply, predation, the seasons, and birth rates. A **limiting factor,** such as water, light, or food, can affect population survival and growth. The **carrying capacity** of an environment is the maximum population it can support. At carrying capacity a population stops growing.

2. **Ecosystems change over time.**
Succession is a gradual series of changes that take place in an ecosystem after a disturbance.
    - **Primary succession** starts from an environment that is mostly empty of life. After the retreat of a glacier, for example, or on new rock produced by a volcano, life can begin to return. **Pioneer species** move into the barren environment and begin the task of creating soil.
    - **Secondary succession** occurs in areas that have soil with roots and seeds below the surface. In such cases, life already survives. Living things produce new generations and attract the return of diverse species. Secondary succession may begin after a fire or flood disturbs the ecosystem.

The pictures on the right show the difference at the start of two successional sequences. In both types of natural succession, plants may facilitate the establishment of other plants by creating a hospitable habitat. Some species, however, create conditions that prevent competitors from moving in.

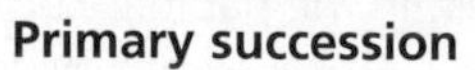

Primary succession

Secondary succession

A key difference between primary and secondary succession is the presence of soil in the environment at the start of the series of changes.

Common Misconceptions

MISCONCEPTION DATABASE
CLASSZONE.COM Background on student misconceptions

MATTER CHANGES FORM Most students think that matter can be destroyed. They often think that dead or decaying matter rots away to nothing. In fact, living and decaying matter is constantly transforming, changing from one form into another.

This misconception is addressed on p. 530.

Previewing Labs

Lab Generator CD-ROM
Edit these Pupil Edition labs and generate alternative labs.

EXPLORE the BIG idea

How Do Living Things Interact Where You Live? p. 507 Students observe how plants and animals interact in an environment.	**TIME** 10 minutes **MATERIALS** notebook, outdoor area, hand lens (optional)
How Many Roles Can a Living Thing Have in an Ecosystem? p. 507 Students analyze how an organism fits with an environment.	**TIME** 10 minutes **MATERIALS** notebook, outdoor area, hand lens (optional)
Internet Activity: Carrying Capacity, p. 507 Students change a population size in a virtual habitat to explore carrying capacity.	**TIME** 20 minutes **MATERIALS** computer with Internet access

SECTION 1

EXPLORE Counting Animals, p. 509 Students use rice and graph paper to estimate population size.	**TIME** 10 minutes **MATERIALS** handful of rice, large-grid graph paper, marker, calculator
CHAPTER INVESTIGATION **Estimating Populations,** pp. 516–517 Students use beans in a paper bag to learn the mark-recapture method of estimating populations. They model the effects of disease on their populations and their estimates.	**TIME** 40 minutes **MATERIALS** about 100 white kidney beans, paper bag, 2 colored markers, calculator

SECTION 2

INVESTIGATE Species Interactions, p. 521 Students use cardboard and paper pieces to analyze the effects of predators on prey and vice versa over 15 generations.	**TIME** 30 minutes **MATERIALS** 20 10-cm squares of cardboard, 200 3 cm squares of paper, masking tape, graph paper, 2 colored pencils

SECTION 3

EXPLORE Population Growth, p. 527 Students observe the effects of different sugar concentrations on the growth of yeast.	**TIME** 20 minutes **MATERIALS** 3 clear plastic cups, warm water, sugar, dry yeast, measuring spoons, measuring cup, stirring rod, marker, ruler
INVESTIGATE Limiting Factors, p. 529 Students design an experiment to test whether space is a limiting factor for the growth of radishes.	**TIME** 20 minutes **MATERIALS** paper cups, potting soil, radish seeds, water, pencil, ruler

R **Additional INVESTIGATION,** Prey Survival, A, B, & C, pp. 130–138; Teacher Instructions, pp. 200–201

Previewing Chapter Resources

INTEGRATED TECHNOLOGY | **LABS AND ACTIVITIES**

CHAPTER 15
Interactions Within Ecosystems

Integrated Technology

CLASSZONE.COM
- eEdition Plus
- EasyPlanner Plus
- Misconception Database
- Content Review
- Test Practice
- Resource Centers
- Internet Activity: Carrying Capacity
- Math Tutorial

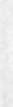
SCILINKS.ORG
SCILINKS

CD-ROMS
- eEdition
- EasyPlanner
- Power Presentations
- Content Review
- Lab Generator
- Test Generator

AUDIO CDS
- Audio Readings
- Audio Readings in Spanish

Labs and Activities

EXPLORE the Big Idea, p. 507
- How Do Living Things Interact Where You Live?
- How Many Roles Can a Living Thing Have in an Ecosystem?
- Internet Activity: Carrying Capacity

UNIT RESOURCE BOOK
Unit Projects, pp. 5–10

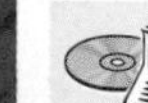
Lab Generator CD-ROM
Generate customized labs.

SECTION

1 Groups of living things interact within ecosystems.
pp. 509–517

Time: 3 periods (1.5 blocks)

 Lesson Plan, pp. 82–83

UNIT TRANSPARENCY BOOK
- Big Idea Flow Chart, p. T9
- Daily Vocabulary Scaffolding, p. T10
- Note-Taking Model, p. T11
- 3-Minute Warm-Up, p. T12
- "Levels in the Environment" Visual, p. T14

- EXPLORE Counting Animals, p. 509
- CHAPTER INVESTIGATION, Estimating Populations, pp. 516–517

UNIT RESOURCE BOOK
CHAPTER INVESTIGATION, Estimating Populations, A, B, & C, pp. 121–129

SECTION

2 Organisms can interact in different ways.
pp. 518–526

Time: 2 periods (1 block)

 Lesson Plan, pp. 92–93

RESOURCE CENTER, Symbiotic Relationships

UNIT TRANSPARENCY BOOK
- Daily Vocabulary Scaffolding, p. T10
- 3-Minute Warm-Up, p. T12

- INVESTIGATE Species Interactions, p. 521
- Think Science, p. 526

UNIT RESOURCE BOOK
- Datasheet, Species Interactions, p. 101
- Additional INVESTIGATION, Prey Survival, A, B, & C, pp. 130–138

SECTION

3 Ecosystems are always changing.
pp. 527–533

Time: 3 periods (1.5 blocks)

 Lesson Plan, pp. 103–104

- **RESOURCE CENTER,** Succession
- **MATH TUTORIAL**

UNIT TRANSPARENCY BOOK
- Big Idea Flow Chart, p. T9
- Daily Vocabulary Scaffolding, p. T10
- 3-Minute Warm-Up, p. T13
- Chapter Outline, pp. T15–T16

- EXPLORE Population Growth, p. 527
- INVESTIGATE Limiting Factors, p. 529
- Math in Science, p. 533

UNIT RESOURCE BOOK
- Datasheet, Limiting Factors, p. 112
- Math Support, p. 119
- Math Practice, p. 120

KEY TO ICONS

 CD/CD-ROM

 Teacher Edition

 UNIT TRANSPARENCY BOOK

 SPANISH ASSESSMENT BOOK

INTERNET

Pupil Edition

UNIT RESOURCE BOOK

UNIT ASSESSMENT BOOK

SCIENCE TOOLKIT

READING AND REINFORCEMENT

- Four Square, B22–23
- Outline, C43
- Daily Vocabulary Scaffolding, H1–8

 **UNIT RESOURCE BOOK**

- Vocabulary Practice, pp. 116–117
- Decoding Support, p. 118
- Summarizing the Chapter, pp. 139–140

Audio Readings CD
Listen to Pupil Edition.

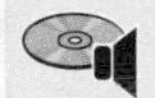

Audio Readings in Spanish CD
Listen to Pupil Edition in Spanish.

ASSESSMENT

- Chapter Review, pp. 535–536
- Standardized Test Practice, p. 537

UNIT ASSESSMENT BOOK

- Diagnostic Test, pp. 21–22
- Chapter Test, A, B, & C, pp. 26–37
- Alternative Assessment, pp. 38–39

Spanish Chapter Test, pp. 69–70

Test Generator CD-ROM
Generate customized tests.

Lab Generator CD-ROM
Rubrics for Labs

STANDARDS

National Standards
A.2–8, A.9.a–c, A.9.e–f, C.1.a, C.4.a, C.4.d, E.2, E.3, G.1.b

See p. 506 for the standards.

 **UNIT RESOURCE BOOK**

- Reading Study Guide, A & B, pp. 84–87
- Spanish Reading Study Guide, pp. 88–89
- Challenge and Extension, p. 90
- Reinforcing Key Concepts, p. 91

 Ongoing Assessment, pp. 510–514

 Section 15.1 Review, p. 515

UNIT ASSESSMENT BOOK
Section 15.1 Quiz, p. 23

National Standards
A.2–7, A.9.a–c, A.9.e–f, C.1.a, C.4.a, G.1.b

UNIT RESOURCE BOOK

- Reading Study Guide, A & B, pp. 94–97
- Spanish Reading Study Guide, pp. 98–99
- Challenge and Extension, p. 100
- Challenge Reading, pp. 114–115
- Reinforcing Key Concepts, p. 102

Ongoing Assessment, pp. 518, 520, 522–525

Section 15.2 Review, p. 525

UNIT ASSESSMENT BOOK
Section 15.2 Quiz, p. 24

National Standards
A.2–8, A.9.a–c, A.9.e–f, C.4.d, G.1.b

 **UNIT RESOURCE BOOK**

- Reading Study Guide, A & B, pp. 105–108
- Spanish Reading Study Guide, pp. 109–110
- Challenge and Extension, p. 111
- Reinforcing Key Concepts, p. 113

 Ongoing Assessment, pp. 529, 531

 Section 15.3 Review, p. 532

UNIT ASSESSMENT BOOK
Section 15.3 Quiz, p. 25

National Standards
A.2–8, A.9.a–c, A.9.e, C.4.d, E.2, E.3, G.1.b

Previewing Resources for Differentiated Instruction

CHAPTER INVESTIGATION

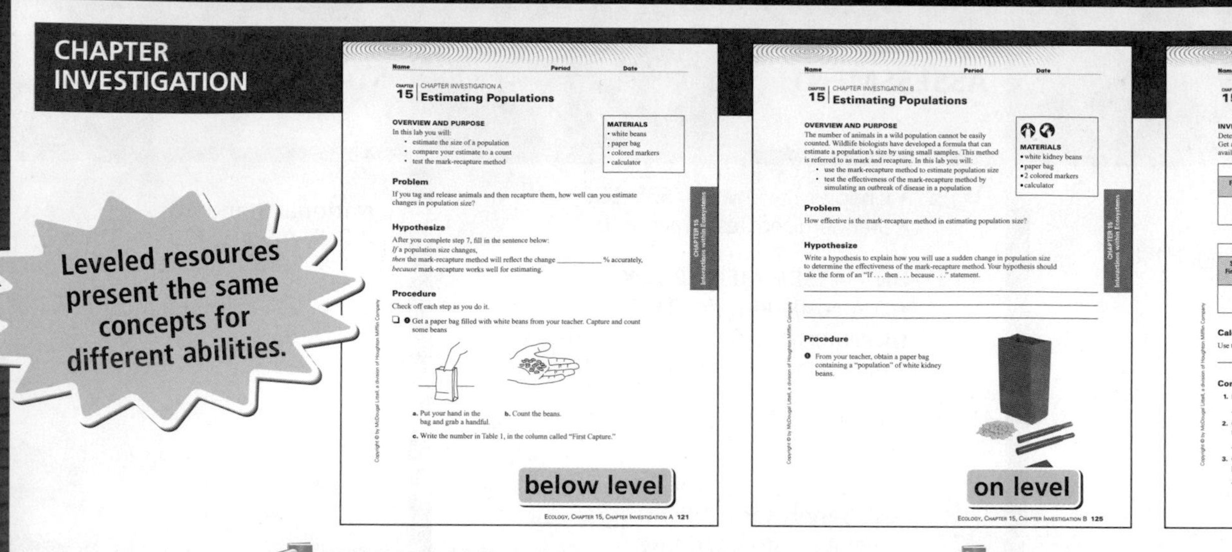

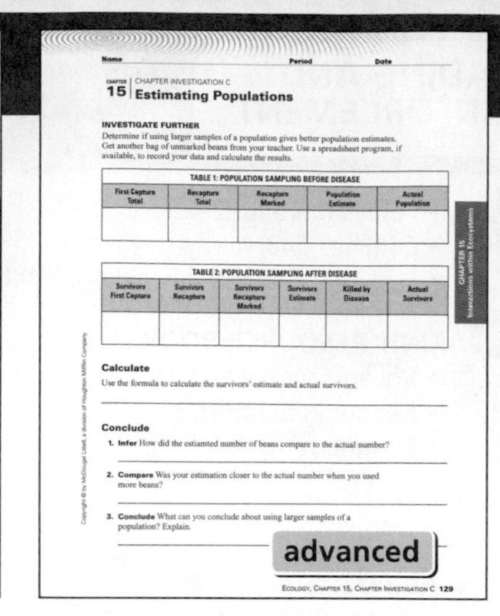

UNIT RESOURCE BOOK, pp. 121–124

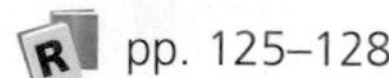
pp. 125–128

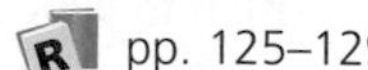
pp. 125–129

READING STUDY GUIDE

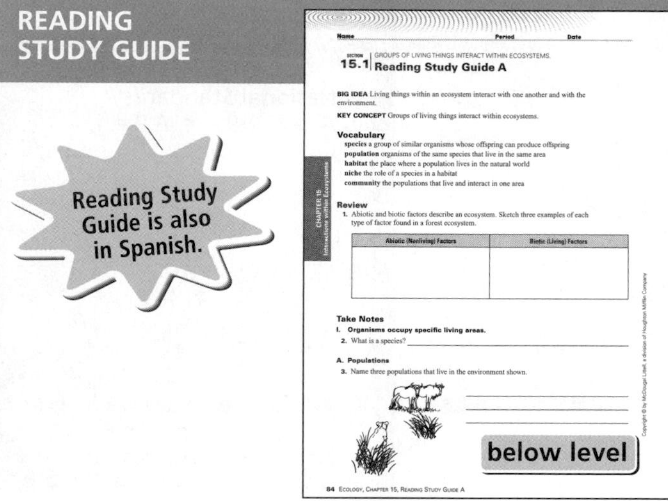

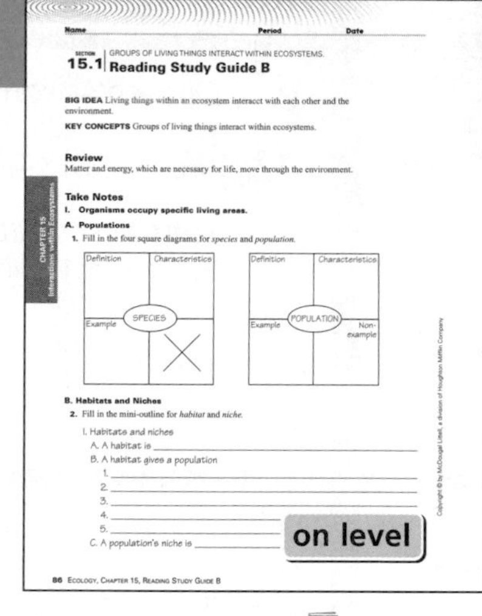

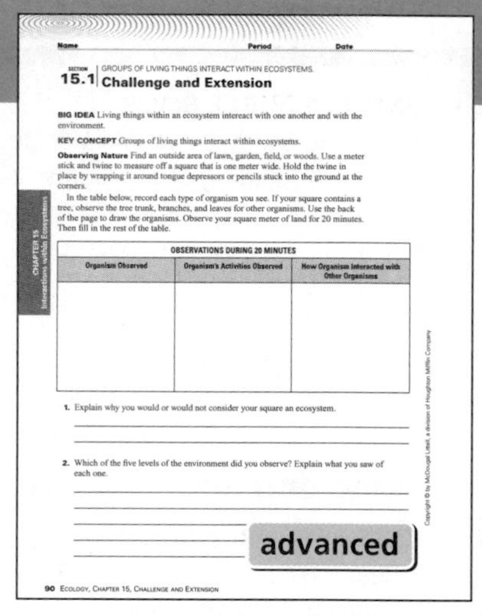

UNIT RESOURCE BOOK, pp. 84–85

pp. 86–87

p. 90

CHAPTER TEST

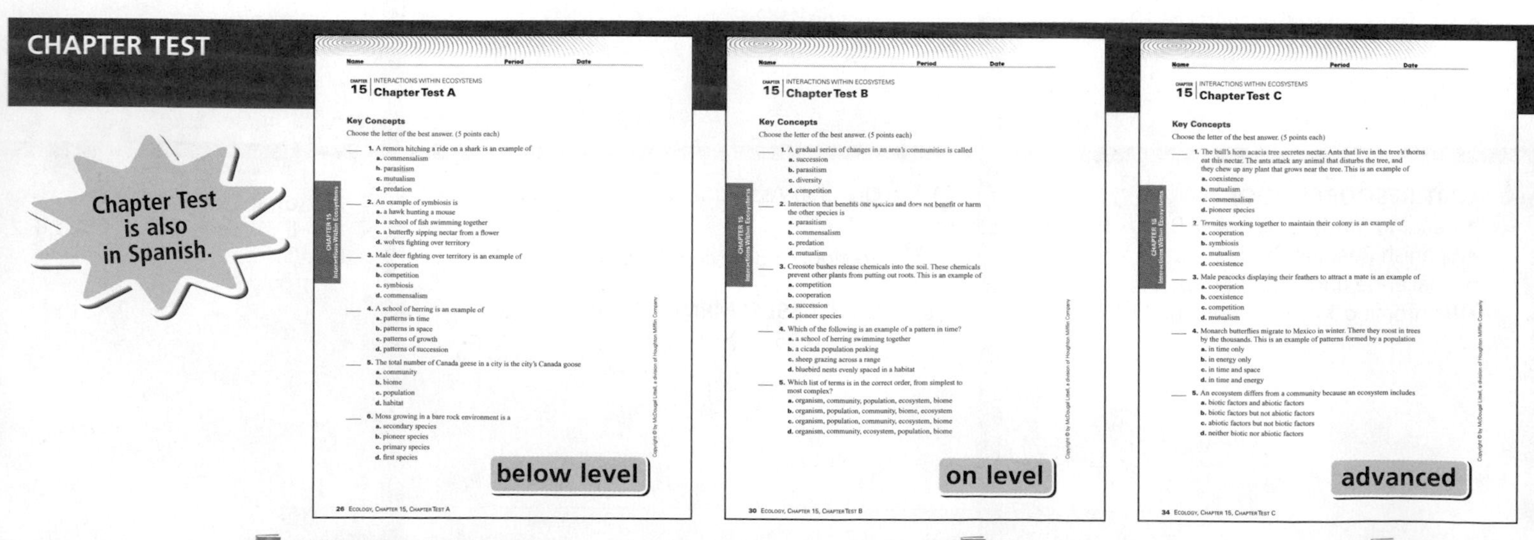

UNIT ASSESSMENT BOOK, pp. 26–29

pp. 30–33

pp. 34–37

TECHNOLOGY

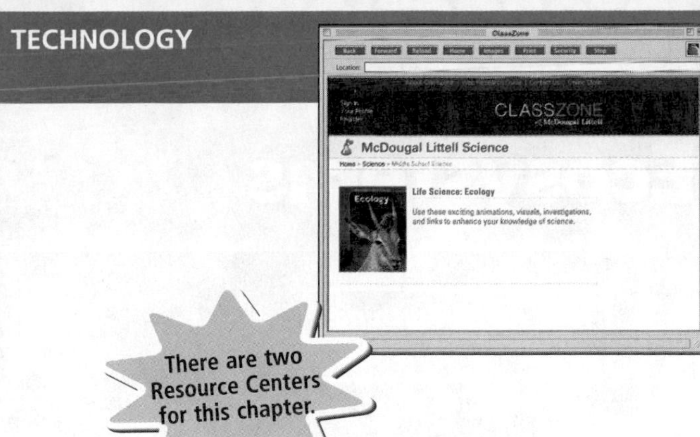

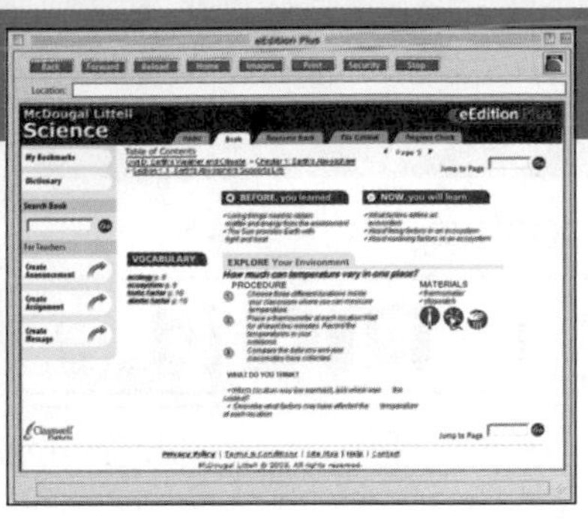

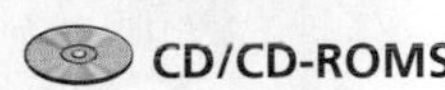

VISUAL CONTENT

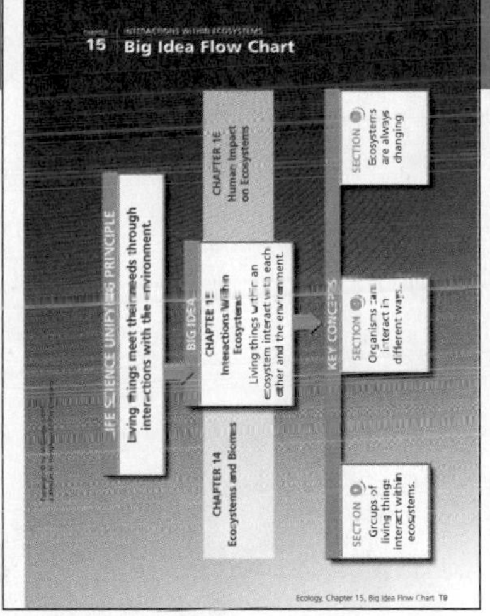

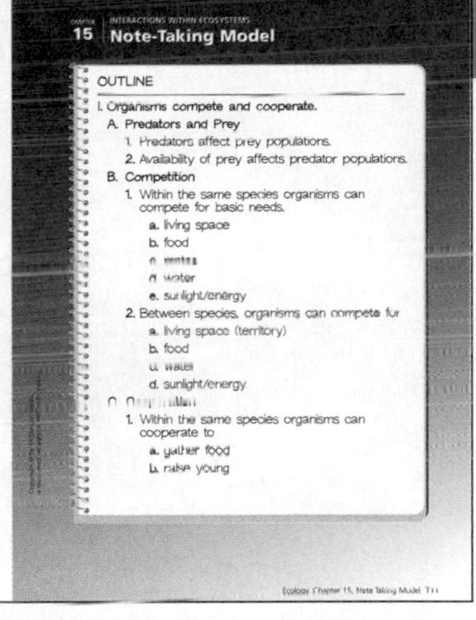

UNIT TRANSPARENCY BOOK, p. T9

p. T11

p. T14

MORE SUPPORT

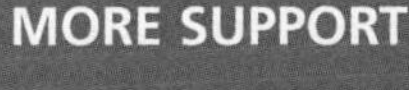

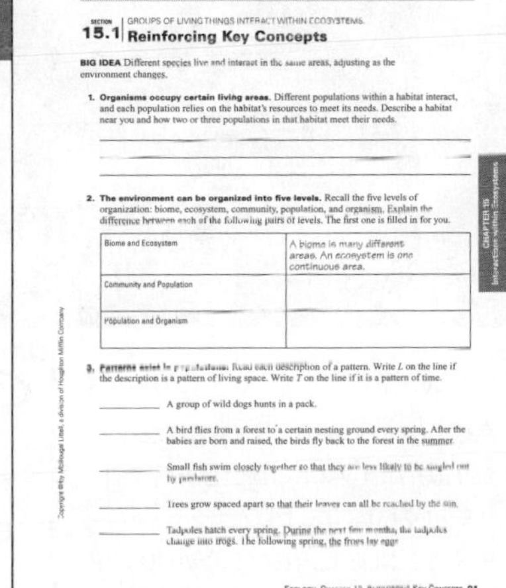

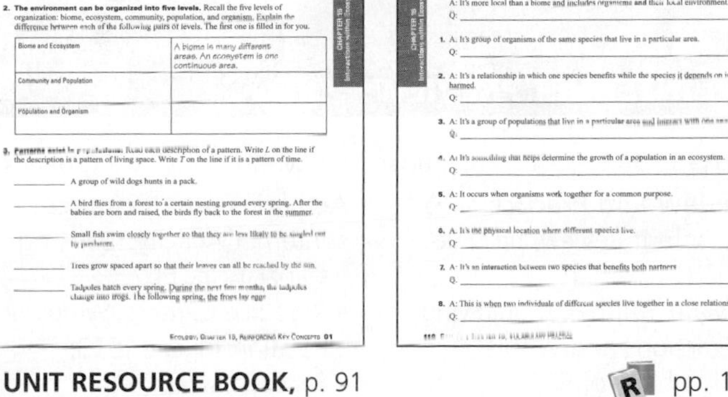

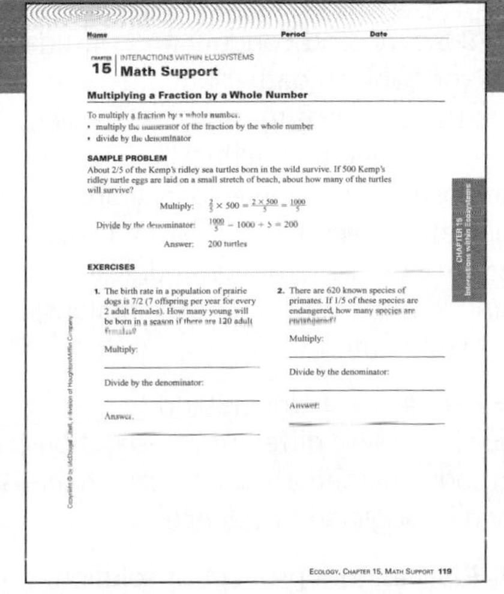

UNIT RESOURCE BOOK, p. 91

pp. 116–117

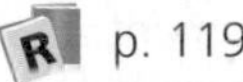
p. 119

CHAPTER 15 Interactions Within Ecosystems

INTRODUCE

the BIG idea

Have students look at the photograph of the reef lizardfish with the goby inside its mouth. Discuss how the question in the box links to the Big Idea:

- Ask: How does the reef lizardfish seem to be interacting with the goby?
- Have students brainstorm a quick class list of ways living things interact.

National Science Education Standards

Content

C.1.a Important levels of organization for living systems include cells, organs, tissues, organ systems, whole organisms, and ecosystems.

C.4.a A population consists of the individuals of a species together at a given place and time. All populations in an area and physical factors compose an ecosystem.

C.4.d The number of organisms an ecosystem can support depends on the resources available and abiotic factors.

Process

A.2–8 Design and conduct an investigation; use tools to gather and interpret data; use evidence to describe, predict, explain, model; think critically to make relationships between evidence and explanation; recognize different explanations and predictions; communicate scientific procedures and explanations; use mathematics.

A.9.a–c, A.9.e–f Understand scientific inquiry by using different investigations, methods, mathematics, and explanations based on logic and evidence.

E.2, E.3 Design a product or solution, implement a solution.

G.1.b Science requires different abilities.

CHAPTER 15 Interactions Within Ecosystems

the BIG idea

Living things within an ecosystem interact with each other and the environment.

Key Concepts

SECTION 1 **Groups of living things interact within ecosystems.**
Learn about how different organisms share living areas, interact in larger communities, and show different patterns within those communities.

SECTION 2 **Organisms can interact in different ways.**
Learn about the different types of interactions in an ecosystem, including competition, cooperation, and symbiosis.

SECTION 3 **Ecosystems are always changing.**
Learn about the limits and boundaries of organisms within an ecosystem and how ecosystems may change over time.

Internet Preview

CLASSZONE.COM

Chapter 15 online resources: Content Review, Simulation, two Resource Centers, Math Tutorial, Test Practice

How do living things interact?

INTERNET PREVIEW

CLASSZONE.COM For student use with the following pages:

Review and Practice

- Content Review, pp. 508, 534
- Math Tutorial: Multiplying Fractions and Whole Numbers, p. 533
- Test Practice, p. 537

Activities and Resources

- Internet Activity: Carrying Capacity, p. 507
- Resource Centers: Symbiotic Relationships, p. 523; Succession, p. 531

Populations and Communities
Code: MDL002

EXPLORE the BIG idea

How Do Living Things Interact Where You Live?

Take your notebook outside. Observe how different living things interact. Record your observations.

Observe and Think Do the interactions you see benefit both living things or just one? Do they involve just animals or plants and animals?

How Many Roles Can a Living Thing Have in an Ecosystem?

While you are outside, choose an organism within your view and think about how it fits into the ecosystem.

Observe and Think In what way does the organism fit into feeding relationships in the ecosystem? What are some other roles the organism plays?

Internet Activity: Carrying Capacity

Go to **ClassZone.com** to simulate the carrying capacity of an area for a population of deer.

Observe and Think What factors other than available food might affect the carrying capacity for a popuation of deer?

Populations and Communities **Code: MDL002**

TEACHING WITH TECHNOLOGY

Spreadsheets and Visual Displays Students could use a spreadsheet for recording data while investigating predator-prey relationships, p. 521. They could also enter and plot the data on a graphing calculator.

Digital Camera You might want to take daily photographs of the radish plants, p. 529. Students could use the photographs to construct a presentation of the experiment. They could create a time-lapse slideshow with fades.

EXPLORE the BIG idea

These inquiry-based activities are appropriate for use at home or as a supplement to classroom instruction.

How Do Living Things Interact Where You Live?

PURPOSE To demonstrate to students how plants and animals interact, and to have students recognize that they are part of the environment.

TIP *10 min.* If you need to do the activity indoors, students could observe interactions in a fish tank.

Answers should mention plants, animals, and resources, and should describe various behaviors.

REVISIT after p. 521.

How Many Roles Can a Living Thing Have in an Ecosystem?

PURPOSE To introduce students to the concept of roles in an ecosystem.

TIP *10 min.* If you cannot go outdoors, photographs or videotapes might help students examine one organism with many roles. It is important to view the organism in context.

Answers should mention feeding other organisms, and the various ways that the organism meets its own needs.

REVISIT after p. 511.

Internet Activity: Carrying Capacity

PURPOSE To model how carrying capacity can limit population size in an environment.

TIP *20 min.* You may wish to have students compare their results.

Answers might include predators, climate, human impact, and natural disasters.

REVISIT after p. 529.

PREPARE

CONCEPT REVIEW

Activate Prior Knowledge

- Ask students to name some living and nonliving factors that make it possible to live in your town.
- Discuss how these factors affect different species in varying ways.
- Help students identify what biome they live in.

TAKING NOTES

Outline

Students can rely on the blue and red headings in the textbook to form the basic structure of their outlines. In an outline, one idea hangs off another, which helps link the ideas in a student's memory. Encourage students to discuss how ideas in the outline are related. Encourage them to use their outlines to study.

Vocabulary Strategy

The four square diagram organizes all aspects of a word into a coherent pattern. By filling in their own words, students personalize their understanding. Be sure students know they can leave a square blank in the diagram. Many words, such as *species* and *habitat*, have no clear "Nonexamples."

Vocabulary and Note-Taking Resources

- Vocabulary Practice, pp. 116–117
- Decoding Support, p. 118

- Daily Vocabulary Scaffolding, p. T10
- Note-Taking Model, p. T11

- Four Square, B22–23
- Outline, C43
- Daily Vocabulary Scaffolding, H1–8

CHAPTER 15

Getting Ready to Learn

CONCEPT REVIEW

- Ecosystems support life.
- Different ecosystems make up a biome.

VOCABULARY REVIEW

producer p. 487 **food chain** p. 490
consumer p. 488 **food web** p. 490
interaction *See Glossary.*

CLASSZONE.COM

Review concepts and vocabulary.

TAKING NOTES

OUTLINE

As you read, copy the headings on your paper in the form of an outline. Then add notes in your own words that summarize what you read.

VOCABULARY STRATEGY

Write each new vocabulary term in the center of a **four square** diagram. Write notes in the squares around each term. Include definition, some characteristics, and some examples of the term. If possible, write some things that are not examples of the terms.

See the Note-Taking Handbook on pages R45–R51.

SCIENCE NOTEBOOK

I. Groups of living things interact within ecosystems.
   A. Organisms occupy specific living areas.
      1. populations: same species in one area
      2. habitat and niche: place where organisms live; role of organisms
      3. community: several populations living together

Definition where something lives	Characteristics supplies shelter and food
Examples a tree is a habitat for a bird	**Nonexamples** (you won't always use this square)

HABITAT

CHECK READINESS

Administer the Diagnostic Test to determine students' readiness for new science content and their mastery of requisite math skills.

 Diagnostic Test, pp. 21–22

Technology Resources

Students needing content and math skills should visit **ClassZone.com**.

- CONTENT REVIEW
- MATH TUTORIAL

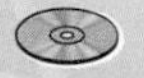 CONTENT REVIEW CD-ROM

KEY CONCEPT

Groups of living things interact within ecosystems.

BEFORE, you learned

- Abiotic and biotic factors interact in an ecosystem
- Matter and energy necessary for life move through the environment

NOW, you will learn

- How groups of organisms interact in an ecosystem
- About levels of organization in an ecosystem
- About living patterns of different groups of organisms

VOCABULARY

species p. 509
population p. 510
habitat p. 510
niche p. 511
community p. 512

EXPLORE Counting Animals

How can you use a grid to estimate the number of animals in an area?

PROCEDURE

1. Mark off an area on the graph paper as shown. Count the number of large squares in that area.
2. Use a handful of rice to represent a group of animals. Spread the rice evenly within the area you marked. Count the number of "animals" inside one large square.
3. Use a calculator to multiply the counts from steps 1 and 2. This will give you an estimate of the total number of "animals." Check your answer by counting all the grains of rice.

WHAT DO YOU THINK?

- How close was your estimate to the actual number?
- What would prevent a scientist from making an actual count of animals in an area?

MATERIALS

- handful of rice
- large-grid graph paper
- marker
- calculator

Organisms occupy specific living areas.

On a walk through the woods, you may see many different plants and animals. These organisms, like all living things, depend on their environment to meet their needs. The particular types of living things you see will depend on the characteristics of the area you are visiting.

Scientists group living things according to their shared characteristics. The smallest grouping is the species. Scientists consider organisms to be members of the same **species** (SPEE-sheez) if the organisms are so similar that they can produce offspring that can also produce offspring. Members of a species can successfully reproduce.

READING TIP

The terms *species, specific,* and *special* come from the same Latin root meaning "kind." A species is a kind, or type, of organism.

15.1 FOCUS

Set Learning Goals

Students will

- Describe how groups of organisms interact.
- Analyze different levels of organization in the environment.
- Recognize patterns found in groups of organisms.
- Use common items to estimate population size.

3-Minute Warm-Up

Display Transparency 12 or copy this exercise on the board:

Imagine that a pond in the park is a thriving ecosystem. A brick wall is built to separate the pond from a new playground. The wall is high enough to keep stray kickballs and other toys from falling into the pond. What might be the effect of the wall on the ecosystem of the pond? *Sample answer: The wall will reduce sunlight reaching the pond. Some organisms may die from lack of light; organisms that like shade may increase. The wall may also affect water runoff.*

 3-Minute Warm-Up, p. T12

15.1 MOTIVATE

EXPLORE Counting Animals

PURPOSE To introduce a scientific method for estimating populations

TIPS *10 min.* You might put sample counts for one column on the board. Prompt students to think about how this method would work for grasshoppers in a field.

WHAT DO YOU THINK? *Estimates should be within 80% accuracy or better. Possible limitations: vast numbers, motion, hidden locations of nests and homes, similar coloring, or similar appearance.*

RESOURCES FOR DIFFERENTIATED INSTRUCTION

Below Level

UNIT RESOURCE BOOK

- Reading Study Guide A, pp. 84–85
- Decoding Support, p. 118

AUDIO CDS

Advanced

UNIT RESOURCE BOOK

Challenge and Extension, p. 90

English Learners

UNIT RESOURCE BOOK

Spanish Reading Study Guide, pp. 88–89

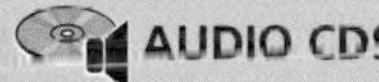

AUDIO CDS

- Audio Readings in Spanish
- Audio Readings (English)

15.1 INSTRUCT

Teach from Visuals

To help students connect the three photographs, remind them of what they learned in Chapter 14: matter cycles through ecosystems, and energy flows through ecosystems. Ask:

- What are some activities of the three species in the photographs? *growing, breathing, photosynthesis, getting water, eating, moving*
- How might the activities move and transform matter in the ecosystem? *Sample: drinking or absorbing water moves it inside an organism. The water can become part of that organism's structure.*
- What effect do you think these species might have on each other? *All use water; cacti release oxygen, which the crabs and the iguana breathe; iguana wastes fertilize the cacti; the crabs clean the beach.*

Ongoing Assessment

CHECK YOUR READING *Answer: A population exists within a certain boundary. A species may exist in many places worldwide.*

Galápagos Island Populations

A population is a group of the same organisms that live in the same area.

Cacti

Crabs

Iguanas

VOCABULARY
Add a four square for *population* to your notebook. Include the word *habitat* in your diagram.

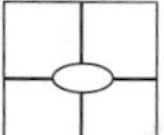

Populations

A

Scientists use the term **population** to mean a group of organisms of the same species that live in a particular area. In a way, this is similar to the population of people who live in a particular city or town. You can then think of those people who live in different cities or towns as belonging to different populations. It is the boundary of an area that defines a population. In the study of ecology, members of the same species that live in different areas belong to different populations.

A biological population can be a group of animals or a group of plants. It can be a group of bacteria or fungi or any other living thing. Populations of many different species will be found living in the same area. For example, the photographs above show different populations of organisms that all live in the same place—on one of the Galápagos Islands. The island has a population of cacti, a population of crabs, and a population of iguanas.

CHECK YOUR READING What is the difference between a species and a population?

Habitats and Niches

B

The Galápagos Islands are a small group of volcanic islands, off the coast of South America, that are famous for their unusual plant and animal life. These islands are the **habitat**—the physical location—where these plants and animals live. Island habitats have certain physical characteristics that describe them, including the amount of precipitation, a range of temperatures, and the quality of the soil. Different habitats have different characteristics.

DIFFERENTIATE INSTRUCTION

More Reading Support

A How does a boundary define a population? *Members are within the boundary.*

B What is a habitat? *the natural home of a population*

English Learners Students new to English may find the following science words challenging: *environment, characteristics, offspring, reproduce, boundary (-ies), precipitation, vegetation, fertilize, toxin.* Preview vocabulary by adding these words and their definitions to a Science Word Wall.

Students who are from South or Central America, Mexico, or the Southwest may be familiar with iguanas and cacti. They can share observations or knowledge.

Galápagos Island Habitat

This island habitat is home to many different populations.

READING VISUALS What resources are available in this habitat?

A habitat is filled with different species, each of which depends on the habitat's resources to meet its needs. The characteristics of a habitat determine the species of plants that can grow there. The species of plants found in a habitat, in turn, determine the species of animals and other organisms that will do well there.

Different populations within a habitat interact. They are part of the flow of energy and matter through an ecosystem. For example, in the Galápagos Island scene above, the cacti capture the Sun's energy and store fresh water. They also provide food for the iguana, who eats the cactus leaves. The cactus is a producer and the iguana is a primary consumer. The crabs of the Galápagos are secondary consumers that feed on other shellfish. Each of these organisms has a role to play in the habitat, a role which is referred to as its **niche** (nihch). C

The niche an organism fills in a habitat is not limited to its place in a food web. Plants provide nesting sites as well as food. The droppings left behind by animals fertilize soil and often spread seed. Generally, no two species will fill exactly the same niche in a habitat. D

DIFFERENTIATE INSTRUCTION

More Reading Support

C What is a niche? *a species' role in a habitat*

D What things about an animal show us its niche? *what it eats or uses, what it is eaten by*

Advanced Have students name habitats other than those already listed—for example, rainforest or swamp. Challenge them to find plants, animals, or insects that live in these habitats, and to describe the niches of the organisms.

R Challenge and Extension, p. 90

Teach from Visuals

To help students interpret the relationships shown in the illustration, ask:

- What niche do the crabs fill? *They pass matter and energy up the food chain to gulls and large fish. Some crabs clean the beach as they feed.*
- Which living thing in the picture might be a primary consumer? *iguanas* Why? *because they eat plants*
- Can you infer some animals or plants that aren't in the pictures but that you would expect to find in this habitat? *Sample answer: insects, birds, grasses, seaweed, fish*

Teach Difficult Concepts

Students may not fully understand the relationship between a species' habitat and its niche. Habitat is a location. Niche is a role. Different species may share a habitat, but each species fills a particular niche within that habitat. Using a familiar local habitat as an example, have students list elements of several species' niches.

EXPLORE the BIG idea

Revisit the activity and observations from "How Many Roles Can a Living Thing Have in an Ecosystem?" on p. 507. How have students' understandings changed?

Ongoing Assessment

Describe how groups of organisms interact.

Give an example of a population of organisms interacting with its habitat. *Sample answer: The cacti population stores fresh water and energy from sunlight.*

READING VISUALS *Answer: The cacti are green plants, so they are producers for this ecosystem. They are food and shelter for animals.*

Develop Critical Thinking

APPLY Have students discuss these examples of habitats: grassy field, pond, park. For each example, ask students to name some of the species that live in the habitat and to describe the niches they fill. *Sample answer: The meadow might contain grasses, worms, flowers, and insects. Insects feed on flowers and pollinate them. Worms loosen and fertilize the soil. Grasses anchor the soil and provide oxygen.*

Metacognitive Strategy

Ask students to restate the definitions for the five levels of organization in their own words. Encourage them to move from one to the next in order. What analogy or mnemonic device might help them recall the five levels?

Ongoing Assessment

Analyze different levels of organization in the environment.

Ask: Starting from an individual organism, describe the different levels into which scientists organize the environment. *An organism is a single living thing. Groups of individuals of the same species that live in the same area are a population. All living things within one ecosystem are a community. An ecosystem includes the living and nonliving factors in a local environment. A biome consists of similar places that have the same type of climate and vegetation.*

CHECK YOUR READING *Answer: A school community has many people that share the same space and use the same resources. A biological community has many organisms that share the same habitat and natural resources.*

Communities

Take a mental tour of your school. Note that you share space with people who do many different things—students, teachers, custodians, librarians, counselors, and many others. They all work together and help each other. We often say that a school is a community.

E

Scientists use the term *community* in a slightly different way. A biological **community** is a group of populations that live in a particular area and interact with one another. Cacti, iguanas, and crabs are part of the Galápagos Island community. This community also includes populations of tortoises, finches, fleas, bacteria, and many other species.

CHECK YOUR READING How is a school community similar to a community of living things?

The environment can be organized into five levels.

OUTLINE Add the different levels of the environment to your outline. Make sure to explain each term in the supporting details.

F

The five terms—biome, ecosystem, community, population, and organism—describe the environment at different levels.

1. **Biome** A biome describes in very general terms the climate and types of plants that are found in similar places around the world.
2. **Ecosystem** Within each biome are many ecosystems. Inside an ecosystem, living and nonliving factors interact to form a stable system. An ecosystem is smaller than a biome and includes only organisms and their local environment.
3. **Community** A community is made up of the living components of the ecosystem. In a community, different plants, animals, and other organisms interact with each other.
4. **Population** A population is a group of organisms of the same species that live in the same area.
5. **Organism** An organism is a single individual animal, plant, fungus, or other living thing. As the picture on page 513 shows, an organism plays a part in each level of the environment.

Patterns exist in populations.

Members of a population settle themselves into the available living space in different ways, forming a pattern. Populations may be crowded together, be spread far apart, or live in small groups. A population may also show a pattern over time. The number of individuals in the population may rise and fall, depending on the season or other conditions, or as a result of interactions with other organisms.

DIFFERENTIATE INSTRUCTION

More Reading Support

E What is a community? *many populations that interact in one area*

F Name 5 levels of the environment. *organism, population, community, ecosystem, biome*

English Learners Students will find the visual on p. 513 especially helpful. They can take notes in a step diagram, adding definitions in their own words.

- biome
- ecosystem
- community
- population
- organism

Levels in the Environment

Organisms living in an African savannah illustrate the different levels of the environment.

Equator

Grassland

1 Biome
The African savannah is part of a grassland biome.

2 Ecosystem
The community of organisms, along with water, soil, and other abiotic factors, make up an ecosystem.

3 Community
Populations of wildebeests, gazelles, lions, and grasses share the same living areas and resources. These and other populations form a savannah community.

4 Population
Gazelles travel together in herds looking for areas to graze in. The total number of gazelles in an ecosystem is called a population of gazelles.

5 Organism
The gazelle lives in various grassland habitats in eastern Africa and fills a particular niche.

READING VISUALS Describe the gazelle's place in each level of the environment.

513

DIFFERENTIATE INSTRUCTION

Advanced Challenge advanced students to choose a different biome, and create a poster or illustration similar to the one on this page showing the relationship of one organism to its population, community, and larger environment.

For a further challenge, students could add more specific levels of organization within the organism, down to the cellular level.

Teach from Visuals

To help students interpret the levels in the environment illustration, ask:

- What is the most specific level pictured? *organism*
- What level of organization do we have in this classroom? *population*
- Is the water in the picture part of the ecosystem, population, or community? *ecosystem*

The visual "Levels in the Environment" is available as T14 in the Unit Transparency Book.

Address Misconceptions

IDENTIFY Ask students to list the factors in a familiar local ecosystem. If they do not include human beings in their list, they may hold the common misconception that humans are not part of an ecosystem.

CORRECT Have students list the effects that human beings have had on the local ecosystem.

REASSESS Ask students to describe what the local ecosystem might be like if human beings were not part of it. *Descriptions may include the following: more animals; different types of plants; no pollution; no buildings, roads, or other structures; no cats, dogs, or other domestic animals; and so on.*

Technology Resources

Visit **ClassZone.com** for background on common student misconceptions.

MISCONCEPTION DATABASE

Ongoing Assessment

READING VISUALS *Answer: One gazelle is a single organism. A group of gazelles that live in one area is a population. All of the organisms that live in the same place as the gazelle population make up a community. These gazelles live within one African savannah ecosystem, made up of the community and its environment. Finally, gazelles are one kind of animal that lives in the grassland biome.*

Teach Difficult Concepts

To help students visualize population patterns in time and space, give a very dramatic example: Wildebeests show three unique patterns in populations:

- At night wildebeests sleep on the ground in rows, so they have the security of the large group and the space to run if necessary.
- Most calves are born within two to three weeks at the start of the rainy season. The huge number of calves increases an individual's chance of surviving, because predators can only kill so many prey at once.
- Wildebeest herds may grow to a million animals when they migrate in search of pasture.

Teacher Demo

Try using a game of jacks to demonstrate population patterns. It is easier to "pick off" individuals when they are spread out. It is easier to "wipe out" a group when it is closer together.

Ongoing Assessment

Recognize patterns found in groups of organisms.

Tell students about the three unique patterns shown by wildebeests, described above. Ask: Which are patterns in time, and which in space? *space, time, time and space*

CHECK YOUR READING *Answer: Different organisms meet their needs in different ways, so they need different amounts of space.*

READING VISUALS *Answer: The elephants are widely spread compared to the wildebeests.*

Patterns in Living Space

 G

The patterns formed by a population often show how the population meets its needs. For example, in California's Mojave desert the pale soil is dotted with dark-green shrubs called creosote bushes. A surprising thing about the bushes is their even spacing. No human shaped this habitat, however. The bushes are the same distance from each other because the roots of each bush release a toxin, a type of poison, that prevents the roots of other bushes from growing.

The distribution of animals in a habitat is often influenced by how they meet their needs. Animals must be able to reach their food supply and have places to raise their young. If you put up bird houses for bluebirds on your property, they must be spaced at least a hundred meters apart. Bluebirds need a large area of their own around their nest in order to collect enough insects to feed their young.

READING TIP As you read this paragraph, note the pattern of wildebeests and elephants in the photograph.

Sometimes, the particular pattern of individuals in a living space helps a population survive. Herring swim in schools, with the individual fish spaced close together. Wildebeests roam African grasslands in closely packed herds. These animals rely on the group for their safety. Even if one member of the group is attacked, many more will survive. H

CHECK YOUR READING What are some reasons for the spacing patterns observed in different populations?

READING VISUALS **COMPARE AND CONTRAST** How would you describe the spacing of these elephants and wildebeests?

DIFFERENTIATE INSTRUCTION

More Reading Support

G Is the herd a pattern in space or in time? *space*

H How does living in large herds meet animals' needs? *protects them from predators*

Below Level When geese migrate or fly south for the winter, they travel in a "V" formation. This example contains within it both a pattern in time and a pattern in space. Ask students to tell how the example shows both patterns. *time: seasonal movement, southward in winter; space: flying in formation*

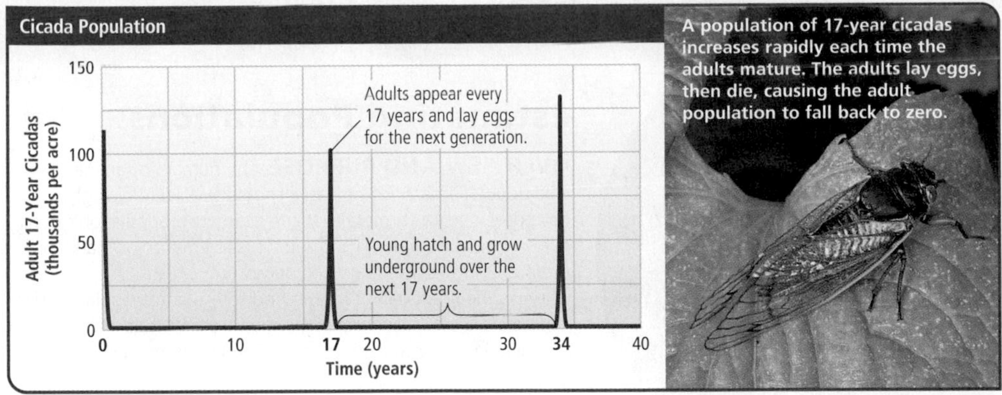

A population of 17-year cicadas increases rapidly each time the adults mature. The adults lay eggs, then die, causing the adult population to fall back to zero.

Patterns in Time

At a spring picnic, you would rarely see the wasps called yellow jackets. At a fall picnic, however, they swarm to the food. This is an example of a population whose size changes with time. In spring, the queen wasp lays eggs and new wasps hatch. She continues to lay eggs all summer and the population grows. When winter comes, all the wasps except the queen die, and the population decreases.

Many birds that nest in North America in summer fly south to Central and South America in winter. There they find enough food and good nesting sites. In North America, this seasonal pattern leads to small bird populations in winter and large ones in summer.

The graph above shows an unusual pattern of population growth. Certain species of cicadas appear only every 17 years. Because no other species can rely on these insects as their main source of food, the cicadas survive long enough to lay eggs when they do appear.

15.1 Review

KEY CONCEPTS

1. What are two characteristics of a population?
2. Order these terms from the simplest to the most complex: biome, community, ecosystem, organism, population.
3. How do the terms *habitat* and *niche* relate to each other?

CRITICAL THINKING

4. **Apply** Choose a biological community in your region. Describe some of the populations that make up that community.
5. **Infer** How might the seasonal patterns of insect populations relate to the seasonal patterns of bird populations?

CHALLENGE

6. **Apply** The Explore activity on page 509 shows one way in which scientists sample a population to determine its total size. Would this method work for estimating the size of a population of 17-year cicadas? Why or why not?

ANSWERS

1. organisms of same species; living in same area

2. organism, population, community, ecosystem, biome

3. Habitat refers to the physical setting a population lives in; niche is the role any one population fills in that habitat.

4. Sample answer: Pond will have fish, insects, frogs, birds, and surrounding plants

5. Population booms for insects would allow bird populations to thrive and vice versa.

6. Yes, only during the few weeks the adults are above ground; or No, it would give deceptive results if the population was young.

Teach from Visuals

To help students interpret the cicada population graph, ask:

- What is represented on the vertical axis? *thousands of adult cicadas in a given area*
- What is represented on the horizontal axis? *time in years*
- How many complete population cycles are shown on the graph? *two*

Reinforce the BIG idea

Have students relate the section to the Big Idea.

 Reinforcing Key Concepts, p. 91

15.1 ASSESS & RETEACH

Assess

 Section 15.1 Quiz, p. 23

Reteach

Have students identify an animal in their neighborhood. Ask for volunteers to explain

- the animal's niche *Answers should include what the animal eats and whether another animal eats it.* (Point out that a niche is the animal's role in the transfer of matter and energy though the entire system.)
- any patterns in space or in time that it fits. Does it migrate? Does it flock? Are groups spaced closely together or far apart? *Answers will vary.*
- how it fits into scientific organization of the environment *Answers should show levels of organism, population, community, ecosystem, and biome.*

Technology Resources

Have students visit **ClassZone.com** for reteaching of Key Concepts.

 CONTENT REVIEW

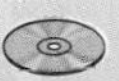 CONTENT REVIEW CD-ROM

CHAPTER INVESTIGATION

Focus

PURPOSE To learn how scientists estimate animal populations and how to use estimates to reflect a change in the ecosystem

OVERVIEW Students will use marked white beans to generate data, which they will record and analyze. Students will determine the following:

- an actual population total
- an estimated population total
- the effectiveness of the estimate

Lab Preparation

- The day before doing the lab, have volunteers make up the bags. Bags should contain around 100 beans, but the number should vary.
- Prior to the investigation have students read through the investigation and prepare their data tables. Or you may wish to copy and distribute datasheets and rubrics.

 UNIT RESOURCE BOOK, pp. 121–129

 SCIENCE TOOLKIT, F14

Lab Management

- Have students work in pairs, with one student handling the beans and the other recording the data. Have them switch roles throughout the lab.
- Tell students to take small handfuls, or demonstrate what a "handful" means here.
- White beans work well for marking. Avoid pinto or other spotted beans.

INCLUSION If students have learning disabilities, have them handle and count the "population" samples, while a partner reads directions and records data. If a student has poor fine motor control and is physically unable to perform the population counts, he or she could read and record the procedure aloud, and could present the results. You might use a tape recorder for results if writing is problematic. If a student is colorblind, be sure the two markers are not red and green.

CHAPTER INVESTIGATION

Estimating Populations

OVERVIEW AND PURPOSE The number of animals in a wild population cannot be easily counted. Wildlife biologists have developed a formula that can estimate a population's size by using small samples. This method is referred to as mark and recapture. In this investigation you will

- use the mark-recapture method to estimate population size
- test the effectiveness of the mark-recapture method by simulating an outbreak of disease in a population

MATERIALS
- paper bag
- white kidney beans
- 2 colored markers
- calculator

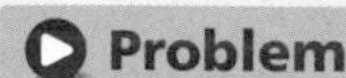

Problem

How effective is the mark-recapture method in estimating population size?

Hypothesize

Write a hypothesis to explain how you will use a sudden change in population size to determine the effectiveness of the mark-recapture method. Your hypothesis should take the form of an "If . . . , then . . . , because . . ." statement.

Procedure

1. Make two data tables in your **Science Notebook,** like the ones shown on page 517.
2. From your teacher, obtain a paper bag containing a "population" of white kidney beans.
3. Remove a small handful of beans. Count the sample and record the count in Table 1, under First Capture Total.
4. Use a colored marker to mark your sample population. Return the beans to the bag, and gently shake the bag to mix all the beans.

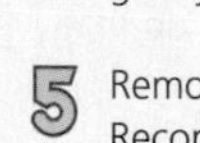
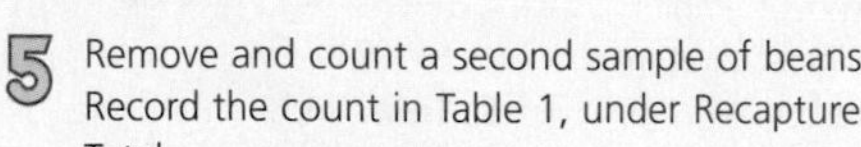

5. Remove and count a second sample of beans. Record the count in Table 1, under Recapture Total.

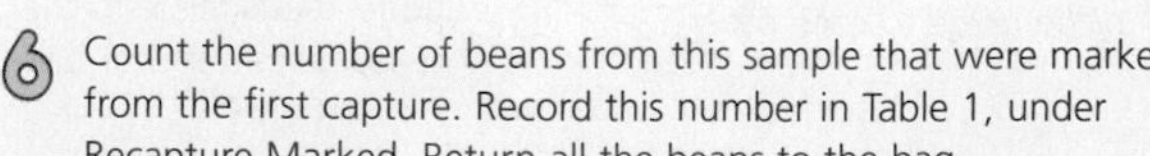

6. Count the number of beans from this sample that were marked from the first capture. Record this number in Table 1, under Recapture Marked. Return all the beans to the bag.

step 3

INVESTIGATION RESOURCES

 CHAPTER INVESTIGATION, Estimating Populations
- Level A, pp. 121–124
- Level B, pp. 125–128
- Level C, p. 129

Advanced students should complete Levels B & C.

 Writing a Lab Report, D12–13

Technology Resources

Customize this student lab as needed or look for an alternative. Print rubrics to assess student lab reports.

 **Lab Generator CD-ROM**

7 Use a calculator and the following formula to estimate the population size. Record the estimate in Table 1 as the Calculated Population Estimate.

$$\frac{\text{First Capture Total} \times \text{Recapture Total}}{\text{Recapture Marked}} = \text{Population Estimate}$$

8 Disease strikes. Remove a small handful of beans from the bag. Count the beans, and record this count in Table 2, under Killed by Disease. Set these beans aside.

9 Repeat steps 3–7 to mark and recapture your survivor population. This time use a different colored marker to mark your sample population, and only include the beans marked in the second color in your counts.

10 Fill in Data Table 2 for the survivor population. Use the formula from step 7 to calculate your estimate of the survivor population.

11 Once you have calculated your estimate of survivors, dump out the paper bag and count all the beans that were inside. Record this count in Table 2, under Actual Survivors Total.

Observe and Analyze

Write It Up

1. **CALCULATE** From Table 2 add together the number of actual survivors and the number killed by disease. Put this in Table 1, under Actual Population Total.
2. **CALCULATE** Find the percentage of the population affected by disease using the following formula:

$$\frac{\text{Killed by disease} \times 100}{\text{Actual Population Total}} = \text{Percentage affected}$$

Conclude

1. **INFER** How did the estimated number of beans compare with the actual number?
2. **IDENTIFY LIMITS** What aspects of this investigation most likely would not be possible in a natural habitat? Why not?
3. **EVALUATE** Compare your results with your hypothesis. Do your data support your hypothesis?

INVESTIGATE Further

CHALLENGE Determine if using larger samples of a population gives better population estimates. Get another bag of unmarked beans from your teacher. Use a spreadsheet program, if available, to record your data and calculate the results.

Estimating Populations

Table 1. Population sampling before disease

First Capture Total	Recapture Total	Recapture Marked	Calculated Population Estimate	Actual Population Total

Table 2. Population sampling after disease

Survivors First Capture Total	Survivors Recapture Total	Survivors Recapture Marked	Calculated Survivors Estimate	Killed by Disease	Actual Survivors Total

517

Post-Lab Discussion

- Discuss whether the percent difference between the estimate and the actual counts would be acceptable or not to working ecologists. *The small difference would be acceptable in most cases. Ecologists can not possibly track every member of a population. Accuracy to 100% becomes more important in small endangered populations.*
- Discuss how the mark-recapture method might be used to study different populations. What data could be collected? *migration patterns, birth rates, predator-prey interactions*

Observe and Analyze

1. *SAMPLE DATA Table 1: First Capture Total, 22; Recapture Total, 28; Recapture Marked, 6; Calculated Population Estimate, 102; Actual Population Total, 100.*
2. *SAMPLE DATA Table 2: Survivors First Capture Total, 26; Survivors Recapture Total, 22; Survivors Recapture Marked, 4; Calculated Survivors Estimate, 71; Killed by Disease, 14; Actual Survivors Total, 86 (Percentage affected, 16%).*

Conclude

1. *SAMPLE DATA The estimate should be within 20% of the actual number.*
2. *It might not be possible to know exactly when disease strikes a population. Also, capturing the required number of animals would be difficult. It most likely would not be possible to catch them all at once. When they are released, they likely would not all stay in one small area.*
3. *Answers will vary. Students who predicted effective correlation (80% or better) between the estimated and actual count will say the hypothesis was supported by the results.*

INVESTIGATE Further

CHALLENGE Answers will vary, but results should indicate that the larger samples are more effective.

15.2 FOCUS

Set Learning Goals

Students will

- Describe the different types of interactions in an ecosystem.
- Describe symbiotic relationships in which one or more species benefits.
- Describe symbiotic relationships in which one species is harmed.

3-Minute Warm-Up

Display Transparency 12 or copy this exercise on the board:

Decide if these statements are true. If not true, correct them.

1. An ecosystem is composed of biotic factors. *An ecosystem is composed of both biotic and abiotic factors.*
2. In a species, the organisms' offspring must be able to breed. *true*
3. The same niche in a habitat may be occupied by more than one species. *Different species never occupy exactly the same niche.*

 3-Minute Warm-Up, p. T12

15.2 MOTIVATE

THINK ABOUT

PURPOSE To understand ways people interact

DISCUSS Brainstorm situations in which two or more people transact. Begin with a game, a group project, a purchase, and so on. Then revisit the list and discuss whether the interaction is competitive or cooperative.

Sample answer: Players on opposite teams compete to score points. Players on the same team pass the ball to each other and divide the field to defend it. Fans give energy by cheering. Both cooperative and competitive relationships are shown in the picture.

Ongoing Assessment

 *Sample answer: sharing food, a water source, living in the same place*

KEY CONCEPT

Organisms can interact in different ways.

BEFORE, you learned

- Different populations live together in a habitat
- Different species fill different niches in a habitat
- There are patterns in the ways organisms interact with each other and their environment

NOW, you will learn

- About different types of interactions in an ecosystem
- How some species benefit from interactions
- How some species are harmed by interactions

VOCABULARY

predator p. 519
prey p. 519
competition p. 519
cooperation p. 521
symbiosis p. 522
mutualism p. 522
commensalism p. 523
parasitism p. 523

THINK ABOUT

What are some of the ways people interact?

People in a community interact with each other in many ways. An interaction is the way a person behaves toward or responds to another person. This photograph shows groups of people at a soccer game. There are players from two teams and fans who are watching the game. How would you describe the interactions among the people in this photograph?

Organisms interact in different ways.

The photograph above shows how members of a human community both compete and cooperate. Different members of the populations of a biological community also compete and cooperate. They not only share a habitat, but they also share the resources in that habitat. How different organisms interact depends on their relationship to each other.

A robin in a meadow finds a caterpillar and swallows it. This is one obvious way organisms in an ecosystem interact—one eats, and the other gets eaten. Organisms also compete. The robin may have to compete with a flicker to get the caterpillar. And organisms can cooperate. Ants work together to build a nest, collect food, and defend their colony.

 Name three ways organisms may interact with each other in an ecosystem.

RESOURCES FOR DIFFERENTIATED INSTRUCTION

Below Level

UNIT RESOURCE BOOK

- Reading Study Guide A, pp. 94–95
- Decoding Support, p. 118

AUDIO CDS

 **Additional INVESTIGATION,** Prey Survival, A, B, & C, pp. 130–138; Teacher Instructions, pp. 200–201

Advanced

UNIT RESOURCE BOOK

- Challenge and Extension, p. 100
- Challenge Reading, pp. 114–115

English Learners

UNIT RESOURCE BOOK

Spanish Reading Study Guide, pp. 98–99

- Audio Readings in Spanish
- Audio Readings (English)

Predator and Prey

Many interactions between organisms in an ecosystem involve food. A food chain shows the feeding relationships between different species. There are producers and consumers. Another way to look at a food chain is through the interactions of predators and prey. The **predator** is an animal that eats another. The **prey** is an animal that is eaten by a predator. In a food chain, an organism can be both predator and prey. A meadowlark that feeds on a grasshopper is, in turn, eaten by a prairie falcon.

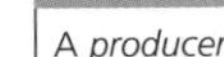

A *producer* is an organism that makes its own food; a *consumer* is an organism that eats another organism for food.

Predators can affect how members of their prey populations are distributed. Herring move together in a school and wildebeests travel in herds to protect themselves. It is the sick or older members of the population that will most likely be eaten by predators. Species of prey may also have adaptations that relate to the behavior of predators. This is true of cicadas and their long reproductive cycles.

Prey populations, in turn, affect the location and number of predator populations. For example some birds are predators feeding on insects. One factor that may affect movement of birds from one location to another is the availability of insects.

Competition

In a team game, two teams compete against each other with the same goal in mind—to win the game. In a biological community, competition is for resources, not wins. **Competition** is the struggle between individuals or different populations for a limited resource.

In an ecosystem, competition may occur within the same species. Individual plants compete with each other for light, space, and nutrients. For example, creosote bushes compete with other creosote bushes for the same water supply. The toxins produced by the roots of one creosote bush prevent other creosote bushes from growing.

Competition also occurs between members of different species. In the tropical rain forests of Indonesia, vines called strangler figs compete with trees for water, light, and nutrients. The vine attaches itself to a host tree. As it grows, the vine surrounds and eventually kills the tree by blocking out sunlight and using up available water and nutrients.

INFER Do you think a strangler fig could survive on its own?

15.2 INSTRUCT

Teach from Visuals

To help students interpret the photograph of the strangler fig and the host tree, ask:

- What is it like on the floor of the rain forest? *deep shade, damp, moist*
- What is at the top of the rainforest? *lots of sunlight, leafy*
- What does the tree give to the fig vine? *support so it can grow up towards the sunlight*

Teach Difficult Concepts

Predator-prey relationships are not the only sort of feeding relationships in ecosystems. Point out that predators and prey are both always animal species. Foraging is another type of interaction. It takes place when an organism eats a producer, such as a plant, protist, bacteria, or fungus.

Social Studies Connection

In order to link the concept of competition among species in an ecosystem with social studies curriculum, discuss with students how competition functions in a free enterprise economic system.

As in an ecosystem, a decrease in the supply of a resource results in an increase in competition. In an economic system, for example, when the need for workers is greater than the supply, employers compete with one another by paying workers higher wages. On the other hand, when the number of workers exceeds the number of available jobs, wages usually fall and workers must compete with one another for a limited supply of jobs.

DIFFERENTIATE INSTRUCTION

More Reading Support

A Is a robin a predator? If so, what is its prey? *yes; earthworms*

B What do plants compete for? *light, space, nutrients, water*

English Learners Have students write the definitions for *symbiosis, mutualism, commensalism,* and *parasitism* in their Science Word Dictionaries. English learners probably do have prior knowledge of soccer which is pictured on p. 518. Ask students to think of predator-prey relationships between animals found in their home countries.

Teach from Visuals

To help students interpret the photographs of interspecies and intraspecies competition, ask:

- In what ways do organisms of the same or different species compete? *for food, space, water, other resources*
- What groups of organisms compete for mates? *males or females of the same species*

Develop Critical Thinking

INFER Ask students to decide whether they think competing for mates or competing for food is more common within a species and which is more common between species.

Ongoing Assessment

Describe the different types of interaction in an ecosystem.

Ask: When animals mark their territory, how are they relating to other members of their species? *They are competing.* How are they relating when they hunt in packs? *They are cooperating within their species, and they are preying on another species.*

Answer: space, light, water, nutrients

Competition

Competition between species Two different species, hyenas and vultures, compete for the remains of a dead animal.

Competition within species Two male deer lock horns as they battle over territory.

Competition occurs between species and within species. For example, vultures and hyenas will compete over the food left in the remains of a dead animal. Wolves will compete with one another over territory. A wolf will mark its territory by urinating on trees and so warn off other wolves. Animals also compete over territory by fighting, using threatening sounds, and putting on aggressive displays.

Competition within species often occurs during the mating season. Male birds use mating songs and displays of feathers to compete for the attention of females. Male hippopotamuses fight to attract female hippopotamuses. Male crickets chirp to attract female crickets.

What sorts of resources do plants and animals compete for?

READING TIP
Compare and contrast the meanings of *competition* and *coexistence.*

Competition does not occur between all populations that share the same resources. Many populations can coexist in a habitat—different species can live together without causing harm to one another. Many different populations of plants coexist in a forest. Maple trees, beech trees, and birch trees can live side by side and still have enough water, nutrients, and sunlight to meet their needs.

DIFFERENTIATE INSTRUCTION

C What are examples of competition among animals? *marking territory, fighting for mates*

Advanced Have students search news sources for stories about interactions between species. Encourage them to generate new questions about species interactions that might be appropriate for current science research.

Have students who are interested in interactions between species read the following article:

Challenge Reading, pp. 114–115

INVESTIGATE Species Interactions

SKILL FOCUS
Analyzing data

MATERIALS
- 20 10 × 10 cm cardboard squares—predators
- 200 3 × 3 cm paper squares—prey
- masking tape

for Challenge:
- graph paper
- 2 colored pencils

TIME
30 minutes

How do predator-prey populations interact?

Use these rules for predator-prey interaction for each round. If a predator card touches three or more prey cards, remove the prey cards touched. If the predator card does not touch at least three prey cards, remove the predator card and leave the prey cards. Predator cards are large, prey cards are small.

PROCEDURE

1. Use masking tape to mark a boundary on a table top.
2. Scatter five prey cards into the area. Take a predator card and toss it, trying to get it to land on the prey.
3. According to the rules above, remove the predators and prey that have "died." Record the number of predators and prey that have "survived." This represents one generation.
4. Double the populations of predators and prey—they have "reproduced."
5. Scatter the prey cards into the area and then toss the predator cards as before. Repeat steps 3 and 4 for a total of 15 rounds (generations).

WHAT DO YOU THINK?

- How does the size of the prey population affect the predator population?
- How might the size of a habitat affect the interaction of predators and prey?

CHALLENGE Use graph paper and colored pencils to make a graph of your results. Or use a spreadsheet program if one is available to you.

Cooperation

D Not all interactions in an ecosystem involve competition. **Cooperation** is an interaction in which organisms work in a way that benefits them all. Some predators cooperate when they hunt. Although individual lions may hunt on their own, they also hunt in packs to kill large prey.

Killer whales also cooperate when they hunt. The whales swim in packs called pods. The pod swims in circles around a school of fish, forcing the fish close together so they are easier to catch. Pod members may also take turns chasing a seal until it gets tired and is easily killed. The pod may even work together to attack larger species of whales.

Ants, bees, and termites are social insects. Members of a colony belong to different groups, called castes, and have different responsibilities. Some groups gather food while others defend the colony. Other animals, like apes and monkeys, live in family groups. Members of the family cooperate to care for their young.

Cooperation
Driver ants work together to bring food to their nest.

INVESTIGATE Species Interactions

PURPOSE Simulate predator-prey relationships to generate and analyze data

TIPS *30 min.* Limit area to two feet by two feet, perhaps by using tape to mark boundaries. You might use sticky notepads and cut off the sticky side of the pad instead of cutting squares individually.

WHAT DO YOU THINK? *Results should show a cycle, with the number of prey increasing for several generations, then predators increasing, then prey decreasing, and repeating.*

CHALLENGE Student graphs will vary but should show the trends described above.

Datasheet: Species Interactions, p. 101

Technology Resources

Customize this student lab as needed or look for an alternative. Print rubrics to assess student lab reports.

Lab Generator CD-ROM

Teaching with Technology

If spreadsheet software is available, have students use it to record data for the investigation. They can also use a graphing calculator to show the data visually.

EXPLORE the BIG idea

Revisit "How Do Living Things Interact Where You Live?" on p. 507. Now that students have studied the basic types of interactions between and within species, have them explain their observations.

DIFFERENTIATE INSTRUCTION

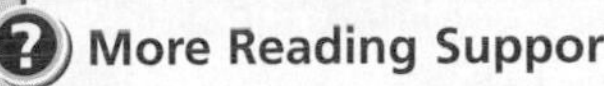

More Reading Support

D Besides competition, what is another way for animals to interact?
cooperation

Additional Investigation

To reinforce Section 15.2 learning goals, use the following full-period investigation:

Additional INVESTIGATION, Prey Survival, A, B, & C, pp. 130–138; 200–201
(Advanced students should complete Levels B and C.)

Teach from Visuals

To help students interpret the photograph of the hummingbird, ask:

- Which structures and behaviors of the hummingbird enable it to get nectar from the flower? *It has a long thin beak and can hover.*
- How is the structure of the flower suited to its interaction with the hummingbird? *Its blooms are deep; it is colorful, bright, and produces sweet food; its pollen can be spread by the interaction helping it to reproduce.*
- Why is this a good example of mutualism? *Two different species interact. They each get a different need met.*

Ongoing Assessment

Describe a symbiotic relationship in which one species benefits from another.

Ask: What is the difference between a mutualistic relationship and a commensal relationship between species? *In a mutualistic relationship both species get something they need. In a commensal relationship, only one species gets something, but the other is unharmed.*

The survival of one species might depend on another species.

OUTLINE
Add a sentence about *symbiosis* to your outline and define the three types of symbiosis in the supporting details.

You have learned that many different organisms live together in a habitat. The fact that organisms live together forces them to interact in different ways. For example, an organism preys upon another for food. Or perhaps there is competition among organisms over resources such as food, water, and territory.

The actions of different organisms can be so closely related that the survival of one species depends on the action or presence of another. In such a relationship, at least one of the species is getting a resource that it needs to survive. Benefits of the relationship may include food, reproductive help, or protection.

E The relationship between individuals of two different species who live together in a close relationship is called **symbiosis** (SIHM-bee-OH-sihs). This word means "living together." A symbiotic relationship may affect the partners in different ways.

- Both species benefit from the relationship.
- One species benefits while the other is not affected.
- One species benefits while the other is harmed.

Here are some examples for each of the three types of symbiosis.

Both Species Benefit

Stroll through a garden on a sunny day and notice the bees buzzing from flower to flower. Look closely at a single bee and you may see yellow pollen grains sticking to its hairy body. The relationship between the flower and the bee is an example of **mutualism** (MYOO-choo-uh-LIHZ-uhm)—an interaction between two species that benefits both. The bees get food in the form of nectar, and the flowers get pollen from other flowers, which they need to make seeds. F

Mutualism The interaction between the hummingbird and the flower benefits both.

Many plants rely on mutualism to reproduce. The pollen needed to make seeds must be spread from flower to flower. The birds and insects that feed on the nectar in these flowers transfer pollen from one flower to the next. The seeds produced are then moved to new ground by animals that eat the seeds or the fruits that hold the seeds. This form of mutualism doesn't benefit the individual flower but instead ensures the survival of the species.

DIFFERENTIATE INSTRUCTION

More Reading Support

E What does *symbiosis* mean? *living together*

F What happens when two species act in mutualism? *They interact in a way that is good for both partners.*

Below Level Struggling readers may not know the words *benefit* and *mutual.* Both words are key to understanding the material on pp. 522–525. Define these words for students (*benefit* = have some need met, have some help; *mutual* = shared, equally taking part in). Then have them make their own word webs, in which *mutual* is the central word and *benefit* is one of the many related words.

In some cases, mutualism is necessary for the survival of the organisms themselves. For example, termites are able to live off a food that most animals cannot digest: wood. The termites, in fact, can't digest wood either. However, they have living in their guts tiny single-celled organisms, protozoans, that can break the wood down into digestible components. The protozoans get a safe place to live, and the termites can take advantage of a plentiful food source.

Explore symbiotic relationships.

Describe how a bee and a flower benefit from a symbiotic relationship.

One Species Benefits

Commensalism (kuh-MEHN-suh-LIHZ-uhm) is a relationship between two species in which one species benefits while the other is not affected. Orchids and mosses are plants that can have a commensal relationship with trees. The plants grow on the trunks or branches of trees. They get the light they need as well as nutrients that run down along the tree. As long as these plants do not grow too heavy, the tree is not affected.

Commensal relationships are very common in ocean ecosystems. Small fish called remoras use a type of built-in suction cup to stick to a shark's skin and hitch a ride. When the shark makes a kill, the remora eats the scraps. The shark makes no attempt to attack the remora. The remora benefits greatly from this commensal relationship; the shark is barely affected.

Not all commensal relationships involve food. Some fish protect themselves by swimming among the stinging tentacles of a moon jellyfish. The fish benefit from the relationship because the tentacles keep them safe from predators. The jellyfish is not helped or hurt by the presence of the fish. As in this example, it is common in commensal relationships for the species that benefits to be smaller than the species it partners with.

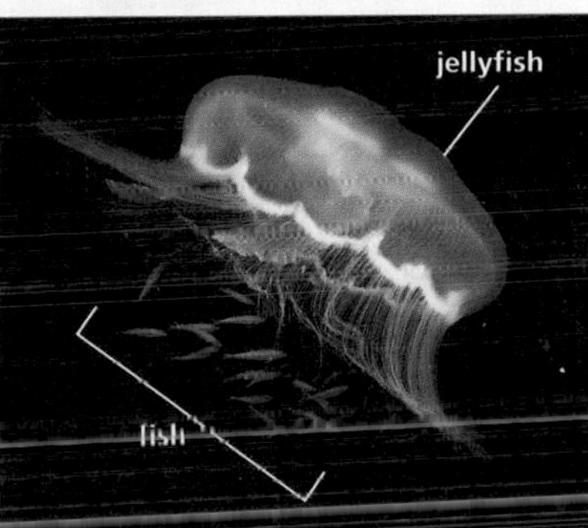

Commensalism The interaction between the jellyfish and the fish benefits the fish only.

One Species Is Harmed

There is one symbiotic relationship in which a small partner can harm a much larger host. **Parasitism** (PAR-uh-suh-TIHZ-uhm) is a relationship between two species in which one species benefits while the species it depends on, its host, is harmed. Parasites are often tiny organisms that feed off, and weaken, their hosts. Ticks, lice, and mites are external parasites that live on or attach to their host's skin. Other parasites, like tapeworms and ringworms, are internal parasites that live inside their hosts.

Real World Example

All humans have resident populations of bacteria, fungi, and protozoans. These are called the "normal flora" of the body, and an average body has more of them than it has cells. Normal flora live on the skin, in the eyes, nose, mouth, upper throat, urethra, and small intestine, and in especially high numbers in the large intestine. The relationships of these species to humans are mainly commensal. In some cases they are mutualistic. Some flora compete with disease-causing microorganisms.

Teach from Visuals

To help students interpret the photograph of the moon jellyfish, ask:

Why is the size of the fish a factor in this method of protection? *The fish have to be small enough to swim among the tentacles. If the fish were larger, they might not need this type of protection.*

Teach Difficult Concepts

The three types of relationships can be hard to remember, especially mutualism and commensalism. Ask the class to bring in pictures of examples for display on a bulletin board that you have started.

Ongoing Assessment

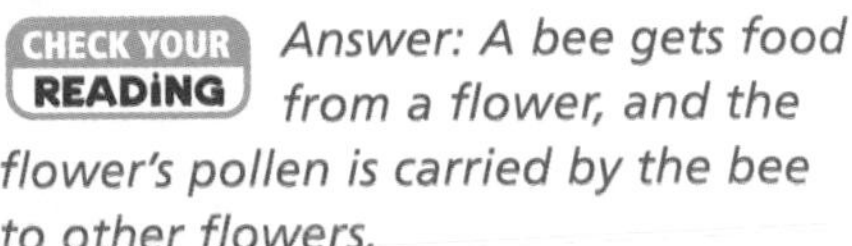

Answer: A bee gets food from a flower, and the flower's pollen is carried by the bee to other flowers.

DIFFERENTIATE INSTRUCTION

More Reading Support

G How are species affected in commensalism? *one species gains; one is not affected*

H How are species affected in parasitism? *one gains; one is harmed*

Below Level Have students make a two-column chart with the types of relationships in one column. In the other column, have them draw a picture or paste a photograph of animals and plants that illustrate each relationship.

Teach from Visuals

To help students interpret the illustration of symbiotic relationships, ask:

- What are the parasites shown in the image? *mistletoe and ticks*
- In the commensal relationships shown, which species benefit? Which species are unaffected? *Lichens and mice benefit; trees and humans are unaffected.*
- What might be another example of mutualism that you would find in this environment? *Sample answer: Bees feed on nectar and help flowers pollinate.*

Ongoing Assessment

Describe symbiotic relationships where one species is harmed.

Ask: What are some ways that one plant can be a parasite of another plant? *Sample answer: A vine might climb a taller or stronger plant to get light and choke or shade the stronger plant; one plant might take nutrients from another plant.*

DIFFERENTIATE INSTRUCTION

Advanced Have students choose one of the relationships in the Symbiotic Relationships illustration, p. 524, and find out more about it. Ask them to consider just one of these three issues:

- Do organisms shown on p. 524 participate in a parasitic relationship?
- Where do disruptions of a mutualistic relationship occur?
- How could a commensal relationship become parasitic?

Challenge and Extension, p. 100

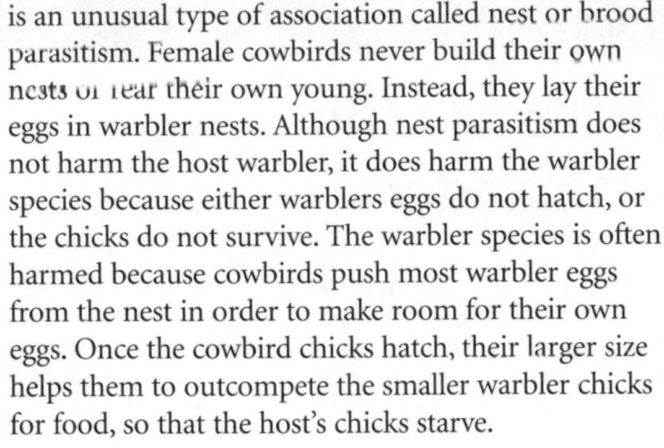

The relationship between cowbirds and warblers is an unusual type of association called nest or brood parasitism. Female cowbirds never build their own nests or rear their own young. Instead, they lay their eggs in warbler nests. Although nest parasitism does not harm the host warbler, it does harm the warbler species because either warblers eggs do not hatch, or the chicks do not survive. The warbler species is often harmed because cowbirds push most warbler eggs from the nest in order to make room for their own eggs. Once the cowbird chicks hatch, their larger size helps them to outcompete the smaller warbler chicks for food, so that the host's chicks starve.

Parasitism The larger cowbird chick is cared for by a warbler at the expense of the smaller warbler chick.

CHECK YOUR READING How is parasitism different from commensalism?

Interactions in an ecosystem are complex.

Different types of symbiosis occur throughout an ecosystem and often overlap. They may occur in the same locations, and the same species might be involved in more than one symbiotic relationship. The illustration on page 524 shows different symbiotic relationships that may occur in a backyard.

Symbiosis is just one of many interactions that take place in an ecosystem. The yard may have a garden, with individual tomato plants competing for water and nutrients; it may have ants cooperating to maintain a successful colony. An ecosystem is more than just a collection of biotic and abiotic factors. Interactions within an ecosystem help explain how resources are shared and used up and how energy flows through the system.

15.2 Review

KEY CONCEPTS

1. Name two ways in which members of the same species interact.
2. In what ways do members of different species interact?
3. Give an example of each type of symbiotic relationship: mutualism, commensalism, and parasitism.

CRITICAL THINKING

4. **Apply** Think of a biological community near you, and give an example of how one population has affected another.
5. **Compare and Contrast** Explain how symbiotic relationships are similar to and different from predator-prey interactions.

CHALLENGE

6. **Synthesize** Mutualism is more common in tropical ecosystems such as rain forests and coral reefs than in other ecosystems. Why do you think this is so?

ANSWERS

1. compete for mates, cooperate for resources

2. compete, cooperate, or form symbiotic relationships

3. Sample answer: mutualism—bee and flower; commensalism—fish and jellyfish; parasitism—tapeworms in humans

4. Sample answer: Bittersweet competes with trees for space and sunlight, and has stunted their growth.

5. In a predator-prey relationship, one species benefits and the other is harmed. Parasitism is similar, but the effect is more dramatic because the parasite relies on its host for survival.

6. Sample answer: Tropical rainforests and coral reefs have many more species than other ecosystems; more opportunities for mutualism.

Ongoing Assessment

CHECK YOUR READING *Answer: In parasitism, one organism is harmed by another. In commensalism, neither organism is harmed.*

Reinforce the BIG idea

Have students relate the section to the Big Idea.

 Reinforcing Key Concepts, p. 102

15.2 ASSESS & RETEACH

Assess

 Section 15.2 Quiz, p. 24

Reteach

Explain each concept. Have students name examples from the text or elsewhere.

- Organisms interact.
- Organisms may be predators or prey—some animals are both.
- Organisms compete for light, space, nutrients, territory, or mates. Members of the same species may compete, or different species may compete.
- Some organisms cooperate. They accomplish things together that they couldn't do as individuals.
- Symbiosis means living in a close relationship. If all the organisms benefit, it is called mutualism.
- If one organism benefits at the expense of another, it is called parasitism.
- If one organism benefits while the other is unaffected, it is called commensalism.

Technology Resources

Have students visit **ClassZone.com** for reteaching of Key Concepts.

 CONTENT REVIEW

 CONTENT REVIEW CD-ROM

THINK SCIENCE
Scientific Methods of Thinking

Set Learning Goal
To make inferences by combining new knowledge with past knowledge

Present the Science
Salamanders absorb water through their skin. These amphibians generally live in freshwater wetlands and damp woods. They range from 5 cm to 1.5 m long, and are bright orange or yellow with stripes or spots. They feed on insects, worms, snails, and other small animals.

Guide the Activity
- Remind students that an inference is a statement that is probably true, based on other information. It must be supported by prior knowledge and observations or data.
- The first notebook contains evidence. Ask: Which statements are qualitative observations—those that must be described? *(b, e)* Which are quantitative—those that can be counted, measured, or calculated? *(a, c, d)*
- The second notebook shows inferences that may or may not be supported. They have not been directly observed or measured. Explain that students must decide which ones are reasonable.

COOPERATIVE LEARNING STRATEGY
Divide the class into groups of five. Have each group brainstorm inferences. A time keeper can keep track of 10 minutes, while a recorder quickly writes all suggestions. Group members suggest which inferences to keep, and which to cross out. They must support their choices.

Close
Ask: Why is it important to study what killed the salamanders? *Sample answer: All organisms have a niche, and their disappearance can affect the entire community. It may be possible to prevent spread of the disease to other populations.*

This barred tiger salamander can be found in many wetlands in the Great Plains.

SKILL: INFERRING

Where Are the Salamanders?

At the Cottonwood Lake Study Area in rural Stutsman County, North Dakota, U.S. Fish and Wildlife Service biologists have been studying wetland ecosystems for more than 30 years. Salamanders are one of the most abundant species in these wetlands. But in May 2000, the researchers started noticing sick salamanders in one wetland. By July, most salamanders had died. What killed them?

Observations

a. In the past, cold winter weather and food shortages have killed salamanders at Cottonwood Lake.
b. The sick salamanders had discolored skin and enlarged livers.
c. The previous year, leopard frogs in a nearby wetland were found dying from a contagious fungal infection.
d. A viral disease has killed tiger salamanders elsewhere in the West.
e. Both large, well-fed salamanders and small, poorly nourished salamanders died.

Inferences
The following statements are possible inferences:

a. A food shortage caused salamanders to starve.
b. The fungal disease that killed leopard frogs also killed the salamanders
c. Salamanders were killed by a viral disease.

Evaluate Inferences
On Your Own Which of the inferences are supported by the observations? Write the observations that support each of the inferences you identify.

As a Group Discuss your decisions. Come up with a list of reasonable inferences.

CHALLENGE What further observations would you make to test any of these inferences?

ANSWERS
Inference a is not supported. Large well-fed salamanders died off. This does not support the animals starving to death.

Inference b is partly supported. Frogs and salamanders share many traits. It is reasonable to think that they could be killed by the same infection. But, they also have differing traits. They may be unharmed by it.

Inference c is supported. The exact same species of salamanders died in both locations. Viral diseases can spread over large areas.

CHALLENGE Study other tiger salamanders for symptoms of the virus, and leopard frogs for symptoms of the fungal infection. Dissect dead salamanders for clues.

KEY CONCEPT

Ecosystems are always changing.

BEFORE, you learned
- Populations in an ecosystem interact in different ways
- Organisms can benefit from interactions in an ecosystem
- Organisms can be harmed by interactions in an ecosystem

NOW, you will learn
- How different factors affect the size of a population
- How biological communities get established
- How biological communities change over time

VOCABULARY

limiting factor p. 528
carrying capacity p. 529
succession p. 530
pioneer species p. 530

EXPLORE Population Growth

How does sugar affect the growth of yeast?

PROCEDURE

1. Use a marker to label the cups A, B, C. Pour 150 mL of warm water into each cup. Mark the water level with the marker.
2. Add 1/2 teaspoon of dry yeast to each plastic cup and stir.
3. Add 1/4 teaspoon of sugar to cup B. Add 1 teaspoon of sugar to cup C. Stir.
4. Wait 15 minutes. Measure the height of the foam layer that forms in each cup.

WHAT DO YOU THINK?
- Which cup had the most foam, which cup had the least?
- Describe the effect of sugar on a population of yeast.

MATERIALS
- 3 clear plastic cups
- warm water
- sugar
- dry yeast
- measuring spoons
- measuring cup
- stirring rod
- marker
- ruler

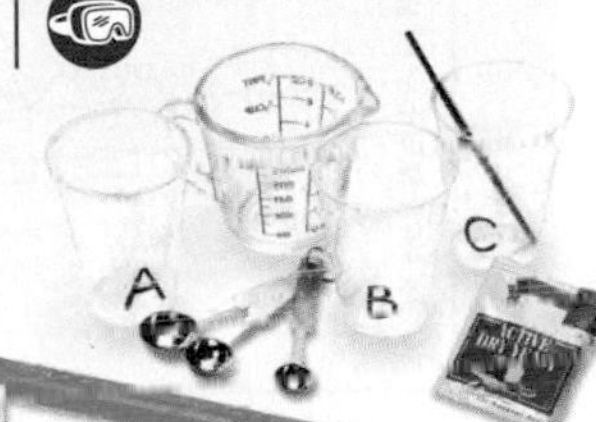

Populations change over time.

REMINDER
A *population* is a group of organisms of the same species that live together in the same habitat.

You may have a strong memory of a park you visited as a little child. You remember collecting pine cones, listening to woodpeckers, and catching frogs. Then you visit again, years later, and the park has changed. Maybe more land has been added, there are more birds and trees. Or maybe the area around the park has been developed. There seem to be fewer woodpeckers, and you can't find any frogs. The community has changed. There are a lot of factors that affect the populations within a biological community. Some have to do with the organisms themselves. Others relate to the habitat.

15.3 FOCUS

Set Learning Goals

Students will
- Explain what affects the size of a population.
- Explore ways that biological communities are established.
- Describe how ecosystems change over time.
- Observe the effects of sugar on the growth of yeast.

3-Minute Warm-Up

Display Transparency 13 or copy this exercise on the board:

Match the definitions to the words.

Definitions
1. a relationship in which two organisms both try to get the same thing *d*
2. a relationship in which both of the organisms benefit *e*
3. the role a species fills in a habitat *b*

Terms
- a. parasitism
- b. niche
- c. habitat
- d. competition
- e. mutualism

 3-Minute Warm-Up, p. T13

15.3 MOTIVATE

EXPLORE Population Growth

PURPOSE To introduce students to limiting factors affecting growth of a population of yeast

TIP *20 min.* Check the yeast before the lab to make sure it's alive.

WHAT DO YOU THINK? *Cup C had the most foam; cup A had the least; yeast feeds on sugar, so the more food, the more foam.*

RESOURCES FOR DIFFERENTIATED INSTRUCTION

Below Level
UNIT RESOURCE BOOK
- Reading Study Guide A, pp. 105–106
- Decoding Support, p. 118

AUDIO CDS

Advanced
UNIT RESOURCE BOOK
Challenge and Extension, p. 111

English Learners
UNIT RESOURCE BOOK
Spanish Reading Study Guide, pp. 109–110

AUDIO CDS
- Audio Readings in Spanish
- Audio Readings (English)

15.3 INSTRUCT

Teach from Visuals

To help students interpret the graphs, ask:

- What was the moose population in 1970? *about 1,300* The wolf population in 1970? *20*
- How did the moose population change between 1970 and 1975? How did the wolf population change in the same period? *The moose population peaked. The wolf population grew.*
- What time period did the wolf population decrease as the moose population decreased? *1980–1982*

Real World Example

In the United States, many animal populations are endangered as a result of human use of their habitat. Whooping cranes are endangered because their wetland habitat has been drained for farmland. The endangered sawback turtle's food (snails and insects) has been reduced by flood controls, siltation, and pollution.

Population Growth and Decline

One factor that obviously affects population size is how often organisms reproduce. Birth rate is a measure of the number of births in an animal population. It can also be a measure of the stability of an ecosystem. For example, black bears reproduce once every two years. If there is not enough food available, however, the female bear's reproductive cycle is delayed, and the bear population does not grow.

A

Predator-prey interactions also affect population size. The graphs show how an increase in the moose population—the prey—in Isle Royale National Park was followed by an increase in the island's population of wolves—the predators. The wolves preyed upon the moose, the moose population decreased, then the wolf population decreased.

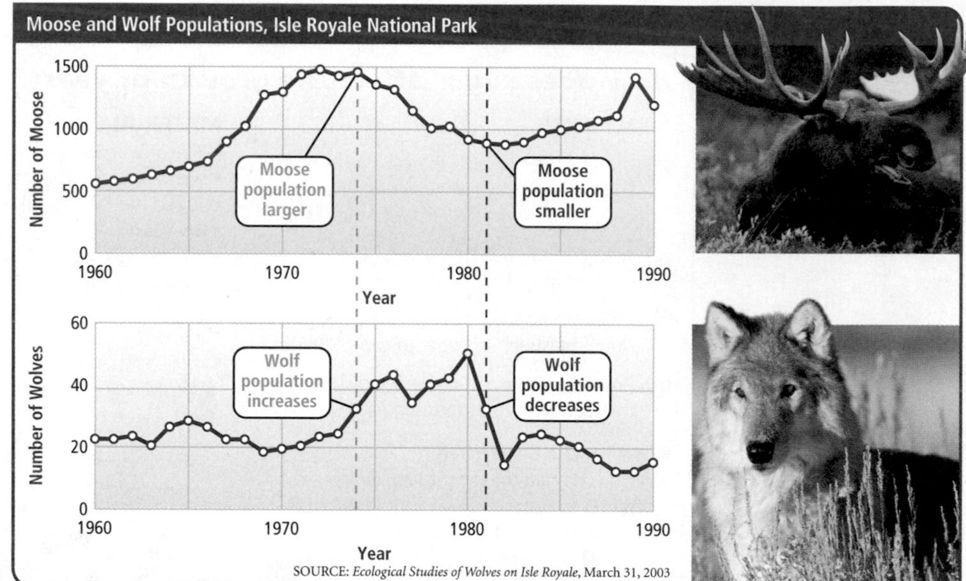

READING TIP
Note in the graphs above that it can take some time for the size of one population to affect the size of the other.

B

Any factor or condition that limits the growth of a population in an ecosystem is called a **limiting factor.** A large population of predators will limit the population of prey; a small population of prey will limit the population of predators. Too much or too little of any biotic or abiotic factor—like food, water, or light—makes an ecosystem unstable and brings about change.

A lack of nutrients in the soil is a limiting factor for plants. That is why farmers fertilize their crops. That same fertilizer, if it runs off into a lake, can increase the population of algae, another photosynthetic organism. A large population of algae can cover a lake with scum and use up oxygen needed by fish. This then limits the fish population.

DIFFERENTIATE INSTRUCTION

More Reading Support

A What can cause a population to grow? *fewer predators*

B What does a limiting factor do? *limits the growth of a population*

English Learners There are many different kinds of charts and graphs. English learners may be unfamiliar with some uncommon types. Help students understand how to read the population chart on the page above.

INVESTIGATE Limiting Factors

What effect does spacing have upon a population of plants?

DESIGN — YOUR OWN — EXPERIMENT

Using the materials listed, design an experiment to test this hypothesis: "If plants grow too close together, the health of the population will be affected because the individual plants do not get enough of the nutrients and water that they need."

PROCEDURE

1. Decide how to use the seeds, cups, and soil to test the hypothesis.
2. Write up your experimental procedure. Include safety tips.

WHAT DO YOU THINK?

- What are the variables in your experiment?
- What evidence would you expect to see if your hypothesis is true?

CHALLENGE Conduct your experiment. Note that seeds must be planted near the top of the soil. A good measure for this is the tip of a pencil. Measure and record the growth of the seedlings. Allow the seedlings to grow for two weeks before drawing your conclusions.

SKILL FOCUS
Designing experiments

MATERIALS
- paper cups
- potting soil
- radish seeds
- water
- pencil
- ruler

TIME
20 minutes

Maintaining a Balance

Living things have certain minimum requirements for food, water, and living space. When a population reaches a state where it can no longer grow, the population has reached its **carrying capacity,** the maximum number of individuals that an ecosystem can support. You can see on page 528 that the graph for the moose population does appear to peak around 1500. Even if there were no wolves on the island of Isle Royale, the population of moose would still be limited because there is only so much food and space available.

VOCABULARY
Remember to make a four square diagram for *carrying capacity* in your notebook. Try to use *limiting factor* in your diagram.

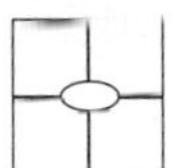

CHECK YOUR READING Explain the term *carrying capacity.*

An ecosystem's carrying capacity is different for each population. A meadow ecosystem will support many more bees and ants than bluebirds, for example. Isle Royale supports many more moose than wolves. The moose is a primary consumer of plants. It is at a lower level of the energy pyramid than the wolf, a secondary consumer.

Biotic factors can be limiting factors. These factors include the interactions between populations, such as competition, predation, and parasitism. Abiotic factors, such as temperature, availability of water or minerals, and exposure to wind, are also limiting.

DIFFERENTIATE INSTRUCTION

More Reading Support

C What's the name for the largest population that an environment can support? *carrying capacity*

Below Level Students may have trouble with the concept of carrying capacity. Use the analogy of a group of people on a boat. Ask: What are the factors that limit the number of people that can safely board the boat? *buoyancy of the boat relative to weight of passengers and supplies; space available to fit people without hurting each other; also could be food and water available for a trip* What are factors that limit the number of organisms that can survive in a population? *food, water, space, light*

INVESTIGATE Limiting Factors

PURPOSE To observe how space can be a limiting factor for plants

TIPS *20 min.*

- Do not plant seeds any deeper than twice their length.
- To accentuate the effects of limited space, crowd the 20 seeds closely together. Using 3-oz. cups for this experiment will dramatize the results.

WHAT DO YOU THINK?

- *The space given to the radish seeds should be the only variable.*
- *Radish seeds given less space would grow less successfully. There would be fewer and/or smaller plants.*

 Datasheet, Limiting Factors, p. 112

Technology Resources

Customize this student lab as needed or look for an alternative. Print rubrics to assess student lab reports.

 **Lab Generator CD-ROM**

Teaching with Technology

Use a digital camera to take daily photos of the plants. Students can use them in a presentation of the experiment.

EXPLORE the BIG idea

Revisit "Internet Activity: Carrying Capacity" on p. 507. Have students explain how limiting factors affected carrying capacity in their simulations.

Ongoing Assessment

Explain what affects the size of a population.

Ask: What factors affect the carrying capacity of a population of trees? *nutrients, space, light, and water; disease, competition, predation*

CHECK YOUR READING *Answer: Carrying capacity is the maximum population that an environment can support.*

Address Misconceptions

IDENTIFY Ask: What happens to organic material as it decays? If students answer that it "disappears" or "is destroyed," they may hold the misconception that decay causes matter to break down into nothing.

CORRECT Direct students to the primary succession diagram on p. 530. Explain that the broken-down rocks contribute to the mineral content of soil. As the first plants that grow on the thin, rocky soil die and decay, the materials that made up their living tissues become the soil's organic content. As this process continues, the soil layer eventually becomes deep enough to support trees.

REASSESS Ask: What else besides plants and rock particles contributes to soil content? *dead and decaying animal matter* What happens to the decaying organic matter after it becomes part of the soil? *Living organisms eat or absorb the nutrients it contains to carry on their life processes; organic matter becomes part of the life cycle in an altered form.*

Technology Resources

Visit **ClassZone.com** for background on common student misconceptions.

MISCONCEPTION DATABASE

Integrate the Sciences

In 1980 Mount St. Helens in Washington erupted, causing a blast of hot gas and debris that reached 300°C. The surface was new rock or scorched ash. Soon after the eruption, the Forest Service reported seeing long earth cores on top of the ash layer. The northern pocket gopher had made tunnels in the snow and filled them with fertile soil from underground burrows. The soil mixture became a seed bed for new plant life.

Teach from Visuals

To help students interpret the sequence of illustrations, ask:

- How is the underground different in the three pictures? *It is rock; then partly rock, partly soil; then soil.*
- What caused this difference? *Pioneering species broke down rock and contributed organic material.*

Ecosystems change over time.

Take a walk in a New Hampshire woods and you may see the remains of old stone walls scattered about. A hundred years ago this land was mostly farmland. The farms were abandoned. And now, new trees have grown where farm animals once grazed.

D

Succession (suhk-SEHSH-uhn) is the gradual change in an ecosystem in which one biological community is replaced by another. The change from field to forest is an example of succession. Over time the grasses of open farmland are slowly replaced by small plants and shrubs, then trees.

Primary Succession

READING TIP

Succeed and *succession* come from the same Latin root word, *succedere*, meaning to go up or to follow after.

Very few places on Earth are without some form of life. Even when a lava flow covers an area or a glacier retreats and leaves behind an empty and barren environment, plants will move into the area and bring it back to life. These are examples of primary succession, the establishment of a new biological community.

E

Pioneer species are the first living things to move into a barren environment. In the illustration below, moss and lichen move in after a glacier retreats. There is little or no topsoil. Moss and lichen are common pioneers because they have tiny rootlike structures that can take hold on exposed rock.

Primary Succession

Primary succession can occur after a glacier retreats, when little topsoil is present.

1 Moss and lichen grow on rock with little or no soil. These pioneer species break apart the surface rock.

2 Over time, the rock breaks down further, forming soil. Larger plants take root. These support populations of animals.

3 Coniferous trees take root in a deep layer of soil. A diversity of plants and animals are supported in this habitat.

DIFFERENTIATE INSTRUCTION

More Reading Support

D What is succession? *a gradual change in the plant and animal communities in an area*

E Give an example of a pioneer species. *moss, lichens*

Advanced Challenge students to come up with examples of how secondary succession could be followed by primary succession in a particular environment.

Challenge and Extension, p. 111

As the pioneers grow, they gradually weaken the rock surface. The rock breaks down and weathers over time. Decaying plant matter adds nutrients, forming soil. Now a variety of small plants and shrubs can take root. These plants, in turn, support insects, birds, and small rodents. Eventually there is enough soil to support coniferous trees. Forests grow, providing a stable habitat for larger animals.

RESOURCE CENTER CLASSZONE.COM

Learn more about succession.

Secondary Succession

F Secondary succession takes place after a major disturbance to the biological community in a stable ecosystem. Despite the disturbance, the soil remains. A community can be disturbed by a natural event, like fire or flood, or it can be disturbed by human activity. A forest cleared or farmland abandoned can lead to secondary succession.

G The illustration below shows secondary succession following a forest fire. The damage, as bad as it is, is surface damage. Below the surface, seeds and plant roots survive. After a time, grasses and small shrubs grow up among the decaying remains of the original plants. Birds, insects, and rodents return. Alder trees take root—alders are trees that put nutrients into the soil. Over time, a variety of trees and plants grow, providing food for a variety of animals.

CHECK YOUR READING What is the difference between primary and secondary succession?

Secondary Succession

Secondary succession occurs if soil remains after a disturbance, such as a forest fire.

1 Plants at the surface are burned; however, below the surface seeds and some plant roots survive.

2 Grasses and small shrubs sprout among the charred trees and vegetation. Smaller animals return.

3 Deciduous trees like elm and maple grow and mature. A forest habitat is reestablished. More animals are supported.

DIFFERENTIATE INSTRUCTION

More Reading Support

F What is secondary succession? *regrowth after a disturbance when the soil remains*

G What can trigger secondary succession? *floods, fires*

Below Level

Use a table to help students understand the different ways ecosystems change over time.

Type of change	Soil	Cause	Pioneer species
primary succession	no	lava flow, glacier movement, landslide	need to move in via seeds and spores
secondary succession	yes	fire, flooding, land-use change	survive in soil

Teach from Visuals

To help students interpret the sequence of illustrations, ask:

- What kind of soil is still on the surface in the first image? *topsoil*
- Why are some plants able to grow back quickly? *because some roots and seeds survive below the surface*
- What lures animals and insects back to the area? *new plant life*

Teach Difficult Concepts

Give more extreme examples to help students distinguish between primary and secondary succession. Primary succession examples: the surface of new construction such as a building or wall, a sterilized canning jar. Secondary succession examples: ice-scoured riverbank, scrubbed footstep, a rinsed-out cup. To help students understand, try the following demonstration.

Teacher Demo

Collect a newly broken rock and a moss- or lichen-covered stone from an old wall, or a new brick and a mossy one. Show them to the class and point out the totally bare sharp surface of the new rock. Describe the succession that could lead to the lichen-covered rock. Pioneer species trap dirt and litter and provide hiding places for small organisms and rooting material for plants.

Ongoing Assessment

Describe how ecosystems change over time.

Ask: When a glacier retreats or a forest burns, how does the ecosystem recover? *After a glacier retreats, primary succession occurs. Pioneer species add soil, small plants and animals move in, then large plants and animals arrive. After a fire, secondary succession occurs. Small plants and shrubs grow from roots and seeds that survived underground. Large plants and animals return.*

CHECK YOUR READING *Answer: Primary succession occurs when life moves to a barren, soilless area. In secondary succession, the ecosystem changes after a disturbance, when there is still soil for life to gain a foothold.*

Reinforce  the BIG idea

Have students relate the section to the Big Idea.

 Reinforcing Key Concepts, p. 113

15.3 ASSESS & RETEACH

Assess

Section 15.3 Quiz, p. 25

Reteach

Write the following terms on the board:

- carrying capacity
- limiting factors
- pioneer species
- predator-prey interaction
- primary succession
- secondary succession

Have students tell whether each term relates more closely to the concept of "population change" or the concept of "ecosystem change." Encourage them to explain their answers. Then discuss how population changes cause overall ecosystem changes and vice versa. Point out that the ecosystem includes all the populations within it.

Technology Resources

Have students visit **ClassZone.com** for reteaching of Key Concepts.

 CONTENT REVIEW

 CONTENT REVIEW CD-ROM

Patterns of Change

All types of ecosystems go through succession. Succession can establish a forest community, a wetland community, a coastal community, or even an ocean community. Succession can happen over tens or hundreds of years. The pattern is the same, however. First a community of producers is established. These are followed by decomposers and consumers, then more producers, then more decomposers and consumers. Over time, a stable biological community develops.

In a way, the establishment of a biological community is like planting a garden. You first prepare the soil. Perhaps you add compost. This adds organic matter and nutrients to the soil, which helps the soil hold water. With the right preparation, your vegetables and flowers should grow well.

READING TIP As you read about the two ways plant species function in succession, think in terms of cooperation and competition.

Pioneer species can function in one of two ways in an ecological succession. They can help other species to grow or they can prevent species from getting established.

- Some plant species function a bit like gardeners. Trees such as alders have nitrogen-fixing bacteria on their roots that improve the nutrient content of the soil and allow other tree seedlings to grow. Pioneering species may also stabilize the soil, shade the soil surface, or add nutrients to the soil when they die and decay.
- Other plant species produce conditions that keep out other plants. The plants may release chemicals that keep other plants from taking root. Or a new species may outcompete other species by using up resources or better resisting a disease.

Such interactions between living things help to determine succession in an ecosystem.

15.3 Review

KEY CONCEPTS

1. Describe three factors that could limit the size of a population in a habitat.
2. List two natural disturbances and two human-made disturbances that can lead to succession.
3. What role do pioneer species play in succession?

CRITICAL THINKING

4. **Infer** How and why would secondary succession in a tundra habitat differ from secondary succession in a rainforest habitat?
5. **Predict** Suppose you are clearing an area in your yard to construct a small pond. Sketch the stages of succession that would follow this disturbance.

CHALLENGE

6. **Synthesize** Imagine you are the wildlife manager for a forest preserve that supports both moose and wolves. What types of information should you collect to determine the carrying capacity for each species?

ANSWERS

1. predators, parasites, food, space, nutrients, disease, etc.

2. volcanic eruptions, glacier retreat, fire, flooding, abandoned fields

3. Moss, lichen, and plants can move into a barren area on the wind. Over time they help break rock into soil, die into the soil, and attract insects and other animals.

4. Succession occurs more slowly in the tundra because of cold temperatures and a short growing season.

5. Sketches could include pioneering seeds, insects, and small lifeforms in the pond. Vegetation and larger animals might be shown around an older pond.

6. Sample answer: a census of animals, including their sex; plants; food sources; breeding sites; human factors that may affect population

MATH TUTORIAL
CLASSZONE.COM
Click on Math Tutorial for more help with multiplying fractions and whole numbers.

SKILL: MULTIPLYING A FRACTION BY A WHOLE NUMBER

Birth Rates and Populations

Ecologists pay careful attention to the yearly birth rates of endangered species. A birth rate is usually expressed as a fraction. It is the number of births divided by the number of adult females. A 2/5 birth rate for a population means that there are 2 births for every 5 adult females.

Example

Suppose at a national park in Borneo, there is a 2/5 birth rate among orangutans. There are 150 adult females in the park. Estimate how many young will be born. To find out, multiply the fraction by the number of adult females.

(1) Multiply the numerator of the fraction by the whole number.

$$150 \text{ females} \times \frac{2 \text{ births}}{5 \text{ females}} = \frac{150 \times 2}{5} = \frac{300}{5}$$

(2) Divide by the denominator.

$$\frac{300}{5} = 300 \div 5 = 60$$

ANSWER 60 young

Answer the following questions.

1. In 2001, there were about 72 adult female right whales. Scientists observing the whales reported a 1/3 birth rate. About how many right whales were born in 2001?
2. Giant pandas are severely endangered. Currently about 140 giant pandas live in captivity, in zoos and parks. About 3/5 of these were born in captivity. How many is that?
3. The orangutan population of the world has decreased sharply. At one time there were over 100,000 ranging across Asia. Now there may be 21,000, of which, 2/3 live in Borneo. About how many orangutans live in Borneo?

CHALLENGE Suppose 1/1 is given as the desired birth rate to save an endangered population. If the population is currently at 4 births per 20 adult females, by how many times does the rate need to increase to reach the desired rate?

ANSWERS

1. $\frac{72}{3} = 24$ *calves*
2. $\frac{140 \times 3}{5} = \frac{420}{5} = 84$ *pandas*
3. $\frac{21{,}000 \times 2}{3} = \frac{42{,}000}{3} = 14{,}000$ *orangutans*

***CHALLENGE** The rate is 20% of what is desired. The desired rate represents 100%. It needs to increase by 5 times its current rate.*

MATH IN SCIENCE
Math Skills Practice for Science

Set Learning Goal

To calculate birth rates and populations by multiplying fractions and whole numbers

Present the Science

Animals become endangered for various reasons. Right whales were hunted to near extinction, not only because they had thick blubber and valuable baleen, but also because they swam slowly and floated when killed.

Develop Calculation Skills

Remind students that the numerator of the fraction is above the line, and the denominator is below.

To help them remember which part of the fraction to multiply, emphasize that they can think of "below the line" as "division." If you multiply "below the line," you are really dividing, making the total decrease: $\frac{1}{16}$ is less than $\frac{1}{2}$.

DIFFERENTIATION TIP Use grid paper or graph paper to model some simple problems multiplying friendly fractions such as $\frac{1}{2}$, $\frac{3}{4}$, $\frac{2}{3}$ by small whole numbers, such as 4, 5, 6. In each case, shade squares that show the fraction as a portion of a larger square. Students will see that repeated addition gets the same result as multiplying.

Close

Ask students to brainstorm how scientists can increase the population of an endangered species. *Raise birth rates by encouraging captive breeding, restore habitat, protect animals from hunting.*

- Math Support, p. 119
- Math Practice, p. 120

Technology Resources

Students can visit **ClassZone.com** to practice multiplying fractions and whole numbers.

MATH TUTORIAL

BACK TO

the BIG idea

Have students choose one of the habitats discussed in the chapter and give examples of the different types of relationships found there. Ask them to propose a natural disaster that could occur in that habitat and to explain how the habitat will recover.

KEY CONCEPTS SUMMARY

SECTION 15.1

Ask students to describe the habitat in which the crabs live, as shown in the picture on the right. *The crabs live in a rocky, beach habitat, next to the ocean.* Based on the crabs' habitat, what niche do you think the crabs fill? *Crabs gather food from the beach and the ocean. They use the beach and the ocean for reproduction and shelter. The crabs are also food for other animals in the habitat.*

SECTION 15.2

Ask students to explain how the faces represent the different symbiotic relationships. *For mutualism, both faces are smiles, meaning both benefit. For commensalism, one face is smiling and one is blank, meaning one benefits and the other is not affected. For parasitism, one face is smiling and the other is frowning, meaning one benefits and the other is harmed.*

SECTION 15.3

Ask: What types of succession are shown? *primary and secondary* What is the main difference between them? *In secondary succession, there is soil that remains.*

Review Concepts

- Big Idea Flow Chart, p. T9
- Chapter Outline, pp. T15–T16

15 Chapter Review

the BIG idea

Living things within an ecosystem interact with each other and the environment.

KEY CONCEPTS SUMMARY

Groups of living things interact within ecosystems.

- Members of the same species form a population within a habitat.
- Each species has a distinct role within a habitat. This is its niche.

Population of Crabs

Island Habitat for Crabs

VOCABULARY
species p. 509
population p. 510
habitat p. 510
niche p. 511
community p. 512

Organisms can interact in different ways.

Organisms within a community interact with each other in many ways. Some are predators, some are prey. Some compete with one another, some cooperate. Some species form symbiotic relationships with other species:

Mutualism
benefits both

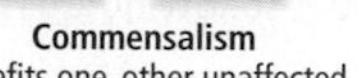
Commensalism
benefits one, other unaffected

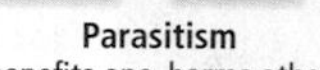
Parasitism
benefits one, harms other

VOCABULARY
predator p. 519
prey p. 519
competition p. 519
cooperation p. 521
symbiosis p. 522
mutualism p. 522
commensalism p. 523
parasitism p. 523

Ecosystems are always changing.

Primary Succession
In a barren area, a new community is established with pioneer species, like mosses, that do well with little or no soil. Mosses eventually give way to coniferous trees.

Secondary Succession
When a disturbance damages a community but soil remains, the community gets reestablished from seeds and roots left behind. Grasses grow, then small shrubs, and eventually trees.

VOCABULARY
limiting factor p. 528
carrying capacity p. 529
succession p. 530
pioneer species p. 530

Technology Resources

Have students visit **ClassZone.com** or use the CD-ROM for a cumulative review of concepts.

CONTENT REVIEW

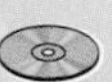
CONTENT REVIEW CD-ROM

Engage students in a whole-class interactive review of Key Concepts. Edit content as you wish.

POWER PRESENTATIONS

Reviewing Vocabulary

Draw a Venn diagram for each pair of terms. Put shared characteristics in the overlap area, put differences to the outside. A sample diagram is provided.

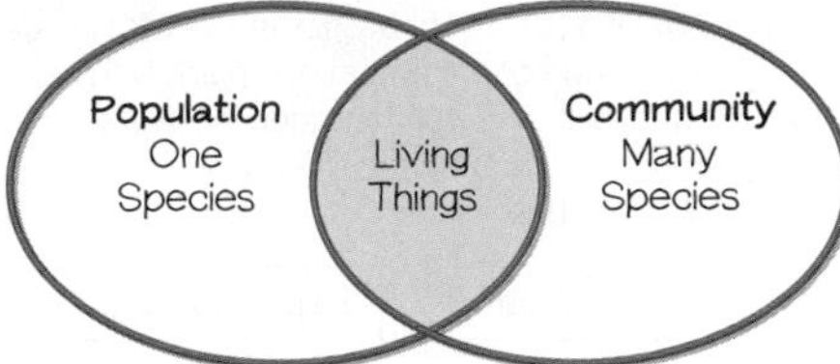

1. habitat, niche
2. mutualism, commensalism
3. mutualism, parasitism
4. competition, cooperation
5. primary succession, secondary succession

Reviewing Key Concepts

Multiple Choice *Choose the letter of the best answer.*

6. What is carrying capacity?
   a. the largest population an ecosystem can support
   b. the smallest population an ecosystem can support
   c. the number of species an ecosystem can support
   d. the number of habitats in an ecosystem
7. A new species of bird moves into a habitat. The birds feed on a particular caterpillar, so that the resulting population of butterflies is small. What can be said of the relationship between the birds and the butterflies?
   a. The birds and the butterflies have a commensal relationship.
   b. The birds and butterflies compete.
   c. The birds are a limiting factor for the butterflies.
   d. The birds and butterflies cooperate.
8. Certain types of worms live in the mud at the bottom of lakes. What does the mud represent for the worm?
   a. an ecosystem
   b. a niche
   c. a community
   d. a habitat
9. What is a pioneer species?
   a. a species that travels within an ecosystem
   b. a species that is among the first to move into an area after a natural disaster
   c. a species that depends upon animal life
   d. a species that cannot return after a natural disaster
10. Which is an example of competition within the same species?
    a. whales in a pod
    b. wildebeests in a herd
    c. creosote bushes in a desert
    d. birds that fly south
11. Which is an example of parasitism?
    a. dog and tick
    b. termite and protozoans
    c. shark and remora
    d. flower and hummingbird
12. Which is an example of secondary succession?
    a. succession after a forest fire
    b. succession after a large volcanic lava flow devastates an area
    c. succession after a glacier retreats, leaving bare rock
    d. succession after a hurricane washes away all the sand from a beach

Short Answer *Write a short answer to each question.*

13. Put the terms in order, starting with the term that includes the largest number of individuals and ending with the group containing the fewest individuals: community, population, ecosystem, biome.
14. List four ways in which members of the same species can cooperate with each other.
15. Describe three different types of symbiosis.

ASSESSMENT RESOURCES

UNIT ASSESSMENT BOOK
- Chapter Test A, pp. 26–29
- Chapter Test B, pp. 30–33
- Chapter Test C, pp. 34–37
- Alternative Assessment, pp. 38–39

SPANISH ASSESSMENT BOOK
Spanish Chapter Test, pp. 69–72

Technology Resources

Edit test items and answer choices.

Test Generator CD-ROM

Visit **ClassZone.com** to extend test practice.

Test Practice

Reviewing Vocabulary

1. habitat: environment surrounding a living thing;
both: within a boundary; relate to matter and energy;
niche: role of one type of living thing in moving matter and energy

2. mutualism: two species benefit by interactions;
both: symbiotic relationships; benefit at least one species; neither is harmed;
commensalism: one species benefits from an interaction, the other remains neutral.

3. mutualism: two species benefit by an interaction;
both: symbiotic relationships, benefit at least one species;
parasitism: one species benefits from an interaction, the other is harmed.

4. competition: two living things are in conflict or oppose each other;
both: types of interactions, can be between or within species;
cooperation: two living things work together or help each other.

5. primary succession: takes place in a barren landscape;
both: series of changes in an ecosystem; take place after disaster or erosion;
secondary succession: takes place after most living things have died, soil remains

Reviewing Key Concepts

6. a	*10. c*
7. c	*11. a*
8. d	*12. a*
9. b	

13. biome, ecosystem, community, population

14. hunt together (whales), move together for protection (wildebeest, herring), share different tasks (ants), care for young (primates)

15. benefits to both species (mutualism), benefits one, but harms another (parasitism), benefits one while other is unaffected (commensalism)

Thinking Critically

16. Years 1–7: steady increase in both; Years 8–10: a decline in both.

17. It is reasonable to infer that the larger a population of lynx or hare, the more pelts traders would sell. The data given is not for populations, but it does suggest increase and decrease in the populations.

18. limiting factors for hares: predator, food, weather, and area of habitat

19. No. Trees function in similar ways, but each species has its niche. Birds, insects, and mammals feed on different trees; shade and nutrients vary plants and fungi around trees.

20. All plants need sunlight. In early stages of succession, small plants grow fastest. Eventually, shrubs, then trees grow, blocking light for smaller plants. Large trees limit growth of small trees.

21. any three: clearing land for development, abandoning farmland, logging, fires, flooding from dams

22. Creosotes are part of a desert community in which populations compete for limited resources. They spread widely and evenly. The roots release a toxin that is a limiting factor for other bushes. Thus, each creosote gets the resources it needs.

23. It would cause populations that rely on those trees for food or shelter to decrease; however, open space might increase low bushes, grasses, and animals that feed on them.

the BIG idea

24. One fish eating another is a predator-prey interaction. Fish may clean, protect, or attract food to one another.

25. Answers should use correct terms in ecology, and should address interactions and carrying capacity.

UNIT PROJECTS

Collect schedules, materials lists, and questions. Be sure dates and materials are obtainable, and questions are focused.

 Unit Projects, pp. 5–10

Thinking Critically

The data in the table below come from the records of a Canadian trading company that, in the late 1800s, bought lynx and hare pelts from hunters and trappers. The Canadian lynx and varying hare share the same habitat. The lynx relies on the hare as a food source. Use the table to answer the next three questions.

Year	Lynx	Hare
1	2	30
2	15	55
3	65	90
4	75	160
5	100	200
6	95	140
7	75	80
8	40	35
9	20	3
10	3	4
11	30	40
12	55	95

16. **ANALYZE** How would you describe the pattern that emerges between the two populations in years 1–7? How does the pattern change in years 8–10?

17. **EVALUATE** The data on the lynx and hare pelts have been used to suggest the sizes of the lynx and hare populations. Is this a reasonable approach to take? Why or why not?

18. **ANALYZE** Scientists have observed that hare populations will go through cycles of increasing and decreasing populations even when the lynx is not part of the habitat. How would you explain this observation?

19. **APPLY** A forest has pine trees, along with oak trees and birch trees. All the trees provide shelter and food for different animals in the habitat. Do these trees occupy the same niche? Explain.

20. **INFER** Explain why low-growing plants like mosses are eventually replaced by shrubs, and shrubs replaced by trees, in both primary and secondary successions.

21. **PROVIDE EXAMPLES** List three human activities that could lead to secondary succession.

22. **ANALYZE** Creosote bushes in the Mojave desert are spread out, so that each plant is about an equal distance from another. Write a short paragraph to describe the interaction of the creosote bushes, using the terms from the table.

competition	population pattern
limiting factor	community

23. **APPLY** How might building homes in a wooded area affect carrying capacity of different populations in the area?

the BIG idea

24. **SUMMARIZE** Look again at the photograph on pages 506–507. How would you change or add details to your answer to the question on the photograph?

25. **APPLY** Imagine that you are an ecologist from another galaxy who arrives on Earth. Describe a human community using the terms that an Earth ecologist would use to describe a natural community. Your description should include at least three examples of interactions between individuals (whether the same or different species). Identify the biotic or abiotic factors that serve as limiting factors to human population growth. Also state whether you think the human population is at or below its carrying capacity—and why.

UNIT PROJECTS

By now you should have completed the following items for your unit project.

- questions that you have asked about the topic
- schedule showing when you will complete each step of your project
- list of resources including Web sites, print resources, and materials

MONITOR AND RETEACH

If students are having trouble using the concepts in Chapter Review items 2, 3, 15, and 24, suggest that they review the visual on p. 524. Have them answer the questions using the illustration of the backyard habitat and the organisms that are pictured.

Students may benefit from summarizing one or more sections of the chapter.

 Summarizing the Chapter, pp. 139–140

Standardized Test Practice

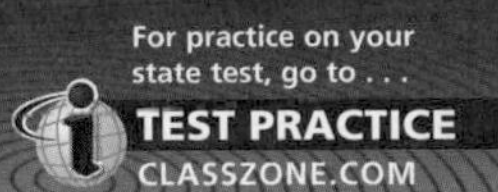

Understanding Symbiosis

Read the following description of the strangler fig and the relationship it has with other species in a rain forest. Then answer the questions that follow.

Strangler figs are part of many symbiotic relationships in a rain-forest ecosystem. In some cases, the symbiotic relationship benefits both the fig and an animal. Fig wasps lay their eggs in the fruit of the strangler fig and, in turn, pollinate it. Many birds feed on the fruit of the strangler fig and, in doing so, spread the seeds of the plant. The fig does not benefit from its interactions with all species. For example, certain butterflies feed on juice from the fruit without affecting the tree in any way.

The symbiotic relationship that gives the strangler fig its name is that between the strangler fig and its host tree. Birds drop seeds onto the top of a tree, and vines of the fig grow downward. Eventually, the vines of the strangler fig touch the ground and join with the roots of the host tree. The host tree is harmed because the leaves of the strangler fig block sunlight and its vines take root, using up nutrients the host tree needs.

1. Which feeding relationship is a form of mutualism in which both species benefit?
- **a.** the strangler fig and its host tree
- **b.** the strangler fig and the butterflies
- **c.** the strangler fig and the birds
- **d.** the strangler fig and the fig wasp

2. Which symbiotic relationship is a form of parasitism in which one species benefits and the other is harmed?
- **a.** the strangler fig and its host tree
- **b.** the strangler fig and the butterflies
- **c.** the strangler fig and the birds
- **d.** the strangler fig and the fig wasp

3. Which symbiotic relationship is a commensal relationship in which one species benefits without affecting the other?
- **a.** the strangler fig and its host tree
- **b.** the strangler fig and the butterflies
- **c.** the strangler fig and the birds
- **d.** the strangler fig and the fig wasp

4. Which word best describes the interaction between the strangler fig and its host?
- **a.** coexistence
- **b.** cooperation
- **c.** competition
- **d.** community

Extended Response

5. Strangler figs attach to trees that are sometimes cut for lumber. Write a paragraph that describes how removal of the host trees would affect these populations.
- butterflies
- birds
- wasps
- strangler figs

6. Write a paragraph describing some of the different roles played by a strangler fig in the rain forest. Use the vocabulary terms listed below in your answer.

habitat	niche	populations
community	ecosystem	

METACOGNITIVE ACTIVITY

Have students answer the following questions in their **Science Notebook:**

1. What did you find the most surprising about interactions in ecosystems?
2. What questions do you still have about interactions in ecosystems?
3. What are the strongest pieces right now in your Unit Project?

Understanding Symbiosis

1. c *2. a* *3. b* *4. c*

Extended Response

5. RUBRIC

4 points for a response that correctly identifies the following effects:
- on butterflies: food lost
- on birds: food lost
- wasps: nesting area lost
- strangler fig: access to sunlight lost

Sample answer: The populations of birds and butterflies will be affected since the strangler fig provides them with food. How much they are affected depends on if they have other food sources. The population of wasps will decrease in the next generation because wasps need the fig to reproduce. The figs will get cut down with the host trees. The strangler fig grows well by reaching the tops of trees for sunlight. It may not grow as well on the ground.

3 points correctly identifies how three populations are affected
2 points correctly identifies how two populations are affected
1 point correctly identifies how one population is affected

6. RUBRIC

4 points for a response that correctly describes the role and uses four of the following terms accurately:
- habitat
- niche
- populations
- community
- ecosystem

Sample answer: The strangler fig fills an important niche in a rainforest habitat. Populations of birds and butterflies depend upon it for food. The fig wasp uses the fruit as part of its reproductive cycle. The wasp in turn helps the reproductive cycle of the fig. Figs are part of a diverse community in a rainforest ecosytem.

3 points describes role adequately and uses three terms accurately
2 points describes role partially and uses two terms accurately
1 point describes role partially and uses 1 term accurately

FOCUS

Set Learning Goals

Students will

- Examine historical steps people have taken to protect ecosystems.
- Learn about some of the tools people have used to study and preserve ecosystems.
- Write a proposal for protecting the ecosystem.

National Science Education Standards

A.9.a–b, A.9.d–g Understandings about Scientific Inquiry

E.6.a–c Understandings about Science and Technology

F.5.a–e, F.5.g Science and Technology in Society

G.1.a–b Science as a Human Endeavor

G.2.a Nature of Science

G.3.a–c History of Science

INSTRUCT

History Connection

Point out to students that the top half of the timeline shows major events in wilderness conservation in the United States starting in the1870s. The bottom half of the timeline illustrates advances in technology and the application of wilderness conservation. The gap between 1910 and 1950 represents a block of time that has been omitted.

Technology

PHOTOGRAPHY First sold in 1888, the Kodak Camera was simple: press a button to expose the film, then turn a key to advance the film. Ask students how this new camera influenced the way conservationists were able to work. *Both conservationists and wildlife photographers could move freely with a lightweight camera to capture images in the environment.*

TIMELINES in Science

WILDERNESS CONSERVATION

The idea of wilderness conservation would have seemed strange to anyone living before the 1800s. The wilderness was vast and much of the wildlife in it dangerous to humans.

In the late 1800s, as smoke from railroads and factories rose in American skies, scientists, artists, even presidents began the work of setting aside land as parks and reservations to protect natural landscapes. Forestry, unpracticed in the U.S. before the 1890s, became a priority of the federal government as the new century dawned. Industries learned to harvest and nurture forests rather than clearing them. Next came the protection of animal species along with a call to control the pollution and depletion caused by human activity.

1872

National Parks Protect Resources

On March 1, 1872, President Ulysses S. Grant signs a law declaring Yellowstone's 2 million acres in northwest Wyoming as the country's first national park. Yellowstone serves as a model, and by 1887, about 45 million acres of forest have been set aside.

EVENTS

1870

APPLICATIONS and TECHNOLOGY

TECHNOLOGY

Seeing the Wilderness

Developments in photography in 1839, and its spread during the Civil War, led to adventurous mobile photographers in the late 1800s. In the early 1860s Mathew Brady and other photographers took mobile studios to the battlefields to bring war news to the public. By the late 1860s and early 1870s the wagonload shrank to a pack load. In 1871, William Henry Jackson balanced his tripod in Yellowstone, as the official photographer of the region's first U.S. Geological Survey.

DIFFERENTIATE INSTRUCTION

Below Level For those students who may have difficulty understanding how information is organized on a timeline, call their attention to the dates on the yellow center line.

Point out how the dates become more recent as they move from left to right. Call attention also to the lines connecting the event boxes to specific dates in the timeline. Emphasize how timelines are a good way of showing quickly a brief or selected history of any subject.

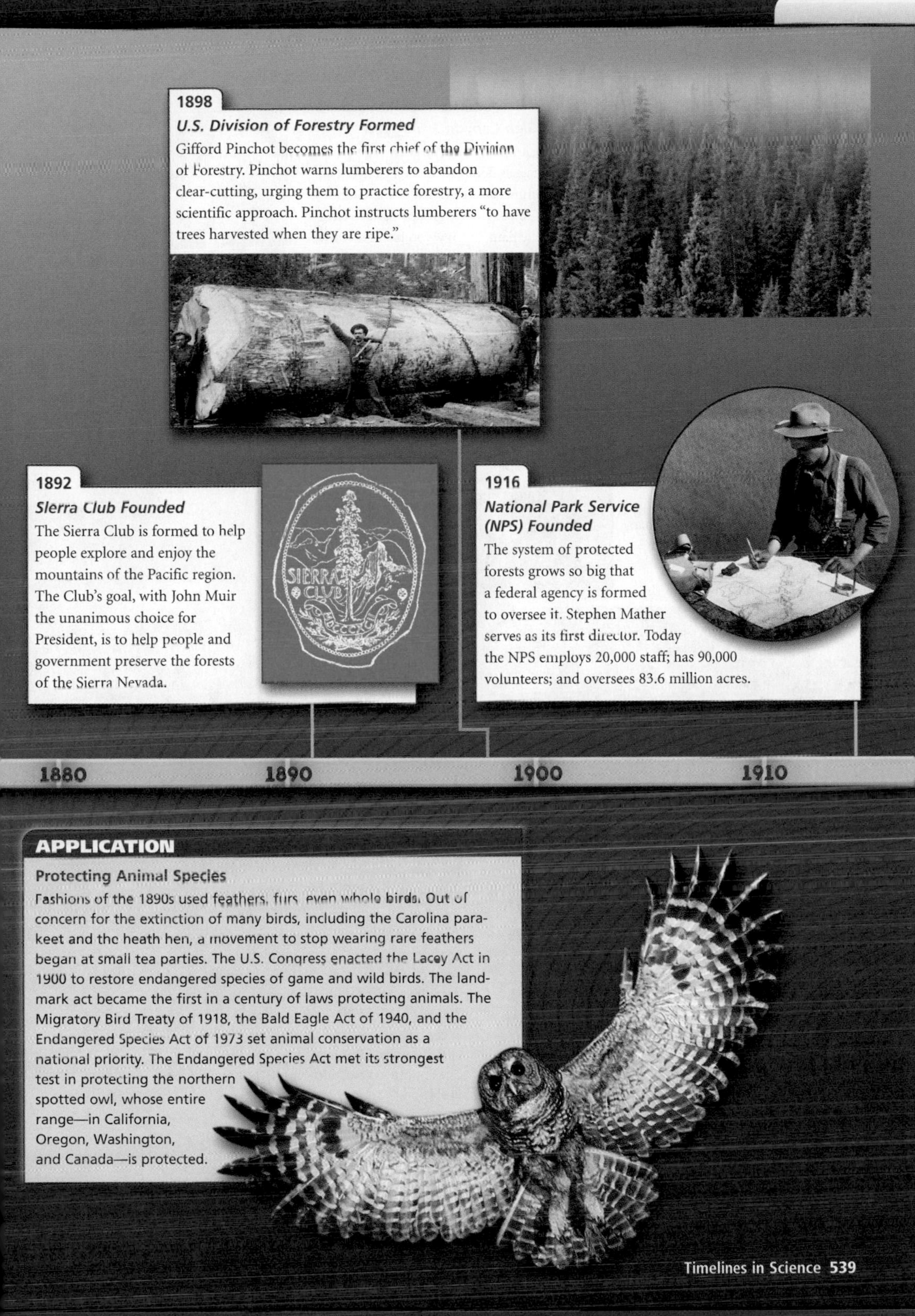

1898
U.S. Division of Forestry Formed
Gifford Pinchot becomes the first chief of the Division of Forestry. Pinchot warns lumberers to abandon clear-cutting, urging them to practice forestry, a more scientific approach. Pinchot instructs lumberers "to have trees harvested when they are ripe."

1892
Sierra Club Founded
The Sierra Club is formed to help people explore and enjoy the mountains of the Pacific region. The Club's goal, with John Muir the unanimous choice for President, is to help people and government preserve the forests of the Sierra Nevada.

1916
National Park Service (NPS) Founded
The system of protected forests grows so big that a federal agency is formed to oversee it. Stephen Mather serves as its first director. Today the NPS employs 20,000 staff; has 90,000 volunteers; and oversees 83.6 million acres.

1880 1890 1900 1910

APPLICATION

Protecting Animal Species
Fashions of the 1890s used feathers, furs, even whole birds. Out of concern for the extinction of many birds, including the Carolina parakeet and the heath hen, a movement to stop wearing rare feathers began at small tea parties. The U.S. Congress enacted the Lacey Act in 1900 to restore endangered species of game and wild birds. The landmark act became the first in a century of laws protecting animals. The Migratory Bird Treaty of 1918, the Bald Eagle Act of 1940, and the Endangered Species Act of 1973 set animal conservation as a national priority. The Endangered Species Act met its strongest test in protecting the northern spotted owl, whose entire range—in California, Oregon, Washington, and Canada—is protected.

Timelines in Science 539

DIFFERENTIATE INSTRUCTION

Advanced Students can visit the website of the U.S. Fish and Wildlife Service and learn about other endangered and threatened species. They can also find out which species have been taken off the endangered list—the success stories.

Students might then select one species and report on what actions are recommended for that species' future. Encourage students to suggest things anyone could do to help ensure the species is protected in a balanced or ecological way.

Scientific Process

Testing hypotheses in ecology takes a long time. A conservationist has no way to be certain about the long-term results of the actions he or she supports. Ecosystems are always larger and more complex than laboratories. When a conservationist takes an action to preserve the environment, he or she must often wait years to fully understand the results. Similarly, the environmental impacts of other human activity, such as industry and agriculture, often take years to truly be felt. As scientists, ecologists have to balance the two.

Art Connection

1892 The Sierra Club has had several logos in its history. The current logo features a giant sequoia tree and the peak of Yosemite's Half Dome mountain. Although the Sierra Club is now a nationwide organization, these symbols were chosen then to symbolize the distinctive beauty of the Sierra Nevada Mountain range. Students may wish to design their own conservation logo. Tell students to think about which natural resources of their region (trees, water, etc.) are most important to preserve and incorporate these into their logos.

Application

PROTECTING ANIMAL SPECIES

The Lacey Act eventually led to the Endangered Species Act, which set up two classes of protected species: *threatened* and *endangered.* The act covers all species of plants and animals. Species classified as threatened are not as in danger of dying out as species classified as endangered. The Fish and Wildlife Service monitors the populations of threatened and endangered species as steps are taken to preserve their habitats. Ask students why they think certain species of plants and animals are threatened. *loss of food and habitat due to human beings' actions on the environment*

Social Studies Connection

1960s The1960s was both an exciting and troubling time in American history. The decade saw the assassinations of President John F. Kennedy in 1963 and civil rights leader Dr. Martin Luther King, Jr. in 1968. College students in the '60s held peaceful protests against American foreign and domestic policies and succeeded in getting much legislation passed by Congress. Some of this legislation eventually led to significant environmental initiatives like the Endangered Species Act and establishment of the Environmental Protection Agency. Ask: Why do you think environmental issues would have concerned people at this time? *Sample answer: People were concerned about their country and wanted to protect it from threats;* or *People were disappointed by human activities and wanted to focus on nature and wildlife.*

Language Arts Connection

1962 Many people consider the publication of *Silent Spring* to be the start of the environmentalist movement. More than simply calling for a stop to the use of pesticides, Carson urged that people needed to adopt a different view of their place in the world. People needed to see themselves as part of nature, not as masters of nature. Ask students why they think this change in view would give people a greater respect for nature. *Sample answer: If people are part of nature, they will want to protect it.*

Social Studies Connection

1968 The Grand Canyon has been considered a sacred site by the Hopi of the southwestern United States. Hopi mythology holds that the first people emerged from inside the Earth through the Grand Canyon.

DIFFERENTIATE INSTRUCTION

English Learners English learners may not know the expression *public outcry* (1968). Students may also need help with words such as *pesticides, publishes,* and *evidence* (1962). You might point out the connection between the terms: *publishes, publicized,* and *public.* Write such terms on the board and put reminder sketches beside them.

Encourage students with limited English to focus mainly on understanding the red headings in the event boxes.

1980 to present

Reservation vs. Resource

In 1980, Congress expands the Arctic National Wildlife Refuge (ANWR) to more than twice its 1960 size. In 2001, President George W. Bush proposes limited oil drilling within the range. Today, debate continues over how to manage its resources and wildlife.

RESOURCE CENTER
CLASSZONE.COM
Read more about current conservation efforts.

1990 2000

APPLICATION

Selling a Service

In New York City in 1996, the water department spent $1.5 billion to protect natural watershed rather than build a $6 billion water treatment plant. In 2001, a group of scientists met to promote the value that ecosystems bring to society — benefits that include pest control, air purification, and water treatment. For example, dragonflies can eat 300 mosquitoes in a single day. Toads and bats can eat a thousand or more mosquitoes in a single day or night.

INTO THE FUTURE

Society has long put a price on natural resources—minerals, water, timber, and so on. But how much is an ecosystem worth? Communities have begun to look at the dollar values of "ecosystem services," the ongoing activities in nature that keep our environment healthy. Data is needed on ecosystem processes. Such data can be compared to the services of human-made treatment plants and agriculture.

Other questions arise with protecting species. Many species, such as wild turkeys and bald eagles, once endangered have come back in great numbers. When a protected species thrives it may endanger another species or bump up against the human landscape and human activity. How can managers of resources set priorities?

ACTIVITIES

Ecosystem Services Proposal

What services to the human population are provided by your local ecosystem? Choose one service and describe how natural processes and interactions within the ecosystem provide the benefits you've identified. What processes are involved?

Write a proposal for protecting the ecosystem. Include a comparison of the estimated cost of protecting the ecosystem and the cost of human services that provide a similar benefit.

Writing Project: The Story Behind the News

Research one of the events described on the timeline. Then write the story behind that event.

DIFFERENTIATE INSTRUCTION

Advanced Encourage motivated students to submit their proposals to their local town or neighborhood board. Tell students that the reports do not need to be comprehensive and numbers exact, but that they should be able to justify how they arrived at the values.

Health Connection

Ask students how the health of our environment and wildlife population affects the health of the human population. Have them to give examples of this interconnectedness. *Sample answer: Fish living in polluted water become contaminated; human beings eat the contaminated fish.*

INTO THE FUTURE

Make three columns on the board. Label the columns *Conservation Activities, Positive Results,* and *Difficulties*. In the first column, have students list ways they can help preserve the ecosystem they live in. *clean up fields, prevent the dumping of trash in water* In the second, have students list the positive impacts of the action. *animal survival, less pollution* In the third, have students identify at least one difficulty they would need to address when taking the action. *waste collecting, effect different animals in the ecosystem*

ACTIVITIES

Ecosystem Services Proposal

Students could get help with this project by contacting their local 4-H, Sierra Club, or chapter of the Forestry Service. Remind students that they need to write persuasively and present their cost estimates clearly when writing their proposals.

Writing Project: The Story Behind the News

Suggest to students that they write their stories from the point of view of one of the participants. If reporting on the founding of the Sierra Club, for example, students could write from the perspective of John Muir, as if he were telling it to a newspaper reporter.

Technology Resources

Students can visit **ClassZone.com** for current news about conservation.

CHAPTER

Human Impact on Ecosystems

Life Science UNIFYING PRINCIPLES

PRINCIPLE 1
All living things share common characteristics.

PRINCIPLE 2
All living things share common needs.

PRINCIPLE 3
Living things meet their needs through interactions with the environment.

PRINCIPLE 4
The types and numbers of living things change over time.

Unit 4: Ecology BIG IDEAS

CHAPTER 14 Ecosystems and Biomes
Matter and energy together support life within a certain environment.

CHAPTER 15 Interactions Within Ecosystems
Living things within an ecosystem interact with each other and the environment.

CHAPTER 16 Human Impact on Ecosystems
Humans and human population growth affect the environment.

CHAPTER 16 KEY CONCEPTS

SECTION 1

Human population growth presents challenges.

1. The human population is increasing.
2. Human populations can put pressure on ecosystems.

SECTION 2

Human activities affect the environment.

1. Humans use many resources.
2. Pollution endangers biodiversity.
3. Habitat loss endangers biodiversity.

SECTION 3

People are working to protect ecosystems.

1. Environmental awareness is growing.
2. Conserving resources protects ecosystems.
3. Think globally, act locally.

The Big Idea Flow Chart is available on p. T17 in the **UNIT TRANSPARENCY BOOK.**

Previewing Content

SECTION

Human population growth presents challenges. pp. 545–552

1. **The human population is increasing.**
Earth's human population was 6 billion in 1999 and is expected to be 9 billion by 2050. Part of the reason for growth is longer life spans, and another reason is the high birth rate.

The human population is not following the usual pattern of leveling off at carrying capacity.

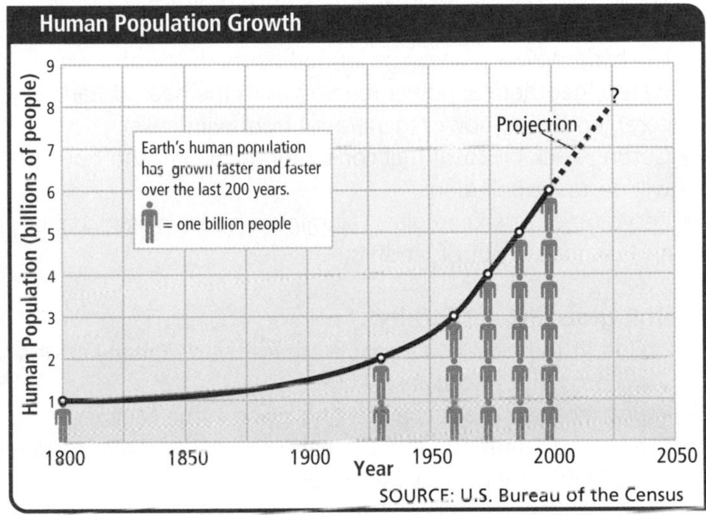

2. **Human populations can put pressure on ecosystems.**
The pressures humans cause to ecosystems arise from waste, resource use, and land-use changes.
   - Waste fills up land with toxic garbage. Sewage releases contaminants into the environment.
   - **Natural resources** are not evenly distributed. Much of the world's population lives in Asia and Africa, where natural resources are often exported for commercial interests.
   - High demand for water is difficult to meet, especially in arid regions. Water is a finite resource.
   - A high **population density** contributes to overuse of resources and disturbance or destruction of natural habitats.

SECTION

Human activities affect the environment. pp. 553–561

1. **Humans use many resources.**
   - Renewable resources include trees, sunlight, and water.
   - Nonrenewable resources include fossil fuels (coal, oil, natural gas) and minerals such as copper and gold.

2. **Pollution endangers biodiversity.**
Biodiversity describes the number and variety of life in an ecosystem. Ecosystems with a variety of species are healthier and more able to recover from problems such as disease.
   - Air and water **pollution** affect entire ecosystems.
   - Use of fossil fuels causes acid rain, which destroys trees, kills fish, and damages soil.
   - Water pollution is caused by oil spills, soil erosion, waste-water, and chemical and waste runoff from farm fields, animal feedlots, and landfills. Water pollution poisons fish, causes algal blooms, and damages the entire food web.
   - Pollution moves across systems.

3. **Habitat loss endangers biodiversity.**
If living space is limited or a food source is removed, then the number of organisms in a biological community will be reduced. Human actions remove habitat, for example, by clear-cutting forests.

Invasive species change habitat. An invasive species is a nonnative species that is introduced by humans or moves in and supplants native species.

Common Misconceptions

MISCONCEPTION DATABASE
CLASSZONE.COM Background on student misconceptions

POLLUTION Most students hold the misconception that air pollution and water pollution affect a limited area. In fact, air pollution can fall to the ground in precipitation, seep into watersheds, and run into bodies of water. Water pollution can evaporate into the air, all the while being carried to larger and larger areas.

 This misconception is addressed on p. 556.

BIODIVERSITY Students sometimes think that changes in population of an organism may not affect an ecosystem because some organisms are not important. They may think that one population can change and have limited or no effects on an ecosystem. In fact, all populations are important and affect the entire ecosystem.

 This misconception is addressed on p. 557.

Previewing Content

SECTION

People are working to protect ecosystems. pp. 562–571

1. **Environmental awareness is growing.**
Awareness of the environment and environmental protection have slowly progressed since the nineteenth century in the United States. Some milestones are
   - Yellowstone National Park, created in 1872, is the first U.S. national park.
   - *Silent Spring,* by Rachel Carson, a book about toxic chemical use published in 1962, raised public awareness about how pollution spreads throughout ecosystems. The author's research on the toxicity of DDT in the environment led to U.S. laws banning its use.
   - Citizen efforts to preserve biodiversity included the founding of the Nature Conservancy and the National Wildlife Federation.
   - More recent government efforts to protect ecosystems have included the Endangered Species Act, the Clean Air Act, Clean Water Act, and the National Environmental Policy Act.

Discontinuing DDT use has permitted several raptors to recover from drastically low populations.

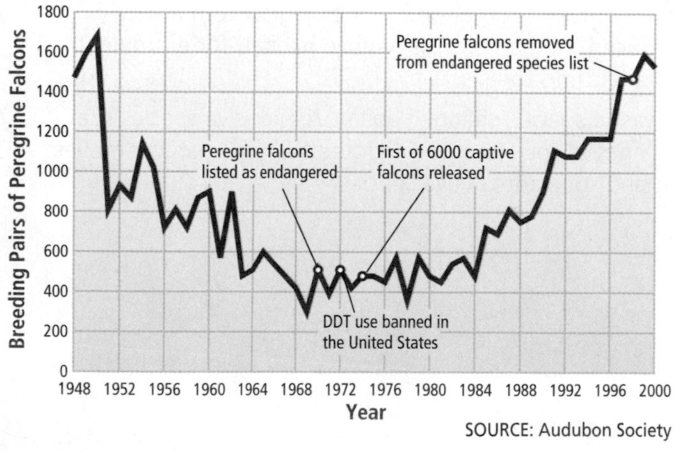

SOURCE: Audubon Society

2. **Conserving resources protects ecosystems.**
Sustainable practices are ways to use resources without using them up. They include the following established practices:
   - U.S. farms practice conservation tillage and use natural fertilizers such as compost and natural pest controls like ladybugs.
   - Forestry practices are changing to strip and selective cutting, which improve regrowth and help prevent erosion.
   - Energy companies are exploring alternative sources of energy like hydropower (energy generated by the force of flowing water), geothermal power (energy from the heat at Earth's core), and wind power (generated from windmills).
   - Cutting back on fossil-fuel consumption in cars and homes will decrease pollution.
   - Recycling efforts keep glass, aluminum, some plastic, paper, and cardboard out of landfills.

3. **Think globally, act locally.**
Working at the local level, people are involved in many efforts to help ecosystems recover.
   - Prairie recovery projects are taking place in the Midwest.
   - The United States and Canada have worked together to clean up Lake Erie, which was heavily polluted by phosphorus.
   - River and watershed restoration takes place in areas throughout the U.S., largely through local community efforts. Businesspeople, economists, and urban planners are also beginning to look at ecosystems as service-providers, with economic value to the community.

Common Misconceptions

INVASIVE SPECIES Some students may think that all plant and animal species, including invasive species, benefit the environment. In fact, because invasive species often have no local predators, they can cause decreases in populations of native organisms through competition. They can use up resources and become difficult to remove or control.

This misconception is addressed on p. 560.

MISCONCEPTION DATABASE
CLASSZONE.COM Background on student misconceptions

SCIENTIFIC MODELS Middle-school students generally think of the world concretely, and often interpret a scientific model too literally. They often believe that scientific models are exact representations of the world. Every model is in some way different from that which it represents.

This misconception is addressed on p. 571.

Previewing Labs

EXPLORE the BIG idea

How Many Is Six Billion? p. 543 Students count rice grains and calculate how much space 6 billion grains would occupy.	**TIME** 10 minutes **MATERIALS** uncooked rice, paper, scissors, tape, ruler, calculator
How Easily Does Polluted Water Move Through Plants? p. 543 Students observe that dye moves through plants, to discover how pollution could affect plants.	**TIME** 10 minutes **MATERIALS** bowl of water, food coloring, stalk of celery
Internet Activity: The Environment, p. 543 Students use the Internet to explore how humans can change ecosystems.	**TIME** 20 minutes **MATERIALS** computer with Internet access

SECTION 1

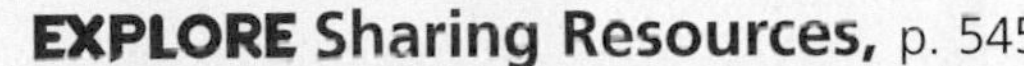

EXPLORE Sharing Resources, p. 545 Students divide objects among members of a group and discover how difficult it is to share unequal resources.	**TIME** 15 minutes **MATERIALS** bag; assorted unlike objects such as pennies, blocks, pencils
INVESTIGATE Resources, p. 548 Students use a map to interpret where their community gets resources and where it disposes of waste.	**TIME** 30 minutes **MATERIALS** recent map of your county, city, or town; tracing paper, ruler

SECTION 2

INVESTIGATE Particles in the Air, p. 555 Students collect and observe samples of local air pollution.	**TIME** 30 minutes **MATERIALS** 2 index cards, marker, hole punch, transparent tape, string, scissors, petroleum jelly, hand lens

SECTION 3

EXPLORE Environmental Impacts, p. 562 Students add water to compressed and uncompressed soil to see how trampling could affect water absorption.	**TIME** 15 minutes **MATERIALS** 2 plant pots with trays, potting soil, measuring cups, stopwatch, water
CHAPTER INVESTIGATION Oil Spills, pp. 570–571 Students create and clean up an oil spill, exploring different methods of cleanup.	**TIME** 40 minutes **MATERIALS** small beaker, vegetable oil, turmeric, spoon, aluminum baking pan, sand, large beaker, water, sponge, dish soap, rubbing alcohol, paper towels, cotton balls, cotton rag, cornstarch, yarn, feather, seaweed

R **Additional INVESTIGATION,** Pollutants on the Move, A, B, & C, pp. 189–197; Teacher Instructions, pp. 200–201

Previewing Chapter Resources

INTEGRATED TECHNOLOGY | LABS AND ACTIVITIES

CHAPTER 16

Human Impact on Ecosystems

Integrated Technology

CLASSZONE.COM
- eEdition Plus
- EasyPlanner Plus
- Misconception Database
- Content Review
- Test Practice
- Visualizations
- Resource Centers
- Internet Activity: The Environment
- Math Tutorial

CD-ROMS
- eEdition
- EasyPlanner
- Power Presentations
- Content Review
- Lab Generator
- Test Generator

AUDIO CDS
- Audio Readings
- Audio Readings in Spanish

SCILINKS.ORG

SCILINKS

Labs and Activities

EXPLORE the Big Idea, p. 543
- How Many Is Six Billion?
- How Easily Does Polluted Water Move Through Plants?
- Internet Activity: The Environment

UNIT RESOURCE BOOK
Unit Projects, pp. 5–10

Lab Generator CD-ROM
Generate customized labs.

SECTION

Human population growth presents challenges.
pp. 545–552

Time: 2 periods (1 block)

 Lesson Plan, pp. 141–142

Integrated Technology

- **VISUALIZATION,** Population Growth
- **RESOURCE CENTER,** Urban Expansion

UNIT TRANSPARENCY BOOK
- Big Idea Flow Chart, p. T17
- Daily Vocabulary Scaffolding, p. T18
- Note-Taking Model, p. T19
- 3-Minute Warm-Up, p. T20
- "Landfill Cross-Section" Visual, p. T22

Labs and Activities

- EXPLORE Sharing Resources, p. 545
- INVESTIGATE Resources, p. 548
- Science on the Job, p. 552

UNIT RESOURCE BOOK
Datasheet, Resources, p. 150

SECTION

Human activities affect the environment.
pp. 553–561

Time: 2 periods (1 block)

 Lesson Plan, pp. 152–153

Integrated Technology

- **RESOURCE CENTER,** Natural Resources
- **MATH TUTORIAL**

UNIT TRANSPARENCY BOOK
- Daily Vocabulary Scaffolding, p. T18
- 3-Minute Warm-Up, p. T20

Labs and Activities

- INVESTIGATE Particles in the Air, p. 555
- Math in Science, p. 561

UNIT RESOURCE BOOK
- Datasheet, Particles in the Air, p. 161
- Math Support, p. 178
- Math Practice, p. 179
- Additional INVESTIGATION, Pollutants on the Move, A, B, & C, pp. 189–197

SECTION

People are working to protect ecosystems.
pp. 562–571

Time: 4 periods (2 blocks)

 Lesson Plan, pp. 163–164

Integrated Technology

RESOURCE CENTER, Ecosystem Recovery

UNIT TRANSPARENCY BOOK
- Big Idea Flow Chart, p. T17
- Daily Vocabulary Scaffolding, p. T18
- 3-Minute Warm-Up, p. T21
- Chapter Outline, pp. T23–T24

Labs and Activities

- EXPLORE Environmental Impacts, p. 562
- CHAPTER INVESTIGATION, Oil Spills, pp. 570–571

UNIT RESOURCE BOOK
CHAPTER INVESTIGATION, Oil Spills, A, B, & C, pp. 180–188

KEY TO ICONS  CD/CD-ROM  Teacher Edition  UNIT TRANSPARENCY BOOK  SPANISH ASSESSMENT BOOK

 INTERNET Pupil Edition UNIT RESOURCE BOOK UNIT ASSESSMENT BOOK SCIENCE TOOLKIT

READING AND REINFORCEMENT	ASSESSMENT	STANDARDS
 • Magnet Words, B24–25 • Supporting Main Idea Notes, C37 • Daily Vocabulary Scaffolding, H1–8  **UNIT RESOURCE BOOK** • Vocabulary Practice, pp. 175–176 • Decoding Support, p. 177 • Summarizing the Chapter, pp. 198–199  **Audio Readings CD** Listen to Pupil Edition.  **Audio Readings in Spanish CD** Listen to Pupil Edition in Spanish.	 • Chapter Review, pp. 573–574 • Standardized Test Practice, p. 575  **UNIT ASSESSMENT BOOK** • Diagnostic Test, pp. 40–41 • Chapter Test, A, B, & C, pp. 45–56 • Alternative Assessment, pp. 57–58 • Unit Test, A, B, & C, pp. 59–70  • Spanish Chapter Test, pp. 65–68 • Spanish Unit Test, pp. 541–80 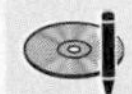 **Test Generator CD-ROM** Generate customized tests.  **Lab Generator CD-ROM** Rubrics for Labs	National Standards A.2–8, A.9.a–c, A.9.e–f, E.2–5, E.6.d–f, F.1.g, F.2.a–b See p. 542 for the standards.
UNIT RESOURCE BOOK • Reading Study Guide A & B, pp. 143–146 • Spanish Reading Study Guide, pp. 147–148 • Challenge and Extension, p. 149 • Reinforcing Key Concepts, p. 151	 Ongoing Assessment, pp. 546–547, 549–551  Section 16.1 Review, p. 551  **UNIT ASSESSMENT BOOK** Section 16.1 Quiz, p. 42	National Standards A.2–7, A.9.a–b, A.9.e–f, F.2.a
UNIT RESOURCE BOOK • Reading Study Guide A & B, pp. 154–157 • Spanish Reading Study Guide, pp. 158–159 • Challenge and Extension, p. 160 • Reinforcing Key Concepts, p. 162 • Challenge Reading, pp. 173–174	 Ongoing Assessment, pp. 554, 556–559  Section 16.2 Review, p. 560 **UNIT ASSESSMENT BOOK** Section 16.2 Quiz, p. 43	National Standards A.2–8, A.9.a–c, A.9.e–f, F.2.b
UNIT RESOURCE BOOK • Reading Study Guide A & B, pp. 165–168 • Spanish Reading Study Guide, pp. 169–170 • Challenge and Extension, p. 171 • Reinforcing Key Concepts, p. 172	 Ongoing Assessment, pp. 563–564, 566–568  Section 16.3 Review, p. 569 **UNIT ASSESSMENT BOOK** Section 16.3 Quiz, p. 44	National Standards A.2–7, A.9.a–b, A.9.d–f, E.2–5, E.6.d–e, F.1.g

Previewing Resources for Differentiated Instruction

CHAPTER INVESTIGATION

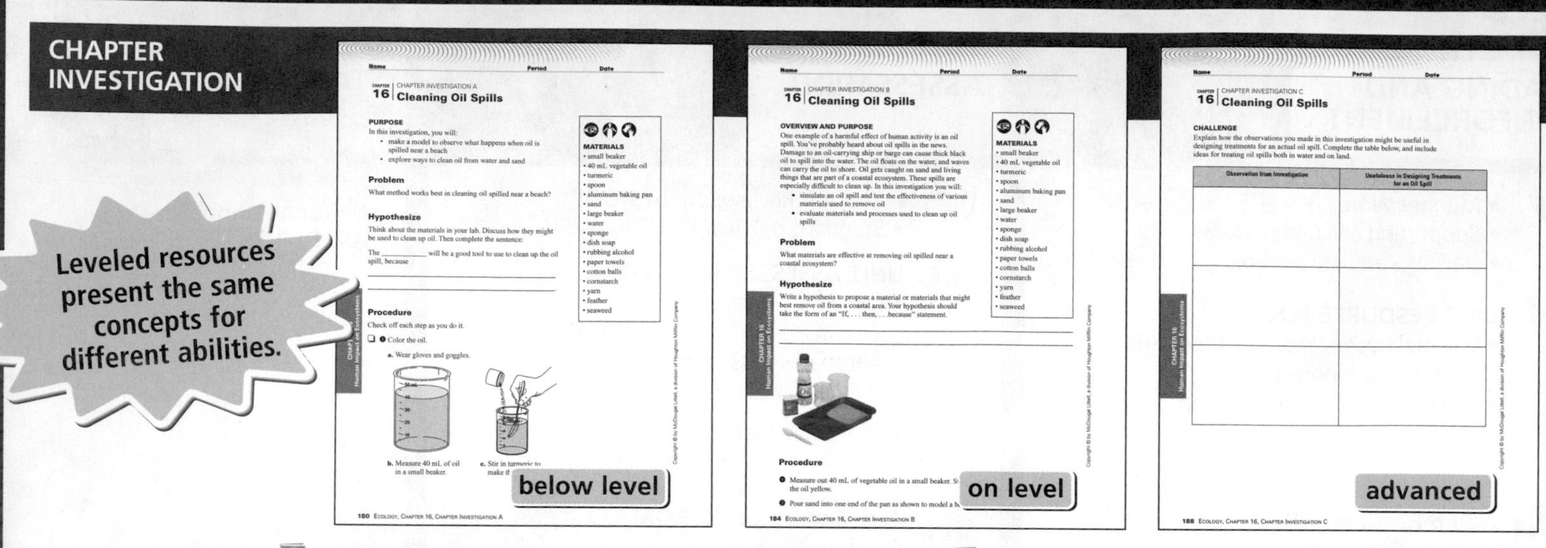

UNIT RESOURCE BOOK, pp. 180–183 | pp. 184–187 | pp. 184–188

READING STUDY GUIDE

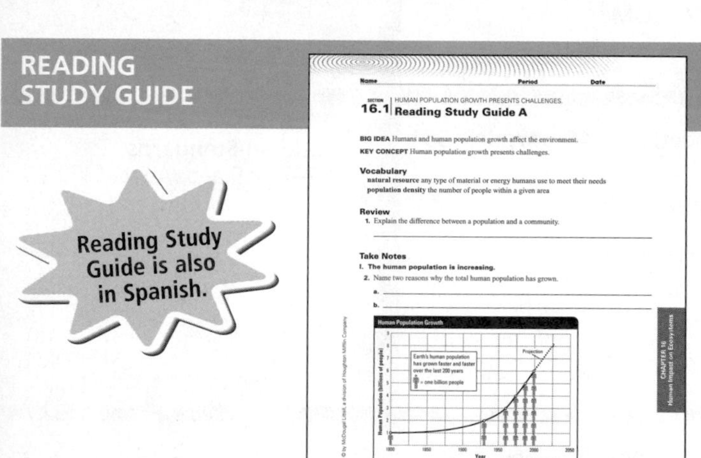

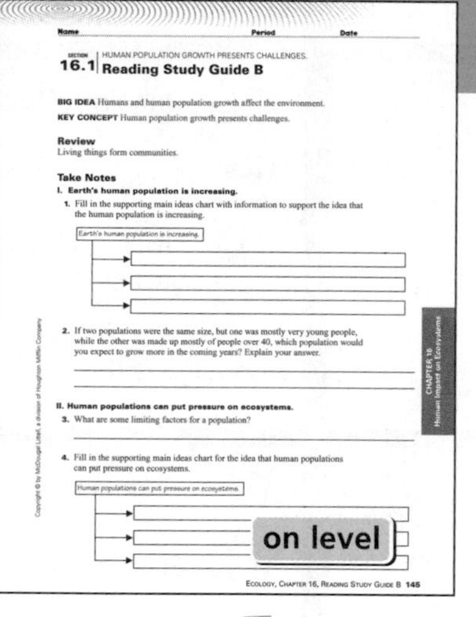

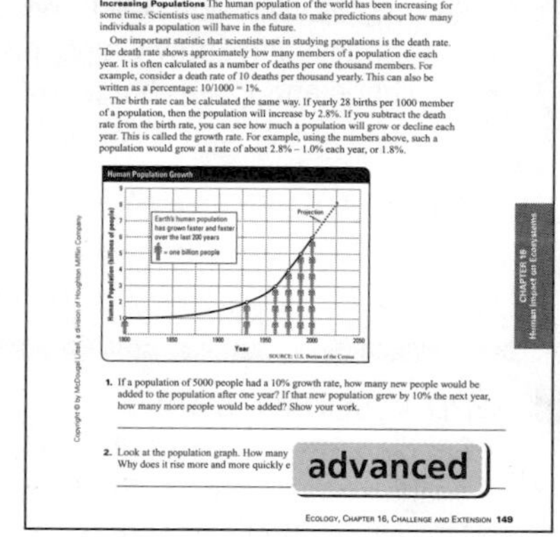

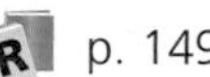

UNIT RESOURCE BOOK, pp. 143–144 | pp. 145–146 | p. 149

CHAPTER TEST

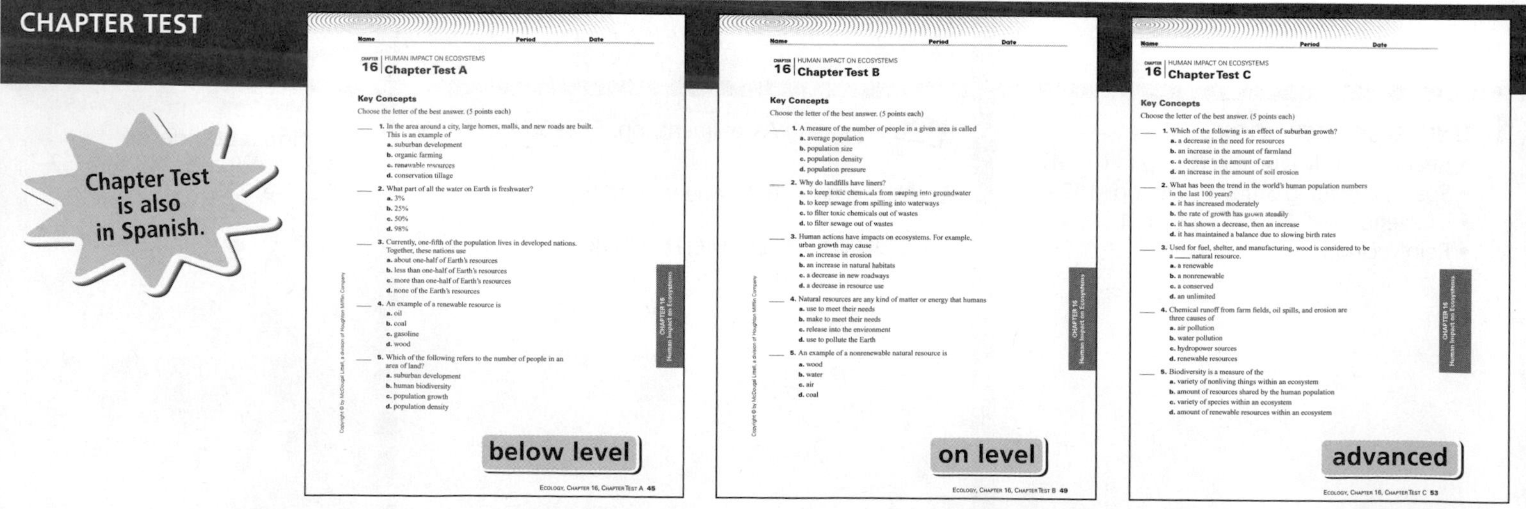

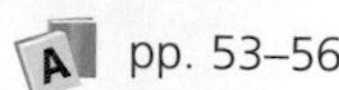

UNIT ASSESSMENT BOOK, pp. 45–48 | pp. 49–52 | pp. 53–56

TECHNOLOGY

There is one Visualization for this chapter.

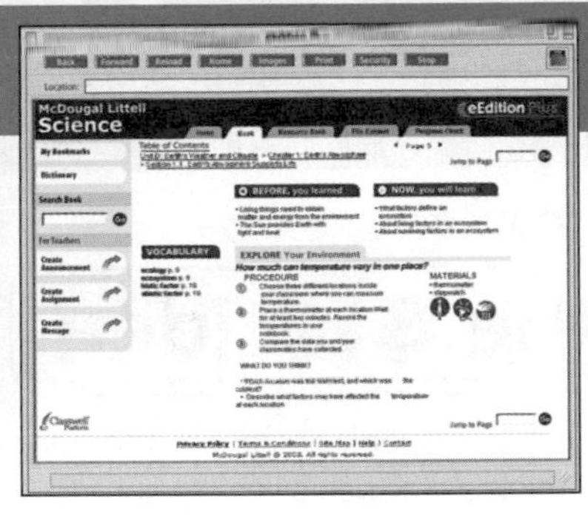

 CLASSZONE.COM

 CD/CD-ROMS

 CLASSZONE.COM

VISUAL CONTENT

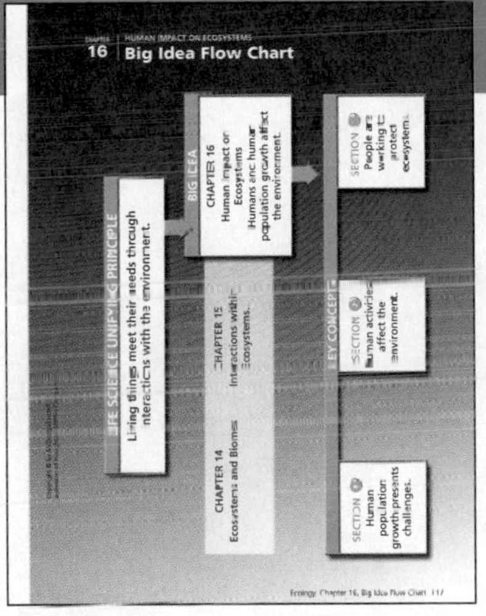

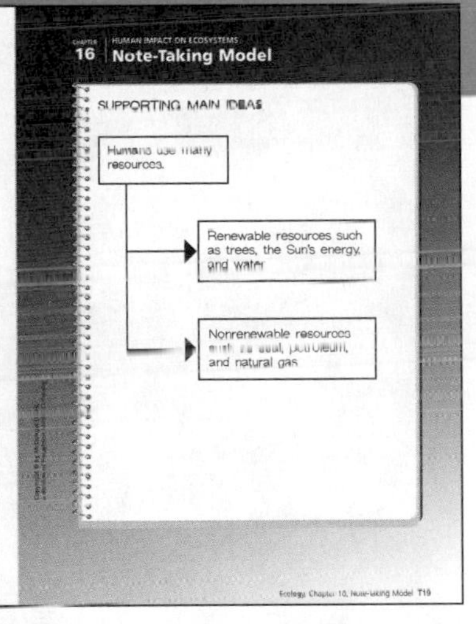

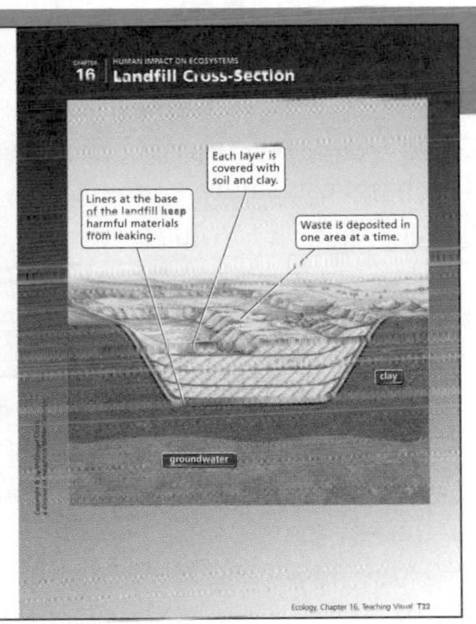

UNIT TRANSPARENCY BOOK, p. T17

p. T19

p. T22

MORE SUPPORT

Reinforcing Key Concepts for each section

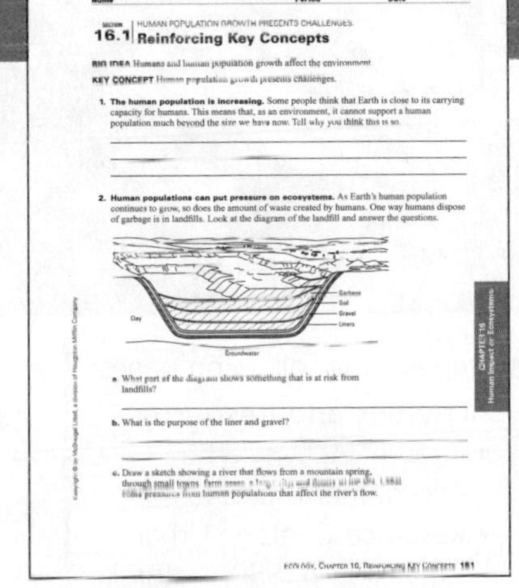

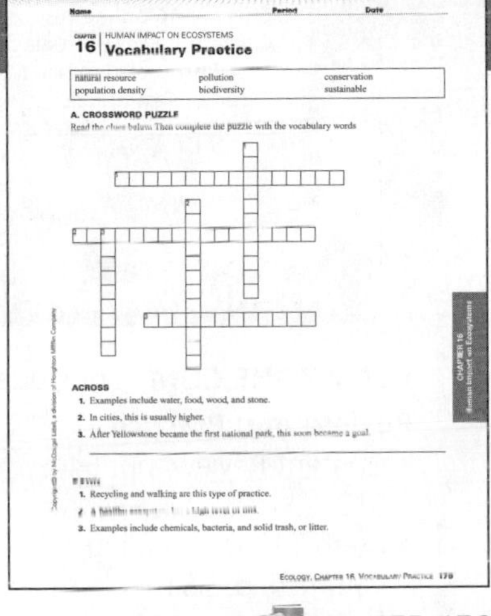

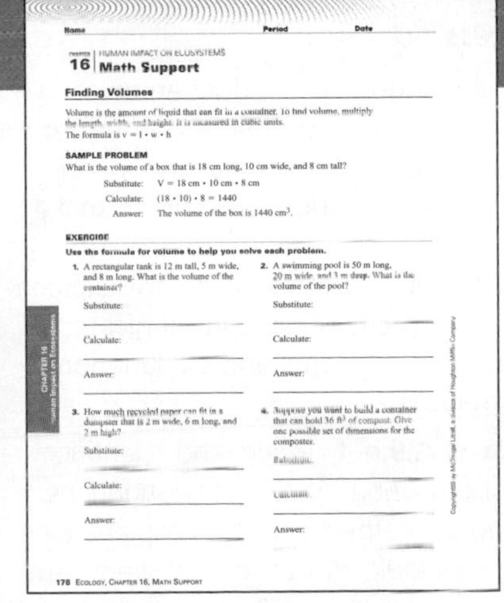

UNIT RESOURCE BOOK, p. 151

pp. 175–176

p. 178

CHAPTER 16 Human Impact on Ecosystems

INTRODUCE

the BIG idea

Have students look at the photograph of cars on a freeway system and discuss how the question in the box links to the Big Idea:

- What items did humans add to this landscape?
- How do you think humans altered the original landscape?

National Science Education Standards

Content

E.6.d All technology has risks and trade-offs such as cost, safety, and efficiency.

E.6.e All designs have limits including availability, safety, and environmental impact.

F.1.g Environmental health relies on monitoring the use of soil, water, and air, as well as the use of harmful substances.

F.2.a When an area becomes overpopulated, the environment will become degraded due to the increased use of resources.

F.2.b Causes of environmental degradation and resource depletion vary in regions and in countries.

Process

A.2–8 Design and conduct an investigation; use tools to gather and interpret data; use evidence to describe, predict, explain, model; think critically to make relationships between evidence and explanation; recognize different explanations and predictions; communicate scientific procedures and explanations; use mathematics.

A.9.a–c, A.9.e–f Understand scientific inquiry by using different investigations, methods, mathematics, and explanations based on logic, evidence, and skepticism.

E.2–5 Design a solution, implement solution, evaluate a solution, and communicate the design process.

CHAPTER

Human Impact on Ecosystems

the BIG idea

Humans and human population growth affect the environment.

Key Concepts

SECTION 
Human population growth presents challenges.
Learn how the increasing human population must share land and resources and dispose of its wastes.

SECTION 
Human activities affect the environment.
Learn how humans may affect natural resources, air and water quality, and biodiversity.

SECTION 
People are working to protect ecosystems.
Learn about federal, local, and scientific efforts to improve resource use and protect ecosystems.

Internet Preview

CLASSZONE.COM
Chapter 16 online resources: Content Review, Visualization, four Resource Centers, Math Tutorial, Test Practice

How have humans affected this landscape?

INTERNET PREVIEW

CLASSZONE.COM For student use with the following pages:

Review and Practice
- Content Review, pp. 544, 572
- Math Tutorial: Finding Volumes, p. 561
- Test Practice, p. 575

Activities and Resources
- Internet Activity: The Environment, p. 543
- Resource Centers: Urban Expansion p. 550; Natural Resources, p. 554; Recovery, p. 563
- Visualization: Population Growth, p. 546

Population Growth
Code: MDL003

EXPLORE the BIG idea

How Many Is Six Billion?

Use a piece of paper, scissors, and some tape to make a box that measures 1 cm by 1 cm by 1 cm. Fill the box with rice. Use the number of grains of rice in 1 cm^3 to calculate the volume of 6,000,000,000 grains of rice.

Observe and Think How many grains of rice are in a cubic centimeter? Do 6 billion grains take up more or less space than you expected?

How Easily Does Polluted Water Move Through Plants?

Place a few drops of food coloring in a half cup of water. Take a leafy stalk of celery and make a fresh cut across the bottom. Place the celery in the water overnight.

Observe and Think What do you observe about the celery and its leaves? What do your observations suggest about plants growing near polluted water?

Internet Activity: The Environment

Go to **ClassZone.com** to explore the effects of human activities on the environment.

Observe and Think How are people working to protect the environment?

NSTA scilinks.org SCILINKS
Population Growth **Code: MDL003**

TEACHING WITH TECHNOLOGY

Online Government Many maps showing land use with community resource data are available at county, city, and town websites. For the Resources activity on p. 548, bookmark these sites or help students find them.

Documentary Film You may wish to introduce the Investigation on p. 570 with a video documentary about oil spills.

EXPLORE the BIG idea

These inquiry-based activities are appropriate for use at home or as a supplement to classroom instruction.

How Many Is Six Billion?

PURPOSE To promote students' understanding of the magnitude of 6 billion.

TIP *10 min.* Make a box template or model to show students.

Typically students relate the volume of 6 billion rice grains to something familiar, like a cereal box. They find that 6 billion is quite a large number.

REVISIT after p. 546.

How Easily Does Polluted Water Move Through Plants?

PURPOSE To introduce students to the way plants absorb pollution from water. Students observe how food coloring moves into celery.

TIP *10 min.* Students will not see the liquid moving. Have them wait until the next class period to observe results.

Answer: The food coloring moved up into the celery. Plants near polluted water would take the pollution into their bodies.

REVISIT after p. 557.

Internet Activity: The Environment

PURPOSE To explore how humans can change ecosystems.

TIP *20 min.* Students can think about steps they can take to protect the environment.

Sample answer: People are building awareness, passing laws, and conserving resources.

REVISIT after p. 569.

PREPARE

CONCEPT REVIEW

Activate Prior Knowledge

- Ask students to list some factors that make up an ecosystem.
- Ask: What would happen if you eliminated light from an ecosystem? If you doubled the light?
- Discuss how changing other factors might affect an ecosystem.

TAKING NOTES

Supporting Main Ideas

Having students take notes as main ideas and supporting details enables students to make connections and see relationships. Remind students to use the blue headings for main ideas and to include only the most important details.

Vocabulary Strategy

Students can use the magnet word strategy for any word or phrase that poses a challenge to them. They do not need to stick to the listed vocabulary items. The strategy can be especially helpful for students learning English.

Vocabulary and Note-Taking Resources

- Vocabulary Practice, pp. 175–176
- Decoding Support, p. 177

- Daily Vocabulary Scaffolding, p. T18
- Note-Taking Model, p. T19

- Magnet Words, B24–25
- Main Idea and Supporting Details Notes, C37
- Daily Vocabulary Scaffolding, H1–8

CHAPTER 16

Getting Ready to Learn

CONCEPT REVIEW

- Both living and nonliving factors affect ecosystems.
- Populations can grow or decline over time.
- Matter and energy move through the environment.

VOCABULARY REVIEW

species p. 509
habitat p. 510

See Glossary for definitions.

diversity, urban

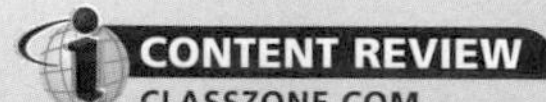

Review concepts and vocabulary.

TAKING NOTES

SUPPORTING MAIN IDEAS

Make a chart to show main ideas and the information that supports them. Copy each blue heading; then add supporting information, such as reasons, explanations, and examples.

VOCABULARY STRATEGY

Think about a vocabulary term as a **magnet word** diagram. Write the other terms or ideas related to that term around it.

See the Note-Taking Handbook on pages R45–R51.

SCIENCE NOTEBOOK

Human populations can put pressure on ecosystems.

- Humans produce waste that must be disposed of.
- Resources must be shared among a growing human population.
- Human population centers are expanding.

BIODIVERSITY

diversity | habitats
populations | variety
life | species

CHECK READINESS

Administer the Diagnostic Test to determine students' readiness for new science content and their mastery of requisite math skills.

 Diagnostic Test, pp. 40–41

Technology Resources

Students needing content and math skills should visit **ClassZone.com**.

- CONTENT REVIEW
- MATH TUTORIAL

 CONTENT REVIEW CD-ROM

KEY CONCEPT

Human population growth presents challenges.

BEFORE, you learned
- Populations have boundaries and are affected by limiting factors
- Living things form communities

NOW, you will learn
- How a growing human population puts pressure on ecosystems
- How sharing resources can be difficult

VOCABULARY
natural resource p. 548
population density p. 550

EXPLORE Sharing Resources

How can you model resource distribution?

PROCEDURE

1. You will work in a group of several classmates. One member of your group gets a bag of objects from your teacher.
2. Each object in the bag represents a necessary resource. Divide the objects so that each member of the group gets the resources he or she needs.
3. After 10 minutes, you may trade resources with other groups.

MATERIALS
bag containing an assortment of objects

WHAT DO YOU THINK?
- Did you get a fair share of your group's objects?
- How does the number of people in each group affect the outcome?
- Was the job made easier when trading occurred across groups?

SUPPORTING MAIN IDEAS
Make a chart to show information that supports the first main idea presented: *The human population is increasing.*

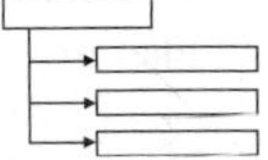

The human population is increasing.

According to the United Nations, on October 12, 1999, Earth's human population reached 6 billion. Until 300 years ago, it had never grown beyond a few hundred million people. Only 200 years ago, the population reached 1 billion. So the increase to 6 billion people has occurred in a very short time. About one-third of all humans alive today are 14 years old or younger. Partly for this reason, experts predict Earth's population will keep growing—to 9 billion or more by the year 2050.

RESOURCES FOR DIFFERENTIATED INSTRUCTION

Below Level
UNIT RESOURCE BOOK
- Reading Study Guide A, pp. 143–144
- Decoding Support, p. 177

AUDIO CDS

Advanced
UNIT RESOURCE BOOK
Challenge and Extension, p. 149

English Learners
UNIT RESOURCE BOOK
Spanish Reading Study Guide, pp. 147–148

AUDIO CDS
- Audio Readings in Spanish
- Audio Readings (English)

16.1 FOCUS

Set Learning Goals
Students will
- Describe how a growing human population puts pressure on ecosystems.
- Explain how sharing resources can be difficult.
- Interpret through maps where the local community gets resources and where it disposes of waste.

3-Minute Warm-Up
Display Transparency 20 or copy this exercise on the board:

Which of the following are populations and which are communities? Write "P" beside a description of a population. Write "C" beside a description of a community.
- group of elephants living in the same grassland *P*
- iguanas and crabs interacting with one another *C*
- group of grasses living on a prairie *P*
- group of fungi living in a pond *P*

3-Minute Warm-Up, p. T20

16.1 MOTIVATE

EXPLORE Sharing Resources

PURPOSE To experience the difficulty of sharing unequal resources

TIPS *15 min.* 4–5 students per group is suggested. Representative or symbolic objects can include: drinking straws for water, kidney beans for food, birthday candles for fuel, and so on.

WHAT DO YOU THINK? *Sample answer: No; group members could not figure out a fair distribution. (Most groups will be unable to divide the objects fairly throughout the exercise.)*

16.1 INSTRUCT

Teach from Visuals

To help students interpret the human population growth graph, ask:

- What is measured on the *x*-axis? *years*
- What is measured on the *y*-axis? *population in billions of people*
- What does the slope of the line tell you? *Human population is growing faster than it used to.*
- What is one problem with using only a mathematical projection for predicting population growth? *Mathematical projection does not account for other factors that might affect future population growth. It only uses current growth rate.*

EXPLORE the BIG idea

Revisit "How Many Is Six Billion?" on p. 543. Have students relate the activity to human population growth.

Ongoing Assessment

CHECK YOUR READING *Answer: The population will continue to grow, threatening the limit of Earth's carrying capacity. Some students may add that population will level off due to carrying capacity.*

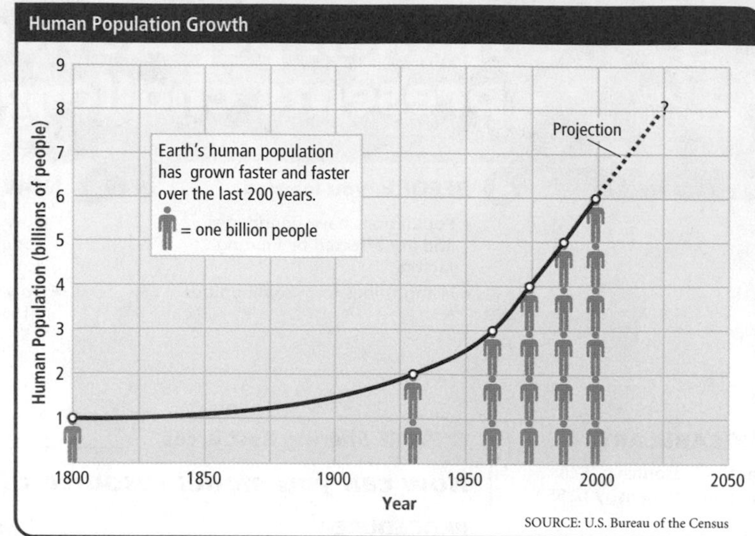

PREDICT The graph shows actual population growth through 2000. Predict how the population will grow in the future.

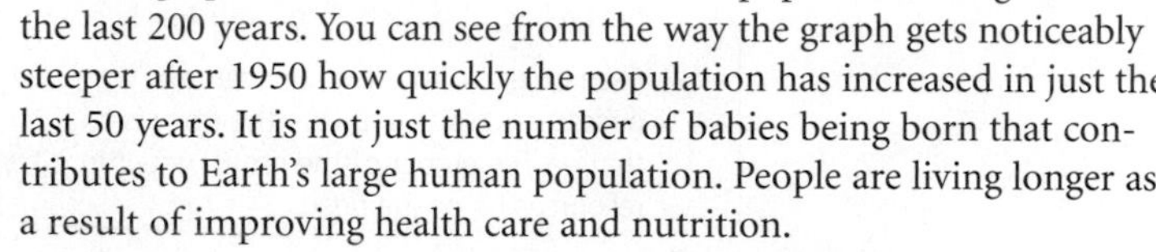

The graph above shows how the human population has grown in the last 200 years. You can see from the way the graph gets noticeably steeper after 1950 how quickly the population has increased in just the last 50 years. It is not just the number of babies being born that contributes to Earth's large human population. People are living longer as a result of improving health care and nutrition.

The dotted line on the graph shows a projection, which helps us predict what the population would be if it continues to grow at the rate it is growing today. However, remember that an ecosystem has a carrying capacity for any given population. At some point, Earth will reach its carrying capacity for the human population. Today, many people think that our planet is close to—if not already at—its carrying capacity for humans.

How might Earth's carrying capacity affect human population growth?

Human populations can put pressure on ecosystems.

Examine how the human population has grown.

If your family has guests for the weekend, you may find that you run out of hot water for showers or do not have enough milk for everyone's breakfast. The resources that would ordinarily be enough for your family are no longer enough.

DIFFERENTIATE INSTRUCTION

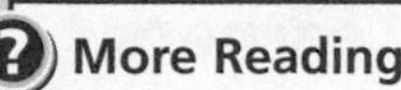

More Reading Support

A Why has the population grown so fast? *longer lifespans, high birth rates*

B Why is part of the graph dotted? *It is a future prediction.*

English Learners Help English learners realize that *may* and *might* indicate that an event is uncertain or hypothetical. For example, if guests visit for the weekend, you *might* run out of hot water for showers. Or you *might* not have enough milk for everyone's breakfast. Have students practice writing science statements using *may* or *might.*

Help English learners visualize the "football field" estimate on p. 547. They can use the trucks in the illustration as a more familiar size reference. For instance, about 15 trucks equal 1 football field.

C You read in Chapter 15 that resources such as food, water, and space can be limiting factors for biological populations. These same resources limit Earth's human population. As the human population grows, it uses more resources—just as your weekend visitors used more of your home's resources. The activities of the growing human population are putting pressure on Earth's ecosystems.

REMINDER

A *limiting factor* is something that prevents a population from continuing to grow.

Pressures of Waste Disposal

As Earth's human population grows, so does the amount of waste produced by humans. Humans, like all living things, produce natural waste. Often, the water that carries this waste is treated to remove harmful chemicals before being cycled back to the environment. However, some of these materials still make it into lakes, rivers, and oceans, harming these ecosystems.

Much of the waste material produced by humans is the result of human activity. Some of this waste is garbage, or food waste. The rest of it is trash, or nonfood waste. In the United States, huge amounts of trash are thrown out each year. Most garbage and trash ends up in landfills.

D Landfills take up a lot of space. The Fresh Kills Landfill in Staten Island, New York, is 60 meters (197 ft) high and covers an area as big as 2200 football fields. Decomposing trash and garbage can release dangerous gases into the air as well as harmful chemicals into the ground. Liners, which are layers of plastic or packed clay, are used to keep chemicals from leaking into surrounding land and water.

DIFFERENTIATE INSTRUCTION

More Reading Support

C What resources limit human population? *food, water, space*

D What is one pressure of disposing garbage in landfills? *It takes up lots of space.*

Below Level Have students make a list of things that they regularly throw away in the trash. Ask them to sort the items or materials in their lists into ones that will probably stay in the environment a long time and ones that will break down quickly.

Develop Critical Thinking

EVALUATE To help students evaluate a problem and solution:

- Tell students that landfills do not actually destroy trash and garbage. Why, then, have they become a widely used method of dealing with solid waste? *They provide a place to store solid waste in a restricted area so that it will have the least impact on the environment. Landfills are also designed to provide a barrier between the solid waste and the soil and groundwater.*
- Ask: What problems with destroying solid waste do landfills avoid? *Landfills eliminate the need to burn solid waste, and so they avoid the air pollution that is produced by burning.*
- Ask: What are some drawbacks of landfills? *Pollutants may leak out and contaminate the soil and groundwater. Landfills may also make an area permanently unsuitable for other uses.*

Teach from Visuals

To help students interpret the drawing of the landfill, ask:

- What is used to cover each layer? *soil and clay*
- What protects chemicals from leaking into the landfill and surrounding areas? *liners made of plastic*
- What lies between the landfill and the groundwater? *clay*

The visual "Landfill Cross-Section" is available as T22 in the Unit Transparency Book.

Ongoing Assessment

Describe how a growing human population puts pressure on ecosystems.

Ask: Why can't the human population just keep growing forever? *There are limited amounts of food, water, and space for humans, as well as limited space for human waste.*

INVESTIGATE Resources

PURPOSE To interpret local maps identifying local resources and refuse facilities

TIP *30 min.* Contact your local city hall, town hall, or county agency for maps.

WHAT DO YOU THINK? *Sample answers: The water reservoir is in another town. A neighboring town uses our landfill and electricity.*

 Datasheet, Resources, p. 150

Technology Resources

Customize this student lab as needed or look for an alternative. Print rubrics to assess student lab reports.

 **Lab Generator CD-ROM**

Another way to get rid of trash and garbage is to incinerate it—burn it. The problem with incineration is that it releases harmful gases and chemicals into the air. To prevent the release of these harmful substances, incinerator smokestacks have filters. To prevent further environmental contamination, used filters must be disposed of safely.

Pressures on Resources

VOCABULARY
Add a magnet word diagram for *natural resource* to your notebook.

You have seen that a growing human population puts pressure on ecosystems by the amount of waste it leaves behind. Human populations also put pressure on ecosystems by what they take away. Humans depend on the environment for resources. A **natural resource** is any type of material or energy that humans use to meet their needs. Natural resources that humans take from their environment include water, food, wood, stone, metal, and minerals.

Clean fresh water is an important resource. Only 3 percent of Earth's water supply is fresh water—and two-thirds of that small amount is locked up in polar ice caps, glaciers, and permanent snow. As the human population grows, sharing this important resource will become more difficult.

INVESTIGATE Resources

How does your community meet its needs?

PROCEDURE

1. Obtain a recent map of your county, city, or town.
2. Using the map, try to identify where your community gets its electricity and water and how it disposes of trash and garbage.
3. Identify locations where food is grown.

WHAT DO YOU THINK?

- How much does your community rely on other communities for resources?
- What resources does your community share with other communities?
- Where does your community dispose of its own waste materials?

CHALLENGE Draw a grid on a piece of tracing paper and place it on top of the map. Use your grid to estimate what percentage of land in your city or town is used for housing and what percentage is used for governmental, agricultural, and commercial purposes.

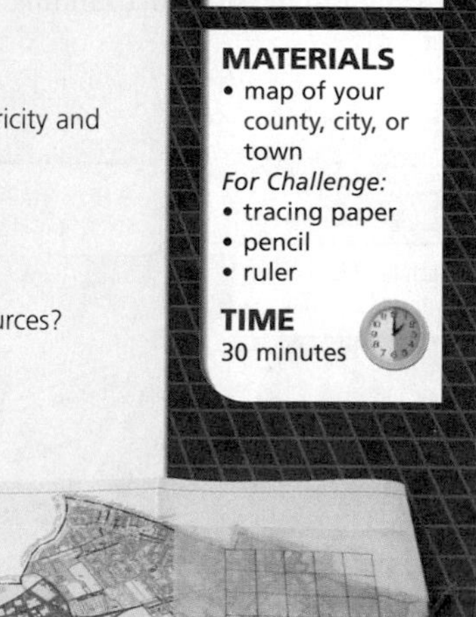

SKILL FOCUS
Interpreting

MATERIALS
- map of your county, city, or town

For Challenge:
- tracing paper
- pencil
- ruler

TIME
30 minutes

Teaching with Technology

Land-use maps and city plans may be available on your city, town, or county website. Show students how this site is set up, and the variety of resources, including e-mail contact with local officials.

Teach Difficult Concepts

Students may have difficulty grasping how much pressure a large population puts on Earth. Give them a simple example, such as foot traffic on a path. If someone occasionally walks across vegetation, the mosses, lichens, and plants can continue to live there. If many people walk on vegetation, vegetation will not grow.

Integrate the Sciences

Glaciers lock up water both as ice and behind glacial dams. When a glacial dam bursts or the glacier melts quickly, the result is a catastrophic flood, called a jökulhlaup. *Jökulhlaup* is an Icelandic word meaning "glacier burst." Iceland has many glaciers with volcanoes underneath. These volcanoes sometimes send out hot emissions that melt a big part of the glacier, causing a flood. In Nepal, glaciers often form dams on streams or lakes. The meltwater rises until the glacier gives way.

DIFFERENTIATE INSTRUCTION

More Reading Support

E What are problems with burning trash? *harmful gases, chemicals*

F What are examples of natural resources? *water, food, wood, metal*

Inclusion As you obtain local maps from government agencies, ask if Braille maps are available. Also request the largest format and type size available. You may need to emphasize the labels, colors, and locations of certain resources, using bold, colored markers.

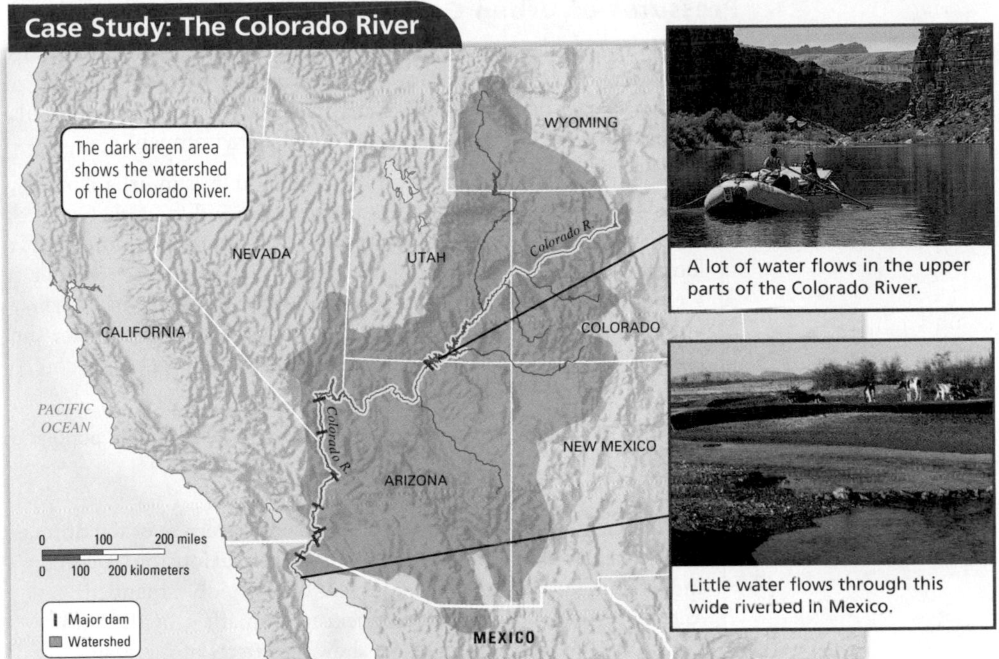

A lot of water flows in the upper parts of the Colorado River.

Little water flows through this wide riverbed in Mexico.

A case study that involves the Colorado River shows how a growing human population puts pressures on natural resources. This example also shows that sharing resources isn't easy. The watershed of this major Western river extends into seven U.S. states and parts of Mexico. The watershed includes all the smaller rivers and streams that flow into the Colorado River. In a region where little rain falls each year, these streams and rivers are an important source of water for drinking and agriculture.

READING TIP As you read about the Colorado River, refer to the map above to see where the river flows and the states that use the Colorado River's water.

As the West was settled, people in the downstream states of California, Arizona, and Nevada worried that the people in the upstream states of Colorado, Utah, Wyoming, and New Mexico would drain too much water from the river. In 1922 the seven states signed an agreement that divided the water between the two groups.

Problems with this agreement soon became apparent. First, the needs of Native American and Mexican populations were not considered. Second, the dams and channels built to prevent floods and transport water harmed river ecosystems. And third, the seven states planned to use more water than the river usually holds. As a result, the river often runs nearly dry at its mouth, in Mexico. G

CHECK YOUR READING List three problems that developed after people made a plan to share Colorado River water.

Teach from Visuals

To help students interpret the map of the Colorado River, ask:

- What is the relationship between the large map and the two small inset photographs? *The small photographs describe details of the large map.*
- If you trace the Colorado River with your finger, how many states and countries do you move through? *five states, two countries*
- Where does more water flow—in the northern parts or toward Mexico? *The amount of water is much greater in the north.*

Geography Connection

You can assess the learning goals for this section by having students work cooperatively to draft and present a plan for sharing the resources of the Colorado River watershed. Be sure they include the interests of the seven states and Mexico, and address ways to solve each of the three problems the original plan encountered.

Ongoing Assessment

Explain how sharing resources can be difficult.

Ask: Why are there international treaties that regulate such things as water rights, fishing, and land boundaries? *Sample answer: Because resources are scarce and people compete for them. Some resources are found in more than one country.*

CHECK YOUR READING *Answer: The agreement ignored Native Americans and Mexicans, the dams and reservoirs destroyed river ecosystems, and there was not enough water in the river to meet the amounts each state wanted to withdraw.*

DIFFERENTIATE INSTRUCTION

More Reading Support

G What happens to the Colorado River when it reaches Mexico? *It runs nearly dry.*

Advanced Have a student bring in a cardboard box large enough to hold the paper that is thrown away in one classroom. Ask them to figure the approximate volume of trash that the class generates each day. Have them use the daily total to estimate the volume of paper waste generated in a year. Have students calculate how many classrooms the trash would fill.

R Challenge and Extension, p. 149

Teach Difficult Concepts

Some students may have a hard time understanding the concept of density. Ask them to imagine two pictures: twenty cows in a field and twenty cows in a barn. Have them contrast the pictures. Point out that density is greater in the barn. To help students understand you might try the demo.

Teacher Demo

Give students the measurements of the classroom and ask them to compute area and number of students. Compare the density of students during class to the density during recess or lunch, when the classroom is mostly empty.

Develop Geometry Skills

Population density is the number of people in a particular area. Students may need a refresher on area calculations.

- Area is expressed in square feet, square miles, square meters, and so forth.
- Area of a square or rectangle, equals length times width or $A = lw$.
- Area of a circle equals πr^2.

Teach from Visuals

To help students interpret the aerial photograph and satellite photographs of Las Vegas:

- Ask: In 1972, about how much of Las Vegas was developed land? *no more than one-third*
- Ask: In 1997, about how much of Las Vegas was developed land? *more than one-half*
- Explain that the largest photograph shows Las Vegas in 2000. Ask students to infer what may have changed for the city between 1997 and 2000. *greater diversity at the city center and outskirts, greater resource use*

Ongoing Assessment

CHECK YOUR READING *Answer: Population density is greater in a city than in suburbs because there are more people in a smaller place.*

Learn more about urban expansion.

Pressures of Urban Growth

Until recently, the majority of Earth's population was spread out, so the population density was low. **Population density** is the measure of the number of people in a given area. Generally, the lower the population density, the less pressure there is on the environment.

H Today, about half of the world's population lives in urban, or city, areas. People are attracted to these areas to live and to work. Over time, suburban areas around a city develop as more and more people look for a place to live. In cities, buildings are spaced close together, so the population density is high. A large number of people in a small area changes the landscape. The local environment can no longer support the number of people living there, and so resources must come from outside.

How does population density in a city differ from the population density of a suburb?

I In recent years, some people have raised concern over the dramatic growth in and around urban areas. Los Angeles; Houston; Atlanta; and Washington, D.C. are all cities that have rapidly expanded. Another urban area that has experienced dramatic growth is Las Vegas, Nevada. The images below show the effects of increasing

The darker colors distinguish the developed land of Las Vegas from the surrounding desert.

Over 25 years, the city expanded in all directions. The population went from 273,000 to 1,124,000.

DIFFERENTIATE INSTRUCTION

More Reading Support

H Where does half of the world's population live? *in cities*

I What has happened to cities in recent years? *Some have grown very fast.*

English Learners Have students write definitions for *population density* and *natural resource* in their Science Word Dictionaries. English learners may not have prior knowledge of the terms *suburban* and *suburb* on this page. Use the aerial photograph of Las Vegas to explain the terms. Students may be unfamiliar with the concept of the mouth of a river on p. 549. Students' abilities to read the text on a map in "Investigate Resources," p. 548, will vary. Encourage students to learn and use the visual key and color codes.

population density around the city between 1972 and 1997. Located in the middle of the desert, Las Vegas depends upon the Colorado River for water and electrical energy. As the population grows, so does the need for natural resources.

INFER What do you think this ecosystem looked like a hundred years ago? two hundred years ago?

Pressures of Expanding Land Use

An increasing demand for resources in a particular area is one consequence of urban growth. But as communities around cities expand onto surrounding land, the environment is affected. Natural habitats, such as forests, are destroyed. Because forests cycle carbon through the environment, cutting down trees affects the carbon cycle. Soil that was held in place by tree roots may wash into lakes and rivers.

Another consequence of widespread development is the loss of productive farmland. Development replaces more than 2.5 million acres of farmland each year in the United States. This means less land is available locally to produce food for the growing population. The result is that food is often transported great distances.

Unlike compact city development, widespread suburban development also increases the need for residents to have cars. This is because most people in suburban areas live farther from where they work, shop, or go to school. A greater number of cars decreases the air quality in communities and requires additional road construction, which can interrupt natural habitats and endanger wildlife.

 CHECK YOUR READING Describe some ways that development harms natural ecosystems.

16.1 Review

KEY CONCEPTS

1. Identify four pressures placed on ecosystems by an increasing human population.
2. Give an example that shows how resources can be difficult to share.

CRITICAL THINKING

3. **Apply** Describe an example of sharing resources that occurs in your home.
4. **Infer** How would a city's population density change if the city increased in area and the number of people in it remained the same?

CHALLENGE

5. **Evaluate** Imagine that you lived along the Colorado River. What information would you need if you wanted to evaluate a water-sharing agreement?

ANSWERS

1. Natural habitats are destroyed, carbon cycle affected, erosion, loss of productive farmland, decreased air quality, construction interrupts habitats and can endanger wildlife.

2. Colorado River case study shows how the use of river water at one location can remove resources from another location.

3. Sample answer: Telephone time is a limited resource. We share by setting a limit on how long one person can use the phone.

4. The population density would decrease.

5. Important information would include how many communities depend on one source, how much water is affected by dams, how much water a town needs.

Ongoing Assessment

Explain how a growing population puts pressure on an ecosystem.

Ask: What happens when the human population grows too fast? *There may be stresses due to increased need for garbage disposal, water, or transport.*

 CHECK YOUR READING *Sample answer: Natural habitats disappear, the carbon cycle is interrupted, local climate may change, and erosion occurs.*

Reinforce the BIG idea

Have students relate the section to the Big Idea.

R Reinforcing Key Concepts, p. 151

16.1 ASSESS & RETEACH

Assess

 Section 16.1 Quiz, p. 42

Reteach

Refer to the graph on p. 546. Have students compare the curve to the moose and wolf graphs on p. 528. Ask:

- How do the graphs differ? *Humans show steady increase, moose and wolf go up and down.*
- Why does the wolf population go down after the moose population does? *The moose provide food for the wolves. When there are too few moose, the wolves do not have enough food.*
- Will the human population have enough or too little food if it continues to grow? *There may be too little.*

Technology Resources

Have students visit **ClassZone.com** for reteaching of Key Concepts.

 **CONTENT REVIEW**

 **CONTENT REVIEW CD-ROM**

SCIENCE ON THE JOB
Relevance of Science to Non-science Jobs

Set Learning Goal
To interest students in a specific use of the science of ecology

Present the Science
Urban planning began with an emphasis on physical factors, but now includes social, economic, and political issues. Urban planners balance economic progress with preserving open spaces and natural habitats. They also consider social goals such as access to education, transportation, and medicine.

Discussion Questions
Ask: What needs are filled by the area in the upper right corner of the urban diagram? *Sample: shelter, jobs, and places to buy, sell, and produce goods.* Does this area address ecological needs? Why or why not? *No; the area meets humans' social and economic needs. Natural features are absent. Or, Yes; all parts are planned with awareness of pollution, waste, and environmental impact.*

Which area of the diagram balances the needs of human beings and of the natural environment? Why? *The lower right corner; it fills humans' need for open spaces and provides other species a habitat. Live plants benefit air quality.*

Ask: What kind of information might an ecologist provide to an urban planner who is designing a railway system to connect a city with its suburbs? *Sample: the types of wild places that may be affected, the species that live there, the presence of watersheds and wetlands*

DIFFERENTIATION TIP Pair some strong readers with students who need support understanding the text. Partners can take turns reading aloud and summarizing as they go along.

Close
Ask: What ecological factors do you think an urban planner should pay most attention to? *Sample answer: environmental impact, safety, availability of resources to all neighborhoods*

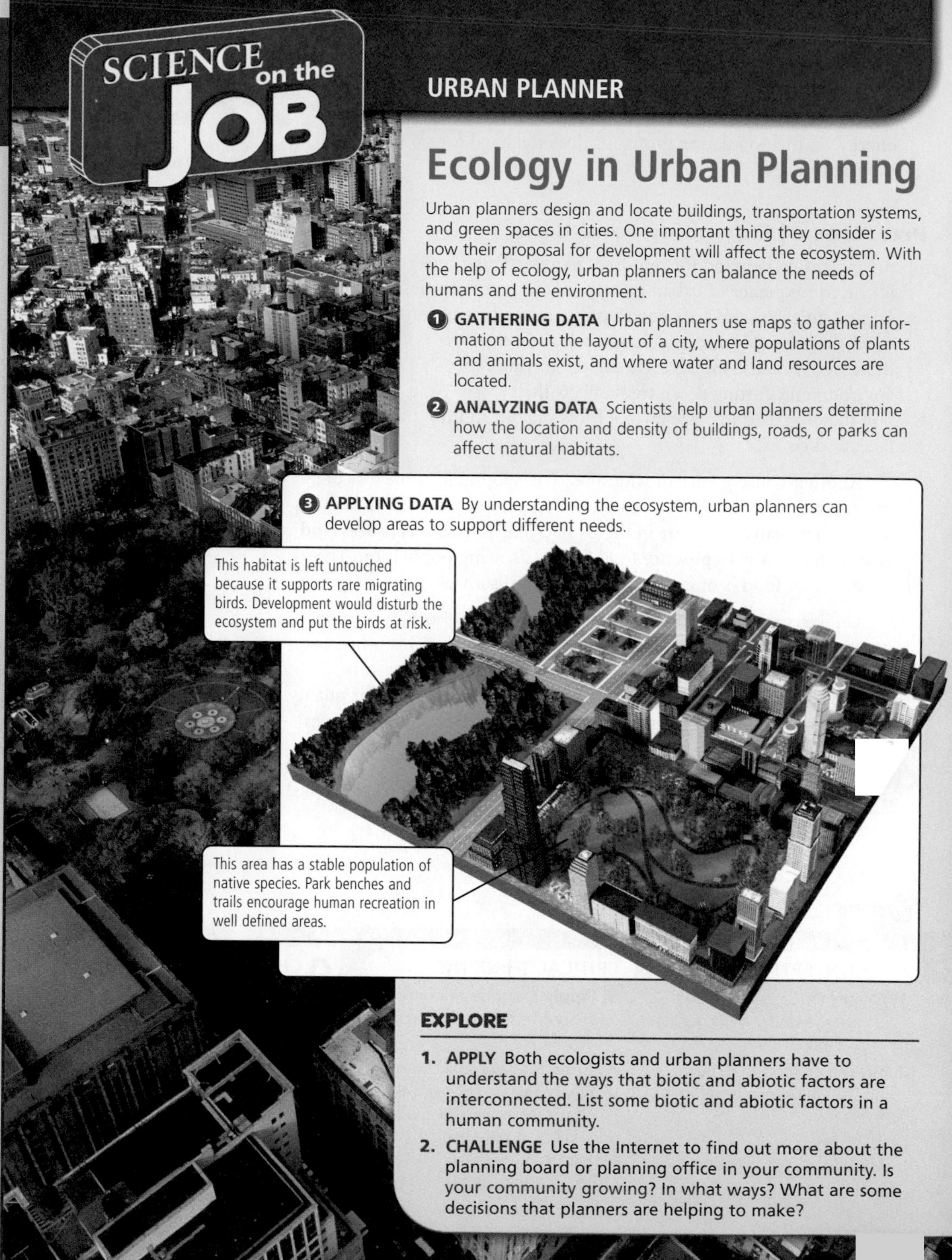

EXPLORE
1. ***APPLY*** *Biotic factors could be population density, park areas, other animals, trees and other plants. Abiotic factors could be light, roads, climate, wind.*
2. ***CHALLENGE*** *Answers should clearly say whether the community is growing and what the planning office is doing to plan for change in population, land use, and so on.*

KEY CONCEPT

Human activities affect the environment.

BEFORE, you learned
- Human populations are increasing
- Human population growth causes problems

NOW, you will learn
- How natural resources are classified
- How pollution affects the environment
- How a loss of diversity affects the environment

VOCABULARY
pollution p. 555
biodiversity p. 555

THINK ABOUT

How do you use water?

Think of the number of times you use water every day. Like all living things, you need water. In fact, more than half of the material that makes up your body is water.

No matter where you live, most of the time you can turn on a faucet and clean water flows out the spout. You use water when you take a shower, fix a snack, or wash a dish. If you've ever lost water service to your home, you've probably been reminded how much you depend upon it. No doubt about it, our need for water is serious.

Humans use many resources.

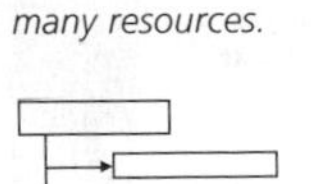

SUPPORTING MAIN IDEAS
Make a chart to show information that supports the main idea: *Humans use many resources.*

Throughout history, people around the world have relied on natural resources for survival. Ancient civilizations used stone to create tools and weapons. And wood was an important fuel for cooking and keeping warm. Today, humans continue to rely on the environment and have discovered additional resources to meet their needs. In Section 16.1 you read about sharing natural resources. Scientists classify these resources into two categories:

- renewable resources
- nonrenewable resources

16.2 FOCUS

Set Learning Goals

Students will
- Classify natural resources.
- Explain how pollution affects the environment.
- Describe how a loss of biodiversity affects the environment.
- Collect and observe air-pollution samples.

3 Minute Warm-Up

Display Transparency 20 or copy this exercise on the board:

Suppose that next week our school had to accept enough new students to double the student population. List five changes that would occur and explain how they would affect you. *Sample answer: The hallways would be much more crowded, so it would be harder to get to class on time. Lunch time would have to last longer to accommodate more students in the same space; I could end up eating lunch at 10:00 in the morning. Classes would be twice as large, and teachers would spend less time with each student. The books and supplies available would become scarce, and we would have to share them. There would be more competition to get on a sports team.*

 3-Minute Warm-Up, p. T20

16.2 MOTIVATE

THINK ABOUT

PURPOSE To understand the importance of water in everyday life

DISCUSS Have students discuss where water comes from at their home. Ask:
- Where is the water that comes from a faucet stored?
- How does it get into the storage tank?
- Does it come from a well, reservoir, or river?
- Under what circumstances could we run out of clean water?

Sample answer: water heater in basement; from pipes from city water source; reservoir; drought

RESOURCES FOR DIFFERENTIATED INSTRUCTION

Below Level

UNIT RESOURCE BOOK
- Reading Study Guide A, pp. 154–155
- Decoding Support, p. 177

AUDIO CDS

Advanced

UNIT RESOURCE BOOK
- Challenge and Extension, p. 160
- Challenge Reading, pp. 173–174

English Learners

UNIT RESOURCE BOOK
Spanish Reading Study Guide, pp. 158–159

AUDIO CDS
- Audio Readings in Spanish
- Audio Readings (English)

R **Additional INVESTIGATION,**
Pollutants on the Move, A, B, & C, pp. 189–197; Teacher Instructions, pp. 200–201

16.2 INSTRUCT

Develop Critical Thinking

INFER Ask students to compare the description of the Northeast 200 years ago to developed areas of the country as they are today.

- What has likely happened to the woodlots of 200 years ago? *They may have been cleared for development or for agriculture.*
- What has happened to pastures and fields? *Many have forests on them. Some have been built on as cities, industry, and highways.*

Teacher Demo

Bring in fresh, living blades of grass and dry, dead ones. Pass the living and dead blades around the class, encouraging students to notice differences in color, texture, flexibility, and overall feel. Help them understand that withdrawal of water results in the dry, dead blade.

Teach from Visuals

To help students interpret the visual of renewable and nonrenewable resources, ask:

- Which two resources are renewable? *trees, water*
- Which two resources are nonrenewable? *oil, coal*
- Are there endless supplies of oil and coal? *No, supplies are limited.*

Ongoing Assessment

Categorize natural resources.

Ask: Coal and oil originally were plant matter. Plants are renewable resources, so why are coal and oil nonrenewable? *Creating coal and oil takes a long time and special geological circumstances.*

CHECK YOUR READING *Answer: trees (they can be planted or regrow); sunlight (Earth receives continuous sunlight); water (water cycle replenishes water in lakes and groundwater)*

RESOURCE CENTER CLASSZONE.COM

Find out more about natural resources.

Renewable Resources

Two hundred years ago, most small towns in the Northeastern part of the United States included farm fields, pasture, and woods. The wooded areas that weren't farmed were used as wood lots. The wood from these lots supplied firewood for towns and was often exported for income.

Trees are an example of a renewable resource—a resource that can be used over and over again. Energy from sunlight is another important renewable resource. Because the Sun is expected to supply energy for another five billion years, energy from sunlight is considered essentially unlimited. As you read earlier in your study of the water cycle, water can be classified as a renewable resource. Renewable resources can be replaced naturally or by humans in a short amount of time, but they may run out if they are overused or managed poorly.

? A

CHECK YOUR READING Give three examples of renewable resources. Explain why each one is considered renewable.

Nonrenewable Resources

? B

Nonrenewable resources are resources that cannot be replaced. In some cases, they may be replenished by natural processes, but not quickly enough for human purposes. Nonrenewable resources are often underground, making them more difficult to reach. But technology has enabled humans to locate and remove nonrenewable resources from places that used to be impossible to reach.

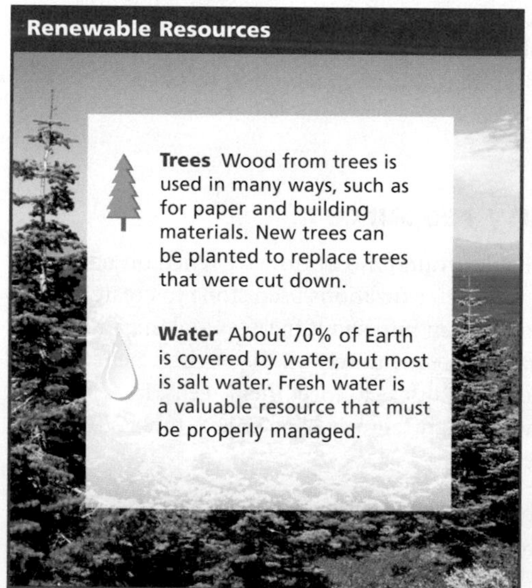

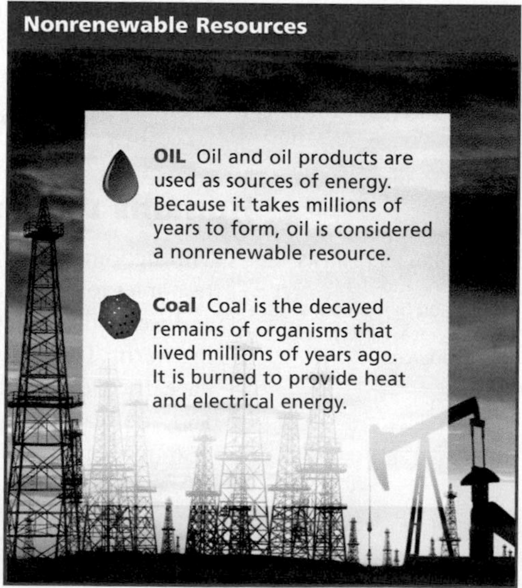

DIFFERENTIATE INSTRUCTION

More Reading Support

A What is a renewable resource? *a resource that can be replenished*

B What is a nonrenewable resource? *a resource that cannot be replaced*

English Learners Encourage English learners to write down the definitions of *renewable* and *nonrenewable resources* in their personal dictionaries. Have students draw a T-chart and list different renewable and nonrenewable resources under the correct heading. Let students compare lists and add new examples like the one shown to their own.

renewable	nonrenewable

Coal, petroleum, and natural gas are nonrenewable resources that are removed from underground by mining or drilling. Also called fossil fuels, they are the main energy source for heating, industry, and transportation and are used to make many products. Many minerals, like copper and gold, are also considered nonrenewable resources.

Pollution endangers biodiversity.

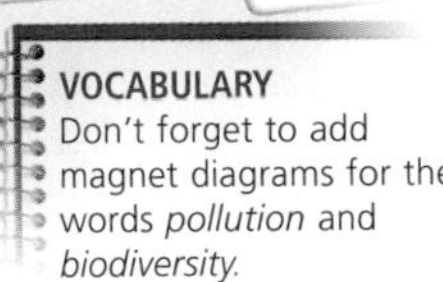

C As you walk along a city street, you may smell exhaust or see litter. These are examples of pollution. **Pollution** is the addition of harmful substances to the environment. Many of the ways humans use natural resources cause pollution to be released into the soil, air, and water. Pollutants include chemicals, bacteria, and dirt. Even materials that are ordinarily not harmful can cause pollution when they build up in one location.

D As pollution becomes common in an ecosystem, living things may be threatened. Plant and animal populations may decrease and biodiversity may decline. **Biodiversity** is the number and variety of life forms within an ecosystem. Healthy ecosystems support a variety of species. An ecosystem with a variety of organisms can recover more easily from disturbances than an ecosystem that has fewer species.

INVESTIGATE Particles in the Air

Where do you find air pollution?

PROCEDURE

1. Use a hole punch to make holes at the ends of two index cards. Cut two pieces of string 30 cm long and tie one string to each card.
2. Choose a different location for each card. Mark the card with its location and the date.
3. Spread a thin film of petroleum jelly on a 3 cm^2 area on each card and hang each card at the location you've chosen.
4. Collect the cards in one week and examine them with the hand lens.

WHAT DO YOU THINK?

- Identify the types of particles collected at each location.
- Do you think of all of the particles collected as pollution?
- Which location had the most pollution?

CHALLENGE Hypothesize why certain locations have more particles in the air than others.

SKILL FOCUS
Observing

MATERIALS
- 2 index cards
- marker
- hole punch
- string
- scissors
- petroleum jelly
- hand lens

TIME
30 minutes

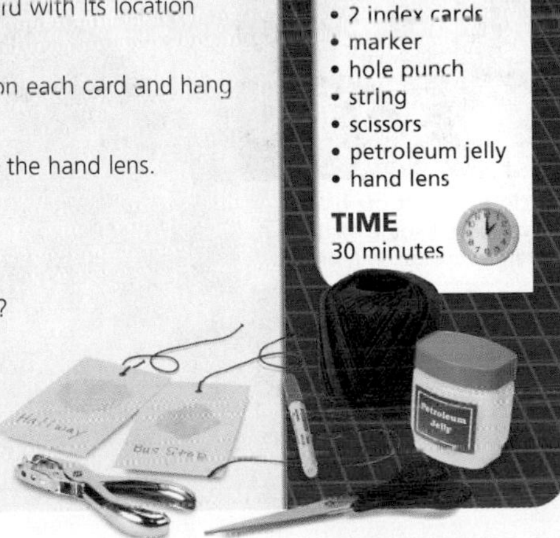

Integrate the Sciences

Fossil fuels are formed from remains of living things 50 to 350 million years ago. Coal was formed in great swamps, where plant remains first formed peat, which was later covered by sand and mud. Oil began as sediment formed from the remains of plants and animals living in shallow seas. Over thousands of centuries, heat and pressure cause chemical changes that form both coal and petroleum.

INVESTIGATE Particles in the Air

PURPOSE To observe air pollution

TIPS *30 min.* The longer you can hang the cards, the better. Some pollutants take a full week to appear. Premake cards for disabled students.

WHAT DO YOU THINK? *Sample answers: dust, dirt, exhaust, pollen, etc.; answers will vary depending on the locations from which samples were collected.*

CHALLENGE *Possibilities include better ventilation or air circulation, proximity to sources of pollution, location inside or outside, amount of people who use the area.*

Technology Resources

Customize this student lab as needed or look for an alternative. Print rubrics to assess student lab reports.

Lab Generator CD-ROM

DIFFERENTIATE INSTRUCTION

More Reading Support

C What is pollution? *substances that harm air, water, or land*

D What is biodiversity? *number and variety of species of living things in an ecosystem*

Below Level To help students distinguish between renewable and nonrenewable resources, have them construct a collage for each category with pictures of examples that they draw or cut from magazines. Display the collages on posters or a bulletin board.

Address Misconceptions

IDENTIFY Ask students to describe or draw the way pollution spreads in water, in air, or on land. If students answer by describing small or isolated areas, they may hold the misconception that air pollution and water pollution affect only limited areas.

CORRECT Demonstrate evaporation by heating a small amount of water on a burner until it boils away. Have students discuss where the water has gone. Pour another pot of water in the sink or on the ground, and discuss where it moved to.

REASSESS Ask: What is likely to happen to pollutants that enter a lake? *Some pollutants would enter the soil around the lake; others might affect living things in the lake. Other pollutants might enter the water cycle through evaporation, move throughout the atmosphere, and fall back to Earth. Evaporated pollutants would enter the air. Precipitation would bring the pollution back down to Earth again.* How would you describe the movement of pollutants through a system? *They move in a cycle, from air to water and soil, into bodies of water, and back to air again.*

Technology Resources

Visit **ClassZone.com** for background on common student misconceptions.

MISCONCEPTION DATABASE

Teach from Visuals

To help students interpret the photographs of acid-rain damage, ask: Why are the spruce needles discolored? *They have been exposed to acid rain.*

Ongoing Assessment

CHECK YOUR READING *Answer: motor vehicles, factory exhaust, and power plant exhaust*

Air Quality

Air quality affects entire ecosystems. For example, in 1980, Mount St. Helens erupted on the West Coast of the United States. Hot ash was blown 15 miles up into the air. Three days later some of that ash reached the East Coast. Although natural events occasionally release air pollutants, human activities pollute every day.

READING TIP *Pollute* and *pollutant* are in the same word family as pollution.

E Today in the United States, motor vehicles, factories, and power plants are the main sources of air pollution. The fossil fuels they burn release sulfur dioxide, nitrogen dioxide, and carbon monoxide into the air. These pollutants affect humans and animals and are the main cause of acid rain, a serious problem affecting ecosystems.

CHECK YOUR READING What air pollutants contribute to acid rain problems in the United States?

F Acid rain occurs when air pollutants such as sulfur dioxide and nitrogen dioxide mix with water in the atmosphere to form acid droplets of rain, ice, snow, or mist. Just as the wind carried ash from Mount St. Helens, wind can carry these droplets for very long distances before they fall as rain.

Acid rain has been very harmful in areas without rich soil to help correct the rain's acidity. In New York's Adirondack Mountains, acid rain has killed all the fish in some lakes. The photograph below shows the impact of acid rain on trees in the Adirondacks. Where acid rain falls, it damages leaves and soil. This damage destroys both habitats and food sources for many animals, eventually reducing biodiversity.

Acid-Rain Damage

A close look at the branch reveals that some of the needles are turning brown.

Air Quality Spruce trees in the Adirondacks show damage caused when pollutants in the air mix with rain.

DIFFERENTIATE INSTRUCTION

More Reading Support

E What are some sources of air pollution? *vehicles, factories, power plants*

F What is acid rain? *rain that has turned acidic from air pollution*

Additional Investigation

To reinforce Section 16.2 learning goals, use the following full-period investigation:

R **Additional INVESTIGATION,** Pollutants on the Move, A, B, & C, pp. 189–197, 200–201 (Advanced students should complete Levels B and C.)

Water Quality

Water quality is another factor that affects biodiversity in ecosystems. Forty years ago, newspaper headlines announced that Lake Erie was "dead" because of pollution. Almost every living thing in the lake had died. Lake Erie suffered for years from pollution by neighborhoods, industries, and farms along its banks. Rivers that emptied into the lake also carried pollution with them.

The pollution found in Lake Erie is common in communities across the United States. Chemicals or waste that drain off of farm fields, animal feedlots, and landfills all cause water pollution. So do oil spills, soil erosion, and the discharging of wastewater from towns and industries.

CHECK YOUR READING Name four different sources of water pollution.

Like air pollution, water pollution affects entire ecosystems. One river that suffers from heavy pollution is the Duwamish River in Washington. Over 600 million gallons of untreated waste and storm water drain off the land into the river. As a result, large amounts of bacteria and harmful chemicals contaminate the water, killing fish and putting humans at risk.

When fish and amphibians in aquatic ecosystems are exposed to pollution, the entire food web is affected. If fish become scarce, some birds may no longer find enough food. The bird population may decrease as birds die or move to a new habitat. The result is that biodiversity in the ecosystem decreases.

Water Quality A scientist tests the water of the Duwamish River after chemicals were released into the river.

Chemical Pollution

Pollution that flows into aquatic ecosystems can harm—even kill—organisms like these fish.

DIFFERENTIATE INSTRUCTION

More Reading Support

G What killed Lake Erie? *water pollution*

H How much of an ecosystem can water pollution affect? *all of it*

Advanced Tell students that scientists have found amphibians with mutations in aquatic ecosystems. Scientists have identified several possible causes such as chemical pollution, UV radiation, disease, and parasites. Have students research and debate whether pollution caused the deformities.

Have students who are interested in amphibians with mutations read the following article:

 Challenge Reading, pp. 173–174

Teach from Visuals

To help students interpret the photographs of chemical pollution, ask:

- Why is the scientist testing the water? *because chemicals were released into the water*
- How does chemical pollution harm fish? *It can kill them.*

Address Misconceptions

IDENTIFY Ask: What types of populations can change without affecting the rest of the ecosystem they are part of? If students name any type of organism, they may hold the misconception that some organisms do not affect the health of an ecosystem. On the contrary, each type of organism is important and affects the entire ecosystem.

CORRECT Use one of the students' answers as an example to illustrate the importance of all organisms to an ecosystem. A sudden decrease in the mosquito population, for example, may cause a decrease in the populations of animals that feed on mosquitoes, such as swallows and bats. The effects continue to move up the food chain.

REASSESS Ask: What species can be removed from an ecosystem without affecting it? *None; all species eat or consume something. Even fleas are predators and serve the purpose of thinning host populations.*

Technology Resources

Visit **ClassZone.com** for background on common student misconceptions.

MISCONCEPTION DATABASE

EXPLORE 

the BIG idea

Revisit "How Easily Does Polluted Water Move Through Plants?" on p. 543. Have students explain how the activity relates to plants near polluted water.

Ongoing Assessment

CHECK YOUR READING *Answer: oil spills, soil erosion, wastewater, chemical runoff*

Teach from Visuals

To help students interpret the diagrams of water and air pollution, ask:

- In the picture on the left, how does pollution move from one place to another? *by water*
- In the picture on the right, how does pollution move from one place to another? *by evaporating into the air*
- How do these pictures suggest a cycle? *the arrows suggest that pollution moves from land to water*
- What might be the next part of the cycle? *pollution in the air might move back to the land by rain or snow*

Integrate the Sciences

Pollutants can move large distances and end up hundreds or thousands of miles away from their source. This "jumping" from one location to another is sometimes referred to as the grasshopper effect. The pollutants move by water or by air. For example, PCBs and mercury can exist as tiny particles that are carried by winds through Earth's atmosphere. These same pollutants can fall to Earth's surface in drops of rain or in snow, where they can enter streams and lakes. Warm temperatures can cause pollutants in the water to vaporize and move back into Earth's atmosphere. The air and the water each represent a different medium that carries the pollutants. This type of interaction is described as cross-media contamination.

Metacognitive Strategy

Ask students to reflect on what they knew about pollution before they studied it in class. Ask them to recall where they got their information, and to assess the reliability of their sources. Have them describe how their thinking has changed.

Ongoing Assessment

Explain how pollution endangers the environment.

Ask: How do air and water pollution harm Earth? *Air pollution causes acid rain and irritation; water pollution poisons fish and other species.*

Pollution Across Systems

As you have learned, pollution can be spread among ecosystems by abiotic factors. For example, wind carried ash from Mount St. Helens to different ecosystems. Wind also carries acid rain to forest ecosystems. Pollution can also move between air and water. For example, some chemical pollutants can run off land and into a body of water. These pollutants, like the water itself, can evaporate from the water's surface and cycle into the air, moving into the atmosphere.

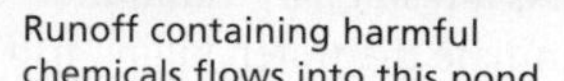

1 Runoff containing harmful chemicals flows into this pond.

2 The chemicals evaporate into the air from the surface of the water.

Habitat loss endangers biodiversity.

Scientists know that an ecosystem with many different species of plants and animals can withstand the effects of flooding, drought, and disease more effectively than an ecosystem with fewer species. But for biodiversity to be maintained, a habitat must be able to support a large number of different species. If living space is limited or a food source is removed, then the number of species in a biological community will be reduced.

Removing Habitat

One way human activities affect habitats is by reducing the amounts of natural resources available to living things. When this occurs, populations that rely on those resources are less likely to survive. For example, if you trim all the dead branches off the trees in your yard and remove them, insects that live in rotting wood will not settle in your yard. As a result, woodpeckers that may have nested in the area will lose their source of food. By removing this food source, you might affect the biodiversity in your backyard.

Now consider altering an ecosystem much larger than your backyard. Instead of removing a single resource, imagine removing a large area of land that is a habitat to many different species. Disturbing habitats removes not only food but space, shelter, and protection for living things.

DIFFERENTIATE INSTRUCTION

More Reading Support

I How does pollution move from land to water? *It dissolves in rainwater or gets eroded in runoff.*

Alternative Assessment Have students design an experiment to test human impact on an ecosystem. Have them study how paving areas affects soil and water in the region. Refer them to the Nature of Science pp. xxii–xxv. Have students identify the information they will need, the way that they can measure results, and the observations they would use.

Removing Habitat

A clear-cut forest provides a dramatic example of habitat loss.

Because of land development, forests that once stretched for hundreds of miles have been fragmented, or broken apart into small patches. Organisms that depend on trees cannot live in woods that have large areas that have been clear-cut. Their habitat is removed or reduced so there is a greater risk of attack by predators. Skunks, raccoons, and crows, which eat the eggs of forest songbirds, will not travel deep into large forests. However, they can reach nests more easily when forests are broken into small areas.

 **CHECK YOUR READING** Why is biodiversity important and how can human activities affect it?

Changing Habitat

Another kind of habitat loss occurs when humans move species into new habitats, either on purpose or by accident. Some species, when released in a new place, successfully compete against the native species, crowding them out. Over time, these species, called invasive species, may replace the native species. **J**

One example of an invasive plant is purple loosestrife. In the 1800s loosestrife from Europe was brought to the United States to use as a garden plant and medicinal herb. One loosestrife plant can make about 2 million seeds a year. These seeds are carried long distances by wind, water, animals, and humans. Loosestrife sprouts in wetlands, where it can fill in open-water habitat or replace native plants such as goldenrod. Most ducks and fish do not feed on purple loosestrife.

DIFFERENTIATE INSTRUCTION

More Reading Support

J What is an invasive species? *a species that moves to a new place and replaces native species*

Advanced In the 1950s, Australia's rabbit population had exploded and caused competition with cattle for pasture to graze. To deal with rabbits that were introduced, officials released a virus that kills rabbits. Rabbit populations then sharply decreased, and native plants and animals rebounded. Ask students to analyze what could go wrong with such a practice. *The virus could affect other organisms, seriously damaging the food web.*

 Challenge and Extension, p. 160

Teach from Visuals

To help students interpret the photograph of a clear-cut forest, ask:

- What has happened in the foreground of the picture? *The forest has been clear-cut.*
- How is the light in the background different from the foreground? *There is much more light in the foreground.*
- How might the ecosystem change from the foreground to the background? *Foreground has dry soil with very little life. Background has variety of life in and under trees; soil is not eroded.*

Real World Example

There are many examples of invasive species. Imported red fire ants were accidentally introduced into Alabama in the ballast of merchant ships. The ants have spread throughout the South. Fire ants are aggressive, their stings are painful, and mainly their mounds can ruin fields of crops. Also in the South, the kudzu vine, imported from Japan, now runs wild, covering small houses and killing trees. Zebra mussels from Europe cover piers, boats, machinery, and clog water supply pipes in the Great Lakes. In Australia, European rabbits have wiped out some native vegetation, severely stressing the local species.

Ongoing Assessment

Describe how loss of diversity affects the environment.

Ask: When land is cleared with a bulldozer, how does loss of diversity affect the environment? *Soil is removed and may become too thin or dry for plants to grow. Plants, insects, and other living things are removed. Many larger animals can no longer live in this habitat. They lose the food and living space they depend on.*

CHECK YOUR READING *Answer: Biodiversity is important because it measures the richness and variety of life in an ecosystem. Human activities can reduce biodiversity by decreasing the amount of land in an ecosystem.*

Address Misconceptions

IDENTIFY Ask students to explain why they think ecologists should or should not work to reduce the growth of some plants. Students may think that all species are beneficial to an environment, and that there is no need to control growth of an invasive species.

CORRECT Have volunteers add steps to a flow chart on the board that illustrates what might happen to the monarch butterfly if the only food source for its larvae were replaced by an invasive plant species.

REASSESS Explain how the growth of a population of a non-native species might limit the growth of another species. *through competition or the destruction of a living area*

Reinforce the BIG idea

Have students relate the section to the Big Idea.

 Reinforcing Key Concepts, p. 162

16.2 ASSESS & RETEACH

Assess

 Section 16.2 Quiz, p. 43

Reteach

Create a three-column chart for students titled "Human Activities Affect the Environment." Use these headings:

- Use Resources
- Release Waste and Pollution
- Alter Habitats

Under each heading have students cite specific activities. Discuss the effects on biodiversity and efficiency of the ecosystem. Have students brainstorm activities that minimize impacts.

Technology Resources

Have students visit **ClassZone.com** for reteaching of Key Concepts.

 CONTENT REVIEW

 CONTENT REVIEW CD-ROM

Changing Habitat

Habitat loss occurs when purple loosestrife fills in open water or crowds out goldenrod.

Invasive Species Purple loosestrife fills in wetlands and crowds out native species, disturbing organisms that rely on native species for food or living space.

Native Species Goldenrod is a native species that is a food source for many wetland populations.

When the native plants that wetland animals depend on are crowded out by loosestrife, the animals disappear, too.

Scientists estimate that Earth supports more than 10 million different species. They also estimate that thousands of species are threatened, and over a hundred species of plants and animals become extinct every year. By protecting biodiversity we can help ecosystems thrive and even recover more quickly after a natural disturbance such as a hurricane. And biodiversity directly benefits humans. For example, many medications are based on natural compounds from plants that only grow in certain types of ecosystems.

16.2 Review

KEY CONCEPTS

1. List some renewable and nonrenewable resources that you need to survive.
2. Describe two ways in which pollution can move through ecosystems.
3. Explain what scientists mean by *biodiversity.*

CRITICAL THINKING

4. **Explain** Under some circumstances, valuable natural resources can be considered pollutants. Explain this statement, giving two examples.
5. **Compare** Identify two natural habitats in your area, one with high biodiversity and one with low biodiversity. Describe the biodiversity of each.

CHALLENGE

6. **Hypothesize** When lakes are polluted by acid rain, the water appears to become clearer, not cloudier. Why do you think this is the case?

560 Unit 4: Ecology

ANSWERS

1. renewable: air, water, wood, crops; nonrenewable: oil, coal, minerals, metals

2. Wind can carry acid rain; chemical pollutants run off land into groundwater.

3. number and variety of life forms in an ecosystem

4. Sample: Natural resources can be pollutants when they end up where they don't belong. Example: when erosion washes soil into streams; carbon from forest fire pollutes the air.

5. Sample: low biodiversity: grass field with insects, worms; high biodiversity: a forest with variety of plant and animal life

6. Acidic water slows the growth of producers in the lake. With fewer producers and less food available, the water appears clearer because there is less life in it.

MATH TUTORIAL
CLASSZONE.COM
Click on Math Tutorial for more help with finding the volume of a rectangular prism.

SKILL: FINDING VOLUMES

How Much Water?

When you take a 10-minute shower, you are using about 190 liters of water. How much is that? Liters are a metric unit of capacity—the amount of liquid that can fit into a container of a certain size. The liter is based on a metric unit of volume. One liter is equal to 1000 cubic centimeters.

Example

A rectangular tank holds the amount of water used for a 10-minute shower. The dimensions of the tank are 250 cm × 40 cm × 19 cm. What is the volume of the tank?

Volume = **length** × **width** × height
$V = l \times w \times h$

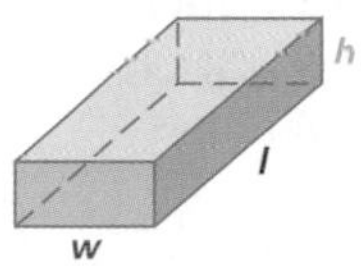

(1) Use the formula for volume.
Replace variables with actual dimensions.
$V = 250 \text{ cm} \times 40 \text{ cm} \times 19 \text{ cm}$

(2) Calculate by multiplying.
$(250 \times 40) \times 19$
$10{,}000 \times 19 = 190{,}000$

(3) Check units:
$\text{cm} \times \text{cm} \times \text{cm} = \text{cm}^3$ (cubic centimeters)

ANSWER $250 \text{ cm} \times 40 \text{ cm} \times 19 \text{ cm} = 190{,}000 \text{ cm}^3$

Find the following volumes or dimensions.

1. Brushing your teeth with the water running uses the water in a tank 14 cm by 45 cm by 12 cm. Sketch an aquarium that holds exactly this amount. Label the dimensions. What is the volume?
2. If you turn off the water while you brush, you use only about half as much water. Sketch a rectangular tank that holds this volume. Label the dimensions. What is the volume?
3. A typical toilet flush uses the water in a 50 cm by 20 cm by 20 cm space. Find the volume in cubic centimeters. Sketch a model of this volume.

CHALLENGE An Olympic swimming pool is 50 m by 25 m by 3 m. What is its volume? There are approximately 5678 cubic meters of water in the water tower shown. How many Olympic pools of water would it take to fill the tower?

ANSWERS

1. Aquariums should have length, width, and height labeled correctly; 7,560 cm³

2. Sample answer: $14 \text{ cm} \cdot 45 \text{ cm} \cdot 6 \text{ cm} = 3780 \text{ cm}^3$

3. $50 \text{ cm} \cdot 20 \text{ cm} \cdot 20 \text{ cm} = 20{,}000 \text{ cm}^3$

CHALLENGE $50 \text{ m} \cdot 25 \text{ m} \cdot 3 \text{ m} = 3750 \text{ m}^3$; $\frac{5678 \text{ cm}^3}{3750 \text{ cm}^3} = 1.5$

MATH IN SCIENCE
Math Skills Practice for Science

Set Learning Goal

To calculate volumes for various scenarios of water usage

Present the Science

From 50–90 percent of the weight of all living things is water. The basic material of cells, protoplasm, is a solution of water and substances like fats, proteins, and salts. Water transports, breaks down, and dissolves these substances.

Develop Geometry Skills

- Remind students that volume adds the third dimension to area.
- Point out that, if a shape is irregular, the standard formula *(lwh)* does not apply.
- Point out that problems asking for volume are easier to solve if you set them up as equations before trying to answer. Have students begin each problem with writing out the $V = l \cdot w \cdot h$ equation.

DIFFERENTIATION TIP Have students who have trouble with the formula keep a cube or rectangular small empty box on their desks as a reminder that volume takes up space, and that it has three dimensions: length, width, and height.

Close

Have students use amounts given in the problems to estimate the volume of water they use in a total day. *Sample answer: 188,500 cm³ for a shower, 5 flushes at 18,850 cm³ per flush, 2 tooth brushings at 950 cm³ each Total = 208,300 cm³ per day*

- Math Support, p. 178
- Math Practice, p. 179

Technology Resources

Students can visit **ClassZone.com** for practice in finding volumes.

 **MATH TUTORIAL**

16.3 FOCUS

Set Learning Goals

Students will

- Consider laws that have been passed to help protect the environment.
- Describe the efforts that are being made to conserve natural resources.

3-Minute Warm-Up

Display Transparency 21 or copy this exercise on the board:

Match the definition to the correct term.

Definitions

1. something from the environment that humans use *c*
2. number of people in a given area *b*
3. the variety of life in an ecosystem *e*

Terms

a. pollution
b. population density
c. natural resource
d. invasive species
e. biodiversity

3-Minute Warm-Up, p. T21

16.3 MOTIVATE

EXPLORE Environmental Impacts

PURPOSE To demonstrate how foot traffic might affect water absorption by soil

TIPS *15 min.* Pots about 4 inches in diameter work well. You do not have to use potting soil. Any soil will do.

WHAT DO YOU THINK? *The pot with the compressed soil took longer to absorb the water; soil that is walked on quite a bit will hold less water, making it more difficult for grass or other plants to get water.*

KEY CONCEPT

16.3 People are working to protect ecosystems.

BEFORE, you learned

- Human activities produce pollutants
- Human activity is depleting some natural resources

NOW, you will learn

- About some of the laws that have been passed to help protect the environment
- About efforts that are being made to conserve natural resources

VOCABULARY

conservation p. 563
sustainable p. 566

EXPLORE Environmental Impacts

What happens when soil is compressed?

PROCEDURE

1. Fill two pots with 1 cup each of potting soil.
2. Compress the soil in the second pot by pushing down hard upon it with your hand.
3. Pour 1 cup of water into the first pot. Start the stopwatch as soon as you start pouring. Stop the watch as soon as all the water has been absorbed. Record the time.
4. Pour 1 cup of water into the second pot and again record how long it takes for the water to be absorbed. Wash your hands.

MATERIALS

- 2 plant pots with trays
- measuring cups
- potting soil
- water
- stopwatch

WHAT DO YOU THINK?

- What effect does compressing the soil have upon how quickly the water is absorbed?
- What might happen to water that is not absorbed quickly by soil?

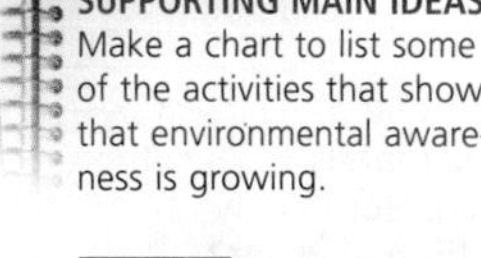

SUPPORTING MAIN IDEAS Make a chart to list some of the activities that show that environmental awareness is growing.

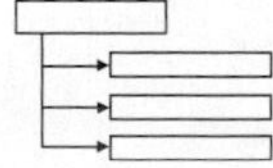

Environmental awareness is growing.

As people moved westward across grassy plains and steep mountain ranges of the United States, many believed our nation's resources were endless. Midwestern prairies were converted to farmland. Forests were clear-cut for lumber. Land was mined for coal.

By the 1800s, foresters and naturalists began to take interest in preserving the wild areas they saw rapidly disappearing. In 1872 our nation's outlook started to change when Yellowstone, the world's first national park, was established. It wasn't long before conservation of

RESOURCES FOR DIFFERENTIATED INSTRUCTION

Below Level

UNIT RESOURCE BOOK

- Reading Study Guide A, pp. 165–166
- Decoding Support, p. 177

AUDIO CDS

Advanced

UNIT RESOURCE BOOK

Challenge and Extension, p. 171

English Learners

UNIT RESOURCE BOOK

Spanish Reading Study Guide, pp. 169–170

- Audio Readings in Spanish
- Audio Readings (English)

wild places became a goal. **Conservation** is the process of saving or protecting a natural resource.

RESOURCE CENTER
CLASSZONE.COM
Discover how people help ecosystems recover.

A

The movement to protect our environment grew rapidly in the 1960s. *Silent Spring,* a book that raised public awareness of the effect of harmful chemicals in the environment, sparked debate about serious pollution problems. As local efforts for environmental protection grew, the United States government responded. Throughout the 1970s important laws were passed to preserve and protect the environment. Today small groups of citizens, along with local and national government efforts, protect America's natural resources.

CHECK YOUR READING List three events in the history of the environmental movement in the United States.

Volunteers work to clean up a stream.

Local Efforts

Maybe you have heard the expression "Think globally, act locally." It urges people to consider the health of the entire planet and to take action in their own communities. Long before federal and state agencies began enforcing environmental laws, individuals were coming together to protect habitats and the organisms that depend on them. These efforts are often referred to as grassroots efforts. They occur on a local level and are primarily run by volunteers.

Often the efforts of a few citizens gather the support and interest of so many people that they form a larger organization. These groups work to bring about change by communicating with politicians, publishing articles, or talking to the news media. Some groups purchase land and set it aside for preservation.

16.3 INSTRUCT

Social Studies Connection

President Theodore Roosevelt is depicted on Mount Rushmore because, more than any other president, he supported conservation. Because of him, Congress created the Forest Service in 1905 to manage federal forest. He set aside about 200 million acres as public lands, protecting them from commercial exploitation. He designated 150 national forests, the first 51 federal bird reservations, and 5 national parks. He pushed for the Reclamation Act of 1902, which established irrigation and other services for western lands. In 1911, the Reclamation Service completed Roosevelt Dam, near Phoenix, Arizona.

History of Science

Rachel Carson wrote four books about the connection between living things and their environment. The most important of these books is *Silent Spring.* Published in 1962, *Silent Spring* exposed the danger of the pesticide DDT. The book depicted how DDT entered the food chain and affected entire ecosystems. Carson kept careful notes and her hard work paid off. Today, *Silent Spring* is credited with starting the environmental movement in the United States.

Ongoing Assessment

CHECK YOUR READING *Answer: creation of first national park (1872), publication of* Silent Spring *(1962), passage of major environmental laws in the 1970s*

DIFFERENTIATE INSTRUCTION

More Reading Support

A When did the movement to protect the environment catch on in a big way? *1960s*

English Learners Encourage English learners to share environmental issues from their native countries. Also encourage them to discuss any local or community conservation efforts.

Teach from Visuals

To help students interpret the graph of peregrine falcon pairs, ask:

- What was happening to the peregrine falcon population until 1968? *The overall trend was that the population declined.*
- In what year was DDT banned? *1972*
- In what year were the first captive falcons released? *1974*
- What has been happening to the peregrine falcon population since 1985? *The number of breeding pairs has risen steeply.*

Real World Example

DDT was once considered very beneficial. After World War II, it was used heavily throughout the world to control the insects that carry life-threatening diseases such as malaria, yellow fever, typhus, and elephantiasis. In the 1950s in India, the use of DDT decreased the number of malaria cases from 75 million to 5 million. Further, crops sprayed with DDT sometimes doubled their yields.

By 1962, however, DDT's damaging effects were being identified. Because DDT is a very stable chemical, it accumulated in the birds and fish that ate the insects, poisoning them and causing reproductive problems. Many insects developed resistance to DDT, and these populations grew unchecked while their natural predators were killed. For these reasons, DDT was banned in the United States in 1972 except for use in extreme health emergencies. Developing countries, such as those in Africa, continue to use DDT to control mosquitoes that can carry malaria.

Ongoing Assessment

CHECK YOUR READING *Answer: the National Environmental Policy Act (NEPA), the Endangered Species Act, the Clean Air Act, and Clean Water Act*

Federal Efforts

B

You have probably heard of the Endangered Species Act or the Clean Air Act. You might wonder, though, exactly what these laws do. The United States government works with scientists to write laws that ensure that companies and individuals work together to conserve natural resources and maintain healthy ecosystems.

In the late 1960s the National Environmental Policy Act, known as NEPA, made the protection of natural ecosystems a national goal. Several important laws followed. For example, the Clean Air Act and Clean Water Act improved the control of different kinds and amounts of pollutants that can be put into the air and water. The Environmental Protection Agency (EPA) enforces all federal environmental laws.

C

CHECK YOUR READING Identify two federal environmental laws.

Over the past decades, chemical waste from factories has piled up in landfills and polluted water sources. These wastes can threaten ecosystems and human health. In 1980, citizen awareness of the dangers led to the Superfund Program. The goal of the program is to identify dangerous areas and to clean up the worst sites.

Helping Endangered Species

Government and private groups have helped peregrine falcon populations to recover.

SOURCE: Audubon Society

DIFFERENTIATE INSTRUCTION

More Reading Support

B What do the Clean Air and Clean Water Acts do? *give government control over pollution*

C What does the EPA do? *enforces all federal environmental laws*

Advanced Suggest that students create political cartoons depicting pollution issues and/or government or civilian responses.

R Challenge and Extension, p. 171

English Learners There are many different types of graphs. Review the graph on endangered species with English learners. Help them understand how the information is arranged and how to interpret it. Encourage them to generate questions that can be answered by the graph.

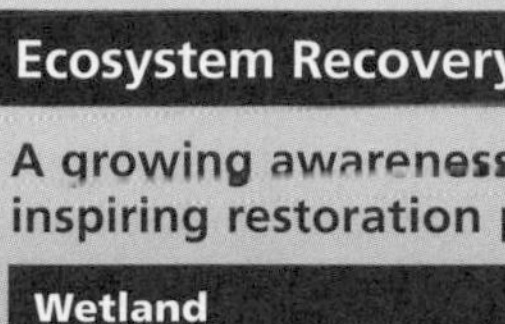

Ecosystem Recovery

A growing awareness of the importance of healthy ecosystems is inspiring restoration projects.

Wetland

Restoration efforts in Galveston Bay, Texas, focus on bringing back the sea-grass meadows near the coast.

Volunteers help replant sea grass around Galveston Island State Park. Sea grass is a major habitat for birds, fish, and crabs and helps prevent erosion by holding bottom sediments in place.

Desert

Members of a restoration group work to restore desert plants and soil in Red Rock Canyon State Park, California.

1 A power auger is used to break up severely compacted soil and prepare it for planting.

2 Seedlings of native species, like the saltbush, are grown off site. Once they reach a more mature size, they are brought in to be planted.

3 Plastic cones are used to protect plants from being disturbed by severe weather or predators.

Teach from Visuals

Ecosystem recovery projects are underway in many areas, including Galveston Island State Park in Texas and Red Rock Canyon State Park in California.

To help students interpret the photographs of wetland and desert, ask:

- How do the seagrass meadows help the marine ecosystem? *Sea grass holds soil in place and keeps the water clear.*
- What were plastic cones used for? *to protect new plants*
- Why did vegetation need to be restored in Red Rock Canyon? *Soil had been compacted and vegetation stripped by vehicles and mining.*

Real World Example

To restore the Galveston Island seagrass meadows—which broke up because of shrimp trawling and pumping groundwater for industrial, commercial, and residential use—an offshore oyster reef had to be replaced. The oyster reef had protected the wetlands from the waves. To replace it, 13,500 geotubes were installed in open water offshore to simulate the reef. Geotubes use a special fabric that contains fill material while allowing water through. These geotubes have helped minimize erosion and improve water clarity.

DIFFERENTIATE INSTRUCTION

Below Level Create a two-column chart on a bulletin board or dry-erase board. Use the column headings: "Sustainable Practices" and "Renewable Resources." Have students brainstorm specific examples of each. Write any "non examples" off to the side to discuss as a contrast.

Integrate the Sciences

One use for recycled newspapers is cellulose insulation. Newspaper is turned into a pulp, which is sprayed into the walls of houses and under rooftops. It fills cavities and so stops air filtration better than fiberglass batting does. Cellulose-insulated buildings may use 20–40 percent less energy than conventional insulated buildings. And it takes less energy to make the insulation than to make fiberglass insulation. Cellulose insulation also increases the fire resistance of a house.

Ongoing Assessment

Consider the kinds of laws that have been passed to help protect the environment.

Ask: What is the goal of the National Environmental Policy Act? *to protect natural ecosystems from damage or destruction*

CHECK YOUR READING *Answer: Sustainable practices use natural resources without using them up.*

INFER At this Superfund site, the chemical cadmium pollutes the soil. Why does this worker need to wear a face mask?

Federal agencies oversee the Superfund Program and other environmental laws. In addition to federal laws protecting the environment, there are state laws. Companies must follow all the laws that apply in each state where they do business. The same company may need to follow different laws in different states.

The United States is just one of many countries learning to deal with the effects of their human population on the environment. Dozens of countries have already met to discuss concerns about clear-cutting, water pollution, and endangered species. At this international level, the United Nations Environment Programme encourages sound environmental practices worldwide.

Conserving resources protects ecosystems.

D

Around the world, individuals and companies are expressing more interest in **sustainable** practices—ways of living and doing business that use natural resources without using them up. Sustainable development allows people to enjoy a high quality of life while limiting harm to ecosystems. Developing new technologies, reducing resource use, and creating less waste are three ways to practice sustainability.

CHECK YOUR READING What are sustainable practices?

Improving Resource Use

As you read in Chapter 15, many different interactions take place in ecosystems. Some organisms form close relationships with one other and their environment. Humans are like other organisms. We depend on the environment to help meet our requirements for life. Because many of the resources we rely on are limited, businesses and governments are changing the way they manage farms, forests, and energy resources. They are adopting sustainable practices.

E

Some farmers are practicing sustainable methods that protect land and provide nutritious food. Nearly one-third of U.S. farms practice conservation tillage, a method that involves planting seeds without plowing the soil. This technique can cut soil erosion by more than 90 percent. Organic farmers reject fertilizers and pesticides made from fossil fuels. Instead they use natural fertilizers, like compost, and natural pest controls, like ladybugs, which eat aphids.

DIFFERENTIATE INSTRUCTION

More Reading Support

D Describe one sustainable practice. *reduce use of resources; lessen waste*

E Name one way organic farms control pests. *use ladybugs to eat aphids*

English Learners English learners may be unfamiliar with words that have multiple meanings. Explain the multiple meanings of the following words in the section. On p. 564, *private* is used to mean non-governmental. On p. 566, *adopting* is used to indicate something being put to use. On p. 566, *practice* is used to mean a policy or way of doing things. On p. 568, *pool* in *carpooling* is used to mean a group.

Forestry practices are also changing. Cutting selectively instead of clear-cutting reduces soil erosion and encourages rapid regrowth. The U.S. Forest Service has adopted an ecosystem-management approach that tries to balance the need for timber with the need to conserve soil and water and preserve wildlife and biodiversity.

CHECK YOUR READING Give two examples of sustainable practices.

F Energy companies are also promoting sustainability by developing alternative energy sources that do not come from fossil fuels. By the time you buy your first car, it may run on fuel cells, and the electricity in your house may be generated by a solar power plant.

Commercial geothermal power plants are a renewable energy source that uses the heat of molten rock in the Earth's interior. Geothermal power already supplies electricity to households in New Zealand, Japan, the United States, and elsewhere.

The energy of falling or flowing water can also be used to generate electricity in a hydropower plant. Commercial hydropower plants generate over half of the alternative energy used in the United States. Like solar and geothermal power, hydropower releases no pollutants. But hydropower often requires dams, which are expensive to build and can flood wildlife habitats and interfere with fish migration.

Wind is another source of energy that is clean and renewable. G Large open areas with relatively constant winds are used as wind farms. Wind turbines are spread across these farms and convert the energy of moving air into electricity. Wind-generating capacity has increased steadily around the world in just the last ten years.

Solar Energy These mirrors collect and concentrate sunlight, which will be used to generate electricity.

DIFFERENTIATE INSTRUCTION

More Reading Support

F Name an energy supply other than fossil fuels. *sunlight, geothermal, hydropower*

G What do windfarms do? *generate electricity from wind power*

Language Arts Connection

As a ranger for the Forest Service and a professor of game management, author Aldo Leopold did more than restore prairie. Leopold became concerned that America was losing too much wilderness. In his most famous book, *A Sand County Almanac,* published in 1949, Leopold laid out a way of thinking called the "land ethic." The land ethic teaches a person to live with greater reverence for Earth's ability to nurture life.

Integrate the Sciences

Geothermal energy comes from the heat at Earth's core. It emerges in volcanoes, hot springs, and geysers. In Iceland, geothermal energy is abundant. Eighty-nine percent of homes are heated with it, and 5 percent of Iceland's electricity is converted geothermal energy. The rest is produced by hydropower, which converts the mechanical energy of moving water into electrical energy.

Teach from Visuals

To help students interpret the photograph of a solar-energy collector:

- Ask: Why is the location of the dishes important? *There is a lot of Sun, and no trees or buildings block sunlight.*
- Tell students the dishes can move to different orientations. Why is that important? *so that they can collect as much sunlight as possible*

Ongoing Assessment

CHECK YOUR READING *Answer: Sustainable farming practices include planting without plowing fields, and using natural fertilizers and pest control.*

Real World Example

Several cities have innovative ways to decrease traffic and pollution. Singapore created a drivable city center by constructing a ring of tollbooths around the city. The toll that people pay varies according to when they are driving and how much pollution there is. It costs more to drive into the city during rush hour than during off-peak periods, and more when pollution is high than when it is low. Licenses for cars are also different prices, depending on how much the car is driven. A license to drive only on weekends costs less than one to drive every day. London uses congestion charging, which charges drivers five pounds a day to drive in central London. This policy is encouraging other modes of transportation such as buses and trains.

Art Connection

In 1970, Container Corporation of America (CCA) sponsored a nationwide contest for students to create a design that would symbolize the paper recycling process. At that time CCA, a paperboard company, was the largest user of recycled fiber in the United States, and it wanted a symbol to identify packages made from recycled materials. Gary Anderson, an architecture student, designed the three-arrow symbol we see so many places today, and won the contest. You may wish to ask students to design a logo for another sustainable practice, such as organic farming.

Ongoing Assessment

Describe the efforts that are being made to conserve natural resources.

Ask: What are some ways that people conserve fossil fuels in their daily transportation to work and school? *carpooling, mass transit, bicycling, and walking*

CHECK YOUR READING *Answer: traffic is reduced; less air and noise pollution; less use of fossil fuels*

INFER What benefits do people get from using mass transit? Why might some people be reluctant to use mass transit?

Reducing Waste and Pollution

Perhaps you are one of the many students who take a bus to school. Buses and trains are examples of mass transit, which move large groups of people at the same time. When you travel by mass transit, you are working to reduce waste and pollution. The photograph to the left shows a light rail train that carries commuters from downtown Portland, Oregon, into suburbs an hour away. In Portland, mass transit like this light rail helps reduce traffic congestion, air pollution, and noise pollution.

Another way to reduce pollution is by carpooling. Many states encourage carpools by reducing tolls or reserving highway lanes for cars carrying more than one person. Traffic is also reduced when workers telecommute, or work from home, using computers and telephones. Of course a telecommuter uses energy at home. But there are many ways to reduce home energy use. You can install compact fluorescent light bulbs, which use less electricity than a regular light bulb. And you can choose energy-efficient appliances.

CHECK YOUR READING How does mass transit benefit the environment?

Most homes are heated with oil or natural gas, two nonrenewable resources. To use less of these resources, you lower your thermostat in winter or add insulation around doors and windows to keep heat inside. Many power companies offer a free energy audit, to show how you can use less energy at home.

READING TIP The prefix *re–* means *again*, so to *recycle* a resource is to use it again.

Recycling is a fairly new idea in human communities, but if you think about it, it's what biological communities have always done to reduce waste and pollution. Resources are used again and again as they move through the water, nitrogen, and carbon cycles. Materials

These students are participating in a local recycling program.

DIFFERENTIATE INSTRUCTION

More Reading Support

H Name some ways to reduce the use of cars. *mass transit, carpool, bike*

I Name some things that are recycled. *glass, aluminum, plastic, paper, cardboard*

Below Level Have students review the ways to conserve natural resources on pp. 568–569 and give an example of each that is practiced in their local neighborhood. Ask for an example of: reducing waste (using a lunch box or canvas grocery bag rather than throw-away packaging), recycling (returning bottles), conserving energy use (lowering heat or air-conditioner use), and reducing air pollution (walking or biking).

that people now commonly recycle include glass, aluminum, certain types of plastic, office paper, newspaper, and cardboard.

Sometimes materials are recycled into the same product. Cans and glass bottles are melted down to make new cans and bottles. Materials can also be recycled into new products. Your warm fleece jacket might be made from recycled soda bottles. The cereal box on your breakfast table might be made from recycled paper.

Name three things people can do at home that reduce waste and pollution.

Think globally, act locally.

Visitors to an ocean beach may find signs like the one on the right. Such signs remind people that small actions—like protecting the nests of sandpipers—make a difference in the preservation of ecosystems.

The challenges facing society are great. Providing Earth's growing population with clean water and air and with energy for warmth and transportation are only some of the many tasks. Scientists continue to learn about the interactions in ecosystems and how important ecosystems are to humans. As you have read about the interactions in ecosystems, you have probably realized that humans—including you—have a large effect on the natural world.

In the coming years, protection of ecosystems will remain a major challenge. By thinking globally, you will be able to understand the effects of society's decisions about resources, development, and transportation. By acting locally you can become involved in efforts to reduce the use of limited resources and to restore ecosystems.

16.3 Review

KEY CONCEPTS

1. List at least five ways that you can reduce your use of natural resources.
2. Describe three ways that resources can be managed in a sustainable way.

CRITICAL THINKING

3. **Infer** Controlling air and water pollution and protecting endangered species usually require the involvement of the federal government. Why can't state or local governments do this on their own?

CHALLENGE

4. **Apply** Explain how efforts to protect endangered species relate to restoration of ecosystems.

ANSWERS

1. volunteer clean up, mass transit, practice sustainable farming, recycling, alternative energy sources

2. Farms can use conservation tillage and natural pest control. Strip cutting and selective cutting can maintain forests. Renewable sources such as wind, solar, and hydropower are alternatives to fossil fuels.

3. Animals migrate; water flows from one state to the next; and pollution created in one state can travel, so the federal government needs to be involved to solve problems and set policies.

4. When efforts to protect or bring back endangered species are successful, more balance and more biodiversity are brought to the ecosystem.

Answer: recycle; lower the thermostat; use compact fluorescent lights

EXPLORE the BIG idea

Revisit "Internet Activity: The Environment" on p. 543. Have students explain their results.

Reinforce the BIG idea

Have students relate the section to the Big Idea.

 Reinforcing Key Concepts, p. 172

16.3 ASSESS & RETEACH

Assess

 Section 16.3 Quiz, p. 44

Reteach

Have the class add to a natural resources problem/possible solutions chart. Students can brainstorm actions that can be taken for the following problems:

- polluted water
- endangered species
- polluted air
- use of nonrenewable energy sources like fossil fuels

Technology Resources

Have students visit **ClassZone.com** for reteaching of Key Concepts.

 **CONTENT REVIEW**

 **CONTENT REVIEW CD-ROM**

CHAPTER INVESTIGATION

Focus

PURPOSE Hypothesize the effects of various methods for containing and cleaning up an oil spill, and design an experimental model to test the effects of a spill on a beach environment

OVERVIEW Using sand and water, students will construct a model of a beach. They will add oil to their "coastal area" and then use materials and solutions to try to remove the oil. Students will find that cotton balls are most absorbent, and detergent most effective at breaking down oil. They will analyze the difference between their models and real oil-spill situations.

Lab Preparation

- Square cake pans work well.
- Prior to the investigation have students read through the investigation and prepare their data tables. Or you may wish to copy and distribute datasheets and rubrics.

 UNIT RESOURCE BOOK, pp. 180–188

 SCIENCE TOOLKIT, F12

Lab Management

- Ensure that all students wear gloves and aprons.
- Spread newspapers on desks to protect from spills.
- Students may dampen the sand for the beach so that it stays where they want it.

Teaching with Technology

You may wish to introduce this activity with a video documentary on cleaning up oil spills.

CHAPTER INVESTIGATION

Cleaning Oil Spills

DESIGN — YOUR OWN —

OVERVIEW AND PURPOSE

One example of a harmful effect of human activity is an oil spill. You've probably heard about oil spills in the news. Damage to an oil-carrying ship or barge can cause thick black oil to spill into the water. The oil floats on the water, and waves can carry the oil to shore. Oil gets caught on sand and living things that are part of a coastal ecosystem. These spills are especially difficult to clean up. In this investigation you will

- simulate an oil spill and test the effectiveness of various materials used to remove oil
- evaluate materials and processes used to clean up oil spills

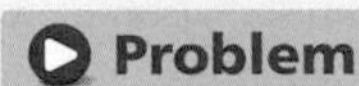

Problem

What materials are effective at removing oil spilled near a coastal ecosystem?

Hypothesize

Write a hypothesis to propose a material or materials that might best remove oil from a coastal area. Your hypothesis should take the form of an "If . . . , then . . . , because . . ." statement.

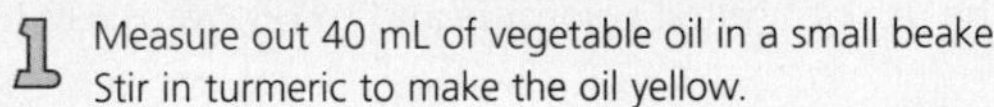

Procedure

1. Measure out 40 mL of vegetable oil in a small beaker. Stir in turmeric to make the oil yellow.
2. Pour sand into one end of the pan as shown to model a beach.
3. Carefully pour enough water into the pan so that it forms a model ocean at least 2 cm deep. Try not to disturb the sand pile.
4. Use the yellow-colored oil to model an oil spill. Pour the oil onto the slope of the sand so that it runs off into the water.

MATERIALS

- small beaker
- 40 mL vegetable oil
- turmeric
- spoon
- aluminum baking pan
- sand
- large beaker
- water
- sponge
- dish soap
- rubbing alcohol
- paper towels
- cotton balls
- cotton rag
- cornstarch
- yarn
- feather
- seaweed

570 Unit 4: Ecology

INVESTIGATION RESOURCES

 CHAPTER INVESTIGATION, Oil Spills
- Level A, pp. 180–183
- Level B, pp. 184–187
- Level C, p. 188

Advanced students should complete Levels B & C.

 Writing a Lab Report, D12–13

Technology Resources

Customize this student lab as needed or look for an alternative. Print rubrics to assess student lab reports.

 **Lab Generator CD-ROM**

Observe and Analyze

1. *Student answers will vary.*
2. *Student answers will vary.*

Conclude

1. *Answers should detail comparisons between hypothesis and results.*
2. *Sample: Cotton balls were most useful to clean water. The sand had soaked up most of the oil, so we needed soap to clean the sand.*
3. *Sample: I would remove as much of the oil surrounding the plant or animal and then clean it. Some animals can be removed immediately and cleaned first.*
4. *Sample: We've created a model of a controlled environment. In real life, oil sinks into the ground and groundwater, making it harder to clean up. In a real ecosystem, you need to worry about the effects of chemicals like detergents on living things.*

INVESTIGATE Further

CHALLENGE Answer: You need something porous and absorbent to clean oil spills on water. On land, you need to get to the oil as soon as possible before the oil sinks into the soil. Soap or detergent is needed to clean the ground.

5 Test the materials for effectiveness in removing the oil from the sand and the water.

6 Place the feather and the seaweed on the beach or in the water, where the oil is. Test materials for effectiveness in removing oil from the feather and seaweed.

7 Make a table in your **Science Notebook** like the one below. Record your observations on the effectiveness of each material.

8 Using your observations from step 7, design a process for removing oil from sand and water. This process may involve several materials and require a series of steps.

Observe and Analyze

1. **RECORD** Write up your procedure for cleaning oil from sand and water. You may want to include a diagram.
2. **EVALUATE** What, if any, difficulties did you encounter in carrying out this experiment?

Conclude

1. **INTERPRET** How do your results compare with your hypothesis? Answer the problem statement.
2. **EVALUATE** Which materials were most useful for cleaning the water? Were they the same materials that were most useful for cleaning the sand?
3. **EVALUATE** Suppose you are trying to clean oil off of living things, such as a bird or seaweed. What process would you use?
4. **IDENTIFY LIMITS** In which ways did this demonstration fail to model a real oil spill?

INVESTIGATE Further

CHALLENGE Explain how the observations you made in this investigation might be useful in designing treatments for an actual oil spill.

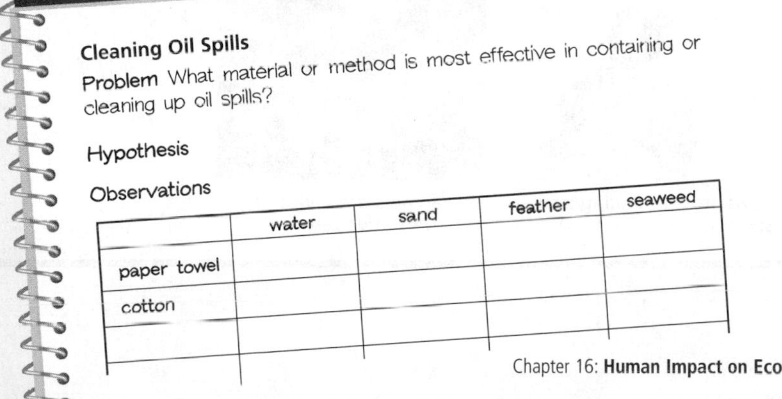
Cleaning Oil Spills

Problem What material or method is most effective in containing or cleaning up oil spills?

Hypothesis

Observations

	water	sand	feather	seaweed
paper towel				
cotton				

Post-Lab Discussion

- With modern technology, why are oil spills a problem? *People can't completely clean up an oil spill, and cleanup operations can pollute the environment.*
- During a real oil spill, how do you think bad weather might affect the cleanup? *Bad weather could spread the oil, interfere with cleanup boats, and add to wildlife stress.*
- What might help prevent an oil spill? *safer ships, safety programs for crew*

Address Misconceptions

IDENTIFY Ask: What can be learned about cleaning real oil spills from making a model? Students may think that the techniques that work in a model would hold true for the real environment. Many students think that scientific models are exact representations.

CORRECT Discuss with students the differences between a real oil spill cleanup and a model oil spill cleanup. Explain that using detergent in a real cleanup could harm living things. Although oil is cleaned from the top layer of sand, oil could seep into lower layers. Also point out that cotton balls and sponges are not available on a large scale.

REASSESS Review students' answers to question 4. Point out that detergent is one method used to clean oil spills, but is much less effective in a real oil spill.

BACK TO

the BIG idea

Use a hypothetical scenario to demonstrate the statement, "Humans and human population growth affect the environment."

Mineral ore is discovered near a small town out in the desert. Quickly, companies arrive to mine for and process the ore, bringing their employees, which in turn attract other businesses (stores, gas stations, restaurants, etc.) to serve them. Explain three ways that this will affect the desert ecosystem. *There will be more waste to dispose of. The limited water supply may run out. Expanding land use will destroy habitats.*

KEY CONCEPTS SUMMARY

SECTION 16.1

Ask: What does the steep curve on the graph imply for the challenges posed by population growth? *We might run out of natural resources.*

SECTION 16.2

Ask: How can pollution change systems? *It can make them unfit for inhabitants and fit for new organisms.*

Ask: How do humans cause habitat loss? *by developing pastures and farms, by clearcutting forests, and by introducing nonnative species*

SECTION 16.3

Ask: What federal laws in the U.S. protect ecosystems? *NEPA, Clean Air and Clean Water Acts, Superfund Program*

Ask students to list some alternative energy resources that lessen impact on the environment. *wind power, hydropower, geothermal power, solar power*

Review Concepts

- Big Idea Flow Chart, p. T17
- Chapter Outline, pp. T23–T24

16 Chapter Review

the BIG idea

Humans and human population growth affect the environment.

KEY CONCEPTS SUMMARY

Human population growth presents challenges.

As the population continues to grow, there is a greater demand for natural resources. Cities and countries share many resources. Increasing populations put pressure on ecosystems.

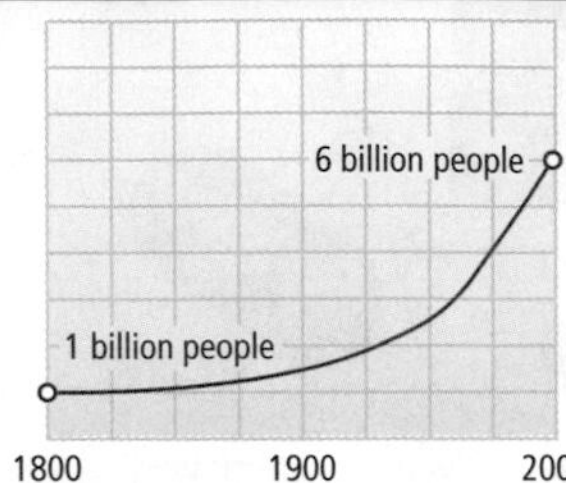

VOCABULARY
natural resource p. 548
population density p. 550

Human activities affect the environment.

Pollution and habitat loss make it difficult for plants and animals to survive. Without the necessary resources, biodiversity of living things decreases, and ecosystems become less stable.

Pollution

Habitat Loss

VOCABULARY
pollution p. 555
biodiversity p. 555

3 Humans are working to protect ecosystems.

Working at local and governmental levels, humans are helping ecosystems recover.

Laws protect endangered species.

Researchers are investigating alternative resources.

VOCABULARY
conservation p. 563
sustainable p. 566

Technology Resources

Have students visit **ClassZone.com** or use the CD-ROM for a cumulative review of concepts.

CONTENT REVIEW

CONTENT REVIEW CD-ROM

Engage students in a whole-class interactive review of Key Concepts. Edit content as you wish.

POWER PRESENTATIONS

Reviewing Vocabulary

Place each vocabulary term at the center of a description wheel diagram. Write some words describing it on the spokes.

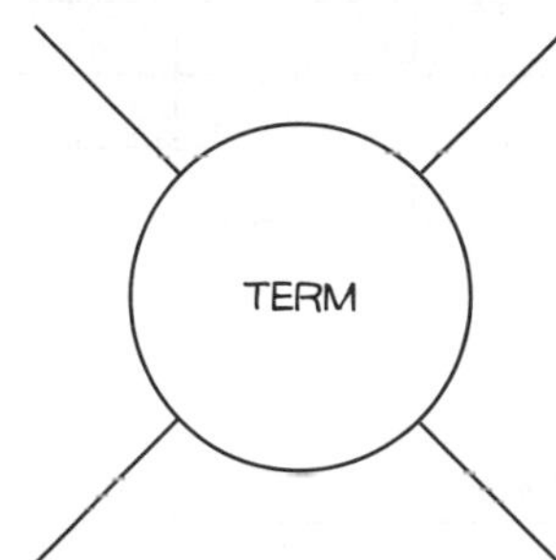

1. population density
2. natural resources
3. pollution
4. biodiversity
5. sustainable
6. conservation

Reviewing Key Concepts

Multiple Choice *Choose the letter of the best answer.*

7. In 2000, how big was Earth's human population?
   a. 1 billion **c.** 6 billion
   b. 3 billion **d.** 9 billion

8. Experts predict that by the year 2050, Earth's population will reach what number?
   a. 3 billion **c.** 9 billion
   b. 6 billion **d.** 12 billion

9. Which statement best explains why Earth's population has grown very rapidly in the last 100 years?
   a. On average, women are having children at an older age.
   b. People live longer because of improved health care and nutrition.
   c. Global warming has enabled farmers to grow more food.
   d. More land has been developed for housing.

10. Which of the four natural resources listed is likely to be used up the soonest?
    a. petroleum **c.** sunlight
    b. water **d.** wood

11. Which of the following is an example of increasing biodiversity?
    a. A forest is clear-cut for its wood, leaving land available for new uses.
    b. New species of animals and plants appear in a wildlife preserve.
    c. A new species of plant outcompetes all of the others around a lake.
    d. A cleared rain forest results in a change to a habitat.

12. Which represents a sustainable practice?
    a. conservation tillage and use of natural fertilizers
    b. more efficient removal of oil
    c. allowing unlimited use of water for higher fees
    d. restocking a lake with fish every year

13. What environmental problem does the Superfund Program address?
    a. habitat loss
    b. land development
    c. biodiversity
    d. pollution

Short Answer *Write a short answer to each question.*

14. List four ways increased human population density affects ecosystems.

15. Three ways that humans dispose of waste are landfills, incineration, and wastewater treatment plants. List one advantage and one disadvantage of each.

16. Write a paragraph to describe how an increase in population density affects land development.

ASSESSMENT RESOURCES

UNIT ASSESSMENT BOOK
- Chapter Test A, pp. 45–48
- Chapter Test B, pp. 49–52
- Chapter Test C, pp. 53–56
- Alternative Assessment, pp. 57–58
- Unit Test, A, B, & C, pp. 59–70

SPANISH ASSESSMENT BOOK
- Spanish Chapter Test, pp. 65–68
- Spanish Unit Test, pp. 77–80

Technology Resources

Edit test items and answer choices.

Test Generator CD-ROM

Visit **ClassZone.com** to extend test practice.

Test Practice

Reviewing Vocabulary

1–6. Answers will vary, but all of the vocabulary terms listed should be used properly.

Reviewing Key Concepts

7. c
8. c
9. b
10. a
11. b
12. a
13. d
14. more pollution, greater demand on limited natural resources like water, destruction of habitats, death of plants and animals
15. Landfill disposal is generally cheap, but trash and materials may stay there for a long time. Incineration reduces the amount of material that needs to stay in the ground, but leads to air pollution. Sewage treatment plants clean water that is released into the environment, but there is still a lot of sludge that must be disposed of.
16. When a population grows to the point that the local environment becomes stressed, people look for other places to live. Land gets developed—forests, farms, and grasslands are destroyed—as roads and buildings are built to create a place for people to live.

Thinking Critically

17. *The population of Atlanta in 2000 was 4 million while that of Las Vegas was 1.5 million. The rate of growth in Atlanta between 1990 and 2000 was about twice that of Las Vegas. At current rates of increase, the population of Las Vegas will not get bigger than the population of Atlanta.*
18. *No; area of both cities*
19. *Sample answer: Carrying capacity is higher in Atlanta as available water sources are greater in a temperate forest biome than in a desert.*
20. *More water would be available for Mexican use and for Mexican wildlife near the mouth of the river.*
21. *Trees are generally considered a renewable resource because a properly managed or natural forest will have new trees grow to replace dead or removed ones. If the land is destroyed or new trees aren't planted, then trees from a forest are a nonrenewable resource.*
22. *RENEWABLE: water, wood, sunlight, soil; NONRENEWABLE: copper, aluminum, petroleum, coal*
23. *3600 kg less carbon dioxide*

the BIG idea

24. *Answers should show a deeper understanding of, not just what was added to the landscape in physical structures, but what was taken away, as well as the pollution and environmental pressures created.*
25. *Answers should list varieties of plants and animals, and should include at least four sustainable practices, including conservation of resources and reduction of waste.*

UNIT PROJECTS

Have students present their projects. Use the appropriate rubrics from the Unit Resource Book to evaluate their work.

 Unit Projects, pp. 5–10

Thinking Critically

Use the graph to answer the next three questions.

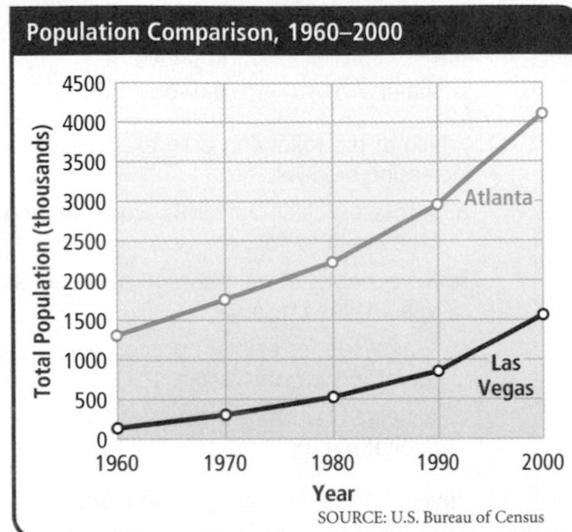

17. **COMPARE AND CONTRAST** Describe the population size and rate of growth for the cities of Atlanta and Las Vegas. Would you expect the population of Las Vegas to ever get bigger than that of Atlanta based on the data supplied?
18. **EVALUATE** Is it possible to determine from the data shown whether the population density is higher in Atlanta than Las Vegas? What other information would you need?
19. **CONNECT** Atlanta is located in a temperate-forest biome and Las Vegas is located in a desert biome. How might the characteristics of these biomes affect the carrying capacity of the human populations in these cities?
20. **PREDICT** If states in the U.S. used less water from the Colorado River, how would the depth of the river in Mexico be affected?
21. **COMPARE AND CONTRAST** Explain why trees are generally considered a renewable resource. Now describe circumstances under which they could be considered a nonrenewable resource.
22. **CLASSIFY** Sort the resources below into the correct categories:

Resource	Renewable	Nonrenewable
Water		
Coal		
Soil		
Wood		
Copper		
Petroleum		
Aluminum		
Sunlight		

23. **CALCULATE** A compact fluorescent bulb uses less energy than a regular bulb. It is estimated that a coal-burning power plant would release 72 kilograms more carbon dioxide (CO_2) a year to power one regular bulb than it would to power one fluorescent bulb. If you replace five regular bulbs with five compact bulbs, how much less CO_2 would be released in a 10-year period?

the BIG idea

24. **PROVIDE EXAMPLES** Look again at the photograph on pages 542–543. How would you change or add details to your answer to the question on the photograph?
25. **APPLY** You are on the town council of a community located on a small island. The council has decided to make a brochure for the town's citizens. In your brochure, describe the island habitat. Include information about natural resources, such as water and soil. List the plants and animals that live there. Establish four rules that the community should follow to preserve the local habitat.

UNIT PROJECTS

Evaluate the materials in your project folder. Finish your project and get ready to present it to your class.

MONITOR AND RETEACH

If students have trouble applying the concepts in items 17–19, explain that upward-trending lines in the graph show that the populations of the two cities have increased steadily over the past 40 years. Ask: What does it mean that Las Vegas is lower on the graph? ***The population numbers are less.*** Review the impacts of population growth.

Students may benefit from summarizing sections of the chapter.

 Summarizing the Chapter, pp. 198–199

Standardized Test Practice

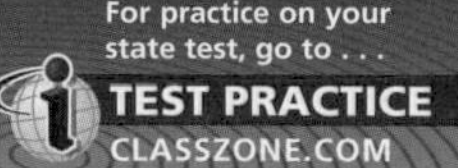

Analyzing Data

Nowhere is the impact of human population growth more obvious than in the growth of urbanized areas. Buildings, parking lots, and roads are replacing forests, farmland, and wetlands. The table below shows the growth of urbanized areas around 10 cities in the United States during a 20-year period.

Growth in land area, 1970–1990

Location	Growth in Land Area (Km²)
Atlanta, GA	1816
Houston, TX	1654
New York City-N.E. New Jersey	1402
Washington, D.C.-MD-VA	1166
Philadelphia, PA	1068
Los Angeles, CA	1020
Dallas-Fort Worth, TX	964
Tampa-St. Petersburg-Clearwater, FL	929
Phoenix, AZ	916
Minneapolis-Saint Paul, MN	885

SOURCE: U.S. Bureau of Census data on Urbanized Areas

1. What patterns can you see in the way information is presented from the top of the table to the bottom?
   - **a.** Cities are arranged alphabetically.
   - **b.** Cities are arranged by growth in population over 20 years.
   - **c.** Cities are arranged by the growth in land area over 20 years.
   - **d.** Cities are arranged by size of urban area.
2. How would you describe the change in the land around Atlanta between 1970 and 1990?
   - **a.** In 1990, more land was used for farming.
   - **b.** The number of buildings and roads increased.
   - **c.** The urbanized area decreased.
   - **d.** Natural habitats for birds increased.
3. Which type of graph would be best for displaying the data in the table?
   - **a.** a bar graph
   - **b.** a circle graph
   - **c.** a line graph
   - **d.** a double bar graph
4. How many square kilometers around Philadelphia were affected by urbanization between 1970 and 1990?
   - **a.** 1116 km^2
   - **b.** 1166 km^2
   - **c.** 1068 km^2
   - **d.** 1020 km^2

Extended Response

5. Write a paragraph to describe how a rural area would change if the land were developed and the area became more urban. Use the vocabulary words listed below in your answer.

population density	biodiversity
renewable resources	nonrenewable resources

6. If you were an urban designer working for a small city that expected to expand rapidly in the next 10 years, what recommendations would you make to the city council on how the land should be developed?

METACOGNITIVE ACTIVITY

Have students answer the following questions in their **Science Notebook:**

1. How has reading the chapter made you think about your own impact on ecosystems?
2. What activity in the chapter posed the biggest challenge? What was important to you about that activity?
3. What have you learned from your research on your Unit Project?

Analyzing Data

1. c *2. b* *3. a* *4. c*

Extended Response

5. RUBRIC

4 points for a response that uses at least three vocabulary words and offers an accurate description of urbanization.

Sample: If a rural area were developed to become more urban, many changes would occur to natural resources. As trees and other vegetation would need to be cleared, available renewable resources would be altered. Nonrenewable resources such as air and water would be affected because construction creates pollution. Many animal species would lose their habitat due to urbanization so there would be a change in biodiversity as well.

3 points description is realistic and uses at least two vocabulary words
2 points description is realistic and uses at least one vocabulary word
1 point attempts to describe the urban area; does not use any vocabulary words

6. RUBRIC

4 points for a response that addresses the following topics:

- wildlife and/or ecosystems
- traffic, transportation, and/or development
- sewage and/or water supply
- waste disposal and/or pollution

Sample: The council should consider any endangered wildlife in the outlying areas. They should preserve open spaces, both for wildlife and for people. They should plan the growth so that traffic heading toward and away from the city doesn't back up. Alternative modes of transportation such as bike paths, trains, buses, and carpool lanes should be planned. Sewage and water supply should not overwork the environment. Recycling should be used to address the extra burden on the landfills.

3 points for a response that correctly addresses the topic and uses three of the topics above
2 points for a response that correctly addresses the topic and uses two of the topics above
1 point for a response that attempts to address the question and uses one of the topics above

McDougal Littell Science

Human Biology

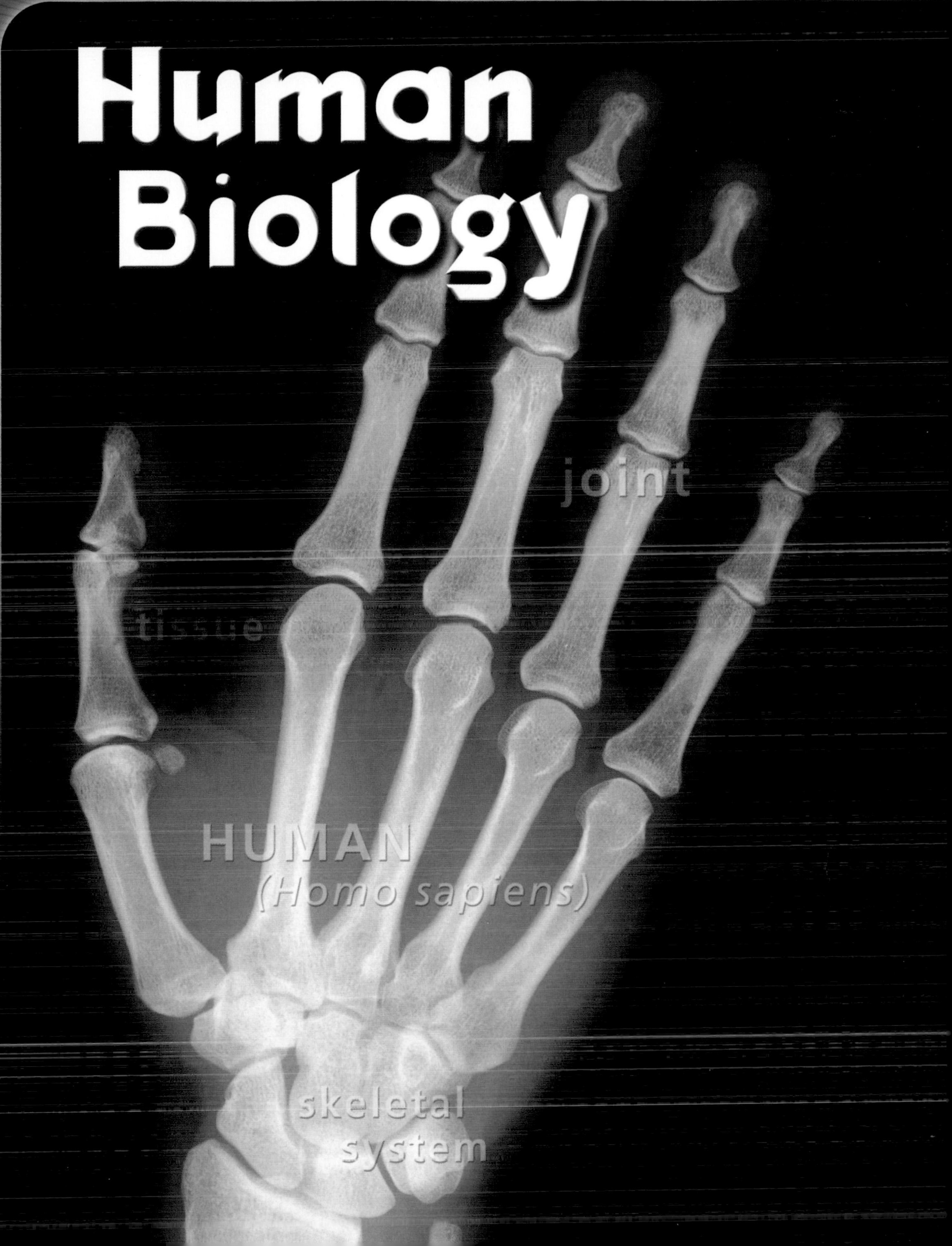

joint

tissue

HUMAN

(Homo sapiens)

skeletal system

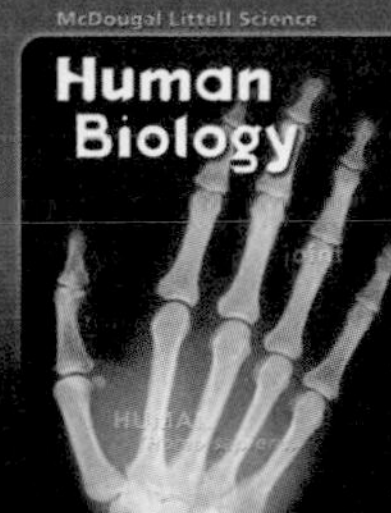

Human Biology
Contents Overview

Unit Features

VIDEO SUMMARY

SCIENTIFIC AMERICAN FRONTIERS

"Sight of Touch," a segment of the *Scientific American Frontiers* series that aired on PBS stations, describes experiments that explore how the brain adapts. Dr. Alvaro Pascual-Leone has found that the brain's visual cortex processes the sense of touch in people born blind. He wants to know if sighted people's brains can adapt in the same way. A sighted volunteer is blindfolded for one week to see if the change in sensory input has an impact on her brain. She studies Braille, and her brain's response to stimuli is tested in an MRI chamber. Toward the end of the week, a magnetic shock is applied to her visual cortex to disrupt its function temporarily. By comparing the volunteer's Braille abilities before and after the shock, Dr. Pascual-Leone confirms his hypothesis: the visual cortex helps process information arriving via the sense of touch. The volunteer's brain has adapted in one short week.

National Science Education Standards

A.1–8 Abilities Necessary to Do Scientific Inquiry

A.9.a–b, A.9.d–g Understandings About Scientific Inquiry

F.5.e Science and Technology in Society

G.1.a–b Science as a Human Endeavor

G.2.a, G.2.c Nature of Science

FRONTIERS in Science

Surprising Senses

SCIENTIFIC AMERICAN FRONTIERS

Learn more about how the brain and senses work. See the video "Sight of Touch."

ADDITIONAL RESOURCES

Technology Resources

Scientific American Frontiers Video: *Sight of Touch:* 11-minute video segment that introduces the unit.

ClassZone.com
CAREER LINK, Neurobiologist

Guide student viewing and comprehension of the video:

Video Teaching Guide, pp. 1–2; Video Viewing Guide, p. 3; Video Wrap-Up, p. 4

Scientific American Frontiers Video Guide, pp. 15–18

Unit projects procedures and rubrics:

Unit Projects, pp. 5–10

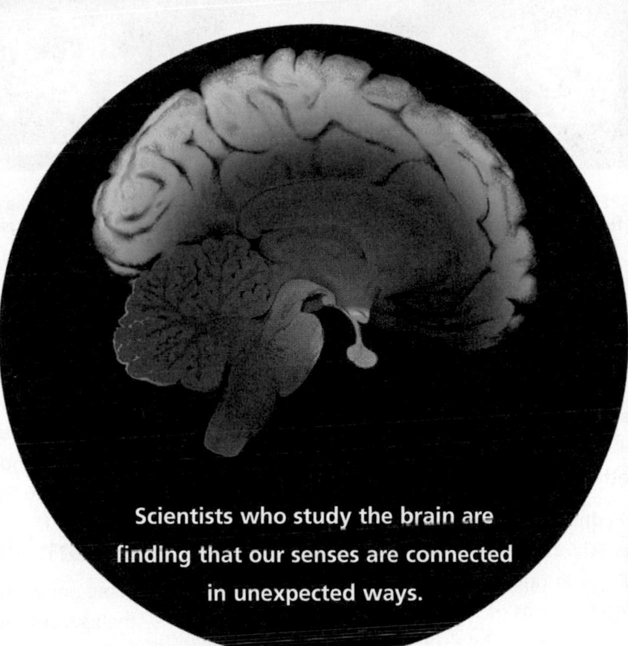

Scientists who study the brain are finding that our senses are connected in unexpected ways.

Senses and the Brain

One of the great mysteries still unsolved in science is what happens inside the brain. What is a thought? How is it formed? Where is it stored? How do our senses shape our thoughts? There are far more questions than answers. One way to approach questions about the brain is to study brain activity at times when the body is performing different functions.

A Most advanced brain functions happen in the part of the brain called the cerebral cortex (suh-REE-bruhl KOR-tehks). That's where the brain interprets information from the senses. The cerebral cortex has many specialized areas. Each area controls one type of brain activity. Scientists are mapping these areas. At first, they studied people with brain injuries. A person with an injury to one area might not be able to speak. Someone with a different injury might have trouble seeing or hearing. Scientists mapped the areas in which damage seemed to cause each kind of problem.

B Now scientists have even more tools to study the brain. One tool is called functional magnetic resonance imaging, or FMRI. Scientists put a person into a machine that uses radio waves to produce images of the person's brain. Scientists then ask the person to do specific activities, such as looking at pictures of faces or listening for specific sounds. The FMRI images show what parts of the person's brain are most active during each activity.

FOCUS

Set Learning Goals

Students will

- Observe how the brain processes information from the senses.
- Analyze how imaging technology is used to map the brain.
- Analyze and model body systems.

The "Sight of Touch" video shows scientists collecting data to use in mapping the functions of areas of the brain. Point out that maps are often a valuable first step in exploring a frontier.

INSTRUCT

Scientific Process

Ask students to identify the skills scientists used when they studied injured people to map the brain. *observation, collecting and analyzing data* Ask: Once scientists realized that they could observe injured people for clues to brain function, what skill did they use to connect an area of the brain with its function? *They made inferences from observations.*

Technology Design

Studying animal brains is not enough to completely understand the human brain. Scientists in the fields of neurology, psychiatry, physiology, and pharmacology all need the information that FMRI studies provide. Aside from information about the senses, researchers wish to understand—among other things—pain, depression, epilepsy, Alzheimer's disease, and how people recover from a stroke. Ask students to discuss how FMRIs could be used to research other areas of study.

DIFFERENTIATE INSTRUCTION

More Reading Support

A Where in the brain do most advanced functions happen? *the cerebral cortex*

B How do scientists use FMRI? *as a tool to study brain activity*

Below Level Have students list three or four common activities and then analyze what senses they use in accomplishing them. You might also suggest that they try tasting their lunches while holding their noses.

Teach from Visuals

To help students interpret the four images of brain activity, focus attention on the image that shows Braille reading (third from left). Explain that when observing people read Braille, it might appear that the sense of touch is stimulated, but in reality many areas of the brain are active. The PET scans show that part of the vision area, part of the hearing area, and part of the thought area all combine in the act of processing Braille.

Scientific Process

Point out that it is not safe to assume that every person has the same brain functioning as another. But you can use information gained from one study subject to form a hypothesis about others. Ask: What hypothesis did Alvaro Pascual-Leone form after studying Gil's brain activity? *The visual center helps the touch center read Braille.* Ask: What skill was Pascual-Leone using when he asked a volunteer to wear a blindfold for a week? *testing a hypothesis*

Asking a Question

Suggest that other situations exist where using a sense to replace one that is impaired might help. Have students form a question and a testable hypothesis that might be investigated to help stroke victims who have trouble speaking.

Technology Design

Translating documents and books into Braille used to be expensive and time-consuming. Software developers have used computers to accomplish what it used to take trained transcriptionists long hours to do. The process now is highly automated, and therefore much faster and cheaper. Ask: Why is this task a good choice for automation? *It is relatively simple, with one-for-one transcription of characters.*

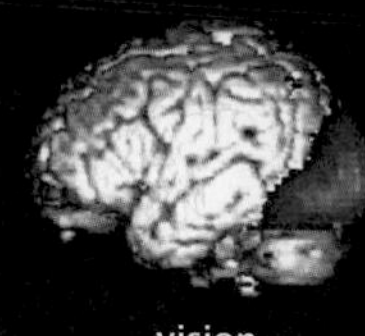

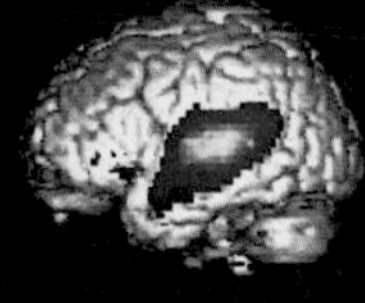

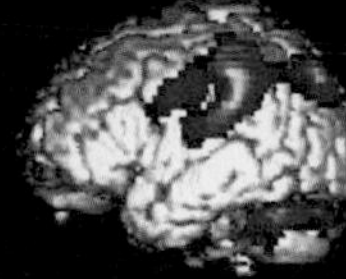

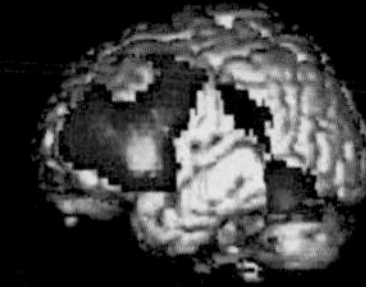

The PET scans show areas of the brain active during particular tasks. Braille is a textured alphabet read by the fingers. Braille reading activates areas associated with touch, vision, hearing, and thought.

Double Duty

Using FMRI and other tools, scientists have identified the parts of the cerebral cortex that are responsible for each of the senses. The vision area is located at the back of the brain. The smell, taste, touch, and hearing areas are all close together in the middle part of the brain. C

People don't usually use just one sense at a time. Scientists have found some unexpected connections. In one study, Marisa Taylor-Clarke poked the arms of some volunteers with either one or two pins. Then she asked them how many pins they felt. Taylor-Clarke found that people who looked at their arms before the test did better than those who didn't. FMRI showed that the part of their brains responsible for touch was also more active when they used their sense of sight.

These connections in the brain show up even when one sense doesn't work. Many people who have hearing impairments read lips to understand what other people are saying. Scientists using FMRI discovered that these people use the part of the brain normally used for hearing to help them understand what they see. This is even true for people who have never been able to hear.

Scrambled Senses

Some people have more connections between their senses than most people have. They may look at numbers and see colors, or associate smells with shapes. Some even get a taste in their mouths when they touch something. All these are examples of synesthesia (sin-uhs-THEE-zhuh). About 1 in 200 people have some kind of synesthesia.  D

View the "Sight of Touch" segment of your Scientific American Frontiers video to learn about another example of connections between the senses.

IN THIS SCENE FROM THE VIDEO Michelle, a research subject, reads Braille with her fingers after wearing a blindfold for three days.

SEEING BY TOUCHING Many blind people read using Braille, a system of raised dots used to represent letters. Some, such as Braille proofreader Gil Busch, can read Braille at astonishing speeds. Scientist Alvaro Pascual-Leone used MRI to study Gil's brain. The visual area of Gil's brain was active while he read Braille.

Gil has been blind since birth, so his brain has had a long time to adjust. Pascual-Leone wanted to know whether the brain could rewire itself in a shorter time. He asked volunteer Michelle Geronimo to wear a blindfold for a week. During that time, she learned to read Braille and experienced the world as a blind person does. At the end of the week, Pascual-Leone was able to demonstrate that Michelle's brain had rewired itself, too. Her visual center was active when she read Braille.

DIFFERENTIATE INSTRUCTION

More Reading Support

C Which sense areas are close together in the brain? *smell, taste, touch, and hearing*

D What is synesthesia? *connecting senses in unusual ways*

Below Level Have students make a poster or bulletin board with a diagram and short summary of the purposes of the different areas of the brain.

E FMRI has made it possible for scientists to learn more about synesthesia. One group of scientists studied people who saw colors when they heard words. FMRI showed that the visual areas of their brains were active along with the hearing areas. (For most people, only the hearing area would be active.)

But why does synesthesia happen? Some scientists think that people with synesthesia have more connections between areas of their brains. Every person has extra connections when they're born, but most people lose many of them in childhood. Perhaps people with synesthesia keep theirs. Another theory suggests that their brains are "cross-wired," so information goes in unusual directions.

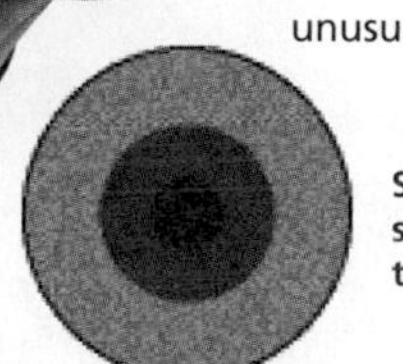

Some people with synesthesia see this colorful pattern when they hear a dog bark.

As scientists explore synesthesia and other connections between the senses, they learn more about how the parts of the brain work together. The human body is complex. And the brain, along with the rest of the nervous system, has yet to be fully understood.

UNANSWERED Questions

Scientists have learned a lot about how senses are connected. Their research leads to new questions.

- How does information move between different areas of the brain?
- How and why does the brain rewire itself?
- How does cross-wired sensing (synesthesia) happen?

UNIT PROJECTS

As you study this unit, work alone or in a group on one of the projects below.

Your Body System

Create one or several models showing important body systems.

- Draw the outline of your own body on a large piece of craft paper.
- Use reference materials to help you place everything correctly. Label each part.

The Brain: "Then and Now"

Compare and contrast past and present understandings of the brain.

- One understanding is that each part of the brain is responsible for different body functions. This understanding has changed over time.
- Research the history of this idea.
- Prepare diagrams of then and now. Share your presentation.

Design an Experiment

Design an experiment that will test one of the senses. You should first identify a problem question you want to explore.

- The experiment may include a written introduction, materials procedure, and a plan for recording and presenting outcomes.
- Prepare a blank written experiment datasheet for your classmates to use.

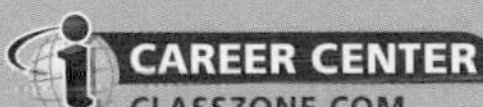

CAREER CENTER
CLASSZONE.COM

Learn more about careers in neurobiology.

UNANSWERED Questions

Have students read the questions and think of some of their own. Remind them that scientists always end up with more questions—that inquiry is the driving force of science.

- With the class, generate on the board a list of new questions.
- Students can add to the list after they watch the *Scientific American Frontiers* Video.
- Students can use the list as a springboard for choosing their Unit Projects.

UNIT PROJECTS

Encourage students to pick the project that most appeals to them. Point out that each is long-term and will take several weeks to complete. You might group or pair students to work on projects and in some cases guide student choice. Some of the projects have student choice built into them. Each project has two worksheet pages, including a rubric. Use the pages to guide students through criteria, process, and schedule.

 Unit Projects, pp. 5–10

REVISIT concepts introduced in this article:

Chapter 17
- The human body is made up of systems that work together to perform necessary functions, pp. 582–588

Timelines in Science
- Seeing inside the body, pp. 670–673

Chapter 20
- The nervous system responds and controls, pp. 677–685
- Sight, hearing, and touch, pp. 678–679
- The central nervous system controls functions, pp. 680–681

DIFFERENTIATE INSTRUCTION

 **More Reading Support**

E What technology has been used to study synesthesia? *FMRI*

Differentiate Unit Projects Projects are appropriate for varying abilities. Allow students to choose the ones that interest them most and let them vary their product. Encourage below level students to give visual or oral presentations or to record audio presentations about their topic.

Below Level Encourage students to try "Your Body System."

Advanced Challenge students to complete "Design an Experiment."

CHAPTER

Systems, Support, and Movement

Life Science UNIFYING PRINCIPLES

PRINCIPLE 1
All living things share common characteristics.

PRINCIPLE 2
All living things share common needs.

PRINCIPLE 3
Living things meet their needs through interactions with the environment.

PRINCIPLE 4
The types and numbers of living things change over time.

Unit 5: Human Biology BIG IDEAS

CHAPTER 17
Systems, Support, and Movement
The human body is made up of systems that work together to perform necessary functions.

CHAPTER 18
Absorption, Digestion, and Exchange
Systems in the body obtain and process materials and remove waste.

CHAPTER 19
Transport and Protection
Systems function to transport materials and to defend and protect the body.

CHAPTER 20
Control and Reproduction
The nervous and endocrine systems allow the body to respond to internal and external conditions.

CHAPTER 21
Growth, Development, and Health
The body develops and maintains itself over time.

CHAPTER 17 KEY CONCEPTS

SECTION 1

The human body is complex.

1. The body has cells, tissues, and organs.
2. The body's systems interact with one another.

SECTION 

The skeletal system provides support and protection.

1. Bones are living tissue.
2. The skeleton is the body's framework.
3. The skeleton changes as the body develops and ages.
4. Joints connect parts of the skeletal system.

SECTION 

The muscular system makes movement possible.

1. Muscles perform important functions.
2. Your body has different types of muscle.
3. Skeletal muscles and tendons allow bones to move.
4. Muscles grow and heal.

The Big Idea Flow Chart is available on p. T1 in the **UNIT TRANSPARENCY BOOK.**

Previewing Content

SECTION

The human body is complex. pp. 585–589

1. The body has cells, tissues, and organs.
The cell is the basic unit of life, and the human body has many specialized cells that perform particular functions. A **tissue** is a group of cells that function together. There are four categories of tissue:

- epithelial, which forms boundaries
- muscle, which enables movement
- nerve, which carries messages
- connective, which supports, protects, pads, insulates, and stores energy

An **organ** is two or more types of tissue that work together to perform a function. For instance, a vein consists of epithelial, muscle, nerve, and connective tissues. Organs work together in **organ systems,** such as the circulatory system, shown below.

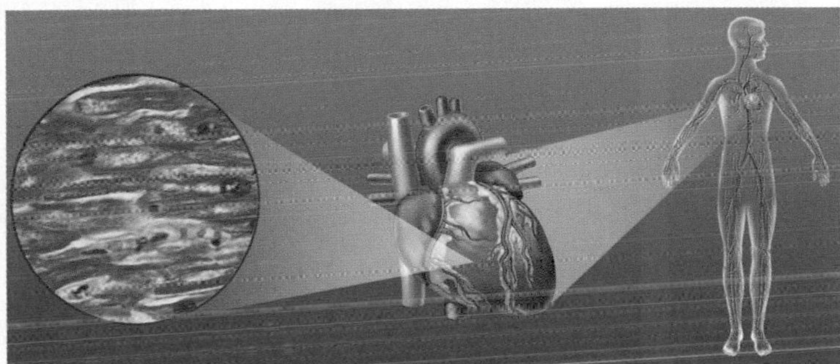

2. The body's systems interact with one another.
The body's levels of organization work together constantly to maintain an internal balance called **homeostasis.** An example of homeostasis is the maintenance of body temperature.

SECTION

The skeletal system provides support and protection. pp. 590–597

1. Bones are living tissue.
The **skeletal system** is composed of bone tissue. Bones are mainly calcium but have a complex structure.

- **Compact bone** is dense tissue that gives bone its strength.
- **Spongy bone** is strong and lightweight.
- Marrow occupies spaces in spongy bone and produces all the body's red blood cells.
- Blood vessels supply oxygen and nutrients to bone and carry away new blood cells.

2. The skeleton is the body's framework.
The skeleton has two main divisions:

- The axial skeleton runs top to bottom and contains the skull (cranium), the vertebrae, and the ribs.
- The appendicular skeleton runs side to side and contains the bones of the shoulders, arms, hips, and legs.

3. The skeleton changes as the body develops and ages.
The skeleton changes as the body ages. In infancy, to allow for rapid growth of the brain, the skull has spaces between the bones, which close up as a baby ages. The bones of the arms and legs, called the long bones, have growth plates at their ends, which allow these bones to grow longer until puberty.

Bone is constantly being broken down and replaced with new bone. As you get older, the replacement may not keep up with loss, and bone density may decrease.

4. Joints connect parts of the skeletal system.
Bones connect to each other at joints.

- Immovable joints lock bones together at places called sutures. The skull is made up of immovable joints.
- Slightly movable joints can flex slightly.
- Tissues called ligaments hold bones together at freely movable joints.
- Freely movable joints are classified by the types of movement they produce.

Common Misconceptions

FEEDBACK MECHANISMS Students sometimes think that the body performs its functions without needing any internal communication mechanism. The body is constantly monitoring itself and making adjustments, without our conscious help.

 This misconception is addressed on p. 587.

MISCONCEPTION DATABASE
CLASSZONE.COM Background on student misconceptions

BONES ARE ALIVE Students sometimes conceive of bones as being solid and inert rather than living and needing nutrients and oxygen. A bone contains different types of tissue that have different densities. A bone is made up of living cells that need energy.

 This misconception is addressed on pp. 591 and 592.

Previewing Content

SECTION

The muscular system makes movement possible. pp. 598–605

1. Muscles perform important functions.
Muscles are made of cells called muscle fibers. They perform three functions.

- Muscles move the body.
- Muscles help maintain the body's temperature by generating heat.
- Muscles maintain upright posture.

2. Your body has different types of muscle.
Skeletal muscles are also called **voluntary muscles.** They allow the body to move when you want it to.

- Slow-twitch muscles allow slow movement.
- Fast-twitch muscles allow rapid movement.

Smooth muscles, also called **involuntary muscles,** are found inside organs and enable the body to perform automatic movements.

Cardiac muscle makes up the heart. Its cells are arranged in webs that contract without conscious control to make the heart beat.

3. Skeletal muscles and tendons allow bones to move.
Tendons attach muscles to bones. Muscles work in pairs to cause bones to move. One muscle contracts, pulling a bone, while the other lengthens.

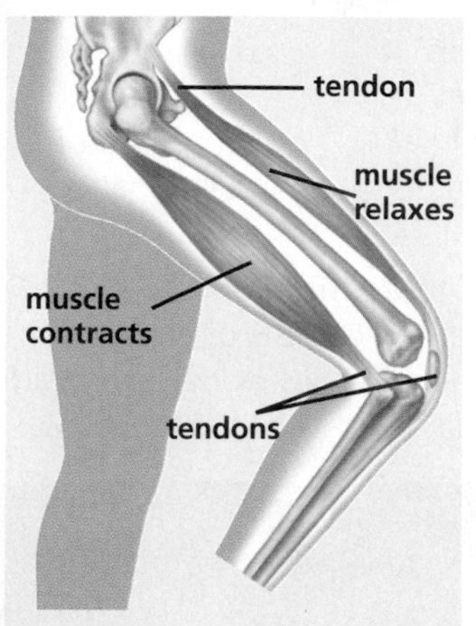

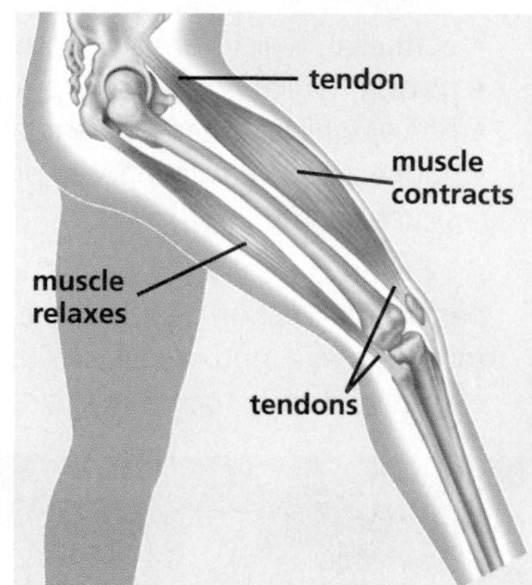

Muscles that cause movement always work in pairs or groups whose movements oppose each other.

4. Muscles grow and heal.
Muscles develop with age. Exercise increases muscle size.

Common Misconceptions

MUSCLES CONTRACT Most middle school students think that muscles can push and pull. In fact, muscles can only pull, which they do by contracting.

This misconception is addressed on p. 602.

MISCONCEPTION DATABASE
CLASSZONE.COM Background on student misconceptions

Previewing Labs

EXPLORE the BIG idea

How Many Bones Are in Your Hand? p. 583 Students examine their own hands to infer the locations of bones and joints.	**TIME** 10 minutes **MATERIALS** paper and pencil
How Does It Move? p. 583 Students compare joints to everyday objects to understand how joints work.	**TIME** 10 minutes **MATERIALS** none
Internet Activity: The Human Body, p. 583 Students compare body systems in different regions to understand the functions of different systems.	**TIME** 20 minutes **MATERIALS** computer with Internet connection

SECTION 1

INVESTIGATE Systems, p. 586 Students identify ways their bodies work to understand the interdependence of body systems.	**TIME** 20 minutes **MATERIALS** 1 large sheet of paper

SECTION 2

EXPLORE Levers, p. 590 Students use a sports bag hung over an arm to demonstrate a lever.	**TIME** 10 minutes **MATERIALS** sports bag
INVESTIGATE Movable Joints, p. 595 Students observe how their joints move.	**TIME** 20 minutes **MATERIALS** book

SECTION 3

EXPLORE Muscles, p. 598 Students perform leg movements to observe how muscles change.	**TIME** 10 minutes **MATERIALS** chair
CHAPTER INVESTIGATION **A Closer Look at Muscles,** pp. 604–605 Students examine a chicken wing to infer how human muscles and bones interact.	**TIME** 40 minutes **MATERIALS** protective gloves, uncooked chicken wing and leg (soaked in bleach solution: 2 Tbsp bleach, dissolved in 1 cup water), paper towels, scissors, dissection tray

R **Additional INVESTIGATION,** Bones and Calcium, A, B, & C, pp. 59–67; Teacher Instructions, pp. 305–306

Previewing Chapter Resources

CHAPTER 17
Systems, Support, and Movement

INTEGRATED TECHNOLOGY

CLASSZONE.COM
- eEdition Plus
- EasyPlanner Plus
- Misconception Database
- Content Review
- Test Practice
- Visualizations
- Resource Centers
- Simulations
- Internet Activity: The Human Body
- Math Tutorial

SCILINKS.ORG
SCILINKS

CD-ROMS
- eEdition
- EasyPlanner
- Power Presentations
- Content Review
- Lab Generator
- Test Generator

AUDIO CDS
- Audio Readings
- Audio Readings in Spanish

LABS AND ACTIVITIES

EXPLORE the Big Idea, p. 583
- How Many Bones Are in Your Hand?
- How Does It Move?
- Internet Activity: The Human Body

UNIT RESOURCE BOOK
- Family Letter, p. ix
- Spanish Family Letter, p. x
- Unit Projects, pp. 5–10

Lab Generator CD-ROM
Generate customized labs.

SECTION

The human body is complex.
pp. 585–589

Time: 2 periods (1 block)

 Lesson Plan, pp. 11–12

UNIT TRANSPARENCY BOOK
- Big Idea Flow Chart, p. T1
- Daily Vocabulary Scaffolding, p. T2
- Note-Taking Model, p. T3
- 3-Minute Warm-Up, p. T4

- INVESTIGATE Systems, p. 586
- Think Science, p. 589

UNIT RESOURCE BOOK
Datasheet, Systems, p. 20

SECTION

The skeletal system provides support and protection.
pp. 590–597

Time: 2 periods (1 block)

 Lesson Plan, pp. 22–23

- **RESOURCE CENTER,** Skeletal System
- **SIMULATION,** Assemble a Skeleton
- **MATH TUTORIAL**

UNIT TRANSPARENCY BOOK
- Daily Vocabulary Scaffolding, p. T2
- 3-Minute Warm-Up, p. T4
- "A Close Look at Bone" Visual, p. T6

- EXPLORE Levers, p. 590
- INVESTIGATE Movable Joints, p. 595
- Math in Science, p. 597

UNIT RESOURCE BOOK
- Datasheet, Movable Joints, p. 31
- Math Support, p. 48
- Math Practice, p. 49
- Additional INVESTIGATION, Bones and Calcium, A, B, & C, pp. 59–67

SECTION

The muscular system makes movement possible.
pp. 598–605

Time: 4 periods (2 blocks)

 Lesson Plan, pp. 33–34

- **RESOURCE CENTER,** Muscles
- **SIMULATION,** Skeletal Muscles

UNIT TRANSPARENCY BOOK
- Big Idea Flow Chart, p. T1
- Daily Vocabulary Scaffolding, p. T2
- 3-Minute Warm-Up, p. T5
- Chapter Outline, pp. T7–T8

- EXPLORE Muscles, p. 598
- CHAPTER INVESTIGATION, A Closer Look at Muscles, pp. 604–605

UNIT RESOURCE BOOK
CHAPTER INVESTIGATION, A Closer Look at Muscles, A, B, & C, pp. 50–58

KEY TO ICONS

 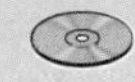 CD/CD-ROM
INTERNET
 Pupil Edition
 Teacher Edition
UNIT RESOURCE BOOK
 UNIT TRANSPARENCY BOOK
UNIT ASSESSMENT BOOK
 SPANISH ASSESSMENT BOOK
SCIENCE TOOLKIT

READING AND REINFORCEMENT	ASSESSMENT	STANDARDS
 • Four Square, B22–23 • Combination Notes, C36 • Daily Vocabulary Scaffolding, H1–8  **UNIT RESOURCE BOOK** • Vocabulary Practice, pp. 45–46 • Decoding Support, p. 47 • Summarizing the Chapter, pp. 68–69 **Audio Readings CD** Listen to Pupil Edition. **Audio Readings in Spanish CD** Listen to Pupil Edition in Spanish.	 • Chapter Review, pp. 606–608 • Standardized Test Practice, p. 609  **UNIT ASSESSMENT BOOK** • Diagnostic Test, pp. 1–2 • Chapter Test, A, B, & C, pp. 6–17 • Alternative Assessment, pp. 18–19  Spanish Chapter Test, pp. 65–68  **Test Generator CD-ROM** Generate customized tests.  **Lab Generator CD-ROM** Rubrics for Labs	National Standards A.1–8, A.9.a–c, A.9.e–g, C.1.a, C.1.d–e, G.1.b See p. 582 for the standards.
UNIT RESOURCE BOOK • Reading Study Guide, A & B, pp. 13–16 • Spanish Reading Study Guide, pp. 17–18 • Challenge and Extension, p. 19 • Reinforcing Key Concepts, p. 21	 Ongoing Assessment, pp. 585–588  Section 17.1 Review, p. 588  **UNIT ASSESSMENT BOOK** Section 17.1 Quiz, p. 3	National Standards A.2–7, A.9.a–b, A.9.e–f, C.1.a, C.1.d, G.1.b
 **UNIT RESOURCE BOOK** • Reading Study Guide, A & B, pp. 24–27 • Spanish Reading Study Guide, pp. 28–29 • Challenge and Extension, p. 30 • Reinforcing Key Concepts, p. 32 • Challenge Reading, pp. 43–44	 Ongoing Assessment, pp. 591–593, 595–596  Section 17.2 Review, p. 596  **UNIT ASSESSMENT BOOK** Section 17.2 Quiz, p. 4	National Standards A.2–8, A.9.a–c, A.9.e–f, C.1.d–e, G.1.b
 **UNIT RESOURCE BOOK** • Reading Study Guide, A & B, pp. 35–38 • Spanish Reading Study Guide, pp. 39–40 • Challenge and Extension, p. 41 • Reinforcing Key Concepts, p. 42	 Ongoing Assessment, pp. 598–601, 603  Section 17.3 Review, p. 603  **UNIT ASSESSMENT BOOK** Section 17.3 Quiz, p. 5	National Standards A.1–7, A.9.a–b, A.9.e–g, C.1.d–e, G.1.b

Previewing Resources for Differentiated Instruction

CHAPTER INVESTIGATION

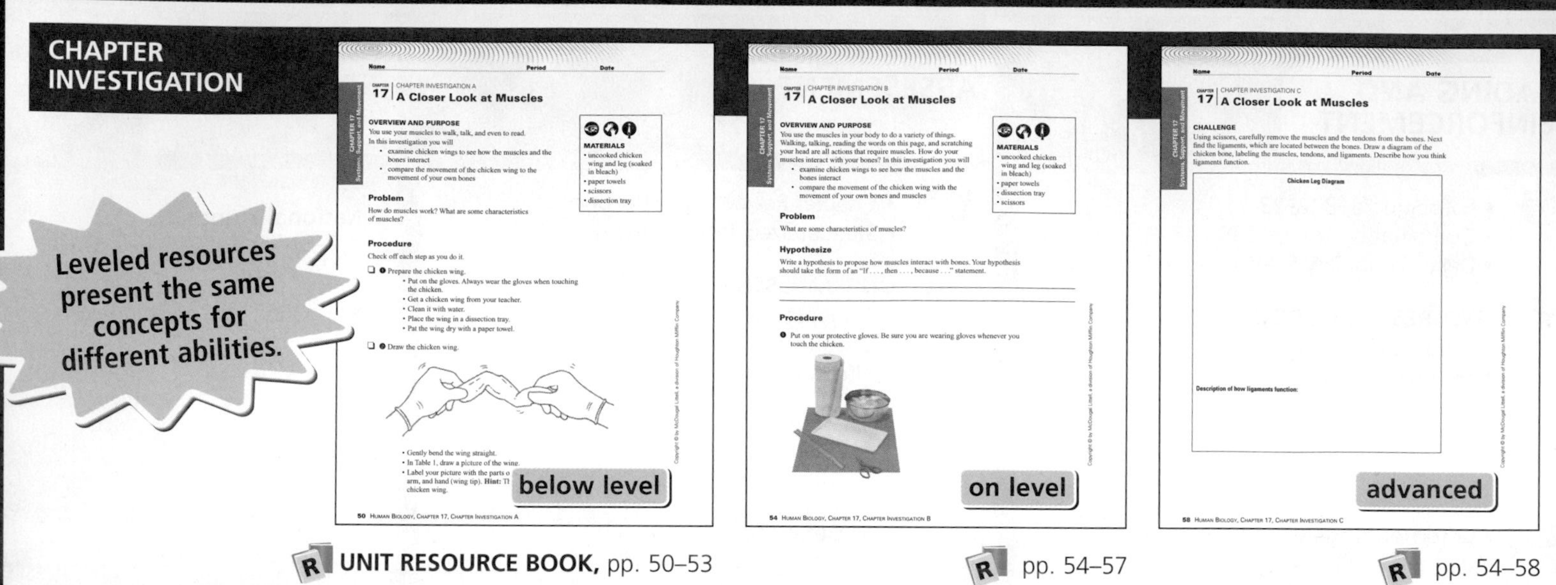

UNIT RESOURCE BOOK, pp. 50–53 | pp. 54–57 | pp. 54–58

READING STUDY GUIDE

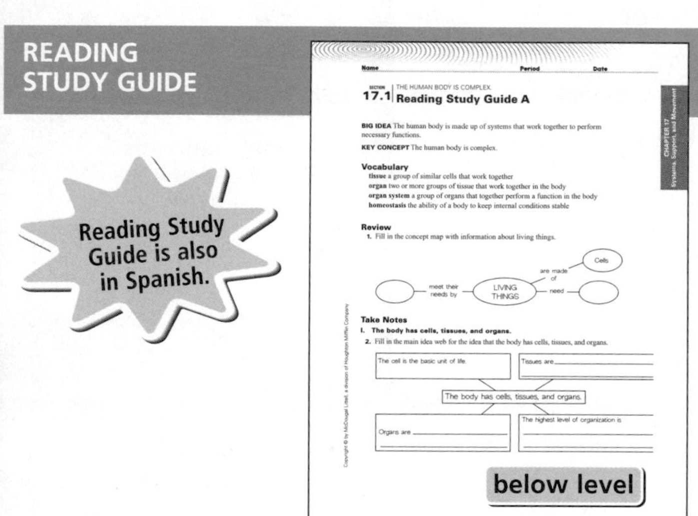

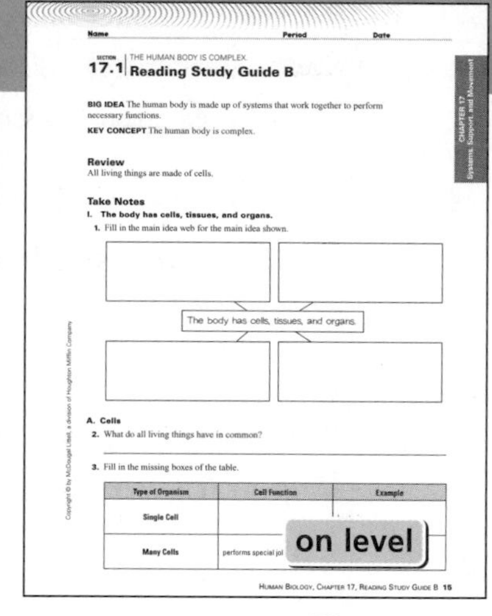

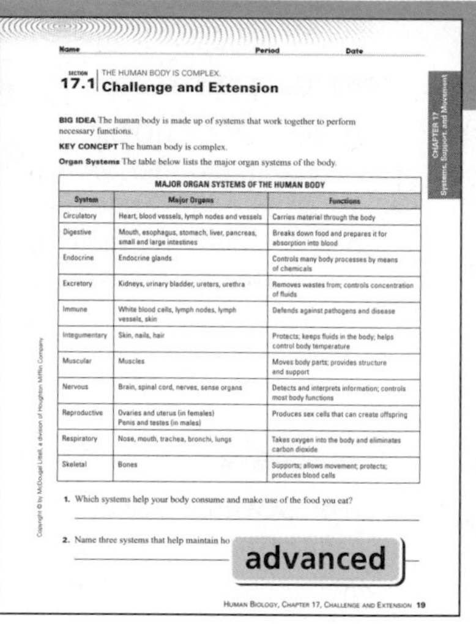

UNIT RESOURCE BOOK, pp. 13–14 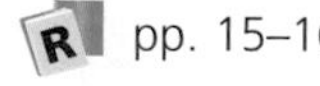 pp. 15–16  p. 19

CHAPTER TEST

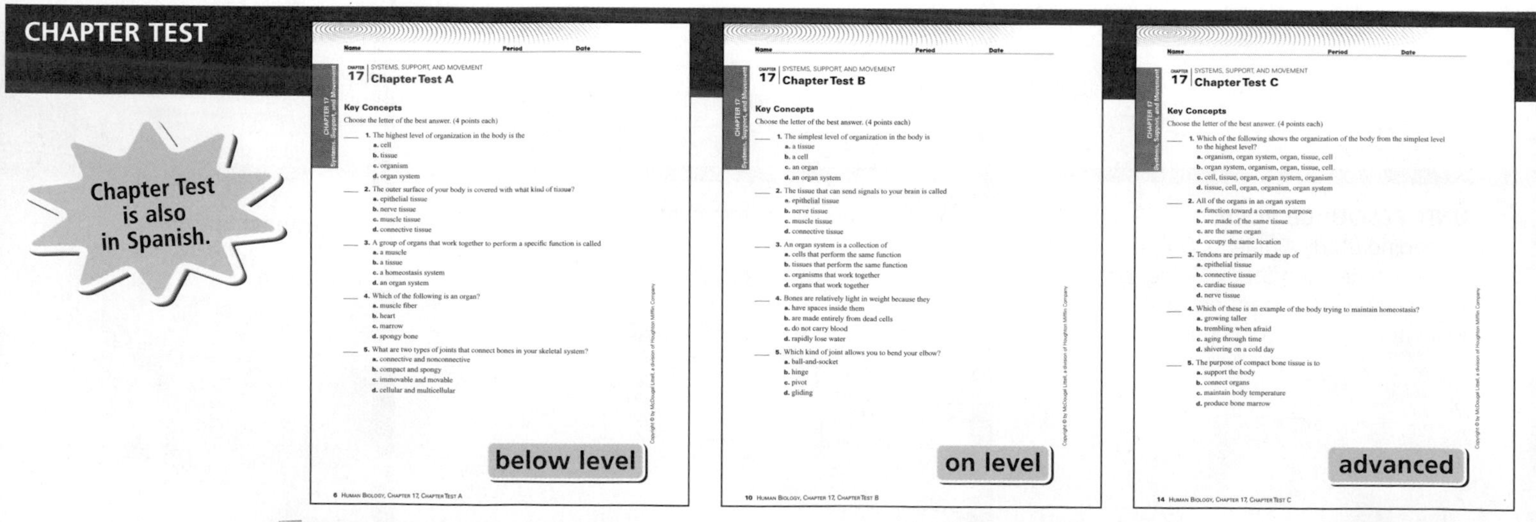

UNIT ASSESSMENT BOOK, pp. 6–9 | pp. 10–13 | pp. 14–17

TECHNOLOGY

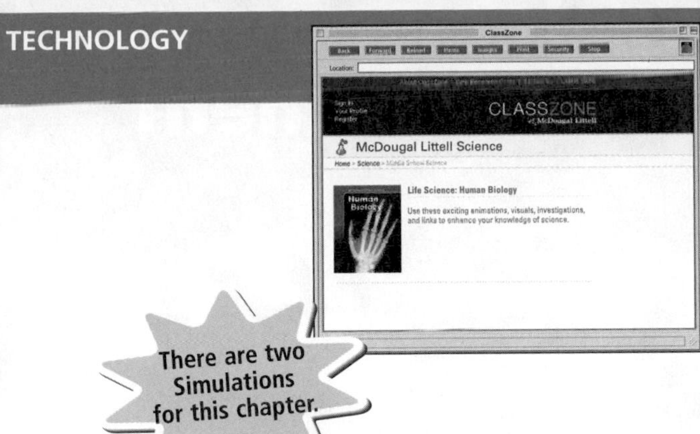

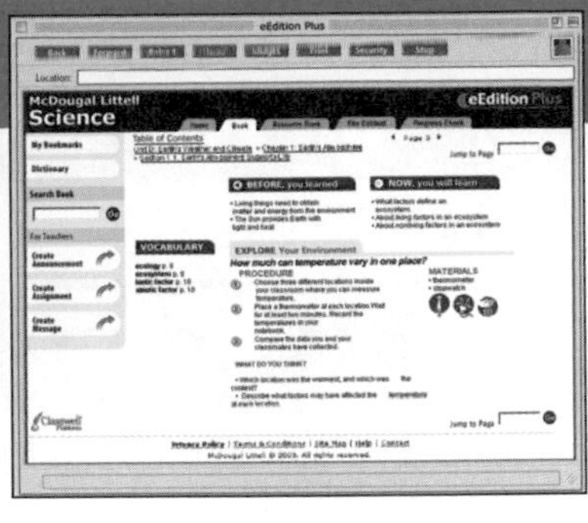

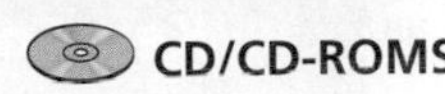

VISUAL CONTENT

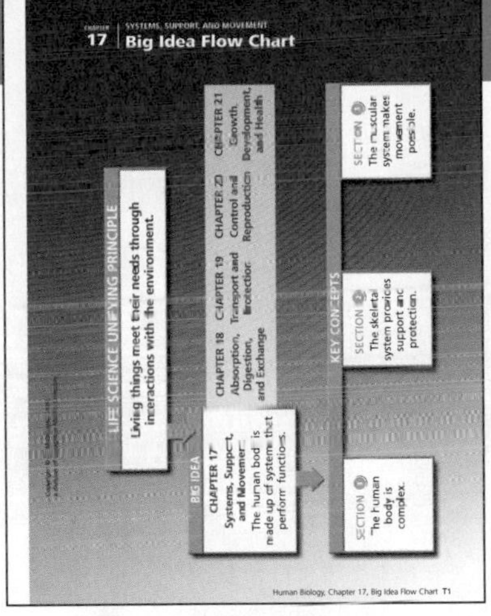

UNIT TRANSPARENCY BOOK, p. T1

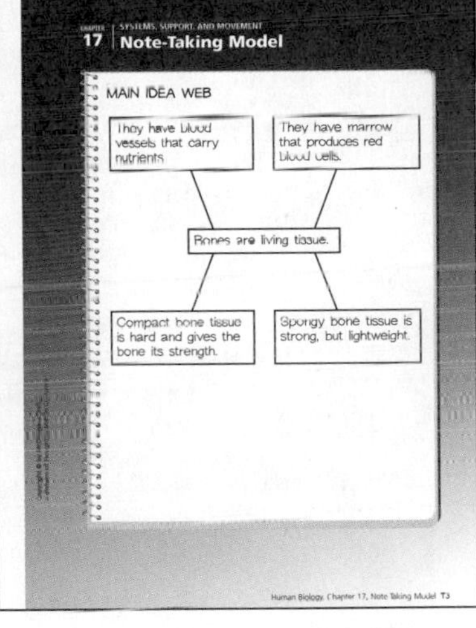

p. T3

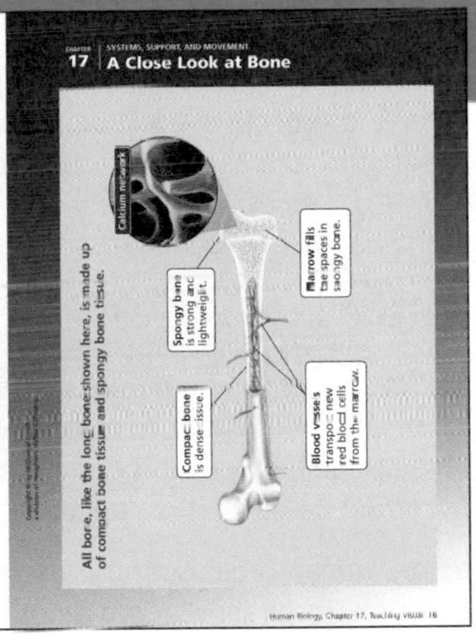

p. T6

MORE SUPPORT

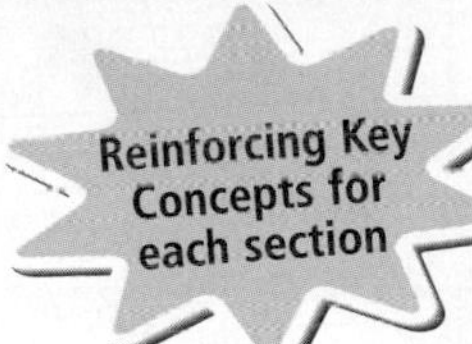

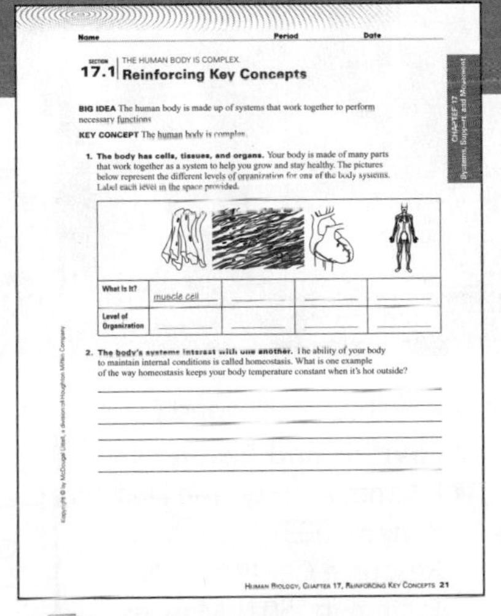

UNIT RESOURCE BOOK, p. 21

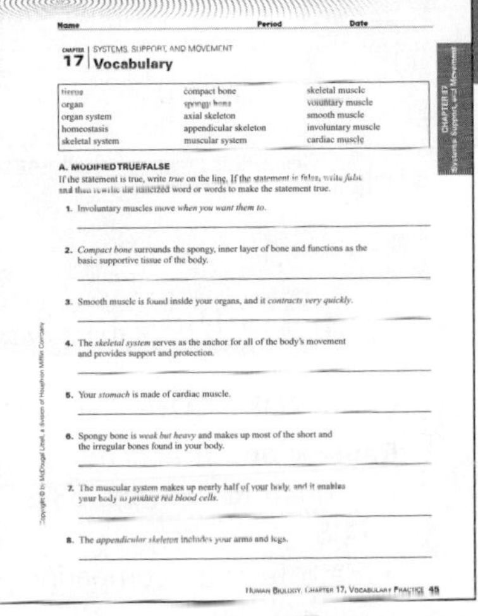

pp. 45–46

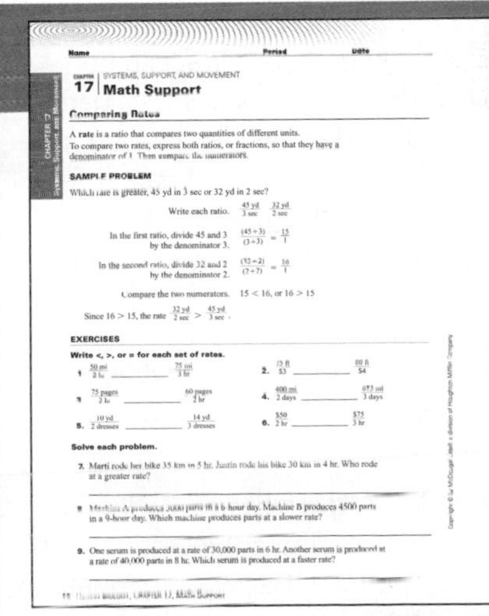

p. 48

CHAPTER

Systems, Support, and Movement

INTRODUCE

the BIG idea

Have students look at the photograph of the wheelchair racer and discuss how the question in the box links to the Big Idea:

- How are joints helping this racer?
- What is the function of the skeletal system? of the muscular system?

National Science Education Standards

Content

C.1.a All living systems demonstrate structure and function. Levels of organization for structure and function include cells, organs, tissues, organ systems, organisms, and ecosystems.

C.1.d Specialized cells perform specialized functions. Groups of specialized cells cooperate to form a tissue, such as a muscle. Different tissues form organs. Each type of cell, tissue, and organ has a distinct structure and set of functions.

C.1.e The human organism has systems for digestion, respiration, reproduction, circulation, excretion, movement, control and coordination, and protection.

Process

A.1–8 Identify questions that can be answered through scientific investigations; design and conduct an investigation; use tools to gather and interpret data; use evidence to describe, predict, explain, model; think critically to make relationships between evidence and explanation; recognize different explanations and predictions; communicate scientific procedures and explanations; use mathematics.

A.9.a–c, A.9.e–g Understand scientific inquiry by using different investigations, methods, mathematics, and explanations based on logic, evidence, and skepticism. Data often results in new investigations.

G.1.b Science requires different abilities.

CHAPTER

Systems, Support, and Movement

the BIG idea

The human body is made up of systems that work together to perform necessary functions.

Key Concepts

SECTION

The human body is complex.
Learn about the parts and systems in the human body.

SECTION

The skeletal system provides support and protection.
Learn how the skeletal system is organized and what it does.

SECTION

The muscular system makes movement possible.
Learn about the different types of muscles and how they work.

What systems make it possible for this racer to move so fast?

Internet Preview

CLASSZONE.COM

Chapter 17 online resources: Content Review, two Simulations, three Resource Centers, Math Tutorial, Test Practice

INTERNET PREVIEW

CLASSZONE.COM For student use with the following pages:

Review and Practice

- Content Review, pp. 584, 606
- Math Tutorial: Comparing Rates, p. 597
- Test Practice, p. 609

Activities and Resources

- Internet Activity: The Human Body, p. 583
- Resource Centers: Skeletal System, p. 591; Muscles, p. 599
- Simulations: Assemble a Skeleton, p. 592; Skeletal Muscles, p. 602

Tissues and Organs
Code: MDL044

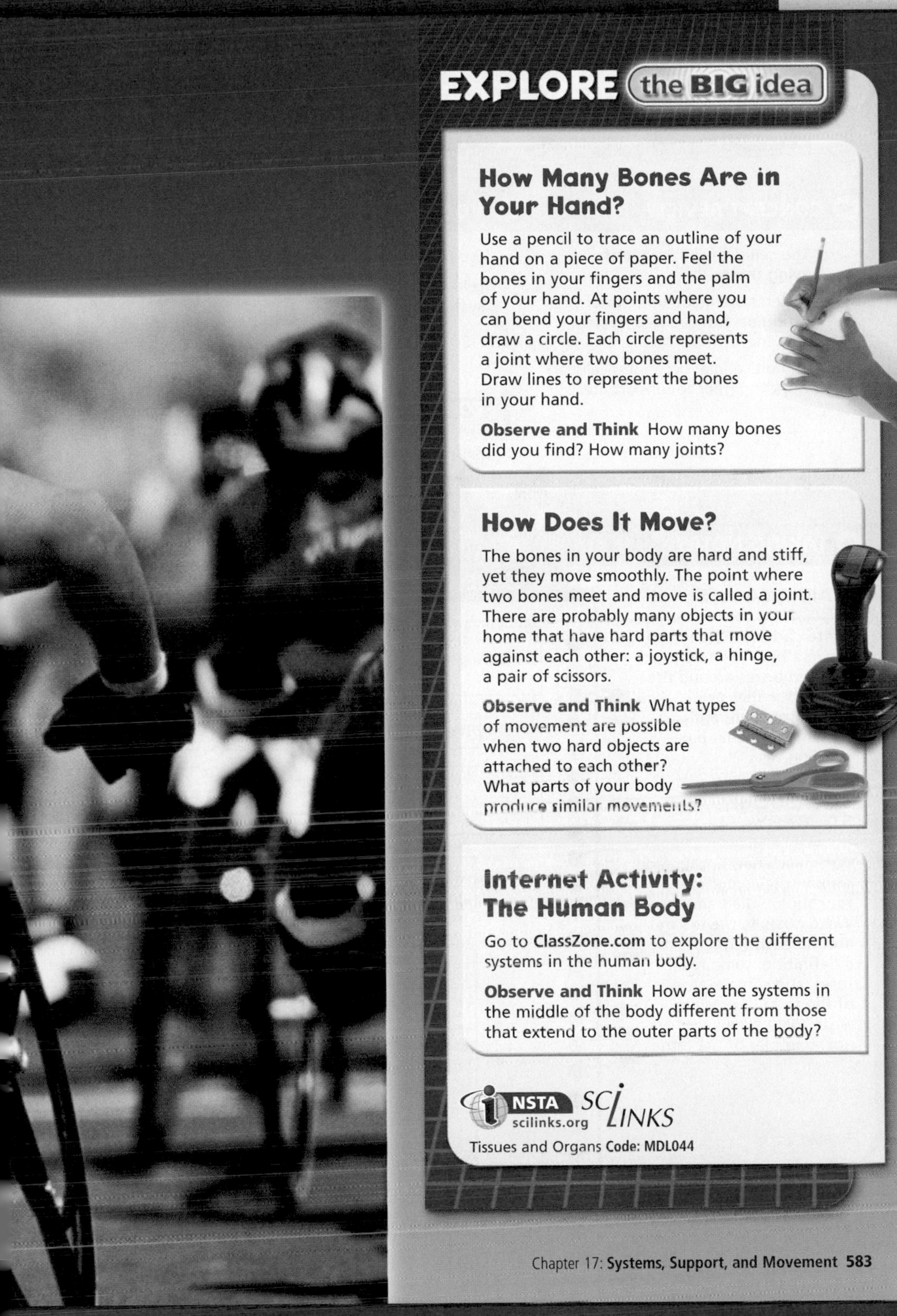

EXPLORE the BIG idea

How Many Bones Are in Your Hand?

Use a pencil to trace an outline of your hand on a piece of paper. Feel the bones in your fingers and the palm of your hand. At points where you can bend your fingers and hand, draw a circle. Each circle represents a joint where two bones meet. Draw lines to represent the bones in your hand.

Observe and Think How many bones did you find? How many joints?

How Does It Move?

The bones in your body are hard and stiff, yet they move smoothly. The point where two bones meet and move is called a joint. There are probably many objects in your home that have hard parts that move against each other: a joystick, a hinge, a pair of scissors.

Observe and Think What types of movement are possible when two hard objects are attached to each other? What parts of your body produce similar movements?

Internet Activity: The Human Body

Go to **ClassZone.com** to explore the different systems in the human body.

Observe and Think How are the systems in the middle of the body different from those that extend to the outer parts of the body?

NSTA scilinks.org SCILINKS

Tissues and Organs **Code: MDL044**

TEACHING WITH TECHNOLOGY

CBL and Probeware For the demonstration of leverage that students perform on p. 590, you may wish to have them take measurements with a force sensor to compare forces.

Digital Camera For the investigation on p. 595, you might want to have students use a digital camera to take pictures of joint movements. They can print the photographs and add labels for their activity write-ups.

EXPLORE the BIG idea

These inquiry-based activities are appropriate for use at home or as a supplement to classroom instruction.

How Many Bones Are in Your Hand?

PURPOSE To introduce students to the structure of bones and joints. By examining their own hands, students will see that movement occurs at joints between bones.

TIP *10 min.* Encourage students to find all the joints in their hands, then have them infer whether the same number might exist in their feet.

Answer: There are 19 bones in a hand and 14 joints. A joint allows movement between two bones.

REVISIT after p. 593.

How Does It Move?

PURPOSE To introduce students to how joints allow movement. Students observe the movements of common household objects and compare them to body movements.

TIP *10 min.* You might display a group of objects from your home or school (hinge, scissors, joystick, tracking ball) instead of eliciting recollection.

Answer: Movement is limited in direction by how the joint is put together. Elbow, knee, and fingers are like hinges; the neck is like the pivot on a pair of scissors; the shoulder and hip are like the joystick.

REVISIT after p. 595.

Internet Activity: The Human Body

PURPOSE To introduce students to the structures and functions of the different systems of the human body.

TIP *20 min.* You might wish to have each student take a different system and then compare notes with other students.

Sample answer: The systems in the middle of the body are more essential to body function than the systems toward the outer parts of the body.

REVISIT after p. 588.

PREPARE

CONCEPT REVIEW

Activate Prior Knowledge

- Ask volunteers to name any systems that make up the human body. *Sample answer: skeletal, circulatory, nervous, respiratory, digestive, immune, reproductive, muscular, integumentary*
- Have them name any organs that they know of in each system. Organize their ideas in a chart on the board. Use the names of the systems as column headings. *Sample answer: heart, lungs, brain, skin*
- Discuss how systems work together—for example, to get nourishment.

TAKING NOTES

Main Idea Web

When students write ideas from the text in a web, they not only practice them but reorganize them from a linear pattern to the more multidimensional patterns that the brain uses.

Vocabulary Strategy

The four square diagram organizes all aspects of a concept into a coherent pattern. By filling in their own words, students personalize their understanding.

Point out that it is okay to have a blank square in the diagram. Some terms, such as *skeletal system,* have no clear nonexamples.

Vocabulary and Note-Taking Resources

- Vocabulary Practice, pp. 45–46
- Decoding Support, p. 47

- Daily Vocabulary Scaffolding, p. T2
- Note-Taking Model, p. T3

- Four Square, B22–23
- Combination Notes, C36
- Daily Vocabulary Scaffolding, H1–8

CHAPTER 17

Getting Ready to Learn

CONCEPT REVIEW

- The cell is the basic unit of living things.
- Systems are made up of interacting parts that share matter and energy.
- In multicellular organisms cells work together to support life.

VOCABULARY REVIEW

See Glossary for definitions.

cell
system

CONTENT REVIEW
CLASSZONE.COM
Review concepts and vocabulary.

TAKING NOTES

MAIN IDEA WEB

Write each new blue heading in a box. Then write notes in boxes around the center box that give important terms and details about that blue heading.

VOCABULARY STRATEGY

Write each new vocabulary term in the center of a **four square** diagram. Write notes in the squares around each term. Include a definition, some features, and some examples of the term. If possible, write some things that are not examples of the term.

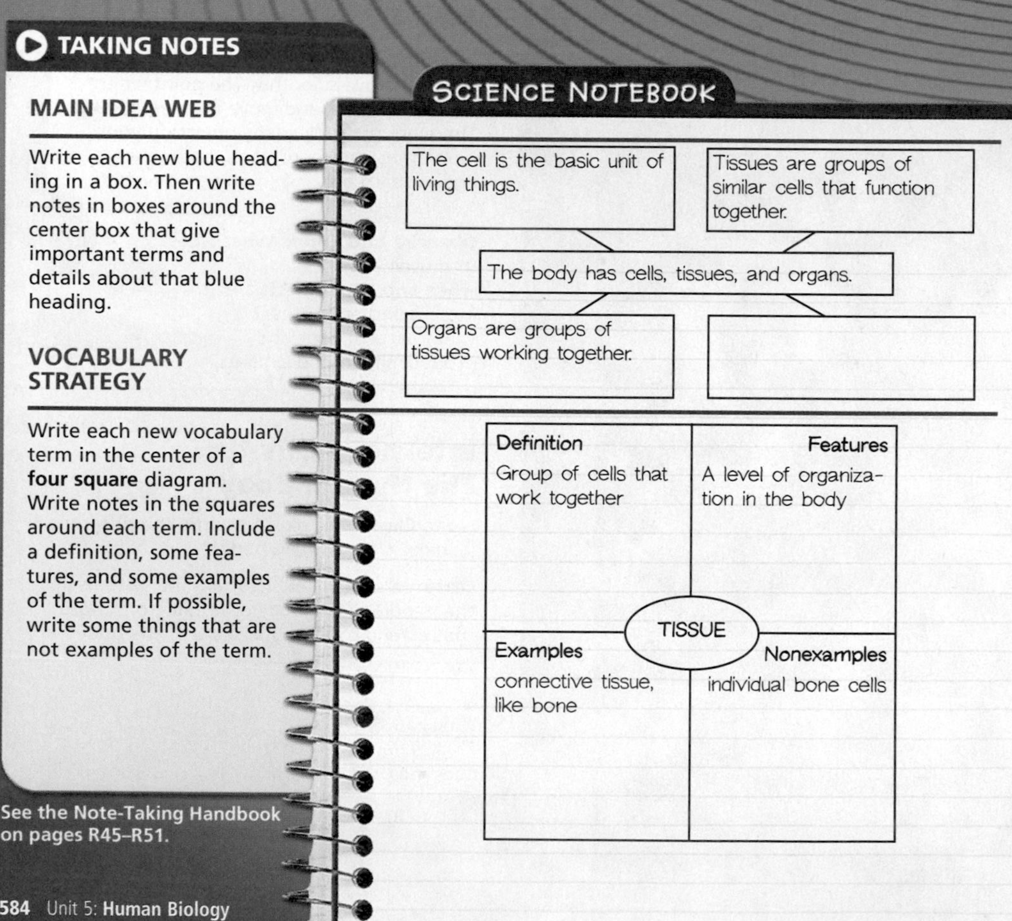

See the Note-Taking Handbook on pages R45–R51.

584 Unit 5: Human Biology

CHECK READINESS

Administer the Diagnostic Test to determine students' readiness for new science content and their mastery of requisite math skills.

 Diagnostic Test, pp. 1–2

Technology Resources

Students needing content and math skills should visit **ClassZone.com**.

- **CONTENT REVIEW**
- **MATH TUTORIAL**

 **CONTENT REVIEW CD-ROM**

KEY CONCEPT

The human body is complex.

BEFORE, you learned

- All living things are made of cells
- All living things need energy
- Living things meet their needs through interactions with the environment

NOW, you will learn

- About the organization of the human body
- About different types of tissues
- About the functions of organ systems

VOCABULARY

tissue p. 586
organ p. 587
organ system p. 588
homeostasis p. 588

THINK ABOUT

How is the human body like a city?

A city is made up of many parts that perform different functions. Buildings provide places to live and work. Transportation systems move people around. Electrical energy provides light and heat. Similarly, the human body is made of several systems. The skeletal system, like the framework of a building, provides support. The digestive system works with the respiratory system to provide energy and materials. What other systems in your body can you compare to a system in the city?

The body has cells, tissues, and organs.

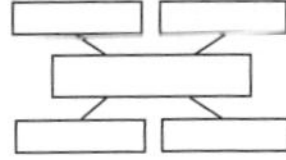

MAIN IDEA WEB
As you read this section, complete the main idea web begun on page 584.

Your body is made of many parts that work together as a system to help you grow and stay healthy. The basic level of organization in your body is the cell. Next come tissues, then individual organs, and then systems that are made up of organs. The highest level of organization is the organism itself. You can think of the body as having five levels of organization: cells, tissues, organs, organ systems, and the organism. Although these levels seem separate from one another, they all work together.

CHECK YOUR READING What are five levels of organization in your body?

RESOURCES FOR DIFFERENTIATED INSTRUCTION

Below Level

UNIT RESOURCE BOOK

- Reading Study Guide A, pp. 13–14
- Decoding Support, p. 47

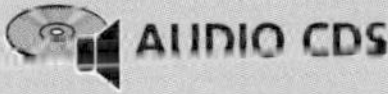

Advanced

UNIT RESOURCE BOOK

Challenge and Extension, p. 19

English Learners

UNIT RESOURCE BOOK

Spanish Reading Study Guide, pp. 17–18

- Audio Readings in Spanish
- Audio Readings (English)

17.1 FOCUS

Set Learning Goals

Students will

- Describe the organization of the human body.
- Describe four types of tissue.
- Explain how organ systems function.
- Predict which body systems are involved in various everyday activities.

3-Minute Warm-Up

Display Transparency 4 or copy this exercise on the board:

Draw a cluster diagram with the words *Living Things* in the center circle and three empty circles connected to it. Fill in the circles with three attributes of all living things. *Sample answer: All consist of cells; all need energy; all interact with their environment to meet their needs.*

3-Minute Warm-Up, p. T4

17.1 MOTIVATE

THINK ABOUT

PURPOSE Have students work in pairs or small groups to make tables comparing the body systems to the various public works systems in a city.

Ongoing Assessment

CHECK YOUR READING *Answer: from smallest to largest: cells, tissues, organs, organ systems, organism*

17.1 INSTRUCT

INVESTIGATE Systems

PURPOSE To understand how body systems work together

TIPS *20 min.*

- Allow students to use the chart from "Activate Prior Knowledge," p. 584.
- Remind students to be aware of their breathing and their hearts beating.
- Suggest that students bring in pictures of people performing everyday tasks, for follow-up discussion.

WHAT DO YOU THINK? *Sample answers: Talking on the phone involves the nervous system, the respiratory system, and the muscular system. When you sleep, your body breathes, excretes waste through the skin and the mouth, moves, and dreams.*

CHALLENGE *Answers will vary, but should group activities appropriately.*

Datasheet, Systems, p. 20

Technology Resources

Customize this student lab as needed or look for an alternative. Print rubrics to assess student lab reports.

Lab Generator CD-ROM

INVESTIGATE Systems

How do the systems in your body interact?

SKILL FOCUS Predicting

MATERIALS large sheet of paper

TIME 20 minutes

PROCEDURE

1. Work with other classmates to make a list of everyday activities.
2. Discuss how your body responds to each task. Record your ideas.
3. Identify and count the systems in your body that you think are used to perform the task.
4. Have someone from your group make a chart of the different activities.

WHAT DO YOU THINK?

- Which systems did you name, and how did they work together to perform each activity?
- When you are asleep, what activities does your body perform?

CHALLENGE How could you make an experiment that would test your predictions?

Cells

A

The cell is the basic unit of life. Cells make up all living things. Some organisms, such as bacteria, are made of only a single cell. In these organisms the single cell performs all of the tasks necessary for survival. That individual cell captures and releases energy, uses materials, and grows. In more complex organisms, such as humans and many other animals and plants, cells are specialized. Specialized cells perform specific jobs. A red blood cell, for example, carries oxygen from the lungs throughout the body.

Tissues

B

A **tissue** is a group of similar cells that work together to perform a particular function. Think of a tissue as a brick wall and the cells within it as the individual bricks. Taken together, the bricks form something larger and more functional. But just as the bricks need to be placed in a certain way to form the wall, cells must be organized in a tissue.

How are cells related to tissues?

The human body contains several types of tissues. These tissues are classified into four main groups according to their function: epithelial tissue, nerve tissue, muscle tissue, and connective tissue.

Develop Critical Thinking

COMPARE Have students list ways in which people are like cells. *No two are exactly alike, both grow and can repair themselves, both have parts that serve to control all functions, both are living and have special jobs, both use food and oxygen to produce energy, both expel wastes, and both will eventually die.*

Ongoing Assessment

Describe the organization of the human body.

Ask: Why are the cells of complex organisms specialized? *Specialized cells perform different jobs necessary for survival.*

Answer: Tissues are made of cells of the same type.

DIFFERENTIATE INSTRUCTION

More Reading Support

A Give an example of a specialized cell. *red blood cell*

B What do you call a group of similar cells that function together? *a tissue*

English Learners Help English learners with different word forms. For example, in the "Cells" paragraph, p. 586, *make* is used in a variety of forms: "Cells make up all living things;" "Some organisms, such as bacteria, are made of only a single cell." This verb can be found as *make, made, make up, made up, made up of,* or *made of.*

- Epithelial (ehp-uh-THEE-lee-uhl) tissue functions as a boundary. It covers all of the inner and outer surfaces of your body. Each of your internal organs is covered with a layer of epithelial tissue.
- Nerve tissue functions as a messaging system. Cells in nerve tissue carry electrical impulses between your brain and the various parts of your body in response to changing conditions.
- Muscle tissue functions in movement. Movement results when muscle cells contract, or shorten, and then relax. In some cases, such as throwing a ball, you control the movement. In other cases, such as the beating of your heart, the movement occurs without conscious control.
- Connective tissue functions to hold parts of the body together, providing support, protection, strength, padding, and insulation. Tendons and ligaments are connective tissues that hold bones and muscles together. Bone itself is another connective tissue. It supports and protects the soft parts of your body.

?C

Organs

?D

Groups of different tissues make up organs. An **organ** is a structure that is made up of two or more types of tissue that work together to carry out a function in the body. For example, the heart that pumps blood around your body contains all four types of tissues. As in cells and tissues, the structure of an organ relates to its function. The stomach's bag-shaped structure and strong muscular walls make it suited for breaking down food. The walls of the heart are also muscular, allowing it to function as a pump.

Levels of Organization

The human body can be studied at different levels of organization.

250 ×

Cells (muscle cells)

Organism (human)

Tissue (cardiac muscle)

Organ (heart)

Organ system (circulatory system)

Address Misconceptions

IDENTIFY Ask: What makes your heart beat? If students respond that the heartbeat is the result of a natural rhythm started at birth, they may hold the misconception that the body does things without needing any internal communications.

CORRECT Have students take their pulse before and after running in place for one minute, noting that their heart rate changes. Point out that the nervous system tells the heart that the legs are moving and that it needs to beat faster.

REASSESS Ask: How do you know when you need to eat? *The brain monitors the body, realizes that the body needs nourishment, and makes me feel hungry.*

Technology Resources

Visit **ClassZone.com** for background on common student misconceptions.

 **MISCONCEPTION DATABASE**

Metacognitive Strategy

Have students devise a strategy for remembering the four tissue types. Possibilities include a graphic organizer, mnemonics, and pictures.

Teach Difficult Concepts

Students may have trouble understanding that epithelial tissue serves as a boundary. Discuss a familiar type of boundary, such as room walls. Ask:

- What do room boundaries do? *keep heat in or out, weather and noise out*
- What do epithelial tissues, such as skin, do? *keep heat and fluid in, bacteria and other unwanted things out*

DIFFERENTIATE INSTRUCTION

More Reading Support

C What type of tissue provides support, protection, strength, and padding? *connective tissue*

D What do you call tissues that work together on one function? *organ*

Advanced Although this module presents the biology of a healthy human body, everyone has strengths and weaknesses. Explain that survival and high achievement are not dependent on full functioning of every organ. Discuss successful individuals with disabilities. Examples: Sir Steve Redgrave, Olympic gold medal for rowing: diabetes, dyslexia; Sir Stephen Hawking, theoretical physicist: amyotrophic lateral sclerosis (ALS); Andrea Bocelli, tenor: blindness; Tionne "T-Boz" Watkins, R&B singer: sickle-cell disease.

R Challenge and Extension, p. 19

Ongoing Assessment

Describe four types of tissue.

Ask: What are the four types of tissue and their functions? *Epithelial tissues act as boundaries; nerves carry messages; muscles enable movement; connective tissues protect, insulate, and support.*

Teach Difficult Concepts

Some students may have a hard time understanding homeostasis. Use a thermostat as an example. Point out that the heat or air conditioning is supplied just long enough to return an area to the set temperature.

EXPLORE the BIG idea

Revisit "Internet Activity: The Human Body" on p. 583. Have students discuss how body structures are related to their functions.

Ongoing Assessment

Explain how organ systems function.

Ask: How do organ systems meet the body's needs? *Each organ system performs a necessary function, and together the systems allow the human organism to grow, reproduce, and maintain life.*

Reinforce the BIG idea

Have students relate the section to the Big Idea.

 Reinforcing Key Concepts, p. 21

Organ Systems

An **organ system** is a group of organs that together perform a function that helps the body meet its needs for energy and materials. For example, your stomach, mouth, throat, large and small intestines, liver, and pancreas are all part of the organ system called the digestive system. The body is made up of many organ systems. In this unit, you will read about these systems. They include the skeletal, muscular, respiratory, digestive, urinary, circulatory, immune, nervous, and reproductive systems. Together, these systems allow the human organism to grow, reproduce, and maintain life.

The body's systems interact with one another.

READING TIP

VOCABULARY
The word *homeostasis* contains two word roots. *Homeo* comes from a root meaning "same." *Stasis* comes from a root meaning "stand still" or "stay."

The ability of your body to maintain internal conditions is called **homeostasis** (HOH-mee-oh-STAY-sihs). Your body is constantly regulating such things as your body temperature, the amount of sugar in your blood, even your posture. The processes that take place in your body occur within a particular set of conditions.

The body's many levels of organization, from cells to organ systems, work constantly to maintain the balance needed for the survival of the organism. For example, on a hot day, you may sweat. Sweating keeps the temperature inside your body constant, even though the temperature of your surroundings changes.

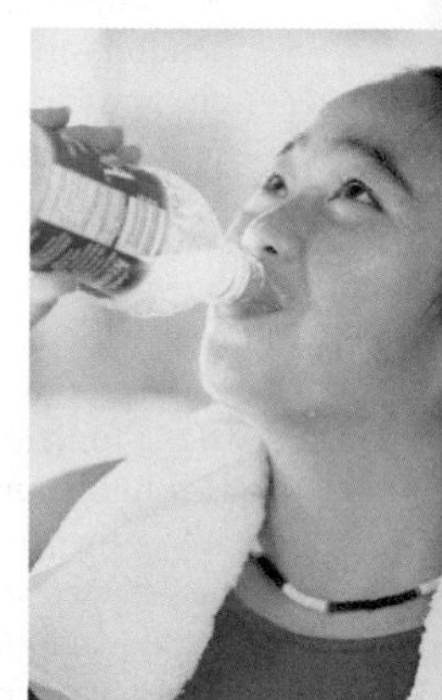

INFER This student is drinking water after exercising. Why is it important to drink fluids after you sweat?

17.1 Review

KEY CONCEPTS

1. Draw a diagram that shows the relationship among cells, tissues, organs, and organ systems.
2. Make a chart of the four basic tissue groups that includes names, functions, and examples.
3. Identify three functions performed by organ systems.

CRITICAL THINKING

4. **Apply** How does drinking water after you sweat help maintain homeostasis?
5. **Compare and Contrast** Compare and contrast the four basic tissue groups. How would all four types of tissue be involved in a simple activity, like raising your hand?

CHALLENGE

6. **Apply** Describe an object, such as a car, that can be used as a model of the human body. Explain how the parts of the model relate to the body.

17.1 ASSESS & RETEACH

Assess

A Section 17.1 Quiz, p. 3

Reteach

Have students draw a flow chart of the progression from cells to tissues to organs to organ systems. In the final drawing, students should make a rough outline of the human body with the systems labeled. Have volunteers share their drawings in a class discussion.

Technology Resources

Have students visit **ClassZone.com** for reteaching of Key Concepts.

 CONTENT REVIEW

 CONTENT REVIEW CD-ROM

ANSWERS

1. Diagrams should show organ systems as groups of organs, as groups of tissues, as groups of cells.

2. Charts should include epithelial, nerve, muscle, and connective tissues, and show understanding of each.

3. Sample answer: digestion, elimination, reproduction

4. When you sweat, your body loses water. Adding new water to the body helps maintain homeostasis.

5. Sample answer: When you raise your hand, nerve tissue carries a message from your brain, and muscle tissue contracts to move the bones, made of connective and epithelial tissues.

6. Answers should mention that the parts work together for the functioning of the whole.

SKILL: INFERRING

What Does the Body Need to Survive?

In 1914, Ernest Shackleton and 27 men set sail for Antarctica. Their goal was to cross the continent by foot and sled. The crew never set foot on Antarctica. Instead, the winter sea froze around their ship, crushing it until it sank. They were stranded on floating ice, over 100 miles from land. How long could they survive? How would their bodies respond? What would they need to stay alive?

You can make inferences in answer to any of these questions. First you need to recall what you know. Then you need new evidence. What was available to the explorers? Did they save supplies from their ship? What resources existed in the environment?

Prior Knowledge

- The human body needs air, water, and food.
- The human body needs to maintain its temperature. The body can be harmed if it loses too much heat.

Observations

Several of Shackleton's explorers kept diaries. From the diaries we know the following:

- The crew hunted seals and penguins for fresh meat.
- The temperature was usually below freezing.
- Tents and overturned lifeboats sheltered the crew from the wind.
- Their clothes were made of thick fabric and animal skins and furs.
- They melted snow and ice in order to have fresh water.

Make Inferences

On Your Own Describe how the explorers met each of the needs of the human body.

As a Group How long do you think these 28 men could have survived these conditions? Use evidence and inferences in your answer.

CHALLENGE How might survival needs differ for sailors shipwrecked in the tropics compared to the Antarctic?

Learn more about Shackleton's expedition.

ANSWERS

ON YOUR OWN For food, they hunted; for shelter, they used tents and overturned lifeboats; their clothes protected them from the cold; for water, they melted snow and ice.

AS A GROUP Sample answer: These men could have survived as long as seals and penguins were available for food. Diseases and injuries may have threatened their survival.

CHALLENGE Protection from sunburn and heat stroke and from harmful insects and other animals would be necessary. Obtaining fresh water might be difficult.

THINK SCIENCE
Scientific Methods of Thinking

Set Learning Goal

To make inferences, using prior knowledge and new evidence

Present the Science

Shackleton and his men rescued themselves. When they had to abandon their ship, they took three small open boats with them and dragged them along as they made their way across the ice that had frozen over the Weddell Sea. When they reached open water, they sailed to Elephant Island. One boat, with Shackleton as part of its crew, set out for South Georgia, 800 miles away. It took them 14 days to reach the island. Then three of them traveled 17 miles across South Georgia's mountains and glaciers to reach a whaling station. It took Shackleton four tries to get back to Elephant Island, but in the end not one member of the expedition was lost.

Guide the Activity

- Suggest that students remember times when they were cold and think about what they needed then.
- Have students share any experiences of outdoor exposure they may have had, such as camping in the rain or extreme heat or cold or being caught outdoors in a storm.
- After they have answered the questions on the page, students may do a Web quest for Shackleton's diary entries.

Close

Ask: How might an expedition today be better equipped? *Sample answer: It might carry global positioning communication devices, special fabrics for warmth and dryness, and compact emergency food.*

Technology Resources

Have students visit **ClassZone.com** to learn more about Shackleton's expedition.

RESOURCE CENTER

17.2 FOCUS

Set Learning Goals

Students will

- Describe different types of bone tissue.
- Explain how the human skeleton is organized.
- Describe how joints allow movement.
- Observe how joints help them perform several activities.

3-Minute Warm-Up

Display Transparency 4 or copy this exercise on the board:

Draw a sequence diagram showing the levels of organization of the human body, from simplest to most complex.

Diagram should show cells, tissues, organs, organ systems, and the organism.

 3-Minute Warm-Up, p. T4

17.2 MOTIVATE

EXPLORE Levers

PURPOSE To observe that bones can act as levers

TIP *10 min.* Students can use a backpack instead of a sports bag.

WHAT DO YOU THINK? *Nearest to the shoulder; in the hand; the action is slowed as the weight travels farther.*

Teaching with Technology

For the demonstration of levers, you may wish to have students use a force sensor if one is available.

KEY CONCEPT

17.2 The skeletal system provides support and protection.

BEFORE, you learned

- The body is made of cells, tissues, organs, and systems
- Cells, tissues, organs, and organ systems work together
- Systems in the body interact

NOW, you will learn

- About different types of bone tissue
- How the human skeleton is organized
- How joints allow movement

VOCABULARY

skeletal system p. 590
compact bone p. 591
spongy bone p. 591
axial skeleton p. 592
appendicular skeleton p. 592

EXPLORE Levers

How can a bone act as a lever?

PROCEDURE

1. A lever is a stiff rod that pivots about a fixed point. Hold the bag in your hand and keep your arm straight, like a lever. Move the bag up and down.
2. Move the handles of the bag over your elbow. Again hold your arm straight and move the bag up and down.
3. Now move the bag to the top of your arm and repeat the procedure.

MATERIALS
sports bag

WHAT DO YOU THINK?

- At which position is it easiest to move the bag?
- At which position does the bag move the farthest?
- How does the position of a load affect the action of a lever?

MAIN IDEA WEB
Make a web of the important terms and details about the main idea: *Bones are living tissue.*

Bones are living tissue.

Every movement of the human body is possible because of the interaction of muscles with the **skeletal system.** Made up of a strong connective tissue called bone, the skeletal system serves as the anchor for all of the body's movement, provides support, and protects soft organs inside the body. Bones can be classified as long bones, short bones, irregular bones, and flat bones. Long bones are found in the arms and legs. Short bones are found in the feet and hands. Irregular bones are found in the spine. Flat bones are found in the ribs and skull.

You might think that bones are completely solid and made up of dead tissue. They actually are made of both hard and soft materials.

RESOURCES FOR DIFFERENTIATED INSTRUCTION

Below Level

UNIT RESOURCE BOOK

- Reading Study Guide A, pp. 24–25
- Decoding Support, p. 47

 **AUDIO CDS**

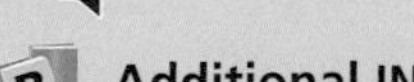 **Additional INVESTIGATION,** Bones and Calcium, A, B, & C, pp. 59–67; Teacher Instructions, pp. 308–309

Advanced

UNIT RESOURCE BOOK

- Challenge and Extension, p. 30
- Challenge Reading, pp. 43–44

English Learners

UNIT RESOURCE BOOK

Spanish Reading Study Guide, pp. 28–29

 **AUDIO CDS**

- Audio Readings in Spanish
- Audio Readings (English)

Like your heart or skin, bones are living tissue. Bones are not completely solid, either; they have spaces inside. The spaces allow blood carrying nutrients to travel throughout the bones. Because bones have spaces, they weigh much less than they would if they were solid.

Explore the skeletal system.

Two Types of Bone Tissue

Every bone is made of two types of bone tissue: compact bone and spongy bone. The hard compact bone surrounds the soft spongy bone. Each individual bone cell lies within a bony web. This web is made up mostly of minerals containing calcium.

Compact Bone Surrounding the spongy, inner layer of the bone is a hard layer called **compact bone.** Compact bone functions as the basic supportive tissue of the body, the part of the body you call the skeleton. The outer layer of compact bone is very hard and tough. It covers the outside of most bones.

Spongy Bone Inside the bone, the calcium network is less dense. This tissue is called **spongy bone.** Spongy bone is strong but lightweight. It makes up most of the short, flat, and irregular bones found in your body. It also makes up the ends of long bones.

Marrow and Blood Cells

Within the spongy bone tissue is marrow, the part of the bone that produces blood cells. The new blood cells travel from the marrow into the blood vessels that run throughout the bone. The blood brings nutrients to the bone cells and carries waste materials away.

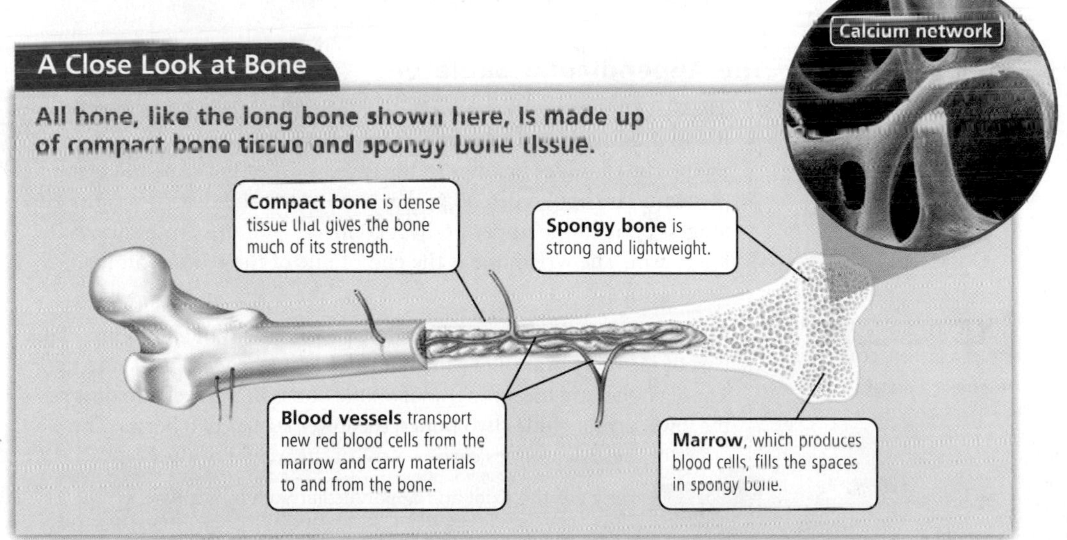

17.2 INSTRUCT

Teach from Visuals

To help students interpret the bone diagram, ask:

- Why is the compact bone able to give the bone strength? *It is dense.*
- How does bone receive nourishment? *Blood vessels bring in nutrients.*
- Where are red blood cells formed? *in the marrow*

Address Misconceptions

IDENTIFY Show students a bone and a solid white rock. Ask: What are some differences between a bone and a rock? If students do not mention the facts that bones have hollow spaces and soft marrow inside them and are living tissues made up of cells, they may hold the misconception that bones are solid and nonliving.

CORRECT Refer students to the bone diagram on p. 591. Have them identify specific differences between rock and bone.

REASSESS Ask: What are the parts of a bone, and what is the function of each? *Dense compact bone gives bones most of their strength; spongy bone is strong but less dense to reduce the weight of bones; marrow produces red blood cells; blood vessels bring nutrients to the bone and carry away waste materials.*

Technology Resources

Visit **ClassZone.com** for background on common student misconceptions.

MISCONCEPTION DATABASE

Ongoing Assessment

Describe different types of bone tissue.

Ask: What kinds of bone tissue make up bones? *Compact bone is dense and gives bones strength; spongy bone is less dense.*

DIFFERENTIATE INSTRUCTION

More Reading Support

A What is the major ingredient of bone? *calcium*

B Name the four parts of a bone. *compact bone, spongy bone, marrow, and blood vessels*

English Learners Demonstrate for English learners how some English sentences can be rearranged without changing the meaning. For example, the sentence "Surrounding the spongy, inner layer of the bone is a hard layer called compact bone," can be rearranged to read "A hard layer called compact bone surrounds the spongy, inner layer of the bone." Write the two sentences on the board and ask students to explain how they are different.

Real World Example

All blood cells begin as stem cells. A disease like leukemia interferes with stem-cell growth. In such cases, a bone marrow transplant can help. A donor provides healthy bone marrow, which is introduced into the patient intravenously. In a successful transplant, the marrow cells find their way to the bone spaces and begin to produce new stem cells after a few weeks.

Develop Critical Thinking

APPLY Have students discuss how the length of one's bones might affect one's athletic abilities. Ask: Would a short femur be more advantageous to a basketball player or to a jockey? *jockey*

Address Misconceptions

IDENTIFY Ask: Why do bones need food and oxygen? If students respond that bones convey food and oxygen to other organs or that they "store" food and oxygen, they may hold the misconception that bones are not alive and do not need nourishment.

CORRECT Ask students to discuss what happens to a bone after it breaks. Remind them that a bone must be alive in order to heal.

REASSESS Ask: How do bones use food and oxygen? *They use them in order to perform their special functions and to grow new cells.*

Technology Resources

Visit **ClassZone.com** for background on common student misconceptions.

MISCONCEPTION DATABASE

Ongoing Assessment

CHECK YOUR READING *Answer: Both divisions of the skeleton work with other systems to allow movement. The axial skeleton provides mainly protection and support, while the appendicular skeleton functions mainly to allow movement.*

The skeleton is the body's framework.

Like the frame of a building, the skeleton provides the body's shape. The skeleton also works with other systems to allow movement. Scientists have identified two main divisions in the skeleton. These are the axial (AK-see-uhl) skeleton, which is the central part of the skeleton, and the appendicular (AP-uhn-DIHK-yuh-luhr) skeleton. Bones in the appendicular skeleton are attached to the axial skeleton. The diagram on page 593 labels some of the important bones in your skeleton.

VOCABULARY
Remember to add four squares for *axial skeleton* and *appendicular skeleton* to your notebook.

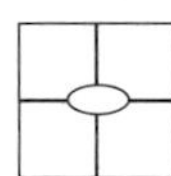

The Axial Skeleton

Imagine a line straight down your back. You can think of that line as an axis. Sitting, standing, and twisting are some of the motions that turn around the axis. The **axial skeleton** is the part of the skeleton that forms the axis. It provides support and protection. In the diagram, parts of the axial skeleton are colored in red.

The axial skeleton includes the skull, or the cranium (KRAY-nee-uhm). The major function of the cranium is protection of the brain. Most of the bones in the cranium do not move. The skull connects to the spinal column in a way that allows the head to move up and down as well as right and left.

C

Your spinal column makes up the main portion of the axial skeleton. The spinal column is made up of many bones called vertebrae. The many bones allow flexibility. If you run your finger along your back you will feel the vertebrae. Another set of bones belonging to the axial skeleton are the rib bones. The ribs function to protect the soft internal organs, such as the heart and lungs.

The Appendicular Skeleton

The diagram shows the bones in the appendicular skeleton in yellow. Bones in the **appendicular skeleton** function mainly to allow movement. The shoulder belongs to the upper part of the appendicular skeleton. The upper arm bone that connects to the shoulder is the longest bone in the upper body. It connects with the two bones of the lower arm. The wristbone is the end of one of these bones in the lower arm.

SIMULATION
CLASSZONE.COM
Assemble a skeleton.

The lower part of the body includes the legs and the hip bones. This part of the body bears all of the body's weight when you are standing. The leg bones are the strongest of all the bones in the skeleton. Just as the lower arm includes two bones, the lower leg has two bones. The larger of these two bones carries most of the weight of the body.

How are the axial and appendicular skeletons alike? How are they different?

DIFFERENTIATE INSTRUCTION

More Reading Support

C What is an advantage of having many bones in the spinal column? *flexibility*

Below Level Have students prepare a Venn diagram to compare and contrast the axial skeleton and the appendicular skeleton.

Axial Skeleton	Both	Appendicular Skeleton
• central part of skeleton • includes skull, spinal column, and ribs • main function is to provide support and protection	• made up of bones • provides body's shape	• attached to axial skeleton • includes bones of the shoulders, hips, arms and legs • main function is to allow movement

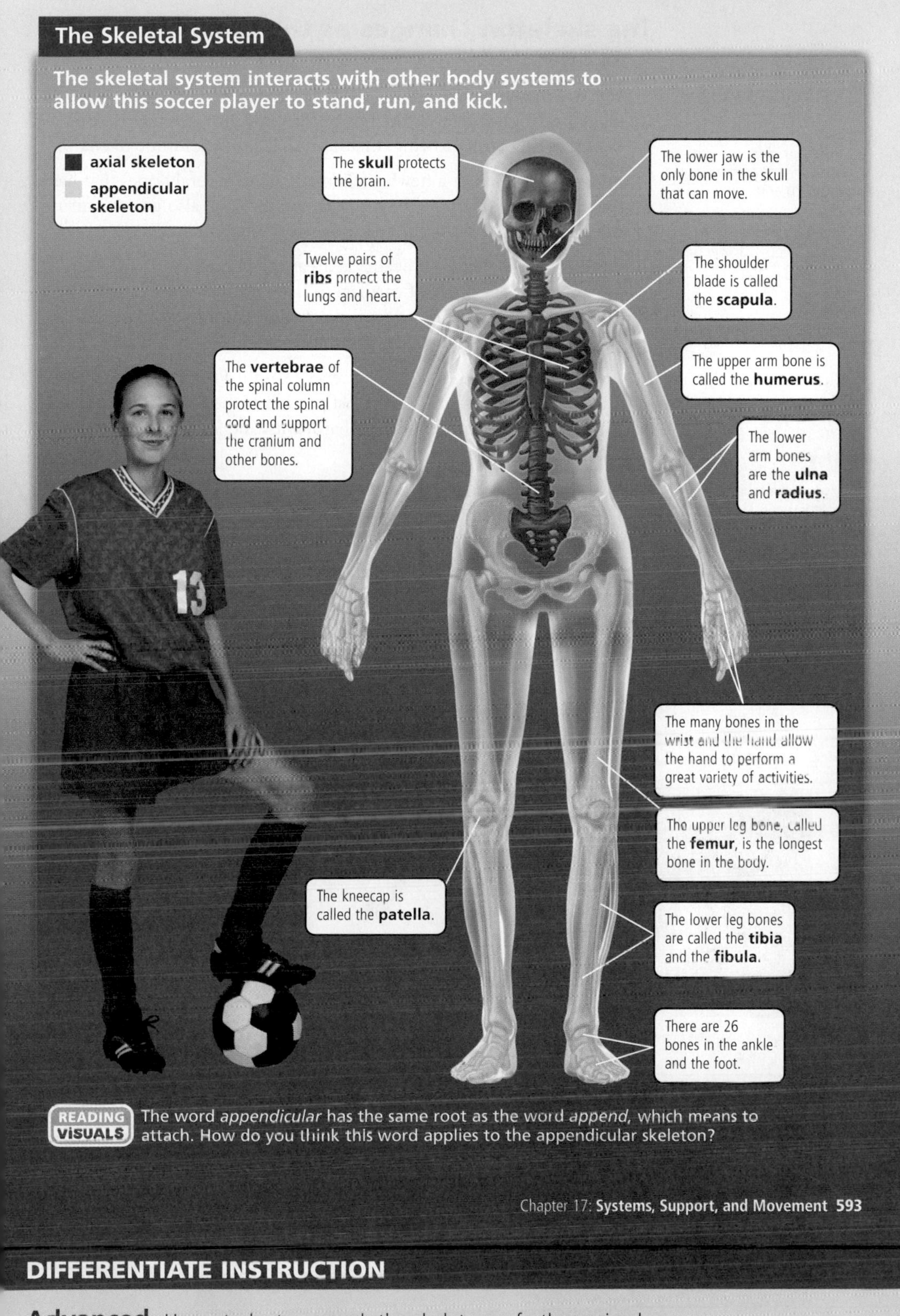

READING VISUALS The word *appendicular* has the same root as the word *append,* which means to attach. How do you think this word applies to the appendicular skeleton?

DIFFERENTIATE INSTRUCTION

Advanced Have students research the skeletons of other animals, such as birds, and infer how differences in movement can result from differences in structure. They could draw and label diagrams and present their findings to the class in posters.

R Challenge and Extension, p. 30

Teach from Visuals

To help students interpret the skeleton diagram, point out that the pelvis bone is sometimes considered to be part of the axial and sometimes part of the appendicular skeleton. Ask:

- What functions do vertebrae perform? *They protect the spinal cord and support the cranium and other bones.*
- How many bones are in the ankle and foot? *26*
- Which division of the skeleton are these bones part of? *appendicular skeleton*
- What is the only bone in the skull that can move? *lower jaw*

EXPLORE the BIG idea

Revisit "How Many Bones Are in Your Hand?" on p. 583. Have students compare the numbers they found with the number of bones shown in the foot.

Arts Connection

Have students draw a skull from an actual model. Compare this activity with drawing the head of a live person. Drawing a skeleton or a part such as a skull can help an artist to understand what he or she is seeing when drawing from life. The artist comes to know where deep shadows and raised highlights should be. These can be harder to find in life.

Ongoing Assessment

Explain how the human skeleton is organized.

Ask: How is the body's framework, the skeleton, structured? *The axial skeleton runs top to bottom. The appendicular skeleton runs side to side.*

READING VISUALS *Answer: The appendicular skeleton attaches the arms and legs to the axial skeleton.*

History of Science

The skeleton has been studied at least since the time of the ancient Greeks. The physician Galen (129–c. 199 C.E.) dissected many animals, drawing logical conclusions about the shape and weight of certain bones. Galen produced many treatises on medicine. His medical writings were translated by Arab thinkers of the ninth century and were highly respected during the European Renaissance.

Integrate the Sciences

Calcium is a major component of bone tissue. It is a silvery white element, one of the alkaline-earth metals. Its atomic number is 20. Calcium is the fifth most abundant element in Earth's crust, but in nature it is always found as part of compounds.

- Marble, limestone, and chalk are calcium carbonate.
- Lime, cement, and mortar are calcium hydroxide.
- Teeth and bones are calcium hydroxyphosphate.

In the body, calcium is essential to the contraction of muscles, the transmission of nerve impulses, and the clotting of blood.

Social Studies Connection

Discuss with students how bone has been used to make tools, musical instruments, decorative inlays, and other objects in many cultures. Other examples include knife and gun handles, spear points, whale-bone sled runners and roof supports, scrimshaw, sewing needles, fishhooks, buttons, beads, and pendants. Keep a bulletin board or scrapbook in the classroom. Each student can contribute a page.

Real World Example

Deterioration of and loss of density in bone lead to a disease called osteoporosis. It is estimated that 10 million Americans have osteoporosis, and 34 million—55 percent of Americans 50 years of age or older—are at risk. Osteoporosis is responsible for more than 1.5 million fractures annually.

The skeleton changes as the body develops and ages.

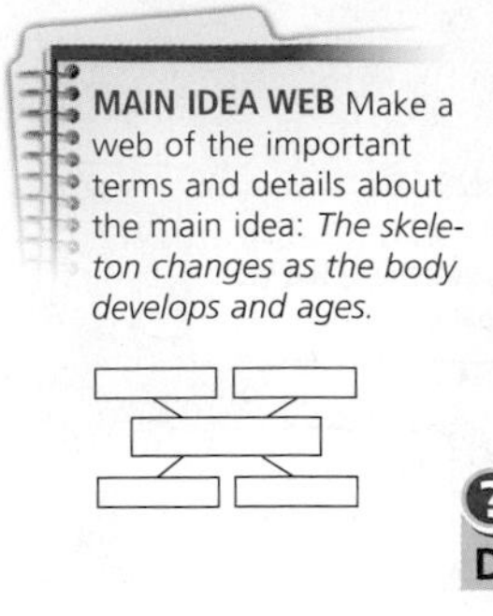

MAIN IDEA WEB Make a web of the important terms and details about the main idea: *The skeleton changes as the body develops and ages.*

You will remember that bones are living tissue. During infancy and childhood, bones grow as the rest of the body grows. Bones become harder as they stop growing. In adulthood, bones continue to change.

Infancy The skull of a newborn is made up of several bones that have spaces between them. As the brain grows, the skull also grows. During the growth of the skull, the spaces between the bones close.

Childhood Bone growth occurs at areas called growth plates. These growth plates are made of cartilage, a firm, flexible connective tissue. The length and shape of bones is determined by growth plates. Long bones grow at the ends of the bone surrounding growth plates.

Adolescence At the end of adolescence (AD-uhl-EHS-uhns) bones stop growing. The growth plate is the last portion of the bone to become hard. Once growth plates become hard, arms and legs stop growing and the skull plates fuse.

REMINDER
Density is the ratio of mass over volume. Bone density is a measure of the mass of a bone divided by the bone's volume.

Adulthood Even after bones stop growing, they go through cycles in which old bone is broken down and new bone is formed. As people age, more bone is broken down than is formed. This can lead to a decrease in bone mass, which causes a decrease in bone density. The strength of bones depends upon their density. As people age, their bone density may decrease. Bones that are less dense may break more easily. Many doctors recommend that adults over a certain age get regular bone density tests.

Test of Bone Density

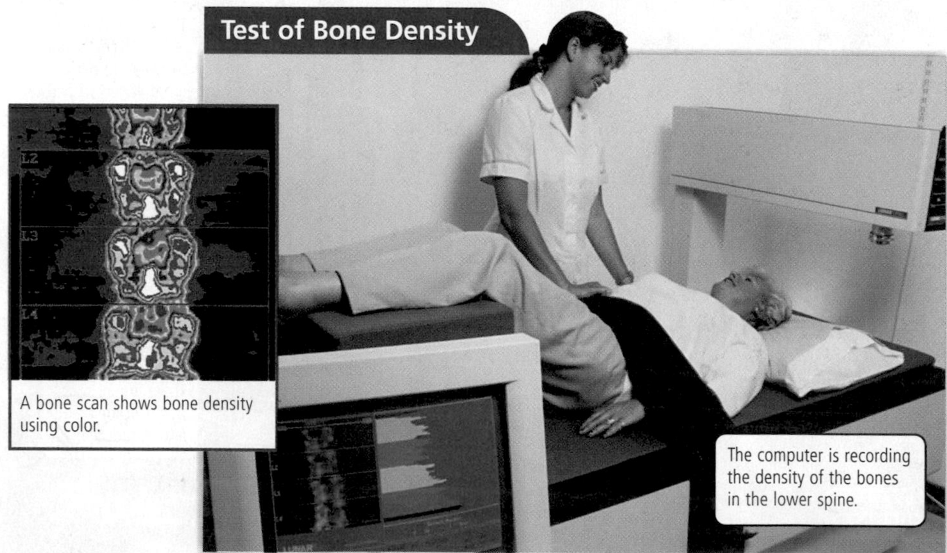

A bone scan shows bone density using color.

The computer is recording the density of the bones in the lower spine.

594 Unit 5: **Human Biology**

DIFFERENTIATE INSTRUCTION

More Reading Support

D Where does bone growth occur? *growth plates*

E When do your arms and legs stop growing? *toward the end of adolescence*

Additional Investigation To reinforce Section 17.2 learning goals, use the following full-period investigation:

Additional INVESTIGATION, Bones and Calcium, A, B, & C, pp. 59–67, 305–306 (Advanced students should complete Levels B and C.)

Below Level Use pictures showing various bonelike parts of animals, such as shells, horns, and beaks. Tell whether each is or is not considered bone.

Joints connect parts of the skeletal system.

A joint is a place at which two parts of the skeletal system meet. There are three types of joints: immovable, slightly movable, and freely movable.

Immovable and Slightly Movable Joints An immovable joint locks bones together like puzzle pieces. The bones of your skull are connected by immovable joints. Slightly movable joints are able to flex slightly. Your ribs are connected to your sternum by slightly movable joints.

Freely Movable Joints Freely movable joints allow your body to bend and to move. Tissues called ligaments hold the bones together at movable joints. Other structures inside the joint cushion the bones and keep them from rubbing together. The entire joint also is surrounded by connective tissue.

Movable joints can be classified by the type of movement they produce. Think about the movement of your arm when you eat an apple. Your arm moves up, then down, changing the angle between your upper and lower arms. This is angular movement. The joint that produces this movement is called a hinge joint.

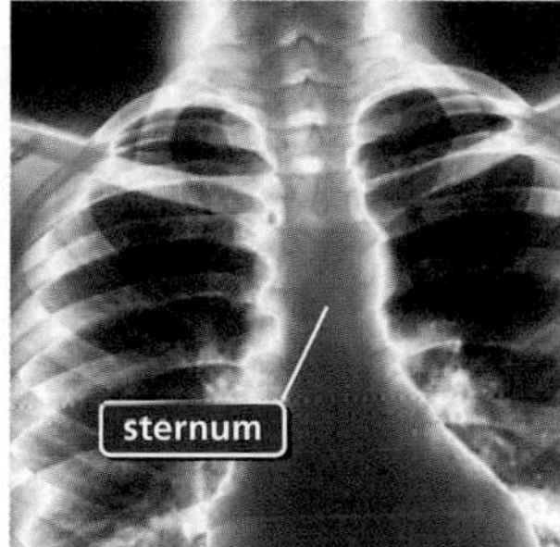

The sternum is an example of a slightly movable joint.

INVESTIGATE Movable Joints

How can you move at joints?

PROCEDURE

1. Perform several activities that involve your joints. Twist at the waist. Bend from your waist to one side. Reach into the air with one arm. Open and close your mouth. Push a book across your desk. Lift the book.
2. Record each activity and write a note describing the motion that you feel at each joint.
3. Try to see how many different ways you can move at joints.

WHAT DO YOU THINK?

- How was the motion you felt similar for each activity? How was it different?
- Based on your observations, identify two or more ways that joints move.

CHALLENGE Draw a diagram showing how you think each joint moves. How might you classify different types of joints based upon the way they move?

SKILL FOCUS Observing

MATERIALS book

TIME 20 minutes

DIFFERENTIATE INSTRUCTION

More Reading Support

F What are the three types of joints? *immovable, slightly movable, and freely movable*

G What holds bones together at joints? *ligaments*

Advanced Osteoporosis is a decrease in bone mass that can put bones at risk of breaking. Have students research statistics on osteoporosis, along with the treatment and prevention. What methods of screening and diagnosis are in current use?

Have students who are interested in the makeup of bones read the following article:

 Challenge Reading, pp. 43–44

EXPLORE the BIG idea

Revisit "How Does It Move?" on p. 583. Have students explain how each type of joint moves.

INVESTIGATE Movable Joints

PURPOSE To make observations about how joints work

TIP *20 min.* Have students remove jackets and roll up sleeves to better observe joint movements.

INCLUSION Include students with restricted movement in this activity by having them serve as recorders and by having them analyze the movements of others.

WHAT DO YOU THINK? *Sample answer: Each motion had a limited range of movement. The types and ranges of movement differed.*

Sample answer: Different joints allow rotational movements, angular movements, and gliding movements.

CHALLENGE *Diagrams may vary, but should show an understanding of the types of joint movements.*

R Datasheet, Movable Joints, p. 31

Technology Resources

Customize this student lab as needed or look for an alternative. Print rubrics to assess student lab reports.

 **Lab Generator CD-ROM**

Teaching with Technology

Students can further investigate movable joints by using a digital camera to record ranges of movement.

Ongoing Assessment

Describe how joints allow movement.

Ask: How are joints classified or grouped into categories?

Answer: Joints are classified by the types of movement they allow: freely movable, slightly movable, and immovable.

Ongoing Assessment

READING VISUALS *Answer: The elbow joint is shaped like a hinge allowing angular movement. The hip joint is shaped like a ball and socket allowing rotational movement.*

Reinforce the BIG idea

Have students relate the section to the Big Idea.

Reinforcing Key Concepts, p. 32

17.2 ASSESS & RETEACH

Assess

Section 17.2 Quiz, p. 4

Reteach

On the board, draw an unlabeled diagram of a cross section of a bone (see p. 591) and an unlabeled diagram of a skeleton. Have students copy the diagrams. Have volunteers suggest labels for the diagrams. *Labels for the cross section should include* compact bone, spongy bone, blood vessels, *and* marrow. *Labels for the skeleton should include* axial skeleton, appendicular skeleton, hinge joint (elbow), ball-and-socket joint (hip), *and* names of individual bones.

Technology Resources

Have students visit **ClassZone.com** for reteaching of Key Concepts.

CONTENT REVIEW

CONTENT REVIEW CD-ROM

Movable Joints

The joints in the elbow and hip allow different types of movement.

Angular movement (elbow)

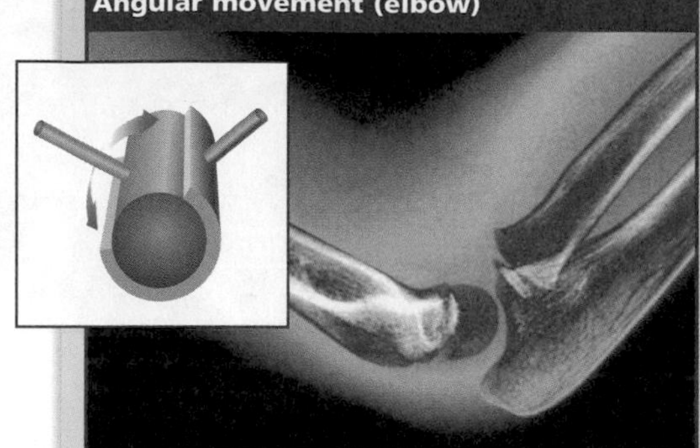

Rotational movement (hip)

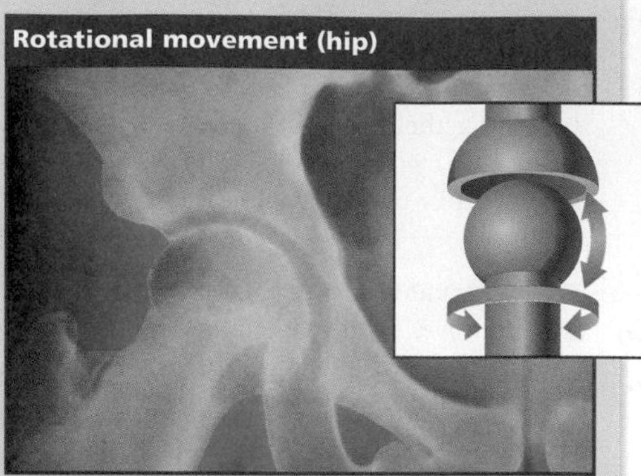

READING VISUALS **INFER** How do the structure and shape of each joint allow bones to move?

Your arm can also rotate from side to side, as it does when you turn a doorknob. Rotational movement like this is produced by a pivot joint in the elbow. You can also rotate your arm in a circle, like the motion of a softball pitcher winding up and releasing a ball. The joint in the shoulder that produces this type of rotational movement is called a ball-and-socket joint.

Joints also produce gliding movement. All joints glide, that is, one bone slides back and forth across another. In some cases, as with the joints in your backbone, a small gliding movement is the only movement the joint produces.

17.2 Review

KEY CONCEPTS

1. What are the functions of the two types of bone tissue?
2. What are the main divisions of the human skeleton?
3. Name three types of movement produced by movable joints and give an example of each.

CRITICAL THINKING

4. **Infer** What function do immovable joints in the skull perform? Think about the different stages of development in the human body.
5. **Analyze** Which type of movable joint allows the most movement? How does the joint's shape and structure contribute to this?

CHALLENGE

6. **Classify** The joints in your hand and wrist produce three different types of movement. Using your own wrist, classify the joint movement of the fingers, palm, and wrist. Support your answer.

ANSWERS

1. Compact bone gives a bone strength. The marrow inside spongy bone produces red blood cells.

2. axial skeleton and appendicular skeleton

3. Ball-and-socket (shoulder) allows movement in almost a full circle. Gliding (wrist) allows movement back and forth or up and down. Hinge (knee) allows movement in one plane.

4. allow rapid brain growth during infancy, then later protect the brain

5. ball-and-socket; ball shape allows movement in all directions

6. Fingers have angular movement, thumb has gliding, and wrist has angular and gliding movement.

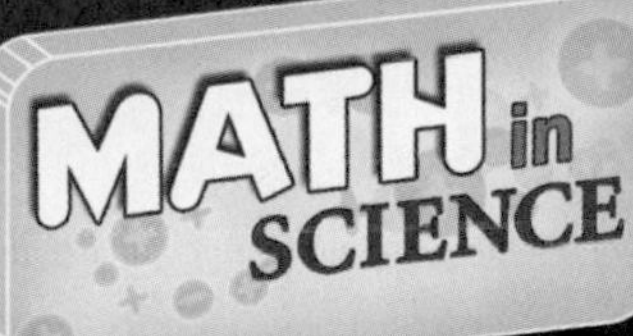

SKILL: COMPARING RATES

Rates of Production

MATH TUTORIAL

Click on Math Tutorial for more help with unit rates.

Where do red blood cells come from? They are produced inside bone marrow at the center of long bones. An average of about 200 billion red blood cells per day are produced by a healthy adult. When a person produces too few red blood cells, a condition called anemia may occur. Doctors study rates of blood cell production to diagnose and treat anemia.

A rate is a ratio that compares two quantities of different units. The number of cells produced per 24 hours is an example of a rate.

Example

A healthy adult produces red blood cells at a rate greater than 166 billion cells per 24 hours. Suppose a man's body produces 8 billion red blood cells per 1 hour. Would he be considered anemic?

(1) Write the two rates as fractions.

$\frac{8}{1}$ $\qquad$ $\frac{166}{24}$

(2) Simplify the fractions, so that the denominators are both 1. To simplify, divide the numerator by the denominator.

$\frac{8}{1}$ $\qquad$ $\frac{6.9}{1}$

(3) Compare the two whole numbers. Is the first number $<$, $>$, or $=$ to the second number?

$8 > 6.9$

ANSWER The rate is greater than 6.9. The patient is not anemic.

Compare the following rates to see if they indicate that a person is anemic or normal.

1. For women, a normal rate is about 178 billion red blood cells per day. A certain woman produces 6 billion red blood cells per hour. Is her rate low or healthy?
2. Suppose a different woman produces 150 million (not billion) red blood cells per minute. How does that rate compare to 178 billion cells per day? Is it $<$, $>$, or $=$ to it?
3. Suppose a certain man is producing 135 million red blood cells per minute. Is that rate low or healthy?

CHALLENGE In the example above of a man producing 166 billion cells per day, calculate the percentage by which the rate would need to increase to bring it up to the average count of 200 billion per day.

ANSWERS

1. low

2. greater than

3. healthy

CHALLENGE 20%

MATH IN SCIENCE

Math Skills Practice for Science

Set Learning Goal

To compare rates of blood-cell production

Present the Science

It is important for the body to maintain an adequate number of red blood cells. Disorders such as iron or vitamin B12 deficiency and diseases such as cancer or leukemia can cause an underproduction of these vital cells. An underproduction of red blood cells is called anemia, and people suffering from it experience fatigue and weakness, shortness of breath, and paleness of skin, eyes, and nails.

Develop Number Sense

- Remind students that both decimals and fractions can represent rates. When a fraction shows a rate, the line may mean "out of."
- Review fraction-to-decimal conversion.

Close

There is a difference between the healthy rate (166 billion per day) and the normal rate (178 billion per day) for women. Ask students to explain this difference. *The normal rate is higher than the rate of cell production needed just to be healthy. That means that if a person's rate decreases due to temporary conditions, they can still be healthy.*

- Math Support, p. 48
- Math Practice, p. 49

Technology Resources

Students can visit **ClassZone.com** for practice in comparing rates.

MATH TUTORIAL

KEY CONCEPT

The muscular system makes movement possible.

BEFORE, you learned
- There are different types of bone tissue
- The human skeleton has two separate divisions
- Joints function in several different ways

NOW, you will learn
- About the functions of muscles
- About the different types of muscles and how they work
- How muscles grow and heal

VOCABULARY

muscular system p. 599
skeletal muscle p. 600
voluntary muscle p. 600
smooth muscle p. 600
involuntary muscle p. 600
cardiac muscle p. 600

EXPLORE Muscles

How do muscles change as you move?

PROCEDURE

1. Sit on a chair with your feet on the floor.
2. Place your hand around your leg. Straighten one leg as shown in the photograph.
3. Repeat step 2 several times.

WHAT DO YOU THINK?
- How did your muscles change during the activity?
- Record your observations.
- What questions do you have about the muscular system?

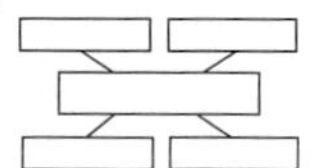

MAIN IDEA WEB
Make a web for the main idea: *Muscles perform important functions.*

Muscles perform important functions.

Every movement of your body—from the beating of your heart, to the movement of food down your throat, to the blinking of your eyes—occurs because of muscles. Some movements are under your control, and other movements seem to happen automatically. However, muscles do more than produce movement. They perform other functions as well. Keeping body temperature stable and maintaining posture are two additional functions of muscles.

What are three functions that muscles perform?

17.3 FOCUS

Set Learning Goals

Students will
- Explain the functions of muscles.
- Describe the different types of muscles and how they work.
- Explain how muscles grow and heal.
- Observe how muscles change with movement.

3-Minute Warm-Up

Display Transparency 5 or copy this exercise on the board:

Match the definitions to the correct terms.

Definitions
1. a bony structure that allows rotation *d*
2. the skeleton division containing the skull *b*
3. the part of a bone that produces red blood cells *e*

Terms
a. compact bone
b. axial skeleton
c. immovable joint
d. ball-and-socket joint
e. marrow

 3-Minute Warm-Up, p. T5

17.3 MOTIVATE

EXPLORE Muscles

PURPOSE To observe how muscles change with movement

TIP *10 min.* Remind students to feel both the top and bottom of the leg during movement.

WHAT DO YOU THINK? *When the leg was straightened, the muscles on the top of the leg got thicker. When the leg was bent, the muscles on the bottom of the leg got thicker. Students' questions should relate to changes during movement of muscles.*

Ongoing Assessment

Answer: Muscles produce movement, keep body temperature stable, maintain posture.

RESOURCES FOR DIFFERENTIATED INSTRUCTION

Below Level

UNIT RESOURCE BOOK
- Reading Study Guide A, pp. 35–36
- Decoding Support, p. 47

AUDIO CDS

Advanced

UNIT RESOURCE BOOK
Challenge and Extension, p. 41

English Learners

UNIT RESOURCE BOOK
Spanish Reading Study Guide, pp. 39–40

- Audio Readings in Spanish
- Audio Readings (English)

Movement

RESOURCE CENTER
CLASSZONE.COM
Discover more about muscles.

The **muscular system** works with the skeletal system to allow movement. Like all muscles, the muscles that produce movement are made up of individual cells called muscle fibers. These fibers contract and relax.

Most of the muscles involved in moving the body work in pairs. As they contract, muscles shorten, pulling against bones. It may surprise you to know that muscles do not push. Rather, a muscle on one side of a bone pulls in one direction, while another muscle relaxes. Muscles are attached to bones by stretchy connective tissue.

Maintaining Body Temperature

Earlier you read that processes within the body require certain conditions, such as temperature and the right amount of water and other materials. The balance of conditions is called homeostasis. One of the functions of the muscular system is related to homeostasis. Muscles function to maintain body temperature.

When muscles contract, they release heat. Without this heat from muscle contraction, the body could not maintain its normal temperature. You may have observed the way your muscles affect your body temperature when you shiver. The quick muscle contractions that occur when you shiver release heat and raise your body temperature.

CHECK YOUR READING How do muscles help maintain homeostasis?

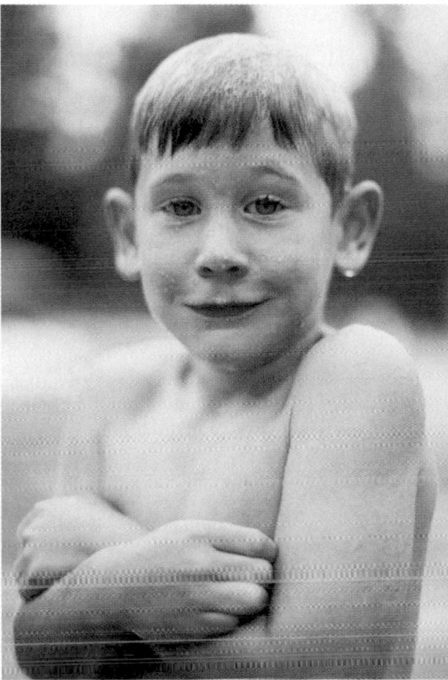
Muscles contract during shivering, raising body temperature.

Maintaining Posture

B Have you ever noticed that you stand up straight without thinking about it, even though gravity is pulling your body down? Most muscles in your body are always a little bit contracted. This tension, or muscle tone, is present even when you are sleeping. The muscles that maintain posture relax completely only when you are unconscious.

Try standing on the balls of your feet for a few moments, or on one leg. When you are trying to balance or hold one position for any length of time, you can feel different muscles contracting and relaxing. Your muscles make constant adjustments to keep you sitting or standing upright. You don't have to think about these tiny adjustments; they happen automatically.

17.3 INSTRUCT

Integrate the Sciences

Muscles atrophy when not used. A person's muscles may atrophy when illness confines the person to bed or when the person has to wear a cast. Muscles also atrophy in space, because there is no gravity for the muscles to resist.

In space, muscles can also change type. Without gravity, the nerve receptors in the muscles that usually carry information about gravitational load and muscle use change because of the lack of resistance. Research in this area is being conducted by NASA and is expected to benefit not only astronauts but also people with spinal-cord injuries and long-term illnesses.

Ongoing Assessment

Explain the functions of muscles.

Ask: How do muscles help maintain posture? *All muscles are always a little bit contracted to hold the body up against gravity.*

CHECK YOUR READING *Answer: They create heat to keep the body warm in a cool environment.*

DIFFERENTIATE INSTRUCTION

More Reading Support

A How do muscles work to maintain body temperature? *They generate heat when they contract.*

B What force pulling the body down do muscles work against? *gravity*

English Learners Students new to English may find the following science words challenging: *fiber, posture, expend, bundles, twitch, coordination.* Preview vocabulary by adding these words and their definitions to a science word wall.

Real World Example

Muscular dystrophy is a disease in which the muscles get progressively weaker and may stop working. Sometimes the protective membranes around the muscles are affected. Muscular dystrophy is a genetic disease that affects how the body makes proteins for muscle. Some current research is aimed at correcting the defective genes; other research is aimed at creating chemicals that act like the missing proteins.

Ongoing Assessment

Describe the different types of muscles and how they work.

Ask: What kind of bundles make up skeletal muscles, and what do they do? *Skeletal muscles are made of fast-twitch and slow-twitch bundles. Fast-twitch bundles can move quickly. Slow-twitch bundles move slowly.*

Answer: They move when you want them to.

Answer: You can consciously control skeletal muscles but not smooth muscles. Smooth muscle contracts slowly, whereas skeletal muscle contains both slow-twitch and fast-twitch bundles. Cardiac muscle is restricted to the heart; the other two can be found throughout the body. Like smooth muscle, cardiac muscle contracts slowly.

Your body has different types of muscle.

Your body has three types of muscle. All three types of muscle tissue share certain characteristics. For example, each type of muscle contracts and relaxes. Yet all three muscle types have different functions, and different types of muscle are found in different locations.

Skeletal Muscle

The muscles that are attached to your skeleton are called **skeletal muscles.** Skeletal muscle performs voluntary movement—that is, movement that you choose to make. Because they are involved in voluntary movement, skeletal muscles are also called **voluntary muscles.**

READING TIP

The root of the word *voluntary* comes from the Latin root *vol-*, meaning "wish." In the word *involuntary* the prefix *in-* suggests the meaning "unwished for." *Involuntary movement* means movement you can't control.

Skeletal muscle, like all muscle, is made of long fibers. The fibers are made up of many smaller bundles, as a piece of yarn is made up of strands of wool. One type of bundle allows your muscles to move slowly. Those muscles are called slow-twitch muscles. Another type of bundle allows your muscles to move quickly. These are called fast-twitch muscles. If you were a sprinter, you would want to develop your fast-twitch muscles. If you were a long distance runner, you would develop your slow-twitch muscles.

What does it mean that skeletal muscles are voluntary muscles?

Smooth Muscle

VOCABULARY

Remember to add four squares for *involuntary muscles* and *voluntary muscles* to your notebook. Note differences in the two diagrams.

Smooth muscle is found inside some organs, such as the intestines and the stomach. Smooth muscles perform automatic movement and are called **involuntary muscles.** In other words, smooth muscles work without your knowing it. You have no control over their movement. For example, smooth muscles line your stomach wall and push food through your digestive system. Smooth muscle fibers are not as long as skeletal muscle fibers. Also, unlike skeletal muscles, smooth muscles are not fast-twitch. Smooth muscles contract slowly.

Cardiac Muscle

Your heart is made of **cardiac muscle.** Like smooth muscle, cardiac muscle moves without conscious control. Each cardiac muscle cell has a branched shape. The cells of the heart connect in a chain. These chains form webs of layered tissue that allow cardiac cells to contract together and make the heart beat. Just like the smooth muscle cells, the cardiac muscle cells contract slowly, except in emergencies.

Compare and contrast the three types of muscle described: skeletal, smooth, and cardiac.

DIFFERENTIATE INSTRUCTION

More Reading Support

C Which muscles perform voluntary movements? *skeletal muscles*

D What kind of muscle makes up the heart? *cardiac muscle*

Advanced Have students research past fat-loss fads, such as vibrating belts and electronic muscle stimulators, and explain why these were ineffective. Have students design an exercise machine that they would enjoy and that would work to help people keep fit.

Challenge and Extension, p. 41

Teach from Visuals

To help students see the science in the photograph of a band, ask:

- What are the voluntary muscles of the band members doing? *controlling their marching, allowing them to play instruments*
- What are involuntary muscles doing in each band member? *making the heart beat, breathing*
- Does everything you do involve all three types of muscle? Explain. *No; when you are asleep, you are not using skeletal muscle.*

Real World Example

A backpack is usually the best way for students to carry all their books and other school supplies. The strongest muscles in the body, the back and abdominal muscles, support the weight of the pack, which is designed to hang evenly. A backpack can overload the body, however, if it is too heavy or hangs unevenly. In such cases, a cart with wheels can help.

Ongoing Assessment

READING VISUALS *Answer: Their walking in time to music and playing instruments are voluntary. Their breathing and the beating of their hearts is involuntary.*

DIFFERENTIATE INSTRUCTION

Below Level Have students find pictures of people performing various movements and use them to make a poster. As captions, have the students name the muscles being used in the pictures.

Address Misconceptions

IDENTIFY Ask: How do muscles push on bones? If students attempt to explain, they may hold the misconception that muscles push and pull, whereas they can only pull.

CORRECT Point out that tendons are like string and that pushing on a string does not work. Explain that muscles and bones are arranged so that pulling the strings—the tendons—moves bones. You may want to include a physical demonstration by giving students lengths of string to manipulate.

REASSESS Ask: How do muscles move bones? *Muscles can only contract or relax. By contracting, they pull on the tendons.*

Technology Resources

Visit **ClassZone.com** for background on common student misconceptions.

 **MISCONCEPTION DATABASE**

Real World Example

Botox injections were first developed to treat problems that involved muscle spasms or rigidity. Examples of such problems are strabismus (crossed eyes) and cervical dystonia (rigidity of the neck muscles). "Botox" is the trade name for botulinum toxin A, a neurotoxin produced by the bacterium *Clostridium botulinum.* People who eat food contaminated by this bacterium can suffer fatal paralysis.

Teach from Visuals

To help students see the differences in the diagrams of muscles and bones, ask:

- In which diagram is the bottom muscle of the thigh contracted? *upper diagram*
- What does that do to the leg? *bends it*
- How does the other muscle in the pair look? *long and flat*

Skeletal muscles and tendons allow bones to move.

Skeletal muscles are attached to your bones by strong tissues called tendons. The tendons on the end of the muscle attach firmly to the bone. As the fibers in a muscle contract, they shorten and pull the tendon. The tendon, in turn, pulls the bone and makes it move.

You can feel your muscles moving your bones. Place your left arm, stretched out flat, in front of you on a table. Place the fingers of your right hand just above your left elbow. Bend your elbow and raise and lower your left arm. You are contracting your biceps. Can you feel the muscle pull on the tendon?

The dancers in the photograph are using many sets of muscles. The diagrams show how muscles and tendons work together to move bones. Muscles are shown in red. Notice how each muscle crosses a joint. Most skeletal muscles do. One end of the muscle attaches to one bone, crosses a joint, then attaches to a second bone. As the muscle contracts, it pulls on both bones. This pulling produces movement—in the case of these dancers, very exciting movement.

Skeletal muscles contract by shortening and pulling the tendon.

Muscle fibers can return to their original length after being shortened.

DIFFERENTIATE INSTRUCTION

More Reading Support

E What attaches skeletal muscles to bone? *tendons*

F How do muscles produce movement? *They contract.*

Below Level Have students write and illustrate a pamphlet or picture storybook for younger students, explaining how to build and strengthen muscles. Alternatively, they may wish to write and illustrate a picture storybook about how muscles produce movement in the body.

Muscles grow and heal.

Developing Muscles An infant's muscles cannot do very much. A baby cannot lift its head, because the neck muscles are not strong enough to support it. For the first few months of life, a baby needs extra support, until the neck muscles grow strong and can hold up the baby's head.

The rest of the skeletal muscles also have to develop and strengthen. During infancy and childhood and into adolescence, humans develop muscular coordination and become more graceful in their movements. Coordination reaches its natural peak in adolescence but can be further improved by additional training.

Exercise and Muscles When you exercise regularly, your muscles may get bigger. Muscles increase in size with some types of exercise, because their cells reproduce more rapidly in response to the increased activity. Exercise also stimulates growth of individual muscle cells, making them larger.

You may have experienced sore muscles during or after exercising. During exercise, chemicals can build up in the muscles and make them cramp or ache. The muscle soreness you feel a day or so after exercise is caused by damage to the muscle fibers. The muscle fibers have been overstretched or torn. Such injuries take time to heal, because the body must remove injured cells, and new ones must form.

Stretching your muscles before exercise helps prevent injury.

17.3 Review

KEY CONCEPTS

1. What are the three main functions of the muscular system?
2. Make a rough outline of a human body and label places where you could find each of the three types of muscles.
3. Explain why you may be sore after exercise.

CRITICAL THINKING

4. **Apply** You are exercising and you begin to feel hot. Explain what is happening in your muscles.
5. **Analyze** Describe what happens in your neck muscles when you nod your head.

CHALLENGE

6. **Infer** The digestive system breaks down food and transports materials. How are the short length and slow movement of smooth muscle tissues in the stomach and intestines related to the functions of these organs?

ANSWERS

1. movement, maintaining temperature, and posture

2. Outlines should label appropriate locations for skeletal, smooth, and cardiac muscles.

3. Muscle fibers can be overstretched or torn. Chemicals can build up in muscles during exercise.

4. Your muscles contract in exercise and expend energy that is converted to heat.

5. The muscles in front of your neck contract to pull your head forward. The muscles behind your spine contract to raise your head.

6. Sample answer: Long, powerful muscle fibers are not needed for involuntary muscle movements. Slow contractions make it possible for involuntary muscle movement to go unnoticed.

Ongoing Assessment

Explain how muscles grow and heal.

Ask: How do you build muscles safely? *Warm up and stretch before exercising, and exercise regularly.*

Reinforce the BIG idea

Have students relate the section to the Big Idea.

 Reinforcing Key Concepts, p. 42

17.3 ASSESS & RETEACH

Assess

 Section 17.3 Quiz, p. 5

Reteach

Write these headings on the board: "Functions," "Structure," "Movement," "Development." Have volunteers help you add under them entries that describe muscles. *Functions: movement, body temperature, posture; Structure: skeletal muscle, smooth muscle, cardiac muscle; Movement: contraction; Development: growth with age and exercise*

Technology Resources

Have students visit **ClassZone.com** for reteaching of Key Concepts.

 **CONTENT REVIEW**

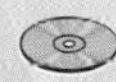 **CONTENT REVIEW CD-ROM**

CHAPTER INVESTIGATION

Focus

PURPOSE To examine how muscles and bones interact

OVERVIEW Students examine the muscles and bones of a chicken wing. Students then use their observations to

- describe the characteristics of muscles
- describe how the interaction of the muscles and bones in the chicken wing compares with the interactions of human muscles and bones

Lab Preparation

- Soak chicken wings in a bleach solution of 2 Tbsp bleach to 1 cup water for at least 5 minutes to kill any surface bacteria. Rinse them thoroughly in water and pat them dry. Store wings in a refrigerator until you are ready to use them.
- Prior to the investigation have students read through the investigation and prepare their data tables. Or you may wish to copy and distribute datasheets and rubrics.

Lab Management

- If necessary, help students locate the muscles, tendons, and ligaments in the chicken wings. Tendons are the tough, shiny white cords that attach the muscles to the bones.
- Arrange for proper disposal of wings at the conclusion of the lab.

SAFETY Caution students not to touch the chicken wings with their bare hands. Disinfect all work surfaces with bleach at the end of the lab.

INCLUSION Prior to the activity, dissect a wing, removing the muscles, tendons, and ligaments. Display the dissected parts of the wings with labels for students to use as a guide. Or, you might provide a full-page unlabeled outline of the wing for students to fill in with labels.

CHAPTER INVESTIGATION

A Closer Look at Muscles

OVERVIEW AND PURPOSE You use the muscles in your body to do a variety of things. Walking, talking, reading the words on this page, and scratching your head are all actions that require muscles. How do your muscles interact with your bones? In this investigation you will

- examine chicken wings to see how the muscles and the bones interact
- compare the movement of the chicken wing with the movement of your own bones and muscles

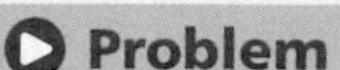

MATERIALS
- uncooked chicken wing and leg (soaked in bleach)
- paper towels
- dissection tray
- scissors

Problem

What are some characteristics of muscles?

Hypothesize

Write a hypothesis to propose how muscles interact with bones. Your hypothesis should take the form of an "If . . . , then . . . , because . . ." statement.

Procedure

1. Make a data table like the one shown on the sample notebook page. Put on your protective gloves. Be sure you are wearing gloves whenever you touch the chicken.
2. Obtain a chicken wing from your teacher. Rinse it in water and pat dry with a paper towel. Place it in the tray.
3. Extend the wing. In your notebook, draw a diagram of the extended wing. Be sure to include any visible external structures. Label the following on your diagram: lower limb, upper joint, and the wing tip.
4. Use scissors to remove the skin. Use caution so that you cut only through the skin. Peel back the skin and any fat so you can examine the muscles.

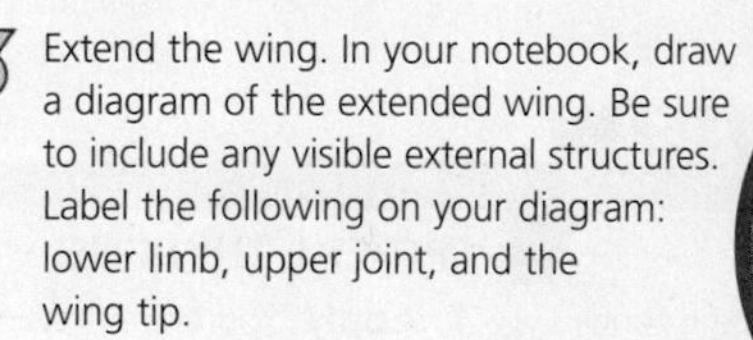

step 3

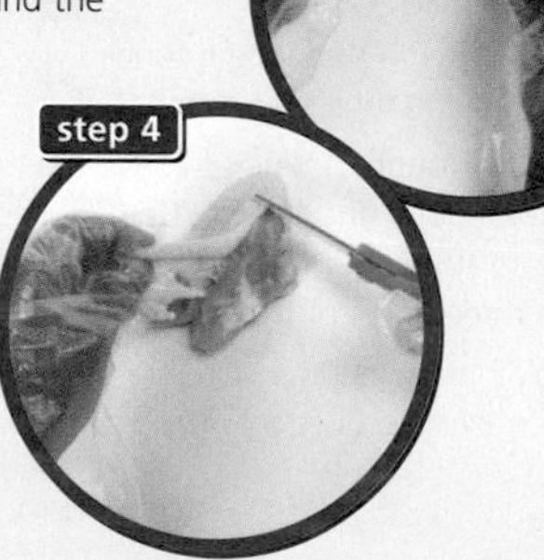

step 4

INVESTIGATION RESOURCES

CHAPTER INVESTIGATION, A Closer Look at Muscles
- Level A, pp. 50–53
- Level B, pp. 54–57
- Level C, p. 58

Advanced students should complete Levels B & C.

Writing a Lab Report, D12–13

Technology Resources

Customize this student lab as needed or look for an alternative. Print rubrics to assess student lab reports.

Lab Generator CD-ROM

5 The muscles are the pink tissues that extend from one end of the bone to the other. Locate these in the upper wing and observe the way they move when you move the wing. Record your observations in your notebook.

6 Repeat this procedure for the muscles in the lower wing. In your notebook, draw a diagram of the muscles in the chicken wing.

7 There are also tendons in the chicken wing. These are the shiny white tissues at the end of the muscles. Add the tendons to your diagram.

8 Dispose of the chicken wing and parts according to your teacher's instructions. **Be sure to wash your hands well.**

Observe and Analyze

Write It Up

1. **RECORD** Write a brief description of how the bones and muscles work together to allow movement.
2. **EVALUATE** What difficulties, if any, did you encounter in carrying out this experiment?

Conclude

1. **INTERPRET** How does the chicken wing move when you bend it at the joint?
2. **OBSERVE** What happens when you pull on one of the wing muscles?
3. **COMPARE** Using your diagram of the chicken wing as an example, locate the same muscle groups in your own arm. How do they react when you bend your elbow?
4. **APPLY** What role do the tendons play in the movement of the muscles or bones?

INVESTIGATE Further

CHALLENGE Using scissors, carefully remove the muscles and the tendons from the bones. Next find the ligaments, which are located between the bones. Add these to your diagram. Describe how you think ligaments function.

A Closer Look at Muscles

Problem: What are some characteristics of muscles?

Table 1. Observations

Draw your diagrams	Write your observations
Extended wing	Muscles in the upper wing
Muscles in the wing	Muscles in the lower wing

Chapter 17: **Systems, Support, and Movement 605**

Post-Lab Discussion

- Ask students why pulling on a muscle in the chicken wing causes the wing to move. *Pulling on the muscle has the same effect as the muscle contracting; it pulls a tendon and thereby moves bones.*
- How are the chicken wing and a human arm similar? *Both have muscles, tendons, and bones that interact to cause movement.*
- Ask students what new questions arose, and discuss ways they could investigate those questions. *Students' questions should relate to the interaction of muscles with bones.*

Observe and Analyze

1. *Skeletal muscles are attached to bones by tendons. When muscles contract, the tendons pull on the bones, causing them to move.*
2. *Answers will vary. Some students may have had difficulty in distinguishing between ligaments and tendons.*

Conclude

1. *It moves with a back-and-forth motion.*
2. *A bone moves.*
3. *When the elbow bends, the biceps contracts and the triceps relaxes. When the arm straightens, the triceps contracts and the biceps relaxes.*
4. *Tendons attach the muscles to the bones and pull the bones when the muscles contract.*

INVESTIGATE Further

CHALLENGE Ligaments hold bones together at movable joints.

BACK TO

the BIG idea

Have students name some of the organ systems of the human body. Then have them tell what each system does and how it may interact with other systems. *Sample answer: When you raise your hand, nerve tissue carries a message from your brain, and muscle tissue contracts to move the bones, made of connective and epithelial tissues.*

KEY CONCEPTS SUMMARY

SECTION 17.1
Ask students to describe the structures of tissues, organs, and organ systems. *Tissues are groups of similar cells that function together. Organs are made up of groups of tissues. Organ systems are made up of groups of organs.*

SECTION 17.2
Ask students to describe the main functions of the skeletal system. *The skeletal system provides a framework for the body that furnishes support, allows movement, and protects organ systems.*

SECTION 17.3
Ask students to identify organs in the body that contain smooth muscle and to explain why they contain that kind of muscle. *Smooth muscle is found in the lining of the stomach and the intestines. Since these organs perform involuntary movements, they need to be lined with smooth muscle.*

Review Concepts

- Big Idea Flow Chart, p. T1
- Chapter Outline, pp. T7–T8

17 Chapter Review

the BIG idea

The human body is made up of systems that work together to perform necessary functions.

KEY CONCEPTS SUMMARY

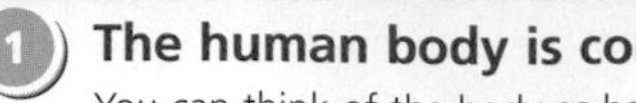

1 The human body is complex.

You can think of the body as having five levels of organization: cells, tissues, organs, organ systems, and the whole organism itself. The different systems of the human body work together to maintain homeostasis.

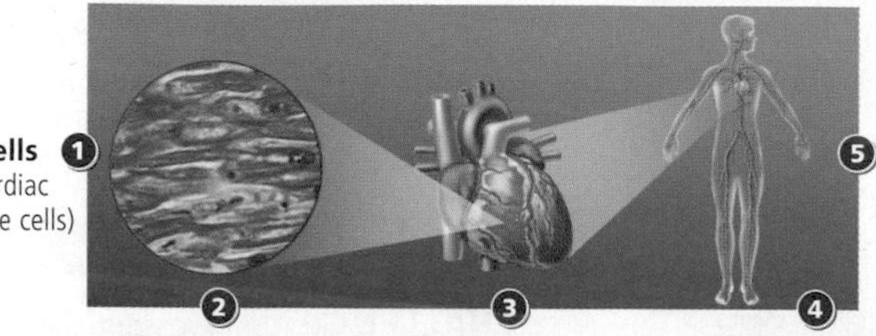

VOCABULARY
tissue p. 586
organ p. 587
organ system p. 588
homeostasis p. 588

2 The skeletal system provides support and protection.

Bones are living tissue. The skeleton is the body's framework and has two main divisions, the **axial skeleton** and the **appendicular skeleton**. Bones come together at joints.

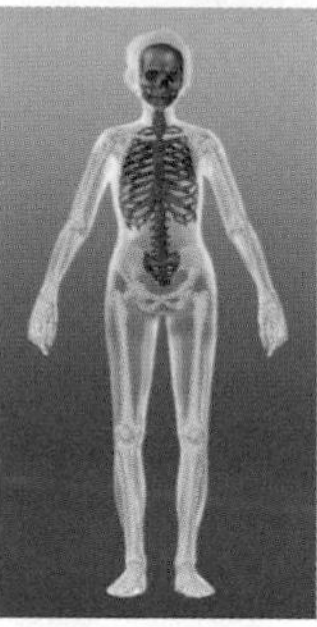

VOCABULARY
skeletal system p. 590
compact bone p. 591
spongy bone p. 591
axial skeleton p. 592
appendicular skeleton p. 592

3 The muscular system makes movement possible.

Types of muscle	Function
skeletal muscle, voluntary	moves bones, maintains posture, maintains body temperature
smooth muscle, involuntary	moves internal organs, such as the intestines
cardiac muscle, involuntary	pumps blood throughout the body

VOCABULARY
muscular system p. 599
skeletal muscle p. 600
voluntary muscle p. 600
smooth muscle p. 600
involuntary muscle p. 600
cardiac muscle p. 600

Technology Resources

Have students visit **ClassZone.com** or use the CD-ROM for a cumulative review of concepts.

CONTENT REVIEW

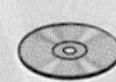
CONTENT REVIEW CD-ROM

Engage students in a whole-class interactive review of Key Concepts. Edit content as you wish.

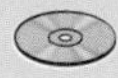
POWER PRESENTATIONS

Reviewing Vocabulary

In one or two sentences describe how the vocabulary terms in each of the following pairs of words are related. Underline each vocabulary term in your answer.

1. cells, tissues
2. organs, organ systems
3. axial skeleton, appendicular skeleton
4. skeletal muscle, voluntary muscle
5. smooth muscle, involuntary muscle
6. compact bone, spongy bone

Reviewing Key Concepts

Multiple Choice *Choose the letter of the best answer.*

7. Which type of tissue carries electrical impulses from your brain?
   a. epithelial tissue
   b. muscle tissue
   c. nerve tissue
   d. connective tissue
8. Connective tissue functions to provide
   a. support and strength
   b. messaging system
   c. movement
   d. heart muscle
9. Bone cells lie within a network made of
   a. tendons
   b. calcium
   c. marrow
   d. joints
10. The marrow produces
    a. spongy bone
    b. red blood cells
    c. compact bone
    d. calcium
11. Which bones are part of the axial skeleton?
    a. skull, shoulder blades, arm bones
    b. skull, spinal column, leg bones
    c. shoulder blades, spinal column, and hip bones
    d. skull, spinal column, ribs
12. Bones of the skeleton connect to each other at
    a. tendons
    b. ligaments
    c. joints
    d. muscles

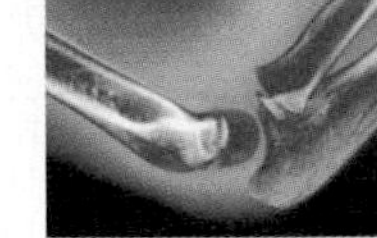

13. How do muscles contribute to homeostasis?
    a. They keep parts of the body together.
    b. They control the amount of water in the body.
    c. They help you move.
    d. They produce heat when they contract.
14. Cardiac muscle is found in the
    a. heart
    b. stomach
    c. intestines
    d. arms and legs
15. The stomach is made up of
    a. cardiac muscle
    b. skeletal muscle
    c. smooth muscle
    d. voluntary muscle

Short Answer *Write a short answer to each question.*

16. What is the difference between spongy bone and compact bone?
17. The root word *homeo* means "same," and the root word *stasis* means "to stay." How do these root words relate to the definition of *homeostasis*?
18. Hold the upper part of one arm between your elbow and shoulder with your opposite hand. Feel the muscles there. What happens to those muscles as you bend your arm?

ASSESSMENT RESOURCES

UNIT ASSESSMENT BOOK
- Chapter Test, Level A, pp. 6–9
- Chapter Test, Level B, pp. 10–13
- Chapter Test, Level C, pp. 14–17
- Alternative Assessment, pp. 18–19

SPANISH ASSESSMENT BOOK
Spanish Chapter Test, pp. 81–84

Technology Resources

Edit test items and answer choices.

Test Generator CD-ROM

Visit **ClassZone.com** to extend test practice.

Test Practice

Reviewing Vocabulary

Sample answers:

1. *Cells are the basic units of life. Tissues are made up of groups of similar cells that function together.*
2. *Organs are body structures that have specific functions. Organ systems are made up of groups of organs that perform related functions.*
3. *There are two main divisions of the human skeleton. The axial skeleton provides support and protection; the appendicular skeleton enables movement.*
4. *Skeletal muscle makes up the muscles attached to the skeleton. Because it produces voluntary movement, such a muscle is called voluntary muscle.*
5. *Smooth muscle is found inside body organs. It produces involuntary movement and is therefore called involuntary muscle.*
6. *Compact bone forms the hard outer layer of bones. Inside it is a strong, lightweight tissue called spongy bone.*

Reviewing Key Concepts

7. *c*
8. *a*
9. *b*
10. *b*
11. *d*
12. *c*
13. *d*
14. *a*
15. *c*
16. *Compact bone makes up a bone's outer layer. Spongy bone is less dense and is surrounded by compact bone.*
17. *Homeostasis is the ability of the body to maintain a stable internal condition—in other words, stay the same.*
18. *The muscle on the top of the arm contracts, and the muscle on the opposite side relaxes.*

Thinking Critically

19. Cells—muscle cell; tissues—bone; organs—heart; organ systems—digestive system

20. connective tissue; blood flows through the body, connecting all organ systems.

21. The bones of the human skeleton contain calcium. The skeleton is hard, providing support and protecting internal organs. It is lightweight, and has joints, much like the hinge of the clam's shells. The difference is that a clam's shell is outside; bones are inside.

22. These are immovable joints. They lock together tissues that support and protect rather than move.

23. The arms and legs belong to the appendicular skeleton. They are attached by ball-and-socket joints, allowing a wide range of movement.

24. The skeleton provides support just like the framework of a house. Unlike the house, the skeleton is made of living tissues and is flexible.

25. The skeleton provides shape and support; it allows the body to move; it protects soft organs.

26. Bringing the toothbrush up involves rotational movement at the shoulder, pivotal of the wrist, angular of the elbow and fingers gripping. The small bones in the hand glide as the hand turns.

27. For movement to occur, muscles on one side of a bone must relax while muscles on the other side contract.

28. More effort means more fibers are contracted.

the BIG idea

29. Answers will depend on students' original answers.

30. Sample answer: Bones come together at joints. Skeletal muscles that are attached to the bones contract and relax, pulling the bones to move the body.

UNIT PROJECTS

Give students unit projects worksheets for their projects. Both directions and rubrics can be used as guides.

 Unit Projects, pp. 5–10

Thinking Critically

19. **PROVIDE EXAMPLES** What are the levels of organization of the human body from simple to most complex? Give an example of each.

20. **CLASSIFY** There are four types of tissue in the human body: epithelial, nerve, muscle, and connective. How would you classify blood? Explain your reasoning.

21. **CONNECT** A clam shell is made of a calcium compound. The material is hard, providing protection to the soft body of a clam. It is also lightweight. Describe three ways in which the human skeleton is similar to a seashell. What is one important way in which it is different?

Use the diagram below to answer the next two questions

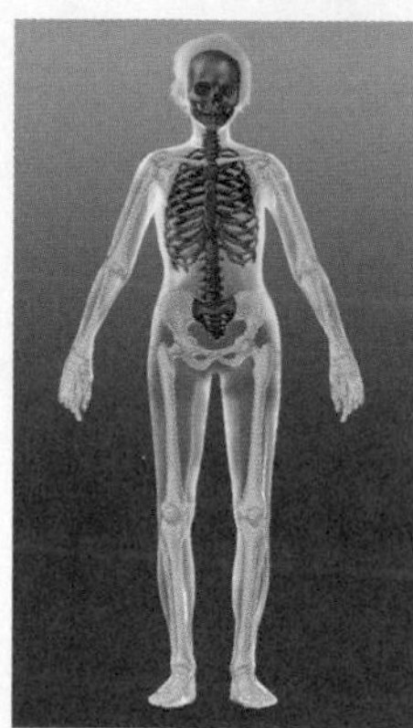

22. **SYNTHESIZE** Identify the types of joints that hold together the bones of the skull and sternum. How do these types of joints relate to the function of the skull and sternum?

23. **SYNTHESIZE** The human skeleton has two main divisions. Which skeleton do the arms and legs belong to? How do the joints that connect the arms to the shoulders and the legs to the hips relate to the function of this skeleton?

24. **COMPARE AND CONTRAST** How is the skeletal system of your body like the framework of a house or building? How is it different?

25. **SUMMARIZE** Describe three important functions of the skeleton.

26. **APPLY** The joints in the human body can be described as producing three types of movement. Relate these three types of movement to the action of brushing your teeth.

27. **COMPARE AND CONTRAST** When you stand, the muscles in your legs help to keep you balanced. Some of the muscles on both sides of your leg bones contract. How does this differ from how the muscles behave when you start to walk?

28. **INFER** Muscles are tissues that are made up of many muscle fibers. A muscle fiber can either be relaxed or contracted. Some movements you do require very little effort, like picking up a piece of paper. Others require a lot of effort, like picking up a book bag. How do you think a muscle produces the effort needed for a small task compared with a big task?

the BIG idea

29. **INFER** Look again at the picture on pages 582–583. Now that you have finished the chapter, how would you change or add details to your answer to the question on the photograph?

30. **SUMMARIZE** Write a paragraph explaining how skeletal muscles, bones, and joints work together to allow the body to move and be flexible. Underline the terms in your paragraph.

UNIT PROJECTS

If you are doing a unit project, make a folder for your project. Include in your folder a list of resources you will need, the date on which the project is due, and a schedule to track your progress. Begin gathering data.

MONITOR AND RETEACH

If students are having trouble applying the concepts in Chapter Review items 22 and 23, suggest that they review the illustration of the skeletal system on p. 593. Then have students create a concept map detailing the functions and structure of the skeleton.

Students may benefit from summarizing one or more sections of the chapter.

 Summarizing the Chapter, pp. 68–69

Standardized Test Practice

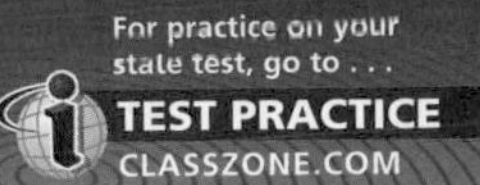

Interpreting Diagrams

The action of a muscle pulling on a bone can be compared to a simple machine called a lever. A lever is a rod that moves about a fixed point called the fulcrum. Effort at one end of the rod can move a load at the other end. In the human body, a muscle supplies the effort needed to move a bone—the lever. The joint is the fulcrum, and the load is the weight of the body part being moved. There are three types of levers, which are classified according to the position of the fulcrum, the effort, and the load.

Read the text and study the diagrams, and then choose the best answer for the questions that follow.

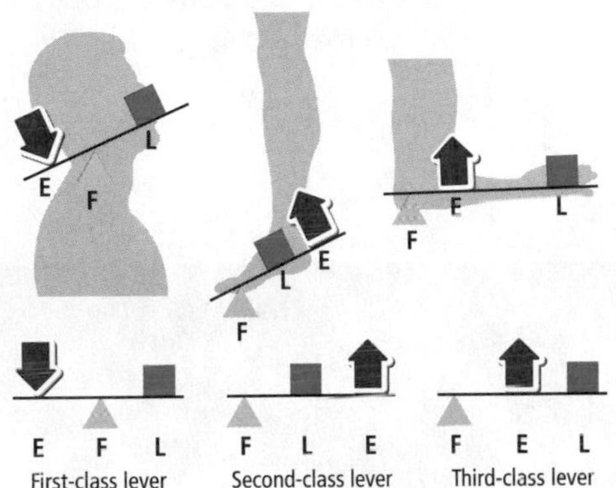

1. In a first-class lever
   a. the load is at end of the lever opposite the fulcrum
   b. the load is between the effort and the fulcrum
   c. the fulcrum is between the load and the effort
   d. the effort and load are on the same side

2. What is true of all levers?
   a. The fulcrum must be located at the center of a lever.
   b. The force of the load and effort point in the same direction.
   c. The load and effort are on the same side of the fulcrum.
   d. The lever exerts a force in a direction opposite the weight of the load.

3. The lever represents what structure in the human body?
   a. a joint
   b. a bone
   c. a muscle
   d. a ligament

4. The main point of the diagram is to show
   a. how bones work
   b. that there are three types of joints and how they are classified as levers
   c. where to apply a force
   d. the forces involved in moving parts of the body

Extended Response

Use the diagrams above and terms from the word box to answer the next question. Underline each term you use in your answer.

fulcrum	load	effort	rod
bone	muscle	joint	

5. Suppose you had a heavy box to lift. Your first thought might be to bend over, stretch out your arms, and grab the box. Your body would be acting as a simple machine. Identify the type of lever this is and the parts of this machine.

6. A doctor would advise you not to lift a heavy object, like a box, simply by bending over and picking it up. That action puts too much strain on your back. It is better to bend your knees, hold the box close to your body, and then lift. How does this way of lifting change how you are using your body?

METACOGNITIVE ACTIVITY

Have students answer the following questions in their **Science Notebook:**

1. Are there any concepts relating to the skeletal and muscular systems that you are still confused about? Explain.
2. What did you learn in this unit that surprised you? Explain.
3. While researching your unit project, how did you prefer to do your research? Why?

Interpreting Diagrams

1. c   *2. d*   *3. a*   *4. d*

Extended Response

5. RUBRIC

4 points for a response that correctly answers the question and includes all of the following terms:

- fulcrum
- load
- bone
- muscle
- effort
- joint
- rod

Sample answer: Your body would be functioning as a third-class lever. The bones of your back act as the rod or lever, the fulcrum is the joint at the lower part of your back, and the load is the box. The muscles in your back provide the effort.

3 points correctly answers the question and includes five or six of the terms listed

2 points correctly answers the question and includes three or four of the terms

1 point correctly answers the question and includes one or two of the terms

6. RUBRIC

4 points for a response that correctly answers the question and includes all of the following points:

- the muscles of the legs are now involved as well.
- more muscles do the same work, so the effort is shared
- the fulcrum has changed
- now the legs are used as levers

Sample answer: By bending down next to the box to pick it up, you have changed the fulcrum to the joints in your legs. Because the legs are now levers, the leg muscles as well as the back muscles are involved in lifting the load. You are putting less strain on your back because your leg muscles are sharing the effort.

3 points includes three of the above points

2 points includes two of the above points

1 point includes one of the above points

CHAPTER

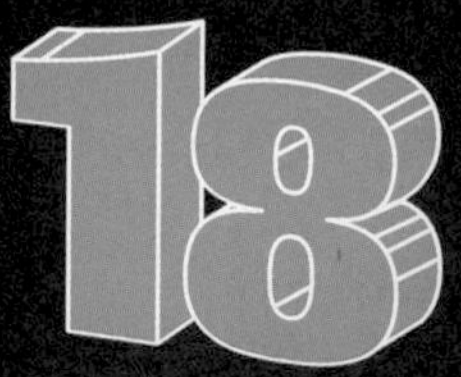

Absorption, Digestion, and Exchange

Life Science

UNIFYING PRINCIPLES

PRINCIPLE 1
All living things share common characteristics.

PRINCIPLE 2
All living things share common needs.

PRINCIPLE 3
Living things meet their needs through interactions with the environment.

PRINCIPLE 4
The types and numbers of living things change over time.

Unit 5: Human Biology

BIG IDEAS

CHAPTER 17
Systems, Support, and Movement
The body is made up of systems that work together to perform necessary functions.

CHAPTER 18
Absorption, Digestion, and Exchange
Systems in the body obtain and process materials and remove waste.

CHAPTER 19
Transport and Protection
Systems function to transport materials and to defend and protect the body.

CHAPTER 20
Control and Reproduction
The nervous and endocrine systems allow the body to respond to internal and external conditions.

CHAPTER 21
Growth, Development, and Health
The body develops and maintains itself over time.

CHAPTER 18

KEY CONCEPTS

SECTION 1

The respiratory system gets oxygen and removes carbon dioxide.

1. Your body needs oxygen.
2. Structures in the respiratory system function together.
3. The respiratory system is also involved in other activities.

SECTION 2

The digestive system breaks down food.

1. The body needs energy and materials.
2. The digestive system moves and breaks down food.
3. Materials are broken down as they move through the digestive tract.
4. Other organs aid digestion and absorption.

SECTION 3

The urinary system removes waste materials.

1. Life processes produce wastes.
2. The urinary system removes waste from the blood.
3. The kidneys act as filters.

The Big Idea Flow Chart is available on p. T9 in the **UNIT TRANSPARENCY BOOK.**

Previewing Content

SECTION

The respiratory system gets oxygen and removes carbon dioxide.
pp. 613–620

1. **Your body needs oxygen.**
During a process called **cellular respiration,** the cells of the body use oxygen in chemical reactions in order to release energy. The respiratory system interacts with the environment and the digestive and circulatory systems to make cellular respiration possible. Carbon dioxide is a byproduct of cellular respiration.

2. **Structures in the respiratory system function together.**
   - Air enters the body through the nose and mouth, then travels down the trachea and into the bronchial tubes that lead to the lungs.
   - The exchange of oxygen and carbon dioxide with the circulatory system takes place in the alveoli, air sacs in the lungs.
   - The diaphragm and involuntary muscles surrounding the ribs control the inhalation and exhalation of gases.

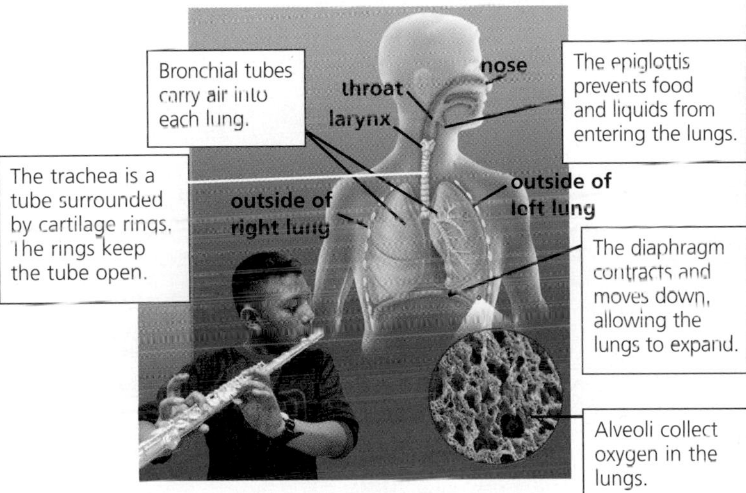

3. **The respiratory system is also involved in other activities.**
Before air passes into the trachea, it moves over the vocal cords of the larynx, allowing sounds to be produced. Water is removed from the respiratory system through the actions of hiccups, coughs, sneezes, and yawns.

SECTION

The digestive system breaks down food. pp. 621–627

1. **The body needs energy and materials.**
Nutrients, such as proteins, carbohydrates, fats, and water, are used by the body during the process of **digestion,** enabling the body to move, grow, and maintain homeostasis.

2. **The digestive system moves and breaks down food.**
Mechanical and chemical digestion both begin in the mouth. The action of physical digestion begins as teeth tear food and mash it. The action of chemical digestion begins as saliva changes starches into sugars. Food passes through the esophagus by the action of **peristalsis** and moves into the stomach.

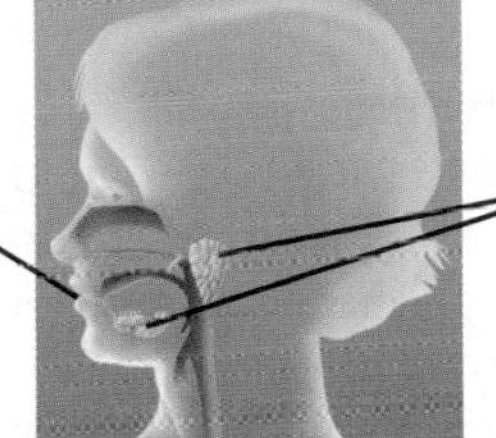

The mouth gives a good example of the difference between mechanical digestion and chemical digestion, and shows how the two work together.

3. **Materials are broken down as they move through the digestive tract.**
   - Muscle contractions in the esophagus allow food to be pushed through it to the stomach.
   - In the stomach, mechanical digestion and chemical digestion continue, aided by acids in the stomach.
   - Partially digested food moves into the small intestine, where digestion is completed. Nutrients are absorbed into the circulatory system through structures called villi.
   - Water is absorbed into the body in the large intestine. Solid wastes pass out of the body through the rectum.

4. **Other organs aid digestion and absorption.**
   - The liver secretes bile, which aids in the breakdown of fats.
   - The gallbladder stores bile produced in the liver and secretes it into the small intestine.
   - The pancreas aids in digestion of proteins, fats, and starch.

Common Misconceptions

FOOD AND GROWTH Middle school students know food is related to growing, but they are not aware of how. They may think that food is only a source of energy, rather than also being a source of matter for growth. The energy gained from food is thought to be for movement or work rather than for all body functions.

This misconception is addressed on p. 622.

MISCONCEPTION DATABASE
CLASSZONE.COM Background on student misconceptions

STOMACH LOCATION Students often think that the stomach is located much lower in the abdomen than it really is.

This misconception is addressed on p. 624.

Previewing Content

SECTION

The urinary system removes waste materials. pp. 628–631

1. Life processes produce wastes.
Removal of wastes is essential in maintaining body functions. In addition to the urinary system, the digestive and respiratory systems and the skin enable the body to remove wastes.

2. The urinary system removes waste from the blood.

- Kidneys filter materials out of the circulatory system. Some of these materials are eliminated as waste. Other materials are returned to the blood.
- From the kidneys, liquid waste material called **urine** travels down structures called ureters and into the bladder. There the urine is eliminated from the body through the urethra.

3. The kidneys act as filters.
Nephrons, which are looping tubes found inside the kidney, act as filters. Blood passes through a structure in the nephron called the glomerulus, where waste materials are filtered out. Once blood passes through the nephron, the waste material passes out of the kidney and into the ureters. The kidneys also regulate the amount of water in the body.

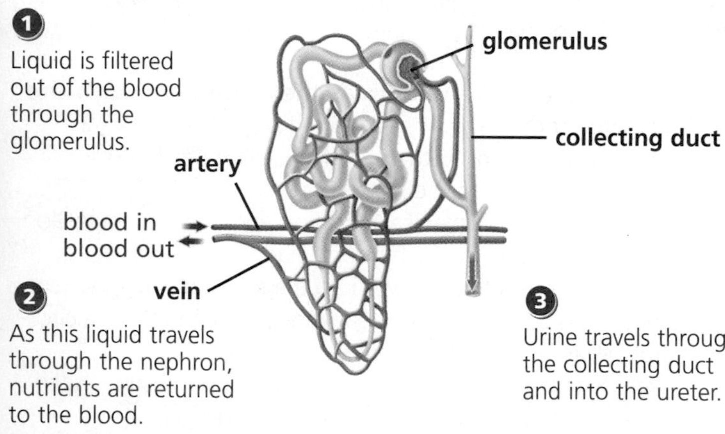

Point out to students that the urinary system is not "breaking down food to obtain nutrients" and so is not part of the digestive system.

Common Misconceptions

MISCONCEPTION DATABASE
CLASSZONE.COM Background on student misconceptions

URINARY BLADDER Many students think that the urinary bladder is a part of the digestive system when in fact it is part of the urinary system.

 This misconception is addressed on p. 629.

Previewing Labs

EXPLORE the BIG idea

Mirror, Mirror, p. 611 Students observe, by exhaling on a mirror, that breath contains water.	**TIME** 10 minutes **MATERIALS** mirror
Water Everywhere, p. 611 Students determine how much liquid they consume in a 24-hour period.	**TIME** 10 minutes **MATERIALS** notebook
Internet Activity: Lung Movement, p. 611 Students observe a simulation of diaphragm and lung movement during respiration.	**TIME** 20 minutes **MATERIALS** computer with Internet access

SECTION 1

EXPLORE Breathing, p. 613 Students observe the movement of the rib cage during respiration.	**TIME** 10 minutes **MATERIALS** notebook
INVESTIGATE Lungs, p. 615 Students design a model of lungs to represent respiration and lung behavior.	**TIME** 15 minutes **MATERIALS** medium balloon, 1L plastic bottle with labels removed, duct tape

SECTION 2

EXPLORE Digestion, p. 621 Students explore how the digestive system breaks down fat.	**TIME** 15 minutes **MATERIALS** graduated cylinders, test tube with caps, test tube stand, 3 graduated cylinders, 5 mL vegetable oil, water, 5 mL dish detergent
INVESTIGATE Chemical Digestion, p. 623 Students model how saliva breaks down food.	**TIME** 25 minutes **MATERIALS** knife, cooked potato, droppers, 50 mL bacterial amylase solution (solution A), water

SECTION 3

EXPLORE Waste Removal, p. 628 Students demonstrate how the skin excretes wastes.	**TIME** 10 minutes **MATERIALS** plastic bag, masking tape, stopwatch
CHAPTER INVESTIGATION **Modeling a Kidney,** pp. 632–633 Students model the filtering process of kidneys to determine what types of materials are filtered by the kidneys.	**TIME** 40 minutes **MATERIALS** small funnel, fine filter paper, 10 g salt dissolved in 1000 mL water (solution A), 10 g glucose dissolved in 1000 mL water (solution B), 10 g albumin powder (or one egg white) dissolved in 1000 mL water (solution C), graduated cylinder, 100 mL beaker, glucose test strips, salinity test strips, protein test strips

R **Additional INVESTIGATION,** How Much Air Can Your Lungs Hold?, A, B, & C, pp. 118–126; Teacher Instructions, pp. 305–306

Previewing Chapter Resources

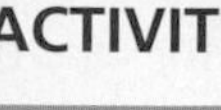

	INTEGRATED TECHNOLOGY	LABS AND ACTIVITIES
CHAPTER 18 **Absorption, Digestion, and Exchange**	 **CLASSZONE.COM** • eEdition Plus • EasyPlanner Plus • Misconception Database • Content Review • Test Practice • Resource Centers • Visualization • Internet Activity: Lung Movement • Math Tutorial  **SCILINKS.ORG** SCILINKS  **CD-ROMS** • eEdition • EasyPlanner • Power Presentations • Content Review • Lab Generator • Test Generator 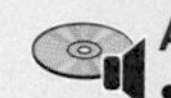 **AUDIO CDS** • Audio Readings • Audio Readings in Spanish	 EXPLORE the Big Idea, p. 611 • Mirror, Mirror • Water Everywhere • Internet Activity: Lung Movement  **UNIT RESOURCE BOOK** Unit Projects, pp. 5–10  **Lab Generator CD-ROM** Generate customized labs.
SECTION 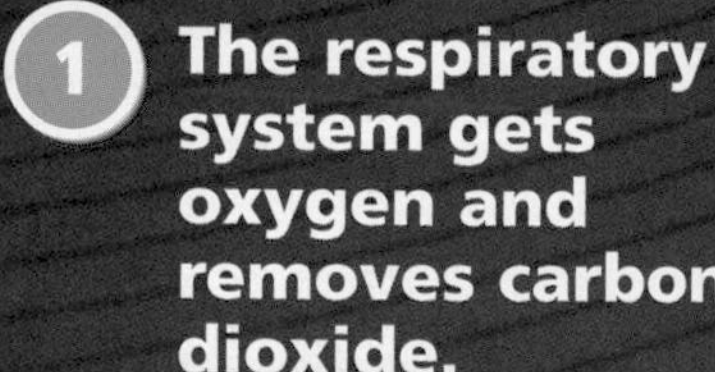 1 **The respiratory system gets oxygen and removes carbon dioxide.** pp. 613–620 Time: 2 periods (1 block) Lesson Plan, pp. 70–71	 **RESOURCE CENTER,** Respiratory System **UNIT TRANSPARENCY BOOK** • Big Idea Flow Chart, p. T9 • Daily Vocabulary Scaffolding, p. T10 • Note-Taking Model, p. T11 • 3-Minute Warm-Up, p. T12	 • EXPLORE Breathing, p. 613 • INVESTIGATE Lungs, p. 615 • Science on the Job, p. 620  **UNIT RESOURCE BOOK** • Datasheet, Lungs, p. 79 • ADDITIONAL Investigation, How Much Air Can Your Lungs Hold?, A, B, & C, pp. 118–126
SECTION 2 **The digestive system breaks down food.** pp. 621–627 Time: 2 periods (1 block)  Lesson Plan, pp. 81–82	 • **VISUALIZATION,** Peristalsis • **MATH TUTORIAL**  **UNIT TRANSPARENCY BOOK** • Daily Vocabulary Scaffolding, p. T10 • 3-Minute Warm-Up, p. T12 • "Digestive System" Visual, p. T14 	 • EXPLORE Digestion, p. 621 • INVESTIGATE Chemical Digestion, p. 623 • Math in Science, p. 627 **UNIT RESOURCE BOOK** • Datasheet, Chemical Digestion, p. 90 • Math Support, p. 107 • Math Practice, p. 108
SECTION  3 **The urinary system removes waste materials.** pp. 628–631 Time: 4 periods (2 blocks) 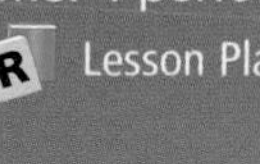 Lesson Plan, pp. 92–93	 **RESOURCE CENTER,** Urinary System  **UNIT TRANSPARENCY BOOK** • Big Idea Flow Chart, p. T9 • Daily Vocabulary Scaffolding, p. T10 • 3-Minute Warm-Up, p. T13 • Chapter Outline, pp. T15–T16	 • EXPLORE Waste Removal, p. 628 • CHAPTER INVESTIGATION, Modeling a Kidney, pp. 632–633  **UNIT RESOURCE BOOK** CHAPTER INVESTIGATION, Modeling a Kidney, A, B, & C, pp. 109–117

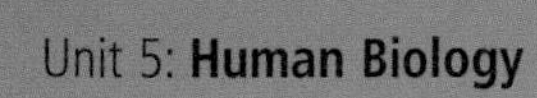

KEY TO ICONS  CD/CD-ROM 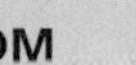 Teacher Edition 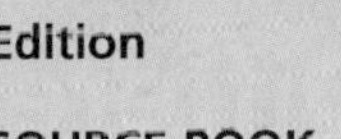 UNIT TRANSPARENCY BOOK  SPANISH ASSESSMENT BOOK

INTERNET · Pupil Edition · UNIT RESOURCE BOOK · UNIT ASSESSMENT BOOK · SCIENCE TOOLKIT

READING AND REINFORCEMENT	ASSESSMENT	STANDARDS
 • Magnet Word Diagram, B24–25 • Outline, C43 • Daily Vocabulary Scaffolding, H1–8  **UNIT RESOURCE BOOK** • Vocabulary Practice, pp. 104–105 • Decoding Support, p. 106 • Summarizing the Chapter, pp. 127–128 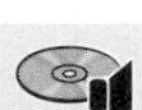 **Audio Readings CD** Listen to Pupil Edition. 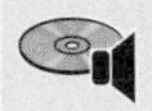 **Audio Readings in Spanish CD** Listen to Pupil Edition in Spanish.	 • Chapter Review, pp. 635–636 • Standardized Test Practice, p. 637  **UNIT ASSESSMENT BOOK** • Diagnostic Test, pp. 20–21 • Chapter Test, A, B, & C, pp. 25–36 • Alternative Assessment, pp. 37–38  Spanish Chapter Test, pp. 85–88  **Test Generator CD-ROM** Generate customized tests.  **Lab Generator CD-ROM** Rubrics for Labs	National Standards A.1–8, A.9.a–c, A.9.e–g, C.1.e, F.1.e, G.1.b See p. 610 for the standards.
 **UNIT RESOURCE BOOK** • Reading Study Guide, A & B, pp. 72–75 • Spanish Reading Study Guide, pp. 76–77 • Challenge and Extension, p. 78 • Reinforcing Key Concepts, p. 80 • Challenge Reading, pp. 102–103	 Ongoing Assessment, pp. 613–618  Section 18.1 Review, p. 619  **UNIT ASSESSMENT BOOK** Section 18.1 Quiz, p. 22	National Standards A.2–7, A.9.a–b, A.9.e–f, C.1.e, G.1.b
 **UNIT RESOURCE BOOK** • Reading Study Guide, A & B, pp. 83–86 • Spanish Reading Study Guide, pp. 87–88 • Challenge and Extension, p. 89 • Reinforcing Key Concepts, p. 91	 Ongoing Assessment, pp. 622–624, 626  Section 18.2 Review, p. 626  **UNIT ASSESSMENT BOOK** Section 18.2 Quiz, p. 23	National Standards A.2–8, A.9.a–b, A.9.e–f, C.1.e, F.1.e, G.1.b
 **UNIT RESOURCE BOOK** • Reading Study Guide, A & B, pp. 94–97 • Spanish Reading Study Guide, pp. 98–99 • Challenge and Extension, p. 100 • Reinforcing Key Concepts, p. 101	 Ongoing Assessment, pp. 628–631  Section 18.3 Review, p. 631  **UNIT ASSESSMENT BOOK** Section 18.3 Quiz, p. 24	National Standards A.1–7, A.9.a–b, A.9.e–g, C.1.e, G.1.b

Previewing Resources for Differentiated Instruction

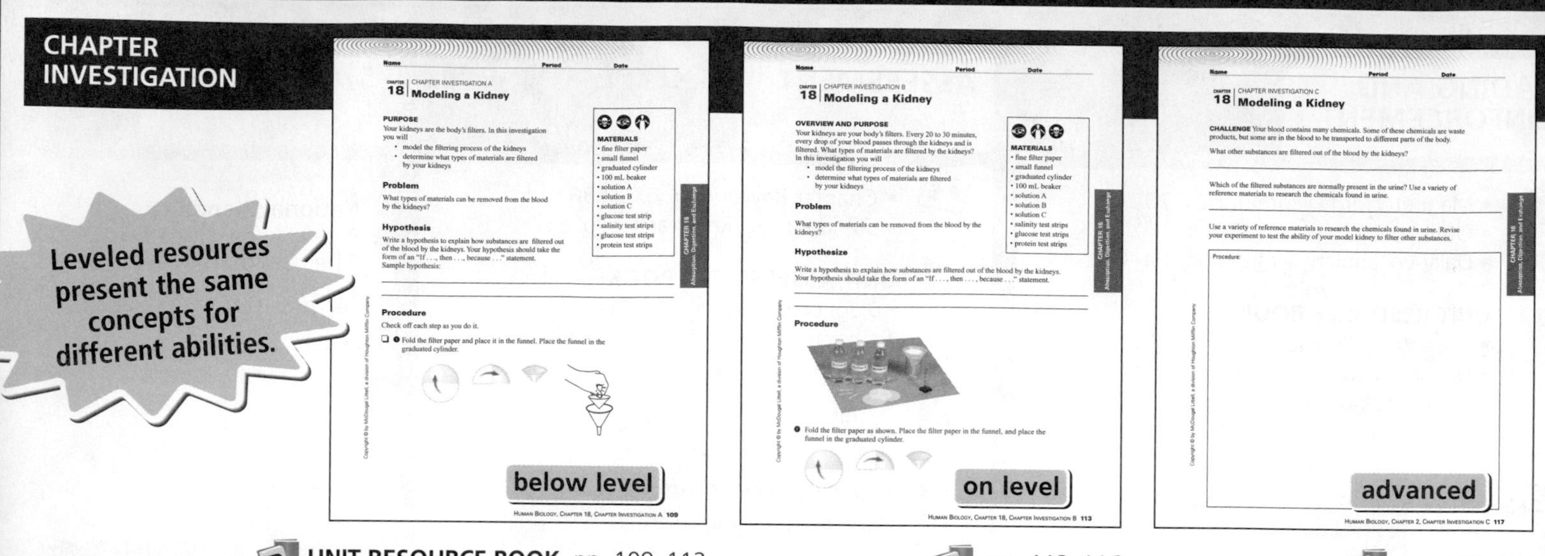

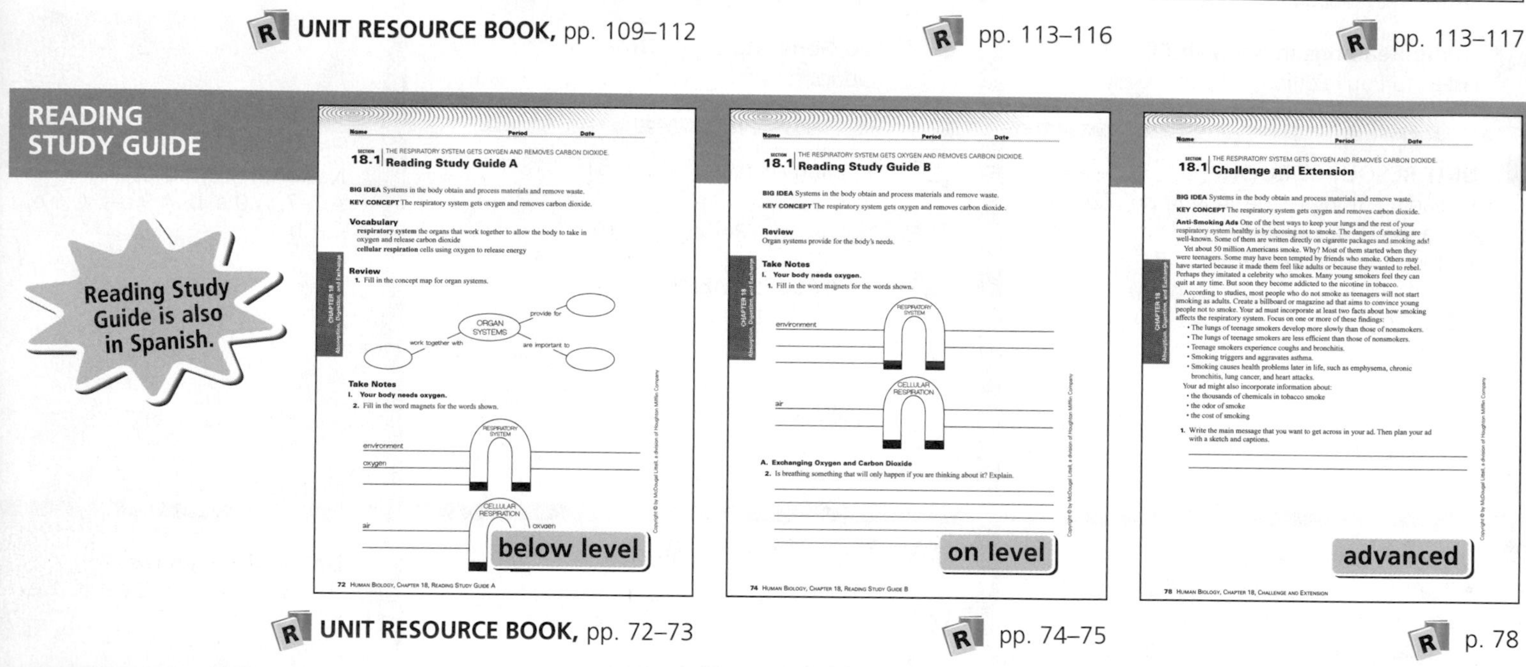

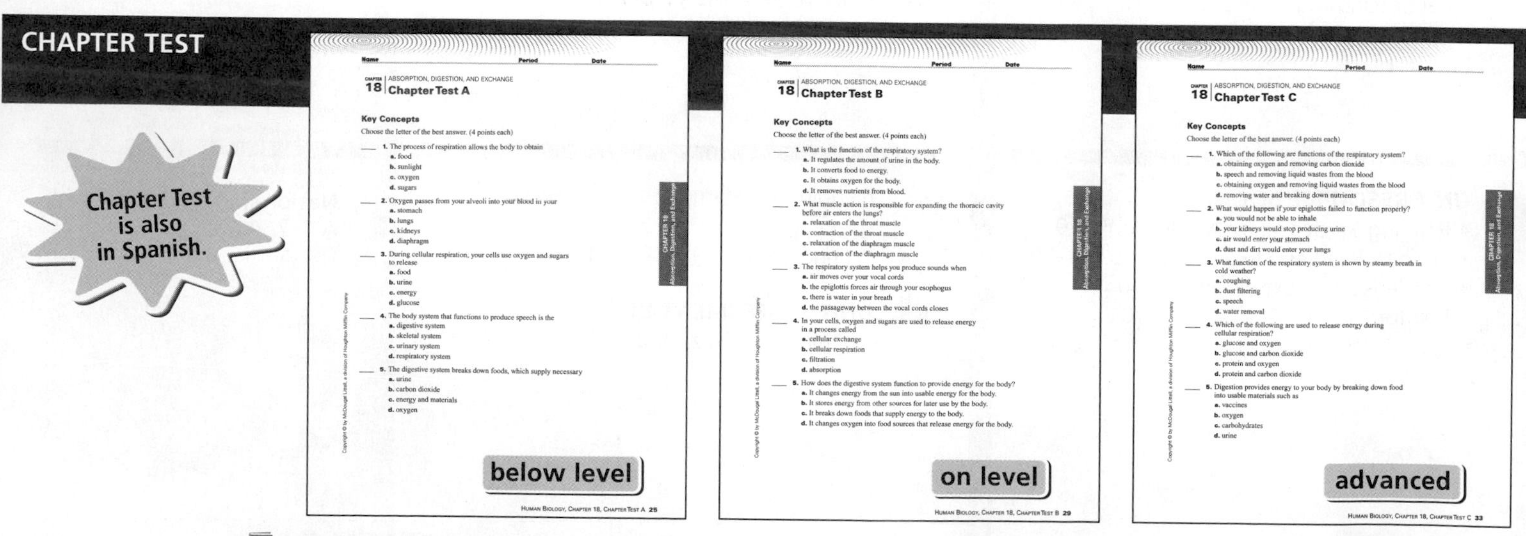

TECHNOLOGY

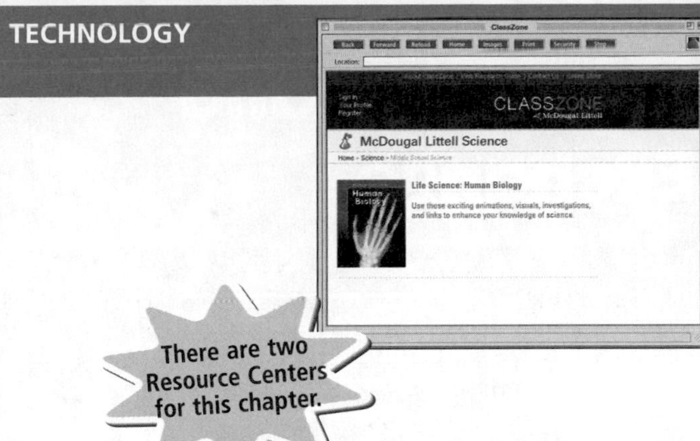

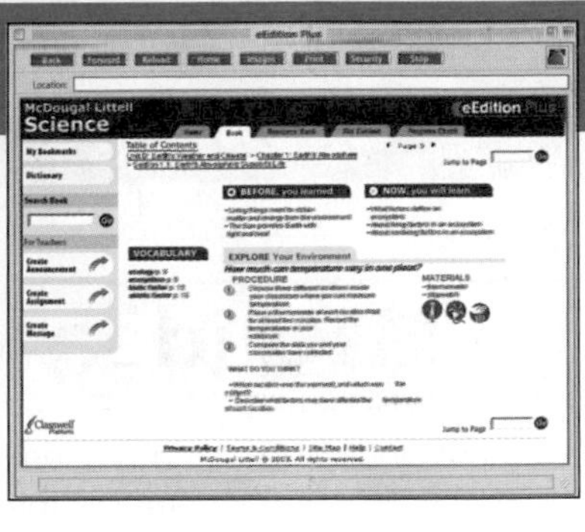

CLASSZONE.COM

CD/CD-ROMS

CLASSZONE.COM

VISUAL CONTENT

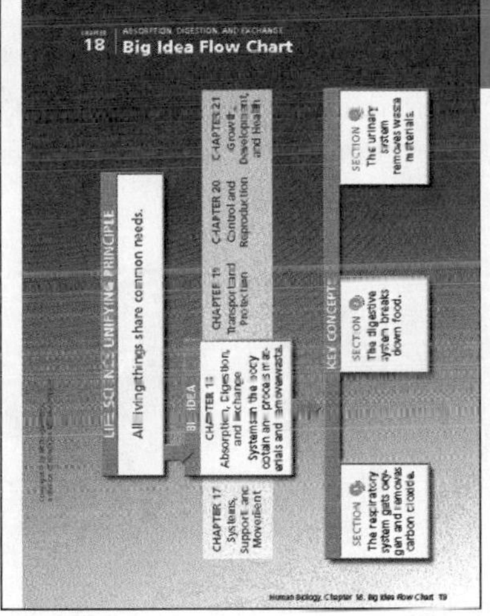

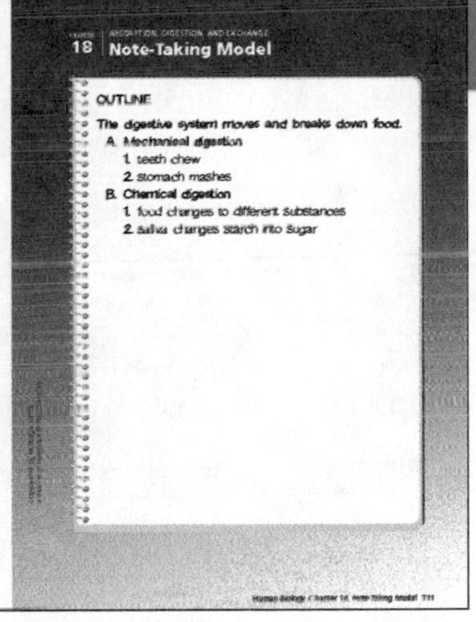

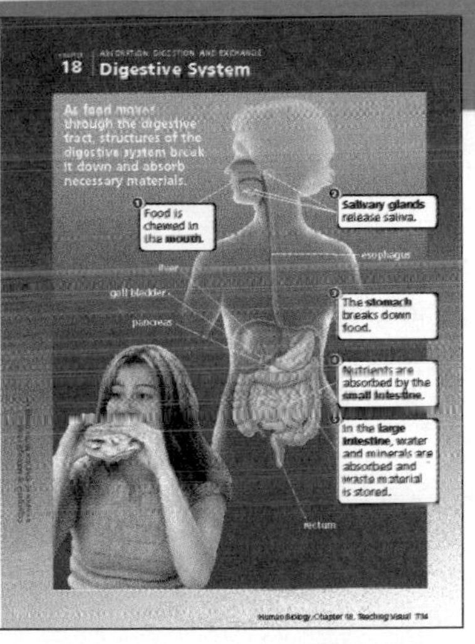

UNIT TRANSPARENCY BOOK, p. T9

p. T11

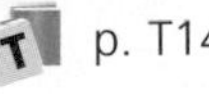
p. T14

MORE SUPPORT

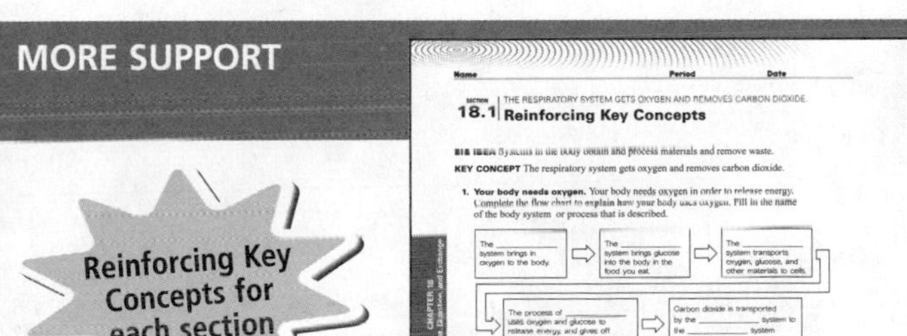

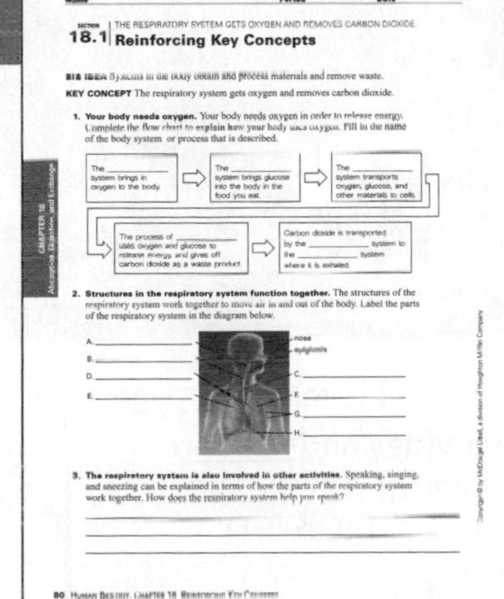

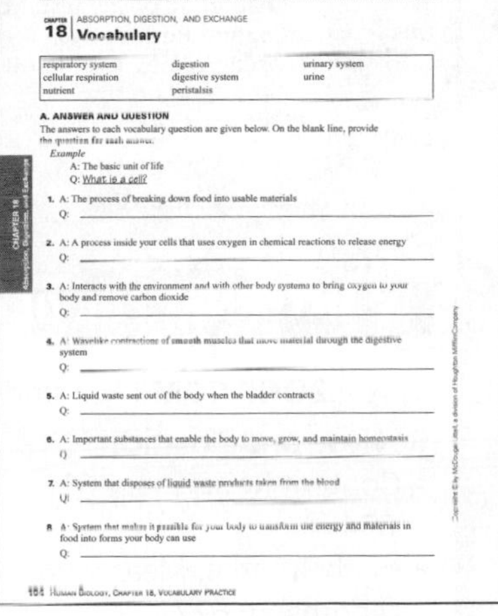

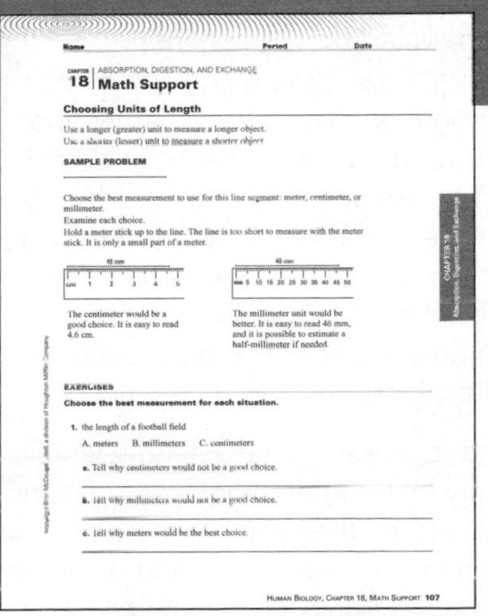

UNIT RESOURCE BOOK, p. 80

pp. 104–105

p. 107

CHAPTER

Absorption, Digestion, and Exchange

INTRODUCE

the BIG idea

Have students look at the photograph and discuss how it shows materials the body needs to function.

- How do these materials get inside the body?
- How does your body manufacture waste materials? How do the waste materials leave the body?

National Science Education Standards

Content

C.1.e The human organism has systems for digestion, respiration, reproduction, circulation, excretion, movement, control, and coordination, and for the protection from disease. These systems interact with one another.

F.1.e Food provides energy and nutrients for growth and development. Nutrition requirements vary with body weight, age, sex, activity, and body functioning.

Process

A.1–8 Identify questions that can be answered through scientific investigations; design and conduct an investigation; use tools to gather and interpret data; use evidence to describe, predict, explain, model; think critically to make relationships between evidence and explanation; recognize different explanations and predictions; communicate scientific procedures and explanations; use mathematics.

A.9.a–c, A.9.e–g Understand scientific inquiry by using different investigations, methods, mathematics, and explanations based on logic, evidence, and skepticism. Data often results in new investigations.

G.1.b Science requires different abilities.

CHAPTER

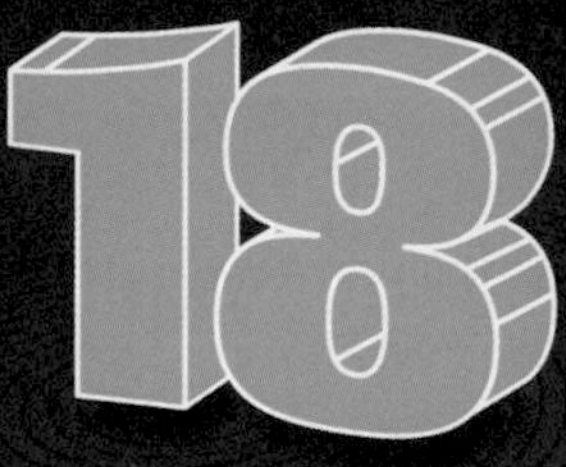

Absorption, Digestion, and Exchange

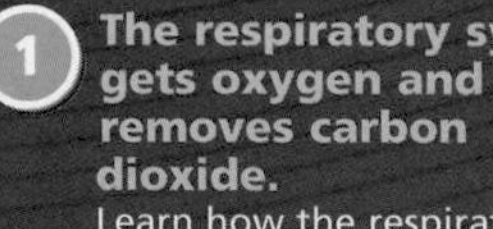

Systems in the body obtain and process materials and remove waste.

Key Concepts

SECTION 1
The respiratory system gets oxygen and removes carbon dioxide.
Learn how the respiratory system functions.

SECTION 2
The digestive system breaks down food.
Learn how the digestive system provides cells with necessary materials.

SECTION 3
The urinary system removes waste materials.
Learn how the urinary system removes wastes.

Internet Preview

CLASSZONE.COM

Chapter 18 online resources: Content Review, two Visualizations, two Resource Centers, Math Tutorial, Test Practice.

INTERNET PREVIEW

CLASSZONE.COM For student use with the following pages:

Review and Practice
- Content Review, pp. 612, 634
- Math Tutorial: Measuring Lengths, p. 627
- Test Practice, p. 637

Activities and Resources
- Internet Activity: Lung Movement, p. 611
- Resource Centers: Respiratory System, p. 616; Urinary System, p. 630
- Visualization: Peristalsis, p. 622

Digestion **Code: MDL045**

EXPLORE the BIG idea

Mirror, Mirror

Hold a small hand mirror in front of your mouth. Slowly exhale onto the surface of the mirror. What do you see? Exhale a few more times onto the mirror, observing the interaction of your breath with the cool surface of the mirror.

Observe and Think What did you see on the surface of the mirror? What does this tell you about the content of the air that you exhale?

Water Everywhere

Keep track of how much liquid you drink in a 24-hour period of time. Do not include carbonated or caffeinated beverages. Water, juice, and milk can count. Add up the number of ounces of liquid you drink in that period of time.

Observe and Think How many ounces did you drink in one day? Do you drink fluids only when you feel thirsty?

Internet Activity: Lung Movement

Go to **ClassZone.com** to watch a visualization of lung and diaphragm movement during respiration. Observe how movements of the diaphragm and other muscles affect the lungs.

Observe and Think How do the diaphragm and lungs move during inhalation? during exhalation? Why do movements of the diaphragm cause the lungs to move?

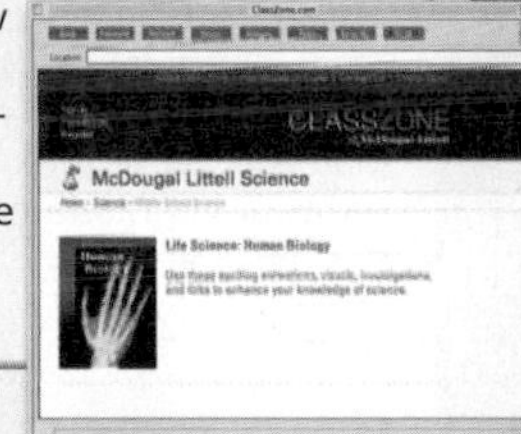

NSTA scilinks.org SCILINKS
Digestion **Code: MDL045**

TEACHING WITH TECHNOLOGY

CBL and Probeware While students are investigating how the lungs work (p. 615), they can use a carbon dioxide sensor to measure the amount of carbon dioxide in their breath before and after exercise. Then they can use a graphing calculator or spreadsheet program to analyze the data.

Graphics Software Students could use drawing software or PowerPoint to create a flowchart that shows how the digestive and circulatory systems interact in transporting materials to the cells of the body (pp. 624–625).

EXPLORE the BIG idea

These inquiry-based activities are appropriate for use at home or as a supplement to classroom instruction.

Mirror, Mirror

PURPOSE To demonstrate to students that breath contains water.

TIP *10 min.* Caution students to be careful when using mirrors.

Answer: There was fog on the mirror. There is moisture in exhalation.

REVISIT after p. 619.

Water Everywhere

PURPOSE To determine how much liquid a student consumes each day.

TIP *10 min.* Supply students with a chart to record their data.

Answer: Answers will vary depending on how much liquid each student consumes.

REVISIT after p. 631.

Internet Activity: Lung Movement

PURPOSE To observe the movement of the lungs and diaphragm.

TIP *20 min.* Encourage students to feel their ribs as they watch the visualization.

Answer: During inhalation, the diaphragm contracts and moves downward, and the ribs expand. During exhalation, the diaphragm relaxes and moves upward, and the ribs contract. When the diaphragm contracts and moves downward, the thoracic cavity expands, putting pressure on the lungs to expand.

REVISIT after p. 616.

PREPARE

CONCEPT REVIEW

Activate Prior Knowledge

- Display a picture of a fish, an insect, and a bird or mammal.
- Ask students how the animals obtain oxygen.
- Discuss how the various structures of spiracles, gills, and lungs enable the animals to interact with their environment.

TAKING NOTES

Outline

Encourage students to use the blue and red headings in their textbooks to form the basis of their outlines. The headings form the main ideas and subtopics of the outlines. Further details can be filled in with information found in the text and visuals.

Vocabulary Strategy

Students can include as many details as they want in a magnet diagram. Words and phrases that are associated with the vocabulary term are useful. The diagrams can become study aids as students read the chapter.

Vocabulary and Note-Taking Resources

- Vocabulary Practice, pp. 104–105
- Decoding Support, p. 106

- Daily Vocabulary Scaffolding, p. T10
- Note-Taking Model, p. T11

- Magnet Word Diagram, B24–25
- Outline, C43
- Daily Vocabulary Scaffolding, H1–8

CHAPTER 18

Getting Ready to Learn

CONCEPT REVIEW

- Cells make up tissues, and tissues make up organs.
- The body's systems interact.
- The body's systems work to maintain internal conditions.

VOCABULARY REVIEW

homeostasis p. 588
smooth muscle p. 600
energy *See Glossary.*

CLASSZONE.COM
Review concepts and vocabulary.

TAKING NOTES

OUTLINE

As you read, copy the blue headings on your paper in the form of an outline. Then add notes in your own words that summarize what you read.

VOCABULARY STRATEGY

Think about a vocabulary term as a **magnet word** diagram. Write the other terms or ideas related to that term around it.

See the Note-Taking Handbook on pages R45–R51.

SCIENCE NOTEBOOK

THE RESPIRATORY SYSTEM GETS OXYGEN AND REMOVES CARBON DIOXIDE.

A. Your body needs oxygen.
   1. Oxygen is used to release energy
   2. Oxygen is in air you breathe
B. Structures in the respiratory system function together
   1. nose, throat, trachea
   2. lungs

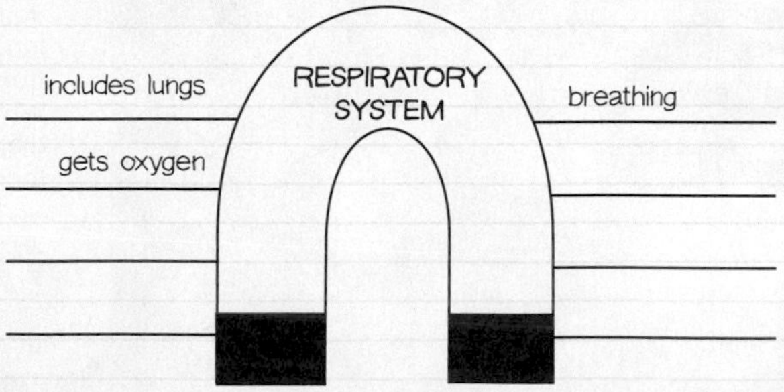

RESPIRATORY SYSTEM

includes lungs

gets oxygen

breathing

CHECK READINESS

Administer the Diagnostic Test to determine students' readiness for new science content and their mastery of requisite math skills.

 Diagnostic Test, pp. 20–21

Technology Resources

Students needing content and math skills should visit **ClassZone.com**.

- CONTENT REVIEW
- MATH TUTORIAL

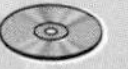 CONTENT REVIEW CD-ROM

KEY CONCEPT

The respiratory system gets oxygen and removes carbon dioxide.

BEFORE, you learned

- Cells, tissues, organs, and organ systems work together
- Organ systems provide for the body's needs
- Organ systems are important to the body's survival

NOW, you will learn

- About the structures of the respiratory system that function to exchange gases
- About the process of cellular respiration
- About other functions of the respiratory system

VOCABULARY

respiratory system p. 613
cellular respiration p. 615

EXPLORE Breathing

How do your ribs move when you breathe?

PROCEDURE

1. Place your hands on your ribs.
2. Breathe in and out several times, focusing on what happens when you inhale and exhale.
3. Record your observations in your notebook.

WHAT DO YOU THINK?

- What movement did you observe?
- Think about your observations. What questions do you have as a result of your observations?

Your body needs oxygen.

During the day, you eat and drink only a few times, but you breathe thousands of times. In fact, breathing is a sign of life. The body is able to store food and liquid, but it is unable to store very much oxygen. The **respiratory system** is the body system that functions to get oxygen from the environment and remove carbon dioxide and other waste products from your body. The respiratory system interacts with the environment and with other body systems.

The continuous process of moving and using oxygen involves mechanical movement and chemical reactions. Air is transported into your lungs by mechanical movements, and oxygen is used during chemical reactions that release energy in your cells.

VOCABULARY
Make a word magnet diagram for the term *respiratory system.*

CHECK YOUR READING What are the two main functions of your respiratory system?

18.1 FOCUS

Set Learning Goals

Students will

- Describe the structures and functions of the respiratory system.
- Analyze the process of cellular respiration.
- Explain other functions of the respiratory system.
- Model how air moves in and out of the lungs.

3-Minute Warm-Up

Display Transparency 12 or copy this exercise on the board:

Draw a diagram that shows how cells, tissues, organs, and organ systems are related. Describe the relationship between cells and tissues, tissues and organs, and organs and organ systems.

The diagram could show four concentric circles, with cells in innermost circle and organ systems in outermost circle. Cells make up tissues; tissues make up organs; organs make up organ systems.

 3-Minute Warm-Up, p. T12

18.1 MOTIVATE

EXPLORE Breathing

PURPOSE To observe the movement of the rib cage during respiration

TIP *10 min.* Be sure that students use a light touch and breathe deeply.

WHAT DO YOU THINK? *Sample answer: During inhalation, the chest expanded; during exhalation, the chest contracted. The ribs moved this way because of air rushing into the lungs. The lungs expand when you take in air. Students' questions should relate to effects of respiration on the body.*

Ongoing Assessment

CHECK YOUR READING *Answer: Respiratory system gets oxygen from environment and removes carbon dioxide and other wastes from body.*

RESOURCES FOR DIFFERENTIATED INSTRUCTION

Below Level

UNIT RESOURCE BOOK

- Reading Study Guide A, pp. 72–73
- Decoding Support, p. 106

Advanced

UNIT RESOURCE BOOK

- Challenge and Extension, p. 78
- Challenge Reading, pp. 102–103

English Learners

UNIT RESOURCE BOOK

Spanish Reading Study Guide, pp. 76–77

- Audio Readings in Spanish
- Audio Readings (English)

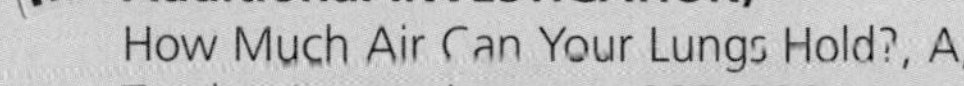

How Much Air Can Your Lungs Hold?, A, B, & C, pp. 118–126; Teacher Instructions, pp. 305–306

18.1 INSTRUCT

Teach from Visuals

To help students interpret the photograph of the diver, ask:

- What kind of gas might be found in the air tank of the diver? *oxygen*
- How do you know? *Humans need oxygen to survive.*

History of Science

Before the mid-1940s, underwater sea exploration was limited to explorers who wore diving suits with air hoses attached to their helmets. In 1943, Jacques Cousteau, with the aid of Emile Gagnan, invented the Aqua Lung, which would eventually come to be known as scuba (self-contained underwater breathing apparatus). Scuba gear became commercially available in 1946. For the first time, divers could move about freely underwater for long periods of time without having to be attached to air hoses from ships above the ocean's surface.

Ongoing Assessment

CHECK YOUR READING *Answer: The air you breathe is made up of a mixture of gases including oxygen and nitrogen.*

Exchanging Oxygen and Carbon Dioxide

A

Like almost all living things, the human body needs oxygen to survive. Without oxygen, cells in the body die quickly. How does the oxygen you need get to your cells? Oxygen, along with other gases, enters the body when you inhale. Oxygen is then transported to cells throughout the body by red blood cells.

B

The air that you breathe contains only about 20 percent oxygen and less than 1 percent carbon dioxide. Almost 80 percent of air is nitrogen gas. The air that you exhale contains more carbon dioxide and less oxygen than the air that you inhale. It's important that you exhale carbon dioxide because high levels of it will damage, even destroy, cells.

In cells and tissues, proper levels of both oxygen and carbon dioxide are essential. Recall that systems in the body work together to maintain homeostasis. If levels of oxygen or carbon dioxide change, your nervous system signals the need to breathe faster or slower.

The photograph shows how someone underwater maintains proper levels of carbon dioxide and oxygen. The scuba diver needs to inhale oxygen from a tank. She removes carbon dioxide wastes with other gases when she exhales into the water. The bubbles you see in the water are formed when she exhales.

What gases are in the air that you breathe?

Gas Exchange

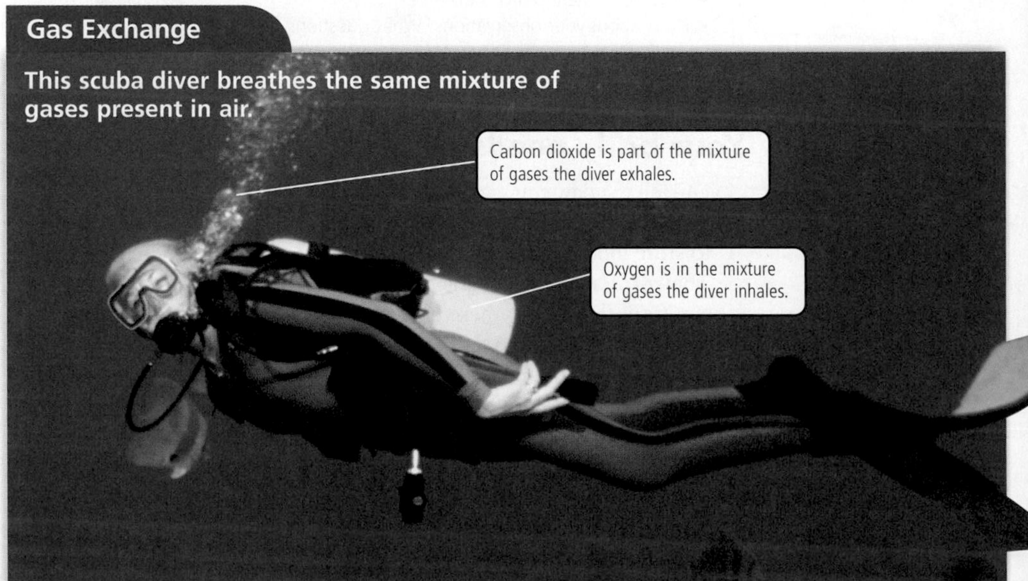

This scuba diver breathes the same mixture of gases present in air.

DIFFERENTIATE INSTRUCTION

More Reading Support

A What gas is necessary in air that you breathe? *oxygen*

B What gas is important to exhale so that cells are not damaged or destroyed? *carbon dioxide*

English Learners Have students write the definitions for the terms *cellular respiration, cilia,* and *alveoli* in their Science Word Dictionaries. Encourage them to add a sketch and a "reminder sentence" for each, based on their reading. Use the Chapter Review, p. 634, to help students focus on key concepts and vocabulary.

INVESTIGATE Lungs

How does air move in and out of lungs?

SKILL FOCUS
Making Models

MATERIALS
- one medium balloon
- 1-L clear plastic bottle with labels removed
- duct tape

TIME
15 minutes

PROCEDURE

1. Create a model of your lungs as shown. Insert an uninflated balloon into the top of the plastic bottle. While squeezing the bottle to force out some air, stretch the end of the balloon over the lip of the bottle. The balloon should still be open to the outside air. Tape the balloon in place with duct tape to make a tight seal
2. Release the bottle so that it expands back to its normal shape. Observe what happens to the balloon. Squeeze and release the bottle several times while observing the balloon. Record your observations.

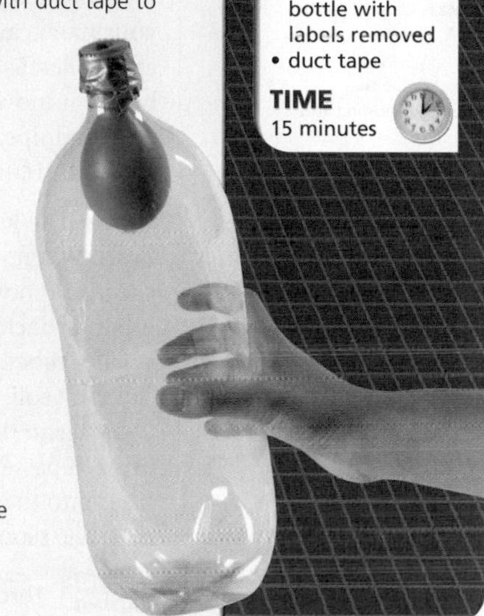

WHAT DO YOU THINK?

- Describe, in words, what happens when you squeeze and release the bottle.
- How do you think your lungs move when you inhale? when you exhale?

CHALLENGE Design an addition to your model that could represent a muscle called the diaphragm. What materials do you need? How would this work? Your teacher may be able to provide additional materials so you can test your model. Be sure to come up with a comprehensive list of materials as well as a specific diagram.

Cellular Respiration

Inside your cells, a process called **cellular respiration** uses oxygen in chemical reactions that release energy. The respiratory system works with the digestive and circulatory systems to make cellular respiration possible. Cellular respiration requires glucose, or sugars, which you get from food, in addition to oxygen, which you get from breathing. These materials are transported to every cell in your body through blood vessels. You will learn more about the digestive and circulatory systems later in this unit.

During cellular respiration, your cells use oxygen and glucose to release energy. Carbon dioxide is a waste product of the process. Carbon dioxide must be removed from cells.

VOCABULARY
Add a magnet diagram for *cellular respiration* to your notebook. Include the word *energy* in your diagram.

CHECK YOUR READING What three body systems are involved in cellular respiration?

DIFFERENTIATE INSTRUCTION

More Reading Support

C How are materials from food transported throughout your body? *blood vessels*

Additional Investigation To reinforce Section 18.1 learning goals, use the following full-period investigation:

 **Additional INVESTIGATION,** How Much Air Can Your Lungs Hold?, A, B, & C, pp. 118–126, 305–306

Advanced Have students draw a diagram or flow chart that shows the process of cellular respiration. Students should include in their diagrams the reaction between glucose and oxygen and both the resulting energy and the byproduct, carbon dioxide.

R Challenge and Extension, p. 78

Teaching with Technology

If a gas sensor is available, have students measure the amount of carbon dioxide exhaled before and after they exercise. Have them plot the data using a graphing calculator or spreadsheet program.

INVESTIGATE Lungs

PURPOSE To create a model showing how the lungs function

TIPS *15 min.*

- Have students stretch the balloon before putting it in the bottle.
- The balloon is best held on with duct tape. Be sure that the tape has made a tight seal.
- Make sure students do not squeeze the bottle too hard while putting in the balloon. The bottle should re-expand once the balloon is in place.

WHAT DO YOU THINK? *When the bottle is squeezed, the balloon deflates. When the bottle is released, the balloon expands slightly. When you inhale, your lungs expand. When you exhale, your lungs shrink.*

CHALLENGE *A diaphragm could be added by cutting off the bottom of the bottle and adding a stretchy material, such as a rubber glove, over the bottom. Pulling on the glove would make the balloon inflate. Releasing the glove would make the balloon deflate.*

 Datasheet, Lungs, p. 79

Technology Resources

Customize this student lab as needed or look for an alternative. Print rubrics to assess student lab reports.

 **Lab Generator CD-ROM**

Ongoing Assessment

Analyze the process of cellular respiration.

Ask: What gas is a waste product of cellular respiration? *carbon dioxide*

 *Answer: The respiratory, circulatory, and digestive systems are involved in cellular respiration.*

Develop Critical Thinking

APPLY To help students understand the structure of the respiratory system, ask:

- By what criteria would biologists include an organ as part of the respiratory system? *Sample answer: The organ must be part of the group of organs that work together to get oxygen into the body and to release carbon dioxide from the body.*
- Have students describe why the organs of the respiratory system are similar to the branches and leaves of a tree. *Sample answer: The bronchial tubes are like the branches of a tree. They separate into smaller and smaller tubes until they end in alveoli. The alveoli are like the leaves of a tree.*

Integrate the Sciences

The contraction of the diaphragm and expansion of the ribs cause the capacity of the thoracic cavity to increase. Air pressure inside the thoracic cavity decreases because there is more room for the air. The difference in the air pressure inside the body and the air pressure outside the body causes air to rush into the lungs.

EXPLORE the BIG idea

Revisit "Internet Activity: Lung Movement" on p. 611. Have students use their own words to explain the movement of the diaphragm and ribs.

Ongoing Assessment

CHECK YOUR READING *Answer: Air inhaled through the nose or mouth enters the throat, passes through the trachea, and moves into the lungs via the bronchial tubes.*

CHECK YOUR READING *Answer: When you inhale, the diaphragm contracts and pulls downward, while other muscles draw the ribs outward.*

Structures in the respiratory system function together.

OUTLINE
Add *Structures in the respiratory system function together* to your outline. Be sure to include the six respiratory structures in your outline.

I. Main idea
  A. Supporting idea
    1. Detail
    2. Detail
  B. Supporting idea

The respiratory system is made up of many structures that allow you to move air in and out of your body, communicate, and keep out harmful materials.

Nose, Throat, and Trachea When you inhale, air enters your body through your nose or mouth. Inside your nose, tiny hairs called cilia filter dirt and other particles out of the air. Mucus, a sticky liquid in your nasal cavity, also helps filter air by trapping particles such as dirt and pollen as air passes by. The nasal cavity warms the air slightly before it moves down your throat toward a tubelike structure called the windpipe, or trachea (TRAY-kee-uh). A structure called the epiglottis (EHP-ih-GLAHT-ihs) keeps air from entering your stomach.

Lungs The lungs are two large organs located on either side of your heart. When you inhale, air enters the throat, passes through the trachea, and moves into the lungs through structures called bronchial tubes. Bronchial tubes branch throughout the lungs into smaller and smaller tubes. At the ends of the smallest tubes, air enters tiny air sacs called alveoli. The walls of the alveoli are only one cell thick. In fact, one page in this book is much thicker than the walls of the alveoli.

Oxygen passes from inside the alveoli through the thin walls and diffuses into the blood. At the same time, carbon dioxide waste passes from the blood into the alveoli.

CHECK YOUR READING Through which structures does oxygen move into the lungs?

Ribs and Diaphragm If you put your hands on your ribs and take a deep breath, you can feel your ribs expand. The rib cage encloses a space inside your body called the thoracic (thuh-RAS-ihk) cavity. Some ribs are connected by cartilage to the breastbone or to each other, which makes the rib cage flexible. This flexibility allows the rib cage to expand when you breathe and make room for the lungs to expand and fill with air.

A large muscle called the diaphragm (DY-uh-FRAM) stretches across the floor of the thoracic cavity. When you inhale, your diaphragm contracts and pulls downward, which makes the thoracic cavity expand. This movement causes the lungs to push downward, filling the extra space. At the same time, other muscles draw the ribs outward and expand the lungs. Air rushes into the lungs, and inhalation is complete. When the diaphragm and other muscles relax, the process reverses and you exhale.

RESOURCE CENTER
CLASSZONE.COM
Explore the respiratory system.

CHECK YOUR READING Describe how the diaphragm and the rib cage move.

DIFFERENTIATE INSTRUCTION

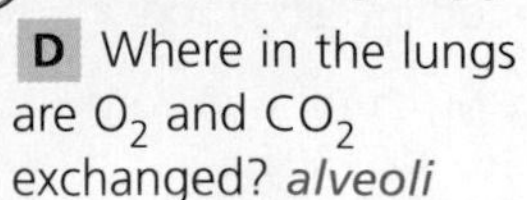

More Reading Support

D Where in the lungs are O_2 and CO_2 exchanged? *alveoli*

E What muscle stretches across the bottom of the thoracic cavity? *diaphragm*

Below Level Have students make a flow chart to show the path of oxygen as it travels through the respiratory system. Students should include the structures listed on p. 616—nose, throat, ribs, lungs, trachea, and diaphragm—and the terms *oxygen* and *carbon dioxide.*

Respiratory System

The structures in the respiratory system allow this flutist to play music.

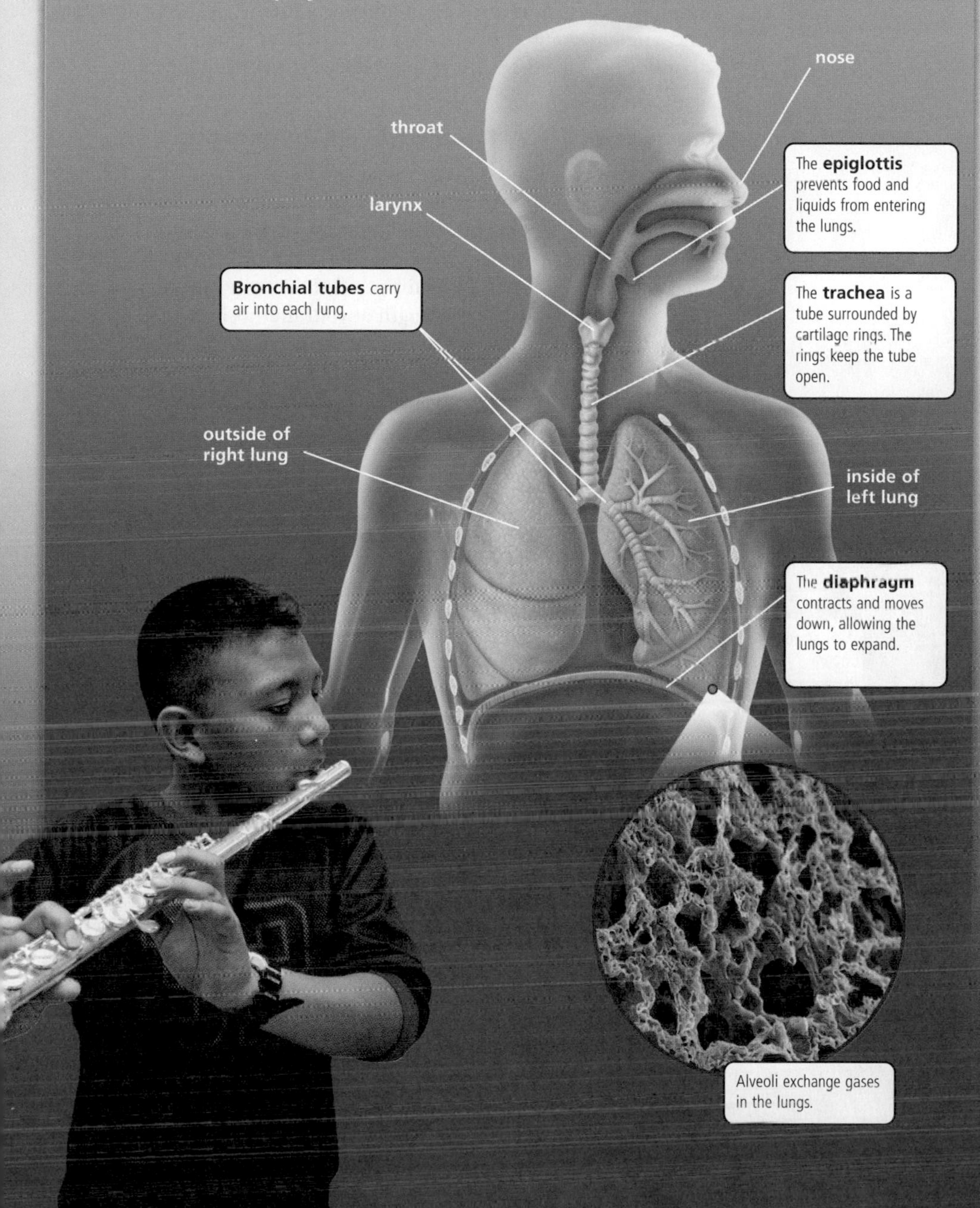

DIFFERENTIATE INSTRUCTION

Advanced Challenge students to time their breathing for one minute. Then have them calculate how many breaths they take in a year and how many in 18 years. Finally, ask students to determine how many breaths they have taken so far in their lives and how many they will have taken when they reach 80 years old.

Have students who are interested in the respiratory system read the following article:

 Challenge Reading, pp. 102–103

Teach from Visuals

To help students interpret the diagram of the respiratory system, ask:

- Which structures in the respiratory system are connected by the trachea? *The trachea connects the larynx and bronchial tubes.*
- Which structure directs air down the trachea? *the epiglottis*

Teacher Demo

Have students breathe normally for about 20 seconds. Then have them pause at the end of an exhalation. Ask them if they can gently push out more air before they breathe in again. Make sure no students have a health condition for which this would be dangerous. Students should discover that not all air is expelled from the lungs during exhalation.

Teach Difficult Concepts

Some students may have a hard time understanding that the diaphragm moves downward. Ask students to recall the Explore activity on p. 613. Have them describe again what they observed about the motion of the ribs as they breathed. Point out that the diaphragm pulls downward when they inhale, even though it feels as if the lungs and diaphragm go up.

Ongoing Assessment

Describe the structures and functions of the respiratory system.

Ask: How does the structure of the bronchial tubes allow air to pass into the lungs? *The bronchial tubes branch throughout the lungs into smaller and smaller tubes.*

Teacher Demo

Help students understand how the vocal cords produce sound.

- Provide pairs of students with different sizes of rubber bands. Invite each pair to the front of the classroom and have one student pull the rubber band taut. Have the other student pluck the rubber band to produce a sound. Relate the vibrating motion of the rubber band to how sound is produced by the vocal cords.
- Encourage students to place their fingers on their throats as they speak. They should be able to feel the vibration of the vocal chords.

Teach from Visuals

To help students understand how sound is produced by the vocal cords, ask:

- What path does air take as it produces sound? *Air from the lungs passes over the vocal cords. The air travels out over the tongue, and sound waves leave the mouth.*
- Is it possible to speak if you are holding your breath? Explain. *No; air is necessary for sounds to be produced.*

Ongoing Assessment

Describe other functions of the respiratory system.

Ask: How do the vocal cords produce sound? *Air from the lungs moves over the vocal cords, causing them to vibrate and produce sound.*

The respiratory system is also involved in other activities.

F

In addition to providing oxygen and removing carbon dioxide, the respiratory system is involved in other activities of the body. Speaking and singing, along with actions such as sneezing, can be explained in terms of how the parts of the respiratory system work together.

Speech and Other Respiratory Movements

G

If you place your hand on your throat and hum softly, you can feel your vocal cords vibrating. Air moving over your vocal cords allows you to produce sound, and the muscles in your throat, mouth, cheeks, and lips allow you to form sound into words. The vocal cords are folds of tissue in the larynx. The larynx, sometimes called the voice box, is a two-inch, tube-shaped organ about the length of your thumb, located in the neck, at the top of the trachea. When you speak, the vocal cords become tight, squeeze together, and force air from the lungs to move between them. The air causes the vocal cords to vibrate and produce sound.

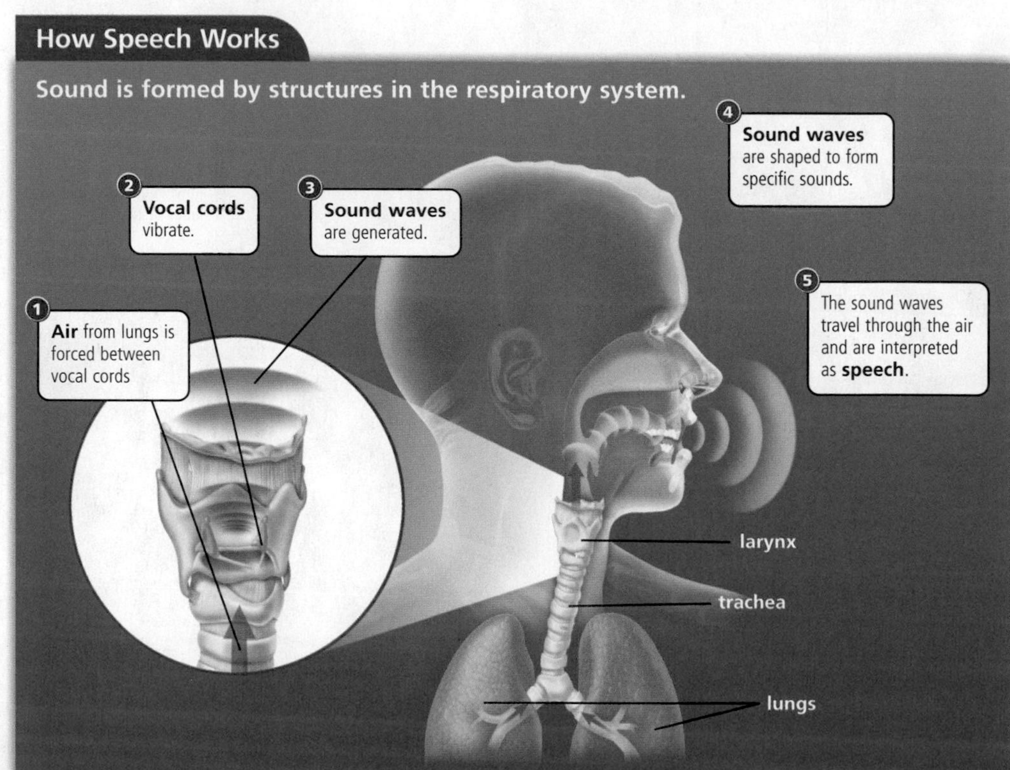

DIFFERENTIATE INSTRUCTION

More Reading Support

F What are some activities the respiratory system is involved in? *speaking, singing, sneezing*

G Where are vocal cords located? *larynx, or voice box*

Below Level Students may confuse the terms *respiration* and *breathing*. Have them write the definitions on index cards to use as study guides. Remind students that respiration is the exchange of gases—and can happen at the level of cell, organ, or organism. Breathing is the movement of air in and out of the body.

Some movements of the respiratory system allow you to clear particles out of your nose and throat or to express emotion. The respiratory system is involved when you cough or sneeze. Sighing, yawning, laughing, and crying also involve the respiratory system.

Sighing and yawning both involve taking deep breaths. A sigh is a long breath followed by a shorter exhalation. A yawn is a long breath taken through a wide-open mouth. Laughing and crying are movements that are very similar to each other. In fact, sometimes it's difficult to see the difference between laughing and crying.

The respiratory system also allows you to hiccup. A hiccup is a sudden inhalation that makes the diaphragm contract. Several systems are involved when you hiccup. Air rushes into the throat, causing the diaphragm to contract. When the diaphragm contracts, the air passageway between the vocal cords closes. The closing of this passageway produces the sound of the hiccup. Hiccups can be caused by eating too fast, sudden temperature changes, and stress.

Water Removal

Hiccups, coughs, yawns, and all other respiratory movements, including speaking and breathing, release water from your body into the environment. Water is lost through sweat, urine, and exhalations of air. When it is cold enough outside, you can see your breath in the air. That is because the water vapor you exhale condenses into larger droplets when it moves from your warm body to the cold air.

Water leaves your body through your breath every time you exhale.

18.1 Review

KEY CONCEPTS

1. How is oxygen used by your body's cells?
2. What are the structures in the respiratory system and what do they do?
3. In addition to breathing, what functions does the respiratory system perform?

CRITICAL THINKING

4. **Sequence** List in order the steps that occur when you exhale.
5. **Compare and Contrast** How is the air you inhale different from the air you exhale?

CHALLENGE

6. **Hypothesize** Why do you think a person breathes more quickly when exercising?

ANSWERS

1. in the respiration process, to release energy

2. Nose, throat, trachea, and bronchial tubes carry air in and out of the lungs, where gas exchange occurs. Diaphragm and ribs move to cause lungs to expand.

3. also filters air and aids in speaking, coughing, sneezing

4. Diaphragm relaxes up to its original position, pushing lungs upward. At the same time, ribs move inward, collapsing lungs inward. Air moves out of lungs through bronchial tubes into trachea, then into throat and out nose or mouth.

5. Air you inhale contains more O_2 and less CO_2 than air you exhale.

6. Energy is expended when you exercise; rapid breathing brings more O_2 into the body, which can add more energy.

EXPLORE the BIG idea

Revisit "Mirror, Mirror" on p. 611 and the observations students made. How has their understanding changed?

Teach Difficult Concepts

Point out that water is released from the body through sweating and urination as well as through exhalation.

Reinforce the BIG idea

Have students relate the section to the Big Idea.

 Reinforcing Key Concepts, p. 80

18.1 ASSESS & RETEACH

Assess

 Section 18.1 Quiz, p. 22

Reteach

With a small group, write a comic strip frame by frame about how oxygen travels through the body. Prompt the group with questions such as:

- Where does oxygen go?
- Through what does oxygen pass?
- Where does oxygen end up?
- How does it leave the body?

Technology Resources

Have students visit **ClassZone.com** for reteaching of Key Concepts.

 CONTENT REVIEW

 CONTENT REVIEW CD-ROM

SCIENCE ON THE JOB
Relevance of Science to Non-science Jobs

Set Learning Goal
To understand why yoga instructors need knowledge of the respiratory system

Present the Science
Remind students that the movement of the diaphragm and the rib cage controls breathing. As the diaphragm contracts and pulls downward, the rib cage expands, and air rushes into the lungs.

SAFETY Find out any health conditions that students may have that might prevent them from doing this activity. Students should not do deep inhalations or hold their breath if they are suffering from hypertension or heart problems. Students should not do deep exhalations if suffering from hypotension or depression. If students become tired, fatigued, or irritated, relax and stop the exercise. If students become hot, it is a sign of strain.

Discussion Questions
Ask: How is full-lung breathing different from the way a person normally breathes? *In full-lung breathing, the belly expands first, then the rib cage, then the upper chest. When a person breathes normally, the breathing does not occur in these stages.*

Ask: What are two functions of nostrils? *filtering dust before air enters lungs and warming air as it enters body*

Use the diagram for students to point out the diaphragm, and discuss how it moves during abdominal breathing.

Close
Ask: Why do yoga instructors need knowledge of the respiratory system? *Yoga instructors need to understand how breathing occurs so they can help their students to exercise and to breathe in healthy ways.*

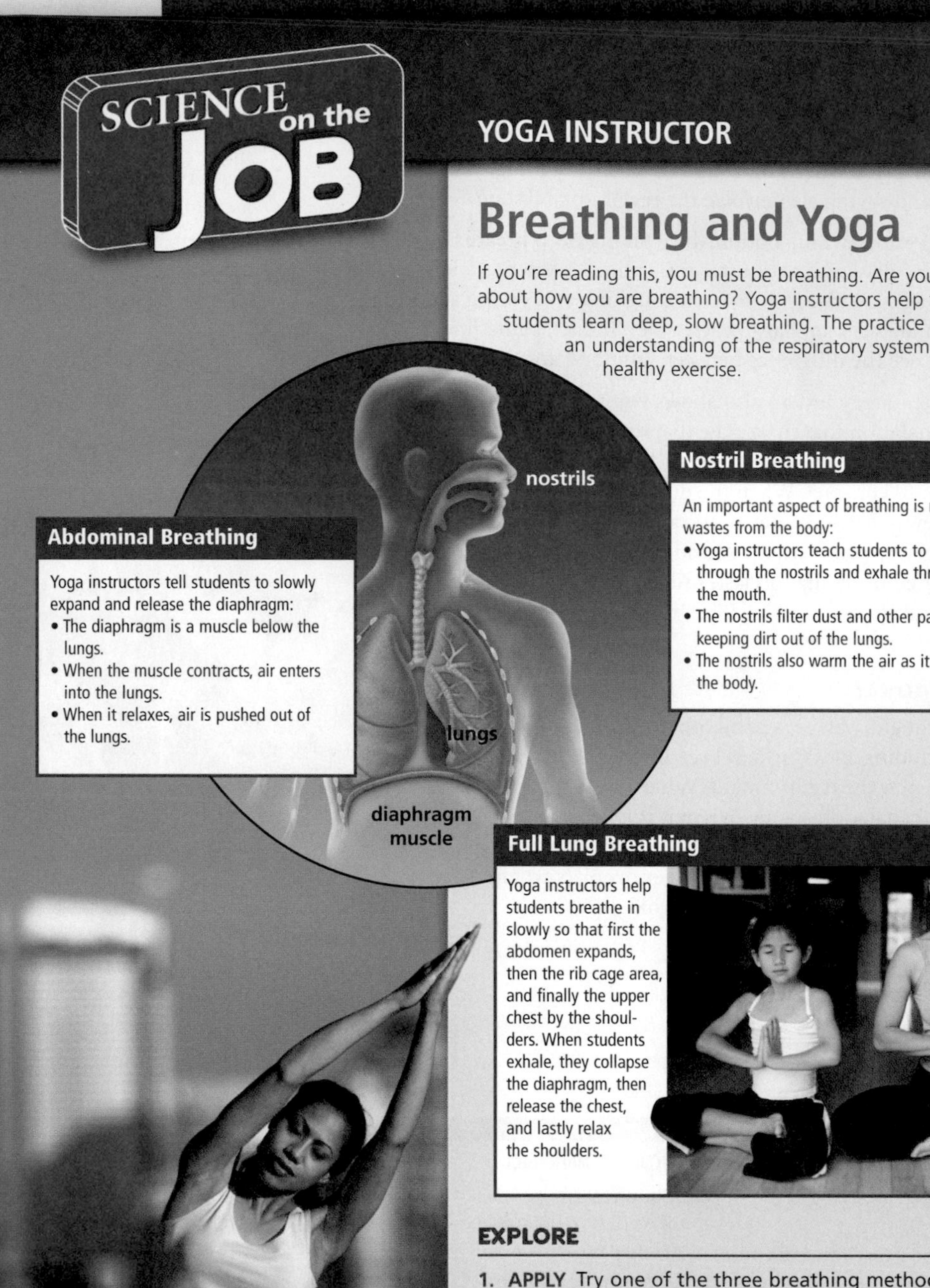

EXPLORE
1. ***APPLY*** *Students may report that they feel relaxed. Others may feel energized. Some may find that their breathing is smoother.*
2. ***CHALLENGE*** *Sample answer: I take in breath through my nostrils. My lungs expand. My diaphragm descends. Then there is a slight pause before I exhale. When I exhale, my lungs deflate, my diaphragm lifts, and air passes out through my nostrils.*

KEY CONCEPT

18.2 The digestive system breaks down food.

BEFORE, you learned
- The respiratory system takes in oxygen and expels waste
- Oxygen is necessary for cellular respiration
- The respiratory system is involved in speech and water removal

NOW, you will learn
- About the role of digestion in providing energy and materials
- About the chemical and mechanical process of digestion
- How materials change as they move through the digestive system

VOCABULARY

nutrient p. 621
digestion p. 622
digestive system p. 622
peristalsis p. 622

EXPLORE Digestion

How does the digestive system break down fat?

PROCEDURE

1. Using a dropper, place 5 mL of water into a test tube. Add 5 mL of vegetable oil. Seal the test tube with a screw-on top. Shake the test tube for 10 seconds, then place it in a test tube stand. Record your observations.
2. Drop 5 mL of dish detergent into the test tube. Seal the tube. Shake the test tube for 10 seconds, then place in the stand. Observe the mixture for 2 minutes. Record your observations.

MATERIALS
- water
- graduated cylinders
- test tube with cap
- vegetable oil
- test tube stand
- liquid dish detergent

WHAT DO YOU THINK?
- What effect does detergent have on the mixture of oil and water?
- How do you think your digestive system might break down fat?

OUTLINE
Remember to add *The body needs energy and materials* to your outline.

I. Main idea
  A. Supporting idea
    1. Detail
    2. Detail
  B. Supporting idea

The body needs energy and materials.

After not eating for a while, have you ever noticed how little energy you have to do the simplest things? You need food to provide energy for your body. You also need materials from food. Most of what you need comes from nutrients within food. **Nutrients** are important substances that enable the body to move, grow, and maintain homeostasis. Proteins, carbohydrates, fats, and water are some of the nutrients your body needs.

You might not think of water as a nutrient, but it is necessary for all living things. More than half of your body is made up of water.

18.2 FOCUS

Set Learning Goals

Students will
- Describe the role of digestion in providing energy for the body.
- Describe the process of digestion.
- Describe changes in materials as they move through the digestive system.
- Model how the stomach breaks down food.

3-Minute Warm-Up

Display Transparency 12 or copy this exercise on the board:

Decide if these statements are true. If not true, correct them.

1. The digestive system works with the respiratory system to make cellular respiration possible. *true*
2. Carbon dioxide is necessary for cellular respiration. *Oxygen is necessary for cellular respiration.*
3. The digestive system is involved in speech and water removal. *The digestive system is involved in digestion and water removal.*

T 3-Minute Warm-Up, p. T12

18.2 MOTIVATE

EXPLORE Digestion

PURPOSE To understand how the digestive system breaks down fat

TIPS *15 min.* Have students predict what they think will happen to the oil. If students work in groups, be sure they work out who is measuring and pouring ahead of time. A well-covered surface, and/or premeasured liquids will help students avoid spills. Smocks and goggles can also be used.

WHAT DO YOU THINK? *The detergent allows the oil to break down. The body breaks down fat into smaller pieces that can be absorbed.*

RESOURCES FOR DIFFERENTIATED INSTRUCTION

Below Level

UNIT RESOURCE BOOK
- Reading Study Guide A, pp. 83–84
- Decoding Support, p. 106

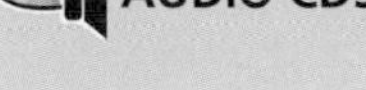
AUDIO CDS

Advanced

UNIT RESOURCE BOOK
Challenge and Extension, p. 89

English Learners

UNIT RESOURCE BOOK
Spanish Reading Study Guide, pp. 87–88

AUDIO CDS
- Audio Readings in Spanish
- Audio Readings (English)

18.2 INSTRUCT

Address Misconceptions

IDENTIFY Ask: What does food provide for the body? If students answer that food provides the body with energy, they may hold the misconception that food is only a source of energy rather than also being a source of matter for growth.

CORRECT Direct students to the definition of digestion on p. 622. Explain that digestion is involved in breaking down food into materials that cells use for growth and repair as well as for energy.

REASSESS Ask: What happens to food during the process of digestion? *Food is broken down into nutrients, used to provide energy for the body as well as material for growth and repair.*

Technology Resources

Visit **ClassZone.com** for background on common student misconceptions.

MISCONCEPTION DATABASE

Teach from Visuals

To help students interpret the sequence in the diagram, ask:

- What structures does the esophagus connect? *the mouth and the stomach*
- Why is the esophagus important in the process of digestion? *It transports food to the next organ of the digestive system.*

Teacher Demo

Model peristalsis by inserting a marble or bead into a piece of rubber tubing. Pinch the tubing so the marble is pushed down through the tubing. Ask:

- What does the tubing represent? *the esophagus*
- What does the marble represent? *food*

Ongoing Assessment

Describe the role of digestion in providing energy for the body.

In what 2 ways does the digestive system process food? *mechanically, chemically*

Protein is another essential nutrient; it is the material that the body uses for growth and repair. Cells in your body—such as those composing muscles, bones, and skin—are built of proteins. Carbohydrates are nutrients that provide cells with energy. Carbohydrates make up cellulose, which helps move materials through the digestive system. Another nutrient, fat, stores energy.

A

Before your body can use these nutrients, they must be broken into smaller substances. **Digestion** is the process of breaking down food into usable materials. Your digestive system transforms the energy and materials in food into forms your body can use.

The digestive system moves and breaks down food.

Observe the process of peristalsis.

B

Your **digestive system** performs the complex jobs of moving and breaking down food. Material is moved through the digestive system by wavelike contractions of smooth muscles. This muscular action is called **peristalsis** (PEHR-ih-STAWL-sihs). Mucous glands throughout the system keep the material moist so it can be moved easily, and the muscles contract to push the material along. The muscles move food along in much the same way as you move toothpaste from the bottom of the tube with your thumbs. The body has complicated ways of moving food, and it also has complicated ways of breaking down food. The digestive system processes food in two ways: physically and chemically.

Peristalsis

The process of peristalsis moves food from the esophagus and into the stomach.

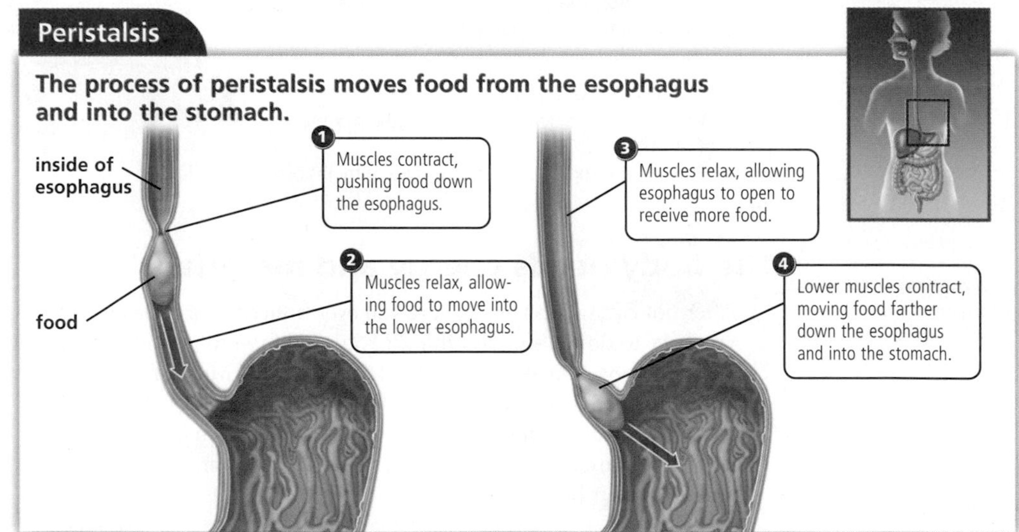

DIFFERENTIATE INSTRUCTION

More Reading Support

A What is digestion? *process of breaking down food into usable materials*

B What is peristalsis? *wavelike contractions of smooth muscles*

English Learners Have students write the definitions for *digestion, digestive system, nutrients, mechanical digestion,* and *chemical digestion* in their Science Word Dictionaries. Beside each word, students can sketch their favorite food being digested. The sketch should have labels and/or arrows to show each aspect of digestion.

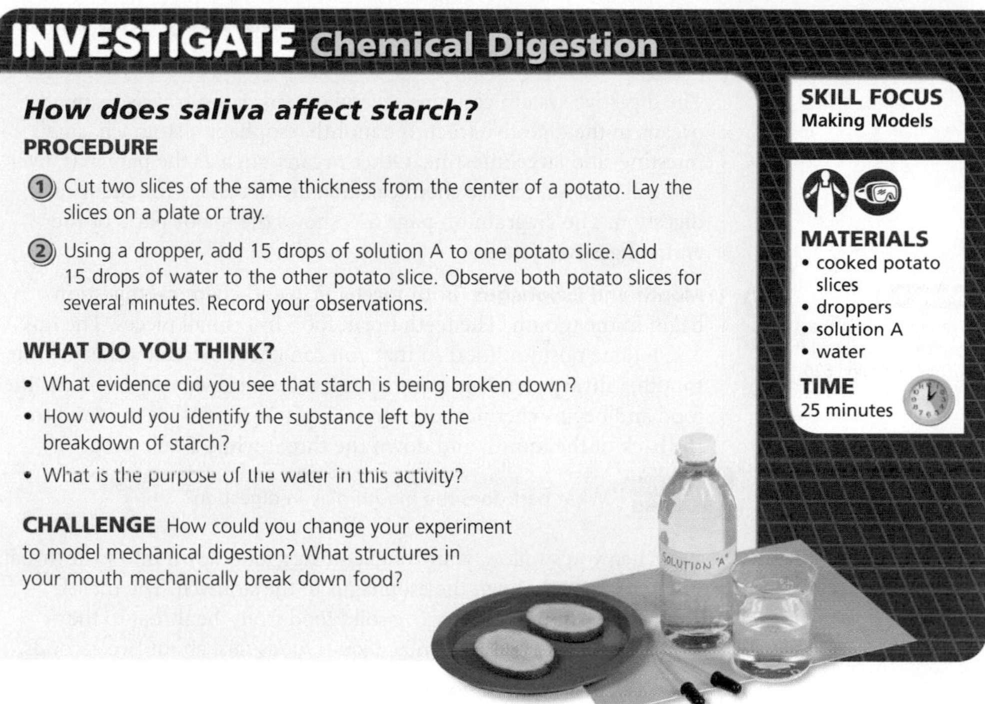

How does saliva affect starch?

PROCEDURE

1. Cut two slices of the same thickness from the center of a potato. Lay the slices on a plate or tray.
2. Using a dropper, add 15 drops of solution A to one potato slice. Add 15 drops of water to the other potato slice. Observe both potato slices for several minutes. Record your observations.

WHAT DO YOU THINK?

- What evidence did you see that starch is being broken down?
- How would you identify the substance left by the breakdown of starch?
- What is the purpose of the water in this activity?

CHALLENGE How could you change your experiment to model mechanical digestion? What structures in your mouth mechanically break down food?

Mechanical Digestion

C

Physical changes, which are sometimes called mechanical changes, break food into smaller pieces. You chew your food with your teeth so you are able to swallow it. Infants without teeth need an adult to cut up or mash food for them. They need soft food that they can swallow without chewing. Your stomach also breaks down food mechanically by mashing and pounding it during peristalsis.

Chemical Digestion

D

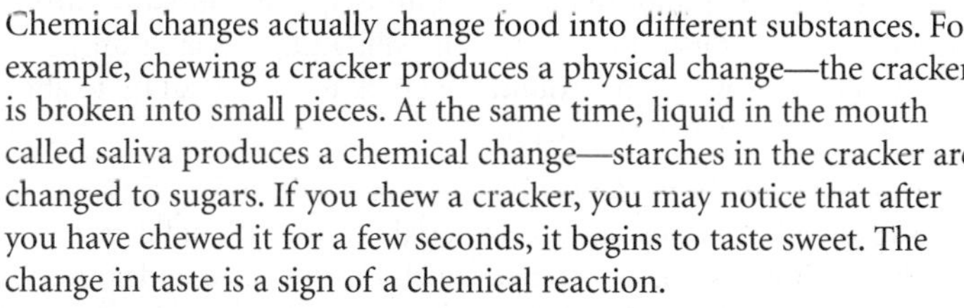
Chemical changes actually change food into different substances. For example, chewing a cracker produces a physical change—the cracker is broken into small pieces. At the same time, liquid in the mouth called saliva produces a chemical change—starches in the cracker are changed to sugars. If you chew a cracker, you may notice that after you have chewed it for a few seconds, it begins to taste sweet. The change in taste is a sign of a chemical reaction.

VOCABULARY
Don't forget to add magnet word diagrams for *digestion, digestive system,* and *peristalsis* to your notebook.

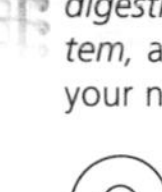

What are the two types of changes that take place during digestion?

DIFFERENTIATE INSTRUCTION

More Reading Support

C Describe mechanical digestion in the mouth. *Teeth chew the food into small pieces.*

D What substance in the mouth causes chemical changes? *saliva*

Advanced Have students find out more about the names and functions of the various types of teeth found in humans. Incisors bite and cut into food. Canines, or eye teeth, tear and break food into smaller pieces. Molars grind and crush food so it can be swallowed. Encourage students to report their findings with diagrams and pictures.

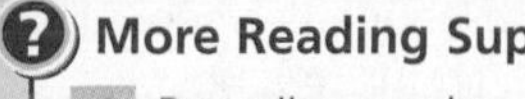
Challenge and Extension, p. 89

INVESTIGATE Chemical Digestion

PURPOSE To create a model of the breakdown of starch by saliva

TIPS *25 min.* Prior to the activity, cook potato slices until soft. Cooking breaks down the cell walls and releases starch for digestion. Amylase solution is available through science supply catalogs. Keep the solution refrigerated. You could do a control with uncooked potato and ask what a lack of a reaction suggests about eating raw potatoes.

WHAT DO YOU THINK? *A hole formed in the potato slice where solution A was dropped on it. The substance left by the breakdown of starch could be identified by adding iodine or by testing it on a glucose test strip. The water is a control.*

CHALLENGE *Mechanical digestion could be modeled by using a grater or masher to break the potato down into smaller pieces. In your mouth, the teeth mechanically break down food.*

Datasheet, Chemical Digestion, p. 90

Technology Resources

Customize this student lab as needed or look for an alternative. Print rubrics to assess student lab reports.

Lab Generator CD-ROM

Teach Difficult Concepts

The concept of chemical change in digestion is not something that students can see happening. To demonstrate, ask volunteers to chew on crackers. Explain that the saliva in the mouth causes the complex starch in the cracker to break down into simple sugar. Students should notice that the crackers begin to taste sweet. Explain that both starch and sugar are carbohydrates, but that starches have larger molecules made up of more atoms.

Ongoing Assessment

Answer: Mechanical digestion breaks down food into smaller pieces, and chemical digestion changes food into different substances.

History of Science

In 1822, an army surgeon named William Beaumont researched the stomach's function. Beaumont treated a patient who had received gunshot wounds. The man, Alexis St. Martin, had one wound that penetrated his stomach. Martin allowed Beaumont to perform experiments and make observations while the wound healed. Beaumont observed stomach secretions and collected samples from Martin's stomach in glass tubes. Beaumont reported the presence of acid in gastric juices, as well as the effects of different types of food.

Address Misconceptions

IDENTIFY Ask: Where is the stomach located in your body? If students answer that the stomach is in the lower abdomen, they may believe that the stomach is lower than it actually is.

CORRECT Point to your left side, just below your rib cage, and explain to students that this is the area where the stomach is located.

REASSESS Have students locate areas on their bodies to show the stomach, small intestine, and the ascending, transversing, and descending sections of the large intestine.

Technology Resources

Visit **ClassZone.com** for background on common student misconceptions.

MISCONCEPTION DATABASE

Ongoing Assessment

Describe the process of digestion.

Ask: Why are the structures called *villi* important in the process of digestion? *Villi allow nutrients to be absorbed by the blood and taken through the body.*

CHECK YOUR READING *Answer: The mouth begins digestion by mechanically breaking down food with teeth and chemically breaking it down with saliva.*

CHECK YOUR READING *Answer: Mechanical digestion occurs primarily in the mouth and stomach.*

Materials are broken down as they move through the digestive tract.

The digestive system contains several organs. Food travels through organs in the digestive tract: the mouth, esophagus, stomach, small intestine, and large intestine. Other organs, such as the pancreas, liver, and gall bladder, release chemicals that are necessary for chemical digestion. The diagram on page 625 shows the major parts of the entire digestive system.

READING TIP
As you read about the digestive tract, look at the structures on page 625.

Mouth and Esophagus Both mechanical and chemical digestion begin in the mouth. The teeth break food into small pieces. The lips and tongue position food so that you can chew. When food is in your mouth, salivary glands in your mouth release saliva, which softens the food and begins chemical digestion. The tongue pushes the food to the back of the mouth and down the throat while swallowing.

CHECK YOUR READING What part does the mouth play in digestion?

When you swallow, your tongue pushes food down into your throat. Food then travels down the esophagus to the stomach. The muscle contractions of peristalsis move solid food from the throat to the stomach in about eight seconds. Liquid foods take about two seconds.

Stomach Strong muscles in the stomach further mix and mash food particles. The stomach also uses chemicals to break down food. Some of the chemicals made by the stomach are acids. These acids are so strong that they could eat through the stomach itself. To prevent this, the cells of the stomach's lining are replaced about every three days, and the stomach lining is coated with mucus.

Villi allow broken-down nutrients to be absorbed into your bloodstream.

Small Intestine Partially digested food moves from the stomach to the small intestine. There, chemicals released by the pancreas, liver, and gallbladder break down nutrients. Most of the nutrients broken down in digestion are absorbed in the small intestine. Structures called villi are found throughout the small intestine. These structures contain folds that absorb nutrients from proteins, carbohydrates, and fats. Once absorbed by the villi, nutrients are transported by the circulatory system around the body. You will read more about the circulatory system in Chapter 19.

Large Intestine In the large intestine, water and some other nutrients are absorbed from the digested material. Most of the solid material then remaining is waste material, which is compacted and stored. Eventually it is eliminated through the rectum.

Where in your digestive system does mechanical digestion occur?

624 Unit 5: Human Biology

DIFFERENTIATE INSTRUCTION

More Reading Support

E Where does chemical digestion begin? *the mouth*

F Once partially digested food leaves the stomach, where does it go? *into the small intestine*

Advanced Have students find out what happens when people choke on pieces of food. Students can make a poster showing how to recognize that a person is choking and how to assist if a choking situation occurs.

Digestive System

As food moves through the digestive tract, structures of the digestive system break it down and absorb necessary materials.

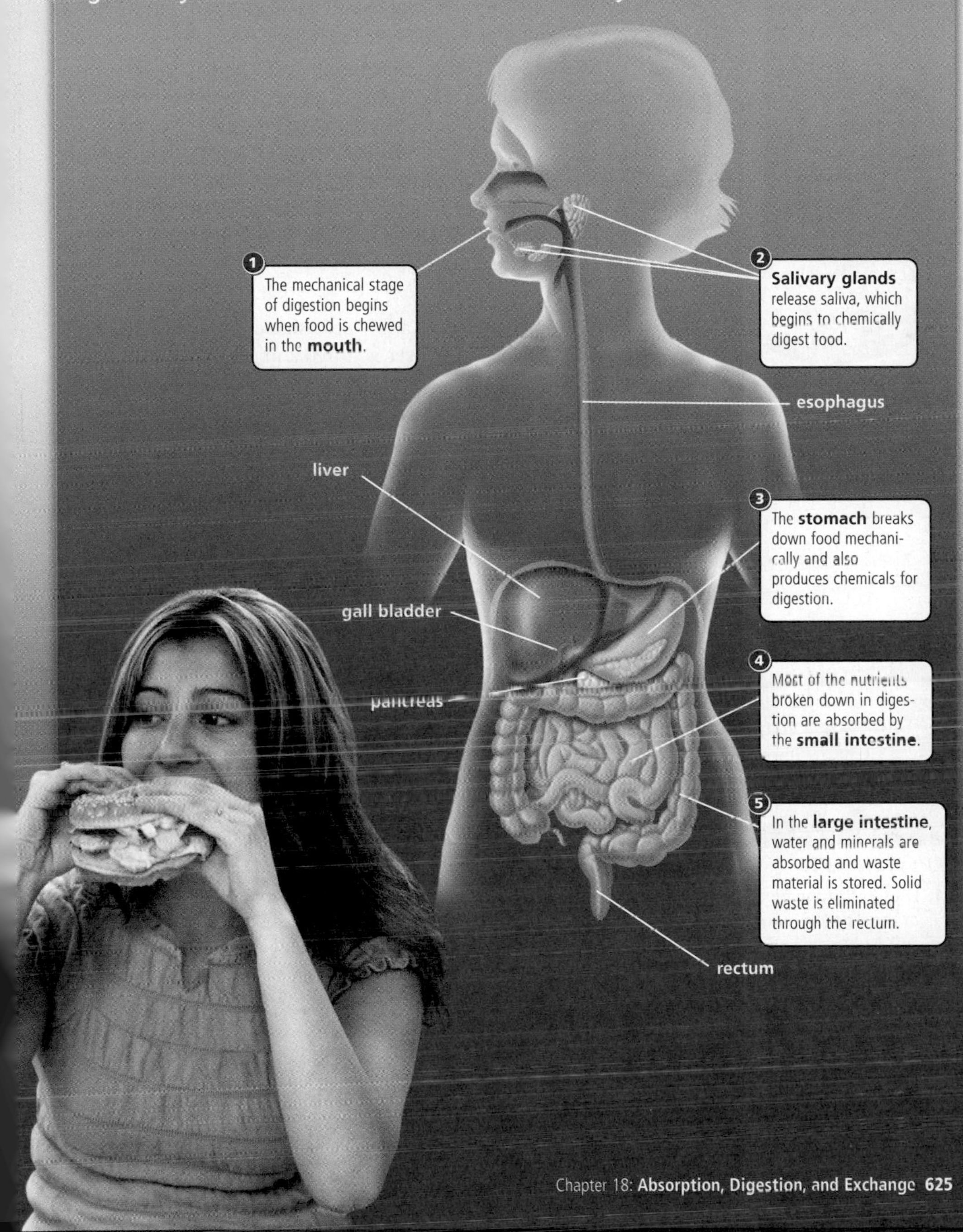

1 The mechanical stage of digestion begins when food is chewed in the **mouth**.

2 **Salivary glands** release saliva, which begins to chemically digest food.

esophagus

liver

3 The **stomach** breaks down food mechanically and also produces chemicals for digestion.

gall bladder

pancreas

4 Most of the nutrients broken down in digestion are absorbed by the **small intestine**.

5 In the **large intestine**, water and minerals are absorbed and waste material is stored. Solid waste is eliminated through the rectum.

rectum

DIFFERENTIATE INSTRUCTION

English Learners English learners may not be familiar with the various uses of the phrase "break down." Commonly, "break down" is used to mean something has broken, either physically (a car) or figuratively (negotiations). In this section, the meaning of "break down" is more complex. It indicates the taking in of food and breaking it into energy, usable materials, and waste materials.

Below Level Have students make a flow chart that shows the path of food as it travels through the digestive system. Students should include the structures listed on p. 624 and the term *villi* in their flow charts.

Teach from Visuals

To help students interpret the diagram of the digestive system, ask:

- What structures in the digestive system are connected by the esophagus? *The esophagus connects the mouth with the stomach.*
- How is the small intestine different from the large intestine? *The small intestine is a coiled tube that sits inside the sections of the large intestine.*

The visual "Digestive System" is available as T14 in the Unit Transparency Book.

Teach Difficult Concepts

Many students confuse the trachea with the esophagus. Have students review the diagram of the respiratory system on p. 617, then compare it with the diagram of the digestive system. Point out that the trachea and the esophagus are two different structures connected with two different systems in the body: The trachea helps transport air to the lungs in the respiratory system; the esophagus helps transport food to the stomach in the digestive system.

Metacognitive Strategy

Challenge students to devise a mnemonic device to remember the order of organs through which materials pass in the digestive tract.

Teaching with Technology

Use graphics software to create a flow chart of the process of digestion. Students can show how the digestive and circulatory systems are related.

Ongoing Assessment

Describe changes in materials as they move through the digestive system.

Ask: How does the sandwich in the picture change as it moves through a person's body? *The mouth softens it and breaks it apart mechanically and chemically. The stomach also breaks it down mechanically and chemically. As it moves through the intestines, it breaks into nutrients such as molecules of carbohydrates, proteins, and fats.*

Ongoing Assessment

CHECK YOUR READING *Answer: The pancreas produces chemicals that lower acidity in the small intestine and help break down proteins, fats, and starch.*

Reinforce the BIG idea

Have students relate the section to the Big Idea.

 Reinforcing Key Concepts, p. 91

18.2 ASSESS & RETEACH

Assess

 Section 18.2 Quiz, p. 23

Reteach

Write these terms on the board: *mouth, esophagus, stomach, small intestine, large intestine, liver, pancreas, gall bladder.* For each term, have students tell (a) whether it is part of the digestive tract, (b) whether mechanical or chemical digestion occurs there, and (c) what the organ's function is in the digestion process.

Technology Resources

Have students visit **ClassZone.com** for reteaching of Key Concepts.

 CONTENT REVIEW

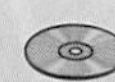 CONTENT REVIEW CD-ROM

Other organs aid digestion and absorption.

The digestive organs not in the digestive tract—the liver, gallbladder, and pancreas—also play crucial roles in your body. Although food does not move through them, all three of these organs aid in chemical digestion by producing or concentrating important chemicals.

Liver The liver—the largest internal organ of the body—is located in your abdomen, just above your stomach. Although you can survive losing a portion of your liver, it is an important organ. The liver filters blood, cleansing it of harmful substances, and stores unneeded nutrients for later use in the body. It produces a golden yellow substance called bile, which is able to break down fats, much like the way soap breaks down oils. The liver also breaks down medicines and produces important proteins, such as those that help clot blood if you get a cut.

Bile is transferred from the liver to the gallbladder and small intestines through the bile duct.

Gallbladder The gallbladder is a tiny pear-shaped sac connected to the liver. Bile produced in the liver is stored and concentrated in the gallbladder. The bile is then secreted into the small intestine.

Pancreas Located between the stomach and the small intestine, the pancreas produces chemicals that are needed as materials move between the two. The pancreas quickly lowers the acidity in the small intestine and breaks down proteins, fats, and starch. The chemicals produced by the pancreas are extremely important for digesting and absorbing food substances. Without these chemicals, you could die of starvation, even with plenty of food in your system. Your body would not be able to process and use the food for energy without the pancreas.

 How does the pancreas aid in digestion?

18.2 Review

KEY CONCEPTS

1. List three of the functions of the digestive system.
2. Give one example each of mechanical digestion and chemical digestion.
3. How does your stomach process food?

CRITICAL THINKING

4. **Apply** Does an antacid deal with mechanical or chemical digestion?
5. **Apply** You have just swallowed a bite of apple. Describe what happens as the apple moves through your digestive system. Include information about what happens to the material in the apple.

CHALLENGE

6. **Compare and Contrast** Describe the roles of the large and the small intestines. How are they similar? How are they different?

ANSWERS

1. Sample answers: breaking food into small pieces; absorbing nutrients; absorbing water; processing waste products

2. Sample answer: bread is broken in small pieces by chewing; saliva changes starches into sugars (chemical)

3. Muscles mix and mash food. Acid breaks down food.

4. An antacid deals with chemical digestion.

5. Answers should include all basic steps and structures in digestion and mention materials in the apple absorbed by intestines, and waste expelled.

6. Both absorb nutrients. The small intestine absorbs more nutrients; the large absorbs water and some nutrients, and stores waste.

MATH in SCIENCE

SKILL: CHOOSING UNITS OF LENGTH

Internal Measurement

It wouldn't be useful if someone told you the length of your tongue in meters, or the length of a tooth in centimeters. To be meaningful, these measurements must be given in appropriate units.

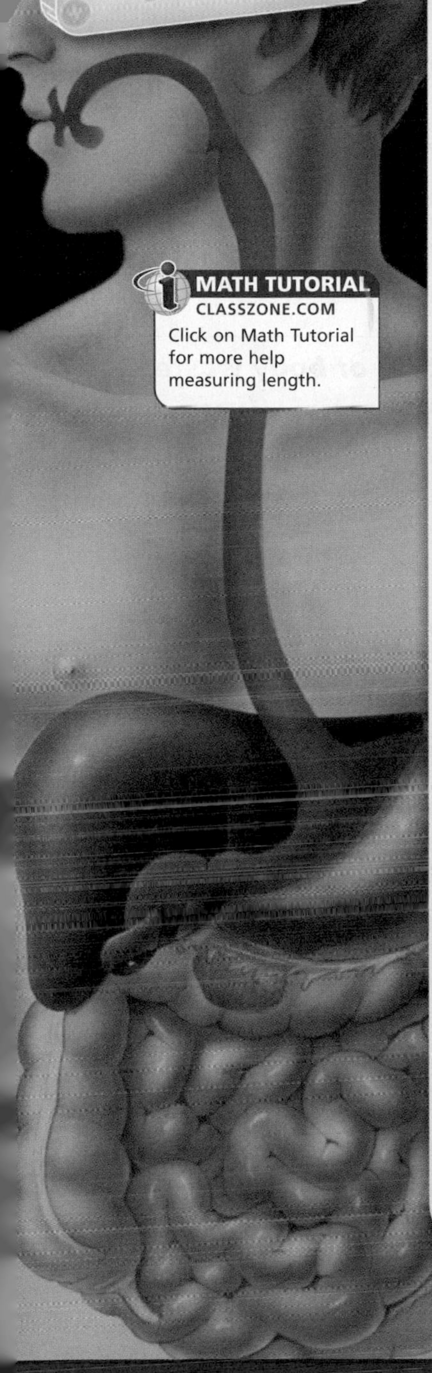

Example

Your esophagus is about the length of your forearm. Choose the appropriate units to measure its length. Would meters, centimeters, or millimeters be most appropriate?

(1) Look at your arm from your wrist to your elbow. It is about the same as a rolling pin. You don't need to measure your forearm to see that a meter would be too large a unit. One meter is about the height of a lab table.

(2) Look at the ruler in the picture. Compare your arm to the centimeters shown and the millimeters.

(3) You can measure your arm with either unit, but if you wiggle a bit, the count of millimeters is thrown off.

ANSWER Centimeters are the most appropriate units.

Answer the following questions.

1. If you uncoiled a human intestine, its length would be about equal to that of 2 cars parked end to end. What would be appropriate units to use to measure that?
2. What units would you use to measure the length of your tongue? The length of a tooth?
3. The large intestine is actually shorter than the small intestine. The small intestine is about the length of a small bus, and the large is about as long as a car's back seat. Tell the units you would choose for each. Explain why.

CHALLENGE Your stomach when empty is about the size of your clenched fist. To measure its volume (the space it takes up), what units would you use?

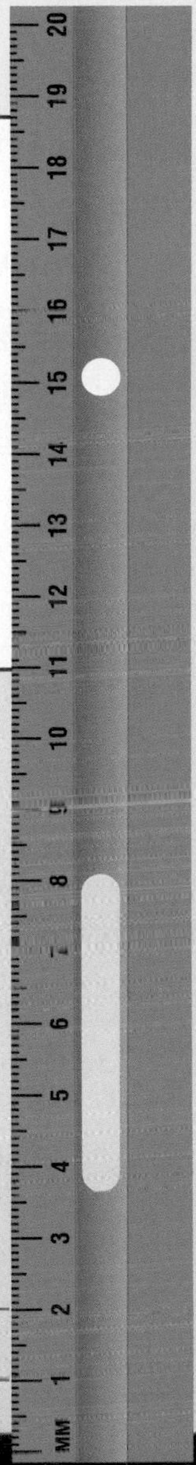

The ruler shows 20 centimeters (cm). There are 10 millimeters (mm) in each centimeter.

1 cm

MATH TUTORIAL
CLASSZONE.COM
Click on Math Tutorial for more help measuring length.

ANSWERS

1. *meters*
2. *centimeters, millimeters*
3. *meters for both, because you can compare both vehicles without changing units*
4. *CHALLENGE The size of my fist would be measured in cubic centimeters. Volume is length · width · height. Centimeters are appropriate for a stomach's length, width, or height.* $cm \cdot cm \cdot cm = cm^3$.

MATH IN SCIENCE

Math Skills Practice for Science

Set Learning Goal

To choose appropriate units for measuring different lengths

Present the Science

Remind students of the differences between the small and large intestines. Point out that the small intestine is actually much longer than the large intestine, but has a smaller diameter.

Develop Measurement Skills

Review metric units of measure: millimeters, centimeters, and meters. Display a meter stick and have students note the differences among the three units of measure.

DIFFERENTIATION TIP Have students use metric rulers to measure parts of the body, for example, the length of a fingernail, a finger, a hand, and an arm, and the height of the whole body. Have them determine which metric unit is right for which body part.

Close

Ask students how they could estimate the length or the surface area of other internal organs. *Use estimation, use formulas for area, use comparison to other organs or to benchmarks, such as a dinner plate or orange skin.*

- Math Support, p. 107
- Math Practice, p. 108

Technology Resources

Students can visit **ClassZone.com** for help with measuring length.

MATH TUTORIAL

18.3 FOCUS

Set Learning Goals

Students will

- Recognize that different body systems remove waste.
- Discuss why kidneys are important organs.
- Analyze the role of the kidneys in homeostasis.
- Model the process of kidney filtration.

3-Minute Warm-Up

Display Transparency 13 or copy this exercise on the board:

Match each definition to the correct term. Show the letter of the correct answer.

Definitions

1. the organ that secretes bile *e*
2. the organ in which acids break down food *b*
3. the organ in which villi absorb nutrients into the bloodstream *c*

Terms

a. mouth	d. large intestine
b. stomach	e. liver
c. small intestine	f. pancreas

3-Minute Warm-Up, p. T13

18.3 MOTIVATE

EXPLORE Waste Removal

PURPOSE To observe how the skin helps to get rid of waste

TIP *10 min.* Have students share their observations in small groups.

WHAT DO YOU THINK? *The bag gets some fog on the inside. It demonstrates that the skin releases moisture through sweat.*

Ongoing Assessment

CHECK YOUR READING *Answer: through the urinary system (eliminates liquid waste), respiratory system (removes water vapor and waste gases), digestive system (removes solid waste from food), and skin (releases waste through sweat glands)*

KEY CONCEPT

The urinary system removes waste materials.

BEFORE, you learned

- The digestive system breaks down food
- Organs in the digestive system have different roles

NOW, you will learn

- How different body systems remove different types of waste
- Why the kidneys are important organs
- About the role of the kidneys in homeostasis

VOCABULARY

urinary system p. 629
urine p. 629

EXPLORE Waste Removal

How does the skin get rid of body waste?

PROCEDURE

1. Place a plastic bag over the hand you do not use for writing and tape it loosely around your wrist.
2. Leave the bag on for five minutes. Write down the changes you see in conditions within the bag.

WHAT DO YOU THINK?

- What do you see happen to the bag?
- How does what you observe help explain the body's method of waste removal?

MATERIALS

- plastic bag
- tape
- stopwatch

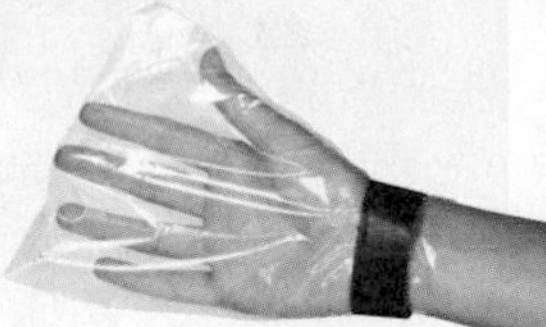

OUTLINE

Add *Life processes produce wastes* to your outline. Include four ways the body disposes of waste products.

I. Main idea
 A. Supporting idea
  1. Detail
  2. Detail
 B. Supporting idea

Life processes produce wastes.

You have read that the respiratory system and the digestive system provide the body with energy and materials necessary for important processes. During these processes, waste materials are produced. The removal of these wastes is essential for the continuing function of body systems. Several systems in your body remove wastes.

- The urinary system disposes of liquid waste products removed from the blood.
- The respiratory system disposes of water vapor and waste gases from the blood.
- The digestive system disposes of solid waste products from food.
- The skin releases wastes through sweat glands.

CHECK YOUR READING What are four ways the body disposes of waste products?

RESOURCES FOR DIFFERENTIATED INSTRUCTION

Below Level

UNIT RESOURCE BOOK

- Reading Study Guide A, pp. 94–95
- Decoding Support, p. 106

AUDIO CDS

Advanced

UNIT RESOURCE BOOK

Challenge and Extension, p. 100

English Learners

UNIT RESOURCE BOOK

Spanish Reading Study Guide, pp. 98–99

AUDIO CDS

- Audio Readings in Spanish
- Audio Readings (English)

The urinary system removes waste from the blood.

If you have observed an aquarium, you have seen a filter at work. Water moves through the filter, which removes waste materials from the water. Just as the filter in a fish tank removes wastes from the water, structures in your urinary system filter wastes from your blood.

As shown in the diagram, the **urinary system** contains several structures. The kidneys are two organs located high up and toward the rear of the abdomen, one on each side of the spine. Kidneys function much as the filter in the fish tank does. In fact, the kidneys are often called the body's filters. Materials travel in your blood to the kidneys. There, some substances are removed, and others are returned to the blood.

A

After the kidneys filter chemical waste from the blood, the liquid travels down two tubes called ureters (yu-REE-tuhrz). The ureters bring the waste to the bladder, a storage sac with a wall of smooth muscle. The lower neck of the bladder leads into the urethra, a tube that carries the liquid waste outside the body. Voluntary muscles at one end of the bladder allow a person to hold the urethra closed until he or she is ready to release the muscles. At that time, the bladder contracts and sends the liquid waste, or **urine,** out of the body.

B

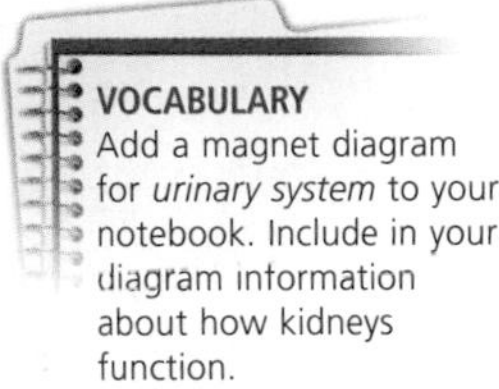

VOCABULARY
Add a magnet diagram for *urinary system* to your notebook. Include in your diagram information about how kidneys function.

Urinary System

The urinary system transports wastes out of the body.

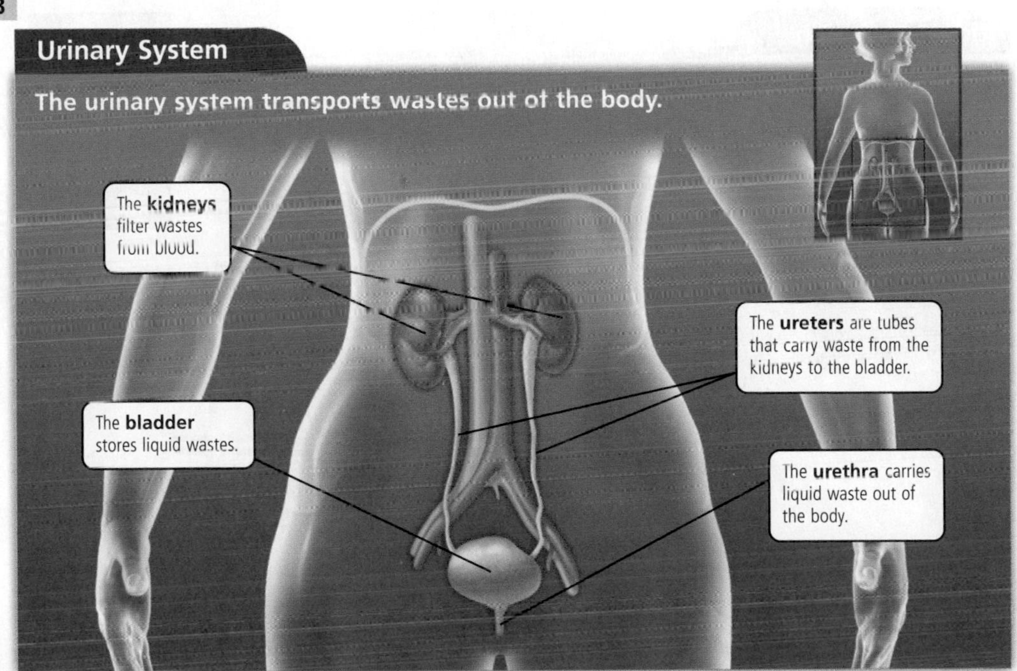

18.3 INSTRUCT

Real World Example

People with compromised kidney function often undergo dialysis, a process in which a patient's blood is removed, purified, and returned to the bloodstream. This process is accomplished with an artificial kidney, called a hemodialyzer. Blood is directed from an artery into the dialyzer. There, it flows along the surface of a membrane where impurities are filtered out. The blood then passes through a trap that removes clots and bubbles and is returned to the bloodstream through a vein, usually in the patient's forearm.

Teach from Visuals

To help students interpret the diagram of the urinary system, ask:

- Which structures make up the urinary system? *kidneys, bladder, ureters, and urethra*
- Through which structure is waste eliminated from the body? *the urethra*

Address Misconceptions

IDENTIFY Ask: The urinary bladder is a part of which body system? Students may hold the misconception that the bladder is part of the digestive system.

CORRECT Have students study the diagram of the urinary system, noting the position of the urinary bladder.

REASSESS Ask students to create a two-column chart, naming the organs of the digestive and respiratory systems.

Technology Resources

Visit **ClassZone.com** for background on common student misconceptions.

MISCONCEPTION DATABASE

DIFFERENTIATE INSTRUCTION

More Reading Support

A Which organs are often called the body's filters? *the kidneys*

B What is the term for the liquid waste that collects in the bladder? *urine*

English Learners Provide students with four index cards. Have them write a different term on the front of each card: *kidney, bladder, urethra, ureter.* On the back of each card, students can draw a picture of the structure and/or write a description of its function. Students can use the cards as they read.

Ongoing Assessment

Recognize that different body systems remove waste.

Ask: What are the four body systems that remove waste from the body? *urinary, digestive, respiratory, skin*

Teach Difficult Concepts

Students may not understand where in the body cavity the kidneys are located. Point to the location of the kidneys on your body (on the back in the lower section of the rib cage) and have students do the same.

Teacher Demo

Some students may not know what a filter is or how it works. To demonstrate this concept, obtain a coffee filter, a glass beaker, a funnel, and some muddy water. Pour the muddy water through the filter and funnel into the beaker. Have students compare the original water with the filtrate. Ask: How is this demonstration similar to the function of the kidneys? *The kidneys filter waste substances out of the blood.*

Teach from Visuals

To help students interpret the diagram of the nephron, ask:

- What structure is made up of a cluster of capillaries? *the glomerulus*
- What is the purpose of the nephron? *The nephron removes waste from the blood and produces urine.*
- What happens to the nutrients and water that are filtered out in the nephron? *Some nutrients are returned to the blood. Some travel into the collecting duct and out through the ureter as urine.*

Ongoing Assessment

Explain why the kidneys are important organs.

Ask: Why is it important that blood be filtered by the kidneys? *Waste materials are filtered out of the blood. If they stayed in the blood, they might damage cells and organs.*

Find out more about the urinary system.

The kidneys act as filters.

At any moment, about one quarter of the blood leaving your heart is headed toward your kidneys to be filtered. The kidneys, which are about as long as your index finger—only 10 centimeters (3.9 in.) long—filter all the blood in your body many times a day.

The Nephron

C

Inside each kidney are approximately one million looping tubes called nephrons. The nephron regulates the makeup of the blood.

1. Fluid is filtered from the blood into the nephron through a structure called the glomerulus (gloh-MEHR-yuh-luhs). Filtered blood leaves the glomerulus and circulates around the tubes that make up the nephron.
2. As the filtered fluid passes through the nephron, some nutrients are absorbed back into the blood surrounding the tubes. Some water is also filtered out in the glomerulus, but most water is returned to the blood.
3. Waste products travel to the end of the nephron into the collecting duct. The remaining liquid, now called urine, passes out of the kidney and into the ureters.

D

Kidney Function

Kidneys filter waste materials out of the blood.

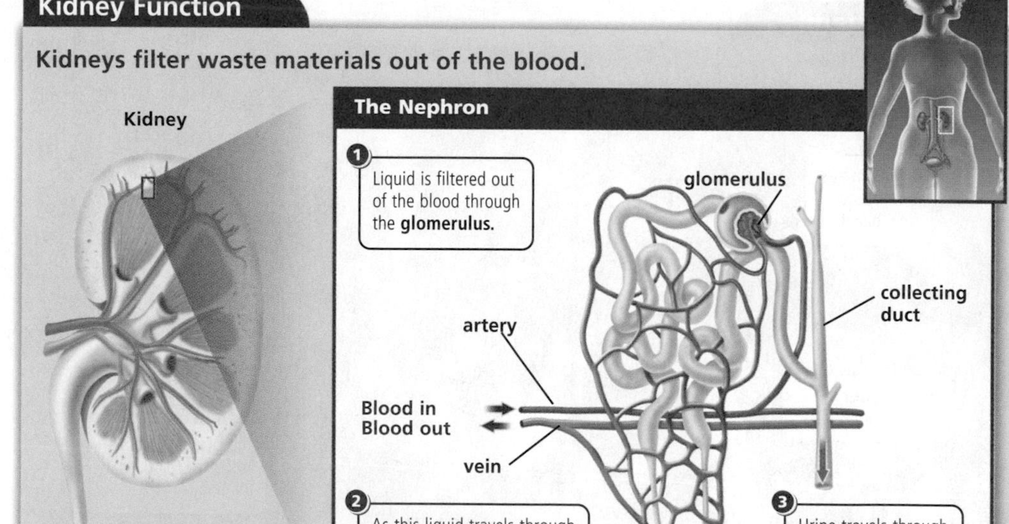

DIFFERENTIATE INSTRUCTION

More Reading Support

C What are the names of the looping tubes that are found inside kidneys? *nephrons*

D What product travels to the end of the nephron and into the ureter? *urine*

Advanced Many English idioms use the names of organs or terms related to organs to describe different emotions or problems that are not related to the function of the organ. For example, we might say that someone "dies of a broken heart." Ask students to research different idioms related to respiratory, digestive, or other organs. Have students prepare a chart to share with the class. *Sample answers: breathless in love, strong of heart, weak-stomached, lily-livered, heartache*

 Challenge and Extension, p. 100

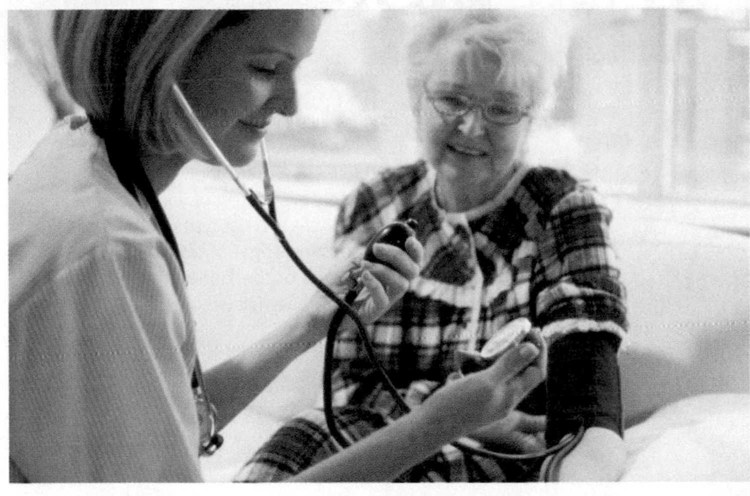

The amount of water in your body affects your blood pressure. Excess water increases blood pressure.

Water Balance

The kidneys not only remove wastes from blood, they also regulate the amount of water in the body. You read in Chapter 17 about the importance of homeostasis—a stable environment within your body. The amount of water in your cells affects homeostasis. If your body contains too much water, parts of your body may swell. Having too little water interferes with cell processes.

About one liter of water leaves the body every day. The kidneys control the amount of water that leaves the body in urine. Depending on how much water your body uses, the kidneys produce urine with more or less water.

 How do your kidneys regulate the amount of water in your body?

18.3 Review

KEY CONCEPTS

1. Describe the four organ systems that remove waste and explain how each removes waste.
2. Describe the function of four organs in the urinary system.
3. Describe homeostasis and explain why the kidneys are important to homeostasis.

CRITICAL THINKING

4. **Connect** Make a word web with the term *kidney* in the center. Add details about kidney function to the web.

CHALLENGE

5. **Synthesize** Explain why you may become thirsty on a hot day. Include the term *homeostasis* in your explanation.

ANSWERS

1. urinary system—removes liquid waste from the blood; respiratory—removes water vapor and waste gases; digestive—removes solid waste; sweat glands—remove waste water

2. Kidneys filter waste from blood. Waste leaves kidneys as urine via ureters to bladder, where stored. Urethra carries urine out of body.

3. Homeostasis is the process of maintaining internal conditions. The kidney helps control the water level in the body.

4. Webs should include the kidney's function as a filter.

5. If you sweat a lot, you will lose fluids. If too little water is in the body, the kidney releases a chemical that makes you thirsty. Drinking fluids helps restore homeostasis.

EXPLORE the BIG idea

Revisit "Water Everywhere" on p. 611. Ask what might happen if a person drinks more than 2 L of water in a day. *The person may produce more urine.*

Ongoing Assessment

Explain the role of the kidneys in homeostasis.

Ask: What might happen if the kidneys were unable to eliminate water from the body? *The body would become swollen.*

CHECK YOUR READING *Answer: The kidneys produce urine with varying amounts of water, depending on how much water the body uses.*

Reinforce the BIG idea

Have students relate the section to the Big Idea.

 Reinforcing Key Concepts, p. 101

18.3 ASSESS & RETEACH

Assess

 Section 18.3 Quiz, p. 24

Reteach

Write the following systems on the board. Have students describe how each system acts to remove wastes from the body.

- respiratory *removes water vapor and gaseous waste from the blood*
- digestive *removes solid waste*
- urinary *removes liquid waste from the blood*
- skin *removes waste via sweat*

Technology Resources

Have students visit **ClassZone.com** for reteaching of Key Concepts.

 **CONTENT REVIEW**

 **CONTENT REVIEW CD-ROM**

CHAPTER INVESTIGATION

Focus

PURPOSE To demonstrate the process of kidney filtration

OVERVIEW Students will use filters and solutions to determine the following:

- how the filtering process of the kidneys can be modeled
- what types of materials are filtered by the kidneys

Lab Preparation

- Prepare solution A: Add 10 g of table salt to 1000 mL of water. Stir until dissolved.
- Prepare solution B: Add 10 g of glucose to 1000 mL of water. Stir until dissolved.
- Prepare solution C: Add 10 g of albumin powder to 1000 mL of water. Stir gently until dissolved. Can substitute the white of one egg if albumin powder is not available.
- Prior to the investigation, have students read through the investigation and prepare their data tables. Or you may wish to copy and distribute datasheets and rubrics.

 UNIT RESOURCE BOOK, pp. 109–117

 SCIENCE TOOLKIT, F14

Lab Management

- Model use of test strips before distributing them.
- Have students work in pairs, one student pouring and testing the solutions, the other student recording the data.
- Have students rinse the funnel and beaker between each testing.
- **SAFETY** Caution students not to touch the solutions or test strips. Make sure they wash their hands when the lab is completed.
- **INCLUSION** To help students new to English or students who have varying abilities, have all students work in cooperative groups where there is a Reader, Leader, Recorder, and Reporter.

CHAPTER INVESTIGATION

Modeling a Kidney

OVERVIEW AND PURPOSE Your kidneys are your body's filters. Every 20 to 30 minutes, every drop of your blood passes through the kidneys and is filtered. What types of materials are filtered by the kidneys? In this investigation you will

- model the filtering process of the kidneys
- determine what types of materials are filtered by your kidneys

Problem

What types of materials can be removed from the blood by the kidneys?

Hypothesize

Write a hypothesis to explain how substances are filtered out of the blood by the kidneys. Your hypothesis should take the form of an "If . . . , then . . . , because . . ." statement.

MATERIALS
- fine filter paper
- small funnel
- graduated cylinder
- 100 mL beaker
- solution A
- solution B
- solution C
- salinity test strips
- glucose test strips
- protein test strips

Procedure

1. Make a data table like the one shown on the sample notebook page. Fold the filter paper as shown. Place the filter paper in the funnel, and place the funnel in the graduated cylinder.

2. Pour 20 mL of solution A into a beaker. Test the solution for salt concentration using a test strip for salinity. Record the results in your notebook. Slowly pour the solution into the funnel. Wait for it all to drip through the filter paper.

632 Unit 5: Human Biology

INVESTIGATION RESOURCES

 CHAPTER INVESTIGATION, Modeling a Kidney
- Level A, pp. 109–112
- Level B, pp. 113–116
- Level C, p. 117

Advanced students should complete Levels B & C.

 Writing a Lab Report, D12–13

Technology Resources

Customize this student lab as needed or look for an alternative. Print rubrics to assess student lab reports.

 **Lab Generator CD-ROM**

4 Test the filtered liquid for salt concentration again. Record the results.

5 Repeat steps 1, 2, and 3 for solution B using glucose test strips. Record the results in your notebook.

Repeat steps 1, 2, and 3 for solution C using protein test strips. Record the results in your notebook.

Observe and Analyze

Write It Up

1. **RECORD** Be sure your data table is complete.
2. **OBSERVE** What substances were present in solutions A, B, and C?
3. **IDENTIFY VARIABLES** Identify the variables and constants in the experiment. List them in your notebook.

Conclude

1. **COMPARE AND CONTRAST** In what ways does your model function like a kidney? How is your model not like a kidney?
2. **INTERPRET** Which materials were able to pass through the filter and which could not?
3. **INFER** What materials end up in the urine? How might materials be filtered out of the blood but not appear in the urine?
4. **APPLY** How could a filtering device be useful in your body?

INVESTIGATE Further

CHALLENGE Your blood contains many chemicals. Some of these chemicals are waste products, but some are in the blood to be transported to different parts of the body. What other substances are filtered out of the blood by the kidneys? Which of the filtered substances are normally present in the urine? Use a variety of reference materials to research the chemicals found in urine. Revise your experiment to test the ability of your model kidney to filter other substances.

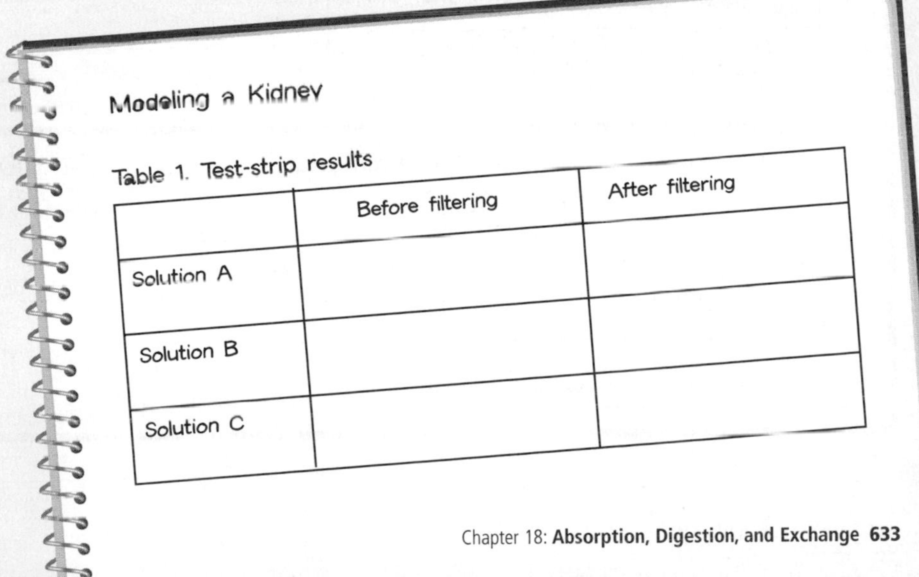

Modeling a Kidney

Table 1. Test-strip results

	Before filtering	After filtering
Solution A		
Solution B		
Solution C		

Observe and Analyze

1. Check to make sure data table is complete.

2. Solution A had salt, solution B had glucose (sugar), and solution C had protein.

3. The variables in the experiment were the different types of solutions. The constants were the filter paper and the amount of solution that was filtered.

Conclude

1. The model acts like a kidney in that it filters some, but not all, substances out of the blood. The model is not like a kidney because some substances that are passed through the filter would be reabsorbed into the blood.

2. Salt and glucose were able to pass through the filter; protein could not.

3. The urine usually contains salt but not glucose. Glucose is reabsorbed into the blood before the urine leaves the kidney.

4. A filtering device could perform the functions of the kidneys in removing specific substances from the blood.

INVESTIGATE Further

CHALLENGE Sample answer: Other substances filtered out of the blood by the kidney include urea, uric acid, calcium, potassium, bicarbonate. All of these substances are normally found in urine. Substances not normally found in urine include protein, glucose, nitrite, hemoglobin, ketones, bilirubin.

Post-Lab Discussion

- Discuss why some substances passed through the filter paper and why others were unable to. *Pores allowed smaller particles to pass through, whereas larger particles were unable to pass through.*
- Discuss how this lab simulates the functions of the kidneys. *Kidneys filter waste out of the blood and return other materials to the blood.*
- Ask: After observing your results, what would you want to study further? What question arise? How would you experiment to find answers?

BACK TO

the BIG idea

For each of the systems discussed in the chapter, have students choose one of the structures in the system and explain how that structure functions within its system to process materials and remove wastes.

KEY CONCEPTS SUMMARY

SECTION 18.1

Have students look at the picture of the respiratory system and describe the path of oxygen as it travels into the lungs. Then have them describe what happens to the oxygen. *Oxygen is inhaled through the nose or mouth, then passes through the larynx, trachea, and bronchial tubes into the lungs. Once inside the lungs, the oxygen travels into smaller vessels, called capillaries, where gas exchange with the circulatory system takes place.*

SECTION 18.2

Ask students to describe the difference between mechanical and chemical digestion. Then have them examine the chart and name the structures of the digestive system in which chemical digestion takes place. *Mechanical digestion physically breaks food into smaller pieces. Chemical digestion changes food into different substances. Chemical digestion takes place in the mouth, stomach, and small intestine.*

SECTION 18.3

Ask: What systems are involved in waste removal? *respiratory, urinary, digestive, (and skin)*

Review Concepts

- Big Idea Flow Chart, p. T9
- Chapter Outline, pp. T15–T16

18 Chapter Review

the BIG idea

Systems in the body obtain and process materials and remove waste.

KEY CONCEPTS SUMMARY

1 The respiratory system gets oxygen and removes carbon dioxide.

- Your body needs oxygen
- Structures in the respiratory system function together
- Your respiratory system is involved in other functions

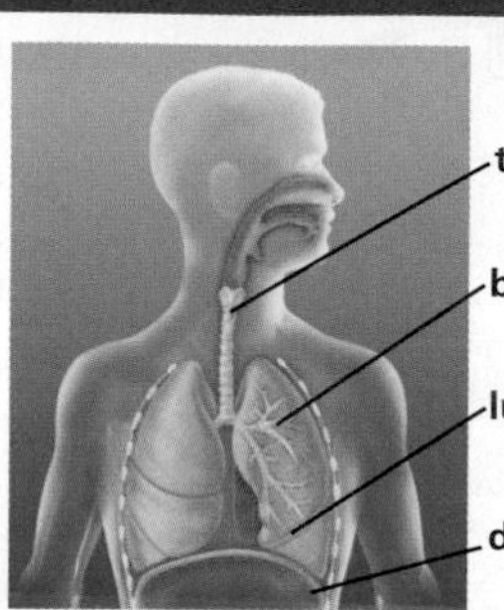

VOCABULARY
respiratory system p. 613
cellular respiration p. 615

2 The digestive system breaks down food.

Structure	Function
Mouth	chemical and mechanical digestion
Esophagus	movement of food by peristalsis from mouth to stomach
Stomach	chemical and mechanical digestion; absorption of broken-down nutrients
Small intestine	chemical digestion; absorption of broken-down nutrients
Large intestine	absorption of water and broken-down nutrients, elimination of wastes

VOCABULARY
nutrient p. 621
digestion p. 622
digestive system p. 622
peristalsis p. 622

3 The urinary system removes waste materials.

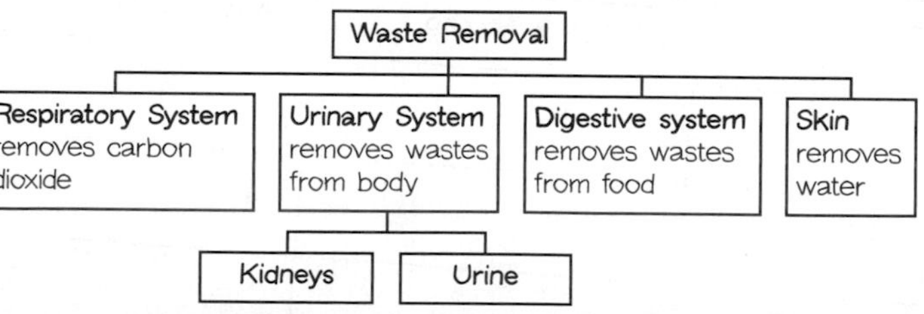

VOCABULARY
urinary system p. 629
urine p. 629

Technology Resources

Have students visit **ClassZone.com** or use the CD-ROM for a cumulative review of concepts.

CONTENT REVIEW

CONTENT REVIEW CD-ROM

Engage students in a whole-class interactive review of Key Concepts. Edit content as you wish.

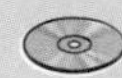
POWER PRESENTATIONS

Reviewing Vocabulary

Copy the chart below and write the definition for each word. Use the meaning of the word's root to help you.

Word	Root Meaning	Definition
EXAMPLE: rib cage	to arch over	bones enclosing the internal organs of the body
1. respiration	to breathe	
2. nutrient	to nourish	
3. digestion	to separate	
4. peristalsis	to wrap around	

Reviewing Key Concepts

Multiple Choice *Choose the letter of the best answer.*

5. Which system brings oxygen into your body and removes carbon dioxide?
   a. digestive system
   b. urinary system
   c. respiratory system
   d. muscular system
6. Which body structure in the throat keeps air from entering the stomach?
   a. trachea
   b. epiglottis
   c. lungs
   d. alveoli
7. Oxygen and carbon dioxide are exchanged through structures in the lungs called
   a. bronchial tubes
   b. alveoli
   c. cartilage
   d. villi
8. Carbon dioxide is a waste product that is formed during which process?
   a. cellular respiration
   b. peristalsis
   c. urination
   d. circulation
9. Carbohydrates are nutrients that
   a. make up most of the human body
   b. make up cell membranes
   c. enable cells to grow and repair themselves
   d. are broken down for energy
10. Which is *not* a function of the digestive system?
    a. absorb water from food
    b. absorb nutrients from food
    c. filter wastes from blood
    d. break down food
11. Which is an example of a physical change?
    a. teeth grind cracker into smaller pieces
    b. liquids in mouth change starches to sugars
    c. bile breaks down fats
    d. stomach breaks down proteins
12. Where in the digestive system is most water absorbed?
    a. kidneys
    b. stomach
    c. large intestine
    d. esophagus
13. Chemical waste is filtered from the blood in which structure?
    a. alveoli
    b. kidney
    c. stomach
    d. villi
14. The kidneys control the amount of
    a. oxygen that enters the blood
    b. blood cells that leave the body
    c. urine that is absorbed by the body
    d. water that leaves the body

Reviewing Vocabulary

Sample answers:

1. *process taking place in cells by which energy is released*
2. *important substance in food that enables the body to grow and maintain homeostasis*
3. *the process of breaking down food into absorbable materials*
4. *wavelike contractions of smooth muscles in the organs of the digestive tract*

Reviewing Key Concepts

5. *c*
6. *b*
7. *b*
8. *a*
9. *d*
10. *c*
11. *a*
12. *c*
13. *b*
14. *c*

(Answers to items that appear on p. 636.)

15. *Students' sketches should show the thoracic cavity increasing in volume.*
16. *energy, water, and carbon dioxide*
17. *mouth, esophagus, stomach, small intestine, large intestine, rectum*
18. *filtering liquid waste from body*

ASSESSMENT RESOURCES

UNIT ASSESSMENT BOOK
- Chapter Test A, pp. 25–28
- Chapter Test B, pp. 29–32
- Chapter Test C, pp. 33–36
- Alternative Assessment, pp. 37–38

SPANISH ASSESSMENT BOOK
Spanish Chapter Test, pp. 85–88

Technology Resources

Edit test items and answer choices.

 **Test Generator CD-ROM**

Visit **ClassZone.com** to extend test practice.

 **Test Practice**

(Answers for items 15–18 appear on p. 635.)

Thinking Critically

19. Air moves into lungs through tubes that branch into smaller tubes and end in alveoli. O_2 moves through the walls of the alveoli and is dissolved into blood. CO_2 moves out of blood and into alveoli to be breathed out.
20. O_2 and sugars combine to release energy. Respiratory system provides the O_2 needed. Digestive system provides sugars.
21. Coughing and sneezing help remove particles from the respiratory system.
22. Water is produced in respiration. When air is exhaled, the water vapor condenses on the glass surface.
23. Mechanical digestion occurs in the mouth and stomach and physically changes food. Chemical digestion breaks chemical bonds.
24. Partially digested food would go straight into the small intestine. No; the small intestine is where nutrients are absorbed.
25. Kidneys regulate water in the body. The athlete will release water through urine, sweat, and water vapor in breath.
26. Nutrients are filtered back into bloodstream.

the BIG idea

27. The body needs oxygen, water, and nutrients.
28. The respiratory system allows O_2 to enter lungs. There, O_2 is exchanged with CO_2 from circulatory system, and CO_2 is exhaled. In the digestive system, nutrients and water are absorbed into circulatory system. In the urinary system, blood passes through the kidneys. Nutrients are returned and liquid waste is eliminated.

UNIT PROJECTS

Collect schedules, materials lists, and questions. Be sure dates and materials are obtainable, questions, focused.

Unit Projects, pp. 5–10

Short Answer *Write a short answer to each question.*

15. Draw a sketch that shows how the thoracic cavity changes as the diaphragm contracts and pulls downward.
16. What are two products that are released into the body as a result of cellular respiration?
17. Through which organs does food pass as it travels through the digestive system?
18. What is the function of the urinary system?

Thinking Critically

19. **SUMMARIZE** Describe how gas exchange takes place inside the lungs.
20. **SYNTHESIZE** Summarize what happens during cellular respiration. Explain how the digestive system and the respiratory system are involved.
21. **ANALYZE** When there is a lot of dust or pollen in the air, people may cough and sneeze. What function of the respiratory system is involved?
22. **INFER** When you exhale onto a glass surface, the surface becomes cloudy with a thin film of moisture. Explain why this happens.
23. **COMPARE AND CONTRAST** Where does mechanical digestion take place? How is it different from chemical digestion?
24. **PREDICT** People with stomach disease often have their entire stomachs removed and are able to live normally. Explain how this is possible. Would a person be able to live normally without the small intestine? Explain your answer.
25. **APPLY** An athlete drinks a liter of water before a basketball game and continues to drink water during the game. Describe how the athlete's body is able to maintain homeostasis during the course of the game.
26. **INTERPRET** Use the diagram of the nephron shown below to describe what happens to the blood as it travels through the vessels surrounding the nephron.

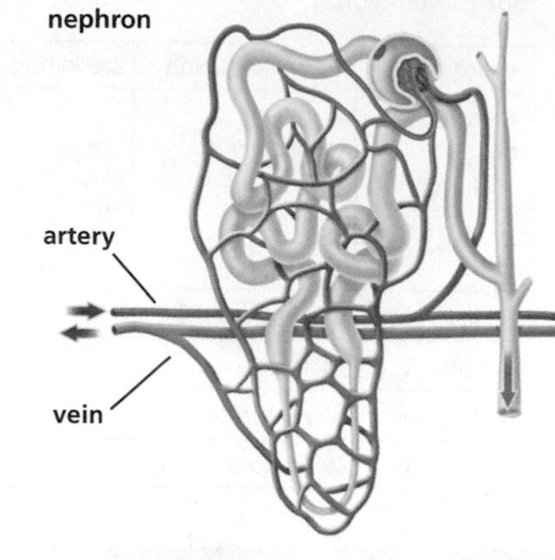

the BIG idea

27. **INFER** Look again at the picture on pages 610–611. Now that you have finished the chapter, how would you change or add details to your answer to the question on the photograph?
28. **SYNTHESIZE** Write a paragraph explaining how the respiratory system, the digestive system, and the urinary system work together with the circulatory system to eliminate waste materials from the body. Underline these terms in your paragraph.

UNIT PROJECTS

Check your schedule for your unit project. How are you doing? Be sure that you've placed data or notes from your research in your project folder.

MONITOR AND RETEACH

If students are having trouble applying the concepts in Chapter Review items 19, 20, and 28, suggest that they create a flow chart that shows how the respiratory, digestive, and urinary systems are connected. Students can refer to the diagrams on pp. 617, 625, and 629 to help them with their graphics.

Students may benefit from summarizing one or more sections of the chapter.

 Summarizing the Chapter, pp. 127–128

Standardized Test Practice

For practice on your state test, go to . . . TEST PRACTICE CLASSZONE.COM

Analyzing Data

The bar graph below shows respiration rates.

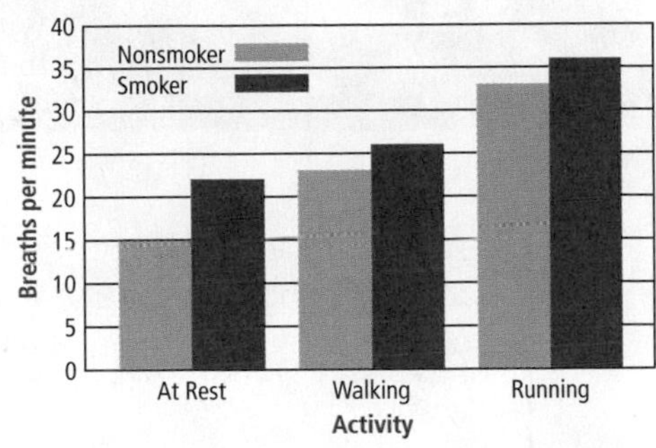

Use the graph to answer the questions below.

1. What is the best title for this graph?
- **a.** Respiration Rates of Smokers and Nonsmokers
- **b.** Cigarettes Smoked During Exercise
- **c.** Activities Performed by Smokers and Nonsmokers
- **d.** Blood Pressure Levels of Smokers and Nonsmokers.

2. How many breaths per minute were taken by a nonsmoker at rest?
- **a.** 15 breaths per minute
- **b.** 22 breaths per minute
- **c.** 26 breaths per minute
- **d.** 33 breaths per minute

3. For the nonsmokers, by how much did the respiration rate increase between resting and running?
- **a.** 15 breaths per minute
- **b.** 18 breaths per minute
- **c.** 23 breaths per minute
- **d.** 33 breaths per minute

4. Which statement is *not* true?
- **a.** The nonsmoker at rest took more breaths per minute than the smoker at rest.
- **b.** The nonsmoker took more breaths per minute running than walking.
- **c.** The smoker took more breaths per minute than the nonsmoker while walking.
- **d.** The nonsmoker took fewer breaths per minute than the smoker while running.

5. Which statement is the most logical conclusion to draw from the data in the chart?
- **a.** Smoking has no effect on respiration rate.
- **b.** Increased activity has no effect on respiration rate.
- **c.** There is no difference in the respiration rates between the smoker and the nonsmoker.
- **d.** Smoking and activity both cause an increase in respiration rate.

Extended Response

6. Tar, which is a harmful substance found in tobacco smoke, coats the lining of the lungs over time. Based on the information in the graph and what you know about the respiratory system, write a paragraph describing how smoking cigarettes affects the functioning of the respiratory system.

7. Ads for cigarettes and other tobacco products have been banned from television. However, they still appear in newspapers and magazines. These ads make tobacco use look glamorous and exciting. Using your knowledge of the respiratory system, design an ad that discourages the use of tobacco products. Create a slogan that will help people remember how tobacco affects the health of the respiratory system.

METACOGNITIVE ACTIVITY

Have students answer the following questions in their **Science Notebook:**

1. What are some strategies that helped you learn about the structures and functions of the respiratory system?
2. What questions do you still have about how the respiratory system works together with the circulatory system?
3. How did your unit project help you gain a better understanding of the systems studied in this chapter?

Analyzing Data

1. a *3. b* *5. d*
2. a *4. a*

Extended Response

6. RUBRIC

4 points for a response that correctly answers the question and uses the following terms accurately:

- bronchial tubes
- tar
- oxygen
- alveoli

Sample answer: Tar coats the lining of the passageways and the bronchial tubes that lead into the lungs. As the amount of tar increases, the smoker no longer is able to keep the passageways of the lungs clear of dust and other harmful particles. Less oxygen is exchanged in the alveoli, and the smoker's rate of respiration increases at rest as well as in other types of activities.

3 points correctly answers the question and uses three terms accurately

2 points correctly answers the question and uses two terms accurately

1 point correctly answers the question and uses one term accurately

7. RUBRIC

4 points for a response in which all requirements of the task are included. *Students' ads should include the following:*

- *knowledge of respiratory system structures (mentions lungs, alveoli, cilia, and/or bronchial tubes)*
- *affect of tobacco on the structures of the respiratory system*
- *respiratory diseases associated with the respiratory system (such as cancer or emphysema)*
- *slogan that describes the effects of smoking (Sample slogan: Today's smoke is tomorrow's choke.)*

3 points response fulfills three of the above items

2 points response fulfills two of the above items

1 point response fulfills one of the above items

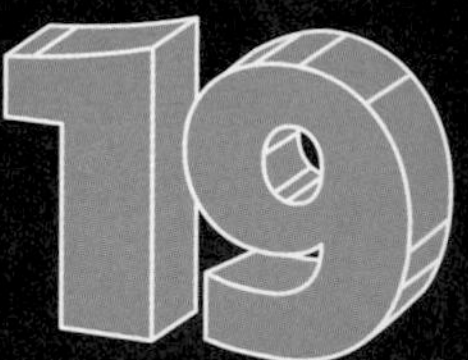

Transport and Protection

Life Science UNIFYING PRINCIPLES

PRINCIPLE 1
All living things share common characteristics.

PRINCIPLE 2
All living things share common needs.

PRINCIPLE 3
Living things meet their needs through interactions with the environment.

PRINCIPLE 4
The types and numbers of living things change over time.

Unit 5: Human Biology BIG IDEAS

CHAPTER 17
Systems, Support, and Movement
The human body is made up of systems that work together to perform necessary functions.

CHAPTER 18
Absorption, Digestion, and Exchange
Systems in the body obtain and process materials and remove waste.

CHAPTER 19
Transport and Protection
Systems function to transport materials and to defend and protect the body.

CHAPTER 20
Control and Reproduction
The nervous and endocrine systems allow the body to respond to internal and external conditions.

CHAPTER 21
Growth, Development, and Health
The body develops and maintains itself over time.

CHAPTER 19 KEY CONCEPTS

SECTION  1

The circulatory system transports materials.

1. The circulatory system works with other body systems.
2. Structures in the circulatory system function together.
3. Blood exerts pressure on blood vessels.
4. There are four different blood types.

SECTION 2

The immune system defends the body.

1. Many systems defend the body from harmful materials.
2. The immune system has response structures.
3. The immune system responds to attack.
4. Most diseases can be prevented or treated.

SECTION  3

The integumentary system shields the body.

1. Skin performs important functions.
2. The structure of skin is complex.
3. The skin grows and heals.

The Big Idea Flow Chart is available on p. T17 in the **UNIT TRANSPARENCY BOOK.**

SECTION

The circulatory system transports materials. pp. 641–649

1. **The circulatory system works with other body systems.** The **circulatory system** transports digested materials from the digestive system to cells of the body. It also transports oxygen to cells of the body and removes carbon dioxide and other wastes through the **blood.**
2. **Structures in the circulatory system function together.** The human heart is divided into four chambers. It pumps oxygen-poor blood from the right ventricle to the lungs. Oxygen-rich blood is pumped from the left ventricle to the rest of the body. The left atrium receives oxygen-rich blood from the lungs, and the right atrium receives oxygen poor blood from the rest of the body.

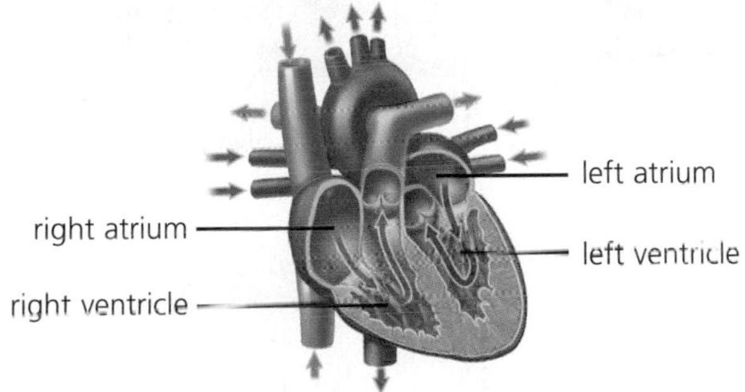

You may wish to leave this simple diagram on the board to emphasize that the heart is not shaped like a valentine and that blood flows both out from and into the heart.

- Blood is a tissue made up of plasma, **red blood cells,** white blood cells, and platelets. Red blood cells carry oxygen to the other cells of the body.
- Blood vessels include **arteries, veins,** and **capillaries.** Most arteries carry blood away from the heart, and most veins carry blood toward the heart. Exchanges of gases and other materials take place in capillaries.

3. **Blood exerts pressure on blood vessels.** Blood pressure is the force that blood exerts on the arteries, veins, and capillaries. High or low blood pressure can cause serious medical conditions.
4. **There are four different blood types.** The four blood types are A, B, AB, and O and are determined by antigens on red blood cells.

SECTION

The immune system defends the body. pp. 650–658

1. **Many systems defend the body from harmful materials.** The integumentary, respiratory, and digestive systems are the first lines of defense against **pathogens,** disease-causing agents that may enter the body.
2. **The immune system has response structures.** White blood cells are produced in the bone marrow, thymus gland, spleen, and lymph nodes. They are specialized to destroy foreign organisms. The lymphatic system transports white blood cells and antibodies throughout the body.
3. **The immune system responds to attack.** Inflammation and fever are two immune responses in the body's defense against pathogens. Histamines are released to raise the temperature of tissues and increase blood flow to an infected area. Fever occurs when many tissues produce histamines. T cells and B cells are two kinds of white blood cells. B cells produce **antibodies** that attack foreign materials.

The diagram below shows the immune responses of T cells and B cells.

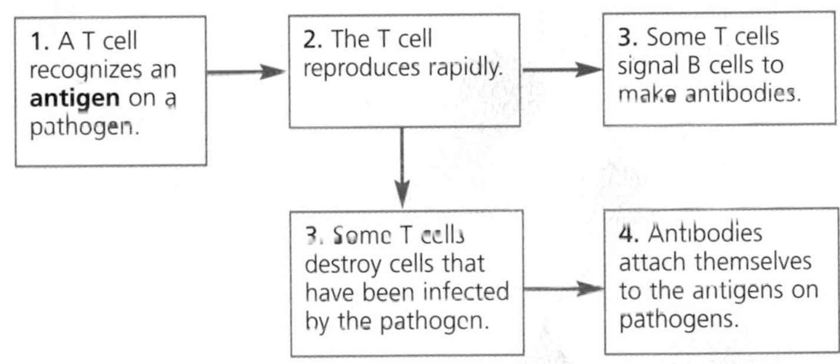

- Active immunity is developed when the body makes its own antibodies after an illness. **Vaccines** provide a form of active immunity. Passive immunity occurs in newborns that inherit antibodies from their mothers.

4. **Most diseases can be prevented or treated.**
   - Vaccines provide a form of active immunity that can prevent some diseases.
   - **Antibiotics** and other medicines are used to treat diseases.

Common Misconceptions

FUNCTION OF THE HEART Many students realize that the heart pumps blood to the extremities, but they are not aware that the blood also returns to the heart. Students often confuse its pump function with functions such as cleaning, filtering, and manufacturing blood.

 This misconception is addressed on p. 642.

MISCONCEPTION DATABASE
CLASSZONE.COM Background on student misconceptions

CIRCULATION AND RESPIRATION Students of all ages hold the misconception that a separate system of tubes carries air to the heart and other organs. Emphasize instead that although oxygen enters the body through the trachea and lungs, it is carried to cells in the blood.

 This misconception is addressed on p. 643.

Previewing Content

SECTION

The integumentary system shields the body. pp. 659–665

1. Skin performs important functions.
The body's integumentary system, which includes hair and nails, repels water, guards against infection, helps maintain homeostasis, and senses the environment.

2. The structure of skin is complex.
Human skin is composed of two layers, the **epidermis** and the **dermis.**
- The epidermis forms a thick, protective outer layer made up of many protein fibers.
- The dermis contains sweat and oil glands, sensory receptors, hair, blood vessels, and muscles.
- Nails grow from epidermal cells in nail beds.

3. The skin grows and heals.
- Growth occurs at the base of the epidermis. This layer completely replaces itself every two to four weeks.
- Serious injuries to the skin include burns, especially sunburn. Repeated burning increases a person's chances of getting skin cancer.

Explain to students that many layers and structures make up the skin they see on their hands.

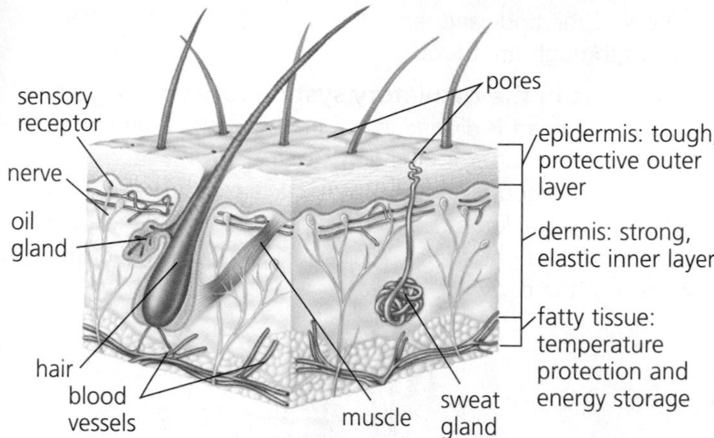

Common Misconceptions

CAUSES OF ILLNESS Many students think that all illnesses are caused by germs and that germs enter only through the mouth during eating. In fact, pathogens can enter the body through a cut in the skin or through the lungs during breathing.

 This misconception is addressed on p. 651.

MISCONCEPTION DATABASE
CLASSZONE.COM Background on student misconceptions

Previewing Labs

EXPLORE the BIG idea

Blood Pressure, p. 639 Students use balloons partially filled with air to simulate the action of blood pressure.	**TIME** 10 minutes **MATERIALS** a few balloons
Wet Fingers, p. 639 Students observe how the skin senses changes in the environment.	**TIME** 10 minutes **MATERIALS** cup, water
Internet Activity: Heart Pumping, p. 639 Students observe how the heart pumps blood to understand that blood circulates.	**TIME** 20 minutes **MATERIALS** computer with Internet access

SECTION 1

EXPLORE The Circulatory System, p. 641 Students take their pulse to measure how fast the heart beats.	**TIME** 10 minutes **MATERIALS** stopwatch
CHAPTER INVESTIGATION, Heart Rate and Exercise, pp. 648–649 Students calculate resting, maximum, and target heart rates and examine the effects of exercise on heart rate.	**TIME** 40 minutes **MATERIALS** notebook, stopwatch, calculator, graph paper

SECTION 2

EXPLORE Membranes, p. 650 Students model working membranes to understand how the body keeps out foreign particles.	**TIME** 15 minutes **MATERIALS** white cloth, zippered sandwich bag, large bowl, water, food coloring, small pin
INVESTIGATE Antibodies, p. 655 Students make models to investigate how antibodies stop pathogens from spreading.	**TIME** 15 minutes **MATERIALS** plastic containers with lids, index cards

SECTION 3

EXPLORE The Skin, p. 659 Students remove the skin from apples to explore the functions of the skin.	**TIME** 10 minutes **MATERIALS** vegetable peeler, apple
INVESTIGATE Skin Protection, p. 661 Students observe how oil protects the skin.	**TIME** 10 minutes **MATERIALS** cotton ball, rubbing alcohol, dropper, water

R **Additional INVESTIGATION,** Listen to Your Heart, A, B, & C, pp. 177–185; Teacher Instructions, pp. 305–306

Previewing Chapter Resources

CHAPTER 19 Transport and Protection

INTEGRATED TECHNOLOGY

 **CLASSZONE.COM**
- eEdition Plus
- EasyPlanner Plus
- Misconception Database
- Content Review
- Test Practice
- Resource Centers
- Internet Activity: Heart Pumping
- Math Tutorial

 **SCILINKS.ORG**

SCiLINKS

 **CD-ROMS**
- eEdition
- EasyPlanner
- Power Presentations
- Content Review
- Lab Generator
- Test Generator

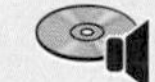 **AUDIO CDS**
- Audio Readings
- Audio Readings in Spanish

LABS AND ACTIVITIES

 EXPLORE the Big Idea, p. 639
- Blood Pressure
- Wet Fingers
- Internet Activity: Heart Pumping

 **UNIT RESOURCE BOOK**
Unit Projects, pp. 5–10

 **Lab Generator CD-ROM**
Generate customized labs.

SECTION

1 The circulatory system transports materials.
pp. 641–649

Time: 3 periods (1.5 blocks)

 Lesson Plan, pp. 129–130

Integrated Technology

 **RESOURCE CENTERS,** The Circulatory System, Blood Types

 **UNIT TRANSPARENCY BOOK**
- Big Idea Flow Chart, p. T17
- Daily Vocabulary Scaffolding, p. T18
- Note-Taking Model, p. T19
- 3-Minute Warm-Up, p. T20
- "The Heart" Visual, p. T22

Labs and Activities

- EXPLORE The Circulatory System, p. 641
- CHAPTER INVESTIGATION, Heart Rate and Exercise, pp. 648–649

 **UNIT RESOURCE BOOK**
- CHAPTER INVESTIGATION, Heart Rate and Exercise, A, B, & C, pp. 168–176
- Additional INVESTIGATION, Listen to Your Heart, A, B, & C, pp. 177–185

SECTION

2 The immune system defends the body.
pp. 650–658

Time: 2 periods (1 block)

 Lesson Plan, pp. 139–140

Integrated Technology

- **RESOURCE CENTER,** Lymphatic System
- **MATH TUTORIAL**

 **UNIT TRANSPARENCY BOOK**
- Daily Vocabulary Scaffolding, p. T18
- 3-Minute Warm-Up, p. T20

Labs and Activities

- EXPLORE Membranes, p. 650
- INVESTIGATE Antibodies, p. 655
- Math in Science, p. 658

 **UNIT RESOURCE BOOK**
- Datasheet, Antibodies, p. 148
- Math Support, p. 166
- Math Practice, p. 167

SECTION

3 The integumentary system shields the body.
pp. 659–665

Time: 3 periods (1.5 blocks)

Lesson Plan, pp. 150–151

Integrated Technology

- **RESOURCE CENTER,** Structure of Skin
- **VISUALIZATION,** How Skin Heals

 **UNIT TRANSPARENCY BOOK**
- Big Idea Flow Chart, p. T17
- Daily Vocabulary Scaffolding, p. T18
- 3-Minute Warm-Up, p. T21
- Chapter Outline, pp. T23–T24

Labs and Activities

- EXPLORE The Skin, p. 659
- INVESTIGATE Skin Protection, p. 661
- Extreme Science, p. 665

 **UNIT RESOURCE BOOK**
Datasheet, Skin Protection, p. 159

KEY TO ICONS  CD/CD-ROM  Teacher Edition  UNIT TRANSPARENCY BOOK  SPANISH ASSESSMENT BOOK

 INTERNET Pupil Edition UNIT RESOURCE BOOK UNIT ASSESSMENT BOOK SCIENCE TOOLKIT

READING AND REINFORCEMENT	ASSESSMENT	STANDARDS
 • Frame Game, B26–27 • Main Idea and Detail Notes, C37 • Daily Vocabulary Scaffolding, H1–8  **UNIT RESOURCE BOOK** • Vocabulary Practice, pp. 163–164 • Decoding Support, p. 165 • Summarizing the Chapter, pp. 186–187  **Audio Readings CD** Listen to Pupil Edition.  **Audio Readings in Spanish CD** Listen to Pupil Edition in Spanish.	 • Chapter Review, pp. 666–667 • Standardized Test Practice, p. 669  **UNIT ASSESSMENT BOOK** • Diagnostic Test, pp. 39–40 • Chapter Test, A, B, & C, pp. 44–55 • Alternative Assessment, pp. 56–57  Spanish Chapter Test, pp. 73–76  **Test Generator CD-ROM** Generate customized tests.  **Lab Generator CD-ROM** Rubrics for Labs	National Standards A.2–8, A.9.a–c, A.9.e–f, C.1.d–f, G.1.b See p. 638 for the standards.
 **UNIT RESOURCE BOOK** • Reading Study Guide, A & B, pp. 131–134 • Spanish Reading Study Guide, pp. 135–136 • Challenge and Extension, p. 137 • Reinforcing Key Concepts, p. 138	 Ongoing Assessment, pp. 642–643, 645–647  Section 19.1 Review, p. 647  **UNIT ASSESSMENT BOOK** Section 19.1 Quiz, p. 41	National Standards A.2–8, A.9.a–c, A.9.e–f, C.1.d–e, G.1.b
 **UNIT RESOURCE BOOK** • Reading Study Guide, A & B, pp. 141–144 • Spanish Reading Study Guide, pp. 145–146 • Challenge and Extension, p. 147 • Reinforcing Key Concepts, p. 149	 Ongoing Assessment, pp. 650–657  Section 19.2 Review, p. 657  **UNIT ASSESSMENT BOOK** Section 19.2 Quiz, p. 42	National Standards A.2–7, A.9.a–b, A.9.e–f, C.1.d–f, G.1.b
 **UNIT RESOURCE BOOK** • Reading Study Guide, A & B, pp. 152–155 • Spanish Reading Study Guide, pp. 156–157 • Challenge and Extension, p. 158 • Reinforcing Key Concepts, p. 160 • Challenge Reading, pp. 161–162	 Ongoing Assessment, pp. 659, 661–664  Section 19.3 Review, p. 664  **UNIT ASSESSMENT BOOK** Section 19.3 Quiz, p. 43	National Standards A.2–7, A.9.a–b, A.9.e–f, C.1.e–f, G.1.b

Previewing Resources for Differentiated Instruction

CHAPTER INVESTIGATION

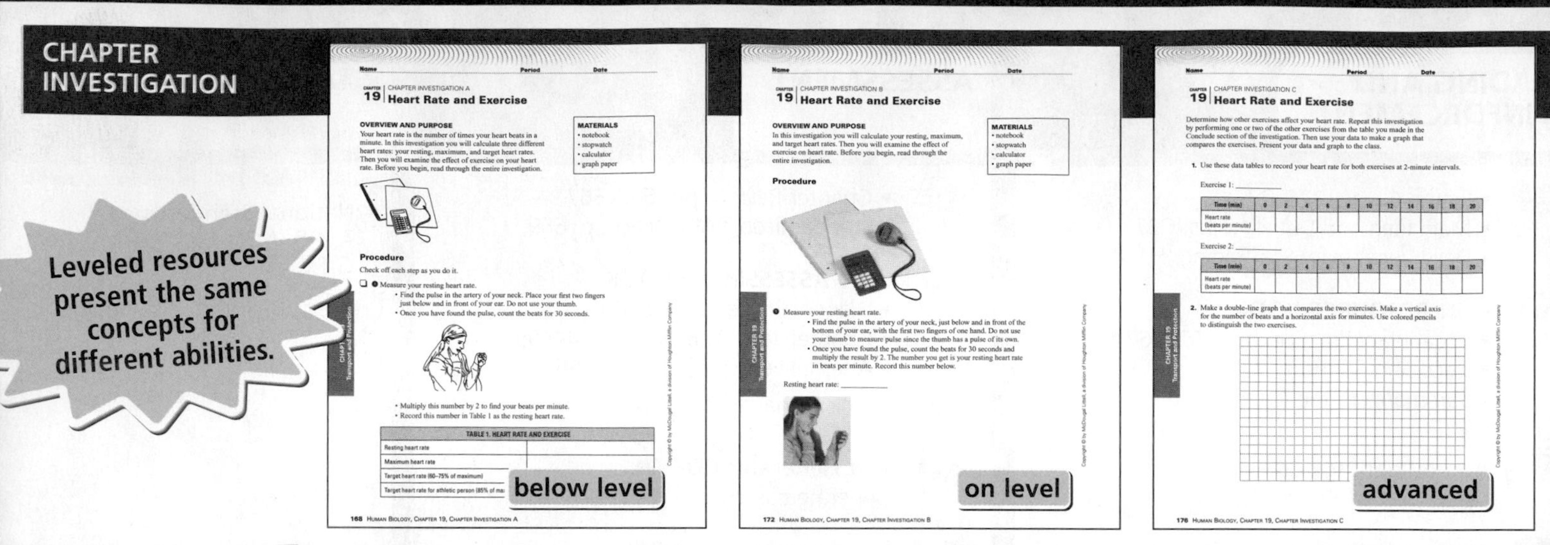

UNIT RESOURCE BOOK, pp. 168–171

pp. 172–175

pp. 172–176

READING STUDY GUIDE

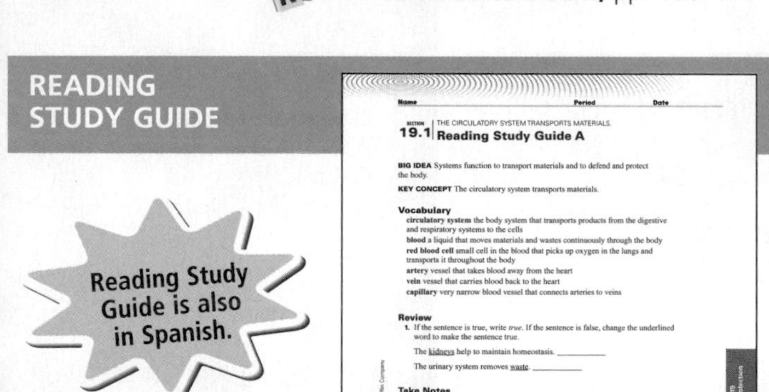

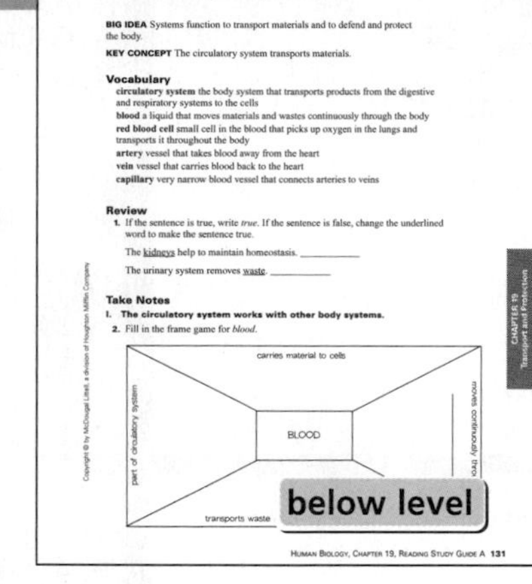

UNIT RESOURCE BOOK, pp. 131–132

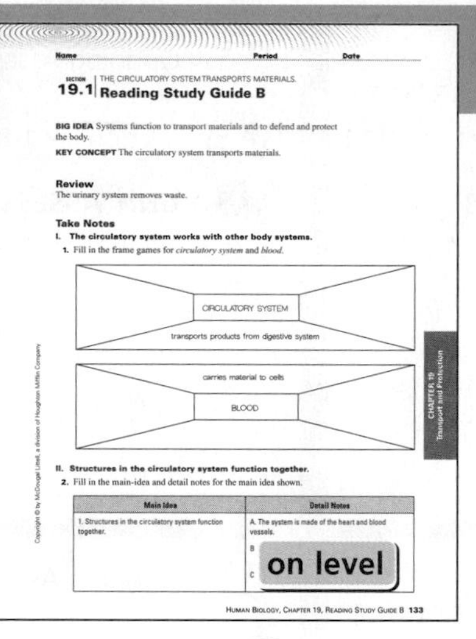

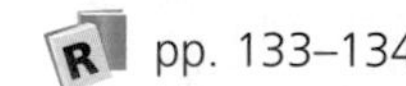
pp. 133–134

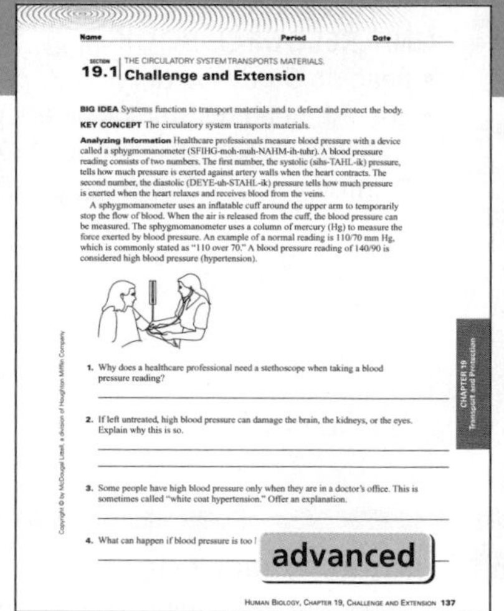

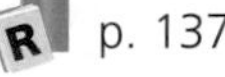
p. 137

CHAPTER TEST

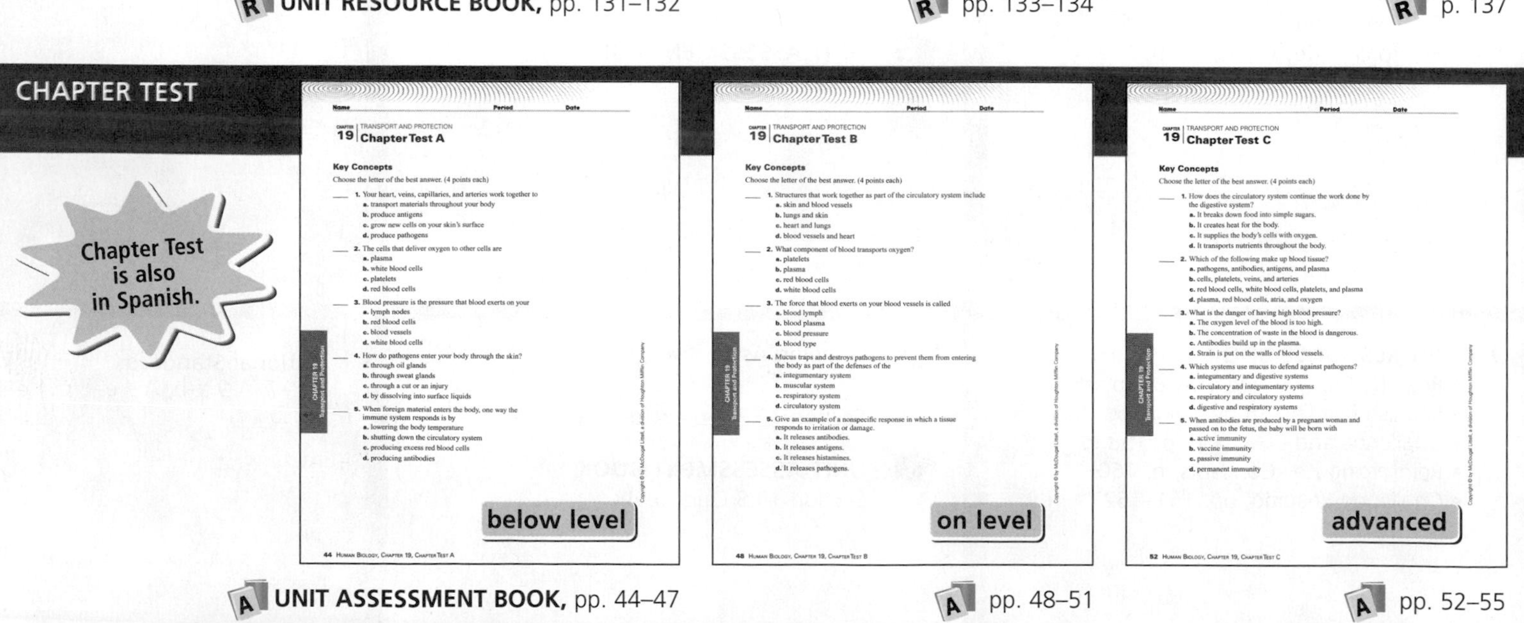

UNIT ASSESSMENT BOOK, pp. 44–47

pp. 48–51

pp. 52–55

TECHNOLOGY

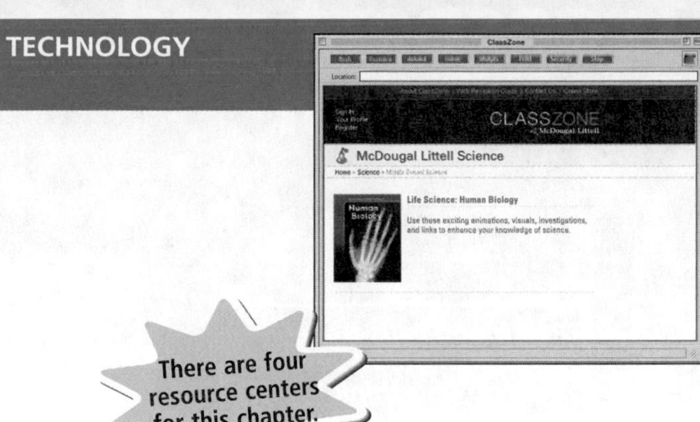

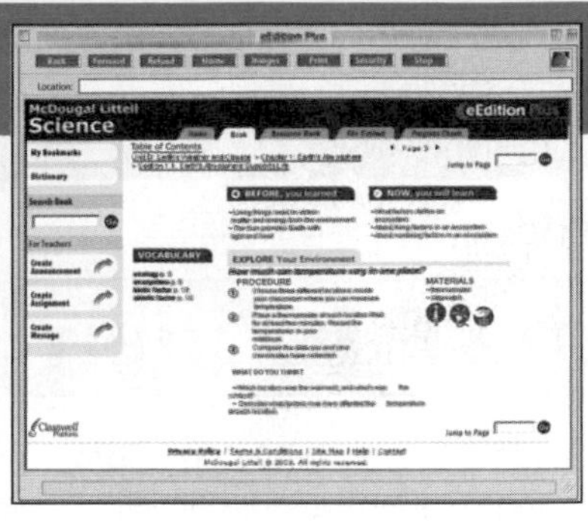

VISUAL CONTENT

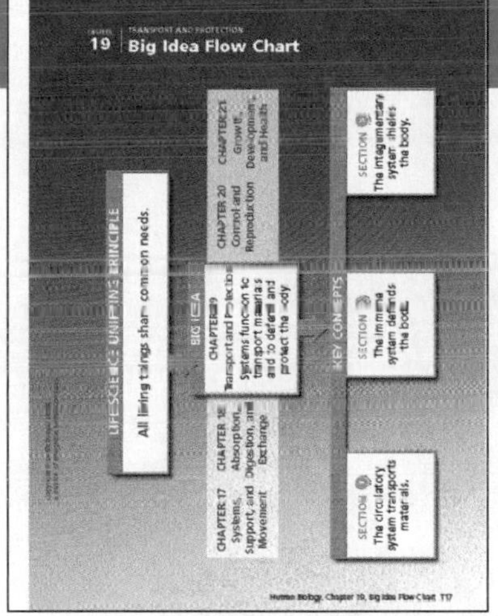

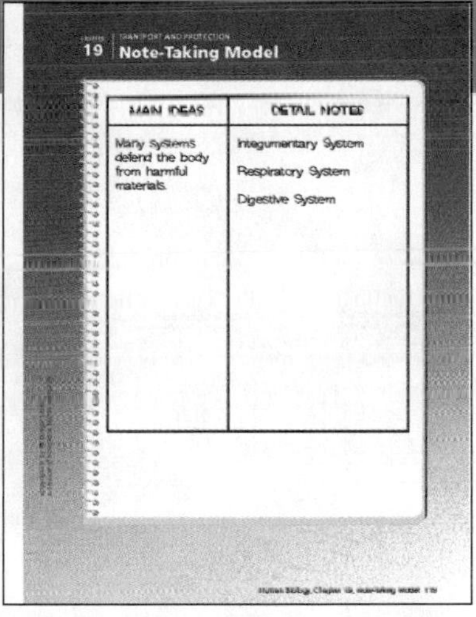

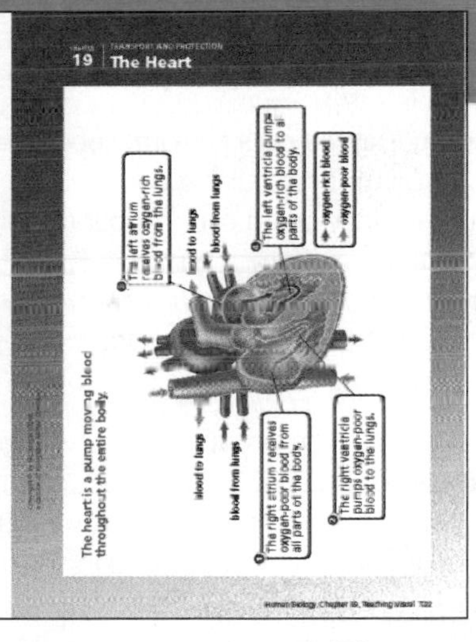

T UNIT TRANSPARENCY BOOK, p. T17 | **T** p. T19 | **T** p. T22

MORE SUPPORT

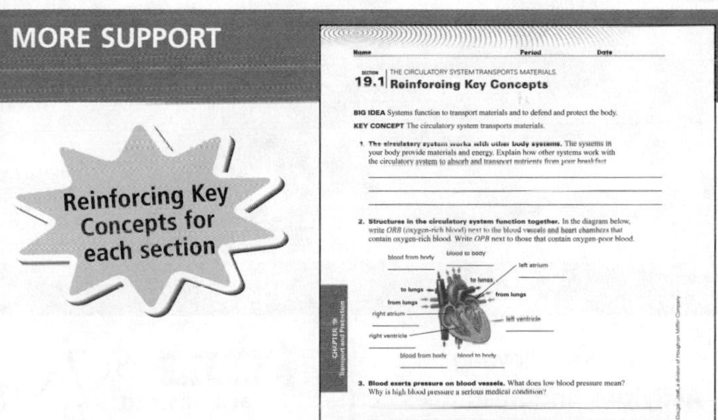

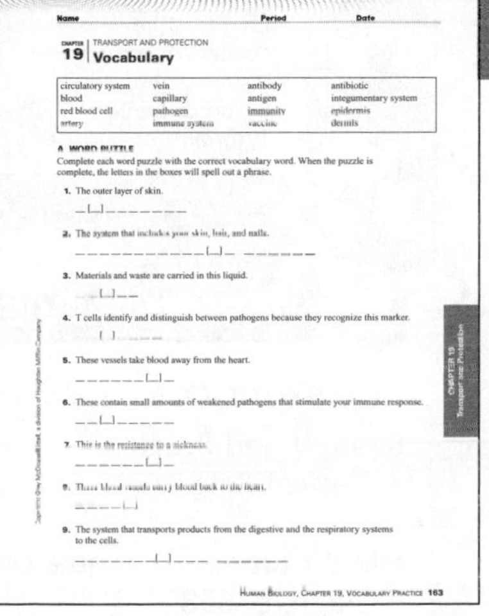

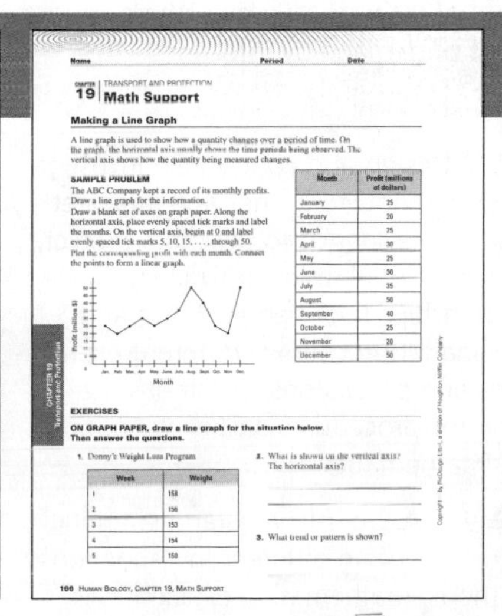

R UNIT RESOURCE BOOK, p. 138 | **R** pp. 163–164 | **R** p. 166

Transport and Protection

INTRODUCE

the BIG idea

Have students look at the photograph of red blood cells and discuss how the question in the box links to the Big Idea. Ask:

- How does the circulatory system act like a transportation system?
- Why are red blood cells key in transporting material to and from cells?

National Science Education Standards

Content

C.1.d Specialized cells perform specialized functions in multicellular organisms. Groups of specialized cells cooperate to form a tissue. Different tissues in turn form larger functional units, called organs. Each type of cell, tissue, and organ has a distinct structure and set of functions.

C.1.e The human organism has systems for digestion, respiration, reproduction, circulation, excretion, movement, control and coordination, and protection from disease. These systems interact.

C.1.f Disease is a breakdown in structures or functions. Some diseases are the result of intrinsic failures. Others are the result of damage by infection.

Process

A.2–8 Design and conduct an investigation; use tools to gather and interpret data; use evidence to describe, predict, explain, model; think critically to make relationships between evidence and explanation; recognize different explanations and predictions; communicate scientific procedures and explanations; use mathematics.

A.9.a–c, A.9.e–f Understand scientific inquiry by using different investigations, methods, mathematics, explanations based on logic, evidence, and skepticism.

G.1.b Science requires different abilities.

CHAPTER

Transport and Protection

the BIG idea

Systems function to transport materials and to defend and protect the body.

Red blood cells travel through a blood vessel. How do you think blood carries materials around your body?

Key Concepts

SECTION

The circulatory system transports materials.
Learn how materials move through blood vessels.

SECTION

The immune system defends the body.
Learn about the body's defenses and responses to foreign materials.

SECTION

The integumentary system shields the body.
Learn about the structure of skin and how it protects the body.

Internet Preview

CLASSZONE.COM

Chapter 19 online resources: Content Review, two Visualizations, four Resource Centers, Math Tutorial, Test Practice

638 Unit 5: **Human Biology**

INTERNET PREVIEW

CLASSZONE.COM For student use with the following pages:

Review and Practice
- Content Review, pp. 640, 666
- Math Tutorial, Making a Line Graph, p. 658
- Test Practice, p. 669

Activities and Resources
- Internet Activity: Heart Pumping, p. 639
- Resource Centers: Circulatory System, p. 642; Blood Types, p. 647; Lymphatic System, p. 652; Skin, p. 661
- Visualization, p. 663

Immune System
Code: MDL046

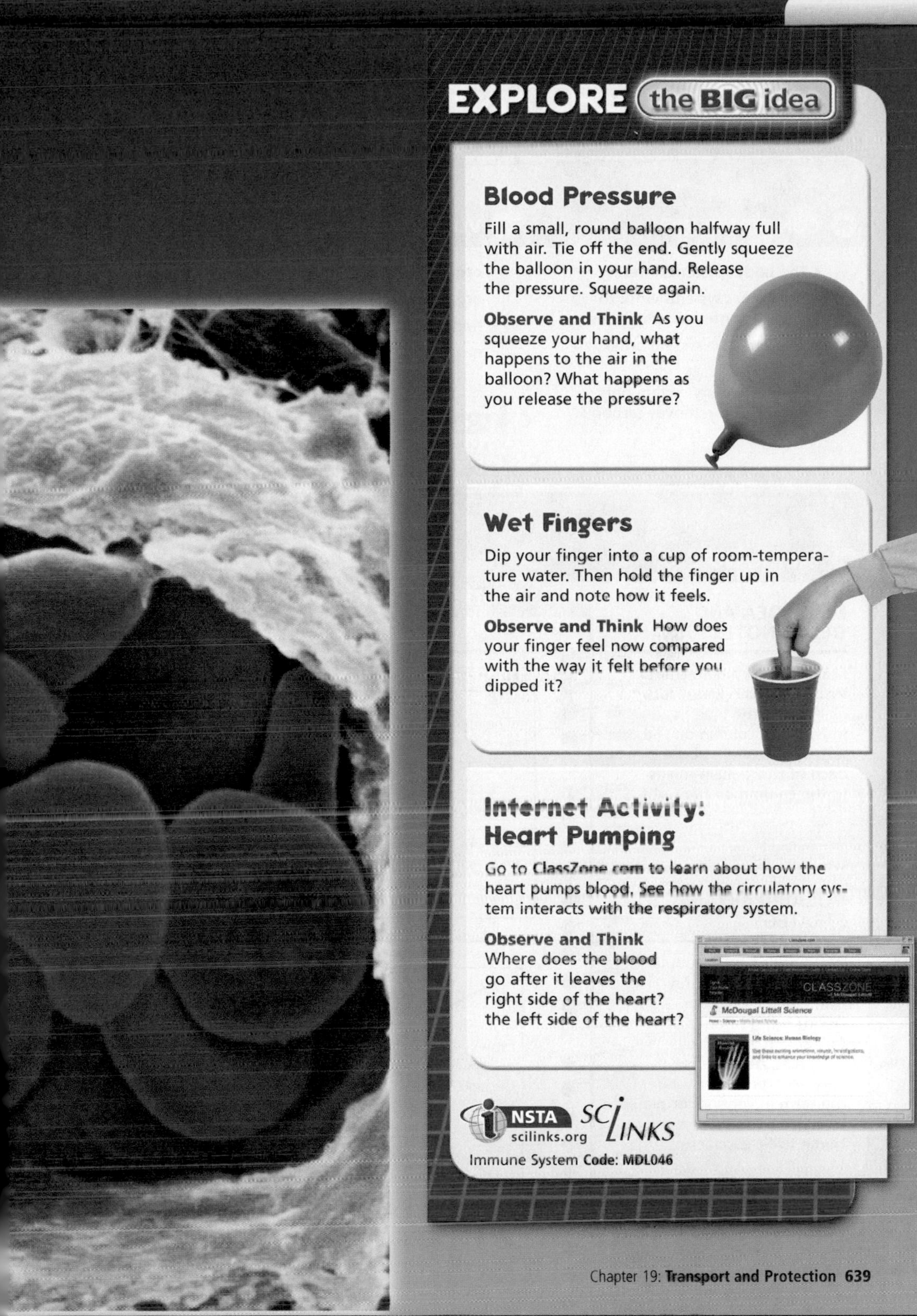

EXPLORE the BIG idea

Blood Pressure

Fill a small, round balloon halfway full with air. Tie off the end. Gently squeeze the balloon in your hand. Release the pressure. Squeeze again.

Observe and Think As you squeeze your hand, what happens to the air in the balloon? What happens as you release the pressure?

Wet Fingers

Dip your finger into a cup of room-temperature water. Then hold the finger up in the air and note how it feels.

Observe and Think How does your finger feel now compared with the way it felt before you dipped it?

Internet Activity: Heart Pumping

Go to **ClassZone.com** to learn about how the heart pumps blood. See how the circulatory system interacts with the respiratory system.

Observe and Think Where does the blood go after it leaves the right side of the heart? the left side of the heart?

NSTA scilinks.org SCILINKS
Immune System **Code: MDL046**

EXPLORE the BIG idea

These inquiry-based activities are appropriate for use at home or as a supplement to classroom instruction.

Blood Pressure

PURPOSE To simulate the action of blood pressure.

TIP *10 min.* Students can try the same activity with water instead of air in the balloon if they are careful not to break the balloon.

Answer: The air inside the balloon moves to one area as the balloon is squeezed. That area of the balloon is stretched by the pressure. When the hand is released, the air once again fills the balloon evenly.

REVISIT after p. 646.

Wet Fingers

PURPOSE To observe how the skin senses changes in the environment.

TIPS *10 min.* You might encourage students to try their other hand or a different temperature of water to compare the observations. A bowl or pan may be used instead of a cup.

Answer: The finger feels colder when exposed to air while wet.

REVISIT after p. 661.

Internet Activity: Heart Pumping

PURPOSE To observe how the heart pumps blood.

TIP *20 min.* Use student observations to introduce the interaction between the circulatory and respiratory systems.

Answer: Blood from the right side of the heart goes to the lungs. Blood from the left side goes to the rest of the body.

REVISIT after p. 642.

TEACHING WITH TECHNOLOGY

CBL and Probeware Students can use a heart rate sensor to measure heart rates before and after mild exercise in the Chapter Investigation on pp. 648–649. Students can use graphing calculators or spreadsheet software to collect, display, and analyze the data.

CBL and Probeware Students can use a skin surface temperature probe to measure the change in skin temperature caused by placing a cold pack or a heat pack on their arms. Relate this measurable change to the change in sensation. Students will learn about sensory receptors in skin on p. 662.

PREPARE

CONCEPT REVIEW

Activate Prior Knowledge

- Ask students to describe how oxygen reaches the cells of the body. *It is exchanged in the alveoli of the lungs and carried by the blood vessels.*
- Discuss how digested food reaches the cells of the body. *Nutrients are absorbed by villi in the intestines and carried by the blood vessels.*

TAKING NOTES

Main Idea and Detail Notes

Remind students that the blue headings in the text should be the main ideas in their graphic organizers. Students can find details in the text as well as in the visuals. Encourage students to compare their notes.

Vocabulary Strategy

The frame game diagrams help students organize facts, descriptions, words, and pictures in a systematic manner. The diagrams can be useful study devices when students look back over their notes.

Students can turn a diagram into a game by leaving the center space blank and asking other students to guess at what the frame is holding.

Vocabulary and Note-Taking Resources

- Vocabulary Practice, pp. 163–164
- Decoding Support, p. 165

- Daily Vocabulary Scaffolding, p. T18
- Note-Taking Model, p. T19

- Frame Game, B26–27
- Main Idea and Detail Notes, C37
- Daily Vocabulary Scaffolding, H1–8

CHAPTER 19

Getting Ready to Learn

CONCEPT REVIEW

- The body's systems interact.
- The body's systems work to maintain internal conditions.
- The digestive system breaks down food.
- The respiratory system gets oxygen and removes carbon dioxide.

VOCABULARY REVIEW

organ p. 587
organ system p. 588
homeostasis p. 588
nutrient p. 621

CLASSZONE.COM
Review concepts and vocabulary.

TAKING NOTES

MAIN IDEA AND DETAIL NOTES

Make a two-column chart. Write the main ideas, such as those in the blue headings, in the column on the left. Write details about each of those main heads in the column on the right.

VOCABULARY STRATEGY

Write each new vocabulary term in the center of a **frame game** diagram. Decide what information to frame it with. Use examples, descriptions, parts, sentences that use the term in context, or pictures. You can change the frame to fit each term.

See the Note-Taking Handbook on pages R45–R51.

SCIENCE NOTEBOOK

MAIN IDEAS	DETAIL NOTES
1. The circulatory system works with other body systems.	1. Transports materials from digestive and respiratory systems to cells 2. Blood is fluid that carries materials and wastes 3. Blood is always moving through the body 4. Blood delivers oxygen and takes away carbon dioxide

carries material to cells
moves continuously through body
BLOOD
carries waste away from cells
circulatory system

640 Unit 5: Human Biology

CHECK READINESS

Administer the Diagnostic Test to determine students' readiness for new science content and their mastery of requisite math skills.

 Diagnostic Test, pp. 39–40

Technology Resources

Students needing content and math skills should visit **ClassZone.com**.

- CONTENT REVIEW
- MATH TUTORIAL

 CONTENT REVIEW CD-ROM

KEY CONCEPT

The circulatory system transports materials.

BEFORE, you learned
- The urinary system removes waste
- The kidneys play a role in homeostasis

NOW, you will learn
- How different structures of the circulatory system work together
- About the structure and function of blood
- What blood pressure is and why it is important

VOCABULARY
circulatory system p. 641
blood p. 641
red blood cell p. 643
artery p. 645
vein p. 645
capillary p. 645

EXPLORE The Circulatory System

How fast does your heart beat?

PROCEDURE

1. Hold out your left hand with your palm facing up.
2. Place the first two fingers of your right hand on your left wrist below your thumb. Move your fingertips slightly until you can feel your pulse.
3. Use the stopwatch to determine how many times your heart beats in one minute.

MATERIALS
stopwatch

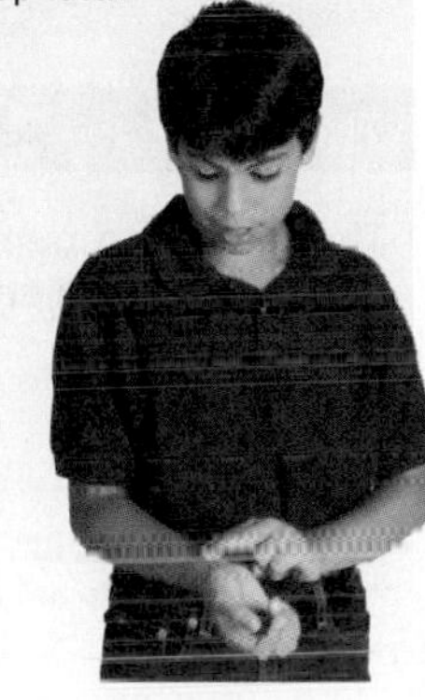

WHAT DO YOU THINK?
- How many times did your heart beat?
- What do you think you would find if you took your pulse after exercising?

The circulatory system works with other body systems.

VOCABULARY
Add a frame game diagram for the term *circulatory system* to your notebook.

You have read that the systems in your body provide materials and energy. The digestive system breaks down food and nutrients, and the respiratory system provides the oxygen that cells need to release energy. Another system, called the **circulatory system**, transports materials from the digestive and the respiratory systems to the cells.

Materials and wastes are carried in a fluid called **blood**. Blood moves continuously through the body, delivering oxygen and other materials to cells and removing carbon dioxide and other wastes from cells.

19.1 FOCUS

Set Learning Goals

Students will
- Describe how the different structures of the circulatory system work together.
- Describe blood's components and functions.
- Explain what blood pressure is and why it is important.
- Determine how heart rate is affected by exercise.

3-Minute Warm-Up

Display Transparency 20 or copy this exercise on the board:

Decide which of these statements are true. If not true, correct them.

1. Blood transports digested food particles to cells of the body. *true*
2. Kidneys filter urine and send it out of the body through the esophagus. *Kidneys filter blood and send urine out of the body through the urethra.*
3. The respiratory system is involved in the exhalation of oxygen from the lungs. *The respiratory system is involved in the exhalation of carbon dioxide from the lungs.*

 3-Minute Warm-Up, p. T20

19.1 MOTIVATE

EXPLORE The Circulatory System

PURPOSE To calculate heart rate

TIPS *10 min.* Remind students not to use their thumb while taking their pulse, since the thumb has its own strong pulse. Encourage students to try other pulse points, such as at a carotid artery in the neck.

WHAT DO YOU THINK? *Sample answer: 72. Pulse rate would increase after exercise.*

RESOURCES FOR DIFFERENTIATED INSTRUCTION

Below Level

UNIT RESOURCE BOOK
- Reading Study Guide A, pp. 131–132
- Decoding Support, p. 165

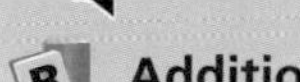 **Additional INVESTIGATION,** Listen to Your Heart, A, B, & C, pp. 177–185; Teacher Instructions, pp. 305–306

Advanced

UNIT RESOURCE BOOK
Challenge and Extension, p. 137

English Learners

UNIT RESOURCE BOOK
Spanish Reading Study Guide, pp. 135–136

- Audio Readings in Spanish
- Audio Readings (English)

19.1 INSTRUCT

Address Misconceptions

IDENTIFY Ask students to describe how the heart functions. They may understand that the heart is a pump but may omit that blood returns to the heart.

CORRECT Create a model of a heart with half of a pear. Refer to the heart illustration on p. 642. Scoop out the flesh to represent the four chambers. Use color-coded tubes to represent the main artery and vein. Explain how blood flows through the chambers of the heart and blood vessels.

REASSESS Where do the inflows come from? *from the lungs and from all other parts of the body*

Technology Resources

Visit **ClassZone.com** for background on common student misconceptions.

MISCONCEPTION DATABASE

Teach from Visuals

Explain that the cross section is a frontal view of the heart. What is on the heart's left is on the right side in the diagram. Ask:

- Which chambers contain oxygen-rich blood? *left atrium and ventricle*
- Why are the walls of the ventricles thicker than those of the atria? *ventricles: pumping chambers that pump blood; atria: filling chambers that simply receive blood*

EXPLORE (the BIG idea)

Revisit "Internet Activity: Heart Pumping" on p. 639.

Ongoing Assessment

Describe how the different structures of the circulatory system work together.

Ask: How do the heart and blood vessels provide the body with nutrients? *The heart pumps blood through blood vessels to all body parts.*

READING VISUALS *Answers: right side pumps blood to lungs; left side pumps blood to body*

Structures in the circulatory system function together.

RESOURCE CENTER
CLASSZONE.COM

Find out more about the circulatory system.

In order to provide the essential nutrients and other materials that your cells need, your blood must keep moving through your body. The circulatory system, which is made up of the heart and blood vessels, allows blood to flow to all parts of the body. The circulatory system works with other systems to provide the body with this continuous flow of life-giving blood. A

The Heart

The heart is the organ that pushes blood throughout the circulatory system. The human heart actually functions as two pumps—one pump on the right side and one on the left side. The right side of the heart pumps blood to the lungs to receive oxygen, and the left side pumps blood to the entire body. The lungs receive oxygen when you inhale and remove carbon dioxide when you exhale. Inside the lungs, the respiratory system interacts with the circulatory system.

The Heart

The heart is a pump moving blood throughout the entire body.

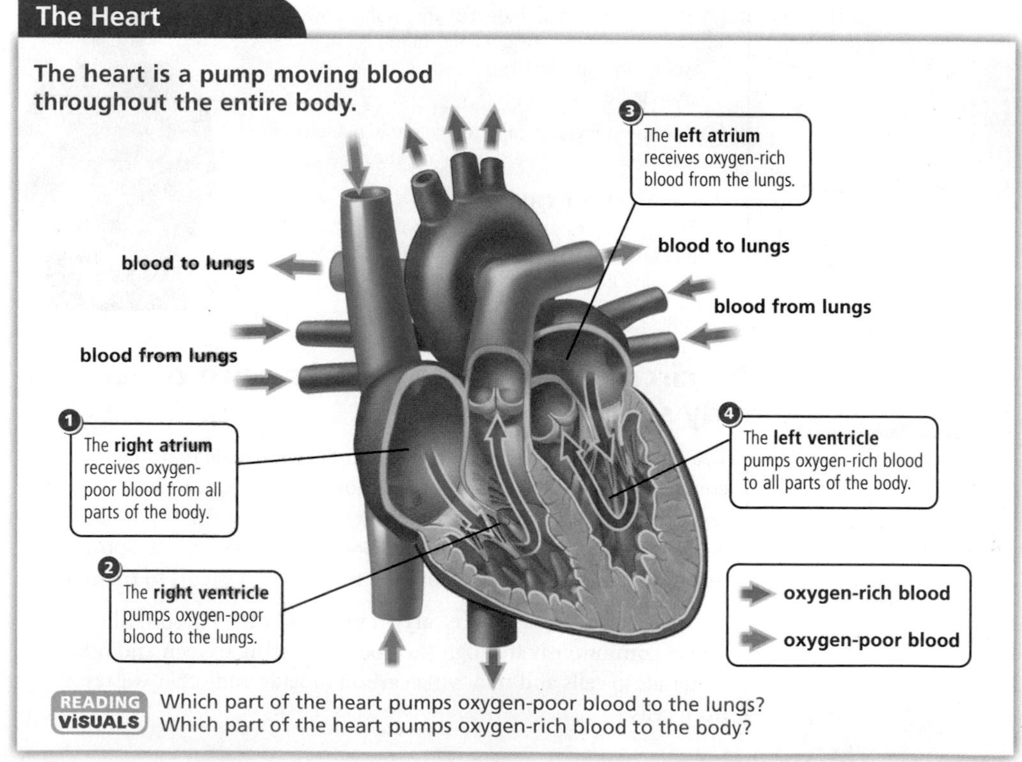

READING VISUALS Which part of the heart pumps oxygen-poor blood to the lungs? Which part of the heart pumps oxygen-rich blood to the body?

642 Unit 5: **Human Biology**

DIFFERENTIATE INSTRUCTION

More Reading Support

A The heart and what other structures make up the circulatory system? *blood vessels*

B To which organs does the right side of the heart pump blood? *the lungs*

English Learners This section of the chapter contains a variety of introductory clauses and phrases. Have students find the commas that separate them from the rest of the sentences. Then help them locate the subject of each sentence. Example: "In order to provide the essential nutrients and other materials that your cells need," p. 642. The subject, "blood," follows the clause.

Each side of the heart is divided into two areas called chambers. Oxygen-poor blood, which is blood from the body with less oxygen, flows to the right side of your heart, into a filling chamber called the right atrium. With each heartbeat, blood flows from the right atrium into a pumping chamber, the right ventricle, and then into the lungs. There the blood releases carbon dioxide waste and absorbs oxygen.

After picking up oxygen, blood is pushed back to the heart, filling another chamber, which is called the left atrium. Blood moves from the left atrium to the left ventricle, a pumping chamber, and again begins its trip out to the rest of the body. Both oxygen-poor blood and oxygen-rich blood are red. However, oxygen-rich blood is a much brighter and lighter shade of red than is oxygen-poor blood. The diagram on page 642 shows oxygen-poor blood in blue, so that you can tell where in the circulatory system oxygen-poor and oxygen-rich blood are found.

CHECK YOUR READING Summarize the way blood moves through the heart. Remember, a summary contains only the most important information.

Blood

The oxygen that your cells need in order to release energy must be present in blood to travel through your body. Blood is a tissue made up of plasma, red blood cells, white blood cells, and platelets. About 60 percent of blood is plasma, a fluid that contains proteins, glucose, hormones, gases, and other substances dissolved in water. C

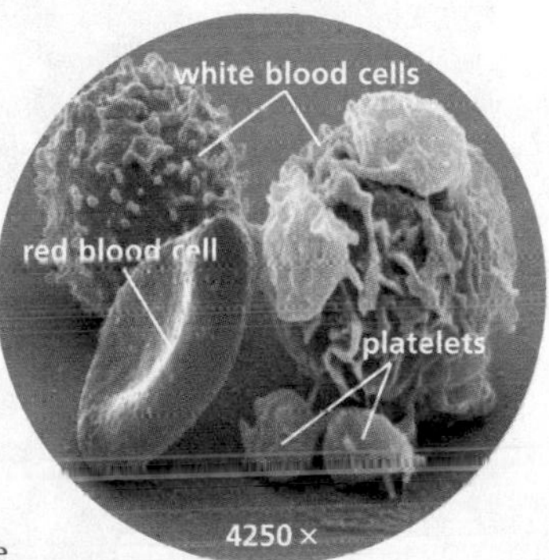

Blood is made mostly of plasma, which transports red blood cells, white blood cells, and platelets.

White blood cells help your body fight infection by attacking disease-causing organisms. **Red blood cells** are more numerous than white blood cells and have a different function. They pick up oxygen in the lungs and transport it throughout the body. As red blood cells travel through the circulatory system, they deliver oxygen to other cells. D

Platelets are large cell fragments that help form blood clots when a blood vessel is injured. You know what a blood clot is if you've observed a cut or a scrape. The scab that forms around a cut or scrape is made of clotted blood. After an injury such as a cut, platelets nearby begin to enlarge and become sticky. They stick to the injured area of the blood vessels and release chemicals that result in blood clotting. Blood clotting keeps blood vessels from losing too much blood.

CHECK YOUR READING What are the four components that make up blood?

Address Misconceptions

IDENTIFY Ask students how oxygen gets to the heart and other parts of the body. Students may hold the misconception that a separate system of tubes carries air to the heart and other body structures.

CORRECT Ask students to study the diagram of the heart on p. 642 and make a flow chart to show how oxygen is transported from the lungs to the heart and from the heart to other parts of the body.

REASSESS Ask: Where does the oxygen in "oxygen-rich blood" come from? *It is breathed into the lungs and enters the bloodstream there.*

Technology Resources

Visit **ClassZone.com** for background on common student misconceptions.

MISCONCEPTION DATABASE

Teach Difficult Concepts

Students may think that blood is simply a liquid as opposed to a tissue containing cells. Ask students to describe the four components of blood. Explain that blood is a fluid tissue, a group of cells working together to perform a function.

Ongoing Assessment

Describe blood's components and functions.

Ask: Why are platelets important? *Platelets cause blood clotting and prevent blood from being lost at a cut.*

CHECK YOUR READING *Sample answer: Oxygen-poor blood flows from the body to the right atrium of the heart. The heart pumps it into the right ventricle, then into the lungs, where it releases CO_2 and picks up O_2. Then the blood flows into the left atrium of the heart and is pumped to the left ventricle. From there it is sent out to the body, and the cycle repeats.*

CHECK YOUR READING *Answer: Blood is made of plasma, red blood cells, white blood cells, and platelets.*

DIFFERENTIATE INSTRUCTION

More Reading Support

C What term refers to the fluid part of blood? *plasma*

D Which cells carry oxygen to other cells of the body? *red blood cells*

Advanced Invite students to create a poster of the different ways to keep the heart healthy. They should include items such as the right foods to eat, the role of exercise in strengthening and improving heart function, and unhealthy behaviors, such as smoking, drug use, and excessive drinking.

 Challenge and Extension, p. 137

Teach from Visuals

To help students interpret the diagram of the circulatory system, ask: What organ pumps blood throughout the entire body? *the heart*

Point out that the left side of the diagram represents the right side of the person shown, who is depicted facing the reader.

History of Science

An artificial heart-lung machine powers blood circulation and oxygenates blood outside a patient's body. The first successful open-heart surgery using such a device was performed in 1953 by the American surgeon Dr. John H. Gibbon, Jr. In 1967 Dr. Christiaan Barnard, a South African surgeon, led a team of 20 surgeons in the first successful heart transplant. The patient, Louis Washkansky, died 18 days later from complications of double pneumonia and immune-suppressant drugs.

Metacognitive Strategy

Have students devise memory strategies or mnemonic devices to remember what happens to the blood as it flows through the heart and lungs to the rest of the body. For example, they might equate "vent" in *ventricle* with *sent* to remember that blood flows out from those chambers and equate "ate" in *atrium* with *gate* to think of going in. Similarly, they can relate *vein* to *vain* to recall "poor" and relate *artery* to *barter* to recall "rich" or perhaps to a highway to recall "traffic."

Mathematics Connection

Have students take their pulse by holding two fingers at the base of the inside of the wrist or just below the jawbone on the neck. Students can compile data on classmates' heartbeats per minute and display the data in a bar graph. Challenge students to find how many times the heart beats in one day, in one month, in one year, and in an average lifetime.

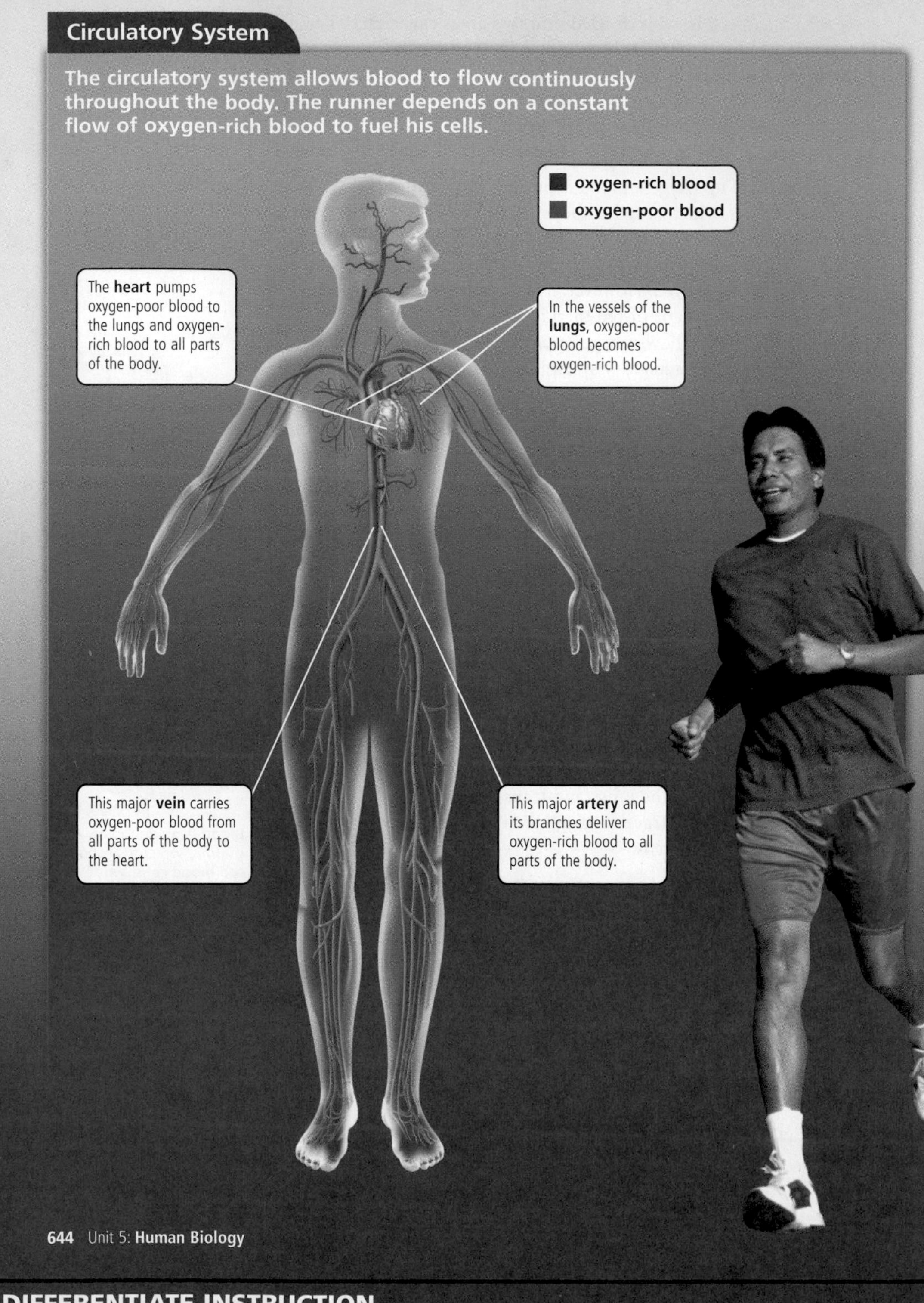

DIFFERENTIATE INSTRUCTION

English Learners Encourage students whose knowledge of English is limited to use the visual in a focused, interactive way. Give them tracing paper to trace the overall path of the circulatory system, using red and blue pencils or markers. Have them label the heart, the lungs, a vein, and an artery and make a key indicating the meanings of red and blue.

As blood travels through blood vessels, some fluid is lost. This fluid, called lymph, is collected in lymph vessels and returned to veins and arteries. As you will read in the next section, lymph and lymph vessels are associated with your immune system. Sometimes scientists refer to the lymph and lymph vessels as the lymphatic system. The lymphatic system helps you fight disease.

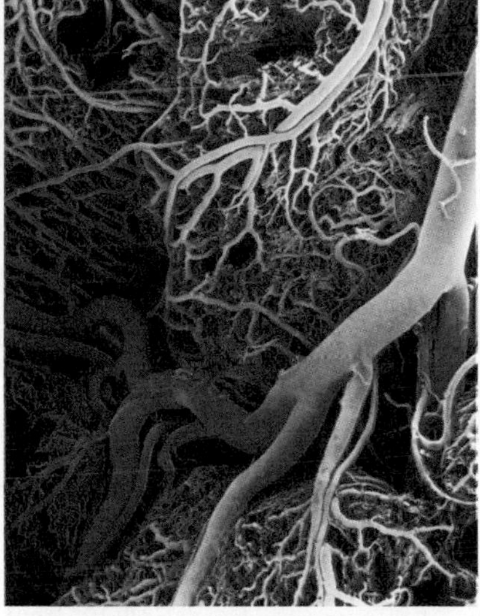
Arteries, capillaries, and veins form a complex web to carry blood to all the cells in the body (30×).

Blood Vessels

Blood moves through a network of structures called blood vessels. Blood vessels are tube-shaped structures that are similar to flexible drinking straws. The structure of blood vessels suits them for particular functions. **Arteries**, which are the vessels that take blood away from the heart, have strong walls. An artery wall is thick and elastic and can handle the tremendous force produced when the heart pumps. **Veins** are blood vessels that carry blood back to the heart. The walls of veins are thinner than those of arteries. However, veins are generally of greater diameter than are arteries.

E Most arteries carry oxygen-rich blood away from the heart, and most veins carry oxygen-poor blood back to the heart. However, the pulmonary blood vessels are exceptions. Oxygen-poor blood travels through the two pulmonary arteries, one of which goes to each lung. The two pulmonary veins carry oxygen-rich blood from the lungs to the heart.

F Veins and arteries branch off into very narrow blood vessels called capillaries. **Capillaries** connect arteries with veins. Through capillaries materials are exchanged between blood and tissues. Oxygen and materials from nutrients move from the blood in the arteries to the body's tissues through tiny openings in the capillary walls. Waste materials and carbon dioxide move from the tissues' cells through the capillary walls and into the blood in the veins.

CHECK YOUR READING Compare and contrast arteries, veins, and capillaries.

Blood exerts pressure on blood vessels.

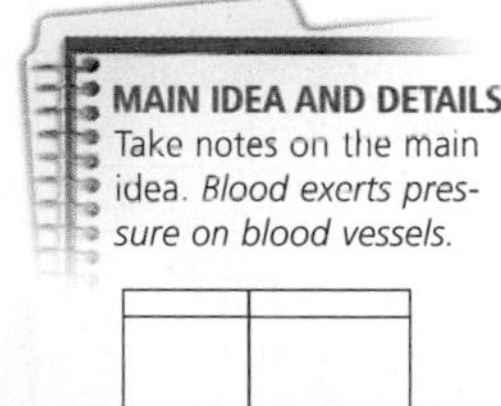
MAIN IDEA AND DETAILS Take notes on the main idea. *Blood exerts pressure on blood vessels.*

As you have read, the contractions of the heart push blood through blood vessels. The force produced when the heart contracts travels through the blood, putting pressure on the blood vessels. This force is called blood pressure. Compare a vessel to a plastic bag filled with water.

Teacher Demo

Ask each student to hold one hand above their head and one hand down by their side for about one minute. Have them compare the two hands. The fingertips of the hand held down will be redder, indicating that blood flowed down. The blood flowed out of the hand held above their head.

Teach Difficult Concepts

To help students understand the difference between arteries and veins, ask:

- How do you know that the blood in most arteries is oxygen-rich? *All arteries carry blood away from the heart. Most of the blood traveling away from the heart is carrying oxygen to the rest of the body.*
- How do you know that the blood in most veins is oxygen-poor? *All veins carry blood toward the heart. Most of the blood traveling toward the heart is coming from the rest of the body, where it has become oxygen-poor.*

Ongoing Assessment

CHECK YOUR READING *Answer: Arteries have strong walls and take blood away from the heart. Veins are blood vessels that carry blood back to the heart. They have thinner walls than arteries. Capillaries connect arteries and veins.*

DIFFERENTIATE INSTRUCTION

More Reading Support

E Which vessels carry blood from the heart to the lungs? *pulmonary arteries*

F In which vessels does exchange take place? *capillaries*

Below Level Have students make flow charts to show the flow of blood through the body. They should include the words *arteries, veins,* and *capillaries* in their diagrams. Once you have reviewed the diagrams for accuracy, have students add the flow of blood to and from the lungs through the pulmonary arteries and veins.

Additional Investigation To reinforce Section 19.1 learning goals, use the following full-period investigation:

R Additional Investigation, Listen to Your Heart, A, B, & C, pp. 177–185, pp. 305–306

EXPLORE the BIG idea

Revisit "Blood Pressure" on p. 639. Ask: How does this activity illustrate blood pressure? *The force against the balloon is like the pressure of blood against the walls of arteries, veins, and capillaries.*

Teach from Visuals

To help students interpret the diagram of blood pressure, ask: Would you expect blood pressure to be higher in arteries or in veins? Explain. *Arteries, because the blood is being pumped by the heart through the arteries. Arteries are closest to the impact of the pump.*

Teach Difficult Concepts

Some students may not understand the difference between pulse rate and blood pressure. Explain that pulse rate is a measure of the frequency of heartbeats, whereas blood pressure is a measure of the pressure that is exerted on the arteries and veins by the pumping action of the heart.

Health Connection

High blood pressure, or hypertension, is a serious condition that affects about one in four adults. It causes stroke and heart and kidney failure. In most cases, the cause of high blood pressure is unknown. However, there are many life choices to help reduce the risk:

- Have blood pressure checked regularly.
- Avoid excessive salt intake.
- Eat a healthy, low-fat diet.
- Exercise regularly.
- Reduce emotional stress; learn stress-reduction techniques.

Ongoing Assessment

Explain what blood pressure is and why is it important.

Ask: Why would a person with high blood pressure have certain health risks? *High blood pressure causes strain on the arteries and veins and can weaken them or cause the heart to work harder than it should.*

If you push down at the center of the bag, you can see the water push out against the sides of the bag.

G The heart pushes blood in a similar way, exerting pressure on the arteries, veins, and capillaries in the circulatory system. It is important to maintain healthy blood pressure so that materials in blood get to all parts of your body. If blood pressure is too low, some of the cells will not get oxygen and other materials. On the other hand, if blood pressure is too high, the force may weaken the blood vessels and require the heart to work harder to push blood through the blood vessels. High blood pressure is a serious medical condition, but it can be treated.

The circulatory system can be considered as two smaller systems: one, the pulmonary system, moves blood to the lungs; the other, the systemic system, moves blood to the rest of the body. Blood pressure is measured in the systemic part of the circulatory system.

You can think of blood pressure as the pressure that blood exerts on the walls of your arteries at all times. Health professionals measure blood pressure indirectly with a device called a sphygmomanometer (SFIHG-moh-muh-NAHM-ih-tuhr).

Blood pressure is expressed with two numbers—one number over another number. The first number refers to the pressure in the arteries when the heart contracts. The second number refers to the pressure in the arteries when the heart relaxes and receives blood from the veins.

Blood Pressure

Blood pressure allows materials to travel to all parts of your body.

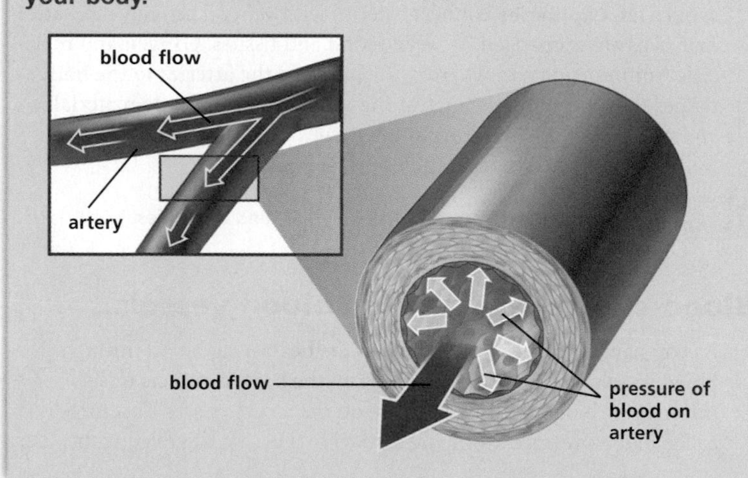

DIFFERENTIATE INSTRUCTION

More Reading Support

G What might happen if a person's blood pressure is too low? *Some cells will not get oxygen or other materials.*

English Learners English learners may be familiar with the *If . . . then* sentence construction. But oftentimes *then* is omitted from a sentence, and cause and effect are to be inferred. Help students recognize *If . . . then* sentences that do not contain *then.* Here are two examples from page 646:

"If you push down at the center of the bag, you can see the water push against the sides."

"If blood pressure is too low, some of the cells will not get oxygen and other materials."

There are four different blood types.

Each red blood cell has special proteins on its surface. One group of surface proteins determines blood type. There are two blood-type proteins, A and B. A person whose blood cells have the A proteins has type A blood. One with cells having B proteins has type B blood. Some people have both proteins—type AB blood. Other people have neither protein, a type of blood referred to as type O.

Maybe you, or someone you know, has had a blood transfusion, a procedure in which one person receives blood donated by another. Knowing blood type is important for transfusions. As you will learn in the next section, the body has structures that protect it from unknown substances. They are part of an immune system that recognizes and protects cells and molecules that are "self" from those that are unrecognized, or "nonself." The body attacks unrecognized substances, including those in donated blood.

The blood used for transfusions is usually the same type as the blood type of the receiver, but sometimes other blood types are used. The diagram shows which blood types are compatible. Because the cells in type O blood have neither protein, the immune system of someone with A, B, or AB blood will not attack O blood cells. A person with type O blood, however, cannot receive any other blood type because that person's immune system would attack A or B surface proteins.

CHECK YOUR READING Why is it important to know your blood type?

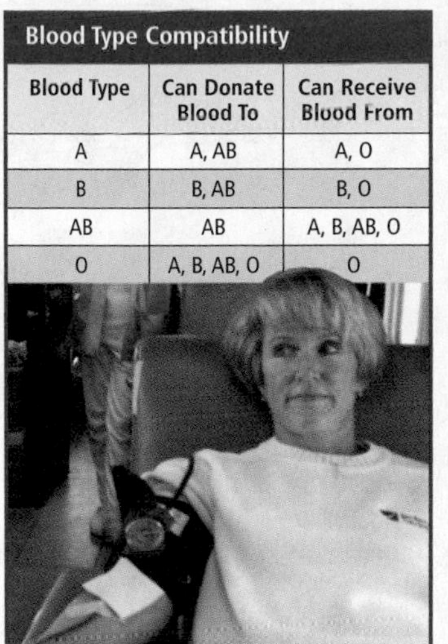

Blood Type Compatibility

Blood Type	Can Donate Blood To	Can Receive Blood From
A	A, AB	A, O
B	B, AB	B, O
AB	AB	A, B, AB, O
O	A, B, AB, O	O

People can donate blood to others.

Learn more about blood types.

19.1 Review

KEY CONCEPTS

1. What are the functions of the two sides of the heart?
2. What is the primary function of red blood cells?
3. Why can both high and low blood pressure be a problem?

CRITICAL THINKING

4. **Apply** List three examples of the circulatory system working with another system in your body.
5. **Compare and Contrast** Explain why blood pressure is expressed with two numbers.

CHALLENGE

6. **Identify Cause and Effect** You can feel the speed at which your heart is pumping by pressing two fingers to the inside of your wrist. This is your pulse. If you run for a few minutes, your pulse rate is faster for a little while, then it slows down again. Why did your pulse rate speed up and slow down?

ANSWERS

1. right side: pumps oxygen-poor blood to the lungs; left side: pumps oxygen-rich blood to the body

2. to carry oxygen to other cells in the body

3. too high: blood vessels can be weakened; too low: some cells won't get oxygen

4. Sample answer: Circulatory system works with muscular system (exercise), with respiratory system (breathing), and with digestive system (eating).

5. first number: pressure in the arteries when the heart contracts; second number: pressure in the arteries when the heart relaxes

6. The pulse rate sped up and slowed down because the body uses more energy when running. To produce extra energy, the body needs more oxygen, so the heart pumps faster to push more blood. Once the body stops running, the extra energy is not needed, and the pumping slows down.

Ongoing Assessment

CHECK YOUR READING *Answer: A person receiving blood may die if the blood is of a type not compatible with his or her own.*

Reinforce the BIG idea

Have students relate the section to the Big Idea.

Reinforcing Key Concepts, p. 138

19.1 ASSESS & RETEACH

Assess

Section 19.1 Quiz, p. 41

Reteach

Put a 4-column chart on the board for the four parts of blood; red blood cells, white blood cells, plasma, and platelets. Have students brainstorm a list of words associated with each, such as *oxygen* for red blood cells, *fluid* for plasma, and *scab* for platelets.

Then ask students to write comic strips about a day in the life of a blood cell. Students' comic strips should show the journey of the blood cell from the heart to the lungs and other parts of the body. They should name the type of cell and the fluid it travels in. Encourage them to have other characters in the comics. They should refer to diagrams in Section 19.1 and may trace them if they find doing so helpful.

Technology Resources

Have students visit **ClassZone.com** for reteaching of Key Concepts.

CONTENT REVIEW

CONTENT REVIEW CD-ROM

CHAPTER INVESTIGATION

Focus

PURPOSE To determine how heart rate is affected by exercise

OVERVIEW In this investigation, students will

- calculate resting, maximum, and target heart rates
- create and analyze graphs of heart rates during and after exercise
- determine a cause of exercise's effect on the heart

Lab Preparation

- Ask volunteers to demonstrate correct use of the stopwatch.
- Inquire about health exemptions for the exercise part of the activity.
- Prior to the investigation have students read through the investigation and prepare their data tables. Or copy and distribute datasheets and rubrics.

 UNIT RESOURCE BOOK, pp. 168–176

 SCIENCE TOOLKIT, F15

Lab Management

- Have students work in pairs. One partner records data, the other exercises.
- If students are able to find their pulse quickly, they can count beats for 15 seconds and multiply by four.

SAFETY Caution students not to exercise beyond their target rate. If students have difficulty breathing, chest discomfort, or feelings of dizziness, they should stop exercising.

INCLUSION Prepare blank graphs for students in advance. The graphs should be titled "Heart Rate During and After Exercise;" the *x*-axis should be labeled "Time" and the *y*-axis labeled "Heart rate (beats per minute)."

INCLUSION Students with mobility limitations can time and/or record data. They may perform modified or assisted exercise.

CHAPTER INVESTIGATION

Heart Rate and Exercise

OVERVIEW AND PURPOSE In this activity, you will calculate your resting, maximum, and target heart rates. Then you will examine the effect of exercise on heart rate. Before you begin, read through the entire investigation.

MATERIALS
- notebook
- stopwatch
- calculator
- graph paper

Procedure

1. Make a data table like the one shown on the sample notebook page.

2. Measure your resting heart rate. Find the pulse in the artery of your neck, just below and in front of the bottom of your ear, with the first two fingers of one hand. Do not use your thumb to measure pulse since the thumb has a pulse of its own. Once you have found the pulse, count the beats for 30 seconds and multiply the result by 2. The number you get is your resting heart rate in beats per minute. Record this number in your notebook.

3. Calculate your maximum heart rate by subtracting your age from 220. Record this number in your notebook. Your target heart rate should be 60 to 75 percent of your maximum heart rate. Calculate and record this range in your notebook.

4. Someone who is very athletic or has been exercising regularly for 6 months or more can safely exercise up to 85 percent of his or her maximum heart rate. Calculate and record this rate in your notebook.

5. Observe how quickly you reach your target heart rate during exercise. Begin by running in place at an intensity that makes you breathe harder but does not make you breathless. As with any exercise, remember that if you experience difficulty breathing, dizziness, or chest discomfort, stop exercising immediately.

INVESTIGATION RESOURCES

 CHAPTER INVESTIGATION, Heart Rate and Exercise
- Level A, pp. 168–171
- Level B, pp. 172–175
- Level C, p. 176

Advanced students should complete Levels B & C.

 Writing a Lab Report, D12–13

Technology Resources

Customize this student lab as needed or look for an alternative. Print rubrics to assess student lab reports.

 **Lab Generator CD-ROM**

6 Every 2 minutes, measure your heart rate for 10 seconds. Multiply this number by 6 to find your heart rate in beats per minute and record it in your notebook. Try to exercise for a total of 10 minutes. After you stop exercising, continue recording your heart rate every 2 minutes until it returns to the resting rate you measured in step 2.

Observe and Analyze

Write It Up

1. **GRAPH DATA** Make a line graph of your heart rate during and after the exercise. Graph the values in beats per minute versus time in minutes. Your graph should start at your resting heart rate and continue until your heart rate has returned to its resting rate. Using a colored pencil, shade in the area that represents your target heart-rate range.
2. **ANALYZE DATA** How many minutes of exercising were needed for you to reach your target heart rate of 60 to 75 percent of maximum? Did your heart rate go over your target range?
3. **INTERPRET DATA** How many minutes after you stopped exercising did it take for your heart rate to return to its resting rate? Why do you think your heart rate did not return to its resting rate immediately after you stopped exercising?

Conclude

1. **INFER** Why do you think that heart rate increases during exercise?
2. **IDENTIFY** What other body systems are affected when the heart rate increases?
3. **PREDICT** Why do you think that target heart rate changes with age?
4. **CLASSIFY** Create a table comparing the intensity of different types of exercise, such as walking, skating, bicycling, weight lifting, and any others you might enjoy.

INVESTIGATE Further

CHALLENGE Determine how other exercises affect your heart rate. Repeat this investigation by performing one or two of the other exercises from your table. Present your data, with a graph, to the class.

Heart Rate and Exercise

Resting heart rate:

Maximum heart rate:

Target heart rate (60–75% of maximum):

Target heart rate (85% of maximum):

Table 1. Heart Rate During and After Exercise

Time (minutes)	0	2	4	6	8	10	12	14	16	18	20
Heart rate (beats per minute)											

Observe and Analyze

1. *Graphs will vary but should show an increase in heart rate during exercise and a return to normal when exercise stops. Target heart-rate range should be similar for all students.*
2. *Answers will vary. Heart rate should reach the target range within 5 minutes. Students should try not to exercise above their target heart rate.*
3. *Answers will vary. Heart rate should return to resting rate within 10 minutes after exercise stops. Heart rate remains elevated for a few minutes after exercise stops because it takes time for the body to restore homeostasis.*

Conclude

1. *Heart rate increases during exercise to pump more oxygen-rich blood to the body cells. The body cells use oxygen at a higher rate during exercise to produce energy.*
2. *The respiratory system is also affected when the heart rate increases, because the breathing rate also increases. The nervous system increases the secretions of sweat glands to get rid of excess heat.*
3. *The heart's ability to pump blood and deliver oxygen decreases as it ages.*
4. *Tables will vary. Exercises such as bicycling are more intense than exercises such as walking or weightlifting.*

INVESTIGATE Further

CHALLENGE Graphs will vary. Exercises of higher intensity will cause the heart to reach its target rate faster than exercises of lower intensity. After higher-intensity exercises, the heart will also take longer to return to its resting rate than it will after lower intensity exercises.

Post-Lab Discussion

- Discuss the connection between heart rate and blood pressure. When heart rate increases, so does blood pressure. Well-conditioned athletes have low resting pulses, and therefore low blood pressure.
- Discuss the health risks of high blood pressure. Point out that proper diet, avoidance of alcohol and tobacco, and exercise can help keep blood pressure at a normal level.

Teaching with Technology

If probeware for monitoring heart rate is available, have students use it to record their heart rates before and after mild exercise. Make sure students do not have any health or heart conditions before allowing them to participate in the activity. They can use a graphing calculator to show the data visually.

19.2 FOCUS

Set Learning Goals

Students will

- Describe how foreign material enters the body.
- Explain how the immune system responds to foreign material.
- Describe ways that the body can become immune to disease.
- Make models to show how antibodies stop pathogens from spreading.

3-Minute Warm-Up

Display Transparency 20 or copy this exercise on the board:

Match the definitions to the correct terms.

Definitions

1. blood cells that carry oxygen *d*
2. blood vessels that carry blood to the heart *e*
3. system for obtaining oxygen *f*

Terms

a. white blood cells	d. red blood cells
b. arteries	e. veins
c. systemic	f. respiratory

 3-Minute Warm-Up, p. T20

19.2 MOTIVATE

EXPLORE Membranes

PURPOSE To understand how the body keeps out foreign particles

TIP *15 min.* Have students start by predicting what will happen. Warn students to use caution handling pins. Provide a pin cushion if possible.

WHAT DO YOU THINK? *When the bag has even a small puncture, it cannot protect the cloth, and the cloth is stained.*

Ongoing Assessment

CHECK YOUR READING *Answer: The integumentary, respiratory, and digestive systems are the first line of defense against pathogens.*

KEY CONCEPT

19.2 The immune system defends the body.

BEFORE, you learned

- The circulatory system works with other systems to fuel the body cells
- Structures in the circulatory system work together
- Blood pressure allows materials to reach all parts of the body

NOW, you will learn

- How foreign material enters the body
- How the immune system responds to foreign material
- Ways that the body can become immune to a disease

VOCABULARY

pathogen p. 650
immune system p. 651
antibody p. 651
antigen p. 654
immunity p. 656
vaccine p. 656
antibiotic p. 657

EXPLORE Membranes

How does the body keep foreign particles out?

PROCEDURE

1. Place a white cloth into a sandwich bag and seal it. Fill a bowl with water and stir in several drops of food coloring.
2. Submerge the sandwich bag in the water. After five minutes, remove the bag and note the condition of the cloth.
3. Puncture the bag with a pin. Put the bag back in the water for five minutes. Remove the bag and note the condition of the cloth.

MATERIALS

- white cloth
- zippered sandwich bag
- large bowl
- water
- food coloring
- small pin

WHAT DO YOU THINK?

- How does a puncture in the bag affect its ability to protect the cloth?

Many systems defend the body from harmful materials.

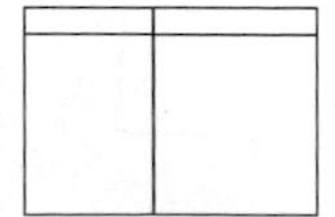

MAIN IDEA AND DETAILS Add the main idea *Many systems defend the body from harmful materials* to your chart along with detail notes.

You might not realize it, but you come into contact with harmful substances constantly. Because your body has ways to defend itself, you don't even notice. One of the body's best defenses is to keep foreign materials from entering in the first place. The integumentary (ihn-TEHG-yu-MEHN-tuh-ree), respiratory, and digestive systems are the first line of defense against **pathogens,** or disease-causing agents. Pathogens can enter through your skin, the air you breathe, and even the food you eat or liquids you drink.

 CHECK YOUR READING Which systems are your first line of defense against pathogens?

RESOURCES FOR DIFFERENTIATED INSTRUCTION

Below Level

UNIT RESOURCE BOOK

- Reading Study Guide A, pp. 141–142
- Decoding Support, p. 165

AUDIO CDS

Advanced

UNIT RESOURCE BOOK

Challenge and Extension, p. 147

English Learners

UNIT RESOURCE BOOK

Spanish Reading Study Guide, pp. 145–146

- Audio Readings in Spanish
- Audio Readings (English)

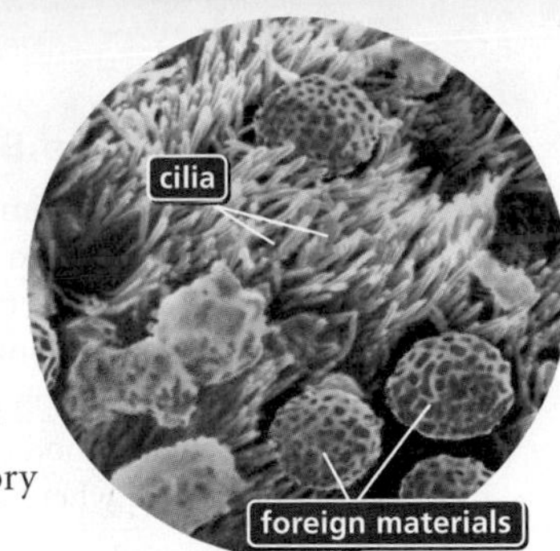

Cilia are hairlike protrusions that trap materials entering your respiratory system (600 ×).

Integumentary System Defenses Most of the time, your skin functions as a barrier between you and the outside world. The physical barrier the skin forms is just one obstacle for pathogens and other foreign materials. The growth of pathogens on your eyes can be slowed by substances contained in tears. The millions of bacteria cells that live on the skin can also kill pathogens. A common way pathogens can enter the body is through a cut. The circulatory system is then able to help defend the body because blood contains cells that respond to foreign materials.

Respiratory System Defenses Sneezing and coughing are two ways the respiratory system defends the body from harmful substances. Cilia and mucus also protect the body. Cilia are tiny, hairlike protrusions in the nose and the lungs that trap dust particles present in the air. Mucus is a thick and slippery substance found in the nose, throat, and lungs. Like the cilia, mucus traps dirt and other particles. Mucus contains substances similar to those in tears that can slow the growth of pathogens.

Digestive System Defenses Some foreign materials manage to enter your digestive system, but many are destroyed by saliva, mucus, enzymes, and stomach acids. Saliva in your mouth helps kill bacteria. Mucus protects the digestive organs by coating them. Pathogens can also be destroyed by enzymes produced in the liver and pancreas or by the acids in the stomach.

The immune system has response structures.

Sometimes foreign materials manage to get past the first line of defense. When this happens, the body relies on the **immune system** to respond. This system functions in several ways:

- Tissues in the bone marrow, the thymus gland, the spleen, and the lymph nodes produce white blood cells, which are specialized cells that function to destroy foreign organisms.
- Some white blood cells produce a nonspecific response to injury or infection.
- Some white blood cells produce proteins called **antibodies,** which are part of a specific immune response to foreign materials.

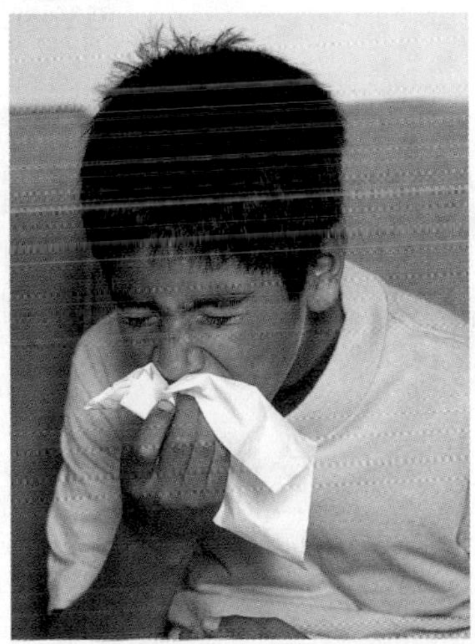
Sneezing helps to expel foreign substances from the body.

19.2 INSTRUCT

Address Misconceptions

IDENTIFY Ask students to describe what causes illness. Some students might hold the misconception that all illnesses are caused by germs and that germs enter through the mouth during eating.

CORRECT Have students make a graphic organizer that shows the body's first line of defense. Students should note the various ways that foreign materials can enter the body.

REASSESS Ask students to extend the diagram to show possible effects of materials such as irritants, bacteria, viruses, and parasites entering the body through each system.

Technology Resources

Visit **ClassZone.com** for background on common student misconceptions.

MISCONCEPTION DATABASE

Teacher Demo

Demonstrate the presence of bacteria on a person's skin. Have a volunteer run his or her fingers across agar in a petri dish. Cover and seal the dish, and place it in a warm place for several days. Students should note that bacteria from the student's hand has grown on the agar. Ask: How does the skin protect the body from these bacteria? *The skin is a protective barrier that prevents bacteria from entering the body.*

Note: This demo is presented as a full-period investigation in Chapter 21.

Ongoing Assessment

Describe how foreign material enters the body.

Ask: How can foreign materials enter through the skin? *If there is a cut in the skin, pathogens may be able to enter the body through it.*

DIFFERENTIATE INSTRUCTION

More Reading Support

A What is the function of cilia? *Cilia trap foreign particles.*

B What proteins are produced by white blood cells? *antibodies*

English Learners English learners may be sensitive to the use of the term *foreign* with regard to human social situations. Point out that *foreign material* is a scientific and medical term and that *foreign* does not correctly describe people who travel or relocate from one country to another. In such a case *immigrant, visitor, guest,* or *newly arrived resident* is preferable and kinder.

Metacognitive Strategy

To help students understand the difference between the circulatory system and the lymphatic system, have them create a Venn diagram comparing and contrasting the two systems. Make sure that students understand that the lymphatic system, like the circulatory system, also contains a network of vessels but that it has no pump.

Teach Difficult Concepts

Some students may not understand the connection between the lymphatic and circulatory systems. The lymphatic system collects fluids that escape from the blood and returns them to the circulatory system. Relate these systems to other real-world systems that have main and secondary or supportive relationships, such as highway systems and computer networks.

Ongoing Assessment

CHECK YOUR READING *Answer: The lymphatic system transports white blood cells throughout the body, so that when they are needed in a part of the body, they are ready to attack.*

White Blood Cells

The immune system has specialized cells called white blood cells that recognize foreign materials in the body and respond. The number of white blood cells in the blood can increase during an immune response. These cells travel through the circulatory system and the lymphatic system to an injured or infected area of the body. White blood cells leave the blood vessels and travel into the damaged tissue, where the immune response takes place.

The Lymphatic System

Learn more about the lymphatic system.

The lymphatic system transports pathogen-fighting white blood cells throughout the body, much as the circulatory system does. The lymphatic system carries lymph, and the circulatory system carries blood. Both fluids transport similar materials, such as white blood cells.

Lymph is the fluid left in the tissues by the circulatory system. It moves through lymph vessels, which are similar to veins. However, the lymphatic system has no pump like the heart to move fluid. Lymph drifts through the lymph vessels when your skeletal muscles contract or when your body changes position. As it moves, it passes through lymph nodes, which filter out pathogens and store white blood cells and antibodies. Because lymph nodes filter out pathogens, infections are often fought in your lymph nodes, causing them to swell when you get sick.

CHECK YOUR READING How does the lymphatic system help the immune system?

The immune system responds to attack.

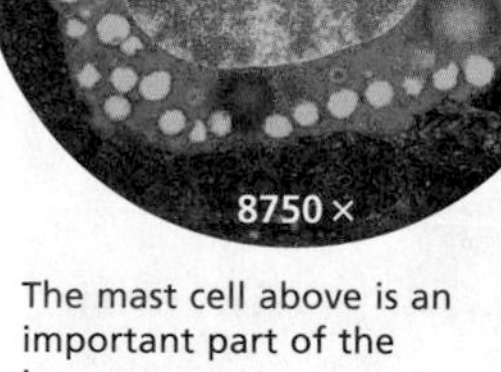

The mast cell above is an important part of the immune system.

Certain illnesses can cause symptoms such as coughing, sneezing, and fever. These symptoms make you uncomfortable when you are sick. But in fact, most symptoms are the result of the immune system's response to foreign materials in the body.

The immune system responds in two ways. The white blood cells that first respond to the site of injury or infection attack foreign materials in a nonspecific response. Some of these cells attack foreign materials and produce chemicals that help other white blood cells work better. The second part of the response is very specific to the types of pathogens invading the body. These white blood cells produce antibodies specific to each pathogen and provide your body with immunity.

DIFFERENTIATE INSTRUCTION

More Reading Support

C What fluid does the lymphatic system transport? *lymph*

D What causes lymph nodes to swell? *the fight against infection carried out in them*

English Learners Have students write the definitions of *pathogen, antibody, antigen, immunity,* and *vaccine* in their Science Word Dictionaries. In the section review on p. 657, students are asked to make two different charts in response to questions. Help English learners by showing them a model of a type of chart that might work for each question.

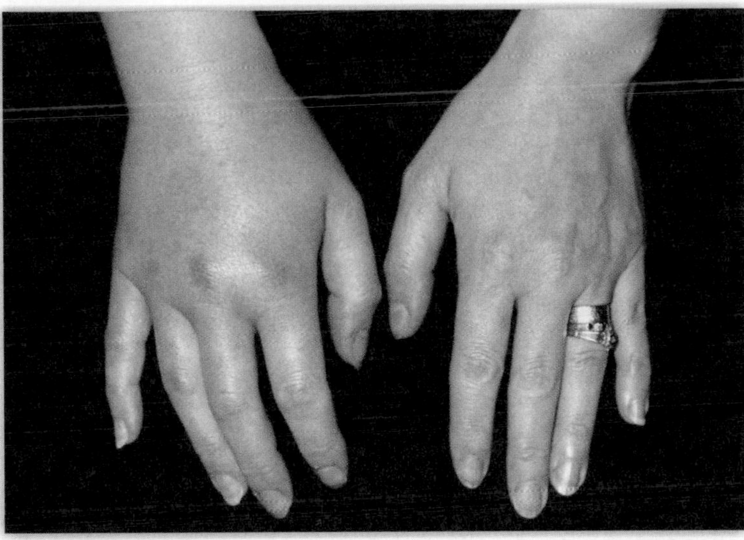

Wasp stings cause an immediate immune response. The area of the sting swells up and increases in temperature while your body battles the injury.

Nonspecific Response

 E

Swelling, redness, and heat are some of the symptoms that tell you that a cut or scrape has become infected by foreign materials. They are all signs of inflammation, your body's first defense reaction against injuries and infections.

F

When tissue becomes irritated or damaged, it releases large amounts of histamine (HIHS-tuh-meen). Histamine raises the temperature of the tissues and increases blood flow to the area. Increased blood flow, which makes the injured area appear red, allows antibodies and white blood cells to arrive more quickly for battle. Higher temperatures improve the speed and power of white blood cells. Some pathogens cannot tolerate heat, so they grow weaker. The swelling caused by the production of histamine can be a small price to pay for this chemical's important work.

When a foreign material affects more than one area of your body, many tissues produce histamine. As a result, the temperature of your whole body rises. Any temperature above 37 degrees Celsius (98.6°F) is considered a fever, but only temperatures hot enough to damage tissues are dangerous. Trying to lower a high fever with medication is advisable in order to avoid tissue damage. When you have a small fever, lowering your body temperature might make you more comfortable, but it will not affect how long you stay sick.

What causes a fever when you are sick?

Teach from Visuals

To help students interpret the photograph showing an immune response, ask: How can you tell that an inflammation has occurred in this person's hand? *Swelling and redness (and an increase in temperature) are signs that an inflammatory response has occurred in the body.*

Real World Example

Influenza is probably one of the last remaining pandemic infections in humans. It is an infectious disease of the respiratory tract caused by any of three types of influenza virus (A, B, and C), with many different strains. Influenza pandemics are periodically caused by new strains of the type-A virus. Most notably, the pandemic of 1918 to 1919 is estimated to have killed about 25 million people worldwide. More recent influenza pandemics include the Asian flu of 1957 and the Hong Kong flu of 1968.

Ongoing Assessment

Answer: Many tissues produce histamine, which raises the body's temperature to help fight illness.

DIFFERENTIATE INSTRUCTION

More Reading Support

E What is the body's first defense reaction against infection? *inflammation*

F How does histamine cause redness? *by increasing blood flow*

Below Level Have students make trading cards with questions and answers about how the immune system protects the body. Allow students time to trade their cards and answer the questions.

Teach Difficult Concepts

Make sure students understand the difference between pathogens and antibodies. Explain that pathogens are foreign materials that can enter the body and cause disease. Antibodies are produced by the body to fight against pathogens. Ask: How does the body produce antibodies? *They are produced by white blood cells.*

Teach from Visuals

To help students interpret the diagram of immune response, ask:

- What are two types of white blood cells? *T cells and B cells*
- What is the role of antibodies in the immune response? *Antibodies attach themselves to antigens on the pathogens.*
- What are antigens? *Antigens are markers that are carried by pathogens.*

Ongoing Assessment

Explain how the immune system responds to foreign material.

Ask: What is the difference between the nonspecific and specific immune responses? *During a nonspecific response to any injury or infection, histamine is released by tissues to cause inflammation. During a specific immune response, antibodies attach to antigens causing pathogens to be contained and eliminated.*

Specific Response

Specific immune responses differ from nonspecific responses in two ways. First, specific responses are triggered by antigens. An **antigen** is a chemical marker on a cell's surface that indicates whether the cell is from your body or is a foreign material. When the body detects a foreign antigen, specific immune responses occur. Second, a specific immune response provides protection from future exposure to the same material. Three major types of white blood cells—phagocytes, T cells, and B cells—function together in a specific response.

Phagocytes and T Cells Phagocytes ingest and break down foreign materials. Small pieces of the foreign materials are incorporated into the surface of the phagocyte's cell membrane. These foreign particles contain antigens that are detected as foreign by T cells. The T cells

Immune Response

When pathogens invade the body, several types of white blood cells function together to identify and attack foreign materials.

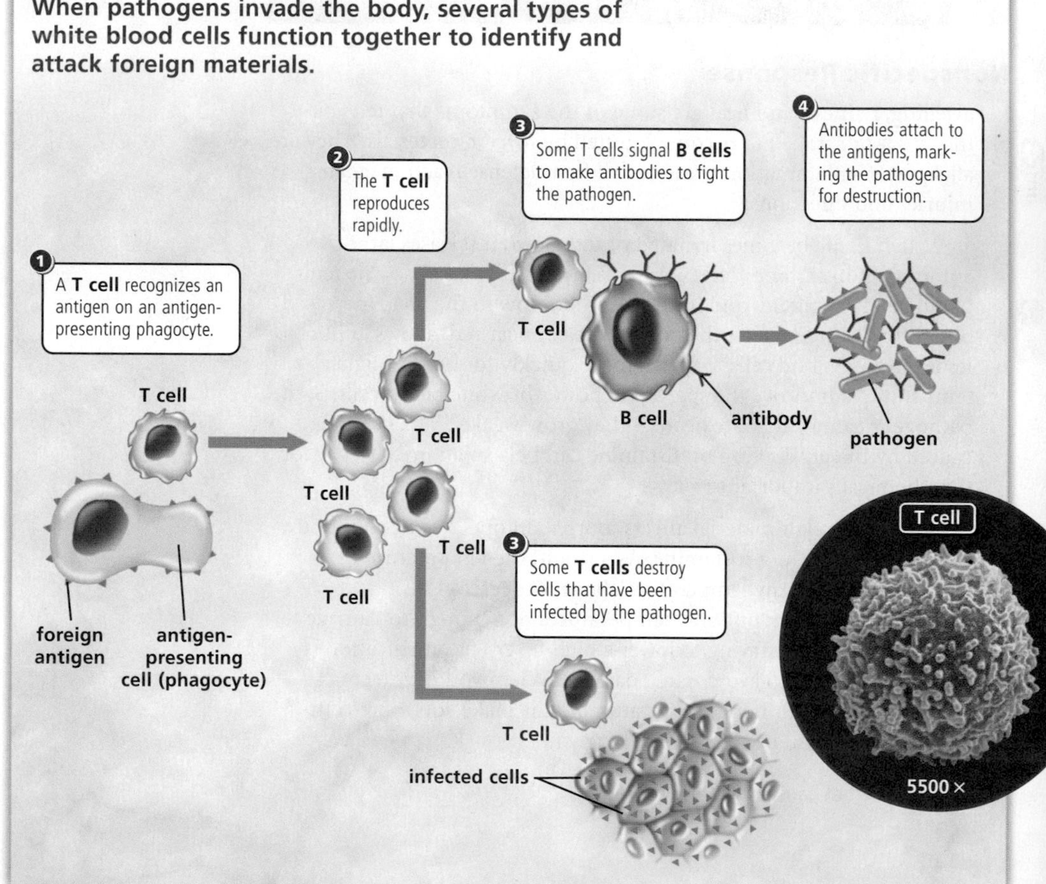

DIFFERENTIATE INSTRUCTION

Below Level Have students draw a chart with two columns headed "B Cells" and "T Cells." Students can write the functions of each, along with the cells' reactions during immune response. Encourage students to draw pictures to illustrate their notes.

INVESTIGATE Antibodies

How do antibodies stop pathogens from spreading?

SKILL FOCUS
Making models

MATERIALS
- plastic containers with lids
- masking tape

TIME
15 minutes

PROCEDURE

1. Your teacher will hand out plastic lids, each labeled with the name of a different pathogen. You will see plastic containers spread throughout the room. There is one container in the room with the same label as your lid.
2. At the signal, find the plastic container with the pathogen that has the same label as your lid and wait in place for the teacher to tell you to stop. If you still haven't found the matching container when time is called, your model pathogen has spread.
3. If your pathogen has spread, write its name on the board.

WHAT DO YOU THINK?

- Which pathogens spread?
- What do you think the lid and container represent? Why?
- How do antibodies identify pathogens?

CHALLENGE Why do you think it is important for your body to identify pathogens?

respond by dividing rapidly. Some types of T cells attack the materials with the foreign antigens, whereas others have different functions. Because antigens that differ from those on a person's cells and provoke an immune response are found on pathogens, the human immune system is necessary for survival in a germ-filled world.

G **B Cells** After T cells divide, B cells that recognize the same foreign antigen are activated and divide rapidly. After several days, many of these B cells begin to produce antibodies that help destroy pathogens. Antibodies attach to the foreign antigens, marking the pathogens for killer T cells or other cells and chemicals that can destroy pathogens.

Some B cells do not make antibodies but remain in the body as a form of immune system memory. If the same pathogen enters the body again, the immune system can respond much more quickly. B cells that recognize the foreign antigen already exist, and antibodies will be produced more quickly.

Why is it important for the body to store B cells?

DIFFERENTIATE INSTRUCTION

More Reading Support

G Which cells can produce antibodies? *B cells*

Advanced Challenge students to create a board game called Invaders from the Outside World. Students should set up the game to model the immune response illustrated on p. 654. The goal of the game is to "collect" enough T cells and B cells to destroy the invading pathogens from the outside world. Allow students class time to play their game.

R Challenge and Extension, p. 147

INVESTIGATE Antibodies

PURPOSE To create a model to show how antibodies keep pathogens from spreading

TIP *15 min.* Prior to the activity, prepare the plastic lids and containers with the names of various pathogens such as *E. coli, streptococcus,* influenza, cold virus (*rhinovirus*), or chicken pox (*varicella*).

WHAT DO YOU THINK? *Students' answers should include any pathogen for which they did not find the container that matched their lid. The lid represents an antibody. The container represents the corresponding pathogen. Antibodies identify pathogens by markers called antigens that are carried by the pathogens.*

CHALLENGE *When the body is able to identify a pathogen, B cells are signaled to make antibodies that destroy the pathogen and prevent it from spreading.*

Datasheet, Antibodies, p. 148

Technology Resources

Customize this student lab as needed or look for an alternative. Print rubrics to assess student lab reports.

Lab Generator CD-ROM

Develop Critical Thinking

ANALYZE Explain to students that HIV is a virus that destroys the body's T cells. Ask: How might HIV eventually affect the ability of the body to defend itself against pathogens? *Since the production of T cells is reduced, the body will lose its ability to fight disease.*

Remind students that HIV spreads only through exchange of internal fluids, such as blood.

Ongoing Assessment

CHECK YOUR READING *Answer: so that antibodies will be available when they are needed to destroy pathogens*

History of Science

The first vaccination is attributed to the British physician Edward Jenner. In 1796 Jenner used the cowpox virus to create a vaccine against smallpox, a disease caused by a similar virus. Jenner had observed that dairymaids who had contracted cowpox, a relatively mild disease, did not contract smallpox when exposed to it. In 1881 Louis Pasteur contributed to the further development of vaccines, immunizing sheep against anthrax by injecting them with forms of the bacteria that cause the disease. Since Pasteur's time, vaccinations have been developed for diphtheria (1891), polio (1955), and measles (1963).

Develop Critical Thinking

APPLY Have students explain the difference between active immunity and passive immunity in their own words. Ask: Why are young schoolchildren more susceptible to flu and colds than older children? *Young children may not have had the chance to build up active immunity and to develop antibodies.*

Ongoing Assessment

Describe ways that the body can become immune to disease.

Ask: What is a vaccine? *A vaccine contains small amounts of weakened pathogens that enable the body to develop an active immunity against the pathogens.*

CHECK YOUR READING *Answer: In active immunity, a body makes its own antibodies. In passive immunity, a body does not develop immunity on its own, as in the case of a baby who inherits immunity from its mother.*

Development of Immunity

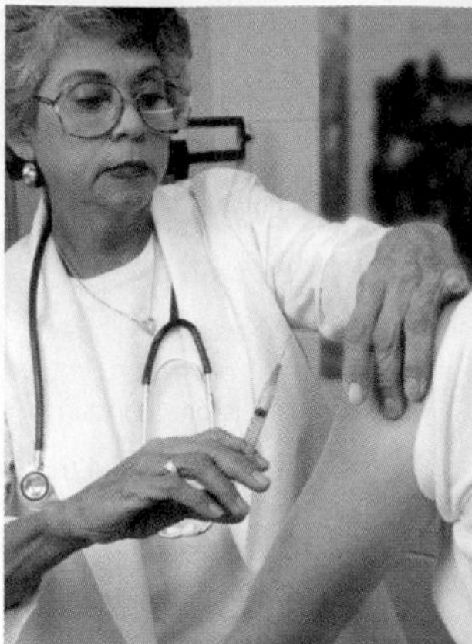

COMPARE A doctor gives a girl a vaccination. Is getting a vaccination an example of passive or active immunity?

After your body has destroyed a specific pathogen, B cells that fight that pathogen remain in your system. If the same pathogen were to enter your body again, your immune system would almost certainly destroy it before you became ill. This resistance to a sickness is called **immunity.**

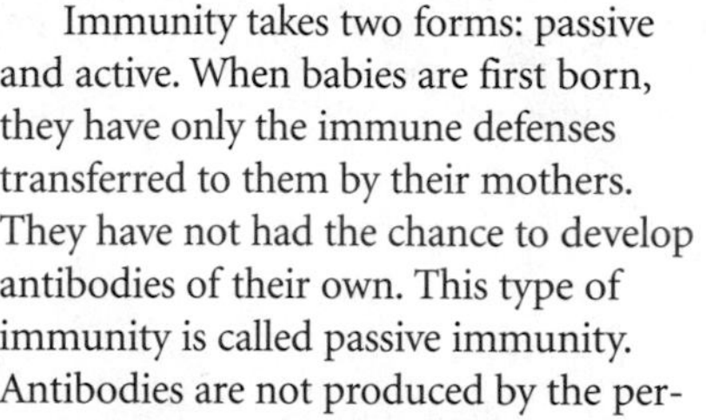

Immunity takes two forms: passive and active. When babies are first born, they have only the immune defenses transferred to them by their mothers. They have not had the chance to develop antibodies of their own. This type of immunity is called passive immunity. Antibodies are not produced by the person's own body but given to the body from another source. Babies develop their own antibodies after a few months.

You have active immunity whenever your body makes its own antibodies. Your body will again fight against any specific pathogen you have developed antibodies against. For example, it is most unlikely that you will get chicken pox twice.

CHECK YOUR READING What is the difference between active and passive immunity?

Most diseases can be prevented or treated.

Given enough time, your immune system will fight off most diseases. However, some infections can cause significant and lasting damage before they are defeated by the body's defenses. Other infections are so strong that the immune system cannot successfully fight them. Medical advances in the prevention and treatment of diseases have reduced the risks of many serious illnesses.

Vaccination

Another way to develop an immunity is to receive a **vaccine.** Vaccines contain small amounts of weakened or dead pathogens that stimulate an immune response. Your B cells are called into action to create antibodies as if you were fighting the real illness. The pathogens are usually weakened or dead so that you will not get sick, yet they still enable your body to develop an active immunity.

DIFFERENTIATE INSTRUCTION

More Reading Support

H What term refers to a resistance to an illness? *immunity*

I Is a baby more likely to have passive immunity or active immunity? *passive immunity*

Advanced Challenge students to find out about the kinds of vaccines they received as young children. Ask them to compare the kinds of vaccines they received with those that were administered to schoolchildren in the 1950s, 1960s, and 1970s. How have the vaccines changed? What might account for the changes?

Today we have vaccines for many common pathogens. Most children who are vaccinated will not get many diseases that their great grandparents, grandparents, and even parents had. Vaccinations can be administered by injection or by mouth. Babies are not the only ones who get them, either. You can be vaccinated at any age.

CHECK YOUR READING Why don't vaccinations usually make you sick?

Treatment

Not all diseases can be prevented, but many of them can be treated. In some cases, treatments can only reduce the symptoms of the disease while the immune system fights the disease-causing pathogens. Other treatments attack the pathogens directly.

In some cases, treatment can only prevent further damage to body tissues by a pathogen that cannot be cured or defeated by the immune system. The way in which a disease is treated depends on what pathogen causes it. Many bacterial infections can be treated with antibiotics. **Antibiotics** are medicines that block the growth and reproduction of bacteria. You may have taken antibiotics when you have had a disease such as strep throat or an ear infection. Other types of medicine can help fight infections caused by viruses, fungi, and parasites.

Types of Pathogens

Disease	Pathogen
Colds, chicken pox, hepatitis, AIDS, influenza, mumps, measles, rabies	virus
Food poisoning, strep throat, tetanus, tuberculosis, acne, ulcers, Lyme disease	bacteria
Athlete's foot, thrush, ringworm	fungus
Malaria, parasitic pneumonia, pinworm, scabies	parasites

19.2 Review

KEY CONCEPTS

1. Make a chart showing three ways that foreign material enters the body and how the immune system defends against each type of attack.
2. What are white blood cells and what is their function in the body?
3. What are two ways to develop immunity?

CRITICAL THINKING

4. **Compare and Contrast** Make a chart comparing B cells and T cells. Include an explanation of the function of antibodies.
5. **Apply** Describe how your immune system responds when you scrape your knee.

CHALLENGE

6. **Hypothesize** Explain why, even if a person recovers from a cold, that person could get a cold again.

Real World Example

Although the measles vaccine has decreased the incidence of measles in the United States, measles remains a health threat in many developing countries. In 2002 the World Health Organization reported that there were 26 million cases of measles worldwide, with 745,000 deaths for the year 2001. Measles results in childhood death from complications like pneumonia, diarrhea, and malnutrition. Measles is also the major cause of preventable blindness in the world.

Ongoing Assessment

CHECK YOUR READING *Answer: You receive a very small amount of a weakened pathogen in a vaccine, which is not usually enough to make you sick.*

Reinforce the BIG idea

Have students relate the section to the Big Idea.

 Reinforcing Key Concepts, p. 149

19.2 ASSESS & RETEACH

Assess

 Section 19.2 Quiz, p. 42

Reteach

Write the following terms on the board: *white blood cells, T cells, B cells, antibodies, antigens, fever, inflammation, mucus, cilia, lymph nodes, vaccine.* For each term have students tell whether it names a part of the body's first line of defense or a function of the immune system. Then have students describe how each item either keeps pathogens from entering the body or fights to destroy or remove pathogens that have entered the body.

Technology Resources

Have students visit **ClassZone.com** for reteaching of Key Concepts.

 CONTENT REVIEW

 CONTENT REVIEW CD-ROM

ANSWERS

1. Charts will vary but should include that foreign materials can enter the body through a wound, during eating or drinking, or during breathing.

2. White blood cells are types of blood cell that destroy foreign materials.

3. through illness and through vaccination

4. Charts will vary but should include that B cells release antibodies, whereas T cells recognize markers called antigens.

5. Answers should show an understanding of the process of inflammation.

6. Students should speculate that different colds are caused by different foreign materials, since getting one cold does not give you immunity against another cold.

MATH IN SCIENCE
Math Skills Practice for Science

Set Learning Goal

To use graphing to explore and represent pollen-count data

Present the Science

Allergies occur when allergens like pollen and dust enter the body. The allergens cause the production of histamine, which results in sneezing, runny nose, and watery eyes.

Develop Graphing Skills

Review the structure of a graph:

- The horizontal axis is the *x*-axis.
- The vertical axis is the *y*-axis.
- The *x*- and *y*-axes intersect at a point, 0.

Line graphs show a relationship between sets of data. Line graphs are particularly effective at showing data that change over time. Double line graphs present two independent sets of data that can be compared.

DIFFERENTIATION TIP A rate is a special kind of ratio in which the denominator is 1. The rate shown in the table is number of grains per 1 cubic meter.

Close

Ask students why labels are important on a graph. *Sample answer: to show exactly what data are measured and how they are being compared*

Suggest that students obtain local pollen counts over a number of days. They can graph the data and post the graph as a community service.

- Math Support, p. 166
- Math Practice, p. 167

Technology Resources

Students can visit **ClassZone.com** to practice graphing skills.

MATH TUTORIAL

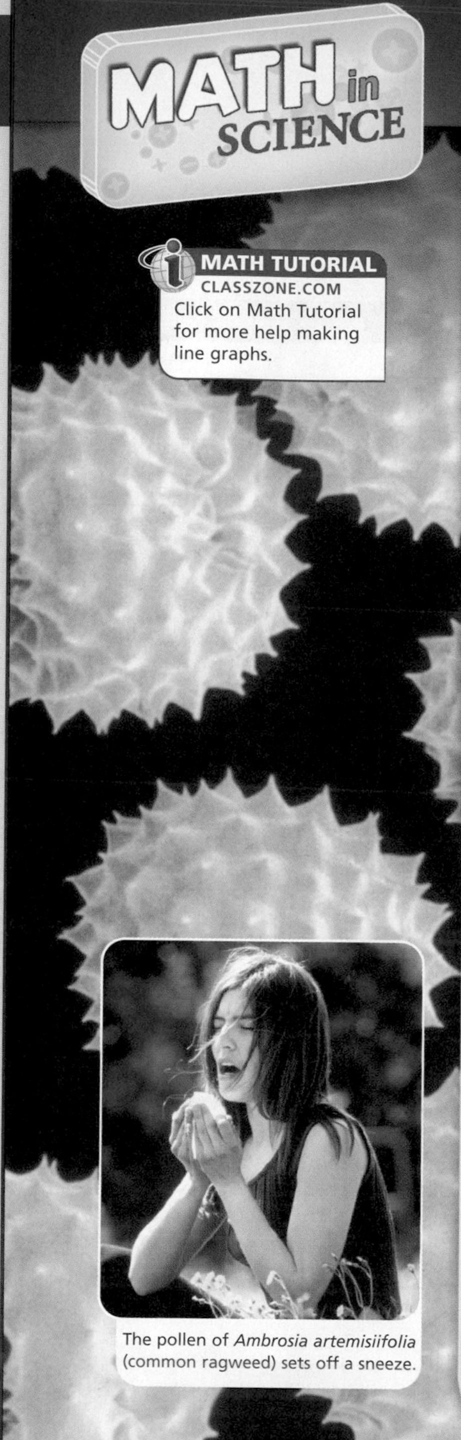

MATH TUTORIAL
CLASSZONE.COM
Click on Math Tutorial for more help making line graphs.

The pollen of *Ambrosia artemisiifolia* (common ragweed) sets off a sneeze.

SKILL: MAKING A LINE GRAPH

Pollen Counts

Every year, sometime between July and October, in nearly every state in the United States, the air will fill with ragweed pollen. For a person who has a pollen allergy, these months blur with tears. Linn County, Iowa, takes weekly counts of ragweed and non-ragweed pollen.

Weekly Pollen Counts, Linn County, Iowa

	Jul. 29	Aug. 5	Aug. 12	Aug. 19	Aug. 26	Sept. 2	Sept. 9	Sept. 16	Sept. 23	Sept. 30	Oct. 7
Ragweed (Grain/m^3)	0	9	10	250	130	240	140	25	20	75	0
Non-Ragweed (Grain/m^3)	10	45	15	50	100	50	40	10	20	25	0

Example

A line graph of the data will show the pattern of increase and decrease of ragweed pollen in the air.

(1) Begin with a quadrant with horizontal and vertical axes.

(2) Mark the weekly dates at even intervals on the horizontal axis.

(3) Starting at 0 on the vertical axis, mark even intervals of 50 units.

(4) Graph each point. Connect the points with line segments.

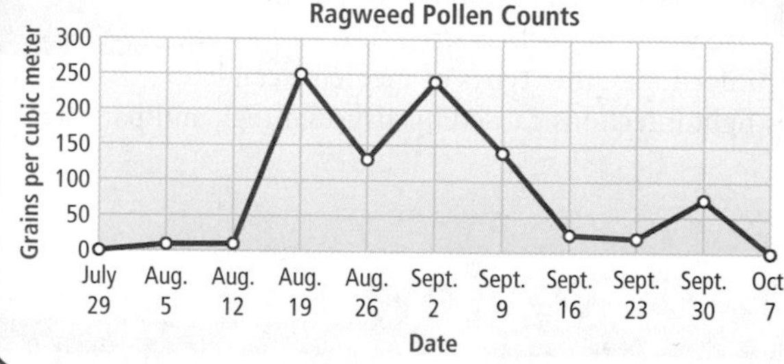

Complete and present your graph as directed below.

1. Use graph paper to make your own line graph of the non-ragweed pollen in Linn County.
2. Write some questions that can be answered by comparing the two graphs. Trade questions with a partner.
3. Which weeks have the highest pollen counts in Linn County?

CHALLENGE Try making a double line graph combining both sets of data in one graph.

ANSWERS

1. Graphs should show an accurate portrayal of the data, with x- and y-axes labeled and a title.

2. Sample answers: Which day had the most pollen? Which had the least? If you have ragweed allergies, which day is the safest to be outside? Which is the worst day for people with allergies?

3. August 19–September 9

CHALLENGE *Graphs should show an accurate portrayal of the data, with the x- and y-axes labeled. It should have a key to the lines and a title.*

KEY CONCEPT

The integumentary system shields the body.

BEFORE, you learned
- The body is defended from harmful materials
- Response structures fight disease
- The immune system responds in many ways to illness

NOW, you will learn
- About the functions of the skin
- How the skin helps protect the body
- How the skin grows and heals

VOCABULARY
integumentary system p. 659
epidermis p. 660
dermis p. 660

EXPLORE The Skin

What are the functions of skin?

PROCEDURE

1. Using a vegetable peeler, remove the skin from an apple. Take notes on the characteristics of the apple's peeled surface. Include observations on its color, moisture level, and texture.
2. Place the apple on a dry surface. After fifteen minutes, note any changes in its characteristics.

WHAT DO YOU THINK?
- What is the function of an apple's skin? What does it prevent?
- What does this experiment suggest about how skin might function in the human body?

MATERIALS
- vegetable peeler
- apple

Skin performs important functions.

MAIN IDEA AND DETAILS Start a two-column chart with the main idea *Skin performs important functions.* Add detail notes about those functions.

Just as an apple's skin protects the fruit inside, your skin protects the rest of your body. Made up of flat sheets of cells, your skin protects the inside of your body from harmful materials outside. The skin is part of your body's **integumentary system** (ihn-TEHG-yu-MEHN-tuh-ree), which also includes your hair and nails.

Your skin fulfills several vital functions:

- Skin repels water.
- Skin guards against infection.
- Skin helps maintain homeostasis.
- Skin senses the environment.

RESOURCES FOR DIFFERENTIATED INSTRUCTION

Below Level
UNIT RESOURCE BOOK
- Reading Study Guide A, pp. 152–153
- Decoding Support, p. 165

Advanced
UNIT RESOURCE BOOK
- Challenge and Extension, p. 158
- Challenge Reading, pp. 161–162

English Learners
UNIT RESOURCE BOOK
Spanish Reading Study Guide, pp. 156–157

- Audio Readings in Spanish
- Audio Readings (English)

19.3 FOCUS

Set Learning Goals

Students will
- Describe the functions of the skin.
- Analyze how the skin protects the body.
- Explain how the skin grows and heals.
- Observe how oil protects the skin.

3-Minute Warm-Up

Display Transparency 21 or copy this exercise on the board:

Complete the chart describing the body's lines of defense against foreign materials.

Body System	Defense(s)
Integumentary System	*skin as barrier*
Respiratory System	*mucus, cilia, coughing, sneezing*
Digestive System	*saliva, mucus, enzymes, acids*
Circulatory System	*white blood cells, antibodies*

 3-Minute Warm-Up, p. T21

19.3 MOTIVATE

EXPLORE The Skin

PURPOSE To understand the functions of skin

TIPS *10 min.* Have students work in groups or pairs. Caution them to avoid touching the sharp edge of the peeler.

WHAT DO YOU THINK? *The apple's skin keeps the apple from turning brown, decaying, and drying out. Skin keeps the inside of the body moist and healthy.*

Ongoing Assessment

Describe the functions of the skin.

Ask: What are the four functions of the integumentary system? *repels water, guards against infection, helps maintain homeostasis, senses the environment*

19.3 INSTRUCT

Teach from Visuals

To help students interpret the diagram of skin structure, ask:

- What structures are found in the dermis layer of the skin? *sensory receptors, nerves, oil glands, hair, blood vessels, muscles, and sweat glands*
- How does the skin provide insulation for the body? *Fatty tissue below the dermis provides protection against extremes in temperature.*
- Which layer of skin protects the body from foreign materials? *epidermis*

Metacognitive Strategy

Many students have trouble remembering the difference between the epidermis and dermis layers of the skin. Challenge students to write a rhyme that will help them remember the difference between the two layers.

Develop Critical Thinking

ANALYZE Ask students how the structure of the skin helps the body maintain homeostasis. *The fatty layer of tissue helps regulate body temperature; sweat glands help cool the body through evaporation.*

Language Arts Connection

The word *epidermis* is derived from the Greek prefix *epi-*, which means "above" or "upon" and the Greek word *derma*, which means "skin." Have students use a dictionary to find the meanings of Greek prefixes such as *neo-*, *peri-*, and *exo-*, which are often used in life science terminology. Ask a few students to list the prefixes and meanings on the board. Challenge others to discover words that contain the prefixes and to add them to the list.

Skin Structure

When you look at your hand, you only see the outer layer of skin. The skin has many structures to protect your body.

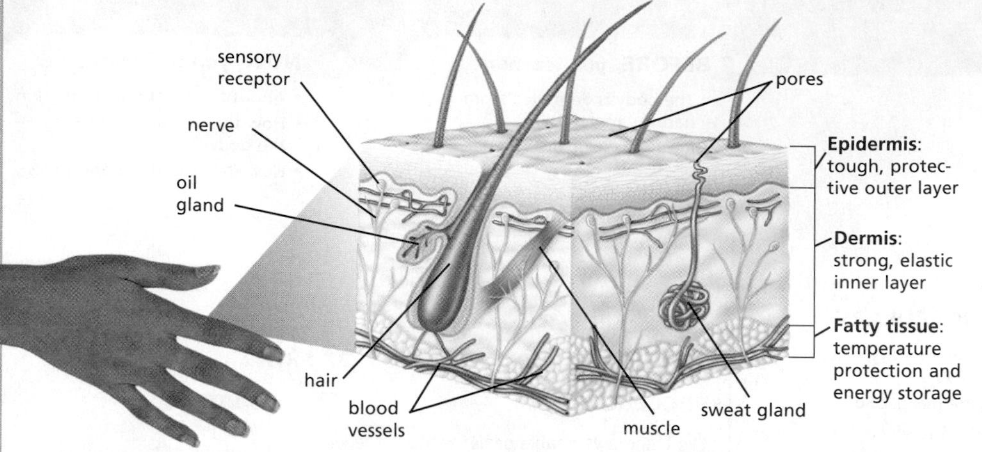

The structure of skin is complex.

Have you ever looked closely at your skin? Your skin is more complex than it might at first seem. It does more than just cover your body. The skin is made up of many structures, which perform many different jobs.

Dermis and Epidermis

VOCABULARY
Add frame games for *epidermis* and *dermis* to your notebook.

As you can see in the diagram above, human skin is composed of two layers: an outer layer, called the **epidermis,** and an inner layer, called the **dermis.** The cells of the epidermis contain many protein fibers that give the skin tough, protective qualities. These cells are formed in the deepest part of the epidermis. Skin cells move upward slowly as new cells form below them. Above new cells, older cells rub off. The surface cells in the epidermis are dead but form a thick, waterproof layer about 30 cells deep.

A

B

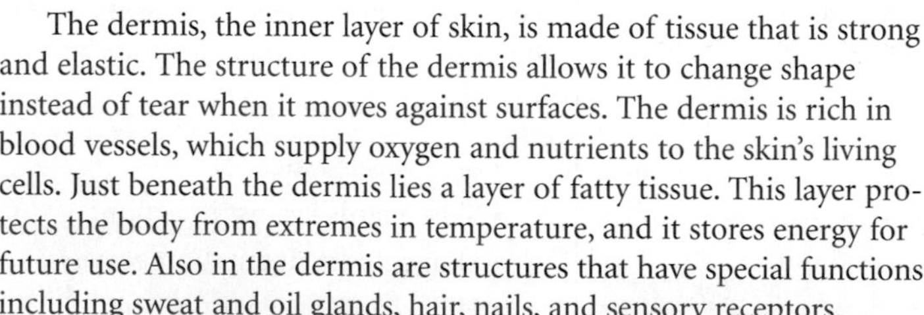

The dermis, the inner layer of skin, is made of tissue that is strong and elastic. The structure of the dermis allows it to change shape instead of tear when it moves against surfaces. The dermis is rich in blood vessels, which supply oxygen and nutrients to the skin's living cells. Just beneath the dermis lies a layer of fatty tissue. This layer protects the body from extremes in temperature, and it stores energy for future use. Also in the dermis are structures that have special functions, including sweat and oil glands, hair, nails, and sensory receptors.

DIFFERENTIATE INSTRUCTION

More Reading Support

A What gives the epidermis its protective qualities? *protein fibers*

B What is formed by the dead surface cells? *a thick, waterproof layer*

English Learners English learners may be unfamiliar with the use of prefixes and suffixes in English. Discuss the terms *dermis* and *epidermis.* Then ask students to look up the prefix *epi-* in the dictionary. Ask students how adding this prefix changes the word *dermis.* Also discuss with students the different words related to *sense* found in this section, such as *sensory, sensor, sensation,* and *sensitive.*

Sweat and Oil Glands

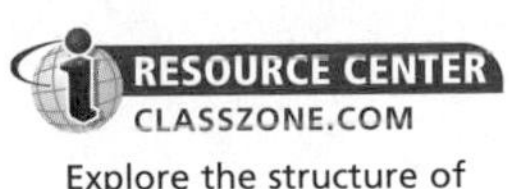

RESOURCE CENTER
CLASSZONE.COM

Explore the structure of skin.

Deep within the dermis are structures that help maintain your body's internal environment. Sweat glands help control body temperature, and oil glands protect the skin by keeping it moist. Both types of glands open to the surface through tiny openings in the skin called pores. Pores allow important substances to pass to the skin's surface. Pores can become clogged with dirt and oil. Keeping the skin clean can prevent blockages.

Sweat glands, which are present almost everywhere on the body's surface, help maintain homeostasis. When you become too warm, the sweat glands secrete sweat, a fluid that is 99% water. This fluid travels from the sweat glands, through the pores, and onto the skin's surface. You probably know already about evaporation. Evaporation is the process by which a liquid becomes a gas. During evaporation, heat is released. Thus, sweating cools the skin's surface and the body.

Like sweat glands, oil glands are present almost everywhere on the body. They secrete an oil that moistens skin and hair and keeps them from becoming dry. Skin oils add flexibility and provide part, but not all, of the skin's waterproofing.

CHECK YOUR READING What are the functions of oil glands?

INVESTIGATE Skin Protection

How does oil protect your skin?

PROCEDURE

1. Rub a cotton ball dampened with alcohol across one of your palms. Alcohol removes the oil from the surface of your skin.
2. Drip a couple of drops of water onto the palm with alcohol. Observe what happens. Record your observations.
3. Drip a couple of drops of water onto your other palm. Observe what happens. Record your observations.

WHAT DO YOU THINK?

- Compare the observations for each palm.
- What does this investigation suggest about the importance of oil and oil glands?

CHALLENGE Predict what might happen to your skin if you removed every trace of oil several times a day.

SKILL FOCUS
Observing

MATERIALS
- cotton ball
- rubbing alcohol
- dropper
- water

TIME
10 minutes

DIFFERENTIATE INSTRUCTION

More Reading Support

C How do oil and sweat reach the surface of the skin? *through pores*

D How does sweat cool the body? *through evaporation*

Alternative Assessment Have students create a 3-D cross section of the skin. They can use materials such as plastic foam, pipe cleaners, yarn, beads, and wires. Ask them to add labels and captions about the three ways skin helps the body.

INVESTIGATE Skin Protection

PURPOSE To observe how oil protects the skin

TIPS *10 min.* Keep the room well ventilated. Caution students not to inhale fumes from the alcohol. You may wish to have petroleum jelly or baby oil available for students whose skin oils are minimal.

WHAT DO YOU THINK? *On the hand without the alcohol, the water formed small beads. On the hand rubbed with alcohol, the water spread thinly over the skin and seemed to sink into the skin. The oil must act as a barrier on the skin. Oil helps keep liquids that don't belong in the skin from sinking into the skin.*

CHALLENGE *The skin would become dry and could absorb foreign materials.*

Datasheet, Skin Protection, p. 159

Technology Resources

Customize this student lab as needed or look for an alternative. Print rubrics to assess student lab reports.

Lab Generator CD-ROM

EXPLORE the BIG idea

Revisit "Wet Fingers" on p. 639. Ask students how this activity demonstrates how evaporation of sweat helps to cool the body.

Ongoing Assessment

Analyze how the skin protects the body.

Ask: What are two types of glands that help the body maintain homeostasis? *oil glands and sweat glands*

CHECK YOUR READING *Answer: Oil glands help to moisten the skin and hair and keep them from drying out.*

Teach from Visuals

Have students compare the magnification photographs of hair and nails. Ask:

- Which magnification shows a greater area? *hair*
- Which image is blown up the most? *nails*
- What do hair and nails have in common with the cells on the surface of the skin? *They are made up of dead cells.*

Teaching with Technology

If skin surface temperature probeware is available, have students use it to measure the change in skin temperature caused by placing a cold pack or a heat pack on their arms. They can use a graphing calculator to show the data visually.

Real World Example

Most students will have experienced getting goosebumps on their skin when they are cold. Explain that the bumps that appear on the surface of the skin are the result of the contraction of tiny muscles at the base of each hair, making the hair stand up.

Integrate the Sciences

Electrical engineers are trying to improve skin for robots. This is a tough problem because robot skin must be elastic but also able to conduct electricity. If sensors and metal wires are used to conduct electricity, they break when the skin stretches. One solution might be to implant broad metal strips that are corrugated. The corrugated metal is stretchy; it can be flattened out or compressed and continue to conduct electricity. Scientists' goal is to make a robot that can "sense" its environment.

Ongoing Assessment

CHECK YOUR READING *Answer: Hair protects your skin and keeps you warm. Nails protect the tips of the fingers and toes from injury.*

Answer: heat, cold, pain, touch, and pressure.

Hair and Nails

In addition to your skin, your integumentary system includes your hair and nails. Many cells in your hair and nails are actually dead but continue to perform important functions.

The hair on your head helps your body in many ways. When you are outside, it shields your head from the Sun. In cold weather, it traps heat close to your head to keep you warmer. Your body hair works the same way, but it is much less effective at protecting your skin and keeping you warm.

E Fingernails and toenails protect the tips of the fingers and toes from injury. Both are made of epidermal cells that are thick and tough. They grow from the nail bed, which continues to manufacture cells as the cells that form the nail bond together and grow.

CHECK YOUR READING What are the functions of hair and nails?

Your hair and nails are made of dead cells, which continue to protect you.

Sensory Receptors

How does your body know when you are touching something too hot or too cold? You get that information from sensory receptors attached to the nerves. These receptors are actually part of the nervous system, but they are located in your skin. Your skin contains receptors that sense heat, cold, pain, touch, and pressure. These sensors help protect the body. For example, temperature receptors sense when an object is hot. If it is too hot and you touch it, pain receptors send signals to your brain telling you that you have been burned.

CHECK YOUR READING What are the five types of sensory receptors in skin?

DIFFERENTIATE INSTRUCTION

More Reading Support

E What are fingernails and toenails made of? *epidermal cells from the nail beds*

F Sensory receptors belong to which body system? *the nervous system*

Advanced Invite interested students to investigate the different types of fingerprints and the way forensic scientists use fingerprinting in helping to solve crimes. Students should research the limitations of using fingerprinting in forensics. Encourage students to make impressions of their own fingerprints for display.

 Challenge and Extension, p. 158

The skin grows and heals.

As a person grows, skin also grows. As you have noticed if you have ever had a bruise or a cut, your skin is capable of healing. Skin can often repair itself after injury or illness.

Growth

As your bones grow, you get taller. As your muscles develop, your arms and legs become thicker. Through all your body's growth and change, your skin has to grow, too.

Most of the growth of your skin occurs at the base of the epidermis, just above the dermis. The cells there grow and divide to form new cells, constantly replacing older epidermal cells as they die and are brushed off during daily activity. Cells are lost from the skin's surface all the time: every 2 to 4 weeks, your skin surface is entirely new. In fact, a percentage of household dust is actually dead skin cells.

Healing Skin

Small injuries to the skin heal by themselves over time.

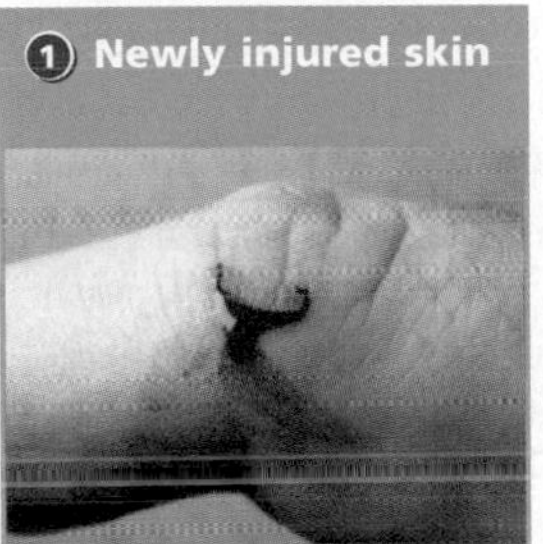

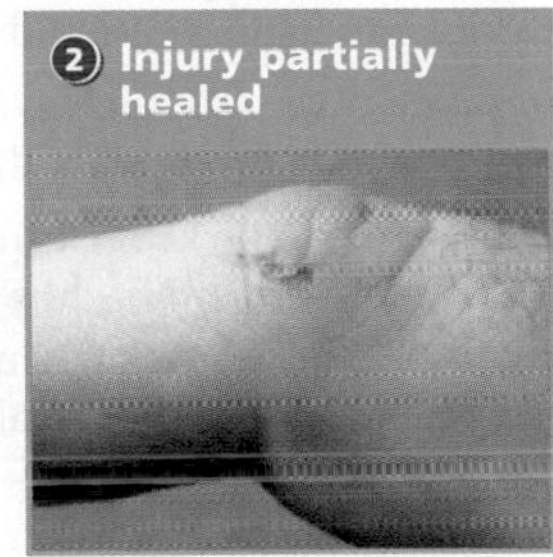

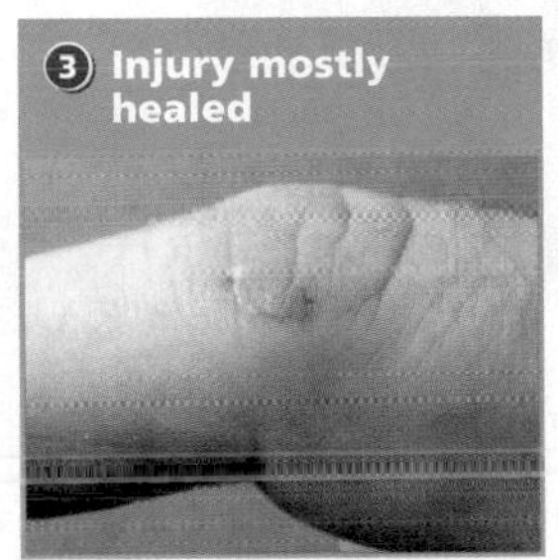

READING VISUALS How do you think small injuries to the skin heal?

Injuries and Healing

You have probably experienced some injuries to your skin, such as blisters, burns, cuts, and bruises. Most such injuries result from the skin's contact with the outside world, such as a concrete sidewalk. In simple injuries, the skin can usually repair itself.

Explore how the skin heals.

Burns can be serious injuries. They can be caused by heat, electricity, radiation, or certain chemicals. In mild cases—those of first-degree burns—skin merely becomes red, and the burn heals in a day or two. In severe cases—those of second-degree and third-degree burns—the body loses fluids, and death can result from fluid loss, infection, and other complications.

DIFFERENTIATE INSTRUCTION

More Reading Support

G How much time does it take for the surface of the skin to replace itself? *two to four weeks*

Below Level Have students create a poster showing the various ways to keep the skin safe from the Sun. Students may include a chart of the UV Index, showing the various dangers at each level in the index. Encourage students to check a local newspaper and report on the daily UV levels. Allow class time for students to present their findings.

Advanced Have students who are interested in the effects of tanning on the skin read the following article.

R Challenge Reading, pp. 161–162

Teach from Visuals

Discuss the photographic sequence of healing skin. At the site of the cut on the finger, three things happen:

- Platelets help the blood clot, or thicken and dry, to form a scab.
- New skin cells grow and cover the area as the scab falls off.
- The new skin and surrounding skin continue to generate new cells while the dead cells form a protective, seamless outer layer.

Integrate the Sciences

The ozone layer is about 6–30 miles (10–50 km) above the surface of Earth. Human activity has caused a thinning of this layer, resulting in higher levels of ultraviolet (UV) radiation. The increase in radiation in turn has elevated the incidence of skin cancers and cataracts. The National Weather Service and the Environmental Protection Agency have developed the UV Index, which predicts daily levels of UV radiation on a 0 to 10+ scale.

Health Connection

About 2.4 million burn injuries to the skin occur each year. Of those, between 8000 and 12,000 result in death. The most frequent place where burns occur in the home is the kitchen. Burns are the most common cause of accidental death for children under the age of 14.

Ongoing Assessment

Explain how the skin grows and heals.

Ask: How are new skin cells formed? *Cells are formed at the base of the epidermis. As new cells are produced, the layer of older epidermal cells is replaced and brushed off during normal daily activity.*

READING VISUALS *Answer: The skin cells at the edge of the injury begin to divide to replace the skin cells that were damaged. Eventually the new skin cells fill in the injured area.*

Ongoing Assessment

 CHECK YOUR READING *Answer: Severe heat and severe cold can damage the skin.*

Reinforce 

Have students relate the section to the Big Idea.

 Reinforcing Key Concepts, p. 160

19.3 ASSESS & RETEACH

Assess

Section 19.3 Quiz, p. 619

Reteach

Write the following notes on the board. For each, have students tell whether it pertains to the dermis or epidermis layer of the skin.

1. contains protein fibers *epidermis*
2. contains nerves and sweat glands *dermis*
3. rich in blood vessels *dermis*
4. forms a waterproof covering *epidermis*
5. Most skin growth occurs at its base. *epidermis*

Then have partners create a Venn diagram comparing the functions of the dermis and the epidermis.

dermis—insulates; cushions; contains glands, vessels, and nerves
both—senses external environment; protects
epidermis—heals surface wounds; releases oil and sweat to surface; acts as shield

Technology Resources

Have students visit **ClassZone.com** for reteaching of Key Concepts.

 CONTENT REVIEW

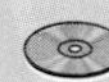 CONTENT REVIEW CD-ROM

Sunburns are usually minor first-degree burns, but that does not mean they cannot be serious. Rays from the Sun can burn and blister the skin much as a hot object can. Repeated burning can increase the chance of skin cancer. Specialized cells in the skin make a pigment that absorbs the Sun's ultraviolet rays and helps prevent tissue damage. These cells produce more of the skin pigment melanin when exposed to the Sun. The amount of melanin in your skin determines how dark your skin is.

Severe cold can damage skin as well. Skin exposed to cold weather can get frostbite, a condition in which the cells are damaged by freezing. Mild frostbite often heals just as well as a minor cut. In extreme cases, frostbitten limbs become diseased and have to be amputated.

CHECK YOUR READING What types of weather can damage your skin?

Wearing sunblock when you are outside protects your skin from harmful rays from the Sun.

Protection

Your skin is constantly losing old cells and gaining new cells. Although your skin is always changing, it is still important to take care of it.

- Good nutrition supplies materials the skin uses to maintain and repair itself. By drinking water, you help your body, and thus your skin, to remain moist and able to replace lost cells.
- Appropriate coverings, such as sunblock in summer and warm clothes in winter, can protect the skin from weather damage.
- Skin also needs to be kept clean. Many harmful bacteria cannot enter the body through healthy skin, but they should be washed off regularly. This prevents them from multiplying and then entering the body through small cuts or scrapes.

19.3 Review

KEY CONCEPTS

1. List four functions of the skin.
2. How do the epidermis and dermis protect the body?
3. Make your own diagram with *How skin grows and repairs itself* at the center. Around the center, write at least five facts about skin growth and healing.

CRITICAL THINKING

4. **Apply** Give three examples from everyday life of sensory receptors in your skin reacting to changes in your environment.
5. **Connect** Describe a situation in which sensory receptors could be critical to survival.

CHALLENGE

6. **Infer** Exposure to sunlight may increase the number of freckles on a person's skin. Explain the connection between sunlight, melanin, and freckles.

ANSWERS

1. It repels water, guards against infection, helps maintain homeostasis, and senses the environment.

2. The epidermis keeps harmful materials out because it contains tough protein fibers. The dermis helps because it is strong elastic tissue that resists tearing.

3. Diagrams will vary but should include five facts about skin growth and healing.

4. Answers should show how sensory receptors respond to the environment.

5. Answers should show the role of sensory receptors in survival.

6. Melanin concentrated in a small place on the skin that is surrounded by skin with less melanin produces a freckle. Exposure to sunlight increases melanin levels in some spots, which become visible as freckles.

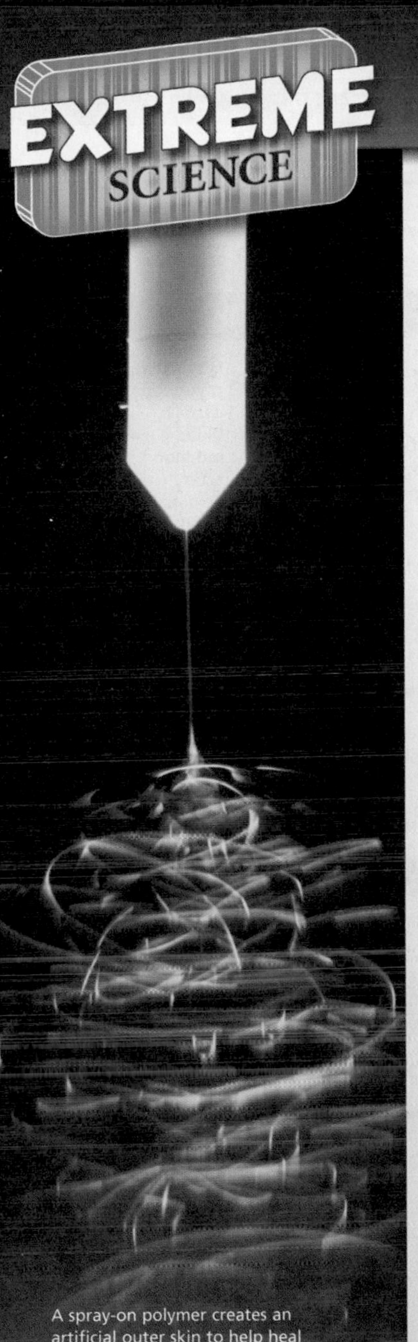

A spray-on polymer creates an artificial outer skin to help heal surface wounds on an arm.

GROWING NEW SKIN

Artificial Skin

Skin acts like a barrier, keeping our insides in and infections out. Nobody can survive without skin. But when a large amount of skin is severely damaged, the body cannot work fast enough to replace it. In some cases there isn't enough undamaged skin left on the body for transplanting. Using skin from another person risks introducing infections or rejection by the body. The answer? Artificial skin.

Here's the Skinny

To make artificial skin, scientists start with cells in a tiny skin sample. Cells from infants are used because infant skin-cell molecules are still developing, and scientists can manipulate the molecules to avoid transplant rejection. The cells from just one small sample of skin can be grown into enough artificial skin to cover 15 basketball courts. Before artificial skin, badly burned victims didn't have much chance to live. Today, 96 out of 100 burn victims survive.

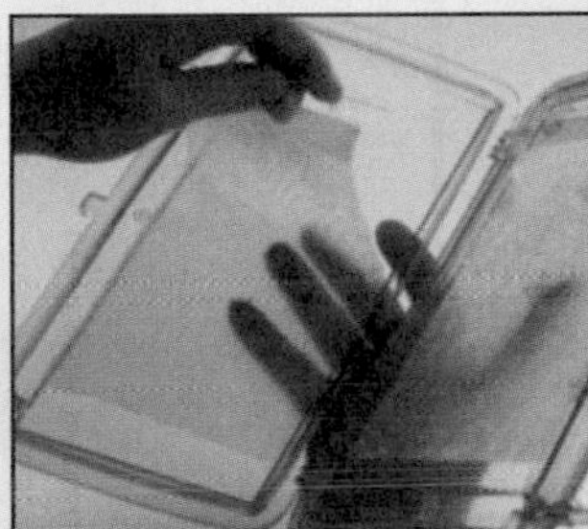

A surgeon lifts a layer of artificial skin. The skin is so thin, a newspaper could be read behind it.

What's Next?

- Scientists are hoping to be able to grow organs using this technology. Someday artificially grown livers, kidneys, and hearts may take the place of transplants and mechanical devices.
- A self-repairing plastic skin that knits itself back together when cracked has been developed. It may someday be used to create organs or even self-repairing rocket and spacecraft parts.
- Artificial polymer "skin" for robots is being developed to help robots do delicate work such as microsurgery or space exploration.

Robot designer David Hanson has developed the K-bot, a lifelike face that uses 24 motors to create expressions.

EXPLORE

1. **COMPARE AND CONTRAST** Detail the advantages and disadvantages of skin transplanted from another place on the body and artificial skin.
2. **CHALLENGE** Artificial skin is being considered for applications beyond those originally envisioned. Research and present a new potential application.

EXPLORE

1. *COMPARE AND CONTRAST Sometimes there is not enough skin to transplant. Transplants from another person can cause infections or rejections. Using artificial skin saves lives. Artificial skin is expensive to produce. Artificial skin can shorten hospital and rehabilitation time.*
2. *CHALLENGE Accept responses that are coherent and research-based.*

EXTREME SCIENCE

Fun and Motivating Science

Set Learning Goal

To understand the uses and future potential uses of artificial skin

Present the Science

Treatment for burns consists of removing the burned tissue and covering the dermis with skin grafts from other parts of the body. For people with large areas of burns, this is not always possible. Artificial skin has made it possible for surgeons to cover burned areas with a temporary synthetic epidermis. Cells from the dermis layer form a "lattice" with the artificial layer, eventually producing a new layer of epidermis.

Discussion Questions

Ask students to brainstorm a "top 10 list" for burn prevention.

Ask: Do you think burns are more severe if they are limited to the epidermis or if they affect the dermis as well? Explain. *Burns are likely to be more severe if they reach down to the dermis, because such burns go deeper into the skin, where live tissue and blood vessels are found.*

Close

Ask: What difficulties do you think scientists might encounter in using the technology of artificial skin for other purposes? *Accept responses that cite qualities of real skin and the difficulties of reproducing it.*

Technology Resources

Students can visit **ClassZone.com** to for more links about artificial skin.

 **RESOURCE CENTER**

BACK TO

the BIG idea

Have students explain how the words *transport, defend,* and *protect* convey how the circulatory and immune systems are related. *The circulatory system transports materials throughout the body; some of these materials are blood cells that defend and protect the body from foreign materials.*

KEY CONCEPTS SUMMARY

SECTION 19.1
Ask students to look at the picture of the heart and identify which chamber of the heart receives oxygen-rich blood. Where does this blood come from? *The left atrium receives oxygen-rich blood from the lungs.*

SECTION 19.2
Ask students to describe the structures and responses of the immune system. *white blood cells, antibodies; inflammation, fever, and development of immunity*

SECTION 19.3
Ask students which layer of the skin protects the body from foreign materials. How does it accomplish this? *The epidermis, the outer layer of skin, prevents foreign materials from entering the body. This layer is made up of tough, waterproof cells.*

Review Concepts

- Big Idea Flow Chart, p. T17
- Chapter Outline, pp. T23–T24

19 Chapter Review

the BIG idea

Systems function to transport materials and to defend and protect the body.

KEY CONCEPTS SUMMARY

1 The circulatory system transports materials.

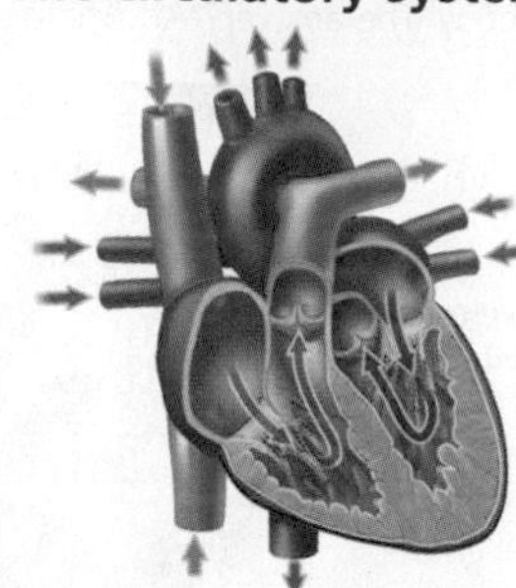

The heart, blood vessels, and blood of the circulatory system work together to transport materials from the digestive and respiratory systems to all cells. The blood exerts pressure on the walls of the blood vessels as the heart keeps the blood moving through the body.

VOCABULARY
circulatory system p. 641
blood p. 641
red blood cell p. 643
artery p. 645
vein p. 645
capillary p. 645

2 The immune system defends the body.

The immune system defends the body from pathogens. White blood cells identify and attack pathogens that find their way inside the body. The immune system responds to attack with inflammation, fever, and development of immunity.

Types of Pathogens

Disease	Pathogen
colds, chicken pox, hepatitis, AIDS, influenza, mumps, measles, rabies	virus
food poisoning, strep throat, tetanus, tuberculosis, acne, ulcers, Lyme disease	bacteria
athlete's foot, thrush, ring worm	fungus
malaria, parasitic pneumonia, pinworm, scabies	parasites

VOCABULARY
pathogen p. 650
immune system p. 651
antibody p. 651
antigen p. 654
immunity p. 656
vaccine p. 656
antibiotic p. 657

3 The integumentary system shields the body.

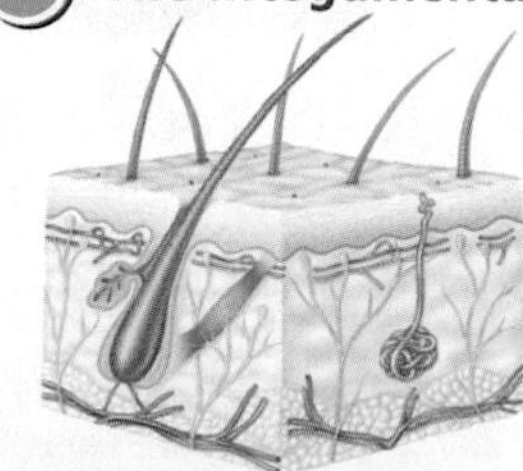

The skin protects the body from harmful materials in the environment, and allows you to sense temperature, pain, touch, and pressure. In most cases the skin is able to heal itself after injury.

VOCABULARY
integumentary system p. 659
epidermis p. 660
dermis p. 660

Technology Resources

Have students visit **ClassZone.com** or use the CD-ROM for a cumulative review of concepts.

 **CONTENT REVIEW**

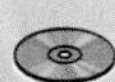 **CONTENT REVIEW CD-ROM**

Engage students in a whole-class interactive review of Key Concepts. Edit content as you wish.

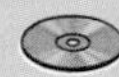 **POWER PRESENTATIONS**

Reviewing Vocabulary

Draw a word triangle for each of the terms below. Write a term and its definition in the bottom section. In the middle section, write a sentence in which you use the term correctly. In the top section, draw a small picture to illustrate the term.

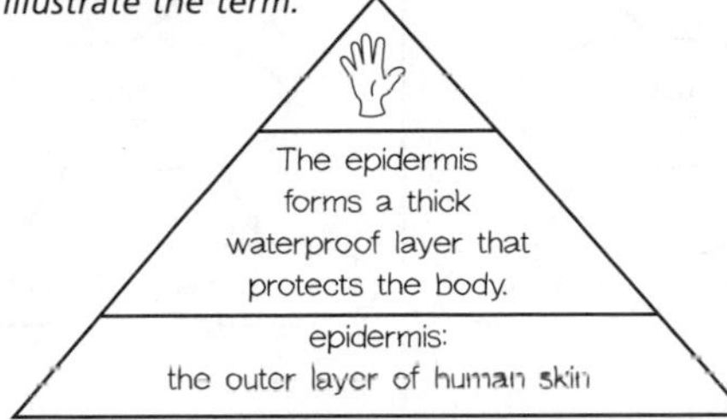

1. capillary
2. blood
3. dermis
4. antigen

Write a sentence describing the relationship between each pair of terms.

5. pathogen, antibody
6. artery, vein
7. immunity, vaccine

Reviewing Key Concepts

Multiple Choice *Choose the letter of the best answer.*

8. Which chamber of the heart pumps oxygen-poor blood into the lungs?
   - **a.** right atrium
   - **b.** right ventricle
   - **c.** left atrium
   - **d.** left ventricle
9. Which structures carry blood back to the heart?
   - **a.** veins
   - **b.** capillaries
   - **c.** arteries
   - **d.** platelets
10. The structures in the blood that carry oxygen to the cells of the body are the
    - **a.** plasma
    - **b.** platelets
    - **c.** white blood cells
    - **d.** red blood cells
11. High blood pressure is unhealthy because it
    - **a.** does not exert enough pressure on your arteries
    - **b.** causes your heart to work harder
    - **c.** does not allow enough oxygen to get to the cells in your body
    - **d.** causes your veins to collapse
12. Which category of pathogens causes strep throat?
    - **a.** virus
    - **b.** bacteria
    - **c.** fungus
    - **d.** parasite
13. Which of the following is a function of white blood cells?
    - **a.** destroying foreign organisms
    - **b.** providing your body with nutrients
    - **c.** carrying oxygen to the body's cells
    - **d.** forming a blood clot
14. Which makes up the integumentary system?
    - **a.** a network of nerves
    - **b.** white blood cells and antibodies
    - **c.** the brain and spinal cord
    - **d.** the skin, hair, and nails
15. Which structure is found in the epidermis layer of the skin?
    - **a.** pores
    - **b.** sweat glands
    - **c.** hair follicles
    - **d.** oil glands
16. The layer of fatty tissue below the dermis protects the body from
    - **a.** cold temperatures
    - **b.** bacteria
    - **c.** sunburn
    - **d.** infection

Short Answer *Write a short answer to each question.*

17. What are platelets? Where are they found?
18. What are antibodies? Where are they found?
19. What special structures are found in the dermis layer of the skin?

ASSESSMENT RESOURCES

UNIT ASSESSMENT BOOK
- Chapter Test A, pp. 44–47
- Chapter Test B, pp. 48–51
- Chapter Test C, pp. 52–55
- Alternative Assessment, pp. 56–57

SPANISH ASSESSMENT BOOK
Spanish Chapter Test, pp. 73–76

Technology Resources

Edit test items and answer choices.

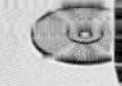

Test Generator CD-ROM

Visit **ClassZone.com** to extend test practice.

Test Practice

Reviewing Vocabulary

1. Sample answer: Capillaries connect arteries with veins. The exchange of oxygen and carbon dioxide takes place in the capillaries.

2. Sample answer: Blood is a fluid that carries materials and wastes through the body. Blood is made up of plasma, red blood cells, white blood cells, and platelets.

3. The dermis is the inner layer of the skin. Sweat glands and oil glands are found in the dermis.

4. Antigens are markers carried by pathogens. T cells recognize antigens on pathogens.

5. Certain white blood cells produce antibodies, which attack and kill pathogens in the body.

6. Arteries are blood vessels that carry blood away from the heart; veins carry blood back from the body to the heart.

7. Vaccines produce immunity, or resistance to diseases caused by viruses or bacteria.

Reviewing Key Concepts

8. b	*11. b*	*14. d*
9. a	*12. b*	*15. a*
10. d	*13. a*	*16. a*

17. Platelets are cell fragments in the blood, which help form blood clots.

18. Antibodies attack specific foreign materials. They are found in the circulatory and lymphatic systems.

19. sweat and oil glands, hair, nails, and sensory receptors

(Answers to items that appear on p. 668)

Thinking Critically

20. Atria receive blood; ventricles pump blood. Ventricles have thicker walls for the pumping of blood.

21. Pumping action pushes blood through the arteries, so valves are not needed.

22. Sweat, tears, and mucus contain substances that attack foreign materials. Tiny hairs in the nose and lungs trap particles and prevent them from passing through membranes.

(Answers for items 20–22 appear on p. 667.)

Thinking Critically

23. T cells identify and destroy pathogens in the blood and the lymph. As these cells are destroyed, the body is less able to protect itself against infection and disease.

24. Histamines raise the temperature of and increase blood flow to the injured area. White blood cells and antibodies move to the injured area.

25. Dead cells that make up the surface form a thick waterproof layer that prevents bacteria from entering the body.

26. Sweat glands: release fluid to cool skin; oil glands: secrete oils that help repel water, kill bacteria; hair: traps heat and keeps body warm.

27. Melanin is a pigment that determines how dark a person's skin is. People with darker skin are less likely to get sunburns. Repeated sunburns can increase a person's chances of getting skin cancer.

28–33. For answers, see p. 666.

the BIG idea

34. Answers should include blood pressure and functions of the heart and circulatory system.

35. The skin of the <u>integumentary system</u> forms a waterproof barrier that protects against foreign substances. Sweat and skin oil and mucus in the nose and throat trap harmful foreign substances and slow the growth of pathogens. White blood cells and antibodies of the <u>immune system</u> work together to kill invading bacteria.

UNIT PROJECTS

Check to make sure students are working on their projects. Check schedules and work in progress.

R Unit Projects, pp. 5–10

Thinking Critically

20. COMPARE AND CONTRAST How do the functions of the atria and ventricles of the heart differ? How are they alike? Use this diagram of the heart as a guide.

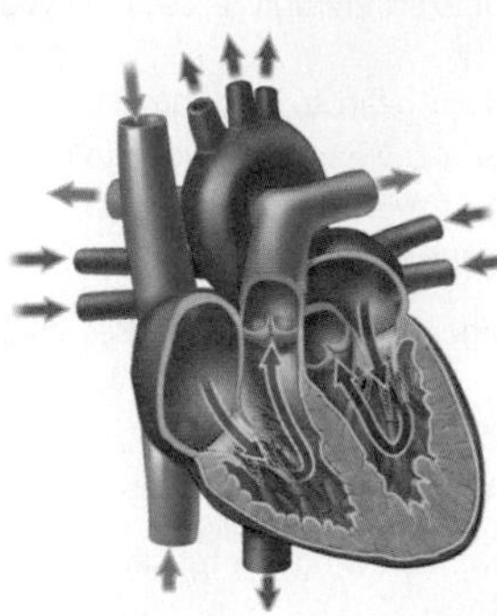

21. APPLY Veins have one-way valves that prevent the blood from flowing backwards. Most arteries do not have valves. Explain how these structures help the circulatory system function.

22. PROVIDE EXAMPLES Describe three structures in the body that help prevent harmful foreign substances from entering the body.

23. IDENTIFY CAUSE HIV is a virus that attacks and destroys the body's T cells. Why is a person who is infected with HIV more susceptible to infection and disease?

24. APPLY You fall and scrape your knee. How does the production of histamines aid the healing of this injury?

25. ANALYZE Describe how the structure of the epidermis helps protect the body from disease.

26. SYNTHESIZE Explain how sweat glands, oil glands, and hair help your body maintain homeostasis.

27. HYPOTHESIZE People with greater concentrations of melanin in their skin are less likely to get skin cancer than people who have lesser concentrations of melanin. Write a hypothesis explaining why this is so.

Answer the next six questions by listing the main structures and functions of the systems shown in the graphic organizer.

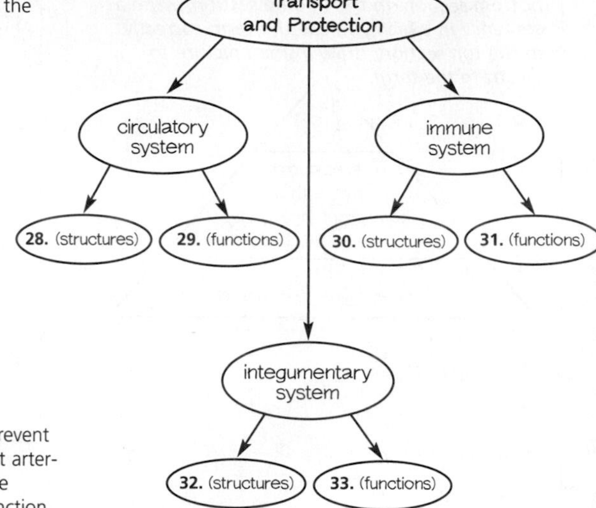

the BIG idea

34. INFER Look again at the picture on pages 638–639. Now that you have finished the chapter, how would you change or add details to your answer to the question on the photograph?

35. SYNTHESIZE Write a paragraph explaining how the integumentary system and the immune system work together to help your body maintain its homeostasis. Underline these terms in your paragraph.

UNIT PROJECTS

If you need to create graphs or other visuals for your project, be sure you have grid paper, poster board, markers, and other supplies.

MONITOR AND RETEACH

If students have trouble applying the concepts in Chapter Review items 22, 25, and 26, suggest they review the diagram on p. 660. Have students create concept maps for the following:

- structures in the body that prevent foreign materials from entering
- structures in the skin that protect the body from disease
- ways in which structures in the skin help the body maintain homeostasis

Students may benefit from summarizing sections of the chapter.

 Summarizing the Chapter, pp. 186–187

Standardized Test Practice

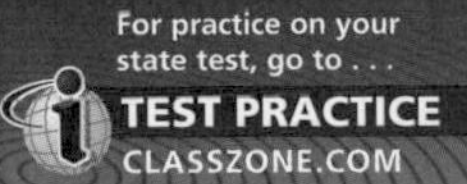

Analyzing Data

Choose the letter of the best answer.

This chart shows the amount of time a person can stay in sunlight without burning, based on skin type and use of a sunscreen with the SPF shown.

Minimum Sun Protection Factors (SPF)

Skin Type	1 hr	2 hr	3 hr	4 hr	5 hr
Very Fair/ Sensitive	15	30	30	45	45
Fair/Sensitive	15	15	30	30	45
Fair	15	15	15	30	30
Medium	8	8	15	15	30
Dark	4	8	8	15	15

1. What is the least SPF that a person with very fair skin should use while exposed to the sun?
a. 8
b. 15
c. 30
d. 45

2. If a person with a medium skin type is exposed to sunlight for 5 hours, which SPF should be used?
a. 4
b. 8
c. 15
d. 30

3. Which skin type requires SPF 30 for three hours of sun exposure?
a. fair/sensitive
b. fair
c. medium
d. dark

4. Based on the data in the chart, which statement is a reasonable conclusion?
a. People with a fair skin type are less prone to UV damage than those with a dark skin type.
b. The darker the skin type, the more SPF protection a person needs.
c. A person with a fair skin type does not need as much SPF protection as a person with a medium skin type.
d. If exposure to sunlight is longer, then a person needs a higher SPF for protection.

5. If a person normally burns after 10 minutes with no protection, an SPF 2 would protect that person for 20 minutes. How long would the same person be protected with SPF 15?
a. 1 hour
b. $1\frac{1}{2}$ hours
c. 2 hours
d. $2\frac{1}{2}$ hours

Extended Response

6. UV index levels are often broadcast with daily weather reports. A UV index of 0 to 2 indicates that it would take an average person about 60 minutes to burn. A UV index level of 10 indicates that it would take the average person about 10 minutes to burn. Write a paragraph describing some variable conditions that would affect this rate. Include both environmental as well as conditions that would apply to an individual.

7. Sun protection factors are numbers on a scale that rate the effectiveness of sunscreen. Without the use of sunscreen, UV rays from the Sun can cause sunburns. People who spend time in sunlight without protection, or who get repeated burns are at a higher risk of developing deadly forms of skin cancer. Based on the information in the table and your knowledge of the layers of the skin, design a brochure encouraging people to protect their skin from sunlight. Include in your brochure the harmful effects on your skin and ways to protect your skin from harmful UV rays.

METACOGNITIVE ACTIVITY

Have students answer the following questions in their **Science Notebook:**

1. What interests you most about the circulatory system?
2. What were you surprised to find out about the immune or integumentary system?
3. How have you accomplished the objectives for your unit project?

Analyzing Data

1. b *3. a* *5. d*
2. d *4. d*

Extended Response

6. RUBRIC

4 points for a response that correctly identifies both environmental and individual factors and includes these terms:

- SPF
- melanin

Sample answer: UV index levels may be affected by environmental conditions such as the time of day, the weather, the amount of cloud coverage, the season, and the location. Conditions that affect an individual would include the fairness or darkness of the skin, the amount of melanin present in the skin, the amount of time spent in the Sun, and the protection used, such as clothing or sunscreen with a particular SPF.

3 points correctly answers the question and includes a description of environmental factors and individual factors
2 points correctly answers the question and includes a description of either environmental factors or individual factors
1 point correctly identifies at least one environmental or individual factor

7. RUBRIC

4 points for a brochure that includes all of the following:

- harmful effects of UV rays
- ways to protect skin from UV rays
- a description of SPF rating
- a description of differences in the skin of individuals

Sample answer: Overexposure to UV rays can eventually lead to skin cancers. Use protection based on your skin type and the length of time you are exposed to the Sun. In addition, stay out of the Sun during peak hours from 10:00 A.M. to 2:00 P.M., wear hats, sunglasses, and cover-ups. Sunscreens are given SPF ratings according to how long they will provide protection from harmful UV rays. People with fair skin should use a sunscreen with an SPF of at least 45 during prolonged exposure to the Sun.

3 points includes at least three of the elements listed above
2 points includes at least two of the elements listed above
1 point includes at least one of the elements listed above

FOCUS

Set Learning Goals

Students will

- Examine technological advances that allow observation of the inner workings of the human body.
- Learn about some of the applications of the new technologies.
- Chart the different types of medical imaging and explain how they work.

National Science Education Standards

A.9.a–g Understandings About Scientific Inquiry

E.6.a–c Understandings About Science and Technology

F.5.a–e, F.5.g Science and Technology in Society

G.1.a–b Science as a Human Endeavor

G.2.a Nature of Science

G.3.a–c History of Science

INSTRUCT

Point out that the top half of the timeline depicts scientific progress in observing the inner workings of the human body. The bottom half of the timeline provides examples of technology and their application to that study. The gaps represent blocks of time that have been omitted.

Integrate the Sciences

Wilhelm Roentgen studied mechanical engineering and taught physics at several universities. When he discovered X-rays, he was studying the passage of electric current through gas. For his discovery he won the Nobel Prize in Physics in 1901.

TIMELINES in Science

SEEING INSIDE the Body

What began as a chance accident in a darkened room was only the beginning. Today, technology allows people to produce clear and complete pictures of the human body. From X-rays to ultrasound to the latest computerized scans, accidental discoveries have enabled us to study and diagnose the inner workings of the human body.

Being able to see inside the body without cutting it open would have seemed unthinkable in the early 1890s. But within a year of the discovery of the X-ray in 1895, doctors were using technology to see through flesh to bones. In the time since then, techniques for making images have advanced to allow doctors to see soft tissue, muscle, and even to see how body systems work in real time. Many modern employ X-ray technology, while others employ sound waves or magnetic fields.

1895

Accidental X-Ray Shows Bones

Working alone in a darkened lab to study electric currents passing through vacuum tubes, William Conrad Roentgen sees a mysterious light. He puts his hand between the tubes and a screen, and an image appears on the screen—a skeletal hand! He names his discovery the X-ray, since the images are produced by rays behaving like none known before them. Roentgen uses photographic paper to take the first X-ray picture, his wife's hand.

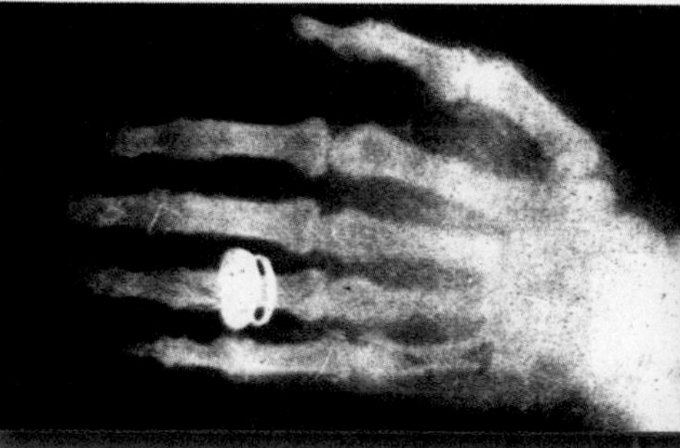

EVENTS

1880 | 1890

APPLICATIONS AND TECHNOLOGY

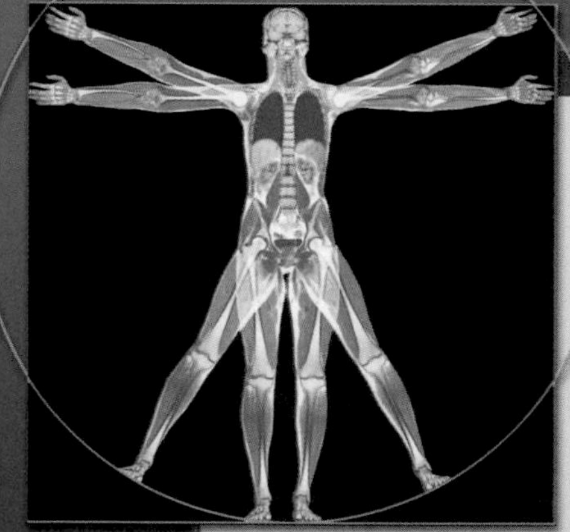

APPLICATION

Doctor Detectives

Within a year of Roentgen's discovery, X-rays were used in medicine for examining patients. By the 1920s, their use was wide-spread. Modern day X-ray tubes are based on the design of William Coolidge. Around 1913, Coolidge developed a new X-ray tube which, unlike the old gas tube, provides consistent exposure and quality. X-ray imaging changed the practice of medicine by allowing doctors to look inside the body without using surgery. Today, X-ray images, and other technologies, like the MRI used to produce the image at the left, show bones, organs, and tissues.

DIFFERENTIATE INSTRUCTION

Below Level Have students make a timeline of their lives with index cards. Each card can represent a year. They can tape the cards together and record special events in news, sports, weather, or their own lives.

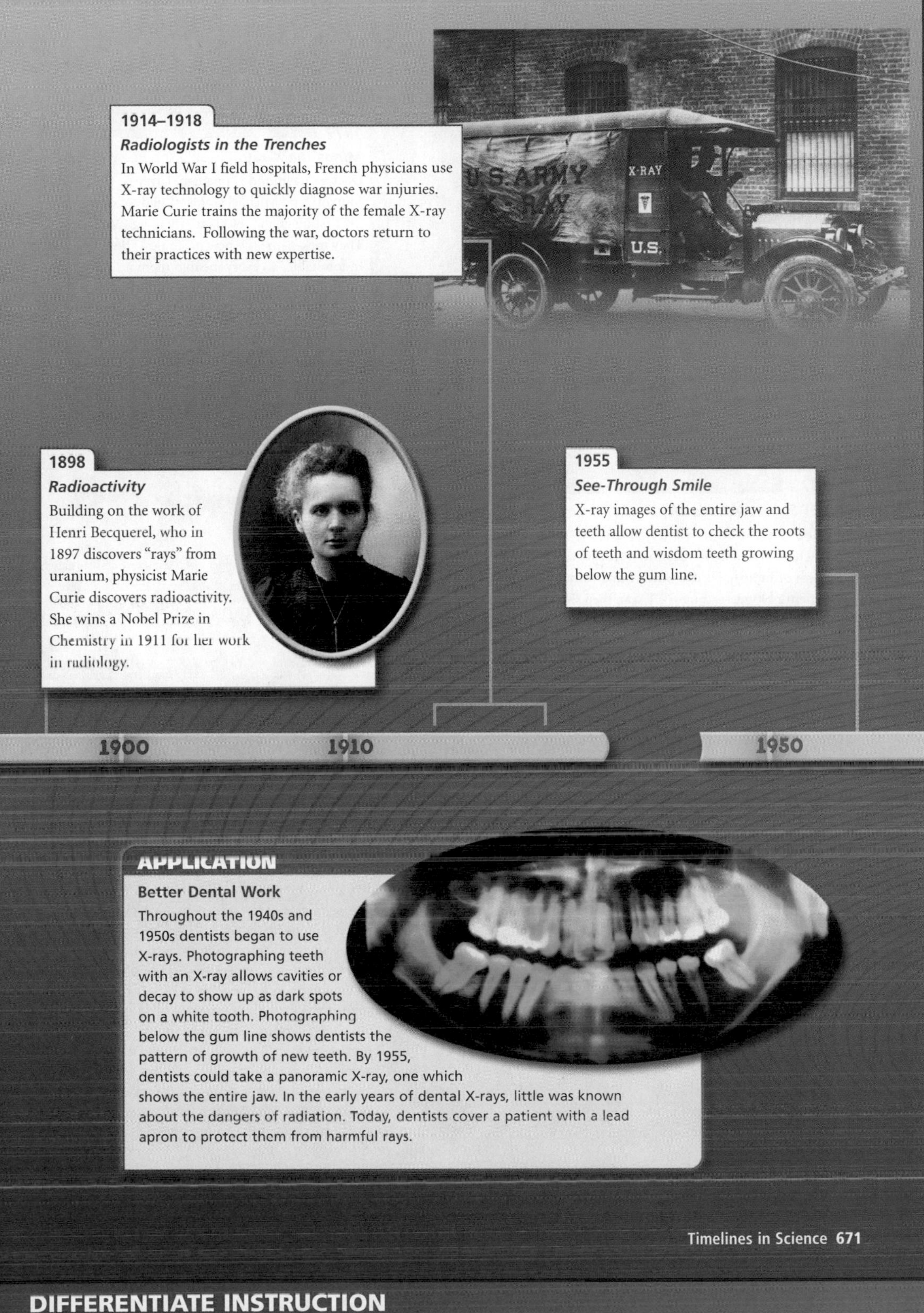

1914–1918

Radiologists in the Trenches

In World War I field hospitals, French physicians use X-ray technology to quickly diagnose war injuries. Marie Curie trains the majority of the female X-ray technicians. Following the war, doctors return to their practices with new expertise.

1898

Radioactivity

Building on the work of Henri Becquerel, who in 1897 discovers "rays" from uranium, physicist Marie Curie discovers radioactivity. She wins a Nobel Prize in Chemistry in 1911 for her work in radiology.

1955

See-Through Smile

X-ray images of the entire jaw and teeth allow dentist to check the roots of teeth and wisdom teeth growing below the gum line.

APPLICATION

Better Dental Work

Throughout the 1940s and 1950s dentists began to use X-rays. Photographing teeth with an X-ray allows cavities or decay to show up as dark spots on a white tooth. Photographing below the gum line shows dentists the pattern of growth of new teeth. By 1955, dentists could take a panoramic X-ray, one which shows the entire jaw. In the early years of dental X-rays, little was known about the dangers of radiation. Today, dentists cover a patient with a lead apron to protect them from harmful rays.

Scientific Process

Have students name the skill that scientists are practicing when they use technology to see inside the body. *making observations*

Technology

1898 Tell students that radioactive elements such as uranium and radium, with which Marie Curie worked extensively, give off radiation that can make a person sick. Ask: What technological step was important in using radiation in medicine? *improvement in safe handling procedures*

Integrate the Sciences

The radioactivity of different elements can vary widely. For example, a gram of radium emits about one million times more radiation than a gram of uranium. Therefore, there are two common units for measuring radioactivity: the becquerel (Bq) and the curie (Ci). One Bq equals one particle of radiation released per second. One Ci is equal to the number of particles of radiation released per second by one gram of radium.

DIFFERENTIATE INSTRUCTION

Advanced One of Marie Curie's legacies is the use of radiation to treat cancer. Have students research this topic and give an oral presentation to the class.

Scientific Process

Have students identify the part of the scientific process undertaken by Damadian, Minkoff, and Goldsmith when they worked on the first MRI, despite being told that it couldn't be done. *proving old theories false*

Application

1976 The use of computers in medicine has opened many doors for doctors today. An entire new field, medical informatics, is developing. For instance, the computer can develop models that take the patient's information, including scan results, and plan a course of treatment.

Technology

ULTRASOUND An echocardiogram uses ultrasound to show a heart beating. It helps doctors diagnose some types of heart disease, find tumors or blood clots in the heart, and monitor the heart after a heart attack.

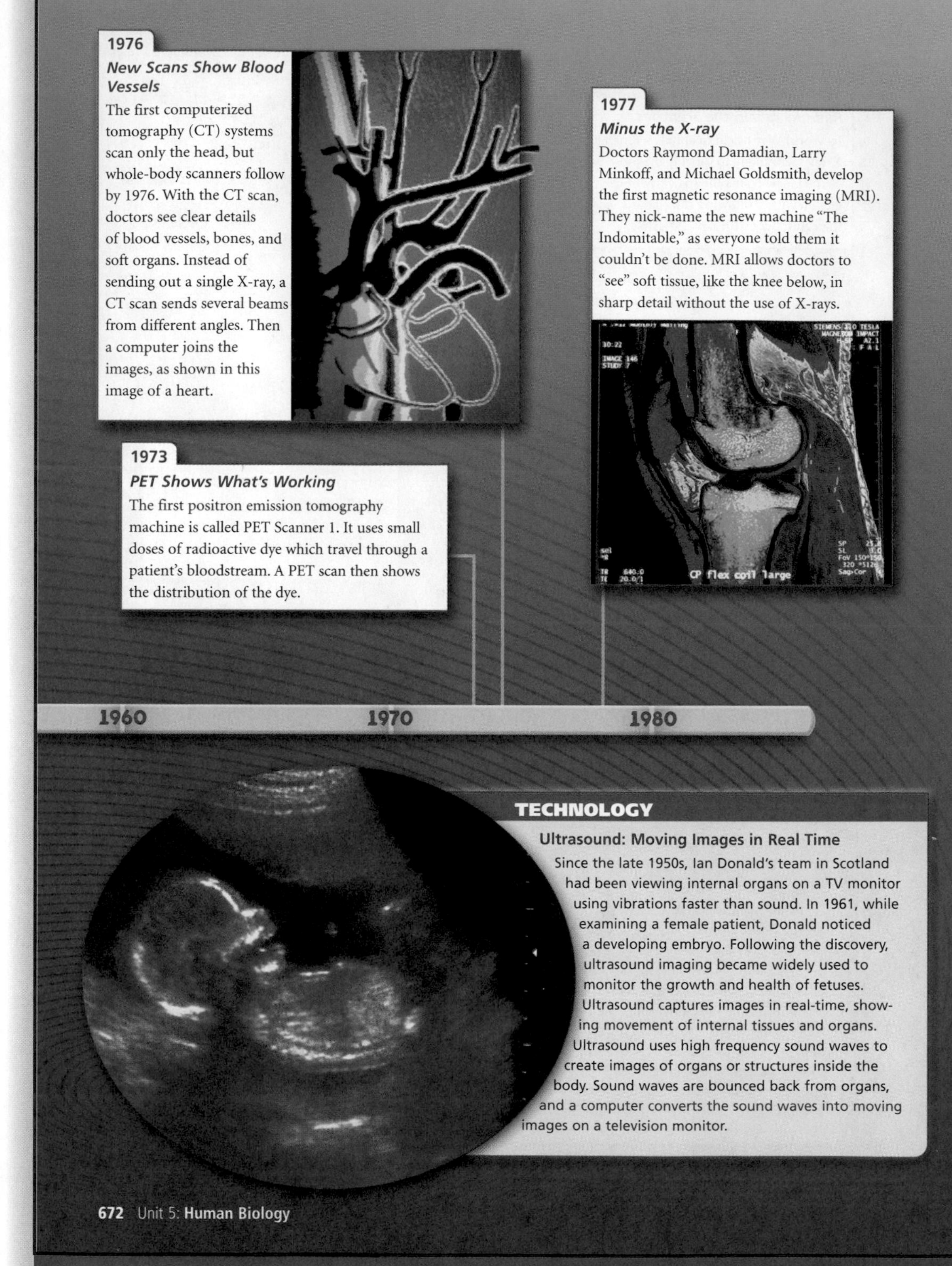

1976

New Scans Show Blood Vessels

The first computerized tomography (CT) systems scan only the head, but whole-body scanners follow by 1976. With the CT scan, doctors see clear details of blood vessels, bones, and soft organs. Instead of sending out a single X-ray, a CT scan sends several beams from different angles. Then a computer joins the images, as shown in this image of a heart.

1977

Minus the X-ray

Doctors Raymond Damadian, Larry Minkoff, and Michael Goldsmith, develop the first magnetic resonance imaging (MRI). They nick-name the new machine "The Indomitable," as everyone told them it couldn't be done. MRI allows doctors to "see" soft tissue, like the knee below, in sharp detail without the use of X-rays.

1973

PET Shows What's Working

The first positron emission tomography machine is called PET Scanner 1. It uses small doses of radioactive dye which travel through a patient's bloodstream. A PET scan then shows the distribution of the dye.

1960 1970 1980

TECHNOLOGY

Ultrasound: Moving Images in Real Time

Since the late 1950s, Ian Donald's team in Scotland had been viewing internal organs on a TV monitor using vibrations faster than sound. In 1961, while examining a female patient, Donald noticed a developing embryo. Following the discovery, ultrasound imaging became widely used to monitor the growth and health of fetuses. Ultrasound captures images in real-time, showing movement of internal tissues and organs. Ultrasound uses high frequency sound waves to create images of organs or structures inside the body. Sound waves are bounced back from organs, and a computer converts the sound waves into moving images on a television monitor.

672 Unit 5: **Human Biology**

DIFFERENTIATE INSTRUCTION

Advanced Have students research the costs of medical imaging, including the cost of buying the machines, training personnel, and performing the procedure. Have them calculate how many patients must use the technology before it starts to make money for the clinic or hospital.

1990s

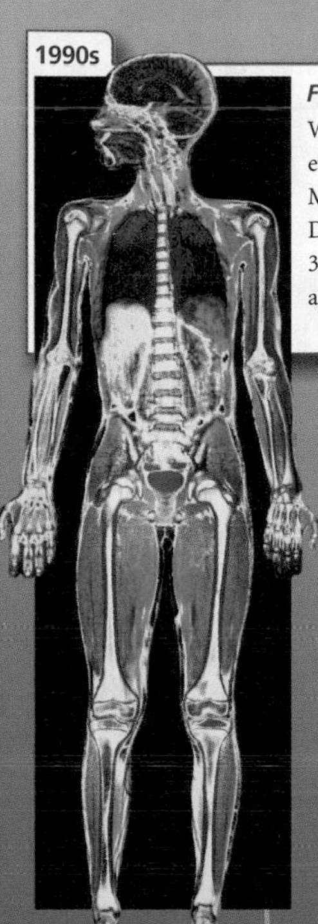

Filmless Images
With digital imaging, everything from X-rays to MRIs is now filmless. Data move directly into 3-D computer programs and shared databases.

2003
Multi-Slice CT
By 2003, 8- and 16-slice CT scanners offer detail and speed. A multi-slice scanner reduces exam time from 45 minutes to under 10 seconds.

RESOURCE CENTER
CLASSZONE.COM
Find more on advances in medical imaging.

1990 2000

TECHNOLOGY

3-D Images and Brain Surgery

In operating rooms, surgeons are beginning to use another type of 3-D ultrasound known as interventional MRI. They watch 3-D images in real time and observe details of tissues while they operate. These integrated technologies now allow scientists to conduct entirely new types of studies. For example, 3-D brain images of many patients with one disease—can now be integrated into a composite image of a "typical" brain of someone with that disease.

INTO THE FUTURE

Although discovered over 100 years ago X-rays are certain to remain a key tool of health workers for many years. What will be different in the future? Dentists have begun the trend to stop using film images, and rely on digital X-rays instead. In the future, all scans may be viewed and stored on computers. Going digital allows doctors across the globe to share images quickly by email.

Magnetic resonance imaging has only been in widespread use for about 20 years. Look for increased brain mapping—ability to scan the brain during a certain task. The greater the collective data on brain-mapping, the better scientists will understand how the brain works. To produce such an image requires thousands of patients and trillions of bytes of computer memory.

Also look for increased speed and mobile MRI scanners, which will be used in emergency rooms and doctor's offices to quickly assess internal damage after an accident or injury.

ACTIVITIES

Writing About Science: Brochure

Make a chart of the different types of medical imaging used to diagnose one body system. Include an explanation of how the technique works and list the pros and cons of using it.

Reliving History

X-rays use radioactivity which can be dangerous. You can use visible light to shine through thin materials that you don't normally see through. Try using a flashlight to illuminate a leaf. Discuss or draw what you see.

DIFFERENTIATE INSTRUCTION

Below Level Have a group of students work on the chart, each student tackling a different kind of imaging. They could find and include photographs of the procedure being done.

Technology

1990s Using digital imaging for dental X-rays reduces the radiation to which patients are exposed by about 90 percent. Instead of inserting film into a patient's mouth, dentists insert electronic sensors. These sensors develop images that are viewed on a computer screen. Ask: Why is this technology an improvement over the old X-rays? *It exposes patients to less radiation, which can be harmful in large doses; it reduces use of film.*

INTO THE FUTURE

Have students brainstorm some technological advances that might further improve our understanding of the inner body. Discuss the feasibility of the fictional *Star Trek* medical tricorder, which reveals a patient's condition after merely skimming the patient's body.

ACTIVITIES

Writing About Science: Brochure

Have students produce a decision tree that a physician could show patients to explain why one imaging technique is best for their circumstances.

Reliving History

Students can also aim a flashlight inside their mouths and see through their cheeks.

Technology Resources

Students can visit **ClassZone.com** for current news about medical imaging.

CHAPTER

Control and Reproduction

Life Science
UNIFYING PRINCIPLES

PRINCIPLE 1
All living things share common characteristics.

PRINCIPLE 2
All living things share common needs.

PRINCIPLE 3
Living things meet their needs through interactions with the environment.

PRINCIPLE 4
The types and numbers of living things change over time.

Unit 5: Human Biology
BIG IDEAS

CHAPTER 17
Systems, Support, and Movement
The human body is made up of systems that work together to perform necessary functions.

CHAPTER 18
Absorption, Digestion, and Exchange
Systems in the body obtain and process materials and remove waste.

CHAPTER 19
Transport and Protection
Systems function to transport materials and to defend and protect the body.

CHAPTER 20
Control and Reproduction
The nervous and endocrine systems allow the body to respond to internal and external conditions.

CHAPTER 21
Growth, Development, and Health
The body develops and maintains itself over time.

CHAPTER 20
KEY CONCEPTS

SECTION 1

The nervous system responds and controls.

1. Senses connect the human body to its environment.
2. The central nervous system controls functions.
3. The peripheral nervous system is a network of nerves.

SECTION 2

The endocrine system helps regulate body conditions.

1. Hormones are the body's chemical messengers.
2. Glands produce and release hormones.
3. Control of the endocrine system includes feedback mechanisms.

SECTION 3

The reproductive system allows the production of offspring.

1. The reproductive system produces specialized cells.
2. The reproduction of offspring includes fertilization, pregnancy, and birth.

T The Big Idea Flow Chart is available on p. T25 in the **UNIT TRANSPARENCY BOOK.**

Previewing Content

SECTION

The nervous system responds and controls. pp. 677–685

1. Senses connect the human body to its environment.
Senses monitor the environment to help maintain homeostasis.
- The eye collects, bends, and focuses light into an image.
- Sensory receptors in the skin detect pressure, texture, pain, and temperature.
- Ears perceive sound waves, which are produced by vibrations.
- Olfactory nerves in the nose perceive the presence of chemicals in the air.
- Taste buds on the tongue perceive chemicals in food.

2. The central nervous system controls functions.
The brain and spinal cord are the **central nervous system.** They communicate with the rest of the nervous system through electrical signals sent to and from neurons.
- Every area of the brain has a specific function, controlling both voluntary and involuntary responses. Some of these areas appear in the figure below.

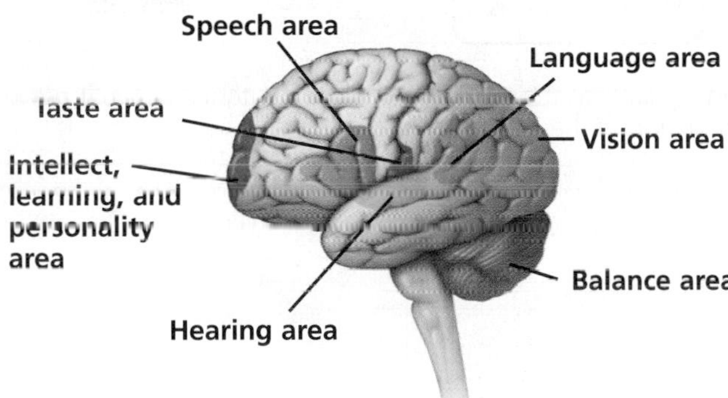

- The spinal cord is the main pathway for information. It is protected and supported by the vertebral column.

3. The peripheral nervous system is a network of nerves.
The **autonomic nervous system** controls involuntary responses such as digestion and heartbeat. The voluntary nervous system monitors and controls conscious functions.

SECTION

The endocrine system helps regulate body conditions. pp. 686–693

1. Hormones are the body's chemical messengers.
Hormones are chemicals made in one organ to trigger response in another organ. The **endocrine system** uses hormones to control conditions in the body.

2. Glands produce and release hormones.
- The pituitary gland directs the endocrine system. Its hormones control growth, sexual development, and water absorption.
- The hypothalamus is the part of the brain that controls the pituitary gland.
- The pineal gland regulates sleep, body temperature, reproduction, and aging.
- The thyroid gland produces hormones for growth and metabolism.
- The thymus helps the body fight disease.
- The adrenal glands produce about 30 hormones that regulate food metabolism, water and salt levels, immunity, and response to stress.
- The pancreas produces insulin, which regulates glucose levels in the blood.

3. Control of the endocrine system includes feedback mechanisms.
- Negative feedback mechanisms help maintain homeostasis.

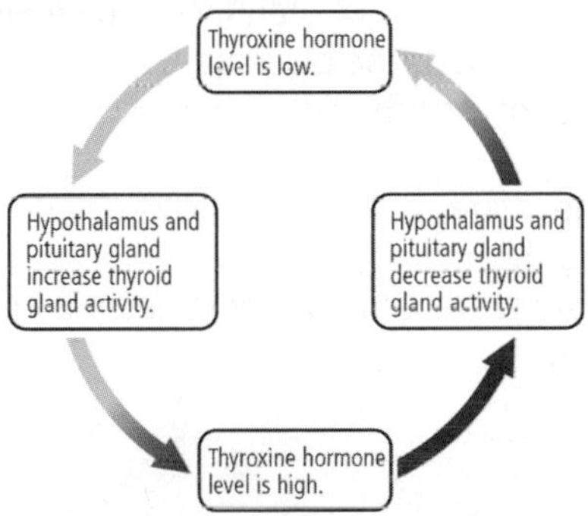

- Positive feedback mechanisms, like blood clotting, result in extreme responses.
- Some hormone action is regulated by a hormone that produces an opposite action.
- Hormone imbalance can cause serious disease.

Common Misconceptions

THE BRAIN Students sometimes think that the body performs some functions without needing the brain. In fact, the brain is in control of all functions of the body.

 This misconception is addressed on p. 682.

MISCONCEPTION DATABASE
CLASSZONE.COM Background on student misconceptions

SECTION

The reproductive system allows the production of offspring.

pp. 694–701

1. **The reproductive system produces specialized cells.** The female produces eggs; the male produces sperm. These specialized cells contain genetic material. The female reproductive system has two functions: to produce eggs and to protect and nourish the offspring until birth.
    - The pituitary gland stimulates eggs in the ovary to grow.
    - An egg is released into the fallopian tube, where it may be fertilized by a sperm cell.
    - The egg moves to the uterus, where, if fertilized, it implants in the uterine wall.
    - If not fertilized, the egg and the uterine lining exit the body through the vagina, in a process called **menstruation.**

    The male reproductive system contains the testes, which produce sperm, and the urethra, which is a canal through the penis. Sperm move through the urethra and exit the penis.

2. **The reproduction of offspring includes fertilization, pregnancy, and birth.**
    - **Fertilization** is the joining of one egg cell and one sperm cell.
    - Once fertilized, the egg divides, producing an **embryo.** Cells in the embryo continue dividing.
    - The embryo implants in the spongy lining of the uterus.
    - During the nine months of pregnancy, the embryo grows and develops, fed through the placenta.
    - The first stage of birth begins with muscular contractions of the uterus.
    - In the second stage, the cervix is fully dilated and the baby leaves the mother.
    - In the third stage the umbilical cord is cut and the placenta exits the body.

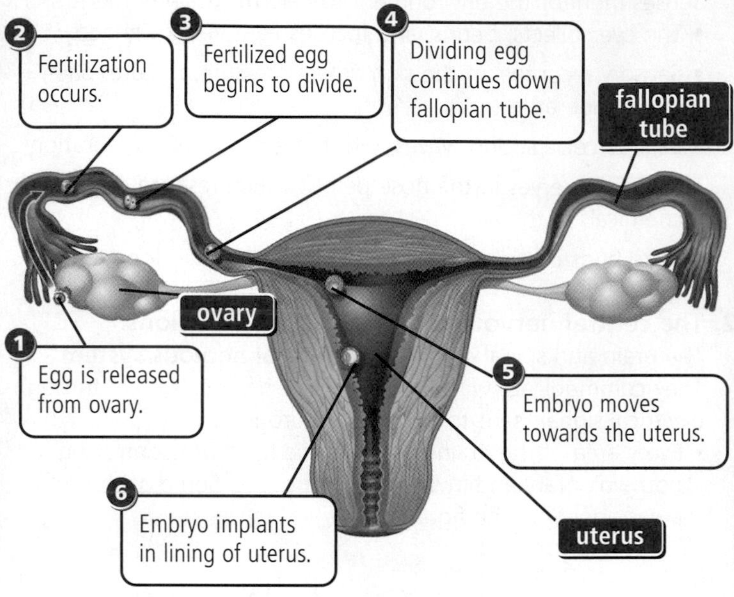

An embryo implants in the spongy lining of the uterus, where it grows and develops during the nine months of pregnancy.

Common Misconceptions

MISCONCEPTION DATABASE
CLASSZONE.COM Background on student misconceptions

THE UNION OF EGG AND SPERM Students sometimes think that the egg contains life, with the sperm needed to trigger growth, or that the sperm contains life, with the egg needed for protection and nourishment. Neither contain life as neither type of cell can divide or reproduce on its own. Life results when they join.

 This misconception is addressed on p. 695.

Previewing Labs

Lab Generator CD-ROM
Edit these Pupil Edition labs and generate alternative labs.

EXPLORE the BIG idea

Color Confusion, p. 675 Students create conflicting visual stimuli with colors and words in order to observe sensory confusion.	**TIME** 10 minutes **MATERIALS** paper, 6 different-colored markers
Eggs, p. 675 Students observe a chicken egg to learn the parts and functions of an egg.	**TIME** 10 minutes **MATERIALS** egg, small bowl
Internet Activity: The Senses, p. 675 Students view how each sense sends specific information to the brain.	**TIME** 20 minutes **MATERIALS** computer with Internet access

SECTION 1

EXPLORE Smell, p. 677 Students explore their sense of smell, testing it with three unknowns.	**TIME** 10 minutes **MATERIALS** 3 bags, an orange, a pine branch, a cinnamon stick
CHAPTER INVESTIGATION **Are You a Supertaster?** pp. 684–685 Students take impressions of their fungiform papillae to infer possible connections between tastebuds and sensitivity to flavors.	**TIME** 40 minutes **MATERIALS** blue food coloring, paper cup, cotton swab, reinforcement circle, paper towel or napkin, white paper, notebook

SECTION 2

INVESTIGATE Response to Exercise, p. 690 Students record their body temperatures before and during exercise to observe a physical response.	**TIME** 30 minutes **MATERIALS** stopwatch, graph paper, mercury-free thermometer, rubbing alcohol or plastic thermometer covers

SECTION 3

EXPLORE Reproduction, p. 694 Students observe and contrast egg and sperm cells under a microscope.	**TIME** 20 minutes **MATERIALS** microscope, slides of egg and sperm cells, paper and pencil

Additional INVESTIGATION, Taste That Smell!, A, B, & C, pp. 235–243; Teacher Instructions, pp. 305–306

Previewing Chapter Resources

	INTEGRATED TECHNOLOGY	LABS AND ACTIVITIES
CHAPTER 20 **Control and Reproduction**	 **CLASSZONE.COM** • eEdition Plus • EasyPlanner Plus • Misconception Database • Content Review • Test Practice • Visualization • Resource Centers • Internet Activity: The Senses • Math Tutorial  **SCILINKS.ORG**   **CD-ROMS** • eEdition • EasyPlanner • Power Presentations • Content Review • Lab Generator • Test Generator **AUDIO CDS** • Audio Readings • Audio Readings in Spanish	 EXPLORE the Big Idea, p. 675 • Color Confusion • Eggs • Internet Activity: The Senses  **UNIT RESOURCE BOOK** Unit Projects, pp. 5–10  **Lab Generator CD-ROM** Generate customized labs.
SECTION 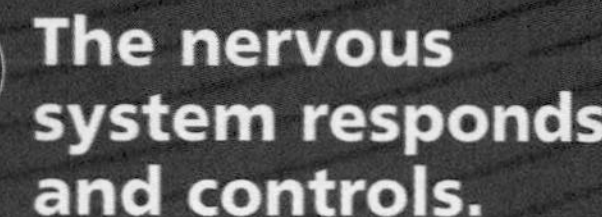 1 **The nervous system responds and controls.** pp. 677–685 Time: 3 periods (1.5 blocks)  Lesson Plan, pp. 188–189	 **RESOURCE CENTER,** Nervous System **UNIT TRANSPARENCY BOOK** • Big Idea Flow Chart, p. T25 • Daily Vocabulary Scaffolding, p. T26 • Note-Taking Model, p. T27 • 3-Minute Warm-Up, p. T28	 • EXPLORE Smell, p. 677 • CHAPTER INVESTIGATION, Are You a Supertaster? pp. 684–685  **UNIT RESOURCE BOOK** • CHAPTER INVESTIGATION, Are You a Supertaster? A, B, & C, pp. 226–234 • Additional INVESTIGATION, Taste That Smell!, A, B, & C, pp. 235–243
SECTION 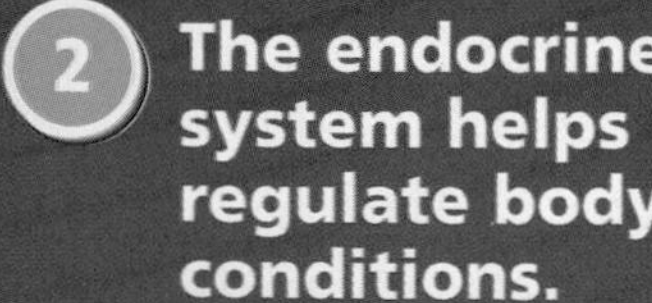 2 **The endocrine system helps regulate body conditions.** pp. 686–693 Time: 2 periods (1 block) Lesson Plan, pp. 198–299	 **RESOURCE CENTER,** Endocrine System  **UNIT TRANSPARENCY BOOK** • Daily Vocabulary Scaffolding, p. T26 • 3-Minute Warm-Up, p. T28 • "Endocrine System" Visual, p. T30	 • INVESTIGATE Response to Exercise, p. 690 • Connecting Sciences, p. 693  **UNIT RESOURCE BOOK** Datasheet, Response to Exercise, p. 207
SECTION  3 **The reproductive system allows the production of offspring.** pp. 694–701 Time: 3 periods (1.5 blocks)  Lesson Plan, pp. 209–210	 • **VISUALIZATION,** Fertilization • **MATH TUTORIAL**  **UNIT TRANSPARENCY BOOK** • Big Idea Flow Chart, p. T25 • Daily Vocabulary Scaffolding, p. T26 • 3-Minute Warm-Up, p. T29 • Chapter Outline, pp. T31–T32	 • EXPLORE Reproduction, p. 694 • Math in Science, p. 701  **UNIT RESOURCE BOOK** • Math Support, p. 224 • Math Practice, p. 225

KEY TO ICONS

 CD/CD-ROM

 Teacher Edition

 UNIT TRANSPARENCY BOOK

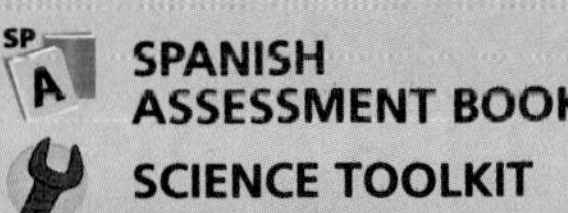 SPANISH ASSESSMENT BOOK

 INTERNET

 Pupil Edition

 UNIT RESOURCE BOOK

 UNIT ASSESSMENT BOOK

SCIENCE TOOLKIT

READING AND REINFORCEMENT

- Description Wheel, B20–21
- Choose Your Own Strategy, C35–44
- Daily Vocabulary Scaffolding, H1–8

UNIT RESOURCE BOOK

- Vocabulary Practice, p. 221–222
- Decoding Support, p. 223
- Summarizing the Chapter, pp. 244–245

Audio Readings CD
Listen to Pupil Edition.

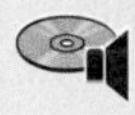

Audio Readings in Spanish CD
Listen to Pupil Edition in Spanish.

ASSESSMENT

- Chapter Review, pp. 703–704
- Standardized Test Practice, p. 705

UNIT ASSESSMENT BOOK

- Diagnostic Test, pp. 58–59
- Chapter Test, A, B, & C, pp. 63–74
- Alternative Assessment, pp. 75–76

Spanish Chapter Test, pp. 93–96

Test Generator CD-ROM
Generate customized tests.

Lab Generator CD-ROM
Rubrics for Labs

STANDARDS

National Standards
A.1–8, A.9.a–c, A.9.e–g, C.1.d–e, C.2.a–c, G.1.b

See p. 674 for the standards.

UNIT RESOURCE BOOK

- Reading Study Guide, A & B, pp. 190–193
- Spanish Reading Study Guide, pp. 194–195
- Challenge and Extension, p. 196
- Reinforcing Key Concepts, p. 1673
- Challenge Reading, pp. 219–220

Ongoing Assessment, pp. 678–681, 683

Section 20.1 Review, p. 683

UNIT ASSESSMENT BOOK
Section 20.1 Quiz, p. 60

National Standards
A.1–7, A.9.a–b, A.9.e–g, C.1.e, G.1.b

UNIT RESOURCE BOOK

- Reading Study Guide, A & B, pp. 200–203
- Spanish Reading Study Guide, pp. 204–205
- Challenge and Extension, p. 206
- Reinforcing Key Concepts, p. 208

Ongoing Assessment, pp. 687–690, 692

Section 20.2 Review, p. 692

UNIT ASSESSMENT BOOK
Section 20.2 Quiz, p. 61

National Standards
A.2–7, A.9.a–b, A.9.e–f, C.1.e, G.1.b

UNIT RESOURCE BOOK

- Reading Study Guide, A & B, pp. 211–214
- Spanish Reading Study Guide, pp. 215–216
- Challenge and Extension, p. 217
- Reinforcing Key Concepts, p. 218

Ongoing Assessment, pp. 695–700

Section 20.3 Review, p. 700

UNIT ASSESSMENT BOOK
Section 20.3 Quiz, p. 62

National Standards
A.2–8, A.9.a–c, A.9.e–f, C.1.d, C.2.a–c, G.1.b

Previewing Resources for Differentiated Instruction

CHAPTER INVESTIGATION

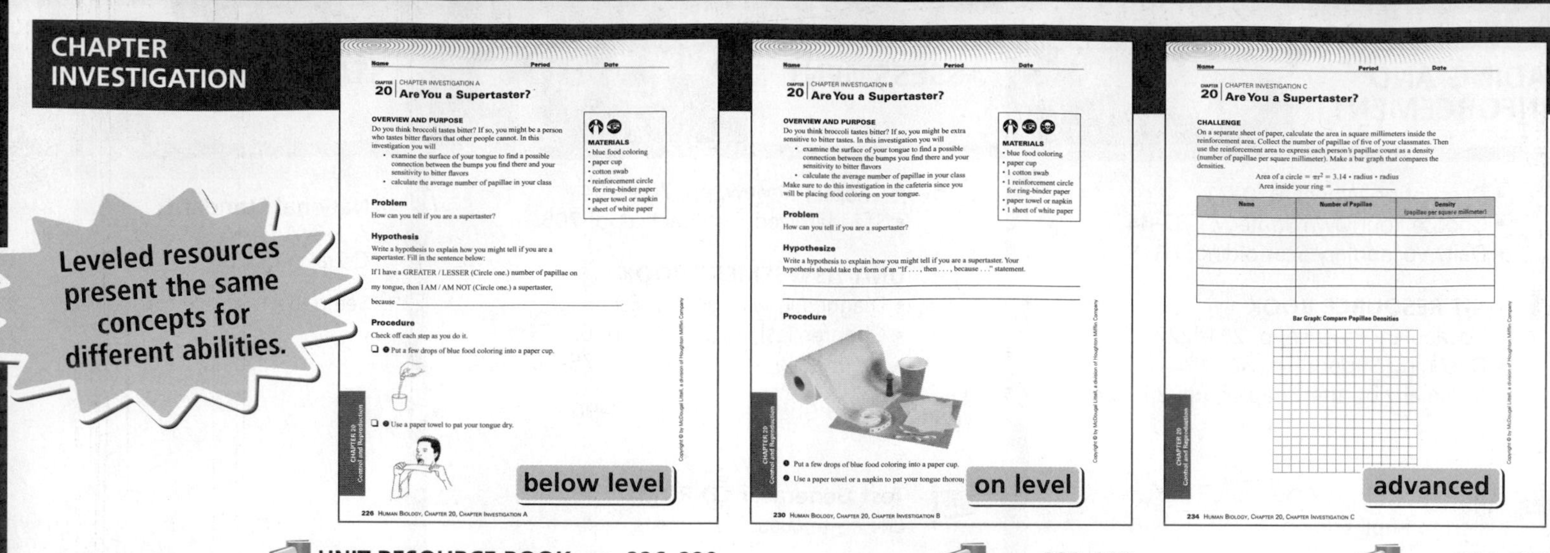

UNIT RESOURCE BOOK, pp. 226–229 pp. 230–233 pp. 230–234

READING STUDY GUIDE

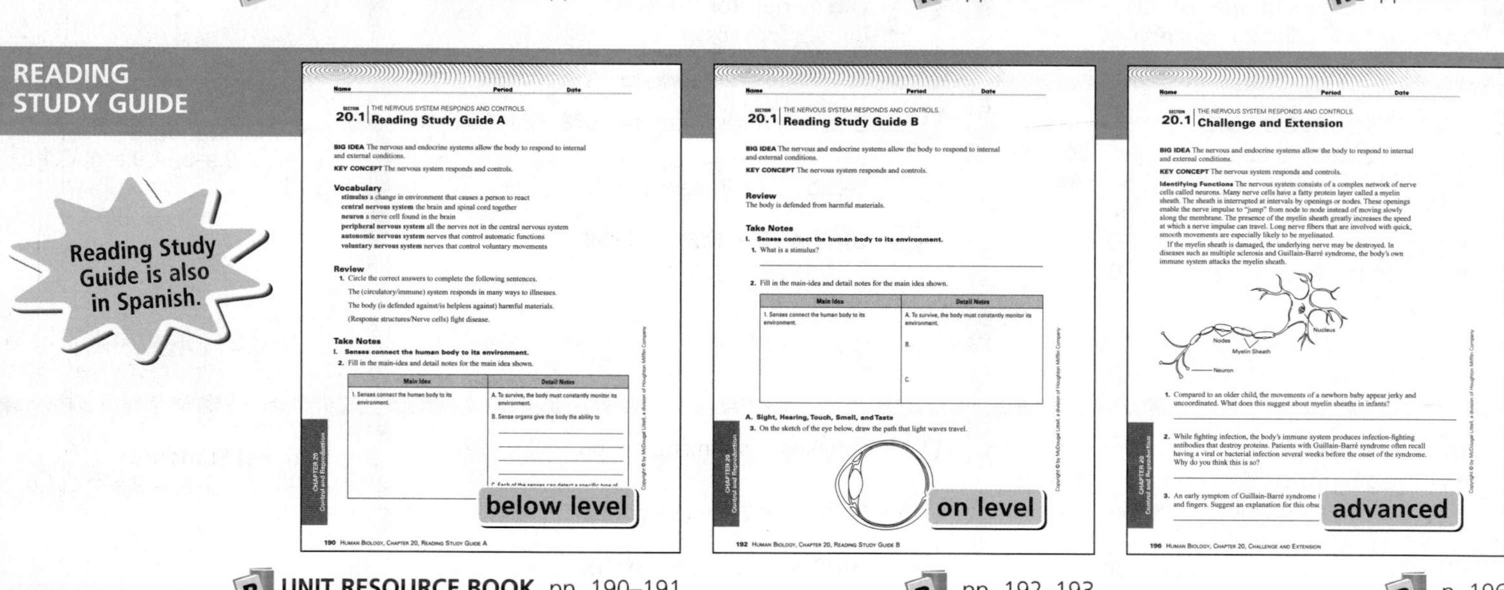

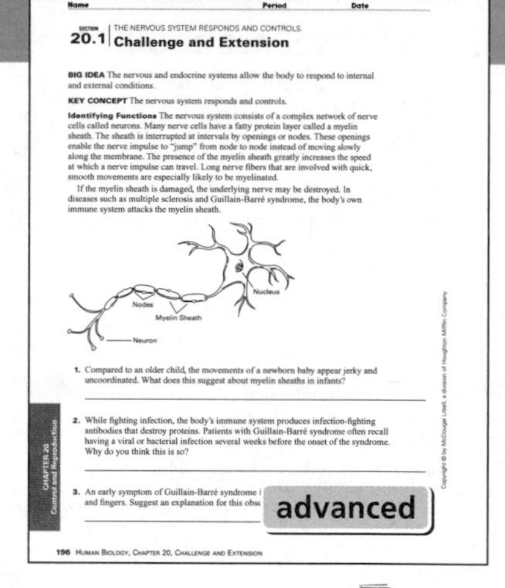

UNIT RESOURCE BOOK, pp. 190–191 pp. 192–193 p. 196

CHAPTER TEST

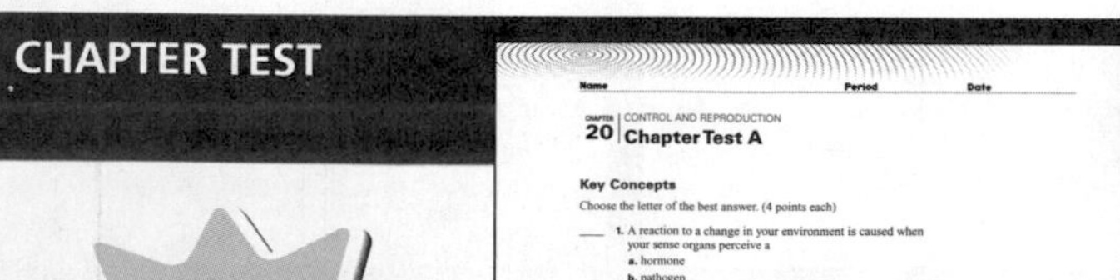

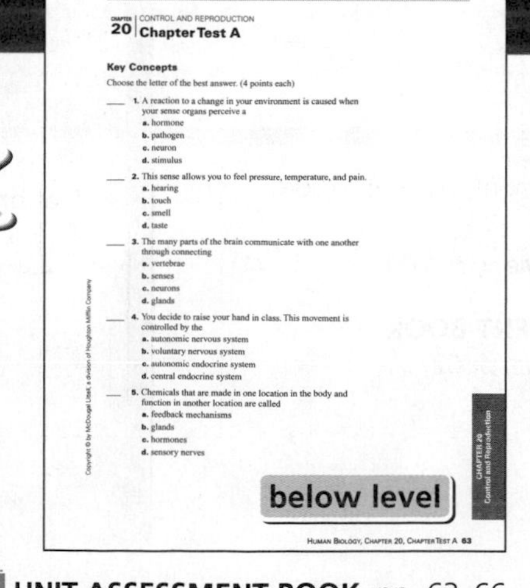

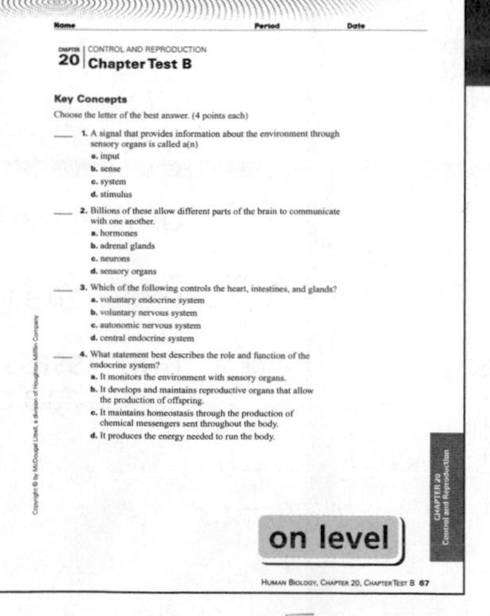

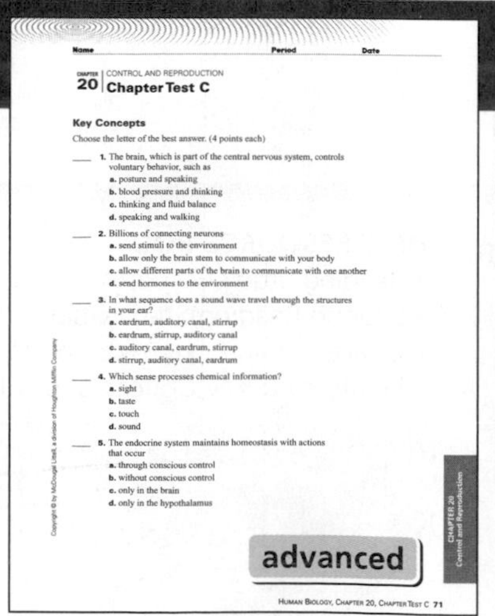

UNIT ASSESSMENT BOOK, pp. 63–66 pp. 67–70 pp. 71–74

TECHNOLOGY

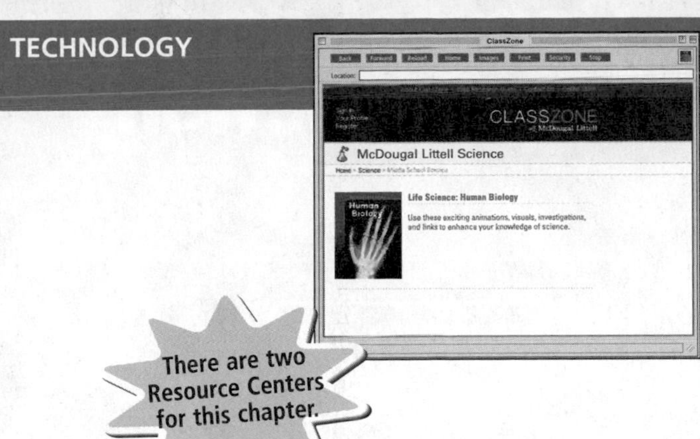

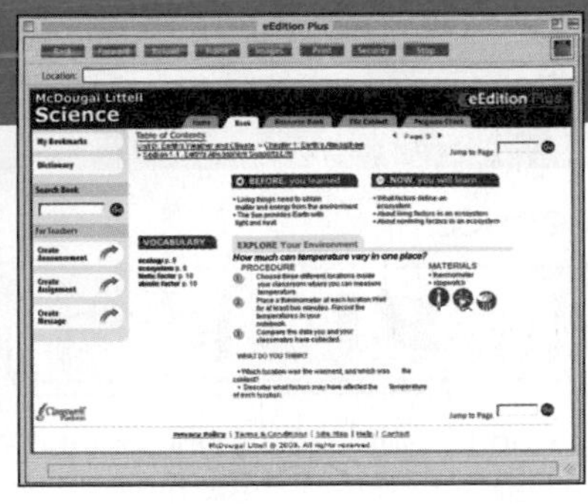

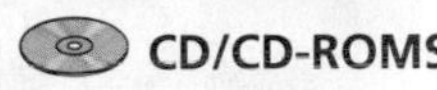

VISUAL CONTENT

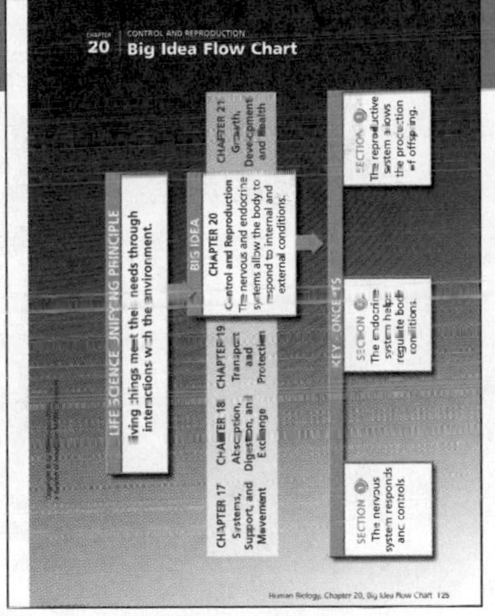

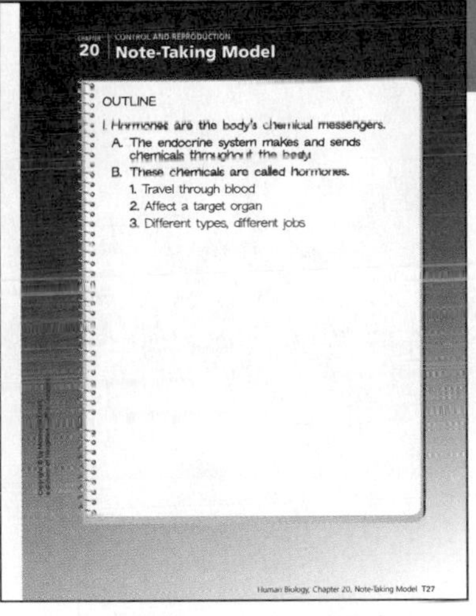

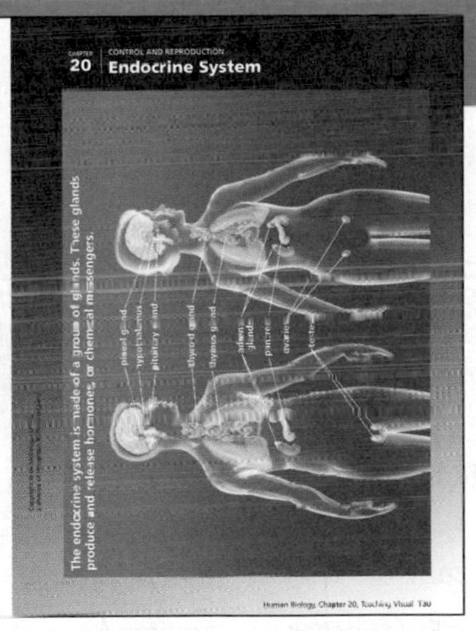

UNIT TRANSPARENCY BOOK, p. T25

p. T27

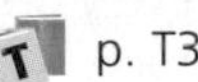
p. T30

MORE SUPPORT

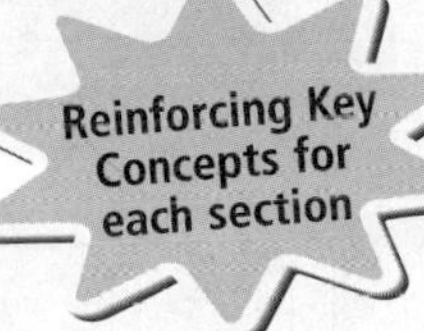

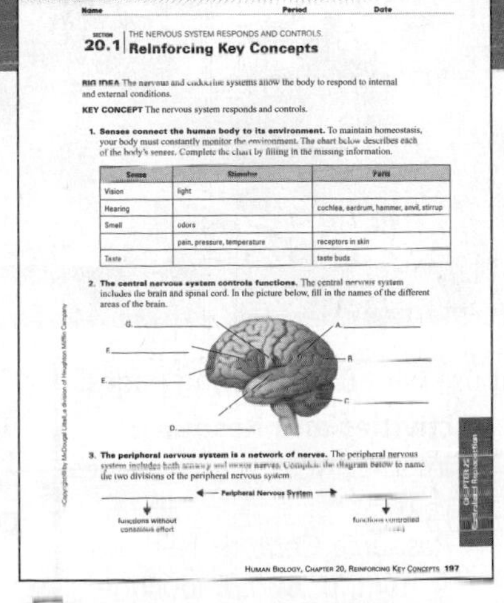

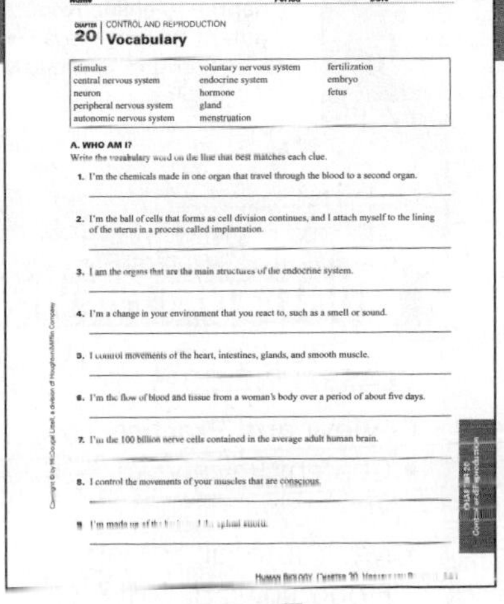

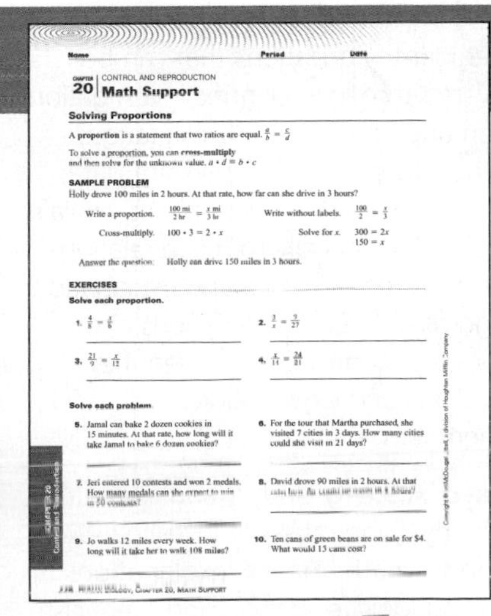

UNIT RESOURCE BOOK, p. 197

pp. 221–222

p. 224

CHAPTER

Control and Reproduction

INTRODUCE

the BIG idea

Have students look at the photograph of nerve cells and discuss how the question in the box relates to the Big Idea. Ask:

- How does your body get the information from words on a page?
- Why might it be necessary for different types of cells to be involved?

National Science Education Standards

Content

C.1.d Specialized cells perform specialized functions in multicellular organisms.

C.1.e The human organism has systems: digestion, respiration, reproduction, circulation, excretion, movement, control and coordination, and protection.

C.2.a Reproduction is essential to the continuation of every species.

C.2.b Females produce eggs, and males sperm, which unite in a new individual.

C.2.c Every organism requires a set of instructions for specifying its traits.

Process

A.1–8 Identify questions that can be answered through scientific investigations; design and conduct an investigation; use tools to gather and interpret data; use evidence to describe, predict, explain, model; think critically to make relationships between evidence and explanation; recognize different explanations and predictions; communicate scientific procedures and explanations; use mathematics.

A.9.a–c, A.9.e–g Understand scientific inquiry by using different investigations, methods, mathematics, explanations based on logic, evidence, and skepticism. Data often result in new investigations.

G.1.b Science requires different abilities.

CHAPTER

Control and Reproduction

the BIG idea

The nervous and endocrine systems allow the body to respond to internal and external conditions.

Key Concepts

SECTION

The nervous system responds and controls.
Learn how the senses help the body get information about the environment.

SECTION

The endocrine system helps regulate body conditions.
Learn the functions of different hormones.

SECTION

The reproductive system allows the production of offspring.
Learn about the process of reproduction.

Internet Preview

CLASSZONE.COM

Chapter 20 online resources: Content Review, Visualization, three Resource Centers, Math Tutorial, Test Practice

These are nerve cells. What do nerves in your body do?

674 Unit 5: **Human Biology**

INTERNET PREVIEW

CLASSZONE.COM For student use with the following pages:

Review and Practice
- Content Review, pp. 676, 702
- Math Tutorial: Solving Proportions, p. 701
- Test Practice, p. 705

Activities and Resources
- Internet Activity: The Senses, p. 675
- Resource Centers: Nervous System, p. 680; Endocrine System, p. 687
- Visualization: Fertilization, p. 696

Reproductive System
Code: MDL047

EXPLORE the BIG idea

Color Confusion

Make a list of six colors using a different color marker or colored pencil to write each one. Make sure not to write the color name with the same color marker or pencil. Read the list out loud as fast as you can. Now try quickly saying the color of each word out loud.

Observe and Think Did you notice a difference between reading the words in the list and saying the colors? If so, why do you think that is?

Eggs

Examine a raw chicken egg. Describe the appearance of the outside shell. Break it open into a small dish and note the different parts inside. Wash your hands when you have finished.

Observe and Think If this egg had been fertilized, which part do you think would have served as the food for the growing chicken embryo? Which part would protect the embryo from impact and serve to cushion it?

Internet Activity: The Senses

Go to **ClassZone.com** to learn how the senses allow the body to respond to external conditions. See how each sense sends specific information to the brain.

Observe and Think How do the different senses interact with one another?

Reproductive System **Code: MDL047**

TEACHING WITH TECHNOLOGY

Graphing Calculator Students can use a graphing calculator to collect and graph data on exercise on p. 690.

PC Microscope Students could use a PC microscope to view eggs and sperm, p. 694, and then create a presentation with screen captures.

EXPLORE the BIG idea

These inquiry-based activities are appropriate for use at home or as a supplement to classroom instruction.

Color Confusion

PURPOSE To look at conflicting stimuli (coloring and word meaning) and observe how the senses can be confused.

TIP *10 min.* To shorten the activity, print a master set of flash cards and show them to the class, or work with three of four colors instead of six.

Answer: It took some extra time to sort out what color was actually being referred to.

REVISIT after p. 678.

Eggs

PURPOSE To examine a chicken egg to infer the parts and functions of an egg

TIPS *10 min.* To conserve eggs, students can work in groups as large as five or six, or the activity can be done as a demo. If possible, show students the membrane that surrounds the egg white. Point out that eggs and embryos in humans do not have shells because the body cushions them, but they have protective membranes.

Answer: the yolk; the white

REVISIT after p. 699.

Internet Activity: The Senses

PURPOSE To learn the function of each of the senses.

TIP *20 min.* Students might try answering the question before and after their observations.

Sample answer: Taste and smell interact; losing sense of smell can decrease ability to taste food.

REVISIT after p. 681.

PREPARE

CONCEPT REVIEW

Activate Prior Knowledge

- Ask student volunteers to name the functions of the circulatory, immune, and integumentary systems.
- You might create a matching game with three types of cards: system, organ, and function. Students can match functions and organs to systems. They can also arrange cards to show interactions and relationships.

TAKING NOTES

Choose Your Own Strategy

Remind students that different graphic organizers may appeal to different types of learners. An outline presents information in linear form, while a main idea web can organize more random thought processes. Main idea and detail notes are particularly helpful for those who draw and visualize what they learn.

Vocabulary Strategy

A description wheel can help students relate new or difficult concepts to familiar or concrete ones.

- Encourage students to create a wheel for each vocabulary term.
- They can set up their wheels in their Science Notebooks before reading the section.
- They can fill in the center of each wheel with a term, and then search or scan the text for details that explain or give context to the term.

Vocabulary and Note-Taking Resources

- Vocabulary Practice, pp. 222–223
- Decoding Support, p. 224

- Daily Vocabulary Scaffolding, p. T26
- Note-Taking Model, p. T27

- Description Wheel, B20–21
- Choose Your Own Strategy, C35–44
- Daily Vocabulary Scaffolding, H1–8

CHAPTER 20

Getting Ready to Learn

CONCEPT REVIEW

- The circulatory system transports materials.
- The immune system responds to foreign materials.
- The integumentary system protects the body.

VOCABULARY REVIEW

homeostasis p. 588
circulatory system p. 641
immune system p. 651
integumentary system p. 659

CONTENT REVIEW
CLASSZONE.COM
Review concepts and vocabulary.

TAKING NOTES

CHOOSE YOUR OWN STRATEGY

Take notes using one or more of the strategies from earlier chapters—**main idea webs, outlines,** or **main idea and detail notes.** You can also use other note-taking strategies that you might already know.

VOCABULARY STRATEGY

Place each vocabulary term at the center of a **description wheel** diagram. Write some words describing it on the spokes.

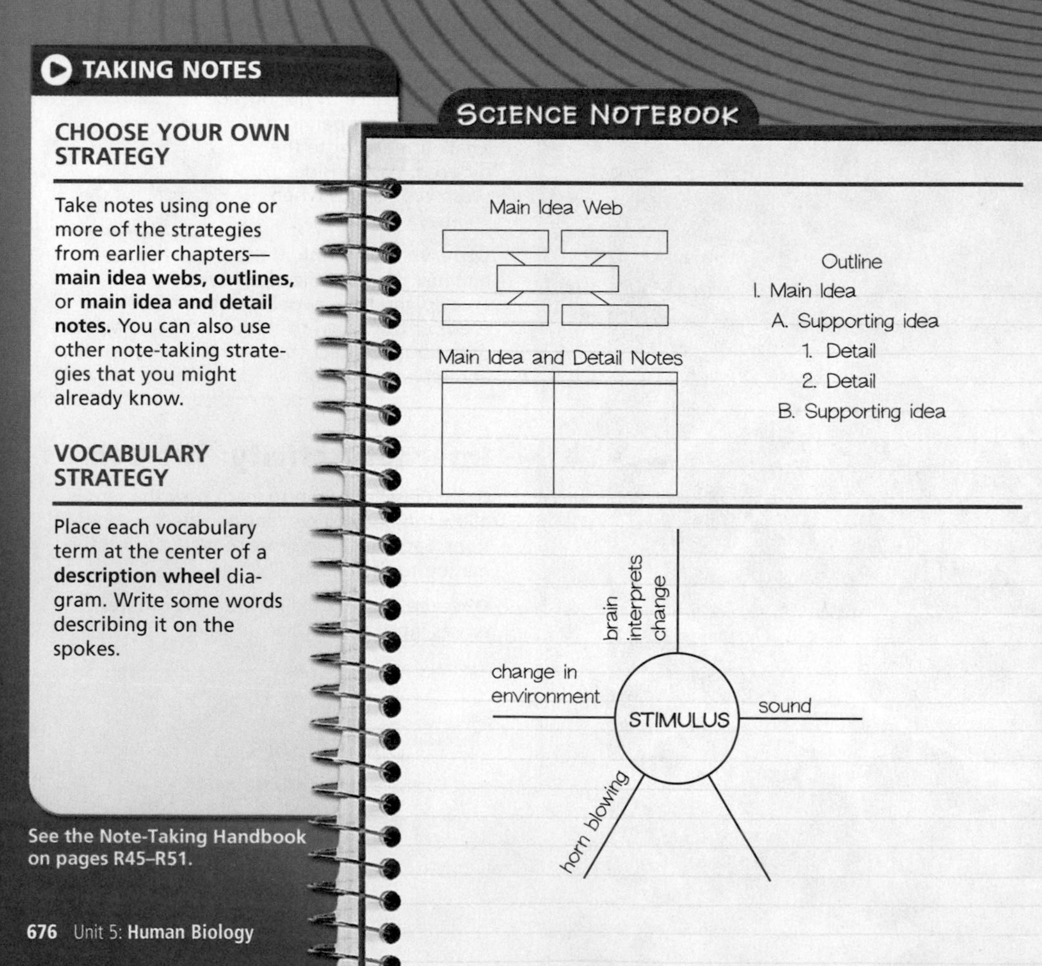

See the Note-Taking Handbook on pages R45–R51.

CHECK READINESS

Administer the Diagnostic Test to determine students' readiness for new science content and their mastery of requisite math skills.

 Diagnostic Test, pp. 58–59

Technology Resources

Students needing content and math skills should visit **ClassZone.com**.

- **CONTENT REVIEW**
- **MATH TUTORIAL**

 **CONTENT REVIEW CD-ROM**

KEY CONCEPT

20.1 The nervous system responds and controls.

BEFORE, you learned

- The body can respond to the presence of foreign materials
- The body is defended from harmful materials
- The immune system responds to pathogens in many ways

NOW, you will learn

- How the body's senses help monitor the environment
- How the sensory organs respond to stimuli
- How the nervous system works with other body systems

VOCABULARY

stimulus p. 678
central nervous system p. 680
neuron p. 681
peripheral nervous system p. 682
autonomic nervous system p. 683
voluntary nervous system p. 683

EXPLORE Smell

Can you name the scent?

PROCEDURE

1. With a small group, take turns smelling the 3 mystery bags given to you by your teacher.
2. In your notebook, write down what you think is inside each bag without showing the people in your group.
3. Compare your answers with those in your group and then look inside the bags.

WHAT DO YOU THINK?

- Did you know what was in the bags before looking inside? If so, how did you know?
- What are some objects that would require more than a sense of smell to identify?

MATERIALS
three small paper bags

CHOOSE YOUR OWN STRATEGY
Use a strategy from an earlier chapter to take notes on the main idea. *Senses connect the human body to its environment.*

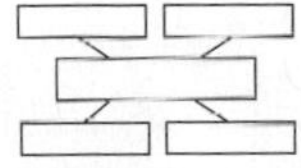

Senses connect the human body to its environment.

To maintain homeostasis and to survive, your body must constantly monitor the environment in which you live. This involves organs that interact so closely with the nervous system that they are often considered extensions of the nervous system. These are your sense organs. They give you the ability to see, smell, touch, hear, and taste.

Each of the senses can detect a specific type of change in the environment. For example, if you have begun to cross the street but suddenly hear a horn blowing, you may stop and step back onto the curb. Your sense of hearing allowed your brain to perceive that a car was coming and thus helped you to protect yourself.

20.1 FOCUS

Set Learning Goals

Students will

- Describe how the body's senses help monitor the environment.
- Explain how the sensory organs respond to stimuli.
- Describe how the nervous system works with other body systems.
- Infer possible connections between taste buds and sensitivity to flavors.

3-Minute Warm-Up

Display Transparency 28 or copy this exercise on the board:

Imagine that for the past three days someone in your household has had a cold, yet you have not caught it. Detail what has been happening in your body to keep you healthy. *Every time the cold virus tried to enter your body, the immune system killed it or your skin and circulatory system repelled it.*

3-Minute Warm-Up, p. T28

20.1 MOTIVATE

EXPLORE Smell

PURPOSE To explore the sense of smell

TIPS *10 min.* Have students close their eyes when smelling the contents of the bags. You may want to tape or staple bags shut to eliminate the chance of peeking. If possible, include mystery smells not pictured in the student book, such as mint, cloves, garlic, lemon, lime, coffee, cedar shavings, or onion. Remind students that they should never smell mystery items without a teacher's permission.

WHAT DO YOU THINK? *You could tell what the items were by their odor. Things such as paper or glass without distinctive odors would require more than the sense of smell to identify them*

RESOURCES FOR DIFFERENTIATED INSTRUCTION

Below Level

UNIT RESOURCE BOOK

- Reading Study Guide A, pp. 190–191
- Decoding Support, p. 223

AUDIO CDS

Additional INVESTIGATION, Taste That Smell!, A, B, & C, pp. 235–243; Teacher Instructions, pp. 305–306

Advanced

UNIT RESOURCE BOOK

- Challenge and Extension, p. 196
- Challenge Reading, pp. 219–220

English Learners

UNIT RESOURCE BOOK

Spanish Reading Study Guide, pp. 194–195

- Audio Readings in Spanish
- Audio Readings (English)

20.1 INSTRUCT

Teach from Visuals

To help students interpret the diagram of the eye, ask:

- Where are light rays bent? *cornea*
- Where are light rays focused? *lens*
- Where do rays form an image? *on the retina at the back of the eye*

Arts Connection

Students are usually fascinated by optical illusions. Show them a piece of M.C. Escher's work, or enter "optical illusions" into the search engine on your computer and download examples from the Internet. Also display samples of pointillism, a style of painting that relies on persistence of vision for viewers to see a field of colored dots as a seamless image.

Teacher Demo

Persistence of vision is an everyday optical illusion that can be easily demonstrated in two ways.

- Show a dollar bill, a page from the Sunday comics, or a printout from an inkjet printer photocopied at an enlarged (200% or greater) size. From a distance of a few inches away students see a seamless image, but their brains are really filling in the spaces between the dots.
- Create or find a flip book. Demonstrate by flipping two or more images in an action sequence how the brain fills in a fluid motion where there are really disjointed, still images.

EXPLORE the BIG idea

Revisit "Color Confusion" on p. 675. Have students explain their results.

Ongoing Assessment

Describe how the body's senses help monitor the environment.

Ask: What does your body do when there is a change in your environment? *The senses perceive the change and the brain makes sense of it, causing the body to respond to maintain homeostasis.*

The sound of the horn is a **stimulus.** A stimulus is a change in your environment that you react to, such as a smell, taste, sound, feeling, or sight. Your brain interprets any such change. If it did not, the information detected by the senses would be meaningless.

Sight

If you have ever tried to find your way in the dark, you know how important light is for seeing. Light is a stimulus. You are able to detect it because your eyes, the sense organs of sight, capture light and help turn it into an image, which is processed by the brain.

Light enters the eye through the lens, a structure made of transparent tissue. Muscles surrounding the lens change its shape so the lens focuses light. Other muscles control the amount of light that enters the eye by altering the size of the pupil, a dark circle in the center of the eye. To reduce the amount of light, the area around the pupil, called the iris, contracts, making the pupil smaller, thus allowing less light to enter. When the iris relaxes, more light can enter the eye.

At the back of the eye, the light strikes a layer called the retina. Among the many cells of the retina are two types of receptors, called rods and cones. Rods detect changes in brightness, while cones are sensitive to color.

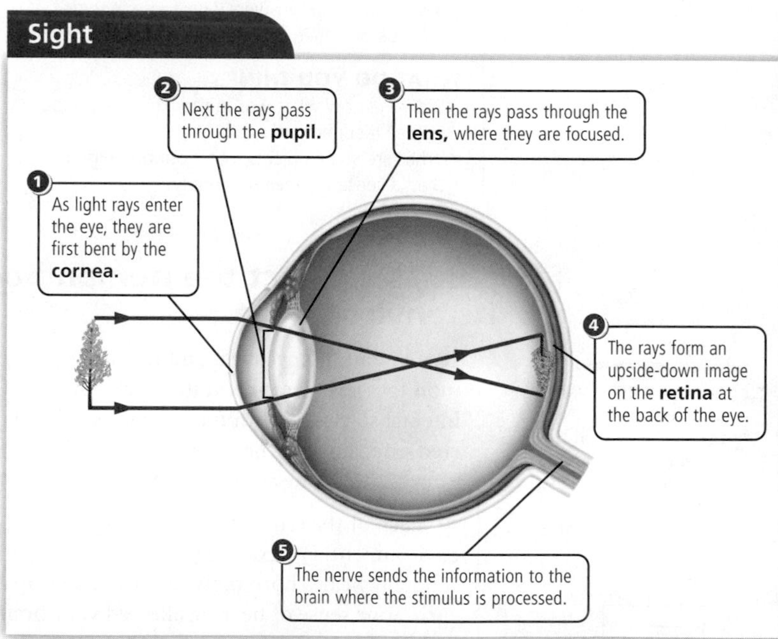

DIFFERENTIATE INSTRUCTION

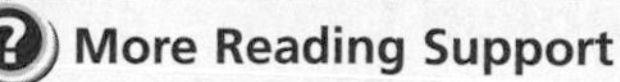

More Reading Support

A What stimulus triggers sight? *light; variations in light*

B What is the lens made of? *transparent tissue*

English Learners Have English learners work in pairs or groups with advanced students to trace the diagram of sight in the human eye. They should leave the boxes blank and unnumbered except for the key terms: *cornea, pupil, lens, retina, nerve.* Then they should take turns explaining orally what happens when an image is seen. (They can continue with the Hearing diagram on p. 679). You may want students who are new to English to preview all the variants of sensory words used in this section, such as *vision, sight, seeing; sound, hearing; touch, feeling; perceive, sense,* and so on.

678 Unit 5: Human Biology

Hearing

Your eyes perceive light waves, but your ears detect a different type of stimulus, sound waves. Sound waves are produced by vibrations. A reed on a clarinet vibrates, and so do your vocal cords. So does a bell after it has been hit by a mallet. The motion causes changes in the air that surrounds the bell. These changes can often be detected by the ear as sound, although many vibrations are too low or high to be heard by humans.

Sound waves enter the ear and are funneled into the auditory canal, a tube-shaped structure that ends at the eardrum. The eardrum vibrates when the sound waves strike it, and it transmits some of the vibrations to a tiny bone called the stirrup. Pressure caused by vibrations from the stirrup causes fluid in the ear to move. The movement of the fluid results in signals sent to the brain that are interpreted as sound.

 How are vibrations involved in hearing?

Hearing

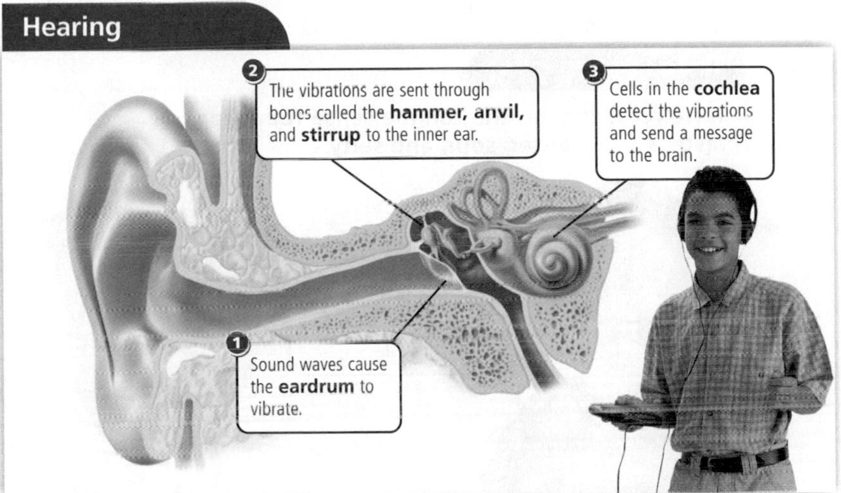

Touch

The sense of touch depends on tiny sensory receptors in the skin. Without these you wouldn't be able to feel pressure, temperature, or pain. Nerves near the top of the inner layer of your skin, or dermis, sense textures, like smooth glass or rough concrete. Nerves deeper in the dermis sense pressure. Other receptors in the dermis sense how hot or cold an object is and can thus help protect you from burning yourself. The sense of touch is important in alerting your brain to danger. Though you might wish that you couldn't feel pain, it serves a critical purpose. Without it, you could harm your body without realizing it.

DIFFERENTIATE INSTRUCTION

More Reading Support

C What produces sound waves? *vibrations*

D What structures give us the sense of touch? *sensory receptors in the skin*

Additional Investigation

To reinforce Section 20.1 learning goals, use the following full-period investigation:

Additional INVESTIGATION, Taste That Smell!, A, B, & C, pp. 235–243, 305–306
(Advanced students should complete Levels B and C.)

Advanced

Have students demonstrate sound waves traveling through a medium. They can use coils, water, rubber bands, or other materials to illustrate vibrations.

Develop Critical Thinking

APPLY Have students describe incidents or situations where their senses have alerted them to an important change in their environment. For example, the sense of smell can alert you to burning food or smoke in the kitchen.

Integrate the Sciences

Many people who have difficulty hearing wear hearing aids. The microphone of a hearing aid converts sound into an electric current, and then the amplifier amplifies the current. An earphone converts the amplified electric current into a sound that is louder than the original one. Hearing aids were large, often handheld devices until transistors were invented in the 1950s. Now hearing aids can often fit inside the ear canal and are barely noticeable. A transistor is an electric device that controls electric current flow using a semiconductor such as silicon.

Teacher Demo

Have students clear their desks of everything but paper and pen. Then have everyone try to be completely quiet for two minutes. At the end of the time, have them write down every sound they heard while the classroom was "silent."

Arts Connection

Point out to students that many famous painters and fine artists have had visual impairments, and that some of the world's best-loved composers—Beethoven is the famous example—had hearing loss. As an exercise, students might try drawing or painting while squinting tightly or looking through a pinhole. Or they could try using earplugs and feeling music by touching a speaker or instrument while it is played.

Ongoing Assessment

 *Vibrations hit sensory receptors in the ear that send impulses to the brain.*

Real World Example

Anyone who has eaten the seasoning monosodium glutamate (MSG) on food has experienced what is sometimes called "the fifth taste, *umami.*" Isolated from kombu seaweed by Kikunae Ikeda of Tokyo Imperial University, glutamate has no smell or texture of its own, but greatly enhances the flavor of other foods. MSG is now a longstanding flavor enhancer for meat, fish, and cheese dishes, and is widely used in processed foods such as canned soups and snack foods.

Teach from Visuals

To help students interpret the map of the taste buds, ask:

- If you bit into a lemon, where on your tongue would you taste it? *on the sides toward the back*
- Where would you taste ice cream? *on the tip of the tongue*

Health Connection

Like the other senses, taste can sometimes get skewed or scrambled. Some people have phantom taste perceptions, some have reduced ability to taste, and others perceive foul tastes from normally pleasant foods. Taste disorders can be congenital or can result from illness or injury. Injuries to the head, exposure to certain chemicals like pesticides, some surgery, and radiation therapy can cause taste disorders. A person with a taste disorder can face diminished quality of life, the loss of an important early warning system, and a reduced desire to eat.

Ongoing Assessment

Explain how the sensory organs respond to stimuli.

Ask: How do the different sense organs process a stimulus? *Eyes respond to light, touch is felt through sensory receptors in the skin, the ear responds to sound waves caused by vibrations, and taste receptors and olfactory nerves sense chemicals in food or the air.*

Smell

E

Whereas sight, touch, and hearing involve processing physical information from the environment, the senses of smell and taste involve detecting chemical information. Much as taste receptors sense chemicals in food, scent receptors sense chemicals in the air. High in the back of your nose, a patch of tissue grows hairlike fibers covered in mucus. Molecules enter your nose, stick to the mucus, and then bind to receptors in the hairlike fibers. The receptors send an impulse to your brain, and you perceive the scent.

Taste

Your tongue is covered with small sensory structures called taste buds, which are also found in the throat and on the roof of the mouth. Each taste bud includes about 100 sensory cells. The receptors are specialized to detect four general tastes: sweet, sour, bitter, and salty. The thousands of tastes you experience are also partially due to sense organs in your nose. That is why when you have a cold, your ability to taste decreases.

Taste

Taste receptors on the tongue sense four types of taste: sweet, bitter, sour, and salty.

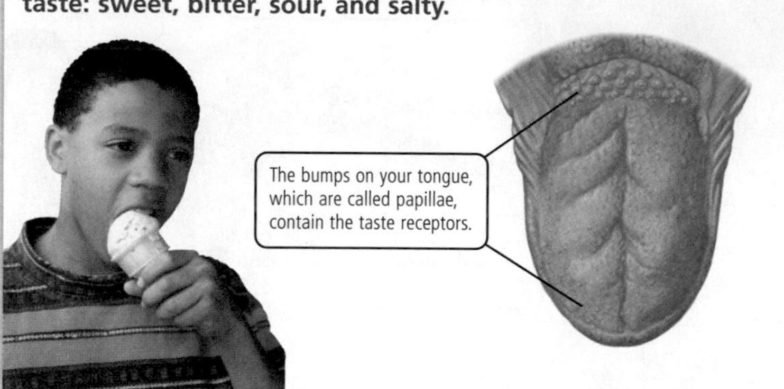

RESOURCE CENTER
CLASSZONE.COM
Explore the nervous system.

The central nervous system controls functions.

F

The **central nervous system** consists of the brain and spinal cord. The brain is located in and protected by the skull, and the spinal cord is located in and protected by the spine. The central nervous system communicates with the rest of the nervous system through electrical signals sent through nerve cells. Impulses travel very quickly, some as fast as 90 meters (295 ft) per second. That's like running almost the entire length of a soccer field in one second.

DIFFERENTIATE INSTRUCTION

More Reading Support

E What kind of information do taste and smell perceive? *chemical*

F What body parts are in the central nervous system? *brain, spinal cord*

Advanced Have students research the structure of a taste bud and build a model to share with the class.

R Challenge and Extension, p. 196

Have students who are interested in the nervous system read the following article:

R Challenge Reading, pp. 219–220

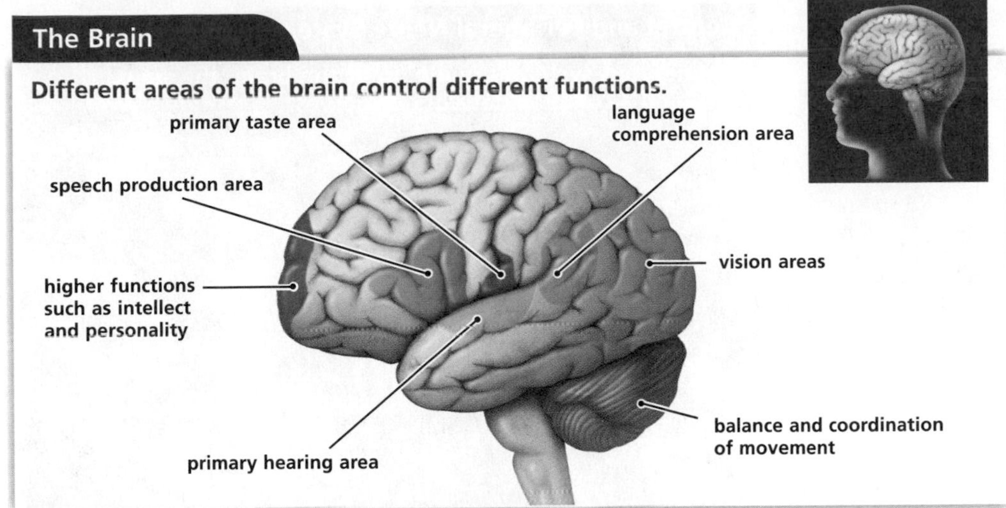

Brain

 G

The average adult brain contains nearly 100 billion nerve cells, called **neurons.** The brain directly controls voluntary behavior, such as walking and thinking. It also allows the body to control most involuntary responses such as heartbeat, blood pressure, fluid balance, and posture.

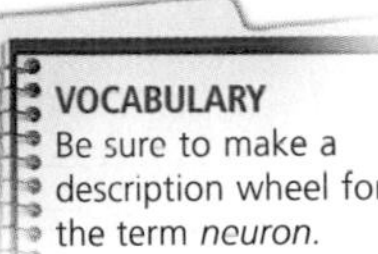

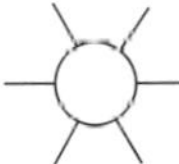

As you can see in the diagram, every area of the brain has a specific function, although many functions involve more than one area. For example, certain areas in the brain process and perceive senses, while other areas help you stand up straight. The lower part of the brain, called the brain stem, controls activities such as breathing and vomiting.

Spinal Cord

 H

The spinal cord is about 44 centimeters (17 in.) long and weighs about 35–40 grams (1.25–1.4 oz). It is the main pathway for information, connecting the brain and the nerves throughout your body. The spinal cord is protected and supported by the vertebral column, which is made up of small bones called vertebrae. The spinal cord itself looks like a double-layered tube with an outer layer of nerve fibers wrapped in tissue, an inner layer of nerve cell bodies, and a central canal that runs the entire length of the cord. Extending from the spinal cord are 31 pairs of nerves, which send sensory impulses into the spinal cord, which in turn sends them to the brain. In a similar way, spinal nerves send impulses to muscles and glands.

Describe the functions performed by the central nervous system.

DIFFERENTIATE INSTRUCTION

More Reading Support

G What is the scientific name for a nerve cell? *neuron*

H What is the main pathway for information in the body? *the spinal cord*

Advanced Have students research neurons and make a model using beads and wire.

Below Level Students may easily confuse the meanings of *nerve, nerve cell, neuron,* and *nerve fiber*. Emphasize that *nerve cell* and *neuron* have the same meaning. They each refer to one cell of nerve tissue. *Nerve* and *nerve fiber* both refer to many cells working together.

EXPLORE (the BIG idea)

Revisit "Internet Activity: The Senses" on p. 675. Ask students how each sense sends specific information to the brain.

Teach from Visuals

To help students interpret the diagram of the brain, ask:

- What functions are handled by the back part of the brain? *vision, balance*
- What functions are handled by the front part of the brain? *intellect, learning, personality*

Real World Example

The first brain structure appeared in reptiles about 300 million years ago and dealt with breathing, heartbeat, and basic motor and foraging skills. This primitive hindbrain is now the human pons and the medulla, for our brains have evolved by adding on sections rather than replacing old ones with new. The hippocampus and cerebellum, or limbic system, developed in mammals 250 million years ago. It governs emotional behavior, balance, and coordination. The newest part of the brain is the cerebrum, which developed about 200 million years ago for functions such as language, thinking, and information processing.

History of Science

Wilder Penfield, the first person ever to perform surgery on the human brain, was also the first to map the brain according to function. In the 1950s, while trying to treat patients with epilepsy, Penfield stimulated parts of the patients' brains in an effort to discover the source of the seizures. He would then remove the disordered tissue. His treatment was often successful, and led to the discovery that memories are stored in particular areas of the temporal lobes.

Ongoing Assessment

Answer: communication with the rest of the nervous system, control of voluntary actions, and control of many involuntary activities

Teach from Visuals

To help students interpret the diagram of the nervous system, ask:

- What part of the nervous system contains sensory and motor nerves? *the peripheral nervous system*
- What part of the nervous system processes information from the peripheral nervous system? *the central nervous system*
- What part of the nervous system carries signals to and from muscles, glands, and other organs? *the peripheral nervous system*

Address Misconceptions

IDENTIFY Ask: What functions does your body carry out without using the brain? If students say anything other than "none" or "no functions," they hold the misconception that some behavior is not controlled by the brain.

CORRECT Use students' answers to the question as examples and take them through how the brain enters the process of the function they named.

REASSESS Ask: What organ is necessary to all human behavior and functions? *the brain*

Technology Resources

Visit **ClassZone.com** for background on common student misconceptions.

 **MISCONCEPTION DATABASE**

Teach Difficult Concepts

If students have trouble differentiating between the autonomic and voluntary nervous systems, have them look up the words *automatic* and *volunteer* in the dictionary, and then suggest actions or events in their lives that were examples of these words. *automatic transmission on a car; volunteering to help around the house.* Connect the meanings with the terms *autonomic* and *voluntary.*

Central and Peripheral Nerve Systems

The nervous system is made up of the brain, the spinal cord and a complex network of nerves.

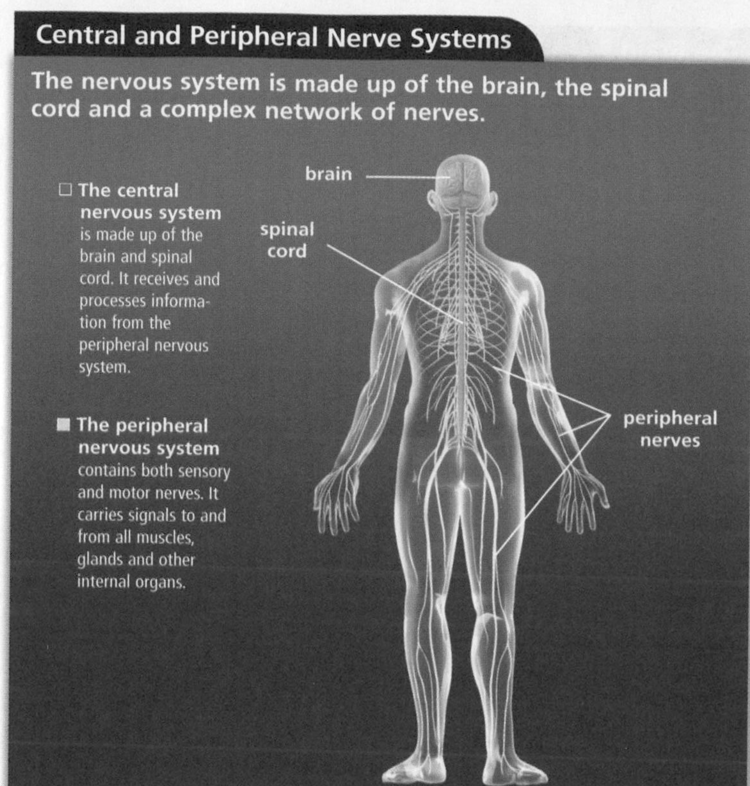

□ **The central nervous system** is made up of the brain and spinal cord. It receives and processes information from the peripheral nervous system.

■ **The peripheral nervous system** contains both sensory and motor nerves. It carries signals to and from all muscles, glands and other internal organs.

The peripheral nervous system is a network of nerves.

Nerves, which are found throughout the body, are often referred to all together as the **peripheral nervous system.** Both sensory and motor nerves are parts of the peripheral nervous system. Sensory nerves receive information from the environment—such as heat or cold—and pass the information to the central nervous system. Motor nerves send signals to your muscles that allow you to move. The peripheral nervous system carries information for both voluntary and involuntary responses.

Involuntary responses of the body are necessary for your survival. In times of danger, there is no time to think. The body must respond immediately. In less stressful situations, the body maintains activities like breathing and digesting food. These functions go on without conscious thought. They are controlled by part of the peripheral nervous system called the autonomic (AW-tuh-NAHM-ihk) nervous system.

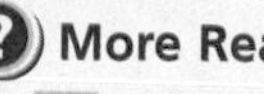

DIFFERENTIATE INSTRUCTION

More Reading Support

I What is the system that runs throughout the body? *peripheral nervous system*

Below Level Help students organize information about the two parts of the nervous system into a table:

System	Functions	Example
autonomic	conserve and store energy, respond to change	digestion, breathing, heartbeat
voluntary	movement, conscious functions	locomotion, speech

The **autonomic nervous system** controls the movement of the heart, the smooth muscles in the stomach, the intestines, and the glands. The autonomic nervous system has two distinct functions: to conserve and store energy and to respond quickly to changes. You can think of the autonomic nervous system as having a division that performs each of these two main functions.

Each division is controlled by different locations on the spinal cord, or within the brain and the brain stem. The cerebellum, which is located at the rear of the brain, coordinates balance and related muscle activity. The brain stem, which lies between the spinal cord and the rest of the brain, controls heartbeat, respiration, and the smooth muscles in the blood vessels.

The autonomic nervous system responds quickly to changes in balance.

When you are under stress, one part of the autonomic nervous system causes what is called the "fight or flight response." Rapid changes in your body prepare you either to fight the danger or to take flight and run away from the danger. The response of your nervous system is the same, whether the stress is a real danger, like falling off a skateboard, or a perceived danger, like being worried or embarrassed.

The **voluntary nervous system** monitors movement and functions that can be controlled consciously. Every movement you think about is voluntary. The voluntary nervous system controls the skeletal muscles of the arms, the legs, and the rest of the body. It also controls the muscles that are responsible for speech and the senses.

CHECK YOUR READING What is the difference between the voluntary and the autonomic nervous systems?

20.1 Review

KEY CONCEPTS

1. Make a chart of five senses that includes a definition and a stimulus for each sense.
2. Explain the process by which you hear a sound.
3. What are two body systems with which the nervous system interacts? How do these interactions take place?

CRITICAL THINKING

4. **Classify** Determine if the following actions involve the autonomic or the voluntary nervous system: chewing, eye blinking, jumping at a loud noise, and riding a bike.
5. **Apply** Describe what messages are sent by the nervous system when you go outside wearing a sweater on a hot day.

CHALLENGE

6. **Hypothesize** When people lose their sense of smell, their sense of taste is often affected as well. Why do you think the ability to taste would be decreased by the loss of the ability to smell?

ANSWERS

1. Charts should include definitions of senses and examples of stimuli for each.

2. Vibration causes sound waves. Waves enter ear through auditory canal and vibrate eardrum to stirrup, which moves liquid in ear, sensed by nerves in brain and interpreted as sound.

3. Sample answer: nervous/muscular: sends messages from brain to muscles; nervous/digestive: controls movements of smooth muscles in stomach

4. autonomic: jumping at a loud noise, eye blinking; voluntary: riding a bike, chewing

5. Autonomic signals to your sweat glands to begin sweating; voluntary signals to muscles to remove sweater.

6. Areas of the brain that process taste and smell area may be connected.

Ongoing Assessment

Describe how the nervous system works with other systems.

Ask: How do the various muscles and organs of the body know what to do? *The peripheral nervous system signals the central nervous system. The brain processes the signal and tells the autonomic and voluntary systems to respond.*

CHECK YOUR READING *Answer: voluntary—can be controlled by conscious thought; autonomic—functions without the brain thinking thoughts about it*

Reinforce the BIG idea

Have students relate the section to the Big Idea.

 Reinforcing Key Concepts, p. 197

20.1 ASSESS & RETEACH

Assess

 Section 20.1 Quiz, p. 60

Reteach

Discuss how the human body maintains its well-being in an ever-changing environment. Have students sketch or discuss an example for each of the following concepts:

- Senses perceive stimuli in the environment.
- The central nervous system processes information collected by the peripheral nervous system.
- The autonomic nervous system controls functions that occur without conscious thought.
- The voluntary nervous system controls conscious actions.

Technology Resources

Have students visit **ClassZone.com** for reteaching of Key Concepts.

 CONTENT REVIEW

 CONTENT REVIEW CD-ROM

CHAPTER INVESTIGATION

Focus

PURPOSE To test the ability to taste

OVERVIEW Students will count the number of taste buds in a sample area of their tongues to determine if they are extra-sensitive to tastes. Students will find the following:

- Different people have different numbers of taste buds.
- The number of taste buds on your tongue can affect your sensitivity to tastes.

Lab Preparation

Prior to the investigation, have students read through the investigation and prepare their data tables. Or you may wish to copy and distribute datasheets and rubrics.

UNIT RESOURCE BOOK, pp. 226–234

SCIENCE TOOLKIT, F14

Lab Management

- Caution students not to swallow too much food coloring and not to get food coloring on their clothing.
- Make sure students properly dispose of cotton swabs after painting their tongues.
- If students have their tongues in the air for long, they may start to drool. They should use paper towels and napkins to wipe away any saliva.
- It may be easier to count taste buds if students paint their tongues, put reinforcement circles directly on their tongues, and count the pink spots on their tongues.
- Note: For the "Calculate" section of "Observe and Analyze," p. 685, help students by keeping a list or chart on the board to provide whole-class data.

CHAPTER INVESTIGATION

Are You a Supertaster?

OVERVIEW AND PURPOSE Do you think broccoli tastes bitter? If so, you might be extra sensitive to bitter tastes. In this investigation you will

- examine the surface of your tongue to find a possible connection between the bumps you find there and your sensitivity to bitter flavors
- calculate the average number of papillae in your class

Make sure to do this investigation in the cafeteria since you will be placing food coloring on your tongue.

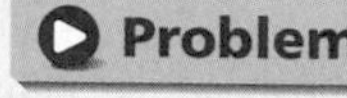

MATERIALS
- blue food coloring
- paper cup
- 1 cotton swab
- 1 reinforcement circle for ring-binder paper
- paper towel or napkin
- 1 sheet of white paper

Problem

How can you tell if you are a supertaster?

Hypothesize

Write a hypothesis to explain how you might tell if you are a supertaster. Your hypothesis should take the form of an "If . . . , then . . . , because . . ." statement.

Procedure

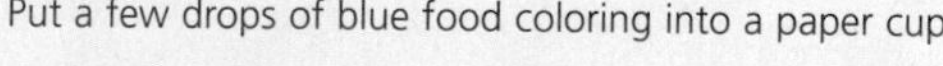

1. Make a data table in your **Science Notebook** like the one shown on page 685.
2. Put a few drops of blue food coloring into a paper cup.
3. Use a paper towel or a napkin to pat your tongue thoroughly dry.
4. Dip the tip of a cotton swab into the blue food coloring, and use it to paint the first 2 centimeters of your tongue.

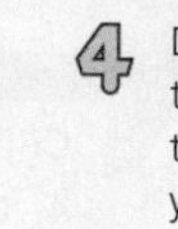

684 Unit 5: Human Biology

INVESTIGATION RESOURCES

CHAPTER INVESTIGATION, Are You a Supertaster?
- Level A, pp. 226–229
- Level B, pp. 230–233
- Level C, p. 234

Advanced students should complete Levels B & C.

Writing a Lab Report, D12–13

Technology Resources

Customize this student lab as needed or look for an alternative. Print rubrics to assess student lab reports.

Lab Generator CD-ROM

5 Press a piece of white paper firmly onto the painted surface of your tongue, and then place the paper on your desk.

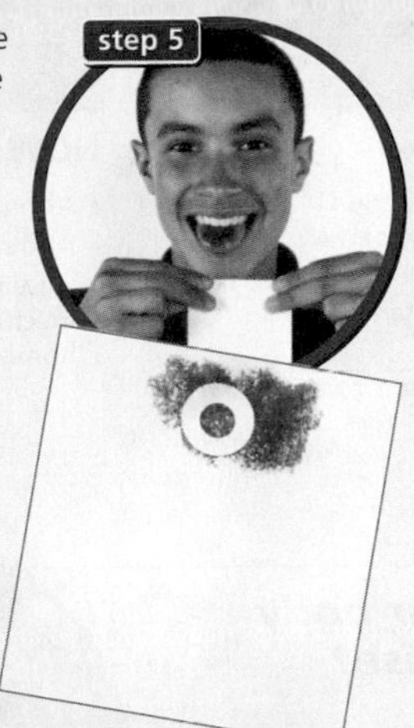

6 Place a notebook reinforcement circle on the blue area.

7 You should see white circles in a field of blue. The white circles are the bumps on your tongue called fungiform papillae, which contain taste buds. Count the number of white circles inside the reinforcement circle. There may be many white circles crammed together that vary in size, or just a few. If there are just a few, they may be larger than the ones on someone who has many white circles close together. If there are too many to count, try to count the number in half of the circle and multiply this number by 2. Record your total count in your data table.

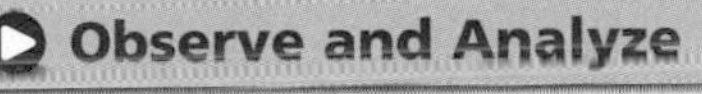

Observe and Analyze

Write It Up

1. **OBSERVE** What did you observe while looking at the tongue print? Is the surface the same all over your tongue?

2. **CALCULATE** Record the number of papillae within the reinforcement circle of all the students in your class.

   AVERAGE Calculate the average number of papillae counted in the class.

$$\text{average} = \frac{\text{sum of papillae in class}}{\text{number of students}}$$

Conclude

1. **INTERPRET** How do the number of fungiform papillae on your tongue compare with the number your partner counted?
2. **INFER** Do you think there is a relationship between the number of fungiform papillae and taste? If so, what is it?
3. **IDENTIFY** What foods might a supertaster not like?
4. **APPLY** Do you think that there are other taste perceptions besides bitterness that might be influenced by the number of fungiform papillae that an individual has? Why do you think so?

INVESTIGATE Further

CHALLENGE Calculate the area in square millimeters inside the reinforcement circle, and use this value to express each person's papillae count as a density (number of papillae per square millimeter).

Are You a Supertaster?

Table 1. Papillae

Name	Number of papillae

Observe and Analyze

1. *Answers will vary. Students should observe different densities of white circles. The density of circles should vary over the surface of the tongue.*
2. *Answers will vary. Check student calculations of average number of papillae in the class.*

Conclude

1. *Answers will vary. Some students will have more papillae and some will have less than others.*
2. *Most fungiform papillae allow for more sensitivity in taste.*
3. *Supertasters might not like foods with a strong bitter taste.*
4. *Sour tastes might be influenced by the number of papillae, because strong sour taste can also cause dislike of foods.*

INVESTIGATE Further

CHALLENGE Area within the reinforcement hole is equal to πr^2. For the typical reinforcement, $r = 3$ mm, giving an area of about 28 mm^2. To get density, divide the number of papillae by the area of the reinforcement hole.

Post-Lab Discussion

Ask: Do you think researchers could adapt this method to determine where on the tongue different types (for different tastes) of fungiform papillae occur? If so, how?

Explain to students that the sense of taste is an early warning system. It helps protect the body from such things as spoiled foods or poisons. Do you think there is an ideal number and size of fungiform papillae for humans? If so, what would it be?

20.2 FOCUS

Set Learning Goals

Students will

- Describe the role of hormones.
- Analyze the function of glands.
- Explain how the body uses feedback mechanisms.
- Determine how body temperature changes during an experiment.

3-Minute Warm-Up

Display Transparency 28 or copy this exercise on the board:

Decide if these statements are true. If not true, correct them.

1. The senses of sight and taste react to chemicals in the environment. *The senses of smell and taste react to chemicals in the environment.*
2. The central nervous system consists of the spinal cord. *The central nervous system consists of the spinal cord and brain.*
3. The peripheral nervous system is a network of sensory and motor nerves. *true*

 3-Minute Warm-Up, p. T28

20.2 MOTIVATE

THINK ABOUT

PURPOSE Determine how the body responds to surprise

DISCUSS Allow students to work in small groups, then share their ideas as a class. Point out that the body's reaction to surprise is an instinctive response to prepare a person to deal with danger. Increased heart rate gets more oxygen and nutrients to the muscles to prepare to fight or run from a source of danger.

KEY CONCEPT

20.2 The endocrine system helps regulate body conditions.

BEFORE, you learned

- Many body systems function without conscious control
- The body systems work automatically to maintain homeostasis
- Homeostasis is important to an organism's survival

NOW, you will learn

- About the role of hormones
- About the functions of glands
- How the body uses feedback mechanisms to help maintain homeostasis

VOCABULARY

endocrine system p. 686
hormone p. 687
gland p. 687

THINK ABOUT

How does your body react to surprise?

In a small group, determine how your body responds to a surprising situation. Have one student in the group pretend he or she is responding to a surprise. The other group members should determine how the body reacts physically to that event. How do your respiratory system, digestive system, circulatory system, muscle system, and skeletal system react?

CHOOSE YOUR OWN STRATEGY
Begin taking notes on the main idea: *Hormones are the body's chemical messengers.* Use a strategy from an earlier chapter or one of your own. Include a definition of *hormone* in your notes.

Hormones are the body's chemical messengers.

Imagine you're seated on a roller coaster climbing to the top of a steep incline. In a matter of moments, your car drops one hundred feet. You might notice that your heart starts beating faster. You grab the seat and notice that your palms are sweaty. These are normal physical responses to scary situations. The **endocrine system** controls the conditions in your body by making and releasing chemicals that are transported thoughout the body. Most responses of the endocrine system are controlled by the autonomic nervous system.

RESOURCES FOR DIFFERENTIATED INSTRUCTION

Below Level

UNIT RESOURCE BOOK
- Reading Study Guide A, pp. 200–201
- Decoding Support, p. 223

AUDIO CDS

Advanced

UNIT RESOURCE BOOK
Challenge and Extension, p. 206

English Learners

UNIT RESOURCE BOOK
Spanish Reading Study Guide, pp. 204–205

- Audio Readings in Spanish
- Audio Readings (English)

Hormones are chemicals that are made in one organ, travel through the blood, and produce an effect in target cells. Target cells have structures that allow them to respond to the chemical. Many hormones, as you can see in the table below, affect all the cells in the body.

Because hormones are made at one location and function at another, they are often called chemical messengers. In order for a hormone to have an effect, it binds to receptors on the surface of or inside the cells. There the hormone begins the chemical changes that cause the target cells to function in a specific way. All of the functions of the endocrine system work automatically, without your conscious control.

Different types of hormones perform different jobs. Some of these jobs are to control the production of other hormones, to regulate the balance of chemicals such as glucose and salt in your blood, or to produce responses to changes in the environment. Some hormones are made only during specific times in a person's life. For example, hormones that control the development of sexual characteristics are not produced in significant amounts during childhood. During adolescence, high levels of these hormones cause major changes in a person's body.

The individuals on this roller coaster are experiencing a burst of the hormone adrenaline.

 How are hormones like messengers?

Hormones

Name	Where produced	Produces responses in
Growth hormone	pituitary gland	all body cells
Antidiuretic hormone	pituitary gland	kidneys
Thyroxine	thyroid gland	all body cells
Cortisol	adrenal glands	all body cells
Adrenaline	adrenal glands	heart, lungs, stomach, intestines, glands
Insulin	pancreas	all body cells
Testosterone (males)	testes	all body cells
Estrogen (females)	ovaries	all body cells

Glands produce and release hormones.

The main structures of the endocrine system are groups of specialized cells called **glands.** Many glands in the body produce hormones and release them into your circulatory system. As you can see in the illustration on page 689, endocrine glands can be found in many parts of your body. However, all hormones move from the cells in which they are produced to cause effects in target cells.

Learn more about the endocrine system.

20.2 INSTRUCT

Real World Example

The roller coaster shown in the photograph is a familiar example of people experiencing a "rush of adrenaline." Have students brainstorm aloud a quick list of other examples. They might give examples from their own life or from films, books, or television.

Ongoing Assessment

Describe the role of hormones.

Ask: What can your pituitary gland produce to communicate with another part of your body? *hormones*

CHECK YOUR READING *Answer: They travel from one location with signals for activity in another location.*

DIFFERENTIATE INSTRUCTION

A Summarize what a hormone is and does. *a chemical made in part of the body that causes reactions in another part*

B What are organs that produce hormones? *glands*

Below Level For students who have difficulty or who have limited attention or skills, you can teach the main concepts of hormones with only one example. Use the example of adrenaline, and refer students to the photograph and caption on p. 687, the paragraph on p. 688, and the illustration on p. 689. Then have them create a flow chart with drawings and/or captions to explain how the hormone adrenaline functions in the body.

Metacognitive Strategy

Have students discuss their own strategies for remembering the main ideas about glands and hormones. Some students will have ways of memorizing the details, while others may generalize. Point out that both are useful, as long as the main ideas are understood.

Health Connection

When the pancreas cannot make enough of the hormone insulin or cannot use insulin properly, diabetes results. The body cannot convert glucose into energy, and glucose builds up in the blood. Many people with diabetes develop it over the course of their lives. This type of diabetes is called adult-onset or Type II diabetes. Diabetes often begins with symptoms such as excessive thirst or hunger, fatigue, and nausea, and if left untreated, can progress to blindness, circulation problems, and kidney failure. It can be treated but not cured. Diabetics who exercise, are careful with diet, and monitor their blood glucose levels can often manage their diabetes and avoid having to take insulin.

History of Science

Until 1922, a diagnosis of diabetes was a death sentence. Canadian surgeon Frederick Banting and his assistant Charles Best were the first to isolate the hormone insulin, which is made in the islets of Langerhans in the pancreas. Once it was isolated, they administered insulin to a diabetic boy and found that it did, as hoped, lower blood glucose levels. It is estimated that today insulin helps 18 million people in the United States with diabetes.

Ongoing Assessment

Analyze the functions of glands.

Ask: What are the main structures of the endocrine system and how do they work? *the glands, which produce and secrete hormones that regulate such things as sleep, growth, calcium levels, and disease fighting*

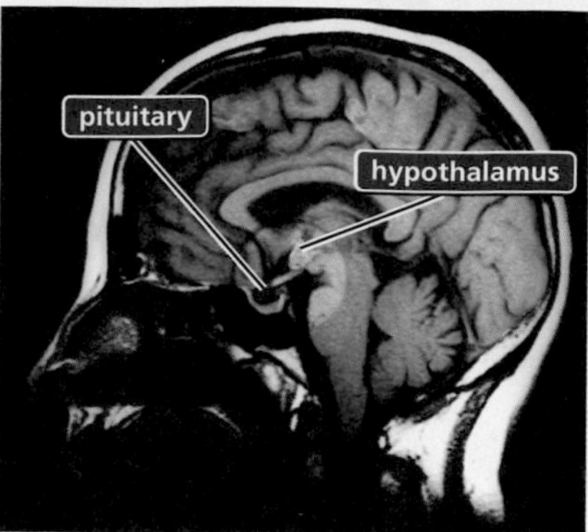

The hypothalamus and the pituitary are important endocrine glands.

Pituitary Gland The pituitary (pih-TOO-ih-TEHR-ee) gland can be thought of as the director of the endocrine system. The pituitary gland is the size of a pea and is located at the base of the brain—right above the roof of your mouth. Many important hormones are produced in the pituitary gland, including hormones that control growth, sexual development, and the absorption of water into the blood by the kidneys. (C)

Hypothalamus The hypothalamus (HY-poh-THAL-uh-muhs) is attached to the pituitary gland and is the primary connection between the nervous and endocrine systems. All of the secretions of the pituitary gland are controlled by the hormones produced in the hypothalamus.

Pineal Gland The pineal (PIHN-ee-uhl) gland is a tiny organ about the size of a pea. It is buried deep in the brain. The pineal gland is sensitive to different levels of light and the hormone it produces is essential to rhythms such as sleep, body temperature, reproduction, and aging.

Thyroid Gland You can feel your thyroid gland if you place your hand on the part of your throat called the Adam's apple and swallow. What you feel is the cartilage surrounding your thyroid gland. The thyroid releases hormones necessary for growth and metabolism. The tissue of the thyroid is made of millions of tiny pouches, which store the thyroid hormones. The thyroid gland also produces the hormone calcitonin, which is involved in the regulation of calcium in the body.

Thymus The thymus is located in your chest. It is relatively large in the newborn baby and continues to grow until puberty. Following puberty, it gradually decreases in size. The thymus helps the body fight disease by controlling the production of white blood cells called T cells.

(D) **Adrenal Glands** The adrenal glands are located on top of your kidneys. The adrenal glands secrete about 30 different hormones that regulate carbohydrate, protein, and fat metabolism and water and salt levels in your body. Some other hormones produced by the adrenal glands help you fight allergies. Roller coaster rides, loud noises, or stress can activate your adrenal glands to produce adrenaline, the hormone that makes your heart beat faster.

Pancreas The pancreas is part of both the digestive and the endocrine systems. The pancreas secretes two hormones, insulin and glucagon. These hormones regulate the level of glucose in your blood. The pancreas sits beneath the stomach and is connected to the small intestine.

Ovaries and Testes The ovaries and testes secrete hormones that control sexual development.

DIFFERENTIATE INSTRUCTION

More Reading Support

C Which gland directs the endocrine system? *pituitary gland*

D Which glands secrete 30 different hormones? *adrenal glands*

Advanced Have students research diabetes and create an educational brochure about it for younger students.

 Challenge and Extension, p. 206

 E

Other Organs Some organs that are not considered part of the endocrine system do produce important hormones. The kidneys secrete a hormone that regulates the production of red blood cells. This hormone is secreted whenever the oxygen level in your blood decreases. Once the hormone has stimulated the red bone marrow to produce more red blood cells, the oxygen level of the blood increases. The heart produces two hormones that help regulate blood pressure. These hormones, secreted by one of the chambers of the heart, stimulate the kidneys to remove more salt from the blood.

 Which glands and organs are part of the endocrine system?

Endocrine System

The endocrine system is made of a group of glands. These glands produce and release hormones, or chemical messengers.

pineal gland
hypothalamus
pituitary gland
thyroid gland
thymus gland
adrenal glands
pancreas
ovaries
testes

DIFFERENTIATE INSTRUCTION

 **More Reading Support**

E Which organs also function as glands? *the brain, heart, and kidney*

Below Level Refer students to the maps of the endocrine system. Have them create their own maps of either the male or female endocrine system by tracing the outline and all of the callout lines on p. 689. Then ask them to sketch or find pictures to illustrate the function of each gland's hormones.

Teach Difficult Concepts

Students may confuse glands with hormones. Point out that glands are a structure, while hormones are a chemical. You might also try the demonstration below.

Teacher Demo

Fill a small plastic bag with colored water. Poke a small hole in the bag with a pin. Hold the bag over a sponge and allow some colored water to drip on it. Ask:

- What correlates to a gland? *the bag*
- What correlates to a hormone? *the colored water*
- What is the sponge? *the target organ*

Develop Critical Thinking

PREDICT Have students choose one of the glands and study the functions performed by that gland's hormones. Ask them to predict what a human being's life would be like if that gland were missing or malfunctioning.

Teach from Visuals

What general area of the body are all the glands of the endocrine system in? *center* What areas do the hormones produced in the glands generally affect? *all parts*

Ask: How do the illustrations show the role of hormones as "chemical messengers"? *The glands are located throughout the body and are able to "deliver" hormones wherever the body needs them.*

 This visual is also available as T30 in the Unit Transparency Book.

Ongoing Assessment

 *Answer: pineal gland, hypothalamus, pituitary gland, thyroid, thymus, adrenal glands, pancreas, ovaries, testes*

INVESTIGATE Response to Exercise

PURPOSE To determine how body temperature changes during exercise

TIPS *30 min.* Encourage students to maintain an even level of intensity as they exercise. Use disposable thermometer covers or rubbing alcohol to maintain proper hygiene.

INCLUSION Sitting-down exercises are less strenuous and will allow inclusion of most students with physical or health limitations.

WHAT DO YOU THINK? *It increased. The amount of exercise, starting body temperature, weight, level of fitness, and gender could all be factors. Answers will vary. Students may say that the person looked more invigorated, rosier, had faster breathing, wider eyes, better posture, and so on.*

CHALLENGE *Graphs should have x-and y-axes labeled with appropriate units of measures. The graph should show an increase in temperature with each round of exercise.*

Datasheet, Response to Exercise, p. 207

Technology Resources

Customize this student lab as needed or look for an alternative. Print rubrics to assess student lab reports.

Lab Generator CD-ROM

Teaching with Technology

Students can use a graphing calculator to collect and graph exercise data.

Ongoing Assessment

CHECK YOUR READING *Answer: to help cells function at their best and for survival*

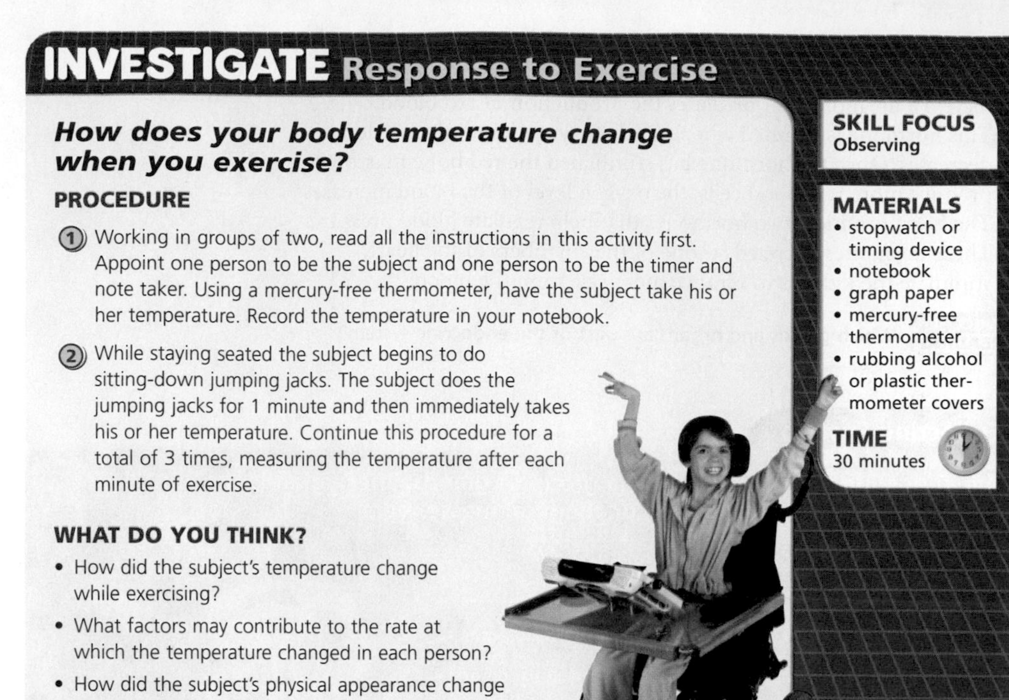

INVESTIGATE Response to Exercise

How does your body temperature change when you exercise?

SKILL FOCUS
Observing

MATERIALS
- stopwatch or timing device
- notebook
- graph paper
- mercury-free thermometer
- rubbing alcohol or plastic thermometer covers

TIME
30 minutes

PROCEDURE

1. Working in groups of two, read all the instructions in this activity first. Appoint one person to be the subject and one person to be the timer and note taker. Using a mercury-free thermometer, have the subject take his or her temperature. Record the temperature in your notebook.
2. While staying seated the subject begins to do sitting-down jumping jacks. The subject does the jumping jacks for 1 minute and then immediately takes his or her temperature. Continue this procedure for a total of 3 times, measuring the temperature after each minute of exercise.

WHAT DO YOU THINK?

- How did the subject's temperature change while exercising?
- What factors may contribute to the rate at which the temperature changed in each person?
- How did the subject's physical appearance change from the beginning of the activity to the end?

CHALLENGE Graph the results on a line graph, with temperature on the *x*-axis and time on the *y*-axis.

Control of the endocrine system includes feedback mechanisms.

As you might recall, the cells in the human body function best within a specific set of conditions. Homeostasis (HOH-mee-oh-STAY-sihs) is the process by which the body maintains these internal conditions, even though conditions outside the body may change. The endocrine system is very important in maintaining homeostasis.

Why is homeostasis important?

Because hormones are powerful chemicals capable of producing dramatic changes, their levels in the body must be carefully regulated. The endocrine system has several levels of control. Most glands are regulated by the pituitary gland, which in turn is controlled by the hypothalamus, part of the brain. The endocrine system helps maintain homeostasis through the action of negative feedback mechanisms.

DIFFERENTIATE INSTRUCTION

More Reading Support

F What is the process of maintaining livable conditions in the body even if the environment outside changes? *homeostasis*

English Learners Demonstrate expected responses to frequently used prompts, such as "What do you think," "How do you know," "What would you predict," etc. For example, the Challenge portion of the Investigate (p. 690) asks the student to create a line graph. Help English learners by providing a model for this answer.

Negative Feedback

Most feedback mechanisms in the body are called negative mechanisms, because the final effect of the response is to turn off the response. An increase in the amount of a hormone in the body feeds back to inhibit the further production of that hormone.

The production of the hormone thyroxine by the thyroid gland is an example of a negative feedback mechanism. Thyroxine controls the body's metabolism, or the rate at which the cells in the body release energy by cellular respiration. When the body needs energy, the thyroid gland releases thyroxine into the blood to increase cellular respiration. However, the thyroid gland is controlled by the pituitary gland, which in turn is controlled by the hypothalamus. Increased levels of thyroxine in the blood inhibit the signals from the hypothalamus and the pituitary gland to the thyroid gland. Production of thyroxine in the thyroid gland decreases.

Negative and Positive Feedback

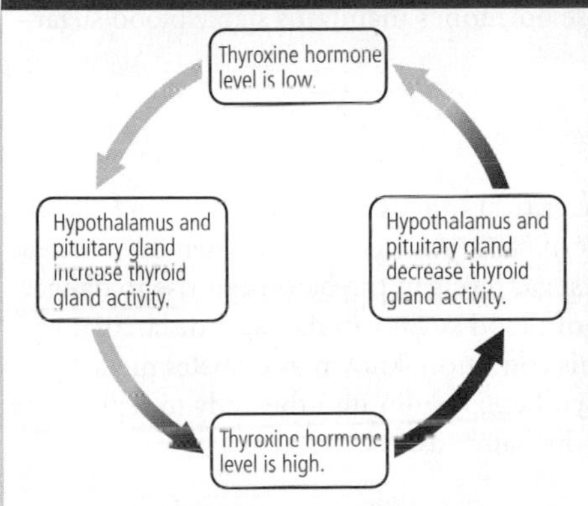

Negative feedback The process shown here regulates levels of thyroid hormone. Feedback keeps conditions within a narrow range to maintain homeostasis.

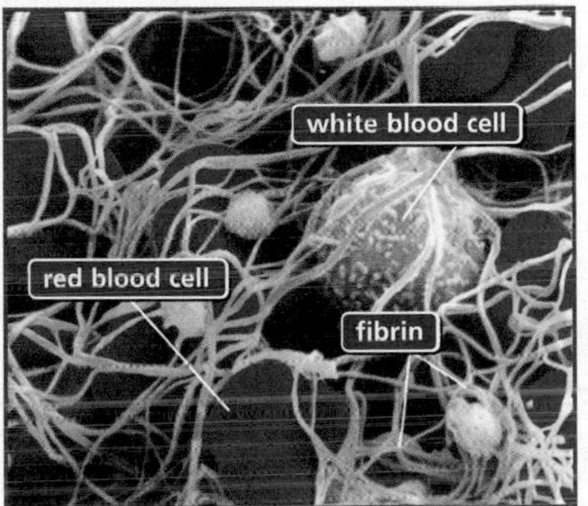

Positive feedback These red blood cells are surrounded by fibrin, a protein that allows them to clot.

Positive Feedback

Some responses of the endocrine system, as well as other body systems, are controlled by positive feedback. The outcome of a positive feedback mechanism is not to maintain homeostasis, but to produce a response that continues to increase. Most positive feedback mechanisms result in extreme responses that are necessary under extreme conditions.

For example, when you cut yourself, the bleeding is controlled by positive feedback. First, the damaged tissue releases a chemical signal.

Teach Difficult Concepts

If students are having trouble understanding homeostasis, call their attention to the *-stasis* part of the word, and relate that part to stability. Point out that homeostasis is a tendency to maintain stability or balance. When students attempt to keep their balance on a bicycle or balance beam, their process correlates to maintaining homeostasis.

DIFFERENTIATE INSTRUCTION

More Reading Support

G Give an example of a negative feedback mechanism. *thyroid hormone production*

!! Give an example of a positive feedback mechanism. *blood clotting*

Below Level Students may need help to relate the negative feedback loop described in the text to the cycle diagram below it. Have pairs of students work to describe to each other in their own words what happens at each stage of the loop. They may want to sketch a simple metaphor as a reminder, such as a fuel pump, a gas gauge, a driver, and a gas tank.

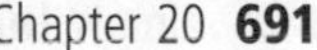

Ongoing Assessment

Explain how the body uses feedback mechanisms.

Ask: How do feedback mechanisms involve cells? What is their general function in the body? *Feedback mechanisms signal cells to produce a response to a change in the environment. Their general function is to maintain healthy conditions.*

Answer: Negative feedback maintains homeostasis; positive feedback starts an increasing response after an extreme change occurs.

Reinforce the BIG idea

Have students relate the section to the Big Idea.

 Reinforcing Key Concepts, p. 208

20.2 ASSESS & RETEACH

Assess

 Section 20.2 Quiz, p. 61

Reteach

Create a table on the board called Feedback Loops in the Body. Make four columns:

- Stimulus (starts activity)
- Response (active change)
- Body Structures (organs involved)
- Positive/Negative/Balance (+, −, =)

Complete the table for some examples in the text, such as cut skin, viral infection, puberty, or labor.

Have students search the text for information to fill in each column. Lead a discussion about how each "loop"—or mechanism—relates to homeostasis.

Technology Resources

Have students visit **ClassZone.com** for reteaching of Key Concepts.

 CONTENT REVIEW

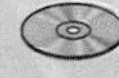 CONTENT REVIEW CD-ROM

The signal starts a series of chemical reactions that lead to the formation of threadlike proteins called fibrin. The fibrin causes the blood to clot, filling the injured area. Other examples of positive feedback include fever, the immune response, puberty, and the process of childbirth.

 **What is the difference between negative and positive feedback?**

Balanced Hormone Action

In the body, the action of one hormone is often balanced by the action of another. When you ride a bicycle, you are able to ride in a straight line, despite bumps and dips in the road, by making constant steering adjustments. If the bicycle is pulled to the right, you adjust the handlebars by turning a tiny bit to the left.

Some hormones maintain homeostasis in the same way that you steer your bicycle. The pancreas, for example, produces two hormones. One hormone, insulin, decreases the level of sugar in the blood. The other hormone, glucagon, increases sugar levels in the blood. The balance of the levels of these hormones maintains stable blood sugar between meals.

Hormone Imbalance

Because hormones regulate critical functions in the body, too little or too much of any hormone can cause serious disease. When the pancreas produces too little insulin, sugar levels in the blood can rise to dangerous levels. Very high levels of blood sugar can damage the circulatory system and the kidneys. This condition, known as diabetes mellitus, is often treated by injecting synthetic insulin into the body to replace the insulin not being made by the pancreas.

20.2 Review

KEY CONCEPTS

1. List three different jobs that hormones perform.
2. Draw an outline of the human body. Add the locations and functions of the pituitary, thyroid, adrenal, and pineal glands to your drawing.
3. What is the function of a negative feedback mechanism?

CRITICAL THINKING

4. **Analyze** Explain why hormones are called chemical messengers.
5. **Analyze** List two sets of hormones that have opposing actions. How do the actions of these hormones help maintain homeostasis?

CHALLENGE

6. **Connect** Copy the diagram below and add three more stimuli and the resulting feedback mechanisms.

692 Unit 5: Human Biology

ANSWERS

1. Sample answer: regulating growth, sexual development, the balance of chemicals in the blood

2. Pituitary: base of brain; growth, sexual development, water absorption. Thyroid: neck; growth and metabolism. Adrenal: above kidneys; carbohydrate, protein, and fat metabolism and water and salt levels. Pineal: brain; body rhythms

3. to help the body maintain homeostasis

4. made in one organ and travel to another, which responds to the chemical

5. insulin and glucagon from the pancreas, insulin decreases blood sugar, glucagon increases blood sugar; hormones controlling salt removal by the kidney, one increases urine, one decreases urine

6. Sample answer: cut skin, clotting; infection, fever; developed baby, labor

CONNECTING LIFE AND PHYSICAL SCIENCE

Heating and Cooling

The cells in our bodies can survive only within a limited temperature range. The body must maintain a constant core temperature at about 37°C (98.6°F). Body temperature is a measure of the average thermal energy in the body. To keep a constant temperature range, our bodies either lose or gain thermal energy.

Energy cannot be created or destroyed, but it can be transferred from one form or place to another. The major source of thermal energy in our bodies is food. When our bodies break down nutrients, some of the chemical energy is released as thermal energy that heats our bodies. Also, some of the kinetic energy from muscle movement is converted into thermal energy.

Body temperature is controlled by the hypothalamus region of the brain. The hypothalamus controls the rate of nutrient use. The hypothalamus also controls shivering and sweating.

Heat is the flow of energy from a warmer to a cooler object. Heat transfer between the body and its surroundings occurs in four ways.

1. **Evaporation:** When water evaporates, or changes from liquid to gas, energy is required. When perspiration evaporates from the surface of our skin, we lose thermal energy as heat.
2. **Radiation:** Heat transfer also occurs through waves that radiate out from a warm object or area. Sitting in the sunshine warms us because we gain thermal energy from the Sun's radiation. Our warm bodies can also radiate energy into cooler air.
3. **Conduction:** When two objects are in direct contact, heat flows by conduction from the warmer to the cooler object. If you stand barefoot on hot sand, heat quickly flows into your feet by conduction.
4. **Convection:** In convection, heat transfer occurs through the movement of particles in a gas or liquid. Your body loses some thermal energy because of convection in the air around you.

EXPLORE

1. **CONNECT** What are some behaviors that help you lose or gain thermal energy?
2. **CHALLENGE** Choose a behavior that either warms or cools your body. Draw a diagram and label it with the types of heat transfer that are occurring.

EXPLORE

1. *CONNECT Sample answer: put on or take off clothes, sit in the shade, build houses, take cold or hot baths, use air conditioning or heating*
2. *CHALLENGE Diagrams should show that some activities promote or prevent radiation and some promote conduction.*

CONNECTING SCIENCES

Integration of Sciences

Set Learning Goal

To apply the physical science concepts of heat transfer and thermal energy to the study of responses in the human body

Present the Science

Energy is the ability to do work or cause change. Heat is a term that describes the felt or measured results of the rapid movement of tiny particles in matter, kinetic energy. Other types of energy can cause kinetic energy and kinetic energy can generate other forms of energy. Students experience kinetic energy and its connection to heat everyday. When they run around a lot, they feel warmer, for example. Hot cocoa and hot tea are liquids in which the tiny particles are set in rapid motion. The same liquids with the particles in slow motion might be cold chocolate milk and iced tea.

Heat transfer happens in all matter (think of ice cubes melting in the tea or steam rising from it). In a living system like an organism, however, heat transfer is controlled. Active parts of the system change in order to keep internal temperatures within a range necessary to survive.

Discussion Questions

Ask: How does shivering warm the body? *movement conduction from muscle*

Ask: Why do we lose heat when sweat evaporates from our skin? *It takes energy to change the molecules of liquid into molecules of gas.*

Close

Ask: Which is more important to our bodies, heating or cooling? *Both are necessary to maintain normal cell temperature. Students in hot areas may say "cooling," and in cold areas may say "heat."*

20.3 FOCUS

Set Learning Goals

Students will

- Describe specialized cells and organs in the male and female reproductive systems.
- Describe the stages of fertilization.
- Describe the development of the embryo and fetus during pregnancy.
- Observe and contrast egg and sperm cells.

3-Minute Warm-Up

Display Transparency 29 or copy this exercise on the board:

Suppose that something occurs that frightens you. What will happen hormonally in your body? What will your physical responses be? *The adrenal glands produce adrenaline, which elevates heart rate. After a while, its effects wear off and you return to normal.*

 3-Minute Warm-Up, p. T29

20.3 MOTIVATE

EXPLORE Reproduction

PURPOSE To observe differences between egg and sperm cells

TIPS *20 min.* Help students focus the microscope and practice moving the slide slightly and slowly so cells can be clearly viewed. Provide images of sperm cells and egg cells or use a microscope projector, or digital images on a computer to assist students with vision limitations.

WHAT DO YOU THINK? *The shapes and sizes are different. The structures of the sperm and egg allow each cell to perform its function.*

Teaching with Technology

Students could use a PC microscope to view eggs and sperm, and then create a presentation with screen captures.

KEY CONCEPT

20.3 The reproductive system allows the production of offspring.

BEFORE, you learned

- Some hormones regulate sexual development
- Glands release hormones

NOW, you will learn

- About specialized cells and organs in male and female reproductive systems
- About fertilization
- About the development of the embryo and fetus during pregnancy

VOCABULARY

menstruation p. 695
fertilization p. 697
embryo p. 697
fetus p. 698

EXPLORE Reproduction

How are sperm and egg cells different?

PROCEDURE

1. From your teacher, gather slides of egg cells and sperm cells.
2. Put each slide under a microscope.
3. Draw a sketch of each cell.
4. With a partner, discuss the differences that you observed.

MATERIALS

- slides of egg and sperm cells
- microscope
- paper
- pencil

WHAT DO YOU THINK?

- What were the differences that you observed?
- What are the benefits of the different characteristics for each cell?

CHOOSE YOUR OWN STRATEGY
Begin taking notes on the idea that the reproductive system produces specialized cells. You might use an outline or another strategy of your choice.

The reproductive system produces specialized cells.

Like all living organisms, humans reproduce. The reproductive system allows adults to produce offspring. Although males and females have different reproductive systems, both systems share an important characteristic. They both make specialized cells. In any organism or any system, a specialized cell is a cell that takes on a special job.

In the female these specialized cells are called egg cells. In the male they are called sperm cells. In the reproductive system, each specialized cell provides genetic material. Genetic material contains the information that an organism needs to form, develop, and grow.

694 Unit 5: **Human Biology**

RESOURCES FOR DIFFERENTIATED INSTRUCTION

Below Level

UNIT RESOURCE BOOK

- Reading Study Guide A, pp. 211–212
- Decoding Support, p. 223

AUDIO CDS

Advanced

UNIT RESOURCE BOOK

Challenge and Extension, p. 217

English Learners

UNIT RESOURCE BOOK

Spanish Reading Study Guide, pp. 215–216

AUDIO CDS

- Audio Readings in Spanish
- Audio Readings (English)

Both the male and female reproductive systems rely on hormones from the endocrine system. The hormones act as chemical messengers that signal the process of sexual development. Sexual development includes the growth of reproductive organs and the development of sexual characteristics. Once mature, the reproductive organs produce hormones to maintain secondary sexual characteristics.

The Female Reproductive System

The female reproductive system has two functions. The first is to produce egg cells, and the second is to protect and nourish the offspring until birth. The female has two reproductive organs called ovaries. Each ovary contains on average hundreds of egg cells. About every 28 days, the pituitary gland releases a hormone that stimulates some of the eggs to develop and grow. The ovaries then produce hormones that get the uterus ready to receive the egg.

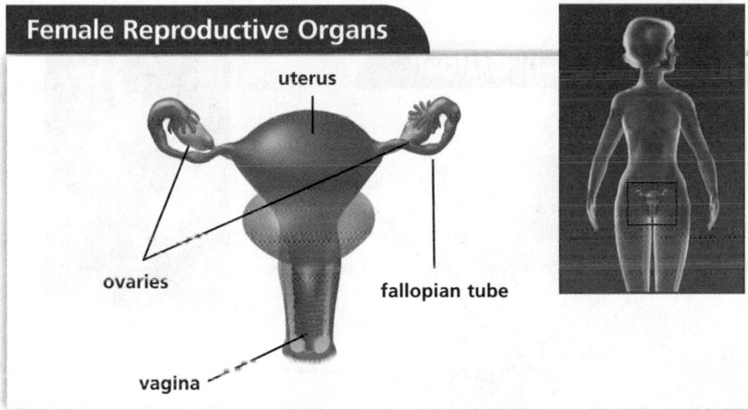

Menstruation

After an egg cell develops fully, another hormone signals the ovary to release the egg. The egg moves from the ovary into a fallopian tube. Within ten to twelve hours, the egg cell may be fertilized by a sperm cell and move to the uterus. Once inside the thick lining of the uterus, the fertilized egg cell rapidly grows and divides.

However, if fertilization does not occur within 24 hours after the egg cell leaves the ovary, both the egg and the lining of the uterus begin to break down. The muscles in the uterus contract in a process called **menstruation.** Menstruation is the flow of blood and tissue from the body through a canal called the vagina over a period of about five days.

 Where does the egg travel after it leaves the ovary?

20.3 INSTRUCT

Address Misconceptions

IDENTIFY Ask students if the material to develop an embryo and then a new human baby is contained in the egg or in the sperm. If they answer either egg or sperm, they hold the misconception either that the developing baby exists in the egg, with the sperm triggering growth, or that the new life exists in the sperm, with the egg required for food and protection.

CORRECT Ask students what traits of each of their parents they have. Point out that they have traits from both parents, and that traits were determined by genetic material in both the egg and the sperm. Explain that neither the egg nor the sperm alone has life, and that what creates life in the process of reproduction is the fusion of egg and sperm.

REASSESS Ask: What makes sperm cells and egg cells different from almost all other types of cells? *They must join one another in order to reproduce.*

Technology Resources

Visit **ClassZone.com** for background on common student misconceptions.

 **MISCONCEPTION DATABASE**

Develop Critical Thinking

COMPARE Have students compare the female and male reproductive systems, focusing on function, structure, and the specialized cells each produces.

Ongoing Assessment

 *Answer: the fallopian tube*

DIFFERENTIATE INSTRUCTION

A Where is an egg cell fertilized? *in the fallopian tube*

B What happens if an egg is not fertilized? *The egg and the lining of the uterus break down.*

English Learners Place the terms *fertilization, menstruation, embryo, sperm, egg,* and *reproduction* on a classroom Science Word Wall with brief definitions for each. Use the chapter summary page to help students focus on key concepts and vocabulary.

Teach from Visuals

Use the illustrations of the female and male reproductive systems (pp. 695–696) to trace the production of eggs and sperm and the process by which they join. Have students individually or in groups find the path of an egg cell in the female organs, and of a sperm cell in the male, and then the female organs.

Ongoing Assessment

Describe specialized cells and organs in the male and female reproductive systems.

Ask: What are the two main functions of the female reproductive system and where do they take place? *to produce egg cells (in the ovaries); to nourish offspring until birth (in the uterus)*

The Male Reproductive System

Testes The organs that produce sperm are called the testes (TEHS-teez). Inside the testes are tiny, coiled tubes hundreds of feet long. Sperm are produced inside these coiled tubes. The testes release a hormone that controls the development of sperm. This hormone is also responsible for the development of physical characteristics in men such as facial hair and a deep voice.

Sperm Sperm cells are the specialized cells of the male reproductive system. Males start producing sperm cells sometime during adolescence. The sperm is a single cell with a head and a tail. The sperm's head is filled with chromosomes, and the tail functions as a whip, making the sperm highly mobile. The sperm travel from the site of production, the testes, through several different structures of the reproductive system. While they travel, the sperm mix with fluids. This fluid is called semen and contains nutrients for the sperm cells. One drop of semen contains up to several million sperm cells.

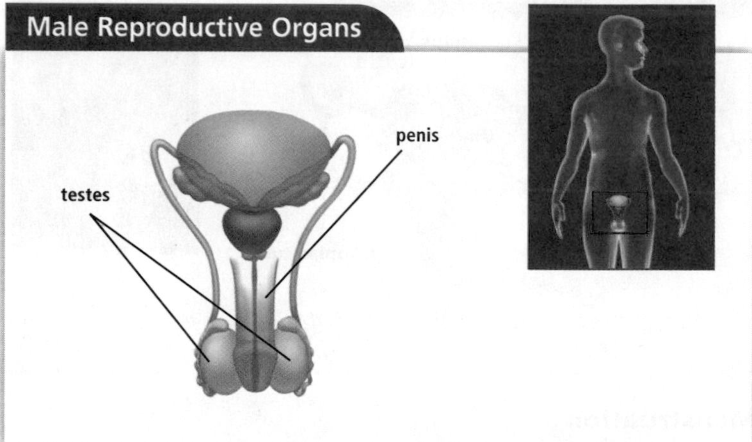

The production of offspring includes fertilization, pregnancy, and birth.

Follow an egg from fertilization to implantation.

Each sperm cell, like each egg cell, has half of the genetic material needed for a human being to grow and develop. During sexual intercourse, millions of sperm cells leave the testes. The sperm cells exit the male's body through the urethra, a tube that leads out of the penis. The sperm cells enter the female's body through the vagina. Next they travel into the uterus and continue on to the fallopian tube.

DIFFERENTIATE INSTRUCTION

More Reading Support

C Where are sperm produced? *in the testes*

D What is the function of the sperm's tail? *makes sperm mobile*

Below Level Help students organize information on the reproductive systems into a chart like the one below:

Gender	Specialized Cell	Organ That Produces Cell	Other Organs
female	egg	ovary	fallopian tube, uterus, vagina
male	sperm	testes	urethra, penis

Fertilization

Fertilization occurs when one sperm cell joins the egg cell. The fallopian tube is the site of fertilization. Immediately, chemical changes in the egg's surface prevent any more sperm from entering. Once inside the egg, the genetic material from the sperm combines with the genetic material of the egg cell. Fertilization is complete.

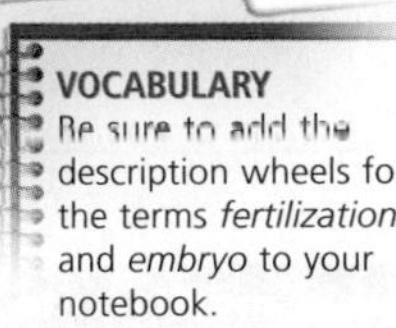

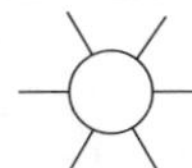

The fertilized egg cell then moves down the fallopian tube toward the uterus. You can trace the path of the egg cell in the diagram on this page. It divides into two cells. Each of those cells divides again, to form a total of four cells. Cell division continues, and a ball of cells forms, called an **embryo** (EM-bree-OH). Within a few days, the embryo attaches itself to the thickened, spongy lining of the uterus in a process called implantation.

F

Fertilization

The egg moves down the fallopian tube following fertilization. Its final destination is the uterus.

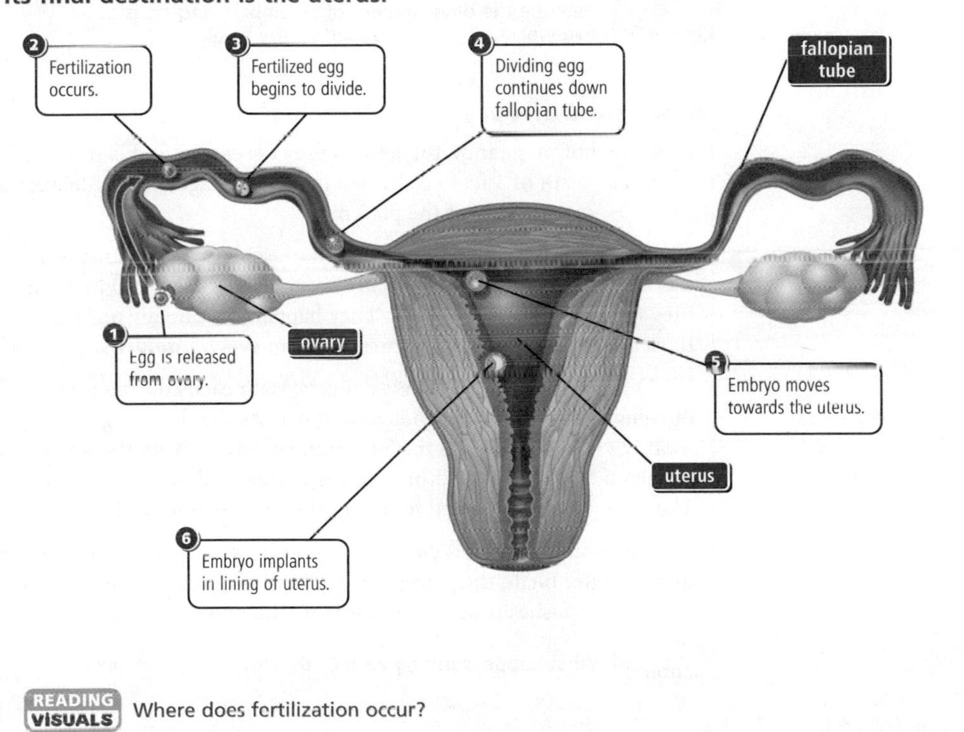

READING VISUALS Where does fertilization occur?

Teach from Visuals

Have students point to the ovary and fallopian tube on the right side of the diagram. Explain that both ovaries and both fallopian tubes are able to produce eggs and carry a fertilized egg to the uterus. To help students interpret the diagram of fertilization, ask:

- Where does the fertilized egg begin to divide? *in the fallopian tubes*
- Where does the embryo implant? *in the uterus*

Ongoing Assessment

Describe the stages of fertilization.

Ask: How does the egg progress to implantation? *A sperm fertilizes the egg in the fallopian tube. The fertilized egg begins to divide as it passes down the tube. Within a few days, a ball of cells is formed and this embryo attaches itself to the wall of the uterus.*

READING VISUALS *Answer: in fallopian tubes*

DIFFERENTIATE INSTRUCTION

More Reading Support

E What is fertilization? *when one sperm cell joins one egg cell*

F What is the ball of cells that grows from a fertilized egg? *an embryo*

Below Level Direct students to view the diagram (p. 697) one stage at a time, following the numbers. Students can render a simple sketch or tracing of the diagram, adding one word for each stage: 1. egg, 2. fertilization, 3. divides, 4. continues, 5. embryo, 6. implants.

Advanced

 Challenge and Extension, p. 217

Health Connection

Drugs, including alcohol and nicotine, interfere with development of an embryo or fetus, killing cells as the body is forming. A classic example is the drug thalidomide, removed from the market in the 1960s, after causing severe birth defects, such as limb abnormalities, to babies of mothers who had taken the drug while pregnant. In the first trimester of a pregnancy a mother may not know she is pregnant and may be taking prescriptions, smoking, or drinking without realizing the impact on her child. Ask students:

- What are some of the reasons why drugs may be especially dangerous to a developing embryo during the first eight weeks of a pregnancy? *During the first trimester, especially when all major organ systems develop, the effects of chemical substances are not only multiplied due to body mass ratios, but also affect growth and health for life.*
- If a woman knows that there is a chance she may become pregnant, what actions could she take to promote health? *She should cease any recreational chemicals, and consult a doctor about prescription or over-the-counter medication.*

Teach Difficult Concepts

Students may have trouble understanding that an entire baby can grow from just two cells. Remind them that the cells contain the DNA instructions for how to grow, and that the mother's body furnishes the raw materials through the placenta.

Ongoing Assessment

CHECK YOUR READING *Answer: 2 weeks—embryo grows rapidly, placenta develops; 8 weeks—embryo becomes a fetus with developing facial features, organ systems, sexual traits, and skeleton; 12 weeks—bones of fetus develop further*

CHECK YOUR READING *Answer: First stage: labor: muscular contractions of the uterus; second stage: delivery: fetus is pushed out; third stage: delivery of the placenta*

Pregnancy

The nine months of pregnancy can be divided into three periods of about the same length. Each period marks specific stages of development. In the first week following implantation, the embryo continues to grow rapidly. Both the embryo and the uterus contribute cells to a new, shared organ called the placenta. The placenta has blood vessels that lead from the mother's circulatory system to the embryo through a large tube called the umbilical cord. Oxygen and nutrients from the mother's body will move through the placenta and umbilical cord to the growing embryo.

Uterus and Placenta

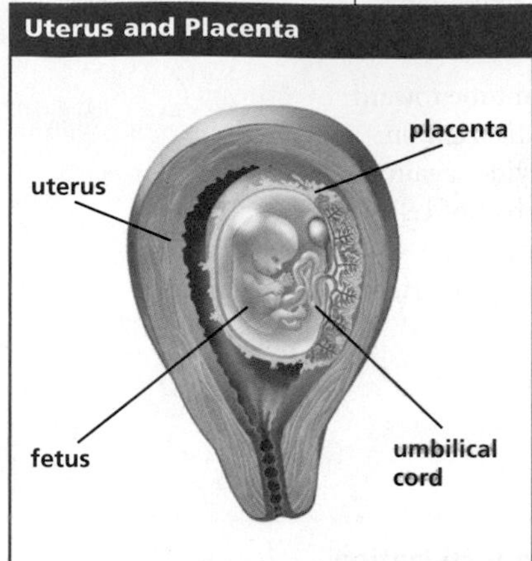

Around the eighth week of pregnancy, the developing embryo is called a **fetus.** The fetus begins to have facial features, major organ systems, and the beginnings of a skeleton. The fetus develops the sexual traits that are either male or female. In the twelfth week, the fetus continues to grow and its bones develop further. In the last twelve weeks, the fetus and all of its organ systems develop fully.

Describe the development of an embryo and fetus at two weeks, eight weeks, and twelve weeks.

Labor and Delivery

At the end of pregnancy, the fetus is fully developed and is ready to be born. The birth of a fetus is divided into three stages; labor, delivery of the fetus, and delivery of the placenta.

The first stage of birth begins with muscular contractions of the uterus. These contractions initially occur at intervals of 10 to 30 minutes and last about 40 seconds. They happen continually until the muscular contractions are occurring about every 2 minutes.

The second stage of birth is delivery. With each contraction, the opening to the uterus expands until it becomes wide enough for the mother's muscles to push the fetus out. During delivery the fetus is pushed out of the uterus, through the vagina, and out of the body. The fetus is still connected to the mother by the umbilical cord.

The umbilical cord is cut shortly after the fetus is delivered. Within minutes after birth, the placenta separates from the uterine wall and the mother pushes it out with more muscular contractions.

What happens during each of the three stages of birth?

DIFFERENTIATE INSTRUCTION

More Reading Support

G How does the first stage of birth begin? *with muscular contractions of the uterus*

English Learners Help students with limited English create a sequence diagram to organize the text into stages of time. They should look for phrases that mention time in the text and diagram and use these phrases in headings in the diagram, as shown.

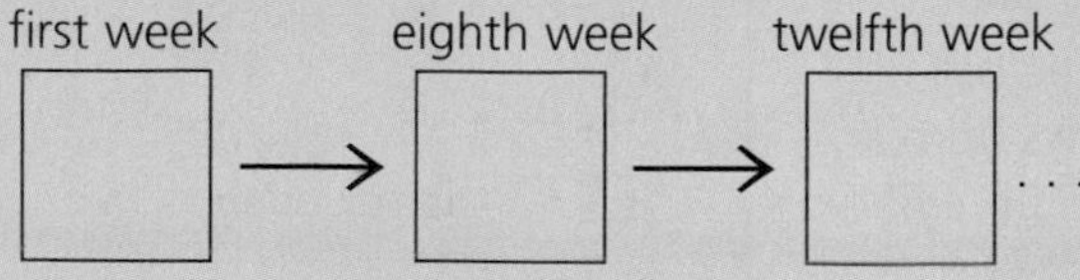

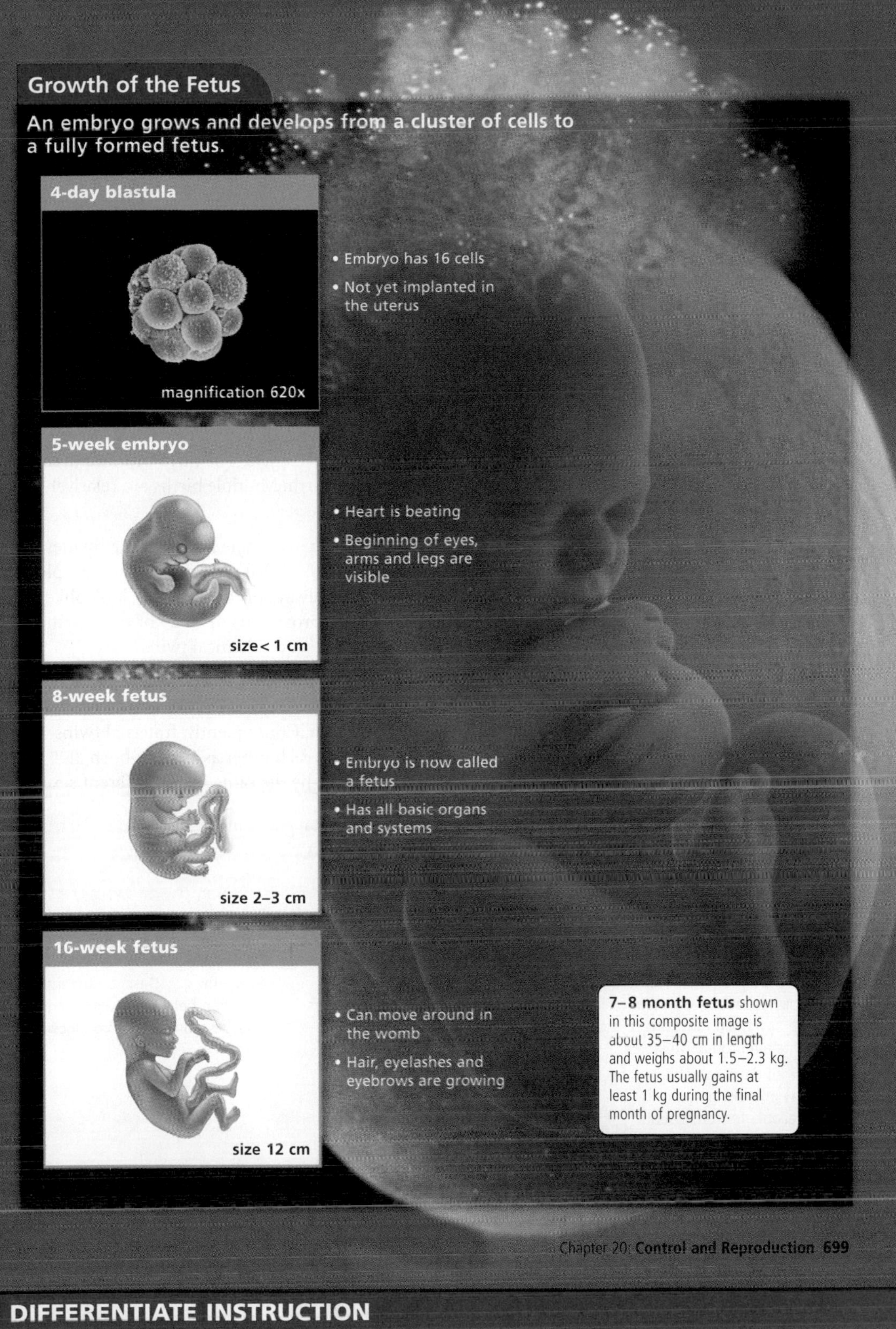

DIFFERENTIATE INSTRUCTION

Below Level Have students create sequence cards for the development of the fetus, drawing pictures of what happens at each stage.

Teach from Visuals

To help students understand the growth and development of a human fetus, ask:

- When does the heart start to beat? *by 5 weeks*
- How big is a 16-week fetus? *about 13 cm long*

Metacognitive Strategy

Have students suggest reasons why it is important to know about sexual reproduction.

EXPLORE the BIG idea

Revisit "Eggs" on p. 675. Have students compare chicken egg structures to human eggs.

Ongoing Assessment

Describe the development of the embryo and fetus during pregnancy.

Ask: How does the embryo change as pregnancy progresses? *By the eighth week the embryo has become a fetus. It begins to have facial features, major organ systems, some of its skeleton, and its sexual traits. In the second trimester the bones continue to grow, and during the third trimester the fetus and all of its systems develop fully.*

Ongoing Assessment

CHECK YOUR READING *Answer: Identical twins come from a single fertilized egg that divides in two. Fraternal twins come from two separate fertilized eggs.*

Reinforce the BIG idea

Have students relate the section to the Big Idea.

 Reinforcing Key Concepts, p. 218

20.3 ASSESS & RETEACH

Assess

 Section 20.3 Quiz, p. 62

Reteach

Draw a sequence or chain of events graphic organizer titled Reproductive System on the board. In the first box, write "male" and "female." Have students help you fill in the rest of the sequence, through fertilization, pregnancy, and birth.

Technology Resources

Have students visit **ClassZone.com** for reteaching of Key Concepts.

 CONTENT REVIEW

CONTENT REVIEW CD-ROM

These twins provide an example of offspring born in a multiple birth.

Multiple Births

Do you have any friends who are twins or triplets? Perhaps you and your brothers or sisters are twins or triplets. The birth of more than one offspring is called a multiple birth. Multiple births are relatively uncommon in humans.

Identical twins are produced when a single fertilized egg divides in half early in embryo development. Each half then forms one complete organism, or twin. Such twins are always of the same sex, look alike, and have identical blood types. Approximately 1 in 29 of twin births, or 4 in every 1000 of all births, is a set of identical twins.

Twins that are not identical are called fraternal twins. Fraternal twins are produced when two eggs are released at the same time and are fertilized by two different sperm. Consequently, fraternal twins may be as similar or different from each other as siblings born at different times. Fraternal twins can be the same sex or different sexes.

CHECK YOUR READING Why are some twins identical and some are not?

20.3 Review

KEY CONCEPTS

1. Describe the function of the male reproductive system and the two main functions of the female reproductive system.
2. Identify two roles hormones play in making egg cells available for fertilization.
3. How is an embryo different from a fetus?

CRITICAL THINKING

4. **Sequence** Describe the sequence of events that occurs between fertilization and the stage called implantation.
5. **Analyze** Detail two examples of hormones interacting with the reproductive system, one involving the male system and one involving the female system.

CHALLENGE

6. **Synthesize** Describe the interaction between the endocrine system and the reproductive system.

ANSWERS

1. male: makes sperm cells; female: makes egg cells; nourishes offspring until birth

2. Hormone stimulates eggs in ovary to develop. Hormone signals egg to move through fallopian tube to uterus.

3. Embryo is ball of cells; fetus has beginnings of features, organs, and skeleton.

4. Fertilized egg moves down fallopian tube; it divides and continues as a ball of cells; forms an embryo; embryo implants in uterus.

5. signal cells in testes to develop into sperm; signal ovaries to release eggs

6. Hormones from endocrine system signal sexual development. In females, hormones make egg develop and make ovary release it.

MATH TUTORIAL

CLASSZONE.COM

Click on Math Tutorial for more help with solving proportions.

SKILL: SOLVING PROPORTIONS

Twins and Triplets

Is the number of twins and triplets on the rise? Between 1980 and 1990, twin births in The United States rose from roughly 68,000 to about 105,000. In 1980, there were about 3,600,000 births total. To convert the data to birth rates, you can use proportions. A proportion is an equation. It shows two ratios that are equivalent.

Example

Find the birth rate of twins born in The United States for 1980. The rate is the number of twin births per 1000 births.

(1) Write the ratio of twin births to total births for that year.

$$\frac{68{,}000 \text{ twin births}}{3{,}600{,}000 \text{ total births}}$$

(2) Write a proportion, using x for the number you need to find.

$$\frac{68{,}000}{3{,}600{,}000} = \frac{x}{1000}$$

(3) In a proportion, the cross products are equal, so

$$68{,}000 \cdot 1000 = x \cdot 3{,}600{,}000$$

(4) Solve for x:

$$\frac{68{,}000{,}000}{3{,}600{,}000} = 18.9$$

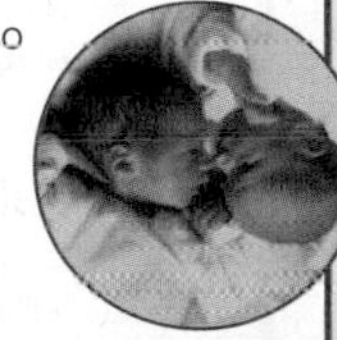

ANSWER There were 18.9 twin births for every 1000 births in 1980.

Find the following birth rates.

1. In 1990, there were about 105,000 twin births and about 3,900,000 total births. What was the birth rate of twins?
2. In 1980, about 1,350 sets of triplets were born, and by 1990, this number had risen to about 6,750. What were the birth rates of triplets in 1980 and in 1990?
3. How much did the birth rate increase for twins between 1980 and 1990? for triplets?
4. Find the overall birth rate of twins and triplets in 1980.
5. Find the overall rate of twin and triplet births in 1990. How much did it increase between 1980 and 1990?

CHALLENGE In 1989, there were about 4 million total births, and the rate of triplets born per million births was about 700. How many triplets were born?

ANSWERS

1. 27 per 1000 births

2. 1980: 0.38 per 1000 births; 1990: 1.7 per 1000 births

3. 42%; 347%

4. 19.3 per 1000 births

5. 28.7 per 1000 births; 49%

CHALLENGE *2800 sets of triplets, or 8400 triplets*

MATH IN SCIENCE

Math Skills Practice for Science

Set Learning Goal

To solve proportions regarding birth rates for twins and triplets

Present the Science

A major reason for the rise in multiple pregnancies in recent decades is the use of fertility drugs and assisted reproductive technology. These advances have helped couples who were unable to have children, but they are not without risks. Multiple fetuses also increase complications of pregnancy and birth. Preterm births occur five times more often for twins than for single fetuses, and 92% of mothers of triplets give birth early. Incidences of gestational diabetes, preeclampsia, and placenta problems are also significantly higher. Anemia is also more common.

Develop Algebra Skills

- It may help students to read the proportions aloud as "68,000 is to 3,600,000 as x is to 1000."
- Describe how to calculate percentage of increase: Subtract the lower number from the greater, and divide the result by the lower number. Multiply by 100 to get a percentage.

Close

Ask: How does using rates help you adjust the data for population growth? *Rates are like percentages. They allow you to compare different-sized populations.*

- Math Support, p. 224
- Math Practice, p. 225

Technology Resources

Students can visit **ClassZone.com** for practice in solving proportions.

MATH TUTORIAL

BACK TO

the BIG idea

Ask students to explain the basic functions of the nervous and endocrine systems. *The nervous system regulates voluntary and involuntary movement of the body and allows it to respond to the environment through the senses. The endocrine system helps the body maintain homeostasis through regulation by hormones.*

KEY CONCEPTS SUMMARY

SECTION 20.1
Have students name an example of something that is controlled by the autonomic nervous system. *The autonomic nervous system controls involuntary movement such as the pumping of the heart and movement of smooth muscles during digestion.*

SECTION 20.2
Ask students why the diagram of the endocrine system is an example of a feedback system in the body. *Feedback systems allow the body to control the levels of hormones that are produced by certain glands, as illustrated in the diagram.*

SECTION 20.3
Ask students to describe the reproductive system shown in the illustration. *The illustration shows the female reproductive system and includes ovaries, fallopian tubes, and uterus.*

Review Concepts

- Big Idea Flow Chart, p. T25
- Chapter Outline, pp. T31–T32

20 Chapter Review

the BIG idea

The nervous and endocrine systems allow the body to respond to internal and external conditions.

KEY CONCEPTS SUMMARY

1 The nervous system responds and controls.

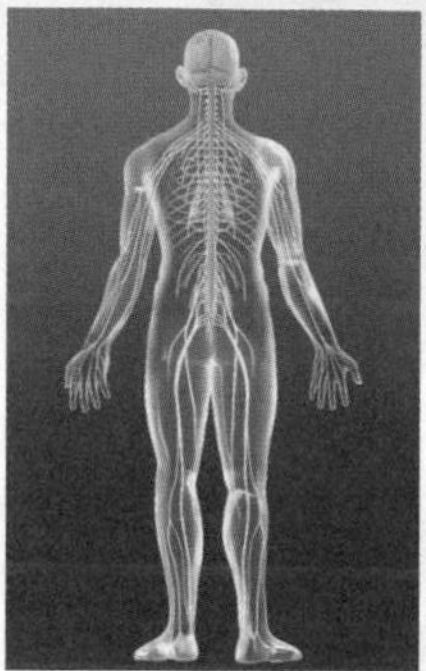

- The nervous system connects the body with its environment using different senses: sight, touch, hearing, smell, and taste. Central nervous system includes the brain, the control center, and the spinal cord.
- The peripheral nervous system includes the autonomic and voluntary systems

VOCABULARY
stimulus p. 678
central nervous system p. 680
neuron p. 681
peripheral nervous system p. 682
autonomic nervous system p. 683
voluntary nervous system p. 683

2 The endocrine system helps regulate body conditions.

The body has chemical messengers called **hormones** that are regulated by the **endocrine system. Glands** produce and release hormones. The endocrine system includes feedback systems that maintain homeostasis.

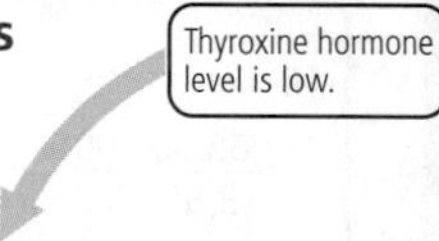

VOCABULARY
endocrine system p. 686
hormone p. 687
gland p. 687

3 The reproductive system allows the production of offspring.

The female produces eggs, and the male produces sperm. Following **fertilization** the fetus develops over a period of about nine months.

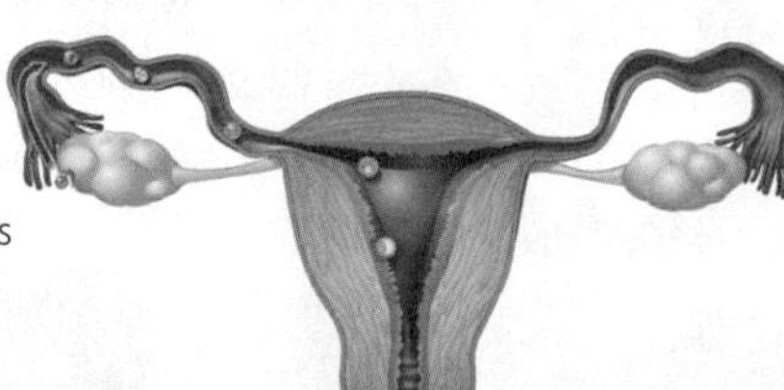

VOCABULARY
menstruation p. 695
fertilization p. 697
embryo p. 697
fetus p. 698

702 Unit 5: **Human Biology**

Technology Resources

Have students visit **ClassZone.com** or use the CD-ROM for a cumulative review of concepts.

CONTENT REVIEW

CONTENT REVIEW CD-ROM

Engage students in a whole-class interactive review of Key Concepts. Edit content as you wish.

POWER PRESENTATIONS

Reviewing Vocabulary

Make a frame for each of the vocabulary words listed. Write the word in the center. Decide what information to frame it with. Use definitions, examples, descriptions, parts, or pictures.

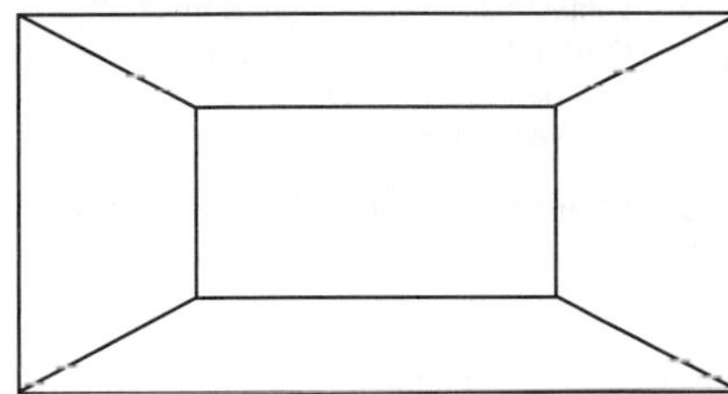

1. stimulus
2. neurons
3. hormones
4. fertilization
5. embryo

Reviewing Key Concepts

Multiple Choice *Choose the letter of the best answer.*

6. Which is a stimulus?
   a. a car horn blowing
   b. jumping at a loud noise
   c. taste buds on the tongue
   d. turning on a lamp
7. Light enters the eye through
   a. the lens
   b. the auditory canal
   c. the olfactory epithelium
   d. the taste buds
8. Which senses allow you to process chemical information?
   a. sight and smell
   b. taste and smell
   c. touch and hearing
   d. hearing and taste
9. What conserves energy and responds quickly to change?
   a. central nervous system
   b. spinal cord
   c. autonomic nervous system
   d. voluntary nervous system
10. Which is not regulated by hormones?
    a. production of white blood cells
    b. physical growth
    c. blood pressure
    d. sexual development
11. Which gland releases hormones that are necessary for growth and metabolism?
    a. thymus
    b. pituitary gland
    c. pancreas
    d. pineal gland
12. Eggs develop in the female reproductive organ called
    a. an ovary
    b. a fallopian tube
    c. a uterus
    d. a vagina
13. The joining of one sperm cell and one egg cell is an event called
    a. menstruation
    b. fertilization
    c. implantation
    d. birth
14. A cluster of cells that is formed by fertilization is called the
    a. testes
    b. urethra
    c. ovary
    d. embryo
15. The period in which a fetus and all of its systems develop fully is the
    a. first three months
    b. second three months
    c. third three months
    d. pregnancy

Short Answer *Write a short answer to each question.*

16. List the parts of the body that are controlled by the autonomic nervous system.
17. What is a negative feedback mechanism? Give an example.
18. How are fertilization and menstruation related?

Reviewing Vocabulary

Sample answers:

1. *sounds, scents, tastes, touch, light; change in environment that people react to; detected by senses; processed by brain*
2. *electrical signals travel through them between body, brain, and spinal cord; make up brain and spinal cord*
3. *made and sent around body by endocrine system; the body's chemical messengers; chemicals made in one structure that are sent to a second structure; growth, antidiuretic, thyroxine, cortisol, insulin, testosterone, estrogen, adrenaline; produced and released by glands*
4. *may lead to pregnancy; results when egg and sperm unite; happens in fallopian tube; may happen as a result of sexual intercourse*
5. *ball of cells that forms from a fertilized egg; implants in lining of uterus; contributes to formation of placenta; attached to placenta by umbilical cord; after eight weeks develops into fetus*

Reviewing Key Concepts

6. a	*11. a*
7. a	*12. a*
8. b	*13. b*
9. c	*14. d*
10. c	*15. c*

16. *The heart and the organs of the digestive system are controlled by the autonomic nervous system.*
17. *A negative feedback system controls the amount of a hormone in the body by signaling the body to stop producing it. Increased levels of thyroxine, for example, inhibit signals from the hypothalamus and pituitary glands that trigger production of thyroxine, and thyroxine production decreases.*
18. *If fertilization does not occur, the egg and the lining of the uterus break down, triggering muscle contractions that expel blood and tissue from the uterus in a process called menstruation.*

ASSESSMENT RESOURCES

UNIT ASSESSMENT BOOK
- Chapter Test, Level A, pp. 63–66
- Chapter Test, Level B, pp. 67–70
- Chapter Test, Level C, pp. 71–74
- Alternative Assessment, pp. 75–76

SPANISH ASSESSMENT BOOK
Spanish Chapter Test, pp. 93–96

Technology Resources

Edit test items and answer choices.

 **Test Generator CD-ROM**

Visit **ClassZone.com** to extend test practice.

 **Test Practice**

Thinking Critically

19. Light enters through lens; pupil gets smaller or larger to control the amount of light that enters; light focused by lens and hits retina at back of eye.

20. Image is like the object but inverted; is corrected by the brain after it receives information from optic nerve.

21. Central and peripheral nervous systems are involved; sensory nerves of peripheral nervous system feel pain and send impulses to central nervous system; motor nerves send signals to muscles to move foot.

22. Response to the stimulus increases stimulus, which then increases response; example: when endocrine system releases hormone that triggers blood clotting.

23. central nervous system: brain, spinal cord; peripheral nervous system: autonomic

24. thyroid gland because it controls metabolism; slow metabolism would likely cause lack of energy

25. Pituitary gland releases a hormone to stimulate egg development; another hormone signals ovary to release egg; egg travels down fallopian tube; not fertilized, egg and uterus lining break down and menstruation begins.

26. Both produce reproductive cells and are regulated by hormones; ovaries produce eggs; testes produce sperm.

the BIG idea

27. Answers will depend on students' original answers.

28. Nervous system controls endocrine and reproductive systems. Sample examples: when frightened, hormones cause heartbeat to increase; hormones control all aspects of male and female reproductive systems.

UNIT PROJECTS

Check to make sure students are working on their projects. Check schedules and work in progress.

 Unit Projects, pp. 5–10

Thinking Critically

Use the diagram to answer the following two questions.

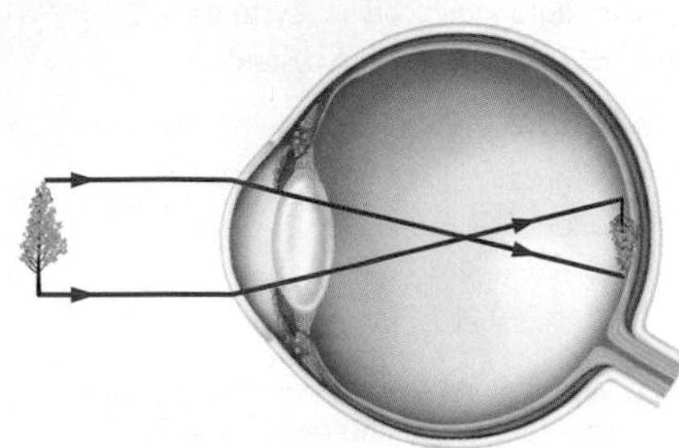

19. SUMMARIZE Use the diagram of the eye to describe how images are formed on the retina.

20. COMPARE AND CONTRAST How is the image that forms on the retina like the object? How is it different? Explain how the viewer interprets the image that forms on the retina.

21. APPLY A person steps on a sharp object with a bare foot and quickly pulls the foot back in pain. Describe the parts of the nervous system that are involved in this action.

22. ANALYZE Explain why positive feedback mechanisms do not help the body maintain homeostasis. Give an example.

23. CONNECT Copy the concept map and add the following terms to the correct box: brain, spinal cord, autonomic.

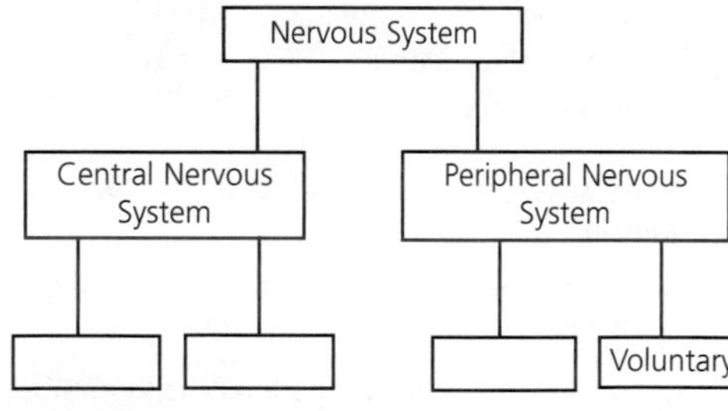

24. DRAW CONCLUSIONS A person who is normally very active begins to notice a significant decrease in energy level. After visiting a doctor, tests results show that one of the endocrine glands is not secreting enough of its hormone. Which gland could this be? Explain your answer.

25. SUMMARIZE Describe the events that occur during the female's 28-day menstrual cycle. Include in your answer how hormones are involved in the cycle.

26. COMPARE AND CONTRAST How are the functions of the ovaries and the testes alike? How are their functions different?

the BIG idea

27. INFER Look again at the picture on pages 674–675. Now that you have finished the chapter, how would you change or add details to your answer to the question on the photograph?

28. SYNTHESIZE How does the nervous system interact with the endocrine and reproductive systems? Give examples that support your answer.

UNIT PROJECTS

If you need to do an experiment for your unit project, gather the materials. Be sure to allow enough time to observe results before the project is due.

MONITOR AND RETEACH

If students are having trouble applying the concepts in items 21–23, suggest that they review the nervous system (pp. 680–683) and feedback mechanisms (pp. 690–692). Have them sketch the situation described in item 21. They can label the activities of various organs involved.

Students may benefit from summarizing one or more sections of the chapter.

 Summarizing the Chapter, pp. 244–245

Standardized Test Practice

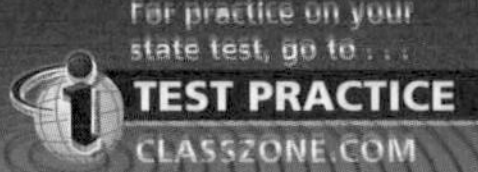

Analyzing Data

This chart shows some of the stages of development of a typical fetus.

Week of Pregnancy	Approximate Length of Fetus (cm)	Developmental Changes in the Fetus
6	1	Primitive heartbeat
10	3	Face, fingers, and toes are formed
14	8.5	Muscle and bone tissue have developed
18	14	Fetus makes active movements
24	30	Fingerprints and footprints forming
28	37.5	Rapid brain development
36	47.5	Increase in body fat
38	50	Fetus is considered full term

Use the chart to answer the questions below.

1. What is the approximate length of the fetus at 10 weeks?
   a. 1 cm
   b. 2 in.
   c. 3 cm
   d. 3 in.
2. At about which week of development does the fetus begin to make active movements?
   a. week 10
   b. week 14
   c. week 18
   d. week 24
3. At about which week of development does the fetus reach a length of about 30 cm?
   a. week 18
   b. week 24
   c. week 36
   d. week 38
4. Which statement is true?
   a. Between weeks 28 and 38, the fetus grows at an average of a little over a centimeter per week.
   b. The fetus begins to develop fingerprints at about week 28.
   c. During week 10, the length of the fetus is about 7.5 cm
   d. The fetus is about 12.5 cm long when muscle and bone tissue develop.
5. Between which two weeks of development does the greatest overall increase in length usually take place?
   a. weeks 6 and 10
   b. weeks 10 and 14
   c. weeks 14 and 18
   d. weeks 24 and 28

Extended Response

6. A pregnancy lasts about 42 weeks, roughly 9 months. The development of the fetus can be broken down into three stages, each 14 weeks long. These stages are referred to as trimesters. Briefly describe changes in length and development that occur during each of these stages.
7. The endocrine system and the nervous system have similar functions. Compare and contrast the two systems including the terms in the box. Underline each term in your answer.

homeostasis	autonomic system	hormones
feedback	smooth muscles	

METACOGNITIVE ACTIVITY

Have students answer the following questions in their **Science Notebook:**

1. What is the most pressing question that you still have about the nervous system?
2. Did you learn anything in this chapter about endocrine, nervous, or reproductive systems that surprised you? Explain.
3. What learning strategies did you use to master a difficult concept in this chapter?

Analyzing Data

1. c *3. b* *5. d*
2. c *4. a*

Extended Response

6. RUBRIC

4 points for a response that correctly answers the question and describes changes in length and development for all three trimesters.

Sample answer: First trimester: fetus grows up to 8.5 cm. Heartbeat, fingers, face, toes, and muscle and bone tissue formed. Second trimester: fetus reaches up to 30 cm. Fetus makes active movements, and fingerprints and footprints are forming. Third trimester: fully developed fetus reaches about 50 cm. Rapid brain development and increase in body fat occurs.

3 points correctly answers question and describes changes in length of all three trimesters of pregnancy and development for at least two trimesters

2 points correctly answers question and describes changes in length of all three trimesters of pregnancy and development for at least one trimester

1 point describes changes in length during all three trimesters or change in development for one trimester

7. RUBRIC

4 points for a response that includes at least four of the following terms:

- homeostasis
- smooth muscles
- feedback
- hormones
- autonomic system

Sample answer: Endocrine and nervous systems control body functions. <u>Autonomic nervous system</u> works with endocrine system to regulate heartbeat, blood pressure, operation of <u>smooth muscles</u>, and secretion of <u>hormones</u> by glands. Endocrine system controls <u>homeostasis</u>, or maintenance of correct body conditions, through negative <u>feedback</u> mechanisms in which increase in amount of a hormone in body triggers decrease in secretion of that hormone.

3 points includes at least three of the terms

2 points includes at least two of the terms

1 point includes at least one of the terms

CHAPTER

Growth, Development, and Health

Life Science
UNIFYING PRINCIPLES

PRINCIPLE 1
All living things share common characteristics.

PRINCIPLE 2
All living things share common needs.

PRINCIPLE 3
Living things meet their needs through interactions with the environment.

PRINCIPLE 4
The types and numbers of living things change over time.

Unit 5: Human Biology
BIG IDEAS

CHAPTER 17
Systems, Support, and Movement
The human body is made up of systems that work together to perform necessary functions.

CHAPTER 18
Absorption, Digestion, and Exchange
Systems in the body obtain and process materials and remove waste.

CHAPTER 19
Transport and Protection
Systems function to transport materials and to defend and protect the body.

CHAPTER 20
Control and Reproduction
The nervous and endocrine systems allow the body to respond to internal and external conditions.

CHAPTER 21
Growth, Development, and Health
The body develops and maintains itself over time.

CHAPTER 21
KEY CONCEPTS

SECTION 1

The human body changes over time.
1. The human body develops and grows.
2. Systems interact to maintain the human body.

SECTION 2

Systems in the body function to maintain health.
1. Diet affects the body's health.
2. Exercise is part of a healthy lifestyle.
3. Drug abuse, addiction, and eating disorders cause serious health problems.

SECTION 3

Science helps people prevent and treat disease.
1. Scientific understanding helps people fight disease.
2. The germ theory describes some causes of disease.
3. Infectious diseases spread in many ways.
4. Noninfectious diseases are not contagious.
5. Scientists continue efforts to prevent and treat illness.

The Big Idea Flow Chart is available on p. T33 in the **UNIT TRANSPARENCY BOOK.**

Previewing Content

SECTION

The human body changes over time. pp. 709–715

1. The human body develops and grows.

- There are several stages of development in a human life. **Infancy** begins at birth and continues as a child learns basic physical skills as well as mental and social skills.

Apgar Score	
Quality	**2 points**
Appearance	Completely pink or good color
Pulse	>100 beats per minute
Grimace	Grimace, cough/ sneeze with suction
Activity	Active motion
Respiration	Good, strong cry

Good health begins in infancy, as the qualities measured in the Apgar test show.

- **Childhood** is the period after infancy and before puberty. Children become more able to care for themselves and learn skills such as cooperation and sharing.
- **Adolescence** begins with puberty, the process of sexual maturation. Hormones signal the reproductive system to mature.
- **Adulthood** occurs when the human body completes its growth and reaches sexual maturity. Mental and social development continue into later adulthood and throughout life.

2. Systems interact to maintain the human body.
All systems in the body constantly interact with other systems to keep the body functioning. Body systems also interact with the external environment to maintain homeostasis.

SECTION

Systems in the body function to maintain health. pp. 716–723

1. Diet affects the body's health.
Nutrition is the study of the materials that affect the body. Six classes of nutrients include carbohydrates, proteins, fats, water, vitamins, and minerals. Food labels use terms such as *low-fat* and *organic* to describe the make-up of food.
More importantly, food labels give nutrition information based on recommended daily amounts, as shown in the chart below.

Nutrition Information		
Nutrient	**Function**	**Daily Amount**
Proteins	Build tissues used for growth and repair	20 percent of the diet
Carbohydrates	Body's most important source of energy	40 to 50 percent of the diet
Fats	Essential for energy	10 to 15 percent of the diet

2. Exercise is part of a healthy lifestyle.
Regular exercise improves respiratory and heart function. It keeps bones and muscles strong and helps to prevent health conditions later in life such as osteoporosis, excess body fat, and heart disease.

3. Drug abuse, addiction, and eating disorders cause serious health problems.
Unhealthy choices may lead to drug abuse, **addiction,** or eating disorders. A drug is a chemical substance that causes a change in the body's function. Tobacco and alcohol are drugs. Nicotine, which is the drug found in tobacco, is addictive. Drugs such as stimulants and narcotics are also addictive and can cause heart failure and death.

Common Misconceptions

FACTORS THAT AFFECT HEALTH Students of all ages focus on the physical dimensions of health and pay less attention to the mental and social dimensions. Students associate health primarily with food and fitness. Many students tend to think that factors important to health and life span are beyond their personal control.

This misconception is addressed on p. 719.

MISCONCEPTION DATABASE
CLASSZONE.COM Background on student misconceptions

Previewing Content

SECTION

Science helps people prevent and treat disease. pp. 724–729

1. **Scientific understanding helps people fight disease.** Disease is a change that disturbs the normal functioning of the body. Infectious diseases are caused by **microorganisms.**

2. **The germ theory describes some causes of disease.** Louis Pasteur's germ theory states that some infectious diseases are caused by germs. Bacteria and viruses are examples of pathogens, which are disease-causing agents. Bacterial diseases can be treated with antibiotics, first discovered by Alexander Fleming.

3. **Infectious diseases spread in many ways.**
   - Pathogens spread in many ways and can be found in food, water, in the air, and on surfaces of objects.
   - Animals and insects carry disease-causing organisms. Lyme disease is carried by deer ticks. Rabies is carried by bats, raccoons, and opossums.
   - Pathogens can also be transmitted by contact with another person, or through the mouth, nose, eyes, and cuts.

4. **Noninfectious diseases are not contagious.** Noninfectious diseases such as hemophilia may be present at birth. Other diseases, such as cancer and diabetes, may occur later in life.

5. **Scientists continue efforts to prevent and treat illness.** Vaccinations have made some diseases nearly extinct. Overuse of antibiotics may cause **resistance** to certain strains of pathogens.

Washing hands and foods and boiling water can help prevent the spread of pathogens, such as this *E. coli* bacteria.

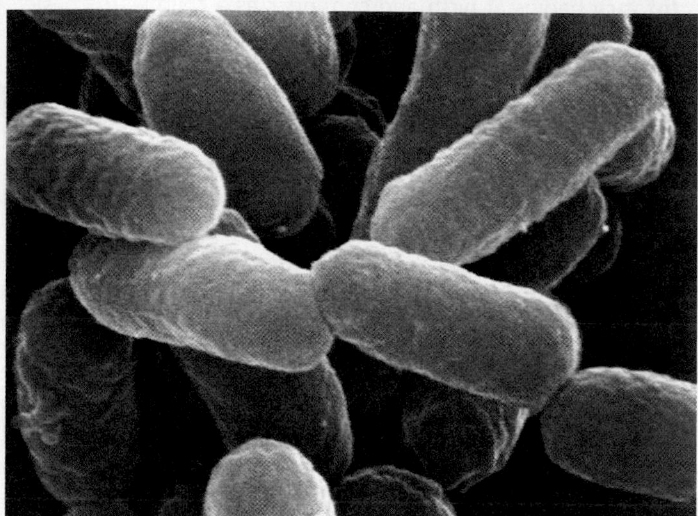

Common Misconceptions

MISCONCEPTION DATABASE
CLASSZONE.COM Background on student misconceptions

CAUSES OF ILLNESS Many students hold the misconception that all illnesses are caused by germs and that germs enter through the mouth by eating. Students may also think that every illness is contagious. As students grow older, their understanding of the causes of illness begins to include malfunctioning of internal organs and systems, poor health habits, and genetics. Upper elementary students can understand that a change in internal body state or the experience of symptoms is the consequence of illness.

TE This misconception is addressed on p. 726.

Previewing Labs

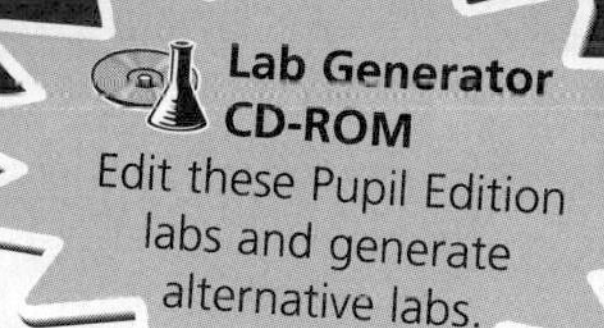

EXPLORE the BIG idea

How Much Do You Exercise? p. 707 Students keep track of how much they exercise in a week in order to understand the connection between exercise and resting heart rate.	**TIME** 10 minutes (per day) **MATERIALS** clock with second hand
How Safe Is Your Food? p. 707 Students analyze freshness dates to learn about food safety.	**TIME** 15 minutes **MATERIALS** various food labels or containers
Internet Activity: Human Development, p. 707 Students observe changes to a person's face during aging.	**TIME** 20 minutes **MATERIALS** computer with Internet access

SECTION 1

EXPLORE Growth, p. 709 Students compile data on body measurements to analyze patterns of growth.	**TIME** 15 minutes **MATERIALS** flexible tape measure, graph paper
INVESTIGATE Life Expectancy, p. 713 Students create a graph to analyze data about life expectancy from 1900–2000 to infer why average life expectancy has changed.	**TIME** 30 minutes **MATERIALS** graph paper, computer graphing program (optional), notebook, pen

SECTION 2

INVESTIGATE Food Labels, p. 719 Students evaluate food labels to determine the nutritional values of a variety of foods.	**TIME** 30 minutes **MATERIALS** nutrition information labels from carbonated soft drink, bag of fresh carrots, canned spaghetti in sauce, potato chips, plain popcorn kernels, unsweetened applesauce, and fruit juice

SECTION 3

EXPLORE The Immune System, p. 724 Students model how easily germs are spread.	**TIME** 10 minutes **MATERIALS** glitter
CHAPTER INVESTIGATION **Cleaning Your Hands,** pp. 730–731 Students sample bacteria on their hands and test the effectiveness of washing their hands with just water compared with soap and water.	**TIME** 40 minutes **MATERIALS** 3 covered petri dishes with sterile nutrient agar, tape, marker, hand soap, hand lens

R **Additional INVESTIGATION,** Where's the Starch?, A, B, & C, pp. 294–302; Teacher Instructions, pp. 305–306

Previewing Chapter Resources

INTEGRATED TECHNOLOGY | **LABS AND ACTIVITIES**

CHAPTER 21
Growth, Development, and Health

Integrated Technology

CLASSZONE.COM
- eEdition Plus
- EasyPlanner Plus
- Misconception Database
- Content Review
- Test Practice
- Resource Centers
- Internet Activity: Human Development
- Math Tutorial

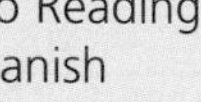

SCILINKS.ORG

CD-ROMS
- eEdition
- EasyPlanner Plus
- Power Presentations
- Content Review
- Lab Generator
- Test Generator

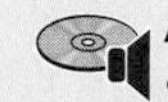

AUDIO CDS
- Audio Readings
- Audio Readings in Spanish

Labs and Activities

EXPLORE the Big Idea, p. 707
- How Much Do You Exercise?
- How Safe Is Your Food?
- Internet Activity: Human Development

UNIT RESOURCE BOOK
Unit Projects, pp. 5–10

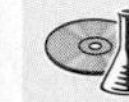

Lab Generator CD-ROM
Generate customized labs.

SECTION

1 The human body changes over time.
pp. 709–715

Time: 2 periods (1 block)

Lesson Plan, pp. 246–247

Integrated Technology

MATH TUTORIAL

UNIT TRANSPARENCY BOOK
- Big Idea Flow Chart, p. T33
- Daily Vocabulary Scaffolding, p. T34
- Note-Taking Model, p. T35
- 3-Minute Warm-Up, p. T36

Labs and Activities

- EXPLORE Growth, p. 709
- INVESTIGATE Life Expectancy, p. 713
- Science on the Job, p. 715

UNIT RESOURCE BOOK
Datasheet, Life Expectancy, p. 255

SECTION

2 Systems in the body function to maintain health.
pp. 716–723

Time: 2 periods (1 block)

Lesson Plan, pp. 257–258

Integrated Technology

- **RESOURCE CENTERS,** Human Health, Principles of Nutrition
- **MATH TUTORIAL**

UNIT TRANSPARENCY BOOK
- Daily Vocabulary Scaffolding, p. T34
- 3-Minute Warm-Up, p. T36

Labs and Activities

- INVESTIGATE Food Labels, p. 719
- Math in Science, p. 723

UNIT RESOURCE BOOK
- Datasheet, Food Labels, p. 266
- Additional INVESTIGATION, Where's the Starch?, Levels A, B, & C, pp. 294–302
- Math Support, p. 283
- Math Practice, p. 284

SECTION

3 Science helps people prevent and treat disease.
pp. 724–729

Time: 4 periods (2 blocks)

Lesson Plan, pp. 268–269

Integrated Technology

RESOURCE CENTER, Ways to Fight Disease

UNIT TRANSPARENCY BOOK
- Big Idea Flow Chart, p. T33
- Daily Vocabulary Scaffolding, p. T34
- 3-Minute Warm-Up, p. T36
- "Pathogens and Disease" Visual, p. T38
- Chapter Outline, pp. T39–T40

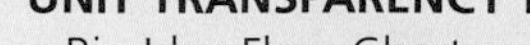

Labs and Activities

- EXPLORE The Immune System, p. 724
- CHAPTER INVESTIGATION, Cleaning Your Hands, pp. 730–731

UNIT RESOURCE BOOK
- CHAPTER INVESTIGATION, Cleaning Your Hands, Levels A, B, & C, pp. 285–293

KEY TO ICONS

 CD/CD-ROM

 Teacher Edition

 UNIT TRANSPARENCY BOOK

 SPANISH ASSESSMENT BOOK

INTERNET

 Pupil Edition

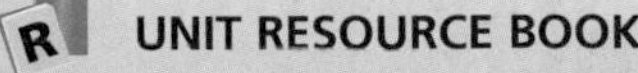 UNIT RESOURCE BOOK

 UNIT ASSESSMENT BOOK

SCIENCE TOOLKIT

READING AND REINFORCEMENT

ASSESSMENT

STANDARDS

- Choose Your Own Strategy, B20–27
- Content Frame, C35
- Daily Vocabulary Scaffolding, H1–8

 **UNIT RESOURCE BOOK**
- Vocabulary Practice, pp. 280–281
- Decoding Support, p. 282
- Summarizing the Chapter, pp. 303–304

 **Audio Reading CD**
Listen to Pupil Edition.

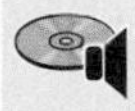 **Audio Readings in Spanish CD**
Listen to Pupil Edition in Spanish.

- Chapter Review, pp. 733–734
- Standardized Test Practice, p. 735

 **UNIT ASSESSMENT BOOK**
- Diagnostic Test, pp. 77–78
- Chapter Test, A, B, & C, pp. 82–93
- Alternative Assessment, pp. 94–95
- Unit Test, A, B, C, pp. 96–107

- Spanish Chapter Test, pp. 97–100
- Spanish Unit Test, pp. 101–104

 **Test Generator CD-ROM**
Generate customized tests.

 **Lab Generator CD-ROM**
Rubrics for Labs

National Standards
A.2–8, A.9.a–c, A.9.e–f, C.1.e–f, C.3.a–b, F.1.c–e, G.1.b

See p. 706 for the standards.

 **UNIT RESOURCE BOOK**
- Reading Study Guide, A & B, pp. 248–251
- Spanish Reading Study Guide, pp. 252–253
- Challenge and Extension, p. 254
- Reinforcing Key Concepts, p. 256
- Challenge Reading, pp. 278–279

 Ongoing Assessment, pp. 711–714

 Section 21.1 Review, p. 714

 **UNIT ASSESSMENT BOOK**
Section 21.1 Quiz, p. 79

National Standards
A.2–7, A.9.a–b, A.9.e–f, C.1.e–f, C.3.a–b, G.1.b

 **UNIT RESOURCE BOOK**
- Reading Study Guide, A & B, pp. 259–262
- Spanish Reading Study Guide, pp. 263–264
- Challenge and Extension, p. 265
- Reinforcing Key Concepts, p. 267

 Ongoing Assessment, pp. 716–717, 720, 722

 Section 21.2 Review, p. 722

 **UNIT ASSESSMENT BOOK**
Section 21.2 Quiz, p. 80

National Standards
A.2–8, A.9.a–c, A.9.e–f, C.1.e, C.3.a, F.1.a, F.1.c–e, G.1.b

 **UNIT RESOURCE BOOK**
- Reading Study Guide, A & B, pp. 270–273
- Spanish Reading Study Guide, pp. 274–275
- Challenge and Extension, p. 276
- Reinforcing Key Concepts, p. 277

 Ongoing Assessment, pp. 726–729

 Section 21.3 Review, p. 729

 **UNIT ASSESSMENT BOOK**
Section 21.3 Quiz, p. 81

National Standards
A.2–7, A.9.a–b, A.9.e–f, C.1.e–f, G.1.b

Previewing Resources for Differentiated Instruction

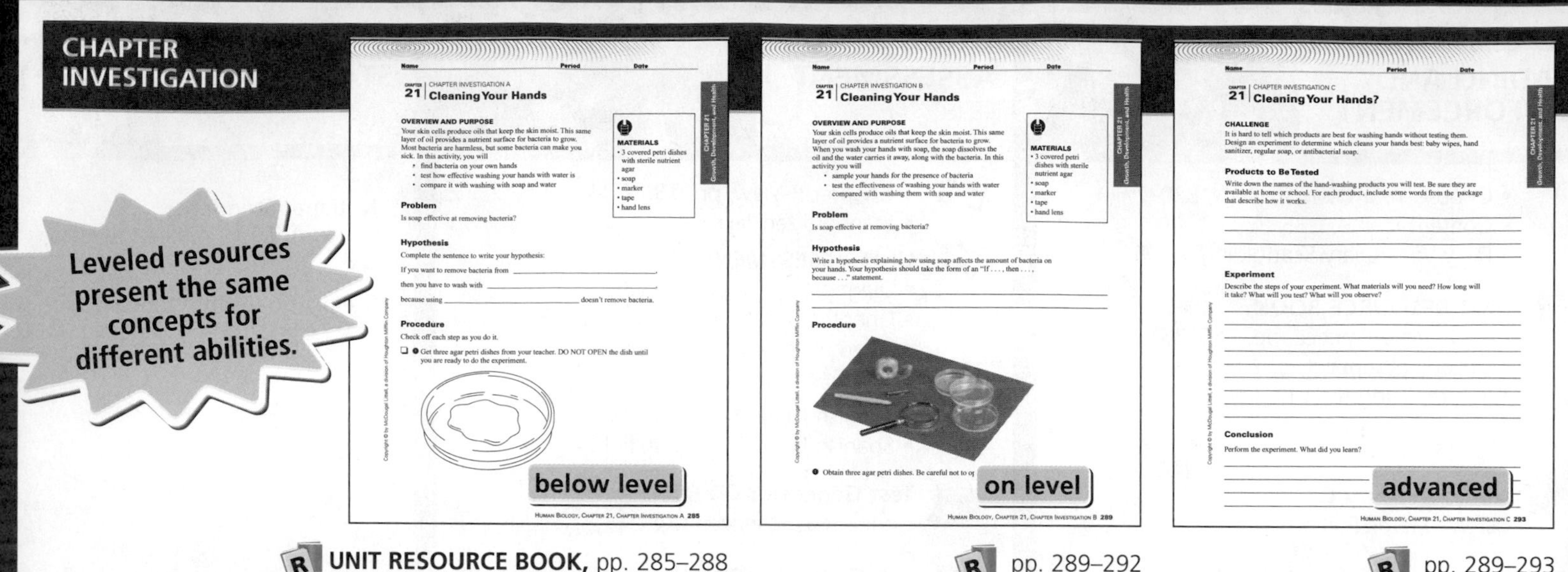

UNIT RESOURCE BOOK, pp. 285–288 | pp. 289–292 | pp. 289–293

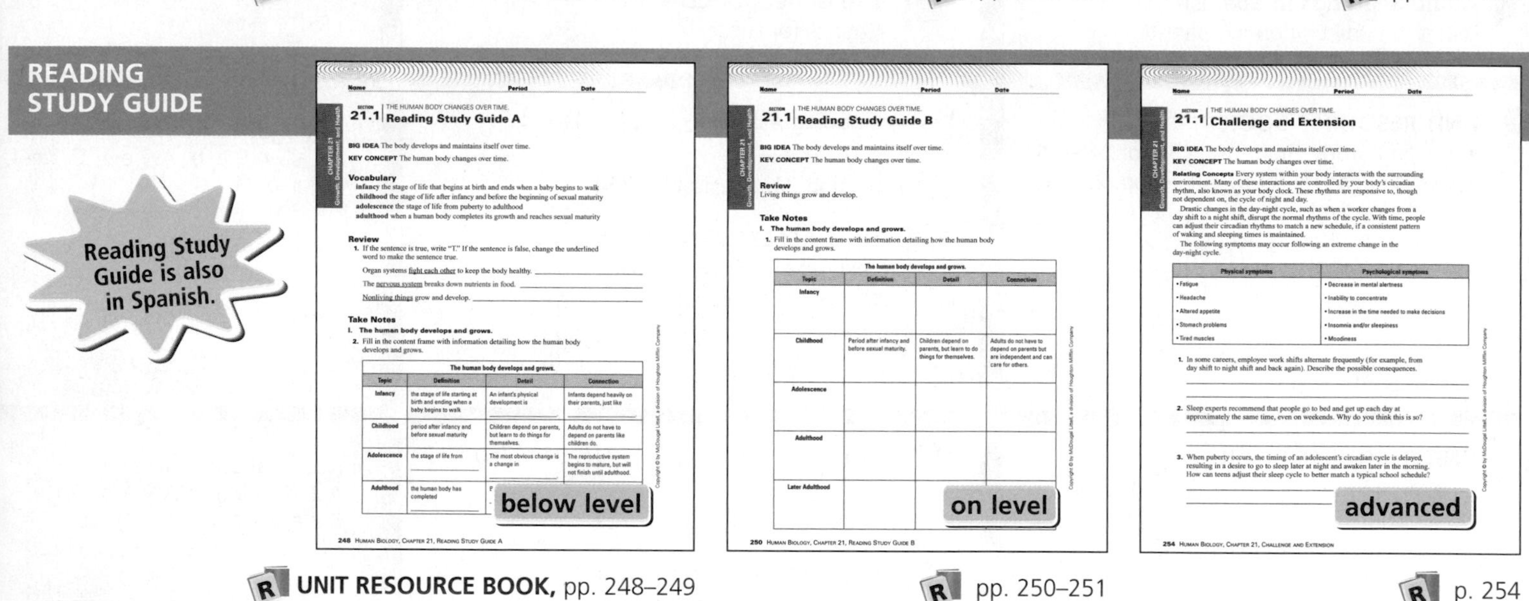

UNIT RESOURCE BOOK, pp. 248–249 | pp. 250–251 | p. 254

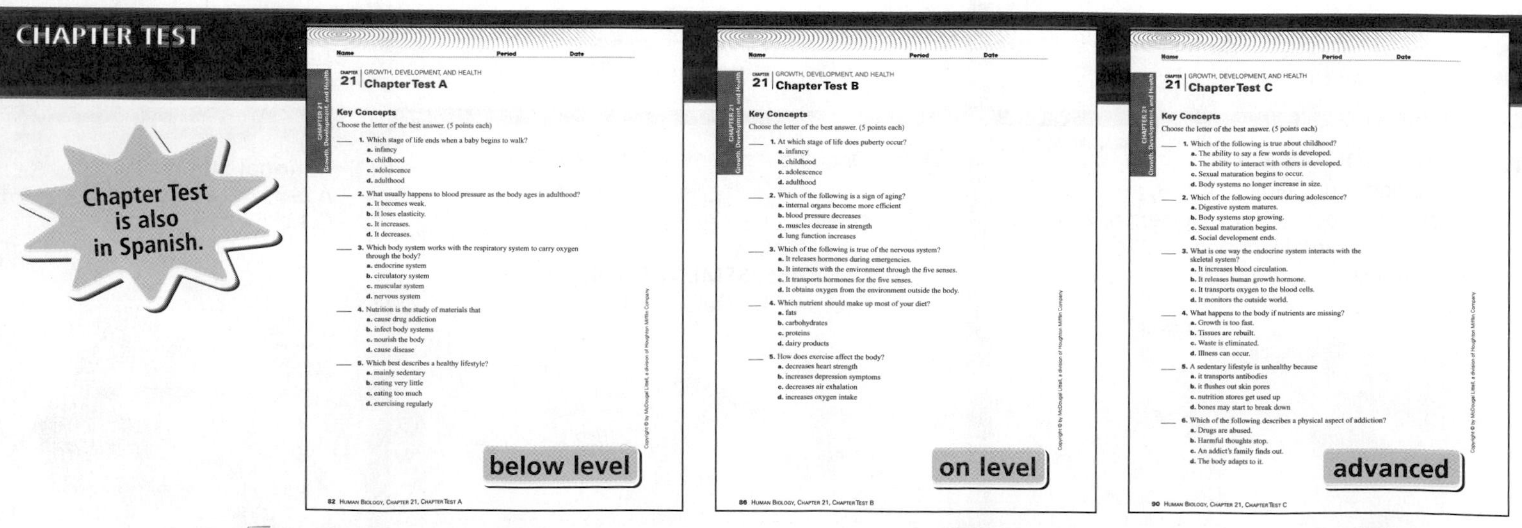

UNIT ASSESSMENT BOOK, pp. 82–85 | pp. 86–89 | pp. 90–93

TECHNOLOGY

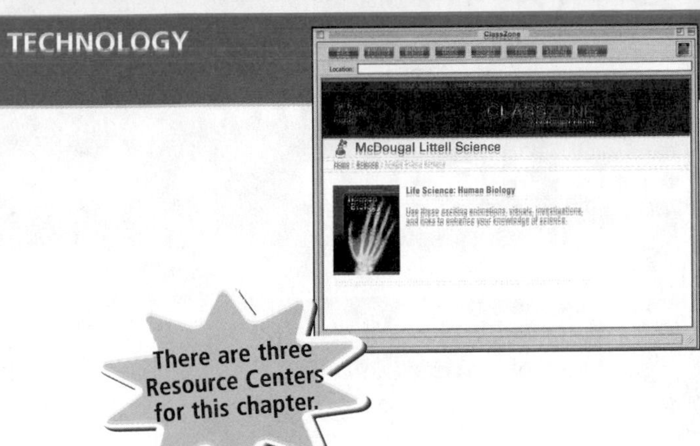

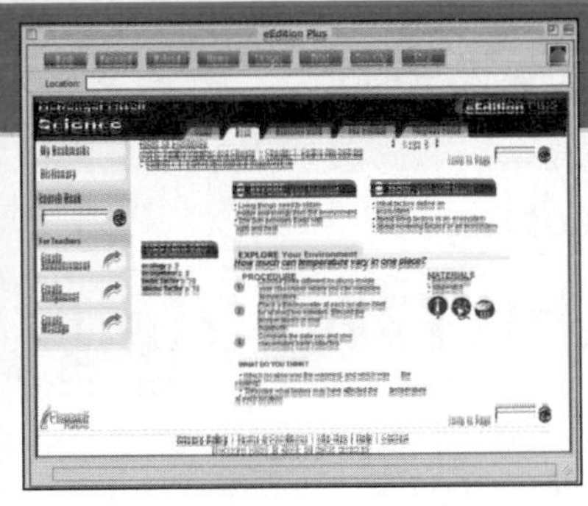

 CLASSZONE.COM

 CD/CD-ROMS

 CLASSZONE.COM

VISUAL CONTENT

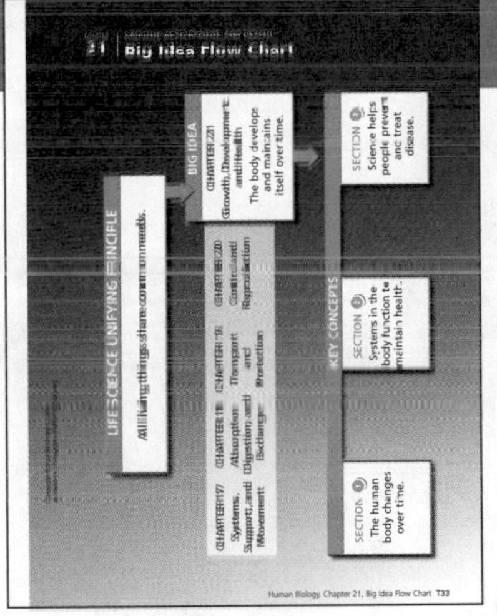

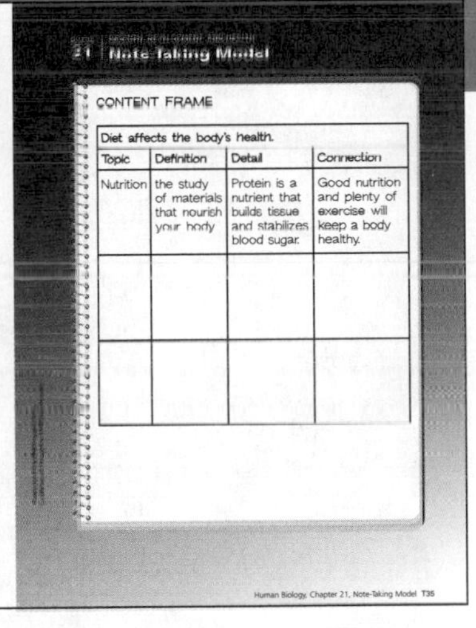

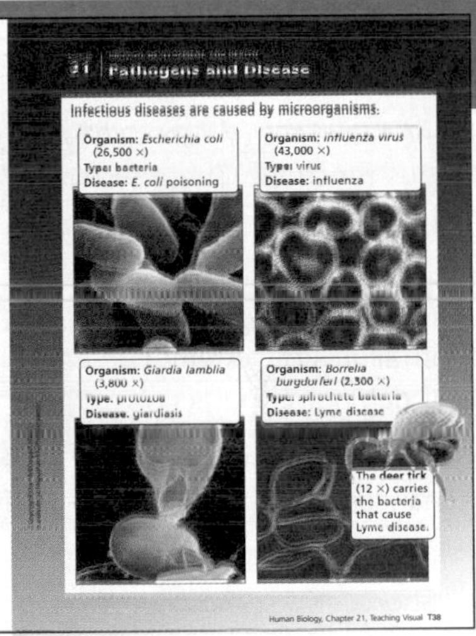

UNIT TRANSPARENCY BOOK, p. T33

p. T35

p. T38

MORE SUPPORT

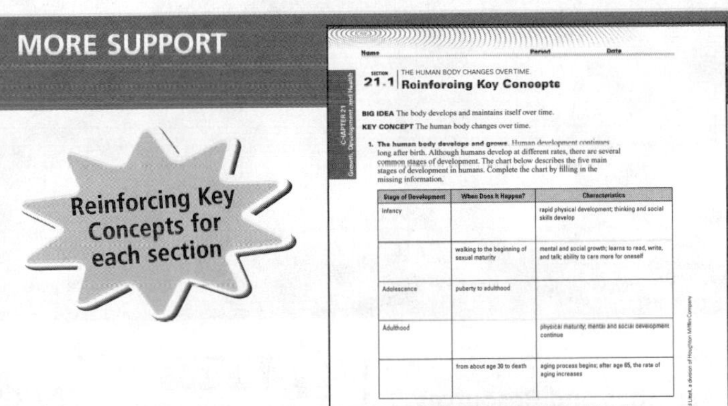

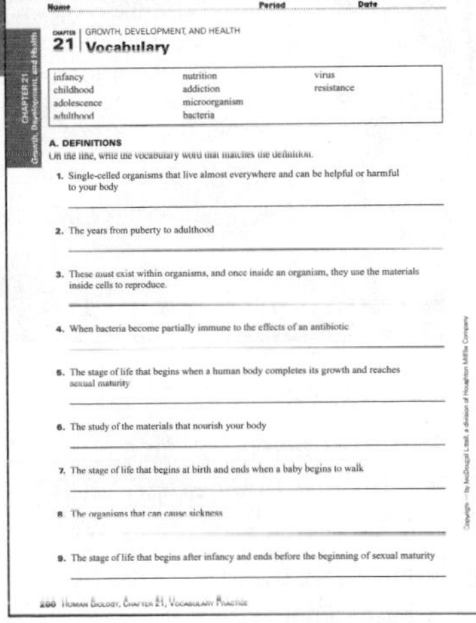

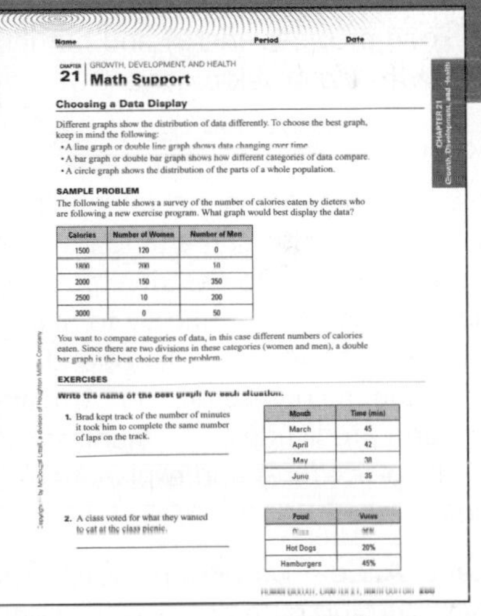

UNIT RESOURCE BOOK, p. 256

pp. 280–281

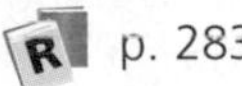 p. 283

Growth, Development, and Health

INTRODUCE

the BIG idea

Have students look at the photograph of a family flying a kite and discuss how the question in the box links to the Big Idea:

- What differences can you notice between the three people?
- How does the photograph relate to being healthy?

National Science Education Standards

Content

C.1.e The human organism has systems for various functions. These systems interact.

C.1.f Disease is a breakdown in structures or functions. Some diseases are the result of failures of system. Others are a result of damage by infection.

F.1.a Regular exercise is important to the maintenance and improvement of health.

F.1.c The use of tobacco increases risk of illness. Short-term social and psychological factors lead to tobacco use.

F.1.d Alcohol and drugs change body function and can lead to addiction.

F.1.e Food provides energy and nutrients for growth and development.

Process

A.2–8 Design and conduct an investigation; use tools to gather and interpret data; use evidence to describe, predict, explain, model; think critically to make relationships between evidence and explanation; recognize different explanations and predictions; communicate scientific procedures and explanations; use mathematics.

A.9.a–c, A.9.e–f Understand scientific inquiry by using different investigations, methods, mathematics, and explanations based on logic, evidence, and skepticism.

CHAPTER

Growth, Development, and Health

the BIG idea

The body develops and maintains itself over time.

Key Concepts

SECTION

The human body changes over time.
Learn about the different stages of human development.

SECTION

Systems in the body function to maintain health.
Learn about what a body needs to be healthy.

SECTION

Science helps people prevent and treat disease.
Learn how to help prevent the spread of disease.

Internet Preview

CLASSZONE.COM

Chapter 21 online resources: Content Review, Visualization, three Resource Centers, Math Tutorial, Test Practice

706 Unit 5: Human Biology

How do people change as they grow?

INTERNET PREVIEW

CLASSZONE.COM For student use with the following pages:

Review and Practice

- Content Review, pp. 708, 732
- Math Tutorial: Choosing a Data Display, p. 723
- Test Practice, p. 735

Activities and Resources

- Internet Activity: Human Development, p. 707
- Resource Centers: Human Health, p. 717; Principles of Nutrition, p. 718; Ways to Fight Disease, p. 725

Human Development
Code: MDL048

TEACHING WITH TECHNOLOGY

Graphing Software Students can use graphing software while investigating how life expectancy has changed over time on p. 713.

Spreadsheet and Slide-Show Software Students could use spreadsheet software and a slide-show program for recording data and outlining the dangers of drugs on p. 721.

EXPLORE the BIG idea

These inquiry-based activities are appropriate for use at home or as a supplement to classroom instruction.

How Much Do You Exercise?

PURPOSE To keep a record of exercise for a week.

TIP *10 min.* Tell students to measure their heart rates by placing their first two fingers at the base of the jaw line to find their pulse.

Answer: Exercising longer and harder increases the heart rate more than exercising for less time or at less intensity. Resting heart rate should decrease with regular exercise. A lower resting heart rate decreases the amount of work the heart does.

REVISIT after p. 720.

How Safe Is Your Food?

PURPOSE To examine food labels and packaging for freshness dates.

TIP *15 min.* Have students look at food packaging at home for "sell by" dates.

Answer: Foods that are perishable have shorter freshness periods than foods that are dried or preserved in some way. Food that is past its freshness date could be contaminated with bacteria or other microorganisms that can make a person sick.

REVISIT after p. 726.

Internet Activity: Human Development

PURPOSE To observe the changes brought about by aging.

TIP *20 min.*

Answer: The skin loosens and wrinkles. Some parts of the face sag, or may fill out with fat deposits. The skin can also change color or develop "age spots."

REVISIT after p. 712.

PREPARE

CONCEPT REVIEW

Activate Prior Knowledge

- Ask students to describe how the skin helps to keep foreign materials from entering the body. *The epidermis is tough and protective. The cells form a thick, waterproof layer.*
- Discuss how white blood cells and antibodies work together to fight foreign materials that enter the body. *White blood cells travel through the circulatory and lymphatic systems to an infected part of the body. These cells produce antibodies, which help fight the foreign materials.*

TAKING NOTES

Content Frame

Students can use the vocabulary lists at the beginning of each section as a guide for topics to use in their content frames. They can add further topics by scanning the red headings in the text. Definitions and details can be found under each red heading, or following each bold-face word in their text. Encourage students to think about how each topic relates to another topic on their list, and have them write a sentence about the connection.

Choose Your Own Strategy

Encourage students to think about their own learning styles and choose a strategy that best suits them. Remind students that different strategies may be appropriate for different vocabulary words.

Vocabulary and Note-Taking Resources

- Vocabulary Practice, pp. 280–281
- Decoding Support, p. 282

- Daily Vocabulary Scaffolding, p. T34
- Note-Taking Model, p. T35

- Choose Your Own Strategy, B20–27
- Content Frame, C35
- Daily Vocabulary Scaffolding, H1–8

CHAPTER 21

Getting Ready to Learn

CONCEPT REVIEW

- The integumentary system protects the body.
- The immune system fights disease.
- A microscope is an instrument used to observe very small objects.

VOCABULARY REVIEW

nutrient p. 621
pathogen p. 650
antibiotic p. 657
hormone p. 687

Review concepts and vocabulary.

TAKING NOTES

CONTENT FRAME

Make a content frame for each main idea. Include the following columns: *Topic, Definition, Detail,* and *Connection.* In the first column, list topics about the title. In the second column, define the topic. In the third column, include a detail about the topic. In the fourth column, add a sentence that connects that topic to another topic in the chart.

CHOOSE YOUR OWN STRATEGY

For each new vocabulary term, take notes by choosing a strategy from earlier chapters—**four square, magnet word, frame game,** or **description wheel.** Or, use a strategy of your own.

See the Note-Taking Handbook on pages R45–R51.

SCIENCE NOTEBOOK

The human body develops and grows.

Topic	Definition	Detail	Connection
Childhood	Period after infancy and before sexual maturity.	Children depend on parents, but learn to do things for themselves, such as get dressed.	Adults do not have to depend on parents; they are independent and can care for others.

Four Square

Frame Game

Magnet Word

Description Wheel

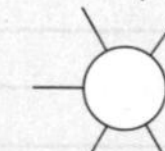

CHECK READINESS

Administer the Diagnostic Test to determine students' readiness for new science content and their mastery of requisite math skills.

 Diagnostic Test, pp. 77–78

Technology Resources

Students needing content and math skills should visit **ClassZone.com**.

- **CONTENT REVIEW**
- **MATH TUTORIAL**

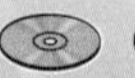 **CONTENT REVIEW CD-ROM**

KEY CONCEPT

21.1 The human body changes over time.

BEFORE, you learned

- Living things grow and develop
- The digestive system breaks down nutrients in food
- Organ systems interact to keep the body healthy

NOW, you will learn

- About four stages of human development
- About the changes that occur as the body develops
- How every body system interacts constantly with other systems to keep the body healthy

VOCABULARY

infancy p. 710
childhood p. 710
adolescence p. 711
adulthood p. 712

EXPLORE Growth

Are there patterns of growth?

PROCEDURE

1. Measure the circumference of your wrist by using the measuring tape as shown. Record the length. Now measure the length from your elbow to the tip of your middle finger. Record the length.
2. Create a table and enter all the data from each person in the class.

MATERIALS

- flexible tape measure
- graph paper

WHAT DO YOU THINK?

- How does the distance between the elbow and the fingertip compare with wrist circumference?
- Do you see a pattern between the size of one's wrist and the length of one's forearm?

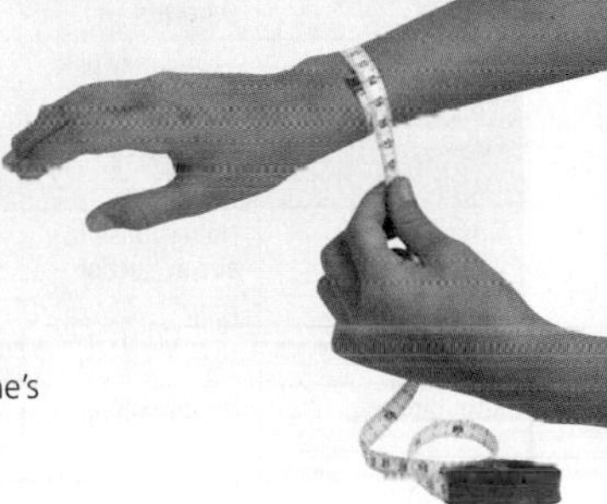

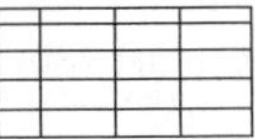

CONTENT FRAME Make a content frame for the first main idea: *The human body develops and grows.* List the red headings in this section in the topics column.

The human body develops and grows.

Have you noticed how rapidly your body has changed over the past few years? Only five years ago you were a young child in grade school. Today you are in middle school. How has your body changed? Growth is both physical and emotional. You are becoming more responsible and socially mature. What are some emotional changes that you have noticed?

Human development is a continuous process. Although humans develop at different rates, there are several stages of development common to human life. In this section we will describe some of the stages, including infancy, childhood, adolescence, and adulthood.

RESOURCES FOR DIFFERENTIATED INSTRUCTION

Below Level

UNIT RESOURCE BOOK

- Reading Study Guide A, pp. 248–249
- Decoding Support, p. 282

AUDIO CDS

Advanced

UNIT RESOURCE BOOK

- Challenge and Extension, p. 254
- Challenge Reading, pp. 278–279

English Learners

UNIT RESOURCE BOOK

Spanish Reading Study Guide, pp. 252–253

AUDIO CDS

- Audio Readings in Spanish
- Audio Readings (English)

21.1 FOCUS

Set Learning Goals

Students will

- Describe the four stages of human development.
- Discuss the changes that happen as the body develops.
- Analyze how body systems interact.
- Graph data about life expectancy.

3-Minute Warm-Up

Display Transparency 36 or copy this exercise on the board:

Decide if these statements are true. If not true, correct them.

1. White blood cells transport oxygen throughout the body. *Red blood cells transport oxygen throughout the body.*
2. Cilia are tiny hairlike projections that trap foreign particles in the nose and lungs. *true*
3. Some white blood cells produce antigens, which attack specific foreign materials. *White blood cells produce antibodies.*

 3-Minute Warm-Up, p. T36

21.1 MOTIVATE

EXPLORE Growth

PURPOSE To compile data on body measurements and analyze patterns of growth

TIPS *15 min.* Have students work in pairs to help one another take the measurements. Demonstrate accurate use of the tape measure. If you do not have a soft tape measure, students can use string and a ruler.

WHAT DO YOU THINK? *There is a difference in length. Generally, students with wider wrists have longer lengths from the elbow to the tip of the finger. The fact that some people have bigger bones can account for this pattern of growth.*

21.1 INSTRUCT

Teach from Visuals

To help students interpret the chart of the Apgar test, ask:

- Which body systems are assessed with the Apgar test? *circulatory, respiratory, muscular, and nervous systems*
- Which five items are tested? *Appearance (color), Pulse (heart rate), Grimace (responsiveness), Activity (muscle tone), and Respiration (breathing)*

History of Science

The Apgar score is named for Dr. Virginia Apgar (1909–1974), a pediatrician who specialized in newborn (neonatal) care. In 1952, she developed a simple way to evaluate a newborn's transition to life outside the uterus. Points are given for each sign at one minute and five minutes after the birth. A score of 7–10 is considered normal. A baby with an Apgar score of 4–7 may need medical attention, and a score of 3 and below requires immediate resuscitation.

Develop Critical Thinking

COMPARE Students can analyze the text by comparing infancy and childhood. Ask: In what ways does a child change between infancy and childhood? What are some things that remain the same? *The child learns to talk, walk, read, write, and communicate. The child is dependent on the parent for food and other needs.*

Infancy

The stage of life that begins at birth and ends when a baby begins to walk is called **infancy.** An infant's physical development is rapid. As the infant's body grows larger and stronger, it also learns physical skills. When you were first born, you could not hold up your head. But as your muscles developed, you gained the ability to hold up your head, to roll over, to sit, to crawl, to stand, and finally to walk. You also learned to use your hands to grasp and hold objects.

Infants also develop thinking skills and social skills. At first, they simply cry when they are uncomfortable. Over time, they learn that people respond to those cries. They begin to expect help when they cry. They learn to recognize the people who care for them. Smiling, cooing, and eventually saying a few words are all part of an infant's social development.

Nearly every body system changes and grows during infancy. For example, as the digestive system matures, an infant becomes able to process solid foods. Changes in the nervous system, including the brain, allow an infant to see more clearly and to better control parts of her or his body.

The Apgar score is used to evaluate the newborn's condition after delivery.

Apgar Score

Quality	0 points	1 point	2 points
Appearance	Completely blue or pale	Good color in body, blue hands or feet	Completely pink or good color
Pulse	No heart rate	<100 beats per minute	>100 beats per minute
Grimace	No response to airway suction	Grimace during suctioning	Grimace, cough/ sneeze with suction
Activity	Limp	Some arm and leg movement	Active motion
Respiration	Not breathing	Weak cry	Good, strong cry

Childhood

The stage called **childhood** lasts for several years. Childhood is the period after infancy and before the beginning of sexual maturity. During childhood, children still depend very much upon their parents. As their bodies and body systems grow, children become more able to care for themselves. Although parents still provide food and other needs, children perform tasks such as eating and getting dressed. In addition, children are able to do more complex physical tasks such as running, jumping, and riding a bicycle.

Childhood is also a time of mental and social growth. During childhood a human being learns to talk, read, write, and communicate in other ways. Along with the ability to communicate come social skills such as cooperation and sharing. A child learns to interact with others.

DIFFERENTIATE INSTRUCTION

More Reading Support

A What are some skills that an infant learns? *lift head, roll over, sit, crawl, stand, walk, and grasp*

B When does childhood end? *at the beginning of sexual maturity*

English Learners Students new to English may find the following science words challenging: *infancy, childhood, adolescence, puberty, maturity, adulthood.* Preview vocabulary by adding these words and their definitions to a Science Word Wall.

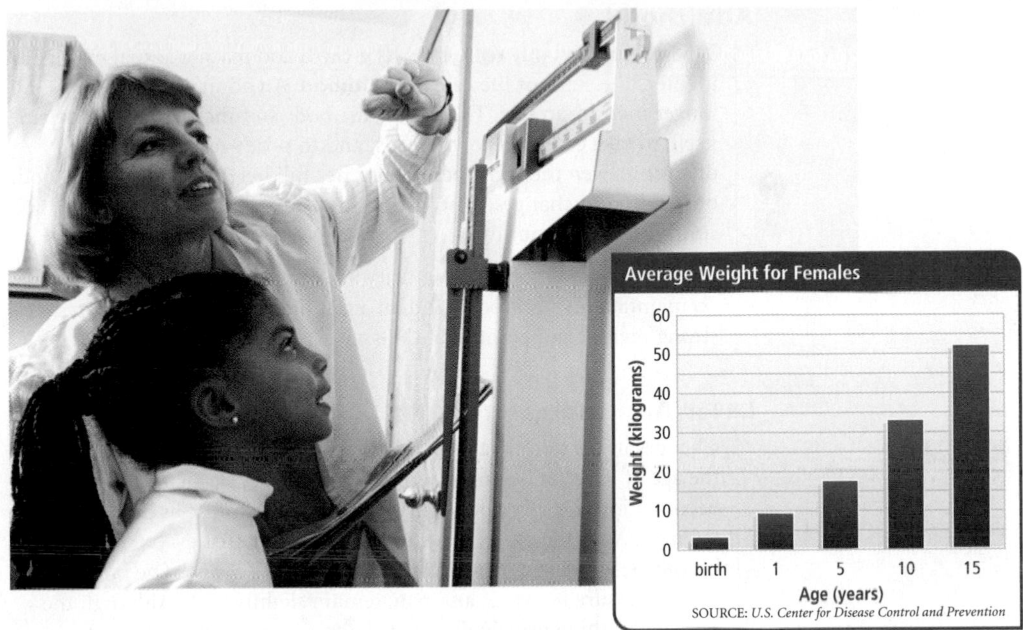

Adolescence

The years from puberty to adulthood are called **adolescence** (AD-uhl-EHS-uhns). Childhood ends when the body begins to mature sexually. This process of physical change is called puberty. Not all people reach puberty at the same age. For girls, the changes usually start between ages eight and fourteen; for boys, puberty often begins between ages ten and sixteen.

C

The human body changes greatly during adolescence. As you learned in Chapter 20, the endocrine system produces chemicals called hormones. During adolescence, hormones signal parts of the reproductive system to mature. At this stage a person's sexual organs become ready for reproduction. These changes are accompanied by other changes. Adolescents develop secondary sexual characteristics. Boys may notice their voices changing. Girls begin developing breasts. Boys and girls both begin growing more body hair.

Probably the change that is the most obvious is a change in height. Boys and girls grow taller by an average of 10 centimeters (3.9 in.) per year during adolescence. Most adolescents eat more as they grow. Food provides materials necessary for growth.

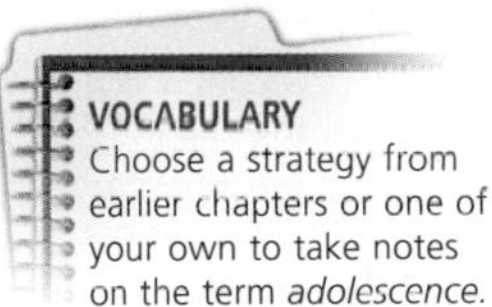

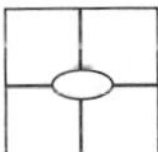

CHECK YOUR READING What are some of the ways the body changes during adolescence?

DIFFERENTIATE INSTRUCTION

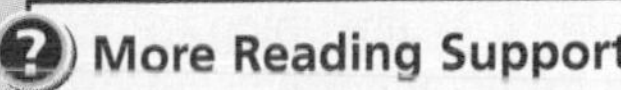

More Reading Support

C What term describes the process of physical change during sexual maturation? *puberty*

Alternative Assessment Have students create a timeline of important events in their lives starting with their birthdays to the present. Students should note in their timelines the stage of life and each important physical, social, and mental change that took place at that stage.

Teach from Visuals

To help students interpret the bar graph of Average Weight for Females, ask:

- Which period shows the greatest weight gain in kilograms? *between ages 10 and 15*
- Which period shows the greatest gain in terms of percent of body weight? Explain. *between birth and 5 years; The bar more than doubles in height.*

Point out to students that the vertical axis shows even intervals, but the horizontal axis shows a jump of one year between the first two bars and five years between the others.

Teach Difficult Concepts

Many students confuse the terms *adolescence* and *puberty* and often interchange the two. Ask students to define each term in their own words. Students may also think there is a "normal" timeline for specific body changes to occur during adolescence. Point out that individuals develop at certain rates depending on their family histories and their own biological clocks. Ask:

- What is the age range when girls reach puberty? *between 8 and 14 years*
- What is the age range when boys reach puberty? *between 10 and 16 years*

Ongoing Assessment

CHECK YOUR READING *Answer: During adolescence, a person grows taller, and sexual organs become ready for reproduction. Boys' voices change and girls develop breasts. There is more body hair.*

Develop Critical Thinking

PREDICT Have students predict how they see themselves as adults and how their lives will change from adolescence to adulthood. Ask them at what age they think adulthood begins and why. *Sample answer: age 18, because the person will not get any taller and has completed sexual maturity*

Real World Example

Ask students to name some television shows that portray people in various stages of life. Ask students if the portrayals are realistic or not. Ask:

- How do the shows you have seen portray teens? Do any of them look and act like typical teens? *Be sure answers mention the variety of individuals as well as some of the traits that scientifically typify each stage.*
- How do the shows portray adults? Do you think the portrayal of adults is realistic or not? Explain. *Student answers should include comparison and contrast with adults they know as well as information in the text.*

EXPLORE the BIG idea

Revisit "Internet Activity: Human Development" on p. 707. Ask students to explain what observations are brought about by aging.

Ongoing Assessment

Describe the changes that happen as the body develops.

Ask: What changes take place in the body as a person reaches later adulthood? *skin begins to wrinkle, eyesight becomes poorer, hair loss, muscle strength loss, internal organs become less efficient, blood vessels are less elastic, blood pressure rises, lung function decreases*

Describe the four stages of human development.

Ask: What are the four stages of human development? *infancy, childhood, adolescence, adulthood*

Adulthood

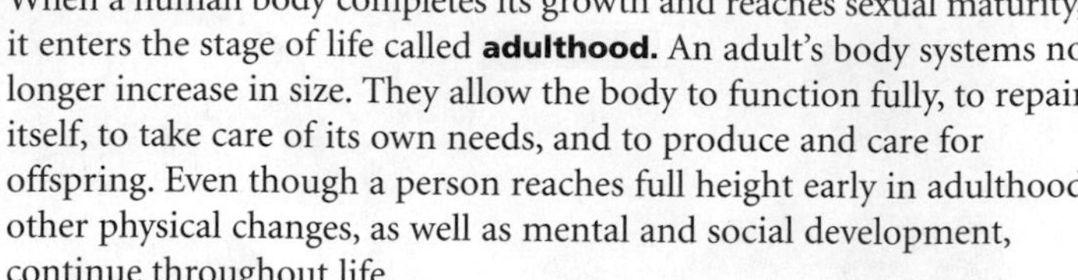

When a human body completes its growth and reaches sexual maturity, it enters the stage of life called **adulthood.** An adult's body systems no longer increase in size. They allow the body to function fully, to repair itself, to take care of its own needs, and to produce and care for offspring. Even though a person reaches full height early in adulthood, other physical changes, as well as mental and social development, continue throughout life. **D**

Mental and emotional maturity are important parts of adulthood. To maintain an adult body and an adult lifestyle, an individual needs strong mental and emotional skills.

Later Adulthood

READING TIP You may find it helpful to review the information on the skeletal and muscular system in Chapter 17.

Changes in the body that you might think of as aging begin at about the age of 30. Skin begins to wrinkle and lose its elasticity. Eyesight becomes increasingly poor, hair loss begins, and muscles decrease in strength. After the age of 65, the rate of aging increases. Internal organs become less efficient. Blood vessels become less elastic. The average blood pressure increases and may remain slightly high. Although the rate of breathing usually does not change, lung function decreases slightly. Body temperature is harder to regulate. However, one can slow the process of aging by a lifestyle of exercise and healthy diet.

Systems interact to maintain the human body.

It's easy to observe the external changes to the body during growth and development. Inside the body, every system interacts constantly with other systems to keep the whole person healthy throughout his or her lifetime. For example, the respiratory system constantly sends oxygen to the blood cells of the circulatory system. The circulatory system transports hormones produced by the endocrine system.

Your body systems also interact with the environment outside your body. Your nervous system monitors the outside world through your senses of taste, smell, hearing, vision, and touch. It allows you to respond to your environment. For example, your nervous system allows you to squint if the sun is too bright or to move indoors if the weather is cold. Your endocrine system releases hormones that allow you to have an increased heart rate and send more blood to your muscles if you have to respond to an emergency.

DIFFERENTIATE INSTRUCTION

More Reading Support

D What development continues in adulthood? *mental, social*

E How does the body know to respond to the outside? *nervous system and senses*

Below Level Have students imagine they are going to teach younger children about what to expect when they reach adolescence. Have students prepare a brochure describing the physical, social, and emotional changes that a young child will go through.

INVESTIGATE Life Expectancy

How has life expectancy changed over time?

In this activity, you will look for trends in the changes in average life expectancy over the past 100 years.

SKILL FOCUS
Graphing

MATERIALS
- graph paper
- computer graphing program

TIME
30 minutes

PROCEDURE

1. Using the following data, create a bar graph to chart changes in life expectancy in the U.S. over the last 100 years.

Life Expectancy 1900–2000

Year	1900	1910	1920	1930	1940	1950	1960	1970	1980	1990	2000
Average Life Expectancy (years)	47.3	50.0	54.1	59.7	62.9	68.2	69.7	70.8	73.7	75.4	76.9

SOURCE: National Center for Health Statistics

2. Study the graph. Observe any trends that you see. Record them in your notebook.

WHAT DO YOU THINK?

- In general, what do these data demonstrate about life expectancy?
- Between which decades did average life expectancy increase the most?

CHALLENGE Using a computer program, create a table and bar graph to chart the data shown above.

Every part of your daily life requires interactions among your body systems. Even during sleep body systems cooperate. When you sleep, your nervous system allows your muscular system to keep your heart pumping and your lungs breathing. The heart pumps blood through your circulatory system, which has received oxygen from your respiratory system. All this cooperation takes place even while you are sleeping. Your endocrine system releases growth hormone during your sleep, allowing your bones and muscles to grow. The activity of neurons in your brain changes when you fall asleep.

Keeping the body healthy is complex. The digestive and urinary systems eliminate solid and liquid wastes from the body. The circulatory and respiratory systems remove carbon dioxide gas. As you will learn in the next section, a healthy diet and regular exercise help the body to stay strong and function properly.

F

CHECK YOUR READING Name three systems that interact as your body grows and maintains itself.

DIFFERENTIATE INSTRUCTION

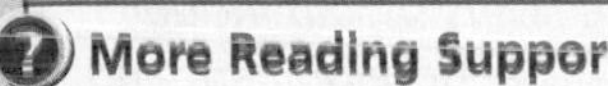
More Reading Support

F Which two systems eliminate solid and liquid wastes? *digestive and urinary systems*

Advanced Write the words *peer pressure* on the board and have students give the definition in their own words. Ask students to brainstorm a list of ways that adolescents may experience both negative and positive peer pressure.

 Challenge and Extension, p. 254

Have students who are interested in the effects of stress on the body read the following article:

 Challenge Reading, pp. 278–279

INVESTIGATE Life Expectancy

PURPOSE To compare the average life expectancy over the last 100 years and to infer why it has changed

TIPS *30 min.* Ask students to think about scale and range for the *x*- and *y*-axes of their graphs before making the graph. Prior to the investigation, prepare tables for visually impaired students to use. Highlight the main heads in the table with colored markers.

WHAT DO YOU THINK? *Life expectancy over the last 100 years has increased. The greatest increases occurred between 1920–1930, and between 1940–1950.*

CHALLENGE *Computer-generated graphs should match data shown.*

 Datasheet, Life Expectancy, p. 255

Technology Resources

Customize this student lab as needed or look for an alternative. Print rubrics to assess student lab reports.

 **Lab Generator CD-ROM**

Teaching with Technology

If graphing software is available, have students use it to record the data for the investigation. They can also use a graphing calculator.

Ongoing Assessment

Analyze how body systems interact.

Ask: How do body systems keep you functioning while you sleep? *Sample answer: Circulatory and respiratory systems keep bringing oxygen to cells. The nervous system keeps signaling the other systems to function. The muscular system keeps the heart pumping. The digestive system brings water and nutrients to cells, while the excretory system removes waste.*

CHECK YOUR READING *Answer: The circulatory, respiratory, and endocrine systems interact when you grow.*

Ongoing Assessment

READING VISUALS *Answer: When you are active, all body systems are working to provide energy to fuel your muscles. When you rest, your body systems cooperate to recharge your body, and to help it grow and maintain itself.*

Reinforce the BIG idea

Have students relate the section to the Big Idea.

Reinforcing Key Concepts, p. 256

21.1 ASSESS & RETEACH

Assess

A Section 21.1 Quiz, p. 79

Reteach

List the four stages of human development on the board and draw a sketch next to each. Tell students that as a group you are going to create a "Progress Report" for each character you drew. Have them search the text or work cooperatively to find ways the person has progressed, or developed, at each stage.

For each of the four stages of development, ask students to name some of the physical, mental, and social changes that take place.

1. infancy—*Sample answers: learns to sit, to cry to show needs, to coo*
2. childhood—*Sample answers: grows taller, learns to read, learns to cooperate with others*
3. adolescence—*Sample answers: sexual organs mature, grows taller, boys' voices change*
4. adulthood—*Sample answers: body systems stop growing, emotional and mental maturity*

Technology Resources

Have students visit **ClassZone.com** for reteaching of Key Concepts.

CONTENT REVIEW

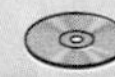

CONTENT REVIEW CD-ROM

READING VISUALS **COMPARE AND CONTRAST** How do the interactions of your body system change when you are active and when you rest?

When body systems fail to work together, the body can become ill. Stress, for example, can affect all the body systems. Some types of stress, such as fear, can be a healthy response to danger. However, if the body experiences stress over long periods of time, serious health problems such as heart disease, headaches, muscle tension, and depression can arise.

All stages of life include different types of stress. Infants and children face stresses as they learn to become more independent and gain better control over their bodies. Adolescents can be challenged by school, by the changes of puberty, or by being socially accepted by their peers. Adults may encounter stress in their jobs or with their families. The stress of aging can be very difficult for some older adults.

21.1 Review

KEY CONCEPTS

1. Make a development timeline with four sections. Write the names of the stages in order under each section. Include a definition and two details.
2. List a physical characteristic of each stage of development.
3. Give an example of an activity that involves two or more body systems.

CRITICAL THINKING

4. **Compare and Contrast** Make a chart to compare and contrast the infancy and childhood stages of development.
5. **Identify Cause and Effect** How is the endocrine system involved in adolescence?

CHALLENGE

6. **Synthesis** How does each of the body systems described change as a human being develops from infancy to older adulthood?

714 Unit 5: **Human Biology**

ANSWERS

1. Timelines show stages with definitions and details.

2. Sample answer: infancy—unable to walk; childhood—learns to talk; adolescence—grows more body hair; adulthood—no new physical growth

3. Sample answer: eating: digestive, muscular, and circulatory systems interact.

4. Charts include ability to walk, increase of independence.

5. Hormones secreted by the endocrine system signal the reproductive system to mature in adolescence.

6. Answers should include details of development and aging of body systems: respiratory/circulatory, digestive, endocrine, integumentary, muscular, nervous, and reproductive.

STAGE MAKEUP ARTIST

Aging the Face

In a movie, characters may go through development stages of a whole lifetime in just over an hour. An actor playing such a role will need to look both older and younger than he or she really is. Makeup artists have a toolbox full of techniques to make the actor look the part.

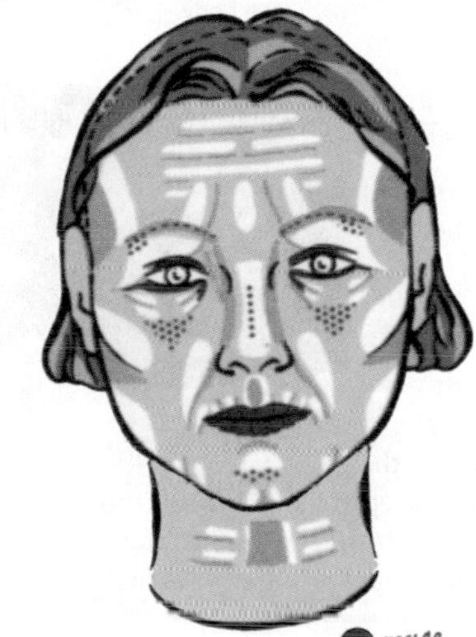

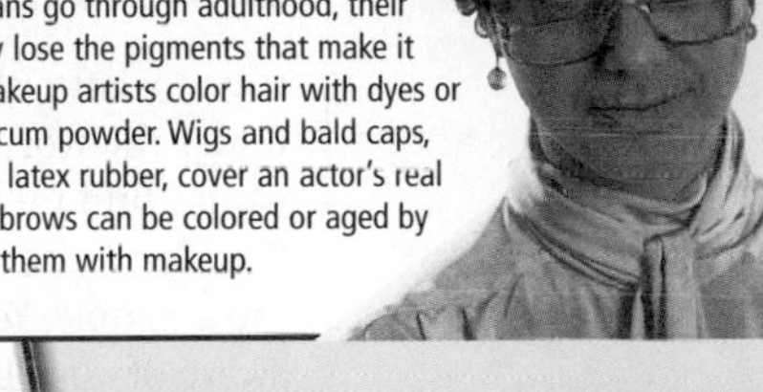

Hair

As humans go through adulthood, their hair may lose the pigments that make it dark. Makeup artists color hair with dyes or even talcum powder. Wigs and bald caps, made of latex rubber, cover an actor's real hair. Eyebrows can be colored or aged by rubbing them with makeup.

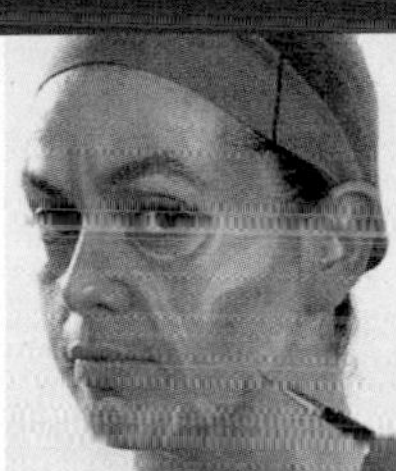

Features

For a bigger-looking nose or extra skin around the neck, makeup artists use foam rubber, or layers of liquid rubber, and, sometimes, wads of paper tissue to build up facial features. For example, building up the cheekbones with layers of latex makes the cheeks appear sharper, less rounded, and more hollow.

Skin

To make wrinkles or scars, makeup artists use light-colored makeup for the raised highlights and dark colored makeup for lower shadows and spots.

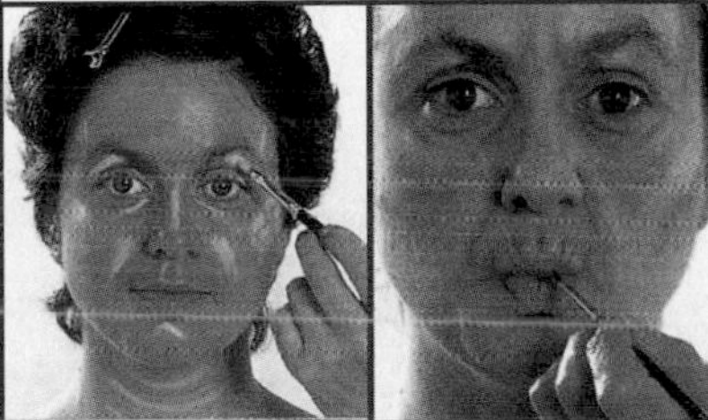

EXPLORE

1. **COMPARE** Look at photos of an older relative at three different stages of life, at about ten years apart. Describe how you might apply makeup to your own face if you were to portray this person's life in three movie scenes. What changes do you need to show?
2. **CHALLENGE** Research to find an image of a character portrayed in a movie by an actor who looked very different in real life. From the picture, describe how the effect was achieved.

SCIENCE ON THE JOB

Relevance of Science to Non-science Jobs

Set Learning Goal

To understand why makeup artists need knowledge of the aging process

Present the Science

Remind students that the integumentary system includes the skin, hair, and nails. The skin helps regulate body temperature as well as protect the body from foreign materials. As we age, skin loses its elasticity and may begin to sag or wrinkle. Hair becomes drier and may begin to turn gray. Hands and other skin that is exposed also show age.

FEATURES Every fold or crease in the skin catches light and creates a different shadow. To begin the aging process with makeup, makeup artists begin by applying a foundation on the face and neck.

SKIN Highlights to make skin age are applied over the muscles of the face. Applying the makeup under an overhead light source can help the makeup artist find the highlights and shadows in the face. Surgical adhesive and liquid latex can create excessive wrinkles and a sagging neck. Age spots can be added to the hands.

HAIR Men can be aged by applying gray at the temples and sideburns as well as on beards and moustaches. Wigs can show thinning hair or a receding hairline.

Discussion Question

Ask: How might creating an aging face with stage makeup assist an actor in developing his or her character? *A realistic look can help the actor portray an age he has not yet experienced. It helps him or her to "become" the character.*

Close

Ask: Why do makeup artists need knowledge of the human body and how it ages? *This knowledge helps them create a realistic accurate look.*

EXPLORE

1. ***COMPARE*** *Students might say that as the person ages, they might want to apply makeup to show wrinkles. They might also need to apply latex or other rubber layers to show various facial features. Students might also suggest using wigs or hair coloring to make the hair look as close to the relative as possible.*
2. ***CHALLENGE*** *Accept all complete responses. Students' answers will vary depending on the movie character that they chose*

21.2 FOCUS

Set Learning Goals

Students will

- Discuss the role of nutrients in health.
- Explain why exercise is needed to keep body systems healthy.
- Describe how drug abuse, eating disorders, and addiction can negatively affect the body.
- Analyze food labels for their nutritional values.

3-Minute Warm-Up

Display Transparency 36 or copy this exercise on the board:

Match the changes to the stages of development.

Changes

1. internal organs stop growing *d*
2. a person reaches puberty *c*
3. a person learns to cooperate with friends *b*

Stages of Development

a. infancy
b. childhood
c. adolescence
d. adulthood
e. later adulthood

 3-Minute Warm-up, p. T36

21.2 MOTIVATE

THINK ABOUT

PURPOSE To write a definition of health and describe ways to protect health

DISCUSS Allow students to work in small groups, then share their ideas as a class. Point out that good health includes factors that affect a person's physical, emotional, and social well-being. Write all ideas on the board and leave them for students to add to or revise as they read the chapter.

Ongoing Assessment

Answer: Your body needs proper nutrition to stay healthy and to function well.

KEY CONCEPT

21.2 Systems in the body function to maintain health.

BEFORE, you learned

- Human development involves all the body systems
- The human body continues to develop throughout life
- Every body system interacts constantly with other systems to keep the body healthy

NOW, you will learn

- About the role of nutrients in health
- Why exercise is needed to keep body systems healthy
- How drug abuse, eating disorders, and addiction can affect the body

VOCABULARY

nutrition p. 716
addiction p. 722

THINK ABOUT

What is health?

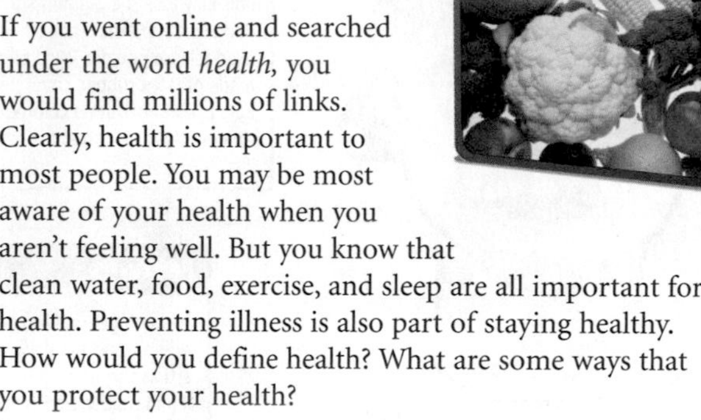

If you went online and searched under the word *health,* you would find millions of links. Clearly, health is important to most people. You may be most aware of your health when you aren't feeling well. But you know that clean water, food, exercise, and sleep are all important for health. Preventing illness is also part of staying healthy. How would you define health? What are some ways that you protect your health?

Diet affects the body's health.

What makes a meal healthy? The choices you make about what you eat are important. Nutrients from food are distributed to every cell in your body. You use those nutrients for energy and to maintain and build new body tissues. **Nutrition** is the study of the materials that nourish your body. It also refers to the process in which the different parts of food are used for maintenance, growth, and reproduction. When a vitamin or other nutrient is missing from your diet, illness can occur. Your body's systems can function only when they get the nutrients they need.

VOCABULARY
Choose a strategy from an earlier chapter, such as a magnet word diagram, for taking notes on the term *nutrition*. Or use any strategy that you think works well.

CHECK YOUR READING How is nutrition important to health?

RESOURCES FOR DIFFERENTIATED INSTRUCTION

Below Level

UNIT RESOURCE BOOK
- Reading Study Guide A, pp. 259–260
- Decoding Support, p. 282

AUDIO CDS

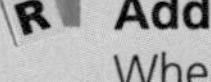 **Additional INVESTIGATION,** Where's the Starch?, A, B, & C, pp. 294–302; Teacher Instructions, pp. 305–306

Advanced

UNIT RESOURCE BOOK
Challenge and Extension, p. 265

English Learners

UNIT RESOURCE BOOK
Spanish Reading Study Guide, pp. 263–264

 **AUDIO CDS**

- Audio Readings in Spanish
- Audio Readings (English)

This family is enjoying a healthy meal that includes proteins, carbohydrates, and fats.

Getting Nutrients

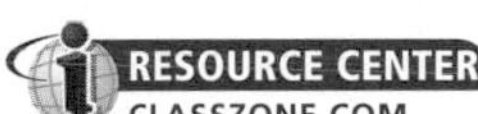

RESOURCE CENTER
CLASSZONE.COM

Discover more about human health.

In order to eat a healthy diet, you must first understand what good nutrition is. There are six classes of nutrients: carbohydrates, proteins, fats, vitamins, minerals, and water. All of these nutrients are necessary for your body cells to carry out the chemical reactions that sustain life.

Proteins are molecules that build tissues used for growth and repair. Proteins provide the building blocks for many important hormones. Good sources of proteins are poultry, red meat, fish, eggs, nuts, beans, grains, soy, and milk. Protein should make up at least 20 percent of your diet.

Carbohydrates are the body's most important energy source and are found in starch, sugar, and fiber. Fiber provides little energy, but is important for regular elimination. Natural sugars such as those found in fruits and vegetables are the best kinds of sugars for your body. Carbohydrates are found in bread and pasta, fruits, and vegetables. Carbohydrates should make up about 40 to 50 percent of your diet.

Fats are essential for energy and should account for about 10 to 15 percent of your diet. Many people eliminate fats from their diet in order to lose weight. But a certain amount of fat is necessary. Fats made from plants have the greatest health benefits. For example, olive oil is better for you than the oil found in butter.

21.2 INSTRUCT

Real World Example

The Food Guide Pyramid was released by the Food and Drug Administration in 1992. Periodically, the FDA reviews and makes changes to the Pyramid. An updated Pyramid is expected to be released in 2005. Changes to the Pyramid include revised daily amounts of food from each of the food groups, suggested energy levels for food intake patterns for different age groups, and target goals for vitamins and minerals. For more information, go to www.cnpp.usda.gov/index.html

Develop Critical Thinking

ANALYZE Ask students to give examples of foods that contain proteins, carbohydrates, and fats. Ask:

- Why does a body need proper nutrition? What happens when nutrition is lacking? *Without the proper nutrients, the body may become ill or may not be able to function efficiently.*
- What are some signs of poor nutrition? *A person might feel tired or sluggish, or be underweight; bones may be weak; skin may look sallow; hair may look dull.*

Ongoing Assessment

Discuss the role of nutrients in health.

Ask: What are the essential nutrients? *carbohydrates, proteins, fats, vitamins, minerals, and water*

DIFFERENTIATE INSTRUCTION

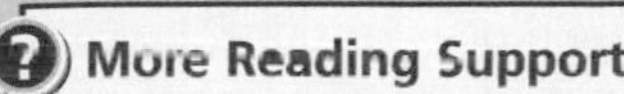

More Reading Support

A What foods are a source of protein? *poultry, red meat, fish, eggs, nuts, grains, beans, milk, soy*

B Name a main food energy source. *carbohydrates*

English Learners On a classroom Science Word Wall, place the terms *protein, carbohydrate,* and *fat.* Ask students to list foods they eat regularly and classify them as one of the above. Have students read their lists aloud. Discuss foods that may be unfamiliar. Then, have students write the food names with a marker on index cards and tape them to the wall under the correct heading.

Teacher Demo

Ask students to list what they ate for breakfast on slips of paper. Read their responses aloud. As you read, have students classify whether the breakfast is a healthful one or if it needs improvement. Write the responses on the board in two columns. In the "needs improvement" category, have students suggest ways to improve the healthfulness of the meal.

Teach from Visuals

To help students interpret the table on vitamins and minerals, ask:

- Why do you think there is a range for the recommended daily allowance? *Vitamin and mineral requirements change during the different stages of life.*
- Which vitamin or mineral does your body need in greatest amounts? in the smallest amounts? *potassium; vitamin A*

Vitamins and minerals are needed by your body in small amounts. Vitamins are small molecules that regulate body growth and development. Minerals help build body tissues. While some vitamins can be made by your body, most of them are supplied to the body in food.

 C

 D

Water is necessary for life. A human being could live for about a month without food, but only about one week without water. Water has several functions. Water helps regulate your body temperature through evaporation when you sweat and breathe. Without water, important materials such as vitamins and other nutrients could not be transported around the body. Water helps your body get rid of the waste products that move through the kidneys and pass out of the body in urine. Urine is composed mostly of water.

To make sure your body can function and maintain itself, you need to drink about two and one half liters, or about eight glasses, of water every day. You also get water when you eat foods with water in them, such as fresh fruit and vegetables.

Vitamins and Minerals

Vitamin or Mineral	Recommended Daily Allowance
Vitamin A	0.3 to 1.3 mg
Niacin	6–18 mg
Vitamin B_2	0.5–1.6 mg
Vitamin B_6	0.5–2.0 mg
Vitamin C	15–120 mg
Vitamin E	6–19 mg
Calcium	500–1300 mg
Phosphorus	460–1250 mg
Potassium	1600–2000 mg
Zinc	3–13 mg
Magnesium	80–420 mg
Iron	7–27 mg

Source: National Institutes of Health

Understanding Nutrition

Examine the basic principles of nutrition.

Ever wonder what the word *lite* really means? What do labels saying that food is fresh or natural or organic mean? Not all advertising about nutrition is reliable. It is important to know what the labels on food really mean. Groups within the government, such as the United States Department of Agriculture, have defined terms that are used to describe food products. For example, if a food label says the food is "all natural," that means it does not contain any artificial flavor, color, or preservative.

Another example is the term *low-fat*. That label means that the food provides no more than 3 grams of fat per serving. The word *organic* means that the produce has been grown using no human-made fertilizers or chemicals that kill pests or weeds. It also means that livestock has been raised on organic feed and has not been given antibiotics or growth hormones. It takes some effort and a lot of reading to stay informed, but the more you know, the better the choices you can make.

DIFFERENTIATE INSTRUCTION

More Reading Support

C About how long can a human being live without water? *about one week*

D How does water help regulate body temperature? *through evaporation of sweat and breathing*

Additional Investigation To reinforce Section 21.2 learning goals, use the following full-period investigation:

Additional INVESTIGATION, Where's the Starch?, A, B, & C, pp. 294–302, 305–306

Advanced Have students create a chart of essential vitamins A, C, D, and E, and the B complex vitamins. For each vitamin, students will list food sources in which the vitamins are found and how the vitamins help the body function.

 Challenge and Extension, p. 265

INVESTIGATE Food Labels

What are you eating?

PROCEDURE

1. Gather nutrition labels from the following products: a carbonated soft drink, a bag of fresh carrots, canned spaghetti in sauce, potato chips, plain popcorn kernels, unsweetened applesauce, and fruit juice. Look at the percent of daily values of the major nutrients, as shown on the label for each food.
2. Make a list of ways to evaluate a food for high nutritional value. Include such criteria as nutrient levels and calories per serving.
3. Examine the nutrition labels and compare them with your list. Decide which of these foods would make a healthy snack.

WHAT DO YOU THINK?

- How does serving size affect the way you evaluate a nutritional label?
- What are some ways to snack and get nutrients at the same time?

CHALLENGE Design a full day's food menu that will give you all the nutrients you need. Use snacks as some of the foods that contribute these nutrients.

SKILL FOCUS
Analyzing

MATERIALS
nutrition labels

TIME
30 minutes

Spaghetti
IN TOMATO SAUCE WITH CHEESE

Nutrition Facts
Serving Size: 1 cup (252g)
Servings Per Container: about 2

Amount Per Serving
Calories 210
Calories from Fat 20

	% Daily Value*
Total Fat 2g	
Saturated Fat 1g	3%
Cholesterol 5mg	5%
Sodium 1,020 mg	2%
Total Carbohydrate 41g	43%
Dietary Fiber 3g	14%
Sugars 14g	12%
Protein 7g	

Vitamin A 10% Vitamin C 0%
Calcium 4% Iron 10%

* Percent Daily Values are based on a 2,000 caloric diet. Your daily values may be higher or lower depending on your calorie needs.

Exercise is part of a healthy lifestyle.

Regular exercise allows all your body systems to stay strong and healthy. You learned that your lymphatic system doesn't include a structure like the heart to pump its fluid through the body. Instead, it relies on body movement and strong muscles to help it move antibodies and white blood cells. Exercise is good for the lymphatic system.

Exercise

When you exercise, you breathe harder and more quickly. You inhale and exhale more air, which exercises the muscles of your respiratory system and makes them stronger. Exercise also brings in extra oxygen. Oxygen is necessary for cellular respiration, which provides energy to other body systems. The circulatory system is strengthened by exercise. Your heart becomes stronger the more it is used. The skeletal system grows stronger with exercise as well. Studies show that older adults who lift weights have stronger bones than those who do not. In addition, physical activity can flush out skin pores by making you sweat, and it reduces the symptoms of depression.

INVESTIGATE Food Labels

PURPOSE To analyze food labels to determine their nutritional values

TIP *15 min.* Prior to the activity, ask students to bring in the nutrition label from a food they have eaten.

WHAT DO YOU THINK? *If a product has more than one serving and you eat the whole product, multiply the nutritional facts by the servings eaten to get the correct nutritional information; sample answer: applesauce, carrots, or fruit juice.*

CHALLENGE *Menus should include food from proteins, carbohydrates, and fats in percentages recommended on p. 717.*

 Datasheet, Food Labels, p. 266

Technology Resources

Customize this student lab as needed or look for an alternative. Print rubrics to assess student lab reports.

 **Lab Generator CD-ROM**

DIFFERENTIATE INSTRUCTION

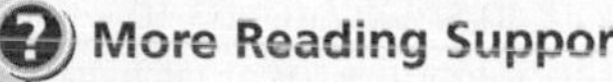

More Reading Support

E What happens to breathing rate during exercise? *It increases.*

Advanced Invite students to create a week's worth of healthy school lunch menus. Menus should have all of the necessary nutritional requirements for proteins, carbohydrates, and fats. For additional guidance, provide a copy of the USDA's most recent Food Guide Pyramid (www.fda.gov) so students can designate the number of servings for each of the food groups per meal.

Address Misconceptions

IDENTIFY Ask students to describe what factors contribute to a healthful lifestyle. If students answer "Eating the right foods and exercising," prompt them to list all factors. They may hold the misconception that good health is associated only with food and physical fitness. Many students focus on the physical dimensions of health and pay no attention to mental and social aspects.

CORRECT Have students write *Physical, Mental,* and *Social* in three corners of a triangle. In the center of the triangle, have students write *Good Health.*

REASSESS Ask students to name one way that good health can be practiced for each corner. *Sample answer: P: exercise; M: relax; S: participate in community activities*

Technology Resources

Visit **ClassZone.com** for background on common student misconceptions.

 **MISCONCEPTION DATABASE**

Teach Difficult Concepts

Some students may think that many factors they consider important to their health and life span are beyond their personal control. Remind students that all people make choices every day that affect the rest of their lives. Ask: What choices can you make today that will help you avoid health risks later on in life? *Sample answers: Not using tobacco can help prevent a person from developing lung cancer later in life. Daily exercise can help people avoid osteoporosis when they are older. Avoiding fatty foods can help a person avoid heart disease and diabetes.*

Teach from Visuals

To help students interpret the photograph showing exercise in a basketball game, ask: Which body systems and related body organs are the students exercising as they play basketball? *respiratory—lungs; circulatory—heart; muscular—muscles; skeletal—bones*

EXPLORE the BIG idea

Revisit "How Much Do You Exercise?" on p. 707. Ask students to explain how exercise affects heart rate.

Ongoing Assessment

Explain why exercise is needed to keep body systems healthy.

Ask: What happens when a person's body does not get an adequate amount of exercise? *The heart and lungs are not strengthened; muscles and bones may begin to break down; body fat is stored and excess fat may cause heart disease and diabetes.*

CHECK YOUR READING *Answer: An active lifestyle can promote good health; a sedentary lifestyle can promote excess body fat and disease.*

By eating healthy meals and exercising, you help your body to grow and develop.

Lifestyle

F

The lifestyles of many people involve regular exercise. Some lifestyles, however, include more sitting still than moving. A lifestyle that is sedentary, associated mostly with sitting down, can harm a person's health. Muscles and bones that are not exercised regularly can begin to break down. Your body stores unused energy from food as fat. The extra weight of body fat can make it harder for you to exercise. Therefore, it is harder to use up energy or to strengthen your skeletal, muscular, and immune systems. Researchers have also made connections between excess body fat and heart disease and diabetes.

CHECK YOUR READING How does lifestyle affect health?

CONTENT FRAME
Make a content frame for the main idea: *Drug abuse, addiction, and eating disorders cause serious health problems.*

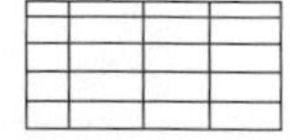

Drug abuse, addiction, and eating disorders cause serious health problems.

Every day, you make choices that influence your health. Some choices can have more serious health risks, or possibilities for harm, than others. You have the option to make healthy choices for yourself. Making unhealthy decisions about what you put into your body can lead to drug abuse, addiction, or eating disorders.

DIFFERENTIATE INSTRUCTION

More Reading Support

F What term describes a lifestyle that is mostly inactive? *sedentary*

Below Level Invite students to work in small groups to create a public service announcement about one aspect of living healthy lifestyles. Record students' announcements and play them for the class. If video equipment is available, have students film and present their public service announcements to the class. You may want to suggest or assign topics and have students focus on the advantages and/or consequences of making healthy or unhealthy choices.

Drug Abuse

A drug is any chemical substance that you take in to change your body's functions. Doctors use drugs to treat and prevent disease and illness. The use of a drug for any other reason is an abuse of that drug. Abuse can also include using too much of a substance that is not harmful in small amounts. People abuse different drugs for different reasons. Drugs often do allow an individual to feel better for the moment. But they can also cause serious harm to an individual's health.

Tobacco Nicotine, the drug in tobacco, increases heart rate and blood pressure and makes it seem as if the user has more energy. Nicotine is also a poison; in fact, some farmers use it to kill insects. Tobacco smoke contains thousands of chemicals. Tar and carbon monoxide are two harmful chemicals in smoke. Tar is a sticky substance that is commonly used to pave roads. Carbon monoxide is one of the gases that cars release in their exhaust. People who smoke or chew tobacco have a higher risk of cancer, and smokers are also at risk for heart disease.

Compounds Found in Unfiltered Tobacco Smoke

Compound	Amount in First-Hand Smoke (mg per cigarette)	Amount in Second-Hand Smoke (mg per cigarette)
Nicotine	1–3	2.1–46
Tar	15–40	14–30
Carbon monoxide	14–23	27–61
Benzene	0.012–0.05	0.4
Formaldehyde	0.07–0.1	1.5
Hydrogen cyanide	0.4–0.5	0.014–11
Phenol	0.08–0.16	0.07–0.25

Source: U.S. Department of Health and Human Services

Alcohol Even a small amount of alcohol can affect a person's ability to think and reason. Alcohol can affect behavior and the ability to make decisions. Many people are killed every year, especially in automobile accidents, because of choices they made while drinking alcohol. Alcohol abuse damages the heart, the liver, the nervous system, and the digestive system.

Other Drugs Some drugs, such as cocaine and amphetamines, can make people feel more energetic and even powerful because they stimulate parts of the nervous system and speed up the heart. These drugs are very dangerous. They can cause heart attacks, and long-term use may cause brain damage.

Drugs called narcotics also affect the nervous system. Instead of stimulating it, however, they decrease its activity. Narcotics are prescribed by doctors to relieve pain and to help people sleep. Because narcotics work by decreasing the function of nerves in some brain regions, large amounts of these drugs can cause the heart and lungs to stop. Abuse of narcotics can also lead to addiction.

History of Science

The tobacco plant is native to the Americas. The practice of smoking tobacco dates back more than 2,000 years ago to the Mayan culture, from which it spread north to Native American tribes. By the mid-16th century, the practice of smoking was introduced in Europe by explorers. Controversy surrounding the ill effects of smoking has existed since then, when James I forbade cultivation of tobacco in England. By the 1960s, clinical studies on smoking and disease concluded that most lung cancer deaths were caused by the use of tobacco. It was also found to be responsible for respiratory illnesses including chronic bronchitis, emphysema, and cardiovascular disease. By 1965, health warnings became mandatory on all cigarette packages. In 1984, the law was expanded to include health warnings on all tobacco advertisements.

Teach from Visuals

To help students interpret the chart of compounds found in tobacco, ask:

- What compounds are found in tobacco? *nicotine, tar, carbon monoxide, benzene, formaldehyde, hydrogen cyanide, phenol*
- Why does second-hand smoke pose a health risk? *Second-hand smoke contains all the dangerous compounds found in first-hand smoke.*

Teach Difficult Concepts

Many students think that tobacco and alcohol are not drugs. Remind students that a drug is any substance that changes the way the body functions. Have students make a list of the effects of both tobacco and alcohol on the body. Point out the the effects of drugs on a user are multiplied when taken in by a growing embryo or fetus. All drugs can cause birth defects if taken by a pregnant woman.

Teaching with Technology

If spreadsheet software is available, have students use it to record and outline the dangers of tobacco, alcohol, and other drugs.

DIFFERENTIATE INSTRUCTION

More Reading Support

G What term names the drug found in tobacco? *nicotine*

H What are two harmful substances in tobacco smoke? *tar and carbon monoxide*

Below Level Ask students to find out the cost of smoking one pack of cigarettes each day for one year. Then have them make a list of how they could use the money instead of smoking.

Ongoing Assessment

Describe how drug abuse, eating disorders, and addiction can negatively affect the body.

Ask: How do stimulants and narcotics affect the body? *Stimulants speed up the nervous system and the heart; narcotics decrease the activity of the nervous system.*

Reinforce the BIG idea

Have students relate the section to the Big Idea.

 Reinforcing Key Concepts, p. 267

21.2 ASSESS & RETEACH

Assess

 Section 21.2 Quiz, p. 80

Reteach

Have students complete the following graphic organizer. Students should write one detail per category as shown.

Good Health Practices Help Maintain a Healthy Body	
Nutrition	*Eating the proper amount of proteins, carbohydrates, and fats helps your body function properly.*
Exercise	*Regular exercise strengthens the heart and keeps muscles and bones strong.*
Lifestyle	*Avoiding drugs keeps your body from becoming addicted to harmful substances that could lead to disease or death.*

Technology Resources

Have students visit **ClassZone.com** for reteaching of Key Concepts.

 CONTENT REVIEW

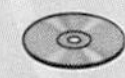 CONTENT REVIEW CD-ROM

Students can be active in protesting drug abuse.

Addiction

Drug abuse can often lead to addiction. **Addiction** is an illness in which a person becomes dependent on a substance or behavior. Repeated use of drugs such as alcohol, tobacco, and narcotics can cause the body to become physically dependent. When a person is dependent on a drug, taking away that drug can cause withdrawal. If affected by withdrawal, a person may become physically ill, sometimes within a very short period of time. Symptoms of withdrawal from some types of drugs can include fever, muscle cramps, vomiting, and hallucinations.

Another type of addiction can result from the effect produced by a drug or even a behavior. Although physical dependency may not occur, a person can become emotionally dependent. Gambling, overeating, and risk-taking are some examples of addictive behaviors. Someone who suffers from an addiction can be treated and can work to live a healthy life, but most addictions never go away completely.

Eating Disorders

An eating disorder is a condition in which people continually eat too much or too little food. One example of an eating disorder is anorexia nervosa. People with this disorder eat so little and exercise so hard that they become unhealthy. No matter how thin they are, they believe they need to be thinner. People with anorexia do not receive necessary nutrients because they don't eat. When the energy used by the body exceeds the energy taken in from food, tissues in the body are broken down to provide fuel. Bones and muscles, including the heart, can be damaged, and the person can die.

21.2 Review

KEY CONCEPTS

1. How do nutrients affect health?
2. Explain the effects of exercise on the respiratory and circulatory systems.
3. Make a chart showing the effects of tobacco, alcohol, and other drugs on the body.

CRITICAL THINKING

4. **Explain** How would you define health? Write your own definition.
5. **Synthesize** Explain how water can be considered a nutrient. Include a definition of *nutrient* in your explanation.

CHALLENGE

6. **Apply** You have heard about a popular new diet. Most of the foods in the diet are fat-free, and the diet promises fast weight loss. How might this diet affect health? Explain your answer.

ANSWERS

1. Nutrients keep the body functioning properly.

2. Exercise causes deeper inhales and exhales that make the heart and muscles of the respiratory system stronger.

3. tobacco—damages respiratory and circulatory systems, high risk of cancer and heart disease; alcohol—damages liver, heart, nervous, and digestive systems; drugs—damage the nervous system and can cause heart and lungs to stop

4. Answers should include a relaxing lifestyle, good nutrition, exercise, and avoiding harmful drugs.

5. Nutrients are sources of energy for the body. A person needs enough water each day to keep body systems functioning.

6. This diet would cause poor health. A diet should contain about 10 to 15 percent fats.

MATH TUTORIAL
CLASSZONE.COM
Click on Math Tutorial for more help with choosing a data display.

SKILL: CHOOSING A DATA DISPLAY

Pumping Up the Heart

Heart rates differ with age, level of activity, and fitness. To communicate the differences clearly, you need to display the data visually. Choosing the appropriate display is important.

Example

The fitness trainer at a gym wants to display the following data:

Maximum heart rate while exercising (beats per minute)		
Age 21	Men	197
	Women	194
Age 45	Men	178
	Women	177
Age 65	Men	162
	Women	164

Here are some different displays the trainer could use:

- A bar graph shows how different categories of data compare. Data can be broken into 2 or even 3 bars per category.
- A line graph shows how data changes over time.
- A circle graph represents data as parts of a whole.

ANSWER The fitness trainer wants to show heart rate according to both age and gender, so a double bar graph would be the clearest.

What would be an appropriate way to display data in the following situations?

1. A doctor wants to display how a child's average heart rate changes as the child grows.
2. A doctor wants to display data showing how a person's resting heart rate changes the more the person exercises.
3. A scientist is studying each type of diet that the people in an experiment follow. She will show what percentage of the people with each diet had heart disease.

CHALLENGE Describe a situation in which a double line graph is the most appropriate data display.

ANSWERS

1. line graph, to show change over time
2. line graph, to show change over time
3. circle graph, to show parts of a whole (subsets of a set)
4. CHALLENGE Answers will vary but should express the idea that two sets of data need to be compared to use a double bar graph.

MATH IN SCIENCE
Math Skills Practice for Science

Set Learning Goal

To determine the appropriate way to display data

Present the Science

Aerobic exercise contributes to cardiovascular health. As the body works to exercise, the aerobic system uses glycogen, fats, and proteins as fuel sources. As the heart rate increases, cardiac output increases. Increased blood flow increases the amount of oxygen sent to the muscles to help them work.

Develop Data Skills

Review the different types of graphs. Line graphs generally show change over a period of time. Circle graphs represent data as percentages of one hundred. Bar graphs compare sets of data using bars across the *x*- or *y*-axis. Remind students that the *x*-axis is the horizontal axis and the *y*-axis is the vertical axis. Both axes intersect at zero.

DIFFERENTIATION TIP Prepare examples of the various types of graphs copied from your school's mathematics texts. Enlarge the graphs for students to examine.

Close

Ask students why neither a line graph nor a circle graph is a good choice for displaying the data in the chart. *Neither graph is useful in comparing two sets of data.*

- Math Support, p. 283
- Math Practice, p. 284

Technology Resources

Students can visit **ClassZone.com** to practice graphing skills.

MATH TUTORIAL

21.3 FOCUS

Set Learning Goals

Students will

- Discuss some of the causes of disease.
- Describe how diseases can be treated.
- Identify ways to prevent the spread of disease.
- Model how germs are spread.

3-Minute Warm-Up

Display Transparency 36 or copy this exercise on the board:

Complete the chart describing how each nutrient benefits the body.

Benefits		Nutrients
main source of energy	←	*carbohydrates*
build tissues, used for growth and repair	←	*proteins*
essential for energy	←	*fats*
transports materials through the body	←	*water*

 3-Minute Warm-Up, p. T36

21.3 MOTIVATE

EXPLORE The Immune System

PURPOSE To model how easily germs are spread

TIP *10 min.* Have students make a list of all the places where they observed the glitter.

WHAT DO YOU THINK? *The glitter was easily transferred to other people and places. Germs are also easily spread by people touching things.*

KEY CONCEPT

21.3 Science helps people prevent and treat disease.

BEFORE, you learned

- Good nutrition and exercise help keep the body healthy
- Drug abuse can endanger health
- Eating disorders can affect the body's health

NOW, you will learn

- About some of the causes of disease
- How diseases can be treated
- How to help prevent the spread of disease

VOCABULARY

microorganism p. 724
bacteria p. 725
virus p. 725
resistance p. 729

EXPLORE The Immune System

How easily do germs spread?

PROCEDURE

1. Early in the day, place a small amount of glitter in the palm of one hand. Rub your hands together to spread the glitter to both palms. Go about your day normally.
2. At the end of the day, examine your environment, including the people around you. Where does the glitter show up?

WHAT DO YOU THINK?

- How easily did the glitter transfer to other people and objects?
- What do you think this might mean about how diseases might spread?

MATERIALS
glitter

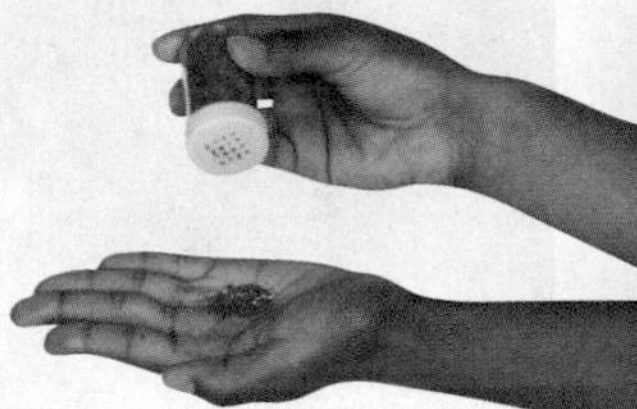

Scientific understanding helps people fight disease.

Disease is a change that disturbs the normal functioning of the body's systems. If you have ever had a cold, you have experienced a disease that affected your respiratory system. What are the causes of disease? Many diseases are classified as infectious diseases, or diseases that can be spread. Viruses, bacteria, and other pathogens cause infectious disease. The organisms that cause sickness are called **microorganisms.**

VOCABULARY
Remember to choose a strategy from earlier chapters or one of your own to take notes on the term *microorganism.*

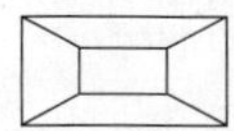

Before the invention of the microscope, people didn't know about microorganisms that cause disease. They observed that people who lived near each other sometimes caught the same illness, but they didn't understand why. Understanding disease has helped people prevent and treat many illnesses.

RESOURCES FOR DIFFERENTIATED INSTRUCTION

Below Level

UNIT RESOURCE BOOK

- Reading Study Guide A, pp. 270–271
- Decoding Support, p. 282

AUDIO CDS

Advanced

UNIT RESOURCE BOOK

Challenge and Extension, p. 276

English Learners

UNIT RESOURCE BOOK

Spanish Reading Study Guide, pp. 274–275

- Audio Readings in Spanish
- Audio Readings (English)

The germ theory describes some causes of disease.

In the 1800s, questions about the causes of some diseases were answered. Scientists showed through experiments that diseases could be caused by very small living things. In 1857, French chemist Louis Pasteur did experiments that showed that microorganisms caused food to decay. Later, Pasteur's work and the work of Robert Koch and Robert Lister contributed to the germ theory. Pasteur's germ theory states that some diseases, called infectious diseases, are caused by germs.

Bacteria and Viruses

Germs are the general name given to organisms that cause disease. **Bacteria** (bak-TEER-ee-uh) are single-celled organisms that live almost everywhere. Within your intestines, bacteria function to digest food. Some bacteria, however, cause disease. Pneumonia (nu-MOHN-yuh), ear infections (ihn-FEHK-shuhnz), and strep throat can be caused by bacteria.

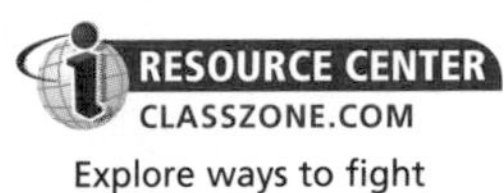

Explore ways to fight disease.

Viruses do not fit all parts of the definition of living things. For example, they must enter and exist inside living cells in order to reproduce. Stomach flu, chicken pox, and colds are sicknesses caused by viruses. Both bacteria and viruses are examples of pathogens, agents that cause disease. The word *pathogen* comes from the Greek *pathos*, which means "suffering." Other pathogens include yeasts, fungi, and protists.

A

Treating Infectious Diseases

Diseases caused by bacteria can be treated with medicines that contain antibiotics. An antibiotic is a substance that can destroy bacteria. The first antibiotics were discovered in 1928 when a scientist named Alexander Fleming was performing experiments on bacteria. Fleming found mold growing on his bacteria samples. While most of the petri dish was covered with bacterial colonies, the area around the mold was clear. From this observation, Fleming concluded that a substance in the mold had killed the bacteria.

Fleming had not intended to grow mold in his laboratory, but the accident led to the discovery of penicillin. Since the discovery of penicillin, many antibiotics have been developed. Antibiotics have saved the lives of millions of people.

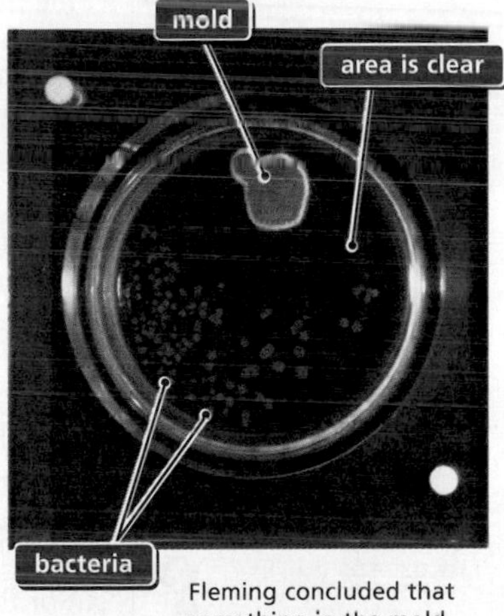

Fleming concluded that something in the mold had killed the bacteria.

21.3 INSTRUCT

History of Science

Prior to the mid 1860s, surgery was risky, with many patients dying of infection after the procedure. In 1865, British surgeon Joseph Lister began to apply Koch's and Pasteur's germ theories to his surgical practices. He hypothesized that microorganisms cause infections and began to use carbolic acid to wash his hands and surgical instruments prior to surgery. He used carbolic acid to cleanse the wounds and bandages. His practice greatly decreased the rate of death from surgical infections.

Real World Example

Bacteria have many industrial uses, including a role in the production of dairy products, vinegar, sauerkraut, and the preparation of certain antibiotics. Bacteria are also used in sewage disposal plants to clean up organic wastes. Certain bacteria decompose oil into small harmless molecules. These are useful when cleaning up oil spills that contaminate plant and animal life.

Teach Difficult Concepts

Some students may think that antibiotics are a cure for most illnesses. In fact, antibiotics are effective against most kinds of bacterial infections, but do not have much effect against viral infections such as influenza, chicken pox, and colds.

DIFFERENTIATE INSTRUCTION

More Reading Support

A What term describes agents of disease, such as bacteria and viruses? *pathogens*

B What substances found in medicines destroy bacteria? *antibiotics*

English Learners Have students write the definitions for the terms *germ, bacteria, virus, pathogen, antibiotic,* and *resistance* in their Science Word Dictionaries. Use the Key Concepts Summary, p. 732, to help students focus on key concepts and vocabulary.

Address Misconceptions

IDENTIFY Ask students to explain what illnesses are caused by germs and how germs cause illness. Many students hold the misconception that every illness is caused by germs, that all diseases are contagious and caused by the same kind of germ. Students may also hold the misconception that all germs enter the body through the mouth when eating.

CORRECT Have students create a chart with three columns: What are germs? What causes diseases? How do germs enter the body? Ask students to fill in the chart as they read pp. 725–731.

REASSESS Have students re-evaluate their charts after the chapter. Have them summarize the ways germs enter the body and the varied causes of illness.

Technology Resources

Visit **ClassZone.com** for background on common student misconceptions.

 **MISCONCEPTION DATABASE**

Social Studies Connection

Interested students may wish to find out about the bubonic plague that occurred in 14th century Europe. Also known as the Black Death, the plague killed over 25 million people. Ask students what caused it and how it changed the history and social structure of medieval Europe. Allow students to share their findings.

EXPLORE the BIG idea

Revisit "How Safe Is Your Food?" on p. 707. Ask students to reassess the dangers of eating food that is past its freshness date.

Ongoing Assessment

Discuss some of the causes of disease.

Ask: What are two types of pathogens that cause disease? *bacteria and viruses*

Identify ways to prevent the spread of disease.

Ask: How can harmful bacteria be killed in food and water? *Wash fruits and vegetables before eating; boil water for cooking.*

Infectious diseases spread in many ways.

READING TIP As you read the text on this page, notice how each pathogen shown on p. 727 spreads.

One of the best ways to protect your health is by being informed and by avoiding pathogens. Pathogens can be found in many places, including air, water, and on the surfaces of objects. By knowing how pathogens travel, people are able to limit the spreading of disease.

Food, Air, and Water

Sometimes people get sick when they breathe in pathogens from the air. The viruses that cause colds can travel through air. If you cover your mouth when you sneeze or cough, you can avoid sending pathogens through the air. Pathogens also enter the body in food or water. Washing fruits and vegetables and cooking meats and eggs kills bacteria. Most cities in the United States add substances, such as chlorine, to the supply of public water. These substances kill pathogens. Boiling water also kills pathogens. People sometimes boil water if their community loses power or experiences a flood. Campers need to boil or filter water taken from a stream before they use it.

Contact with Animals

 C

Animals can also carry organisms that cause disease. The animal itself does not cause the illness, but you can become sick if you take in the pathogen that the animal carries. Lyme disease, for example, is caused by bacteria that inhabit ticks. The ticks are not the cause of illness, but if an infected tick bites you, you will get Lyme disease.

A deadly central nervous system infection called rabies can also come from animal contact. The virus that causes rabies is found in the saliva of an infected animal, such as a bat, raccoon, or opossum. If that animal bites you, you may get the disease. A veterinarian can give your pet an injection to prevent rabies. You can get other infections from pets. These infections include worms that enter through your mouth or nose and live in your intestines. You can also get a skin infection called ringworm, which is actually a fungus rather than a worm.

Person-to-Person Contact

 D

Most of the illnesses you have had have probably been passed to you by another person. Even someone who does not feel sick can have pathogens on his or her skin. If you touch that person or if that person touches something and then you touch it, the pathogens will move to your skin. If the pathogens then enter your body through a cut or through your nose, mouth, or eyes, they can infect your body. The simplest way to avoid giving or receiving pathogens is to wash your hands often and well.

DIFFERENTIATE INSTRUCTION

More Reading Support

C What are two diseases spread by animals? *Lyme disease, rabies*

D How can pathogens enter the body? *nose, eyes, mouth, a cut*

Advanced Invite interested students to investigate some recent diseases or pathogens, their origin, symptoms, and what is being done to contain them. Topics for research might include Ebola virus, giardia, and SARS.

 Challenge and Extension, p. 276

Pathogens and Disease

Infectious diseases are caused by microorganisms.

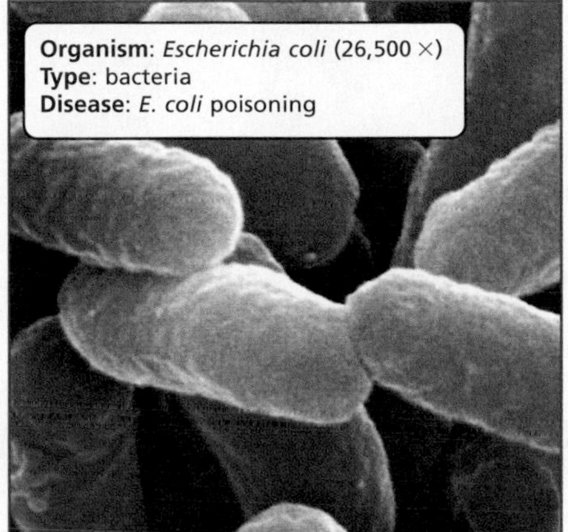

Organism: *Escherichia coli* (26,500 ×)
Type: bacteria
Disease: *E. coli* poisoning

Spread: contaminated food or water
Prevention: handwashing, thoroughly cooking meat, boiling contaminated water, washing fruits and vegetables, drinking only pasteurized milk, juice, or cider

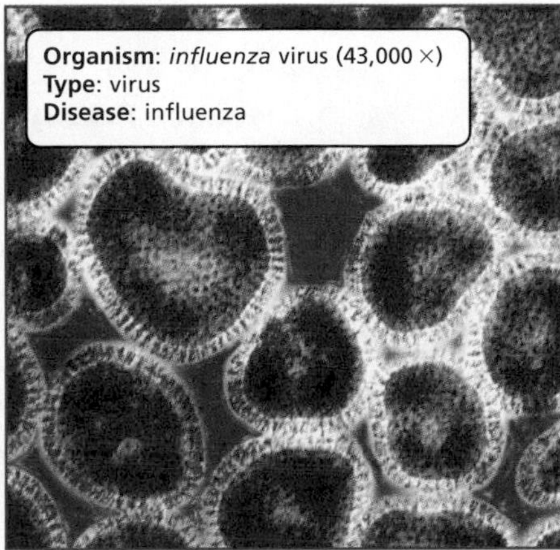

Organism: *influenza* virus (43,000 ×)
Type: virus
Disease: influenza

Spread: inhaling virus from sneezes or coughs of infected person
Prevention: vaccination

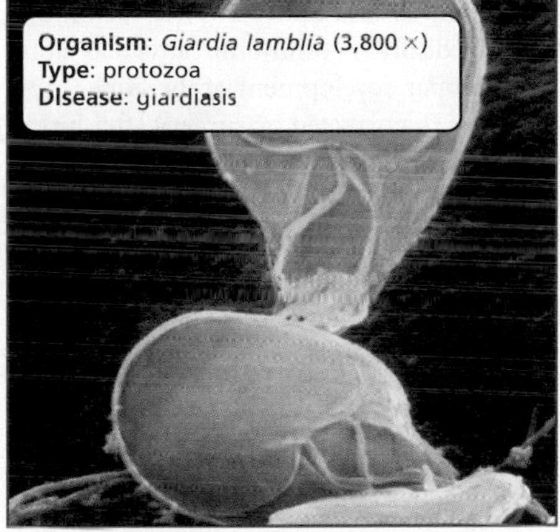

Organism: *Giardia lamblia* (3,800 ×)
Type: protozoa
Disease: giardiasis

Spread: contaminated food or water, close contact with infected person
Prevention: handwashing, thoroughly cooking meat, boiling contaminated water, washing fruits and vegetables, drinking only pasteurized milk, juice, or cider

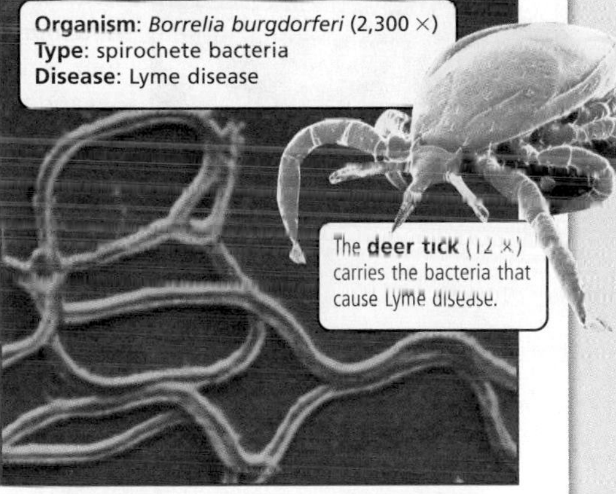

Organism: *Borrelia burgdorferi* (2,300 ×)
Type: spirochete bacteria
Disease: Lyme disease

The **deer tick** (12 ×) carries the bacteria that cause Lyme disease.

Spread: tick bite
Prevention: wear light-colored clothing, tuck pants into socks or shoes, check for ticks after outdoor activities, use repellents containing DEET

READING VISUALS How can people prevent each of these pathogens from spreading?

DIFFERENTIATE INSTRUCTION

Below Level Explain that the common cold can be caused by over 200 different viruses. Persons infected with cold viruses often experience similar symptoms even though the viruses differ. Ask students to develop an inference about why there is still no cure for the common cold. They should support the inference with evidence and try to convince their peers that the inference is valid. *Sample answer: Because there are so many viruses that cause the cold, there would have to be that many cures, and doctors would need to determine which virus is causing the symptoms.*

Teacher Demo

To model how disease is spread, try this demonstration. Prior to class, prepare a class set of envelopes. Place a green strip of paper inside three of the envelopes. Place white strips in the remaining envelopes. Give each student an envelope. Instruct students that the green strips are "infected." Tell students to move about the room for 60 seconds until you say *Stop*. They should whisper the color of the strip that they hold to the nearest person. The students who hear green will now whisper *green* at all future stops. At the end of two rounds, instruct students who have a green slip or who heard green at the first stop to sit down. After the third round, students who heard green at the second stop should sit down. At this point, many students should be "infected." Work with the class to trace the infections back to the original source of infection. Students should record all of their contacts to track how the virus spread.

Teach from Visuals

To help students interpret the photo graphs showing pathogens, ask: What are some different ways shown that diseases are spread? *through contaminated food or water, inhaling viruses, insect bites*

This visual is also available as T38 in the Unit Transparency Book.

Ongoing Assessment

READING VISUALS *Answer: E. coli and Giardia can be stopped by handwashing and avoiding contaminated food and water. Influenza can be prevented by vaccination. Lyme disease can be prevented by wearing proper protective clothing or repellent, and checking for ticks after being outdoors.*

Metacognitive Strategy

Have students make a list of diseases and choose methods of classifying the diseases by what causes them. Encourage students to write definitions for each category of disease classification. Examples include contagious and noncontagious; genetic or environmentally caused.

Health Connection

Point out that some noninfectious diseases can be prevented by practicing good health habits. For example, a person can cut down on the risks of getting lung cancer by not smoking cigarettes and avoiding second-hand smoke. Ask students to give examples of other ways that they can prevent the onset of noninfectious diseases.

Ongoing Assessment

CHECK YOUR READING *Answer: Hemophilia is an inherited disease that is present at birth. Cancer and diabetes are diseases that may come later in life.*

Noninfectious diseases are not contagious.

E Noninfectious diseases are diseases that cannot be spread by pathogens. They are not contagious. People are born with some of these, and others can develop during life.

Diseases Present at Birth

Some diseases present at birth are inherited. Genes, which act as instructions for your cells, are inherited from your parents. Some forms of a gene produce cells that do not function properly. Most genetic disorders are due to recessive forms of a gene, which means that while both parents carry the defective form, neither one has the disorder. Cystic fibrosis and sickle cell disease are diseases inherited this way.

Asthma is a noncontagious disease often present at birth.

The symptoms of some genetic diseases may not be present immediately at birth. Huntington's disease, even though it is an inherited condition, does not begin to produce symptoms until a person reaches adulthood. Other genes can increase the chances of developing a disease later in life, such as cancer or diabetes, but the pattern of inheritance is complex.

The process of human development is complex. Some diseases present at birth may involve both inherited factors and development. Talipes, a disorder commonly known as clubfoot, is due to the improper development of the bones of the leg and foot. Talipes can be corrected by surgery after birth.

Diseases in Later Life

Some diseases, including heart disease, certain forms of cancer, and many respiratory disorders, have much less to do with genetics and more to do with environment and lifestyle. You have learned about the ways in which you can lead a healthy lifestyle. Good nutrition, exercise, and avoiding substances that can damage the body systems not only increase the length of life, but also the quality of life.

While people with family histories of cancer are at higher risk of getting it, environmental factors can influence risk as well. Tar and other chemicals from cigarettes can damage the lungs, in addition to causing cancer. Much is still not known about the causes of cancer.

Name a noninfectious disease that is present at birth and one that may occur later in life.

DIFFERENTIATE INSTRUCTION

E What are noninfectious diseases? *those not spread by pathogens*

Below Level Ask students to create a news conference about a disease outbreak such as SARS or Ebola. Students can role-play doctors and news reporters at the conference. Students should come prepared with questions and answers and be ready to explain how doctors differentiate the outbreak from other illnesses including those that are noninfectious.

Scientists continue efforts to prevent and treat illness.

In spite of all that scientists have learned, disease is still a problem all over the world. Illnesses such as AIDS and cancer are better understood than they used to be, but researchers must still find ways to cure them.

Even though progress is sometimes slow, it does occur. Better education has led to better nutrition. The use of vaccines has made some diseases nearly extinct. However, new types of illness sometimes appear. AIDS was first identified in the 1980s and spread quickly before it was identified. More recently, the West Nile virus appeared in the United States. This virus is transmitted by infected mosquitoes and can cause the brain to become inflamed. Efforts to control the disease continue.

Scientists work hard to fight disease.

Antibiotics fight pathogens, but they can also lead to changes in them. When an antibiotic is used too often, bacteria can develop **resistance,** which means that the strain of bacteria is no longer affected by the drug. Once a strain of bacteria has developed resistance, the resistance will be passed on to new generations of the bacteria. This means that a particular antibiotic will not stop that particular bacterial infection.

Describe the advantages and disadvantages of using an antibiotic when you are sick.

21.3 Review

KEY CONCEPTS

1. Define microorganism and explain how microorganisms can affect health.
2. What is an antibiotic?
3. Make a chart showing ways that infectious diseases spread and ways to keep them from spreading.

CRITICAL THINKING

4. **Connect** Make a list of things you can do to avoid getting Lyme disease or the West Nile virus.
5. **Apply** How does washing your hands before eating help protect your health?

CHALLENGE

6. **Synthesize** How can nutrition help in the prevention of disease? Use these terms in your answer: *nutrients, pathogens,* and *white blood cells.*

ANSWERS

1. a very small organism that can be seen only with a microscope; can bring disease, which disturbs the normal functioning of the body

2. An antibiotic is a substance that can destroy bacteria.

3. Charts should include food, air, water transmission, animal contact, and a prevention method for each transmission.

4. Answers may include wearing long sleeves and pants tucked into boots and using insect repellent.

5. Washing kills pathogens on your skin. This prevents pathogens from moving onto your food.

6. If the body is not healthy, it may not be able to produce enough white blood cells to kill pathogens. Lack of nutrients makes a person vulnerable to diseases.

Ongoing Assessment

Describe how diseases can be treated.

Ask: What are the pathogen-killing drugs used to treat infectious disease? *antibiotics*

Answer: Antibiotics fight diseases, but if they are used too often, bacteria can develop resistance to them and they are no longer effective in treating that bacteria.

Reinforce the BIG idea

Have students relate the section to the Big Idea.

 Reinforcing Key Concepts, p. 278

21.3 ASSESS & RETEACH

Assess

 Section 21.3 Quiz, p. 81

Reteach

Discuss each concept. Have students name examples from the text or elsewhere.

1. Bacteria and viruses are pathogens that can cause disease. (pp. 726–727)
2. Antibiotics are used to treat infectious diseases. (p. 725)
3. Noninfectious diseases cannot be spread by pathogens. (p. 728)

Technology Resources

Have students visit **ClassZone.com** for reteaching of Key Concepts.

 CONTENT REVIEW

 CONTENT REVIEW CD-ROM

CHAPTER INVESTIGATION

Focus

PURPOSE To determine the effectiveness of cleaning hands with soap and water to remove bacteria

OVERVIEW Students will prepare petri dishes with samples of bacteria from their hands before and after washing. Students will do the following:

- sample their hands for the presence of bacteria
- test the effectiveness of washing with water compared with soap and water

Lab Preparation

- Sterile petri dishes may be obtained from biological supply companies.
- Prior to the investigation, have students read through the investigation and prepare their data tables. Or you may wish to copy and distribute datasheets and rubrics.

 UNIT RESOURCE BOOK, pp. 285–293

 SCIENCE TOOLKIT, F14

Lab Management

- Remind students to leave the petri dishes closed. Place the petri dishes in a cool place for several days.
- Dispose of petri dishes in a plastic container filled with dilute bleach. Do not allow students to open the dishes when they record their observations.
- You can prepare your own nutrient agar: boil 31 grams per liter of water for 10–15 minutes. Use a fume hood or leave windows open.

SAFETY Make sure students wash their hands thoroughly after the activity.

INCLUSION Provide a simplified checklist of the procedure steps for students to follow. Give each step a number and a name. Students can check off each step as they complete it. If you have students with limited attention, be sure to review the caution statements first.

CHAPTER INVESTIGATION

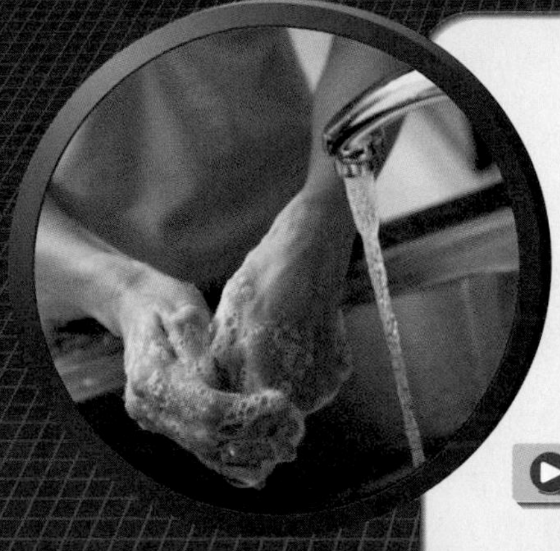

Cleaning Your Hands

OVERVIEW AND PURPOSE Your skin cells produce oils that keep the skin moist. This same layer of oil provides a nutrient surface for bacteria to grow. When you wash your hands with soap, the soap dissolves the oil and the water carries it away, along with the bacteria. In this activity you will

- sample your hands for the presence of bacteria
- test the effectiveness of washing your hands with water compared with washing them with soap and water

Problem

Write It Up

Is soap effective at removing bacteria?

Hypothesize

Write It Up

Write a hypothesis explaining how using soap affects the amount of bacteria on your hands. Your hypothesis should take the form of an "If . . . , then . . . , because . . ." statement.

MATERIALS

- 3 covered petri dishes with sterile nutrient agar
- soap
- marker
- tape
- hand lens

Procedure

1. Make a data table in your **Science Notebook** like the one shown on page 731.
2. Obtain three agar petri dishes. Be careful not to open the dishes accidentally.
3. Remove the lid from one dish and gently press two fingers from your right hand onto the surface of the agar. Close the lid immediately. Tape the dish closed. Mark the tape with the letter *A*. Include your initials and the date.

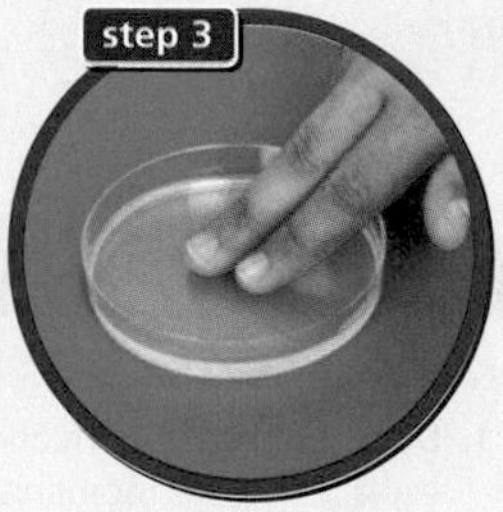

step 3

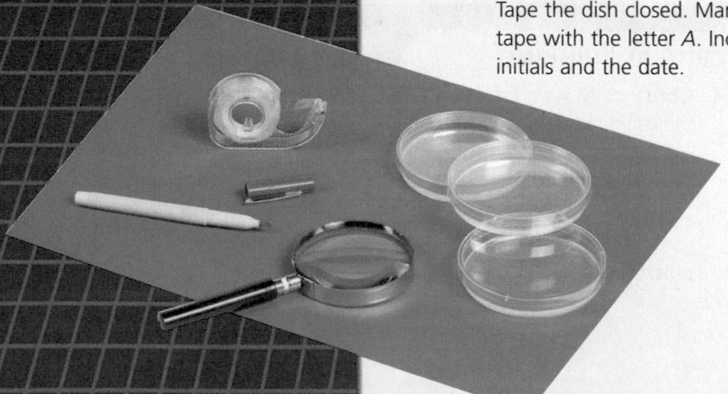

730 Unit 5: Human Biology

INVESTIGATION RESOURCES

 CHAPTER INVESTIGATION, Cleaning Your Hands

- Level A, pp. 285–288
- Level B, pp. 289–292
- Level C, p. 293

Advanced students should complete Levels B & C.

 Writing a Lab Report, D12–13

Technology Resources

Customize this student lab as needed or look for an alternative. Print rubrics to assess student lab reports.

 **Lab Generator CD-ROM**

4 Wash your hands in water and let them air-dry. Open the second dish with your right hand and press two fingers of your left hand into the agar. Close the lid immediately. Tape and mark the dish *B*, as in step 3.

5 Wash your hands in soap and water and let them air-dry. Open the third dish with one hand and press two fingers of the other hand into the agar. Close the lid immediately. Tape and mark the dish *C*, as in step 3.

6 Place the agar plates upside down in a dark, warm place for two to three days. **Caution:** Do not open the dishes. Wash your hands.

Observe and Analyze

Write It Up

1. **OBSERVE** Use a hand lens to observe the amounts of bacterial growth in each dish, and record your observations in Table 1. Which dish has the most bacterial growth? the least growth?
2. **OBSERVE** Is there anything you notice about the bacterial growth in each dish other than the amount of bacterial growth?
3. Return the petri dishes to your teacher for disposal. **Caution:** Do not open the dishes. Wash your hands thoroughly with warm water and soap when you have finished.

Conclude

Write It Up

1. **INFER** Why is it necessary to air-dry your hands instead of using a towel?
2. **INFER** Why is it important to use your right hand in step 3 and your left hand in step 4?
3. **INTERPRET** Compare your results with your hypothesis. Do your observations support your hypothesis?
4. **EVALUATE** Is there much value in washing your hands simply in water?
5. **EVALUATE** How might the temperature of the water you used when you washed your hands affect the results of your experiment?
6. **EVALUATE** Given the setup of your experiment, could you have prepared a fourth sample, for example to test the effectiveness of antibacterial soap?

INVESTIGATE Further

CHALLENGE It is hard to tell which products are best for washing hands without testing them. Design an experiment to determine which cleans your hands best: baby wipes, hand sanitizer, regular soap, or antibacterial soap.

Cleaning Your Hands

Table 1. Observations

Petri Dish	Source	Amount of Bacteria
A	hand	
B	hand washed with water	
C	hand washed with soap and water	

Observe and Analyze

1. *Dish A should have the most bacterial growth. Dish C should have the least growth.*
2. *Observations may vary.*

Conclude

1. *Towel drying would remove additional bacteria by rubbing them off, or might add bacteria to the hands from the towel.*
2. *Pressing the fingers of the right hand to the agar in step 3 removed the bacteria from the fingers and transferred it to the agar.*
3. *Students should provide evidence or explanation for describing whether their hypotheses are correct or incorrect.*
4. *Using water alone did remove some bacteria from the hands, but not as much as using water and soap.*
5. *Hot water would be more effective at killing bacteria than cold water.*
6. *It would be possible to test the effectiveness of antibacterial soap by using two different fingers from those used in steps 3, 4, or 5.*

INVESTIGATE Further

CHALLENGE Students' experiments should include a hypothesis, steps for a procedure, and a method of gathering data. Students may use sterile petri dishes with agar to test the bacteria present on their hands before and after using soap and the antibacterial ingredients.

Post-Lab Discussion

- On the board, keep a running tally of results for each student or group. Have students think about conditions that might cause differences in results. Students can make inferences as to why one surface might contain more bacteria than another.
- Remind students that not all bacteria is harmful. Human beings have bacteria that line the digestive tract to help digest food and keep the digestive system functioning properly.

BACK TO

the BIG idea

Have students choose one of the life stages discussed in the chapter and describe the physical and developmental changes that occur during that stage. *Sample answer: In adulthood the body systems are not increasing in size. The systems continue to function and to repair tissue and to take care of the organism's needs. In adulthood the body can produce and care for offspring. An adult continues to develop mental and social skills and knowledge.*

KEY CONCEPTS SUMMARY

SECTION 21.1

Ask students what is represented by the data in the graph. *average weight for females, birth to age 15*

SECTION 21.2

Have students describe why it is important to read and understand the nutrition labels that are given on food packaging. *Nutrition labels contain information about the nutrients and vitamins that are present in each serving of food. Labels help a person maintain and be knowledgeable about a healthy diet.*

SECTION 21.3

Have students describe different ways that they can prevent infectious disease. *Sample answers: wash hands, get vaccinations, wear insect repellent, avoid contact with persons who are ill, and maintain a healthy lifestyle by eating the right foods and getting exercise.*

Review Concepts

- Big Idea Flow Chart, p. T33
- Chapter Outline, pp. T39–T40

21 Chapter Review

the BIG idea

The body develops and maintains itself over time.

KEY CONCEPTS SUMMARY

The human body changes over time.

Your body changes throughout your entire life. Some changes are physical and some are emotional. The stages of life are infancy, childhood, adolescence, adulthood, and later adulthood. All the different systems in the body interact to maintain your health.

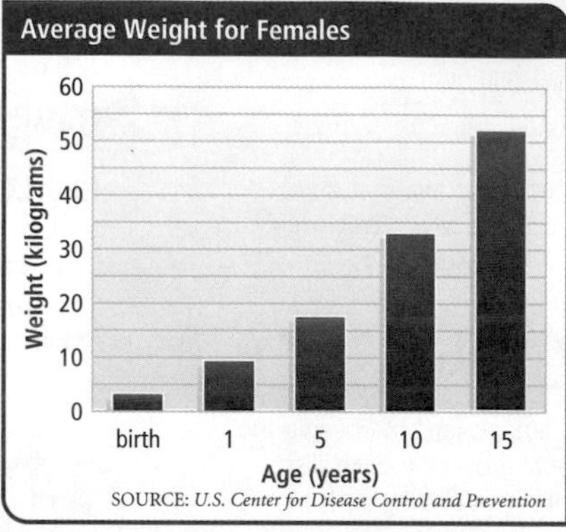

VOCABULARY
infancy p. 710
childhood p. 710
adolescence p. 711
adulthood p. 712

Systems in the body function to maintain health.

Your diet affects your health. Important nutrients include proteins, carbohydrates, fats, vitamins, minerals, and water. Water is also essential to healthy living. Exercise is another ingredient to a healthy life. Problems that can interfere with a healthy life are drug abuse, addiction, and eating disorders.

VOCABULARY
nutrition p. 716
addiction p. 722

Science helps people prevent and treat disease.

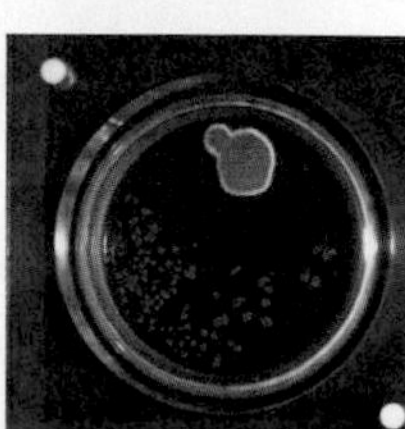

- Science helps people fight disease.
- Antibiotics are used to fight diseases caused by bacteria.
- Infectious disease can spread in many ways including food, air, water, insects, other animals, and person-to-person contact.
- Noninfectious diseases are not contagious. Some noninfectious diseases are present at birth and others occur in later life.

VOCABULARY
microorganism p. 724
bacteria p. 725
virus p. 725
resistance p. 729

Technology Resources

Have students visit **ClassZone.com** or use the CD-ROM for a cumulative review of concepts.

CONTENT REVIEW

CONTENT REVIEW CD-ROM

Engage students in a whole-class interactive review of Key Concepts. Edit content as you wish.

POWER PRESENTATIONS

Reviewing Vocabulary

Make a frame for each of the vocabulary words listed below. Write the word in the center. Decide what information to frame it with. Use definitions, examples, descriptions, parts, or pictures.

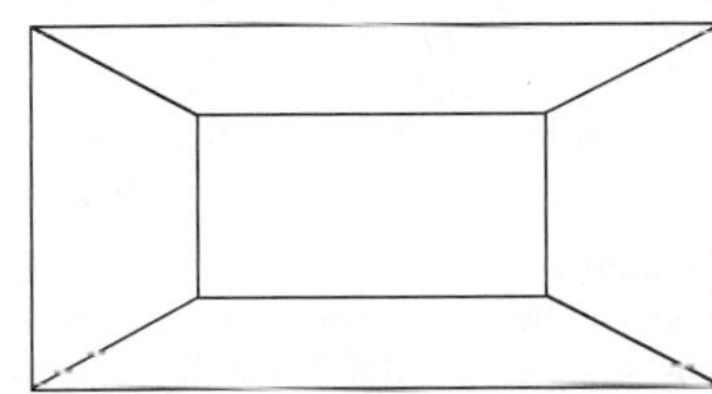

1. infancy
2. childhood
3. adolescence
4. adulthood

Reviewing Key Concepts

Multiple Choice *Choose the letter of the best answer.*

5. The stage of life known as infancy ends when an infant
   a. begins to cry
   b. learns to walk
   c. holds up his head
   d. sees more clearly
6. The process in which the body begins to mature sexually is called
   a. adolescence
   b. adulthood
   c. nutrition
   d. puberty
7. Which nutrients are the main sources of energy for the body?
   a. fats and carbohydrates
   b. water and protein
   c. fats and proteins
   d. water and carbohydrates
8. Which is *not* a benefit of regular exercise?
   a. flushed-out skin pores
   b. stronger skeletal system
   c. increased body fat
   d. strengthened heart
9. A sedentary life style is associated with
   a. a stronger immune system
   b. more sitting than moving
   c. regular exercise
   d. an eating disorder
10. The chemical found in tobacco that increases heart rate and blood pressure is
    a. cocaine
    b. narcotics
    c. tar
    d. nicotine
11. Which term includes all of the others?
    a. bacteria
    b. fungus
    c. virus
    d. pathogen
12. An example of a disease caused by bacteria is
    a. an ear infection
    b. stomach flu
    c. chicken pox
    d. a cold
13. Which statement about viruses is true?
    a. Viruses function to digest food.
    b. Viruses are one-celled organisms.
    c. Viruses need living cells to reproduce.
    d. Examples of viruses are fungi and yeasts.
14. A substance that can destroy bacteria is called
    a. a vitamin
    b. a pathogen
    c. an antibiotic
    d. a mold
15. Lyme disease is spread through
    a. drinking unfiltered water
    b. uncooked meats
    c. the bite of a dog
    d. the bite of a tick

Short Answer *Write a short answer to each question.*

16. In your own words, define *nutrition.*
17. What are pathogens? Give three examples.
18. Explain what happens if antibiotics are used too often.

ASSESSMENT RESOURCES

UNIT ASSESSMENT BOOK

- Chapter Test, Level A, pp. 82–85
- Chapter Test, Level B, pp. 86–89
- Chapter Test, Level C, pp. 90–93
- Alternative Assessment, pp. 94–95
- Unit Test, pp. 96–107

SPANISH ASSESSMENT BOOK

- Spanish Chapter Test, pp. 97–100
- Spanish Unit Test, pp. 101–104

Technology Resources

Edit test items and answer choices.

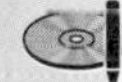 **Test Generator CD-ROM**

Visit **ClassZone.com** to extend test practice.

 **Test Practice**

Reviewing Vocabulary

Sample answers:

1. infancy—rapid physical development; infants learn to roll over, sit, crawl, stand, and walk; development of thinking and social skills; much body system growth and change

2. childhood—period between infancy and adolescence; children learn to care for themselves; mental and social growth—learn to read, write, and communicate

3. adolescence—period between childhood and adulthood; puberty occurs; period of physical growth in boys and girls (as much as 10 cm)

4. adulthood—completes growth and reaches sexual maturity; mental and social development continue throughout life; mental and emotional maturity

Reviewing Key Concepts

5. b

6. d

7. a

8. c

9. b

10. d

11. d

12. a

13. c

14. c

15. d

16. Nutrition is the study of the nutrients, such as proteins and carbohydrates, that keep your body healthy and how these nutrients are used for maintenance, growth, and reproduction.

17. Pathogens are agents that cause disease. Examples may include bacteria, viruses, yeasts, fungi, and protists.

18. When an antibiotic is used too often, bacteria can develop resistance to it.

Thinking Critically

19. *Infants learn that people respond to their crying when they are hungry or have other needs.*
20. *Sample answer: Physical: development of a deeper voice; Mental: learning to communicate better with others; Social: ability to cooperate with others*
21. *Fats provide energy that helps the body absorb vitamins and form parts of cells. A no-fat diet might result in not enough energy, being unable to absorb vitamins, and improper cell function.*
22. *Lack of activity causes muscles and bones to break down. Unused energy from food is stored as fat; excess fat can cause health problems.*
23. *Alcohol damages heart, liver, and body systems. Tobacco affects lungs, heart rate, and blood pressure. The fetus is connected to the mother's circulatory system; alcohol and tobacco could affect the fetus.*
24. *Both are eating disorders. Anorexia: eat so little they become unhealthy and can die; Bulimia: overeat, then force themselves to vomit*
25. *Pasteur showed that tiny organisms caused food decay. Pasteur's germ theory stated that some diseases are caused by germs.*
26. *The disease probably came from water contaminated by a pathogen. Boiling water would kill pathogens.*
27. *Eat nutritious foods, get exercise, stay out of the Sun, avoid tobacco and alcohol use.*

the BIG idea

28. *Answers will depend on students' original answers to the Big Idea question.*
29. *Answers should include concepts from the unit and terminology from the box.*

UNIT PROJECTS

Have students present their projects. Use the appropriate rubrics from the URB to evaluate their work.

Unit Projects, pp. 5–10

Thinking Critically

19. **ANALYZE** Why do you think crying is an example of a social skill that develops during infancy?

20. **ANALYZE** Describe one physical, one mental, and one social change that a ten-year-old boy might experience over the next five years.

21. **EVALUATE** Explain why a diet that doesn't contain any fat would be unhealthy.

22. **APPLY** Explain why people who live sedentary lifestyles should get more exercise.

23. **SYNTHESIZE** Discuss why doctors recommend that women avoid alcohol and tobacco use during pregnancy.

24. **COMPARE AND CONTRAST** People who overeat and then quickly try to lose weight are bulimic. How is bulimia like anorexia? How does it differ?

25. **ANALYZE** Explain why Pasteur's work was important in the understanding of disease.

26. **HYPOTHESIZE** In 1854 a disease called cholera spread through the city of London. Most of the people who contracted the disease lived near the city's various water pumps. What might you hypothesize about the cause of the disease? How could you prevent people from contracting the disease in the future?

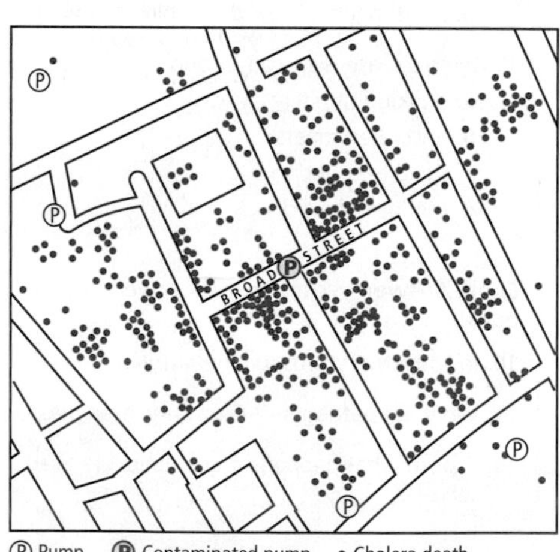

Ⓟ Pump Ⓟ Contaminated pump • Cholera death

27. **PROVIDE EXAMPLES** What are some ways that a person can prevent noninfectious diseases such as cancer or diabetes?

the BIG idea

28. **INFER** Look again at the picture on pages 706–707. Now that you have finished the chapter, how would you change or add details to your answer to the question on the photograph?

29. **SUMMARIZE** Write one or more paragraphs explaining how lifestyle can lead to a healthy body and a longer life. Include these terms in your description.

nutrition	alcohol
exercise	infectious disease
germs	noninfectious disease
tobacco	

UNIT PROJECTS

Evaluate all the data, results, and information from your project folder. Prepare to present your project.

MONITOR AND RETEACH

If students are having trouble applying the concepts in Chapter Review items 19 and 20, suggest that they review the stages of life on pp. 710–711. Then have students create a concept map detailing the events of each stage.

Students may benefit from summarizing one or more sections of the chapter.

 Summarizing the Chapter, pp. 303–304

Standardized Test Practice

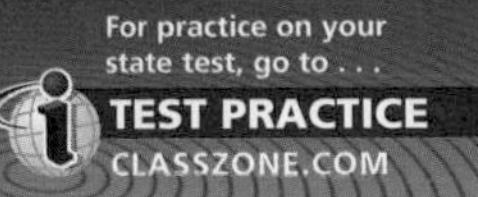

Analyzing Data

The table below presents information about causes of death in the United States.

Leading Causes of Death in the United States

2000		1900	
Cause of Death	**Percent of Deaths**	**Cause of Death**	**Percent of Deaths**
heart disease	31%	pneumonia*	12%
cancer	23%	tuberculosis*	11%
stroke	9%	diarrhea*	11%
lung disease	5%	heart disease	6%
accident	4%	liver disease	5%
pneumonia*	4%	accident	4%
diabetes	3%	cancer	4%
kidney disease	1%	senility	2%
liver disease	1%	diphtheria*	2%

* infectious disease

Use the table to answer the questions below.

1. What was the leading cause of death in 1900?
   a. heart disease c. pneumonia
   b. cancer d. tuberculosis

2. Which infectious disease was a leading cause of death both in 1900 and 2000?
   a. tuberculosis c. stroke
   b. diphtheria d. pneumonia

3. Which was the leading noninfectious cause of death in both 1900 and 2000?
   a. pneumonia c. heart disease
   b. cancer d. accidents

4. Which cause of death showed the greatest increase between 1900 and 2000?
   a. heart disease c. liver disease
   b. cancer d. pneumonia

5. Which statement is true?
   a. The rate of infectious disease as a leading cause of death increased from 1900 to 2000.
   b. The rate of infectious disease as a leading cause of death decreased from 1900 to 2000.
   c. The rate of noninfectious disease as a leading cause of death decreased from 1900 to 2000.
   d. The rate of noninfectious disease as a leading cause of death remained the same.

6. The percent of deaths caused by heart disease in 2000 was how much greater than in 1900?
   a. 37% c. 25%
   b. 31% d. 6%

Extended Response

bacterium	virus	pathogen
antibiotic	resistance	microorganism

7. Write a paragraph explaining the change in the number of deaths due to infectious diseases from 1900 to 2000. Use the information in the data and what you know about infectious disease in your description. Use the vocabulary words in the box in your answer.

8. The spread of infectious disease can be controlled in many different ways. Write a paragraph describing how the spread of infectious disease may be limited. Give at least two examples and describe how these diseases can be prevented or contained.

METACOGNITIVE ACTIVITY

Have students answer the following questions in their **Science Notebook:**

1. Are there any concepts in this chapter that you are still unclear about? Explain.
2. Is there anything else that you would like to know about how human beings grow and develop? Explain.
3. How does working in a group help you learn? Give an example from this chapter.

Analyzing Data

1. c 3. c 5. b
2. d 4. a 6. c

Extended Response

7. RUBRIC

4 points for a response that correctly answers the question and includes at least four of the following terms:

- bacterium
- antibiotic
- virus
- resistance
- pathogen
- microorganism

Sample answer: The discovery of pathogens such as bacteria and viruses led people to a greater understanding of disease and how people become ill. Antibiotics such as penicillin were developed to fight infectious diseases, so people have a better chance of surviving. Improvement in sanitation such as the treatment of water has limited the spread of disease. Vaccinations also help to prevent the spread of many infectious diseases.

3 points correctly answers the question and includes at least three of the terms shown

2 points correctly answers the question and includes at least two of the terms shown

1 point correctly answers the question and includes at least one term shown

8. RUBRIC

4 points for a response that includes two examples and describes how both diseases can be prevented.

Sample answer: Infectious diseases are caused by pathogens such as bacteria and viruses. Diseases caused by bacteria can enter the body through food and water. Washing fruits and vegetables and cooking meats thoroughly can help prevent the spread of disease. Boiling water that may be contaminated is another way to prevent disease. Some infectious diseases like rabies are transmitted by certain animals and are prevented by avoiding contact with these animals.

3 points includes two examples and describes how one disease can be prevented

2 points includes one example and describes how that disease can be prevented

1 point includes two examples, but no description of how the disease can be prevented

736

Student Resource Handbooks

Scientific Thinking Handbook

SCIENTIFIC THINKING HANDBOOK

Making Observations

An **observation** is an act of noting and recording an event, characteristic, behavior, or anything else detected with an instrument or with the senses.

Observations allow you to make informed hypotheses and to gather data for experiments. Careful observations often lead to ideas for new experiments. There are two categories of observations:

- **Quantitative observations** can be expressed in numbers and include records of time, temperature, mass, distance, and volume.
- **Qualitative observations** include descriptions of sights, sounds, smells, and textures.

EXAMPLE

A student dissolved 30 grams of Epsom salts in water, poured the solution into a dish, and let the dish sit out uncovered overnight. The next day, she made the following observations of the Epsom salt crystals that grew in the dish.

To determine the mass, the student found the mass of the dish before and after growing the crystals and then used subtraction to find the difference.

The student measured several crystals and calculated the mean length. (To learn how to calculate the mean of a data set, see page R36.)

Table 1. Observations of Epsom Salt Crystals

Quantitative Observations	Qualitative Observations
• mass = 30 g • mean crystal length = 0.5 cm • longest crystal length = 2 cm	• Crystals are clear. • Crystals are long, thin, and rectangular. • White crust has formed around edge of dish. Epsom salt crystals

Photographs or sketches are useful for recording qualitative observations.

MORE ABOUT OBSERVING

- Make quantitative observations whenever possible. That way, others will know exactly what you observed and be able to compare their results with yours.
- It is always a good idea to make qualitative observations too. You never know when you might observe something unexpected.

Predicting and Hypothesizing

A **prediction** is an expectation of what will be observed or what will happen. A **hypothesis** is a tentative explanation for an observation or scientific problem that can be tested by further investigation.

SCIENTIFIC THINKING HANDBOOK

EXAMPLE

Suppose you have made two paper airplanes and you wonder why one of them tends to glide farther than the other one.

1. Start by asking a question.
2. Make an educated guess. After examination, you notice that the wings of the airplane that flies farther are slightly larger than the wings of the other airplane.
3. Write a prediction based upon your educated guess, in the form of an "If . . . , then . . ." statement. Write the independent variable after the word *if,* and the dependent variable after the word *then.*
4. To make a hypothesis, explain why you think what you predicted will occur. Write the explanation after the word *because.*

1. Why does one of the paper airplanes glide farther than the other?
2. The size of an airplane's wings may affect how far the airplane will glide.
3. Prediction: If I make a paper airplane with larger wings, then the airplane will glide farther.
4. Hypothesis: If I make a paper airplane with larger wings, then the airplane will glide farther, because the additional surface area of the wing will produce more lift.

To read about independent and dependent variables, see page R30.

Notice that the part of the hypothesis after *because* adds an explanation of why the airplane will glide farther.

MORE ABOUT HYPOTHESES

- The results of an experiment cannot prove that a hypothesis is correct. Rather, the results either support or do not support the hypothesis.
- Valuable information is gained even when your hypothesis is not supported by your results. For example, it would be an important discovery to find that wing size is not related to how far an airplane glides.
- In science, a hypothesis is supported only after many scientists have conducted many experiments and produced consistent results.

Inferring

An **inference** is a logical conclusion drawn from the available evidence and prior knowledge. Inferences are often made from observations.

EXAMPLE

A student observing a set of acorns noticed something unexpected about one of them. He noticed a white, soft-bodied insect eating its way out of the acorn.

The student recorded these observations.

Observations

- There is a hole in the acorn, about 0.5 cm in diameter, where the insect crawled out.
- There is a second hole, which is about the size of a pinhole, on the other side of the acorn.
- The inside of the acorn is hollow.

Here are some inferences that can be made on the basis of the observations.

Inferences

- The insect formed from the material inside the acorn, grew to its present size, and ate its way out of the acorn.
- The insect crawled through the smaller hole, ate the inside of the acorn, grew to its present size, and ate its way out of the acorn.
- An egg was laid in the acorn through the smaller hole. The egg hatched into a larva that ate the inside of the acorn, grew to its present size, and ate its way out of the acorn.

When you make inferences, be sure to look at all of the evidence available and combine it with what you already know.

MORE ABOUT INFERENCES

Inferences depend both on observations and on the knowledge of the people making the inferences. Ancient people who did not know that organisms are produced only by similar organisms might have made an inference like the first one. A student today might look at the same observations and make the second inference. A third student might have knowledge about this particular insect and know that it is never small enough to fit through the smaller hole, leading her to the third inference.

Identifying Cause and Effect

In a **cause-and-effect relationship,** one event or characteristic is the result of another. Usually an effect follows its cause in time.

There are many examples of cause-and-effect relationships in everyday life.

Cause	Effect
Turn off a light.	Room gets dark.
Drop a glass.	Glass breaks.
Blow a whistle.	Sound is heard.

Scientists must be careful not to infer a cause-and-effect relationship just because one event happens after another event. When one event occurs after another, you cannot infer a cause-and-effect relationship on the basis of that information alone. You also cannot conclude that one event caused another if there are alternative ways to explain the second event. A scientist must demonstrate through experimentation or continued observation that an event was truly caused by another event.

EXAMPLE

Make an Observation

Suppose you have a few plants growing outside. When the weather starts getting colder, you bring one of the plants indoors. You notice that the plant you brought indoors is growing faster than the others are growing. You cannot conclude from your observation that the change in temperature was the cause of the increased plant growth, because there are alternative explanations for the observation. Some possible explanations are given below.

- The humidity indoors caused the plant to grow faster.
- The level of sunlight indoors caused the plant to grow faster.
- The indoor plant's being noticed more often and watered more often than the outdoor plants caused it to grow faster.
- The plant that was brought indoors was healthier than the other plants to begin with.

To determine which of these factors, if any, caused the indoor plant to grow faster than the outdoor plants, you would need to design and conduct an experiment.

See pages R28–R35 for information about designing experiments.

R5

SCIENTIFIC THINKING HANDBOOK

Recognizing Bias

Television, newspapers, and the Internet are full of experts claiming to have scientific evidence to back up their claims. How do you know whether the claims are really backed up by good science?

Bias is a slanted point of view, or personal prejudice. The goal of scientists is to be as objective as possible and to base their findings on facts instead of opinions. However, bias often affects the conclusions of researchers, and it is important to learn to recognize bias.

When scientific results are reported, you should consider the source of the information as well as the information itself. It is important to critically analyze the information that you see and read.

SOURCES OF BIAS

There are several ways in which a report of scientific information may be biased. Here are some questions that you can ask yourself:

1. **Who is sponsoring the research?**

   Sometimes, the results of an investigation are biased because an organization paying for the research is looking for a specific answer. This type of bias can affect how data are gathered and interpreted.

2. **Is the research sample large enough?**

   Sometimes research does not include enough data. The larger the sample size, the more likely that the results are accurate, assuming a truly random sample.

3. **In a survey, who is answering the questions?**

   The results of a survey or poll can be biased. The people taking part in the survey may have been specifically chosen because of how they would answer. They may have the same ideas or lifestyles. A survey or poll should make use of a random sample of people.

4. **Are the people who take part in a survey biased?**

   People who take part in surveys sometimes try to answer the questions the way they think the researcher wants them to answer. Also, in surveys or polls that ask for personal information, people may be unwilling to answer questions truthfully.

SCIENTIFIC BIAS

It is also important to realize that scientists have their own biases because of the types of research they do and because of their scientific viewpoints. Two scientists may look at the same set of data and come to completely different conclusions because of these biases. However, such disagreements are not necessarily bad. In fact, a critical analysis of disagreements is often responsible for moving science forward.

Identifying Faulty Reasoning

Faulty reasoning is wrong or incorrect thinking. It leads to mistakes and to wrong conclusions. Scientists are careful not to draw unreasonable conclusions from experimental data. Without such caution, the results of scientific investigations may be misleading.

EXAMPLE

Scientists try to make generalizations based on their data to explain as much about nature as possible. If only a small sample of data is looked at, however, a conclusion may be faulty. Suppose a scientist has studied the effects of the El Niño and La Niña weather patterns on flood damage in California from 1989 to 1995. The scientist organized the data in the bar graph below.

Flood and Storm Damage in California

Estimated damage (millions of dollars)
2000
1500
1000
500
0
1989
1992
1995
Starting year of season (July 1–June 30)
Weak–moderate El Niño
Strong El Niño

SOURCE: *Governor's Office of Emergency Services, California*

The scientist drew the following conclusions:

1. The La Niña weather pattern has no effect on flooding in California.
2. When neither weather pattern occurs, there is almost no flood damage.
3. A weak or moderate El Niño produces a small or moderate amount of flooding.
4. A strong El Niño produces a lot of flooding.

For the six-year period of the scientist's investigation, these conclusions may seem to be reasonable. However, a six-year study of weather patterns may be too small of a sample for the conclusions to be supported. Consider the following graph, which shows information that was gathered from 1949 to 1997.

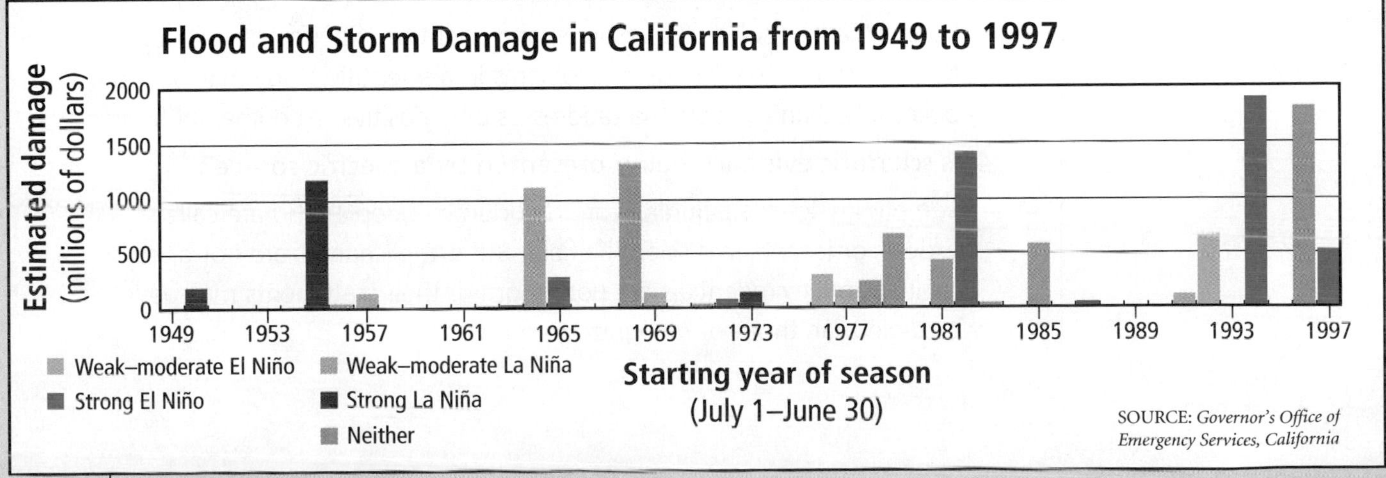

The only one of the conclusions that all of this information supports is number 3: a weak or moderate El Niño produces a small or moderate amount of flooding. By collecting more data, scientists can be more certain of their conclusions and can avoid faulty reasoning.

Analyzing Statements

To **analyze** a statement is to examine its parts carefully. Scientific findings are often reported through media such as television or the Internet. A report that is made public often focuses on only a small part of research. As a result, it is important to question the sources of information.

Evaluate Media Claims

To **evaluate** a statement is to judge it on the basis of criteria you've established. Sometimes evaluating means deciding whether a statement is true.

Reports of scientific research and findings in the media may be misleading or incomplete. When you are exposed to this information, you should ask yourself some questions so that you can make informed judgments about the information.

1. **Does the information come from a credible source?**
   Suppose you learn about a new product and it is stated that scientific evidence proves that the product works. A report from a respected news source may be more believable than an advertisement paid for by the product's manufacturer.
2. **How much evidence supports the claim?**
   Often, it may seem that there is new evidence every day of something in the world that either causes or cures an illness. However, information that is the result of several years of work by several different scientists is more credible than an advertisement that does not even cite the subjects of the experiment.
3. **How much information is being presented?**
   Science cannot solve all questions, and scientific experiments often have flaws. A report that discusses problems in a scientific study may be more believable than a report that addresses only positive experimental findings.
4. **Is scientific evidence being presented by a specific source?**
   Sometimes scientific findings are reported by people who are called experts or leaders in a scientific field. But if their names are not given or their scientific credentials are not reported, their statements may be less credible than those of recognized experts.

Differentiate Between Fact and Opinion

Sometimes information is presented as a fact when it may be an opinion. When scientific conclusions are reported, it is important to recognize whether they are based on solid evidence. Again, you may find it helpful to ask yourself some questions.

1. **What is the difference between a fact and an opinion?**

   A **fact** is a piece of information that can be strictly defined and proved true. An **opinion** is a statement that expresses a belief, value, or feeling. An opinion cannot be proved true or false. For example, a person's age is a fact, but if someone is asked how old they feel, it is impossible to prove the person's answer to be true or false.

2. **Can opinions be measured?**

   Yes, opinions can be measured. In fact, surveys often ask for people's opinions on a topic. But there is no way to know whether or not an opinion is the truth.

HOW TO DIFFERENTIATE FACT FROM OPINION

Human Activities and the Environment

Unfortunately, human use of fossil fuels is one of the most significant developments of the past few centuries. Humans rely on fossil fuels, a nonrenewable energy resource, for more than 90 percent of their energy needs.

This careless misuse of our planet's resources has resulted in pollution, global warming, and the destruction of fragile ecosystems. For example, oil pipelines carry more than one million barrels of oil each day across tundra regions. Transporting oil across such areas can only result in oil spills that poison the land for decades.

Opinions
Notice words or phrases that express beliefs or feelings. The words *unfortunately* and *careless* show that opinions are being expressed.

Opinion
Look for statements that speculate about events. These statements are opinions, because they cannot be proved.

Facts
Statements that contain statistics tend to be facts. Writers often use facts to support their opinions.

R9

Safety Rules

Before you work in the laboratory, read these safety rules twice. Ask your teacher to explain any rules that you do not completely understand. Refer to these rules later on if you have questions about safety in the science classroom.

Directions

- Read all directions and make sure that you understand them before starting an investigation or lab activity. If you do not understand how to do a procedure or how to use a piece of equipment, ask your teacher.
- Do not begin any investigation or touch any equipment until your teacher has told you to start.
- Never experiment on your own. If you want to try a procedure that the directions do not call for, ask your teacher for permission first.
- If you are hurt or injured in any way, tell your teacher immediately.

Dress Code

goggles

apron

gloves

- Wear goggles when
  — using glassware, sharp objects, or chemicals
  — heating an object
  — working with anything that can easily fly up into the air and hurt someone's eye
- Tie back long hair or hair that hangs in front of your eyes.
- Remove any article of clothing—such as a loose sweater or a scarf—that hangs down and may touch a flame, chemical, or piece of equipment.
- Observe all safety icons calling for the wearing of eye protection, gloves, and aprons.

Heating and Fire Safety

fire safety

heating safety

- Keep your work area neat, clean, and free of extra materials.
- Never reach over a flame or heat source.
- Point objects being heated away from you and others.
- Never heat a substance or an object in a closed container.
- Never touch an object that has been heated. If you are unsure whether something is hot, treat it as though it is. Use oven mitts, clamps, tongs, or a test-tube holder.
- Know where the fire extinguisher and fire blanket are kept in your classroom.
- Do not throw hot substances into the trash. Wait for them to cool or use the container your teacher puts out for disposal.

Electrical Safety

electrical safety

- Never use lamps or other electrical equipment with frayed cords.
- Make sure no cord is lying on the floor where someone can trip over it.
- Do not let a cord hang over the side of a counter or table so that the equipment can easily be pulled or knocked to the floor.
- Never let cords hang into sinks or other places where water can be found.
- Never try to fix electrical problems. Inform your teacher of any problems immediately.
- Unplug an electrical cord by pulling on the plug, not the cord.

Chemical Safety

chemical safety

poison

fumes

- If you spill a chemical or get one on your skin or in your eyes, tell your teacher right away.
- Never touch, taste, or sniff any chemicals in the lab. If you need to determine odor, waft. Wafting consists of holding the chemical in its container 15 centimeters (6 in.) away from your nose, and using your fingers to bring fumes from the container to your nose.
- Keep lids on all chemicals you are not using.
- Never put unused chemicals back into the original containers. Throw away extra chemicals where your teacher tells you to.

Wafting

- Pour chemicals over a sink or your work area, not over the floor.
- If you get a chemical in your eye, use the eyewash right away.
- Always wash your hands after handling chemicals, plants, or soil.

Glassware and Sharp-Object Safety

sharp objects

- If you break glassware, tell your teacher right away.
- Do not use broken or chipped glassware. Give these to your teacher.
- Use knives and other cutting instruments carefully. Always wear eye protection and cut away from you.

Animal Safety

- Never hurt an animal.
- Touch animals only when necessary. Follow your teacher's instructions for handling animals.
- Always wash your hands after working with animals.

Cleanup

disposal

- Follow your teacher's instructions for throwing away or putting away supplies.
- Clean your work area and pick up anything that has dropped to the floor.
- Wash your hands.

Using Lab Equipment

Different experiments require different types of equipment. But even though experiments differ, the ways in which the equipment is used are the same.

Beakers

- Use beakers for holding and pouring liquids.
- Do not use a beaker to measure the volume of a liquid. Use a graduated cylinder instead. (See page R16.)
- Use a beaker that holds about twice as much liquid as you need. For example, if you need 100 milliliters of water, you should use a 200- or 250-milliliter beaker.

Test Tubes

- Use test tubes to hold small amounts of substances.
- Do not use a test tube to measure the volume of a liquid.
- Use a test tube when heating a substance over a flame. Aim the mouth of the tube away from yourself and other people.
- Liquids easily spill or splash from test tubes, so it is important to use only small amounts of liquids.

Test-Tube Holder

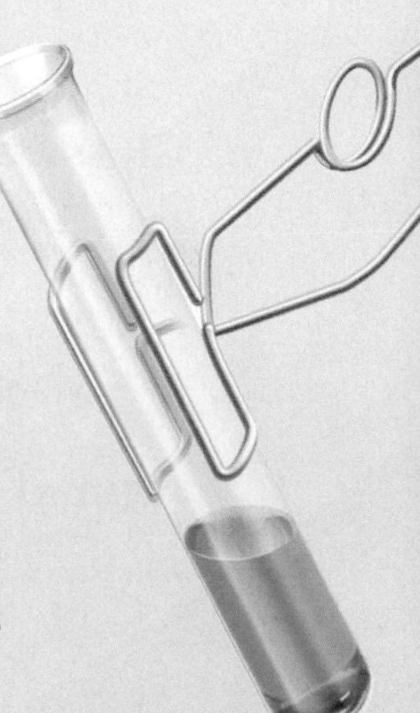

- Use a test-tube holder when heating a substance in a test tube.
- Use a test-tube holder if the substance in a test tube is dangerous to touch.
- Make sure the test-tube holder tightly grips the test tube so that the test tube will not slide out of the holder.
- Make sure that the test-tube holder is above the surface of the substance in the test tube so that you can observe the substance.

Test-Tube Rack

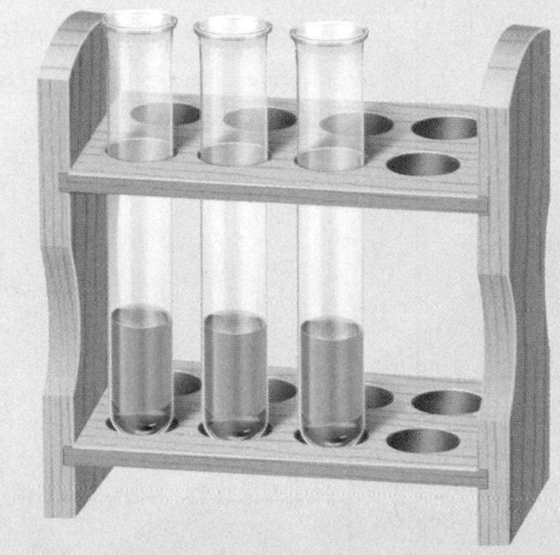

- Use a test-tube rack to organize test tubes before, during, and after an experiment.
- Use a test-tube rack to keep test tubes upright so that they do not fall over and spill their contents.
- Use a test-tube rack that is the correct size for the test tubes that you are using. If the rack is too small, a test tube may become stuck. If the rack is too large, a test tube may lean over, and some of its contents may spill or splash.

Forceps

- Use forceps when you need to pick up or hold a very small object that should not be touched with your hands.
- Do not use forceps to hold anything over a flame, because forceps are not long enough to keep your hand safely away from the flame. Plastic forceps will melt, and metal forceps will conduct heat and burn your hand.

Hot Plate

- Use a hot plate when a substance needs to be kept warmer than room temperature for a long period of time.
- Use a hot plate instead of a Bunsen burner or a candle when you need to carefully control temperature.
- Do not use a hot plate when a substance needs to be burned in an experiment.
- Always use "hot hands" safety mitts or oven mitts when handling anything that has been heated on a hot plate.

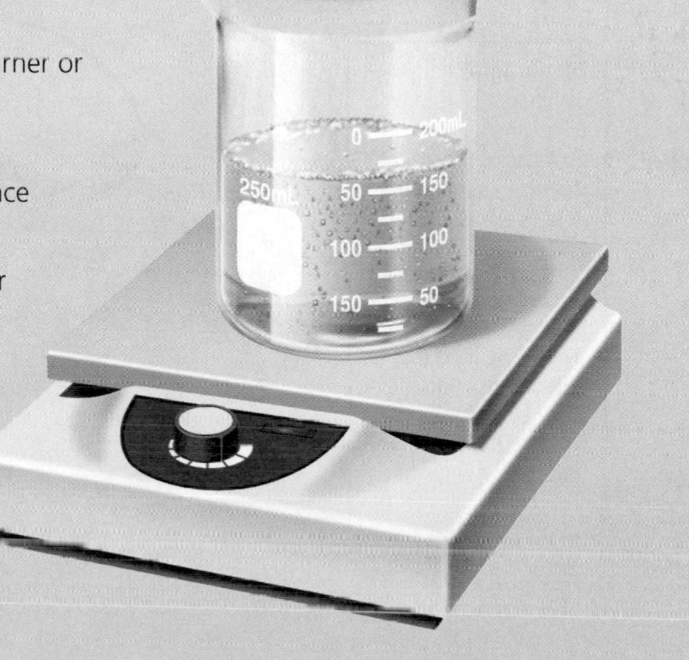

Microscope

Scientists use microscopes to see very small objects that cannot easily be seen with the eye alone. A microscope magnifies the image of an object so that small details may be observed. A microscope that you may use can magnify an object 400 times—the object will appear 400 times larger than its actual size.

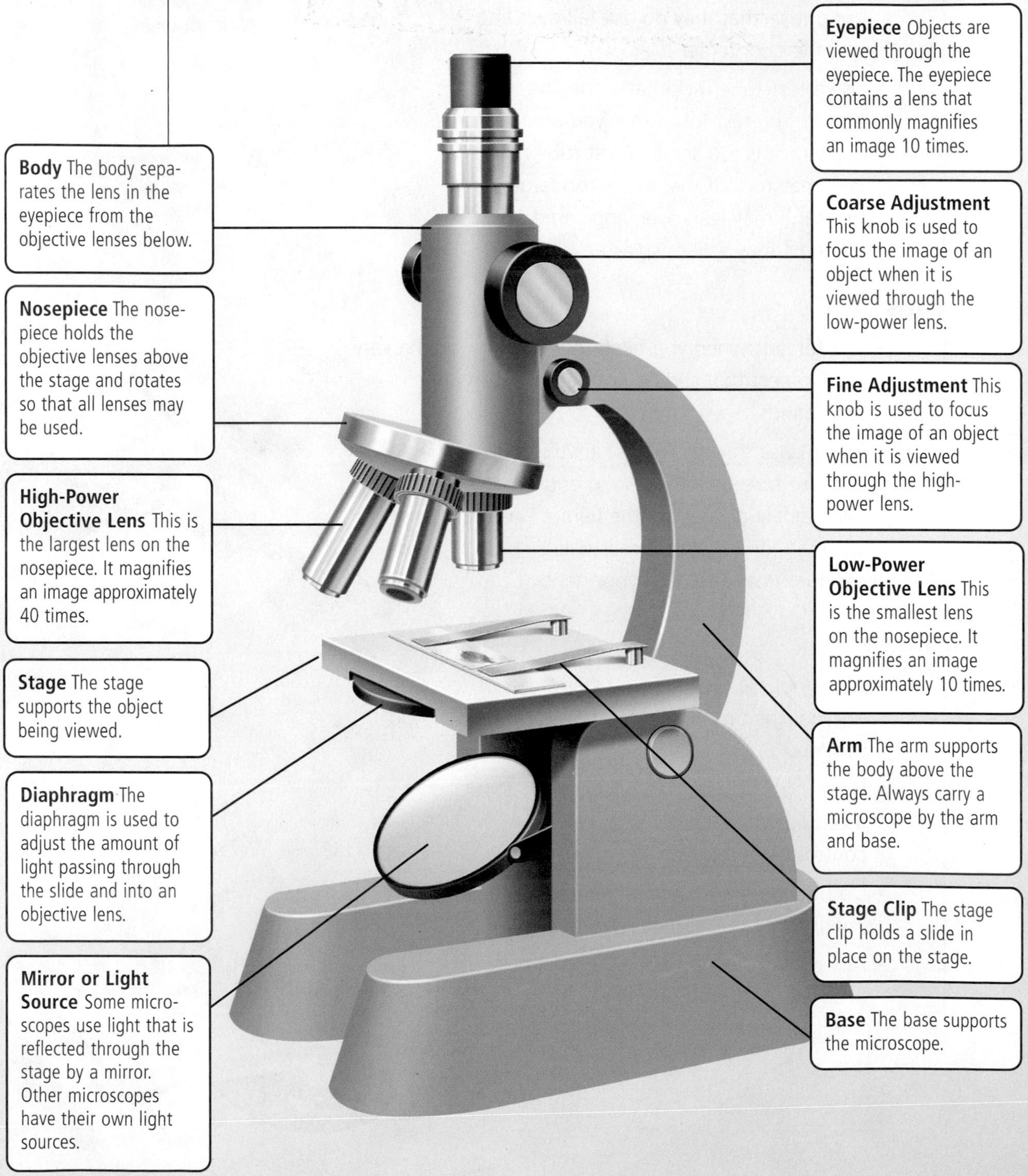

Eyepiece Objects are viewed through the eyepiece. The eyepiece contains a lens that commonly magnifies an image 10 times.

Body The body separates the lens in the eyepiece from the objective lenses below.

Coarse Adjustment This knob is used to focus the image of an object when it is viewed through the low-power lens.

Nosepiece The nosepiece holds the objective lenses above the stage and rotates so that all lenses may be used.

Fine Adjustment This knob is used to focus the image of an object when it is viewed through the high-power lens.

High-Power Objective Lens This is the largest lens on the nosepiece. It magnifies an image approximately 40 times.

Low-Power Objective Lens This is the smallest lens on the nosepiece. It magnifies an image approximately 10 times.

Stage The stage supports the object being viewed.

Arm The arm supports the body above the stage. Always carry a microscope by the arm and base.

Diaphragm The diaphragm is used to adjust the amount of light passing through the slide and into an objective lens.

Stage Clip The stage clip holds a slide in place on the stage.

Mirror or Light Source Some microscopes use light that is reflected through the stage by a mirror. Other microscopes have their own light sources.

Base The base supports the microscope.

LAB HANDBOOK

VIEWING AN OBJECT

1. Use the coarse adjustment knob to raise the body tube.
2. Adjust the diaphragm so that you can see a bright circle of light through the eyepiece.
3. Place the object or slide on the stage. Be sure that it is centered over the hole in the stage.
4. Turn the nosepiece to click the low-power lens into place.
5. Using the coarse adjustment knob, slowly lower the lens and focus on the specimen being viewed. Be sure not to touch the slide or object with the lens.
6. When switching from the low-power lens to the high-power lens, first raise the body tube with the coarse adjustment knob so that the high-power lens will not hit the slide.
7. Turn the nosepiece to click the high-power lens into place.
8. Use the fine adjustment knob to focus on the specimen being viewed. Again, be sure not to touch the slide or object with the lens.

MAKING A SLIDE, OR WET MOUNT

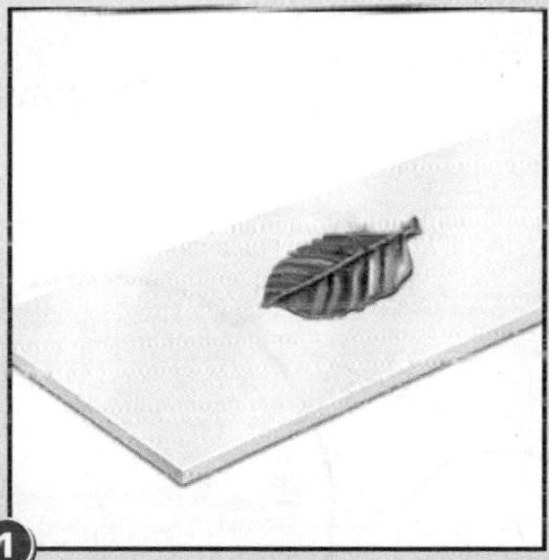

1 Place the specimen in the center of a clean slide.

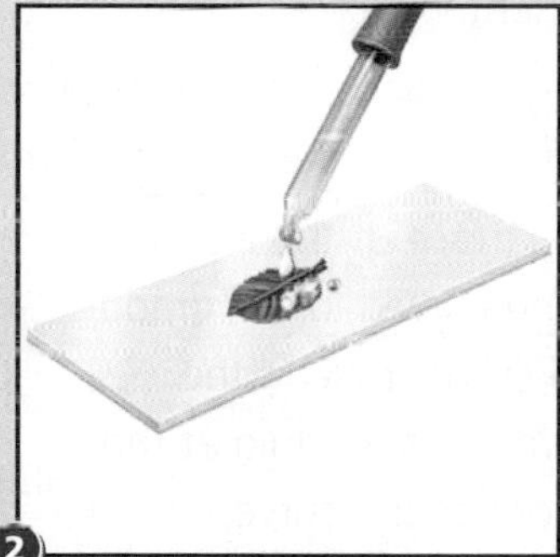

2 Place a drop of water on the specimen.

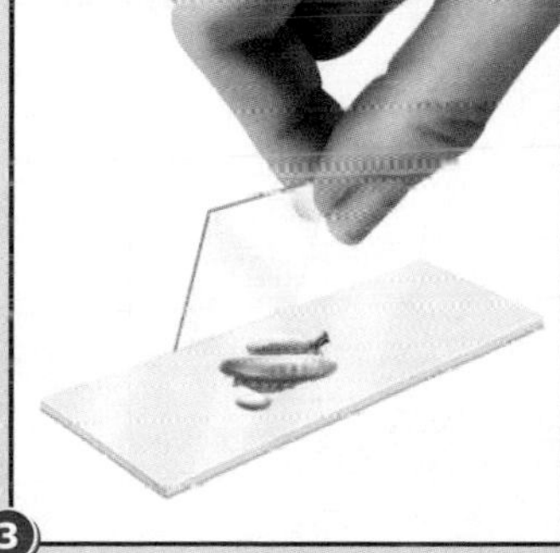

3 Place a cover slip on the slide. Put one edge of the cover slip into the drop of water and slowly lower it over the specimen.

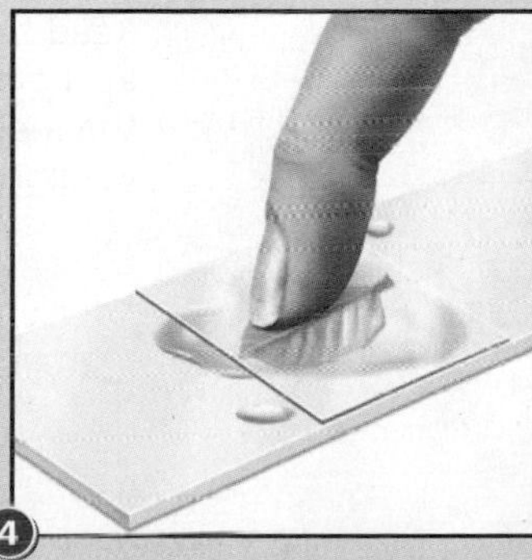

4 Remove any air bubbles from under the cover slip by gently tapping the cover slip.

5 Dry any excess water before placing the slide on the microscope stage for viewing.

Spring Scale (Force Meter)

- Use a spring scale to measure a force pulling on the scale.
- Use a spring scale to measure the force of gravity exerted on an object by Earth.
- To measure a force accurately, a spring scale must be zeroed before it is used. The scale is zeroed when no weight is attached and the indicator is positioned at zero.
- Do not attach a weight that is either too heavy or too light to a spring scale. A weight that is too heavy could break the scale or exert too great a force for the scale to measure. A weight that is too light may not exert enough force to be measured accurately.

Graduated Cylinder

- Use a graduated cylinder to measure the volume of a liquid.
- Be sure that the graduated cylinder is on a flat surface so that your measurement will be accurate.
- When reading the scale on a graduated cylinder, be sure to have your eyes at the level of the surface of the liquid.
- The surface of the liquid will be curved in the graduated cylinder. Read the volume of the liquid at the bottom of the curve, or meniscus (muh-NIHS-kuhs).
- You can use a graduated cylinder to find the volume of a solid object by measuring the increase in a liquid's level after you add the object to the cylinder.

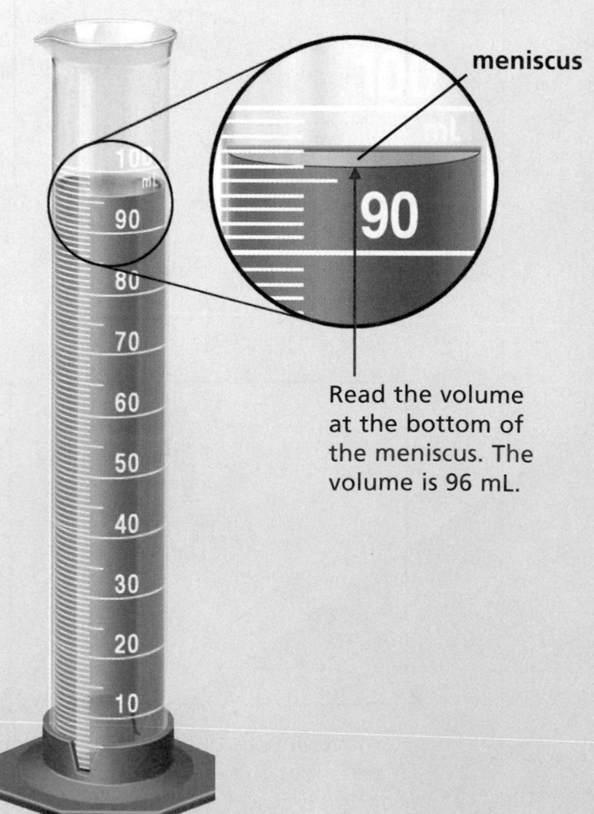

Read the volume at the bottom of the meniscus. The volume is 96 mL.

Metric Rulers

- Use metric rulers or meter sticks to measure objects' lengths.
- Do not measure an object from the end of a metric ruler or meter stick, because the end is often imperfect. Instead, measure from the 1-centimeter mark, but remember to subtract a centimeter from the apparent measurement.
- Estimate any lengths that extend between marked units. For example, if a meter stick shows centimeters but not millimeters, you can estimate the length that an object extends between centimeter marks to measure it to the nearest millimeter.
- **Controlling Variables** If you are taking repeated measurements, always measure from the same point each time. For example, if you're measuring how high two different balls bounce when dropped from the same height, measure both bounces at the same point on the balls—either the top or the bottom. Do not measure at the top of one ball and the bottom of the other.

EXAMPLE

How to Measure a Leaf

1. Lay a ruler flat on top of the leaf so that the 1-centimeter mark lines up with one end. Make sure the ruler and the leaf do not move between the time you line them up and the time you take the measurement.
2. Look straight down on the ruler so that you can see exactly how the marks line up with the other end of the leaf.
3. Estimate the length by which the leaf extends beyond a marking. For example, the leaf below extends about halfway between the 4.2-centimeter and 4.3-centimeter marks, so the apparent measurement is about 4.25 centimeters.
4. Remember to subtract 1 centimeter from your apparent measurement, since you started at the 1-centimeter mark on the ruler and not at the end. The leaf is about 3.25 centimeters long (4.25 cm – 1 cm = 3.25 cm).

LAB HANDBOOK

Triple-Beam Balance

This balance has a pan and three beams with sliding masses, called riders. At one end of the beams is a pointer that indicates whether the mass on the pan is equal to the masses shown on the beams.

1. Make sure the balance is zeroed before measuring the mass of an object. The balance is zeroed if the pointer is at zero when nothing is on the pan and the riders are at their zero points. Use the adjustment knob at the base of the balance to zero it.
2. Place the object to be measured on the pan.
3. Move the riders one notch at a time away from the pan. Begin with the largest rider. If moving the largest rider one notch brings the pointer below zero, begin measuring the mass of the object with the next smaller rider.
4. Change the positions of the riders until they balance the mass on the pan and the pointer is at zero. Then add the readings from the three beams to determine the mass of the object.

300 g	position of largest rider
90 g	position of middle rider
+ 3 g	position of smallest rider
393 g	mass of beaker

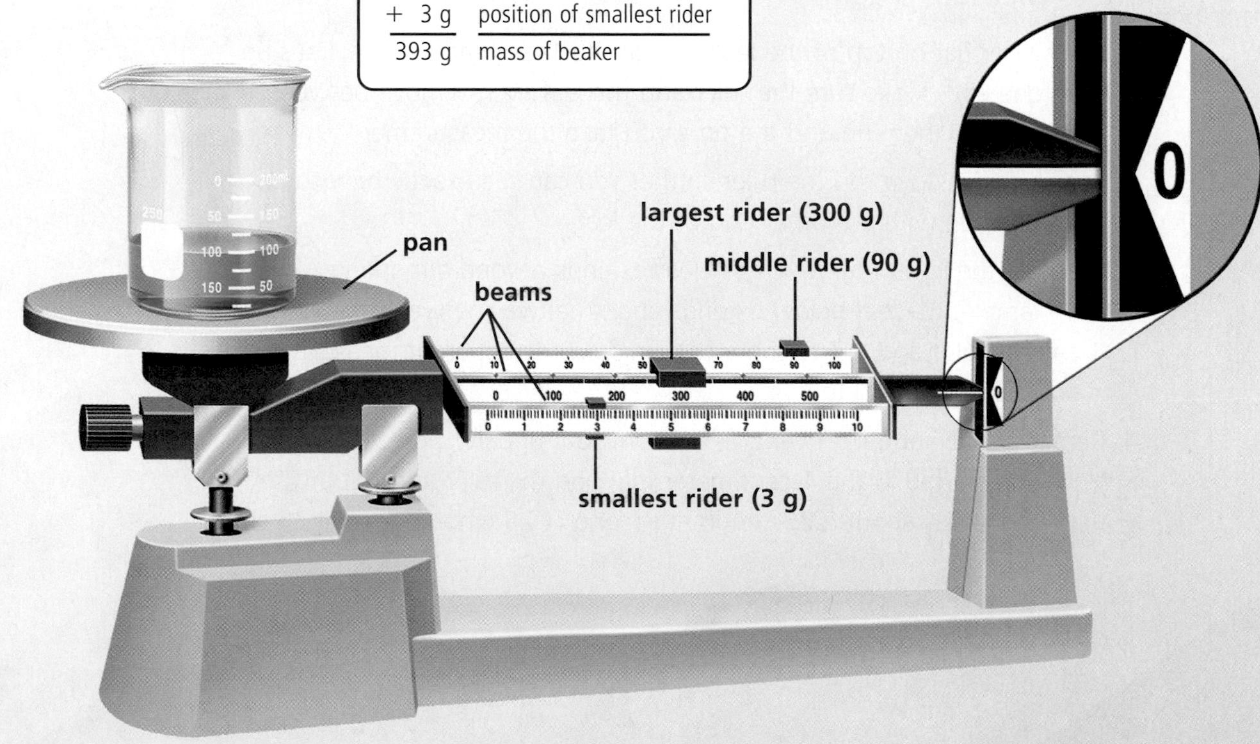

Double-Pan Balance

This type of balance has two pans. Between the pans is a pointer that indicates whether the masses on the pans are equal.

1. Make sure the balance is zeroed before measuring the mass of an object. The balance is zeroed if the pointer is at zero when there is nothing on either of the pans. Many double-pan balances have sliding knobs that can be used to zero them.
2. Place the object to be measured on one of the pans.
3. Begin adding standard masses to the other pan. Begin with the largest standard mass. If this adds too much mass to the balance, begin measuring the mass of the object with the next smaller standard mass.
4. Add standard masses until the masses on both pans are balanced and the pointer is at zero. Then add the standard masses together to determine the mass of the object being measured.

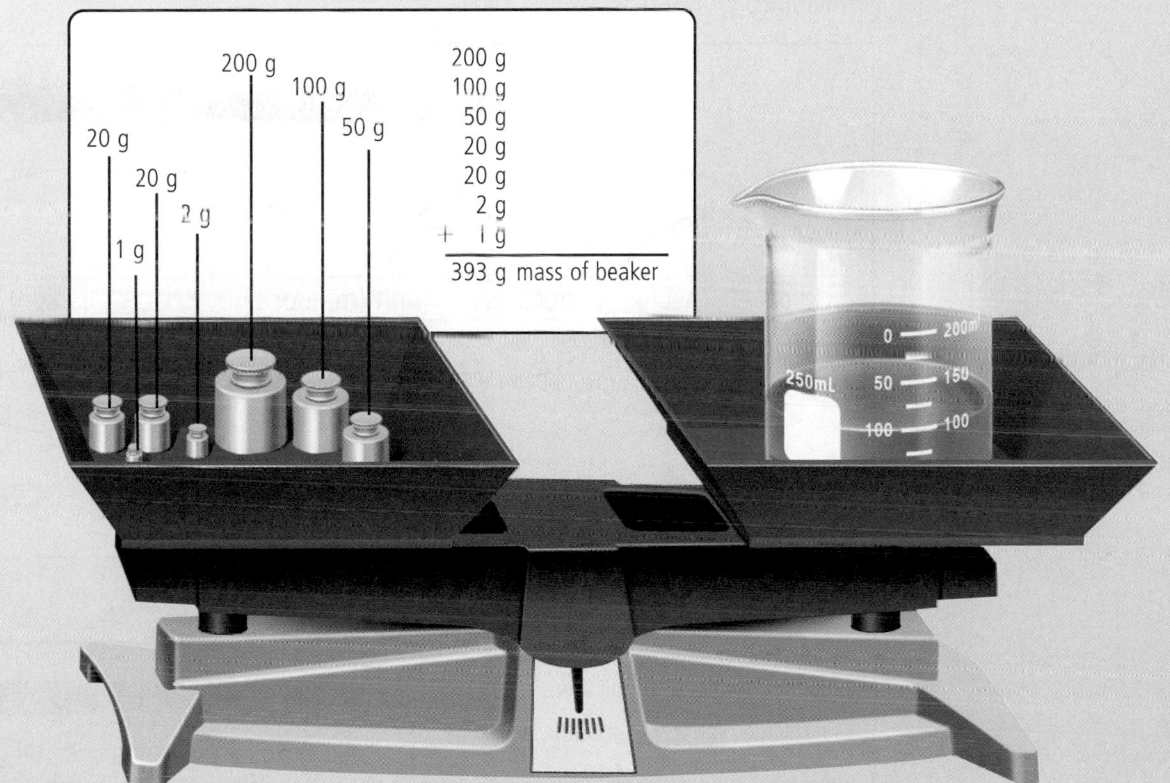

Never place chemicals or liquids directly on a pan. Instead, use the following procedure:

1. Determine the mass of an empty container, such as a beaker.
2. Pour the substance into the container, and measure the total mass of the substance and the container.
3. Subtract the mass of the empty container from the total mass to find the mass of the substance.

R19

The Metric System and SI Units

Scientists use International System (SI) units for measurements of distance, volume, mass, and temperature. The International System is based on multiples of ten and the metric system of measurement.

Basic SI Units		
Property	**Name**	**Symbol**
length	meter	m
volume	liter	L
mass	kilogram	kg
temperature	kelvin	K

SI Prefixes		
Prefix	**Symbol**	**Multiple of 10**
kilo-	k	1000
hecto-	h	100
deca-	da	10
deci-	d	0.1 $(\frac{1}{10})$
centi-	c	0.01 $(\frac{1}{100})$
milli-	m	0.001 $(\frac{1}{1000})$

Changing Metric Units

You can change from one unit to another in the metric system by multiplying or dividing by a power of 10.

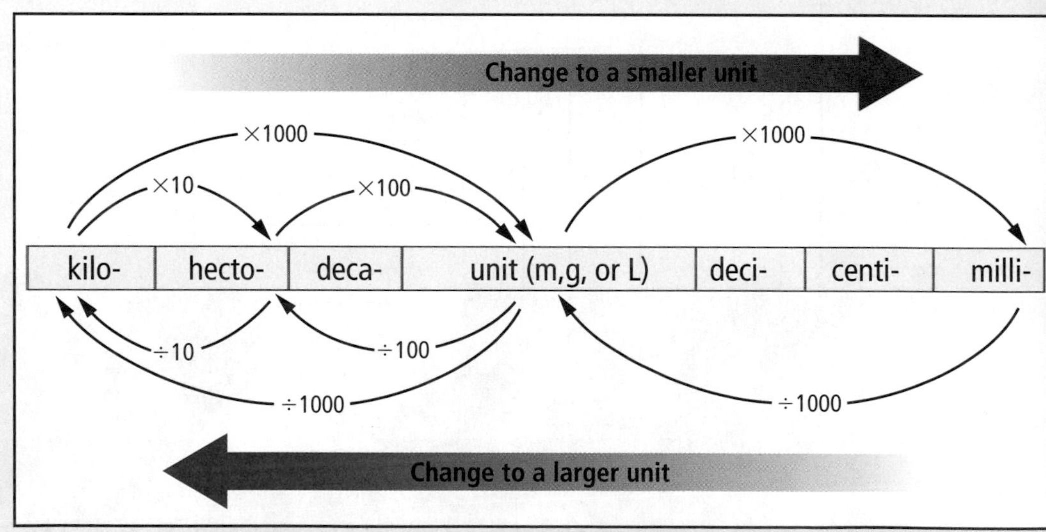

Example

Change 0.64 liters to milliliters.

(1) Decide whether to multiply or divide.

(2) Select the power of 10.

ANSWER 0.64 L = 640 mL

Change to a smaller unit by multiplying.

L —— ×1000 ——→ mL

0.64 × 1000 = **640.**

Example

Change 23.6 grams to kilograms.

(1) Decide whether to multiply or divide.

(2) Select the power of 10.

ANSWER 23.6 g = 0.0236 kg

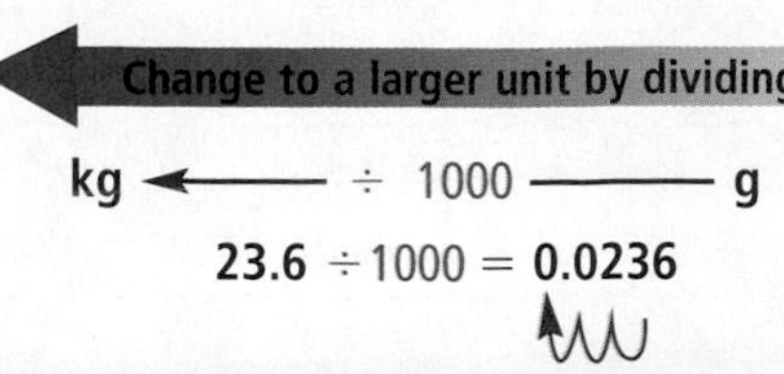

LAB HANDBOOK

Temperature Conversions

Even though the kelvin is the SI base unit of temperature, the degree Celsius will be the unit you use most often in your science studies. The formulas below show the relationships between temperatures in degrees Fahrenheit (°F), degrees Celsius (°C), and kelvins (K).

$$°C = \frac{5}{9}(°F - 32)$$

$$°F = \frac{9}{5}°C + 32$$

$$K = °C + 273$$

See page R42 for help with using formulas.

Examples of Temperature Conversions

Condition	Degrees Celsius	Degrees Fahrenheit
Freezing point of water	0	32
Cool day	10	50
Mild day	20	68
Warm day	30	86
Normal body temperature	37	98.6
Very hot day	40	104
Boiling point of water	100	212

Converting Between SI and U.S. Customary Units

Use the chart below when you need to convert between SI units and U.S. customary units.

SI Unit	From SI to U.S. Customary			From U.S. Customary to SI		
Length	**When you know**	**multiply by**	**to find**	**When you know**	**multiply by**	**to find**
kilometer (km) = 1000 m	kilometers	0.62	miles	miles	1.61	kilometers
meter (m) = 100 cm	meters	3.28	feet	feet	0.3048	meters
centimeter (cm) = 10 mm	centimeters	0.39	inches	inches	2.54	centimeters
millimeter (mm) = 0.1 cm	millimeters	0.04	inches	inches	25.4	millimeters
Area	**When you know**	**multiply by**	**to find**	**When you know**	**multiply by**	**to find**
square kilometer (km^2)	square kilometers	0.39	square miles	square miles	2.59	square kilometers
square meter (m^2)	square meters	1.2	square yards	square yards	0.84	square meters
square centimeter (cm^2)	square centimeters	0.155	square inches	square inches	6.45	square centimeters
Volume	**When you know**	**multiply by**	**to find**	**When you know**	**multiply by**	**to find**
liter (L) = 1000 mL	liters	1.06	quarts	quarts	0.95	liters
	liters	0.26	gallons	gallons	3.79	liters
	liters	4.23	cups	cups	0.24	liters
	liters	2.12	pints	pints	0.47	liters
milliliter (mL) = 0.001 L	milliliters	0.20	teaspoons	teaspoons	4.93	milliliters
	milliliters	0.07	tablespoons	tablespoons	14.79	milliliters
	milliliters	0.03	fluid ounces	fluid ounces	29.57	milliliters
Mass	**When you know**	**multiply by**	**to find**	**When you know**	**multiply by**	**to find**
kilogram (kg) = 1000 g	kilograms	2.2	pounds	pounds	0.45	kilograms
gram (g) = 1000 mg	grams	0.035	ounces	ounces	28.35	grams

Precision and Accuracy

When you do an experiment, it is important that your methods, observations, and data be both precise and accurate.

low precision

precision, but not accuracy

precision and accuracy

LAB HANDBOOK

Precision

In science, **precision** is the exactness and consistency of measurements. For example, measurements made with a ruler that has both centimeter and millimeter markings would be more precise than measurements made with a ruler that has only centimeter markings. Another indicator of precision is the care taken to make sure that methods and observations are as exact and consistent as possible. Every time a particular experiment is done, the same procedure should be used. Precision is necessary because experiments are repeated several times and if the procedure changes, the results will change.

EXAMPLE

Suppose you are measuring temperatures over a two-week period. Your precision will be greater if you measure each temperature at the same place, at the same time of day, and with the same thermometer than if you change any of these factors from one day to the next.

Accuracy

In science, it is possible to be precise but not accurate. **Accuracy** depends on the difference between a measurement and an actual value. The smaller the difference, the more accurate the measurement.

EXAMPLE

Suppose you look at a stream and estimate that it is about 1 meter wide at a particular place. You decide to check your estimate by measuring the stream with a meter stick, and you determine that the stream is 1.32 meters wide. However, because it is hard to measure the width of a stream with a meter stick, it turns out that you didn't do a very good job. The stream is actually 1.14 meters wide. Therefore, even though your estimate was less precise than your measurement, your estimate was actually more accurate.

R22

Making Data Tables and Graphs

Data tables and graphs are useful tools for both recording and communicating scientific data.

Making Data Tables

You can use a **data table** to organize and record the measurements that you make. Some examples of information that might be recorded in data tables are frequencies, times, and amounts.

EXAMPLE

Suppose you are investigating photosynthesis in two elodea plants. One sits in direct sunlight, and the other sits in a dimly lit room. You measure the rate of photosynthesis by counting the number of bubbles in the jar every ten minutes.

1. Title and number your data table.
2. Decide how you will organize the table into columns and rows.
3. Any units, such as seconds or degrees, should be included in column headings, not in the individual cells.

Table 1. Number of Bubbles from Elodea

Time (min)	Sunlight	Dim Light
0	0	0
10	15	5
20	25	8
30	32	7
40	41	10
50	47	9
60	42	9

Always number and title data tables.

The data in the table above could also be organized in a different way.

Table 1. Number of Bubbles from Elodea

Light Condition	Time (min)						
	0	10	20	30	40	50	60
Sunlight	0	15	25	32	41	47	42
Dim light	0	5	8	7	10	9	9

Put units in column heading.

LAB HANDBOOK

Making Line Graphs

You can use a **line graph** to show a relationship between variables. Line graphs are particularly useful for showing changes in variables over time.

EXAMPLE

Suppose you are interested in graphing temperature data that you collected over the course of a day.

Table 1. Outside Temperature During the Day on March 7

	Time of Day						
	7:00 A.M.	9:00 A.M.	11:00 A.M.	1:00 P.M.	3:00 P.M.	5:00 P.M.	7:00 P.M.
Temp (°C)	8	9	11	14	12	10	6

1. Use the vertical axis of your line graph for the variable that you are measuring—temperature.
2. Choose scales for both the horizontal axis and the vertical axis of the graph. You should have two points more than you need on the vertical axis, and the horizontal axis should be long enough for all of the data points to fit.
3. Draw and label each axis.
4. Graph each value. First find the appropriate point on the scale of the horizontal axis. Imagine a line that rises vertically from that place on the scale. Then find the corresponding value on the vertical axis, and imagine a line that moves horizontally from that value. The point where these two imaginary lines intersect is where the value should be plotted.
5. Connect the points with straight lines.

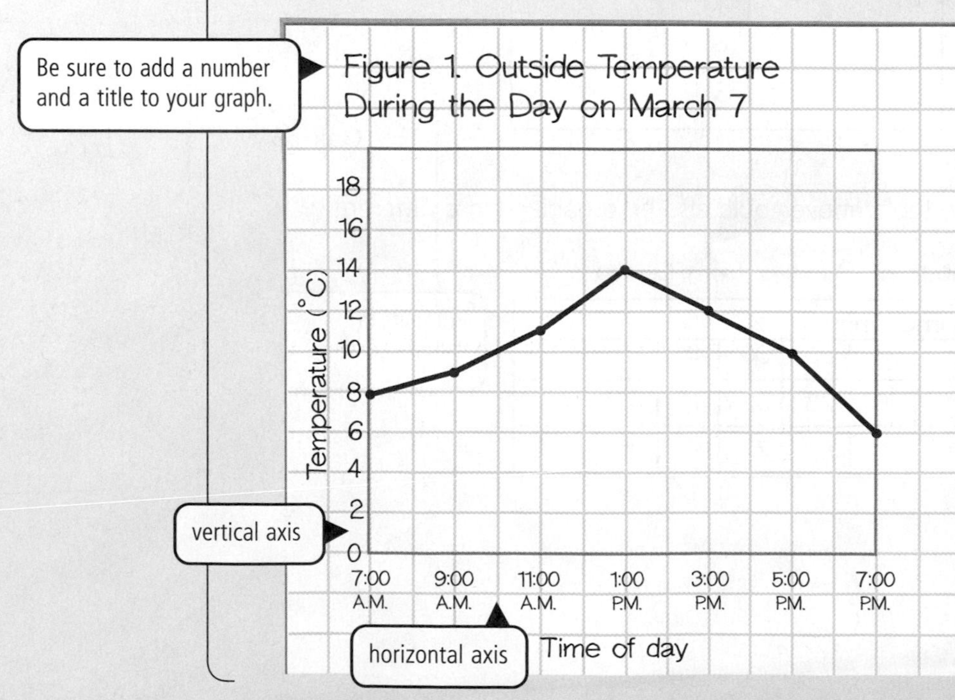

Making Circle Graphs

You can use a **circle graph,** sometimes called a pie chart, to represent data as parts of a circle. Circle graphs are used only when the data can be expressed as percentages of a whole. The entire circle shown in a circle graph is equal to 100 percent of the data.

EXAMPLE

Suppose you identified the species of each mature tree growing in a small wooded area. You organized your data in a table, but you also want to show the data in a circle graph.

1. To begin, find the total number of mature trees.

   $56 + 34 + 22 + 10 + 28 = 150$

2. To find the degree measure for each sector of the circle, write a fraction comparing the number of each tree species with the total number of trees. Then multiply the fraction by 360°.

   Oak: $\frac{56}{150} \times 360° = 134.4°$

3. Draw a circle. Use a protractor to draw the angle for each sector of the graph.
4. Color and label each sector of the graph.
5. Give the graph a number and title.

Table 1. Tree Species in Wooded Area

Species	Number of Specimens
Oak	56
Maple	34
Birch	22
Willow	10
Pine	28

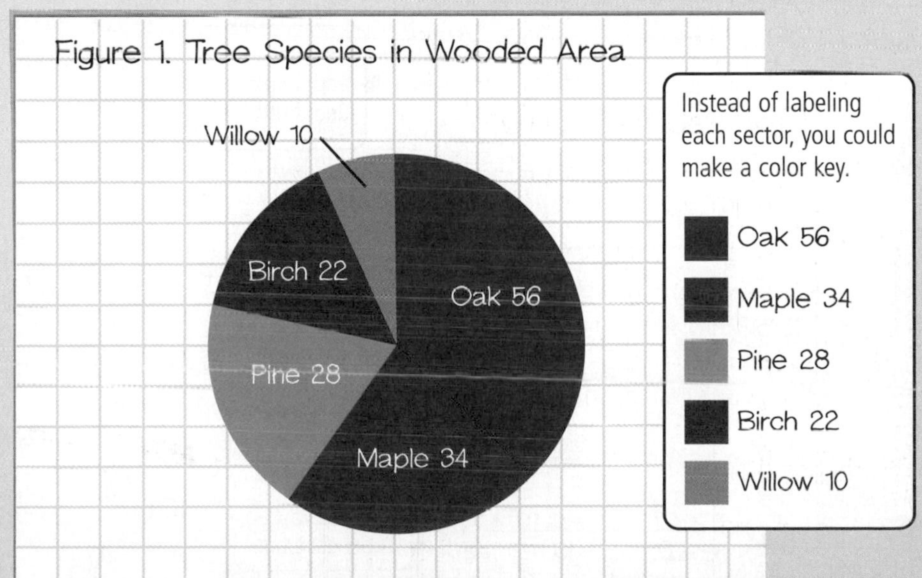

Figure 1. Tree Species in Wooded Area

Instead of labeling each sector, you could make a color key.

- Oak 56
- Maple 34
- Pine 28
- Birch 22
- Willow 10

LAB HANDBOOK

Bar Graph

A **bar graph** is a type of graph in which the lengths of the bars are used to represent and compare data. A numerical scale is used to determine the lengths of the bars.

EXAMPLE

To determine the effect of water on seed sprouting, three cups were filled with sand, and ten seeds were planted in each. Different amounts of water were added to each cup over a three-day period.

Table 1. Effect of Water on Seed Sprouting

Daily Amount of Water (mL)	Number of Seeds That Sprouted After 3 Days in Sand
0	1
10	4
20	8

1. Choose a numerical scale. The greatest value is 8, so the end of the scale should have a value greater than 8, such as 10. Use equal increments along the scale, such as increments of 2.
2. Draw and label the axes. Mark intervals on the vertical axis according to the scale you chose.
3. Draw a bar for each data value. Use the scale to decide how long to make each bar.

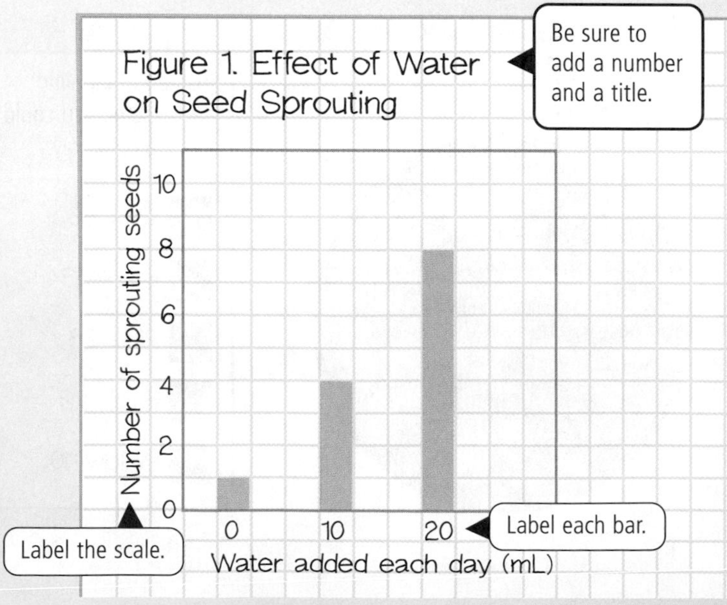

Double Bar Graph

A **double bar graph** is a bar graph that shows two sets of data. The two bars for each measurement are drawn next to each other.

EXAMPLE

The seed-sprouting experiment was done using both sand and potting soil. The data for sand and potting soil can be plotted on one graph.

1. Draw one set of bars, using the data for sand, as shown below.
2. Draw bars for the potting-soil data next to the bars for the sand data. Shade them a different color. Add a key.

Table 2. Effect of Water and Soil on Seed Sprouting

Daily Amount of Water (mL)	Number of Seeds That Sprouted After 3 Days in Sand	Number of Seeds That Sprouted After 3 Days in Potting Soil
0	1	2
10	4	5
20	8	9

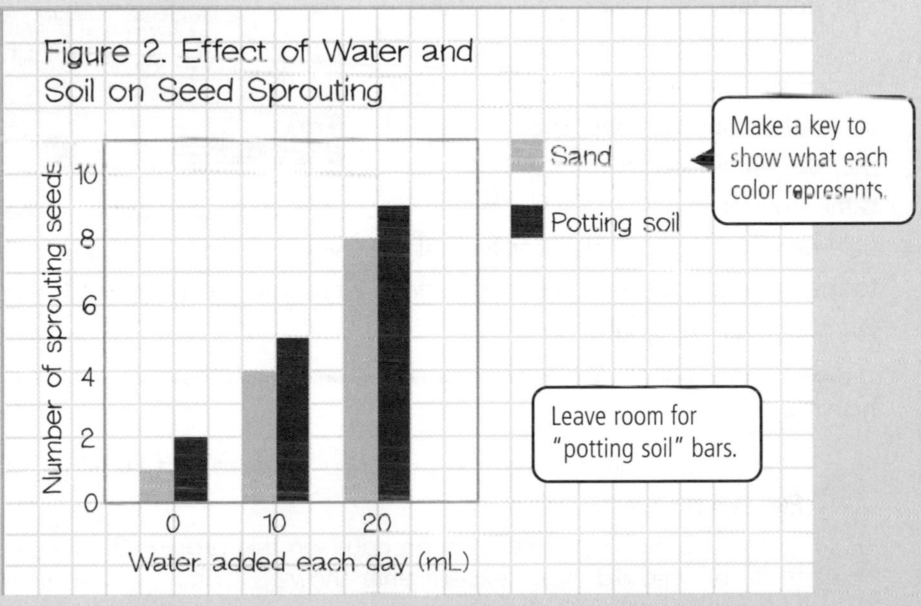

LAB HANDBOOK

Designing an Experiment

Use this section when designing or conducting an experiment.

Determining a Purpose

You can find a purpose for an experiment by doing research, by examining the results of a previous experiment, or by observing the world around you. An **experiment** is an organized procedure to study something under controlled conditions.

Don't forget to learn as much as possible about your topic before you begin.

1. Write the purpose of your experiment as a question or problem that you want to investigate.
2. Write down research questions and begin searching for information that will help you design an experiment. Consult the library, the Internet, and other people as you conduct your research.

EXAMPLE

Middle school students observed an odor near the lake by their school. They also noticed that the water on the side of the lake near the school was greener than the water on the other side of the lake. The students did some research to learn more about their observations. They discovered that the odor and green color in the lake came from algae. They also discovered that a new fertilizer was being used on a field nearby. The students inferred that the use of the fertilizer might be related to the presence of the algae and designed a controlled experiment to find out whether they were right.

Problem

How does fertilizer affect the presence of algae in a lake?

Research Questions

- Have other experiments been done on this problem? If so, what did those experiments show?
- What kind of fertilizer is used on the field? How much?
- How do algae grow?
- How do people measure algae?
- Can fertilizer and algae be used safely in a lab? How?

Research
As you research, you may find a topic that is more interesting to you than your original topic, or learn that a procedure you wanted to use is not practical or safe. It is OK to change your purpose as you research.

R28

Writing a Hypothesis

A **hypothesis** is a tentative explanation for an observation or scientific problem that can be tested by further investigation. You can write your hypothesis in the form of an "If . . . , then . . . , because . . ." statement.

Hypothesis

If the amount of fertilizer in lake water is increased, then the amount of algae will also increase, because fertilizers provide nutrients that algae need to grow.

Hypotheses
For help with hypotheses, refer to page R3.

Determining Materials

Make a list of all the materials you will need to do your experiment. Be specific, especially if someone else is helping you obtain the materials. Try to think of everything you will need.

Materials

- 1 large jar or container
- 4 identical smaller containers
- rubber gloves that also cover the arms
- sample of fertilizer-and-water solution
- eyedropper
- clear plastic wrap
- scissors
- masking tape
- marker
- ruler

Determining Variables and Constants

EXPERIMENTAL GROUP AND CONTROL GROUP

An experiment to determine how two factors are related always has two groups—a control group and an experimental group.

1. Design an experimental group. Include as many trials as possible in the experimental group in order to obtain reliable results.
2. Design a control group that is the same as the experimental group in every way possible, except for the factor you wish to test.

Experimental Group: two containers of lake water with one drop of fertilizer solution added to each

Control Group: two containers of lake water with no fertilizer solution added

Go back to your materials list and make sure you have enough items listed to cover both your experimental group and your control group.

LAB HANDBOOK

VARIABLES AND CONSTANTS

Identify the variables and constants in your experiment. In a controlled experiment, a **variable** is any factor that can change. **Constants** are all of the factors that are the same in both the experimental group and the control group.

1. Read your hypothesis. The **independent variable** is the factor that you wish to test and that is manipulated or changed so that it can be tested. The independent variable is expressed in your hypothesis after the word *if*. Identify the independent variable in your laboratory report.
2. The **dependent variable** is the factor that you measure to gather results. It is expressed in your hypothesis after the word *then*. Identify the dependent variable in your laboratory report.

Hypothesis
If the amount of fertilizer in lake water is increased, then the amount of algae will also increase, because fertilizers provide nutrients that algae need to grow.

Table 1. Variables and Constants in Algae Experiment

Independent Variable	Dependent Variable	Constants
Amount of fertilizer in lake water	Amount of algae that grow	• Where the lake water is obtained • Type of container used • Light and temperature conditions where water will be stored

Set up your experiment so that you will test only one variable.

R30

MEASURING THE DEPENDENT VARIABLE

Before starting your experiment, you need to define how you will measure the dependent variable. An **operational definition** is a description of the one particular way in which you will measure the dependent variable.

Your operational definition is important for several reasons. First, in any experiment there are several ways in which a dependent variable can be measured. Second, the procedure of the experiment depends on how you decide to measure the dependent variable. Third, your operational definition makes it possible for other people to evaluate and build on your experiment.

EXAMPLE 1

An operational definition of a dependent variable can be qualitative. That is, your measurement of the dependent variable can simply be an observation of whether a change occurs as a result of a change in the independent variable. This type of operational definition can be thought of as a "yes or no" measurement.

Table 2. Qualitative Operational Definition of Algae Growth

Independent Variable	Dependent Variable	Operational Definition
Amount of fertilizer in lake water	Amount of algae that grow	Algae grow in lake water

A qualitative measurement of a dependent variable is often easy to make and record. However, this type of information does not provide a great deal of detail in your experimental results.

EXAMPLE 2

An operational definition of a dependent variable can be quantitative. That is, your measurement of the dependent variable can be a number that shows how much change occurs as a result of a change in the independent variable.

Table 3. Quantitative Operational Definition of Algae Growth

Independent Variable	Dependent Variable	Operational Definition
Amount of fertilizer in lake water	Amount of algae that grow	Diameter of largest algal growth (in mm)

A quantitative measurement of a dependent variable can be more difficult to make and analyze than a qualitative measurement. However, this type of data provides much more information about your experiment and is often more useful.

Writing a Procedure

Write each step of your procedure. Start each step with a verb, or action word, and keep the steps short. Your procedure should be clear enough for someone else to use as instructions for repeating your experiment.

If necessary, go back to your materials list and add any materials that you left out.

Procedure

1. Put on your gloves. Use the large container to obtain a sample of lake water.
2. Divide the sample of lake water equally among the four smaller containers.
3. Use the eyedropper to add one drop of fertilizer solution to two of the containers.
4. Use the masking tape and the marker to label the containers with your initials, the date, and the identifiers "Jar 1 with Fertilizer," "Jar 2 with Fertilizer," "Jar 1 without Fertilizer," and "Jar 2 without Fertilizer."
5. Cover the containers with clear plastic wrap. Use the scissors to punch ten holes in each of the covers.
6. Place all four containers on a window ledge. Make sure that they all receive the same amount of light.
7. Observe the containers every day for one week.
8. Use the ruler to measure the diameter of the largest clump of algae in each container, and record your measurements daily.

Controlling Variables The same amount of fertilizer solution must be added to two of the four containers.

Controlling Variables All four containers must receive the same amount of light.

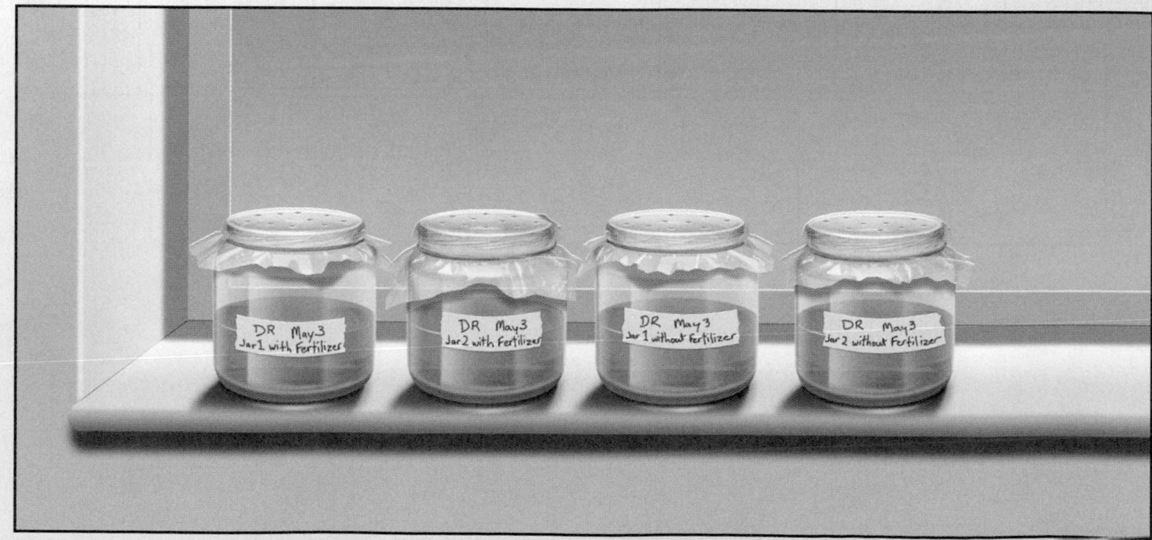

LAB HANDBOOK

Recording Observations

Once you have obtained all of your materials and your procedure has been approved, you can begin making experimental observations. Gather both quantitative and qualitative data. If something goes wrong during your procedure, make sure you record that too.

Observations
For help with making qualitative and quantitative observations, refer to page R2.

For more examples of data tables, see page R23.

Table 4. Fertilizer and Algae Growth

	Experimental Group		Control Group		
Date and Time	Jar 1 with Fertilizer (diameter of algae in mm)	Jar 2 with Fertilizer (diameter of algae in mm)	Jar 1 without Fertilizer (diameter of algae in mm)	Jar 2 without Fertilizer (diameter of algae in mm)	Observations
5/3 4:00 P.M.	0	0	0	0	condensation in all containers
5/4 4:00 P.M.	0	3	0	0	tiny green blobs in jar 2 with fertilizer
5/5 4:15 P.M.	4	5	0	3	green blobs in jars 1 and 2 with fertilizer and jar 2 without fertilizer
5/6 4:00 P.M.	5	6	0	4	water light green in jar 2 with fertilizer
5/7 4:00 P.M.	8	10	0	6	water light green in jars 1 and 2 with fertilizer and in jar 2 without fertilizer
5/8 3:30 P.M.	10	18	0	6	cover off jar 2 with fertilizer
5/9 3:30 P.M.	14	23	0	8	drew sketches of each container

Notice that on the sixth day, the observer found that the cover was off one of the containers. It is important to record observations of unintended factors because they might affect the results of the experiment.

Drawings of Samples Viewed Under Microscope on 5/9 at 100x

Use technology, such as a microscope, to help you make observations when possible.

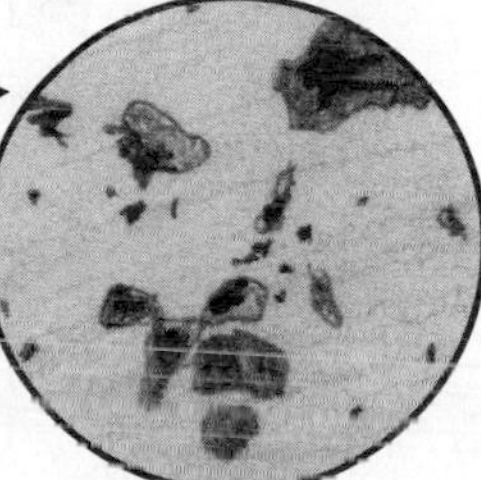
Jar 1 with Fertilizer

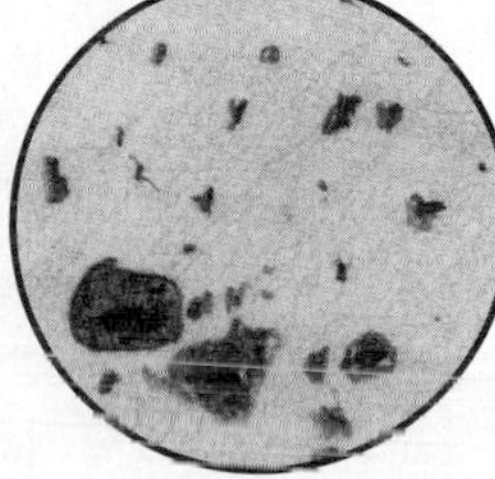
Jar 2 with Fertilizer

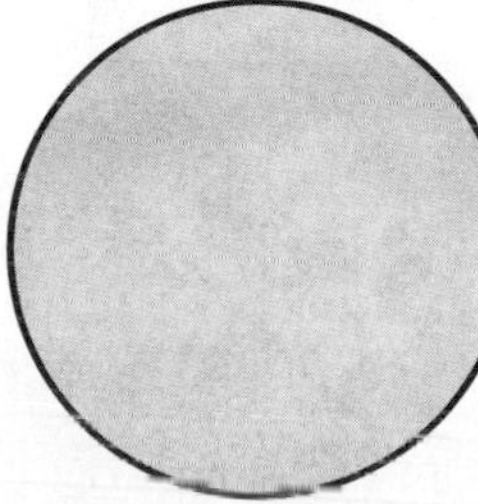
Jar 1 without Fertilizer

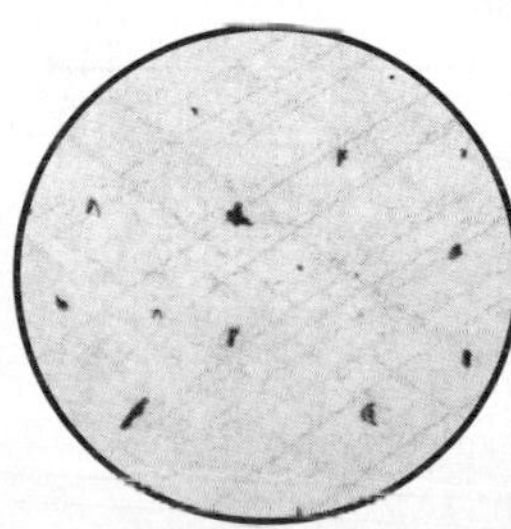
Jar 2 without Fertilizer

LAB HANDBOOK

Summarizing Results

To summarize your data, look at all of your observations together. Look for meaningful ways to present your observations. For example, you might average your data or make a graph to look for patterns. When possible, use spreadsheet software to help you analyze and present your data. The two graphs below show the same data.

EXAMPLE 1

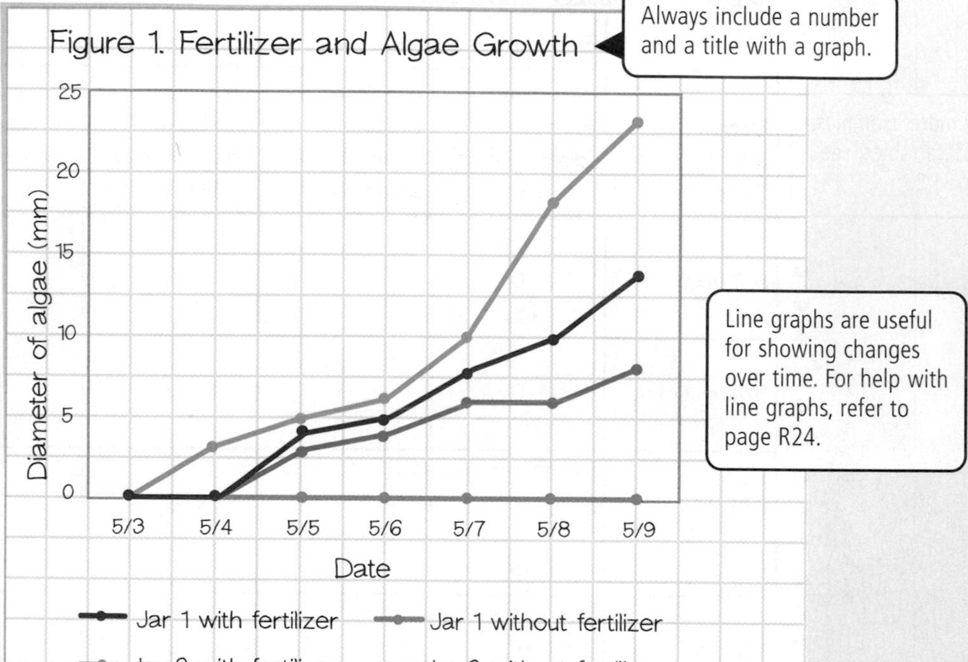

Line graphs are useful for showing changes over time. For help with line graphs, refer to page R24.

EXAMPLE 2

Bar graphs are useful for comparing different data sets. This bar graph has four bars for each day. Another way to present the data would be to calculate averages for the tests and the controls, and to show one test bar and one control bar for each day.

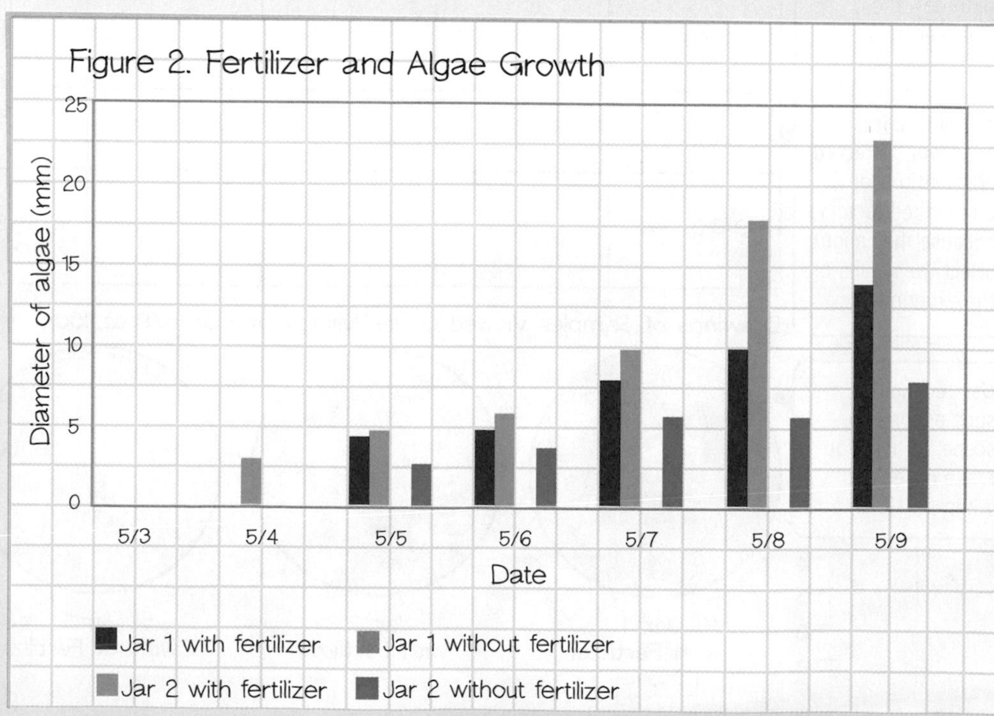

LAB HANDBOOK

Drawing Conclusions

RESULTS AND INFERENCES

To draw conclusions from your experiment, first write your results. Then compare your results with your hypothesis. Do your results support your hypothesis? Be careful not to make inferences about factors that you did not test.

For help with making inferences, see page R4.

Results and Inferences

The results of my experiment show that more algae grew in lake water to which fertilizer had been added than in lake water to which no fertilizer had been added. My hypothesis was supported. I infer that it is possible that the growth of algae in the lake was caused by the fertilizer used on the field.

Notice that you cannot conclude from this experiment that the presence of algae in the lake was due only to the fertilizer.

QUESTIONS FOR FURTHER RESEARCH

Write a list of questions for further research and investigation. Your ideas may lead you to new experiments and discoveries.

Questions for Further Research

- What is the connection between the amount of fertilizer and algae growth?
- How do different brands of fertilizer affect algae growth?
- How would algae growth in the lake be affected if no fertilizer were used on the field?
- How do algae affect the lake and the other life in and around it?
- How does fertilizer affect the lake and the life in and around it?
- If fertilizer is getting into the lake, how is it getting there?

Describing a Set of Data

Means, medians, modes, and ranges are important math tools for describing data sets such as the following widths of fossilized clamshells.

13 mm 25 mm 14 mm 21 mm 16 mm 23 mm 14 mm

Mean

The **mean** of a data set is the sum of the values divided by the number of values.

Example

To find the mean of the clamshell data, add the values and then divide the sum by the number of values.

$$\frac{13\text{ mm} + 25\text{ mm} + 14\text{ mm} + 21\text{ mm} + 16\text{ mm} + 23\text{ mm} + 14\text{ mm}}{7} = \frac{126\text{ mm}}{7} = 18\text{ mm}$$

ANSWER The mean is 18 mm.

Median

The **median** of a data set is the middle value when the values are written in numerical order. If a data set has an even number of values, the median is the mean of the two middle values.

Example

To find the median of the clamshell data, arrange the values in order from least to greatest. The median is the middle value.

13 mm 14 mm 14 mm 16 mm 21 mm 23 mm 25 mm

ANSWER The median is 16 mm.

Mode

The **mode** of a data set is the value that occurs most often.

Example

To find the mode of the clamshell data, arrange the values in order from least to greatest and determine the value that occurs most often.

13 mm 14 mm 14 mm 16 mm 21 mm 23 mm 25 mm

ANSWER The mode is 14 mm.

A data set can have more than one mode or no mode. For example, the following data set has modes of 2 mm and 4 mm:

2 mm 2 mm 3 mm 4 mm 4 mm

The data set below has no mode, because no value occurs more often than any other.

2 mm 3 mm 4 mm 5 mm

Range

The **range** of a data set is the difference between the greatest value and the least value.

Example

To find the range of the clamshell data, arrange the values in order from least to greatest.

13 mm 14 mm 14 mm 16 mm 21 mm 23 mm 25 mm

Subtract the least value from the greatest value.

13 mm is the least value.
25 mm is the greatest value.

25 mm – 13 mm = 12 mm

ANSWER The range is 12 mm.

R37

Using Ratios, Rates, and Proportions

You can use ratios and rates to compare values in data sets. You can use proportions to find unknown values.

Ratios

A **ratio** uses division to compare two values. The ratio of a value a to a nonzero value b can be written as $\frac{a}{b}$.

Example

The height of one plant is 8 centimeters. The height of another plant is 6 centimeters. To find the ratio of the height of the first plant to the height of the second plant, write a fraction and simplify it.

$$\frac{8 \text{ cm}}{6 \text{ cm}} = \frac{4 \times \overset{1}{\cancel{2}}}{3 \times \underset{1}{\cancel{2}}} = \frac{4}{3}$$

ANSWER The ratio of the plant heights is $\frac{4}{3}$.

You can also write the ratio $\frac{a}{b}$ as "a to b" or as $a{:}b$. For example, you can write the ratio of the plant heights as "4 to 3" or as 4:3.

MATH HANDBOOK

Rates

A **rate** is a ratio of two values expressed in different units. A unit rate is a rate with a denominator of 1 unit.

Example

A plant grew 6 centimeters in 2 days. The plant's rate of growth was $\frac{6 \text{ cm}}{2 \text{ days}}$. To describe the plant's growth in centimeters per day, write a unit rate.

Divide numerator and denominator by 2: $\frac{6 \text{ cm}}{2 \text{ days}} = \frac{6 \text{ cm} \div 2}{2 \text{ days} \div 2}$

Simplify: $= \frac{3 \text{ cm}}{1 \text{ day}}$

You divide 2 days by 2 to get 1 day, so divide 6 cm by 2 also.

ANSWER The plant's rate of growth is 3 centimeters per day.

Proportions

A **proportion** is an equation stating that two ratios are equivalent. To solve for an unknown value in a proportion, you can use cross products.

Example

If a plant grew 6 centimeters in 2 days, how many centimeters would it grow in 3 days (if its rate of growth is constant)?

Write a proportion: $\frac{6\text{ cm}}{2\text{ days}} = \frac{x}{3\text{ days}}$

Set cross products: $6\text{ cm} \cdot 3 = 2x$

Multiply 6 and 3: $18\text{ cm} = 2x$

Divide each side by 2: $\frac{18\text{ cm}}{2} = \frac{2x}{2}$

Simplify: $9\text{ cm} = x$

ANSWER The plant would grow 9 centimeters in 3 days.

Using Decimals, Fractions, and Percents

Decimals, fractions, and percentages are all ways of recording and representing data.

Decimals

A **decimal** is a number that is written in the base-ten place value system, in which a decimal point separates the ones and tenths digits. The values of each place is ten times that of the place to its right.

Example

A caterpillar traveled from point *A* to point *C* along the path shown.

A 36.9 cm B 52.4 cm C

ADDING DECIMALS To find the total distance traveled by the caterpillar, add the distance from *A* to *B* and the distance from *B* to *C*. Begin by lining up the decimal points. Then add the figures as you would whole numbers and bring down the decimal point.

$$\begin{array}{r} 36.9\text{ cm} \\ +\ 52.4\text{ cm} \\ \hline 89.3\text{ cm} \end{array}$$

ANSWER The caterpillar traveled a total distance of 89.3 centimeters.

MATH HANDBOOK

Example *continued*

SUBTRACTING DECIMALS To find how much farther the caterpillar traveled on the second leg of the journey, subtract the distance from *A* to *B* from the distance from *B* to *C*.

$$\begin{array}{r} 52.4 \text{ cm} \\ -\ 36.9 \text{ cm} \\ \hline 15.5 \text{ cm} \end{array}$$

ANSWER The caterpillar traveled 15.5 centimeters farther on the second leg of the journey.

Example

A caterpillar is traveling from point *D* to point *F* along the path shown. The caterpillar travels at a speed of 9.6 centimeters per minute.

D E **33.6 cm** F

MULTIPLYING DECIMALS You can multiply decimals as you would whole numbers. The number of decimal places in the product is equal to the sum of the number of decimal places in the factors.

For instance, suppose it takes the caterpillar 1.5 minutes to go from *D* to *E*. To find the distance from *D* to *E*, multiply the caterpillar's speed by the time it took.

$$\begin{array}{r} 9.6 \\ \times\ 1.5 \\ \hline 480 \\ 96\ \ \\ \hline 14.40 \end{array} \qquad \begin{array}{rl} 1 & \text{decimal place} \\ +\ 1 & \text{decimal place} \\ \hline \\ \\ 2 & \text{decimal places} \end{array}$$

Align as shown.

ANSWER The distance from *D* to *E* is 14.4 centimeters.

DIVIDING DECIMALS When you divide by a decimal, move the decimal points the same number of places in the divisor and the dividend to make the divisor a whole number.

For instance, to find the time it will take the caterpillar to travel from *E* to *F*, divide the distance from *E* to *F* by the caterpillar's speed.

$9.6\overline{)33.6}$

Move each decimal point one place to the right.

$$\begin{array}{r} 3.5 \\ 96\overline{)336.} \\ \underline{288}\ \ \\ 480 \\ \underline{480} \\ 0 \end{array}$$

Line up decimal points.

ANSWER The caterpillar will travel from *E* to *F* in 3.5 minutes.

Fractions

A **fraction** is a number in the form $\frac{a}{b}$, where b is not equal to 0. A fraction is in **simplest form** if its numerator and denominator have a greatest common factor (GCF) of 1. To simplify a fraction, divide its numerator and denominator by their GCF.

Example

A caterpillar is 40 millimeters long. The head of the caterpillar is 6 millimeters long. To compare the length of the caterpillar's head with the caterpillar's total length, you can write and simplify a fraction that expresses the ratio of the two lengths.

Write the ratio of the two lengths: $\frac{\text{Length of head}}{\text{Total length}} = \frac{6 \text{ mm}}{40 \text{ mm}}$

Write numerator and denominator as products of numbers and the GCF: $= \frac{3 \times 2}{20 \times 2}$

Divide numerator and denominator by the GCF: $= \frac{3 \times \overset{1}{\cancel{2}}}{20 \times \underset{1}{\cancel{2}}}$

Simplify: $= \frac{3}{20}$

ANSWER In simplest form, the ratio of the lengths is $\frac{3}{20}$.

Percents

A **percent** is a ratio that compares a number to 100. The word *percent* means "per hundred" or "out of 100." The symbol for *percent* is %.

For instance, suppose 43 out of 100 caterpillars are female. You can represent this ratio as a percent, a decimal, or a fraction.

Percent	Decimal	Fraction
43%	0.43	$\frac{43}{100}$

Example

In the preceding example, the ratio of the length of the caterpillar's head to the caterpillar's total length is $\frac{3}{20}$. To write this ratio as a percent, write an equivalent fraction that has a denominator of 100.

Multiply numerator and denominator by 5: $\frac{3}{20} = \frac{3 \times 5}{20 \times 5}$

$= \frac{15}{100}$

Write as a percent: $= 15\%$

ANSWER The caterpillar's head represents 15 percent of its total length.

MATH HANDBOOK

Using Formulas

A **formula** is an equation that shows the general relationship between two or more quantities.

In science, a formula often has a word form and a symbolic form. The formula below expresses Ohm's law.

Word Form

$$\text{Current} = \frac{\text{voltage}}{\text{resistance}}$$

Symbolic Form

$$I = \frac{V}{R}$$

The term *variable* is also used in science to refer to a factor that can change during an experiment.

In this formula, I, V, and R are variables. A mathematical **variable** is a symbol or letter that is used to represent one or more numbers.

Example

Suppose that you measure a voltage of 1.5 volts and a resistance of 15 ohms. You can use the formula for Ohm's law to find the current in amperes.

Write the formula for Ohm's law: $I = \frac{V}{R}$

Substitute 1.5 volts for V and 15 ohms for R: $I = \frac{1.5 \text{ volts}}{15 \text{ ohms}}$

Simplify: $I = 0.1 \text{ amp}$

ANSWER The current is 0.1 ampere.

If you know the values of all variables but one in a formula, you can solve for the value of the unknown variable. For instance, Ohm's law can be used to find a voltage if you know the current and the resistance.

Example

Suppose that you know that a current is 0.2 amperes and the resistance is 18 ohms. Use the formula for Ohm's law to find the voltage in volts.

Write the formula for Ohm's law: $I = \frac{V}{R}$

Substitute 0.2 amp for I and 18 ohms for R: $0.2 \text{ amp} = \frac{V}{18 \text{ ohms}}$

Multiply both sides by 18 ohms: $0.2 \text{ amp} \cdot 18 \text{ ohms} = V$

Simplify: $3.6 \text{ volts} = V$

ANSWER The voltage is 3.6 volts.

Finding Areas

The area of a figure is the amount of surface the figure covers.

Area is measured in square units, such as square meters (m^2) or square centimeters (cm^2). Formulas for the areas of three common geometric figures are shown below.

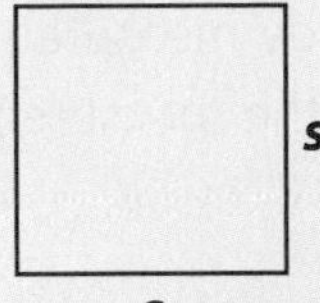

Area = (side length)^2
$A = s^2$

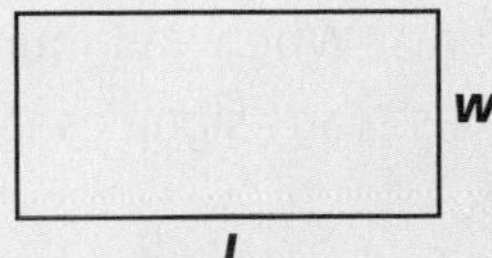

Area = length × width
$A = lw$

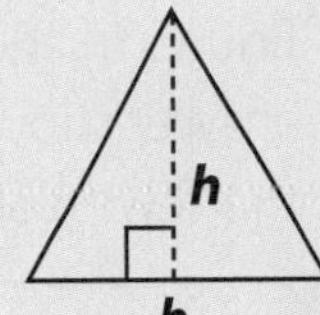

Area = $\frac{1}{2}$ × base × height
$A = \frac{1}{2}bh$

Example

Each face of a halite crystal is a square like the one shown. You can find the area of the square by using the steps below.

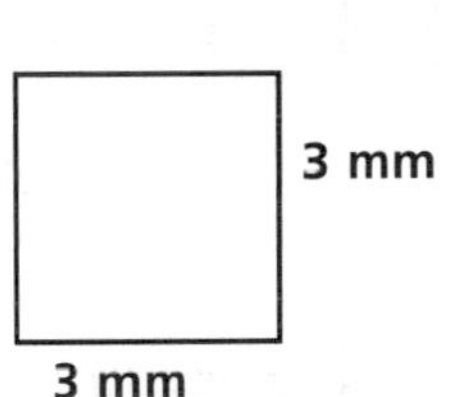

Write the formula for the area of a square:	$A = s^2$
Substitute 3 mm for s:	$= (3\text{ mm})^2$
Simplify:	$= 9\text{ mm}^2$

ANSWER The area of the square is 9 square millimeters.

Finding Volumes

The volume of a solid is the amount of space contained by the solid.

Volume is measured in cubic units, such as cubic meters (m^3) or cubic centimeters (cm^3). The volume of a rectangular prism is given by the formula shown below.

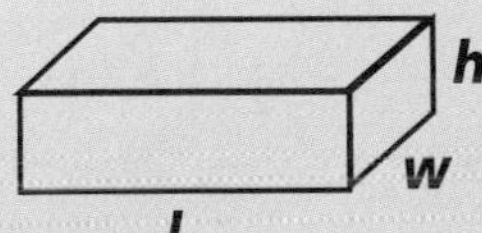

Volume = length × width × height
$V = lwh$

Example

A topaz crystal is a rectangular prism like the one shown. You can find the volume of the prism by using the steps below.

10 mm
12 mm
20 mm

Write the formula for the volume of a rectangular prism:	$V = lwh$
Substitute dimensions:	$= 20\text{ mm} \times 12\text{ mm} \times 10\text{ mm}$
Simplify:	$= 2400\text{ mm}^3$

ANSWER The volume of the rectangular prism is 2400 cubic millimeters.

Using Significant Figures

The **significant figures** in a decimal are the digits that are warranted by the accuracy of a measuring device.

When you perform a calculation with measurements, the number of significant figures to include in the result depends in part on the number of significant figures in the measurements. When you multiply or divide measurements, your answer should have only as many significant figures as the measurement with the fewest significant figures.

Example

Using a balance and a graduated cylinder filled with water, you determined that a marble has a mass of 8.0 grams and a volume of 3.5 cubic centimeters. To calculate the density of the marble, divide the mass by the volume.

Write the formula for density: Density $= \frac{\text{mass}}{\text{Volume}}$

Substitute measurements: $= \frac{8.0 \text{ g}}{3.5 \text{ cm}^3}$

Use a calculator to divide: $\approx 2.285714286 \text{ g/cm}^3$

ANSWER Because the mass and the volume have two significant figures each, give the density to two significant figures. The marble has a density of 2.3 grams per cubic centimeter.

Using Scientific Notation

Scientific notation is a shorthand way to write very large or very small numbers. For example, 73,500,000,000,000,000,000,000 kg is the mass of the Moon. In scientific notation, it is 7.35×10^{22} kg.

Example

You can convert from standard form to scientific notation.

Standard Form	Scientific Notation
720,000	7.2×10^5
5 decimal places left	Exponent is 5.
0.000291	2.91×10^{-4}
4 decimal places right	Exponent is –4.

You can convert from scientific notation to standard form.

Scientific Notation	Standard Form
4.63×10^7	46,300,000
Exponent is 7.	7 decimal places right
1.08×10^{-6}	0.00000108
Exponent is –6.	6 decimal places left

MATH HANDBOOK

Note-Taking Handbook

Note-Taking Strategies

Taking notes as you read helps you understand the information. The notes you take can also be used as a study guide for later review. This handbook presents several ways to organize your notes.

Content Frame

1. Make a chart in which each column represents a category.
2. Give each column a heading.
3. Write details under the headings.

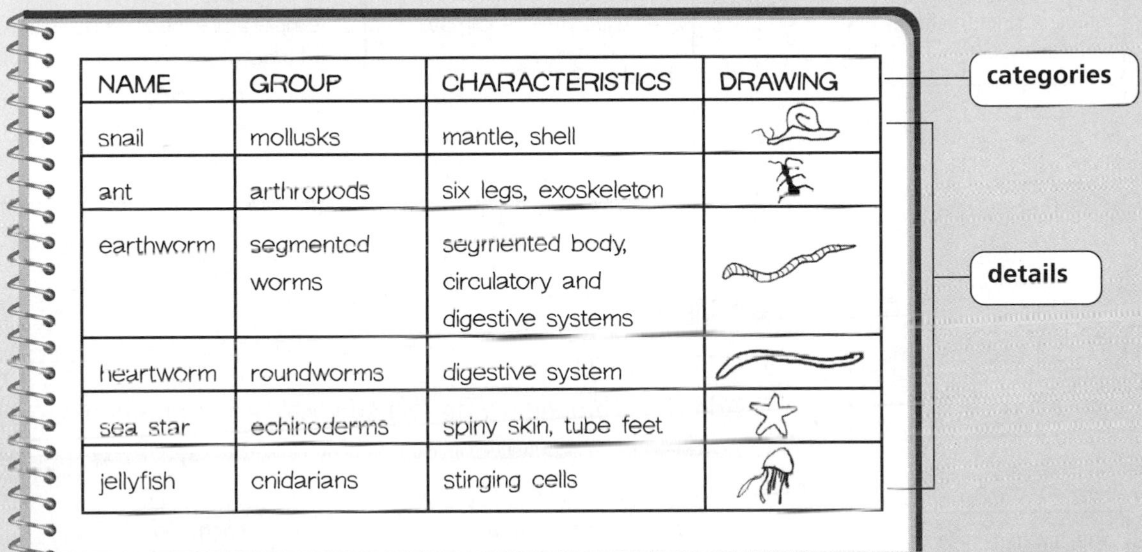

NAME	GROUP	CHARACTERISTICS	DRAWING
snail	mollusks	mantle, shell	
ant	arthropods	six legs, exoskeleton	
earthworm	segmented worms	segmented body, circulatory and digestive systems	
heartworm	roundworms	digestive system	
sea star	echinoderms	spiny skin, tube feet	
jellyfish	cnidarians	stinging cells	

Combination Notes

1. For each new idea or concept, write an informal outline of the information.
2. Make a sketch to illustrate the concept, and label it.

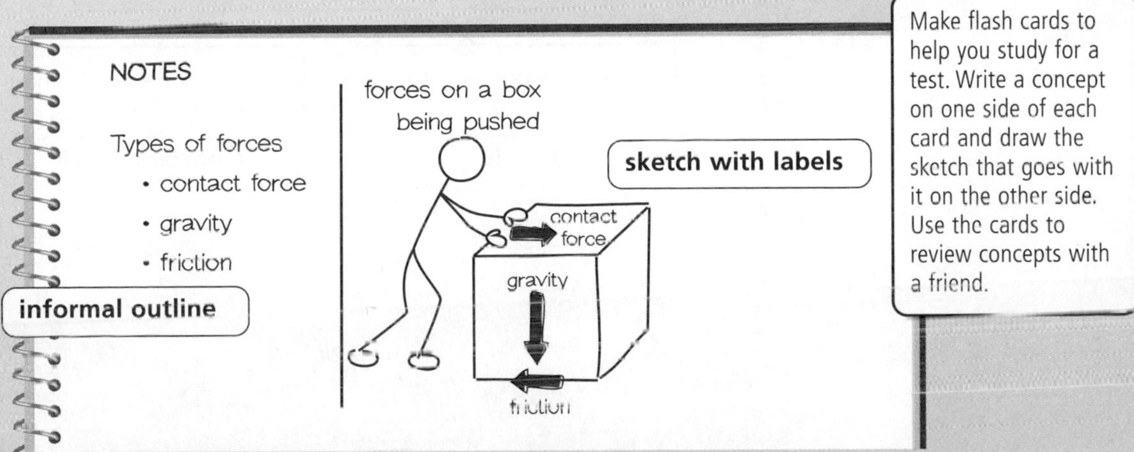

Make flash cards to help you study for a test. Write a concept on one side of each card and draw the sketch that goes with it on the other side. Use the cards to review concepts with a friend.

Main Idea and Detail Notes

1. In the left-hand column of a two-column chart, list main ideas. The blue headings express main ideas throughout this textbook.
2. In the right-hand column, write details that expand on each main idea.

You can shorten the headings in your chart. Be sure to use the most important words.

When studying for tests, cover up the detail notes column with a sheet of paper. Then use each main idea to form a question—such as "How does latitude affect climate?" Answer the question, and then uncover the detail notes column to check your answer.

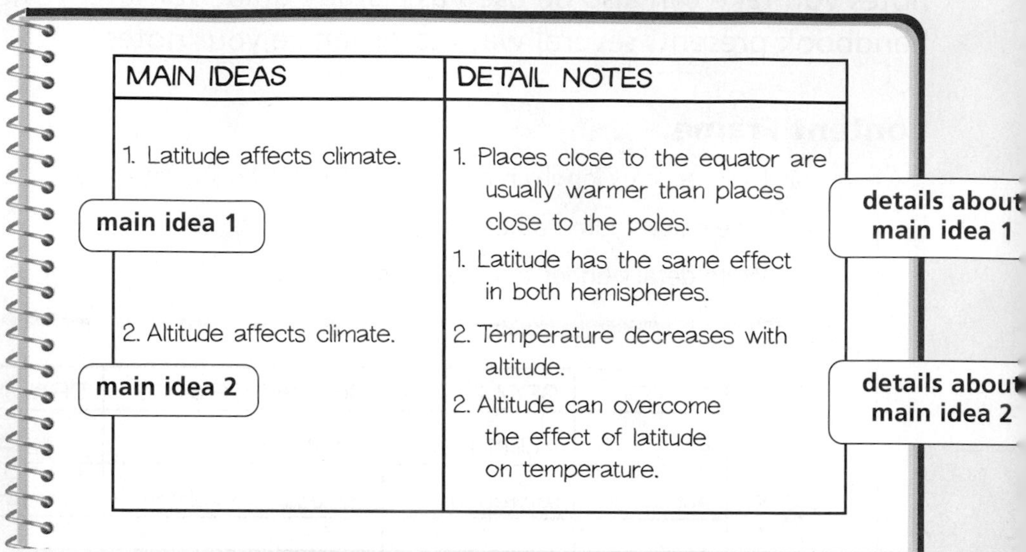

MAIN IDEAS	DETAIL NOTES
1. Latitude affects climate.	1. Places close to the equator are usually warmer than places close to the poles.
	1. Latitude has the same effect in both hemispheres.
2. Altitude affects climate.	2. Temperature decreases with altitude.
	2. Altitude can overcome the effect of latitude on temperature.

Main Idea Web

1. Write a main idea in a box.
2. Add boxes around it with related vocabulary terms and important details.

You can find definitions near highlighted terms.

definition of *work*

Work is the use of force to move an object.

formula

Work = force · distance

main idea

Force is necessary to do work.

The joule is the unit used to measure work.

definition of *joule*

Work depends on the size of a force.

important detail

NOTE-TAKING HANDBOOK

Mind Map

1. Write a main idea in the center.
2. Add details that relate to one another and to the main idea.

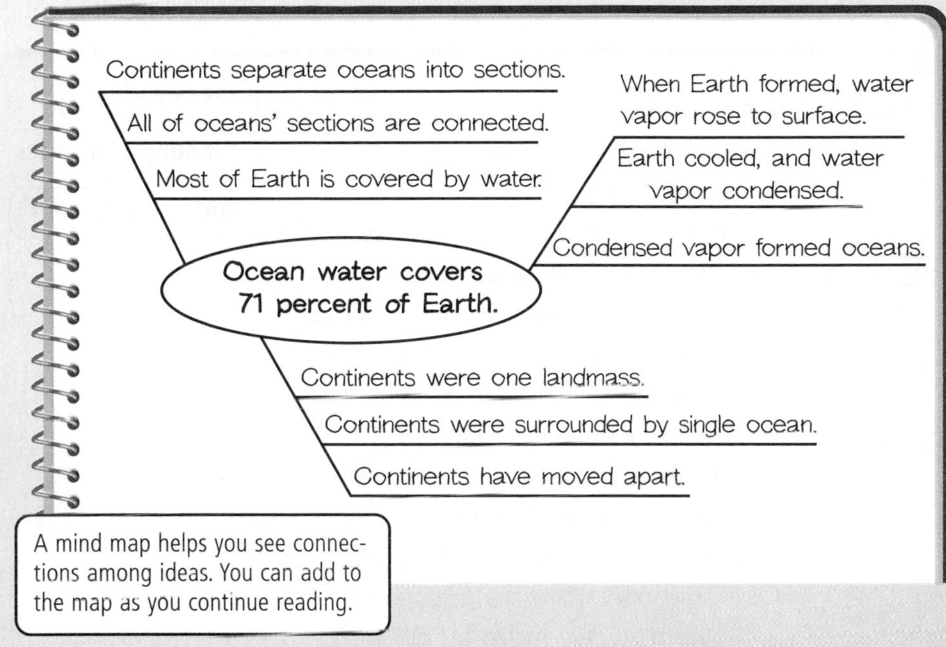

Supporting Main Ideas

1. Write a main idea in a box.
2. Add boxes underneath with information—such as reasons, explanations, and examples—that supports the main idea.

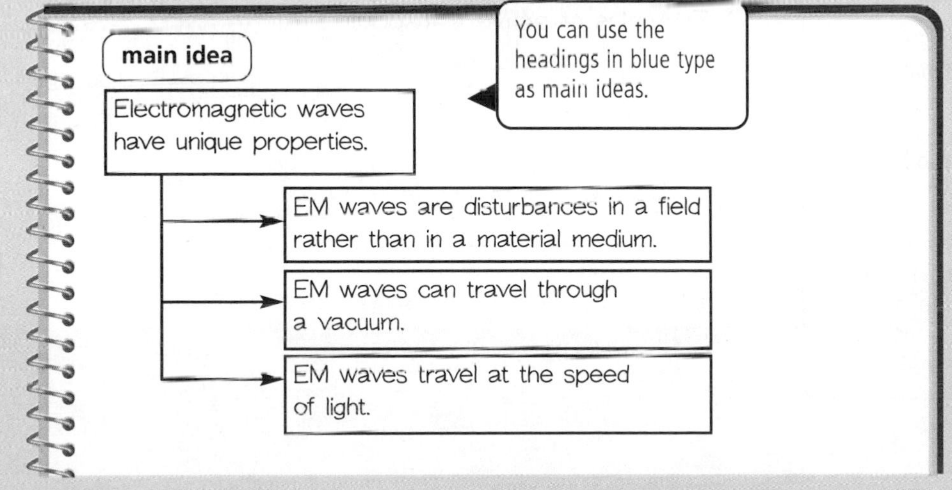

NOTE-TAKING HANDBOOK

Outline

1. Copy the chapter title and headings from the book in the form of an outline.
2. Add notes that summarize in your own words what you read.

Cell Processes

I. Cells capture and release energy. — 1st key idea
   A. All cells need energy. — 1st subpoint of I
   B. Some cells capture light energy. — 2nd subpoint of I
      1. Process of photosynthesis — 1st detail about B
      2. Chloroplasts (site of photosynthesis) — 2nd detail about B
      3. Carbon dioxide and water as raw materials
      4. Glucose and oxygen as products
   C. All cells release energy.
      1. Process of cellular respiration
      2. Fermentation of sugar to carbon dioxide
      3. Bacteria that carry out fermentation
II. Cells transport materials through membranes.
   A. Some materials move by diffusion.
      1. Particle movement from higher to lower concentrations
      2. Movement of water through membrane (osmosis)
   B. Some transport requires energy.
      1. Active transport
      2. Examples of active transport

Correct Outline Form
Include a title.

Arrange key ideas, subpoints, and details as shown.

Indent the divisions of the outline as shown.

Use the same grammatical form for items of the same rank. For example, if A is a sentence, B must also be a sentence.

You must have at least two main ideas or subpoints. That is, every A must be followed by a B, and every 1 must be followed by a 2.

Concept Map

1. Write an important concept in a large oval.
2. Add details related to the concept in smaller ovals.
3. Write linking words on arrows that connect the ovals.

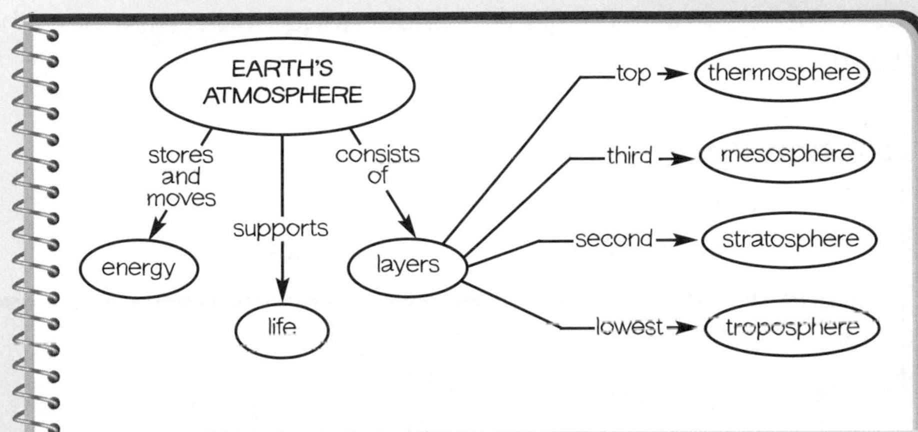

The main ideas or concepts can often be found in the blue headings. An example is "The atmosphere stores and moves energy." Use nouns from these concepts in the ovals, and use the verb or verbs on the lines.

Venn Diagram

1. Draw two overlapping circles, one for each item that you are comparing.
2. In the overlapping section, list the characteristics that are shared by both items.
3. In the outer sections, list the characteristics that are peculiar to each item.
4. Write a summary that describes the information in the Venn diagram.

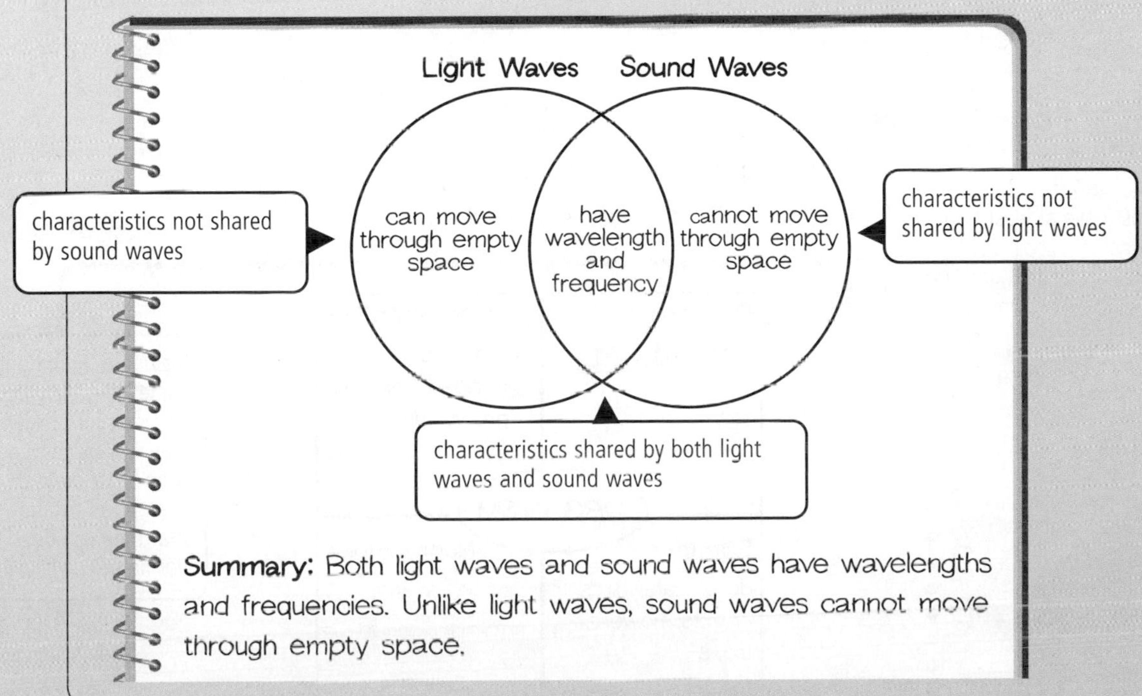

Vocabulary Strategies

Important terms are highlighted in this book. A definition of each term can be found in the sentence or paragraph where the term appears. You can also find definitions in the Glossary. Taking notes about vocabulary terms helps you understand and remember what you read.

Description Wheel

1. Write a term inside a circle.
2. Write words that describe the term on "spokes" attached to the circle.

When studying for a test with a friend, read the phrases on the spokes one at a time until your friend identifies the correct term.

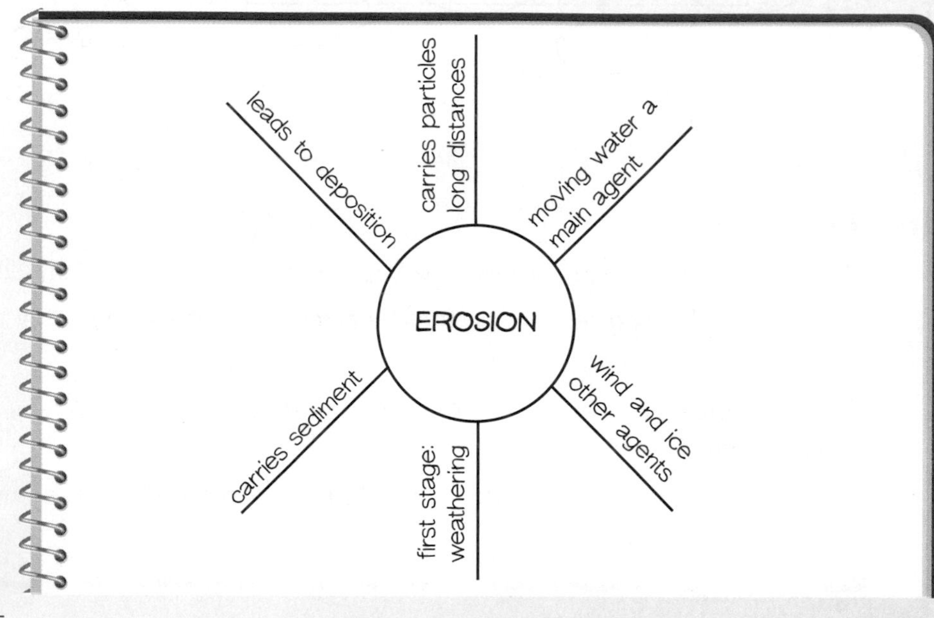

Four Square

1. Write a term in the center.
2. Write details in the four areas around the term.

Definition	**Characteristics**
any living thing	needs food, water, air; needs energy; grows, develops, reproduces
Examples	**Nonexamples**
dogs, cats, birds, insects, flowers, trees	rocks, water, dirt

Center term: ORGANISM

Include a definition, some characteristics, and examples. You may want to add a formula, a sketch, or examples of things that the term does *not* name.

Frame Game

1. Write a term in the center.
2. Frame the term with details.

Include examples, descriptions, sketches, or sentences that use the term in context. Change the frame to fit each new term.

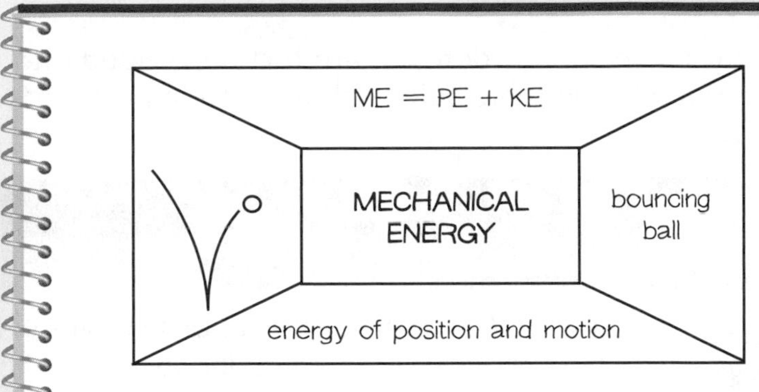

Magnet Word

1. Write a term on the magnet.
2. On the lines, add details related to the term.

You can also use phrases or sentences on the lines.

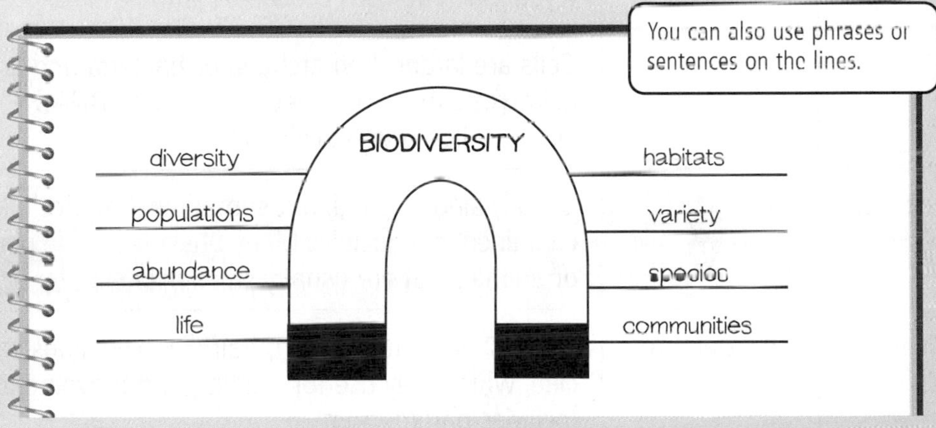

Word Triangle

1. Write a term and its definition in the bottom section.
2. In the middle section, write a sentence in which the term is used correctly.
3. In the top section, draw a small picture to illustrate the term.

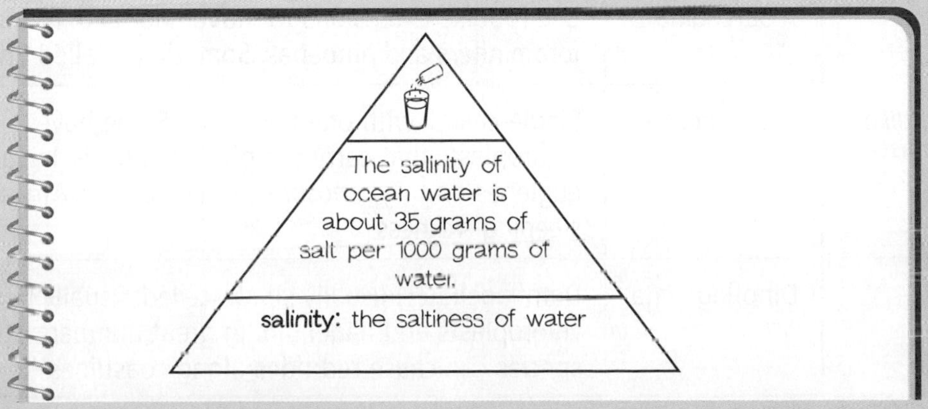

Appendix

Classification of Living Things

Living things are classified into three domains. These domains are further divided into kingdoms, and then phyla. Major phyla are described in the table below, along with important features that are used to distinguish each group.

Classification of Living Things

Domain	Kingdom	Phylum	Common Name and Description
Archaea	**Archaea**		Single-celled, with no nucleus. Live in some of Earth's most extreme environments, including salty, hot, and acid environments, and the deep ocean.
Bacteria	**Bacteria**		Single-celled, with no nucleus, but chemically different from Archaea. Live in all types of environments, including the human body; reproduce by dividing from one cell into two. Includes blue-green bacteria (cyanobacteria), *Streptococcus,* and *Bacillus.*
Eukarya			Cells are larger than archaea or bacteria and are eukaryotic (have a nucleus containing DNA). Single-celled or multicellular.
	Protista		Usually single-celled, but sometimes multicellular. DNA contained in a nucleus. Many phyla resemble plants, fungi, or animals but are usually smaller or simpler in structure.
	Animal-like protists	Ciliophora	Ciliates; have many short, hairlike extensions called cilia, which they use for feeding and movement. Includes paramecium.
		Zoomastigina	Zooflagellates; have usually one or two long, hairlike extensions called flagella.
		Sporozoa	Cause diseases in animals such as birds, fish, and humans. Includes *Plasmodium,* which causes malaria.
		Sarcodina	Use footlike extensions to move and feed. Includes foraminifers and amoebas. Sometimes called Rhizopoda.
	Plantlike protists	Euglenozoa	Single-celled, with one flagellum. Some have chloroplasts that carry out photosynthesis. Includes euglenas and *Trypanosoma,* which causes African sleeping sickness.
		Dinoflagellata	Dinoflagellates; usually single-celled; usually have chloroplasts and flagellum. In great numbers, some species can cause red tides along coastlines.

APPENDIX

Classification of Living Things (cont.)

Domain	Kingdom	Phylum	Common Name and Description
		Chrysophyta	Yellow algae, golden-brown algae, and diatoms; single-celled; named for the yellow pigments in their chloroplasts (*chrysophyte*, in Greek, means "golden plant").
		Chlorophyceae	Green algae; have chloroplasts and are chemically similar to land plants. Unicellular or forms simple colonies of cells. Includes *Chlamydomonas, Ulva* (sea lettuce), and *Volvox.*
		Phaeophyta	Brown seaweed; contain a special brown pigment that gives these organisms their color. Multicellular, live mainly in salt water; includes kelp.
		Rhodophyta	Red algae; contain a red pigment that makes these organisms red, purple, or reddish-black. Multicellular, live in salt water.
	Funguslike protists	Acrasiomycota	Cellular slime molds; live partly as free-living single-celled organisms, then fuse together to form a many-celled mass. Live in damp, nutrient-rich environments; decomposers.
		Myxomycota	Acellular slime molds; form large, slimy masses made of many nuclei but technically a single cell.
		Oomycota	Water molds and downy mildews; produce thin, cottonlike extensions called hyphae. Feed off of dead or decaying material, often in water.
	Fungi		Usually multicellular; eukaryotic; cells have a thick cell wall. Obtain nutrients through absorption; often function as decomposers.
		Chytridiomycota	Oldest and simplest fungi; usually aquatic (fresh water or brackish water); single-celled or multicellular.
		Basidiomycota	Multicellular; reproduce with a club-shaped structure that is commonly seen on forest floors. Includes mushrooms, puffballs, rusts, and smuts.
		Zygomycota	Mostly disease-causing molds; often parasitic.
		Ascomycota	Includes single-celled yeasts and multicellular sac fungi. Includes *Penicillium.*

APPENDIX

Classification of Living Things (cont.)			
Domain	**Kingdom**	**Phylum**	**Common Name and Description**
	Plantae		Multicellular and eukaryotic; make sugars using energy from sunlight. Cells have a thick cell wall of cellulose.
		Bryophyta	Mosses; small, grasslike plants that live in moist, cool environments. Includes sphagnum (peat) moss. Seedless, nonvascular plants.
		Hepatophyta	Liverworts; named for the liver-shaped structure of one part of the plant's life cycle. Live in moist environments. Seedless, nonvascular plants.
		Anthoceratophyta	Hornworts; named for the visible hornlike structures with which they reproduce. Live on forest floors and other moist, cool environments. Seedless, nonvascular plants.
		Psilotophyta	Simple plant, just two types. Includes whisk ferns found in tropical areas, a common greenhouse weed. Seedless, vascular plants.
		Lycophyta	Club mosses and quillworts; look like miniature pine trees; live in moist, wooded environments. Includes *Lycopodium* (ground pine). Seedless vascular plants.
		Sphenophyta	Plants with simple leaves, stems, and roots. Grow about a meter tall, usually in moist areas. Includes *Equisetum* (scouring rush). Seedless, vascular plants.
		Pterophyta	Ferns; fringed-leaf plants that grow in cool, wooded environments. Includes many species. Seedless, vascular plants.
		Cycadophyta	Cycads; slow-growing palmlike plants that grow in tropical environments. Reproduce with seeds.
		Ginkgophyta	Includes only one species: *Ginkgo biloba,* a tree that is often planted in urban environments. Reproduce with seeds in cones.
		Gnetophyta	Small group includes desert-dwelling and tropical species. Includes *Ephedra* (Mormon tea) and *Welwitschia,* which grows in African deserts. Reproduce with seeds.
		Coniferophyta	Conifers, including pines, spruces, firs, sequoias. Usually evergreen trees; tend to grow in cold, dry environments; reproduce with seeds produced in cones.

APPENDIX

Classification of Living Things (cont.)			
Domain	Kingdom	Phylum	Common Name and Description
		Anthophyta	Flowering plants; includes grasses and flowering trees and shrubs. Reproduce with seeds produced in flowers, becoming fruit.
	Animalia		Multicellular and eukaryotic; obtain energy by consuming food. Usually able to move around.
		Porifera	Sponges; spend most of their lives fixed to the ocean floor. Feed by filtering water (containing nutrients and small organisms) through their body.
		Cnidaria	Aquatic animals with a radial (spokelike) body shape; named for their stinging cells (cnidocytes). Includes jellyfish, hydras, sea anemones, and corals.
		Ctenophora	Comb jellies; named for the comblike rows of cilia (hairlike extensions) that are used for movement.
		Platyhelminthes	Flatworms; thin, flattened worms with simple tissues and sensory organs. Includes planaria and tapeworms, which cause diseases in humans and other hosts.
		Nematoda	Roundworms; small, round worms; many species are parasites, causing diseases in humans, such as trichinosis and elephantiasis.
		Annelida	Segmented worms; body is made of many similar segments. Includes earthworms, leeches, and many marine worms.
		Mollusca	Soft-bodied, aquatic animals that usually have an outer shell. Includes snails, mussels, clams, octopus, and squid.
		Arthropoda	Animals with an outer skeleton (exoskeleton) and jointed appendages (for example, legs or wings). Very large group that includes insects, spiders and ticks, centipedes, millipedes, and crustaceans.
		Echinodermata	Marine animals with a radial (spokelike) body shape. Includes feather stars, sea stars (starfish), sea urchins, sand dollars, and sea cucumbers.
		Chordata	Mostly vertebrates (animals with backbones) that share important stages of early development. Includes tunicates (sea squirts), fish, sharks, amphibians, reptiles, birds, and mammals.

The Periodic Table of the Elements

	1	2	3	4	5	6	7	8	9
1	1 H Hydrogen 1.008								
2	3 Li Lithium 6.941	4 Be Beryllium 9.012							
3	11 Na Sodium 22.990	12 Mg Magnesium 24.305							
4	19 K Potassium 39.098	20 Ca Calcium 40.078	21 Sc Scandium 44.956	22 Ti Titanium 47.87	23 V Vanadium 50.942	24 Cr Chromium 51.996	25 Mn Manganese 54.938	26 Fe Iron 55.845	27 Co Cobalt 58.933
5	37 Rb Rubidium 85.468	38 Sr Strontium 87.62	39 Y Yttrium 88.906	40 Zr Zirconium 91.224	41 Nb Niobium 92.906	42 Mo Molybdenum 95.94	43 Tc Technetium (98)	44 Ru Ruthenium 101.07	45 Rh Rhodium 102.906
6	55 Cs Cesium 132.905	56 Ba Barium 137.327	57 La Lanthanum 138.906	72 Hf Hafnium 178.49	73 Ta Tantalum 180.95	74 W Tungsten 183.84	75 Re Rhenium 186.207	76 Os Osmium 190.23	77 Ir Iridium 192.217
7	87 Fr Francium (223)	88 Ra Radium (226)	89 Ac Actinium (227)	104 Rf Rutherfordium (261)	105 Db Dubnium (262)	106 Sg Seaborgium (266)	107 Bh Bohrium (264)	108 Hs Hassium (269)	109 Mt Meitnerium (268)

Period

Each row of the periodic table is called a **period.** As read from left to right, one proton and one electron are added from one element to the next.

58 Ce Cerium 140.116	59 Pr Praseodymium 140.908	60 Nd Neodymium 144.24	61 Pm Promethium (145)	62 Sm Samarium 150.36
90 Th Thorium 232.038	91 Pa Protactinium 231.036	92 U Uranium 238.029	93 Np Neptunium (237)	94 Pu Plutonium (244)

Group

Each column of the table is called a **group.** Elements in a group share similar properties. Groups are read from top to bottom.

APPENDIX

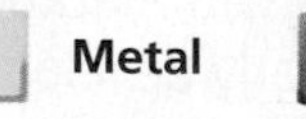 Metal  Metalloid  Nonmetal **Fe** Solid  Liquid 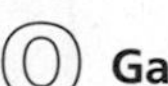 Gas

Metals and Nonmetals

This zigzag line separates metals from nonmetals.

10	11	12	13	14	15	16	17	18
								2 **He** Helium 4.003
			5 **B** Boron 10.811	6 **C** Carbon 12.011	7 **N** Nitrogen 14.007	8 **O** Oxygen 15.999	9 **F** Fluorine 18.998	10 **Ne** Neon 20.180
			13 **Al** Aluminum 26.982	14 **Si** Silicon 28.086	15 **P** Phosphorus 30.974	16 **S** Sulfur 32.066	17 **Cl** Chlorine 35.453	18 **Ar** Argon 39.948
28 **Ni** Nickel 58.69	29 **Cu** Copper 63.546	30 **Zn** Zinc 65.39	31 **Ga** Gallium 69.723	32 **Ge** Germanium 72.61	33 **As** Arsenic 74.922	34 **Se** Selenium 78.96	35 **Br** Bromine 79.904	36 **Kr** Krypton 83.80
46 **Pd** Palladium 106.42	47 **Ag** Silver 107.868	48 **Cd** Cadmium 112.4	49 **In** Indium 114.818	50 **Sn** Tin 118.710	51 **Sb** Antimony 121.760	52 **Te** Tellurium 127.60	53 **I** Iodine 126.904	54 **Xe** Xenon 131.29
78 **Pt** Platinum 195.078	79 **Au** Gold 196.967	80 **Hg** Mercury 200.59	81 **Tl** Thallium 204.383	82 **Pb** Lead 207.2	83 **Bi** Bismuth 208.980	84 **Po** Polonium (209)	85 **At** Astatine (210)	86 **Rn** Radon (222)
110 **Ds** Darmstadtium (269)	111 **Uuu** Unununium (272)	112 **Uub** Ununbium (277)						

Lanthanides & Actinides

The lanthanide series (elements 58–71) and actinide series (elements 90–103) are usually set apart from the rest of the periodic table.

63 **Eu** Europium 151.964	64 **Gd** Gadolinium 157.25	65 **Tb** Terbium 158.925	66 **Dy** Dysprosium 162.50	67 **Ho** Holmium 164.930	68 **Er** Erbium 167.26	69 **Tm** Thulium 168.934	70 **Yb** Ytterbium 173.04	71 **Lu** Lutetium 174.967
95 **Am** Americium (243)	96 **Cm** Curium (247)	97 **Bk** Berkelium (247)	98 **Cf** Californium (251)	99 **Es** Einsteinium (252)	100 **Fm** Fermium (257)	101 **Md** Mendelevium (258)	102 **No** Nobelium (259)	103 **Lr** Lawrencium (262)

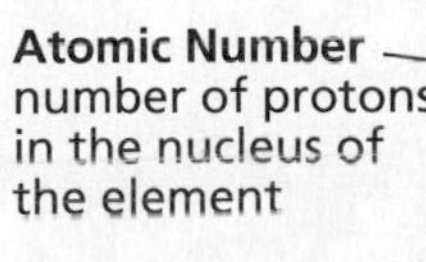

Atomic Number
number of protons in the nucleus of the element

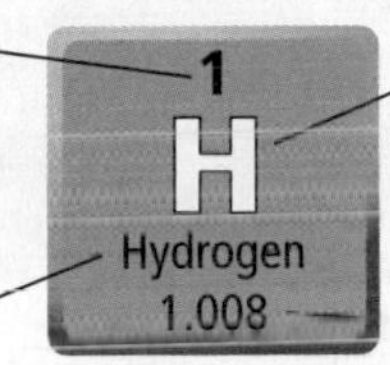

Name

Symbol
Each element has a symbol. The symbol's color represents the element's state at room temperature.

Atomic Mass
average mass of isotopes of this element

Divisions of Geologic Time

The geologic time scale is divided into eons, eras, periods, epochs (ehp-uhks), and ages. Unlike divisions of time such as days or minutes, the divisions of the geologic time scale have no exact fixed lengths. Instead, they are based on changes or events recorded in rocks and fossils.

Eon The largest unit of time is an eon. Earth's 4.6-billion-year history is divided into four eons.

The Hadean, Archean, and Proterozoic eons together are called Precambrian time and make up almost 90 percent of Earth's history.

Geologic Time Scale

This geologic time scale shows the longest divisions of Earth's history: eons, eras, and periods.

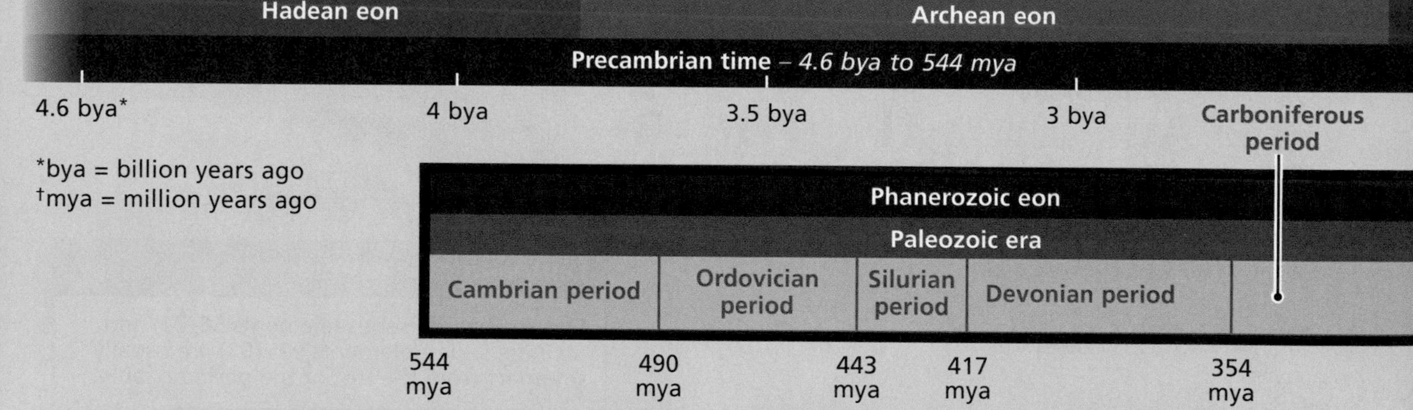

Precambrian Time at 3.6 Billion Years Ago

For nearly 4 billion years, during most of Precambrian time, no plants or animals existed.

Paleozoic Era at 544 Million Years Ago

At the beginning of the Paleozoic era, all life lived in the oceans.

APPENDIX

The fossil record for Precambrian time consists mostly of tiny organisms that cannot be seen without a microscope. Other early forms of life had soft bodies that rarely formed into fossils.

The Phanerozoic eon stretches from the end of Precambrian time to the present. Because so many more changes are recorded in the fossil record of this eon, it is further divided into smaller units of time called eras, periods, epochs, and ages.

The Phanerozoic eon is divided into three eras: the Paleozoic, the Mesozoic, and the Cenozoic. Each era is subdivided into a number of periods. The periods of the Cenozoic, the most recent era, are further divided into epochs, which are in turn further divided into ages. The smaller time divisions relate to how long certain conditions and life forms on Earth lasted and how quickly they changed or became extinct.

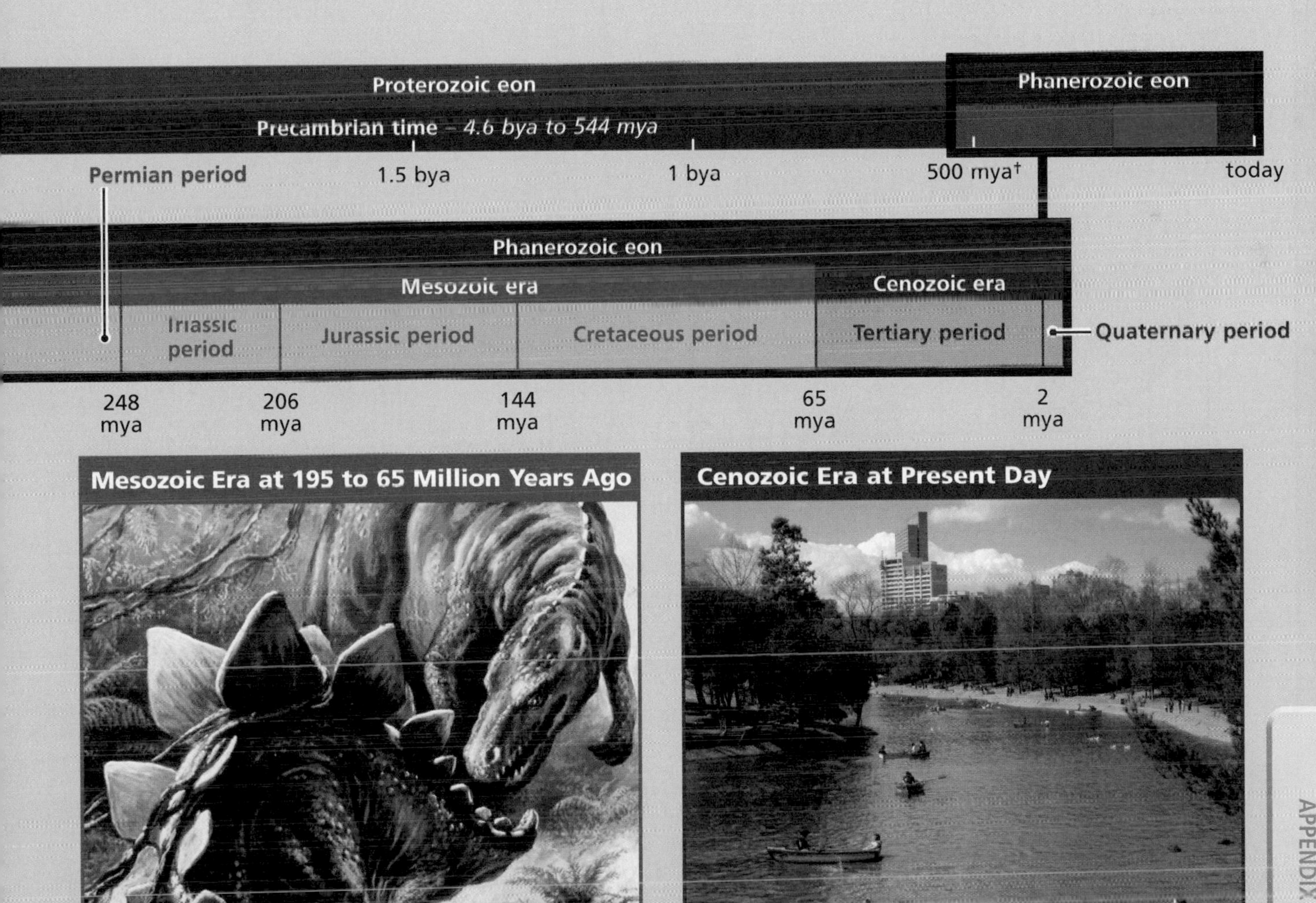

During the Mesozoic era, dinosaurs lived along with the first mammals, birds, and flowering plants.

The first humans appeared in the later part of the Cenozoic era, which continues today.

APPENDIX

Fossils in Rocks

If an organism is covered by or buried in sediment, it may become a fossil as the sediments become rock. Many rock fossils are actual body parts, such as bones or teeth, that were buried in sediment and then replaced by minerals and turned to stone. Fossils in rock include molds and casts, petrified wood, carbon films, and trace fossils.

❶ **Molds and Casts** Some fossils that form in sedimentary rock are mold fossils. A mold is a visible shape that was left after an animal or plant was buried in sediment and then decayed away. In some cases, a hollow mold later becomes filled with minerals, producing a cast fossil. The cast fossil is a solid model in the shape of the organism. If you think of the mold as a shoeprint, the cast would be what would result if sand filled the print and hardened into stone.

Fossils in Rocks

Rock fossils show shapes and traces of past life.

① Molds and Casts

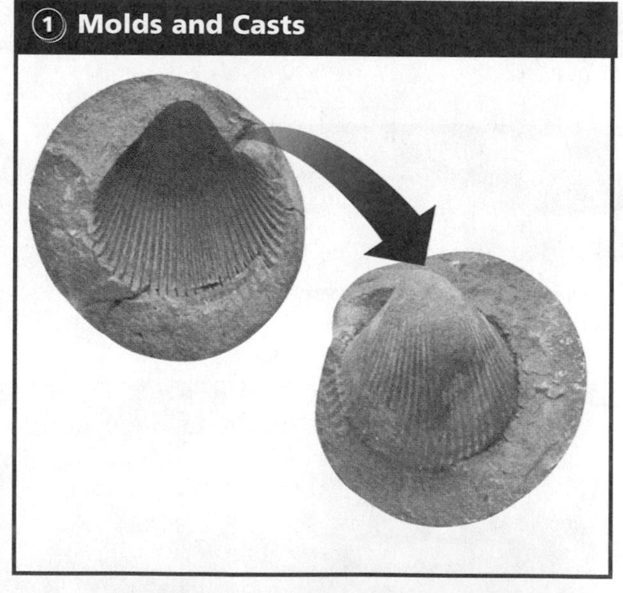

An organism dies and falls into soft sediment.

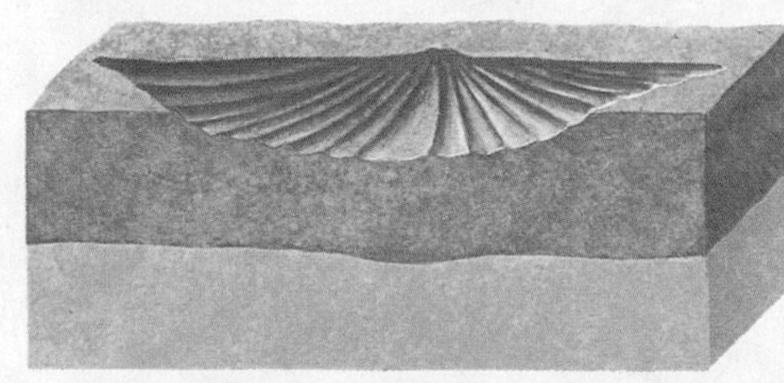

Over time, the sediment becomes rock and the organism decays, leaving a mold.

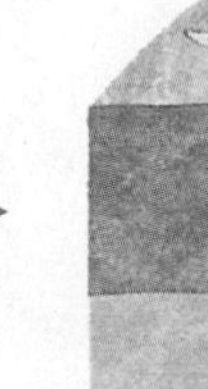

Minerals fill the mold and make a cast of the organism.

APPENDIX

2 Petrified Wood The stone fossil of a tree is called petrified wood. In certain conditions, a fallen tree can become covered with sediments. Over time, water passes through the sediments and into the tree's cells. Minerals that are carried in the water take the place of the cells, producing a stone likeness of the tree.

In this close-up, you can see the minerals that replaced the wood, forming petrified wood.

3 Carbon Films Carbon is an element that is found in every living thing. Sometimes when a dead plant or animal decays, its carbon is left behind as a visible layer. This image is called a carbon film. Carbon films can show details of soft parts of animals and plants that are rarely seen in other fossils.

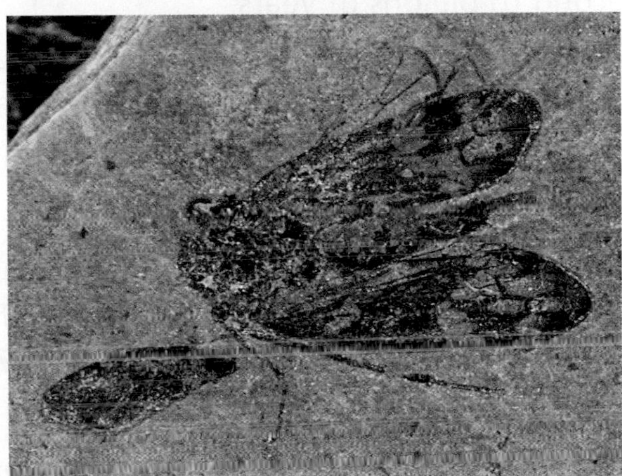

This carbon film of a moth is about 10 million years old. Carbon films are especially useful because they can show details of the soft parts of organisms.

4 Trace Fossils Do you want to know how fast a dinosaur could run? Trace fossils might be able to tell you. These are not parts of an animal or impressions of it, but rather evidence of an animal's presence in a given location. Trace fossils include preserved footprints, trails, animal holes, and even feces. By comparing these clues with what is known about modern animals, scientists can learn how prehistoric animals may have lived, what they ate, and how they behaved.

A trace fossil, such as this footprint of a dinosaur in rock, can provide important information about where an animal lived and how it walked and ran.

Half-Life

Over time, a radioactive element breaks down at a constant rate into another form.

The rate of change of a radioactive element is measured in half-lives. A half-life is the length of time it takes for half of the atoms in a sample of a radioactive element to change from an unstable form into another form. Different elements have different half-lives, ranging from fractions of a second to billions of years.

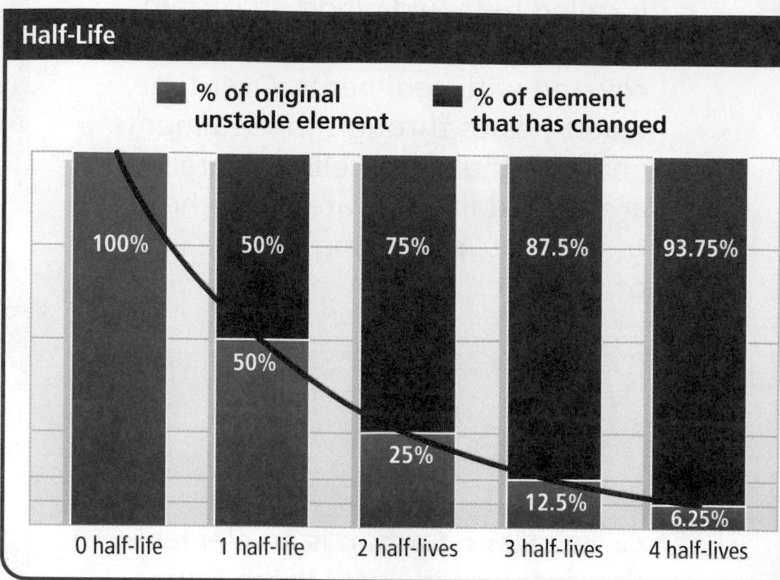

Radiometric Dating

Radiometric dating works best with igneous rocks. Sedimentary rocks are formed from material that came from other rocks. For this reason, any measurements would show when the original rocks were formed, not when the sedimentary rock itself formed.

Elements with half-lives of millions to billions of years are used to date rocks.

When magma first hardens into rock, it contains some uranium 235 and no lead 207.

APPENDIX

Uranium 235, an unstable element found in some igneous rocks, has a half-life of 704 million years. Over time, uranium 235 breaks down into lead 207.

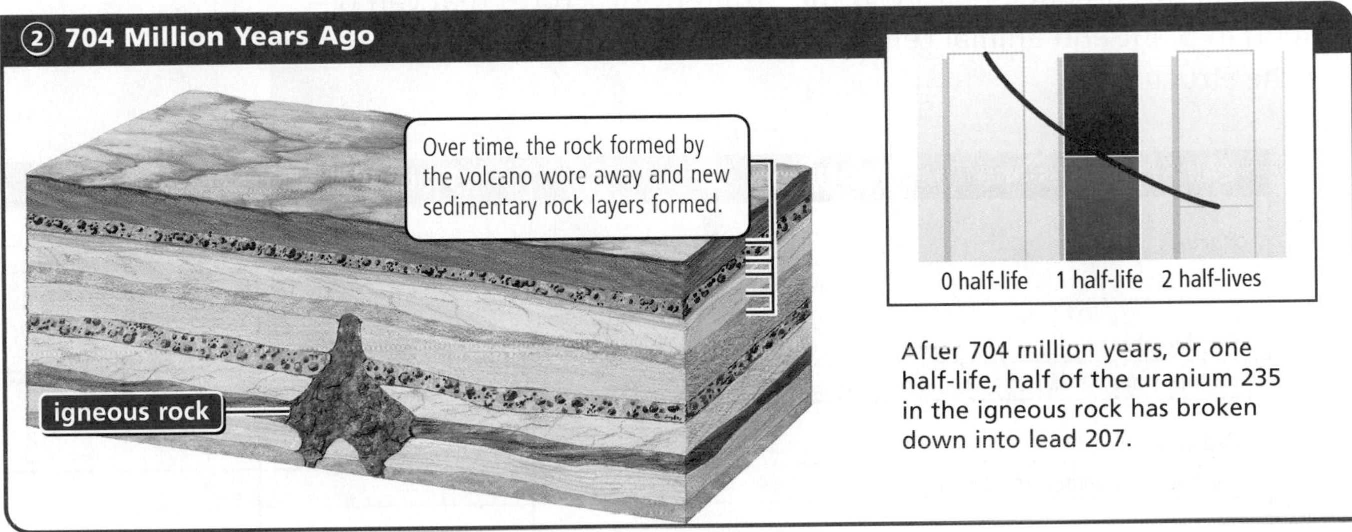

After 704 million years, or one half-life, half of the uranium 235 in the igneous rock has broken down into lead 207.

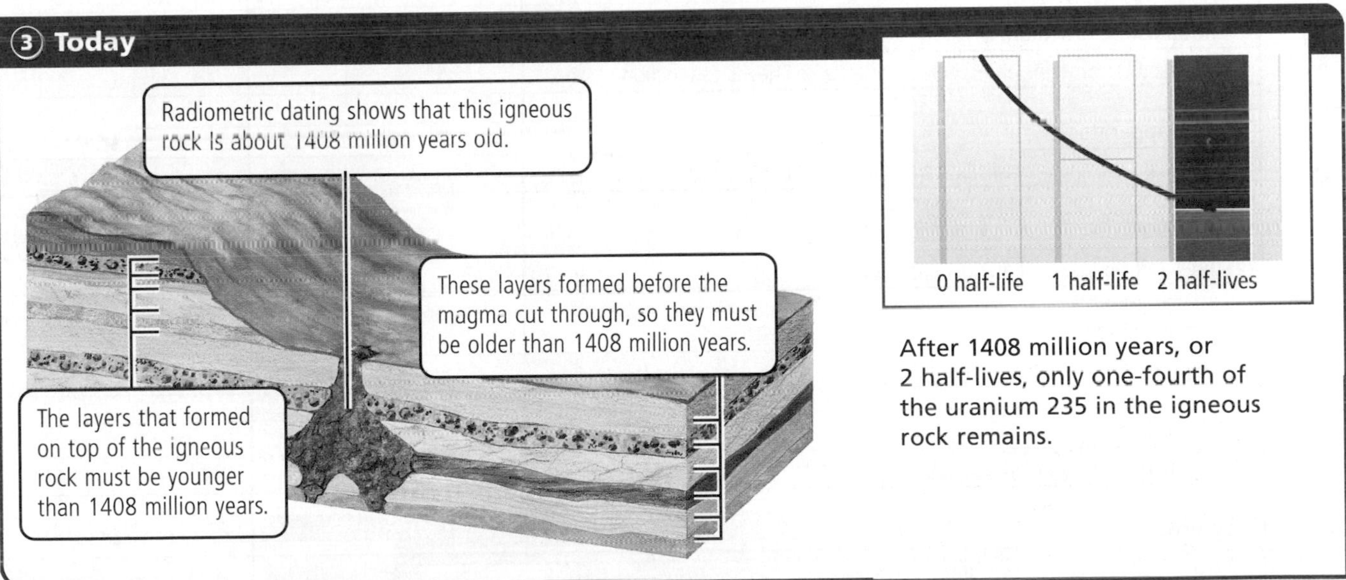

After 1408 million years, or 2 half-lives, only one-fourth of the uranium 235 in the igneous rock remains.

Just as uranium 235 can be used to date igneous rocks, carbon 14 can be used to find the ages of the remains of some things that were once alive. Carbon 14 is an unstable form of carbon, an element found in all living things. Carbon 14 has a half-life of 5730 years. It is useful for dating objects between about 100 and 70,000 years old, such as the wood from an ancient tool or the remains of an animal from the Ice Age.

APPENDIX

Plant and Animal Cells

Plants and animals are eukaryotes, that is, their cells contain a nucleus and other membrane-bound structures called organelles. The diagrams on page R65 show the different structures that can be found in plant and animal cells. The table below lists the functions of the structures.

Cell Structures and Their Functions	Plant Cell	Animal Cell
Nucleus stores genetic material that enables a cell to function and divide	✔	✔
Cell Membrane controls what comes into and goes out of a cell	✔	✔
Cell wall tough outer covering provides support	✔	
Ribosome uses genetic material to assemble materials needed to make proteins	✔	✔
Endoplasmic reticulum manufactures proteins and other materials a cell needs to function	✔	✔
Golgi apparatus finishes processing proteins and transports them	✔	✔
Vesicle stores and transports materials and wastes	✔	✔
Mitochondrion releases chemical energy stored in sugars	✔	✔
Chloroplast uses energy from sunlight to make sugars	✔	
Lysosome breaks down food particles and wastes		✔

APPENDIX

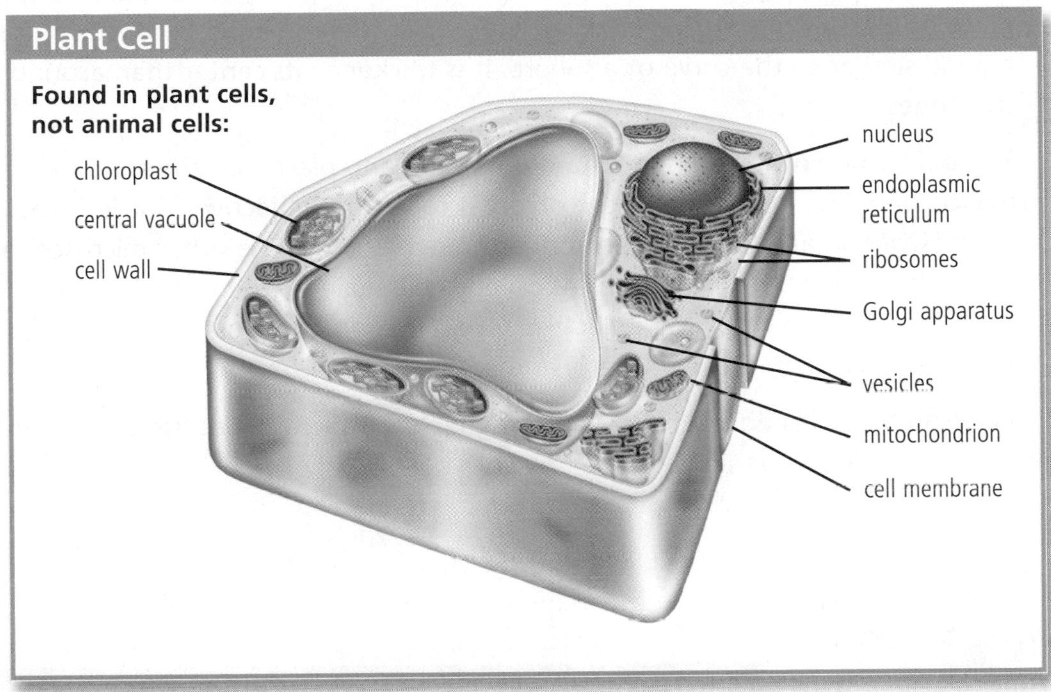
Plant Cell
Found in plant cells, not animal cells:
chloroplast
central vacuole
cell wall
nucleus
endoplasmic reticulum
ribosomes
Golgi apparatus
vesicles
mitochondrion
cell membrane

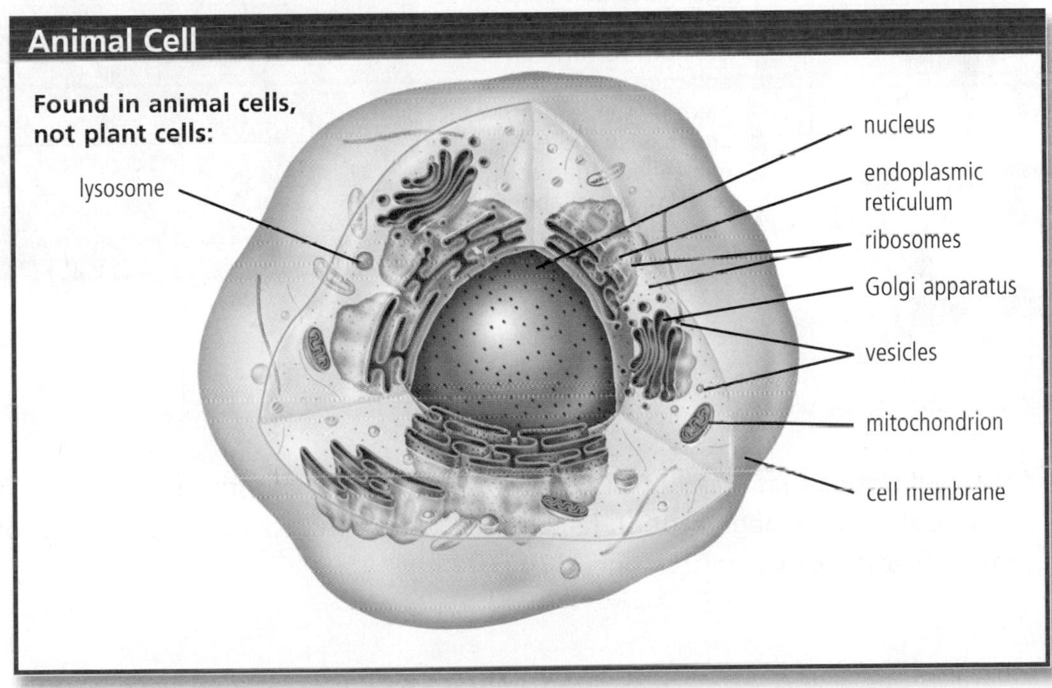
Animal Cell
Found in animal cells, not plant cells:
lysosome
nucleus
endoplasmic reticulum
ribosomes
Golgi apparatus
vesicles
mitochondrion
cell membrane

APPENDIX

How a Light Microscope Works

Microscopes are used to see objects that are too small to see well with the naked eye. An ordinary light microscope works by combining convex lenses. A lens is a piece of glass or plastic shaped in such a way as to bend light. A convex lens has a bend similar to the curve of a sphere. It is thicker at its center than around the edges.

The object being viewed is mounted on a slide and placed on the stage of the microscope. The lens closer to the object is called the objective. This lens focuses an enlarged image of the object inside the microscope. The other microscope lens—the one you look through—is called the eyepiece. You use this lens to look at the image formed by the objective. Like a magnifying glass, the eyepiece lens forms an enlarged image of the first image.

Very small objects do not reflect much light. Most microscopes use a lamp or a mirror to shine more light on the object.

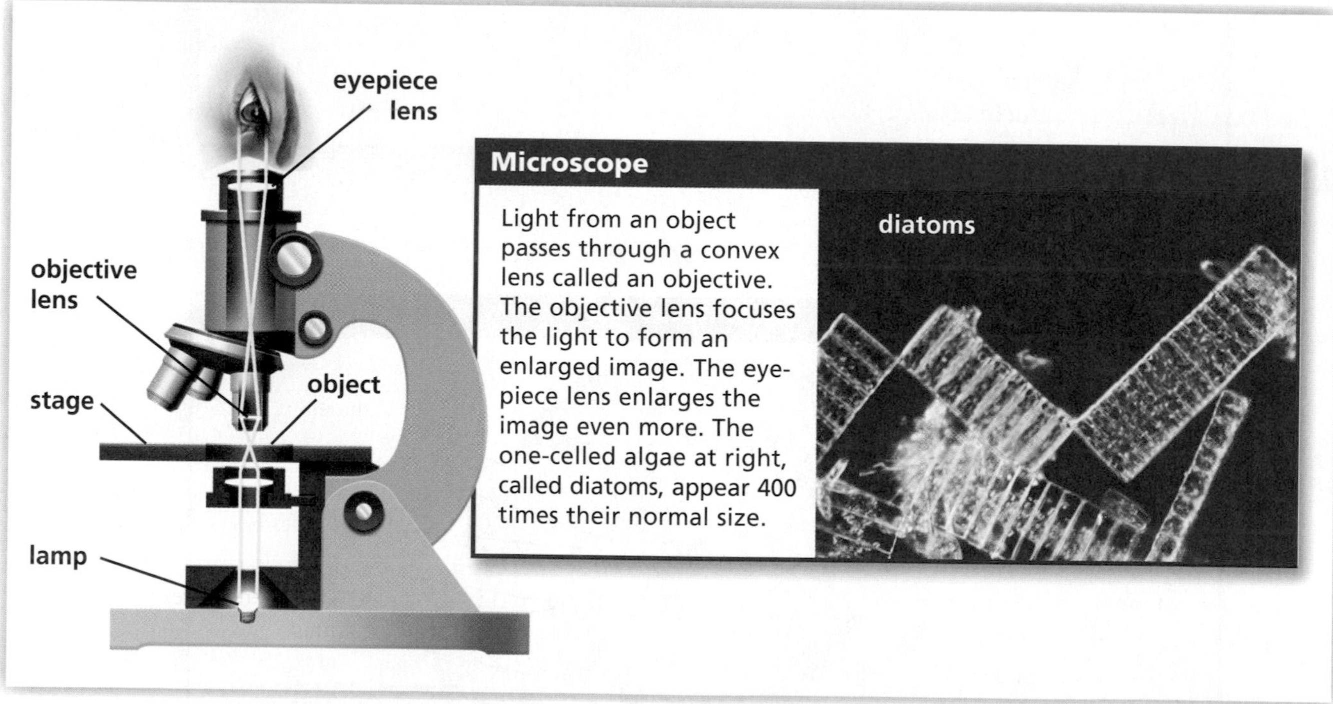

Microscope

Light from an object passes through a convex lens called an objective. The objective lens focuses the light to form an enlarged image. The eyepiece lens enlarges the image even more. The one-celled algae at right, called diatoms, appear 400 times their normal size.

You will notice that many of the photographs of microscopic images included in this book have a magnification factor, for example 400×. This is the power of magnification of the microscope.

Glossary

A

abiotic factor (AY-by-AHT-ihk)
A nonliving physical or chemical part of an ecosystem. (p. 474)

factor abiótico Una parte física o química sin vida de un ecosistema.

active transport
The process of using energy to move materials through a membrane. (p. 60)

transporte activo El proceso de usar energía para mover sustancias a través de una membrana.

adaptation
A characteristic, a behavior, or any inherited trait that makes a species able to survive and reproduce in a particular environment. (p. xxxvii)

adaptación Una característica, un comportamiento o cualquier rasgo heredado que permite a una especie sobrevivir o reproducirse en un medio ambiente determinado.

addiction
A physical or psychological need for a habit forming substance, such as alcohol or drugs. (p. 722)

adicción Una necesidad física o psicológica de una sustancia que forma hábito, como el alcohol o las drogas.

adolescence (AD-uhl-EHS-uhns)
The stage of life from the time a human body begins to mature sexually to adulthood. (p. 711)

adolescencia La etapa de la vida que va desde que el cuerpo humano empieza a madurar sexualmente hasta la edad adulta.

adulthood
The stage of life that begins once a human body completes its growth and reaches sexual maturity. (p. 712)

edad adulta La etapa de la vida que empieza una vez que el cuerpo humano completa su crecimiento y alcanza la madurez sexual.

algae
Protists that live mostly in water and use sunlight as a source of energy. *Algae* is a plural word; the singular is *alga.* (p. 303)

algas Protistas que viven principalmente en el agua y que usan la luz solar como fuente de energía.

allele (uh-LEEL)
An alternate form of a gene for a specific trait or gene product. (p. 103)

alelo Una forma alterna de un gen para un rasgo específico o un producto del gen.

amphibian
A cold-blooded vertebrate animal that lives in water and breathes with gills when it is young; as an adult, it moves onto land and breathes air with lungs. (p. 439)

anfibio Un vertebrado de sangre fría que vive en el agua y respira con branquias cuando es juvenil; cuando es adulto, se mueve a la tierra y respire aire con pulmones.

ancestor
A distant or early form of an organism from which later forms descend. (p. 189)

ancestro Una forma distante o temprana de un organismo a partir de la cual descienden formas posteriores.

angiosperm (AN-jee-uh-SPURM)
A plant that has flowers and produces seeds enclosed in fruit. (p. 379)

Angiosperma Una planta que tiene flores y que produce semillas dentro de frutas.

Animalia (AN-uh-MAL-yuh)
Part of a classification system that divides all living things into six kingdoms. Kingdom Animalia includes multicellular organisms, from humans and lions to insects and microbes, that rely on food for energy. (p. 223)

Animalia Parte de un sistema de clasificación que divide a todos los organismos vivos en seis reinos. El reino Animalia incluye a organismos multicelulares, desde humanos y leones hasta insectos y microbios, que dependen del alimento como fuente de energía.

GLOSSARY

GLOSSARY

antibiotic
A medicine that can block the growth and reproduction of bacteria. (p. 657)

antibiótico Una medicina que puede impedir el crecimiento y la reproducción de las bacterias.

antibody
A protein produced by some white blood cells to attack specific foreign materials. (p. 651)

anticuerpo Una proteína producida por algunos glóbulos blancos para atacar materiales extraños específicos.

antigen
A particular substance that the body recognizes as foreign and that stimulates a response. (p. 654)

antígeno Una sustancia que el cuerpo reconoce come extraña y que causa una respuesta.

appendicular skeleton (AP-uhn-DIHK-yuh-luhr)
The bones of the skeleton that function to allow movement, such as arm and leg bones. (p. 592)

esqueleto apendicular Los huesos del esqueleto cuya función es permitir el movimiento, como los huesos del brazo y los huesos de la pierna.

archaea (AHR-kee-uh)
Single-celled organisms without nuclei that can survive in extreme environments. *Archaea* is a plural word; the singular is *archaeon.* (p. 290)

archaea Organismos de una célula sin nucléo que pueden sobrevivir en medios ambientes extremosos.

Archaea (AHR-kee-uh)
Part of a classification system that divides all living things into six kingdoms. Kingdom Archaea includes microscopic single-celled organisms with a distinctive cell structure that allows them to live in extreme environments. (p. 223)

Archaea Parte de un sistema de clasificación que divide a todos los organismos vivos en seis reinos. El reino Archaea incluye a organismos microscópicos de una sola célula con una estructura celular distintiva que les permite vivir en medios ambientes extremosos.

artery
A blood vessel with strong walls that carries blood away from the heart. (p. 645)

arteria Un vaso sanguíneo con paredes fuertes que lleva la sangre del corazón hacia otras partes del cuerpo.

arthropod
An invertebrate animal with an exoskeleton, a segmented body, and jointed legs. (p. 414)

artrópodo Un animal invertebrado con un exoesqueleto, un cuerpo segmentado y patas articuladas.

asexual reproduction
The process by which a single organism produces offspring that have the same genetic material. (p. 88)

reproducción asexual El proceso mediante el cual un solo organismo produce crías que tienen el mismo material genético.

atom
The smallest particle of an element that has the chemical properties of that element.

átomo La partícula más pequeña de un elemento que tiene las propiedades químicas de ese elemento.

autonomic nervous system
The part of the nervous system that controls involuntary action and responses. (p. 683)

sistema nervioso autónomo La parte del sistema nervioso que controla la acción involuntaria y las respuestas.

autotroph (AW-tuh-TRAHF)
An organism that captures energy from sunlight and uses it to produce energy-rich carbon compounds, usually through the process of photosynthesis. (p. 324)

autótrofo Un organismo que capta energía de la luz solar y la usa para producir compuestos de carbono ricos en energía, usualmente mediante el proceso de fotosíntesis.

axial skeleton
The central part of the skeleton, which includes the cranium, the spinal column, and the ribs. (p. 592)

esqueleto axial La parte central del esqueleto que incluye al cráneo, a la columna vertebral y a las costillas.

B

bacteria (bak-TEER-ee-uh)
A large group of one-celled organisms that sometimes cause disease. *Bacteria* is a plural word; the singular is *bacterium.* (pp. 14, 725)

bacterias Un grupo grande de organismos unicelulares que algunas veces causan enfermedades.

Bacteria (bak-TEER-ee-uh)
Part of a classification system that divides all living things into six kingdoms. Kingdom Bacteria includes microscopic single celled organisms found in many environments. Bacteria can be associated with disease in other organisms. (p. 223)

Bacteria Parte de un sistema de clasificación que divide a todos los organismos vivos en seis reinos. El reino Bacteria incluye a organismos microscópicos de una sola célula que se encuentran en muchos medios ambientes. Las bacterias pueden estar asociadas a enfermedades en otros organismos.

behavior
An organism's action in response to a stimulus. (p. 334)

comportamiento La acción de un organismo en respuesta a un estímulo.

binary fission
A form of asexual reproduction by which some single-celled organisms reproduce. The genetic material is copied, and one cell divides into two independent cells that are each a copy of the original cell. Prokaryotes such as bacteria reproduce by binary fission. (pp. 89, 284)

fisión binaria Una forma asexual de reproducción mediante la cual algunos organismos unicelulares se reproducen. El material genético se copia y una célula se divide en dos células independientes las cuales son copias de la célula original. Los organismos procariotas, tales como las bacterias, se reproducen mediante fisión binaria.

binomial nomenclature
(by-NOH-mee-uhl NOH-muhn-KLAY-chuhr)
The two-part naming system used to identify species. The first part of the name is the genus, and the second part of the name is the species. (p. 212)

nomenclatura biológica El sistema de denominación de dos partes que se usa para identificar a las especies. La primera parte del nombre es el género y la segunda parte del nombre es la especie.

biodiversity
The number and variety of living things found on Earth or within an ecosystem. (p. 555)

biodiversidad La cantidad y variedad de organismos vivos que se encuentran en la Tierra o dentro de un ecosistema.

biology
The scientific study of life and all living things; ecology, zoology, and botany are examples of biological sciences.

biología El estudio científico de la vida y de todos los organismos vivos; la ecología, la zoología y la botántica son ejemplos de ciencias biológicas.

biome (BY-OHM)
A region of Earth that has a particular climate and certain types of plants. Examples are tundra, taiga, desert, grassland, temperate and tropical forests. (p. 494)

bioma Una región de la Tierra que tiene un clima particular y ciertos tipos de plantas. La tundra, la taiga, el desierto, la estepa, la selva tropical y el bosque templado son ejemplos de biomas.

biotic factor (by-AHT-ihk)
A living thing in an ecosystem. (p. 494)

factor biótico Un organismo vivo en un ecosistema.

blood
A fluid in the body that delivers oxygen and other materials to cells and removes carbon dioxide and other wastes. (p. 641)

sangre Un fluido en el cuerpo que reparte oxígeno y otras sustancias a las células y elimina dióxido de carbono y otros desechos.

blubber
A layer of fat in some sea mammals that lies beneath the skin. It insulates the animal from cold and stores reserve energy. (p. 456)

grasa de ballena Una capa de tejido graso en algunos mamíferos marinos que yace bajo la piel. Aísla al animal del frió y almacena energía de reserva.

budding
A process of asexual reproduction in which an organism develops as an outgrowth of the parent. Each bud can grow into a new organism, breaking free and becoming separate and independent. (p. 89)

gemación Un proceso de reproducción asexual en el cual un organismo se desarrolla a partir de una porción del progenitor. Cada yema puede convertirse en un nuevo organismo, separándose del progenitor y volviéndose independiente.

C

capillary
A narrow blood vessel that connects arteries with veins. (p. 645)

capilar Un vaso sanguíneo angosto que conecta a las arterias con las venas.

carbohydrate (KAHR-boh-HY-drayt)
A type of molecule made up of subunits of sugars and used for energy and structure. (p. 42)

carbohidrato Un tipo de molécula compuesta de unidades de azúcares y usada como fuente de energía y como material estructural.

GLOSSARY

GLOSSARY

carbon cycle
The continuous movement of carbon through Earth, its atmosphere, and the living things on Earth. (p. 482)

ciclo del carbono El movimiento continuo del carbono en la Tierra, su atmósfera y todos los seres vivos en ella.

cardiac muscle
The muscle that makes up the heart. (p. 600)

músculo cardiaco El músculo del cual está compuesto el corazón.

carrying capacity
The maximum size that a population can reach in an ecosystem. (pp. 242, 529)

capacidad de carga El tamaño máximo que una población puede alcanzar en un ecosistema.

cell
The smallest unit that is able to perform the basic functions of life. (p. xxxi)

célula La unidad más pequeña capaz de realizar las funciones básicas de la vida.

cell cycle
The normal sequence of growth, maintenance, and division in a cell. (p. 80)

ciclo celular La secuencia normal de crecimiento, mantenimiento y división en una célula.

cell membrane
The outer boundary of the cytoplasm, a layer that controls what enters or leaves the cell; a protective covering enclosing an entire cell. (p. 20)

membrana celular El límite exterior del citoplasma, una capa que controla lo que entra y sale de la célula, una cubierta protectora que encierra una célula entera.

cellular respiration
A process in which cells use oxygen to release energy stored in sugars. (pp. 50, 325, 615)

respiración celular Un proceso en el cual las células usan oxígeno para liberar energía almacenada en las azúcares.

cell wall
A protective outer covering that lies just outside the cell membrane of plant cells. (p. 21)

pared celular Una cubierta exterior protectora que se encuentra justo fuera de la membrana celular de las células vegetales.

central nervous system
The brain and spinal cord. The central nervous system communicates with the rest of the nervous system through electrical signals sent to and from neurons. (p. 680)

sistema nervioso central El cerebro y la médula espinal. El sistema nervioso central se comunica con el resto del sistema nervioso mediante señales eléctricas enviadas hacia y desde las neuronas.

chemical energy
Energy that is stored in the chemical composition of matter. The amount of chemical energy in a substance depends on the types and arrangement of its atoms. When wood or gasoline burns, chemical energy produces heat. The energy used by the cells in your body comes from chemical energy in the foods you eat. (p. 47)

energía química Energía almacenada en la composición química de la materia. La cantidad de energía química en una sustancia depende de los tipos y la disposición de sus átomos. Cuando se quema madera o gasolina, la energía química produce calor. La energía usada por las células en tu cuerpo proviene de la energía química en los alimentos que comes.

chemical reaction
The process by which chemical changes occur. In a chemical reaction, atoms are rearranged, and chemical bonds are broken and formed. (p. 42)

reacción química El proceso mediante el cual ocurren cambios químicos. En una reacción química, se reacomodan átomos y se rompen y se forman enlaces químicos.

childhood
The stage of life after infancy and before the beginning of sexual maturity. (p. 710)

niñez La etapa de la vida después de la infancia y antes del comienzo de la madurez sexual.

chlorophyll (KLAWR-uh-fihl)
A light-absorbing chemical, a pigment, that traps the energy in sunlight and converts it to chemical energy. Found in chloroplasts of plant cells and the cells of other photosynthetic organisms. (p. 48)

clorofila Una sustancia química que absorbe luz, un pigmento, que atrapa la energía de la luz solar y la convierte a energía química. Se encuentra en los cloroplastos de células vegetales y en las células de otros organismos fotosintéticos.

chloroplast (KLAWR-uh-PLAST)
An organelle in a plant cell that contains chlorophyll, a chemical that uses the energy from sunlight to make sugar. (p. 23)

cloroplasto Un organelo en una célula vegetal que contiene clorofila, una sustancia química que usa la energía de la luz solar para producir azúcar.

chromosome
The physical struture in a cell that contains the cell's genetic material. (p. 75)

cromosoma Una estructura corporal en la célula que contiene el material genético de la célula.

circulatory system
The group of organs, consisting of the heart and blood vessels, that circulates blood through the body. (p. 641)

sistema circulatorio El grupo de órganos, que consiste del corazón y los vasos sanguíneos, que hace circular la sangre por el cuerpo.

classification
The systematic grouping of different types of organisms by their shared characteristics. (p. 204)

clasificación La agrupación sistemática de diferentes tipos de organismos en base a las características que comparten.

cloning
The process of using DNA technology to produce an offspring that is genetically identical to its one parent. (p. 154)

clonación El proceso de usar tecnología de ADN para producir una cría que es genéticamente idéntica a su único progenitor.

cnidarian (ny-DAIR-ee-uhn)
An invertebrate animal such as a jellyfish that has a body with radial symmetry, tentacles with stinging cells, and a central internal cavity. (p. 400)

cnidario Un animal invertebrado tal como una medusa que tiene un cuerpo con simetría radial, tentáculos con células urticantes y una cavidad central interna.

commensalism (kuh-MEHN-suh-LIHZ-uhm)
An interaction between two species in which one species benefits without harming the other; a type of symbiosis. (p. 523)

comensalismo Una interacción entre dos especies en la cual una especie se beneficia sin causar daño a la otra; un tipo de simbiosis.

community
All the populations that live and interact with each other in a particular place. The community can live in a place as small as a pond or a park, or it can live in a place as large as a rain forest or the ocean. (p. 512)

comunidad Todas las poblaciones que viven e interactúan entre sí en un lugar. La comunidad puede vivir en un lugar tan pequeño como una laguna o un parque o en un lugar tan grande como un bosque tropical o el océano.

compact bone
The tough, hard outer layer of a bone. (p. 591)

hueso compacto La capa exterior, resistente y dura de un hueso.

competition
The struggle between two or more living things that depend on the same limited resource. (p. 519)

competencia La lucha entre dos o más organismos vivos que dependen del mismo recurso limitado.

competitor
A species characterized by a relatively longer life span, with relatively few offspring, when compared with an opportunist species. (p. 256)

competidor Una especie caracterizada por una vida relativamente larga, con relativamente pocas crías, en comparación con una especie oportunista.

compound
A substance made up of two or more different types of atoms.

compuesto Una sustancia formada por dos o más diferentes tipos de átomos enlazados.

coniferous (koh-NIHF-uhr-uhs)
A term used to describe cone-bearing trees and shrubs that usually keep their leaves or needles during all the seasons of the year; examples are pine, fir, and spruce trees. (p. 496)

conífero Un término usado para describir a los árboles y los arbustos que producen conos o piñas y que generalmente conservan sus hojas o agujas durante todas las estaciones del año; el pino, el abeto y la picea son ejemplos de coníferas.

conservation
The process of saving or protecting a natural resource. (p. 563)

conservación El proceso de salvar o proteger un recurso natural.

GLOSSARY

consumer
A living thing that gets its energy by eating other living things in a food chain; consumers are also called heterotrophs. (pp. 330, 488)

consumidor Un organismo vivo que obtiene su energía alimentándose de otros organismos vivos en una cadena alimentaria; los consumidores también son llamados heterótrofos.

cooperation
A term used to describe an interaction between two or more living things in which they are said to work together. (p. 521)

cooperación Un término que describe la interacción entre dos or más organismos vivos en la cual se dice que trabajan juntos.

cycle
n. A series of events or actions that repeat themselves regularly; a physical and/or chemical process in which one material continually changes locations and/or forms. Examples include the water cycle, the carbon cycle, and the rock cycle.
v. To move through a repeating series of events or actions.

ciclo Una serie de eventos o acciones que se repiten regularmente; un proceso físico y/o químico en el cual un material cambia continuamente de lugar y/o forma. Ejemplos: el ciclo del agua, el ciclo del carbono y el ciclo de las rocas.

cytokinesis (SY-toh-kuh-NEE-sihs)
The division of a parent cell's cytoplasm following mitosis. (p. 81)

citocinesis La división del citoplasma de la célula madre después de la mitosis.

cytoplasm (SY-tuh-PLAZ-uhm)
A thick, gelatin-like material contained within the cell membrane. Most of the work of the cell is carried out in the cytoplasm. (p. 20)

citoplasma Un material espeso, parecido a la gelatina, contenido dentro de la membrana celular. La mayor parte del trabajo de la célula se realiza en el citoplasma.

D

data
Information gathered by observation or experimentation that can be used in calculating or reasoning. *Data* is a plural word; the singular is *datum.*

datos Información reunida mediante observación o experimentación y que se puede usar para calcular o para razonar.

deciduous (dih-SIHJ-oo-uhs)
A term used to describe trees and shrubs that drop their leaves when winter comes; examples are maple, oak, and birch trees. (p. 497)

caducifolio Un término usado para describir árboles y arbustos que dejan caer sus hojas cuando llega el invierno; el arce, el roble y el abedul son ejemplos de árboles caducifolios.

decomposer
An organism that feeds on and breaks down dead plant or animal matter. (pp. 291, 489)

descomponedor Un organismo que se alimenta de y degrada materia vegetal o animal.

density
A property of matter representing the mass per unit volume.

densidad Una propiedad de la materia que representa la masa por unidad de volumen.

dermis
The inner layer of the skin. (p. 660)

dermis La capa interior de la piel.

dichotomous key (dy-KAHT-uh-muhs)
A series of questions, each with only two answers, that can be used to help identify an organism's genus and species. (p. 216)

clave dicotómica Una serie de preguntas, cada una con solo dos respuestas, que puede usarse para ayudar a identificar el género y especie de un organismo.

diffusion (dih-FYOO-zhuhn)
The tendency of a substance to move from an area of higher concentration to an area of lower concentration. (p. 56)

difusión La tendencia de una sustancia a moverse de un área de mayor concentración a un área de menor concentración.

digestion
The process of breaking down food into usable materials. (p. 622)

digestión El proceso de descomponer el alimento en sustancias utilizables.

digestive system
The structures in the body that work together to transform the energy and materials in food into forms the body can use. (p. 622)

sistema digestivo Las estructuras en el cuerpo que trabajan juntas para transformar la energía y las sustancias en el alimento a formas que el cuerpo puede usar.

diversity
A term used to describe the quality of having many differences. *Biodiversity* describes the great variety and many differences found among living things.

diversidad Un término usado para describir la cualidad de tener muchas diferencias. La biodiversidad describe la gran variedad y las muchas diferencias encontradas entre organismos vivos.

DNA
The genetic material found in all living cells that contains the information needed for an organism to grow, maintain itself, and reproduce. Deoxyribonucleic acid (dee-AHK-see-RY-boh-noo-KLEE-ihk). (p. 74)

ADN El material genético que se encuentra en todas las céulas vivas y que contiene la información necesaria para que un organismo crezca, se mantenga a sí mismo y se reproduzca. Ácido desoxiribunucleico.

domain
One of three divisions in a classification system based on different types of cells. The six kingdoms of living things are grouped into three domains: Archaea, Bacteria, and Eukarya. (p. 221)

dominio Una de las tres divisiones en un sistema de clasificación basado en los diferentes tipos de células. Los seis reinos de los organismos vivos esta agrupados en tres dominios: Archaea, Bacteria y Eukarya.

dominant
A term that describes the allele that determines the phenotype of an individual organism when two different copies are present in the genotype. (p. 107)

dominante Un término que describe al alelo que determina el fenotipo de un organismo cuando están presentes dos copias diferentes en el genotipo.

E

echinoderm
An invertebrate sea animal with a spiny skeleton, a water vascular system, and tube feet. (p. 411)

equinodermo Un animal invertebrado marino con esqueleto espinoso, sistema vascular acuífero y pies ambulacrales.

ecology
The scientific study of how living things interact with each other and their environment. (p. 473)

ecología El estudio científico de cómo interactúan los organismos vivos entre sí y con su medio ambiente.

ecosystem
All the living and nonliving things that interact in a particular environment. An ecosystem can be as small as a meadow or a swamp or as large as a forest or a desert. (p. 473)

ecosistema Todos los organismos vivos y las cosas que interactúan en un medio ambiente específico. Un ecosistema puede ser tan pequeño como un prado o un pantano, o tan grande como un bosque o un desierto.

ectotherm
An animal whose body temperature changes with environmental conditions. (p. 442)

poiquilotermo o poiquilotérmico Un animal cuya temperatura corporal cambia con las condiciones del medio ambiente.

egg
A female reproductive cell (gamete) that forms in the reproductive organs of a female and has just a single copy of the genetic material of the parent. (p. 118)

óvulo Una célula reproductiva femenina (gameto) que se forma en los órganos reproductivos de una hembra y tiene una sola copia del material genético de la madre.

element
A substance that cannot be broken down into a simpler substance by ordinary chemical changes. An element consists of atoms of only one type.

elemento Una sustancia que no puede descomponerse en otra sustancia más simple por medio de cambios químicos normales. Un elemento consta de átomos de un solo tipo.

embryo (EHM-bree-OH)
A multicellular organism, plant or animal, in its earliest stages of development. (pp. 370, 697)

embrión Una planta o un animal en su estadio mas temprano de desarrollo.

emigration
In population studies, the movement of individuals out of an ecosystem. (p. 251)

emigración En estudios poblacionales, el movimiento de individuos fuera de un ecosistema.

endocrine system
A group of organs called glands and the hormones they produce that help regulate conditions inside the body. (p. 686)

sistema endocrino Un grupo de órganos llamados glándulas y las hormonas que producen que ayudan a regular las condiciones dentro del cuerpo.

endoskeleton
An internal support system; such a skeleton made of bone tissue is a distinguishing characteristic of vertebrate animals. (p. 429)

endoesqueleto Un sistema de soporte interno, como un esqueleto formado de tejido óseo es una característica distintiva de los animales vertebrados.

endotherm
An animal that maintains a constant body temperature. (p. 446)

homeotermo o endotermo Un animal que mantiene una temperatura corporal constante.

energy
The ability to do work or to cause a change. For example, the energy of a moving bowling ball knocks over pins; energy from food allows animals to move and to grow; and energy from the Sun heats Earth's surface and atmosphere, which causes air to move.

energía La capacidad para trabajar o causar un cambio. Por ejemplo, la energía de una bola de boliche en movimiento tumba los pinos; la energía proveniente de su alimento permite a los animales moverse y crecer; la energía del Sol calienta la superficie y la atmósfera de la Tierra, lo que ocasiona que el aire se mueva.

energy pyramid
A model used to show the amount of energy available to living things in an ecosystem. (p. 492)

pirámide de energía Un modelo usado para mostrar la cantidad de energía disponible para organismos vivos en un ecosistema.

environment
Everything that surrounds a living thing. An environment is made up of both living and nonliving factors. (p. xxxv)

medio ambiente Todo lo que rodea a un organismo vivo. Un medio ambiente está compuesto de factores vivos y factores sin vida.

epidermis
The outer layer of the skin. (p. 660)

epidermis La capa exterior de la piel.

estuary
The lower end of a river where it meets the ocean and fresh and salt waters mix. (p. 500)

estuario La parte baja de un río donde desemboca en el océano y donde el agua dulce del río se mezcla con el agua salada del mar.

eukaryotic cell (yoo-KAR-ee-AHT-ihk)
A cell in which the genetic material is enclosed within a nucleus, surrounded by its own membrane. (p. 20)

célula eucariota Una célula en la cual el material genético esta dentro de un núcleo, rodeado por su propia membrana.

evolution
The process through which species change over time; can refer to the changes in a particular population or to the formation and extinction of species over the course of Earth's history. (p. 177)

evolución El proceso mediante el cual las especies cambian con el tiempo; puede referirse a cambios en una población en particular o a la formación y extinción de especies en el curso de la historia de la Tierra.

exoskeleton
The strong, flexible outer covering of some invertebrate animals, such as arthropods. (p. 415)

exoesqueleto La cubierta exterior fuerte y flexible de algunos animales invertebrados, como los artrópodos.

experiment
An organized procedure to study something under controlled conditions. (p. xl)

experimento Un procedimiento organizado para estudiar algo bajo condiciones controladas.

extinction
The permanent disappearance of a species. (p. xxxvii)

extinción La desaparición permanente de una especie.

F

fermentation
A chemical process by which cells release energy from sugar when no oxygen is present. (p. 52)

fermentación Un proceso químico mediante el cual las células liberan energía del azúcar cuando no hay oxígeno presente.

fertilization
Part of the process of sexual reproduction in which a male reproductive cell and a female reproductive cell combine to make a new cell that can develop into a new organism. (pp. 118, 320, 697)

fertilización El proceso mediante el cual una célula reproductiva masculina y una célula reproductiva femenina se combinan para formar una nueva célula que puede convertirse en un organismo nuevo.

fetus
The developing human embryo from eight weeks to birth. (p. 698)

feto El embrión humano en desarrollo de las ocho semanas al nacimiento.

flower
The reproductive structure of an angiosperm, containing male and female parts. (p. 380)

flor La estructura reproductiva de una angiosperma, contiene las partes masculinas y femeninas.

food chain
A model used to show the feeding relationship between a single producer and a chain of consumers in an ecosystem. In a typical food chain, a plant is the producer that is eaten by a consumer, such as an insect; then the insect is eaten by a second consumer, such as a bird. (p. 490)

cadena alimentaria Un modelo usado para mostrar la relación de ingestión entre un solo productor y una cadena de consumidores en un ecosistema. En una cadena alimentaria típica, una planta es la productora que es ingerida por un consumidor como un insecto, y luego el insecto es ingerido por un segundo consumidor como un pájaro.

food web
A model used to show a feeding relationship in which many food chains overlap in an ecosystem. (p. 490)

red trófica Un modelo usado para mostrar una relación de consumo en la cual muchas cadenas alimentarias se empalman en un ecosistema.

fossil
The imprint or hardened remains of a plant or animal that lived long ago. (p. 169)

fósil La huella o los restos endurecidos de una planta o un animal que vivió hace mucho tiempo.

fruit
The ripened ovary of a flowering plant that contains the seeds. (p. 380)

fruta El ovario maduro de una planta floreciente que contiene las semillas.

Fungi (FUHN-jy)
Part of a classification system that divides all living things into six kingdoms. Kingdom Fungi includes multicellular mushrooms and molds and single-celled yeasts. (p. 223)

Fungi Parte de un sistema de clasificación que divide a todos los organismos vivos en seis reinos. El reino Fungi incluye a los hongos multicelulares, a los mohos y a las levaduras unicelulares.

G

gamete
A sperm or egg cell, containing half the usual number of chromosomes of an organism (one chromosome from each pair), which is found only in the reproductive organs of a plant or animal. (p. 118)

gameto Un óvulo o un espermatozoide, que contiene la mitad del número usual de cromosomas de un organismo (un cromosoma de cada par), que se encuentra sólo en los órganos reproductivos de una planta o de un animal.

gene
The basic unit of heredity that consists of a segment of DNA on a chromosome. (pp. 102, 193)

gen La unidad básica de herencia que consiste en un segmento de ADN en un cromosoma.

genetic engineering
The scientific process in which DNA is separated from an organism, changed, and then reinserted into the same or a different organism. (p. 151)

ingeniería genética El proceso científico en el cual se extrae el ADN de un organismo, se modifica y luego se reinserta en el mismo organismo o en uno diferente.

genetic material
The nucleic acid DNA that is present in all living cells and contains the information needed for a cell's growth, maintenance, and reproduction.

material genético El ácido nucleico ADN, ue esta presente en todas las células vivas y que contiene la información necesaria para el crecimiento, el mantenimiento y la reproducción celular.

genome (JEE-nohm)
All the DNA of an organism, including its genes; the genetic material of an organism. (p. 154)

genoma Todo el ADN de un organismo, incluyendo sus genes; el material genético de un organismo.

genotype (JEHN-uh-TYP)
The genetic makeup of an organism; all the genes that an organism has. (p. 106)

genotipo La estructura genética de un organismo; todos los genes que tiene un organismo.

genus
The first part of a binomial name that groups together closely related species. The genus *Felis* includes all species of small cats. (p. 212)

género La primera parte de un nombre biológico que agrupa a especies muy relacionadas entre sí. El género Felis incluye a todas las especies de gatos pequeños.

GLOSSARY

germination (JUR-muh-NAY-shuhn)
The beginning of growth of a new plant from a spore or a seed. (p. 371)

germinación El inicio del crecimiento de una nueva planta a partir de una espora o una semilla.

gestation
In mammals, the period of time spent by a developing offspring inside the mother's body. (p. 458)

gestación En los mamíferos, el periodo de tiempo que pasa una cría en desarrollo dentro del cuerpo de la madre.

gill
A respiratory organ that filters oxgen dissolved in water. (p. 409)

branquia Un órgano respiratorio que filtra oxígeno disuelto en el agua.

gland
An organ in the body that produces a specific substance, such as a hormone. (p. 687)

glándula Un órgano en el cuerpo que produce una sustancia específica, como una hormona.

glucose
A sugar molecule that is a major energy source for most cells, produced by the process of photosynthesis. (p. 47)

glucosa Una molécula de azúcar que es la principal fuente de energía para la mayoría de las células, producida mediante el proceso de fotosíntesis.

gymnosperm (JIHM-nuh-SPURM)
A plant that produces seeds that are not enclosed in flowers or fruit. (p. 374)

Gimnosperma Una planta que produce semillas que no están dentro de las flores o las frutas.

H

habitat
The natural environment in which a living thing gets all that it needs to live; examples include a desert, a coral reef, and a freshwater lake. (p. 510)

hábitat El medio ambiente natural en el cual un organismo vivo consigue todo lo que requiere para vivir; ejemplos incluyen un desierto, un arrecife coralino y un lago de agua dulce.

heredity
The passing of genes from parents to offspring; the genes are expressed in the traits of the offspring. (p. 102)

herencia La transferencia de genes de los progenitores a la crías; los genes se expresan en los rasgos de las crías.

heterotroph (HEHT-uhr-uh-TRAWF)
An organism that consumes other organisms to get energy. (p. 330)

heterótrofo Un organismo que consume a otros organismos para obtener energía.

hibernation
A sleeplike state in which certain animals spend the winter. Hibernation reduces an animal's need for food and helps protect it from cold. (p. 336)

hibernación Un estado parecido al de sueño en el cual ciertos animales pasan el invierno. La hibernación reduce la necesidad de alimento de un animal y le ayuda a protegerse del frío.

homeostasis (HOH-mee-oh-STAY-sihs)
A condition needed for health and functioning in which an organism or cell maintains a relatively stable internal environment. (p. 588)

homeostasis Una condición necesaria para la salud y el funcionamiento en la cual un organismo o una célula mantiene un medio ambiente estable e interna.

hormone
A chemical that is made in one organ and travels through the blood to another organ. (p. 687)

hormona Una sustancia química que se produce en un órgano y viaja por la sangre a otro órgano.

host cell
A cell that a virus infects and uses to make copies of itself. (p. 298)

célula hospedera Una célula que un virus infecta y usa para hacer copias de sí mismo.

hyphae
Threadlike tubes that form the structural parts of the body of a fungus. *Hyphae* is a plural word; the singular is *hypha.* (p. 339)

hifas Los tubos, similares a hilos, que forman las partes estructurales del cuerpo de un hongo.

hypothesis
A tentative explanation for an observation or phenomenon. A hypothesis is used to make tentative predictions. (p. xl)

hipótesis Una explicación provisional de una observación o de un fenómeno. Una hipótesis se usa para hacer predicciones que se pueden probar.

I, J, K

immigration
In population studies, the movement of an organism into a range inhabited by individuals of the same species. (p. 251)

inmigración En estudios poblacionales, el movimiento de un organismo hacia un territorio habitado por individuos de la misma especie.

immune system
A group of organs that provides protection against disease-causing agents. (p. 651)

sistema inmune o inmunológico Un grupo de órganos que provee protección contra agentes que causan enfermedades.

immunity
Resistance to a disease. Immunity can result from antibodies formed in the body during a previous attack of the same illness. (p. 656)

inmunidad La resistencia a una enfermedad. La inmunidad puede resultar de anticuerpos formados en el cuerpo durante un ataque previo de la misma enfermedad.

incubation
The process of keeping eggs warm by bodily heat until they hatch. (p. 451)

incubación El proceso de mantener huevos cálidos por medio de calor corporal hasta que eclosionen.

infancy
The stage of life that begins at birth and ends when a baby begins to walk. (p. 710)

infancia La etapa de la vida que inicia al nacer y termina cuando el bebe empieza a caminar.

insect
An arthropod with three body segments, six legs, two antennae, and compound eyes. (p. 417)

insecto Un artrópodo con tres segmentos corporales, seis patas, dos antenas y ojos compuestos.

integumentary system (ihn-TEHG-yu-MEHN-tuh-ree)
The body system that includes the skin and its associated structures. (p. 659)

sistema tegumentario El sistema corporal que incluye a la piel y a sus estructuras asociadas.

interaction
The condition of acting or having an influence upon something. Living things in an ecosystem interact with both the living and nonliving parts of their environment. (p. xxxv)

interacción La condición de actuar o influir sobre algo. Los organismos vivos en un ecosistema interactúan con las partes vivas y las partes sin vida de su medio ambiente.

interphase
The period in the cell cycle in which a cell grows, maintains itself, and prepares for division. (p. 81)

interfase El período en el ciclo celular en el cual una célula crece, se mantiene y se prepara para la división.

invertebrate
An animal that has no backbone. (p. 395)

invertebrado Un animal que no tiene columna vertebral.

involuntary muscle
A muscle that moves without conscious control. (p. 600)

músculo involuntario Un músculo que se mueve sin control consciente.

L

larva
A free-living early form of a developing organism that is very different from its adult form. (p. 398)

larva Una etapa temprana de vida libre de un organismo en desarrollo que es muy diferente a su etapa adulta.

law
In science, a rule or principle describing a physical relationship that always works in the same way under the same conditions. The law of conservation of energy is an example.

ley En las ciencias, una regla o un principio que describe una relación física que siempre funciona de la misma manera bajo las mismas condiciones. La ley de la conservación de la energía es un ejemplo.

lichen (LY-kuhn)
An organism that results from a close association between single-celled algae and fungi. (p. 342)

liquen Un organismo que resulta de una asociación cercana entre algas unicelulares y hongos.

GLOSSARY

GLOSSARY

limiting factor
A factor or condition that prevents the continuing growth of a population in an ecosystem. (pp. 252, 528)

factor limitante Un factor o una condición que impide el crecimiento continuo de una población en un ecosistema.

lipid
A type of molecule made up of subunits of fatty acids. Lipids are found in the fats, oils, and waxes used for structure and to store energy. (p. 43)

lípido Un tipo de molécula compuesta de unidades de ácidos grasos. Los lípidos se encuentran en las grasas, los aceites y las ceras usadas como materiales estructurales y para almacenar energía.

lung
A respiratory organ that absorbs oxygen from the air. (p. 409)

pulmón Un órgano respiratorio que absorbe oxígeno del aire.

M

mammal
A warm-blooded vertebrate animal whose young feed on milk produced by the mother's mammary glands. (p. 455)

mamífero Un animal vertebrado de sangre caliente cuyas crías se alimentan de leche producida por las glándulas mamarias de la madre.

mass
A measure of how much matter an object is made of.

masa Una medida de la cantidad de materia de la que está compuesto un objeto.

mass extinction
One of several periods in Earth's history when large numbers of species became extinct at nearly the same time. (p. 174)

extinción masiva Uno de varios períodos en la historia de la Tierra cuando grandes números de especies se extinguieron casi al mismo tiempo.

matter
Anything that has mass and volume. Matter exists ordinarily as a solid, a liquid, or a gas.

materia Todo lo que tiene masa y volumen. Generalmente la materia existe como sólido, líquido o gas.

meiosis (my-OH-sihs)
A part of sexual reproduction in which cells divide to form sperm cells in a male and egg cells in a female. Meiosis occurs only in reproductive cells. (pp. 119, 320)

meiosis Una parte de la reproducción sexual en la cual las células se dividen para formar espermatozoides en los machos y óvulos en las hembras. La meiosis sólo ocurre en las células reproductivas.

menstruation
A period of about five days during which blood and tissue exit the body through the vagina. (p. 695)

menstruación Un período de aproximadamente cinco días durante el cual salen del cuerpo sangre y tejido por la vagina.

metamorphosis
The transformation of an animal from its larval form into its adult form. (p. 418)

metamorfosis La transformación de un animal de su forma larvaria a su forma adulta.

microorganism
A very small organism that can be seen only with a microscope. Bacteria are examples of microorganisms. (pp. 282, 724)

microorganismo Un organismo muy pequeño que solamente puede verse con un microscopio. Las bacterias son ejemplos de microorganismos.

microscope
An instrument that uses glass lenses to magnify an object. (p. 12)

microscopio Un instrumento que usa lentes de vidrio para magnificar un objeto.

migration
The movement of animals from one region to another in response to changes in the seasons or the environment. (p. 336)

migración El movimiento de animales de una región a otra en respuesta a cambios en las estaciones o en el medio ambiente.

mitochondria (MY-tuh-KAWN-dree-uh)
Organelles that release energy by using oxygen to break down sugars. (p. 23)

mitocondrias Organelos que liberan energía usando oxígeno para romper los azúcares.

mitosis
The phase in the cell cycle during which the nucleus divides. (p. 81)

mitosis La fase en el ciclo celular durante la cual se divide el núcleo.

mobile
Able to move from place to place. (p. 402)

móvil Capaz de moverse de un lugar a otro.

molecule
A group of atoms that are held together by covalent bonds so that they move as a single unit.

molécula Un grupo de átomos que están unidos mediante enlaces covalentes de tal manera que se mueven como una sola unidad.

mollusk
An invertebrate animal with a soft body, a muscular foot, and a mantle. Many mollusks have a hard outer shell. (p. 408)

molusco Un animal invertebrado con cuerpo blando, un pie muscular y un manto. Muchos moluscos tienen una concha exterior dura.

molting
The process of an arthropod shedding its exoskeleton to allow for growth. (p. 415)

muda El proceso mediante el cual un artrópodo se despoja de su exoesqueleto para poder crecer.

multicellular
A term used to describe an organism that is made up of many cells. (p. 11)

multicelular Un término usado para describir a un organismo que esta formado por muchas células.

multicellular organism
An organism that is made up of many cells. (p. 173)

organismo multicelular Un organismo compuesto de muchas células.

muscular system
The muscles of the body that, together with the skeletal system, function to produce movement. (p. 599)

sistema muscular Los músculos del cuerpo que, junto con el sistema óseo, sirven para producir movimiento.

mutation
Any change made to DNA. (p. 145)

mutación Cualquier cambio hecho al ADN.

mutualism (MYOO-choo-uh-LIHZ-uhm)
An interaction between two species in which both benefit; a type of symbiosis. (p. 522)

mutualismo Una interacción entre dos especies en la cual ambas se benefician; un tipo de simbiosis.

N

natural resource
Any type of matter or energy from Earth's environment that humans use to meet their needs. (p. 548)

recurso natural Cualquier tipo de materia o energía del medio ambiente de la Tierra que usan los humanos para satisfacer sus necesidades.

natural selection
The process through which members of a species that are best suited to their environment survive and reproduce at a higher rate than other members of the species. (p. 181)

selección natural El proceso mediante el cual los miembros de una especie que están mejor adecuados a su medio ambiente sobreviven y se reproducen a una tasa más alta que otros miembros de la especie.

neuron
A nerve cell. (p. 681)

neurona Una célula nerviosa.

niche (nihch)
The role a living thing plays in its habitat. A plant is a food producer, whereas an insect both consumes food as well as provides food for other consumers. (p. 511)

nicho El papel que juega un organismo vivo en su hábitat. Una planta es un productor de alimento mientras que un insecto consume alimento y a la vez sirve de alimento a otros consumidores.

nitrogen cycle
The continuous movement of nitrogen through Earth, its atmosphere, and the living things on Earth. (p. 483)

ciclo del nitrógeno El movimiento continuo de nitrógeno por la Tierra, su atmósfera y los organismos vivos de la Tierra.

nucleic acid (noo-KLEE-ihk)
A type of molecule, made up of subunits of nucleotides, that is part of the genetic material of a cell and is needed to make proteins. DNA and RNA are nucleic acids. (p. 43)

ácido nucleico Un tipo de molécula, compuesto de unidades de nucleótidos, que es parte del material genético de una célula y se necesita para producir proteínas. El ADN y el ARN son ácidos nucleicos.

GLOSSARY

nucleus (NOO-klee-uhs)
The structure in a eukaryotic cell that contains the genetic material a cell needs to reproduce and function. (p. 20)

núcleo La estructura en una célula eucariota que contiene el material genético que la célula necesita para reproducirse y funcionar.

nutrient (NOO-tree-uhnt)
A substance that an organism needs to live. Examples include water, minerals, and materials that come from the breakdown of food particles. (p. 621)

nutriente Una sustancia que un organismo necesita para vivir. Ejemplos incluyen agua, minerales y sustancias que provienen de la descomposición de partículas de alimento.

nutrition
The study of the materials that nourish the body. (p. 716)

nutrición El estudio de las sustancias que dan sustento al cuerpo.

O

offspring
The new organisms produced by one or two parent organisms.

crías Los nuevos organismos producidos por uno o dos organismos progenitores.

opportunist
A species characterized by a relatively short life span, with relatively large quantities of offspring, as compared with a competitor species. (p. 255)

oportunista Una especie caracterizada por una vida relativamente corta, que produce relativamente grandes cantidades de crías, en comparación con una especie competidora.

organ
A structure in a plant or an animal that is made up of different tissues working together to perform a particular function. (pp. 30, 316, 587)

órgano Una estructura en una planta o en un animal compuesta de diferentes tejidos que trabajan juntos para realizar una función determinada.

organelle (AWR-guh-NEHL)
A structure in a cell that is enclosed by a membrane and that performs a particular function. (p. 20)

organelo Una estructura en una célula, envuelta en una membrana, que realiza una función determinada.

organism
An individual living thing, made up of one or many cells, that is capable of growing and reproducing. (p. xxxi)

organismo Un individuo vivo, compuesto de una o muchas células, que es capaz de crecer y reproducirse.

organ system
A group of organs that together perform a function that helps the body meet its needs for energy and materials. (p. 588)

sistema de órganos Un grupo de órganos que juntos realizan una función que ayuda al cuerpo a satisfacer sus necesidades energéticas y de materiales.

osmosis (ahz-MOH-sihs)
The movement of water through a membrane from an area of higher concentration to an area of lower concentration. (p. 59)

osmosis El movimiento de agua a través de una membrana desde un área de mayor concentración hacia un área de menor concentración.

P, Q

parasite
An organism that absorbs nutrients from the body of another organism, often harming it in the process. (p. 291)

parásito Un organismo que absorbe nutrientes del cuerpo de otro organismo, a menudo causándole daño en el proceso.

parasitism (PAR-uh-suh-TIHZ-uhm)
A relationship between two species in which one species is harmed while the other benefits; a type of symbiosis. (p. 523)

parasitismo Una relación entre dos especies en la cual una especie es perjudicada mientras que la otra se beneficia; un tipo de simbiosis.

parent
An organism that produces a new organism or organisms similar to or related to itself. (p. 93)

progenitor Un organismo que produce un nuevo organismo u organismos parecidos a o relacionados a él.

passive transport
The movement of materials through a membrane without any input of energy. (p. 58)

transporte pasivo El movimiento de sustancias a través de una membrana sin aporte de energía.

pathogen
An agent that causes disease. (p. 650)

patógeno Un agente que causa una enfermedad.

pedigree
A chart that shows family relationships, including two or more generations. (p. 147)

pedigrí Un diagrama de las relaciones de dos o más generaciones de una familia.

percentage
A ratio that states the number of times an outcome is likely to occur out of a possible 100 times. (p. 112)

porcentaje Una razón que establece el número de veces que es probable que ocurra un resultado en 100 veces.

peripheral nervous system
The part of the nervous system that lies outside the brain and spinal cord. (p. 682)

sistema nervioso periférico La parte del sistema nervioso que se encuentra fuera del cerebro y la médula espinal.

peristalsis (PEHR-ih-STAWL-sihs)
Wavelike contractions of smooth muscles in the organs of the digestive tract. The contractions move food through the digestive system. (p. 622)

peristalsis Contracciones ondulares de músculos lisos en los órganos del tracto digestivo. Las contracciones mueven el alimento por el sistema digestivo.

phenotype
The observable characteristics or traits of an organism. (p. 106)

fenotipo Las características o rasgos visibles de un organismo.

photosynthesis (FOH-toh-SIHN-thih-sihs)
The process by which green plants and other producers use simple compounds and energy from light to make sugar, an energy-rich compound. (pp. 48, 324, 487)

fotosíntesis El proceso mediante el cual las plantas verdes y otros productores usan compuestos simples y energía de la luz para producir azúcares, compuestos ricos en energía.

pioneer species
The first species to move into a lifeless environment. Plants like mosses are typical pioneer species on land. (p. 530)

especie pionera La primera especie que ocupa un medio ambiente sin vida. Las plantas como los musgos son típicas especies pioneras terrestres.

placenta
An organ that transports materials between a pregnant female mammal and the offspring developing inside her body. (p. 458)

placenta Un órgano que transporta sustancias entre un mamífero hembra preñado y la cría que se está desarrollando dentro de su cuerpo.

plankton
Mostly microscopic organisms that drift in great numbers through bodies of water. (p. 305)

plancton Organismos, en su mayoría microscópicos, que se mueven a la deriva en grandes números por cuerpos de agua.

Plantae (PLAN-tee)
Part of a classification system that divides all living things into six kingdoms. Kingdom Plantae includes multicellular organisms, such as trees, grass, and moss, that are capable of photosynthesis, capturing energy from the Sun. (p. 223)

Plantae Parte de un sistema de clasificación que divide a todos los organismos vivos en seis reinos. El reino Plantae incluye a organismos multicelulares, como árboles, pasto y musgo, que son capaces de fotosintetizar, capturando la energía del Sol.

pollen
Tiny multicellular grains that contain the undeveloped sperm cells of a plant. (p. 372)

polen Los diminutos granos multicelulares que contienen las células espermáticas sin desarrollar de una planta.

pollution
The release of harmful substances into the air, water, or land. (pp. 264, 555)

contaminación La descarga de sustancias nocivas al aire, alagua o a la tierra.

population
A group of organisms of the same species that live in the same area. For example, a desert will have populations of different species of lizards and cactus plants. (p. 510)

población Un grupo de organismos de la misma especie que viven en la misma área. Por ejemplo, un desierto tendrá poblaciones de distintas especies de lagartijas y de cactus.

R81

population density
A measure of the number of organisms that live in a given area. The population density of a city may be given as the number of people living in a square kilometer. (pp. 245, 550)

densidad de población Una medida de la cantidad de organismos que viven un área dada. La densidad de población de una ciudad puede expresarse como el número de personas que viven en un kilómetro cuadrado.

population dynamics
The study of the changes in the number of individuals in a population and the factors that affect those changes. (p. 241)

dinámica de población El estudio de los cambios en el número de individuos en una población y los factores que afectan a estos cambios.

population size
The number of individuals of the same species that live in a given area. (p. 244)

tamaño de la población El número de individuos de la misma especie que vive en un área determinada.

predator
An animal that hunts other animals and eats them. (pp. 335, 519)

predador Un animal que caza otros animales y se los come.

prey
An animal that other animals hunt and eat. (pp. 335, 519)

presa Un animal que otros animales cazan y se comen.

probability
The likelihood or chance that a specific outcome will occur out of a total number of outcomes. (p. 112)

probabilidad La posibilidad de que ocurra un resultado específico en un número total de resultados.

producer
An organism that captures energy from sunlight and transforms it into chemical energy that is stored in energy-rich carbon compounds. Producers are a source of food for other organisms. (pp. 291, 487)

productor Un organismo que capta energía de la luz solar y la transforma a energía química que se almacena en compuestos de carbono ricos en energía. Los productores son una fuente de alimento para otros organismos.

prokaryotic cell (proh-KAR-ee-AWT-ihk)
A cell that lacks a nucleus and other organelles, with DNA that is not organized into chromosomes. (p. 20)

célula procariota Una célula que carece de núcleo y otros organelos, con ADN que no esta organizado en cromosomas.

protein
One of many types of molecules made up of chains of amino acid subunits. Proteins control the chemical activity of a cell and support growth and repair. (p. 43)

proteína Uno de muchos tipos de moléculas formadas por cadenas de aminoácidos. Las proteínas controlan la actividad química de una célula y sustentan el crecimiento y la reparación.

Protista (proh-TIHS-tuh)
Part of a classification system that divides all living things into six kingdoms. Kingdom Protista includes mostly single-celled organisms with cells similar to those of the Plantae, Animalia, and Fungi kingdoms. (p. 223)

Protista Parte de un sistema de clasificación que divide a todos los organismos vivos en seis reinos. El reino Protista incluye principalmente a organismos unicelulares con células parecidas a las de los reinos Plantae, Animalia y Fungi.

protozoa
Animal-like protists that eat other organisms or decaying parts of other organisms. *Protozoa* is a plural word; the singular is *protozoan.* (p. 306)

protozoarios Protistas parecidos a los animales que comen otros organismos o partes en descomposición de otros organismos.

Punnett square
A chart used to show all the ways genes from two parents can combine and be passed to offspring; used to predict all genotypes that are possible. (p. 110)

cuadro de Punnett Una tabla que se usa para mostrar todas las formas en que los genes de dos progenitores pueden combinarse y pasarse a la crías; se usa para predecir todos los genotipos que son posibles.

R

ratio
A comparison between two quantities, often written with a colon, as 3 : 4. (p. 112)

razón Una comparación entre dos cantidades, a menudo se escribe con dos puntos, como 3 : 4.

recessive
A term that describes an allele that is not expressed when combined with a dominant form of the gene. (p. 107)

recesivo Un término que describe un alelo que no se expresa cuando se combina con una forma dominante del gen.

red blood cell
A type of blood cell that picks up oxygen in the lungs and delivers it to cells throughout the body. (p. 643)

glóbulos rojos Un tipo de célula sanguínea que toma oxígeno en los pulmones y lo transporta a células en todo el cuerpo.

regeneration
In some organisms, the process by which certain cells produce new tissue growth at the site of a wound or lost limb; also a form of asexual reproduction. (p. 90)

regeneración En algunos organismos, el proceso mediante el cual ciertas células producen crecimiento de tejido nuevo en el sitio de una herida o de una extremidad perdida; también un tipo de reproducción asexual.

replication
The process by which DNA is copied before it condenses into chromosomes. Replication takes place before a cell divides. (p. 137)

replicación El proceso mediante el cual el ADN se copia antes de condensarse en los cromosomas. La replicación se realiza antes de que una célula se divida.

reptile
A cold-blooded vertebrate that has skin covered with scales or horny plates and has lungs. (p. 440)

reptil Un vertebrado de sangre fría que tiene la piel cubierta de escamas o placas callosas y que tiene pulmones.

resistance
The ability of an organism to protect itself from a disease or the effects of a substance. (p. 729)

resistencia La habilidad de un organismo para protegerse de una enfermedad o de los efectos de una sustancia.

respiration
The physical and chemical processes by which a living thing exchanges gases with the environment. In cellular respiration, cells take in oxygen and release the energy stored in carbon compounds.

respiración Los procesos físicos y químicos mediante los cuales un organismo vivo toma oxígeno y libera energía. En la respiración celular, las células absorben oxígeno y liberan la energía almacenada en compuestos de carbono.

respiratory system
A system that interacts with the environment and with other body systems to bring oxygen to the body and remove carbon dioxide. (p. 613)

sistema respiratorio Un sistema que interactúa con el medio ambiente y con otros sistemas corporales para traer oxígeno al cuerpo y eliminar dióxido de carbono.

RNA
A molecule that carries genetic information from DNA to a ribosome, where the genetic information is used to bring together amino acids to form a protein. Ribonucleic acid (RY-boh-noo-KLEE-ihk). (p. 138)

ARN Una molécula que lleva información genética del ADN al ribosoma, donde la información genética se usa para unir aminoácidos para formar una proteína. Ácido ribonucleico.

S

scale
One of the thin, small, overlapping plates that cover most fish and reptiles and some other animals. (p. 433)

escama Una de las pequeñas y delgadas placas traslapadas que cubren a la mayoría de los peces y reptiles y algunos otros animales.

seed
A plant embryo that is enclosed in a protective coating and has its own source of nutrients. (p. 370)

semilla El embrión de una planta que esta dentro de una cubierta protectora y que tiene su propia fuente de nutrientes.

selective breeding
The process of breeding plants and animals with specific traits to produce offspring that have these traits. (p. 151)

reproducción selectiva El proceso de reproducir plantas y animales con rasgos específicos para producir crías que tengan estos rasgos.

sessile (SEHS-EEL)
The quality of being attached to one spot; not free-moving. (p. 397)

sésil La cualidad de estar sujeto a un punto; sin libre movimiento.

GLOSSARY

GLOSSARY

sexual reproduction
A type of reproduction in which male and female reproductive cells combine to form offspring with genetic material from both cells. (pp. 102, 320)

reproducción sexual Un tipo de reproducción en el cual se combinan las células reproductivas femeninas y masculinas para formar una cría con material genético de ambas células.

skeletal muscle
A muscle that attaches to the skeleton. (p. 600)

músculo esquelético Un músculo que está sujeto al esqueleto.

skeletal system
The framework of bones that supports the body, protects internal organs, and anchors all the body's movement. (p. 590)

sistema óseo El armazón de huesos que sostiene al cuerpo, protege a los órganos internos y sirve de ancla para todo el movimiento del cuerpo.

smooth muscle
Muscle that performs involuntary movement and is found inside certain organs, such as the stomach. (p. 600)

músculo liso Músculos que realizan movimiento involuntario y se encuentran dentro de ciertos órganos, como el estómago.

specialization
The specific organization of a cell and its structure that allows it to perform a specific function. (p. 28)

especialización La organización específica de una célula y de su estructura que le permite realizar una función específica.

speciation
The evolution of a new species from an existing species. (p. 184)

especiación La evolución de una nueva especie a partir de una especie existente.

species
A group of living things that are so closely related that they can breed with one another and produce offspring that can breed as well. (p. xxxvii)

especie Un grupo de organismos que están tan estrechamente relacionados que pueden aparearse entre sí y producir crías que también pueden aparearse.

sperm
A male reproductive cell (gamete) that forms in the reproductive organs of a male and has just a single copy of the genetic material of the parent. (p. 118)

espermatozoide Una célula reproductiva masculina (gameto) que se forma en los órganos reproductivos de un macho y tiene una sola copia del material genético del progenitor.

sponge
A simple multicellular invertebrate animal that lives attached to one place and filters food from water. (p. 397)

esponja Un animal invertebrado multicelular simple que vive sujeto a un lugar y filtra su alimento del agua.

spongy bone
Strong, lightweight tissue inside a bone. (p. 591)

hueso esponjoso Tejido fuerte y de peso ligero dentro de un hueso.

spore
A single reproductive cell that can grow into a multicellular organism. (p. 339)

espora Una célula reproductiva individual que puede convertirse en un organismo multicelular.

stimulus
Something that causes a response in an organism or a part of the body. (pp. 327, 678)

estímulo Algo que causa una respuesta en un organismo o en una parte del cuerpo.

succession (suhk-SEHSH-uhn)
A natural process that involves a gradual change in the plant and animal communities that live in an area. (p. 530)

sucesión Un proceso natural que involucra un cambio gradual en las comunidades de plantas y animales que viven en un área.

sustainable
A term that describes the managing of certain natural resources so that they are not harmed or used up. Examples include maintaining clean groundwater and protecting top soil from erosion. (p. 566)

sostenible Un término que describe el manejo de ciertos recursos naturales para que no se deterioren o se terminen. Ejemplos incluyen mantener limpia el agua subterránea y proteger de la erosión a la capa superficial del suelo.

symbiosis (SIHM-bee-OH-sihs)
The interaction between individuals from two different species that live closely together. (p. 522)

simbiosis La interacción entre individuos de dos especies distintas que viven en proximidad.

system
A group of objects or phenomena that interact. A system can be as simple as a rope, a pulley, and a mass. It also can be as complex as the interaction of energy and matter in the four parts of the Earth system.

sistema Un grupo de objetos o fenómenos que interactúan. Un sistema puede ser algo tan sencillo como una cuerda, una polea y una masa. También puede ser algo tan complejo como la interacción de la energía y la materia en las cuatro partes del sistema de la Tierra.

T

taxonomy
The science of classifying and naming organisms. (p. 204)

taxonomía La ciencia de clasificar y ponerle nombre a los organismos.

technology
The use of scientific knowledge to solve problems or engineer new products, tools, or processes.

tecnología El uso de conocimientos científicos para resolver problemas o para diseñar nuevos productos, herramientas o procesos.

tentacle
A long, slender, flexible extension of the body of certain animals, such as jellyfish. Tentacles are used to touch, move, or hold. (p. 400)

tentáculo Una extensión larga, delgada y flexible del cuerpo de ciertos animales, como las medusas. Los tentáculos se usan para tocar, mover o sujetar.

theory
In science, a set of widely accepted explanations of observations and phenomena. A theory is a well-tested explanation that is consistent with all available evidence.

teoría En las ciencias, un conjunto de explicaciones de observaciones y fenómenos que es ampliamente aceptado. Una teoría es una explicación bien probada que es consecuente con la evidencia disponible.

tissue
A group of similar cells that are organized to do a specific job. (pp. 29, 316, 586)

tejido Un grupo de células parecidas que juntas realizan una función específica en un organismo.

trait
Any type of feature that can be used to tell two species apart, such as size or bone structure.

rasgo Cualquier característica que puede usarse para diferenciar a dos especies, como el tamaño o la estructura ósea.

transpiration (TRAN-spuh-RAY-shuhn)
The movement of water vapor out of a plant and into the air. (p. 360)

transpiración El movimiento de vapor de agua hacia fuera de una planta y hacia el aire.

U

unicellular
A term used to describe an organism that is made up of a single cell. (p. 11)

unicelular Un término usado para describir a un organismo que está compuesto de una sola célula.

unicellular organism
An organism that is made up of a single cell. (p. 172)

organismo unicelular Un organismo compuesto de una sola célula.

urban
A term that describes a city environment.

urbano Un término que describe el medio ambiente de una ciudad.

urinary system
A group of organs that filter waste from an organism's blood and excrete it in a liquid called urine. (p. 629)

sistema urinario Un grupo de órganos que filtran desechos de la sangre de un organismo y los excretan en un líquido llamado orina.

urine
Liquid waste that is secreted by the kidneys. (p. 629)

orina El desecho líquido que secretan los riñones.

vaccine
A small amount of a weakened pathogen that is introduced into the body to stimulate the production of antibodies. (p. 656)

vacuna Una pequeña cantidad de un patógeno debilitado que se introduce al cuerpo para estimular la producción de anticuerpos.

GLOSSARY

variable
Any factor that can change in a controlled experiment, observation, or model. (p. R30)

variable Cualquier factor que puede cambiar en un experimento controlado, en una observación o en un modelo.

vascular system (VAS-kyuh-lur)
Long tubelike tissues in plants through which water and nutrients move from one part of the plant to another. (p. 359)

sistema vascular Tejidos largos en forma de tubo en las plantas a través de los cuales se mueven agua y nutrientes de una parte de la planta a otra.

vein
A blood vessel that carries blood back to the heart. (p. 645)

vena Un vaso sanguíneo que lleva la sangre de regreso al corazón.

vertebrate
An animal with an internal backbone. (p. 429)

vertebrado Un animal que tiene columna vertebral interna.

vestigial organ (veh-STIHJ-ee-uhl)
A physical structure that was fully developed and functional in an earlier group of organisms but is reduced and unused in later species. (p. 190)

órgano vestigial Una estructura física que fue completamente desarrollada y funcional en un grupo anterior de organismos pero que está reducido y en desuso en especies posteriores.

virus
A nonliving disease-causing particle that uses the materials inside cells to make copies of itself. A virus consists of genetic material enclosed in a protein coat. (pp. 286, 725)

virus Una particular sin vida, que causa enfermedad y que usa los materiales dentro de las células para reproducirse. Un virus consiste de material genético encerrado en una cubierta proteica.

volume
An amount of three-dimensional space, often used to describe the space that an object takes up.

volumen Una cantidad de espacio tridimensional; a menudo se usa este término para describir el espacio que ocupa un objeto.

voluntary muscle
A muscle that can be moved at will. (p. 600)

músculo voluntario Un músculo que puede moverse a voluntad.

voluntary nervous system
The nerves that govern consciously controlled function and movement. (p. 683)

sistema nervioso voluntario Los nervios que gobiernan las funciones y el movimiento cuyo control es consciente.

W, X, Y, Z

water cycle
The continuous movement of water through Earth, its atmosphere, and the living things on Earth. (p. 481)

ciclo del agua El movimiento continuo de agua por la Tierra, su atmósfera y los organismos vivos de la Tierra.

Index

Page numbers for definitions are printed in **boldface** type.
Page numbers for illustrations, maps, and charts are printed in *italics*.

A

INDEX

B

INDEX

D

INDEX

R91

INDEX

E

F

INDEX

G

INDEX

H

INDEX

I

J

K

L

INDEX

M

INDEX

N

O

P, Q

R

INDEX

S

INDEX

T

U

V

INDEX

INDEX

Acknowledgments

Photography

Cover Terry Whittaker/Photo Researchers, Inc.; i Terry Whittaker/Photo Researchers, Inc.; **iii** Photograph of James Trefil by Evan Cantwell; Photograph of Rita Ann Calvo by Joseph Calvo; Photograph of Kenneth Cutler by Kenneth A. Cutler; Photograph of Douglas Carnine by McDougal Littell; Photograph of Linda Carnine by Amilcar Cifuentes; Photograph of Donald Steely by Marni Stamm; Photograph of Sam Miller by Samuel Miller; Photograph of Vicky Vachon by Redfern Photographics; **vi** *bottom* © Kent Foster Photographs/Bruce Coleman, Inc.; **viii** *bottom* © Richard T. Nowitz/Corbis; **ix** © Burke/Triolo/Artville: Bugs and Insects; **x** © Orion Press/Corbis; **xii** © Jeff Schultz/Alaska Stock.com; **xiii** © Wolcott Henry/National Geographic Image Collection; **xiv** © Larry Dale Gordon/Getty Images; **xv** © Professors P.M. Motta & S. Correr/Photo Researchers, Inc.; **xx** Photograph by Ken O'Donoghue; **xxi** *bottom left* Photograph by Ken O'Donoghue *bottom right* Photograph by Frank Siteman, **xxx–xxxi** © Mark Hamblin/Age Fotostock; **xxxii–xxxiii** © Georgette Duowma/Taxi/Getty Images; **xxxiv–xxxv** © Ron Sanford/Corbis; **xxxvi–xxxvii** © Nick Vedros & Assoc./Stone/Getty Images; **xxxviii** *left* © Michael Gadomski/Animals Animals; *right* © Shin Yoshino/Minden Pictures; **xxxix**© Laif Elleringmann/Aurora Photos; **xl** © Pascal Goetgheluck/Science Photo Library/Photo Researchers, Inc.; **xli** *top left* © David Parker/Science Photo Library/Photo Researchers, Inc.; *top right* © James King-Holmes/Science Photo Library/Photo Researchers, Inc.; *bottom* Sinsheimer Labs/University of California, Santa Cruz; **xlii–xliii** *background* © Maximillian Stock/Photo Researchers, Inc.; **xlii** Courtesy, John Lair, Jewish Hospital, University of Louisville; **xliii** *top* © Brand X Pictures/Alamy; *center* Courtesy, AbioMed; **xlviii** © Chedd-Angier Production Company.

Cells and Heredity

Divider © Dr. Gopal Murti/Photo Researchers, Inc.; **2, 3** © Mark Smith/Photo Researchers, Inc.; **4** *top left to right* © Dr. Richard Kessel and Dr. Gene Shih/Visuals Unlimited; *bottom* © Chedd-Angier Production Company; **5** *left* © Carolina Biological/Visuals Unlimited; *right* © Inga Spence/Visuals Unlimited; **6, 7** © Biophoto Associates/Photo Researchers, Inc.; **7** *top right* Photograph by Ken O'Donoghue; *center right* Photograph by Frank Siteman; **9** Photograph by Ken O'Donoghue; **10** © Heintges/Premium Stock/PictureQuest ; **11** *bottom* © David Stone/Rainbow/ PictureQuest; *inset* © Science VU/Visuals Unlimited; **12** *left* © American Registry of Photography; *right* Library of Congress, Prints and Photographs Division, #LC-USZ62-95187; **13** *bottom* © Tom Walker/Visuals Unlimited; *inset* © Greg Theiman; **14** © Will & Demi McIntyre/Corbis; **16** *top* © Science VU/Visuals Unlimited; *center* Photograph by Frank Siteman; *bottom left, bottom right* Photographs by Ken O'Donoghue; **18** *left* Photograph by Ken O'Donoghue; *right* © Dr. Gary Gaugler/Visuals Unlimited **19** © Eye of Science/Photo Researchers, Inc., **20** *left* © Eric Grave/Photo Reseachers, Inc.; *right* © CNRI/Photo Reseachers, Inc ; **21** *bottom left* © Biophoto Associates/Science Source/Photo Researchers, Inc.; *bottom right* © Dennis Kunkel/Phototake; **22** *background* © John Edwards/Getty Images; *inset* © Gary Braasch/Getty Images; **23** © Dr. Martha Powell/Visuals Unlimited; **24** *top* © Dr. Henry Aldrich/Visuals Unlimited, *bottom* © Biophoto Associates/Photo Researchers, Inc.; **25** *top* © Dr. Gary Gaugler/Visuals Unlimited; *bottom* © Dr. Tony Brain and David Parker/Photo Reseachers, Inc., **26** Photograph by Ken O'Donoghue; **27** *center* © Ralph White/Corbis; *inset* © Alfred Pasieka/Photo Researchers, Inc.; **28** © Stan Flegler/Visuals Unlimited; **29** *left to right* © Ted Whittenkraus/Visuals Unlimited; © Gustav Verderber/Visuals Unlimited; © Dwight R. Kuhn; **30** *left* © Eric and David Hosking/Corbis; *right* © Frans Lanting/Minden Pictures; **31** Photograph by Ken O'Donoghue; **32** *top* © Ken Eward/BioGrafx/Photo Researchers, Inc.; *inset* © A. Barrington Brown/Photo Researchers, Inc.; **33** *left* © Photo Researchers, Inc.; *inset* © Dr. Linda Stannard, UCT/Photo Researchers, Inc.; **34** *top left* David Stone/Rainbow/PictureQuest; *top right* © Science VU/Visuals Unlimited; *center left* © CNRI/Photo Reseachers, Inc.; © *bottom* Frans Lanting/Minden Pictures; **35** © Dr. Martha Powell/Visuals Unlimited; **36** *top* © Tom Walker/Visuals Unlimited; *inset* © Greg Theiman; **38, 39** © Kent Foster Photographs/Bruce Coleman, Inc.; **39** *top, center* Photographs by Ken O'Donoghue; **41** Photograph by Ken O'Donoghue; **42** © Corbis-Royalty Free; **44** *top* © Alfred Pasieka/Photo Researhers, Inc.; *bottom* Photograph by Ken O'Donoghue; **46** *background* © Andrew Syred/Photo Researchers, Inc.; *bottom left* © Anna Clopet/Corbis; *center right* Photograph by Tim Nihoff; *montage top to bottom* © Dr. Jeremy Burgess/Photo Researchers, Inc.; © Andrew Syred/Photo Researchers, Inc.; **47** *top right* © David Young-Wolff/PhotoEdit; *top inset* John Durham/Photo Researchers, Inc.; *bottom inset* © Innerspace Imaging/Photo Researchers, Inc.; **48** © Dr. Jeremy Burgess/Photo Researchers, Inc.; **49** *top center* © Biophoto Associates/Science Source/Photo Researchers, Inc.; **51** *top left* © Dr. Gopal Murti/Photo Researchers, Inc.; *top right* © Biophoto Associates/Science Source/Photo Researchers, Inc.; **53** Photograph by Ken O'Donoghue; **54** © Bob Daemmrich Photo, Inc.; **55** © Roger Ressmeyer/Corbis; **56** Photograph by Ken O'Donoghue; **59** © Marilyn Schaller/Photo Researchers, Inc.; **60** © Fred Bavendam/Peter Arnold, Inc.; **62** Photograph by Frank Siteman; **64** *top* Corbis/Royalty Free; *all others* Photograph by Frank Siteman; **66** *bottom left* Photograph by Frank Siteman; *bottom right* © Fred Bavendam/Peter Arnold, Inc.; **70, 71** © CNRI/Photo Researchers, Inc.; **71** *top right* Photograph by Ken O'Donoghue; *center right* Photograph by Frank Siteman; **73** Photograph by Ken O'Donoghue; **74** © Will & Deni McIntyre/Photo Researchers, Inc.; **76** Photograph by Frank Siteman; **77** *background* © Rudiger Lehnen/Photo Researchers, Inc.; *left inset* © Alexis Rosenfeld/Photo Researchers, Inc.; *right inset* © David Hughes/Bruce Coleman, Inc.; **79** *left* © Nancy Kedersha/UCLA/Photo Researchers, Inc.; *top right* Photograph of Elizabeth Gould by Denise Applewhite; **80** © IFA/eStock Photo/PictureQuest; **83** © Ed Reschke; **84** Photograph by Ken O'Donoghue; **85** *left* © Dr. Gopal Murti/Photo Researchers, Inc.; *right* © Carolina Biological/Visuals Unlimited; **86** *top* © Michael Newman/PhotoEdit, Inc., *top right, bottom left, bottom right* Photographs by Ken O'Donoghue; *center right* © Science VU/Visuals Unlimited; *center* © Custom Medical Stock Photo; **88** © M.I. Walker/Photo Researchers, Inc.; **89** *top* © CNRI/Photo Researchers, Inc.; *bottom* © Biophoto Associates/Photo Researchers, Inc.; **90** © David B. Fleetham/Visuals Unlimited; **91** *top* © Cytographics/Visuals Unlimited; *bottom* Photograph by Ken O'Donoghue; **93** © CNRI/Phototake; **94** © Will & Deni McIntyre/Photo Researchers,

ACKNOWLEDGMENTS

Inc.; **98, 99** © Norbert Rosing/National Geographic Image Collection; **99** *top right* © Photodisc/Getty Images; *center right* Photograph by Ken O'Donoghue; **101** © Florence Delva/Getty Images; **103** *left* © CNRI/Photo Researchers, Inc.; *right* © Biophoto Associates/Photo Researchers, Inc.; **106** © Mary Kate Denny/PhotoEdit; **107** © Ken Weingart/Corbis; **108** *top* © Johnny Johnson/Animals Animals; *bottom* Photograph by Ken O'Donoghue; **109, 110** Photographs by Ken O'Donoghue; **113** *background* © Ludovic Maisant/Corbis; *bottom right* © Jane Burton/Bruce Coleman, Inc.; **114** Photograph by Frank Siteman; **116** © Robert Dowling/Corbis; **117** Photograph by Ken O'Donoghue; **118** © Pascal Goetgheluck/Photo Researchers, Inc.; **119** Photograph by Ken O'Donoghue; **123** © David M. Phillips/Photo Researchers, Inc.; **128** *center* Library of Congress, Prints and Photographs Division, #LC-USZ62-95187; *center right* Courtesy of The Royal Society of London; *bottom* Courtesy of Professor John Doebley, Genetics Department, University of Wisconsin; **129** *top left* Library and Archives of the Royal Botanical Gardens, Kew; *center* Drawing by Edward Strasburger; *center left* © Margaret Stones; *center right* © Oliver Meckes/Photo Researchers, Inc.; *bottom* © Vic Small; **130** *top left* Reproduced from *The Journal of Experimental Medicine*, 1944, vol. 79, 158-159, by copyright permission of the Rockefeller University Press; *top right* © Dr. Gopal Murti/Photo Researchers, Inc.; *center* © Omikron/Photo Researchers, Inc.; *bottom left* © Lennart Nilsson/Albert Bonniers Forlag AB; **131** *top* © David Parker/Photo Researchers, Inc.; *center* Courtesy of The Whitehead Institute/MIT Center for Genome Research and reprinted by permission of Nature, 409:745-964 (2001), Macmillan Publishers Ltd.; *bottom* Courtesy of the USC-Keck School of Medicine and Ashanti DeSilva; **132, 133** © Ted Horowitz/Corbis; **133** *top right* Photograph by Ken O'Donoghue; *bottom right* © Corbis-Royalty Free; **135** Photography by Ken O'Donoghue; **139** Photograph by Ken O'Donoghue; **142** *top* © Ken Eward/Photo Researchers, Inc.; *center* Photograph by Frank Siteman; *bottom* Photography by Ken O'Donoghue; **143** Photograph by Frank Siteman; **144** Photograph by Ken O'Donoghue; **145** © David Pollack/Corbis; **146** Photograph by Frank Siteman; **147** © Meckes/Ottawa/Photo Researchers, Inc.; **148** © Gladden Willis/Visuals Unlimited, Inc; **149** © Dennis Kunkel Microscopy, Inc.; **150** © Geoff Tompkinson/Photo Researchers, Inc.; **151** © Doug Loneman/AP Wide World Photos; **152** © Richard T. Nowitz/Corbis; **153** © Mark C. Burnett/Stock Boston, Inc./PictureQuest ; **154** © Getty Images; **155** *left* © ImageState-Pictor/PictureQuest; *right* © PJ Green/Ardea London Limited; **156** © Getty Images.

Life Over Time

Divider © Martin Siepman/Age Fotostock America Inc.; **162, 163** *background* © Alfredo Maiquez/Lonely Planet Images; **163** *top left* © Donald Windsor; *bottom right* Reprinted with permission from "Timing the Radiations of Leaf Beetles: Hispines on Gingers from Latest Cretaceous to Recent" Peter Wilf and Conrad C. Labandeira, SCIENCE V. 289:291-294 (2000). © 2000 AAAS.; **164** *bottom* © The Chedd-Angier Production Company; *top* Courtesy, Earth Sciences and Image Analysis, NASA-Johnson Space Center; **165** © The Natural History Museum, London; **166, 167** © Richard T. Nowitz/Corbis; **170** *top* © Mark A. Schneider/Photo Researchers, Inc.; *center* © Sinclair Stammers/Photo Researchers, Inc.; *bottom* © Novosti/Science Photo Library/Photo Researchers, Inc.; **171** *bottom* © Field Museum/Photo Researchers, Inc.; **173** *top* © Ken M. Johns/Photo Researchers, Inc.; **174** *bottom* © Lynette Cook/Photo Researchers, Inc.; **175** *top right* © D. Van Ravenswaay/Photo Researchers, Inc.; *bottom right* © David Parker/Photo Researchers, Inc.; *top left* © D. Van Ravenswaay/Photo Researchers, Inc.; **176** *top* © Paddy Ryan/Animals Animals; *bottom* © Layne Kennedy/Corbis; **177** *left* © Corbis-Royalty Free; **178, 179** *background* © Ralph Lee Hopkins/Lonely Planet Images; *bottom* © The Natural History Museum, London; *top* © The Granger Collection, New York; **179** *top right* © Volker Steger/Photo Researchers, Inc.; *right* © Zig Leszczynski/ Animals Animals; *left* © Theo Allots/Visuals Unlimited; **180** *bottom right, top left, top right* © Tui De Roy/Minden Pictures; *bottom left* © Richard l'Anson/Lonely Planet Images; *background* © Ralph Lee Hopkins/Lonely Planet Images; **181** *right* © Hans Reinhard/Bruce Coleman, Inc.; center, *left* © Larry Allan/Bruce Coleman, Inc.; **183** *top left* © Bruce Coleman, Inc.; *background* © Paul Souders/Accent Alaska; **184** *top* © Hans Reinhard/Bruce Coleman, Inc.; *bottom, center* © Jane Burton/Bruce Coleman, Inc.; **185** © John Winnie, Jr./DRK Photo; **186** *top* © Marian Bacon/Animals Animals; **188** © Ed Degginger/Color-Pic, Inc.; **189** © Mark A. Schneider/Photo Researchers, Inc.; **191** *background* © Corbis-Royalty Free; **192** *center, left* © Photodisc/Getty Images; *right* © Mark Smith/Photo Researchers, Inc.; **194** © Photodisc/Getty Images; **195** © Norbert Wu; **196** *bottom* © Mark A. Schneider/Photo Researchers, Inc.; *top* © Tui de Roy/Bruce Coleman, Inc.; **198** © Hans Reinhard/Bruce Coleman, Inc.; **200, 201** © Burke/Triolo/Artville: Bugs and Insects; **201** *top right* © Ed Block/Corbis; **203** *top* © Robert Pickett/Corbis; *bottom* © U.S. Fish & Wildlife Service; **204** *right* © David I. Roberts/Photo Researchers, Inc.; *left* © S.J. Krasemann/Photo Researchers, Inc.; **205** *center* © Renee Lynn/Photo Researchers, Inc.; *bottom left* © Tom McHugh/Photo Researchers. Inc.; *top right* © Len Rue, Jr./Bruce Coleman, Inc.; *bottom right* © Frans Lanting/Minden Pictures; **207** *right* © Bill Kamin/Visuals Unlimited; *bottom left* © Norbert Wu; center, *top left* © Dave Fleetham/Tom Stack & Associates; *background* © E.R. Degginger/Photo Researchers, Inc.; **208** *top* © D. Ditchburn/Visuals Unlimited; *bottom* © M.H. Sharp/Photo Researchers, Inc.; **209** *top right* © Tom Brakefield/Bruce Coleman, Inc.; *top left* © Fritz Polking/POLKI/Bruce Coleman, Inc.; *bottom left* © G.C. Kelley/Photo Researchers, Inc.; *bottom right* © Tom McHugh/Photo Researchers, Inc.; *background* © Corbis-Royalty Free; **210** © Mary Evans Picture Library; **211** *top* © Photodisc/Getty Images; **213** *left, right* © Judy White/GardenPhotos.com; *center* © Tom J. Ulrich; **214** *left* © Joe McDonald/Visuals Unlimited; *right* © Photodisc/Getty Images; **215** *right* © John Mitchell/Photo Researchers, Inc.; *background* © Visuals Unlimited; **217** *top right* © Robert Della-Piana/photolibrary/PictureQuest; *background* © Photodisc/Getty Images; **218** From *A Field Guide To The Birds Of Eastern And Central North America,* Fifth Edition by Roger Tory Peterson. Text copyright © 2002 by Marital Trust B u/a Roger Tory Peterson and the Estate of Virginia Peterson. Reprinted by permission of Houghton Mifflin Company. All rights reserved.; **219** *background* © Link/Visuals Unlimited; *bottom* © George Bryce/Animals Animals; **220** © Ken Lucas/Visuals Unlimited; **221** *left* © CNRI/Photo Researchers, Inc.; *center* © Wolfgang Baumeister/Photo Researchers, Inc.; *right* © Biophoto Associates/Photo Researchers, Inc.; **222** *top to bottom* © Corbis-Royalty Free; © Sharna Balfour/Gallo Images/Corbis; © Eric Grave/Photo Researchers, Inc.; © Rico & Ruiz/Nature Picture Library; © Dr. Jeremy Burgess/Photo Researchers, Inc.; © Eye of Science/Photo Researchers, Inc.; *background* © Courtesy of NASA/Corbis; **224** *center* © Jim Zuckerman/Corbis; *right* © Masa Ushioda/Bruce Coleman, Inc.; *left* © M. & C. Photography/Peter Arnold, Inc.; *top* © Ed Degginger/Earthscenes; **225** © Jeff Foott/Bruce Coleman, Inc.; **226** *right* © Mark Taylor, Warren Photographic/Bruce Coleman, Inc.; *bottom* © Dr. M. Rohde, GBF/Photo Researchers, Inc.; *left* © Cordelia Molloy/Photo Researchers, Inc.; **227** © Gary Gaugler/Visuals Unlimited; **228** © Corbis-Royalty Free; **230** © John Mitchell/Photo Researchers, Inc.; **234** *bottom right* © Visuals Unlimited; *bottom left, top right* The Natural History Museum Picture Library, London; **235** *top left* American

Museum of Natural History Library; *bottom right* © O. Louis Mazzatenta/National Geographic Image Collection; *center* © Peter Scoones/Photo Researchers, Inc.; *top right* © Geoff Bryant/Photo Researchers, Inc.; **236** *top left* © Science/Visuals Unlimited; *top right* © Kevin O. Mooney/Odyssey/Chicago; *center right* © Ira Block/National Geographic Image Collection; *bottom left* © James King-Holmes/Photo Researchers, Inc.; **237** *top left* © John Reader/Science Photo Library; *bottom left* © David Parker/Photo Researchers, Inc.; **238, 239** *background* NASA, **241** © David M. Phillips/Photo Researchers, Inc.; **243** *left* © Photo Researchers, Inc.; *right* © Wayne Lynch/DRK Photo; **244** *right* © Darrell Gulin/DRK Photo; *left* © Thomas Wiewandt/Corbis; **245** *left* © Stephen J. Krasemann/DRK Photo; *right* © D. Cavagnaro/DRK Photo; **246** *center* © Visuals Unlimited; *right* © Judy White/GardenPhotos.com; *left* © Betty Press/Animals Animals; **247** © Jim Sulley/The Image Works; **248** © Anthony Mercieca/Photo Researchers, Inc.; **249** *left* © Rod Planck/Photo Researchers, Inc.; *right* © Michael Abbey/Photo Researchers, Inc.; **251** © OSF/N. Rosing/Animals Animals; **252** © Tom Brakefield/Corbis; **253** © Najlah Feanny/Corbis; **255** *right* © Martha Cooper/Peter Arnold, Inc.; *bottom* © Dennis Flaherty/Photo Researchers, Inc.; **256** © Stephen J. Krasemann/DRK Photo; **257** *left* © Ted Spiegel/Corbis; *top right* © Wesmar; **259** *bottom right* © Rob Crandall/The Image Works; *bottom left* © Grant Heilman/Grant Heilman Photography; *top right* © Ed Degginger/Color-Pic, Inc.; **260** *left* © Bob Daemmrich/The Image Works; *right* © Geri Engberg/The Image Works; **261** NASA; **263** *top* © Ray Coleman/Photo Researchers, Inc.; *bottom* © John Serrao/Photo Researchers, Inc.; **264** *top* © Donald Speckler/Animals Animals; *bottom* © Janis Burger/Bruce Coleman, Inc.; **265** © Jeff Greenberg/The Image Works; **266** © Gaetano/Corbis; **268** *center* © Najlah Feanny/Corbis; *bottom* © Bob Daemmrich/The Image Works; **270** © Photo Researchers, Inc.; **271** © Wayne Lynch/DRK Photo.

Diversity of Living Things

Divider © Buddy Mays/Corbis; **274, 275** © *background* Yva Momatiuk/John Eastcott/Minden Pictures; **275** *top* © Pat O'Hara/Corbis; *bottom* © Darrell Gulin/Corbis; **276** *top left* © Bruce Marlin/Cirrus Digital Imaging; *top right* © A.B. Sheldon; *bottom* © Chedd-Angier Production Company; **278, 279** © Science VU/Visuals Unlimited; **279** *top* Photograph by Frank Siteman; *center* Photograph by Ken O'Donoghue; *bottom* © Custom Medical Stock Photo; **281** Photograph by Ken O'Donoghue; **282** *background* © Lynda Richardson/Corbis; *inset* © Astrid & Hanns-Frieder Michler/Photo Researchers, Inc.; **284** © A.B. Dowsett/Science Photo Library/Photo Researchers, Inc.; **285** Photograph by Ken O'Donoghue; **286** *right* © Dr. Gopal Murti/Photo Researchers, Inc.; *left* © K.G. Murti/Visuals Unlimited; **287** © CNRI/Photo Researchers, Inc.; **288** © Dennis Kunkel/Visuals Unlimited; **289** *left* © Tina Carvalho/Visuals Unlimited; *center* © D.M. Phillips/Visuals Unlimited; *right* © CNRI/Photo Researchers, Inc.; **290** *left* © Grant Heilman/Grant Heilman Photography; *left inset* © Dr. Kari Lounatmaa/Photo Researchers, Inc.; *center* © Roger Tidman/Corbis; *center inset* © Alfred Pasieka/Science Photo Library/Photo Researchers, Inc.; *right* © ML Sinbaldi/Corbis; *right inset* © Wolfgang Baumeister/Photo Researchers, Inc.; **291** *left* © Jack Novak/Photri-Microstock; *left inset* © Dr. Kari Lounatmaa/Photo Researchers, Inc.; *center* © Dennis Flaherty/Photo Researchers, Inc.; *center inset* © Microfield Scientific LTD/Science Photo Library/Photo Researchers, Inc.; *right* © Dr. P. Marazzi/Science Photo Library/Photo Researchers, Inc.; *right inset* © Dr. Kari Lounatmaa/Photo Researchers, Inc.; **292** © *background* Runk/Schoenberger/Grant Heilman Photography; *left inset* © Simko/Visuals Unlimited; *right inset* © Dwight R. Kuhn; **293** © T.A. Zitter/Cornell University; **294** *top* © Adam Hart-Davis, Leeds Public Health Laboraory/Photo Researchers, Inc.; *bottom (both)* Photographs by Ken O'Donoghue; **296, 297** Photographs by Frank Siteman; **298** © Hans Gelderblom/Visuals Unlimited; **299** *(both)* © Lee D. Simon/Photo Researchers, Inc.; **300** © Bettmann/Corbis; **301** *left* © Judy White/GardenPhotos.com; *right* © Dennis Kunkel Microscopy, Inc.; **302** © Corbis; **303** Photograph by Ken O'Donoghue; **304** *left* © R. Kessel-G. Shih/Visuals Unlimited; *center* © Jan Hinsch/Photo Researchers, Inc.; *right* © Runk/Schoenberger/Grant Heilman Photography; **305** © R. Kessel-C.Y. Shih/Visuals Unlimited; **306** © Andrew Syred/Photo Researchers, Inc.; **307** © Ed Reschke/Peter Arnold, Inc.; **308** *bottom left* © Runk/Schoenberger/Grant Heilman Photography; *bottom center* © Ed Reschke/Peter Arnold, Inc.; *bottom right* © Andrew Syred/Photo Researchers, Inc.; **310** *left* © A.B. Dowsett/Science Photo Library/Photo Researchers, Inc.; *right* © Science VU/Visuals Unlimited; **312, 313** © Orion Press/Corbis; **313** *top, center* Photographs by Ken O'Donoghue; **315** © David G. Massey/AP Wide World Photos; **316** Photograph by Frank Siteman; **317** © Joe McDonald/Bruce Coleman, Inc.; **318** © Michael Doolittle/ PictureQuest; **319** *background* © Photospin; *top* © A. Mercieca/Photo Researchers, Inc.; *center* © Jim Brandenburg/Minden Pictures; *center inset* © Yva Momatiuk/John Eastcott/Minden Pictures; *bottom* © Tim Fitzharris/Minden Pictures; **320** © Matt Brown/Corbis; **321** *left* © Joe McDonald/Corbis; *right* © David J. Wrobel/Visuals Unlimited; **322** © Frans Lanting/Minden Pictures; **323, 324** Photographs by Ken O'Donoghue; **325** *top* © Peter Dean/Grant Heilman Photography; *inset* © Pascal Goetgheluck/Science Photo Library/Photo Researchers, Inc.; **326** *(both)* © D. Suzio/Photo Researchers, Inc.; **327** *left* © Joel Arrington/Visuals Unlimited; *right* © Gary W. Carter/Visuals Unlimited; **329** © Josiah Davidson/Picturesque/PictureQuest; **330** © Yva Momatiuk/John Eastcott/Minden Pictures; **331** *left* © Brandon Cole; *right* © Rauschenbach/Premium Stock/PictureQuest ; **332** Photograph by Frank Siteman; **333** *left and left inset* © Dwight R.Kuhn; *center* © Steve Maslowski/Visuals Unlimited; *right* © Belinda Wright/DRK Photo; **334** © J. Sneesby/B. Wilkins/Getty Images; **335** *top* © Shin Yoshino/Minden Pictures; *bottom left* © Charles V. Angelo/Photo Researchers, Inc.; *bottom right* © Fred McConnaughey/Photo Researchers, Inc.; **336** *left* © Ron Austing/Photo Researchers, Inc.; *right* © Kevin Schafer; **337** *left, top right* © Steve Winter/National Geographic Image Collection; *bottom right* © Brian J. Skerry/National Geographic Image Collection; **338** Photograph by Ken O'Donoghue; **340** © IFA/eStock Photography/PictureQuest ; **341** *top* © Andrew Syred/Science Photo Library/Photo Researchers; *bottom* © Simko/Visuals Unlimited; **343** *(both)* © Lennart Nilsson/Albert Bonniers Forlag AB; **344** *top* © Bob Daemmrich/Stock Boston, Inc./PictureQuest; *bottom* Photograph by Ken O'Donoghue; **345** Photograph by Frank Siteman; **346** *top* © Matt Brown/Corbis; *center* © Rauschenbach/Premium Stock/PictureQuest ; *bottom* © IFA/eStock Photography/PictureQuest; **350** *top* © Academy of Natural Sciences of Philadelphia/Corbis; *bottom* © The Granger Collection, New York; **351** *top left, top right* © The Natural History Museum, London; *bottom left* © Photo Researchers, Inc.; *bottom right* © The Granger Collection, New York; **352** *top left* © B. Boonyaratanakornit & D.S. Clark, G. Vrdoljak/EM Lab, UC Berkeley/Visuals Unlimited, Inc.; *top right* © OAR/National Undersea Research Program; *center* © Terry Erwin/ Smithsonian Institution; *bottom* © Emory Kristoff/National Geographic Image Collection; **353** © Michael Bordelon/Smithsonian Institution; **354, 355** © David J. Job/AlaskaStock.com; **355** *(both)* Photographs by Ken O'Donoghue; **357** Photograph by Ken O'Donoghue; **358** *left* © Nick Garbutt/Nature Picture Library; *center* © D. Cavagnaro/Visuals Unlimited; *right* © Hal Horwitz/Corbis; **359** © Andrew Syred/Photo Researchers, Inc.; **360** *(both)* © Dr. Jeremy Burgess/Science Photo Library/Photo

ACKNOWLEDGMENTS

Researchers, Inc.; **361** *background* © Donna Disario/Corbis; *top left* © Photodisc/Getty Images; **362** © Craig K. Lorenz/Photo Researchers, Inc.; **363** *top* © Delphoto/Premium Stock/ PictureQuest; *inset* © Unicorn Stock Photo; **364** Photograph by Frank Siteman; **365** *top* © Ray Simmons/Photo Researchers, Inc.; *bottom* The Field Museum of Natural History, #GEO85637c; **366** Photograph by Frank Siteman; **367** © Dwight R. Kuhn; **368** *left* © Dr. Jeremy Burgess/Science Photo Library/Photo Researchers, Inc.; *inset* School Division, Houghton Mifflin Co.; *right* © Michael & Patricia Fogden/Corbis; **369** *left* © Dwight R. Kuhn; *right* © Sylvester Allred/Fundamental Photographs; **370** © Keren Su/Corbis; **371** © Dwight R. Kuhn; **372** © Martha Cooper/Peter Arnold, Inc.; **373** *background* © Photospin; *top* © Scott Barrow/ImageState; *bottom* © Bryan Mullenix/Getty Images; **374** Photograph by Ken O'Donoghue; **375** © Robert Gustafson/Visuals Unlimited; **376** *top* © Michael J. Doolittle/The Image Works; *bottom right* © James A. Sugar/Corbis; **377** Photograph by Frank Siteman; **378** *left* © Raymond Gehman/Corbis; *top right* © David Sieren/Visuals Unlimited, Inc.; *bottom right* © George Bernard/Science Photo Library; **379** Photograph by Ken O'Donoghue; **381** *background* © John Marshall; *left* © George D. Lepp/Corbis; *center* © Sergio Piumatti; *right* © Gary Braasch/Corbis; **382** © Ed Reschke; **383** *top* Photograph by Ken O'Donoghue; *bottom* © Custom Medical Stock Photo; **384** *left* © Frank Lane Picture Agency/Corbis; *right* © Eastcott/Momatiuc/Animals Animals; **385** *right* © Craig Aurness/Corbis; *inset* © Michael Newman/PhotoEdit; **386** *background* © Lance Nelson/Corbis; *top, left* National Cotton Council of America; *right* © Mary Kate Denny/PhotoEdit; **387** *left* © Patricia Agre/Photo Researchers, Inc.; *right* © Martin B. Withers, Frank Lane Picture Agency/Corbis; **388** *top* © Hal Horwitz/Corbis; *center left* © Martha Cooper/Peter Arnold, Inc.; *center right* © Dwight R. Kuhn; *bottom left* © Gary Braasch/Corbis; *bottom right* © George D. Lepp/Corbis; **389** *(both)* © Wolfgang Bayer/Bruce Coleman, Inc./PictureQuest ; **392, 393** © Norbert Wu; **393** *top* Photograph by Frank Siteman; *bottom* © Photospin; **395** © Andrew J. Martinez/Visuals Unlimited; **396** Photograph by Ken O'Donoghue; **397** *background* © Viola's Photo Visions, Inc./Animals Animals; **398** © Marty Snyderman/Visuals Unlimited; **399** *background* © Kevin Schafer/Getty Images; **400** Photograph by Ken O'Donoghue; **401** © Photodisc/Getty Images; **402** *top left, bottom left* © John D. Cunningham/Visuals Unlimited; **403** *left* © Bob Evans/Peter Arnold, Inc.; *right* © Visuals Unlimited; **404** © Dwight R. Kuhn; **405** *top* © Larry Lipsky/DRK Photo; *center* © A. Flowers & L. Newman/Photo Researchers, Inc.; *bottom* © Richard Kessel/Visuals Unlimited; **406** *top* © Robert Pickett/Corbis; *bottom* Photograph by Ken O'Donoghue; **407** *top* Photograph by Ken O'Donoghue; *bottom* Photograph by Frank Siteman; **408** © Sinclair Stammers/Photo Researchers, Inc.; **409** *top* © Andrew J. Martinez/Photo Researchers, Inc.; *bottom* © Konrad Wothe/Minden Pictures; **410** *top* Photograph by Ken O'Donoghue; *bottom* © Fred Bavendam/Minden Pictures; **411** *top* © Andrew J. Martinez; *bottom* © David Wrobel/Visuals Unlimited; **412** *left* © Fred Winner/Jacana/Photo Researchers, Inc.; *right* © Gerald & Buff Corsi/Visuals Unlimited; **413** *background* © Dwight R. Kuhn; *inset* © Thomas Kitchin/Tom Stack & Associates; **414** Photograph by Frank Siteman; **415** *top* © Kelvin Aitken/Peter Arnold, Inc.; *bottom* © Barry Runk/Grant Heilman Photography; **416** *background* © Corbis-Royalty Free; *top* © Tim Davis/Corbis; *center* © Steve Wolper/DRK Photo; *bottom* © George Calef/DRK Photo; **418** Photograph by Ken O'Donoghue; **419** *top (all)* © Dwight R. Kuhn; *bottom* © Frans Lanting/Minden Pictures; **420** *top* © David Scharf/Peter Arnold, Inc.; *bottom* © E.R. Degginger/Color-Pic, Inc.; **421** *left* © Science Photo Library/Photo Researchers, Inc.; *right* © Claus Meyer/Minden Pictures; **422** *top right* © Viola's Photo Visions, Inc./Animals Animals; *center left* © John D. Cunningham/Visuals Unlimited; *bottom left* © Konrad Wothe/Minden Pictures; *bottom right* © Gerald & Buff Corsi/Visuals Unlimited; **426, 427** © Paul A. Souders/Corbis; **427** *top* Photograph by Frank Siteman; *center left* © Steven Frame/Stock Boston Inc./PictureQuest; *center right* © Rod Planck/Photo Researchers, Inc.; **429** Photograph by Frank Siteman; **430** © Corbis-Royalty Free; **431** *background* © SeaLifeStyles Signature Series/Imagin; **432** *background* © Colla - V&W/Bruce Coleman, Inc.; *left* © Norbert Wu; *left inset* © Brandon Cole; *center* © Georgienne E. Bradley & Jay Ireland/Bradley Ireland Productions; *right* © Brandon Cole; **434** © David Doubilet; **435** *left* © Kennan Ward/Corbis; *right* © Frans Lanting/Minden Pictures; **436** *left* © Bianca Lavies/National Geographic Image Collection; *right* Photograph by Frank Siteman; **437** *left* © Dwight R. Kuhn; *right* © Joe McDonald/Bruce Coleman, Inc.; **438** *all* © Dwight R. Kuhn; **440** © Francois Gohier/Photo Researchers, Inc.; **441** © Carmela Leszczynski/Animals Animals; **442** *top* Photograph by Frank Siteman; *bottom* © Tui de Roy/Minden Pictures; **443** © Michael Fogden/Animals Animals; **444** *left* ©Frans Lanting/Minden Pictures; *center* © E.R. Degginger/Color-Pic, Inc.; *right* © Science Photo Library/Photo Researchers, Inc.; **445** Photograph by Ken O'Donoghue; **446** © Michael Quinton/Minden Pictures; **447** *left* © Julie Habel/Corbis; *center* © Randy Faris/Corbis; *right* © David-Young Wolff/PhotoEdit; **449** *background* © Tim Bird/Corbis; **450** *left* © Jim Brandenburg/Minden Pictures; *right* © Fritz Polking/Visuals Unlimited; **451** *top* © Ron Austing/Photo Researchers, Inc.; *bottom* © S. Nielsen/DRK Photo; **452** *top* © DigitalVision/PictureQuest; *bottom* Photograph by Frank Siteman **453** *top* Photograph by Frank Siteman; *bottom left* © Corbis-Royalty Free; *bottom center* © Frans Lemmens/Getty Images; *bottom right* © Arthur Morris/Corbis; **454** © Carleton Ray/Photo Researchers, Inc.; **455** *top* © Mitsuaki Iwago/Minden Pictures; *bottom* © Don Enger/Animals Animals; **456** Photograph by Frank Siteman; **457** *background* © Stephen Frink/Corbis; **458** *left* © Photodisc/Getty Images; *right* © Frans Lanting/Minden Pictures; **459** © Comstock; **460** *top left* © Dwight R. Kuhn; *top right* © Michael Fogden/Animals Animals; *center right* © Fritz Polking/Visuals Unlimited; *bottom left* © Frans Lanting/Minden Pictures; *bottom right* © Photodisc/Getty Images.

Ecology

Divider © Richard du Toit/Nature Picture Library; **466, 467** *background* © Mark Thiessen/National Geographic Image Collection; **467** *top* © Frank Oberle/Getty Images; *bottom* © Hal Horwitz/Corbis; **468** *top (both)* © Lawrence J. Godson; *bottom* Chedd-Angier Production Company; **470, 471** © Jeff Schultz/Alaska Stock.com; **471** *top* Photograph by Ken O'Donoghue; *center* Photograph by Frank Siteman; **473** Photograph by Frank Siteman; **474** © Mark Allen Stack/Tom Stack & Associates; **475** *left* © Jim Brandenburg/Minden Pictures; *right* © Ted Kerasote/Photo Researchers, Inc.; **476** *bottom left* © Grant Heilman Photography; **477** © Frans Lemmens/Getty Images; **478** *top* © Michael J. Doolittle/The Image Works, Inc.; *bottom* Photograph by Ken O'Donoghue; **480** Photograph by Ken O'Donoghue; **483** Photograph by Frank Siteman; **485** © Randy Wells/Corbis; **486** Photograph by Frank Siteman; **487** *left* © Eric Crichton/Corbis; *top right* © E.R. Degginger/Color-Pic, Inc.; *bottom right* © T.E. Adams/Visuals Unlimited, Inc.; **488** © Anthony Mercieca Photo/Photo Researchers, Inc.; **489** *top* © Fred Bruemmer/DRK Photo; *bottom* Photograph by Ken O'Donoghue; **491** *background* © Raymond Gehman/Corbis; **493** *left* © Arthur Gurmankin & Mary Morina/Visuals Unlimited, Inc.; *top right* © Carmela Leszczynski/Animals Animals; **494** © Charles Melton/Visuals Unlimited, Inc.; **495** © Michio Hoshino/Minden Pictures; **496** *top left* © Tom Bean; *top right* © E.R. Degginger/Color-Pic, Inc.; *bottom* © Joe McDonald/Visuals Unlimited, Inc.; **497** *left* © David Wrobel/Visuals Unlimited, Inc.; *right* © Tom Bean; **498** *left* ©

Owaki-Kulla/Corbis; *right* © Frans Lanting/Minden Pictures; **499** *top* Photograph by Ken O'Donoghue; *bottom* © Stephen Dalton/Photo Researchers, Inc.; **500** *left* © Aaron Horowitz/Corbis; *center* © Hans Pfletschinger/Peter Arnold, Inc.; *right* © Arthur Gurmankin & Mary Morina/Visuals Unlimited, Inc.; **501** *left* © Paul Rezendes; *center* © Richard Herrmann/Visuals Unlimited, Inc.; *right* © Norbert Wu; **506, 507** © Wolcott Henry/National Geographic Image Collection; **507** *top* Photograph by Frank Siteman; *center* Photograph by Ken O'Donoghue; **509** Photograph by Frank Siteman; **510** *left and center* © Frans Lanting/Minden Pictures; *right* © Robin Karpan/Visuals Unlimited, Inc.; **514** © Walt Anderson/Visuals Unlimited, Inc.; **515** © Alan & Linda Detrick/Photo Researchers, Inc.; **516** *top* © Patrick J. Endres/Visuals Unlimited, Inc.; *bottom left* Photograph by Frank Siteman; *bottom right* Photograph by Ken O'Donoghue; **517** Photograph by Ken O'Donoghue; **518** © Spencer Grant/PhotoEdit, Inc.; **519** © Gary Braasch; **520** *top* © Joe McDonald/Visuals Unlimited, Inc.; *bottom* © Stephen J. Krasemann/Photo Researchers, Inc.; **521** *top* Photograph by Ken O'Donoghue; *bottom* © Michael Fogden/Bruce Coleman Inc.; **522** © Michael & Patricia Fogden/Minden Pictures; **523** © Bradley Sheard; **524** *clockwise from top* © S.J. Krasemann/Peter Arnold, Inc.; © Ray Coleman/Visuals Unlimited, Inc.; © Astrid & Hanns-Frieder Michler/Science Photo Library; © E.R. Degginger/Color-Pic, Inc.; © Dwight R. Kuhn; © Phil Degginger/Color-Pic, Inc.; **525** © Arthur Morris/Visuals Unlimited, Inc.; **526** *left* © Kevin Fleming/Corbis; *inset* © David M. Dennis/Animals Animals; **527** Photograph by Ken O'Donoghue; **528** *top* © Shin Yoshino/Minden Pictures; *bottom* © Tim Fitzharris/Minden Pictures; **529** Photograph by Frank Siteman; **530** *bottom (background)* © Leo Collier/Getty Images; **531** *bottom* (background) © David R. Frazier/Getty Images; **533** © A. & J. Visage/Peter Arnold, Inc.; **534** *top left* © Frans Lanting/Minden Pictures; **538** *bottom left* Denver Public Library, Western History Collection, call#F-4659; *top center* © James Randklev/Getty Images; *bottom right* Library of Congress, Prints and Photographs Division (LC-USZ62-16709 DLC) cph 3a18915; **539** *top left* © H.H. French/Corbis; *top right* © Bill Ross/Corbis; *center left* The Bancroft Library, University of California, Berkeley; *center right* © Corbis; *bottom* © Michael Sewell/Peter Arnold, Inc.; **540** *top left* © Alfred Elsenstaedt/Getty Images; *top right* © Tom Bean/DRK Photo; *center right* © David Muench/Corbis; *bottom left* © Kevin Schafer/Corbis; *bottom right* Habitat Quality for San Joaquin Kit Fox on Managed and Private Lands reprinted from ESRI Map Book, Vol. 16 and used herein with permission. Copyright © 2001 ESRI. All rights reserved.; **541** *top* © Tom Soucek/Alaska Stock Images; *bottom* © Richard Galosy/Bruce Coleman, Inc.; **542, 543** © Alex Maclean/Photonica; **543** *top and center* Photographs by Ken O'Donoghue; **545** Photograph by Frank Siteman; **547** © Ray Pfortner/Peter Arnold, Inc.; **548** Photograph by Ken O'Donoghue; **549** *top* © John Elk III; *bottom* © Ted Spiegel/Corbis; **550** *background* © ChromoSohm/Sohm/Photo Researchers, Inc.; *insets* Courtesy, USGS: EROS Data Center; **551** © Mark E. Gibson/Visuals Unlimited, Inc.; **552** © David Zimmerman/Corbis; **553** © David Young-Wolff/PhotoEdit, Inc.; **554** *left* © Richard Stockton/Iguazu Falls/Index Stock Imagery, Inc.; *right* © Bill Ross/Corbis; **555** Photograph by Ken O'Donoghue; **556** *bottom* © Tom Bean/DRK Photo; *inset* © Jenny Hager/The Image Works, Inc.; **557** *bottom* © Natalie Fobes/Corbis; *inset* © Natalie Fobes/Getty Images; **559** © Kent Foster Photgraphs/Visuals Unlimited, Inc.; **560** *top* © Andrew J. Martinez/Photo Researchers, Inc.; *inset* © D. Cavagnaro/Visuals Unlimited, Inc.; **561** © Tom Edwards/Visuals Unlimited, Inc.; **562** Photographs by Ken O'Donoghue and Frank Siteman; **563** © Frank Pedrick/The Image Works, Inc.; **564** © Joe McDonald/Visuals Unlimited, Inc.; **565** *top (background)* © Jim Wark/Airphoto; *top (inset)* Photograph by Scott Williams/U.S. Fish and Wildlife Service; *bottom (background)* © Tom Bean/Corbis; *bottom (insets)* Courtesy, San Diego State University, Soil Ecology and Restoration Group; **566** © Melissa Farlow/National Geographic Image Collection; **567** © Klein/Hubert/Peter Arnold, Inc.; **568** *top* © Janis Miglavs; *bottom* © David Young-Wolff/PhotoEdit, Inc.; **569** © Kevin Schafer/Corbis; **570** *top* Tom Myers/Photo Researchers, Inc.; *bottom* Photograph by Frank Siteman; **572** *center left* © Natalie Fobes/Corbis; *center right* © Kent Foster Photographs/Visuals Unlimited, Inc.; *bottom left* © Joe McDonald/Visuals Unlimited, Inc.; *bottom right* © Klein/Hubert/Peter Arnold, Inc.

Human Biology

Divider RNHRD NHS Trust; **578–579** © Peter Byron/PhotoEdit; **579** *top right* © ISM/Phototake; **580** *top* © Wellcome Department of Cognitive Neurology/Photo Researchers, Inc., *bottom* Chedd-Angier Production Company; **581** © Myrleen Ferguson Cate/PhotoEdit; **582–583** © Chris Hamilton/Corbis; **583** *top* Frank Siteman, *bottom* Ken O'Donoghue; **585** © SuperStock; **586** Frank Siteman; **587** *left* © Martin Rotker/Phototake; **588** © SW Production/Index Stock Imagery/PictureQuest; **589** *background* © Hulton-Deutsch Collection/Corbis, *center* © Underwood & Underwood/Corbis; **590** Frank Siteman; **591** © Prof. P. Motta/Dept. of Anatomy/University "La Sapienza," Rome/Photo Researchers, Inc.; **592** © Photodisc/Getty Images; **594** *bottom* © Science Photo Library/Photo Researchers, Inc., *bottom left* © Zephyr/Photo Researchers, Inc.; **595** *top* © Zephyr/Photo Researchers, Inc., *bottom* Frank Siteman; **596** *top left* © Stock Image/SuperStock, *top right* © Science Photo Library/Photo Researchers, Inc.; **597** © Dennis Kunkel/Phototake; **598** Frank Siteman; **599** © Kevin R. Morris/Corbis; **601** *background* © Mary Kate Denny/PhotoEdit, *top* © Martin Rotker/Phototake, *left* © Triarch/Visuals Unlimited, *bottom* © Eric Grave/Phototake; **602** © Ron Frehm/AP Wide World Photos; **603** © Jeff Greenberg/PhotoEdit; **604** *top* © Gunter Marx Photography/Corbis, *bottom, all* Frank Siteman; **606** © Martin Rotker/Phototake; **607** *top* © Stock Image/SuperStock; **610–611** © Larry Dale Gordon/Getty Images; **611** *top* Frank Siteman, *bottom* Ken O'Donoghue; **613** Frank Siteman; **614** © Amos Nachoum/Corbis; **615** Ken O'Donoghue; **617** *bottom left* © Michael Newman/PhotoEdit, *bottom right* © Science Photo Library/Photo Researchers, Inc.; **619** © Kennan Harvey/Getty Images; **620** *background* © Jim Cummins/Getty Images, *center* © Steve Casimiro/Getty Images; **621** Ken O'Donoghue; **623** Ken O'Donoghue; **624** © Professors P. Motta & A. Familiari/University "La Sapienza," Rome/Photo Researchers, Inc.; **625** © David Young-Wolff/PhotoEdit; **626** © Dr. Gladden Willis/Visuals Unlimited; **627** © David Gifford/SPL/Custom Medical Stock Photo; **628** Frank Siteman; **631** © LWA-Dann Tardif/Corbis; **632** *top* © Myrleen Ferguson Cate/PhotoEdit, *bottom left* Ken O'Donoghue, *bottom right* Frank Siteman; **633** Frank Siteman; **638–639** © Professors P.M. Motta & S. Correr/Photo Researchers, Inc.; **639** *both* Frank Siteman; **641** Frank Siteman; **643** © Science Photo Library/Photo Researchers, Inc.; **644** © Myrleen Ferguson Cate/PhotoEdit; **645** © Susumu Nishinaga/Photo Researchers, Inc.; **647** © Journal Courier/The Image Works; **648** *top left* © Michael Newman/PhotoEdit, *bottom left* Ken O'Donoghue, *center right, bottom right* Frank Siteman; **650** Frank Siteman; **651** *top* © Eddy Gray/Photo Researchers, Inc., *bottom* © Mary Kate Denny/PhotoEdit; **652** © Science Photo Library/Photo Researchers, Inc.; **653** *top* © Dr. P. Marazzi/Photo Researchers, Inc., *top right* © Dr. Jeremy Burgess/Photo Researchers, Inc.; **654** © Science Photo Library/Photo Researchers, Inc.; **655** Frank Siteman; **656** © Bob Daemmrich/The Image Works; **657** © Richard

ACKNOWLEDGMENTS

Lord/The Image Works; **658** *background* © SCIMAT/Photo Researchers, Inc., *inset* © Vision/Photo Researchers; **659** Ken O'Donoghue; **660** RMIP/Richard Haynes; **661** Frank Siteman; **662** *top inset* © Dennis Kunkel/Phototake, *bottom inset* © Andrew Syred/Photo Researchers, Inc., *center* © Photodisc/Getty Images; **663** *all* © Eric Schrempp/Photo Researchers, Inc.; **664** © The Image Bank/Getty Images; **665** *background* © James King-Holmes/Photo Researchers, Inc., *top right* © Sygma/Corbis, *bottom right* © David Hanson; **670** *top* © Hulton Archive/Getty Images, *bottom* © Simon Fraser/Photo Researchers, Inc.; **671** *top* © Bettmann/Corbis, *center* © Underwood & Underwood/Corbis, *bottom* © George Bernard/Photo Researchers, Inc.; **672** *top left* © Collection CNRI/Phototake, *top right* © Geoff Tompkinson/Photo Researchers, Inc., *bottom* © Josh Sher/Photo Researchers, Inc.; **673** *top* © Simon Fraser/Photo Researchers, Inc., *bottom* © GJLP/Photo Researchers, Inc.; **674–675** © Photo Researchers, Inc.; **675** *top* Ken O'Donoghue, *center* © Photospin; **677** Ken O'Donoghue; **679** RMIP/Richard Haynes; **680** © David Young-Wolff/PhotoEdit; **683** © Royalty-Free/Corbis; **684** *top* © Ed Young/Corbis, *bottom* Ken O'Donoghue; **685** *top* Frank Siteman, *bottom* Ken O'Donoghue; **686** © David Young-Wolff/PhotoEdit; **687** © Kwame Zikomo/SuperStock; **688** © ISM/Phototake; **690** Frank Siteman; **691** © CNRI/Photo Researchers, Inc.; **693** *left* © David Young-Wolff/PhotoEdit, *bottom right* © Glenn Oakley/ImageState/PictureQuest; **694** Ken O'Donoghue; **699** *background* © Yoav Levy/Phototake, *top left* © Dr. Yorgos Nikas/Photo Researchers, Inc.; **700** © David Degnan/Corbis; **701** *left* © Christopher Brown/Stock Boston, Inc./PictureQuest, *right* © Nissim Men/Photonica; **706–707** © Brooklyn Productions/Corbis; **707** *top* Ken O'Donoghue; **709** Frank Siteman; **710** © Tom Galliher/Corbis; **711** © Tom Stewart/Corbis; **712** © Novastock/Index Stock Imagery, Inc.; **714** *left* © Spencer Grant/PhotoEdit, *right* © Michael Newman/PhotoEdit; **715** *all* from STAGE MAKEUP, STEP BY STEP. Courtesy of Quarto Publishing, Inc.; **716** © Ed Young/Corbis; **717** © Ronnie Kaufman/Corbis; **718** © Photodisc/Getty Images; **720** © Don Smetzer/PhotoEdit; **722** © Brett Coomer/HO/AP Wide World Photos; **723** *left* © Eric Kamp/Index Stock Photography, Inc., *top right* © Ariel Skelley/Corbis; **724** Frank Siteman; **725** © Mediscan/Visuals Unlimited; **727** *top left* © Dr. Kari Lounatmaa/Science Photo Library/Photo Researchers, Inc., *top right* © Dr. Gopal Murti/Photo Researchers, Inc., *bottom left* © Professors P.M. Motta & F.M. Magliocca/Photo Researchers, Inc., *bottom right* © Microworks/Phototake, *bottom right inset* © Andrew Spielman/Phototake; **728** © Mary Steinbacher/PhotoEdit; **729** © Srulik Haramary/Phototake; **730** *top left* © Kwame Zikomo/Superstock, *bottom left* Ken O'Donoghue, *bottom right* Frank Siteman; **731** Ken O'Donoghue; **732** © Mediscan/Visuals Unlimited.

Backmatter

R28 © PhotoDisc/Getty Images, **R58** *bottom left* Mural by Peter Sawyer © National Museum of Natural History, Smithsonian Institution, Washington, D.C.; *bottom right* Exhibit Museum of Natural History, The University of Michigan, Ann Arbor, Michigan; **R59** *bottom left* © Ludek Pesek/Photo Researchers; *bottom right* © Steve Vidler/SuperStock; **R60** © Dorling Kindersley; **R61** *top right* © John Elk III; *center right* © Kaj R. Svensson/Photo Researchers; *bottom right* © Francesco Muntada/Corbis; **R66** © Andrew Syred/Photo Researchers.

Illustration and Maps

Richard Bonson/Wildlife Art Ltd. **172, 173, 196** *(top)*, **492, 511, 513, 524** *(background)*, **534** *(top right)*; Robin Boutell/Wildlife Art Ltd. **404, 422** *(center right)*; Peter Bull/Wildlife Art Ltd. **32, 298, 305, 306**; Sandra Doyle/Wildlife Art Ltd. **491** *(all)*, **502** *(bottom)*; Luigi Galante **530–531** *(all insets)*, **534** *(bottom)*; Patrick Gnan/Deborah Wolfe Ltd. **61, 215**; Dan Gonzalez **552, 558**; Gary Hincks **476** *(bottom right)*, **481, 482, 484, 500–501** *(background)*, **502** *(center)*, **547**; Ian Jackson/Wildlife Art Ltd. **191, 339, 342, 417, 422** *(bottom)*, **449**; Keith Kasnot **49, 51, 52, 66**; George Kelvin **15, 17**; George Kelvin and Richard McMahon **19** *(montage)*; Myriam Kirkman-Oh/KO Studios **43** *(center)*, **140, 359**; Debbie Maizels **3** *(right)*, **22, 30, 34, 42, 43** *(top, bottom)*, **45, 58, 60, 61, 75** *(center right)*, **136** *(bottom)*, **317, 328** *(inset)*, **361, 371, 373, 381, 390, 430, 591, 602, 660, 666, 678, 680, 704, R65**; MapQuest.com, Inc. **178–179, 248, 259, 319, 495, 511** *(top right)*, **513** *(top)*, **549**; Linda Nye **587, 606, 622, 642, 646, 666, 668, 695, 696, 697, 698, 699, 702**; Steve Oh/KO Studios **75** *(left)*, **83, 96** *(right)*, **121, 122, 124, 136, 137, 139, 289, 299, 308, 654, 681**; Laurie O'Keefe, **189, 192, 196** *(bottom)*, **397, 402, 431, 457, 493**; Mick Posen/Wildlife Art Ltd. **78, 105, 111, 113, 116, 183, 217, 232, 401**; Precision Graphics **257**; Tony Randazzo/American Artists Rep. Inc. **328** *(background)*; Peter Scott/Wildlife Art Ltd. **180, 184, 196** *(center)*; Dan Stuckenschneider/Uhl Studios **R11–R19, R22, R32, R66**; UNEP-WCMC, 2002 World Atlas of Biodiversity **353**; Bart Vallecoccia and Richard McMahon **3** *(montage)*, **587, 593, 606, 608, 617, 618, 620, 622, 625, 629, 630, 634, 636, 644, 679, 681, 682, 689, 695, 696, 702.**

Content Standards: 5–8

A. Science as Inquiry

As a result of activities in grades 5–8, all students should develop

Abilities Necessary to do Scientific Inquiry

A.1 Identify questions that can be answered through scientific investigations. Students should develop the ability to refine and refocus broad and ill-defined questions. An important aspect of this ability consists of students' ability to clarify questions and inquiries and direct them toward objects and phenomena that can be described, explained, or predicted by scientific investigations. Students should develop the ability to identify their questions with scientific ideas, concepts, and quantitative relationships that guide investigation.

A.2 Design and conduct a scientific investigation. Students should develop general abilities, such as systematic observation, making accurate measurements, and identifying and controlling variables. They should also develop the ability to clarify their ideas that are influencing and guiding the inquiry, and to understand how those ideas compare with current scientific knowledge. Students can learn to formulate questions, design investigations, execute investigations, interpret data, use evidence to generate explanations, propose alternative explanations, and critique explanations and procedures.

A.3 Use appropriate tools and techniques to gather, analyze, and interpret data. The use of tools and techniques, including mathematics, will be guided by the question asked and the investigations students design. The use of computers for the collection, summary, and display of evidence is part of this standard. Students should be able to access, gather, store, retrieve, and organize data, using hardware and software designed for these purposes.

A.4 Develop descriptions, explanations, predictions, and models using evidence. Students should base their explanation on what they observed, and as they develop cognitive skills, they should be able to differentiate explanation from description—providing causes for effects and establishing relationships based on evidence and logical argument. This standard requires a subject matter knowledge base so the students can effectively conduct investigations, because developing explanations establishes connections between the content of science and the contexts within which students develop new knowledge.

A.5 Think critically and logically to make the relationships between evidence and explanations. Thinking critically about evidence includes deciding what evidence should be used and accounting for anomalous data. Specifically, students should be able to review data from a simple experiment, summarize the data, and form a logical argument about the cause-and-effect relationships in the experiment. Students should begin to state some explanations in terms of the relationship between two or more variables.

A.6 Recognize and analyze alternative explanations and predictions. Students should develop the ability to listen to and respect the explanations proposed by other students. They should remain open to and acknowledge different ideas and explanations, be able to accept the skepticism of others, and consider alternative explanations.

A.7 Communicate scientific procedures and explanations. With practice, students should become competent at communicating experimental methods, following instructions, describing observations, summarizing the results of other groups, and telling other students about investigations and explanations.

A.8 Use mathematics in all aspects of scientific inquiry. Mathematics is essential to asking and answering questions about the natural world. Mathematics can be used to ask questions; to gather, organize, and present data; and to structure convincing explanations.

Understandings about Scientific Inquiry

A.9.a Different kinds of questions suggest different kinds of scientific investigations. Some investigations involve observing and describing objects, organisms, or events; some involve collecting specimens; some involve experiments; some involve seeking more information; some involve discovery of new objects and phenomena; and some involve making models.

A.9.b Current scientific knowledge and understanding guide scientific investigations. Different scientific domains employ different methods, core theories, and standards to advance scientific knowledge and understanding.

A.9.c Mathematics is important in all aspects of scientific inquiry.

A.9.d Technology used to gather data enhances accuracy and allows scientists to analyze and quantify results of investigations.

A.9.e Scientific explanations emphasize evidence, have logically consistent arguments, and use scientific principles, models, and theories. The scientific community accepts and uses such explanations until displaced by better scientific ones. When such displacement occurs, science advances.

A.9.f Science advances through legitimate skepticism. Asking questions and querying other scientists' explanations is part of scientific inquiry. Scientists evaluate the explanations proposed by other scientists by examining evidence, comparing evidence, identifying faulty reasoning, pointing out statements that go beyond the evidence, and suggesting alternative explanations for the same observations.

A.9.g Scientific investigations sometimes result in new ideas and phenomena for study, generate new methods or procedures for an investigation, or develop new technologies to improve the collection of data. All of these results can lead to new investigations.

B. Physical Science

As a result of their activities in grades 5–8, all students should develop an understanding of

Properties and Changes of Properties in Matter

B.1.a A substance has characteristic properties, such as density, a boiling point, and solubility, all of which are independent of the amount of the sample. A mixture of substances often can be separated into the original substances using one or more of the characteristic properties.

B.1.b Substances react chemically in characteristic ways with other substances to form new substances (compounds) with different characteristic properties. In chemical reactions, the total mass is conserved. Substances often are placed in categories or groups if they react in similar ways; metals is an example of such a group.

B.1.c Chemical elements do not break down during normal laboratory reactions involving such treatments as heating, exposure to electric current, or reaction with acids. There are more than 100 known elements that combine in a multitude of ways to produce compounds, which account for the living and nonliving substances that we encounter.

Motions and Forces

B.2.a The motion of an object can be described by its position, direction of motion, and speed. That motion can be measured and represented on a graph.

B.2.b An object that is not being subjected to a force will continue to move at a constant speed and in a straight line.

B.2.c If more than one force acts on an object along a straight line, then the forces will reinforce or cancel one another, depending on their direction and magnitude. Unbalanced forces will cause changes in the speed or direction of an object's motion.

Transfer of Energy

B.3.a Energy is a property of many substances and is associated with heat, light, electricity, mechanical motion, sound, nuclei, and the nature of a chemical. Energy is transferred in many ways.

B.3.b Heat moves in predictable ways, flowing from warmer objects to cooler ones, until both reach the same temperature.

B.3.c Light interacts with matter by transmission (including refraction), absorption, or scattering (including reflection). To see an object, light from that object—emitted by or scattered from it—must enter the eye.

B.3.d Electrical circuits provide a means of transferring electrical energy when heat, light, sound, and chemical changes are produced.

B.3.e In most chemical and nuclear reactions, energy is transferred into or out of a system. Heat, light, mechanical motion, or electricity might all be involved in such transfers.

B.3.f The sun is a major source of energy for changes on the earth's surface. The sun loses energy by emitting light. A tiny fraction of that light reaches the earth, transferring energy from the sun to the earth. The sun's energy arrives as light with a range of wavelengths, consisting of visible light, infrared, and ultraviolet radiation.

C. Life Science

As a result of their activities in grades 5–8, all students should develop understanding of

Structure and Function in Living Systems

C.1.a Living systems at all levels of organization demonstrate the complementary nature of structure and function. Important levels of organization for structure and function include cells, organs, tissues, organ systems, whole organisms, and ecosystems.

C.1.b All organisms are composed of cells—the fundamental unit of life. Most organisms are single cells; other organisms, including humans, are multicellular.

C.1.c Cells carry on the many functions needed to sustain life. They grow and divide, thereby producing more cells. This requires that they take in nutrients, which they use to provide energy for the work that cells do and to make the materials that a cell or an organism needs.

C.1.d Specialized cells perform specialized functions in multicellular organisms. Groups of specialized cells cooperate to form a tissue, such as a muscle. Different tissues are in turn grouped together to form larger functional units, called organs. Each type of cell, tissue, and organ has a distinct structure and set of functions that serve the organism as a whole.

C.1.e The human organism has systems for digestion, respiration, reproduction, circulation, excretion, movement, control, and coordination, and for protection from disease. These systems interact with one another.

C.1.f Disease is a breakdown in structures or functions of an organism. Some diseases are the result of intrinsic failures of the system. Others are the result of damage by infection by other organisms.

Reproduction and Heredity

C.2.a Reproduction is a characteristic of all living systems; because no individual organism lives forever, reproduction is essential to the continuation of every species. Some organisms reproduce asexually. Other organisms reproduce sexually.

C.2.b In many species, including humans, females produce eggs and males produce sperm. Plants also reproduce sexually—the egg and sperm are produced in the flowers of flowering plants. An egg and sperm unite to begin development of a new individual. That new individual receives genetic information from its mother (via the egg) and its father (via the sperm). Sexually produced offspring never are identical to either of their parents.

C.2.c Every organism requires a set of instructions for specifying its traits. Heredity is the passage of these instructions from one generation to another.

C.2.d Hereditary information is contained in genes, located in the chromosomes of each cell. Each gene carries a single unit of information. An inherited trait of an individual can be determined by one or by many genes, and a single gene can influence more than one trait. A human cell contains many thousands of different genes.

C.2.e The characteristics of an organism can be described in terms of a combination of traits. Some traits are inherited and others result from interactions with the environment.

National Science Education Standards

Regulation and Behavior

C.3.a All organisms must be able to obtain and use resources, grow, reproduce, and maintain stable internal conditions while living in a constantly changing external environment.

C.3.b Regulation of an organism's internal environment involves sensing the internal environment and changing physiological activities to keep conditions within the range required to survive.

C.3.c Behavior is one kind of response an organism can make to an internal or environmental stimulus. A behavioral response requires coordination and communication at many levels, including cells, organ systems, and whole organisms. Behavioral response is a set of actions determined in part by heredity and in part from experience.

C.3.d An organism's behavior evolves through adaptation to its environment. How a species moves, obtains food, reproduces, and responds to danger are based in the species' evolutionary history.

Populations and Ecosystems

C.4.a A population consists of all individuals of a species that occur together at a given place and time. All populations living together and the physical factors with which they interact compose an ecosystem.

C.4.b Populations of organisms can be categorized by the function they serve in an ecosystem. Plants and some microorganisms are producers—they make their own food. All animals, including humans, are consumers, which obtain food by eating other organisms. Decomposers, primarily bacteria and fungi, are consumers that use waste materials and dead organisms for food. Food webs identify the relationships among producers, consumers, and decomposers in an ecosystem.

C.4.c For ecosystems, the major source of energy is sunlight. Energy entering ecosystems as sunlight is transferred by producers into chemical energy through photosynthesis. That energy then passes from organism to organism in food webs.

C.4.d The number of organisms an ecosystem can support depends on the resources available and abiotic factors, such as quantity of light and water, range of temperatures, and soil composition. Given adequate biotic and abiotic resources and no disease or predators, populations (including humans) increase at rapid rates. Lack of resources and other factors, such as predation and climate, limit the growth of populations in specific niches in the ecosystem.

Diversity and Adaptations of Organisms

C.5.a Millions of species of animals, plants, and microorganisms are alive today. Although different species might look dissimilar, the unity among organisms becomes apparent from an analysis of internal structures, the similarity of their chemical processes, and the evidence of common ancestry.

C.5.b Biological evolution accounts for the diversity of species developed through gradual processes over many generations. Species acquire many of their unique characteristics through biological adaptation, which involves the selection of naturally occurring variations in populations. Biological adaptations include changes in structures, behaviors, or physiology that enhance survival and reproductive success in a particular environment.

C.5.c Extinction of a species occurs when the environment changes and the adaptive characteristics of a species are insufficient to allow its survival. Fossils indicate that many organisms that lived long ago are extinct. Extinction of species is common; most of the species that have lived on the earth no longer exist.

D. Earth and Space Science

As a result of their activities in grades 5–8, all students should develop an understanding of

Structure of the Earth System

D.1.a The solid earth is layered with a lithosphere; hot, convecting mantle; and dense, metallic core.

D.1.b Lithospheric plates on the scales of continents and oceans constantly move at rates of centimeters per year in response to movements in the mantle. Major geological events, such as earthquakes, volcanic eruptions, and mountain building, result from these plate motions.

D.1.c Land forms are the result of a combination of constructive and destructive forces. Constructive forces include crustal deformation, volcanic eruption, and deposition of sediment, while destructive forces include weathering and erosion.

D.1.d Some changes in the solid earth can be described as the "rock cycle." Old rocks at the earth's surface weather, forming sediments that are buried, then compacted, heated, and often recrystallized into new rock. Eventually, those new rocks may be brought to the surface by the forces that drive plate motions, and the rock cycle continues.

D.1.e Soil consists of weathered rocks and decomposed organic material from dead plants, animals, and bacteria. Soils are often found in layers, with each having a different chemical composition and texture.

D.1.f Water, which covers the majority of the earth's surface, circulates through the crust, oceans, and atmosphere in what is known as the "water cycle." Water evaporates from the earth's surface, rises and cools as it moves to higher elevations, condenses as rain or snow, and falls to the surface where it collects in lakes, oceans, soil, and in rocks underground.

D.1.g Water is a solvent. As it passes through the water cycle it dissolves minerals and gases and carries them to the oceans.

D.1.h The atmosphere is a mixture of nitrogen, oxygen, and trace gases that include water vapor. The atmosphere has different properties at different elevations.

D.1.i Clouds, formed by the condensation of water vapor, affect weather and climate.

D.1.j Global patterns of atmospheric movement influence local weather. Oceans have a major effect on climate, because water in the oceans holds a large amount of heat.

D.1.k Living organisms have played many roles in the earth system, including affecting the composition of the atmosphere, producing some types of rocks, and contributing to the weathering of rocks.

Earth's History

D.2.a The earth processes we see today, including erosion, movement of lithospheric plates, and changes in atmospheric composition, are similar to those that occurred in the past. Earth history is also influenced by occasional catastrophes, such as the impact of an asteroid or comet.

D.2.b Fossils provide important evidence of how life and environmental conditions have changed.

Earth in the Solar System

D.3.a The earth is the third planet from the sun in a system that includes the moon, the sun, eight other planets and their moons, and smaller objects, such as asteroids and comets. The sun, an average star, is the central and largest body in the solar system.

D.3.b Most objects in the solar system are in regular and predictable motion. Those motions explain such phenomena as the day, the year, phases of the moon, and eclipses.

D.3.c Gravity is the force that keeps planets in orbit around the sun and governs the rest of the motion in the solar system. Gravity alone holds us to the earth's surface and explains the phenomena of the tides.

D.3.d The sun is the major source of energy for phenomena on the earth's surface, such as growth of plants, winds, ocean currents, and the water cycle. Seasons result from variations in the amount of the sun's energy hitting the surface, due to the tilt of the earth's rotation on its axis and the length of the day.

E. Science and Technology

As a result of activities in grades 5–8, all students should develop

Abilities of Technological Design

E.1 Identify appropriate problems for technological design. Students should develop their abilities by identifying a specified need, considering its various aspects, and talking to different potential users or beneficiaries. They should appreciate that for some needs, the cultural backgrounds and beliefs of different groups can affect the criteria for a suitable product.

E.2 Design a solution or product. Students should make and compare different proposals in the light of the criteria they have selected. They must consider constraints—such as cost, time, trade-offs, and materials needed—and communicate ideas with drawings and simple models.

E.3 Implement a proposed design. Students should organize materials and other resources, plan their work, make good use of group collaboration where appropriate, choose suitable tools and techniques, and work with appropriate measurement methods to ensure adequate accuracy.

E.4 Evaluate completed technological designs or products. Students should use criteria relevant to the original purpose or need, consider a variety of factors that might affect acceptability and suitability for intended users or beneficiaries, and develop measures of quality with respect to such criteria and factors; they should also suggest improvements and, for their own products, try proposed modifications.

E.5 Communicate the process of technological design. Students should review and describe any completed piece of work and identify the stages of problem identification, solution design, implementation, and evaluation.

Understandings about Science and Technology

E.6.a Scientific inquiry and technological design have similarities and differences. Scientists propose explanations for questions about the natural world, and engineers propose solutions relating to human problems, needs, and aspirations. Technological solutions are temporary; technologies exist within nature and so they cannot contravene physical or biological principles; technological solutions have side effects; and technologies cost, carry risks, and provide benefits.

E.6.b Many different people in different cultures have made and continue to make contributions to science and technology.

E.6.c Science and technology are reciprocal. Science helps drive technology, as it addresses questions that demand more sophisticated instruments and provides principles for better instrumentation and technique. Technology is essential to science, because it provides instruments and techniques that enable observations of objects and phenomena that are otherwise unobservable due to factors such as quantity, distance, location, size, and speed. Technology also provides tools for investigations, inquiry, and analysis.

E.6.d Perfectly designed solutions do not exist. All technological solutions have trade-offs, such as safety, cost, efficiency, and appearance. Engineers often build in back-up systems to provide safety. Risk is part of living in a highly technological world. Reducing risk often results in new technology.

E.6.e Technological designs have constraints. Some constraints are unavoidable, for example, properties of materials, or effects of weather and friction; other constraints limit choices in the design, for example, environmental protection, human safety, and aesthetics.

E.6.f Technological solutions have intended benefits and unintended consequences. Some consequences can be predicted, others cannot.

F. Science in Personal and Social Perspectives

As a result of activities in grades 5–8, all students should develop understanding of

Personal Health

F.1.a Regular exercise is important to the maintenance and improvement of health. The benefits of physical fitness include maintaining healthy weight, having energy and strength for routine activities, good muscle tone, bone strength, strong heart/lung systems, and improved mental health. Personal exercise, especially developing cardiovascular endurance, is the foundation of physical fitness.

F.1.b The potential for accidents and the existence of hazards imposes the need for injury prevention. Safe living involves the development and use of safety precautions and the recognition of risk in personal decisions. Injury prevention has personal and social dimensions.

F.1.c The use of tobacco increases the risk of illness. Students should understand the influence of short-term social and psychological factors that lead to tobacco use, and the possible long-term detrimental effects of smoking and chewing tobacco.

F.1.d Alcohol and other drugs are often abused substances. Such drugs change how the body functions and can lead to addiction.

F.1.e Food provides energy and nutrients for growth and development. Nutrition requirements vary with body weight, age, sex, activity, and body functioning.

F.1.f Sex drive is a natural human function that requires understanding. Sex is also a prominent means of transmitting diseases. The diseases can be prevented through a variety of precautions.

F.1.g Natural environments may contain substances (for example, radon and lead) that are harmful to human beings. Maintaining environmental health involves establishing or monitoring quality standards related to use of soil, water, and air.

Populations, Resources, and Environments

F.2.a When an area becomes overpopulated, the environment will become degraded due to the increased use of resources.

F.2.b Causes of environmental degradation and resource depletion vary from region to region and from country to country.

Natural Hazards

F.3.a Internal and external processes of the earth system cause natural hazards, events that change or destroy human and wildlife habitats, damage property, and harm or kill humans. Natural hazards include earthquakes, landslides, wildfires, volcanic eruptions, floods, storms, and even possible impacts of asteroids.

F.3.b Human activities also can induce hazards through resource acquisition, urban growth, land-use decisions, and waste disposal. Such activities can accelerate many natural changes.

F.3.c Natural hazards can present personal and societal challenges because misidentifying the change or incorrectly estimating the rate and scale of change may result in either too little attention and significant human costs or too much cost for unneeded preventive measures.

Risks and Benefits

F.4.a Risk analysis considers the type of hazard and estimates the number of people that might be exposed and the number likely to suffer consequences. The results are used to determine the options for reducing or eliminating risks.

F.4.b Students should understand the risks associated with natural hazards (fires, floods, tornadoes, hurricanes, earthquakes, and volcanic eruptions), with chemical hazards (pollutants in air, water, soil, and food), with biological hazards (pollen, viruses, bacterial, and parasites), social hazards (occupational safety and transportation), and with personal hazards (smoking, dieting, and drinking).

F.4.c Individuals can use a systematic approach to thinking critically about risks and benefits. Examples include applying probability estimates to risks and comparing them to estimated personal and social benefits.

F.4.d Important personal and social decisions are made based on perceptions of benefits and risks.

Science and Technology in Society

F.5.a Science influences society through its knowledge and world view. Scientific knowledge and the procedures used by scientists influence the way many individuals in society think about themselves, others, and the environment. The effect of science on society is neither entirely beneficial nor entirely detrimental.

F.5.b Societal challenges often inspire questions for scientific research, and social priorities often influence research priorities through the availability of funding for research.

F.5.c Technology influences society through its products and processes. Technology influences the quality of life and the ways people act and interact. Technological changes are often accompanied by social, political, and economic changes that can be beneficial or detrimental to individuals and to society. Social needs, attitudes, and values influence the direction of technological development.

F.5.d Science and technology have advanced through contributions of many different people, in different cultures, at different times in history. Science and technology have contributed enormously to economic growth and productivity among societies and groups within societies.

F.5.e Scientists and engineers work in many different settings, including colleges and universities, businesses and industries, specific research institutes, and government agencies.

F.5.f Scientists and engineers have ethical codes requiring that human subjects involved with research be fully informed about risks and benefits associated with the research before the individuals choose to participate. This ethic extends to potential risks to communities and property. In short, prior knowledge and consent are required for research involving human subjects or potential damage to property.

F.5.g Science cannot answer all questions and technology cannot solve all human problems or meet all human needs. Students should understand the difference between scientific and other questions. They should appreciate what science and technology can reasonably contribute to society and what they cannot do. For example, new technologies often will decrease some risks and increase others.

G. History and Nature of Science

As a result of activities in grades 5–8, all students should develop understanding of

Science as a Human Endeavor

G.1.a Women and men of various social and ethnic backgrounds—and with diverse interests, talents, qualities, and motivations—engage in the activities of science, engineering, and related fields such as the health professions. Some scientists work in teams, and some work alone, but all communicate extensively with others.

G.1.b Science requires different abilities, depending on such factors as the field of study and type of inquiry. Science is very much a human endeavor, and the work of science relies on basic human qualities, such as reasoning, insight, energy, skill, and creativity—as well as on scientific habits of mind, such as intellectual honesty, tolerance of ambiguity, skepticism, and openness to new ideas.

National Science Education Standards

Nature of Science

G.2.a Scientists formulate and test their explanations of nature using observation, experiments, and theoretical and mathematical models. Although all scientific ideas are tentative and subject to change and improvement in principle, for most major ideas in science, there is much experimental and observational confirmation. Those ideas are not likely to change greatly in the future. Scientists do and have changed their ideas about nature when they encounter new experimental evidence that does not match their existing explanations.

G.2.b In areas where active research is being pursued and in which there is not a great deal of experimental or observational evidence and understanding, it is normal for scientists to differ with one another about the interpretation of the evidence or theory being considered. Different scientists might publish conflicting experimental results or might draw different conclusions from the same data. Ideally, scientists acknowledge such conflict and work towards finding evidence that will resolve their disagreement.

G.2.c It is part of scientific inquiry to evaluate the results of scientific investigations, experiments, observations, theoretical models, and the explanations proposed by other scientists. Evaluation includes reviewing the experimental procedures, examining the evidence, identifying faulty reasoning, pointing out statements that go beyond the evidence, and suggesting alternative explanations for the same observations. Although scientists may disagree about explanations of phenomena, about interpretations of data, or about the value of rival theories, they do agree that questioning, response to criticism, and open communication are integral to the process of science. As scientific knowledge evolves, major disagreements are eventually resolved through such interactions between scientists.

History of Science

G.3.a Many individuals have contributed to the traditions of science. Studying some of these individuals provides further understanding of scientific inquiry, science as a human endeavor, the nature of science, and the relationships between science and society.

G.3.b In historical perspective, science has been practiced by different individuals in different cultures. In looking at the history of many peoples, one finds that scientists and engineers of high achievement are considered to be among the most valued contributors to their culture.

G.3.c Tracing the history of science can show how difficult it was for scientific innovators to break through the accepted ideas of their time to reach the conclusions that we currently take for granted.

Project 2061
Benchmarks for Science Literacy

1. The Nature of Science

By the end of the 8th grade, students should know that

1.A The Scientific World View

1.A.1 When similar investigations give different results, the scientific challenge is to judge whether the differences are trivial or significant, and it often takes further studies to decide. Even with similar results, scientists may wait until an investigation has been repeated many times before accepting the results as correct.

1.A.2 Scientific knowledge is subject to modification as new information challenges prevailing theories and as a new theory leads to looking at old observations in a new way.

1.A.3 Some scientific knowledge is very old and yet is still applicable today.

1.A.4 Some matters cannot be examined usefully in a scientific way. Among them are matters that by their nature cannot be tested objectively and those that are essentially matters of morality. Science can sometimes be used to inform ethical decisions by identifying the likely consequences of particular actions but cannot be used to establish that some action is either moral or immoral.

1.B Scientific Inquiry

1.B.1 Scientists differ greatly in what phenomena they study and how they go about their work. Although there is no fixed set of steps that all scientists follow, scientific investigations usually involve the collection of relevant evidence, the use of logical reasoning, and the application of imagination in devising hypotheses and explanations to make sense of the collected evidence.

1.B.2 If more than one variable changes at the same time in an experiment, the outcome of the experiment may not be clearly attributable to any one of the variables. It may not always be possible to prevent outside variables from influencing the outcome of an investigation (or even to identify all of the variables), but collaboration among investigators can often lead to research designs that are able to deal with such situations.

1.B.3 What people expect to observe often affects what they actually do observe. Strong beliefs about what should happen in particular circumstances can prevent them from detecting other results. Scientists know about this danger to objectivity and take steps to try and avoid it when designing investigations and examining data. One safeguard is to have different investigators conduct independent studies of the same questions.

1.C The Scientific Enterprise

1.C.1 Important contributions to the advancement of science, mathematics, and technology have been made by different kinds of people, in different cultures, at different times.

1.C.2 Until recently, women and racial minorities, because of restrictions on their education and employment opportunities, were essentially left out of much of the formal work of the science establishment; the remarkable few who overcame those obstacles were even then likely to have their work disregarded by the science establishment.

1.C.3 No matter who does science and mathematics or invents things, or when or where they do it, the knowledge and technology that result can eventually become available to everyone in the world.

1.C.4 Scientists are employed by colleges and universities, business and industry, hospitals, and many government agencies. Their places of work include offices, classrooms, laboratories, farms, factories, and natural field settings ranging from space to the ocean floor.

1.C.5 In research involving human subjects, the ethics of science require that potential subjects be fully informed about the risks and benefits associated with the research and of their right to refuse to participate. Science ethics also demand that scientists must not knowingly subject coworkers, students, the neighborhood, or the community to health or property risks without their prior knowledge and consent. Because animals cannot make informed choices, special care must be taken in using them in scientific research.

1.C.6 Computers have become invaluable in science because they speed up and extend people's ability to collect, store, compile, and analyze data, prepare research reports, and share data and ideas with investigators all over the world.

1.C.7 Accurate record-keeping, openness, and replication are essential for maintaining an investigator's credibility with other scientists and society.

3. The Nature of Technology

By the end of the 8th grade, students should know that

3.A Technology and Science

3.A.1 In earlier times, the accumulated information and techniques of each generation of workers were taught on the job directly to the next generation of workers. Today, the knowledge base for technology can be found as well in libraries of print and electronic resources and is often taught in the classroom.

3.A.2 Technology is essential to science for such purposes as access to outer space and other remote locations, sample collection and treatment, measurement, data collection and storage, computation, and communication of information.

3.A.3 Engineers, architects, and others who engage in design and technology use scientific knowledge to solve practical problems. But they usually have to take human values and limitations into account as well.

3.B Design and Systems

3.B.1 Design usually requires taking constraints into account. Some constraints, such as gravity or the properties of the materials to be used, are unavoidable. Other constraints, including economic, political, social, ethical, and aesthetic ones, limit choices.

3.B.2 All technologies have effects other than those intended by the design, some of which may have been predictable and some not. In either case, these side effects may turn out to be unacceptable to some of the population and therefore lead to conflict between groups.

3.B.3 Almost all control systems have inputs, outputs, and feedback. The essence of control is comparing information about what is happening to what people want to happen and then making appropriate adjustments. This procedure requires sensing information, processing it, and making changes. In almost all modern machines, microprocessors serve as centers of performance control.

3.B.4 Systems fail because they have faulty or poorly matched parts, are used in ways that exceed what was intended by the design, or were poorly designed to begin with. The most common ways to prevent failure are pretesting parts and procedures, overdesign, and redundancy.

3.C Issues in Technology

3.C.1 The human ability to shape the future comes from a capacity for generating knowledge and developing new technologies—and for communicating ideas to others.

3.C.2 Technology cannot always provide successful solutions for problems or fulfill every human need.

3.C.3 Throughout history, people have carried out impressive technological feats, some of which would be hard to duplicate today even with modern tools. The purposes served by these achievements have sometimes been practical, sometimes ceremonial.

3.C.4 Technology has strongly influenced the course of history and continues to do so. It is largely responsible for the great revolutions in agriculture, manufacturing, sanitation and medicine, warfare, transportation, information processing, and communications that have radically changed how people live.

3.C.5 New technologies increase some risks and decrease others. Some of the same technologies that have improved the length and quality of life for many people have also brought new risks.

3.C.6 Rarely are technology issues simple and one-sided. Relevant facts alone, even when known and available, usually do not settle matters entirely in favor of one side or another. That is because the contending groups may have different values and priorities. They may stand to gain or lose in different degrees, or may make very different predictions about what the future consequences of the proposed action will be.

3.C.7 Societies influence what aspects of technology are developed and how these are used. People control technology (as well as science) and are responsible for its effects.

4. The Physical Setting

By the end of the 8th grade, students should know that

4.A The Universe

4.A.1 The sun is a medium-sized star located near the edge of a disk-shaped galaxy of stars, part of which can be seen as a glowing band of light that spans the sky on a very clear night. The universe contains many billions of galaxies, and each galaxy contains many billions of stars. To the naked eye, even the closest of these galaxies is no more than a dim, fuzzy spot.

4.A.2 The sun is many thousands of times closer to the earth than any other star. Light from the sun takes a few minutes to reach the earth, but light from the next nearest star takes a few years to arrive. The trip to that star would take the fastest rocket thousands of years. Some distant galaxies are so far away that their light takes several billion years to reach the earth. People on earth, therefore, see them as they were that long ago in the past.

4.A.3 Nine planets of very different size, composition, and surface features move around the sun in nearly circular orbits. Some planets have a great variety of moons and even flat rings of rock and ice particles orbiting around them. Some of these planets and moons show evidence of geologic activity. The earth is orbited by one moon, many artificial satellites, and debris.

4.A.4 Large numbers of chunks of rock orbit the sun. Some of those that the earth meets in its yearly orbit around the sun glow and disintegrate from friction as they plunge through the atmosphere—and sometimes impact the ground. Other chunks of rocks mixed with ice have long, off-center orbits that carry them close to the sun, where the sun's radiation (of light and particles) boils off frozen material from their surfaces and pushes it into a long, illuminated tail.

4.B The Earth

4.B.1 We live on a relatively small planet, the third from the sun in the only system of planets definitely known to exist (although other, similar systems may be discovered in the universe).

4.B.2 The earth is mostly rock. Three-fourths of its surface is covered by a relatively thin layer of water (some of it frozen), and the entire planet is surrounded by a relatively thin blanket of air. It is the only body in the solar system that appears able to support life. The other planets have compositions and conditions very different from the earth's.

4.B.3 Everything on or anywhere near the earth is pulled toward the earth's center by gravitational force.

4.B.4 Because the earth turns daily on an axis that is tilted relative to the plane of the earth's yearly orbit around the sun, sunlight falls more intensely on different parts of the earth during the year. The difference in heating of the earth's surface produces the planet's seasons and weather patterns.

4.B.5 The moon's orbit around the earth once in about 28 days changes what part of the moon is lighted by the sun and how much of that part can be seen from the earth—the phases of the moon.

4.B.6 Climates have sometimes changed abruptly in the past as a result of changes in the earth's crust, such as volcanic eruptions or impacts of huge rocks from space. Even relatively small changes in atmospheric or ocean content can have widespread effects on climate if the change lasts long enough.

4.B.7 The cycling of water in and out of the atmosphere plays an important role in determining climatic patterns. Water evaporates from the surface of the earth, rises and cools, condenses into rain or snow, and falls again to the surface. The water falling on land collects in rivers and lakes, soil, and porous layers of rock, and much of it flows back into the ocean.

4.B.8 Fresh water, limited in supply, is essential for life and also for most industrial processes. Rivers, lakes, and groundwater can be depleted or polluted, becoming unavailable or unsuitable for life.

4.B.9 Heat energy carried by ocean currents has a strong influence on climate around the world.

4.B.10 Some minerals are very rare and some exist in great quantities, but—for practical purposes—the ability to recover them is just as important as their abundance. As minerals are depleted, obtaining them becomes more difficult. Recycling and the development of substitutes can reduce the rate of depletion but may also be costly.

4.B.11 The benefits of the earth's resources—such as fresh water, air, soil, and trees—can be reduced by using them wastefully or by deliberately or inadvertently destroying them. The atmosphere and the oceans have a limited capacity to absorb wastes and recycle materials naturally. Cleaning up polluted air, water, or soil or restoring depleted soil, forests, or fishing grounds can be very difficult and costly.

4.C Processes that Shape the Earth

4.C.1 The interior of the earth is hot. Heat flow and movement of material within the earth cause earthquakes and volcanic eruptions and create mountains and ocean basins. Gas and dust from large volcanoes can change the atmosphere.

4.C.2 Some changes in the earth's surface are abrupt (such as earthquakes and volcanic eruptions) while other changes happen very slowly (such as uplift and wearing down of mountains). The earth's surface is shaped in part by the motion of water and wind over very long times, which act to level mountain ranges.

4.C.3 Sediments of sand and smaller particles (sometimes containing the remains of organisms) are gradually buried and are cemented together by dissolved minerals to form solid rock again.

4.C.4 Sedimentary rock buried deep enough may be reformed by pressure and heat, perhaps melting and recrystallizing into different kinds of rock. These re-formed rock layers may be forced up again to become land surface and even mountains. Subsequently, this new rock too will erode. Rock bears evidence of the minerals, temperatures, and forces that created it.

4.C.5 Thousands of layers of sedimentary rock confirm the long history of the changing surface of the earth and the changing life forms whose remains are found in successive layers. The youngest layers are not always found on top, because of folding, breaking, and uplift of layers.

4.C.6 Although weathered rock is the basic component of soil, the composition and texture of soil and its fertility and resistance to erosion are greatly influenced by plant roots and debris, bacteria, fungi, worms, insects, rodents, and other organisms.

4.C.7 Human activities, such as reducing the amount of forest cover, increasing the amount and variety of chemicals released into the atmosphere, and intensive farming, have changed the earth's land, oceans, and atmosphere. Some of these changes have decreased the capacity of the environment to support some life forms.

4.D Structure of Matter

4.D.1 All matter is made up of atoms, which are far too small to see directly through a microscope. The atoms of any element are alike but are different from atoms of other elements. Atoms may stick together in well-defined molecules or may be packed together in large arrays. Different arrangements of atoms into groups compose all substances.

4.D.2 Equal volumes of different substances usually have different weights.

4.D.3 Atoms and molecules are perpetually in motion. Increased temperature means greater average energy, so most substances expand when heated. In solids, the atoms are closely locked in position and can only vibrate. In liquids, the atoms or molecules have higher energy, are more loosely connected, and can slide past one another; some molecules may get enough energy to escape into a gas. In gases, the atoms or molecules have still more energy and are free of one another except during occasional collisions.

4.D.4 The temperature and acidity of a solution influence reaction rates. Many substances dissolve in water, which may greatly facilitate reactions between them.

4.D.5 Scientific ideas about elements were borrowed from some Greek philosophers of 2,000 years earlier, who believed that everything was made from four basic substances: air, earth, fire, and water. It was the combinations of these "elements" in different proportions that gave other substances their observable properties. The Greeks were wrong about those four, but now over 100 different elements have been identified, some rare and some plentiful, out of which everything is made. Because most elements tend to combine with others, few elements are found in their pure form.

4.D.6 There are groups of elements that have similar properties, including highly reactive metals, less-reactive metals, highly reactive nonmetals (such as chlorine, fluorine, and oxygen), and some almost completely nonreactive gases (such as helium and neon). An especially important kind of reaction between substances involves combination of oxygen with something else—as in burning or rusting. Some elements don't fit into any of the categories; among them are carbon and hydrogen, essential elements of living matter.

4.D.7 No matter how substances within a closed system interact with one another, or how they combine or break apart, the total weight of the system remains the same. The idea of atoms explains the conservation of matter: If the number of atoms stays the same no matter how they are rearranged, then their total mass stays the same.

4.E Energy Transformations

4.E.1 Energy cannot be created or destroyed, but only changed from one form into another.

4.E.2 Most of what goes on in the universe—from exploding stars and biological growth to the operation of machines and the motion of people—involves some form of energy being transformed into another. Energy in the form of heat is almost always one of the products of an energy transformation.

4.E.3 Heat can be transferred through materials by the collisions of atoms or across space by radiation. If the material is fluid, currents will be set up in it that aid the transfer of heat.

4.E.4 Energy appears in different forms. Heat energy is in the disorderly motion of molecules; chemical energy is in the arrangement of atoms; mechanical energy is in moving bodies or in elastically distorted shapes; gravitational energy is in the separation of mutually attracting masses.

4.F Motion

4.F.1 Light from the sun is made up of a mixture of many different colors of light, even though to the eye the light looks almost white. Other things that give off or reflect light have a different mix of colors.

4.F.2 Something can be "seen" when light waves emitted or reflected by it enter the eye—just as something can be "heard" when sound waves from it enter the ear.

4.F.3 An unbalanced force acting on an object changes its speed or direction of motion, or both. If the force acts toward a single center, the object's path may curve into an orbit around the center.

4.F.4 Vibrations in materials set up wavelike disturbances that spread away from the source. Sound and earthquake waves are examples. These and other waves move at different speeds in different materials.

4.F.5 Human eyes respond to only a narrow range of wavelengths of electromagnetic radiation—visible light. Differences of wavelength within that range are perceived as differences in color.

4.G Forces of Nature

4.G.1 Every object exerts gravitational force on every other object. The force depends on how much mass the objects have and on how far apart they are. The force is hard to detect unless at least one of the objects has a lot of mass.

4.G.2 The sun's gravitational pull holds the earth and other planets in their orbits, just as the planets' gravitational pull keeps their moons in orbit around them.

4.G.3 Electric currents and magnets can exert a force on each other.

5. The Living Environment

By the end of the 8th grade, students should know that

5.A Diversity of Life

5.A.1 One of the most general distinctions among organisms is between plants, which use sunlight to make their own food, and animals, which consume energy-rich foods. Some kinds of organisms, many of them microscopic, cannot be neatly classified as either plants or animals.

5.A.2 Animals and plants have a great variety of body plans and internal structures that contribute to their being able to make or find food and reproduce.

5.A.3 Similarities among organisms are found in internal anatomical features, which can be used to infer the degree of relatedness among organisms. In classifying organisms, biologists consider details of internal and external structures to be more important than behavior or general appearance.

5.A.4 For sexually reproducing organisms, a species comprises all organisms that can mate with one another to produce fertile offspring.

5.A.5 All organisms, including the human species, are part of and depend on two main interconnected global food webs. One includes microscopic ocean plants, the animals that feed on them, and finally the animals that feed on those animals. The other web includes land plants, the animals that feed on them, and so forth. The cycles continue indefinitely because organisms decompose after death to return food material to the environment.

5.B Heredity

5.B.1 In some kinds of organisms, all the genes come from a single parent, whereas in organisms that have sexes, typically half of the genes come from each parent.

5.B.2 In sexual reproduction, a single specialized cell from a female merges with a specialized cell from a male. As the fertilized egg, carrying genetic information from each parent, multiplies to form the complete organism with about a trillion cells, the same genetic information is copied in each cell.

5.B.3 New varieties of cultivated plants and domestic animals have resulted from selective breeding for particular traits.

5.C Cells

5.C.1 All living things are composed of cells, from just one to many millions, whose details usually are visible only through a microscope. Different body tissues and organs are made up of different kinds of cells. The cells in similar tissues and organs in other animals are similar to those in human beings but differ somewhat from cells found in plants.

5.C.2 Cells repeatedly divide to make more cells for growth and repair. Various organs and tissues function to serve the needs of cells for food, air, and waste removal.

5.C.3 Within cells, many of the basic functions of organisms—such as extracting energy from food and getting rid of waste—are carried out. The way in which cells function is similar in all living organisms.

5.C.4 About two-thirds of the weight of cells is accounted for by water, which gives cells many of their properties.

5.D Interdependence of Life

5.D.1 In all environments—freshwater, marine, forest, desert, grassland, mountain, and others—organisms with similar needs may compete with one another for resources, including food, space, water, air, and shelter. In any particular environment, the growth and survival of organisms depend on the physical conditions.

5.D.2 Two types of organisms may interact with one another in several ways: They may be in a producer/consumer, predator/prey, or parasite/host relationship. Or one organism may scavenge or decompose another. Relationships may be competitive or mutually beneficial. Some species have become so adapted to each other that neither could survive without the other.

5.E Flow of Matter and Energy

5.E.1 Food provides molecules that serve as fuel and building material for all organisms. Plants use the energy in light to make sugars out of carbon dioxide and water. This food can be used immediately for fuel or materials or it may be stored for later use. Organisms that eat plants break down the plant structures to produce the materials and energy they need to survive. Then they are consumed by other organisms.

5.E.2 Over a long time, matter is transferred from one organism to another repeatedly and between organisms and their physical environment. As in all material systems, the total amount of matter remains constant, even though its form and location change.

5.E.3 Energy can change from one form to another in living things. Animals get energy from oxidizing their food, releasing some of its energy as heat. Almost all food energy comes originally from sunlight.

5.F Evolution of Life

5.F.1 Small differences between parents and offspring can accumulate (through selective breeding) in successive generations so that descendants are very different from their ancestors.

5.F.2 Individual organisms with certain traits are more likely than others to survive and have offspring. Changes in environmental conditions can affect the survival of individual organisms and entire species.

5.F.3 Many thousands of layers of sedimentary rock provide evidence for the long history of the earth and for the long history of changing life forms whose remains are found in the rocks. More recently deposited rock layers are more likely to contain fossils resembling existing species.

6. The Human Organism

By the end of the 8th grade, students should know that

6.A Human Identity

6.A.1 Like other animals, human beings have body systems for obtaining and providing energy, defense, reproduction, and the coordination of body functions.

6.A.2 Human beings have many similarities and differences. The similarities make it possible for human beings to reproduce and to donate blood and organs to one another throughout the world. Their differences enable them to create diverse social and cultural arrangements and to solve problems in a variety of ways.

6.A.3 Fossil evidence is consistent with the idea that human beings evolved from earlier species.

6.A.4 Specialized roles of individuals within other species are genetically programmed, whereas human beings are able to invent and modify a wider range of social behavior.

6.A.5 Human beings use technology to match or excel many of the abilities of other species. Technology has helped people with disabilities survive and live more conventional lives.

6.A.6 Technologies having to do with food production, sanitation, and disease prevention have dramatically changed how people live and work and have resulted in rapid increases in the human population.

6.B Human Development

6.B.1 Fertilization occurs when sperm cells from a male's testes are deposited near an egg cell from the female ovary, and one of the sperm cells enters the egg cell. Most of the time, by chance or design, a sperm never arrives or an egg isn't available.

6.B.2 Contraception measures may incapacitate sperm, block their way to the egg, prevent the release of eggs, or prevent the fertilized egg from implanting successfully.

6.B.3 Following fertilization, cell division produces a small cluster of cells that then differentiate by appearance and function to form the basic tissues of an embryo. During the first three months of pregnancy, organs begin to form. During the second three months, all organs and body features develop. During the last three months, the organs and features mature enough to function well after birth. Patterns of human development are similar to those of other vertebrates.

6.B.4 The developing embryo—and later the newborn infant—encounters many risks from faults in its genes, its mother's inadequate diet, her cigarette smoking or use of alcohol or other drugs, or from infection. Inadequate child care may lead to lower physical and mental ability.

6.B.5 Various body changes occur as adults age. Muscles and joints become less flexible, bones and muscles lose mass, energy levels diminish, and the senses become less acute. Women stop releasing eggs and hence can no longer reproduce. The length and quality of human life are influenced by many factors, including sanitation, diet, medical care, sex, genes, environmental conditions, and personal health behaviors.

6.C Basic Functions

6.C.1 Organs and organ systems are composed of cells and help to provide all cells with basic needs.

6.C.2 For the body to use food for energy and building materials, the food must first be digested into molecules that are absorbed and transported to cells.

6.C.3 To burn food for the release of energy stored in it, oxygen must be supplied to cells, and carbon dioxide removed. Lungs take in oxygen for the combustion of food and they eliminate the carbon dioxide produced. The urinary system disposes of dissolved waste molecules, the intestinal tract removes solid wastes, and the skin and lungs rid the body of heat energy. The circulatory system moves all these substances to or from cells where they are needed or produced, responding to changing demands.

6.C.4 Specialized cells and the molecules they produce identify and destroy microbes that get inside the body.

6.C.5 Hormones are chemicals from glands that affect other body parts. They are involved in helping the body respond to danger and in regulating human growth, development, and reproduction.

6.C.6 Interactions among the senses, nerves, and brain make possible the learning that enables human beings to cope with changes in their environment.

6.D Learning

6.D.1 Some animal species are limited to a repertoire of genetically determined behaviors; others have more complex brains and can learn a wide variety of behaviors. All behavior is affected by both inheritance and experience.

6.D.2 The level of skill a person can reach in any particular activity depends on innate abilities, the amount of practice, and the use of appropriate learning technologies.

6.D.3 Human beings can detect a tremendous range of visual and olfactory stimuli. The strongest stimulus they can tolerate may be more than a trillion times as intense as the weakest they can detect. Still, there are many kinds of signals in the world that people cannot detect directly.

6.D.4 Attending closely to any one input of information usually reduces the ability to attend to others at the same time.

6.D.5 Learning often results from two perceptions or actions occurring at about the same time. The more often the same combination occurs, the stronger the mental connection between them is likely to be. Occasionally a single vivid experience will connect two things permanently in people's minds.

6.D.6 Language and tools enable human beings to learn complicated and varied things from others.

6.E Physical Health

6.E.1 The amount of food energy (calories) a person requires varies with body weight, age, sex, activity level, and natural body efficiency. Regular exercise is important to maintain a healthy heart/lung system, good muscle tone, and bone strength.

6.E.2 Toxic substances, some dietary habits, and personal behavior may be bad for one's health. Some effects show up right away, others may not show up for many years. Avoiding toxic substances, such as tobacco, and changing dietary habits to reduce the intake of such things as animal fat increases the chances of living longer.

6.E.3 Viruses, bacteria, fungi, and parasites may infect the human body and interfere with normal body functions. A person can catch a cold many times because there are many varieties of cold viruses that cause similar symptoms.

6.E.4 White blood cells engulf invaders or produce antibodies that attack them or mark them for killing by other white cells. The antibodies produced will remain and can fight off subsequent invaders of the same kind.

6.E.5 The environment may contain dangerous levels of substances that are harmful to human beings. Therefore, the good health of individuals requires monitoring the soil, air, and water and taking steps to keep them safe.

6.F Mental Health

6.F.1 Individuals differ greatly in their ability to cope with stressful situations. Both external and internal conditions (chemistry, personal history, values) influence how people behave.

6.F.2 Often people react to mental distress by denying that they have any problem. Sometimes they don't know why they feel the way they do, but with help they can sometimes uncover the reasons.

8. The Designed World

By the end of the 8th grade, students should know that

8.A Agriculture

8.A.1 Early in human history, there was an agricultural revolution in which people changed from hunting and gathering to farming. This allowed changes in the division of labor between men and women and between children and adults, and the development of new patterns of government.

8.A.2 People control the characteristics of plants and animals they raise by selective breeding and by preserving varieties of seeds (old and new) to use if growing conditions change.

8.A.3 In agriculture, as in all technologies, there are always trade-offs to be made. Getting food from many different places makes people less dependent on weather in any one place, yet more dependent on transportation and communication among far-flung markets. Specializing in one crop may risk disaster if changes in weather or increases in pest populations wipe out that crop. Also, the soil may be exhausted of some nutrients, which can be replenished by rotating the right crops.

8.A.4 Many people work to bring food, fiber, and fuel to U.S. markets. With improved technology, only a small fraction of workers in the United States actually plant and harvest the products that people use. Most workers are engaged in processing, packaging, transporting, and selling what is produced.

8.B Materials and Manufacturing

8.B.1 The choice of materials for a job depends on their properties and on how they interact with other materials. Similarly, the usefulness of some manufactured parts of an object depends on how well they fit together with the other parts.

8.B.2 Manufacturing usually involves a series of steps, such as designing a product, obtaining and preparing raw materials, processing the materials mechanically or chemically, and assembling, testing, inspecting, and packaging. The sequence of these steps is also often important.

8.B.3 Modern technology reduces manufacturing costs, produces more uniform products, and creates new synthetic materials that can help reduce the depletion of some natural resources.

8.B.4 Automation, including the use of robots, has changed the nature of work in most fields, including manufacturing. As a result, high-skill, high-knowledge jobs in engineering, computer programming, quality control, supervision, and maintenance are replacing many routine, manual-labor jobs. Workers therefore need better learning skills and flexibility to take on new and rapidly changing jobs.

8.C Energy Sources and Use

8.C.1 Energy can change from one form to another, although in the process some energy is always converted to heat. Some systems transform energy with less loss of heat than others.

8.C.2 Different ways of obtaining, transforming, and distributing energy have different environmental consequences.

8.C.3 In many instances, manufacturing and other technological activities are performed at a site close to an energy source. Some forms of energy are transported easily, others are not.

8.C.4 Electrical energy can be produced from a variety of energy sources and can be transformed into almost any other form of energy. Moreover, electricity is used to distribute energy quickly and conveniently to distant locations.

8.C.5 Energy from the sun (and the wind and water energy derived from it) is available indefinitely. Because the flow of energy is weak and variable, very large collection systems are needed. Other sources don't renew or renew only slowly.

8.C.6 Different parts of the world have different amounts and kinds of energy resources to use and use them for different purposes.

8.D Communication

8.D.1 Errors can occur in coding, transmitting, or decoding information, and some means of checking for accuracy is needed. Repeating the message is a frequently used method.

8.D.2 Information can be carried by many media, including sound, light, and objects. In this century, the ability to code information as electric currents in wires, electromagnetic waves in space, and light in glass fibers has made communication millions of times faster than is possible by mail or sound.

8.E Information Processing

8.E.1 Most computers use digital codes containing only two symbols, 0 and 1, to perform all operations. Continuous signals (analog) must be transformed into digital codes before they can be processed by a computer.

8.E.2 What use can be made of a large collection of information depends upon how it is organized. One of the values of computers is that they are able, on command, to reorganize information in a variety of ways, thereby enabling people to make more and better uses of the collection.

8.E.3 Computer control of mechanical systems can be much quicker than human control. In situations where events happen faster than people can react, there is little choice but to rely on computers. Most complex systems still require human oversight, however, to make certain kinds of judgments about the readiness of the parts of the system (including the computers) and the system as a whole to operate properly, to react to unexpected failures, and to evaluate how well the system is serving its intended purposes.

8.E.4 An increasing number of people work at jobs that involve processing or distributing information. Because computers can do these tasks faster and more reliably, they have become standard tools both in the workplace and at home.

8.F Health Technology

8.F.1 Sanitation measures such as the use of sewers, landfills, quarantines, and safe food handling are important in controlling the spread of organisms that cause disease. Improving sanitation to prevent disease has contributed more to saving human life than any advance in medical treatment.

8.F.2 The ability to measure the level of substances in body fluids has made it possible for physicians to make comparisons with normal levels, make very sophisticated diagnoses, and monitor the effects of the treatments they prescribe.

8.F.3 It is becoming increasingly possible to manufacture chemical substances such as insulin and hormones that are normally found in the body. They can be used by individuals whose own bodies cannot produce the amounts required for good health.

9. The Mathematical World

By the end of the 8th grade, students should know that

9.A Numbers

9.A.1 There have been systems for writing numbers other than the Arabic system of place values based on tens. The very old Roman numerals are now used only for dates, clock faces, or ordering chapters in a book. Numbers based on 60 are still used for describing time and angles.

9.A.2 A number line can be extended on the other side of zero to represent negative numbers. Negative numbers allow subtraction of a bigger number from a smaller number to make sense, and are often used when something can be measured on either side of some reference point (time, ground level, temperature, budget).

9.A.3 Numbers can be written in different forms, depending on how they are being used. How fractions or decimals based on measured quantities should be written depends on how precise the measurements are and how precise an answer is needed.

9.A.4 The operations + and – are inverses of each other—one undoes what the other does; likewise x and ÷ .

9.A.5 The expression *a/b* can mean different things: *a* parts of size *1/b* each, *a* divided by *b,* or *a* compared to *b.*

9.A.6 Numbers can be represented by using sequences of only two symbols (such as 1 and 0, on and off); computers work this way.

9.A.7 Computations (as on calculators) can give more digits than make sense or are useful.

9.B Symbolic Relationships

9.B.1 An equation containing a variable may be true for just one value of the variable.

9.B.2 Mathematical statements can be used to describe how one quantity changes when another changes. Rates of change can be computed from differences in magnitudes and vice versa.

9.B.3 Graphs can show a variety of possible relationships between two variables. As one variable increases uniformly, the other may do one of the following: increase or decrease steadily, increase or decrease faster and faster, get closer and closer to some limiting value, reach some intermediate maximum or minimum, alternately increase and decrease indefinitely, increase or decrease in steps, or do something different from any of these.

9.C Shapes

9.C.1 Some shapes have special properties: triangular shapes tend to make structures rigid, and round shapes give the least possible boundary for a given amount of interior area. Shapes can match exactly or have the same shape in different sizes.

9.C.2 Lines can be parallel, perpendicular, or oblique.

9.C.3 Shapes on a sphere like the earth cannot be depicted on a flat surface without some distortion.

9.C.4 The graphic display of numbers may help to show patterns such as trends, varying rates of change, gaps, or clusters. Such patterns sometimes can be used to make predictions about the phenomena being graphed.

9.C.5 It takes two numbers to locate a point on a map or any other flat surface. The numbers may be two perpendicular distances from a point, or an angle and a distance from a point.

9.C.6 The scale chosen for a graph or drawing makes a big difference in how useful it is.

9.D Uncertainty

9.D.1 How probability is estimated depends on what is known about the situation. Estimates can be based on data from similar conditions in the past or on the assumption that all the possibilities are known.

9.D.2 Probabilities are ratios and can be expressed as fractions, percentages, or odds.

9.D.3 The mean, median, and mode tell different things about the middle of a data set.

9.D.4 Comparison of data from two groups should involve comparing both their middles and the spreads around them.

9.D.5 The larger a well-chosen sample is, the more accurately it is likely to represent the whole. But there are many ways of choosing a sample that can make it unrepresentative of the whole.

9.D.6 Events can be described in terms of being more or less likely, impossible, or certain.

9.E Reasoning

9.E.1 Some aspects of reasoning have fairly rigid rules for what makes sense; other aspects don't. If people have rules that always hold, and good information about a particular situation, then logic can help them to figure out what is true about it. This kind of reasoning requires care in the use of key words such as if, and, not, or, all, and some. Reasoning by similarities can suggest ideas but can't prove them one way or the other.

9.E.2 Practical reasoning, such as diagnosing or troubleshooting almost anything, may require many-step, branching logic. Because computers can keep track of complicated logic, as well as a lot of information, they are useful in a lot of problem-solving situations.

9.E.3 Sometimes people invent a general rule to explain how something works by summarizing observations. But people tend to overgeneralize, imagining general rules on the basis of only a few observations.

9.E.4 People are using incorrect logic when they make a statement such as "If *A* is true, then *B* is true; but *A* isn't true, therefore *B* isn't true either."

9.E.5 A single example can never prove that something is always true, but sometimes a single example can prove that something is not always true.

9.E.6 An analogy has some likenesses to but also some differences from the real thing.

10. Historical Perspectives

By the end of the 8th grade, students should know that

10.A Displacing the Earth from the Center of the Universe

10.A.1 The motion of an object is always judged with respect to some other object or point and so the idea of absolute motion or rest is misleading.

10.A.2 Telescopes reveal that there are many more stars in the night sky than are evident to the unaided eye, the surface of the moon has many craters and mountains, the sun has dark spots, and Jupiter and some other planets have their own moons.

10.F Understanding Fire

10.F.1 From the earliest times until now, people have believed that even though millions of different kinds of material seem to exist in the world, most things must be made up of combinations of just a few basic kinds of things. There has not always been agreement, however, on what those basic kinds of things are. One theory long ago was that the basic substances were earth, water, air, and fire. Scientists now know that these are not the basic substances. But the old theory seemed to explain many observations about the world.

10.F.2 Today, scientists are still working out the details of what the basic kinds of matter are and of how they combine, or can be made to combine, to make other substances.

10.F.3 Experimental and theoretical work done by French scientist Antoine Lavoisier in the decade between the American and French revolutions led to the modern science of chemistry.

10.F.4 Lavoisier's work was based on the idea that when materials react with each other many changes can take place but that in every case the total amount of matter afterward is the same as before. He successfully tested the concept of conservation of matter by conducting a series of experiments in which he carefully measured all the substances involved in burning, including the gases used and those given off.

10.F.5 Alchemy was chiefly an effort to change base metals like lead into gold and to produce an elixir that would enable people to live forever. It failed to do that or to create much knowledge of how substances react with each other. The more scientific study of chemistry that began in Lavoisier's time has gone far beyond alchemy in understanding reactions and producing new materials.

10.G Splitting the Atom

10.G.1 The accidental discovery that minerals containing uranium darken photographic film, as light does, led to the idea of radioactivity.

10.G.2 In their laboratory in France, Marie Curie and her husband, Pierre Curie, isolated two new elements that caused most of the radioactivity of the uranium mineral. They named one radium because it gave off powerful, invisible rays, and the other polonium in honor of Madame Curie's country of birth. Marie Curie was the first scientist ever to win the Nobel prize in two different fields—in physics, shared with her husband, and later in chemistry.

10.I Discovering Germs

10.I.1 Throughout history, people have created explanations for disease. Some have held that disease has spiritual causes, but the most persistent biological theory over the centuries was that illness resulted from an imbalance in the body fluids. The introduction of germ theory by Louis Pasteur and others in the 19th century led to the modern belief that many diseases are caused by microorganisms—bacteria, viruses, yeasts, and parasites.

10.I.2 Pasteur wanted to find out what causes milk and wine to spoil. He demonstrated that spoilage and fermentation occur when microorganisms enter from the air, multiply rapidly, and produce waste products. After showing that spoilage could be avoided by keeping germs out or by destroying them with heat, he investigated animal diseases and showed that microorganisms were involved. Other investigators later showed that specific kinds of germs caused specific diseases.

10.I.3 Pasteur found that infection by disease organisms—germs—caused the body to build up an immunity against subsequent infection by the same organisms. He then demonstrated that it was possible to produce vaccines that would induce the body to build immunity to a disease without actually causing the disease itself.

10.I.4 Changes in health practices have resulted from the acceptance of the germ theory of disease. Before germ theory, illness was treated by appeals to supernatural powers or by trying to adjust body fluids through induced vomiting, bleeding, or purging. The modern approach emphasizes sanitation, the safe handling of food and water, the pasteurization of milk, quarantine, and aseptic surgical techniques to keep germs out of the body; vaccinations to strengthen the body's immune system against subsequent infection by the same kind of microorganisms; and antibiotics and other chemicals and processes to destroy microorganisms.

10.I.5 In medicine, as in other fields of science, discoveries are sometimes made unexpectedly, even by accident. But knowledge and creative insight are usually required to recognize the meaning of the unexpected.

10.J Harnessing Power

10.J.1 Until the 1800s, most manufacturing was done in homes, using small, handmade machines that were powered by muscle, wind, or running water. New machinery and steam engines to drive them made it possible to replace craftsmanship with factories, using fuels as a source of energy. In the factory system, workers, materials, and energy could be brought together efficiently.

10.J.2 The invention of the steam engine was at the center of the Industrial Revolution. It converted the chemical energy stored in wood and coal, which were plentiful, into mechanical work. The steam engine was invented to solve the urgent problem of pumping water out of coal mines. As improved by James Watt, it was soon used to move coal, drive manufacturing machinery, and power locomotives, ships, and even the first automobiles.

11. Common Themes

By the end of the 8th grade, students should know that

11.A Systems

11.A.1 A system can include processes as well as things.

11.A.2 Thinking about things as systems means looking for how every part relates to others. The output from one part of a system (which can include material, energy, or information) can become the input to other parts. Such feedback can serve to control what goes on in the system as a whole.

11.A.3 Any system is usually connected to other systems, both internally and externally. Thus a system may be thought of as containing subsystems and as being a subsystem of a larger system.

11.B Models

11.B.1 Models are often used to think about processes that happen too slowly, too quickly, or on too small a scale to observe directly, or that are too vast to be changed deliberately, or that are potentially dangerous.

11.B.2 Mathematical models can be displayed on a computer and then modified to see what happens.

11.B.3 Different models can be used to represent the same thing. What kind of a model to use and how complex it should be depends on its purpose. The usefulness of a model may be limited if it is too simple or if it is needlessly complicated. Choosing a useful model is one of the instances in which intuition and creativity come into play in science, mathematics, and engineering.

11.C Constancy and Change

11.C.1 Physical and biological systems tend to change until they become stable and then remain that way unless their surroundings change.

11.C.2 A system may stay the same because nothing is happening or because things are happening but exactly counterbalance one another.

11.C.3 Many systems contain feedback mechanisms that serve to keep changes within specified limits.

11.C.4 Symbolic equations can be used to summarize how the quantity of something changes over time or in response to other changes.

11.C.5 Symmetry (or the lack of it) may determine properties of many objects, from molecules and crystals to organisms and designed structures.

11.C.6 Cycles, such as the seasons or body temperature, can be described by their cycle length or frequency, what their highest and lowest values are, and when these values occur. Different cycles range from many thousands of years down to less than a billionth of a second.

11.D Scale

11.D.1 Properties of systems that depend on volume, such as capacity and weight, change out of proportion to properties that depend on area, such as strength or surface processes.

11.D.2 As the complexity of any system increases, gaining an understanding of it depends increasingly on summaries, such as averages and ranges, and on descriptions of typical examples of that system.

12. Habits of Mind

By the end of the 8th grade, students should know that

12.A Values and Attitudes

12.A.1 Know why it is important in science to keep honest, clear, and accurate records.

12.A.2 Know that hypotheses are valuable, even if they turn out not to be true, if they lead to fruitful investigations.

12.A.3 Know that often different explanations can be given for the same evidence, and it is not always possible to tell which one is correct.

12.B Computation and Estimation

12.B.1 Find what percentage one number is of another and figure any percentage of any number.

12.B.2 Use, interpret, and compare numbers in several equivalent forms such as integers, fractions, decimals, and percents.

12.B.3 Calculate the circumferences and areas of rectangles, triangles, and circles, and the volumes of rectangular solids.

12.B.4 Find the mean and median of a set of data.

12.B.5 Estimate distances and travel times from maps and the actual size of objects from scale drawings.

12.B.6 Insert instructions into computer spreadsheet cells to program arithmetic calculations.

12.B.7 Determine what unit (such as seconds, square inches, or dollars per tankful) an answer should be expressed in from the units of the inputs to the calculation, and be able to convert compound units (such as yen per dollar into dollar per yen, or miles per hour into feet per second).

12.B.8 Decide what degree of precision is adequate and round off the result of calculator operations to enough significant figures to reasonably reflect those of the inputs.

12.B.9 Express numbers like 100, 1,000, and 1,000,000 as powers of 10.

12.B.10 Estimate probabilities of outcomes in familiar situations, on the basis of history or the number of possible outcomes.

12.C Manipulation and Observation

12.C.1 Use calculators to compare amounts proportionally.

12.C.2 Use computers to store and retrieve information in topical, alphabetical, numerical, and key-word files, and create simple files of their own devising.

12.C.3 Read analog and digital meters on instruments used to make direct measurements of length, volume, weight, elapsed time, rates, and temperature, and choose appropriate units for reporting various magnitudes.

12.C.4 Use cameras and tape recorders for capturing information.

12.C.5 Inspect, disassemble, and reassemble simple mechanical devices and describe what the various parts are for; estimate what the effect that making a change in one part of a system is likely to have on the system as a whole.

12.D Communication Skills

12.D.1 Organize information in simple tables and graphs and identify relationships they reveal.

12.D.2 Read simple tables and graphs produced by others and describe in words what they show.

12.D.3 Locate information in reference books, back issues of newspapers and magazines, compact disks, and computer databases.

12.D.4 Understand writing that incorporates circle charts, bar and line graphs, two-way data tables, diagrams, and symbols.

12.D.5 Find and describe locations on maps with rectangular and polar coordinates.

12.E Critical-Response Skills

12.E.1 Question claims based on vague attributions (such as "Leading doctors say...") or on statements made by celebrities or others outside the area of their particular expertise.

12.E.2 Compare consumer products and consider reasonable personal trade-offs among them on the basis of features, performance, durability, and cost.

12.E.3 Be skeptical of arguments based on very small samples of data, biased samples, or samples for which there was no control sample.

12.E.4 Be aware that there may be more than one good way to interpret a given set of findings.

12.E.5 Notice and criticize the reasoning in arguments in which (1) fact and opinion are intermingled or the conclusions do not follow logically from the evidence given, (2) an analogy is not apt, (3) no mention is made of whether the control groups are very much like the experimental group, or (4) all members of a group (such as teenagers or chemists) are implied to have nearly identical characteristics that differ from those of other groups.